G000268812

Sports Lighting

Specialists in the Lighting of all Sports Applications

Tel; 01803 844 833   Fax; 01803 844 835

www.sportslighting.co.uk

APPROVED
CONTRACTOR

Sports Lighting has been a family run business for the last 15yrs.

We do nationwide installations.

All our work comes with a 12months parts and labour guarantee.

We make on site surveys and advise for installation to suit your needs.

We make life easy for you, by supplying all the lux and spillage charts for your planning application FREE OF CHARGE.

Our light fittings are all asymmetric which cut out any possibility of light pollution and spillage.

All out work comes with the backing of the NICEIC as we are an approved contractor.

We are the main floodlighting contractor for Torquay Utd.

Sports lighting is always prepared to put money back into local sports by means of sponsorships tailored to meet the requirements of both parties.

ISBN 9-781-869833-55-8
ISBN 1-869-833-55-4

Published by Tony Williams Publications Ltd
Printed by MPG impressions Ltd (Chessington)
All distributing queries to Pat Vaughan
Tel: 01823 490 080 or 01458 241592

Front Cover caption:
Bradford Pak Avenue`s Luke Caulfield surges away from Prescot Cables Adam Flynn
during his sides 1-0 opening day victory.
Photo: Darren Thomas.

NON LEAGUE CLUB DIRECTORY 2007

(29th Edition)

EDITORS
MIKE & TONY WILLIAMS

FIELD turf™

IF YOU'RE THINKING OF BUYING SYNTHETIC GRASS...
BUY THE BEST

FOREWORD

Every summer is the season of optimism, of expectations for the season to come. After a disappointing World Cup when managing expectations was the most difficult task, we must put it behind us and look forward with anticipation to the new season both on and of the field.

Off the field we need the conclusion of the restructuring of the National League System and more importantly, the implementation of the Lord Burns Report. A further major consideration is for the 'three up three down' between the League and the Football Conference. A change of heart there would be a great fillip to the National game.

Over the years football outside The Premiership and The Football League, whilst improving its profile and credibility has been very patient in awaiting due recognition and an invitation to join the decision table. It is time that the National Game, in its own right, had a presence on the FA Council, it is long overdue.

The World Cup threw doubt on the "spirit" of the game. It is a challenge and an opportunity in the new season for footballers at all levels of the game to play the game skilfully and fairly. Remember, if you do not play the game fairly then you cannot play the game skilfully. That, together with respect for and towards Officials and the laws of the game could see a dramatic reversal of the trends shown in Germany.

On the following pages you will read of the exploits of Burton Albion in the FA Cup, of Grays Athletic in the FA Trophy, of Nantwich Town in the FA Vase and of the Isle of Man winning the FA National League Systems Cup and representing us in Europe.
You will read about Accrington Stanley and Hereford United returning to The Football League and former First Division Oxford United joining The Conference. You will then read all about the other promotion and relegated teams in The National League System but whilst there can be one winner of a match both teams can be winners for the game.

To be selected to represent your country at whatever level is the ultimate individual accolade in sport and we wish Paul Fairclough and the England National Game X1 all success, when they play Holland at Burton Albion in November, a win would clinch the inaugural European Challenge Cup – no mean achievement.

The Non-league Directory is a must for every Club Secretary and the bookshelf of every 'football buff,' it contains a wealth of vital information and our thanks and congratulations go to Tony.and Mike Williams.
Tony is an exceptional football man who I have known for many years, a man of thoughtful innovation with a passion and love for the game unsurpassed.
Sometimes this book comes with the help and sponsorship of others, but irrespective of outside help or not, it still comes, as 29 consecutive editions have proved.

In thanking them on your behalf, may I wish you all a successful season at whatever level you are involved. Temper your expectations with reality, control your finances, play within the spirit and laws of the game and seize your opportunities as and when they arise. There is so much to look forward to – I can't wait!

Brian Lee
Ex Manager and Chairman of Wycombe Wanderers,
and now a Vice President of the Nationwide Conference.

CONTENTS

Welcome to the start of four years of The FA Cup sponsored by E.ON.

As the proud new sponsor of this competition, I'd like to take this opportunity to introduce E.ON to you.

E.ON UK is the UK's largest integrated power and gas company with around 13,000 employees at over 40 different sites. We have 11 power stations producing enough electricity for around nine million homes and have one of the largest green generation portfolios in the UK. As Central Networks, we operate the power distribution network for 4.9m customers in central England. Our retail business (branded Powergen) is a leading energy supplier in the UK, with around six million electricity and gas customers, both residential and small business. E.ON UK forms part of the E.ON group, the world's largest investor-owned power and gas company.

Our partnership with The FA isn't solely about The FA Cup sponsored by E.ON. We are also sponsor of The FA Women's Cup, The FA Youth Cup and are The FA Schools Football Development Partner. The sponsorship of The FA Cup provides a fantastic opportunity for the business to raise awareness of who we are and what we do.

We recognise and respect that The FA Cup is the best domestic knockout cup competition in the world and take immense pride in the fact that, for the next four years, the competition will be The FA Cup sponsored by E.ON.

Operating as a good and responsible neighbour wherever E.ON works is at the heart of our business. The FA Cup sponsored by E.ON will allow us to connect with people who are involved in football at all levels, and build on our existing commitment to the communities where we operate and beyond.

We believe the success of our four-year partnership with The FA lies in our relationship with you and with all of the clubs who have helped to make The FA Cup such a truly fantastic competition.

I would like to wish you all the very best of luck in this season's FA Cup sponsored by E.ON.

Yours sincerely,

Mike Thompson
Head of Sponsorship

ACKNOWLEDGMENTS

As football seasons tend to run into one another, reducing the close season break every year Mike and I seem to miss the Summer altogether. The task of compiling the book really depends on the amount of co operation we receive from club and league officials and our sincere thanks go to the vast majority who enthusiastically help us ensure their up to date information is received.

As regular readers know, one of our ambitions has been to include a team photo for every club that qualifies for at least a page of its own. This is a huge 'exercise ' and our appreciation goes to the club officials who organise a pre season photo call and provide a group photo with a caption and of course to the photographers who also provide action photos. Such stalwarts as **Peter Barnes, Graham Brown, Paul Carter, Keith Clayton,Alan Coomes, Graham Cotterill, Ken Gregory,Tim Lancaster, Gary Letts,Peter Lirettoc, Eric Marsh, Dennis Nicholson, Francis Short, Neil Thaler, Darren Thomas, Roger Thomas, Roger Turner, John Vass, Alan Watson, Bill Wheatcroft, Gordon Whittington** and **Mark Wood.**

You will see from our efforts this year that we are a little nearer our ambition and for this, a great deal of credit should go to **Bill Mitchell** who has tirelessly phoned and phoned again to encourage overworked club officials to organise club photos with captions. Thanks for the efforts of all those who made this year's selection the best yet. It should mean we have photos of about 3,000 of the country's leading non-league footballers, a feat of which we are quite proud and which I hope you will enjoy.

Team Photos & Programmes

The majority of team photos we feature on the club pages show club squads as they lined up last season or at photo calls before the current campaigns. When these were not available we decided it was better to feature a collector's piece and a vintage programme which we hope will still be of interest to the fans and collectors alike.

We have spent hours chasing copy for these pages and our sincere thanks go to the vast majority of club officials who have bent over backwards to help us hit deadlines and to those who we haven't heard from we can only apologise if we haven't been able to fully update their information.

The all round work of **Arthur Evans** with pen and camera are always appreciated as are the regular contributions of **Mike Simmonds** (Schools), **Wally Goss & Mike Brown** (A.F.A.), **Stewart Davidson** and **Bill Mitchell** (Scotland) and Island football correspondents such as **Graham Skuse** (Channel Islands) and **Adam Kelso** (Isle of Man).

The Football Association Competitions Department are always ready to help and special support was given this year by **Danny Jackman** while a new name to emerge in the 'squad' in this Directory is statistician **Craig Pottage** who has supplied most of the senior players' details. Also thanks goes to **Rob Grillo**, who supplied the Yorkshire League tables.

It's an absolute pleasure working with someone as dedicated as my son **Mike** and as he and I collate information from over a thousand clubs, search for team photos from all the senior leagues and collect programmes for the top six divisions plus many action pictures from all levels, co-operation and understanding are obviously needed from the club and league officials.

T.W

Educated at Malvern College, one of the country's best football schools in the late sixties, he represented England Under 18 against Scotland at Celtic Park before serving as an administrative officer in the Royal Air Force for five years.

He was on Reading's books from the age of 16 to 22, but also represented F.A. Amateur XI's and the R.A.F. while playing mainly in the old Isthmian League for Corinthian Casuals, Dulwich Hamlet and Kingstonian and joining Hereford United and Grantham during R.A.F. postings.

After taking an F.A. Coaching badge he coached at Harrow Borough, Epsom & Ewell and Hungerford Town and was asked to edit Jimmy Hill's Football Weekly after initial experience with the Amateur Footballer. Monthly Soccer and Sportsweek followed before he had the idea for a football Wisden and was helped by The Bagnall Harvey Agency to find a suitable generous sponsor in Rothmans.

After launching the Rothmans Football Yearbook in 1970 as its founder and co-compiler with Roy Peskett, he was asked to join Rothmans (although a non-smoker!) in the company's public relations department and was soon able to persuade the Marketing Director that Rothmans should become the first ever sponsor of a football league.

After a season's trial sponsoring the Hellenic and Isthmian Leagues, it was decided to go national with the Northern and Western Leagues and for four years he looked after the football department at Rothmans, with Jimmy Hill and Doug Insole presenting a brilliant sponsorship package which amongst many other innovations included three points for a win and goal difference.

So Non-League football led the way with league sponsorship and two, now well accepted, innovations.

Sportsmanship and goals were also rewarded in a sponsorship that proved a great success for football and for Rothmans. Indeed the sportsmanship incentives could be of great value to-day in the Football Association's bid to improve the game's image by ridding the game of dissent and cheating.

After the cigarette company pulled out of their sports sponsorship Tony produced the first Non-League Annual and later The Football League Club Directory, launching 'Non-League Football' magazine with "The Mail on Sunday" and then "Team Talk."

After his ten years with Hungerford Town, he moved West and served Yeovil Town as a Director for seven years but was thrilled when David Emery's plans for the exciting Non-League Media emerged and came into reality, thus giving the grass roots of the game the publicity and promotion that he and his team had been attempting to set up since the Annual (now Directory) was launched in 1978.

Sadly, Non-League Media Plc is no more, but Greenways Media helped The Non-League Paper develop successfully to the benefit of their levels of the football world. Tony Williams Publications was brought back into action and after producing a Fair Play magazine for members of a non league enthusiasts' club, the company now publishes football books, produces a non-league diary and promotes an annual non-league quiz with finals at an F.A.Trophy week-end celebration.

Books published this year included 'Alliance to Conference - The First Twenty One Years' and a Centenary celebration of the Channel Islands' Muratti inter Island Competition. The aim of the company has always been to promote the non-league 'family,' its spirit and and its general development. So a plaque from The Football Association inscribed 'To Tony Williams for his continued promotion of all that's good in football' was greatly appreciated as was the recent GLS "Lifetime Award' for promoting non-league football.

W hat started out as a holiday job in 1988 helping put together (literally in those days) the Non-League Club Directory and League Club Directory, in the end forged a career which saw him work for Coventry City Football Club, e-comsport in London and finally return to Tony Williams Publications in 2003.

During his eight year spell with TW Publications he learned the ropes of all aspects of publishing culminating in the roll of production manager for the Non-League Directory, Team Talk Magazine, the League Club Directory and many more publications published by the company.

1995 saw the opportunity to take up the post of Publications Manager at Coventry City Football Club, and the transfer was made in the April of that year. Sky Blue Publications was formed and the League Club Directory became their leading title. Rebranded as the Ultimate Football Guide he was to deal with all aspects of the book, from design to sales and was also put on a steep learning curve into the world of Premiership programme production.

The three years spent at the Midland's club gave him a great incite into all departments of a Premiership club, having produced publications for them all, but by 1998 it was time to move on again and the world of freelance design and editing beckoned. That was until, at the final hour, Grant Bovey and his newly formed company Sportscheck diverted his route back to the West Country by luring him to London.

The challenge of creating an online data base of football players from europe and the rest of world, to aid professional clubs in their quest to better their squads, was one which he relished and the company rapidly grew. Juggling the day job with the editing of the Ultimate Football Guide proved to be even more of a challenge, which ultimately was to no avail as Sky Blue Publications did not publish the 1999 edition.

This released him to work full time on the players data-base for the newly named e-comsport and in the January of 2000 he was promoted to Data Manager, looking after a multi-national team of football analysts. As with most 'dot com' companies of that time flotation was shortly followed by closure and in 2001 the move back to the West Country, which had been on hold since 1998, was finally made.

The desire to start up his own design/publishing company still remained and in the April of 2003 MCsolutions was officially formed and his return to the 'non-league' family was complete.

Having gone to a rugby school his football playing career was delayed. However, becoming the youngest player to have played for the First XV and representing Torbay Athletics club at 100 and 200m proved his sporting background. At the age of 20 he begun his football career which, at it's height, saw him playing for Chard Town in the Western League Premier Division. Now 36, officially a veteran(!), he has the 'experience' but, unfortunately, not the legs! Nevertheless he enjoys turning out for Loddiswell Athletic in the South Devon Football League every Saturday, and was recently voted in as Secretary for the club. Another challenge he relishes as the Devon club look to gain promotion into the Premier Division for the first time in their history.

arena
SEATING

AFFORDABLE SEATING FOR SALE

Take a Seat!

from our broad range of seating products

From 50 to 50,000... Arena Seating have the solution

Arena Seating has invested in the design and development of a comprehensive range of tiered seating products, which provide solutions for the smallest to the very largest of clubs, venues and clients.

From bespoke designed covered and uncovered stands for larger venues, to our LT Portastand that is aimed at smaller local clubs and is delivered on a truck fully assembled, we have a product range to suit every seating requirement.

Contact us to see how we can enhance your venue.

WWW.ARENASEATING.COM

Arena Seating
Arena House Membury Lambourn Woodlands Hungerford Berkshire RG17 7TQ
T. 01488 67 48 00 **W.** www.arenaseating.com **E.** info@arenaseating.com

PART OF THE ARENA GROUP

arena
SEATING

AFFORDABLE SEATING FOR SALE

Take a Seat!
with The Arena Tiered Seating System

royal windsor

From 50 to 50,000... Arena Seating have the solution

The classic Arena demountable tiered seating system upon which we have built our reputation is available for sale. The system can be supplied for sale in 254mm or 152mm rise format as standard, providing a cost effective permanent or demountable grandstand solution for sports clubs and venues.

It can be permanently in position, moved around the venue or even added to on a sale or hire basis as requirements change.

Contact us to see how we can enhance your venue.

WWW.ARENASEATING.COM

Arena Seating
Arena House Membury Lambourn Woodlands Hungerford Berkshire RG17 7TQ
T. 01488 67 48 00 **W.** www.arenaseating.com **E.** info@arenaseating.com

REVIEWOF THE

The second season featuring the restructured 'steps' on the National Game pyramid kicked off with the vast majority of clubs pleased with their initial experience.

However, at Step One The Conference now contained nearly half their members wishing they weren't there at all, as they had lost their valued Football League membership. While many of their fellow members had decided to raise their budgets to cope with a full time squad but realised too late that they were just not ready for the responsibilities involved.

Even in the North and South feeder divisions where many clubs are pleased to attract crowds of just 500, the money spent on the required upgrading of ground facilities and the cost of a squad capable of promotion often proved too much of a strain and took a great deal of the enjoyment away for those battling to keep their respective clubs making progress on and off the field.

Sensible club chairmen avoided the temptation of immediate overspending and once they find they can cope with a step up then gradually they can strengthen the squad and ensure their ground is ready for possible promotion.

St.Albans City and Stafford Rangers have done just that, and were promoted with outstanding champions in Northwich Victoria and a Weymouth club who shook off rumour after rumour to remain steady and once again prove that given the resources Gary Hill is a very successful manager.

· Northwich manager Steve Burr has benefited from a great working relationship with chairman Mike Connett and despite the excitement of a new ground and a spectacular F.A.Cup run, their excellent initial league form was recovered and a tremendous finish to the season saw the Vics back into the top division with a wonderful twin strike force of Jon Allan(31)and Paul Brayson(30) finishing with an impressive 61 senior goals.

As the season settled down, Grays Athletic appeared to be the outstanding footballing side in the Nationwide Conference but it turned out to be Accrington Stanley who had the consistency and it wasn't until their 43rd senior game of the season that they failed to score. Stanley pulled away to win the championship with ease and completed a fairy tale return to The Football League, especially as they took the place of Oxford United the club who initially had replaced them in 1962.

Financial troubles at Scarborough, Crawley Town and Canvey Island and a wretched points loss at Altrincham for including a player who hadn't obtained   official clearance at his previous club after playing abroad, left most fans completely confused for weeks after the playing had stopped. Forest Green Rovers officially survived with a battling finish to the season and Tamworth were saved by the surrounding chaos which eventually saw Canvey Island volunteer to drop two steps down to the Isthmian Division One and Scarborough drop to Nationwide North. One can only hope that Crawley can survive until the start of the coming season and most supporters will be pleased that Alty kept their Conference place as their problem hardly appeared to be a direct fault of their own. What a shambles!

In contrast the Conference promotion play-offs were a great success once again and everyone except the Halifax Town supporters probably felt that Hereford United deserved to return to The Football League after so many near misses.The actual final was a credit to The Conference in every way. The attendance, the presentation of the fixture, the quality football and the spirit in which the very important game was played all brought great credit to the competition.

2005-06 SEASON

Another excellent day's football was enjoyed at Upton Park where Grays Athletic retained The F.A.Challenge Trophy against Woking in a another splendid display of attractive sporting football. So with Burton Albion's wonderful F.A.Cup draw at Old Trafford which set up a glorious evening replay at Albion's impressive new ground The Nationwide Conference had some very special days to show the best characteristics of top non-league football.

The quite extraordinary number of cautions handed out during the World Cup must act as a very clear warning that life throughout non-league football could change dramatically.

We have read that F.I.F.A.are worried about bringing in technology to decide goalmouth arguments as to whether or not the ball crossed the line for a goal. One of the reasons that technology may not be used is that F.I.F.A.consider all changes to the game should apply to all levels and obviously cameras would not be available to most competitions below national professional leagues.

However, in the modern game the only infringement that according to the rules has to be'deliberate' is handball. Apparently fouls don't have to be deliberate. We have seen players cautioned for honest tackles that are mistimed without any malice or intent, we have seen them booked for falling over players, losing their balance, being out skilled and sometimes even without touching an opponent. The players are regularly booked without having any intent to foul whatsoever so if this is a F.I.F.A. policy that will apply to all levels of the game, what hope have the players got in competitions where innocent, mistimed and clumsy tackles and par for the course.

It seems quite ludicrous that cautions can be given out in this way while players who head butt, go over the top in tackles and deliberately chop down players moving into dangerous areas of the pitch are often seen on television to receive exactly the same punishment.

Referees don't need to know the game or show any common sense any more, they can hide behind the instructions passed down to them and there is no doubt the game, especially at our levels could suffer. How can the whole game be treated in this way when non-league football and local leagues consist of many players who, with the best will in the world cannot always time their tackles perfectly?

My worst moment of referees' madness last season was shared by supporters of both sides at Woking for their F.A.Cup tie against Northwich Victoria. The game was completely defused and ruined as any sort of spectacle by a referee who booked perfect tackles, honest collisions and ensured that after half time both sides had given up tackling and both sets of supporters were silenced as a potentially thrilling cup tie fizzled out to a boring draw.

Who in this country can prevent the game at the lower levels from disintegrating? Many matches probably wouldn't last until half time if the principles of refereeing we saw in the world cup were to be used strictly in non-league football.

A sensible reaction at the top would be for referees to be told to use their common sense in this situation.

But there again they have not been encouraged to do this at senior levels for many years now, so what can we expect in the season ahead?

It's our game. So don't just criticise it. Save It!

We were all excited by the prospect of a Summer dominated by the World Cup, especially as we had a team who were expected to bring us some excitement and possibly even a trophy to lift the country's morale.

Referees had been told to clamp down on tough tackling so perhaps we could expect exciting flowing football with talented attackers providing great entertainment.

Early games were generally encouraging apart from own English performances, but gradually as players and the coaches realised that the slightest nudge, especially if followed by a tumble, scream or a couple of rolls and a clutching of the face, would at best bring the opposition a red or yellow card or at worst 'win' a free kick.

The Portugal v Holland game made me feel physically sick. The Game I loved, the tournament I had been looking forward to so much and two talented sides had all let millions of us down very badly.

The anti football brigade were having a field day as the star footballers on show couldn't take a knock like a true sportsman (especially Rugby players) or even just like men (as they used to be). The histrionics and cheating were horrendous and referees had no idea which offence was deliberate or not and which was in fact an offence anyway, so they booked just about everybody and hardly a game was allowed to flow.

Where was the disciplined, physical game for sportsman that we had believed in for years. The game that we were proud for our youngsters to copy as they learnt to give and take a knock, cope graciously with winning and losing and respecting the officials?

I still believe that 90% of everyone involved with the game admires fair play and good sportsmanship, we don't believe in winning at all costs, although we expect our teams to give everything for the cause as they strive to be successful within the rules. However, F.I.F.A. in their wisdom instructed their referees to issue cautions for every nudge or fall and they no longer had to judge whether the offences were deliberate other than those for handball.

So referees to-day need to know absolutely nothing about the game itself or its spirit- just the laws of the game. Ex -players have been kept out of the higher ranks of match officials as they just haven't time to reach the top if they carry on playing to their late twenties.

Anyone who had played could sense what was going to happen in the Wayne Rooney clash. He had been fouled by two players, but unlike just about every other player in the tournament, refused to claim the foul by falling over. The referee could see this and also that the three players were thrashing away dangerously with a disaster ready to happen. Did he read the situation, step in and defuse it and give a free kick? No,common sense or reading the game sensibly isn't now part of the referees job and we all know what happened to bring the game further into disrepute!

The best Football League referee I ever saw for understanding the game and spotting potential trouble before it happened was Steve Baines an ex player of over 300 appearances but as an ex player he wasn't popular with the other referees. He understood things about the game that they would never know about and it showed and they didn't like it.

Most people will only remember The World Cup Final for one thing and the rubbish talked about the sending off incident to the extent that lip readers were guessing at what was said (in which language I wonder) and a player who finished the tournament with three yellow cards and a red was given the top award and will of course be copied by youngsters all over the world. Once again well done F.I.F.A!

Any referee who had played the game would sense when rival players are on the verge of a flare up. A quiet word to both, or individually, would normally defuse the trouble.

In this case the referee wasn't even keeping an eye on things as the situation developed. Incidentaly any schoolboy, youth player or junior professional will have learnt to cope with insults and swearing early in his football career. To a youngster, being told you are too small, too fat, too ugly, too pretty, you speak too posh or you are even too tall are all hurtful but you have to overcome the sniping. You learn to cope especially if you are in a very rough area so when you are older whatever the insult, you learn to laugh it off and if you really feel annoyed there is always a time and a place to sort your opponent out on or off the field, but not in an obvious pre-meditated loss of control in front of millions including thousands of youngsters.

Yes, I know the referee featuring in these two incidents was the same and presumably he was considered the best in the world. I rest my case.

The instructions given to the referees obviously didn't help them.The players adopted disgraceful tactics giving the officials no chance to know whether the contact was worthy of a foul, a booking or sending off (or even if there was contact). So they booked everybody for everything and our game as we knew it died in front of our eyes.

It is our game so what we are going to do about it?
No doubt the Football Association have seen that everyone has had enough. Even senior retired professionals are sick of some of the modern attitudes. We all want leadership but we must also put our own houses in order.

Youth coaches - make sure the youngsters don't think it clever to copy the cheats

Chairmen - instruct your Managers to ensure their players don't miss games through stupid bookings and dismissals.

Managers - ensure that your teams are respected for their football and tactical skills not their pathetic cheating. Behave with some sort of discipline in the dug out where supporters see your behaviour and hear your language..

Players - make sure you don't become the saddest bunch of losers as you scream at officials, dive, cheat and look quite pathetic while losing all respect as you drive supporters away.

The media - praise good sportsmanship and make sure those misbehaving are made to look really pathetic and be seen to be letting everyone else down.

Referees- respond to any club attempting to play in the right spirit by making sure cautions are deserved but punish the cheats severely.

The wonderful 'family' of Non-League football can lead the way by making football a happier place for the young referees coming through the system. How about only the captains speaking to the officials?

I hope it will be a happy season for us all and that we will discover the game we love is still there somewhere, that it will survive and underline the fact that it really can be the beautiful game.

Tony Williams

WHAT DO YOU THINK?

A new feature for the Directory this year involves Questions to three prominent football personalities whose lives are dedicated to football in different ways. We thank them for giving their opinions on topical subjects and hope their answers will be of interest.

First we asked Barry Bright, Chairman of the F.A.'s Disciplinary Committee and newly   appointed Vice Chairman of the Football Association:

At a time when the example of our top Premier League players is so influential to non-league, youth and schools players, do you get the impression that they care about their attitude? Or is cheating to gain an extra point or an opponent booked more important to coaching staff and players?
Yes, I believe that the vast majority of players do certainly care about their attitude and recognise that they are role models. Footballers do a lot of work with charities, youth and grassroots initiatives and other good causes that is often unseen. At the same time, it's important to recognise that the modern game is played for increasingly high stakes; this means that the players are under a lot of pressure and the importance of winning, whether to win trophies, avoid relegation or ensure the financial stability of the club, has never been greater. We have to recognise that players are only human and will sometimes cross the line of what we consider to be fair or appropriate behaviour. It is our duty to ensure that when this happens, there is a fair and effective disciplinary process to ensure standards in the game are maintained. I firmly believe that the FA has this.

Do chairmen ever take responsibility for the attitude and behaviour of their managers and staff?
At the very top level, chairmen will often not have much direct contact with their players. Nonetheless, there are plenty of examples where clubs have taken a hard line regarding their responsibilities for player/staff behaviour. You only need to look at the example of the Lee Bowyer/Keiron Dyer incident last season where the players were heavily fined by their club (as well as being appropriately sanctioned by the FA) to see evidence of that.

Could the Football Association show more leadership by stricter punishments for clubs whose players take part in mass brawls or concentrated bullying of referees? For example, instead of fines surely the threat of a ten point loss would ensure the incidents would never ever occur again?
The FA does take a lead in this area and last season sent out specific guidance to clubs on the issue of harassment of match officials. This was followed up by a number of disciplinary cases where clubs were fined for the behaviour of their players. On the issue of punishments, it's important to recognise that the FA has a duty to ensure that any sanction is proportionate and reasonable given the particular circumstances of an incident. Again, I believe the FA deals with serious incidents in a robust way and shows leadership by adopting a proper and responsible approach as the sport's governing body.

Apparently referees no longer need to be able to tell the difference between a deliberate malicious foul and a slightly mistimed or clumsy honest tackle. If the latter is accompanied by a tumble from the opponent both offences often produce a yellow card. Is this fair? If this policy continues, players with lower levels of skill will not dare to tackle at all? Can your committee help?
This is really a question for the FA Referees Committee or the General Manager of the Professional Game Match Officials and I cannot comment on the policy issue. However, it is worth noting that match officials are instructed to differentiate between careless or clumsy tackles and reckless ones, punishable by a yellow card or even a red card if the safety of an opponent is endangered. What I can say is that foul tackles (whether deliberate or clumsy) should be punished, not least because they can be dangerous and can threaten careers. It is very important to offer protection to participants in the game whilst,of course, recognising that football is a contact sport.

Do you think it would be a good idea for only the captains to be allowed to speak to the referee?

My personal view is that I would like to see a limit on approaches to the referee and this is in line with the messages the FA's Disciplinary Committee has given out over the last few seasons. The FA has worked alongside the leagues, the PFA, the LMA and match officials to address abusive and confrontational behaviour towards match officials. Limiting the ability to address the referee to just the captain is probably unrealistic given how the game is played (eg. if there is an incident on the edge of one penalty area involving a forward and his captain is the goalkeeper or centre half). It is certainly an area that we are keenly aware of, and constantly reviewing, to see if changes can be made that are practical and that will improve behaviour.

Next up to answer a few questions, is Barnet and England National Team boss, Paul Fairclough:

The honour of representing your country can hardly be bettered. Do you feel the National Game Eleven who represent the largest section of footballers in England, are given the publicity and praise they deserve? So do they feel special when in an England shirt?

The profile of the side has been raised enormously over the last two years but there is still a long way to go.The Girls team receive more coverage and recognition although out team has been more successful than any other England team for decades. However, the players take their role and responsibility of representing the nation with huge enthusiasm, passion and desire.

How would you describe the differences in attitude and skill between the players in your England side and the opponents you have faced from other countries?

English players have an honesty about them that is quite unique. They are salso very committed physically and are more desciplinerd in their decision making and playing as a unit. Techinically they are a match for any nation.

What has been your best moment so far as England manager?

Winning the Four Nations Tournament (v Wales, Scotland & Republic of Ireland) in was superb and travelling to the States a real eye opener as to how the Americans are approaching the game of football.

The current Euro Trophy we are involved in has given everyone a real target and crowds to go with it.

Which of the England players you have selected have most obviously been proud to be in the England party and wearing the England shirt?

Every single player is consumed with pride. However, Glen Southam of Dagenham & Redbridge has always made it very clear that nothing would be more important to him than wearing the three lions. He has been left out of the original selection then been brought in via the contingency squad and is always just as keen to play.

Can you understand the atttitude of the club officials who sometimes make it difficult for their players to join England squads and decry non-league International football in general?

Of course I can understand them, unfortunateley they do not get the bigger picture. Clubs are desperate to gain promotion and view the England squad as a distraction and hinderance. We look after the play ers extremely well and they learn so much with our squad. In the main, clubs are becoming more sup portive and consider it an honour. I had five players from Barnet in the squad during one season and it helped gain promotion. Players often return to their clubs refreshed from the break of the usual day to day routine.

improving facilities
creating opportunities
building communities

cash in on our support for
- **pitches**
- **social inclusion projects**
- **changing rooms**
- **education schemes**
- **kit and equipment**
- **pavilions**

funding partners

FootballFoundation

football's biggest supporter

And finally, we get the points of view on a few topics from Northwich Victoria manager Steve Burr:

Which clubs do you enjoy playing against for their style, honesty and attitude on and off the field?
Hereford Utd - good footballing side with flair. Under Graham Turner they will always create and score goals. Never seen any of their players hound referees or abuse them, great discipline.

With many non-league players on full time contracts, do you consider that clubs get their moneys' worth at this level from ability, attitude and dedication?
Money is always a big issue, if a player is not performing he's on too much money, if he is performing well then nothing is ever said about is wages. Clubs agree wages before a player signs, so for me it never becomes a problem. Players with bad attitudes soon get found out.

Do you think referees respond to well behaved sides or take the easy option and give way to the abusers and respond to constant appealing, cheating and bullying?
I think in general referees respond to well behaved sides. the more you antagonise a referee the more he will turn against you.

In your experience, are the majority of senior non-league managers free from boardroom pressure regarding team selection and the signing of new players?
Chairmen and directors have all got opinions, just like fans. As a manager you are employed to manage and so far I have never been told to buy a certain player or play a player that I didn't want. The pressure to win games is always there whether it be at the top of the league or at the bottom. Good chairmen are the one's who stick by you when things aren't going so well and are not influenced by all the 'crap' from web sites and 'phone ins.

If players in your team constantly cheat on the field do you keep quiet if they get away with it and are pleased if it benefits the team?
If a player in my team cheats and it benefits us in the game, I will either pull him after the game or during the next training session and tell him he may have got away with it this time, but could cost us with another referee who may send him off. What goes around, comes around. I don't like cheats. We had an incident of bad sportsmanship last season which, thankfully, didn't cost us the title.

MOST NON-LEAGUE CLUBS APPRECIATE HELP

Having enjoyed life as a player, coach, manager, general manager, sponsor, director and journalist within the massive world of non-league football I do realise that most clubs are continually looking for ways in which they can boost funds to help improve facilities and of course attract better players.

With this in mind, we have agreed to promote some ideas that we consider should benefit any non-league clubs who are lucky enough to have the right type of positive personnel who can take advantage of new ideas.

If you are interested in any of the opportunities below please phone me on 01823 490684 or 01823 490080 or contact me by E-Mail: twpublications@tiscali.co.uk

Do you know anyone who would benefit from:-
Losing weight?
Improving their diet?
Gaining more energy?
and consecuently benefiting from a more neutricious lifestyle?
while at the same time
Would you like to raise extra funds for your club?

2. Does your club need advice on looking after your playing surface? Do you need Advice on Turf and its treament ?

3. Would your social manager like the opportunity to sell special quality wines at reasonable prices in your bars?

4. As you can see from the wonderful service Arena Seating gives to Non-League Football all types of stands with seating or covered standing areas can be supplied depending on your requirements and if you need any help contacting the Arena Seating executives please let us know.

INTRODUCTION TO THE BOOK

As with last year's Directory the Non-League awards 'kick-off' our publication, followed by the 'Non-League Club Directory' which is broken down into Steps, as per the new structure published by Mike Appleby.

Where a league covers more than one Step, the clubs and tables from each division follow on. For example: Isthmian Premier (Step 3), Isthmian Division One (Step 4) and Isthmian Division Two (Step 5) are all contained within the same section.

The Step 5 and 6 section is in alphabetical order with Step 7 following on, again with leagues listed alphabetically.

The 'Non-League Club Directory' is followed by the Football Association's Competition section which this year includes a club by club break-down of the F.A. Cup, Trophy and Vase, as well as all the results, statistics and photographs from all the other F.A. competitions played during the 2005-06 season.

Finally the end section of the book includes the County Association Football, Amateur Football, Schools, Women's and Scottish football, plus much much more.

Key to results

			Att.
Team A	v Team B	0-3* 2-2r 4-3p	120

* - After Extra Time r - Reply p - Penalties

Where a cup tie was contested over two legs, the first named club played the 1st Leg at home.

(H) after a clubs name indicates that they were the current holders of the competition.

HW or AW as a result, indicates either a Home Win or an Away Win has been awarded.

The Non-League Club Directory

2005-2006
AWARDS

· ROLL OF HONOUR ·

FOOTBALLER OF THE YEAR
Stuart Thurgood (Grays Athletic)

MANAGER OF THE YEAR
Steve Burr (Northwich Victoria)

ENGLAND PLAYER OF THE YEAR
Ian Craney (Accrington Stanley)

REGIONAL AWARDS
Blyth Spartans ~ Accrington Stanley
Chasetown ~ Histon ~ St Albans City
Horsham YMCA ~ Braintree Town ~ Boreham Wood
Hillingdon Borough ~ Hereford United

F.A. CUP
Burton Albion

INDIVIDUAL MERIT AWARDS
Mrs Jane Phillips ~ Steve Davis ~ Alan Carey
Wolverhampton University Students
Andy Morris

· REGIONAL CLUB AWARDS 2005-06 ·

These awards are not necessarily given to the best clubs in each area but go to clubs who have recorded special achievements which reflect well on their resources and position in the non-league pyramid.

NORTH WEST

Accrington Stanley scored in every one of their first 42 senior games of the season and by the time this sequence was broken, Stanley were red hot favourites for the Football League. The whole club has been preparing for their return for many seasons and standards on and off the field have been steadily improved until last season when John Colemans squad clicked into gear in October and with machine like reliability never looked like faltering as they stormed to the championship. To take the place of Oxford United, the club who had displaced them was an amazing coincidence and their return will give great satisfaction to all those who have worked so hard to see Stanley back where they belong.

NORTH EAST

Blyth Spartans storming finish to the season swept them to the championship of the Northern Premier League and saw them take over as the senior Non-League club in the North East. Apart from an F.A.Trophy defeat and a loss at Ossett Town, Spartans were unbeaten in their other eighteen games of which only four were drawn. The club faced eight games in the last fortnight to complete their wonderful season and also had time to fit in a County Cup Final. Spartans were previously famous for their cup run in 1977-78 but from now on their wonderful promotion season and Robert Dale's 33 senior goals will challenge for pride of place.

WEST MIDLANDS

Chasetown hit the headlines by qualifying for the First Round of the F.A.Cup and impressed the nation with their courageous battle against Oldham Athletic over two games. This run obviously inspired everyone at the club as they stormed to the Midland Football Alliance Championship and a place in Step 4 where they will compete in the Southern League Divison One Midlands. Chasetown are another fine example of a small club steadily growing at a sensible rate on and off the field. benefitting from good leadership from Michael Joiner, and now after some Cup and Vase highlights, they are ready to move on and hopefully will be able to consolidate at the higher level.

EAST MIDLANDS

If ever a club were on an inspired 'roll' it must be **Histon**. The club is led by a team of dedicated, hard working club fabnatics who have come through the ranks together from virtually village status, through the Eastern Counties and Southern Leagues into the Nationwide Conference South for the first time last season. Despite the distraction of an F.A.Cup run that practically took them into the Third Round Proper, 'The Stutes' re-assembled their wounded and managed to qualifying for the play offs on the last day of the season while also winning the League's sportsmanship award.
This club is an example of all that is special about non-league football.

HOME COUNTIES - NORTH

St Albans City started last season as outsiders but it was soon very clear that the financially powerful Weymouth squad might just be overtaken. Experienced managerColin Lippiatt built a well balanced squad capable of producing goals from all positions. Skipper Lee Clarke started the season by scoring in the first eight matches and finished in much the same vein.A massive crowd of 5,022 saw Weymouth hang on to a 3-2 home victory and the championship but the Saints held their composure and won the play offs in style to take their place in the Nationwide Conference for the first time.

HOME COUNTIES - SOUTH

For the first time in their history **Horsham YMCA** are to play in the Isthmian League. They won the Sussex County Championship in style, finishing nine points ahead of the runners up with a goaldifference of 83-31 and were only defeated four times. The Management team is as impressive as you will see in non-league football as Chairman and ex Amateur International Mick Browning and Secretary Bob Brading are backed up by an excellent committee and long serving manager John Suter who has experienced coach who took Deal Town to Wembley as his right hand man. Of course god father Victor Gladwish is also a tremendous inspiration behind the scenes. Congatulations to them all!

HOME COUNTIES - EAST

It took about half a sea son for **Braintree Town** to establish themselves at the top of the Ryman Premier Division. But once there they made sure no one would catch them, in fact from Boxing day onwards they didn't lose one of their 23 games of which only seven were drawn! An exciting F.A.Cup run took'The Iron' to the Fourth Qualifying Round where they just lost by the only goal of the game at Crawley.Their experienced manager George Borg had done it again and a first campaign at the highest non-league level was their's to cherish.

HOME COUNTIES - WEST

Boreham Wood enjoyed a dream season winning promotion and the championship in a thrilling climax to the campaign when Corby Town were pipped on goal difference. An impressive goal tally of 84-41 and only six defeats made the vital.difference. The excitement of a thrilling F.A.Trophy run to the semi-final in which they took the scalps of Conference clubs Gravesend & Northfleet and Crawley Town may well have affected their concentartion on league matters but 'Wood' are expected to continue their progress up the pyramid this season with a challenge at the top of the Ryman Premier Division.

SOUTH EAST

When a club has enjoyed successful campaigns in an impresive past it is always extra special for the modern squad to hit the headlines. Ther new **Hillingdon Borough** certainly did that with their thrilling F.A.Vase run to the final and promotion to the Southern League Division One South West. Borough had just been pipped for the Spartan South Midlands Championship by Oxford City on goal difference but a wonderful season was capped by a memorable Vase Final against a very good Nantwich side at St Andrews.

SOUTH WEST

Hereford United's return to the Football League wiill surely have been welcomed by everyone except their nearest Conference rivals. Graham Turner the owner/chairman/manager had dedicated himself to the club's successful recovery and after two heartbreaking play-off disappointments, the 'Bulls' did him proud and their two impressive displays in superb playoffs saw his club qualify to return where they belong. Good luck to them all.

F.A.CUP - BURTON ALBION

Fairy stories don't often come true in football but when a Manchester United X1 kindly helped 'The Brewers' open their glorious new ground the locals could hardly have imagined the two clubs would be playing for an F.A.Cup Fourth Round place just a few weeks later. Nigel Clough's team had beaten Leek Town, Peterborough United (after an away draw) and Burscough, conceding just one goal and their 0-0 home draw with United set up the dream match at Old Trafford. What a joy it was to seet the Chairman's face at the biig game and to watch how Nigel's son enjoyed the involvement on the bench.

NON LEAGUE FOOTBALLER OF THE YEAR
STUART THURGOOD
(Grays Athletic)

Most followers of Conference football last season would probably consider Grays Athletic as the most entertaining club in the competition and until a mid season dip in form the Essex club were favourites for promotion. Their skipper and inspirational play maker in midfield was Stuart Thurgood who was also a regular in the successful England squad. Grays finished the season in style and swept all opposition away to retain the F.A.Trophy and finished the season in third place with a 36 goals in the last fourteen games. Stuart just missed double figures with 9 goals but his assists helped five colleagues to reach ten or more in a great team season.

PAST WINNERS

2004-05	Terry Fearns (Southport)	1993-94	Chris Brindley (Kidderminster H.)
2003-04	Andrew Forbes (Winchester City)	1992-93	Steve Guppy (Wycombe Wndrs)
2002-03	Darren Way (Yeovil Town)	1991-92	Tommy Killick (Wimborne Town)
2001-02	Daryl Clare (Boston United)	1990-91	Mark West (Wycombe Wndrs)
2000-01	Ray Warburton (Rushden & Dia)	1989-90	Phil Gridelet (Barnet)
1999-00	Gary Abbott (Aldershot Town)	1988-89	Steve Butler (Maidstone Utd)
1998-99	Neil Grayson (Cheltenham Town)	1987-88	David Howell (Enfield)
1997-98	Phil Everett (Tiverton Town)	1986-87	Mark Carter (Runcorn)
1996-97	Howard Forinton (Yeovil Town)	1985-86	Jeff Johnson (Altrincham)
1995-96	Barry Hayles (Stevenage Boro)	1984-85	Alan Cordice (Wealdstone)
1994-95	Kevan Brown (Woking)	1983-84	Brian Thompson (Maidstone Utd)

NON LEAGUE MANAGER OF THE YEAR
STEVE BURR
(Northwich Victoria)

Despite the sickening disappointment of losing their treasured Nationwide Conference place after administrative rather then playing problems, manager Steve Burr stood by his Northwich Victoria squad and inspired them to bounce straight back to the top flight after a magnificent season's football. The Nationwide North Championship was won in style and an exciting F.A.Cup run was only ended by Premier League Sunderland. The Victoria Stadium was christened in a season in which the Vics scored an impressive 116 goals in senior competitions and the manager's season was capped when he was invited to assist Paul Fairclough in the management of the England squad.

PAST WINNERS

2004-05 Paul Fairclough (Barnet)	1997-98 Steve Cotterill (Cheltenham Town)
2003-04 Graham Turner (Hereford United)	1996-97 Paul Futcher (Southport)
2002-03 Gary Johnson (Yeovil Town)	1995-96 Paul Fairclough (Stevenage Boro)
2001-02 Nigel Clough (Burton Albion)	1994-95 Sammy McIlroy (Macclesfield T)
2000-01 Jeff King (Canvey Island)	
1999-00 Jan Molby (Kidderminster Harr.)	1993-94 Bill Punton (Diss Town)
1998-99 Brendan Phillips (Nuneaton Boro)	1992-93 Martin O'Neill (Wycombe Wndrs)

ENGLAND PLAYER OF THE YEAR
(Nominated by Manager Paul Fairclough)
IAN CRANEY
(Accrington Stanley)

Ian has been part of my plans for so long
and it has been a pleasure to watch him develop.
John Coleman, his club manager, has done a superb job with Ian, and he
will be missed now that they have moved into The Football League.
Ian is another player who has really exerted himself for his country.
Paul Fairclough

· INDIVIDUAL MERIT AWARDS 2005-06 ·

Mrs Jane Phillips (Godalming Town)

Godalming Town completed a spectacular 'double' by winning the Combined Counties Championship by fourteen points with a goal difference of 97-32 and the League Cup. Their hard working secretary is Mrs Jane Phillips who is dedicated to her club in a high quality residential area of Surrey, the club's committee have created a popular niche for themselves in the community and all their hard work has been rewarded with promotion to the Ryman Division One South for the first time in their history. Jane epitomises the spirit that enables little clubs like Godalming to move into a senior competition with confidence.

Steve Davis (Nantwich Town)

After a long and distinguished career in the Football League, forty year old Steve Davis probably thought he had seen the last of the big occasions as a player. So a thrilling F.A.Vase run culminating in a final at St Andrews was a tremendous reward for the player manager who had already helped his club qualify for promotion to the Northern Premier League Division One. His squad could hardly have played better in the final where controlled passing football brought three spectacular goals and a fine 3-1 victory.

Alan Carey (Bodmin Town)

In recent years Alan Carey has known what it was like to be brave runners-up as he attempted to catch St Blazey at the top of the South West Counties League with his Porthleven and later Bodmin Town clubs. Exciting successes were enjoyed in the F.A.Vase and County Cups but until last season the League seemed out of reach. Despite the emergence of the new ambitious Truro City, Bodmin held on to take the championship, so with his colleague Roger Fice and his loyal band of local playing heroes a special ambition was deservedly achieved.

Wolverhampton University Students

Last season a band of Wolverhampton University students based in Walsall, 'adopted' the Isle of Man representative side with colourful and noisy support that never got out of hand and was appreciated by all concerned. The Islanders played all their games away in the F.A.'s National League System Cup culminating in a winning final against the Cambridge County League at The Abbey Stadium and their 'supporters club were appreciated wherever they went. with noisy and happy support which gave a popular competition an extra attraction.

Andy Morris (Westfields)

Forty years ago England won the World Cup and all over the country many youngsters fell in love with the game. In Hereford a young sixteen year old Andy Morris formed a new club and became their goalkeeper for another twenty years. That club is now called Westfields F.C, competes in the Midland Football Alliance and with Hereford United's return to the Football League is the county's senior non-league club and won their Senior Cup last season. Allpay park is a lovely new home with plans in hand for a new standing enclosure and balcony for the dressing room complex. It's all a dream coming true for another of the game's real enthusiasts who could never have imagined this when Bobby Moore picked up that famous trophy.

PECKING ORDER 2005-2006   by A J Sarnecki

Position in Season 04-05	05-06	League	Lge Code	FA Cup ent (1)	FA Cup xmt (2/10)	FA Cup won (1)	FA Trophy ent (3)	FA Trophy xmt (2/6)	FA Trophy won (1)	FA Vase ent (1)	FA Vase xmt (4/6)	FA Vase won (1)	C pts	T pts	V pts	Total pts
1	1	FOOTBALL CONFERENCE National	fca	22	220	21	22	176	33				263	231		494
2	2	FOOTBALL CONFERENCE North	fcn	22	132	36	22	88	24				190	134		324
3	3	FOOTBALL CONFERENCE South	fcs	22	132	33	22	88	23				187	133		320
4	4	ISTHMIAN Premier	isa	22	88	37	22	44	25				147	91		238
5	5	SOUTHERN Premier	soa	22	88	33	22	44	23				143	89		232
6	6	NORTHERN PREMIER Premier	npa	22	88	32	23	44	19				142	85		227
8	7	ISTHMIAN First	isb	22	44	37	22	44	16				103	82		185
7	8	SOUTHERN First West	sobw	22	44	29	22	44	17				95	83		178
9	9	SOUTHERN First East	sobe	22	44	18	22	44	26				84	92		176
10	10	NORTHERN PREMIER First	npb	21	44	22	22	44	17				87	83		170
15	11	MIDLAND ALLIANCE	mda	21	0	23				22	30	31	44		83	127
12=	12=	NORTH WEST COUNTIES First	nwca	22	0	23				22	20	37	45		79	124
11	12=	EASTERN COUNTIES Premier	ecoa	19	0	18				19	28	40	37		87	124
16	14	NORTHERN First	nora	21	0	21				21	32	21	42		74	116
14	15	WESSEX Premier	wsxa	19	0	21				22	16	31	40		69	109
12=	16	NORTHERN COUNTIES EAST Premier	ncea	19	0	12				19	20	33	31		72	103
17=	17	WESTERN Premier	wesa	20	0	6				20	38	16	26		74	100
25	18	SPARTAN SOUTH MIDLANDS Premier	ssma	18	0	16				20	12	29	34		61	95
17=	19	UNITED COUNTIES Premier	ucoa	15	0	17				20	20	21	32		61	93
20	20	HELLENIC Premier	hela	14	0	21				19	14	22	35		55	90
19	21	ISTHMIAN Second	isd	17	0	15				15	18	18	32		51	83
21	22	KENT	kena	15	0	9				18	18	22	24		58	82
22	23	SUSSEX COUNTY First	ssxa	17	0	12				16	12	17	29		45	74
23	24	ESSEX SENIOR	esxs	15	0	10				21	16	7	25		44	69
26	25	COMBINED COUNTIES Premier	coca	15	0	11				16	8	16	26		40	66
24	26=	NORTHERN Second	norb	14	0	11				16	0	22	25		38	63
25	26=	NORTHERN COUNTIES EAST First	nceb	13	0	12				19	0	19	25		38	63
27=	28	NORTH WEST COUNTIES Second	nwcb	14	0	13				13	6	8	27		27	54
27=	29	EASTERN COUNTIES Second	ecob	9	0	10				14	0	15	19		29	48
29	30	SOUTH WESTERN	swe	9	0	3				13	6	15	12		34	46
30	31	WESTERN First	wesb	9	0	4				9	6	8	13		23	36
31	32=	WEST MIDLAND REGIONAL Premier	wmda	0	0	0				14	0	11	0		25	25
33=	32=	LEICESTERSHIRE SENIOR Premier	lesa	0	0	0				13	0	12	0		25	25
35	34	SUSSEX COUNTY Second	ssxb	8	0	2				9	0	5	10		14	24
32=	35=	MIDLAND COMBINATION Premier	mdca	0	0	0				14	0	9	0		23	23
34	35=	CENTRAL MIDLANDS Supreme	cmda	8	0	0				9	0	6	8		15	23
36	37	SPARTAN SOUTH MIDLANDS First	ssmb	0	0	3				8	0	4	3		12	15
38	38	WESSEX First	wsxb	4	0	0				6	0	2	4		8	12
37	39	DEVON COUNTY LEAGUE	dvc	0	0	0				4	0	4	0		8	8
40	40	UNITED COUNTIES First	ucob	0	0	0				2	0	5	0		7	7
39	41=	WEST CHESHIRE First	wcha	0	0	0				3	0	3	0		6	6
44=	41=	HELLENIC First West	hebw	0	0	0				2	0	4	0		6	6
43	43=	COMBINED COUNTIES First	cocb	0	0	0				2	0	3	0		5	5
42=	43=	CENTRAL MIDLANDS Premier	cmdb	0	0	0				3	0	2	0		5	5
42=	45	HELLENIC First East	hebe	0	0	0				1	0	3	0		4	4
41	46	WEARSIDE	wea	0	0	0				2	0	1	0		3	3
44	47	NORTHERN ALLIANCE Premier	nala	0	0	0				1	0	1	0		2	2
45	48=	SUSSEX COUNTY Third	ssxc	0	0	0				1	0	0	0		1	1
-	48=	DORSET PREMIER	dspr	0	0	0				1	0	0	0		1	1

Note: This season no Trophy Exemptions were given below Conference level.

Points are given for status (acceptance into each of the three competitions), for prestige (exemption from early rounds) and performance (number of wins, however achieved, even by walkover). Entry to the Vase is valued at one point, that to the Trophy at 4. Cup entry gives a further bonus of one point. Points for exemptions are valued at two for each round missed. The entry in the table is of the total points so gained by the given league, not the number of teams given exemptions. Finally, all wins are valued at one point, regardless of opposition: giving extra points for defeating 'stronger' opponents would be too arbitrary. After all, if they lost then they were not stronger on the day!

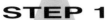

FOOTBALL LEAGUE

STEP 1

| FOOTBALL |
| CONFERENCE |

STEP 2

| CONFERENCE NORTH | CONFERENCE SOUTH |

STEP 3

| SOUTHERN PREMIER | NORTHERN PREMIER | ISTHMIAN PREMIER |

STEP 4

| SOUTHERN DIVISION 1 SOUTH &WEST MIDLAND | NORTHERN PREMIER DIV.1 | ISTHMIAN DIVISION 1 NORTH   SOUTH |

STEP 5/6

Combined Counties	Hellenic	Northern League	Spartan South Midlands	Wessex
Eastern Counties	Kent	Northern Counties East	Sussex County	Western
Essex Senior	Midland Alliance	North West Counties	United Counties	

STEP 7

Anglian Combination	Dorset County	Kent County	Midland Combination	Peterborough & District	West Cheshire
Bedford & District	Dorset Premier	Leicestershire Senior	Midland League	Reading League	West Lancashire
Brighton & Hove	East Sussex	Liverpool County	North Berkshire	Somerset County	West Midlands (reg)
Cambridgeshire County	Essex & Suffolk Border	Manchester Football	Northampton Town Lge	South Western	West Sussex
Central Midlands	Essex Intermediate	Mid Cheshire League	Northamptonshire Comb.	Suffolk & Ipswich	Wiltshire League
Crawley & District	Gloucesterhisre Co.	Mid Sussex	Northern Alliance	Teeside League	Worthing & District
Devon County	Herts Senior County	Middlesex County	Oxfordshire Senior	Wearside League	

SPONSORED BY: NATIONWIDE
Founded 1979
President: J C Thompson MBIM, Minst.M
Chairman: W J King   **Chief Executive:** J A Moules
Secretary: Kellie Discipline
51 Highfield Road, Dartford, Kent DA1 2JS
Tel: 01322 280837   Fax: 01322 294480   email: kellie@footballconference.co.uk

FINAL LEAGUE TABLE 2005-06

		P	W	D	L	F	A	Pts
1.	Accrington Stanley	42	28	7	7	76	45	91
2.	Hereford United*	42	22	14	6	59	33	80
3.	Grays Athletic	42	21	13	8	94	55	76
4.	Halifax Town	42	21	12	9	55	40	75
5.	Morecambe	42	22	8	12	68	41	74
6.	Stevenage Borough	42	19	12	11	62	47	69
7.	Exeter City	42	18	9	15	65	48	63
8.	York City	42	17	12	13	63	48	63
9.	Burton Albion	42	16	12	14	50	52	60
10.	Dagenham & Redbridge	42	16	10	16	63	59	58
11.	Woking	42	14	14	14	58	47	56
12.	Cambridge United	42	15	10	17	51	57	55
13.	Aldershot Town	42	16	6	20	61	74	54
14.	Canvey Island	42	13	12	17	47	58	51
15.	Kidderminster Harriers	42	13	11	18	39	55	50
16.	Gravesend & Northfleet	42	13	10	19	45	57	49
17.	Crawley Town	42	12	11	19	48	55	47
18.	Southport	42	10	10	22	36	68	40
19.	Forest Green Rovers	42	8	14	20	49	62	38
20.	Tamworth	42	8	14	20	32	63	38
21.	Scarborough (Relegated)	42	9	10	23	40	66	37
22.	Altrincham (-18)•	42	10	11	21	40	71	23

*Promoted via the play-offs.
•Avoided relegation after appeal.

	1	2	3	4	5	6	7	8	9	10	11	12	13	14	15	16	17	18	19	20	21	22
1 Accrington Stanley		3-2	1-0	2-1	1-0	1-0	4-2	1-0	1-2	2-0	1-1	2-3	1-1	2-1	2-0	2-0	1-0	4-0	1-1	2-1	2-1	2-1
2 Aldershot Town	1-4		0-2	1-1	1-3	2-2	3-2	3-1	1-0	2-1	3-2	0-3	3-1	0-1	1-0	2-0	0-1	2-0	2-2	0-2	1-1	2-1
3 Altrincham	0-1	5-1		1-2	2-1	0-1	1-1	0-5	1-1	2-1	2-2	0-2	1-2	0-1	3-0	2-0	1-1	1-0	1-1	2-0	0-4	0-3
4 Burton Albion	0-2	1-2	1-0		2-0	1-2	3-1	2-2	2-0	1-0	0-0	1-1	1-2	0-1	1-0	0-4	2-1	0-0	3-1	1-1	1-1	0-0
5 Cambridge Utd	3-1	0-2	4-0	2-2		3-1	2-1	1-2	2-1	2-2	1-1	1-1	1-1	2-1	0-2	2-2	2-1	2-1	1-0	2-1	0-2	2-0
6 Canvey Island	0-2	2-1	1-1	0-2	1-1		1-0	1-2	1-1	1-1	1-2	2-1	0-1	1-1	2-1	3-3	1-0	2-1	1-1	1-2	0-2	1-1
7 Crawley Town	0-1	2-0	2-0	1-1	1-0	3-1		0-0	0-2	1-0	1-2	1-3	2-2	0-2	2-0	1-3	2-0	2-0	1-2	3-0	2-2	0-1
8 Dagenham & R	1-2	2-0	2-4	3-1	1-0	2-2	0-3		2-2	1-1	1-2	1-2	1-0	0-1	3-0	3-1	0-2	3-1	2-2	2-1	1-3	0-2
9 Exeter City	1-3	4-0	3-1	1-2	4-0	0-2	4-0	3-1		0-0	1-0	1-2	4-2	1-2	1-0	2-0	1-1	5-0	0-2	3-0	1-1	1-3
10 Forest Green	1-2	4-2	5-0	1-0	1-0	1-2	2-2	0-3	0-0		0-0	1-2	2-2	2-2	0-0	1-0	5-1	1-2	2-0	1-3	0-3	1-2
11 Gravesend & N.	1-3	0-3	2-0	0-1	0-0	2-0	1-1	1-3	0-2	2-0		1-3	4-0	1-2	1-0	0-0	2-1	0-2	2-0	2-0	2-0	2-2
12 Grays Ath.	1-2	2-1	1-1	2-3	5-3	1-2	1-0	0-4	3-0	2-2	6-1		1-1	2-2	2-2	1-2	5-0	1-1	2-2	5-0	2-2	1-1
13 Halifax Town	2-2	1-1	2-0	1-0	1-0	0-2	2-2	3-0	2-0	1-0	2-0	2-1		2-1	0-0	0-0	1-0	2-1	1-1	4-0	1-0	1-0
14 Hereford United	2-2	2-1	0-0	2-0	3-0	1-1	2-1	1-1	0-2	1-1	1-1	0-2	1-0		0-1	1-0	4-0	1-1	2-0	1-0	4-0	1-0
15 Kidderminster	2-0	1-4	1-1	0-1	1-0	3-2	1-0	3-1	1-2	1-3	0-2	0-5	0-1	1-1		1-0	2-1	1-1	0-0	0-1	2-1	0-0
16 Morecambe	3-2	5-2	2-0	3-1	0-1	1-0	3-0	2-0	2-2	3-2	3-0	3-0	1-0	2-2	2-0		0-3	0-0	4-1	0-0	3-1	2-0
17 Scarborough	2-2	2-2	1-2	3-0	1-2	1-2	1-2	0-1	0-1	1-0	3-1	2-7	2-0	0-1	1-1	0-1		0-1	1-1	0-0	1-1	2-2
18 Southport	2-0	0-1	1-1	3-2	2-2	2-0	0-2	1-2	0-3	3-1	1-0	1-4	0-2	1-2	1-4	0-3	0-2		3-2	1-1	1-0	1-4
19 Stevenage B.	3-1	2-1	3-0	2-3	3-1	3-0	2-1	2-1	2-0	2-1	2-0	1-0	1-0	0-0	3-1	1-0	2-0	0-1		3-1	1-1	1-1
20 Tamworth	1-2	2-1	1-1	1-1	1-1	1-0	0-0	2-2	1-1	0-0	1-0	2-2	1-2	0-1	1-0	1-3	0-1	0-0	2-0		0-1	0-3
21 Woking	0-1	1-2	3-1	2-2	0-1	1-1	0-0	0-0	1-0	2-1	1-3	1-1	2-2	1-1	0-1	0-1	4-0	1-0	3-2	5-0		2-0
22 York City	2-4	3-2	5-0	0-1	1-0	2-1	0-0	1-1	4-2	5-1	1-0	1-2	0-2	1-3	2-2	1-1	3-1	0-0	0-1	2-1	2-1	

STEP 1
CONFERENCE
STEP 2 - P177
CONFERENCE Nth & 5th
STEP 3 - P269
NPL - SOUTHERN - ISTHMIAN PREM
STEP 4 - P269
NPL - SOUTHERN - ISTHMIAN
STEP 5/6 - P473
STEP 7 - P713

A T T E N D A N C E S

		05-06	04-05					
		Lge Pos	Lge Pos	Highest	Lowest	05-06 Average	04-05 Ave.	Diff(+/-)
1	Exeter City	7	6	6682	1782	3756	3335	421
2	York City	8	17	4921	2153	2845	2331	514
3	Hereford United	2	2	4497	1950	2793	3068	-275
4	Cambridge United	12	n/a	3697	1821	2607	n/a	n/a
5	Aldershot Town	13	4	3136	1645	2294	3043	-749
6	Stevenage Borough	6	5	3463	1403	2178	2095	83
7	Woking	11	8	3244	890	1950	2273	-323
8	Accrington Stanley	1	10	3320	959	1895	1537	358
9	Morecambe	5	7	2788	1413	1780	1751	29
10	Kidderminster	15	n/a	3241	1220	1775	n/a	n/a
11	Halifax Town	4	9	2688	1284	1749	1719	30
12	Burton Albion	9	16	2680	1235	1724	1368	356
13	Scarborough	21	13	4057	1152	1606	1791	-185
14	Crawley Town	17	12	2454	1012	1533	2018	-485
15	Grays Athletic	3	n/a	2910	858	1444	n/a	n/a
16	Tamworth	20	15	2151	823	1247	1296	-49
17	Southport	18	n/a	1807	901	1244	n/a	n/a
18	Dagenham & Redbridge	10	11	2017	932	1243	1378	-135
19	Gravesend & Northfleet	16	14	1616	618	1092	1336	-244
20	Altrincham	22	n/a	1447	688	1048	n/a	n/a
21	Forest Green Rovers	19	20	1957	548	977	855	122
22	Canvey Island	14	18	1458	358	807	804	3

Conference Play-off Action
Photos: Peter Barnes.

Play off Action

Conference South Play-off Action
Photos: Peter Barnes.

FOOTBALL LEAGUE TROPHY - CONFERENCE CLUBS ONLY

SOUTHERN SECTION

ALDERSHOT TOWN

Round	Opponents (Division)	Venue	Res	FT	HT	Goalscorers	Att.
1st Round	AFC Bournemouth (D1)	A	L	1-4	1-0	Heald 65	2,657

CRAWLEY TOWN

1st Round	Gillingham (D1)	A	L	0-2*	0-0		1, 988

DAGENHAM & REDBRIDGE

1st Round	Wycombe Wanderers (D2)	A	L	1-2*	1-0	Benson 26	1,094

EXETER CITY

1st Round	Milton Keynes (D1)	A	L	2-3	0-1	Phillips 73, Taylor 83	2,745

STEVENAGE BOROUGH

1st Round	Swindon Town (D1)	A	L	0-2	0-1		1,771

WOKING

1st Round	Nottingham Forest (D1)	H	W	3-2	1-2	Rawle 11, 53, Richards 65	3,127
2nd Round	Cheltenham Town (D2)	H	L	1-5*	1-0	Blackman 18	883

NORTHERN SECTION

ACCRINGTON STANLEY

1st Round	Rotherham United (D1) (Rotherham won 3-2 on pens)	A	D	3-3*	1-2	Mangan 18, Williams 75 Brown 104	1,888

CAMBRIDGE UNITED

1st Round	Chester City (D2)	H	W	3-0	0-0	Bridges 65, Smith 79, Onibuje 90	1,224
2nd Round	Doncaster Rovers (D2)	H	W	3-2	2-1	Morrison 8, Onibuje 34, Hanlon 78	1,435
Quarter-Final	Macclesfield Town (D2)	A	L	2-4	1-3	Bridges 17, Atkins 47	860

HALIFAX TOWN

1st Round	Bury (D2)	H	W	6-1	2-0	Midgley 17(p), Mansaram 29, 47, Haslam 52,	1,191
2nd Round	Scunthorpe United (D1)	H	L	1-3	0-1	Doughty 88	1,124

HEREFORD UNITED

1st Round	Mansfield Town (D2)	A	W	1-0	1-0	Day 12(og), Killeen 56, Parrish 76 (og)	1,393
2nd Round	Port Vale (D1)	H	W	2-1*	1-1	Carey-Bertram 14, Mkandawire 102	1,355
Quarter-Final	Scunthorpe United (D1)	H	W	2-0	2-0	Stansfield 17, Mkandawire 44	1,452
Semi-Final	Macclesfield Town (D2)	A	L	0-2	0-2		1,315

KIDDERMINSTER HARRIERS

1st Round	Darlington (D2)	H	W	2-1	1-1	Hatswell 45, Sheldon 83(p)	696
2nd Round	Boston United (D2)	A	W	3-0	3-0	Christie 26,28, Blackwood 40	1,131
Quarter-Final	Bradford (D1)	H	W	2-1	1-0	Christie 16, Penn 60	1,276
Semi-Final	Carlisle United (D2)	A	L	0-1	0-0		4,432

MORECAMBE

1st Round	Grimsby Town (D2)	A	D	1-1*	1-0	Lloyd 45 (won 4-3 on pens)	1,131
2nd Round	Bradford City (D1)	H	L	0-1	0-0		1,649

CONFERENCE v LEAGUE			PENS	PENS			D1 CLUBS	D2 CLUBS
	P	W	D	W	L	F	A	BEATEN	BEATEN
Kidderminster	4	3	0	0	0	7	3	1/1	2/3
Hereford United	4	3	0	0	0	5	3	2/2	1/2
Cambridge United	3	2	0	0	0	8	6	0/0	2/3
Halifax Town	2	1	0	0	0	7	4	0/1	1/1
Woking	2	1	0	0	0	4	7	1/1	0/1
Morecambe	2	0	0	1	0	1	2	0/1	1/0
Accrington Stanley	1	0	0	0	1	3	3	0/1	0/0
Exeter City	1	0	0	0	0	2	3	0/1	0/0
Dagenham & Redbridge	1	0	0	0	0	1	2	0/0	0/1
Crawley Town	1	0	0	0	0	0	2	0/1	0/0
Stevenage Borough	1	0	0	0	0	0	2	0/1	0/0
Aldershot Town	1	0	0	0	0	1	4	0/1	0/0

ALDERSHOT TOWN

Club Colours: Red and Blue quarters/Red/Bllue.
Change Colours: White shirts/silver/White
Club Sponsor: EBB Paper
Previous League: Isthmian League 2003
LAST SEASON
League: 13th   **F.A. Cup:** 2nd Round   **F.A. Trophy:** 1st Round
BEST PERFORMANCES
League: 4th (Conference) 2004-05 **F.A. Cup:** 2nd Round 1999-00, 2004-05, 2005-06   **Re-Founded:** 1992
F.A. Trophy: Semi-Final 2003-04 **F.A. Vase:** Quarter Final 1993-94   **Nickname:** Shots

Back row,left to right: Louis Soares, Ryan Scott,Phil Anderson, Louis Wells, Nicki Bull, Ricky Newman, John Grant and Jason Milletti. Middle Row: Sue Brown (Physio), Will Salmon, Rhys Day, Dave Wingfield, Marcus Gayle, Jamie Whisken (Physio), Mark Molesley, Andy Edwards and Paul Priddy (Goalkeeping Coach). Front Row: Sean Ridgway, Kirk Hudson, Dean Smith, Terry Brown (Manager), Mark Pritchard, Martin Kuhl (Team Coach) Darren Barnard, Ryan Williams and David Lee.

CLUB PERSONNEL

Chairman:	Karl Prentice	**Commercial Manager:**	Andy Morgan
		Press Officer:	Nick Fryer
Vice Chairman:	John McGinty	**Tel Nos:**	(B) 01483 411 500
Other Directors	Peter Bloomfield, Simon Groves		(M) 07710 947571
	John Leppard,Paul Muddell,Aidan Whelan	**Email:**	nick.fryer@isscoflex.com
President:	Bob Potter OBE		
Vice President:	Jack Rollin		

Football Secretary (c/o club):   Andy Morgan
Tel & Fax: 01252 320 211 Fax: 01252 324 347
e-mail: clubsecretary@theshots.co.uk

MANAGEMENT TEAM

Manager:	Terry Brown	**Assistant Manager:**	Martin Kuhl
Previous clubs as a manager:	Hayes (93-02)		
As a player: Hayes (twice) Wokingham Town, Slough T		**Goalkeeping Coach:**	Paul Priddy
Honours		**Youth Team Manager:**	Chris Palmer
As a manager:	Isthmian Lge 95-96, 02-03		
	Conference Play-Offs 2004-05	**Physio:**	Sue Bowen

ALDERSHOT TOWN

BEST LGE ATT.: 3,136 v Exeter City
LOWEST: 1,512 v Dagenham & Red.

No.	Date	Comp	H/A	Opponents	Att:	Result	Goalscorers	Pos
1	Aug 13	C	H	Tamworth	2641	L 0 - 2		19
2	16		A	Canvey Island	1210	L 1 - 2	Guyett 20	19
3	20		A	Halifax Town	1571	D 1 - 1	McPhee 51 (pen)	21
4	27		H	Altrincham	2235	L 0 - 2		22
5	29		A	Grays Athletic	1869	L 1 - 2	Crittenden 54	22
6	Sept 5		H	Crawley Town	2371	W 3 - 2	Robinson 29 **Sills** 43 69 (pen)	21
7	10		A	Morecambe	1429	L 2 - 5	Heald 32 McPhee 45	22
8	17		H	Stevenage Borough	2563	D 2 - 2	Williams 48 **Sills** 82	22
9	20		A	Accriington Stanley	1114	L 2 - 3	Somner 24,**Sills**71	21
10	24		H	York City	2470	W 2 - 1	Crittenden 20 Barnard 80	19
11	27		H	Hereford United	2656	L 0 - 1		21
12	Oct 2		A	Burton Albion	1493	W 2 - 1	**Sills** 65 Crittenden 66	19
13	9		H	Dagenham & Redbridge	1512	L 0 - 2		22
14	15		H	Kidderminster Harriers	2315	W 1 - 0	Coleman 62	18
15	18	LDV Vans T	A	**Bournemouth**	2657	L 1 - 4	Heald 64	
16	22	FAC 4Q	A	**Bromley**	1454	W 1 - 0	Sills 1	
17	29	C	A	Scarborough	1682	D 2 - 2	Jinadu 45 Hughes 49 (og)	16
18	Nov 5	FAC 1R	A	**Burnham**	1623	W 3 - 1	**Brough 54 Heald 71 Deen 85**	
19	12	C	H	Gravesend & Northfleet	2415	W 3 - 2	**Sills** 4 90 Barnard 31 (pen)	15
20	19		A	Cambridge United	2905	W 2 - 0	Tinnion 4 **Sills** 68	12
21	26		H	Forest Green Rovers	2290	W 2 - 1	Heald 19 Jinadu 31	11
22	Dec 3	FAC 2R	H	**Scunthorpe United**	3548	L 0 - 1		
23	10	C	H	Southport	2066	W 2 - 0	Somner 26 Barnard 36 (pen)	11
24	17	FAT 1	H	**Grays Athletic**	1771	D 1 - 1	**Barnard 50 (pen)**	
25	20	FAT 1r	A	**Grays Athletic**	852	L 0 - 1*		
26	26	C	A	Exeter City	4989	L 0 - 4		13
27	31		A	Forest Green Rovers	1051	L 2 4 4	**Sills** 45 Sulamini 90	14
28	Jan 2		H	Exeter City	3136	W 1 - 0	Somner 16	14
29	21		H	Halifax Town	2417	W 3 - 1	Holloway 21 Griffiths 45 72	12
30	24		H	Canvey Island	1800	D 2 2 2	**Sills** 52 Griffiths 75	11
31	28		A	Altrincham	1115	L 1 - 5	Barnard 33 (pen)	13
32	Feb 4		A	Stevenage Town	2010	L 1 - 2	Crittenden 17	14
33	12		A	York City	2401	L 2 - 3	Dixon 17 Williams 82	15
34	18		H	Burton Albion	2248	D 1 - 1	Dixon 44	15
35	21		H	Hererford United	2205	L 1 - 2	Holloway 60	16
36	25		H	Morecambe	1868	W 2 - 0	Dixon 2 Griffiths 46	14
37	Mar 7		H	Accrington Stanley	1645	L 1 - 4	Griffiths 71	14
38	11		H	Dagenham & Redbridge	2010	W 3 - 1	Barnard 20 Williams 45 Holloway 84	13
39	16		A	Kidderminster Harriers	1630	W 4 - 1	Barnard 5 Crittendon 16 Williams 33 Hudson 45	12
40	21		A	Woking	3244	W 2 - 1	Crittenden 28 Barnard 32 (pen)	10
41	25		H	Scarborough	2245	L 0 - 1		10
42	April 1		A	Gravesned & Northfleet	1131	W 3 - 0	Williams 44 45 Hudson 55	10
43	4		A	Tamworth	914	L 1 - 2	Matthews 53	10
44	8		H	Cambridge United	2198	L 1 - 3	Griffiths 34	11
45	15		A	Crawley Town	1764	L 0 - 2		12
46	17		H	Grays Athlettic	1879	L 0 - 3		12
47	22		H	Woking	2704	D 1 - 1	Dixon 55	12
48	29		A	Southport	1709	W 1 - 0	Barnard 68 (pen)	13

Ave. League Home Attendance: 2366   **Goals** 66 81   **Top Goalscorer:** Sills (11)

Best Position: 10th   **Worst:** 22nd

* After extra time

CONFERENCE — CONFERENCE Nth & Sth — NPL – SOUTHERN · ST'WAYS PREM — NPL – SOUTHERN · ISTHMIAN

	BULL 1	HAMILTON 12	BROUGH 5	GUYETT 15	SULAIMAN 14	CRITTENDEN 20	LEE 7	DEEN 18	BRAYLEY 22	MCPHEE 16	JINADU 6	GORDON 25	SILLS 9	SCOTT 17	WEAIT 21	WINFIELD 19	COZIC 27	SOMNER 26	MUSTAFA 2	WATSON 8	HEALD 4	WILLIAMS 28	GEARING 29	BOUCAUD 22	REED 25	HOLLOWAY 11	BARNARD 3	COLEMAN 27	FIELD 16	TINNION 15	WALKER 16	VINCENT 16	TURNER 30	SALMON 23	GRIFFITHS 27	HUDSON 22	ELPHICK 24	DIXON 10	SIMPEMBA 15	MATTHEWS 16	AHMAD 30	CROCKFORD 24	
X	X	X	X	X	X	X	X	X	S	S	S		U	U																														1
X	X		X	X	X	X	X	X	X	U		X	X	U	S																												2
X	X		X	X	X		X	S	X	X		X	S	U	U	X	X	S																								3
X	X		X	S	X		S	X	X			X	U	U	U	X	X	X	X																							4
X	S		X	X	X		X	S	X	X		X	U	S		X	X	X																								5
X	X		X	U	X		U		X			X	U	U		X	X	X	X	S																						6
X	X	S	X	S	X			X				X	U	U		X	X	X	X	X	S																					7
X	X		X	S	S			X				X	U	U		X	X	X	X	X	U	X																				8
X	S		X	X	X		U		X			X	S	U		X			X	X		X	X	S																		9
X	X		X	U	X		X		X			X	U	U					X	X		X	X	S	S																	10
X	X		X	U	X		X		X			X	S	U					X	X		X	X	S	S																	11
X	X			U	X		S		X	X		X		U					S	X	X		X	X	S	X																12
X			X	U	X							S				X	S	U	U			X		X	X		X	X	X													13
X	X		X		X			X				S	S		X	S	U		X				X	U	X	X	X															14
X	**U**			**X**	**S**		**S**			**X**		**X**	**X**	**U**			**X**	**U**		**X**	**U**			**X**	**X**	**X**			**X**													15
X	**U**			**U**	**X**		**S**			**X**		**X**	**X**	**U**			**X**	**U**		**X**				**X**	**X**	**X**	**X**														16
X		S		X	X		X			X		X	U				S			X				X	X	X	X															17
X	**X**		**U**	**X**			**S**			**U**		**X**	**X**	**U**			**X**			**X**				**X**	**X**	**X**	**X**	**U**													18
X	X		S	X	X					U		X	X	U			X			X			S	X	X				X	S												19
X	X		S	X	U				U	U		X	X	U			X			X			U	X	X				X	X												20
X			U	U			X			X		X	X	U			X			X	S			X	X				X	X	S											21
X	**X**		**U**	**X**			**X**			**S**			**X**	**U**			**X**			**S**	**X**		**S**	**X**	**X**				**X**	**X**												22
X	X		U	X			S						X	U			X			S	X		S	X	X				X	X	X											23
X	**X**		**S**	**X**			**X**						**S**	**U**	**U**		**X**			**X**	**X**		**S**	**X**	**X**				**X**	**X**												24
X	**X**		**S**	**X**			**U**						**X**	**X**	**U**	**U**	**X**			**X**	**X**		**S**	**X**	**X**				**X**													25
X	X		X	X			S						X	X	U	S	X			X	S			U	X	X			X			X										26
X	X		S	X									X	X	U	S	X			X			U		X	X			X			X	U									27
X			U	X			U						X	S	U	S	X			X	X	X			X	X			X			X										28
X	X	X		S	X								X	X	U	U	X	U		X	X				X									X	S							29
X	X	U		S	X								X	U	U		X			X	X				X									X	U	X						30
X	S	S		S	X								X	U	U		X			S	X	X			X	X								X								31
X	X			U	X									U	U		X			S	X	X	X		X	X								X		U	X					32
X	X			U	X					U				S	U		X			X	X	X			X									X		S	X					33
X	X	X		S	X									U	U		X			X	X	X			X									X	U	U	X					34
X	X	X		X									S				U			X			X	X		X	X									U	X	S	U	X		35
X			U		X					X					X		X			X					X										X	U	U	U	X			36
X	X		U		X					X					X		X	U		X					X	X									S	U	U	X				37
X	X		S		X					X					X		S	U		X					X	X									X	S		X				38
X	X		U		X									U	U				S	X	X	X			X	X									X	X			X	S		39
X	X		S		X									U	U		U			X	X	X			X	X									X	X			X	S		40
X	X		S		X									U	U		X			X	X	X			X	X									X	X			X	S		41
X				X	X								U	U	U	X			X			X			X										X	X		X	S	S	S	42
X	X			X	X								X	U	S		X			X			X												X	X		X	S	S	S	43
X	X			X						U			X	S	X	X					X				U									X	X		X	U	S	X		44
X	X			X						U			S	U	X	X					X				X									S	X		X	X	S	X		45
X	X			X									X	U	X	U		X		S					X									X			X	X	U	S	U	46
X	X			X									U	U	X	X					X				X	X								X			X	X	S	X	S	47
X	U			S	S								S	U	X		X			X					X	X								X			X	X		X	X	48

Total Appearances (Conference)

42	27	12	13	10	38	2	9	2	12	10	0	20	16	0	6	2	29	5	24	28	24	0	8	4	25	24	3	0	7	0	3	3	0	15	9	2	10	10	2	2	3	**X**
3	3	0	13	3	0	0	3	3	2	3	1	1	11	1	6	0	2	3	2	0	1	4	1	4	2	0	0	1	0	1	0	2	3	1	0	0	0	5	5	3		**S**
1	1	0	14	0	0	0	5	0	0	6	1	0	13	41	4	0	2	1	0	0	0	3	1	1	0	1	0	0	0	0	0	0	0	0	0	2	0	4	5	0	0	**U**

Cup Appearances

6	0	4	0	1	5	0	2	0	0	2	0	4	5	0	0	0	6	0	2	6	0	0	3	1	6	5	3	0	3	0	1	1	0	0	0	0	0	0	0	0	0	**X**
0	0	0	2	1	0	0	3	0	1	0	0	1	0	0	0	0	0	0	0	0	0	3	0	0	3	0	0	0	1	0	0	0	0	0	0	0	0	0	0	0	0	**S**
0	2	0	0	3	0	0	0	1	0	0	1	0	0	0	6	2	0	0	2	0	0	0	0	0	0	0	0	1	0	0	0	0	0	0	0	0	0	0	0	0	0	**U**

Also played: Nurse (23): X (M1). Kitson (24) S (3). Rose (16): U 1(17)

CURRANT SQUAD AS OF BEGINING OF 2006-07 SEASON

GOALKEEPERS	SQ NO.	HT	WT	D.O.B	AGE	P.O.B	CAREER	APPS	GOA
Nikki Bull	1	6'01"	11 03	2/10/81	24	Hastings	Aston Villa (Trainee), QPR 98/99 Rel c/s 02, Hayes (SL) 3/02, Aldershot 5/02	42	0
Louis Wells							Hayes, Aldershot 6/06		

DEFENDERS	SQ NO.	HT	WT	D.O.B	AGE	P.O.B	CAREER	APPS	GOA
Dean Smith		5'10"	11 05	13/8/86	20	Islington	Chelsea, Aldershot 6/06		
Darren Barnard	3	5'09"	12 03	30/11/71	34	Rintein	Wokingham, Chelsea £50,000 7/90, Reading (L) 11/94, Bristol C £175,000 10/95, Barnsley £750,000 8/97 Rel c/s 02, Northampton (Trial) 7/02, Grimsby 8/02 Rel c/s 04, Kilmarnock (Trial) 7/04, Mansfield (Trial) 7/04, Aldershot 8/04	26	8
Rhys Day		6'02"	13 06	31/8/82	24	Bridgend	Man City, Blackpool (3ML) 12/01, Cambridge U (L) 9/02, Mansfield (2ML) 11/02 Perm 1/03 Rel c/s 05, Aldershot 7/06		
Andy Edwards		6'02"	12 00	17/9/71	34	Epping	Southend, Birmingham £400,000 7/95, Peterborough P/E 11/96, Rushden & D 3/03 Rel c/s 04, Southend 7/04 Rel 5/06, Grays (3ML) 1/06 (05/06 5,0), Aldershot 7/06		
Louis Soares		5'09"	10 03	8/1/85	21	Reading	Reading Rel 5/05, Tamworth (2ML) 2/05, Bristol R (L) 4/05, Barnet 8/05 Rel 5/06, Aldershot 5/06		
Phil Anderson				1/3/87	19		Southend, Aldershot 7/06		
Dave Winfield	19			24/3/88	18	Aldershot	Aldershot, Staines (2ML) 2/06	12	0
Magnus Okuonghae		6'03"	13 04	16/2/86	20	Nigeria	Rushden & D, Aldershot 8/06		

MIDFIELDERS	SQ NO.	HT	WT	D.O.B	AGE	P.O.B	CAREER	APPS	GOA
Ricky Newman		5'10"	12 06	5/8/70	36	Guildford	C.Palace, Maidstone (SL) 2/92, Millwall £500,000 7/95, Reading (SL) 3/00, Reading 7/00, Brentford 7/05, Aldershot 8/06		
Mark Molseley							Hayes, Cambridge C 5/05, Aldershot 5/06		
David Lee	7	5'11"	11 08	28/3/80	26	Basildon	Tottenham cc c/s 00, Southend 8/00, Hull C 6/01, Brighton P/E 1/02, Bristol R (L) 10/02, Yeovil (Trial) 2/03, Cambridge U (Trial) 4/03, Thurrock (L) 10/03, Thurrock c/s 04, Oldham 9/04, Thurrock 12/04, Kidderminster (Trial) 1/05, Stevenage 2/05, Aldershot	2	0
Ryan Williams	28	5'04"	11 02	31/8/78	28	Chesterfield	Mansfield, Tranmere £70,000 + 8/97, Chesterfield (3ML) 11/99 £80,000 2/00, Hull C £150,000 7/01, Bristol R (2ML) 10/03 Perm 12/03, Forest Green (2ML) 12/04, Aldershot (L) 8/05, Aldershot 1/06	25	7
Sean Ridgway		5'11"	12 02	10/12/86	19		Rushden & D, Aldershot (Trial), Chesham (L) 2/06, Aldershot 6/06		
Ryan Scott	17			27/12/86	19	Aldershot	Aldershot	27	0
James Field	16					Aldershot	Aldershot, Fleet T (Season Dual)) 9/05	0	0

FORWARDS	SQ NO.	HT	WT	D.O.B	AGE	P.O.B	CAREER	APPS	GOA
John Grant		5'11"	10 07	9/8/81	24	Manchester	Crewe Rel c/s 02, Hyde (SL) 3/01, Rushden (L) 11/01, Northwich (SL) 2/02, Hereford 6/02, Telford 7/03, Shrewsbury Free c/s 04, Halifax 3/05, Aldershot 7/06		
Marcus Gayle		6'02"	14 03	27/9/70	35	Hammersmith	Brentford, Wimbledon £250,000 3/94, Rangers £900,000 3/01, Watford £900,000 8/01, Brentford 3/05, Aldershot 7/06		
Mark Pritchard		5'09"	11 00	23/11/85	20	Tredegar	Swansea, Merthyr (L) 3/05, Aldershot 7/06		
Kirk Hudson	22	6'00"	10 10	12/12/86	19	Rochford	Ipswich (Yth), Celtic 6/03, Bournemouth 8/05 Rel 10/05, Aldershot 1/06	12	2
Luke Walker	16			17/7/86	20	Basingstoke	Aldershot	1	0
Will Salmon	23			25/11/86	19	Basingstoke	Aldershot	0	0

PLAYING SQUAD

LOANEES	SN	HT	WT	DOB	AGE	POB	FROM - TO	APPS	GOA
(D)Scott Guyett	15	6'02"	13 01	20/1/76	30	Ascot	Yeovil (3M) 8/05 -	13	1
(F)Chris McPhee	16	5'11"	11 09	20/3/83	23	Eastbourne	Brighton (3M) 8/05 - Swindon (SL) 3/06, Rel 5/06, Torquay 7/06	14	2
(F)Matthew Gearing	29						Northampton (3M) 9/05 - Bedford (L) 1/06, Rugby T (L) 3/06, Rel 5/06, Rugby T 8/06	4	0
(M)Andre Boucaud	22	5'10"	11 04	10/10/84	21	Enfield	Peterborough (4M) 9/05 - Kettering 5/06	9	0
(D)Stephen Reed	25	5'08"	12 02	18/6/85	21	Barnstaple	Yeovil 9/05 - Torquay (2ML) 3/06, Rel 5/06, Torquay 5/06	5	0
(F)OmariColeman	27	5'11"	11 13	23/11/80	25	London	Lincoln C 10/05 - Gravesend (L) 11/05, Crawley 1/06, Carshalton 8/06	3	1
(D)Jason Rose	16	6'01"	10 13	28/1/85	21	Sidcup	Millwall 10/05 - Rel 1/06, Fisher 1/06, Walton & H 4/06	0	0
(F)Ashley Vincent	16	6'00"	11 07	26/5/85	21	Birmingham	Cheltenham 11/05 -	3	0
(F)John Turner	30	5'10"	11 00	12/2/86	20	Harrow	Cambridge U 11/05 - Rushden & D 1/06, Grays 8/06	4	0
(F)Leroy Griffiths	27	5'11"	13 05	30/12/76	29	London	Fisher (3M) 1/06 -	17	6
(D)Gary Elphick	24	6'01"	13 02	17/10/85	20	Brighton	Brighton (2M) 1/06 - St Albans 3/06	3	0
(F)Jonny Dixon	10	5'09"	11 01	16/1/84	22	Murcia	Wycombe (SL) 1/06 -	10	4
(M)Ian Simpemba	15	6'02"	12 08	28/3/83	23	Dublin	Crawley (SL) 3/06 - Lewes 6/06	10	0
(F)Kyle Matthews	16			18/10/87	18	Park Royal	Watford (SL) 3/06 - Northwood 7/06	7	1
(M)Ryan Crockford	24			3/12/86	19		Reading (SL) 3/06 - Sutton U 8/06	6	0

DEPARTURES	SN	HT	WT	DOB	AGE	POB	FROM - TO	APPS	GOA
(F)Bertie Brayley	22	5'09"	12 07	5/9/81	24	Basildon	Thurrock 8/05 - Margate 9/05, Grays 9/05, Margate (L) 10/05, Margate 12/05	5	0
(M)Bertrand Cozic	27	5'10"	12 06	18/5/78	28	Quimper	Kidderminster 8/05 - Rel 9/05 Team Bath 9/05, Exeter 7/06	2	0
(M)Michael Gordon	25	5'06	10 04	11/10/84	21	Wandsworth	Havant & W 8/05 - Crawley 9/05, Sutton U 12/05	1	0
(F)Chris Nurse	23			7/5/84	22	London	Sutton U 8/05 - Moor Green 10/05, Hinckley U 5/06	1	0
(F)Paul Kitson	24	5'11"	10 12	9/1/71	35	Murton	Rushden & D 8/05 - Rel 11/05 Rushden & D (Coach)	1	0
(F)Tim Sills	9	6'02"	12 02	10/9/79	26	Romsey	Kingstonian 5/03 - Oxford U 1/06, Hereford 6/06	21	10
(M)Ahmed Deen	18	5'09"	10 09	30/6/85	21		Peterborough 8/05 - Rel 1/06, Fisher 1/06	12	0
(D)Brian Tinnion	15	5'11"	12 13	28/3/68	38	Stanley	Bristol C 11/05 - Rel 1/06	7	1
(D)Tarkan Mustafa	2	5'11"	12 01	28/8/73	33	Islington	Hornchurch 1/05 - Billericay (2ML) 11/05, Rel 2/06, Worthing 3/06	8	0
(D)John Brough	5	6'00"	12 11	8/1/73	33	Heanor	Cheltenham Rel c/s 05, 6/05 - Rel 2/06, Newport C 3/06	15	0
(D)Greg Heald	4	6'01"	13 01	26/9/71	34	Enfield	Ashton U 9/05 - Retired 3/06, Thurrock 6/06	28	2
(M)Mazin Ahmad	30			2/2/85	21		Kingstonian 3/06 - Rel 5/06	7	0
(G)Dan Weait	21			12/7/87	19	Ascot	Basingstoke 8/05 - Rel 5/06	1	0
(D)Tobi Jinadu	6	6'03"		14/7/84	22	London	Sutton U 7/04 - Rel 5/06, Hayes 8/06	13	2
(D)Lewis Hamilton	12	6'00"	11 08	21/11/84	21	Derby	QPR 8/05 - Rel 5/06, Lewes 5/06	30	0
(D)Hassan Sulaiman	14			26/9/85	20	London	Wigan 7/05 - Rel 5/06	23	1
(M)Steve Watson	8			23/12/71	34	Croydon	Stevenage 7/04 - Rel 5/06, AFC Wimbledon 6/06	26	0
(M)Nick Crittenden	20	5'08"	10 11	11/11/78	27	Ascot	Yeovil 6/04 - Weymouth 5/06	41	6
(M)Gary Holloway	11			19/3/79	27	Surrey	Farnborough 3/05 - Lewes 6/06	29	3
(M)Matt Somner	26	5'11"	12 00	10/1/83	23	London	Brentford, Cambridge AL 12/04, Bristol R NC 8/05, Aldershot 8/05 - Notts County 6/06	31	3

ALDERSHOT TOWN

Ground Address:	Recreation Ground,High Street,Aldershot, Hants. GU11 1TW
Telephone:	01252 320 211
Fax:	01252 324 347
General email address:	clubsecretary@theshots.co.uk
Official website:	www.theshots.co.uk
Shots Line	09066 555 855 (Graham Brookland)
Office Opening Hours:	Monday -Friday: 9.00am-5.00pm.
	Saturday Matchdays: 9.30am-until end of match

SIMPLE DIRECTIONS:

By Road: From M3 jct 4 take A325 to Aldershot. After 5 miles take1st exit marked town centre (A323) into Wellington Ave.At Burger King roundabout take 2nd exit into High St. Ground is at eastern end of High St next to large multi storey BT Building.

By Rail: Five minutes walk from Aldershot (British Rail)

MATCH TICKETS:

Ticket office Telephone:	01252 320 211
Ticket Prices	Seats: Adults £15 OAP & U18 £8 U16-£5 Standing: Adults £12. OAP & U16 £7
Midweek Home Matchday:	Tuesday

CAPACITY:	7,500
Seats:	1,800
Covered:	6,850

Clubhouse: Open on matchdays and for special functions.
Steward: Wally Clarke 01252 320211 x 212

Refreshments: Hot and Cold snacks available on match days

Club Shop: Open matchdays with range of souvenirs, programmes replica kits available.
David Child & Janet Guest (01252 528007) for mail order. Also online sales

MATCHDAY PROGRAMME
Pages: 44 Price: £2.00
Editor: Karl Prentice, Rachel Pearce
Contact details: 01256 471 630
Local Press: Aldershot News, Farnham Herald
Local radio: County Sound (96.4, 1476khz),
BBC Southern Counties (104.6 fm)

CLUB STATISTICS

RECORDS

Attendance:	7,500
	v Brighton & Hove Albion F.A.Cup 1st Rd 18.11.00
Victory	8-0
	v Bishop's Stortford (A) League 05.09.98
Defeat	0-6
	v Worthing (A) Lg.Cup 02.03.99
Career Goalscorer:	Mark Butler 155 (92-96)
Season Goalcsorer	
Career Appearances:	Jason Chewings 400 (93)
Transfer Fee Paid:	£20,000
	to Woking for Grant Payne
Transfer Fee Received:	£6,000
	from Bedford Town for Leon Gurzmore

SENIOR HONOURS

Isthmian League Champions 2002-03
Runners-Up 1999-00

PREVIOUS LEAGUES

Isthmian: Prem 98-03, Div 1 94-98,
Div 2 93-4, Div 3 92-3

ALTRINCHAM

Club Colours: Red & white stripes/black/red
Change Colours: Blue/navy/blue
Club Sponsor: Go Goodwins Coaches
Previous League: Conference North
LAST SEASON
Conference: 18th   **F.A. Cup:** 4th Qualifying   **F.A. Trophy:** 1st Round
BEST PERFORMANCES
League: Alliance Premier Champions 79-80 80-81
F.A. Cup: 4th Round 1985-86
F.A. Trophy: Winners 1977-78 & 1985-86

Formed: 1903
Nickname: The Robins

Back Row (L-R): Stuart Coburn, Andy Cummins, Richard Acton. **Middle:** Andy Hosgood (physio), Joe O'Neill, Lewis Chalmers, Gary Talbot, Peter Band, Peter Thomson, Graham Heathcote (manager), Karl Munroe, Stephen Rose, Val Owen, Robbie Lawton, Gary Scott, Dan Heathcote (kitman). **Front:** Charles Heathcote (kitman), Steve Aspinall, Justin Bowler, Warren Peyton, Lee Hendley, Colin Potts, Steve Bushell, Eddie Hussin, Kieran Lugsden, Colin Little, Pat McFadden, Rod Thornley, Alan Ainsley (physio).

CLUB PERSONNEL

Chairman:	Geoffrey Goodwin	**Commercial Manager:**	Barry Pond
President:	Noel White	**Tel.Nos.**	(H) 0161 973 0381
			(B) 0161 928 1045
Directors:	Grahame Rowley and Andrew Shaw		(M) 07870 852 042
Secretary:	Graham Heathcote	**Press Officer:**	John Laidlar
Tel Nos:	(H) 01619 739 325	**Tel.Nos:**	(H) 0161 969 0089
	(B) 0161 928 1045		(B) 0161 928 1045
	(M) 07867 523 286		(M) 07947 769 214
e-mail:	g.heathcote@tesco.net		

MANAGEMENT TEAM

Manager: Graham Heathcote
Assistant Manager: Dalton Steele
Physio: Sean Riley
Reserve Team Manager: Neil Brown
Youth Team Manager: George Heslop
Assistants: Neil Thamason and Tony Spilsbury

ALTRINCHAM

No.	Date	Comp	H/A	Opponents	Att:	Result	Goalscorers	Pos
1	Aug 13	C	A	Stevenage Borough	2008	L 0 - 3		21
2	16		H	Accrington Stanley	1264	L 0 - 1		19
3	20		H	Forest Green Rovers	804	W 2 - 1	Searle 24 (og) Potts 51	16
4	27		A	Aldershot Town	2235	W 2 0	Olsen 71 **Little** 78	10
5	29		H	Morecambe	1447	W 2 - 0	**Little** 30 Potts 34	5
6	Sept 3		A	Hererford United	2318	D 0 - 0		7
7	10		H	Dagenham & Redbridge	876	L 0 - 5		11
8	17		A	York City	2834	L 0 - 5		13
9	20		H	Scarborough	862	D 1 - 1	**Little** 59	13
10	24		A	Cambridge United	2199	L 0 - 4		15
11	27		A	Halifax Town	1453	L 0 - 2		17
12	Oct 1		H	Crawley Town	819	D 1 - 1	**Little** 68 (pen)	18
13	8		A	Canvey Island	835	D 1 - 1	**Little** 45 (pen)	18
14	15		H	Southport	1225	W 1 - 0	Potts 69	14
15	**22**	**FAC 4Q**	**A**	**Tamworth**	**801**	**L 1 - 3**	**Smith 65 (og)**	
16	29	C	A	Burton Albion	1375	L 0 1 1		15
17	Nov 12		H	Exeter City	1366	D 1 - 1	**Little** 69	17
18	19		A	Gravesend & Northfleet	1091	L 0 - 2		19
19	26		H	Tamworth	824	W 2 - 0	**Little** 89 Robinson 90	18
20	Dec 3		A	Accrington Stanley	1436	L 0 - 1		18
21	7		A	Grays Athletic	1028	D 1 - 1	Lugsden 90	16
22	10		H	Woking	825	L 0 - 4		17
23	**17**	**FAT 1**	**A**	**Accrington Stanley**	**810**	**L 0 - 2**		
24	26	C	A	Kidderminster Harriers	2206	D 1 - 1	Aspinall 80 (pen)	17
25	31		A	Tamworth	1064	D 1 - 1	Peyton 45	16
26	Jan 2		H	Kidderminster Harriers	1165	W 3 - 0	**Little** 11 77 Thornley 36	16
27	7		H	Stevenage Borough	914	D 1 - 1	**Little** 75	17
28	21		A	Forest Green Rovers	995	L 0 - 5		17
29	28		H	Aldershot Town	1115	W 5 - 1	Robinson 7 45 Thornley 40 77 **Little** 79	17
30	Feb 4		A	Scarborough	1405	W 2 - 1	**Little** 25 Aspinall 68 (pen)	16
31	11		H	Cambridge United	1151	W 2 - 1	Robinson 3 Thormley 25	13
32	18		A	Crawley Town	1085	L 0 - 2		14
33	21		H	Halifax Town	1139	L 1 - 2	Peyton 61	15
34	Mar 11		H	Canvey Island	903	L 0 - 1		17
35	18		A	Southport	1278	D 1 - 1	Talbot 90	17
36	25		H	Burton Albion	1214	L 1 - 2	**Little** 6	17
37	April 1		A	Exeter City	3134	L 1 - 3	**Little** 18	18
38	4		H	York City	1237	L 0 - 3		18
39	8		H	Gravesend & Northfleet	688	D 2 - 2	Murphy 20 **Little** 21	18
40	11		A	Dagenham & Redbridge	1058	W 4 - 2	Potts 9 Murphy 13 Band 38 **Little** 70	18
41	15		H	Hereford United	1251	L 0 - 1		18
42	17		A	Morecambe	2118	L 0 - 2		18
43	22		H	Grays Athletic	917	L 0 - 2		18
44	29		A	Woking	1650	L 1 - 3	**Little** 71	18

Ave. League Home Attendance: 1109   **Goals**   40   76   **Top Goalscorer:** Little (17)
Best Position: 5th   **Worst:** 21st

STEP 1 — CONFERENCE

#	COBURN 1	BAND 15	MADDOX 4	TALBOT 5	ADAMS 3	MUNROE 17	HAWES 12	OWEN 8	CHALMERS 14	LITTLE 9	WILLIAMS 19	POTTS 7	THORNLEY 10	LUGSDEN 20	ACTON 13	MCKENZIE 25	ROSE 21	OLSEN 16	HENDLEY 26	MELLING 24	ASPINALL 2	HILTON 23	CLOHERTY 27	SCOTT 11	JAMES 18	WILSON 29	MCFADDEN 28	PEYTON 12	BUTLER 16	ROBINSON 19	BUSHELL 30	MURPHY 37	NORTON 18
1	X	X	X	X	X	X	X	X	X	X	X	S	S	S	U	U																	
2	X	X	X	X	X		X	X	X	X	X	X				S	U	S	S		S	U											
3	X	X		X	X		X	X	X	X	X	X		U	S		U	S	X	S													
4	X	X		X	X		X	X	X	X	X	X			U	S	X	S	S	U													
5	X	X			X		X	X	S	X	S	X			U	X	X	X	U	X	S												
6	X	X	S	X	X		X	X	S	X	X		X	X	X	S		U	X	X	U	S											
7	X	X	U	X	X	S	X	X		X	X	X	S		U	S	X	X															
8	X	X	X		X	X	X	X		X	S		U		X	X		S	S		X	U											
9	X	X	X		X	S	X	X		X		X	X	S		U	X	U	X		S												
10	X	X	X			S	X	X	U	X	S		X	X		U	X	S	X		X												
11	X	X	X		X	X	X	X	X	X	X		U	S		U	S		X	X													
12	X	X	X	X	X	X	X	X	U	X	S	X	X		S		U		S														
13	X	X	X	X	X	X	X	X	S	X	S	X		U			S	U		X													
14	X	X	S	X	X	X	X	X	S	X		X	X			U		U	X	S													
15	X	X		X	X	X	X	X	S	X		X	S			U			U	X	X	S											
16	X	X	X		X	X		X	S	X		X	S			U			U	X	X	X	S										
17	X	X	X	X	X			X	X		S		S		S		X	X	X		X	U	U										
18	X	X	X		U		X	X	X		S		S			U	X		X		X	X	S										
19	X	X	X		X	U		X	S	X		X		S			X		X		U	X	S	X									
20	X	X	X		X	U		X	S	X		X		S			X		U		S	X	X										
21	X			X	X		X	U	X		X		S		S			X		S	U	X	X	X									
22	X			X	X		X	X	X		X		S	U	S		X		S		U	X		X									
23	X	X	X				X	S	X		X	S	X	U			X		X		U	U	X		X								
24	X	X	X		X			X	X		S	X	S		S			X			U	X	U	X	X								
25	X	U	X				X	X	U	X	S		X			X		X		U	X	S	X	X									
26	X	X				U	X	X		X	S	X			X		X		U	X	S	X	X										
27	X	X	X			X	U	X		S	X	S		U			X		X		X	S	X	X									
28	X	X	X	U			X	S	X		S	X	S		U			X			X		X	X									
29	X	X	X		X			X	S	X		X	X	S			S	U	X		U		X										
30	X	X	X		X			X	S	X		X	X	S			S	U	X		U		X										
31	X	X	X		X			X	S	X		X	X	S			X		X		U		X										
32	X	X	X	S	X			X	U	X		X	X	S			U		X		X		S		X	X							
33	X	X	X	S				X	S	X		X	X	S			U	U	X		X		U	X	X								
34	X	X	U	X	X			X	S	X		S		S			U		X		X		X		X	X							
35	X	X		X	X	S		X	U	X		S	X	U			X		X		S		X		X	X							
36	X	X		X	X	U		X	S	X		X	X	S			U		X		X		X		X	X							
37	X	X	X		X	X	X		X		S	U					X		X		U	X		S	S								
38	X	X		X	X	X		X		X		S	U	S			X		X		S	X		X	U								
39	X	X		X	X	S		U	X		X	X	S			X		X		U	X		X	U									
40	X	X		X	U	S		X	X		X	X	S			X		X		S	X		X	S									
41	X	X		X	U	S		X	X		X	X	S			X		X		U	X		X	S									
42	X	X	X	X	S			S	S		X	U				X		X		X	X		X	U									
43	X	X	X	S	U	X		U	X		X	X	S			X		X		S	X		X										
44	X	X	X	X	S	X		S	X		X	X				S		X		U	X		X	U									

Total Appearances (Conference)

	COBURN	BAND	MADDOX	TALBOT	ADAMS	MUNROE	HAWES	OWEN	CHALMERS	LITTLE	WILLIAMS	POTTS	THORNLEY	LUGSDEN	ACTON	MCKENZIE	ROSE	OLSEN	HENDLEY	MELLING	ASPINALL	HILTON	CLOHERTY	SCOTT	JAMES	WILSON	MCFADDEN	PEYTON	BUTLER	ROBINSON	BUSHELL	MURPHY	NORTON	
	42	39	27	20	31	13	14	32	13	41	6	19	21	1	0	3	11	5	0	3	20	3	0	27	2	4	1	23	1	8	7	22	3	X
	0	0	2	3	1	8	0	0	16	1	6	16	3	26	0	4	5	4	4	2	3	1	0	1	1	5	1	0	6	0	1	3		S
	0	1	2	0	4	4	0	1	8	0	0	1	7	3	7	1	9	1	8	1	1	4	1	0	0	13	0	2	2	0	0	4		U

Cup Appearances

	COBURN	BAND	MADDOX	TALBOT	ADAMS	MUNROE	HAWES	OWEN	CHALMERS	LITTLE	WILLIAMS	POTTS	THORNLEY	LUGSDEN	ACTON	MCKENZIE	ROSE	OLSEN	HENDLEY	MELLING	ASPINALL	HILTON	CLOHERTY	SCOTT	JAMES	WILSON	MCFADDEN	PEYTON	BUTLER	ROBINSON	BUSHELL	MURPHY	NORTON	
	2	2	1	1	1	1	1	2	0	2	0	2	0	1	0	0	0	0	0	1	0	0	2	1	0	0	1	0	0	0	1	0		X
	0	0	0	0	0	0	0	0	2	0	0	0	2	0	0	0	0	0	0	0	0	0	0	0	0	1	0	0	0	0	0	0		S
	0	0	0	0	0	0	0	0	0	0	0	0	1	0	1	0	0	0	0	1	0	0	0	1	1	0	0	0	0	0	0	0		U

ALTRINCHAM

CURRANT SQUAD AS OF BEGINING OF 2006-07 SEASON

GOALKEEPERS	SQ NO.	HT	WT	D.O.B	AGE	P.O.B	CAREER	APPS	GOA
Stuart Coburn	1	6'01"	14 00	5/5/75	31	Manchester	Maine Road, Irlam, Trafford 94/95, Altrincham 3/97,		
							Leigh RMI 5/02, Altrincham 10/03	42	0
Richard Acton	13	6'02"	14 00	16/10/79	26	Manchester	Man City Rel 98, Woodley Sports, Runcorn, Hyde 3/01,		
							Altrincham 9/02, TNS 3/04, Altrincham c/s 04,		
							Woodley Sports (Dual) 8/04, Bangor C 9/04, Altrincham 2/05,		
							Woodley Sports (Cover) 2/05, TNS 7/05, Altrincham c/s 05	0	0

DEFENDERS									
Steve Aspinall	2			10/5/76	30		Tranmere (Jun), Poulton Vic, Macclesfield, Caernarfon, Knowsley U,		
							Winsford, Chorley, Bamber Bridge 7/99, Runcorn 12/01,		
							Vauxhall Motors, Altrincham 7/03	23	2
Gary Talbot	5			6/10/70	35	Manchester	Rhyl, Wilmslow A, Barnton, Winsford, Altrincham,		
							Northwich £2,500 1/01, Altrincham 7/02	23	1

MIDFIELDERS									
Gary Scott	3	5'08"	11 02	3/2/78	28	Liverpool	Tranmere Rel c/s 97, Rotherham 8/97 Rel c/s 99,		
							Northwich (Trial) c/s 99, Barrow, Marine 8/99, Leigh RMI 9/00,		
							Altrincham 10/00	28	0
Peter Band	4			18/12/73	32	Lancashire	Bollington U, Hyde 6/98, Altrincham 7/02, Northwich 12/04,		
							Altrincham 6/05	39	1
Steve Bushell	6	5'09"	11 06	28/12/72	33	Manchester	York, Blackpool 7/98 Rel c/s 01, Stalybridge 7/01,		
							Halifax 11/01 Rel 5/06, Altrincham (L) 11/05, Altrincham 7/06	7	0
Robbie Lawton	7			14/6/79	27	Liverpool	Marine, Vauxhall Motors, Caernarfon, Vauxhall Motors 7/99, Altrincham 6/06		
Val Owen	8			11/2/71	35	Manchester	Local, Hyde c/s 95, Northwich 6/98, Hednesford 6/00,		
							Southport 9/01, Northwich 10/01, Halifax AL 12/03 Rel 4/04,		
							Altrincham 10/04	32	0
Warren Peyton	11	5'09"	11 03	13/12/79	26	Manchester	Bolton, Rochdale 10/99 Rel c/s 00, Bury 9/00, Nuneaton 7/01,		
							Doncaster 12/02, Leigh RMI 7/03 Rel c/s 05, Altrincham 11/05	24	2
Lewis Chalmers	14			4/2/86	20		Altrincham	29	0
Karl Munroe	17	6'00"	10 08	23/9/79	26	Manchester	Swansea, Macclesfield 10/99 Rel c/s 04, Halifax 8/04 Rel 3/05,		
							Northwich 3/05, Altrincham 7/05	21	0
Stephen Rose	20	6'00"	10 07	23/11/80	25	Salford	Man Utd Rel c/s 00, Bournemouth (L) 2/00, Bristol R 8/00 Rel c/s 01,		
							York C (Trial) 3/01, Chester 7/01 Rel 5/02, Droylsden (L) 12/01,		
							Altrincham 8/02, Radcliffe B (L) 11/05	16	0
Eddie Hussin		5'10"	12 00	13/12/77	28	Liverpool	Everton Rel c/s 97, Northwich, Winsford, Chorley, Marine, Winsford,		
							Marine 8/00, Altrincham 6/04		
Colin Potts				26/2/78	28	Lancashire	Rochdale, Chorley, Bamber Bridge, Morecambe, Lancaster C 12/00,		
							Stalybridge 5/02, Northwich 11/03, Stalybridge 2/04, Northwich 7/04,		
							Altrincham 8/04	35	4

FORWARDS									
Colin Little	9	5'10"	11 00	4/11/72	33	Wythenshawe	Rossendale, Hyde, Crewe £50,000 2/96 Rel c/s 03,		
							Mansfield (2ML) 10/02, Macclesfield (L) 12/02, Macclesfield (L) 3/03,		
							Macclesfield 5/03 Rel 3/04, Halifax 3/04, Altrincham 7/04	42	17
Rod Thornley	10	5'09"	11 05	2/4/77	29	Bury	Warrington T, Doncaster 9/97, Warrington T 11/97, Salford C,		
							Congleton, Altrincham 3/01, Trafford (L) 9/04	24	4
Joe O'Neill	12	6'00"	10 05	28/10/82	23	Blackburn	Preston, Bury (SL) 7/03, Mansfield (3ML) 8/04, Chester (3ML) 1/05,		
							York 7/05 Rel 5/06, Altrincham 6/06		
Justin Bowler	15	5'07"	12 00	26/6/86	20	Leeds	Leeds, Halifax 8/05, Altrincham 7/06		
Peter Thomson	16	6'03"	12 06	30/6/77	29	Crumpsall	Stand Ath, Bury 11/95 Rel c/s 97, Chorley c/s 97, Lancaster,		
							NAC Breda £10,000, Luton £100,000 9/00 Rel 1/02,		
							Rushden & D (L) 11/01, Chester (Trial), Morecambe 3/02,		
							Southport 7/02, Lancaster 12/03, Stafford 7/05, Altrincham 6/06		
Pat McFadden	18			4/4/87	19		Fletcher Moss, Altrincham 10/05, Trafford (Dual) 2/06, Radcliffe B (Dual) 8/06	6	0
Lee Hendley	19			7/4/87	19		Altrincham, Trafford (Dual) 2/06	4	0
Kieran Lugsden	21			4/4/86	20		New Mills, Altrincham 4/03, Radcliffe (L) 10/05, Radcliffe (Dual) 8/06	27	1

PLAYING SQUAD

Loanees	HT	WT	DOB	AGE	POB	From - To	APPS	GOA
(G)Chris Cloherty	6'01"					Trafford 9/05 -	0	0
(F)Kyle Wilson	5'10"	11 05	14/11/85	20	Wirral	Crewe (2M) 10/05 - Barrow (3ML) 12/05, Rel 5/06, Barrow 8/06	5	0
(G)Kurt Edginton			30/10/68	37		Flixton (Cover) 3/06 -		

DEPARTURES	HT	WT	DOB	AGE	POB	FROM - TO	APPS	GOA
(D)George Melling						Morecambe - Clitheroe 10/05, Lancaster 11/05, Clitheroe 1/06, Leigh RMI 2/06	5	0
(M)James Olsen	5'10"	12 00	23/10/81	24	Bootle	Vauxhall Motors 7/05 - Rel 10/05, Vauxhall Motors 10/05, Barrow 2/05, Southport 7/06	9	1
(M)Steve Hawes	5'08"	11 04	17/7/78	28	High Wycombe	Stocksbridge PS 6/05 - Rel 10/05, Stocksbridge P S 10/05	14	0
(F)Gary Williams			19/7/79	27	Burnley	Leigh RMI 8/05 - Rel 10/05, Colne 11/05, Clitheroe 11/05, Leigh RMI 1/06	12	0
(F)Lutel James	5'08"	11 00	2/6/72	34	Manchester	Accrington 7/05 - Garforth (L) 8/05, Rel 11/05, Bradford PA 3/06	3	0
(D)Chris Butler			18/10/84	21	Wavertree	Accrington 11/05 - Vauxhall Motors 12/05, Barrow 1/06	1	0
(D)Kirk Hilton	5'07"	10 00	2/4/81	25	Flixton	Halifax 2/05 - Ashton U (L) 11/05, Rel 12/05, Ashton U 12/05	4	0
(M)Nehru McKenzie			26/4/82	24	Manchester	Hyde c/s 05 - Mossley (L) 10/05, Rel	7	0
(M)James Robinson	5'09"	10 05	18/9/82	23	Whiston	Accrington 11/05 - Richmond Eagles (Aust) 2/06	14	4
(M)Ged Murphy	5'10"	11 03	19/12/78	27	Manchester	Droylsden 11/05 - Radcliffe B (L) 11/05 Rel 6/06, Stafford R 8/06	23	2
(D)Mark Maddox	6'01"	12 07	1/3/73	33	Liverpool	Barrow 12/98 - Rel 6/06, Leigh RMI 7/06	29	0
(M)Blake Norton			10/12/83	22	Manchester	Worksop 3/06 - Rel 7/06, Worksop 8/06	6	0
(M)Richard Norris			5/1/78	28	Birkenhead	Northwich 2/05 - Rel 7/06		
(D)Chris Adams			10/10/75	30	Manchester	Ashton U 5/01 - Rel 7/06	32	0

ALTRINCHAM

Ground Address:	Moss Lane, Altrincham,Cheshire WA15 8AP
Tel No:	0161 928 1045
Fax:	0161 926 9934
General email address:	g.heathcote@tesco.net
Official website:	www.altrinchamfc.com
Club call:	09066 555902

SIMPLE DIRECTIONS

By Road	From M6 junction19, turn right towards Altrincham into town centre (approx 15 minutes). Turn down Lloyd Street, past Sainsburys on the right. Tesco Extra on left. Then follow signs for Altrincham F.C.
Parking:	Carpark adjoining ground.

MATCH TICKETS

Ticket office Telephone:	0161 928 1045
Ticket Prices:	Seats: £12 OAP & U16 £7-5 Standing: £10 OAP & U16 £6-4
Capacity:	6,085
Seats:	1,154
Covered:	Three sides
Clubhouse:	Bar under th stand open on matchdays only.
Refreshments:	Two snack bars on the ground
Club Shop:	Yes. Contact: Jenny Heslop 0161 928 1045

Local Press:	Sale & Altrincham Messenger and Manchester Eevening News
Local Radio:	Piccadilly Radio, Signal Radio and GMR (BBC)

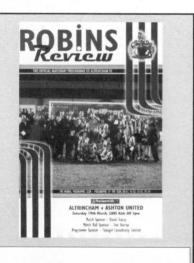

MATCHDAY PROGRAMME
Pages: 40   Price: £1.80
Editor: Grahame Rowley
Contact Details: (H) 0161 980 1741
(M) 07720 606 897

CLUB STATISTICS

RECORDS

Attendance:	10,275 Altrincham Boys v Sunderland Boys English Schools Shield 1925
Victory:	9-2 V Merthyr Tydfil Conference 1990-1991
Defeat:	Unknown
Career Goalscorer:	Jack Swindells 252 1965-71
Career Appearances:	John Davison 677 1071-86
Transfer Fee Paid:	£15,000 tp BLackpool for Keith Russell
Transfer Fee Received:	£45,000 from Scarborough for Kevin Ellison

SENIOR HONOURS   F.A.Trophy Winners 77-78 85-86
Football Alliance Champions 79-80 80-81
Condference North v South Play Off Winners 2004-05
Northern Premier League Champions 98-99
Cheshire Senior Cup Winners 04-05 33-34 66-67 81-82

PREVIOUS

Leagues:	Manchester 03-11, Lancashire Comb.11-19, Cheshire County 19-68, N.P.L. 68-79 97-99 Conference 79-97 99-00 Conference North 2004-2005
Grounds:	Pollitts Field 1903-1910

BURTON ALBION

Club Colours: Yellow /black/black
Change Colours: All gray & royal blue
Club Sponsor: Bison Concrete Products Ltd and Knott Ltd.
Previous League: Northern Premier
LAST SEASON
League: Conference: **F.A. Cup:** 3rd Round   **F.A. Trophy:** 1st Round
BEST PERFORMANCES
League: 14th (Conference) 2003-2004
F.A. Cup: 3rd Rd 1955-56 1984-85 2005-06
F.A. Trophy: Finalists 1986-87

Formed: 1950
Nickname: Brewers

The squad that won the Bass Charity Vase competition durign the pre-season.

CLUB PERSONNEL

Chairman:	Ben Robinson	**Commercial Manager:**	Fleur Robinson
Vice-Chairman:		**Tel Nos:**	As for secretary
Company & Club Secretary:	F.E.L.Spires		
Additional Directors:	P.Brown, P.Simpson,	**Press Officer:**	Rex Page
	C. Simpson, C.Brodie, D.Amott,	**Tel No:**	(B) 01283 512 345
	J.Williams and R. Bowring		

Secretary:	Fleur Robinson c/o BAFC
Tel Nos:	(B) 01283 565 938
	(M) 07774 102 485
E-mail:	fleur@burtonalbionfc.co.uk

MANAGEMENT TEAM

Manager:	Nigel Clough	**Coach**	Andy Garner
Previous clubs as a manager:	None		
As a player:	Heanor Town, Nottingham Forest	**Physio:**	Matt Brown
	Liverpool and England		
Honours as a manager:	N.P.L. Champions 2001		
As a player:	England Full & u21 caps		

BURTON ALBION

No.	Date	Comp	H/A	Opponents	Att:	Result	Goalscorers	Pos
1	Aug 13	C	H	Grays Athletic	1654	D 1 - 1	Webster 49 (pen)	10
2	16		A	Halifax Town	1681	L 0 - 1		17
3	20		A	Woking	1692	D 2 - 2	**Shaw** 10 Harrad 32	19
4	27		H	Canvey Island	1423	L 1 - 2	Todd 8	20
5	29		A	Southport	1253	L 2 - 3	Krief 70 (og) Hall 73	20
6	Sept 3		H	Scarborough	1336	W 2 - 1	Webster 23 (pen) 52	18
7	10		H	Accrington Stanley	1374	L 0 - 2		20
8	17		A	Dagenham & Redbridge	1149	L 1 - 3	Anderson 78	20
9	20		H	Morecambe	1352	L 0 - 4		22
10	24		A	Exeter City	4025	W 2 2 1	Stride 81 **Shaw** 85	21
11	27		A	Cambridge United	2298	D 2 - 2	Anderson 11 Gilroy 70	20
12	Oct 2		H	Aldershot Town	1493	L 1 - 2	Todd 30	22
13	8		H	Stevenage Borough	1319	W 3 - 1	Webster 5 **Shaw** 11 30	19
14	15		A	Hereford United	2493	L 0 - 2		21
15	22	FAC 4Q	H	**Leek Town**	**1467**	W 2 - 0	**Shaw 8 23**	
16	29	C	A	Altrincham	1375	W 1 - 0	Anderson 20	18
17	Nov 5	FAC 1R	A	**Peterborough United**	**3856**	D 0 - 0		
18	12	C	A	York City	2411	W 1 - 0	Hall 77	16
19	16	FAC 1R r	H	**Peterborough United**	**2511**	W 1 - 0	**Harrad 73**	
20	19	C	H	Crawley Town	1353	W 3 - 1	Harrad 12 **Shaw** 75 80	13
21	26		H	Kidderminster Harriers	1847	W 1 - 0	Bell 50	12
22	Dec 6	FAC2R	H	**Burscough**	**4499**	W 4 - 1	**Gilroy 8 37 Stride 16 Harrad 84**	
23	10	C	H	Gravesend & Northfleet	1733	D 0 - 0		13
24	13		A	Forest Green Rovers	548	L 0 - 1		13
25	17	FAT 1	H	**Worksop Town**	**1359**	L 0 - 1		
26	26		H	Burton Albion	2151	D 1 - 1	Melton 35	15
27	30		A	Kidderminster Harriers		W 1 - 0	Gilroy 65	
28	Jan 2		H	Tamworth	2680	D 1 - 1	**Shaw** 58	13
29	8	FAC 3R	H	**Manchester United**	**6191**	D 0 - 0		
30	18	FAC 3Rr	A	**Manchester United**	**53564**	L 0 - 5		
31	21	C	H	Woking	2061	D 1 - 1	Hall 43	14
32	24		H	Halifax Town	1540	L 1 - 2	Taylor K 8	15
33	28		A	Canvey Island	741	W 2 - 0	Taylor 26 43	12
34	31		A	Grays Athletic	858	W 3 - 2	**Shaw** 17 Hall 23 Webster 57	10
35	Feb 4		A	Morecambe	1855	L 1 - 3	Ducros 83	10
36	10		H	Exeter City	1924	W 2 - 0	Gilroy 62 Harrad 64	9
37	18		A	Aldershot Town	2248	D 1 - 1	Webster 3	19
38	21		H	Cambridge United	1577	W 2 - 0	Moore 46 Harrad 60	10
39	25		A	Accrington Stanley	1946	L 1 - 2	**Shaw** 45	10
40	Mar 11		A	Stevenage Borough	2081	W 3 - 2	**Shaw** 63 Webster 79 Moore 90	9
41	18		H	Hereford United	2512	L 0 - 1		9
42	25		A	Aldershot town	1214	W 2 - 1	Webster 3 Harrod 47	9
43	April 1		H	York City	2605	D 0 - 0		9
44	8		A	Crawley Town	1341	D 1 - 1	Clare 59	9
45	15		A	Scarborough	1808	L 0 - 3		9
46	18		H	Southport	1488	D 0 - 0		9
47	22		H	Forest Green Rovers	2331	W 1 - 0	Harrad 44	9
48	25		H	Dagenham & Redbridge	1235	D 2 - 2	Clare 14 Harrad 23	9
49	29		A	Gravesend & Northfleet	912	W 1 - 0	Taylor 35	9

Ave. League Home Attendance: 2590   **Goals** 57 59   **Top Goalscorer:** John Shaw (12)

Best Position: 9th   **Worst:** 22nd

CRANE 1	HENSHAW 2	TINSON 5	STRIDE 7	WEBSTER 3	CORBETT 4	GILROY 11	DUCROS 10	TODD 19	SHAW 9	HARRAD 14	CLOUGH 20	HALL 12	ANDERSON 8	AUSTIN 6	GRAVES 15	M TAYLOR 13	BACON 18	DEENEY 31	BELL 22	SEDGEMORE 16	ROWETT 17	AYRES 21	K TAYLOR 23	MOORE 24	BRAYFORD 25	CLARE 26	#
X	X	X	X	X	X	X	X	X	X	X	S	S	S	U	U												1
X	X	X	X	X	X	X	X	X	X	X	S	S	S	U	U												2
X	X	X	X	X	X	X	X	X	X	X	U	S	S	U	S												3
X	X	X	X	X	X	X	X	X	X	X	U	S	S	U	S												4
X	X	X	X	X	X	U	S	S	X	X	X	S	X	U	X												5
X	X	X	X	X	X			S	X	X	X	S	U	X	U	U											6
X	X	X	X	X	X			X	X	U	U	S	S	X	U		X										7
X	X	X	X	X	X			S	X	S	X	U	S	X	U		X										8
X	U	X	X	X	X			X	X	X	U	S	S	X	U		X										9
X	X	X	X	X	S	S	U	X	X	U	X	S	X				X										10
X	U	X	X	X	X	X	S	U	U	X	X	U					X										11
X	U	X	X	X		X	X	U	X	X	X	U	U	U	S												12
U	S	X	X	X	X	U	S	X	S		X	X	X						X	X							13
U	U	X	X	X	X		S	X	X	S		X	X	X	S				X	X							14
	X	X	X	X	X	X	S	X	S	S	X	X	X			U		X				U					15
U	X	X	X	X	X	U	S	X	S		X	X	X		U		X	X									16
	X	X	X	X		U	S	X	X	U	X	U	X		U		X		X								17
X	X	X	X	S		U	S	X	X	U	X		X		U		X	X	X								18
X	X	X	X	S	X	U	S	X	X	U	X		X		U		X		X								19
U	X	X	X	S	X	S	S	S	X	X	U	X			X	X	X										20
X	X	U		X	X	U	U	X	X		X	U	X			X	X	X	S								21
X	X	X		X	X	S	X	X		X	U	X		U		X	X	S									22
X	X	X		X	X	S	S	X	X		X	S	X	U	U		X										23
U	X	X		X		X	X	S	X		S	X	X	U	U		X		X								24
X	X	X		X	X	S	U	X	X		S	S	X		U		X	X	X								25
S	X	X		X	X	X	U	X	X		X	S	X		U		X		U								26
X	X	S		X	X	X	S	X	X	U	X	S	X		U		X										27
S	X	X		X	X	X	X	S	U		X		U		X		X	X	U								28
U	X	X		X	X	X	S	X	X	U	X	S	X		U		X										29
S	X	X	S		X	X	X	X		X	S	X		U		X		X									30
U	X	X	S	X	X	S	U	X	X		X	U	X		X			X									31
X	X	X	X	X	X	U	X	S		X	U	X		X		U	S		X								32
S	X		X		X	X	S	X	X	U	X	S	X				X		X								33
S		X	X	X	X	X		X	X	U	X		X							U	X	S					34
S	X	X	X	X	X		X	X	U		X		X							X	S	U					35
U	X	S	X	X	X	U		X	X		X		S	U	X		X	X	X								36
S	X		X	X	X	S		X	X	U	X		X		X		X	X									37
S	X		X	X	X	X		S	X	U	S		X		X		X	X									38
X	X	S	X	X	S	X		X	X	U	X		X				X	S									39
U	X	X	X	X	X	S		X	X		X	U	X		X		X	S									40
U	X	X	X	X	X	S		X	X		X	U	X		X		X	S									41
S	X		X	X	X	X		X	X		X	U	X		X		X	S		S							42
U	X	X	X	X	X	X		S	X		X	U		X		S	U		X								43
S	X	X	X	X	U	X		S	X		X	U		X		X	S		X								44
S	X	X	X	X	U	X		S	X		X		U		X		X	S	U	X							
U	X	S	X	X		X	X		X				S		X		X	S	U	X							
S	X	X	X		X	X		X	S		X	U		X		X	S	U	X								
X	X	X		X		X		U	X		X	U	U	U	X		X		S	U	X						
X	X	X	U	X		X	X	S	X		X		U		X	S	S	S	X								

Total Appearances (Conference)

12	16	41	34	33	38	31	23	10	35	32	4	27	8	28	1	0	4	30	6	9	15	0	16	2	0	7	X
0	12	0	3	1	2	3	7	11	6	7	3	10	12	2	3	0	1	0	0	0	2	0	2	13	1	1	S
2	13	0	1	1	0	2	6	5	1	3	16	1	4	10	11	23	0	0	0	1	0	3	0	1	4	0	U

Cup Appearances

0	5	7	6	3	5	6	3	1	7	6	0	6	1	7	0	0	0	7	0	6	1	0	0	0	0	0	X
0	1	0	0	1	1	0	3	4	0	1	1	1	3	0	0	0	0	0	0	1	0	0	0	0	0	0	S
0	1	0	0	0	0	1	1	2	0	0	3	0	2	0	0	7	0	0	0	0	0	1	0	0	0	0	U

BURTON ALBION

CURRANT SQUAD AS OF BEGINING OF 2006-07 SEASON

GOALKEEPERS	SQ NO.	HT	WT	D.O.B	AGE	P.O.B	CAREER	APPS	GOA
Stuart Tomlinson	1	6'01"	11 02	10/5/85	21	Chester	Crewe, Stafford R (3ML) 12/04, Burton (SL) 5/06		
Martin Taylor	13	5'11"	13 11	9/12/66	39	Tamworth	Mile Oak, Derby 7/86 Rel c/s 97, Carlisle (3ML) 9/87,		
							Scunthorpe (2ML) 12/87, Crewe (L) 9/96, Wycombe (L) 3/97,		
							Wycombe 6/97, Barnsley (L) 3/03, Telford (Pl/Coach) 5/03,		
							Burton 5/04	0	0
Kevin Poole	30	5'10"	11 11	21/7/63	43	Bromsgrove	Aston Villa, Northampton (Loan) 11/84, Middlesbrough 8/87,		
							Hartlepool (L) 3/91, Leicester £40,000 7/91, Birmingham 8/97,		
							Bolton 10/01, Derby 7/05, Burton 8/06		

DEFENDERS									
Gary Rowett	2	6'00"	12 10	6/3/74	32	Bromsgrove	Cambridge U, Everton £200,000 3/94, Blackpool (3ML) 1/95,		
							Derby £300,000 7/95, Birmingham £1 mill 8/98,		
							Leicester £3 mill 7/00, Charlton £2.5 mill 5/02 Ret 5/04,		
							Derby U18 Coach, Burton 11/05 (05/06 17,0)	17	0
Aaron Webster	3			19/12/80	25	Burton	Burton	34	8
Darren Tinson	5	6'00"	11 04	15/11/69	36	Birmingham	Connahs Quay, Colwyn Bay, Northwich, Macclesfield £10,000 2/96,		
							Shrewsbury 7/03 Rel c/s 05, Burton 6/05	41	0
Ryan Austin	6	6'03"	13 08	15/11/84	21	Stoke	Crewe (Sch), Burton (3ML) 8/04, Burton 12/04	30	0
Terry Henshaw	15	5'10"	10 10	29/2/80	26	Nottingham	N.County, Burton (L) 3/99, Burton 7/99	28	0
John Brayford	17			29/12/87	18		Burton	1	0

MIDFIELDERS									
Andrew Corbett	4	6'00"	11 04	20/2/82	24	Worcester	Kidderminster, Redditch (L) 3/01, Solihull (L) 8/02, Solihull 11/02,		
							Nuneaton 7/03, Burton 11/03	40	0
Darren Stride	7			28/9/75	30	Burton	Burton	37	1
Lee Fowler	8	5'07"	10 00	10/6/83	23	Cardiff	Coventry, Cardiff (L) 3/03, Huddersfield (3ML) 8/03 (Perm) 11/03,		
							Scarboough (L) 11/05 (Perm) 1/06, Burton 5/06		
Andy Ducros	10	5'04"	9 08	16/8/77	28	Evesham	Coventry Rel c/s 99, Nuneaton 8/99, Wigan (Trial) 11/99,		
							Kidderminster £100,000 7/00, Nuneaton (L) 10/02 (L) 12/02,		
							Burton Free 2/03	30	1
Keith Gilroy	11	5'10"	10 13	8/7/83	23	Sligo	Sligo R, Middlesbrough 9/00, Scarborough Free 3/03,		
							Darlington 2/05 Rel c/s 05, Burton 7/05	34	3
Chris Hall	12			3/3/83	23	Lincoln	Lincoln U, Burton 5/04	37	4
Shaun Harrad	14	5'10"	12 04	11/12/84	21	Nottingham	N.County, Gresley (4ML) 9/02, Tamworth (L) 9/04, Burton 7/05	39	7
Danny Holmes	19	6'00"		17/11/86	19		Port Vale Rel c/s 06, Burton 7/06		
Nigel Clough	20	5'09"	12 03	19/3/66	40	Sunderland	AC Hunters, N.Forest 9/84, Liverpool £2.275 mill 6/93,		
							Man City 1/96 £1.5 mill, N.Forest (3ML) 12/96, Sheff Wed (L) 9/97,		
							Burton 10/98 Pl/Man 3/99	7	0

FORWARDS									
Daryl Clare	9	5'09"	11 00	1/8/78	28	Jersey	Grimsby Rel c/s 01, Northampton (3ML) 11/99,		
							Northampton (L) 11/00, Cheltenham (L) 12/00, Boston U 7/01,		
							Chester £25,000 10/02, Boston U Undisc 11/04, Crawley 8/05,		
							Burton 3/06	8	0
Jon Shaw	16	6'01"	12 09	10/11/83	22	Sheffield	Sheff Wed Rel 11/04, York (2ML) 11/03 Burton 11/04,		
							Cheltenham (Trial) 11/04	41	11
Steve Scoffham	18	5'11"	11 04	12/7/83	23	Munster, Ger	Gedling, Notts County 2/04, Burton 8/06		

PLAYING SQUAD

LOANEES	HT	WT	DOB	AGE	POB	FROM - TO	APPS	GOA
(F)Danny Bacon	5'10"	10 12	20/9/80	25	Mansfield	Lincoln C 9/05 -	5	0
(M)Lee Bell	5'11"	11 05	26/1/83	23	Crewe	Crewe 10/05 -	6	1
(M)Jake Sedgemore	6'01"	12 10	20/10/78	27	Wolverhampton	Bury 11/05 - Rel 1/06, Kidderminster 1/06	9	0
(M)Kris Taylor	5'09"	13 05	12/1/84	22	Stafford	Walsall (SL) 1/06 -	18	4

DEPARTURES	HT	WT	DOB	AGE	POB	FROM - TO	APPS	GOA
(D)Barry Miller	6'00"	11 07	29/3/76	30	Ealing	Leigh RMI 12/04 - Rel 8/05, Worksop 9/05, Ilkeston 3/06		
(F)Craig Dudley	5'11"	11 02	12/9/79	26	Ollerton	Oldham 5/02 - Hyde U 8/05, Ashton U 12/05		
(G)Daniel Crane	6'03"	14 11	27/5/84	22	Birmingham	WBA 8/04 - Moor Green (3ML) 10/05, Rushden & D 1/06	12	0
(D)Lee Ayres	6'01"	11 00	28/8/82	23	Birmingham	Tamworth £10,000 8/04 - Rel 4/06	0	0
(G)Saul Deeney	6'01"	11 07	12/3/83	23	Derry	N.County 10/05 - Rel 5/06, N.County 7/06	30	0
(F)Dale Anderson	5'11"	11 12	10/11/79	26	Birmingham	Bromsgrove 3/99 - Northwich (L) 2/06,		
						Moor Green (SL) 3/06, Rel 5/06, Moor Green 5/06	20	3
(F)Christian Moore			4/11/72	33	Derby	Kettering 1/06 - Hucknall 5/06	15	2
(M)Eric Graves	5'08"		8/9/86	19	Derby	Stoke c/s 05 - Gresley R (L) 10/05, Gainsborough T (4ML) 1/06,		
						Gainsborough T 6/06	4	0
(F)Andy Todd	6'00"	11 03	22/2/79	27	Nottingham	Hucknall T 7/05 - Accrington (L) 1/06, Accrington 6/06	21	3

BURTON ALBION

Ground Address: Pirelli Stadium, Princess Way, Burton DE13 0AR

Tel No: 01283 565 938

Fax: 01283 565 938

General email address: bafc@burtonalbionfc.co.uk

Official website: www.burtonalbionfc.co.uk

Simple Directions: From South - M1 -take junction 23A onto the A50 towards Derby, then A3.and tfrom the south take the second Burton exit. and from North - take the first exit onto A5121 Burton/VClay Mills -over the first island and right at the next one into Princess Way. Ertrance is 300 yards on right .

Rail Travel: Nearest railway stationis Burton on Trent (one mile)

Pirelli Stadium   Capacity
Seats
Cover:
Clubhouse:
Shop:
Refreshments

Local Press:
Local Radio:

MATCHDAY PROGRAMME
Pages: 48   Price: £2.00
Editor: Ian Hawkins
Tel No: 0870 190 0060
email: bafc@burtonalbionfc.co.uk

CLUB STATISTICS

RECORDS

Attendance: 6,191
v Manchester Utnited, 3rd Rd F.A.Cup 2005-2006
(22,500 v Leicester City F.A.Cup at Derby Co. 1984)

Career Goalscorer: Ritchie Barker 157

Career Appearances: Phil Annable 567

Transfer Fee Paid: £21,000
To Kidderminster Harriers for R.Jones and J.Pearson

Transfer Fee Received: £60,000
From Crystal Palace for Darren Carr

SENIOR HONOURS   F.A.Trophy Finalists 1986-87
Southern League Div1 North R-up (2)
Northern Premier League Champions 2001-02
Birmingham Senior Cup 53-54 70-71 R-Up 86-87
Staffordshire Senior Cup 1955-56

PREVIOUS

Leagues: W. Midlands 1950-58,
Southern 58-79 80-2001,
N.P.L. 79-80 01-02

Ground: Wellington Street 50-57
Eton Park 57-2005

CAMBRIDGE UNITED

Club Colours: Amber/black/amber
Change Colours: Navy & sky blue/sky blue/sky blue
Club Sponsor: The Global Group
Previous League: Football League
LAST SEASON
Conference: 12th   **F.A. Cup:** 4th Qual. Rd.   **F.A.Trophy:** 1st Round
LDV Trophy: Regional Quarter Final.
BEST PERFORMANCES
League: 5th Div.2 91-2 **F.A. Cup:** 6th Rd 1990 (Div 4 record) **F.League.Cup:** 5th Rd 1993

Founded: 1912
Nickname: The 'U's'

Back Row (L-R): Andy Duncan, Mark Peters, Robbie Simpson, Michael Morrison, Michael Gash, Adam Davies, David Bridges, Danny Carey-Bertram. **Middle:** Josh Simpson, Rob Wolleaston, Paul Crichton, Ritchie Hanlon, Shane Herbert, Chris Gordon, Matt Bloomer, Greg Reid (physio). **Front:** Darren Quinton, Jon Brady, Tommy Jaszczun, Rob Newman (manager), Charlie Dyke, Tony Spearing (assistant manager), Stephen Smith, Courtney Pitt

CLUB PERSONNEL

Chairman:	Roger Hunt	**Commercial Manager:**	Heather Wilkanowski
		Tel No:	(B) 01223 729 205
Directors	John Howard, Brian Attmore,		(M) 07899 947 979
T.H.Baker, Paul Barry, Justyn Medd, Nick Pomery.			
		Press Officer:	James Smith
Associate Director	R.L. Sargent		

Club Secretary   Wayne Purser
Tel Nos: (B) 01223 566500

Assistant Secretary: James Smith

e-mail: matt.wildr@cambridge-united.co.uk

MANAGEMENT TEAM

Manager:	Rob Newman	**Assistant Manager:**	Tony Spearing
As a player:	Bristol City, Norwich City	**Physio:**	Greg Reid
	Motherwell, Wigan, Southend		

CAMBRIDGE UNITED

BEST LGE ATT.: **4,188** v York City
LOWEST: **2,924** v Hereford

No.	Date	Comp	H/A	Opponents	Att:	Result	Goalscorers	Pos
1	Aug 13	C	A	Forest Green Rovers	1112	L 0 - 1		15
2	16		H	Hereford United	2.924	W 2 - 1	Smith 44 Bridges 70	12
3	20		H	Accrington Stanley	2730	W 3 - 1	Angel 17 Quinton 34, Bridges 45	3
4	27		A	Burton Albion	1379	D 0 - 0		5
5	29		H	Kidderminster Harriers	3161	L 0 - 2		11
6	Sept 2		A	York City	2666	L 0 - 1		13
7	10		A	Exeter City	3407	L 0 - 4		16
8	17		H	Woking	2345	L 0 - 2		18
9	20		A	Grays Athletic	1543	L 3 - 5	Hanlon 13 82 Peters 58	19
10	24		H	Altrincham	2199	W 4 - 0	Pitt 15 **Onibuje** 18 79 Atkins 54	17
11	27		H	Burton Albion	2298	D 2 - 2	**Onibuje** 46 Pitt 66	14
12	Oct 1		A	Southport	1204	D 2 - 2	**Onibuje** 4 Westcarr 82	15
13	7		H	Tamworth	2606	W 2 - 1	**Onibuje** 22 Duncan 71	14
14	15		A	Halifax Town	1621	L 0 - 1		15
15	**18**	**LDV Vans T 1**	**H**	**Chester Cioty**	**1224**	**W 3 - 0**	**Bridges 64 Smith 78 Onibuje 90**	
16	**22**	**FAC 4Q**	**A**	**Weymouth**	**1652**	**L 1 - 2**	**Peters 42**	
17	29	C	H	Crawley Town	2413	W 2 - 1	Chick 31 Hamlon 36	13
18	Nov 12		A	Morecambe	1648	W 1 - 0	Bridges 16	10
19	19		H	Aldershot Town	2905	L 0 - 2		
20	**22**	**LDV Vans T 2**	**H**	**Doncaster Rovers**	**1435**	**W 3 - 2**	**Morrison 7 Onibuje 33 Hanlon 77**	
21	26	C	A	Canvey Island	842	D 1 - 1	Duncan 52	13
22	Dec 3		H	Scarborough	2809	W 2 - 1	Westcarr 30 Morrison 34	11
23	10		A	Dagenham & Redbridge	1271	L 0 - 1		12
24	**13**	**LDV Vans T 3**	**A**	**Macclesfield Town**	**860**	**L 2 - 4**	**Bridges 17 Atkins 47**	
25	**17**	**FAT 1**	**A**	**Dorchester Town**	**426**	**L 2 - 3**	**Morrison 13 Bridges 90**	
26	26	C	H	Stevenge Borough	3697	W 1 - 0	Bridges 19	11
27	31		H	Canvey Island	2594	W 3 - 1	Westcarr 47 **Onibuje** 51 78	9
28	Jan 2		A	Stevenage Borough	3463	L 1 - 3	Pitt 7	11
29	7		H	Forest Greeen Rovers	2344	D 2 - 2	Duncan 17 **Onibuje** 66	11
30	21		A	Accrington Stanley	1837	L 0 - 1		13
31	28		H	Gravesend & Northfleet	2459	D 1 - 1	Pitt 76	14
32	31		H	Hereford United	2142	L 0 - 3		15
33	Feb 11		A	Altrincham	1151	L 1 - 2	Bridges 34	16
34	18		H	Southport	2310	W 2 - 1	Wollaston 14 Peters 84	13
35	21		A	Burton Albion	1577	L 0 - 2		14
36	Mar 4		A	Woking	2066	W 1 - 0	Guy 71	14
37	7		H	Grays Athletic	1821	D 1 - 1	Westcarr 13	
38	11		A	Tamworth	1325	D 1 - 1	Westcarr 5	12
39	18		H	Halifax Town	2288	D 1 - 1	Westcarr 1	14
40	25		A	Crawley Town	1472	L 0 - 1		14
41	April 1		H	Morecambe	2129	D 2 - 2	Brady 20 Smith 70	14
42	4		A	Exeter City	2358	W 2 - 1	**Onibuje** 14 Guy 90	13
43	8		A	Aldershot Town	2198	W 3 - 1	Morrison 48 Jelleyman 58 Westcarr 75	13
44	14		H	York City	4188	W 2 - 0	Westcarr 61(pen) Hotte 79 (og)	9
45	17		A	Kidderminster Harriers	1665	L 0 - 1		10
46	22		A	Scarborough	1831	W 2 - 1	Wolleaston 44 73	10
47	29		H	Dagenham & Redbridge	3161	L 1 - 2	Peters 58	12

Ave. League Home Attendance: 2642   **Goals** 62 68   **Top Goalscorer:** Folawiyo Onibuje (11)

Best Position: 3rd   **Worst:** 19th

Player	No.	1	2	3	4	5	6	7	8	9	10	11	12	13	14	15	16	17	18	19	20	21	22	23	24	25	26	27	28	29	30	31	32	33	34	35	36	37	38	39	40	41	42	43	44	45	46	47
BEHCET	1	X	X	X	X	X	X	X								U	U	U		U		U				U															U	S					X	X
GLEESON	2	X	X	X	X	X	X	X	X	X	X	X	S	X	X	X	X	X	X	X	X	X	X	X	X	X	X	X	X	X	X	X	X	X	X	X	X	X	X	X		X		X			X	X
DUNCAN	4	X	X	X	X	X	X	X	X	X	X	X	X	X	X	X	X	X	X	X	X	X	X	X	X	X	X	X	X	X	X	X	X	X	X	X	X	X	X	X	X	X	X		X	X		X
PETERS	5	X	X	X	X	X	X	X	U	U	S	S	U	U	S	S	S	U	X	X	X	X	X	S	X	X	X	X	X	X	X	X	X	X	X	X	X	X			X	U	S					
CHICK	3	X	X	X	X	X	U	U																S						S																		
ANGEL	25	X	X					U	U	U	X	X	X	U	X	X	X	X	X	X	X	X	X	X	X	X	X																					
BRIDGES	8	X	X	X	X	X	X		X	X	X	X	X	X	X	X	X	X	X	X	X	X	X	X	X	X	X	X	X	X	X	X	X	X	X	X	X	X	X	X	X	X	X	X	X	X	X	X
QUINTON	16	X	X	X	X	X	U	X	X	X	S	S	U	S	X	U	X	X	U	X	U	X	X	S	X	S	X	S	U	S																		
SMITH	18	X	X	X	X	S	X	X	X	X	X	X	X	X	X	X	X	X	X	X	X	X	X	X	X	S	X	U	X	S	U	X	X	X	X	X	X		X	X	X	X	X	S	U	U	X	X
TURNER	10	X	X	X	X	X	X	X		X	X	X	X	X	X	X	X	X	X	X	X	X	X	S	X	S	S	U	S	X								U	X	X	X	X	X	U	U	U	X	X
ONIBUJE	9	X	X	X	X	X	X	X																	S																						U	S
R DUFFY	24	S	S	S	S	X	S	S	S	S	X	X	X	X	X	S	S	S	U	S	U		X	X	X	X	S	X	U	U	U	U	U	U	U	S	U	U	U	U	X	X		U	S	S	S	S
OKAI	11	S	S	U	S	X	X	X	X	X	X	X	X	X																																		
DANIELS	7	S	U	U	S	X	X	U	S	S	U	U	U	U	U				U	S	U																X	U			X	X	S	U	S	S	S	S
DAVIES	15	U	U	S	S	U	S	S	X	X	X	X	X	X	X	X	X	X		S	U	U	X	X	X	U	U	X	U	U	U	S	U	S	U	S				X	X						U	
NOLAN	15	U	U	S		S				X				S	S	U	U	U				U	S	U		S	S		U	U	U	U	U	U	U													
ROBBINS	23						S	S	X	X	X	X	X	X	X	X	X	X	X	S	S	X	X	X	X	U	U	U	U	U								S										U
HARKNESS	6		U		U	X	X	X	U	U				U	X	X	X	U	U	U	U	S	U	U	U	X	X	X	U	S	S	X	S	X	X	S						X						
HANLON	28			X			X	X	X	X	X	X	X	X	X	X	X	X	X	X	X	X	X	X	X	X	X	X	X	X	X	X	X	X	X	X	X	X	X	X	S	X	X	X	X	X	X	X
PITT	29				X	X	X	X	X	X	X	X	X	X	X	X	X	X	X	X	X	X	X	X	X	X	X	X	X	X	X	X	X	X	X	X	X	X	X	X	X	X	X	X	X	X	X	X
ROBERTSON	22						X	U																														S	U	U		S						
HOWIE	13								X	X	X	X	X	X	X	X	X	X	X	X	X	X	X	X	X	X	X	X	X	X	X	X	X	X	X	X	X	X	X	X	X	X	X	X	X	X	X	X
WESTCARR	30								S	S	X	X	X	X	X	X	X	X	S	S	X	X	X	U	X	U	X	X	U	U	X	X	S	S	U	X	X	X	X	X	U	S	X	S	X	X	S	X
ATKINS	14									S	X	X	X	U	U	S	X	X	X	X	X	U	U	S	S	X	X	X	S	X	U	X	X	X	X	U	U	U	S	U					X	X	X	X
MORRISON	21								X	X	X	X	X	U	U	X	X	X	X	X	X	X	X	X	X	X	X	X	X	X	X	X	X	X	X	X	X	X	U	U	S	S	S	X	X	X	X	X
FULLER	17								S											X		X		X	X	U	U																					
NICHOLLS	24									S									X	X											U										U	S	U	U	U	X	U	S
BUNCE	26													X	X	X	X	X	X	X	X	U	S	X	X	S	S	S	S	S		U	U	U	U	U	S	S	S	S	S	S	S	U	X	X	U	S
PORTER	33													U	U	S	S	U	X	X	X	U	X	U	S	X	X	X	X	U	U	U																
MANN	34													U	S				X		X				X	X	X	X	X																	X		
HEEROO	31								X	X	X	X	X	X	X	X	X	X	X	X	X	X	X	X	S	S	S	S	S	S	U	U	U	U	U	U	U	U	S	S	S	S	S	U	U	U	U	U
ROBINSON	11								S	S	X	X	X	U	U	S	S	U	X	X	U	S	X	X	X	X	X	X	U	U	X	X	X	X	X	X	X	X	X	X	X	X	X	X	X	X	X	U
BRADY	12									S					S				X	X	U					U	U	U	X	X	U	X	X						X						X	X	X	
JASZCZUN	19														X														U	X	X	X	X	X	X	X	X											
MEDINE	20																										X	X	U	U	U	X	X	X	X	X			X	X	X	X	X	X	X	X	X	U
COLDICOTT	17																												X	X	X	X	S	X	X	X	X	S	X	S	X	U	U	X	X	X	X	X
WOLLEASTON	23																												U	X	S	X	X	X	X	U	X	X	U	X	X	X	X	X	X	X	X	X
GUY	10																													X	X	X	S	X	X	X	U	S	X	X	X		U					
BLOOMER	25																													X	X		X	X	X	X	X	X	X	X	X	X	X	X	X	X	X	X
A DUFFY	1																												S			X	X	X	X	X	X	S	X	X	X	X	X					
WAITE	27																																	X	X	X	X	X	X	X	X	X		X	X	U	U	U

Total Appearances (Conference)

	X	7	23	31	34	6	6	33	11	21	6	25	3	6	1	8	3	3	7	22	29	0	33	23	1	21	1	3	5	3	0	8	3	19	16	2	4	13	12	8	2	0
	S	0	1	1	1	1	2	2	6	5	3	9	4	7	2	4	7	1	0	3	1	0	0	8	8	1	0	1	8	5	0	1	1	0	0	3	0	0	0	0	0	0
	U	1	1	2	0	0	7	2	5	11	4	2	0	5	2	11	6	12	0	0	0	1	0	3	8	7	0	1	7	5	0	5	1	0	0	2	0	1	0	0	0	2

Cup Appearances

	X	0	2	5	5	0	0	5	4	3	0	1	0	2	0	0	2	0	0	2	0	0	5	0	0	5	5	2	5	0	0	3	1	0	0	0	0	0	0	0	0	0
	S	0	0	0	0	0	0	2	0	0	0	0	4	0	1	0	0	0	1	1	0	0	0	0	0	0	2	0	0	0	0	1	0	0	0	0	0	0	0	0	0	0
	U	4	0	0	0	1	0	0	1	0	0	0	0	1	0	3	0	0	0	0	0	0	0	0	0	0	0	0	0	1	1	1	0	0	0	0	0	0	0	0	0	0

CURRANT SQUAD AS OF BEGINING OF 2006-07 SEASON

GOALKEEPERS	SQ NO.	HT	WT	D.O.B	AGE	P.O.B	CAREER	APPS	GOA
Paul Crichton	1	6'00"	13 08	3/10/68	37	Pontefract	Notts Forest, Notts C (2ML) 9/86, Darlington (L) 1/87, Peterborough (SL) 3/87, Darlington (L) 9/87, Swindon (L) 12/87, Rotherham (L) 3/88, Torquay (3ML) 8/88, Peterborough 11/88 Rel c/s 90, Doncaster 8/90 Rel c/s 93, Grimsby 7/93, WBA (L) 9/96 £250,000 10		
Jamie Waite	13			22/2/86	20		Rotherham (Sch) Rel c/s 04, Braintree, Kettering, Barrow 2/05, Stevenage 3/05, Cambridge U (NC) 8/05, Chelmsford (Dual) 9/05, AFC Sudbury (Dual) 1/06	0	0
Shane Herbert	20			23/9/86	19	Hethersett	Norwich (Scholar) Rel c/s 06, Gorleston (L) 12/04, Gillingham (SL) 11/05, Cambridge U (Trial) 5/06, Kings Lynn 7/06, Cambridge U 7/06		
Matthew Mann				14/11/87	18		Cambridge U, AFC Sudbury (L) 1/06	0	0
DEFENDERS									
Adam Davies	2	6'02"	13 05	23/7/87	19	Peterborough	Peterborough (Jun), Cambridge U	12	0
Matthew Bloomer	3	6'00"	12 00	3/11/78	27	Cleethorpes	Grimsby Rel c/s 01, Hull C (Trial) 4/01, Hull C 7/01, Lincoln C (L) 3/02, Telford (3ML) 8/02, Lincoln C 12/02 Rel 5/06, Grimsby (L) 1/06, Cambridge U (2ML) 3/06, Cambridge U 7/06	8	0
Andy Duncan	4	5'11"	13 04	20/10/77	28	Hexham	Man Utd, Cambridge U (3ML) 1/98 Undisc 4/98, Peterborough (Trial) 7/05	32	3
Mark Peters	5	6'00"	13 03	6/7/72	34	Rhyl	Man City Rel c/s 92, Norwich 9/92 Rel c/s 93, Peterborough 8/93, Mansfield 9/94 Rel c/s 99, Bromsgrove (SL) c/s 96, Rushden & D 7/99, L.Orient 9/03 Rel c/s 05, Aldershot (L) 11/04, Aldershot (Trial) 7/05, Cambridge U 8/05	35	3
Tommy Jaszczun	19	5'11"	11 02	16/9/77	28	Kettering	Aston Villa, Blackpool £30,000 1/00 Rel c/s 04, Northampton 7/04, Rochdale 7/05, Cambridge U (SL) 1/06, Cambridge U 7/06	16	0
Michael Morrison	21			3/3/88	18		Cambridge U, Newcastle (Trial) 7/06, Chelsea (Trial) 7/06	22	2
Chris Gordon	22	6'00"	13 10	18/10/85	20	Grimsby	Lincoln C, Gainsborough (L) 8/05, Cambridge U 8/06		
MIDFIELDERS									
Ritchie Hanlon	6	5'10"	11 12	25/5/78	28	Kenton	Chelsea (Trainee), Southend 7/96, Dover (L) 12/96, Welling 9/97, Rushden & D 5 fig 7/98, Peterborough P/E 12/98, Welling (L) 3/99, Welling 8/99, Peterborough 12/99, Rushden & D £30,000 9/01 Rel 5/04 Stevenage 7/04, Lincoln C (L) 12/04 Perm 12/04 Rel c/s 0	25	3
Jon Brady	7	5'10"	11 02	14/1/75	31	Newcastle (Aus)	Adamstown Rosebuds (Aust), Brentford (Trainee), Swansea 7/93 Rel c/s 94, Wycombe, Brentford (Trial), Hayes 11/94, Mjolner (Nor) 3/95, Hayes c/s 95, Rushden & D £40,000 7/98 Rel c/s 02, Woking Free 8/02), Chester Free 10/02, Stevenage 12/03, Hereford 6/05,	19	1
David Bridges	8	6'00"	12 00	22/9/82	23	Huntingdon	Cambridge U, New England Rev (USA) (Trial) c/s 04, Chesterfield (Trial) 7/04, Northampton (Trial) 8/04, Latvia c/s 04, Braintree 1/05, Rushden & D 2/05, Histon 3/05, Cambridge U 8/05	35	5
Courtney Pitt	11	5'07"	10 08	17/12/81	24	Paddington	Chelsea, Portsmouth £200,000 7/01, Luton (3ML) 8/03, Coventry (L) 12/03, Oxford U 3/04 Rel c/s 04, Luton (Trial) 7/04, Boston U 8/04 Rel c/s 05, Colchester (Trial) 7/05, Port Vale (Trial) 8/05, Cambridge U 9/05	30	5
Josh Simpson	12			6/3/87	19		Cambridge C, Cambridge U 6/06		
Darren Quinton	16	5'08"	9 11	28/4/86	20	Romford	Cambridge U	17	1
Robert Wolleaston	17	5'11"	11 07	21/12/79	26	Perivale	Chelsea Rel c/s 03, Bristol R (L) 3/00, Portsmouth (SL) 3/01, Northampton (3ML) 7/01, Luton (Trial) 3/03, Bradford C 7/03, Wimbledon (Trial) 3/04, Oxford U 7/04 Rel 10/05, USA, Cambridge U 2/06	13	3
Stephen Smith	18	5'08"	11 07	19/9/86	19	Harlow	Cambridge U	26	2
Jordan Collins	24						Cambridge U		
Dave Robertson				19/11/73	32		Deeping R, Cambridge U NC c/s 05	0	0A
FORWARDS									
Marcus Richardson	9	6'02"	13 02	31/8/77	29	Reading	Slough, Cambridge U (Trial) 7/00, Reading (Trial) 8/00, Wycombe (Trial), Harrow 1/01, Cambridge U 3/01, Torquay (L) 9/01 £5,000 10/01, Hartlepool 10/02, Lincoln C (2ML) 8/03, Lincoln C (L) 12/03 Perm 1/04, Rochdale (L) 2/05, Yeovil 3/05 Rel c/s 05, Chester		
Danny Carey-Bertram	10	5'11"	13 00	14/6/84	22	Birmingham	WBA, Hereford 9/03 Rel 6/06, Cambridge U 6/06		
Michael Gash	14			3/9/86	19		Cambridge C, Cambridge U 6/06		
Robbie Simpson	15			18/3/85	20		Norwich (Jun), Cambridge C 7/01, Cambridge U 6/06		
Dave Lawrence	23					Hayes	Hillingdon, Cambridge U 8/06		

PLAYING SQUAD

LOANEES	HT	WT	DOB	AGE	POB	FROM - TO	APPS	GOA
(G)Darren Behcet			8/10/86	19		West Ham (4M) 8/05 - Southend (Trial) 1/06,		
						Margate (SL) 1/06, Rel 5/06, Yeovil 6/06	7	0
(M)Mark Angel	5'08"	11 01	23/8/75	31	Newcastle	Kings Lynn (3M) 8/05 - Stamford 2/06	8	1
(D)Johnny Harkness	6'00"	12 09	18/11/85	20	Belfast	Walsall 8/05 - Halesowen T (L) 10/05, Rel 1/06, Kidderminster 1/06	7	0
(M)Gavin Heeroo	6'00"	11 06	2/9/84	21	Haringey	Farnborough (SL) 11/05 - Chelmsford 8/06	9	0
(M)Trevor Robinson	5'09"	12 11	20/9/84	21	St Catherines, Jam	Millwall 1/06 - Rel 5/06	4	0
(M)Stacy Coldicott	5'08"	12 00	29/4/74	32	Redditch	Hereford 2/06 - Rel 5/06	4	0
(F)Jamie Guy	6'01"	13 00	1/8/87	19	Barking	Colchester 2/06 + 3/06 -	12	2
(G)Ayden Duffy			16/11/86	19	Kettering	Lincoln C 3/06 - Stamford (L) 4/06, Stamford (L) 8/06	2	0

DEPARTURES	HT	WT	DOB	AGE	POB	FROM - TO	APPS	GOA
(F)Robert Duffy	6'01"	12 04	2/12/82	23	Swansea	Rushden & D 8/05 - Rel 9/05, Kettering 10/05, Gainsborough 1/06,		
						Stevenage 3/06, Oxford U 8/06	7	0
(F)Matt Nolan	6'01"	12 00	25/2/82	24	Hitchin	Peterborough 8/05 - Rel 12/05, Kings Lynn 12/05	10	0
(M)Parys Okai	5'09"	11 05	23/11/84	21	London	Bedford T c/s 05 - Rel 12/05, Hitchin 12/05, Kettering 3/06	13	0
(M)Ashley Nicholls	5'11"	11 11	30/10/81	24	Ipswich	Darlington 2/04 - Rushden & D (3ML) 8/05, Rushden & D 1/06, Grays 8/06	4	0
(F)Ryan Lockett	5'10"	11 08	11/11/86	19	Cambridge	Youth - Cambridge C (Trial) 11/05 Rel 1/06, Cambridge C 1/06		
(M)Ashley Fuller	5'09"	10 10	14/11/86	19	Bedford	Peterborough (Sch) - Cambridge C (Trial) 11/05, Rel 1/06,		
						Gravesend 1/06 Rel 5/06, Bishops Stortford 7/06	1	0
(D)Duane Eastall		-	29/9/86	19		Youth - Fakenham T (L), Cambridge C (Trial) 11/05, Rel 1/06		
(F)John Turner	5'10"	11 00	12/2/86	20	Harrow	Youth - Rushden & D (Trial) 10/05, Scunthorpe (Trial) 11/05,		
						Aldershot (L) 11/05, Rushden & D 1/06, Grays 8/06	9	0
(D)David Chick			27/2/85	21	Norwich	Kings Lynn 7/05 - Rel 2/06	7	1
(D)Nick Robbins	5'10"		30/11/85	20		Ipswich (Sch) - Norwich U (L) 2/06, Rel 3/06	4	0
(F)Dave Daniels	5'08"	10 10	14/9/85	20	Bedford	Yth - Hitchin (2ML) 1/06, Rel 3/06, Mildenhall 5/06	3	0
(F)Paul Atkins			21/10/86	19		Yth - Norwich U (L) 2/06, Rel 3/06, Kings Lynn 8/06	9	1
(F)Mbiyeye Medine			3/9/87	18		Waltham Forest 8/05 - Chelmsford (L) 11/05, Rel 3/06,		
						Waltham Forest 3/06	5	0
(D)Dan Gleeson	6'03"	13 02	17/2/85	21	Cambridge	Welling 2/04 - Rel 5/06, Notts County 7/06	24	0
(D)Danny Bunce			30/4/86	20		West Ham Rel c/s 05, 11/05 - Rel 5/06, Woking 7/06	13	0
(G)Scott Howie	6'03"	13 07	4/1/72	34	Motherwell	Shrewsbury 8/05 - Retired 5/06	33	0
(F)Fola Onibuje	6'07"	12 00	25/9/84	21	Lagos	Peterborough 8/05 - Rel 5/06, Swindon 8/06	34	9
(F)Craig Westcarr	5'11"	11 04	29/1/85	21	Nottingham	N.Forest Rel c/s 05, 9/05 - Kettering 5/06	31	8
(M)Max Porter	5'10"		29/6/87	19		Southend AL 11/05 - Bishops Stortford 6/06	8	0

CAMBRIDGE UNITED

Ground Address: Abbey Stadium, Newmarket Road, Cambridge CB5 8LN

Telephone: 01223 566 500

Fax: 01223 566 502

General email address: web@cambridge-united.co.uk

Official website: www.cambridge-united.co.uk

Midweek Home Matchday: Tuesday

MATCH TICKETS:
Ticket office Telephone: 01223 566 500

Ticket Prices
Seats   £15
Standing   £12

Capacity: 9,217
Seats   2,500
Cover   5,000

Clubhouse: Open matchdays

Club Shop: Yes.

Refreshments Restaurant and Burger bars

MATCHDAY PROGRAMME
Pages: 52   Price: £2.50
Editor:James Smith.

CLUB STATISTICS
RECORDS
Attendance: 14,000
                    v Chelsea, Friendly 1st May 1970
Victory: 5-1
                   v Bristol City F.A.Cup 5th Rd 89-90
Defeat: 0-7
              v Sunderland League Cup 2nd Rd 02-3
Career Goalscorer: John Taylor 86
                               1988-92 1996-2001
Career Appearances: Steve Spriggs 416 1975-87
Transfer Fee Paid: £192,000 Nov. 92
                       to Luton Town for Steve Claridge
Transfer Fee Received: £1,000,000
        from Manchester United for Dion Dublin Aufust 92
    from Leicester City for Trevor Benjaminn July 2000
SENIOR HONOURS   Football League Div 3
         Champions 1990-91, Runners-Up 77-78 98-99
                         Football League Division 4
         Champions 1976-77 Promoted from Play offs 89-90
PREVIOUS
    Leagues: United Counties, Eastern Counties 1951-58
    Southern League 1958-1970 Football League 1970-2005
Name: Abbey United: 1919-1951

STEP 1
CONFERENCE

STEP 2 - P177
CONFERENCE Nth & Sth

STEP 3 - P269
NPL - SOUTHERN - ETHIHIM PREM

STEP 4 - P269
NPL - SOUTHERN - ISTHMIAN

STEP 5/6 - P473

STEP 7 - P713

CRAWLEY TOWN

Club Colours: All Red
Change Colours: All Royal Blue
Club Sponsor: TBC
Previous League: Southern
LAST SEASON: Conference: 17th   **F.A.Cup:** 4th Qualifying Round **F.A.Trophy:** 3rd Round
BEST PERFORMANCES
League: Conference 2004-2005 **F.A. Cup:** 3rd Rd. 1991-92 **F.A. Trophy:** 3rd Rd 1998-99

Formed: 1896
Nickname: Red Devils

CLUB PERSONNEL

Chairman: Azwar Majeed

Club Secretary: Barry Munn
Tel Nos: (H) 01293 529 493
                                             (B) 01293 410 000
                                             (M) 07764 951 577
             Email: barry.munn@crawley-town-fc.com
Commercial Manager   Victor Marley
                                             (B) 01293 410 000

                    Email: info@crawley-townfc.com

MANAGEMENT TEAM

Manager: John Hollins   **Physio:**   Richard Massimo

Assistant Manager: Alan Lewer

Physiotherpist   Richard Massino

CRAWLEY TOWN

BEST LGE ATT.: 2,454 v Exeter City
LOWEST: 1,012 v Kidderminster H.

No.	Date	Comp	H/A	Opponents	Att:	Result	Goalscorers	Pos
1	Aug 13	C	A	York City	2276	D 0 0		12
2	16		H	Dagenham & Redbridge	1734	D 0 0 0		16
3	20		H	Hereford United	1842	L 0 - 2		20
4	27		A	Morecambe	1473	L 0 - 3		
5	29		H	Stevenage Borough	2019	L 1 - 2	Douglas 59	21
6	Sept 5		A	Aldershot Town	2371	L 2 - 3	**Clare** 8 Wormull 83	22
7	10		H	Canvey Island	1335	W 3 - 1	Armstrong 44 Opinel 50 Burton 72	21
8	17		A	Accrington Stamley	1365	L 2 - 4	Burton 23 **Clare** 67	20
9	20		A	Forest Green Rovers	916	D 2 - 2	**Clare** 84 (pen) Judge 88	20
10	24		H	Grays Athletic	1471	L 1 - 3	Wormull 12	22
11	27		H	Kidderminster Harriers	1012	W 2 - 0	Burgess 3 (og) Cade 82	20
12	Oct 1		A	Altrincham	819	D 1 - 1	Lindegaard 45	20
13	8		A	Scarborough	1257	W 2 - 1	Wormull 8 Giles 90	17
14	15		H	Exeter City	2454	L 0 - 2		20
15	**18**	**LDV Vans T**	**A**	**Gillingham**	**1988**	**L 0 - 2**		
16	**22**	**FAC 4Q**	**H**	**Braintree Town**	**970**	**L 0 - 1**		
17	29	C	A	Cambridge United	2413	L 1 - 2	Cade 2	20
18	Nov 12		H	Southport	2055	W 2 - 0	Cade 21 **Clare** 34	18
19	19		A	Burton Albion	1353	L 1 - 3	**Clare** 77	20
20	26		H	Gravesend & Northfleet	1426	L 1 - 2	Armstrong 71	20
21	Dec 3		A	Halifax Town	1616	D 2 - 2	**Clare** 12 (pen) Whitman 91	19
22	10		H	Tamworth	1448	W 3 - 0	Woozley 78 Burton 85 90	18
23	**17**	**FAT 1**	**A**	**Stevengae Borough**	**610**	**W 2 - 0**	**Wormull 33 Burton 45**	
24	26	C	A	Woking	2643	D 0 - 0		18
25	Jan 2		H	Woking	2073	D 2 - 2	**Clare** 60 (pen) 64	18
26	7		H	York City	1514	L 0 - 1		19
27	**14**	**FAT 2**	**H**	**Worcester City**	**878**	**W 3 1**	**Giles 47 Scully 59 Burton 73**	
28	21		A	Hereford United	2782	L 1 - 2	Brown 62	20
29	28		H	Morecambe	1253	L 1 - 3	**Clare** 75 (pen)	21
30	**Feb 4**	**FAT 3**	**H**	**Boreham Wood**	**929**	**L 0 - 2**		
31	11	C	A	Grays Athletic	1038	L 0 - 1		22
32	18		H	Altrincham	1085	W 2 - 0	**Clare** 34 59	21
33	21		A	Kidderminster Harriers	1302	L 0 - 1		21
34	25		A	Canvey Island	698	L 0 - 1		21
35	28		A	Gravesend & Northfleet	698	D 1 - 1	Jenkins 90	21
36	Mar 4		H	Accrington Stanley	1361	L 0 - 1		21
37	11		H	Scarborough	1181	W 2 - 0	Scully 42 Coleman 76	19
38	18		H	Forest Green Rovers	1067	W 1 - 0	Burton 37	19
39	25		H	Cambridge United	1472	W 1 - 0	Giles 55	18
40	28		A	Dagenah & Redbridge	932	W 3 - 0	Coleman 57 Burton 66 72	17
41	April 1		A	Southport	1308	W 2 - 0	Clay 73 Coleman 90	17
42	8		H	Burton Albion	1341	D 1 - 1	Scully 89	17
43	15		H	Aldershot Town	1764	W 2 - 0	Coleman 27 Bostwick 54	16
44	17		A	Stevenage Borough	2410	L 1 2 2	Ekoku 20	17
45	22		H	Halifax Town	1285	D 2 - 2	Bostwick 8 15	17
46	25		A	Exeter City	1782	L 0 - 4		17
47	29		A	Tamworth	1709	D 0 - 0		17

Ave. League Home Attendance:	1655		**Goals**	53 61	**Top Goalscorer:** Daryl Clare (11)
Best Position: 12th	**Worst:** 22nd				

	SMITH	JUDGE	SIMPEMBA	WOOZLEY	JENKINS	ELAM	BROWN	WORMULL	HODGSON	BURTON	CADE	BLACKBURN	EKOKU	DOUGLAS	WARD	GILES	OPINEL	ARMSTRONG	DAVIDSON	DONOVAN	KEEHAN	CLARE	KEMBER	LINDEGAARD	M GORDON	BOTTING	SACKMAN	HUNTLEY	WHITMAN	PROFFITT	SCULLY	MENDY	EL-ABD	GRANT	MARSHALL	COLEMAN	CLAY	G GORDON	BANKS	BOSTWICK	MACLEOD	#
No.	1	2	5	12	11	6	4	7	25	10	27	23	9	18	14	26	17	8	24	15	28	30	16	19	20	21	29	25	24	22	18	6	3	20	31	19	20	33	40	34	35	
	X	X	X	X	X	X	X	X	X	X	S	S	S	U	U																											1
	X	X	X	X	X	X		X	X	X	X	X	S	U	U		U	U																								2
	X	X	X	X	X	X	U	X	X	X	X	X		S	U	U					S																					3
	X	X	X	X			X	X	X	X	S	X	X		U				S	S	U																					4
	X	X	X	X			X	X		S	S		X	X	U	X	X	X			U	U																				5
	X	X		X			X	X		U	S		S	X	U	X	X	X		X		X	S																			6
	X	X	X	X		U		X		X	X		U	U	U	X	X	X			U	X																				7
	X	X	X	X				X		X	S	S	S		U	X	X	X		U	X		X																			8
	X	X	X	X			S		X		S	X	X		U	X	X	X	U		X		X	U																		9
	X		X	X		S		X	X	S	U	U	U	X	X	X	X	X			X		X																			10
	U	X	X	X			X		X	X	S	U	S	X	S	X	X	X			X		X																			11
	U	X	X	X			X		X	X	S		S	X	U	X	X	X			U	X	X																			12
	U	X	X	X	S		X		X	X			U	X	S	X	X	X			U	X	X																			13
	U	X		X	X		U	X		X	X	S		S	X	X	X			S	X		X																			14
	X	X		X	X		U	X		X	S	S		S	U	X	X	X			X		X																			15
	U	X		X	X		U	X		X	U		X	X	X	X	X		U	X			U																			16
	X	X		X	X					X	X		U	X	X	X	U	U	U	U																						17
	X	X	X	X			X			X		S		U	S	X	X	X			U	X		X	S																	18
	X	X	X	X			X			X		X		U	S	X	X	X			U	X		X	S																	19
	X	X	X	X			X		S	X		S		U	S	X	X				U	X		X		X																20
	X	X	X	X			X		X		S		U	X	X	X			U	X			X		S		X	U														21
	X	X	X	X			X	X		S	S	U		X						X	U	X	U																			22
	X	X	X		X		X	X		X	S			U	X	S	X					X		X	U		S															23
	X		X	X	X		X	X		X	S			U		X					X		U	X	X	U	U															24
	X	X	X		X		X	X		X	X			U	X	S					X		U	X	X	U	U	U														25
	X	X	X		X		X			X	S			U	X	S					S		X	X	U																	26
	X	X	X	S			X	X		X	S			U	X	X	X				S		X	X	U																	27
	X	X	X	U	U		X			X		X	S	U	X	X	X				U		X																			28
	X		X	X	S		X	X		X		S	S	U	X	X	X			X	U																					29
	X	X	X	U	X		X	X		U	U		U	X	X	U	X			X	X																					30
	X	X	X	X	X			S		X	S		U	U	X	X	X			X									S													31
	X	X	X	X	U					X	S		U		X	X	X			X									S		S											32
	X	X	X	X			U			S	X	S		X	X	X			X										S		X	U										33
	X	X	X	X			U			X	X	S		U	X	X	X			X									S		S											34
	X	X		S			X			S	X	S		X	U	X			X										X		X	U										35
	X	X	U	S			X			X	X	S		X	U	X			X										X		S	X										36
	X	X	U	S			X			X	X			U	X	U	X												X		S	X										37
	X	X	U	S			X			X	X	U		U	X														X		X	X						S				38
	X	X	U	U			X			X	X			U	X	U	X												X		X	X										39
	X	X	U	S			X			X	X	S		U	X	U	X												X		X	X										40
	X	X	U				X			X	X	U		U	X	S	X												X		S	X	X				S					41
	X	X		U			X			X	X			U	X	X	X		U										X		X	X	X	U		S					42
	X	X	S	S			X			X	X	U		X	U														X		X	S	X									43
	X	X		X	X		X			X		U	U	S					X										X	U		U						X				44
	X	X		X	S		X			X		U	S	U					X										X	U		U						X				45
	X	X	X	X			X			S		X	X	U	X	S													X	U		S						X				46
	X	X		X			X			S	X	X	X			U							X						X	U		U						X	X			47

Total Appearances (Conference)

38	39	26	29	14	4	23	21	4	29	15	24	8	2	4	22	19	29	0	1	25	4	10	0	0	0	3	0	20	21	1	0	3	6	8	3	0	5	1			X
0	0	0	1	9	1	0	2	0	7	4	11	19	5	0	6	4	1	2	0	1	0	1	0	0	0	0	2	2	0	0	0	3	3	3	2	0	3	0			S
4	0	0	7	4	1	4	0	0	1	0	0	4	4	35	4	9	1	0	3	9	0	0	0	2	1	1	3	0	0	3	6	4	3	0	0	1	2	0			U

Cup Appearances

4	5	3	2	4	0	3	5	0	3	1	0	0	1	1	5	4	4	0	0	3	0	1	0	0	0	0	0	1	0	3	2	0	0	0	0	0	0	0	0	0	X
0	0	0	0	1	0	0	0	0	0	1	3	0	1	0	0	1	0	0	0	0	0	0	0	0	0	0	0	0	0	1	0	0	0	0	1	0	0	0	0	0	S
1	0	0	1	0	0	2	0	0	0	2	1	0	4	0	0	1	0	0	0	1	0	0	0	0	0	0	0	1	0	1	0	0	0	0	0	0	0	0	0	0	U

CRAWLEY TOWN

CURRANT SQUAD AS OF BEGINING OF 2006-07 SEASON

GOALKEEPERS	SQ NO.	HT	WT	D.O.B	AGE	P.O.B	CAREER	APPS	GOA
Ben Hamer	1			20/11/87	18		Reading, Crawley (L) 8/06		
Rob Tolfrey	22						Dulwich H, Beckenham, Crawley 8/06		

DEFENDERS									
Ben Judge	2					London	C.Palace (Jun), Croydon, Crawley 11/01	39	1
Scott Hiley	4	5'09"	11 12	27/9/68	37	Plymouth	Exeter, Birmingham £100,000 3/93, Man City (2ML) 2/96 £250,000 4/96,		
							Southampton 8/98, Portsmouth £200,000 12/99,		
							Exeter (2ML) 9/02 Perm 11/02 Rel 2/06, Crawley 8/06		
Patrick Sappleton	5					London	Hendon, Boreham Wood 10/02, Farnborough 8/03, Billericay 12/03,		
							Crawley 8/06		
Michael Bostwick	7						Millwall, Crawley (SL) 3/06, Crawley (L) 8/06	8	3
Jack MacLeod	12						Millwall, Crawley (L) 3/06 (05/06 1,0), Crawley 8/06	1	0
John Huckle	14						Crawley		
David Woozley	26	6'00"	12 10	6/12/79	26	Ascot	C.Palace, Bournemouth (L) 9/00, Torquay (L) 8/01, Torquay 3/02,		
							Oxford U 7/04, Yeovil (L) 3/05, Aldershot (Trial) 7/05, Crawley 8/05	30	1

MIDFIELDERS									
Danny Brown	3	6'00"	12 06	12/9/80	25	Bethnal Green	L.Orient, Barnet £40,000 5/99 Rel c/s 03, Oxford U 7/03 Rel c/s 05,		
							Crawley 8/05	23	1
Garry Mills	6	5'09"	11 06	20/5/81	25	Sheppey	Rushden & D, Yeovil (Trial) 6/06, Crawley 8/06		
Lee Blackburn	8	5'08"	10 05	1/10/85	20	Romford	Norwich (C.o.E), Chelsea (Sch) c/s 98, Norwich (Sch) 3/02,		
							Notts County (Trial) 2/05, Cambridge U 2/05, Crawley 8/05	35	0
Tony Scully	11	5'07"	11 05	12/6/76	30	Dublin	C.Palace, Bournemouth (2ML) 10/94, Cardiff (L) 1/96,		
							Portadown (L) 3/97, Man City £80,000 8/97, Stoke (L) 1/98,		
							QPR £155,000 3/98 Rel c/s 01, Walsall (L) 3/00,		
							Cambridge U 7/01 Rel c/s 03, Southend (L) 11/02,		
							Northampton (Trial) 2/03 Peterborough (L) 3/03	20	2
Abdul Osman	17						Crawley		
Mark E'Beyer	18	5'11"	11 05	21/9/84	21	Stevenage	Watford (Scholar), Wimbledon (Scholar), Stevenage 3/04,		
							Oxford U 7/04 Rel 5/06, Northampton (Trial) 5/06, Crawley 8/06		

FORWARDS									
Jake Edwards	9	6'01"	12 08	11/5/76	30	Prestwich	James Maddison Univ (USA), Tranmere (Trial), Wrexham 8/98,		
							Blackpool (L) 3/99, Telford (2ML) 11/99 £20,000 1/00,		
							Charleston Batt (USA) 7/02, Yeovil 8/03 Rel c/s 04, Exeter 7/04,		
							Tamworth (3ML) 10/05, Chester (SL) 3/06, Crawley 8/06		
Ben Strevens	10	6'01"	11 00	24/5/80	26	Islington	Wingate & Finchley, Barnet 1/99 Rel 5/06, Slough (L) 1/00,		
							St Albans (2ML) 1/01, Crawley 8/06		
Scott Rendell	16	6'01"		21/10/86	19	Ashford	Reading (Sch), Aldershot (2ML) 2/05, Forest Green (5ML) 8/05,		
							Crawley (L) 8/06		
Mark Rawle	19	5'11"	12 04	27/4/79	27	Leicester	Leicester YMCA, Rushden & D 9/97, Boston U 2/99,		
							Hibernian (Trial) 12/00, Southend £60,000 + 2/01, Oxford U 7/03,		
							Tamworth (L) 1/05, Rushden & D (Trial) 1/05,		
							Kidderminster 2/05 Rel c/s 05, Barnet (Trial) 7/05, Woking 7/05,		
							Gravesend (SL) 1/06, Crawley 8/06		
Scott Marshall	20						Crawley	6	0
Luke Townsend	28	6'00"	11 10	28/9/86	19	Guildford	QPR, Maidenhead (L), Notts County (Trial) 2/05, Woking (L) 2/06, Crawley 8/06		

OTHERS									
Jamie Lovegrove	15						Crawley		
Carl Baker	21						Crawley		
Daniel Hutchings	23						Crawley		
Sam Belton	24						Crawley		
Lee Wragg	25						Crawley		
James Dadson	27						Crawley		
Mithan Nayee	29						Crawley		

PLAYING SQUAD

LOANEES	HT	WT	DOB	AGE	POB	FROM - TO	APPS	GOA
(M)Andy Lindegaard	5'08"	11 04	10/9/80	25	Taunton	Yeovil (2M) 9/05 -	10	1
(F)Tristram Whitman	5'07"	11 00	9/6/80	26	Nottingham	Tamworth (3M) 11/05 - Hinckley (L) 2/06, Rel 5/06, Alfreton 6/06	5	1
(M)Daniel Clay			15/12/85	20	Doncaster	Exeter (SL) 2/06 -	11	1
(G)Rikki Banks	6'03"	13 08	13/5/88	18	Brighton	C.Palace 2/06 - Hendon (SL) 3/06	0	0
(D)Dean Pooley						Millwall 3/06 -		

DEPARTURES	HT	WT	DOB	AGE	POB	FROM - TO	APPS	GOA
(M)Lee Elam	5'08"	10 12	24/9/76	29	Bradford	Morecambe 7/05 - Rel 9/05, Weymouth 9/05	5	0
(D)James Donovan	6'04"	13 12	11/9/84	21	Sidcup	Millwall 3/05 - Rel 9/05, Margate 10/05	1	0
(M)Richard Hodgson	5'10"	11 06	1/10/79	26	Sunderland	Pahang (Mal) 6/05 - Rel 10/05, Carshalton 10/05,		
						Gravesend 1/06 Rel 2/06, Bognor 2/06, Eastleigh 3/06	4	0
(F)Danny Davidson	6'05"		23/10/79	26	Derby	Stafford R 8/05 - Rel 11/05, Nuneaton 11/05, Tamworth 1/06 Rel 5/06	2	0
(F)Stuart Douglas	5'08	11 05	9/4/78	28	London	ex Dag & Red 8/05 - Rel 11/05, Eastleigh 12/05	7	1
(M)Michael Gordon	5'06	10 04	11/10/84	21	Wandsworth	Aldershot 9/05 - Sutton U 12/05	0	0
(M)Joe Keehan			7/1/87	19		Worthing - Eastbourne B 12/05	2	0
(F)Kim Grant	5'10"	11 05	25/9/72	33	Sekondi-Takoradi	Gravesend 12/05 - AFC Wimbledon 2/06	0	0
(F)Darryl Proffitt			2/5/85	21		ex Leek T 11/05 - Rel 2/06, Hinckley U 2/06	2	0
(M)Simon Wormull	5'10"	12 03	1/12/76	29	Crawley	Hornchurch 11/04 - Caretaker Man 10/05-11/05, Lewes 3/06	23	3
(F)Daryl Clare	5'09"	11 00	1/8/78	28	Jersey	Boston U 9/05 - Burton 3/06	25	11
(F)Danny Ekoku	5'11"	11 08	9/10/85	20	London	Bradford C (Sch) 8/05 - Sutton U (L) 9/05, Gravesend 6/06	27	1
(M)Ian Simpemba	6'02"	12 08	28/3/83	23	Dublin	Wycombe 7/04 - Aldershot (SL) 3/06, Lewes 6/06	26	0
(M)Paul Armstrong	5'10"	10 09	5/10/78	27	Dublin	Airdrie U 6/03 - Eastbourne 6/06	30	2
(F)Jamie Cade	5'08"	10 11	15/1/84	22	Durham	Colchester 8/05 - Lewes (3ML) 1/06, Lewes 7/06	19	3
(D)Chris Giles	6'02"	13 00	16/4/82	24	Milborne Port	Aldershot 7/05 - Forest Green 7/06 Rel 7/06	28	2
(D)Sasha Opinel	5'09"	12 00	9/4/77	29	Saint Maurice	Farnborough 1/05 - Gravesend 7/06	23	1
(G)Phil Smith	6'01"	13 00	14/12/79	26	Harrow	Margate 7/04 - Swindon 7/06	38	0
(F)Steve Burton	6'01"	12 11	9/10/83	22	Doncaster	Scarborough 3/05 - Tamworth 8/06	36	7
(G)James Plumley			15/7/87	18		Horsham YMCA, Crawley, Ramsgate (2ML) 1/06		
(G)Scott Ward	6'02"	13 00	5/10/81	24	Brent	Margate, Crawley 10/04	4	0
(D)Sami El-Abd			1/1/88	18		Brighton - Burgess Hill (2ML) 9/05, Team Bath 8/06	1	0
(D)Leonard Mendy	6'00"	12 04	22/3/82	24	Evreux	Dieppe 12/05 -	21	0
(D)Neil Jenkins	5'06"	10 08	6/1/82	24	Carshalton	Southend 6/04 - Eastbourne 7/06	23	1
(D)Matthew Percival			7/12/87	18		Brighton -		
(D)Owen Botting						Yth - Horsham 8/06	0	0
(D)Dan Sackman						Yth	0	0
(M)Robert Kember			21/8/81	24	Wimbledon	Basingstoke 3/04 - Lewes (3ML) 2/06	5	0
(F)Omari Coleman	5'11"	11 13	23/11/80	25	London	Lincoln C 2/06 - Carshalton 8/06	9	4
(F)Gavin Gordon	6'01"	12 00	24/6/79	27	Manchester	N.County 2/06	5	0
(F)Billy Huntley			23/9/88	17	Portsmouth	Southampton, Crawley	0	0

CRAWLEY TOWN

Ground Address:	Broadfield Stadium, Brighton Road, Crawley RH 11 9RX
Tel No:	01293 41000
Fax:	01293 410009
General email address:	info@crawley-town.fc.com
Official website:	www.crawley-town-fc.com

SIMPLE DIRECTIONS

By Road	From M23 Jct. 11 take second exit off roundabout which is A23 towrds Crawley. Turn left at net roundabout to ground
Parking:	Large Car Park at ground

MATCH TICKETS

Ticket office Telephone:	01293 41000
Capacity:	4,996
Seats:	1.080
Covered:	4,200
Clubhouse:	Open matchdays and for private bookings plus evenings and week end lunchtimes
Refreshments:	Available on matchdays.
Club Shop:	Yes, fully stocked
Local Press:	Crawley Observer, Crawley News and The Argus.
Local Radio:	Radio Mercury and BBC Southern Counties

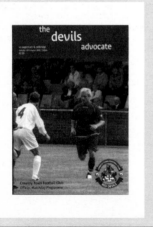

MATCHDAY PROGRAMME
Pages: 48   Price: £2.50
Editor: Ben Taylor
Tel No:01293 410000
07710508066 (M)

CLUB STATISTICS

RECORDS

Attendance: 4,522
v Weymouth Southern Premier 06.03.04

Victory: 10-0
v Chichester United Sussex Lg 1955
and v Crowborough Sussex Fllodlit Cup 2001

Defeat: 0-10
Career Goalscorer: Phil Basey 108 (1968-72)
Career Appearances: John Maggs 652(63-73 75-79)
Transfer Fee Paid: Undisclosed to Wycombe W
for Simpemba July 2004
Transfer Fee Received: £75,000
From Brentford for Jay Lovett in 2000
SENIOR HONOURS   Southern League Champions 2003-04
Southern League Southern Division R-Up 1983-84
Southern League Championship Match 2002-03 2003-04
Sussex Senior Cup 88-89 90-91 02-03 R-Up (2)

PREVIOUS
Leagues: Sussex County 1951-56, Metroplitan 56-63
Southern 1964-2003
Grounds: Malthouse Farm 1896-1914,1938-40,
Victory Hall & Rectory Field 1918-38,Yetmans Field 45-49,
Town Mead 49-53 54-97 and Ifield Recreation Ground 53-54

STEP 1
CONFERENCE

STEP 2 - P177
CONFERENCE Nth & Sth

STEP 3 - P269
NPL-SOUTHERN-ISTHMIAN PREM

STEP 4 - P269
NPL-SOUTHERN-ISTHMIAN

STEP 5/6 - P473

STEP 7 - P713

DAGENHAM & REDBRIDGE

Club Colours: Red/White/Red
Change Colours: Blue/Blue/Black
Club Sponsor: Compass Plumbing & Engineering
Previous League: Isthmian
BEST PERFORMANCES
League: Conference 2nd 2001-02 **F.A.Cup:** 4th Round 2002-2003
F.A.Trophy: Finalists 1996-97 (as Dagenham F.C. Winners 1980)
LAST SEASON
League: 10th Conference: **F.A.Cup:** 1st Round   **F.A.Trophy:** 4th Round Replay   **Formed:** 1992
                                                                                                      Nickname: Daggers

Back Row (L-R): Anwar Uddin, Shane Blacket, Tim Cole, Tony Roberts, Dave Hogan, Shaun Batt, Michael Olayle, Lee Goodwin.
Middle: John Gowan (Physio), Sam Saunders, Sam Sloma, Cliff Akurang, Paul Benson, Bai Mas Lettejallow, Craig Mackail-Smith, Peter Brady (Masseur). **Front:** Dave Rainford, Paul Bruce, Danny Foster, Terry Harris (Coach), John Still (Manager), Robbie Garvey (Coach), Glen Southam, Scott Griffiths, Tommy Laxton.

CLUB PERSONNEL

Chairman: Dave Andrews
Presidents: John & Brian East
Vice-Chairman: David Ward
Club Secretary: Derek Almond
97 Clays Rd, Walton on the Naze, Essex CO14 8SD
Tel Nos: 01255 677086 (H), 07768 506741(M)
and 0208 5927194 Ext 29
Correspondence to Secretary at Home

Commercial Manager: Steve Thompson
Tel Nos: 01708 702484 (H) 0208 5927194 (W) and
7811 426745 (M)
Press Officer: David Simpson
Tel Nos: 07860 119430 (W & M)

MANAGEMENT TEAM

Manager: John Still
Previous clubs as a manager: Dartford,
Maidstone United and Leytonstone Ilford
Honours as a Manager: Conference,Isthmian,
Southern champions Essex, Kent and London
Senior Cup winners
Prevous clubs as a player: Leyton Orient,
Ilford, Dagenham and Bishop Stortford

Honours as a Player: F.A.Amateur Cup Winners 1974

Coach: Terry Harris
Assistant Manager: Robbie Garvey
Physio: John Gowens

DAGENHAM & REDBRIDGE

No.	Date	Comp	H/A	Opponents	Att:	Result	Goalscorers	Pos
1	Aug 13	C	H	Southport	1265	W 3 - 1	Mackail-Smith 31 90 Leberi 51	3
2	16		A	Crawley Town	1734	D 0 - 0		6
3	20		A	Tamworth	1.04	D 2 - 2	Goodwin 21 **Moore** 45	8
4	27		H	Scarborough	1.074	L 0 - 2		11
5	29		A	Canvey island	1458	W 2 - 1	Goodwin 27 Mackail-Smith 79	9
6	Sept 3		H	Exeter City	1372	D 2 - 2	Southam 5 **Moore** 58	11
7	10		A	Altrincham	876	W 5 - 0	Kandol 37 57 **Moore** 51 Leberi 70 Mackail-Smith 81	7
8	17		A	Burton Albion	1.149	W 3 - 1	Goodwin 23 **Moore** 63 Kandol 82	5
9	29		A	York City	2927	D 1 1	Griffiths 90	6
10	24		H	Accrington Stanley	1331	L 1 - 2	Kandol 64	8
11	27		H	Grays Athletic	2017	L 1 - 2	**Moore** 48	10
12	Oct 5		A	Stevenage Borough	2447	L 1 - 2	Mackail-Smith 72	10
13	9		A	Aldershot Town	1512	W 2 - 0	Kandol 26 63	8
14	15		A	Morecambe	1718	L 0 - 2		10
15	18	LDV VansT	A	**Wycombe Wanderers**	1094	L 1 - 2*	Benson 26	
16	22	FAC 4Q	A	**Forest Green Rovers**	751	W 3 - 2	Moore 38 65 Kandol 74	
17	29	C	H	Forest Green Rovers	1325	D 1 - 1	**Moore** 5	10
18	Nov 5	FAC 1R	A	**Hartlepool United**	3655	L 1 - 2	Kandol 32	
19	12	C	A	Hoalifax Town	1532	L 0 - 3		11
20	19		H	Hereford UNited	1294	L 0 - 1		14
21	26		H	Woking	1138	L 1 - 3	Bruce 12	15
22	Dec 3		A	Kidderminster Harriers	1559	L 1 - 3	Southam 80	16
23	10		A	Cambridge United	1271	W 1 - 0	Akurang 45	15
24	17	FAT 1	H	**Thurrock**	797	W 2 - 0	**Moore** 60 (pen) Southam 90	
25	26	C	A	Gravesend & Northfleet	1391	W 3 - 1	Goodwin 32 **Moore** 87 90	14
26	31		A	Woking	1806	D 0 - 0		12
27	Jan 2		H	Gravesened & Northfleet	1405	L 1 - 2	Bruce 60	15
28	7		A	Southport	1002	W 2 - 1	Leberi 68 Mackail-Smith 16	12
29	14	FAT 2	H	**Kettering Town**	931	W 2 - 1	**Mackail-Smith 80 McIllain (og)**	
30	21	C	A	Tamworth	1352	W 2 - 1	**Moore** 13 62	11
31	28		A	Scarborough	1506	W 1 - 0	Griffiths 69	10
32	Feb 4	FAT 3	A	**Tamworth**	920	D 0 - 0		
33	7	FAT 3R	H	**Tamworth**	922	W 3 - 0	Moore 18 64 Southam 66	
34	11	C	A	Accriungton Stanley	2156	L 0 - 1		12
35	18		H	Stevenage Borough	1427	D 2 - 2	Cole 10 Saunders 16	12
36	21		A	Grays Athetic	1065	W 4 - 0	Bruce 11 Akurang 18 66 Southam 44	11
37	25	FAT 4	A	**Grays Athetic**	2321	D 1 - 1	**Mackail-Smith 16**	
38	28	FAT 4R	H	**Grays Athletic**	1526	L 2 - 4	**Mackail-Smith 36 Saunders 57**	
39	Mar 7	C	H	York City	973	L 0 - 0		
40	11		A	Aldershot Town	2010	L 1 - 3	Mackail-Smith 69	14
41	18		H	Morecambe	960	W 3 - 1	Mackail-Smith 45 Southam 62 Akurang 71	13
42	25		A	Forest Green Rovers	625	W 3 - 0	Cole 61 Foster 70 **Moore** 90	11
43	28		H	Crawley Town	932	L 0 - 3		11
44	April 1		H	Halifax Town	1078	W 1 - 0	Mackail-Smith 14	11
45	8		A	Hereford United	2561	D 1 - 1	Southam 83 (pen)	10
46	11		H	Altrincham	1058	L 2 4 4	Bruce 41 Griffiuths 45	10
47	15		A	Exeter City	3186	L 1 - 3	Cole 34	11
48	17		H	Canvey Island	1139	D 2 - 2	**Moore** 19 82 (pen)	11
49	22		H	Kiddermionster Harriers	1038	W 3 - 0	Saunders 33 Mackail-Smith 43 45	11
50	25		A	Burton Albion	1235	D 2 - 2	**Moore** 3 Akurang 72	10
51	29		A	Cambridge United	3161	W 2 1	**Moore** 54 (pen) Benson 78	10

Ave. League Home Attendance:	1132	**Goals**	75 68	**Top Goalscorer:** Chris Moore (20)
Best Position: 3rd	**Worst:** 16th			

CONFERENCE | CONFERENCE Nth & Sth | NPL - SOUTHERN - ISTHMIAN PREM | NPL - SOUTHERN - ISTHMIAN

#	ROBERTS 19	FOSTER 15	UDDIN 5	BLACKETT 12	GRIFFITHS 8	SOUTHAM 4	GOODWIN 6	LEBERL 22	BRUCE 10	MACKAIL-SMITH 23	MOORE 3	VICKERS 14	BENSON 27	OVERLAND 7	SAUNDERS 18	FOWLER 9	KANDOL 11	MARWA 20	CLARK 21	FRANCIS 17	LATTEJALLOW 24	MCGOWAN 18	FROTA 16	WARD 2	COLE 13	FILLETTI 9	AKURANG 26	HOGAN 16	BATT 16	ALI 18	JOHNSON 18	SCHOBURG 18	BRYANT 16
1	X	X	X	X	X	X	X	X	X	X	S	S	U	U	U																		
2	X	X	X	X	X	X	X	X	X	X	S	S	U		U	U																	
3	X	X	X		X	X	X	X	X	X	X	X	U	U	S	U	U																
4	X	X	X	X	X	X	X		X	X			S	U	S	U	S																
5	X	X	X	X	X	X	X		X	X		X	U	S	U	S	U																
6	X	X	X	X	X	X	X		X	X	S	X	U	U	U		S																
7	X	X	X	X	X	X	X	X	U	X	X			X	U	U	U																
8	X	X	X	X	X	X	X		X	X		S	U	X	S	U		U															
9	X	X	X	X	X	X	X		X	X		S	U	X	X	U	U																
10	X	X	X	X	X	X	X		X	X	S	S	U	X	X	U		U															
11	X	X	X	X	X	X	X		X	X	X	U	U	X	U	U	U																
12	X		X	X	X	X	X		X	X	X	S	U	X	X	U	U	U															
13	X		X	X	X	X	X		X	X	U	X	U	X	X	U	U	U															
14	X		X	X	X	X	X		X	X	S	X	U	X	X	U	U	U															
15	X		X	X	X	X			X	S	X	U	X	X	S	U		S															
16	X	U	X	X	X	X			U	X	S	X	U	X	X	U																	
17	X	U	X	X	X	X			S	X	X	X	U	S	X	X	U																
18	X	X	X	X	X	X	U		S	X	X	S	U	X	X	U																	
19	X	X	X	X	X	X			X	X	X	U	X	U	U	S	U																
20	X	X	X	X	X	X			X	X	X	U	X	U	U	U	S																
21	X	X	X	X	X	X			X		X	S	U	X	U	U	U	X															
22	X	X	X	X	X	X			X		X	S	U	X	U	U	X																
23	X	X	X	X	X	X			X		X	U	U	X	U	X	U	U															
24	X	X	X		X	X	X		X	U	X	X	X	U	U	X	U	U															
25	X	X	X	X	X	X			X	X	S	U	X	U	X	U	S																
26	X	X	X	X	X	X	X		X	X	X	U	U	U	X	U	U																
27	X	X	X	X	X		X	X	S	X	U	X	U	X	U	U																	
28	X	X	X	X	X		X	X	S	U	X	U	X	U	U																		
29	X	X	X	X	X	X			X	X	X	S	S	X	U	X	U	U															
30	X	X	X	X	X	X			X	X	U	X	X	U	U	S	U																
31	X	X	X	X	X	X			X	X	S	S	U	X	U	U																	
32	X	X	X	X	X	X	X	X	X	X	U	S	X	U	U																		
33	X	X	X	X		X	U	X	X	X	X	X	U	U	X	U	S																
34	X		X	X	X	X			X	X	X	S	X	U	X	X	U	U	U														
35	X	X	X	X	X	X			X	X	X	U	X	U	X	S	U	U															
36	X	X	X		X	X	U	S	X	X	S	X	X	S	X	X	U																
37	X	X	X	X	X	X	U		X	X	X	X	X	X	U	U																	
38	X	X	X	X		X		X	X	X	S	X	X	U	U	S																	
39	X	X	X	X	X	X			X	S	S	X	U	X	X	U	U																
40	X	X	X	X	X	X			X	X	S	X	X	X	S	U	U	U															
41	X	X	X	X	X	X			X	X	U	X	U	U	X	X	U																
42	X	X	X	X	X	X			X	X	S	S	X	U	X	X	U																
43	X	X	X	X	X	X			X	X	S	S	X	U	X	X	U																
44	X	X	X	X	X	X			X	X	X	U	U	S	X	S	U																
45	X	X	X	X	X	X			X	X	X	U	S	X	S	U																	
46	X	X	X	X	X	X			X	X	X	U	S	X	S	U																	
47	X	X	X		X	X			X	S	X	S	X	U	U	X	X	U															
48	X	X		X	X	X			S	X	X	X	S	U	U	X	X	U															
49	X	X		X	X	X			X	X	S	X	X	S	X	U	U	S															
50	X	X		X	X	X			X	X	X	X	S	S	X	U	U	U															
51	X	X		X	X	X			X	X	X	X	X	U	U	S	U	U															

Total Appearances (Conference)

	X	42	37	38	39	42	42	22	10	26	36	33	9	13	0	15	0	10	10	2	0	4	0	0	20	0	12	0	0	0	0	0	0	0
S	0	0	0	0	0	0	0	1	0	3	7	12	13	0	7	0	2	2	0	0	3	0	0	3	0	6	0	2	0	0	0	0
U	0	1	0	0	0	0	1	0	1	0	0	12	4	19	4	6	2	6	13	9	13	3	7	3	3	2	1	23	6	0	8	2	0

Cup Appearances

	X	9	7	9	8	8	8	6	2	4	6	9	3	3	0	5	0	3	4	0	0	0	0	0	0	5	0	0	0	0	0	0	0	0
S	0	0	0	0	0	0	0	0	1	0	0	3	2	0	2	0	0	0	0	0	0	1	0	0	1	0	0	0	0	0	0	1	1
U	0	1	0	0	0	0	2	1	0	2	0	2	0	3	0	0	0	1	4	2	0	2	0	0	1	1	0	6	0	1	0	3	1

DAGENHAM & REDBRIDGE

CURRANT SQUAD AS OF BEGINING OF 2006-07 SEASON

GOALKEEPERS

	SQ NO.	HT	WT	D.O.B	AGE	P.O.B	CAREER	APPS	GOA
Tony Roberts	1	6'00"	12 00	4/8/69	36	Holyhead	QPR Rel c/s 98, Millwall 8/98 Rel 4/99, St Albans c/s 99, Coaching in USA 3/00, Dag & Red 8/00	42	0
David Hogan	26						Dag & Red	0	0
Simon Overland	27	6'04"				London	Millwall Rel 2/04, Kettering (L) 3/00, Kettering NC 2/04, Gravesend 3/04, Grays 8/04, Dag & Red 1/05, Redbridge (L) 2/05, Maldon T 3/05, Dag & Red 6/05, Fisher (Dual) 11/05, Ashford T (L) 3/06	0	0

DEFENDERS

	SQ NO.	HT	WT	D.O.B	AGE	P.O.B	CAREER	APPS	GOA
Tim Cole	2			9/10/76	29	London	Walthamstow Pennant, Leyton Pennant, Dag & Red 4 fig 3/97, Billericay (L) 3/02, Gravesend (L) 9/02, East Thurrock (L) 9/05	23	3
Sam Sloma				29/10/82	23	London	Wimbledon, Hampton & R (L) 12/01, Aylesbury c/s 02, Wingate & F 12/02 Rel 2/06, Milwaukee Wave United (USA) (L) (2005), Wealdstone 2/06, Thurrock (Dual) 3/06, Dag & Red 7/06		
Lee Goodwin	4			5/9/78	27	Stepney	West Ham Rel c/s 98, Dag & Red 8/98, Bromley (L) 8/99, Grays (L) 2/03	22	4
Shane Blackett	5			3/10/82	23	Luton	Dunstable, Arlesey 8/03, Dag & Red 5/04	39	0
Scott Griffiths	12			10/2/86	20	Essex	Aveley, Dag & Red 8/04	42	3
Anwar Uddin	15	6'02"	13 00	1/11/81	24	London	West Ham, Cheltenham (Trial) 10/01, Sheff Wed 2/02 Rel c/s 02, Bristol R 7/02 Rel 5/04, Hereford (2ML) 12/03, Telford (L) 3/04, Dag & Red 7/04	38	0
Danny Foster	19			23/9/84	21	Enfield	Tottenham Rel c/s 04, Dag & Red 7/04	37	1
Michael Filletti	13	6'03"					Clapton, B.Stortford 4/05, Dag & Red 11/05, East Thurrock (Dual) 11/05	0	0
Mehmet Ali							Dag & Red	0	0

MIDFIELDERS

	SQ NO.	HT	WT	D.O.B	AGE	P.O.B	CAREER	APPS	GOA
Jake Leberl	6			2/4/77	29	Morden	Crewe, Dover 8/97 Rel c/s 02, Margate 8/02, Dag & Red 6/04	11	3
Sam Saunders	7			29/8/83	22		QPR (Jun), Welling, Hastings T, Ashford T 2/02, Carshalton 2/04. Dag & Red 5/05	22	2
Glen Southam	8			10/6/80	26	London	Fulham (Jun), Tottenham (Jun), Enfield, B.Stortford 7/00, Boreham Wood (L), Dag & Red 5/04	42	5
David Rainford		6'00"	11 11	21/4/79	27	Stepney	Colchester Rel c/s 99, Scarborough (L) 12/98, Slough 6/99, Grays c/s 01, Heybridge S 7/02, Slough 11/02, Ford U 1/03, B.Stortford 3/03, Dag & Red 5/06		
Baimass Lettejallow	17	5'09"	10 11	16/4/84	22	London	Barnet, Braintree 10/03, Harlow 1/04, Dag & Red 1/05	7	0
Paul Bruce	22	5'10"	12 06	18/2/78	28	London	QPR Rel c/s 02, Cambridge U (L) 3/99, Southend (Trial) 4/02, Dag & Red 7/02	26	4
Michael Olayle							Dag & Red		
Seb Schoburgh							Dulwich Hamlet, Dag & Red 2/06	0	0
David Bryant								0	0

Forwards

	SQ NO.	HT	WT	D.O.B	AGE	P.O.B	CAREER	APPS	GOA
Cliff Akurang	9			27/2/81	25		Chelsea (Jun), Luton (Trainee), Chesham, Hitchin 8/00 Rel 12/01, Purfleet/Thurrock 12/01, Heybridge Swifts 2/05, Dag & Red (L) 11/05, Dag & Red 1/06	18	5
Craig Mackail-Smith	10			25/2/84	22	Hertfordshire	St Albans, Arlesey 8/03, Dag & Red 5/04	39	11
Paul Benson	14	6'02"				Essex	White Ensign, Southend (Trial), Dag & Red 5/05	26	1
Shaun Batt	16					Luton	Stevenage, Dag & Red 7/05, Ilford (L) 8/05, Leyton (2ML) 10/05, East Thurrock (3ML) 1/06	2	0
Taiwo Atieno		6'02"	12 13	6/8/85	21	Brixton	Walsall Rel 5/06, Nuneaton (WE) 2/04, Rochdale (L) 10/04, Chester (L) 2/05, Kidderminster (5ML) 8/05, Darlington (L) 3/06, Dag & Red 8/06		
Liam Francis	21			15/3/86	20	Edmonton	Tottenham (Trainee), Redbridge, Dag & Red 12/04, Redbridge (L) 12/04, Ilford (Dual) 10/05, Lewes (L) 1/06	0	0

PLAYING SQUAD

LOANEES	SN	HT	WT	DOB	AGE	POB	FROM - TO	APPS	GOA
(M)Thomas Ward	20						Luton (1M) 10/05 - B.Stortford 1/06	0	0
(M)Luis Frota	17						Stansted (Dual) 10/05 -	0	0
(D)Ryan Johnson	18			15/1/87	19	Dartford	QPR (Sch) (2M) 1/06 - Maidenhead (SL) 3/06	0	0

DEPARTURES	SN	HT	WT	DOB	AGE	POB	FROM - TO	APPS	GOA
(M)Jordan Fowler	18	5'10"	11 00	1/10/84	21	Barking	Arsenal 8/05 - Rel 9/05, Arsenal 9/05, Kettering 11/05,		
							Havant & W 1/06, Bishops Stortford 8/06	0	0
(D)Tom McGowan	24						Dartford 9/05 - Maldon 11/05	0	0
(F)Tresor Kandol	9	6'01"	11 07	30/8/81	24	Banga	Thurrock 5/05 - Darlington (L) 11/05, Barnet £50,000 1/06	12	6
(M)Rambir Marwa	11			10/1/80	25	Barkingside	St Albans 5/05 - St Albans (L) 2/06 (Perm) 3/06	12	0
(D)Ashley Vickers	3	6'03"	13 10	14/6/72	34	Sheffield	St Albans 3/00 - Weymouth 5/06	21	0
(D)Kenny Clark	20						Dag & Red - Heybridge (L) 3/06, Thurrock 6/06	2	0
(F)Chris Moore	23			13/1/80	26	Middlesex	Northwood 11/03 - Brentford 7/06	40	15

Dagenham & Redbridge

Ground Address:	Glyn Hopkin Stadium, Victoria Road, Dagenham, essex RM10 7XL
Tel No:	0208 592 7194/1549
Fax:	0208 5937227
General email address:	info@daggers.co.uk
Official website:	www.daggers.co.uk
SIMPLE DIRECTIONS	
By Road	The Ground is on the A112 between A12 and A13
Parking:	Club car park plus ample parkingin surrounding streets
By Rail:	Dagenham East Tube (District Line) is 500 yards from ground.

MATCH TICKETS	
Ticket office Telephone:	02085927194/1549
Capacity:	6,077
Seats:	1,028
Covered:	3,000
Clubhouse:	0208 592 7194/1549
Refreshments:	Available at ground
Club Shop:	Open on matchdays Contact: Steve Thompson
Club Manager:	Tel No: 0208 592 7194
Clubcall:	

Local Press:	Dagenham Post, Yellow Advertiser, Walthamstow Guardian and Barking & Dagenham Recorder.
Local Radio:	BBC Radio Essex, Time FM and GLR London Live.

MATCHDAY PROGRAMME
Pages: 48   Price: `32.50
Editor: Dave Simpson
Tel No: 07860 119430 (M)

CLUB STATISTICS

RECORDS

Attendance: 5,949
v Ipswich Town F.A.Cup 3rd Rd. 03.01.02

Victory: 8-1
v Woking (A) Conference 19.04.94

Defeat: 0-9 v Hererford U (H) Conference 03-04
Career Goalscorer: Danny Shipp 102 (1995-2004)
Career Appearances: Jason Broom 338
Transfer Fee Paid: £15,000 to Purfleet for Paul Cobb1997
Transfer Fee Received: £65,000 from Birmingham City for
Ian Richardson in May 1995

SENIOR HONOURS Isthmian League Champions 1999-2000
Conference Runners Up 2001-02
F.A.Trophy Finalists 1996-97
Essex Senior Cup 1997-98

PREVIOUS
Leagues: GMV Conference 92-96 Isthmian League 96-00
Names: Ilford (1881) & Leytonstone (1886) merged in 1979
to form Leytonstone-Ilford
They & Walthamstowe Avenue (1900) merged in1986
to form Redbridge Forest
who in turn merged with Dagenham (1949) in 1992
to form Dagenham & Redbridge

EXETER CITY

Club Colours: Red & white stripes/black/black
Change Colours: All Sky Blue
Club Sponsor: Flybe
Previous League: Football League
BEST PERFORMANCES
League: 8th Division Three (Now Div 1) 1979-80 **F.A. Cup:** Quarter Final 1931 and 1981.
F.A. Trophy: Quarter Final 2003-04
LAST SEASON
League: 7th Conference   **F.A.Cup:** 4th Qual. Round   **F.A.Trophy:** Semi-Final

Formed: 1904
Nickname: Grecians

Back row.left to right: Steven Humt,Chris Wright, Jamie Mackie, Dean Moxey, Bertrand Cozic, Patrick Ada and Adam Stansfield. Middle Row: Jon Richardson, Danny Seaborne, Billy Jones, Martin Rice, Paul Jones, George Friend, Jon Challinor and Danny Woodards. Front row: Matt Gill, Danny Clay, Paul Buckle (Asssistant Manager), Steve Perryman (Director of Football), Chris Todd (Captain), Paul Tisdale (Manager) Claire Turner (Sports Therapist), Andy Taylor and Lee Påhillips.

CLUB PERSONNEL

Chairperson: Denise Watts

Vice-Chairman: Julian Tagg

Additional Directors: Dave Newbury, Geoffrey Styles

Roger Hamilton-Kendal, Frances Farley, Paul Morrish

Honorary President: Ivor Doble

Honorary Life President: Clifford Hill

Head of Operations: Andy Gillard
Tel No: 01392 413954

Club Secretary: Sally Cooke
Tel Nos: H) 01884 32275
(B) 01395 232 784. (M) 07703 323769
Email: sally.cooke@exetercityfc.co.uk

Commercial Manager: Bruce Henderson
Tel No: 01395 413953
e-mail: bruce.henderson@exetercityfc.co.uk

Press Officer   John Fournier
e-mail: john.fournier@exetercityfc.co.uk
Tel No: 01392 411243

MANAGEMENT TEAM

Director of Football: Steve Perryman M.B.E.

Manager: Paul Tisdale

Player/Assitant Manager: Paul Buckle

Youth Development Officer: Mike Radford

Physio: Claire Turner

EXETER CITY

No.	Date	Comp	H/A	Opponents	Att:	Result	Goalscorers	Pos
1	Aug 13	C	A	Gravesend & Northfleet	1578	W 2 - 0	Phillips 44 73 (pen)	4
2	16		H	Kidderminster Harriers	4914	W 1 - 0	Farrell 69	1
3	20		H	Morecambe	3978	W 2 - 0	Phillips 24 Todd 33	1
4	27		A	Accrington Stanley	1312	W 2 - 1	Watkins 68 Todd 71	1
5	29		H	Forest Green Rovers	4696	D 0 - 0		1
6	Sept 3		A	Dagenham & Redbridge	1372	D 2 - 2	Challinor 12 Todd 90	2
7	10		H	Cambridge United	3407	W 4 - 0	Scully 4 Phillips 14 Buckle 63 Challinor 67	1
8	17		A	Southport	1423	W 3 - 0	Farrell 46 56 Phillips 48	1
9	20		A	Stevenage Borough	2445	L 0 - 2		1
10	24		H	Burton Albion	4025	L 1 - 2	Jones 17	3
11	27		H	Woking	3082	D 1 - 1	Scully 27	5
12	Oct 1		A	York City	3503	L 2 - 4	Flack 22 Jones 73 (pen)	5
13	8		H	Halifax Town	3154	W 4 - 2	Jones 10 (pen) Flack 45 Afful 73 Farrell 74	4
14	15		A	Crawley Town	2454	W 2 - 0	Chalinor 90 90	3
15	18	LDV Vans T	A	MK Dons	2745	L 2 - 3	Phillips 72 Taylor 82	
16	22	FAC 4Q	H	Stevenage Borough	3421	L 0 - 1		
17	29	C	H	Tamworth	3369	W 3 - 0	Phillips 43 Farrell 66 90	2
18	Nov 5		A	Kidderminster Harriers	1869	W 2 - 1	Todd 59 Scully 77	2
19	12		A	Altrincham	1366	D 1 - 1	Challinor 31	1
20	19		H	Grays Athletic	6682	L 1 - 2	Challinor 86	3
21	26		A	Hereford United	3754	W 2 - 0	Mackie 61 Challinor 67	3
22	Dec 3		H	Canvey Island	3465	L 0 - 2		3
23	10		A	Scarborough	1428	W 1 - 0	Farrell 45	3
24	18	FAT 1	H	Bishop's Stortford	1807	W 2 - 1	Jones 5 Robinson 41	
25	26	C	H	Aldershot Town	4989	W 4 - 0	Buckle 33 B.Jones 38 (pen) Challinor 61 Phillips 70	2
26	30		H	Hereford United	4433	L 1 2	Phillips 5	2
27	Jan 2		A	Aldershot Town	3136	L 0 - 1		2
28	7		H	Gravesend & Northfleet	3396	W 1 - 0	Phillips 79	2
29	14	FAT 2	H	Histon	2103	W 3 - 2	Jones 23, Mackie 25 Challinor 81	
30	21	C	A	Morecambe	2073	D 2 - 2	Jones 54 (pen) Challinor 90	2
31	30		H	Accrington Stanley	4624	L 1 - 3	Edwards 72	2
32	Feb 4	FAT 3	H	Cambridge City	2166	W 1 - 0	Pope 86 (og)	
33	10	C	A	Burton Albion	1824	L 0 - 2		7
34	18		H	York City	3381	L 1 - 3	Carlisle	7
35	21		A	Woking	1536	L 0 - 1		8
36	25	FAT 4	H	Salisbury City	3653	W 3 - 0	Phillips 15 59 Flack 29	
37	Mar 4	C	A	Southport	3485	W 5 - 0	Flack 3 (2 4 13) Phillips 32 (pen) Buckle 81	7
38	11		A	Halifax Toiwn	2104	L 0 - 2		8
39	14		H	Stevenage Borough	3026	L 0 - 2		8
40	18	FAT S-F1	H	Grays Athletic	3051	W 2 - 1	Todd 63 Phillips 76	
41	25	FAT S-F2	A	Grays Athletic	3693	L 0 - 2		
42	28	C	A	Tamworth	823	D 1 - 1	Challinor 1	8
43	April 1		H	Altrincham	3134	W 3 - 1	Phillips 8 Mackie 28 Challinor 49	8
44	4		A	Cambridge United	2358	L 1 - 2	Phillips 82	8
45	10		A	Grays Athletic	1369	L 0 - 3		8
46	15		H	Dagenham & Redbridge	3186	W 3 - 1	Jones 45 (pen) Phillips 47 Gill 88	8
47	17		A	Forset Greeen Rovers	1334	D 0 - 0		8
48	22		A	Canvey Island	641	D 1 - 1	Jones 83	8
49	25		H	Crawley Town	1782	W 4 - 0	Mackie 34 Seaborne 38 Farrell 41 Moxey 62	8
50	29		H	Scarborough	3382	D 1 - 1	Challinor 85	7

Ave. League Home Attendance:	2122	**Goals**	77 58	**Top Goalscorer:** Lee Phillips (17)
Best Position: 1st	**Worst:** 8th			

	P JONES 27	HILEY 2	GAIA 5	TODD 6	MOXEY 21	TAYLOR 7	CHALLINOR 10	BUCKLE 18	VINNICOMBE 30	PHILLIPS 11	FLACK 14	AFFUL 17	FARRELL 9	CRONIN 8	RICE 1	SEABORNE 22	B JONES 3	EDWARDS 19	MACKIE 12	SAWYER 4	WATKINS 16	SCULLY 24	CLAY 20	MCCONNELL 15	GHIGLIA 33	BUCKLER 31	LELIUGA 23	WOODARDS 25	ROBINSON 26	CARLISLE 26	GILL 15	FRIEND 2	BYE 29	
	X	X	X	X	X	X	X	X	X	X	X	S	S	S	U	U																		1
	X	X	X	X			X	X	X	U	X	X		S	X	X	U	U	X	S														2
	X	X	X	X		S	X	X	X	S	X	S		X	X	U		X	X	U														3
	X	X	X	X			X	X	X	U	X	X		X	U		X	S		S	S													4
	X	X		X		X	X	X	U	X	S	S		X	U		X	X		X	S													5
	X	X	U	X		X	X	X		X	X		S	X	U		X			X	S	S												6
	X	X	U	X		S	X	X		X	S	S	X	X	X	U		X			X		X											7
	X	X	U	X		S	X	X		X	S		X	X	U		X			X	S	X												8
	X	X	U	X		X	X	X		X	S		S	X	U		X	X		X		S												9
	X	X	U	X		S	X	X		X	S	S	X	X	U		X			X		X												10
	X	X	S	X		X	X			X	U	X		U		X	S	S	X		X													11
	X	X	U	X		X	X			X	X	S	X	U		X	X	S	S															12
	X	X	X	X		X	X			S	X	S	X	X	U		X	U		S		X												13
	X	S	X	X		X	X			X	S	X	X	X	U		X		U	S		X												14
		X	X			X				X	X		X	U			X	X	X		X	S	S	U	U									15
	X	X		X		X	X			S	X	X	X	X			X		S	X														16
	X		X	U		X	X	S		X	U		X	X	U		X		S	X		X						X						17
	X		X	X	S	X	X			X	S		X	X	U		X		S	U		X						X						18
	X		X	X	S	X	X			X	S		X	X	U		X		S	U		X						X						19
	X		U	X	X	S	X			X	S		X	X	U		X		S	X		X						X						20
	X			X	S	X	X	U			S		X	X	U		X		X	X	U							X						21
	X		U	S	X	X	X			S	X		X	X	U		X		X	X								X						22
	X		X	X	U	S	X	X			X	U	X	X	U		X		S									X						23
	X		X	U		X	U			X	U	U	X	X	U		X		X	X								X	X					24
	X		U	X	S	X	X	X		X	S		X	X	U		X		S	X								X						25
	X		S	X	S	X	X	X		X	S		X	X	U		X		U	X								X						26
	X		U	X	X	X	X			X	S		X	X	U		X		S	X								X	S					27
	X		U	X	X	X	X			X	S		X	S	U		X		S	X								X						28
	X		X		X		X	X		X	S	S	S	X			X		X	X								X						29
	X		U	X		X	X			X	S		S	X	U		X	X		X	X							X		X	S			30
	X		S	X		X	S			X	S		X		U		X	X	U	X								X		X	X			31
	X		X	S		X	X			X	S		X	X			X		U	X								X		X	X			32
	X		X	X	X	X	X			S	X		S	X	U		X	X	X	U								X			S			33
	X		X	X	X	X				S	X	U		X	X	U		S	S									X		X	U			34
	X		X	X	X	X				S	S		X	X	U		U	X	S									X			X			35
	X		X	X	X	X	X			X	X		U	X	U		U	U										X			X			36
	X		U	X	X	X	X			X	X			X	U		S	S												S	X			37
	X		U	X	X	X	S	X			S		S	X	U		X	X	X									X			X			38
	X		U	X		X	X	X			X		X	X	U		X	S										X		S	S			39
	X		U	X	S	X	X			X	X		S	X	U		X		X									X		S	X			40
	X		U	X	X	X	X	S		X	S		S		U		X		X									X		X	X			41
	X		U	X	S	X	X	S		X	S		X		U		X		X									X			X			42
	X		U	X	S	X	X			X	U		S		U		X		X	X								X			X			43
	X		U	X	S	X	X	X			X		S		U		X		S	X								X			X			44
	X		X	X	X	U	X	X			X	S		U		U		X		X								X			X			45
	U		X	X	X	X				X	S	S		X	X	X		X	X						S			X			X			46
	U		X		X	S				X	S	S		X	U	X		X	U		X				X			X		X	X	X		47
	U		X	X	X		S			X	S		S		X	X	X		X	X					U			X			X			48
	U		U	X	X		X		S	X	U		X		X	X	X								S			X			X			49
	U		X	X			X			U	X	S		X		X	X	X		X	U							X			X	S		50

Total Appearances (Conference)

37	13	14	41	12	29	40	24	1	34	11	4	26	28	5	4	36	8	13	26	0	10	1	0	0	0	0	27	0	4	13	1	0	X
0	1	3	0	9	6	2	4	2	3	26	6	12	2	0	0	1	6	11	4	5	3	2	0	0	0	0	1	2	3	0	1		S
5	0	20	1	1	1	0	1	4	0	5	1	1	0	37	3	2	1	4	5	1	0	1	0	0	0	0	0	0	1	0	0		U

Cup Appearances

7	2	5	4	3	5	7	2	1	7	3	2	3	6	1	0	6	0	3	7	1	0	1	0	0	0	0	6	1	2	4	0	0	X
0	0	0	1	1	0	0	0	2	0	1	3	1	3	0	0	0	0	0	1	0	0	0	0	0	1	1	0	0	0	1	0	0	S
0	0	2	1	0	0	0	1	0	0	1	1	1	0	5	1	1	1	0	0	0	0	0	0	0	1	1	0	0	0	0	0	0	U

EXETER CITY

CURRANT SQUAD AS OF BEGINING OF 2006-07 SEASON

GOALKEEPERS	SQ NO.	HT	WT	D.O.B	AGE	P.O.B	CAREER	APPS	GOA
Martin Rice	1	5'09"		7/3/86	20	Exeter	Exeter	5	0
Paul Jones	27	6'03"		28/6/86	20	Maidstone	L.Orient, Exeter (SL) 11/04, Exeter 7/05	37	0
Tom Buckler	31			15/10/87	18	Torquay	Exeter, Taunton (L) 3/06	0	0

DEFENDERS

DEFENDERS	SQ NO.	HT	WT	D.O.B	AGE	P.O.B	CAREER	APPS	GOA
Danny Woodards	25	5'11"	11 01	7/10/83	22	Forest Gate	Chelsea Rel c/s 05, Wycombe (Trial) 10/05, Exeter 10/05	27	0
Billy Jones	3	6'00"	11 05	26/3/83	23	Gillingham	L.Orient, Kidderminster 1/05, Exeter 5/05	37	7
Daniel Seaborne	22			5/3/87	19	Barnstaple	Exeter, Tiverton (L) 9/05, Taunton (2ML) 1/06	4	1
Chris Todd	6	6'01"	12 01	22/8/81	24	Swansea	Swansea Rel c/s 02, Drogheda 8/02, Exeter 1/03	41	4
Rob Edwards		6'00"	12 07	1/7/73	33	Kendal	Carlisle, Bristol C £135,000 3/91, Preston 8/99 Rel c/s 04, Blackpool 8/04 Rel 5/06, Exeter 8/06		
Patrick Ada		6'00"		14/1/85	21	Cameroon	Redbridge 7/04, Aldershot (Trial), Barnet 3/05, St Albans 7/05, Exeter 7/06		
Jon Richardson		6'01"	12 02	29/8/75	31	Nottingham	Exeter, C. Palace (Trial) (95/96), Oxford U 8/00 Rel c/s 02, Forest Green 8/02 Rel 5/06, Exeter 7/06		
Dean Moxey	21	5'11"		14/1/86	20	Exeter	Exeter	21	1
George Friend	2						Exeter, Tiverton (L) 8/05	1	0

MIDFIELDERS

MIDFIELDERS	SQ NO.	HT	WT	D.O.B	AGE	P.O.B	CAREER	APPS	GOA
Matthew Gill	15	5'11"	11 10	8/11/80	25	Cambridge	Peterborough, Notts County 6/04, Exeter 1/06	16	1
Andrew Taylor	7	5'09"	12 10	17/9/82	23	Exeter	Man Utd Rel c/s 02, Northwich 7/02 Rel c/s 03, Kidsgrove A (L) 3/03, Cheltenham (Trial) 9/03, Exeter 10/03	35	0
Jon Challinor	10	5'11"		2/12/80	25	Northampton	Rushden & D, Stamford 4/99, Cambridge C 2/01 , Kalamazoo Kingdom (USA), St Albans 8/02, Aldershot 8/03 Rel 5/05, Exeter 5/05	42	12
Bertrand Cozic		5'10"	12 06	18/5/78	28	Quimper, Fr	Quimper (Fr), Guincamp (Fr), Bihorel (Fr), Team Bath 7/00, Cheltenham 8/03 Rel 1/04, Notts County (Trial) 2/04, Hereford 3/04 Rel 5/04, Northampton 8/04, Kidderminster 2/05 Rel c/s 05, Aldershot 8/05 Rel 9/05 Team Bath 9/05, Exeter 7/06		
Daniel Clay	20			15/12/85	20	Doncaster	Exeter, Tiverton (2ML) 12/05, Crawley (2ML) 2/06	3	0
Paul Buckle	18	5'08"	11 10	16/12/70	35	Welwyn	Brentford, Wycombe (L) 12/92, Torquay 2/94, Exeter (L) 10/95 Perm 11/95 Rel c/s 96, Northampton 8/96, Wycombe 10/96, Colchester 11/96, Exeter 7/99, Aldershot 8/02, Weymouth 8/03, Exeter 12/04, Tiverton 12/04, Exeter Pl/Coach 3/05	28	3
Rytis Leliuga	23			4/1/87	19		SM Mazeikiai, Exeter, Taunton (L) 12/05	0	0
Matt Bye	29						Exeter	1	0

FORWARDS

FORWARDS	SQ NO.	HT	WT	D.O.B	AGE	P.O.B	CAREER	APPS	GOA
Jamie Mackie	12	5'08"	11 02	22/9/85	20	London	Leatherhead, Wimbledon/MK Dons 1/04 Rel c/s 05, Havant & W (L) 2/05, Exeter (Trial) 7/05, Exeter 8/05, Sutton U (L) 8/05	24	3
Adam Stansfield		5'11"	11 02	10/9/78	27	Plymouth	Cullompton R, Tiverton T, Cullompton R, Elmore, Exeter Res (Dual), Yeovil 11/01 Rel c/s 04, Hereford 6/04, Exeter 6/06		
Lee Phillips	11	5'10"	12 00	16/9/80	25	Penzance	Plymouth, Weymouth (3ML) 12/00 Perm 3/01, Exeter 2/05	37	13

PLAYING SQUAD

LOANEES	SN	HT	WT	DOB	AGE	POB	FROM - TO	APPS	GOA
(D)Gary Sawyer	4		5/7/85		21	Bideford	Plymouth (SL) 8/05 -	30	0
(M)Tony Scully	24	5'07"	11 05	12/6/76	30	Dublin	N.County 9/05 - Crawley (L) 11/05, Rel 1/06, Crawley 1/06	13	3

DEPARTURES	SN	HT	WT	DOB	AGE	POB	FROM - TO	APPS	GOA
(M)Barry McConnell	15	5'11"	10 03	1/1/77	29	Exeter	Youth 8/95 - Bath C 11/05, Tamworth 12/05 Rel 1/06,		
							Forest Green 2/06, Tiverton 3/06	0	0
(M)Anton Robinson	26	5'09"	10 03	17/2/86	20	Brent	Margate 12/05 - Rel 1/06, Eastbourne 2/06 Rel 5/06, Fisher 5/06	1	0
(D)Scott Hiley	2	5'09"	11 12	27/9/68	37	Plymouth	Portsmouth - Rel 2/06, Crawley 8/06	14	0
(F)Craig Watkins	18					Croydon	Sutton U 8/05 - Sutton U (L) 10/05, Lewes (L) 12/05,		
							Staines (L) 1/06, Rel 2/06, Havant & W 3/06	5	1
(D)Chris Vinnicombe	30	5'08"	10 12	20/10/70	35	Exeter	Tiverton 8/05 - Rel 5/06, Tiverton	3	0
(M)Les Afful	17	5'06"	10 00	4/2/84	22	Liverpool	Yth 8/02 - Torquay (SL) 1/06, Rel 5/06, Forest Green 5/06	10	1
(F)Craig Farrell	9	6'00"	12 11	5/12/82	23	Middlesbrough	Carlisle 8/05 - Rel 5/06, York 6/06	38	8
(F)Steve Flack	14	6'01"	11 04	29/5/71	35	Cambridge	Cardiff 9/96 - Rel 5/06, Tiverton (Pl/Coach) 5/06	37	5
(F)Jake Edwards	19	6'01"	12 08	11/5/76	30	Prestwich	Yeovil 7/04 - Tamworth (3ML) 10/05, Chester (SL) 3/06, Rel 5/06,		
							Crawley 8/06	14	1
(D)Santos Gaia	5	6'00"	12 04	8/9/78	27	Sao-Mateus-Es	Agremiacao (Bra) 7/02 - Stevenage 6/06	17	0
(M)Glenn Cronin	8	5'08"	10 11	14/9/81	24	Dublin	Yth - Chester 7/06	30	0
(F)Loris Ghiglia	33						Yth - Taunton (SL) 2/06, Taunton 7/06, Clyst 8/06	0	0
(M)Wayne Carlisle	26	6'00"	11 06	9/9/79	26	Lisburn	L.Orient 1/06 - Rel c/s 06	6	1

EXETER CITY

Ground Address:	St James' Park, Exeter EX4 6PX
Tel No:	01392 411 243
Fax:	01392 413 959
General email address:	enquiries@exetercityfc.co.uk
Official website:	www.exetercityfc.co.uk

SIMPLE DIRECTIONS

By Road   Take the M5 exiting at junction 30, follow signs for Exeter City Centre, along Sidmouth Road and onto Heavitree Road, at the roundabout take the 4th exit into Western Way and then the second exit onto Tiverton road, then take the next left into St. James Road. On-street car parking, otherwise city centre car parks and walk to ground.

By Rail: Nearest station: St James' Park. served by Exmouth branch line trains. Half hourly throughout the day.Nearest main line stations, Exeter Central or Exeter St Davids

MATCH TICKETS

Ticket office Telephone:	01392 411 243.
Capacity:	9,036

Clubhouse:	Centre Spot Social Club in adjacent St Jame's Centre. Tel No: 01392 413 955
Refreshments:	Social Club, hospitality suits and kiosks around the ground.
Club Shop:	At ground in St James' Centre; In city centre at Bedford street, Exeter (manned voluntarily by members of Exeter City Supporters Trust).

Local Press:	Express & Echo; Western Morning News
Local Radio:	Local radio: BBC Radio Devon; Gemini Radio

Football in the Community:	Jamie Vittals
Centre of Excellence:	Mel Gwinnett

MATCHDAY PROGRAMME
WINNER OF THE WIRRAL PROGRAMME
AWARD 2003/04, 2004/05

Pages: 48   Price: £2.50
Editor: Mike Blackstone
Tel No: (H) 01524 853 605
Email: mj.blackstone@virgin.net

CLUB STATISTICS

RECORDS

Attendance: 21,018
v Sunderland, FA Cup quarter-final replay, 1931

Victory (League): 8-1
v Coventry City, Div. 3 South 1926
v Aldershot, Div. 3 South 1935

Cup: 14-0
v Weymouth, FA Cup, 1908

Defeat (League): 0-9
v Notts County, Div. 3 South 1948
v Nothampton Town, Div. 3 South 1958

Career Goalscorer: Tony Kellow - 129
1976-79, 1980-83, 1985-88

Career Appearances: Arnold Mitchell - 495
1952-66

Transfer Fee Paid: £65,000
to Blackpool for Tony Kellow, March 1980

Transfer Fee Received: £500,000
from Manchester City for Martin Phillips, November 1995

SENIOR HONOURS   Fourth Division 1990
Third Division South Cup 1934

PREVIOUS
Leagues: East Devon Senior League - 1904-05
Plymouth & District - 1905-08
Southern League - 1908-20
Football League - 1920 - 2003

FOREST GREEN ROVERS

Club Colours: Black & white stripes/black/black

Change Colours: Green & white

Club Sponsor: Sheffield Insulations.

Previous League: Southern

BEST PERFORMANCES

League: 12th Conference 98-99 **F.A. Cup:** 2nd Rd 99-00 **F.A. Trophy:** R-Up 98-99 00-01

LAST SEASON

Conference: 20th   **F.A.Cup:** 4th Qual. Round   **F.A.Trophy:** 3rd Round

Founded: 1890
Nickname: Rovers

Back row, left to right: Alex Lawless, Allan Russell, Alex Meecham, Paul Wanless, Darren Jones, and Simon Clist Middle row: Jack Russell (Goalkeeping Coach), Tony Butler, Mark Preece, Steve Williams, Keith Marfel (Physio), Ryan Harrison, Charlie Griffin, Matt McEntegart, and Mike Bullock. Front Row: Paul Stonehouse, Mark Beesley, Michael Brough, Gary Owers (Manager), Shaun Taylor (Assistant Manager), Jamie Pitman, Les Afful and Kevin Nicholson.

CLUB PERSONNEL

Chairman:	Colin Gardner M.B.E.	**Press Officer:**	Colin Peake
Vice Chairman:	Trevor Horsley	**Tel No:**	07788 188688
Directors:	Jenny Anns, John Clapp	**Programme Editor:**	Clive White
	Jenny Anns, Ken Boulton & Mark Coles	**Tel No:**	01453 750099 (w) 07884 030859 (M)
Company Secretary:	Doug O'Brien		
Football Administrator	Colin Peake	**e-mail:**	clivemwhite@aol.com
Tel Nos:	01453 834860 Ext 22	**Programme;:**	52 pages £2.50
Fax:	01453 835291	**Website:**	www.fgrfc.co.uk
e-mail:	member@roversfc.freeserve.co.uk	**Club Shop:**	Open on matchdays only
General Manager:	Robin Eaves	**Contact:**	Andy Whiting
Tel.No:	1453 834860 Ext 23		
e.mail:	t.eaves@roversfc.freeserve.co.uk		
Commercial Manager:	Natalie Ward		

MANAGEMENT TEAM

Manager:	Gary Owers
Previous club as Manager:	Bath City
Assistant Manager:	Shaun Taylor
Goalkeepeting Coach:	Mick Byrne
Physiothapist:	Keith Marvell

FOREST GREEN ROVERS

No.	Date	Comp	H/A	Opponents	Att:	Result	Goalscorers	Pos
1	Aug 13	C	H	Cambridge United	1112	W 1 - 0	Rendell 49	8
2	16		A	Tamworth	1258	D 0 - 0		8
3	20		A	Altrincham	804	L 1 - 2	**Wanless** 71 (pen)	12
4	27		H	Halifax Town	905	D 2 - 2	**Wanless** 2 82	13
5	29		A	Exter City	4696	D 0 - 0		15
6	Sept 2		H	Grays Athletic	1152	L 1 - 2	**Wanless** 23 (pen)	15
7	10		H	York City	889	L 1 - 2	Teixeira 89	17
8	17		A	Kidderminster Harriers	1818	W 3 - 1	**Wanless** 19 Abbey 34 74	
9	20		H	Crawley Town	916	D 2 - 2	**Wanless** 2 Meechan 5	14
10	24		A	Scarborough	1341	L 0 1		16
11	27		A	Gravesend & Northfleet	706	L 0 - 2		18
12	Oct 1		H	Morecambe	802	W 1 - 0		14
13	7		A	Southport	1087	L 1 - 3	Richardson 16	16
14	15		H	Woking	875	L 0 - 3		19
15	**22**	**FAC 4Q**	**H**	**Dagenham & Redbridge**	**751**	**L 2 - 3**	**Beswetherick 4 Meechan 27**	
16	29	C	A	Dagenham & Redbridge	1325	D 1 - 1	**Wanless** 33 (pen)	18
17	Nov 12		H	Canvey Island	678	L 1 - 2	Meechan 22	21
18	18		A	Accrington Stanley	1506	L 0 - 2		22
19	26		A	Aldershot Town	2290	L 1 - 2	Madjo 7	22
20	Dec 10		A	Stevenage Borough	1771	L 1 - 2	Harding 4	22
21	13		H	Burton Albion	548	W 1 - 0	Alsop 45	20
22	**17**	**FAT 1**	**A**	**Weymouth**	**1120**	**W 1 - 0**	**Gadsby 88**	
23	24	C	H	Hereford United	1957	D 2 - 2	Meechan 34 Madjo 80	20
24	31		H	Aldershot Town	1051	W 4 - 2	Alsop 7 **Wanless** 10 Madjo 48 71	19
25	Jan 2		A	Hereford United	3507	D 1 - 1	Madjo 58	19
26	7		A	Cambridge United	2344	D 2 - 2	Richardson 2 Teixeira 90	18
27	**14**	**FAT 2**	**H**	**Dorchester Town**	**861**	**W 3 - 1**	**Hayes 24 Harding 35 Wanless 51**	
28	21		H	Altrincham	995	W 5 - 0	Madjo 11 72 Alsop 17 Meechan 65 Rendell 87	18
29	24		H	Tamworth	788	L 1 - 3	**Wanless** 75	19
30	28		A	Halifax Town	1284	L 0 1 1		19
31	**Feb 4**	**FAT 3**	**A**	**Stafford Rangers**	**1178**	**L 1 - 2**	**Madjo 45**	
32	11	C	H	Scarborough	732	W 5 - 1	Alsop 1 Sall 4 **Wanless** 43 (pen) Hayes 79 Teixeira 88	18
33	18		A	Morecambe	1486	L 2 - 3	Madjo 15 Sall 87	18
34	21		H	Gravesend & Northfleet	582	D 0 - 0		18
35	25		A	York City	2314	L 1 - 5	Sall 33	18
36	Mar 4		H	Kidderminster Harriers	1033	D 0 - 0		18
37	11		H	Southport	846	L 1 - 2	Sall 3	18
38	18		H	Crawl;ey Town	1067	L 0 - 1		19
39	25		H	Dagenham & Redbridge	625	L 0 - 3		20
40	April 1		A	Canvey Island	426	D 1 - 1	Brough 70 (pen)	19
41	7		H	Accrington Stanley	1187	D 1 - 1	Meechan 74	18
42	15		A	Grays Athletic	1205	D 2 - 2	Brough 37 (pen) Madjo 90	22
43	17		H	Exteer City	1334	D 0 - 0		22
44	22		H	Burton albion	2331	L 0 - 1		22
45	25		A	Woking	890	L 1 - 2	Brough 38 (pen)	22
46	29		H	Stevenage Borough	1510	W 2 - 0	Teixeira 42 Alsop 60	20

Ave. League Home Attendance: 1054   **Goals**   56 68   **Top Goalscorer:** Paul Wanless (11)

Best Position: 8th   **Worst:** 22nd

Player	No	1	2	3	4	5	6	7	8	9	10	11	12	13	14	15	16	17	18	19	20	21	22	23	24	25	26	27	28	29	30	31	32	33	34	35	36	37	38	39	40	41	42	43	44	45	46
CLARKE	1	X	X	X	X	X	X	X	X	X	X	X	X	X	X	X	X	X	X	X	X	X	X	X	X	X	X	X	X	X	X	X	X	X	X	X	X	X	X	X	X	X	X	X	X	X	X
RICHARDSON	6	X	X	X	X	X	X	X	X	X	X	X	X	X	X	X	X	X	X	X	X	X	U	X	X	X	X	X	X																		
SALL	5	X				U	U	S	X	X	X	X	X		U	U			X	X			X			U	U			S							S									S	
GRAHAM	17	X	X	X	X		U		U	X	U	U		U	U	U	X	X			X	X	X	X	X	X	X	X	X	X	X	X	X	X	S	X	X	X	X	X	X	X	X	X	X		S
GADSBY	4	X	X	X	X	S				X			S	S	X	X	X	S	X		X	X	X	X	X	X	X	S	X	S	X	X	S	U	S	X	X		U	U	X	X	X	S	U		X
MEECHAN	16	X	X	X	X	X	X	X	X	X	X	X	X	X	X	X	X	X	X	X	X	X	X	X	X	X	X	X	X	X	X	X	X	X	X	X	X	X	X	X	X	X	X	X	X	X	X
WANLESS	7	X	X	X	X	X	X	X	X	X	X	X	X	X	X	X	X	X	X	X	X	X	X	X	X	X	X	X	X	X	X	X	X							X							
SEARLE	3	X	X	X	X	X	X				X	X	X	X	X	X	X	U	X	X	X	X	X	X	X	X	X	X	X	X	X	X		X						X							X
SIMPSON	2	X	X	X	X	X	X	X	X	X				X	X	X	X	X	X	X	S	S	S	X	S	S	S	S	U	U	S	X	S	X	X	S	X	X	S	X	X	X	X	X	X	X	X
RENDELL	25	X	X	X	U	S	U	S	X	X	X	S	S	X	X	X	U	X	U	U	U	U	S	X	U	U	U	U	S	S		U		U	X	S	U	U	S	U	U	U	U	U	S	X	X
TEIXEIRA	11	S	S	S	S	S	U	S	X	U	X	X	X	X	S	X	X	S	U	S	U	U	S	U	S	U	U	U	U	U	S	S	S	U	S	S	U	U	U	U	U	U	X	U	U	U	X
HALDANE	22	S	S		X	X	X	X	X	U	X	X	X	U	S	X	U	X	U	U	U	U	U	X	U	U	U	U	S	U	U	U	U	U	U	X	X		S	X	X	S	S	X	X	U	X
BESWETHERICK	24	U	U	U	S	X	U	U	U	U	U	U	U	X	X	X	X	U	X	U	U	U	U	U	U	U	U	U	U	X	X	U	X	S	X	S	X	X	X	X	X	S	X	X	X	X	
HARRISON	20	U	X	X	U	X	U	X	X	U	X	X	X	S	X	X	U	U	U	U	U	U	X	U	U	U	U	S	U	X	U	U	X	U	U	X	U	U	S	U	U	S	X	U	S	U	U
GARNER	14	U	S	X	X	X	X	S	X	X	S	S	U	X	X	S	X	X		U	U			S	U	U	U	U	S	X	X	U	X	X	U	X	X	X	X	S	X	X	X	S	X	X	X
GOSLING	23		U	X		X				U	X	X				S	X	X	X	S	X	X	X	X	X	X	X	X	X	X	X	X	X	X	X	S	X	X	X	S	S	X	X	S	X		
DANKS	19		U	X			S		X			U	X		S		S		X	U	X	X	U	X	X	X	X	X	X	X	S	X	X	X	U	X	X	X	X	S	X	X	X	X	X	X	X
ABBEY	9			S	S	X	S		U		U	U		S	X	S	U	U	X	X	X	X	X	X	X	X	X	X	X	X	U	X	X	U	X	U	X	X	X	X	X	X	X	X	X	X	X
ROGERS	8			U	U	X	U	U	X	U	X	X	U	X	U	S	U	X	X	X	X	X	X	X	X	X	X	X	X	X	X	X	X	X	X	X	S	S	S	S	S	S	S	S	S	X	X
DAVIES	15				X	S	X	X	S	X	S	S	U	X	U	S	X	U	S	X	X	X	X	X	X	X	X	X	X	X	S	S	X	S	X	S	X	X	X	S	X	X	X	X	X	X	X
HOWELL	21		S			X			U	X					S			X	X	X	X	X	X	X					X	X		X		X	X	X	X	X	X	X	X	X	X	X	X	X	X
WHITTINGTON	22		U		U	X		U		U	X	X		X	U	S	X	X	X	X																											
HARLEY	26			U		X	S	X				X		U	U				X	X																											
ALSOP	12			U		S	U	U	S		U	U	U		U	U	U	U	U	X	U	U	U	U	U	U	U	X	X	X	X	X	X	X	X	X	S	S	X	X	X	X	X	X	X	X	X
HARDING	10								X	X				S	U	U	X	X	X	X	U	U	U	U	X	X	X	X	X	X	X	X					X										
MADJO	27														U	U	X	X	X	X	X	X	X	X	X	X	X	X	X	X	X	X	X	X	X	X	X	X	X	X	X	X	X	X	X	X	X
HAYES	22																			X															U		X	X									
BEESLEY	18																												X	X	X	X	X	X	X	X	X	X	X	X	X	X	X	X	X	X	X
BROUGH	10																												S	X	S	U	X	X	X	X	X	X	S	X	X	X	X	X	X	X	X
ANTHONY	22																												S	X	X	X	X	X	X	X	X	S	S	S	X	X	X	X	X	X	X
MCCONNELL	26																													S	X	S	X	X	X	X	S	X									
TAYLOR	24																														X	S	X	X	U	X	X	X	X	X	X	X	X	X	X	X	X
JONES	23																															S		X	X	X	X	S	X	X	X	X	X	X	X	X	X
DOVE	22																																			U	S	X	X	X	X	X	X	X	X	X	X
COLEMAN	26																																			U	X	S	U	X	U	U	S	S	S		
OWERS	28																																						X	U	X	U				U	U
STONEHOUSE	15																																													S	S

Total Appearances (Conference)

		X	42	25	24	24	20	41	30	37	31	8	12	3	11	0	16	3	0	18	5	0	6	0	3	20	9	18	4	11	13	4	2	10	9	1	2	0	0
		S	0	0	2	3	8	0	0	0	2	10	15	4	4	1	4	6	0	8	5	0	1	1	0	3	0	6	0	5	1	0	2	0	1	4	0	0	2
		U	0	0	2	10	2	0	0	2	1	4	11	2	0	40	5	4	2	1	7	4	4	1	1	0	0	0	0	1	0	0	0	1	2	4	1	0	

Cup Appearances

		X	4	2	1	3	3	4	4	4	0	1	0	1	0	2	0	0	1	0	0	0	0	0	4	2	2	2	0	0	0	0	0	0	0	0	0	0	0
		S	0	0	0	0	0	1	0	0	0	0	2	2	0	0	0	1	1	0	0	1	0	0	0	0	0	0	0	1	0	0	0	0	0	0	0	0	0
		U	0	0	1	1	0	0	0	0	0	1	1	0	0	3	1	0	0	0	0	2	1	0	0	0	0	0	0	0	0	0	0	0	0	0	0	0	0

FOREST GREEN ROVERS

CURRANT SQUAD AS OF BEGINING OF 2006-07 SEASON

GOALKEEPERS	SQ NO.	HT	WT	D.O.B	AGE	P.O.B	CAREER	APPS	GOA
Steve Williams	1	6'06"	13 10	21/4/83	23	Oxford	Wycombe, Winsor & E (L) 12/02, Forest Green (SL) 8/06		
Ryan Harrison	20	6'03"	14 09	6/12/86	19	Kettering	Swansea (Sch), Canvey Island 10/04, Hastings T 12/04, Wrexham 2/05, Forest Green 7/05	1	0

DEFENDERS									
Alex Lawless	2	5'11"	10 08	5/2/83	23	Llwynupion	Fulham, Torquay 7/05 Rel 5/06, Forest Green 8/06		
Darren Jones	4	6'01"	14 00	28/8/83	23	Newport	Bristol C, Forest Green (SL) 9/02, Cheltenham (3ML) 8/03, Forest Green (3ML) 11/03, Newport C 2/04 Rel 12/05, Jail, Forest Green 3/06	10	0
Tony Butler	5	6'02"	12 00	28/9/72	33	Stockport	Gillingham, Blackpool £225,000 7/96, Port Vale £115,000 3/99, West Brom £140,000 3/00, Bristol C (3ML) 8/02 Perm 11/02, Blackpool 2/05, Forest Green 7/06		
Mark Preece	12			3/6/87	19	Bristol	Bristol R Rel c/s 06, Gloucester (SL) 1/06, Kidderminster (Trial) 7/06, Forest Green 7/06		
Matthew McEntegart	15			31/8/83	23	Australia	Adelaide Panthers (Aust), Southend, Cirencester, Chippenham 7/04, Forest Green 6/06		
Christian Edwards	24			23/11/75	30	Caerphilly	Swansea, Notts Forest (Trial) 1/98, Notts Forest £175,000 3/98, Bristol C (L) 12/98, Oxford U (L) 2/00, C.Palace (2ML) 11/01, Tranmere (3ML) 9/02, Oxford U (L) 1/03, Wimbledon (Trial) 4/03, Bristol R 7/03 Rel 5/06, Swansea (L) 8/05, Forest Green 8/06		

MIDFIELDERS									
Kevin Nicholson	3	5'08"	11 05	2/10/80	25	Derby	Sheff Wed, Northampton NC 1/01, Forest Green (L) 1/01, N.County Free 3/01 Rel c/s 04, Scarborough (2ML) 3/04, Scarborough 8/04, Forest Green 5/06		
Jamie Pitman	6	5'09"	10 09	6/1/76	30	Trowbridge	Swindon, Hereford 2/96, Yeovil 8/98, Woking c/s 00, Hereford 6/02 Rel 5/06, Forest Green 5/06		
Paul Wanless	7	6'01"	13 11	14/12/73	32	Banbury	Oxford U Rel c/s 95, Lincoln C 7/95, Woking (L) 1/96, Cambridge U (SL) 3/96, Cambridge U c/s 96, Oxford U 8/03 Rel c/s 05, Forest Green 7/05	30	10
Simon Clist	8	5'10"	11 05	13/6/81	25	Bournemouth	Tottenham (Trainee) Rel c/s 99, Bristol C 7/99, Torquay (2ML) 2/03, Barnet AL 1/04 Rel 5/06, Forest Green 5/06		
Michael Brough	10	6'00"	11 07	1/8/81	25	Nottingham	N.County Rel 1/04, Spalding (L) 1/00, Macclesfield (Trial) 1/04, Lincoln C (Trial) 2/04, Stevenage 3/04, Forest Green 1/06	14	3
Les Afful	17	5'06"	10 00	4/2/84	22	Liverpool	Exeter Rel 5/06, Torquay (SL) 1/06, Forest Green 5/06		
Paul Stonehouse	19						Forest Green	2	0
Gary Owers	23	5'11"	12 07	3/10/68	37	Newcastle	Sunderland, Bristol C £250,000 12/94, Notts County £15,000 7/98 Rel c/s 02, Forest Green 8/02 (02/03 36,0, 03/04 14,1), Bath C (Pl/Man) 10/03, Forest Green (Pl/Man) c/s 05	0	0

FORWARDS									
Allan Russell	9	6'00"	12 03	13/12/80	25	Glasgow	Hibernian, Hamilton 6/99, St Mirren 6/03, Macclesfield 8/05, Mansfield (2ML) 11/05, Perm 1/06, Forest Green 8/06		
Arkadiusz Zarczynski	11	6'01"	12 13	23/4/75	31	Lubin (Pol)	FC Lausitz Hoyerswerda, FC Freienbach, Linzer ASK, Odra Opole, Altmark Stendal, Miedz Legnica, 1. FC Magdeburg, Zaglebie Lubin, FC Sion, Ceramika Paradyz, KS Paradyz (Pol), Mansfield (Trial) 7/06, Aberdeen (Trial) 7/06, Forest Green 8/05		
Charlie Griffin	14	6'00"	12 07	25/6/79	27	Bath	Bristol R (Ass Sch), Melksham, Chippenham T 7/98, Swindon £10,000 1/99, Yeovil (L) 10/99, Woking (L) 10/00 £15,000 11/00, Havant (L) 11/01, Chippenham T (L) 2/02, Chippenham 9/02, Forest Green 5/04, Wycombe Free 5/05, Forest Green (SL) 7/06		
Alex Meechan	16	5'08"	10 10	29/1/80	26	Plymouth	Swindon, Bristol C 7/98, Forest Green (2ML) 8/00, Yeovil (L) 11/00, Forest Green 12/00, Dag & Red Free 6/03, Forest Green (3ML) 11/03 Perm 2/04 Rel 6/04, Luton (Trial) 7/04, Leigh RMI 8/04 Rel 11/04, Halifax 11/04 Rel 4/05, Forest Green 7/05	41	5
Mark Beesley	18	5'10"	11 10	10/11/81	24	Burscough	Preston Rel c/s 00, Chester 7/00, Southport (L) 9/03, Hereford 12/03 Rel 5/04, Forest Green 6/04	16	0

82

PLAYING SQUAD

LOANEES	HT	WT	DOB	AGE	POB	FROM - TO	APPS	GOA
(G)Ryan Clarke	6'03"	12 13	30/4/82	24	Bristol	Bristol R (SL) 7/05 - Rel 5/06, Salisbury 8/06	42	0
(D)Luke Graham	6'03"	12 07	27/4/86	20	Kettering	Northampton (SL) 8/05 - Rel 5/06, Kettering 5/06	27	0
(M)Simieon Howell	5'11"	12 00	26/8/85	21	Reading	Reading (4ML) 8/05 - Farnborough 2/06, Sutton U 3/06 Rel 5/06, Basingstoke 8/06	7	0
(F)Lewis Haldane	6'00"	11 03	13/3/85	21	Trowbridge	Bristol R (2ML) 8/05 -	7	0
(F)Scott Rendell	6'01"		21/10/86	19	Ashford	Reading (SL) 8/05 - Hayes (L) 3/05, Crawley (L) 8/06	18	2
(F)Michael Whittington						Cheltenham 10/05 - Gloucester (2ML) 1/06	1	0
(D)Ryan Harley	5'09"	11 00	22/1/85	21	Bristol	Bristol C 10/05 - Rel 5/06	3	0
(M)Ben Harding	5'10"	11 02	6/9/84	21	Carshalton	MK Dons (2ML) 11/05 -	9	1
(F)Jonathan Hayes	5'07"	11 00	9/7/87	19	Ballyfermot	Reading 1/06 -	4	1
(D)Byron Anthony	6'01"	11 00	20/9/84	21	Newport	Cardiff 2/06 - Rel c/s 06, Bristol R 8/06	4	0
(D)Michael Taylor	6'02"	13 10	21/11/82	23	Liverpool	Cheltenham (2M) 3/05 - Halifax 7/06 Rel 7/06, Lancaster 7/06	10	0
(M)Craig Dove	5'08"	11 00	6/8/83	23	Hartlepool	Chester (SL) 3/06 - Rel 5/06	5	0
(M)Liam Coleman	5'09"	10 05	11/1/86	20	Colchester	Torquay (SL) 3/06 - Rel 5/06, Gravesend 8/06	2	0

DEPARTURES	HT	WT	DOB	AGE	POB	FROM - TO	APPS	GOA
(F)Ian Foster	5'07"	10 07	11/11/76	29	Liverpool	Kidderminster 6/05 - Rel 11/05, Nuneaton 11/05, Kidderminster (Physio) 5/06		
(M)Jamie Gosling	6'00"	10 06	21/3/82	24	Bristol	Woking 8/05 - Rel 11/05, Basingstoke 3/06	9	0
(D)Jon Beswetherick	5'11"	11 04	15/1/78	28	Liverpool	Kidderminster 1/05 - Rel 11/05, Salisbury 12/05	15	0
(D)Darren Davies	5'08"	11 07	13/8/78	28	Port Talbot	Dover 5/04 - Tiverton 10/05	0	0
(F)Mark Danks	5'09"	10 09	8/2/84	22	Worley	Aberystwyth 8/04 - Bromsgrove (2ML) 9/05, Cirencester (L) 12/05, Worcester 1/06	0	0
(M)Barry McConnell	5'11"	10 03	1/1/77	29	Exeter	Tamworth Rel 1/06, 2/06 - Rel 3/06, Tiverton 3/06	4	0
(M)Scott Rogers	5'11"	11 00	23/5/79	27	Bristol	Tiverton 8/03 - Weston-s-Mare (L) 11/05, Bath C 3/06	10	0
(D)Sekani Simpson	5'10"	11 10	11/3/84	22	Bristol	Bristol C 7/05 - Rel 5/06, Weston-s-Mare 8/06	33	0
(D)Jon Richardson	6'01"	12 02	29/8/75	31	Nottingham	Oxford U 8/02 - Rel 5/06, Exeter 7/06	25	2
(D)Adam Garner	6'02"	12 00	22/7/84	22	Oxford	Gravesend 9/04 - Rel 5/06, Chippenham 7/06	20	0
(F)Zema Abbey	6'01"	12 11	17/4/77	29	Luton	Torquay 8/05 - Rel 5/06, Kettering 8/06	26	2
(D)Damon Searle	5'10"	11 00	26/10/71	34	Cardiff	Hornchurch 11/04 - Newport C 5/06	37	0
(D)Abdou Sall	6'04"	14 00	1/11/80	25	Dakar	Kidderminster 7/05 - St Pauli (Ger) 5/06	26	4
(F)Guy Madjo			1/6/84	22	Cameroon	Bristol C (L) (Perm) 11/05 - Rel 5/06, Stafford R 8/06	24	9
(D)Matthew Gadsby	6'01"	11 12	6/9/79	26	Sutton Coldfield	Kidderminster 6/04 - Hinckley U 6/06	28	0
(D)Chris Giles	6'02"	13 00	16/4/82	24	Milborne Port	Crawley 7/06 - Rel 7/06		
(F)Bruno Teixeira	5'11"	11 09	8/10/82	23	Portugal	Leca 8/05 - Rel 7/06	27	5
(F)Julian Alsop	6'04"	14 03	28/5/73	33	Nuneaton	Tamworth AL 10/05 - Newport 7/06	23	5

FOREST GREEN ROVERS

Ground Address: Nympsfield Road, Forest Green, Nailsworth, GlosGL6 0ET
Telephone: 01453 834860
Fax: 01453 835291
General email address: members@roversfc,freeserve.co.uk
Official website: www.fgrfc.co.uk
Office Opening Hours: 9.00am -5.00 pm

SIMPLE DIRECTIONS:
By Road: Nailsworth is on the A46 between Stroud and Bath, At mini roundabout in centre of town, turm to Forest Green. Ground is at top of the hill

MATCH TICKETS:
Ticket office Telephone: 01453 834860 Ext 22
Midweek Home Matchday: Tuesday
Capacity: 5,141
Seats: 2,000
Covered Terracing: 1,000
Green Man Public House Tel No: 01453 833295 Open normal pub hours.
Restaurant Five Valley's Leisure (01453 832268) Available for bookings daily and open for meals on matchdays

Club Shop: Open on matchdays only with souvenirs, programmes and memorabilia

Local Press: troud News & Journal and Gloucester Citizen
Local Radio: Star FM, BBC Radio Gloucestershire

MATCHDAY PROGRAMME
Pages: 52   **Price:** £2.50
Editor: Clive White
Contact details:
Tel Nos: 01453 750099 (H)
07884 030859 (M)
e-mail: clivemwhite@aol.com

CLUB STATISTICS
RECORDS
Attendance: 3,002
v St Albans City .F.A.Trophy S-Final 18.04.99
Victory: 8-0
v Fareham Town, Southern League Southern Div. 96-97
Defeat: 0-7
v Moor Green, Southern League, Midland Div. 85-86
Career Goalscorer: Karl Bayliss
Career Appearances: Alex Sykes
Transfer Fee Paid: £20,000
to Salisbury City for Adrian Randall
Transfer Fee Received: £35,000
from Nuneaton Boroughfor Marc McGregor
from Oxford United for Wayne Haswell

SENIOR HONOURS
F.A.Trophy	Runners-up	98-99 2000-01
F.A.VASE	Winners	1981-82
Southern League Premier Diviision Champions		1996-97
Hellenic League	Champions	1981-82
Gloucestershire Senior Cup	Winners	84-5 85-6 86-7
Gloucestershire Senior Professional Cup		84-5 85-6 86-7

PREVIOUS
Leagues: Stroud & Dist 1890-192, Glos Northern Sen.22-67
Glos.Co. 67-73, Hrellenic 73-82, Southern League 82-89

GRAVESEND & NORTHFLEET

Club Colours: Red/White/Red

Change Colours: Sky Blue/Navy Blue/Sky Blue

Club Sponsor: T.B.A.

Previous League: Isthmian League

BEST PERFORMANCES

League: Conference: 5th **F.A. Cup:** 4th Rd replay 1962-163 **F.A. Trophy:** 6th Rd 2004-05

LAST SEASON:

Conference: 16th **F.A.Cup:** 4th Qual.Round **F.A.Trophy:** 2nd Round

Re-Formed: 1946

Nickname: The Fleet

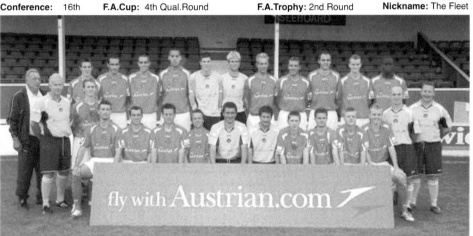

Back Row (L-R): Luke Moore, Peter Hawkins, Jack Roberts, Danny Ekoku, Sam Mott, Lance Cronin, Ross Smith, Paul McCarthy, James Smith, Mark Ricketts, John Akinde. **Middle:** Maurice Cox (Kit Man), Ron Hillyard (Goalkeeping Coach), Danny Slatter, Paul Wilson (Physio), Ian Docker (Youth Team Coach). **Front:** Rob Quinn, Mark De Bolla, Charlie MacDonald, Jon Keeling, Liam Daish (Manager), Alan Kimble (Assistant Manager), Stacy Long, Liam Coleman, George Purcell, Mike McKenna

CLUB PERSONNEL

Chairman:	Jason Botley
Directors:	Bob Gunton,Adrian Felstead,
	Duncam Holt, Brian Kilcullen
	Mick Ward and Roly Edwards
Company & Club Secretary:	Roly Edwards
Tel Nos:	01474533796
Fax:	01474 324754
e-mail:	info@gnfc.co.uk
Commercial Manager:	Frank Walter
Tel No:	01474 533796
E-mail:	wicksy@gnfc.co.uk
Press Officers:	Cheryl Wanless & Tracy Richardson
Tel No:	01474 533796
e-mail:	info@gnfc.co.uk

MANAGEMENT TEAM

Manager:	Liam Daish	**Assistant Manager:**	Alan Kimble
Previous clubs as a manager:	Havant & Water'ville	**Coaches:**	Ron Hillyard & Ian Docker
	Welling United	**Physio:**	Paul Wilson
As a player:	Portsmouth, Cambridge United,Barnet,		
	Birmingham City, Coventry City & Eire	**Club Playing Status:**	Full Time

GRAVESEND & NORTHFLEET

BEST LGE ATT.: 1,616 v Accrington Stanley
LOWEST: **618** v Hereford United

No.	Date	Comp	H/A	Opponents	Att:	Result	Goalscorers	Pos
1	Aug 13	C	H	Exeter City	1578	L 0 - 2		20
2	16		A	Grays Athletic	1562	L 1 - 6	**MacDonald** 59	22
3	20		A	Canvey Island	1070	W 2 - 1	**Macdonald** 36 (pen) 90	18
4	27		H	Cambridge United	1379	D 0 - 0		19
5	29		A	Woking	1770	W 3 - 1	Jackson 8 Saunders 14 50	14
6	Sept 3		H	Southport	813	W 2 - 1	McCarthy 15 Slatter 67	10
7	10		A	Scarborough	1307	L 1 - 3	Drury 72	12
8	17		H	Halifax Town	918	W 4 - 0	Graham-Smith 36 **MacDonald** 47 Slatter 49 Drury 90 (pen)	9
9	20		A	Hereford United	2396	D 1 - 1	Bowry 89	10
10	24		H	Kidderminster Harriers	1054	L 1 - 2	**MacDonald** 62	12
11	27		H	Forest Green Rovers	706	W 2 - 0	**MacDonald** 35 Jackson 66	
12	Oct 1		A	Accrington Stanley	1206	D 1 - 1	Sodje 65	10
13	8		H	York City	1133	D 2 - 2	Grant 29 Sodje 88	10
14	15		A	Tamworth	1003	L 0 - 1		11
15	**22**	**FAC 4Q**	**A**	**Kettering Town**	**1647**	**L 0 - 3**		
16	29	C	H	Stevenage Borough	1372	L 0 - 2		12
17	Nov 12		A	Aldershot Town	2415	L 2 - 3	**MacDonald** 20 (pen) 85	13
18	19		H	Altrincham	1091	W 2 - 0	Drury 42 **MacDonald** 52	10
19	26		A	Crawley Town	1426	W 2 - 1	Johnson 25 Coleman 27	10
20	Dec 3		H	Morecambe	1172	W 1 - 0	**MacDonald** 30	9
21	10		A	Burton Albion	1733	D 0 - 0		10
22	**17**	**FAT 1**	**A**	**East Thurrock**	**381**	**W 2 - 0**	**Smith 40 MacDonald 67**	
23	26	C	H	Dagenham & Redbridge	1391	L 1 - 3	**MacDonald** 41	10
24	Jan 2		A	Dagenham & Redbridge	1405	W 2 - 1	Graham-Smith 86 Johnson 90	10
25	7		A	Exeter City	3396	L 0 - 1		10
26	**14**	**FAT 2**	**A**	**Boreham Wood**	**462**	**L 1 - 3**	MacDonald 68	
27	21	C	H	Canvey Island	1560	W 2 - 0	McCarthy 38 **MacDonald** 90	9
28	28		A	Cambridge United	2459	D 1 - 1	Jackson 32	11
29	Feb 11		A	Kidderminster Harriers	1575	W 2 - 0	Sodje 17 Drury 73	10
30	17		H	Accrington Stanley	1616	L 1 - 3	Graham-Smith 90	11
31	21		A	Forest Green Rovers	582	D 0 - 0		12
32	25		H	Scarborough	930	D 0 - 0		11
33	28		H	Crawley Town	698	D 1 - 1	Rawle 60	11
34	Mar 7		H	Hereford United	618	L 1 - 2	Jackson 33	11
35	11		A	York City	2902	L 0 - 1		
36	18		H	Tamworth	841	W 2 - 0	Smith 42 Jackson 59	11
37	25		A	Stevenage Borough	1873	L 0 - 2		13
38	April 1		H	Aldershot Town	1131	L 0 - 3		13
39	4		H	Grays Athletic	1245	L 1 - 3	Johnson 51	14
40	8		A	Altrincham	688	D 2 - 2	Smith 34 Johnson 90 (pen)	13
41	15		A	Southport	1301	L 0 - 1		14
42	17		H	Woking	776	W 2 - 0	Johnson 45 Moore 76	14
43	22		A	Morecambe	1991	L 0 - 3		13
44	25		A	Halifax Town	1680	L 0 - 2		14
45	29		H	Burton Albion	912	L 0 - 1		16

Ave. League Home Attendance: 1092 **Goals** 48 63 **Top Goalscorer:** Charlie MacDonald (14)
Best Position: 9th **Worst:** 22nd

STEP 1
CONFERENCE

STEP 2 - P177   STEP 3 - P269   STEP 4 - P269   STEP 5/6 - P473   STEP 7 - P713
CONFERENCE Nth & Sth   NPL SOUTHERN - STHN/MIDFRN   NPL - SOUTHERN - ISTHMIAN

HOLLOWAY 12	GOODING 2	R SMITH 20	McCARTHY 3	SLATTER 6	BOWRY 15	SAUNDERS 17	JACKSON 8	GRANT 11	MACDONALD 18	KERR 10	OMOYINMI 1	SUREY 21	DRURY 14	GLOZIER 23	J SMITH 19	MOTT 5	McSHANE 27	PROTHEROE 30	SESTANOVICH 16	MOORE 24	SODJE 22	GUY 24	TANN 25	BRAD JOHNSON 25	PORTER 31	BRETT JOHNSON 4	COLEMN 32	HODGSON 27	FULLER 18	WATKINS 14	RAWLE 21	McKIMM 9	HAWKINS 7	DARVILLE 25	26	#
X	X	X	X	X	X	X	X	X	X	X	S	U	U	U																						1
X	X	X	X	X	X	X	X	X	X	X	S	U	U	S	X	S																				2
U	X	X	X	X	X		X		X			X		S	X			U	X	X	U	U														3
U	X	X	X	X	X	X			X		U	X		U		U		X	X		S															4
S	X	X	X	X	X	X	X		U		X	U	X	S				X	X		S															5
U	X	X	X	X	X	X			X		U	X	U	X	S			X	X																	6
S	X	X	X	X	X	X			U		U	X	S					X	X		S	X														7
X	U	X	X	X	X	X	X			X	U	S	S	X				X				S														8
X	U	X		X	X	X	X	U	X	U	S	S	X	X				X																		9
X	U	X	X	X	X	X	X	U	X	U	S	U	X					X																		10
X	U	X	X	X	X	X	X	S	X	U	S	S	X					X																		11
X	U	X	X	X	X	X	X		U	U	S	X	X					X			S															12
X	S	X	X	X	X	X	X		U	U	S							X			X	S														13
X	U	X	X	X		X	X	X		U	S	X	S	S				X			X															14
X	X	X	X		X		X	X	S	X	U	S	S	X	U			X			X															15
X		X		X	X	X		X	S	X	U	X	S	X	X				U		S	X														16
X	S	X		X		X	X		X	U	U		U		X			S	X		S	X		X												17
X	X	X	S		X	X	X		X	U		X	U	X				X	S		X	U		X	U											18
X	X	X	U		X	X	S		X	U		X		X		S		S			X			X	X	X										19
X	X	X		S	X	X	U		X	U		X		X				U			X			X	X	X	S									20
X	X		X	S	X	X			X			X		X		X	U	U		U	U			X	X	X	S									21
X	X		U	X	S	X	X		X			X		X	X	U		S			X			X	X	X	S									22
X	X	U	U	X	X	X			X	U		X		X				S			X			X	X	X	S									23
X	U	X	X	X	X					U		X		S		X		S			X	U		X	X											24
X	U	X	X	X	X				X	U		X		S		X		S			X			X	S											25
X	U	X	X	X	X	X			S		X	U		X		U		X	S			X	X													26
X	X	X		X	X	X		X		X	U		X		U		S		X			X		U	S											27
X	X	X		X	X		X		X	U		X		S				X						U	U	X	S									28
X	X	X		X	X		X		U			X	X		U	S	X						S	X	X	S										29
X	X	X	U	U	X	X			U			X	X		S	X	X						S	X	X	S										30
X	X	X	X	X	X			U		X	U		S	X	S							S	X	X	X											31
X	X	X	X	X		S		U		X	U		S	X	S							X	X	S	X											32
X	X	X	X	X		X		U		X	U		X	U	X							S	X	S	X											33
X	X	X	X	X	U	X		U		S			X	S	X							S	S	X	U	X	X	X								34
X	X		X	X	S	X		U		X	X		S	S								S	X	X	U	X	X	X								35
X	X		X	X	X	X		U		X			X		S							S	X	X	S	X	X	U								36
X	X	X	X	X	X	X		U		X			S		X							S	X	X	S	X	U	S								37
X	X	X		X	X	X		U		U	X		S		X							X	S	X	U	X										38
U	X	X	U		X	X		X		X		U	X		S							U	X		X	X										39
U	X	X	S		X	X		X		X		X	X		S							S	X		X	U	X									40
S	X	X	X	X	X	X	U	U		X	X	S	X		S							X			X											41
X	X	X	U	X	X	X	S	U		X	X	X	U		X							U			X											42
X	X	X	S	X	U	X		U		X	X	X	X		X							X			X		S			U						43
X		X	X	X	X	X		U		X	X	X		X								X			U		U	U		S						44
	X	X	X	U	X	S	X		X	X			X								X	U	S	X	S											45
																																				46
																																				47
																																				48
																																				49
																																				50

Total Appearances (Conference)

HOLLOWAY	GOODING	R SMITH	McCARTHY	SLATTER	BOWRY	SAUNDERS	JACKSON	GRANT	MACDONALD	KERR	OMOYINMI	SUREY	DRURY	GLOZIER	J SMITH	MOTT	McSHANE	PROTHEROE	SESTANOVICH	MOORE	SODJE	GUY	TANN	BRAD JOHNSON	PORTER	BRETT JOHNSON	COLEMN	HODGSON	FULLER	WATKINS	RAWLE	McKIMM	HAWKINS	DARVILLE	26	
32	24	38	19	30	37	35	24	26	5	20	5	5	1	30	6	19	0	5	15	0	10	8	0	1	21	0	4	6	1	4	12	9	6	4	0	X
1	4	0	3	0	2	0	2	3	2	0	1	7	9	2	4	4	1	0	1	0	18	6	1	0	4	0	0	0	4	9	1	2	4	1	2	S
2	11	1	4	1	0	2	2	3	3	0	33	3	5	2	5	6	3	0	4	1	3	1	0	0	0	2	0	1	1	5	0	2	4	0	2	U

Cup Appearances

HOLLOWAY	GOODING	R SMITH	McCARTHY	SLATTER	BOWRY	SAUNDERS	JACKSON	GRANT	MACDONALD	KERR	OMOYINMI	SUREY	DRURY	GLOZIER	J SMITH	MOTT	McSHANE	PROTHEROE	SESTANOVICH	MOORE	SODJE	GUY	TANN	BRAD JOHNSON	PORTER	BRETT JOHNSON	COLEMN	HODGSON	FULLER	WATKINS	RAWLE	McKIMM	HAWKINS	DARVILLE	26	
3	2	2	2	2	2	2	1	0	3	0	0	3	0	1	0	0	2	0	0	1	0	0	1	0	1	2	1	0	0	0	0	0	0	0	0	X
0	0	0	0	0	1	0	0	1	1	0	0	1	1	0	0	0	0	0	0	0	2	0	0	0	0	0	0	1	0	0	0	0	0	0	0	S
0	1	0	1	0	0	0	0	0	0	0	2	0	0	0	1	1	1	0	0	0	0	0	0	0	0	0	0	0	0	0	0	0	0	0	0	U

CURRANT SQUAD AS OF BEGINING OF 2006-07 SEASON

GOALKEEPERS	SQ NO.	HT	WT	D.O.B	AGE	P.O.B	CAREER	APPS	GOA
Lance Cronin	1	6'01"	13 02	11/9/85	20	Brighton	Brighton (Jun), C.Palace, Wycombe (L) 3/05,		
							Oldham 11/05 Rel 2/06, Shrewsbury 2/06, MK Dons (Trial) 4/06,		
							Gravesend 8/06		
Sam Mott	21						Gravesend, Whitstable (L) 1/06	1	0
Craig Holloway		6'01"	12 11	10/8/84	22	Blackheath	Arsenal Rel c/s 04, Farnborough 6/04, Southend 2ML 1/05,		
							Gravesend 8/05	33	0

DEFENDERS									
Peter Hawkins	2	6'00"	11 04	19/9/78	27	Maidstone	Wimbledon Rel c/s 04, York (SL) 2/00, Rushden & D 7/04, Gravesend 3/06	5	0
Sasha Opinel	3	5'09"	12 00	9/4/77	29	Saint Maurice	Lille (Fr), Ajaccio GFCO 7/99, Stockport (Trial) 10/99, Raith 12/99,		
							N.County (Trial) 10/00, Plymouth 12/00, Bournemouth (Trial) 1/01,		
							L.Orient 2/01 Rel c/s 01,, Billericay 11/01, Casteinau-le-Cres (Fr),		
							Farnborough 7/03, Crawley P/E + Fee 1/05, Gravesend		
James Smith	5	6'01"		30/8/86	20	London	Cambridge U (Sch), Welling 10/04, Gravesend £3,000 + 6/05,		
							Margate (L) 9/05	23	3
Paul McCarthy	6	5'10"	13 10	4/8/71	35	Cork	Brighton, Wycombe £100,000 7/96 Rel c/s 03, Oxford U (SL) 3/03,		
							Oxford U 7/03, Rel c/s 04, Hornchurch 6/04, Gravesend 11/04	30	2
Mark Ricketts	15	6'00"	11 02	7/10/84	21	Sidcup	Charlton Rel c/s 06, MK Dons (3ML) 11/05, Gravesend 8/06		
Ross Smith	20	6'00"	12 07	4/11/80	25	Ontario (Can)	Mississauga Dixie (Can), Margate 10/04, Gravesend 8/05	38	2

MIDFIELDERS									
Stacy Long	4	5'08"	10 00	11/1/85	21	Bromley	Charlton Rel 5/05, Luton (Trial) 3/05, Bristol C (Trial) 3/05,		
							Notts County (Trial) 4/05, Notts County 8/05 Rel 5/06, Gravesend 7/05		
Danny Slatter	7	5'08"	10 02	15/11/80	25	Cardiff	Chelsea Rel c/s 02, Chelmsford 9/02, Welling 7/03,		
							Gravesend 6/05	39	2
Rob Quinn	8	5'11"	11 02	8/11/76	29	Sidcup	C.Palace, Brentford £40,000 7/98, Oxford U £75,000 1/01,		
							Bristol R 7/02 Rel c/s 04, Stevenage 5/04 Rel 5/06, Gravesend 6/06		
Jon Keeling	11					Essex	Concord R, Tilbury, Purfleet 2/98, Dag & Red 7/02, Purfleet 10/02,		
							Hornchurch 7/03 Rel 5/04, Canvey Island 7/04, Gravesend 6/06		
Liam Coleman	16	5'09"	10 05	11/1/86	20	Colchester	Colchester (Scholar), Wivenhoe, Torquay 7/05 Rel 5/06,		
							Forest Green (SL) 3/06, Gravesend 8/06	0	0
George Purcell	17			8/4/88	18		Gillingham, Gravesend 8/06		
Jack Roberts	22						Gravesend		

FORWARDS									
Mark De Bolla	9	5'07"	11 09	1/1/83	23	London	Aston Villa, Charlton Nominal 1/01 Rel 3/04, Oxford U (Trial) 4/03,		
							Chesterfield (2ML) 9/03, Chesterfield (L) 3/04 Perm 3/04,		
							Notts County (L) 11/05, Notts County 1/06, Grays 3/06 Rel 5/06,		
							Gravesend 7/06		
Charlie MacDonald	10	5'08"	12 10	13/2/81	25	Southwark	Charlton Rel c/s 02, Cheltenham (SL) 3/01, Torquay (L) 2/02,		
							Colchester (L) 3/02, Margate 8/02, Stevenage 9/02, Crawley 8/03,		
							Weymouth 3/05, Gravesend 5/05	20	12
Danny Ekoku	14	5'11"	11 08	9/10/85	20	London	Bradford C (Sch), Crawley 8/05, Sutton U (L) 9/05, Gravesend 6/06		
Luke Moore	18			27/4/88	18		Gravesend	28	1
John Akinde	19						Gravesend		
Mike McKenna	23						Gravesend		
Jamie Darville							Gravesend	2	0

PLAYING SQUAD

LOANEES	HT	WT	DOB	AGE	POB	FROM - TO	APPS	GOA
(G)Luke McShane	6'01"	10 09	6/11/85	20	Peterborough	Peterborough 8/05 -	5	0
(F)Onome Sodje			17/7/88	18	Nigeria	Charlton (3M) 9/05, 2/06 - Rel 5/06	14	3
(F)Jamie Guy	6'01"	13 00	1/8/87	19	Barking	Colchester 10/05 - Staines (2ML) 10/05, Staines (L) 1/06,		
						Cambridge U (SL) 1/06	1	0
(D)Adam Cottrell			15/11/86	19		Charlton 10/05 - Walton & H (L) 3/06, Rel 5/06, Millwall 5/06		
(M)Bradley Johnson	6'00"	12 10	28/4/87	19	London	Northampton (SL) 11/05 -	25	5
(F)Omari Coleman	5'11"	11 13	23/11/80	25	London	Lincoln C (L) 11/05 - Crawley 2/06, Carshalton 8/06	6	1
(D)Brett Johnson	6'01"		15/8/85	21	Hammersmith	Northampton 11/05 - Grays (L) 1/06	4	0
(F)Mark Rawle	5'11"	12 04	27/4/79	27	Leicester	Woking (SL) 1/06 - Rel 5/06, Crawley 8/06	11	1
(D)Robert Watkins	5'10"		14/10/85	20	Sutton	Fulham (3M) 1/06 - Rel 5/06	13	0

DEPARTURES	HT	WT	DOB	AGE	POB	FROM - TO	APPS	GOA
(M)Ashley Sestanovich	6'03"	13 00	18/9/81	24	London	Chester 8/05 - Rel 9/05, Farnborough 9/05 Rel 6/06, Grays 6/06 Rel 7/06	0	0
(D)Adam Tann	6'00"	11 05	12/5/82	24	Fakenham	Cambridge U 10/05 - N.County 11/05, L.Orient 1/06	1	0
(F)Emmanuel Omoyinmi	5'06"	10 07	28/12/77	28	Nigeria	Oxford U 5/04 - Lewes 12/05	12	0
(F)Kim Grant	5'10"	11 05	25/9/72	33	Sekondi-Takoradi	Shonan Bellmare (Jap) 8/05 - Rel 12/05, Crawley 12/05,		
						AFC Wimbledon 2/06	7	1
(M)Ben Surey	5'10"	11 00	18/12/82	23	Camberley	C.Palace 7/04 - Basingstoke (L) 11/05 (Perm) 12/05	10	0
(M)Richard Hodgson	5'10"	11 06	1/10/79	26	Sunderland	Carshalton 12/05 - Rel 2/06, Bognor Regis 2/06, Eastleigh 3/06,		
						Farnborough 8/06	5	0
(D)Graham Porter			29/10/74	31	Kent	Margate 5/04 - Maidenhead (L) 1/06, Rel 3/06	0	0
(D)Lee Protheroe			5/11/75	30	Edmonton	Canvey Island 4/04 - Margate (SL) 3/06, Rel 4/06, Margate 5/06	16	0
(G)Aaron Kerr	6'02"	13 00	8/12/82	23	Carrickfergus	Worcester 7/05 - Rel 5/06, Tonbridge 6/06	6	0
(D)Scott Gooding	5'10"	11 07	2/1/82	24	Croydon	Crawley 5/05 - Rel 5/06, Tonbridge 5/06	28	0
(D)Justin Skinner	5'07"	11 00	17/9/72	33	Dorking	Aylesbury c/s 01 - Rel 5/06, Margate 5/06	22	0
(D)Daniel Glozier			3/9/86	20	Rush Green	L.Orient 7/05 - Tonbridge (4ML) 12/05, Rel 5/06	10	0
(M)Steve McKimm			30/7/75	31	London	Kingstonian 10/01 - Rel 5/06, Margate 5/06	10	0
(M)Jay Saunders			15/1/79	27	Kent	Margate 5/04 - Rel 5/06, Lewes 6/06	26	2
(M)Jimmy Jackson			10/7/76	30	Gravesend	Dag & Red 5/04 - Rel 5/06, Margate 5/06	29	5
(M)Ashley Fuller	5'09"	10 10	14/11/86	19	Bedford	Cambridge U 1/06 - Rel 5/06, Bishops Stortford 7/06	13	0
(M)Bobby Bowry	5'09"	10 08	19/5/71	35	Croydon	Colchester 7/05 - Rel 5/06, Bromley (Pl/Coach) 5/06	35	1
(M)Andy Drury	5'11"	12 06	28/11/83	22	Sittingbourne	Sittingbourne £1,700 7/03 - Rel 5/06, Lewes 6/06	32	4

GRAVESEND & NORTHFLEET

Ground Address: Stonebridge Road,Northfleet, Kent DA11 9GN
Tel No: 01474 533796
Fax: 01474324754
General email address: info@gnfc.co.uk
Official website: www.gnfc.co.uk
Clubcall: 09068 664660

SIMPLE DIRECTIONS
By Road From A2 take Northfleet/Southfleet exit (B262) folow to Northfleet then B2175 (Springflet Road) to junction A226. Turn left (THe H~III, Northflet) and road becomes Stonebridge Road. Ground is at the bottom of a steep hill on the right after a mile.

Parking: Room for about 500 cars.

By Rail: Ground is two minutes from Norfleet (BR) station

MATCH TICKETS
Ticket office Telephone: 01474 533796
Capacity: 4,184
Seats: 500
Covered: 3,000
Clubhouse: Fleet Social Centre
Refreshments: Hot and Cold food available on matchdays
Club Shop: Sells all types of club products
Club Manageress: Jesica McQueen (c/o club)

Local Press: Gravesend Report, Kent Messenge and Gravesend Messenger
Local Radio: Radio Kent.

MATCHDAY PROGRAMME
Pages: 46   **Price:** £2.50
Editor: Rachell Willett
Tel No: e-mail: editor@gnfc.co.uk

CLUB STATISTICS & RECORDS
Attendance: 12,036
v Sunderland F.A.Cup 4th Rd.12.02.63
Victory: 8-1
v Clacton Town Southern League1962-63
Defeat: 0-9
v Trowbridge Town Southern League Premeir 1991-92
Career Goalscorer: Steve Portway 152 (92-94 97-01)
Career Appearances: Ken Burrett 537
Transfer Fee Paid: £8,000
to Wokingham Town for Richard Newbery 1996
and to Tonbridge for Craig Williams 1997
Transfer Fee Received: £35,000
from West Ham United for Jimmy Bullard 1998
SENIOR HONOURS
Isthmian League Champions 2001-2002
Southern League Champions 1956-1957
Southern Division 1994-95
Division One South1974-75
Kent Senior Cup 48-49 52-53 80-81 99-00 00-01 01-02
PREVIOUS
Leagues: Kent (as Gravesend Utd)
Southern 46-79 80-96
Alliance Premier 1979-80
Isthmian 1997-2002

Names: Gravesend Utd. & Northfleet Utd. merghged in 1946
Grounds : Central Avenue (Gravesend Utd)
(Northfleet always played at Stonebridge Road)

STEP 1
CONFERENCE

STEP 2 - P177
CONFERENCE Nth & Sth

STEP 3 - P269
NPL - SOUTHERN - ISTHMIAN PREV

STEP 4 - P269
NPL - SOUTHERN - ISTHMIAN

STEP 5/6 - P473

STEP 7 - P713

GRAYS ATHLETIC

Club Colours: Sky Blue

Change Colours: All Yellow

Club Sponsor: Westview Rail Ltd

Previous League: Conference South

Last Season

Confernce: 3rd **F.A. Cup:** 2nd Round **F.A. Trophy:** Winners

BEST PERFORMANCES **Founded:** 1890

League: 3rd Conference **F.A. Cup:** 2nd Round 2005-06 **F.A. Trophy:** Winners 04-05 05-06 **Nickname:** The Blues

Back Row (L-R): Andy Sambrook, Nathan Moulds, Ashley Bayes, Jamie Slabber, Daniel Knowles, John Turner, Jim Sangare. **Middle:** Steve Snelling (physio)Lee Boylan, Ashley Nicholls, Cam Mawer, Jay Smith, Mark Wright, Tom Williamson, Adam Green, Glenn Poole, Gerry Murphy (coach). **Front:** Aaron Mclean, Michael Kightly, Stuart Thurgood, Frank Gray (Manager) Jamie Stuart, John Martin, Scott Canhan.

CLUB PERSONNEL

Chairman: Alan Barnard
Vice-Chairman: Mick Woodward
Directors: Phil O'Reilly (Company Secretary), Jamie Lee, Gordon Norman, and Anthony Leeman.

Club Secretary & Press Officer: Phil O'Reilly, 102 Luxborough Lane, Chigwell, Essex IL7 5AA
Tel No: 07980 643832
e-mail: philoreilly33@hotmail.com

Commercial Manager: Gerard Rice
Tel.No: 07939917350
e.mail: grice@blueyonder.co.uk

Programme: 48 Pages £2.00

Club Shop: Well stocked. Contact: Secretary

Commercial Office : Willie Wordsworth

Clubhouse Steward : Chris Reilly

Tel No: 01375 377753

MANAGEMENT TEAM

Manager: Frank Gray

Coach: Gerry Murphy and Colin Barnes

Physio: Steve Snelling

GRAYS ATHLETIC

No.	Date	Comp	H/A	Opponents	Att:	Result	Goalscorers	Pos
1	Aug 13	C	A	Burton Albion	1654	D 1 - 1	Battersby 74	11
2	16		H	Gravesend & Northfleet	1562	W 6 - 1	Martin 3 (33,63,72 (pen) Oli 42, **Poole** 88, Slabber 90	4
3	20		H	York City	1272	D 1 - 1	Thurgood 90 (pen)	6
4	27		A	Hereford United	2997	W 2 - 0	Battersby 14 Hooper 90	3
5	29		H	Aldershot Town	1869	W 2 - 1	**Poole** 35 Battersby 46	2
6	Sept 2		A	Forest Green Rovers	1152	W 2 - 1	Oli 18 Stuart 90	1
7	10		A	Kidderminster Harriers	1316	D 2 - 2	Hooper 53 Danby 90 (og)	2
8	17		A	Tamworth	1078	D 2 - 2	Oli 36 **Poole** 69	3
9	20		H	Cambridge United	1543	W 5 - 3	Slabber 3 (7 39 48 pen) How 25 (og) Hooper 35	2
10	24		A	Crawley Town	1471	W 3 - 1	Slabber 42 Oli 76 90	1
11	27		A	Dagenham & Redbridge	2017	W 2 - 1	Thurgood 37 Angus 87	1
12	Oct 1		H	Halifax Town	1807	D 1 - 1	Matthews 41	1
13	8		A	Woking	1995	D 1 - 1	Thurgood 23 (pen)	1
14	15		H	Scarborough	1515	W 5 - 0	Slabber 26 **Poole** 52 Hooper 68 Kightly 81 Thurgood 90 (pen)	1
15	22	FAC4Q	H	**Cray Wanderers**	1316	W 2 - 0	**McLean 25 Kightly 88**	
16	29	C	A	Southport	1148	W 4 - 1	Kightly 6 Slabber 21 Stuart 66 Hooper 86	1
17	Nov 5	FAC 1R	A	**York City**	3586	W 3 - 0	**Bishop (og) 15 Slabber 58 Poole 87**	
18	12	C	H	Accrington Stanley	185	L 1 - 2	Kightly 51	2
19	19		A	Exeter City	6682	W 2 - 1	Martin 55 Hooper 89	2
20	26		A	Stevenage Borough	2753	W 1 - 0	Hooper 84	1
21	Dec 2	FAC 2R	A	**Mansfield Town**	2992	L 0 - 3		
22	7	C	H	Altrincham	1028	D 1 - 1	McLean 4	2
23	10		A	Morecambe	1785	L 0 - 3		2
24	17	FAT 1	A	**Aldershot Town**	1771	D 1 - 1	**Kightly 42**	
25	20	FAT 1r	H	**Aldershot Town**	852	W 1 - 0*	**Poole 118**	
26	27	C	H	Canvey Island	2910	L 1 - 2	Martin 64	3
27	31		H	Stevenage Borough	1214	D 2 - 2	Kightly 16 73	2
28	Jan 2		A	Canvey Island	1445	L 1 - 2	Kightly 4	3
29	14	FAT 2	A	**Kidderminster H**	1456	W 1 - 0	**McLean 90**	
30	21	C	A	York City	2461	W 2 - 1	McLean 29 88	3
31	28		H	Hereford United	1528	D 2 - 2	McLean 27 Thurgood 42	4
32	31		A	Burton Albion	858	L 2 - 3	Martin 20 Thurgood 51 (pen)	5
33	Feb 4	FAT 3	A	**Hereford United**	1609	W 1 - 0	**Kightly 60**	
34	11	C	H	Crawley Town	1038	W 1 - 0	Oli 60	4
35	18		A	Halifax Town	16666	L 1 - 2	Stuart 10	6
36	21		H	Dagenham & Redbridge	1065	L 0 - 4		6
37	25	FAT 4	H	**Dagenham & Redbridge**	2321	D 1 - 1	**Poole 6**	
38	28	FAT 4R	A	**Dagenham & redbridge**		W 4 - 2	**Nutter 23 Oli 34 Poole 52 Stuart 68**	
39	Mar 4	C	H	Tamworth	1117	W 5 - 0	McLean 11 Thurgood 27 Slabber 45 54 Kightly 86	5
40	7		A	Cambridge City	1821	D 1 - 1	Slabber 38	
41	11		H	Woking	1256	D 2 - 2	Slabber 20 McLean 22	6
42	18	FAT S-F1	A	**Exeter City**	3051	L 1 - 2	**Slabber 32**	
43	25	FAT S-F2	H	**Exeter City**	3693	W 2 - 0	**Poole 6 McLean 32**	
44	28	S	A	Kidderminster Harriers	1220	W 5 - 0	Oli 6 Kightly 32 **Poole** 47 Thurgood 72 (pen) Hooper 89	7
45	April 1		A	Accrington Stanley	2642	W 3 - 2	**Poole** 57 62 McLean 79	5
46	4		A	Gravesend & Northfleet	1245	W 3 - 1	**Poole** 68 Kightly 70 72	4
47	10		A	Exeter City	1369	W 3 - 0	**Poole** 34 Oli 64 Martin 70	4
48	15		H	Forest Green Rovers	1205	D 2 - 2	OLi 12 **Poole** 71	4
49	17		A	Aldershot Town	1879	W 3 - 0	Kightly 10 **Poole** 19 McLean 27	4
50	19		A	Scarborough	1560	W 7 - 2	McLean 6 56 KIGHTLY 3 (17 80 90) **Poole** 43 71	3
51	22		H	Altrincham	917	W 2 - 0	Maddox 54 (og) Thurgood 63 (pen)	3
52	25		H	Southport	918	D 1 - 1	DeBolla 49	3
53	29		H	Morecambe	1950	L 1 - 2	de Bolla 7	3
54	May 6	Play Off SF1	A	**Halifax Town**	3848	L 2 - 3	**Oli 65 77**	
55	10	Play Off SF2	H	**Halifax Town**	2886	D 2 - 2	**Kightly 56 Nutter 57 Grays lose 4-5 on agg.**	
56	14	FAT Final	N	**Woking**	13997	W 2 - 0	**Oli 41 Poole 45**	
				Ave. League Home Attendance:	3239	**Goals**	115 69 **Top Goalscorer:** Glenn Poole (19)	
				Best Position: 1st **Worst:** 11th				

STEP 1
CONFERENCE

STEP 2 - P177
CONFERENCE Nth & Sth

STEP 3 - P269
NPL - SOUTHERN - ISTHMIAN PREM

STEP 4 - P269
NPL - SOUTHERN - ISTHMIAN

STEP 5/6 - P473

STEP 7 - P713

#	BAYES 1	SAMBROOK 2	STUART 4	MATTHEWS 5	NUTTER 3	KIGHTLY 14	THURGOOD 6	OLI 7	POOLE 23	MARTIN 10	SLABBER 25	HOOPER 8	BATTERSBY 9	BRENNAN 15	EYRE 16	BRUCE 18	MAWER 20	ANGUS 17	MCLEAN 11	BRAYLEY 21	WILLIAMSON 12	OLAYINKA 19	KOO-BOOTHE 22	EDWARDS 27	HANSON 26	JOHNSON 24	STIMSOM 15	DE BOLLA 21	#
1	X	X	X	X	X	X	X	X	X	X	S	X	S	X	S	U	U	U											1
2	X	X	X	X	X	S	X	X	X	X	S	X		X	U	U													2
3	X	X	X	X	S	X	X	X	X	S	X		X	U	U	U													3
4	X		X	U	X	U	X	X	X	X	S	X	X	S	U	X	X												4
5	X		X		X	U	X		X	X	S	U	X	X	U	S	X	X	X										5
6	X		X		X	U	X		X	X	X		X	U	U	X	X	U	S										6
7	X		X	U	X		X	X	X	X		X	U	U	X	X		S	S										7
8	X	X		X		X	X	X		S	X		X	U	X	X	U	X	U	S	U								8
9	U		X	U	X	S	X	X	X		X	X		X	X		X	X		U		S							9
10	U		X	U	X	S	X	X	X		X	X		X	X		X	X		S		S							10
11	U		X	S	X		X	X	X		X	S		X	X	X	X	S		U									11
12	U		X	X	S	X	X	X	S	X	S		X	X		X	X	X		U									12
13	U		X	U	X	U	X	X	X	X	S		X			X	X		U										13
14	U	X	X	U	X	X	X	X	X	X	S		X			X	X		S										14
15	U	X	X	U	X	U	X	X	X	X	U		X			X	X		U										15
16	U	X	X	U	X	X	X	X	S	X	X		X			X	X		S										16
17	U	X	X	U	X	X	X	X	S	X	X		X			X	X		U										17
18	U	X	X	U	X	X	X	U	X	X	S		X			X	X		U										18
19	X	X	X	X	X	X	X	X	S	X	X	S		U		U		X	S										19
20	X	X		X	X	X	X	S	X	X	S		U		U		U	X											20
21	X	X		X	X	X	X	S	X	X	S		U			X	X		U	U									21
22	U		X	X	X	X	S	S	X	X	X		X			X	X	X		U	U								22
23	U		X	S	X	X	X		S	X	X	X		S		X	X	X		S	U	X							23
24	U		X	U	X	X		X	X	X	S		X	X	S	X	X		X	U									24
25	U	U	X	X	X		X	X	X	X	S	S		X	X		X		X	S									25
26	U		X	X	X	X	X	X	X	X	S		X	X	U		U	U											26
27	U	X	X		X	X	X	X	X	U	S	X		X	X			X	U	U									27
28	U	X	X		X	X	X	S		X	U	S	X		X	S	X	X		X									28
29	X	X		X	X	X		U		X	S	X	X		U	U	X		X		U		X						29
30	X	X		U	X	X			X	S	X	X		U		U		X		S		X	X	X					30
31	X	X		U	X	S			X	S	X	X		U		U		X				X	X	X					31
32	X	X		X	S	X	S			X	S	X	X		U		U		X				X	X	X				32
33	X	X	X		X	X	X	S	U	X	X			U		U		X		X		X		U					33
34	X	X		X	X	X	S	S	X	X			U		U		S	X		X		S	X	X					34
35	X	X	X		X	X		X	X	S	X	X		U		S		X		S	X	U							35
36	X	X	X		X	X	X	X	S	X	X		U	X	X			S		X	S								36
37	X		X		X	X	X	S	X	S	U	X		U		X		X	U	X		X							37
38	X		X		X	X	X	X	S	S	U		U		X		X		U	X		X							38
39	U	S	X		X	X	X	X		S	U		X		X		X		S	X		X							39
40	U	U	X		X	X	X	X	X	X	S	U		X		X		S		X									40
41	U	S	X		X	X		X	X	X	U		X		X		X	U	U	X									41
42	X	X	X		X	X	S	X	X	U		U	U		X		S		X										42
43	X	X	X		X	X	X	X	S		U	U		X		U		X											43
44	X	X	X		X	X	X	X		S		U	U		X		S	X		X		S							44
45	X	X	X		X	X	S	S			U	U		X		U	X		X		X								45
46	X	X	X		X	X	S	S			U	U		X		S	X		X		X								46
47	X	X	X		X	X	X		S		U	U		X			S		X		X								47
48	X	X	X		X	X	X		S		U	U		X			S		X		S								48
49	X	X	X		X	X	S	X		X	S		U	U		X	X	S		X									49
50	X	X	X		X	X	X	X		S		U	S		X		S	U		X									50
51	X		X		X	X	X	X		S		U	X		X		S	U		X		S							51
52	X		X		X	X	X	X		S		U	X			S	S		X	U		X							52
53	U		S	X	S		X	X	U		X	X	X		X	X		X	S	X									53
54	X	S	X		X	X	X	X	X		U		X	U	X		U		X		U								54
55	X	X	X		X	X	X	X		S		U	X		X		U		X		U								55
56	X	X	X		X	X	X	X		S		S		S	X		S		X										56

Total Appearances (Conference)

25	23	34	8	40	27	40	26	31	31	18	16	13	6	17	9	16	11	28	0	4	6	2	4	18	4	0	5	X
0	2	0	3	0	8	0	8	6	3	10	22	1	2	0	3	2	0	2	4	10	9	0	1	1	1	0	3	S
17	1	0	8	2	4	0	0	1	1	3	3	2	4	25	9	6	2	0	1	5	12	1	0	0	1	1	0	U

Cup Appearances

10	9	12	2	14	12	13	9	10	12	6	2	1	0	4	2	5	4	14	0	3	2	0	0	8	0	0	0	X
0	1	0	0	0	0	0	4	2	2	3	7	0	0	1	0	2	0	0	0	1	3	0	0	0	0	0	0	S
4	1	0	3	0	1	0	0	2	0	1	4	1	0	9	3	0	0	0	0	3	7	1	0	1	0	1	2	U

GRAYS ATHLETIC

CURRANT SQUAD AS OF BEGINING OF 2006-07 SEASON

GOALKEEPERS	SQ NO.	HT	WT	D.O.B	AGE	P.O.B	CAREER	APPS	GOA
Ashley Bayes	1	6'01"	13 05	19/4/72	34	Lincoln	Brentford Rel c/s 93, Torquay 8/93 Rel c/s 96, Exeter 7/96 Rel c/s 99, L.Orient 7/99 Rel c/s 02, Bohemians (Ire) c/s 02, Woking 3/03, Hornchurch 5/04, Grays 11/04	25	0
Danny Knowles	15	6'00"	12 00	7/1/86	20	Sidcup	Gillingham Rel 4/06, Welling (L) 1/05, East Thurrock (3ML) 11/05, Grays 8/06		

DEFENDERS	SQ NO.	HT	WT	D.O.B	AGE	P.O.B	CAREER	APPS	GOA
Andrew Sambrook	2	5'10"	11 09	13/7/79	27	Chatham	Gillingham (AS), USA Scholarship (Hartwick College) c/s 97, Gillingham 3/01 Rel 6/01, Rushden & D 8/01 Rel c/s 05, Grays 7/05	25	0
Adam Green	3	5'11"	10 11	12/1/84	22	Hillingdon	Fulham Rel 5/06, Sheff Wed (L) 1/05, Bournemouth (L) 3/05, Bristol C (SL) 1/06, Grays 7/06		
Jamie Stuart	4	5'10"	11 00	15/10/76	29	Southwark	Charlton cc 12/97, Millwall 9/98 Rel c/s 01, Cambridge U (Trial) 7/01, Bury 10/01, Southend 6/03 Rel c/s 04, Hornchurch 7/04, Grays 11/04	34	3
Djoumin Sangare	5			16/12/83	22	Dunkerque	Wasquehal (Fra), Redbridge 9/04, Chelmsford 1/05, Redbridge 1/05, Lewes, St Albans (L) 8/05, Grays 8/06		
Mark Wright	16			20/1/87	19	London	Norwich (Jun), Tottenham (Scholar), Charlton (Scholar), Southend, Lewes (L) 12/05, Grays 8/06		
Jay Smith	17	5'11"	11 07	29/12/81	24	Hammersmith	Brentford, Farnborough 10/04 Rel 5/05 Re-signed, Grays 6/06		
Nathan Moulds	19			14/1/83	23		APIA Leichhardt Tigers (Wal), Grays 8/06		
Cameron Mawer	20	5'10"	11 06	21/2/86	20	Stevenage	Watford (Scholar), Wealdstone 1/05, Stoke, Stockport (Trial) c/s 05, Grays 7/05	18	0

MIDFIELDERS	SQ NO.	HT	WT	D.O.B	AGE	P.O.B	CAREER	APPS	GOA
Stuart Thurgood	6	5'08"	11 10	4/11/81	24	Enfield	Tottenham (Scholar), Shimuzu S Pulse (Jap) 7/00, Southend 1/01, Grays 8/03	40	9
John Martin	10	5'05"	10 00	15/7/81	25	Bethnal Green	L.Orient Rel c/s 03, Woking (Trial) 7/03, Farnborough 8/03, Hornchurch 9/03, Grays 11/04	34	7
Tom Williamson	12	5'09"	10 02	24/12/84	21	Leicester	Leicester Rel c/s 04, Canvey Island 10/04 Rel 4/05, Grays 7/05	14	0
Michael Kightly	14	5'09"	9 11	24/1/86	20	Basildon	Tottenham (Jun), Southend (from trainee) 12/03, Farnborough (3ML) 10/04, Grays 7/05	35	14
Scott Canham	18	5'09"	11 03	5/11/74	31	Newham	West Ham, Torquay (L) 11/95, Brentford (SL) 1/96, Brentford £25,000 8/96 Rel c/s 98, L.Orient 8/98 Rel c/s 00, Chesham (2ML) 11/99, Chesham 9/00, L.Orient 7/01, Woking (2ML) 3/03 (02/03 10,2), Woking 5/03 (03/04 37,2, 04/05 15,2), Farnborough 2/05 (04/05		
Ashley Nicholls	22	5'11"	11 11	30/10/81	24	Ipswich	Ipswich Wan, Ipswich 7/00 Rel c/s 02, Canvey Island (L) 2/02, Hereford (trial) 7/02, Darlington 8/02, Cambridge U (SL) 2/04, Cambridge U 7/04, Rushden & D (3ML) 8/05, Rushden & D 1/06, Grays 8/06		
Glenn Poole	23			3/2/81	25	Essex	Tottenham (Trainee), Witham T 99/00, Yeovil 11/99, Bath C (L) 9/01, Ford U/Redbridge 2/02, Thurrock 11/04, Grays 7/05	37	13

FORWARDS	SQ NO.	HT	WT	D.O.B	AGE	P.O.B	CAREER	APPS	GOA
Dennis Oli	7	6'00"	12 02	28/1/84	22	Newham	QPR Rel 6/04, Gravesend (2ML) 11/03, Farnborough (L) 2/04, Swansea 8/04, Cambridge U 9/04 Rel 10/04, Grays 11/04	34	9
Lee Boylan	9	5'06"	11 06	2/9/78	27	Witham	West Ham Rel c/s 99, Kingstonian (L) 12/98, Trelleborgs (Swe) c/s 99, Exeter (2ML) 11/99, Kingstonian 2/00 Rel c/s 00, Southend (Trial), Hayes 10/00, Stevenage, Heybridge S, Canvey Island 8/01, Grays 7/06		
Aaron McLean	11	5'06"	10 02	25/5/83	23	Hammersmith	L.Orient, Grays (2ML) 9/02, Aldershot 3/03, Colchester (Trial) 4/03, Grays 2/05	30	10
Jamie Slabber	25	6'02"	11 10	31/12/84	21	Enfield	Tottenham, AB Copenhagen (L) 3/04, Swindon (L) 12/04, Aldershot 3/05 Rel 5/05, Grays 7/05	28	11
John Turner	26	5'10"	11 00	12/2/86	20	Harrow	Cambridge U, Rushden & D (Trial) 10/05, Scunthorpe (Trial) 11/05, Aldershot (L) 11/05, Rushden & D 1/06, Grays 8/06		

PLAYING SQUAD

LOANEES	HT	WT	DOB	AGE	POB	FROM - TO	APPS	GOA
(D)Nathan Koo-Boothe	6'04"	13 12	18/7/85	21	Westminster	MK Dons (1M) 11/05 - Rel 2/06, Kettering 2/06	2	0
(D)Brett Johnson	6'01"		15/8/85	21	Hammersmith	Northampton (SL) 1/06 -	5	0
(D)Andy Edwards	6'02"	12 00	17/9/71	34	Epping	Southend (3M) 1/06 - Rel 5/06, Aldershot 7/06	5	0

DEPARTURES	HT	WT	DOB	AGE	POB	FROM - TO	APPS	GOA
(F)Steve West			15/11/72	33	Essex	Hornchurch 11/04 - East Thurrock 8/05, Fisher 1/06 Rel 5/06, Leyton 7/06		
(M)Dean Brennan	5'09"	11 08	17/6/80	26	Dublin	Stevenage AL 8/04 - Lewes 10/05, Kettering 1/06, AFC Wimbledon 2/06	8	0
(F)Bertie Brayley	5'09"	12 07	5/9/81	24	Basildon	Margate 9/05 - Margate (L) 10/05, Margate 12/05	4	0
(F)Tony Battersby	6'00"	12 09	30/8/75	31	Doncaster	Kings Lynn 10/04 - Rel 3/06, AFC Wimbledon 3/06	14	3
(D)Lee Matthews			30/5/73	33	Wickford	Hornchurch 11/04 - Rel 5/06	11	1
(D)Stevland Angus	6'00"	12 00	16/9/80	25	Westminster	Cambridge U 8/05 - Barnet (SL) 1/06, Rel 5/06, Torquay 7/06	11	1
(D)Joe Bruce	6'00"	12 00	5/7/83	23	London	Hitchin 8/03 - Maidenhead (2ML) 1/06, Rel 5/06, Basingstoke 6/06	12	0
(M)Christian Hanson	6'01"	11 05	3/8/81	25	Middlesbrough	L.Orient 1/06 - Rel 5/06, Durham C 8/06	19	0
(F)Mark De Bolla	5'07"	11 09	1/1/83	23	London	Notts County 3/06 - Rel 5/06, Gravesend 7/06	8	2
(D)Mark Stimson	5'11"	11 00	27/12/67	38	Plaistow	Canvey Island (Pl/Coach) 4/02 (Pl/Man) 9/02 - Stevenage (Manager) 5/06	0	0
(D)John Nutter	5'10"	11 09	13/6/82	24	Taplow	Aldershot 6/04 - Stevenage 5/06	40	0
(M)Ade Olayinka	5'11"		16/6/83	22	London	Barnet 8/03 - Hampton & R (L) 1/06, Basingstoke 6/06	15	0
(M)Gary Hooper			26/1/88	18	Loughton	Tottenham (Jun) 7/04 - Reading (Trial) 7/05 Rel 7/06	38	8
(F)Charlie Henry						Arlesey, Wycombe 3/06 - Rel c/s 06, Haverhill 7/06		
(M)Ashley Sestanovich	21	6'03"	13 00	18/9/81	24	London	Farnborough 6/06 - Rel 7/06		
(G)Nicky Eyre	16	5'10"	10 10	7/9/85	20	Braintree	Tottenham 7/05 - Rel 7/06, Rushden & D 8/06	17	0

GRAYS ATHLETIC

Ground Address: REcreation Ground, Bridge Road, Grays RM17 6BZ
Telephone: 01375 391649
Fax:
General email address:
Official website:
Office Opening Hours: Monday -Friday: 9.00am-5.00pm.
Saturday Matchdays: 9.30am-until end of match

SIMPLE DIRECTIONS:
Seven minutes walk from Grays BR station. Turn right round one way system then right into Clarence Road and at end into Bridge Road. Or from A13 towards Southend from London, take Grays exit towards town centre, keep left on one way sytem, continue up hill for about half a mile, turn right into Bridge Street and ground is half a mile on left. Bus No 370 passes Bridge Road..

MATCH TICKETS:
Ticket office Telephone: 01375 391649

Midweek Home Matchday: Tuesday 7.45 pm

Capacity: 4,000 **Seats:** 950 **Covered:** 1,500

Clubhouse: open Daily (01375 37753).
Steward: Chris Riley
Refreshments:

Club Shop: On ground and open on matchdays

Local Press: Thurrock Gazette

Local Radio: BBC Essex, Radio Essex

MATCHDAY PROGRAMME
Pages: 48 **Price:** £2.00
Editor: Kevin Lamb
Tel No: 07810 898572

CLUB STATISTICS

RECORDS
Attendance: 9,500 v Chelmsford City F.A.Cup 4th Qualifying Round 1959
Victory: 12-0 v Tooting & Mitcham United London League 24.02.23

Defeat: 0-12 v Enfield (A) Athenian League 20.04.63
Career Goalscorer: Harry Brand 269 (1944-520)

Career Appearances: Phil Sammons 673 (1982-97)

Transfer Fee Paid: to Canvey Island for Ian Durant
Transfer Fee Received: from Crystal Palace for Tony Witter Plymouth A for Dwight Marshall & Wycombe E for Matt Lawrence

SENIOR HONOURS Conference South Champions 2004-05
F.A.Trophy Winners 2004-05 2005-06
Isthmian Div 1 R-up 87-88 99-00
Athenian Lg R-up 82-83
Essex Senior Cup (8) R-up (9)

PREVIOUS LEAGUES: Athenian 1912-14, 1958-83
London 1914-1924 1926-1939
Kent 1924-1926 Corinthian 1945-1958 Isthmian 1958-2004

HALIFAX TOWN

Club Colours: Blue & white stripes/blue/blue
Change Colours: Tangerine/white/white
Club Sponsor: Grand Central Rail
Previous League: Football Laegue
LAST SEASON
League: 4th Nationwide Conference **F.A. Cup:** 1st Round Replay **F.A. Trophy:** 2nd Round
BEST PERFORMANCES
League: 3rd, Division 3(out of fourdivisions) 1969-70 **F.A. Cup:** 5th Rd 191314 52-53
F.A. Trophy: 3rd Round

Founded: 1911
Nickname: The Shaymen

Back Row (L-R):   S Smeltz M Roberts C Mawson R Sugden L Butler A Quinn G Young.
Middle: R Toulson D Forrest A Campbell A Russell-Cox(Physio)S Haslam J Wright S Torpey
Front: G Uhlenbeek L Killeen M Foster C Wilder (Manager) W Jacobs (Assistant Manager) C Senior M Doughty T Thompson

CLUB PERSONNEL

President:	Bob Holmes
Chairman:	Geoff Ralph
Vice Chairman:	Adrian Hall
Directors:	Bob Bland,Richard Harrisoin,
	Stuart Byrnes (HTST representative)
Club Secretary	Angie Firth c/o Club
Tel Nos: 01422 341222	**Fax:** 01422 349487
e-mail:	secretary@halifaxafc.co.uk
Commercial Manager:	Matthew Band
e.mail:	commercial@halifax.co.uk
Press Officer:	Chairman/Secretary
	Tel Nos: 01422 341222

MANAGEMENT TEAM

Manager:	Chris Wilder
Previous clubs as player/manager:	Alfreton Town
Assistant Manager:	Wayne Jacobs
Player-Coach:	Lee Butler
Physio:	Alan Russell-Cox

HALIFAX TOWN

BEST LGE ATT.: 2,688 v Accrington Stanley
LOWEST: 1,284 v Forest Green Rovers

No.	Date	Comp	H/A	Opponents	Att:	Result	Goalscorers	Pos
1	Aug 13	C	A	Morecambe	2150	L 0 1		17
2	16		H	Burton Albion	1681	W 1 0	Brabin 71	15
3	20		H	Aldershot Town	1571	D 1 1	**Grant** 4	13
4	27		A	Forest Green Rovers	905	D 2 2	Midgley 54 (pen) Senior 65	14
5	29		H	York City	2078	W 1 0	Midgley 62 (pen)	10
6	Sept 3		A	Stevenage Borough	1382	L 0 1		12
7	10		H	Tamworth	1453	W 4 - 0	Midgley 46 Forrest 64 **Grant** 69 Senior 72	9
8	17		A	Gravesend & Northfleet	918	L 0 - 4		11
9	20		A	Kidderminster Harriers	1566	W 1 - 0	Killeen 27	9
10	24		H	Hereford United	1559	W 2 - 1	**Grant** 48 Senior 86	7
11	27		H	Altrincham	1453	W 2 - 0	Midgley 21 (pen) **Grant** 83	6
12	Oct 1		A	Grays Athletic	1807	D 1 - 1	**Grant** 57	6
13	8		A	Exeter City	3154	L 2 2 4	**Grant** 1 Killeen 26	7
14	15		H	Cambridge United	1621	W 1 - 0	Senior 76	7
15	18	LDV Vans 1	H	**Bury**	1191	W 6 - 1	Midgley (pen) 16 Mansaram 28 46 Haslam 51 Killeen 55 Parish (og) 75	
16	22	FAC 4Q	H	**Farsley Celtic**	1469	W 2 - 0	**Senior** 44 67	
17	29	C	A	Woking	2054	D 2 - 2	Killeen 50 Quinn 86	7
18	Nov 5	FAC 1R	H	**Rushden & Diamonds**	2303	D 1 - 1	**Senior** 44	
19	12		H	Dagenham & redbridge	1532	W 3 - 0	Mansaram 70 90 Killeen 85	6
20	15	FAC 1Rr	A	**Rushden & Diamonds**	2133	D 0 - 0	Lost 4-5 after penalties	
21	19	C	A	Southport	1402	W 2 - 0	Foster 21 Forrest 22	
22	26		A	Scarborough	1843	L 0 - 2		6
23	Dec 3		H	Crawley Town	1616	D 2 - 2	Forrest 56 **Grant** 61	5
24	10		A	Canvey Island	664	W 1 - 0	Quinn 89	5
25	13	LDV Vans 2	H	**Scunthorpe United**	1124	L 1 - 3	**Doughty** 88	
26	17	FAT 1	H	**Southport**	1101	D 0 - 0		
27	20	FATR 1r	A	**Southport**	589	W 1 - 0	**Forrest** 80	
28	24	C	H	Accrington Stanley	2688	D 2 - 2	Killeen 45 **Grant** 68	5
29	30		H	Scarborough		W 1 - 0	Foster 83	
30	Jan 2		A	Accrington Stanley	3014	D 1 - 1	Forrest 58	5
31	9		H	Morecambe	1962	D 0 - 0		5
32	14	FAT 2	H	**Hereford United**	1220	L 0 - 1		
33	21	C	A	Aldershot Town	2417	L 1 - 3	Killeen 15	7
34	24		A	Burton Albion	1540	W 2 - 1	**Grant** 45 Foster (pen ?) 76	4
35	28		H	Forest Green Rovers	1284	W 1 - 0	Quinn 18	3
36	Feb 4		H	KidderminsterHarrirs	1544	D 0 - 0		3
37	11		A	Hereford United	2555	L 0 - 1		6
38	18		H	Grays Athletic	1666	W 2 - 1	Thompson 21 **Grant** 88	4
39	21		A	Altrincham	1139	W 2 - 1	Killeen 5 Sugden 88	3
40	25		A	Tamworth	1672	W 2 - 1	Killeen 1 Senior 69	2
41	Mar 11		H	Exeter City	2104	W 2 - 0	Sugden 5 38	3
42	18		A	Cambridge United	2288	D 1 - 1	**Grant** 83	3
43	28		H	Woking	1465	W 1 - 0	Bushell 38	3
44	April 1		A	Dagenham & Redbridge	1078	L 0 - 1		3
45	8		H	Southport	1791	W 2 1 1	Forrest 47 Sugden	3
46	14		H	Stevenage Borough	2253	D 1 - 1	Young 35	3
47	17		A	York City	4085	W 2 - 0	**Grant** 48 Bushell 83	3
48	22		A	Crawley Town	1285	D 2 - 2	Senior 56 Killeen 68	4
49	25		H	Gravesend & Northfleet	1680	W 2 - 0	Sugden 52 54	4
50	29		H	Canvey Island	2049	L 0 - 2		4
51	May 6	Play Off SF1	H	**Grays Athletic**	3848	W 3 - 2	**Bushell** 17 **Sugden** 30 **Killeen** 32	
52	10	Play Off SF2	A	**Grays Athletic**	2886	D 2 2	**Foster** 6 63 (pen) Halifax Town win 5-4 on agg.	
53		Play Off F	N	**Hereford United**	15499	L 2 - 3	**Killean** 27 **Grant** 73	
Ave. League Home Attendance:				2253		Goals	72 52	Top Goalscorer: John Grant (13)
Best Position:	2nd			Worst:	17th			

98

DUNBAVIN 1	HASLAM 2	INGRAM 6	ATHERTON 19	YOUNG 16	MIDGLEY 7	BRABIN 21	FOSTER 8	KILLEEN 10	SUGDEN 11	GRANT 20	BOWLER 23	SENIOR 15	THOMPSON 18	DOUGHTY 3	BUTLER 24	LEISTER 14	TOULSON 12	QUINN 5	JACOBS 17	FORREST 26	WRIGHT 25	MANSARAM 22	LEGZDINS 21	PRENDERGAST 27	BUSHELL 4	YATES 6	KENNEDY 1	SMIKLE 25	HOWELL 21	
X	X	X	X	X	X	X	X	X	X	S	S	S	S	U	U															1
X	X	X	X	X	X	X	X	X	X	S	S	S	S	U	U															2
X	X	X	X	X	X	X	X	X	X	S	S	S	S	U	U															3
X	X	X	X	X	X	X			S	X	U	X	X	S	U	S														4
X		X				X		X	X	X	U	U	X	X	U	S		X	X	S										5
X	X	X			X		X	X	U	X	S		S	X	X			X	X	S	U									6
X	X	X		S	X		X	U	S	X	U	X	X	X				X		X	S									7
X	X	X			X	X		X	S	S	X	S	X	X				X	U	X	U									8
X	X	X		S	S		X	X	X	S	U	U	X					X	X	X	X									9
X	X	X		S	S		X		X	X	U	X	S	X		U		X	X	X	X									10
X	X	X		S	X		X		U	X	S	X	X	U		S		X		X	X									11
X	X	X		U			X	X	S	U	S	X	X		S			X	X	X	X									12
X	X	X		S	U		X		X	U	S	X	X		S			X	X	X	X									13
X	X			X	S		X		X	U	S	X	U	S		U		X	X	X	X									14
U	X		X	X		X	X		X	U	S	X	X	X	X		X		S	S	X									15
X	X	X	U	X		X	U	X	S	X	X	U	U	X		X		X	X										16
X	X	U		X	X	X	S	S	X	X	U	X	X		X	X	S													17
X	X	U	S	X	S	X	X	X	X	X	U	X	U	X	X	U														18
X	X	U	S	X	S	X	X	X	X	U	X	X	X	S	X															19
X	X	U	S	X	X	S	X	S	X	X	U	X	X	X	X															20
X	X	U	X	X	X	S	S	U	X	S	X	X	X	X	X															21
X	X	S	U	X	X	X	U	S	X	X	X	X	U	X	X															22
X	X	S	X	X	X	U	U	X	X	X	S	X	X	X																23
X	X	U	S	X	X	X	S	X	X	U	X	X	X																	24
X	X	X	X	X	S	X	X	S	X	X	U	U	X	X	S															25
X	U	X	U	S	X	X	S	X	X	X	U	X	X	X	X															26
X	S	X	U	X	X	X	S	X	X	X	U	X	U	X	X															27
X	S	X	X	X	X	S	U	X	X	X	U	X	X	X																28
X	S	X	U	X	X	S	S	X	X	X	U	X	X	X																29
X	X	X	U	U	X	S	X	S	X	X	X	U	X	X	X															30
X	X	U	S	X	X	X	S	X	X	U	X	X	X	X																31
X	X	U	S	X	X	X	S	X	X	X	U	X	X	S																32
X	X	U	X	X	U	S	X	X	X	U	X	X	X	S																33
X	X	U	X	X	S	U	X	X	X	X	X	S	X	X	U															34
X	X	X	X	X	X	S	X	X	X	U	X	U	X	S	U															35
X	X	S	X	S	X	X	X	X	U	X	U	X	X	U	X															36
X	X	S	X	X	S	X	U	X	X	X	X	U	S	X																37
X	X	X	S	U	X	S	X	X	X	U	S	X	X	X																38
X	X	U	X	S	X	S	X	X	X	X	S	U	X	X																39
X	X	X	X	X	S	X	X	X	U	S	S	U	X	X																40
X	S	X	X	X	S	X	U	X	X	X	U	S	X	X																41
X	U	X	U	X	X	S	X	X	X	X	S	X	X	X																42
X	X	U	S	X	X	U	X	X	X	X	X	S	X	S	X	S														43
X	U	X	X	X	X	S	S	X	X	X	U	X	U	X	X															44
X	U	X	S	X	X	S	X	X	X	X	U	X	X	U																45
X	U	X	X	X	X	S	U	X	X	U	X	S	X	X																46
X	U	X	X	X	S	X	U	X	X	U	X	S	X	X																47
X	U	X	X	X	S	X	S	X	X	U	X	S	X	X																48
X	U	X	X	X	X	S	S	X	X	U	X	S	X	X																49
X	X	X	X	X	S	X	X	S	X	S	U	U	X	X	X															50
X	S	X	X	X	X	X	U	S	X	U	X	X	X	U																51
X	X	X	X	X	X	S	S	X	X	U	X	X	X	U																52
X	X	X	X	X	X	S	S	X	X	U	X	X	X	U																53

Total Appearances (Conference)

14	40	18	12	24	14	4	35	32	12	30	5	10	37	31	3	2	1	37	8	32	10	1	10	6	7	0	15	11	1	X
0	0	2	2	6	10	0	1	4	10	10	14	20	4	1	0	7	1	0	3	4	1	2	0	0	7	3	0	1	0	S
0	0	0	7	10	5	0	2	1	3	1	13	8	0	4	10	5	3	1	11	1	2	1	0	0	2	6	0	1	0	U

Cup Appearances

1	10	4	6	5	4	0	11	8	3	4	4	3	8	8	4	1	0	10	1	10	3	3	3	3	1	0	3	0	0	X
0	0	1	1	0	4	0	0	2	0	3	1	6	3	0	0	0	0	0	0	1	1	0	0	2	0	0	0	0	0	S
1	0	1	0	6	0	0	0	1	0	0	0	2	0	0	4	4	0	1	3	0	0	2	0	0	1	0	0	3	0	U

HALIFAX TOWN

CURRANT SQUAD AS OF BEGINING OF 2006-07 SEASON

GOALKEEPERS

GOALKEEPERS	SQ NO.	HT	WT	D.O.B	AGE	P.O.B	CAREER	APPS	GOA
Craig Mawson		6'02"	13 04	16/5/79	27	Keighley	Burnley, Lincoln (2ML) 9/00, Halifax 2/01 Rel c/s 01, Morecambe 8/01 Rel c/s 04, Oldham 8/04 Rel 10/04, Hereford 10/04, Halifax 6/06		
Lee Butler	24	6'02"	13 00	30/5/66	40	Sheffield	Haworth Coll, Lincoln C 8/86, Boston U (L) 1/87, Aston Villa £100,000 8/87, Hull (L) 3/91, Barnsley £165,000 7/91 Rel c/s 96, Scunthorpe (L) 2/96, Wigan 7/96, Dunfermline 7/98, Halifax 8/99, Doncaster 1/02, Alfreton 5/02, Halifax (Pl/Ass Man) 6/02, Alfret	3	0

DEFENDERS

DEFENDERS	SQ NO.	HT	WT	D.O.B	AGE	P.O.B	CAREER	APPS	GOA
Steve Haslam	2	5'11"	11 00	6/9/79	26	Sheffield	Sheff Wed Rel 5/04, Halifax 8/04, Northampton 8/04, Halifax 9/04	40	0
Matt Doughty	3	5'11"	11 00	2/11/81	24	Warrington	Chester, Rochdale 7/01 Rel 5/04, Halifax 5/04	32	0
Greg Young	16	6'02"	12 03	24/4/83	23	Doncaster	Sheff Wed (Scholar), Shrewsbury (Trial) 3/02, Grimsby 7/02, Northwich (L) 10/04, Northwich (L) 12/04, Halifax 2/05	30	1
Adam Quinn	5			2/6/83	23	Sheffield	Sheff Wed, Carlisle (Trial) 3/02, Halifax 8/02	37	3
Jake Wright	25	5'11"	10 07	11/3/86	20	Keighley	Bradford C Rel 5/06, Halifax (3M) 8/05, Halifax 6/06	11	0
Mark Roberts		6'01"	12 00	16/10/83	22	Northwich	Crewe, Southport (2ML) 11/05, Chester (L) 1/06, Southport (SL) 3/06, Halifax (5ML) 8/06		
Wayne Jacobs	17	5'08"	12 01	3/2/69	37	Liverpool	Sheff Wed, Hull C £27,000 3/88, Rotherham 8/93, Bradford C 8/94 Caretaker Man 11/03 Rel c/s 05, Halifax (Pl/Ass Man) 6/05	11	0
Gus Uhlenbeek		5'10"	12 06	20/8/70	36	Paramaribo, Sur	Ajax (Holl), Cambuur (Holl), Tops SV (Holl), Ipswich £100,000 8/95, Fulham 7/98 Rel c/s 00, Sheff Utd 8/00 Rel c/s 02, Walsall (L) 3/02, Bradford C 8/02 Rel c/s 03, Chesterfield 8/03 Rel 4/04, Wycombe 7/04, Mansfield 8/05, Halifax 8/06		

MIDFIELDERS

MIDFIELDERS	SQ NO.	HT	WT	D.O.B	AGE	P.O.B	CAREER	APPS	GOA
Tom Kearney		5'09"	10 12	7/10/81	24	Liverpool	Everton, Bradford C 3/02 Rel 5/06, Halifax c/s 06		
Martin Foster	8	5'05"	9 10	29/10/77	28	Sheffield	Leeds Rel c/s 98, Blackpool (L) 12/97, Morton 7/98, Doncaster 4/99, Ilkeston (L) 9/00, Forest Green AL 1/01, Halifax 7/04	36	3
Ryan Toulson	12			18/11/85	20		Halifax, Stocksbridge (L) 9/05	2	0
Tyrone Thompson	18	5'09"	11 02	8/5/81	24	Sheffield	Sheff Utd Rel c/s 03, Halifax (Trial) 9/01, Lincoln C (L) 10/02, Doncaster (L) 3/03, Huddersfield 8/03 Rel 4/04, Scarborough 6/04, Halifax 8/05	41	1

FORWARDS

FORWARDS	SQ NO.	HT	WT	D.O.B	AGE	P.O.B	CAREER	APPS	GOA
Danny Forrest	26	5'10"	11 07	23/10/84	21	Keighley	Bradford C Rel 5/06, Halifax (SL) 8/05, Halifax 6/06	36	5
Shane Smeltz		6'01"	12 08	29/8/81	25	Goppegan, Ger	Gold Coast City (Aust), Brisbane Strikers (Aust), Napier City (NZ), Adelaide C (Aust), Adelaide U (Aust) Rel 10/04, Mansfield 1/05, Rushden (Trial), AFC Wimbledon 3/05, Halifax 7/06		
Lewis Kileen	10	5'09"	10 07	23/9/82	23	Peterborough	Sheff Utd Rel c/s 03, Halifax (3ML), Halifax 6/03	36	9
Ryan Sugden	11	6'00"	12 06	26/12/80	25	Bradford	Oldham, Burton (SL) 3/01, Scarborough 2/02, Chester 6/02, Burton 6/03, Morecambe 5 fig 8/03), Halifax 7/04	22	6
Chris Senior	15	5'06"	9 01	18/11/81	24	Huddersfield	Huddersfield, Wakefield-Emley 7/02, Scarborough 8/03 OOC 5/05, Halifax 8/05	30	6
Steve Torpey		5'09"	10 08	16/9/81	24	Kirkby	Liverpool Rel c/s 01, Chesterfield (Trial) 7/01, Port Vale 8/01 Rel 9/01, Scarborough 10/01 Rel 12/01, Prescot Cables 8/02, Altrincham 10/04, Prescot Cables 2/05, FCUM 7/05, Halifax 8/06		
Andy Campbell		5'11"	11 07	18/4/79	27	Stockton	Middlesbrough, Sheff Utd (2ML) 12/98, Sheff Utd (SL) 3/99, Bolton (SL) 3/01, Cardiff (L) 2/02 £950,000 3/02, Doncaster (L) 1/05, Oxford U (3ML) 9/05, Dunfermline 1/06, York C (Trial) 7/06, Halifax 8/06		

PLAYING SQUAD

LOANEES	SN	HT	WT	DOB	AGE	POB	FROM - TO	APPS	GOA
(G)Adam Legzdins	21						Birmingham (3M) 11/05 -	10	0
(M)Rory Prendergast	27	5'08"	12 00	6/4/78	28	Pontefract	Blackpool (2M) 11/05 -	6	0
(M)Brian Smikle	25			3/11/85	20		West Brom (2M) 2/06 - Rel 6/06, Kidderminster 7/06	12	0

DEPARTURES	SN	HT	WT	DOB	AGE	POB	FROM - TO	APPS	GOA
(D)Mark Monington	14	6'01"	14 00	21/10/70	35	Bilsthorpe	Boston U 11/02 - Rel 8/05, Woodley Sports 9/05		
(M)Gary Brabin	21	5'11"	14 08	9/12/70	35	Liverpool	Witton 7/05 - Rel 11/05 Banned, Lancaster 1/06, Southport 1/06	4	1
(G)Ian Dunbavin	1	6'01"	10 10	27/5/80	26	Knowsley	Shrewsbury 7/04 - Rel 11/05,		
							Scarborough (L) 11/05 (Perm) 12/05 Rel 5/06, Accrington 8/06	14	0
(D)Denny Ingram	6	5'11"	11 13	27/6/76	30	Sunderland	Forest Green 3/04 - Scarborough 1/06	20	0
(F)Darren Mansaram	22	6'02"	11 07	25/6/84	22	Doncaster	Grimsby £5,000 1/05 - York (L) 8/05, Tamworth (L) 9/05,		
							Worksop (L) 12/05, Sligo Rovers 1/06	3	2
(M)Steve Bushell	4	5'09"	11 06	28/12/72	33	Manchester	Stalybridge 11/01 - Altrincham (2ML) 11/05, Rel 5/06, Altrincham 7/06	14	2
(F)Craig Midgley	7	5'07"	11 00	24/5/76	30	Bradford	Hartlepool 7/01 - Rel 5/06, Farsley Celtic 7/06	24	4
(G)Jon Kennedy	1	6'01"	14 03	30/11/80	25	Rotherham	Witton 1/06 - Rel 5/06, Lancaster 6/06	15	0
(M)Dean Howell	21	6'01"	12 05	29/11/80	25	Burton	Colchester 2/06 - Rel 5/06, Weymouth 6/06	1	0
(D)Steve Yates	6	5'10"	12 02	29/1/70	36	Bristol	Scarborough 1/06 - Rel 5/06	3	0
(D)Brenton Leister	14	5'11"	11 12	3/6/85	21	Leeds	Leeds 8/05 - Hull (Trial) 4/06, Rel 5/06	9	0
(F)John Grant	20	5'11"	10 07	9/8/81	24	Manchester	Shrewsbury 3/05 - Aldershot 7/06	40	12
(F)Justin Bowler	23	5'07"	12 00	26/6/86	20	Leeds	Leeds 8/05 - Altrincham 7/06	19	0
(D)Michael Taylor		6'02"	13 10	21/11/82	23	Liverpool	Cheltenham 7/06 - Rel 7/06, Lancaster C 7/06		
(D)Peter Atherton	19	5'11"	13 13	6/4/70	36	Wigan	Bradford C 7/05 - Retired 8/06	14	0

HALIFAX TOWN

Ground Address:	The Shay Stadium, Halifax, HX1 2TS
Capacity	9,500
Telephone:	01422 341222
General email address:	secretary@halifaxafc.co.uk
Official website:	www.halifaxafc.co.uk
SIMPLE DIRECTIONS:	M62 Jct 24 head towards town centre on A629, 3-4 miles ground is on right (ShawHill) signposted The Shay.
By Rail:	Halifax BR -One mile
MATCH TICKETS:	
Ticket office Telephone:	01422 341222
Midweek Home Matchday:	Tuesday
Clubhouse:	Open normal licensing hours.
Refreshments:	Available on matchdays
Club Shop:	At The Shay (0970 411 7111)

MATCHDAY PROGRAMME
Pages: 32   Price: £2.50
Editor: Matt Wall
Tel Nos: 01562 513955 (W)
07725 536272 (M)

CLUB STATISTICS

RECORDS

Attendance:	36,885
	v Tottenham Hotspur F.A.Cup 5th Rd. 14.02.53
Victory:	12-0
	v West Vale Ramblers F.A.Cup 1st Qual. Rd 1913-14
Defeat:	0-13
	v Stockport County Div.3 North 1933-34
Career Goalscorer:	Albert Valentine
Career Appearances:	John Pickering
Transfer Fee Paid:	£50,000
	to Hereford United for Ian Jurieff
Transfer Fee Received:	£250,000
	from Watford for Wayne Allison

SENIOR HONOURS

Promotion to Division 3 in 1968-69
Conference Champions1997-98

PREVIOUS

Leagues: Yorkshire Comb.1911-12, Midland League 1912-21, Football League-Division 3 North 1921-58, Division 3, 1958-63 69-76 98-02 Division 4 1963-69 76-93 Conference 94-98

Grounds: Sandhall Lane 1911-15 Exley 1919-2

KIDDERMINSTER HARRIERS

Club Colours: Red/white/red

Change Colours: Navy/white/navy

Club Sponsor: HIRE-IT

Previous League: Football League

BEST PERFORMANCES: League:10th in Div 3(out of four divisions)**F.A. Cup:** 5th Rd 1994

Football League Cup: 2nd Rd.   **F.A. Trophy:** Winners 1986-87

LAST SEASON:

Conference: 15th   **F.A.Cup:** 2nd Round   **F.A.Trophy:** 2nd Round

Founded: 1886

Nickname: Harriers

Back row (L-R): Jamie McClen, Luke Reynolds, Michael McGrath, Mark Creighton, Andy White, Dwane Lee, Jake Sedgemore, Simon Russell. **Middle:** Graham Devenport (Kit Man), Brian Smikle, Jonny Harkness, Steve Taylor, Scott Bevan, Gavin Hurren, Scott Eaton, Ian Foster (Physio). **Front:** Dean Sturridge, Jeff Kenna, Neil Howarth (Assistant Manager), Stuart Whitehead, Mark Yates (Manager), Russell Penn, Michael Blackwood.

CLUB PERSONNEL

Chairman:	Barry Norgrove	**President:**	Colin Youngjohns
Vice Chairman:	Neil Savery		
Directors: Wayne Allen, John Baldwin,Gordon Howard			
Company Secretary:	Richard Painter	**Clubhouse Manager**	
Club Secretary	Roger Barlow	Tel.No:	
Tel Nos:	01562 513954		
Mobile:	07973 237626		
CommercialManager:	Helen MacDonald	**Club Shop Manager**	Helen MacDonald
TelNo:	01562 513952	**Tel No:**	01562 823931
e.mail:	helen.macdonald@harriers.co.uk	**Football in the Community:**	Nick Griffiths
Press Officer:	MattWall	**Tel No:**	01562 863821
Tel No:	01562 513955		
e-mail:	mattwall@harriers.co.uk		

MANAGEMENT TEAM

Manager:	Mark Yates
Assistant Manager:	N/A
Reserves Manager:	N/A
Physio:	Jim Conway

KIDDERMINSTER HARRIERS

BEST LGE ATT.: 3,241 v Hereford United
LOWEST: **1,220** v Grays Athletic

No.	Date	Comp	H/A	Opponents	Att:	Result	Goalscorers	Pos
1	Aug 13	C	H	Woking	1926	W 2 - 1	Atieno 82 (pen) 90	6
2	16		A	Exeter City	4914	L 0 - 1		14
3	20		A	Scarborough	1401	D 1 - 1	Jackson 31	11
4	27		H	Southport	1753	D 1 - 1	Hatswell 85	15
5	29		A	Cambridge United	3161	W 2 - 0	Atieno 74 Sheldon 86	8
6	Sept 2		H	Canvey Island	1842	W 3 - 2	Fleming 42 **Christie** 90 Atieno 90 (pen)	5
7	10		A	Grays Athletic	1316	D 2 - 2	**Christie** 48 63	8
8	17		H	Forest Green Rovers	1818	L 1 - 3	**Christie** 73	10
9	20		H	Halifax Town	1566	L 0 - 1		11
10	24		A	Gravesend & Northfleet	1054	W 2 - 1	**Christie** 25 Hatswell 57	10
11	27		A	Crawley Town	1012	L 0 - 2		12
12	Oct 1		H	Tamworth	1961	L 0 - 1		13
13	8		H	Morecambe	1481	W 1 - 0	Sheldon 45	12
14	15		A	Aldershot Town	2315	L 0 - 1		12
15	18	LDV Vans T	H	**Darlington**	**696**	**W 2 - 1**	**Hatswell 45 (pen) Sheldon 83 (pen)**	
16	22	FAC 4Q	A	**Southport**	**1108**	**L 0 - 1**		
17	29	C	H	Hereford United	3241	D 1 - 1	Atieno 27	11
18	Nov 5		H	Exeter City	1869	L 1 - 2	Heslop 49	12
19	12		A	Stevenage Borough	2207	L 1 - 3	**Christie** 66	14
20	19		H	York City	1768	D 0 - 0		16
21	23	LDV Vans T 2	A	**Boston United**	**1131**	**W 3 - 0**	**Christie** 26 28 Blackwood 40	
22	26	C	A	Burton Albion	1847	L 0 - 1		16
23	Dec 3		H	Dagenham & Redbridge	1559	W 3 - 1	**Christie** 40 65 Pugh 45	
24	10		A	Accrington Stanley	1366	L 0 - 2		16
25	17	FAT 1	H	**Scarborough**	**957**	**W 4 - 0**	**Thompson 14 Blackwood 24 Christie 42 Heslop 72**	
26	20	LDV NQF	H	**Bradford PA**	**1276**	**W 2 - 1**	**Christie 16 Penn 60**	
27	26	C	H	Altrincham	2206	D 1 - 1	**Christie** (pen) 23	16
28	30		H	Burton Albion	1740	L 0 - 1		
29	Jan 2		A	Altrincham	1165	L 0 - 3		17
30	7		A	Woking	1514	W 1 - 0	Mullins 68	16
31	14	FAT 2	H	**Grays Athletic**	**1456**	**L 0 - 1**		
32	21	C	A	Scarborough	1740	W 2 - 1	Jackson 45 Mullins 49	16
33	24	LDV N S-F	A	**Carlisle United**	**4432**	**L 0 - 1**		
34	28		A	Southport	1076	W 4 - 1	Jackson 14 Harkness 24 **Christie** 33 Russell 57	15
35	Feb 4		A	Halifax Town	1544	D 0 - 0		13
36	11		H	Gravesend & Northfleet	1575	L 0 2 2		14
37	18		A	Tamworth	1278	D 1 - 1	White 47	15
38	21		H	Crawley Town	1302	W 1 - 0	Russell 24	13
39	Mar 4		A	Forest Green Rovers	1033	D 0 - 0		18
40	11		A	Morecambe	1662	L 0 - 2		15
41	18		H	Aldershot Town	1630	L 1 - 4	Reynolds 52	16
42	25		H	Hereford United	4223	W 1 - 0	Blackwood 72	15
43	28		A	Grays Athletic	1220	L 0 - 5		15
44	April 1		H	Stevenage Borough	1490	D 0 - 0		16
45	9		A	York City	3376	D 2 - 2	Fleming 72 77	16
46	14		H	Canvey Island	621	L 1 - 2	Reynolds 72	17
47	17		H	Cambridge United	1665	W 1 - 0	Peters 14 (og)	15
48	22		A	Dagenham & Redbridge	1038	L 0 - 3		16
49	29		H	Accrington Stanley	1934	W 2 - 0	Thompson 47 Reynolds 55	15

Ave. League Home Attendance: 1984 **Goals** 50 60 **Top Goalscorer:** Iysden Christie (14)
Best Position: 5th **Worst:** 18th

	DANBY 1	EVANS 2	JACKSON 4	BURGESS 6	HATSWELL 5	RUSSELL 15	O'CONNOR 7	FLEMING 8	BLACKWOOD 11	CHRISTIE 9	THOMPSON 10	SHELDON 14	ATIENO 18	LEWIS 13	BURTON 3	WILSON 12	GRAVES 17	HURREN 21	PENN 20	HESLOP 23	MULLINS 24	MCHALE 16	PUGH 26	BUTLER 25	FLYNN 2	HARKNESS 5	FRANCIS 18	SEDGEMORE 7	WHITE 9	HOWARTH 3	SMITH 16	OSBORNE 19	HANLEY 9	REYNOLDS 18	MCGRATH 4	REA 23	NEWBY 22	WALKER 25	BYRNE	
	X	X	X	X	X	X	X	X	X	X	S	S	U	U	U																									1
	X	X	X	X	X	X	X	X	X	X	S	U	U	S																									2
	X	X	X	X	X	X			X	X	X	U	S	X	S	S	U																						3
	X	X	X	X	X	X	X		X	U	X	S	U	U	X				S																				4
	X	X	X	X	X	X	X		X	S	S	X	U	U	S				X																				5
	X	X	X	X	X	X	S	X	S	U	X		U	S					X																				6
	X	X	X	X	S	X	X		X	U	X		U	S	S	X																							7
	X	X	X	X	U		X	S	X	S	X	X		U	X	X			S																				8
	X	X	X	X	S	X	X	S	X	X	U	X		U		X			S																				9
	X	X	X	X	X	X	X	U	S	S		S	X		U		X																						10
	X	X	X	X	X		X	X	S	S	S		U	X		U		X																					11
	X	U	X	X	S			S	X	X	X		X	X	U	U		X																					12
	X	X	X	X	X	X	X	X	X	U	X	S		U	S			S																					13
	X	X	X	X	X	X	X		X	S	X	S		U	S		U		X																				14
	U	X	X	X	X	X	X		X	U	X		X	U	S		U	X																					15
	U	X	X	X	X	X	X		X	S	X		X	U	S		S	X																					16
	U		X	X	X	X	X		S	X	X	X		U	U		U		X	X																			17
	U		X	X	X	X	X		S	S	X	X		S				X	X	U																			18
	U		X	X	X			X	X	U		X	X		X	U	U		X	X	U																		19
	U		X	X				X	X	U		X	X		U	U	U	X	X	X		X																	20
		X	X	X				X	X	S		X	X		S	S	U	X	X	X		X	U																21
	U	X	X	X			S	X	X	U		X	X		U	X	X	X	X		X																		22
	U		X		X	U	X	X		U	X		U	U	X	X	X		X	X	X	X																	23
	U	X	U	X		X	S		X		X	X		S		U	X	X	X	X	X	X																	24
	U	X	U	X			X	X	X	X	S	U	X			S	X	X	X		X																		25
	U	X	U	X			X	X	X	X	S	U	X			U	X	X	X		X																		26
	U	X	U	X			X	X	X	X	S	S	X			U	X	X	X		X																		27
		X	U	X			X	X	X	X	X	S	X		U		U	X	S	X		X																	28
	X		X	X	X	S		X	X	X	X	X				U	U	U	U	X		X																	29
	X	X	X	X	S		X	X	X	U	X		U				X	S	X		X		U																30
	X		X	X	S		X	X	X	S	X		U		X		X		X		X		U																31
	X	X	X		X		X	X	X	U	X		U				S		X		X		S		X	S													32
	X	X	X		X		X	X		X	U						X	U	X		S		X	S			S												33
	X	X	X		X		X	X	X	S		U			S	U		X	S	X		X	X																34
	X		X		X		X	X	U	S		U				X		X		X	X	X	X	S	S														35
	X		X		X		X	X	S	X		U			S	U		X		X	X	X	X	U															36
	X		X		X		X	X		X	U		S			X	U	X		X		U	X	X	S	X													37
	X		X		X		X		X	X	U		S		X		X		X		U	X	X	U	S	X													38
	X		X		X			S		X	X		U		S		X	X		X		X	S	X	X		U												39
	X		X		X		U	X		S	X		U		X		S	X		X		X	S			X		X	S										40
	X		X		X		X	X		S	X		U			U	X		X		X		X			X	S						X	X					41
	X		X		S		X	X		S	X		U				X		X		X		X			X	U							U	X	X			42
	X		X		X		X	X		S	X		U				X		X		X		X			X	U								U	X	X		43
	U		X		S		X	X		U	S		X				X	X		X		X			S		X						X		X	X			44
	U		U		X		X	X		S	S		X				X	X		X		X			X		X					X	U	X	X			45
	U				X			S		S	S		X				X	X		X		X			X		X	U				X	X	X	X	X	S		46
	U		X				X			X	X		X				X	X		X		X			X	S	X	S	U	U								47
	U	X		S			X	X		S	X		X				X	X		X		X			X				X	X	S	U						48
	U		X		X			X	X		X		X			U	X	X		X					X				X	S		S	S					49

Total Appearances (Conference)

	DANBY	EVANS	JACKSON	BURGESS	HATSWELL	RUSSELL	O'CONNOR	FLEMING	BLACKWOOD	CHRISTIE	THOMPSON	SHELDON	ATIENO	LEWIS	BURTON	WILSON	GRAVES	HURREN	PENN	HESLOP	MULLINS	MCHALE	PUGH	BUTLER	FLYNN	HARKNESS	FRANCIS	SEDGEMORE	WHITE	HOWARTH	SMITH	OSBORNE	HANLEY	REYNOLDS	MCGRATH	REA	NEWBY	WALKER	BYRNE	
	27	13	26	34	24	23	12	37	24	23	16	24	13	15	1	8	3	10	22	15	25	0	5	0	5	13	3	11	5	0	0	3	0	8	1	7	5	1	0	X
	0	0	0	0	0	8	0	1	6	1	15	10	9	0	3	14	2	3	0	7	0	0	1	0	0	1	3	0	0	1	3	0	1	0	3	0	2	1	2	S
	14	1	0	3	0	2	0	1	1	0	11	2	1	18	11	7	9	14	2	0	0	1	1	0	1	0	2	2	0	3	0	1	0	0	2	0	0	2	1	U

Cup Appearances

	DANBY	EVANS	JACKSON	BURGESS	HATSWELL	RUSSELL	O'CONNOR	FLEMING	BLACKWOOD	CHRISTIE	THOMPSON	SHELDON	ATIENO	LEWIS	BURTON	WILSON	GRAVES	HURREN	PENN	HESLOP	MULLINS	MCHALE	PUGH	BUTLER	FLYNN	HARKNESS	FRANCIS	SEDGEMORE	WHITE	HOWARTH	SMITH	OSBORNE	HANLEY	REYNOLDS	MCGRATH	REA	NEWBY	WALKER	BYRNE	
	22	7	4	6	3	2	6	5	7	2	4	1	5	0	0	1	0	5	5	5	0	2	0	2	1	0	0	0	0	0	0	0	0	0	0	0	0	0	0	X
	0	0	0	0	0	1	0	0	0	0	3	2	0	0	0	3	1	2	0	0	0	0	1	0	0	0	1	0	0	1	0	0	1	0	0	0	0	0	0	S
	4	0	0	2	0	0	0	0	0	0	1	0	2	2	2	1	0	3	0	1	0	0	0	1	1	0	0	0	0	0	0	0	0	0	0	0	0	0	0	U

CURRANT SQUAD AS OF BEGINING OF 2006-07 SEASON

GOALKEEPERS	SQ NO.	HT	WT	D.O.B	AGE	P.O.B	CAREER	APPS	GOA
Scott Bevan	1	6'06"	15 03	16/9/79	26	Southampton	Southampton, Stoke (L) 2/02, Woking (L) 3/02, Huddersfield (SL) 7/02, Woking (L) 11/03, Wycombe (L) 1/04, Wimbledon/MK Dons Free 3/04, Tamworth (3ML) 10/05 (Perm) 1/06, Kidderminster 6/06		
Steve Taylor	13			17/12/85	20		AFC Telford, Kidderminster 5/06		

DEFENDERS

DEFENDERS	SQ NO.	HT	WT	D.O.B	AGE	P.O.B	CAREER	APPS	GOA
Jeff Kenna	2	5'11"	12 02	27/8/70	36	Dublin	Southampton, Blackburn £1.5 mill 3/95, Tranmere (SL) 3/01, Wigan (L) 11/01, Birmingham (2ML) 12/01 Perm 2/02, Derby 3/04 Rel 5/06, Kidderminster 8/06		
Jonny Harkness	3	6'00"	12 09	18/11/85	20	Belfast	Linfield (Jun), Coventry (Jun), Walsall Rel 1/06, Cambridge U (L) 8/05, Halesowen T (L) 10/05, Kidderminster 1/06	14	1
Gavin Hurren	4	5'08"	13 07	22/10/85	20	Birmingham	N.Forest Rel c/s 05, Kidderminster 7/05, Bromsgrove (L) 1/06	13	0
Mark Creighton	5					Birmingham	Kidderminster (Yth), Moor Green, Paget R, Halesowen T, Redditch, Bromsgrove, Willenhall 1/02, Redditch 8/05, Kidderminster 6/06		
Stuart Whitehead	6	6'00"	12 02	17/7/76	30	Bromsgrove	Bromsgrove, Bolton 9/95 Rel c/s 98, Carlisle 7/98, Darlington 10/02, Telford 6/03, Shrewsbury 6/04, Kidderminster 5/06		
Neil Howarth	20	6'03"	13 07	15/11/71	34	Bolton	Burnley, Macclesfield (L) 9/93, Macclesfield (SL) 2/94), Macclesfield c/s 94, Cheltenham £7,000 £7,500 2/99 Rel c/s 03, Telford 6/03, AFC Telford 5/04, Kidderminster 1/06	1	0
Gavin Cowan	21	6'04"	14 04	24/5/81	25	Hanover(Ger)	Exeter (Trainee), Braintree 7/99, Canvey Island 12/02, Nuneaton (L) 12/04, Nuneaton (L) 2/05, Shrewsbury £5,000 + 3/05, Kidderminster (L) 8/06		
Ashley Walker							Kidderminster	2	0

MIDFIELDERS

MIDFIELDERS	SQ NO.	HT	WT	D.O.B	AGE	P.O.B	CAREER	APPS	GOA
Jake Sedgemore	7	6'01"	12 10	20/10/78	27	Wolverhampton	WBA (Jun), Hednesford 12/97, Hereford 8/01, Northwich 9/01, Shrewsbury 7/03 Rel c/s 05, Bury 7/05 Rel 1/06, Burton (2ML) 11/05, Kidderminster 1/06	11	0
Jamie McClen	10	5'08"	10 12	13/5/79	27	Newcastle	Newcastle Rel c/s 05, Motherwell (3ML) 10/00, Carlisle 8/05 Rel 12/05, Blyth Sp 1/06, Stockport (Trial) 2/06, Shrewsbury 2/06 Rel 4/06, Kidderminster 6/06		
Simon Russell	15	5'07"	10 06	19/3/85	21	Hull	Hull C, Kidderminster 7/04	31	2
Russell Penn	16	5'11"	11 05	8/11/85	20	Wordsley	Scunthorpe, Kidderminster 7/05, Alvechurch (L) 10/05	22	0
Michael McGrath	17						Kidderminster, Bromsgrove (L), Redditch (7ML) 8/05	4	0
Brian Smikle	18			3/11/85	20		WBA Rel 6/06, Hereford (SL) 2/05, Halifax (SL) 2/06, Kidderminster 7/06		
Dwane Lee	23	6'03"	13 09	26/11/79	26	Hillingdon	Yeading, Exeter 7/03, Stoke (Trial) 7/04, Barnet 8/04 Rel 4/06, Kidderminster 8/06		
Mark Yates		5'11"	13 02	24/1/70	36	Birmingham	Burnley (Ass Man), Kidderminster (Man) 1/06		

FORWARDS

FORWARDS	SQ NO.	HT	WT	D.O.B	AGE	P.O.B	CAREER	APPS	GOA
Dean Sturridge	8	5'08"	12 02	27/7/73	33	Birmingham	Derby, Torquay (2ML) 12/94, Leicester £350,000 1/01, Wolves (L) 11/01 £350,000 12/01, Sheff Utd (L) 1/04, QPR 3/05, Kingstonian 6/06		
Andy White	9	6'04"	14 03	6/11/81	24	Derby	Hucknall, Mansfield 7/00, Crewe (L) 10/02, Boston U (L) 9/03, Kidderminster (L) 10/03, Burton (L) 2/04, Crewe Free c/s 04 Rel c/s 05, N.County 8/05 Rel 5/06, Kidderminster (L) 1/06, Kidderminster 5/06	5	1
Michael Blackwood	11	5'10"	11 04	30/9/79	26	Birmingham	Aston Villa Rel c/s 00, Chester (2ML) 9/99, Wrexham 6/00 Rel c/s 02, Worcester 8/02, Stevenage Free 9/02, Halesowen 3/03, Telford 8/03, Lincoln C Free 7/04 Rel c/s 05, Kidderminster 7/05	30	1
Luke Reynolds	14			5/6/79	26	Birmingham	Tividale, Willenhall 2/01, Market Drayton, AFC Telford 9/05 Rel 2/06, Market Drayton 2/06, Kidderminster (NC) 3/06 (Perm) 5/06	8	4
Scott Eaton	19			28/10/87	18		Kidderminster		
Mitch Butler				5/3/88	18		Kidderminster	0	0
Tom Byrne				17/5/88	18		Kidderminster	2	0

PLAYING SQUAD

LOANEES	HT	WT	DOB	AGE	POB	FROM - TO	APPS	GOA
(F)Taiwo Atieno	6'02"	12 13	6/8/85	20	Brixton	Walsall (5M) 8/05 - Darlington (L) 3/06, Rel 5/06, Dag & Red 8/06	22	5
(M)Simon Heslop	5'11"	11 00	1/5/87	19	York	Barnsley (5M) 8/05 -	22	1
(D)Johnny Mullins	5'11"	12 07	6/11/85	20	Hampstead	Reading (SL) 10/05 - Mansfield 5/06	25	2
(M)Marc Pugh	5'11"	11 05	2/4/87	19	Bacup	Burnley 11/05 + 1/06 - Bury 3/06	6	1
(F)Francino Francis			18/1/87	19	Jamaica	Watford (2M) 1/06 - Wealdstone (SL) 3/06	6	0
(D)Junior Osborne	5'10"	10 12	12/2/88	18	Watford	Watford 2/06 - Redditch 7/06	3	0
(F)Cayne Hanley	5'10"				Manchester	Burnley 3/06 - Hyde (L) 3/06	1	0
(D)Simon Rea	6'01"	13 00	20/9/76	29	Coventry	Nuneaton 3/06 - Rel 5/06, Redditch 7/06	7	0
(F)Jon Newby	6'00"	12 00	28/11/78	27	Warrington	Bury 3/06 - Rel 5/06, Wrexham 8/06	7	0

DEPARTURES	HT	WT	DOB	AGE	POB	FROM - TO	APPS	GOA
(D)Wayne Evans	5'10"	12 03	25/8/71	34	Welshpool	Rochdale 7/05 - Retired 11/05	13	0
(D)Steve Burton	6'01"	11 05	10/10/82	23	Hull	Hull C 3/04 - Rel 11/05, Australia	4	0
(D)Wayne Hatswell	6'00"	13 03	8/2/75	31	Swindon	Chester £15,000 10/03 - Rushden & D 1/06	24	2
(M)Chris McHale	6'00"	12 00	4/11/84	21	Birmingham	Youth - Stourport S (L) 11/05 Rel 1/06, Bromsgrove 1/06	0	0
(D)Jermain Hollis	5'10"	11 00	7/10/86	19	Nottingham	Eastwood T 11/04 - Alvechurch (L) 10/05, Rel 1/06, Hucknall 2/06		
(D)Daniel Ludlow			4/6/88	18		Youth - Stourport S (L) 11/05, Worcester 1/06		
(D)Mark Jackson	6'00"	12 10	30/9/77	28	Barnsley	Scunthorpe 2/05 - Rochdale 1/06	26	3
(F)Iyseden Christie	5'10"	12 02	14/11/76	29	Coventry	Mansfield 8/04 - Rochdale 1/06	24	10
(D) Patrick Flynn	5'11"	11 04	13/1/85	21	Dublin	Torquay 11/05 - Rel 2/06, Waterford Utd (Ire)	5	0
(M)Martin O'Connor	5'08"	10 08	10/12/67	38	Walsall	Shrewsbury - Caretaker Manager 12/05-1/06, Rel 2/06, Hednesford 3/06	12	0
(M)Laurie Wilson	5'10"	11 03	5/12/84	21	Brighton	Burton 7/05 - Rel 3/06, Hucknall 3/06	22	0
(M)Paul Smith	6'00"	13 03	22/7/76	30	Leeds	Sheff Wed Rel c/s 05, Kendal T 12/05, Alfreton 1/06, Kidderminster 1/06 - Rel 4/06	3	0
(G)John Danby	6'02"	14 07	20/9/83	22	Stoke On Trent	Yth 12/01 - Rel 5/06, Chester 5/06	27	0
(G)Daniel Lewis	6'01"	14 00	18/6/82	24	Redditch	Studley 7/04 - Rel 5/06, Moor Green 6/06	15	0
(D)Daryl Burgess	5'11"	11 04	24/1/71	35	Birmingham	Rochdale 7/05 - Rel 5/06, Nuneaton 7/06	34	0
(M)Terry Fleming	5'09"	10 01	5/1/73	36	Marston Green	Grimsby 7/05 - Rel 5/06, Moor Green 8/06	38	2
(M)Lee Thompson	5'07"	10 10	25/3/83	23	Sheffield	Boston U 7/05 - Rel 5/06, Worksop 8/06	31	1
(M)Wayne Graves	5'08"	10 07	18/9/80	25	Scunthorpe	Scunthorpe 8/05 - Rel 5/06	5	0
(F)Gareth Sheldon	5'11"	11 10	21/1/80	26	Birmingham	Exeter Undisc 7/05 - Rel 5/06, Hereford 6/06	34	2
Danny Mason						Yth - Stourport 7/06		

Kidderminster Harriers

Ground Address:	Aggborough Stadium, Hoo Road, Kidderminster DY10 1NB
Telephone:	01562 823931
Fax:	01562 827329
General email address:	info@harriers.co.uk
Official website:	www.harriers.co.uk
Office Opening Hours:	9.00a.m. -5.00pm(Mon-Fri) Sat Matchdays 11am -5pm
SIMPLE DIRECTIONS:	
By Road:	There are signs for the ground on all the main approach roads into Kidderminster

MATCH TICKETS:	Adults £16	Concessions available. (£11)
Ticket office Telephone:	01562 823931	

Midweek Home Matchday:	Tuesday

Capacity:	6,419
Seats:	3,175
Covered:	3,062
Social facilities	Harriers Arms (Pub lic House
For Home supporters:	Aggborough Suite (Hospitality)
For Away Supporters:	As home subject to availability plus Supporters Club.
Refreshments at the ground:	Hot and Cold fod in all areas
Club Shop:	Souvenirs & leisurewear
	(01562 63341)
Local Press:	Kidderminster Shuttle
Local Radio:	BBC Hereford & Worcester

MATCHDAY PROGRAMME
Pages:52   Price: £2.50
Editor:Matt Wall
01562 513955(W)
07725 536272 (M)

CLUB STATISTICS

RECORDS

Attendance:	9,155
	Hereford United 27 Nov. 1948
Victory:	25-0
	v Hereford (H) Birmingham Senior Cup 12.10.1889
Defeat:	0-13 v Darwen (A) F.A.Cup1st 24.01.1891
Career Goalscorer:	Peter Wassell 432 1963-1974
Career Appearances:	Brendan Wassall 686 1962-1974
Transfer Fee Paid:	£80,000 to Nuneaton B
	for Andy Ducross July 2000
Transfer Fee Received:	£380,000 from W.B.A.
	for Lee Hughes July 1997

SENIOR HONOURS

Conference Champions 1993-94 1999-2000
Runners-Up 1996-97
F.A.Trophy Winners 1986-87
Runners-Up 1990-91 1994-95
Welsh F.A. Cup Runners-Up 1985-86 1988-89
Birmingham Senior Cup (7) Staffs Sen Cup (5)

PREVIOUS

Leagues: **Birmingham**1889-90,1891-1939, 47-48, 60-62
Midland 1890-1891 Southern 39-45 48-60 72-83
Birmingham Combination 45-47 and West Midlands.62-72

MORECAMBE

Club Colours: Red/white/black

Change Colours: All Blue

Club Sponsor: Wright & Lord and Umbro

Previous League: Northern Premier League

LAST SEASON

League: 5th Conference :   **F.A. Cup:** 1st Rd proper   **F.A. Trophy:** 2nd Round.

BEST PERFORMANCES

League: Conference: 3rd 99-00 **F.A. Cup:** 3rd Rd 61-62 00-01 **F.A. Trophy:** Winners 73-74

Founded: 1920

Nickname: The Shrimps

CLUB PERSONNEL

Chairman:	Peter McGuigan
Vice Chairman:	Graham Hodgson
Directors	Peter Cross, Mark Mace & David Robinson
Club Secretary	Neil Marsdin

6 Palmer Grove, Bare Village, Morecambe LA46BQ
Tel Nos: 01524 833358(H) 07325 370842(W)
Fax: 01524 831367 **e-mail:** neil@morecambefc.com

CommercialManager: Peter Howard
commercil officeopen Monday-Friday
TelNo: 01524 411794 **e.mail:**office@morecambefc.com

Press Officer: Derek Quinn
Tel Nos: 01524 411797 (W) 07944480796 (M)

Website: http://www.morecambefc.com

Club Shop: On ground and open on matchdays.

MANAGEMENT TEAM

Manager:	Sammy McIlroy
Assistant Manager:	Andy Mutch
Reserves Manager:	Jeff Udall
Res. Asst. Man:	Tony Gibbons
Sports Therapist:	David Edge

MORECAMBE

No.	Date	Comp	H/A	Opponents	Att:	Result	Goalscorers	Pos
1	Aug 13	C	H	Halifax Town	2150	W 1 - 0	Curtis 21	9
2	16		A	Scarborough	1759	W 1 - 0	**Carlton** 81	3
3	20		A	Exeter City	3978	L 0 - 2		5
4	27		H	Crawley Town	1473	W 3 - 0	Twiss 54 Thompson 65 76	2
5	29		A	Altrincham	1447	L 0 - 2		6
6	Sept 3		H	Tamworth	1413	D 0 - 0		8
7	10		H	Aldershot Town	1.429	W 5 - 2	Curtis 28 O'Connor 45 Twiss 48 84 **Carlton** 80	5
8	17		A	Hereford United	2422	L 0 - 1		8
9	20		A	Burton Albion	1352	W 4 - 0	**Carlton** 14 Curtis 40 O'Connor 60 Twiss 75	7
10	24		H	Stevenage Borough	1738	W 4 - 1	Twiss 12 Hunter 25 Thompson 40 Curtis 90	4
11	27		H	Accrington Stanley	2162	W 3 - 2	Twiss 33 51 **Carlton** 73	2
12	Oct 1		A	Forest Green Rovers	802	L 0 - 1		4
13	8		A	Kiddermoinster Harriers	1461	L 0 - 1		5
14	15		H	Dagenham & Redbridge	1718	W 2 - 0	Moore 6 (og) Curtis 74	5
15	18	LDV Vans T1	A	**Grimsby Town**	1131	D 1 - 1*	**Lloyd** 45	
16	22	FAC 4Q	A	**Bromsgrove Rovers**	919	W 2 - 0	O'Connor 7 Walmsley 60	
17	29	C	A	Canvey Island	480	D 3 - 3	Bentley 58 Twiss 73 81	6
18	Nov 5	FAC 1R	H	**Northwich Victoria**	2166	L 1 - 3	**Carlton** 84	
19	12	C	H	Cambridge United	1648	L 0 - 1		7
20	19		A	Woking	2069	W 1 - 0	**Carlton** 18	7
21	22	LDV Vans T2	H	**Bradford City**	1649	L 0 - 1		
22	26	C	H	York City	1778	W 2 - 0	Thompson 29 O'Connor 81	4
23	Dec 3		A	Gravesend & Northfleet	1172	L 0 - 1		4
24	10		H	Grays Athletic	1785	W 3 - 0	Thompson 21 **Carlton** 37 Bentley 57	4
25	17	FAT 1	A	**Vauxhall Motors**	322	W 4 - 0	**Bentley** 15 Twiss 16 51 Curtis 49	
26	24	C	A	Southport	1807	W 3 - 0	**Carlton** 32 Thompson 59 Roberts (og) 88	4
27	31		A	York City	2712	D 1 - 1	Curtis 54	3
28	Jan 2		H	Southport	2788	D 0 - 0		4
29	9		A	Halifax Town	1962	D 0 - 0		3
30	14	FAT 2	A	**Stafford Rangers**	1121	L 0 - 1		
31	21	C	H	Exeter City	2073	D 2 - 2	Barlow 67 Brannan74	
32	24		H	Svarborough	1478	L 0 - 3		7
33	28		A	Crawley Town	1253	W 3 - 0	Barlow 48 55 Perkins 77	5
34	Feb 4		H	Burton Albion	1855	W 3 - 1	Blackburn 39 Barlow 87 Thompson 90	2
35	11		A	Stevenage Borough	2068	L 0 - 1		5
36	18		H	Forest Green Rovers	1486	W 3 - 2	Kelly 29 Barlow 45 Curtis 70	2
37	20		A	Accrington Town	3008	L 0 - 2		2
38	25		A	Aldershot Town	1868	L 0 - 2		5
39	Mar 11		H	Kidderminster Harriers	1662	W 2 - 0	Twiss 30 Curtis 86	5
40	18		A	Dagenham & Redbridge	960	L 1 - 3	Thompson 48	6
41	25		H	Canvey Island	1471	W 1 - 0	**Carlton** 43	6
42	April 1		A	Cambridge United	2129	D 2 - 2	**Carlton** 22 53	7
43	4		H	Hereford United	1699	D 2 - 2	Teiss 3 **Carlton** 51	7
44	8		H	Woking	1468	W 3 - 1	Curtis 32 **Carlton** 37 Hunter 45	6
45	15		A	Tamworth	1178	W 3 - 0	Curtis 1 Thompson 11 **Carlton** 76	5
46	17		H	Altrincham	2118	W 2 - 0	Bentley 44 **Carlton** 63	5
47	22		A	Gravesned & Northfleet	1991	W 3 - 0	Curtis 14 **Carlton** 38 46	5
48	29		A	Grays Athletic	1950	W 2 - 1	**Carlton** 32 Bentley 53	5
49	May 6	Play Off SF1	H	**Hereford United**	5208	D 1 - 1	**Bentley** 22	
50	11	Play Off SF2	A	**Hereford United**	6278	L 2 - 3*	**Curtis** 8 (pen) Twiss 53	
Ave. League Home Attendance:				1894	**Goals**	79 46	**Top Goalscorer:** Danny Carlton (18)	
Best Position: 2nd		**Worst:**	9th					

	ROBINSON	HEARD	BENTLEY	KEMPSON	BLACKBURN	HOWARD	THOMPSON	PERKINS	HUNTER	CURTIS	TWISS	CARLTON	O'CONNOR	KELLY	RUFFER	DAVIES	WALMSLEY	STRINGFELLOW	DODGSON	LLOYD	GRAY	SMITH	HARDIKER	BRANNAN	DRENCH	BARLOW	RIGOGLIOSO	MCLACHLAN	
	1	19	5	12	14	4	11	3	17	9	7	15	10	6	2	13	23	8	16	18	21	20	24	25	30	19	10	28	
	X	X	X	X	X	X	X	X	X	X	X	S	S	U	U														1
	X	X	X	X	X	X	X	X	X	X	X	S		S	U	U													2
	X	X	X	X	X	X	X	X	X	X	X	S			U	U	S	S											3
	X	S	X	X	X	X	X	X	X	X	X	U			U	X	S	S											4
	X	S	X	X	X	X	X	X	X	X	X	S			U	U	X	S											5
	X	X	X	X	X	U	X	X	X	X	X	S	S	X		U	U												6
	X		X	X	X	X	X	X	X	X	X	S	X	U		U	S	U											7
	X		X	X	X	X	X	X	X	X	X	S	X	U		U	S	U											8
	X		X	X		X	X	X	X	X	X	S	X	S	U	X		S	U										9
	X		X	X	S		X	X	X	X	X	S	X	S	U	X		U											10
	X		X	X	S		X	X	X	X	X	S	X	U	U	X		U											11
	X		X	X	X		X	X	X	X	X	S	X		U	S	U		U										12
	X		X	X	S	U	X	X	X	X	X	S	X		U	X	S												13
	X		X	X	X			X	S	X	X	S	X	X		U	X	S	U										14
	X		**X**	**X**	**X**		**S**	**X**		**U**	**S**	**X**			**U**		**X**	**X**	**X**	**S**	**X**								15
	X		**X**	**X**	**X**		**X**	**U**	**X**	**X**	**S**	**X**			**U**	**X**	**S**		**S**										16
	X		X	X	X	X	S	X		X	X	S	X	X		U	X	U			S								17
	X		**X**	**X**	**X**	**X**	**S**	**X**		**X**	**X**	**S**	**X**	**X**		**U**	**X**	**S**	**U**										18
	X		X	X		X	X	X		X	X	X	S	U		U	U		U			X	X						19
	X		X	X		X	X	X		X	X	X	S	U		U	S		U			X	X						20
	X		**X**	**X**		**X**	**X**	**X**		**X**	**X**	**X**		**U**		**S**	**X**	**U**	**S**	**U**			**X**						21
			X	X		X	X	X		X	X	X	S	S		U	U		U			X	X	X					22
			X	X	X	X	X	X		X	X	X				S		U	S	U		X	X						23
			X		X	X	X	X		X	X	X				S	U	U	U			S	X	X					24
			X	**U**	**X**	**X**	**X**	**X**		**X**	**X**	**X**				**U**		**U**	**U**			**S**	**X**	**X**	**X**				25
			X	X		X	X	X		X	X	X				U		U	U	U		U	X	X	X				26
			X	U	X	X	X	X		X	X	X				S		U	U			U	X	X	X				27
			X	U	X	X	X			X	X	X				X		U	U	U	S		X	X	X				28
			X	U	X	X	X			X	X	X				U		U	U			U	X	X	X				29
			X	**X**	**X**	**X**	**X**			**X**	**X**	**X**				**U**		**U**	**U**			**S**	**U**	**X**	**X**				30
			X	X		X	X	X		S	X	X				X		U	S		U	S		X	X	X			31
			X	X		X	X	X		S	X	X				X		U	S	U		S	X	X					32
			X	X		X			X	X	X					X		U	U	U		X	U	X	X				33
			X	X		X	X			X	X	S				X		U	U			U	X	S	X	X			34
			X	X		X	X				X	S				X		U	U			U	U	X	X	X	X		35
			X	X		X	X			X	S	X				X		U	S			U	X	S	X	X			36
			X	X		X	X			X	S	S				X		U	U			U	X	X	X	X			37
	X		X	X	X	X	X			X	X	S				X				U	U		U	S	X				38
			X	X	X	X	X		S	S	X	X				U			U			X	X	X	X	S			39
	U		X	S	X	X	X			X	X	X			U							X	X	X	S	S			40
	U		X		X	X	X	X	X	S	X	X			U				U			X	X	X	X			S	41
	U		X	S	X	X		X		U	X	X							U			X	X	X	S	X			42
	U			X	X	X	X			X	X	X			U				S			X	X	S	U	X			43
	U		X	U	X	X		X		X	X	X							U			X	X	U	S	X			44
	U		X	U	X	X		X		X	X	X							S			X	X	S	S	X			45
	U		X	U	X	X	X	S	X	X	X	X										X	X	S	S	X			46
	U		X	U	X	X	S	X	X	X	X	X										X	X	S	S	X			47
	U		X	U	X	X	U	X	X	X	X	X										X	X	S	U	X			48
	U		**X**	**S**	**X**	**X**	**X**	**S**	**X**	**X**	**X**	**X**											**X**	**X**	**U**	**S**	**X**		49
	U		**X**	**S**	**X**	**X**	**X**	**S**	**X**	**X**	**X**	**X**											**X**	**X**	**U**	**S**	**X**		50

Total Appearances (Conference)

	ROBINSON	HEARD	BENTLEY	KEMPSON	BLACKBURN	HOWARD	THOMPSON	PERKINS	HUNTER	CURTIS	TWISS	CARLTON	O'CONNOR	KELLY	RUFFER	DAVIES	WALMSLEY	STRINGFELLOW	DODGSON	LLOYD	GRAY	SMITH	HARDIKER	BRANNAN	DRENCH	BARLOW	RIGOGLIOSO	MCLACHLAN	
	18	4	40	30	35	28	39	34	21	37	40	27	4	16	0	0	10	0	0	0	0	0	15	23	24	10	0	7	X
	0	2	0	2	3	0	1	2	2	3	2	13	10	7	3	0	7	6	4	5	0	0	2	2	1	6	7	1	S
	9	0	0	8	0	2	0	1	0	1	0	1	0	9	4	31	13	4	10	13	7	0	0	2	0	1	2	0	U

Cup Appearances

	ROBINSON	HEARD	BENTLEY	KEMPSON	BLACKBURN	HOWARD	THOMPSON	PERKINS	HUNTER	CURTIS	TWISS	CARLTON	O'CONNOR	KELLY	RUFFER	DAVIES	WALMSLEY	STRINGFELLOW	DODGSON	LLOYD	GRAY	SMITH	HARDIKER	BRANNAN	DRENCH	BARLOW	RIGOGLIOSO	MCLACHLAN	
	4	0	8	5	7	8	5	5	3	7	7	5	3	2	0	0	3	1	1	1	0	1	1	5	4	0	0	2	X
	0	0	0	2	0	0	1	3	0	0	0	3	0	0	0	1	0	2	1	3	1	0	0	0	0	0	2	0	S
	2	0	0	1	0	0	0	0	1	0	1	0	0	3	0	5	2	1	0	2	0	0	1	0	0	2	0	0	U

MORECAMBE

CURRANT SQUAD AS OF BEGINING OF 2006-07 SEASON

GOALKEEPERS	SQ NO.	HT	WT	D.O.B	AGE	P.O.B	CAREER	APPS	GOA
Steven Drench	1	6'01"	12 09	11/9/85	20	Salford	Blackburn Rel 5/06, Morecambe (SL) 11/05, Morecambe c/s 06	25	0
Ryan Robinson	13	6'02"	13 02	13/10/82	23	Tebay	Blackburn, Wigan (Trial) 9/02, Southend 7/03 Rel c/s 04,		
							Wivenhoe (L) 10/03, Morecambe 9/04, Southport (L) 8/06	18	0
Scott Davies	30			27/2/87	19	Blackpool	Morecambe, Leek T (L) 3/06, Leek T (L) 8/06	0	0

DEFENDERS									
Adam Yates	2	5'10"	10 07	28/5/83	23	Stoke	Crewe Rel c/s 04, Halifax (SL) 11/03, Leek T 8/04,		
							Port Vale (Trial) 1/05, Morecambe 8/06		
David Perkins	3			21/6/82	24	Heysham	Morecambe	36	1
Mike Howard	4	5'09"	11 13	2/12/78	27	Birkenhead	Liverpool (Sch), Tranmere, Swansea 2/98 Rel c/s 04, Morecambe 7/04	28	0
Jim Bentley	5	6'01"	13 00	11/6/76	30	Liverpool	Manchester C Rel c/s 97, Telford 9/97, Morecambe 5/02	40	3
Danny Meadowcroft	14	6'04"	12 05	22/5/85	21	Macclesfield	Stockport, Mossley (L) 10/04 Perm 11/04, Morecambe 7/04		
Scott McNiven	19	5'10"	10 08	27/5/78	28	Leeds	Oldham Rel c/s 02, Oxford U 7/02, Mansfield 7/04 Rel c/s 05,		
							Chester Rel 5/06, Morecambe 8/06		
Shaun Gray	21			28/1/87	19	Ormskirk	Morecambe, Fleetwood (L) 1/06	0	0
Jamie Davies	22			11/8/87	19	Preston	Morecambe, Leek T (4ML) 1/06		
Kieran Walmsley	23			11/12/83	22	Preston	Morecambe, Kendal (L) 8/06	17	0
Andy Langford	29			3/7/88	18	Manchester	Morecambe		

MIDFIELDERS									
Craig Stanley	6	5'08"	10 08	3/3/83	23	Bedworth	Walsall, Telford 2/04, Hereford 6/04, Morecambe 6/06		
Garry Hunter	8			1/1/85	21	Morecambe	Morecambe	23	2
Adriano Rigoglioso	10	6'01"	12 07	28/5/79	27	Liverpool	Liverpool (Trainee), Marine 7/98, Morecambe 7/00,		
							Doncaster £30,000 11/03 Rel 2/06, Southport (L) 11/05,		
							Chester (Trial) 1/06, Morecambe 3/06	7	0
Gary Thompson	11			24/11/80	25	Kendal	Morecambe	40	9
Ged Brannan	12	6'00"	12 05	15/1/72	34	Liverpool	Tranmere, Man City £750,000 3/97, Norwich (2ML) 8/98,		
							Motherwell £378,000 10/98, Wigan £195,000 2/01,		
							Dunfermline (3ML) 1/03, Rochdale (2ML) 9/03, Accrington 11/03,		
							Radcliffe B 9/05, Morecambe 11/05	25	1
Chris Blackburn	17	5'07"	10 06	2/8/82	24	Crewe	Chester Rel c/s 03, Northwich 8/03, Morecambe 2/04	38	1
Paul Lloyd	18			26/3/87	19	Preston	Morecambe, Burscough (2ML) 3/06	5	0
Jonathan Smith	20			17/10/86	19	Preston	Morecambe, Fleetwood (3ML) 1/06	0	0
Fraser McLachlan	24	5'11"	12 07	9/11/82	23	Manchester	Stockport, Northwich (L) 8/04, Mansfield (2ML) 11/04 Undisc 1/05 Rel 5/06,		
							Morecambe (SL) 3/06, Morecambe 7/06	8	0
Michael West	27			1/2/88	18	Burnley	Morecambe		
Thomas Pickersgill	28			31/1/88	18	Bolton	Morecambe		

FORWARDS									
Michael Twiss	7	5'11"	13 03	28/12/77	28	Salford	Man Utd Rel c/s 00, Sheff Utd (SL) 8/98, Norwich (Trial) 2/00,		
							Preston (Trial) 3/00, Tranmere (Trial) 3/00, Port Vale 7/00 Rel c/s 01,		
							Chesterfield (Trial) 7/01, Leigh RMI 8/01, Chester 5/02, Morecambe 5/04	42	11
Wayne Curtis	9			6/3/80	26	Barrow	Holker O.B, Morecambe 3/98, Barrow (L) 11/03	40	11
Danny Carlton	15			22/12/83	22	Leeds	Morecambe	40	17
David McNiven	16	5'10"	12 00	27/5/78	28	Leeds	Oldham Rel c/s 00, Linfield (L) 3/97, Scarborough (L) 2/00,		
							Southport (L) 3/00, York 8/00 Rel c/s 01, Chester 7/01, Hamilton 10/01,		
							Northwich 7/02, Kidsgrove (L) 11/02, Leigh RMI 8/03, Q.O.South 7/04,		
							Scarborough 1/06, Morecambe 6/06		

STEP 1 CONFERENCE

STEP 2 - P177
CONFERENCE Nth & Sth

STEP 3 - P269
NPL - SOUTHERN - ISTHMIAN PREM

STEP 4 - P269
NPL - SOUTHERN - ISTHMIAN

STEP 5/6 - P473

STEP 7 - P713

PLAYING SQUAD

LOANEES	HT	WT	DOB	AGE	POB	FROM - TO	APPS	GOA
None								

DEPARTURES	HT	WT	DOB	AGE	POB	FROM - TO	APPS	GOA
(D)Jamie Heard	5'11"	11 00	11/8/83	23	Sheffield	North Ferriby 9/04 - Rel 10/05, Harrogate T 10/05 Rel 5/06, Australia	6	0
(D)Carl Ruffer	6'01"	12 03	20/12/74	31	Chester	Chester 5/04 - Rel 11/05, Droylsden 12/05	3	0
(F)Sean O'Connor	6'03"		7/7/81	25	Wolverhampton	Queen of the South 5/04 - Rel 1/06, Queen of the South 3/06	14	3
(M)James Kelly	5'07"	11 09	14/2/73	33	Liverpool	Scarborough 5/04 - Rel 5/06, Lancaster 7/06	23	2
(M)Michael Stringfellow			9/10/81	24	Lancaster	Yth - Leek T (2ML) 1/06, Lancaster (L) 2/06, Rel 5/06, Barrow 6/06	6	0
(M)Lee Dodgson			24/3/84	22	Lancaster	Yth - Leek T (2ML) 1/06, Fleetwood 7/06	4	0
(D)Darran Kempson	6'02"	12 13	6/12/84	21	Blackpool	Preston (L) 12/04 (Perm) 3/05 - Crewe 7/06	32	0
(D)John Hardiker	6'00"	11 01	7/7/82	24	Preston	Bury (3ML) 10/05 (Perm) 1/06 - Fleetwood 7/06	17	0
(F)Stuart Barlow	5'10"	11 01	16/7/68	38	Liverpool	Bury 1/06 - Rel 6/06, Southport 8/06	16	5
Callum Routledge						Yth - Padiham 8/06		

MORECAMBE

Ground Address: Christie Park'Lancaster Road,Morecambe, Lancashire LA4 5TJ
Telephone: 01524 411797
Fax: 01524 411797
General email address: neil@morecambefc.com
Official website: http//www.morecambefc.com
Office Opening Hours: Monday -Friday: 9.00am-5.00pm.
Saturday Matchdays: 9.30am-until end of match

SIMPLE DIRECTIONS:
By Road:
From South leave M6 motorway at junction 34. Follow signs for Morecambe through Lancastter, on A589, go straight across the first two roundaboutsand at the third (with the Shrimp pub on your left) follow the signs for Town Centre- Christie Park is about 600 yards on the left.

MATCH TICKETS: ?   Concessions available.
Ticket office Telephone: 01524 832230

Midweek Home Matchday: Tuesday 7.45 pm

Capacity: 6,300   **Seats:** 1,200   **Covered:** 4,300

Clubhouse: JB's open normal licensing hours

Clubcall: 09066 555966

Club Shop: On ground and open on matchdays

Club Publication: 'Gazetta de la Shrimpa'

Local Press: Morecambe Visitor,Morecambe Guardian,Lancashire Evening Post and The Citizen

Local Radio: Radio Lancashire. red Rose Radio and Bay Radio

MATCHDAY PROGRAMME
Pages: 48   **Price:** £2.00
Editor: Sean O'Conner
Contact details:
01524 410921 (H)
01524 411797 (W)
e-mail: seanoconnor@morecambefc.com

CLUB STATISTICS

RECORDS

Attendance:	9,324 v Weymouth F.A.Cup 4.1.62
Victory:	14-0 v Rossendale Utd
	Lancs Comb.Sept 1967 (Arlod Yimmins scored 8)
Defeat:	0-14 v Chorley (A)19.04.46
Career Goalscorer:	Keith Borrowdale 289
	1956-68 78-79Lancs Comb.
Career Appearances:	Steve Done 523+7sub 1968-78
Transfer Fee Paid:	£25,000 to Northwich Victoria
	for Steve Walters July 2000
Transfer Fee Received:	£175,000 from Rushden & Diamonds
	for Justin Jackson July 2000

SENIOR HONOURS

F.A.Challenge Trophy 73-74
Conference Runners-Up 2002-03
Spalding Cup 97-98
Northern Premier League R-Up 91-92 94-95
Lancashire Junior Cup Now ATS Trophy x 8

PREVIOUS

Leagues: Lancs Combination 1920-68
Northern Premier League 1968-1995

Grounds: Woodhill Lane 1920-95
(shared with cricket club who stillplay there)

STEP 1
CONFERENCE
STEP 2 - P177
CONFERENCE Nth & Sth
STEP 3 - P269
NPL - SOUTHERN - ISTHMIAN PREM
STEP 4 - P269
NPL - SOUTHERN - ISTHMIAN
STEP 5/6 - P473
STEP 7 - P713

NORTHWICH VICTORIA

Club Colours: Green & White Hoops/White/White
Change Colours: Yellow/Green/Yellow
Club Sponsor: T.B.A.
Previous League: Conferenc North
LAST SEASON
League: Champions Conference North **F.A. Cup:** 3rd Round Replay
F.A.Trophy 2nd Round Replay
BEST PERFORMANCES
League: 4th Conference **F.A. Cup:** Quarter Finals1883-84 **F.A.Trophy Winners** 1983-84
F.A. Trophy: Semi-Final 1998-1999

Founded:1874
Nickname:
Vics, Greens or
Trickies

Front (L-R): Carlos Roca; Paul Brayson; Kevin Townson; Steve Burr (Manager); Stuart Elliot (Cpt); David Moss (Asst Mgr); Michael Byrne; Chris Williams; Ryan Brown.; **Middle (L-R):** Andy Fearn (Scout); Steve Whitehall (Physio); Mark Sale; Jon McCarthy; Richard Battersby; Phil Senior; Ben Connett; Kieran Charnock; Tom Rutter; Garreth Griffiths.; Phil Lea (Physio) **Back (L-R):** Chris Sargent; Michael Carr; Jonothan Allan; Danny Mayman; Steve Payne; Tony Gallimore. Photographs: Courtesy Simon Ellison / Papillon Photo

CLUB PERSONNEL

Chairman: Mike Connett
Directors: Duncan Crawfored and Derek Nuttall
Football Secretary Derek Nuttall
10 Cedar Close,Lostock Gralam, Northwich,
Cheshire CW9 6GB
Tel Nos: 01606 43350 (H)) 07941 229922
e-mail: gnuttall@aol.com
General Manager & Press Officer David Thomas

Tel Nos: 01606 45144 (H07798 564596 (M)
Commercial Manager Roni Melville
Tel No: 01606 41555 (W) 07833 605605
E-mail: roni@n-vics.co.uk

MANAGEMENT TEAM

Manager: Steve Burr
Assitant Manager: Dave Moss
Youth Coach: John McCarthy
Physio: Steve Whitehall

NORTHWICH VICTORIA

No.	Date	Comp	H/A	Opponents	Att:	Result	Goalscorers	Pos
1	Aug 13	NN	A	Stalybridge Celtic	533	D 3 - 3	**Allan** 40 54 Carr 90	10
2	16		H	Gainsborough Trinity	669	W 2 - 0	**Allan** 9 **Brayson** 58	3
3	20		H	Barrow	724	W 2 - 0	**Allan** 38 **Brayson** 70	2
4	27		A	Alfreton Town	385	W 4 - 2	**Brayson** 3 (22 68 (pen) 90) Carr 45	1
5	29		H	Redditch United	784	W 5 - 1	Carr 9 Payne 14 **Allan** 46 **Brayson** 76 (pen) Byrne 80	1
6	Sept 3		A	Hinckley United	703	W 3 - 1	Carr 18 Woolley (OG) 55 Roca 76	1
7	10		A	Hednesford Town	660	W 4 - 1	Sale 15 **Allan** 3 (20 33 64)	1
8	17		H	Vauxhall Motors	778	W 3 - 1	**Brayson** 56 **Allan** 73 (pen) Battersby 90	1
9	24	FAC2Q	A	Frickley Athletic	392	W 4 - 1	**Brayson** 3 (38 51 60) Carr 63	
10	Oct 1	NN	H	Kettering Town	909	W 3 - 1	**Allan** 23 McCarthy 77 **Brayson** 90	1
11	8	FAC 3Q	H	North Ferriby United	684	W 1 - 0	**Brayson** 59	
12	15	NN	A	Worcester City	951	W 1 - 0	**Brayson** 42	1
13	18		A	Worksop Town	446	W 2 - 1	Handyside	1
14	22	FAC 4Q	H	Barrow	1116	W 4 - 1	**Brayson** 11 84 **Allan** 16 Carr 23	
15	29	NN	A	Hucknall Town	620	L 2 - 3	Mayman 44 **Allan** 70 (pen)	2
16	Nov 5	FAC1R	A	Morecambe	2166	W 3 - 1	**Brayson** 3 (19 41 67)	
17	8	NN	H	Nuneaton Borough	1119	D 2 - 2	**Brayson** 10 51	2
18	12		A	Lancaster City	513	W 2 - 1	**Allan** 45 89	1
19	19		H	Moor Green	737	D 1 - 1	Elliott 39	
20	26	FAT 3Q	A	Hucknall Town	439	D 0 - 0		
21	29	FAT3Qr	H	Hucknall Town	500	W 2 1 1	**Allan** 17 **Brayson** 68	
22	Dec 3	FAC 3R	A	Woking	2462	D 0 - 0		
23	10	NN	H	Leigh RMI	755	W 1 - 0	**Brayson** 20	2
24	13	FAC3Rr	H	Woking	2302	W 2 - 1	Elliott 13 **Brayson** 60	
25	17	FAT 1	A	York City	1372	W 2 - 1	**Allan** 11 (pen) 41 (pen)	
26	26	NN	A	Droylsden	701	L 3 - 4	**Allan** 16 **Brayson** 75 Elliott 85	3
27	31		A	Stafford Rangers	1677	L 0 - 2		3
28	Jan 2		H	Droysden	1106	W 2 - 1	Byrne 79 Sale 90	3
29	8	FAC 3R	A	Sunderland	19323	L 0 - 3		
30	14	FAT 2	A	Woking	1071	D 1 - 1	Carr 35	
31	17	FAT2r	H	Woking	888	L 1 - 2	**Allan** 58	
32	21	NN	A	Barrow	1007	D 1 - 1	**Brayson** 38	3
33	24		A	Harrogate Town	502	W 2 - 0	Devlin 44 Rocca 50	3
34	28		H	Alfreton Town	1017	D 1 - 1	**Allan** 85	3
35	Feb 4		A	Kettering Town	1154	L 0 - 2		3
36	7		H	Hyde United	850	L 1 - 2	Mayman	3
37	11		H	Worcester City	1062	L 0 - 1		3
38	18		A	Workington	476	L 2 - 5	**Allan** 62 (pen) Carr 90	3
39	21		H	Worksop Town	479	W 4 - 1	Carr 27 Byrne 50 Mayman 68 Garner 70	3
40	25		H	Hednesford Town	855	W 8 - 0	Dale 4 Byrne 3 (17 65 90) **Brayson** 56 Mayman 71 Williams 73 79	3
41	28		H	Stalybridge Celtic	834	W 1 - 0	**Allan** 69	3
42	Mar 11		H	Hucknall Town	1020	W 2 - 0	**Allan** 11 22	2
43	14		A	Gainsborough Trinity	255	W 2 - 1	Byrne 12 Williams 54	2
44	18		A	Hyde United	667	W 3 - 1	Carr 14 76 Byrne 26	2
45	25		H	Lancaster City	1027	W 3 - 2	Carr 5 Williams 83 90	2
46	28		H	Workington	729	W 4 - 1	Carr 25 **Allan** 27 89 (pen) **Brayson** 84	1
47	April 1		A	Moor Green	384	W 2 - 1	Handyside 49 Penny 86 (og)	2
48	4		A	Vauxhall Motors	529	W 3 - 0	**Allan** 33 **Brayson** 41 72	1
49	8		H	Harrigate Town	1032	W 3 - 0	Williams 51 Byrne 65 **Brayson** 77	1
50	11		A	Nuneaton Borough	1296	W 2 - 1	Williams 7 60	1
51	15		H	Hinckley United	1250	W 2 - 0	**Allan** 11 Williams 71	1
52	17		A	Redditch United	703	W 2 - 1	Payne 45 Taylor 65 (og)	1
53	22	41	H	Stafford Rangers	3154	W 3 - 1	**Allan** 37 45 Williams 76	1
54	29		A	Leigh RMI	629	L 1 - 2	Williams 45	1

Ave. League Home Attendance: 1153   **Goals** 101 53   **Top Goalscorer:** Allan & Brayson (30)
Best Position: 1st   **Worst:** 10th

PLAYING SQUAD

CURRANT SQUAD AS OF BEGINING OF 2006-07 SEASON

GOALKEEPERS	SQ NO.	HT	WT	D.O.B	AGE	P.O.B	CAREER
Phil Senior	1	5'11"	10 12	30/10/82	23	Huddersfield	Huddersfield Rel 5/06, Northwich 6/06
Ben Connett	20			1/9/83	22	Knutsford	Liverpool, Northwich 7/01

DEFENDERS							
Richard Battersby	2	5'08"	10 03	13/6/79	27	York	Oldham Rel c/s 99, Radcliffe B 11/99, Northwich 7/05
Tony Gallimore	3	5'11"	12 06	21/2/72	34	Nantwich	Stoke, Carlisle (2ML) 10/91, Carlisle (L) 2/92, Carlisle (SL) 3/93, Carlisle
£15,000 7/93, Grimsby £125,000 3/96 Rel c/s 04, Barnsley 8/03 Rel c/s 04, Rochdale 8/04 Rel 5/06, Northwich 6/06							
Gareth Griffiths	4	6'04"	14 00	10/4/70	36	Winsford	Rhyl, Port Vale £1,000 2/93, Shrewsbury (L) 10/97, Wigan 7/98 Rel c/s 01,
Rochdale 7/01 Retired Professionally 5/06, Northwich 5/06							
Kieran Charnock	6	5'11"	10 06	3/8/84	22	Preston	Wigan, Southport 3/03, Northwich 8/03
Steve Payne	12	5'11"	12 05	1/8/75	31	Castleford	Huddersfield, Macclesfield (3ML) 9/94 (Perm) 12/94, Chesterfield Undisc 7/99,
							Macclesfield 3/04 Rel 4/05, Northwich 7/05
Ryan Brown	15	5'10"	11 02	15/3/85	21	Stoke	Port Vale Rel c/s 05, Leek T 8/05, Northwich 6/06

MIDFIELDERS							
Stuart Elliott	5	5'08"	11 05	27/8/77	29	Willesden	Newcastle, Hull (L) 2/97, Swindon (L) 2/98, Gillingham (2ML) 10/98,
							Hartlepool (L) 1/99, Wrexham (SL) 3/99, Bournemouth (2ML) 12/99,
							Stockport (3ML) 2/00, Darlington 7/00, Plymouth 3/01 Rel c/s 01,
							Scarborough (Trial) 8/01, Carlisle U 8/01, Durham C 9/01,
Danny Mayman	7			8/5/79	27	Nottingham	Clipstone W, Hucknall T 7/99, Northwich 12/04
Michael Carr	8	5'08"	10 07	6/12/83	22	Crewe	Macclesfield, Northwich 1/05
Carlos Roca	11	5'04"	10 07	4/9/84	21	Manchester	Oldham Rel 5/04, Carlisle 5/04 Rel c/s 05, Northwich (L) 2/05, Northwich 7/05
Jon McCarthy	16	5'09"	11 05	18/8/70	36	Middlesbrough	Hartlepool, Shepshed 3/89, York 3/90, Port Vale £450,000 8/95,
							Birmingham £1.85 mill 9/97 Rel c/s 02, Sheff Wed (L) 3/02, Port Vale 8/02,
							Doncaster 10/02, York Mon 11/02, Carlisle 11/02, Hucknall 8/03, Northwich 7/04

FORWARDS							
Jonny Allan	9	6'00"	11 03	24/5/83	23	Penrith	Carlisle Rel c/s 02, Workington 8/02, Oxford U (Trial) 8/02,
							Northwich 8/02, Tranmere (Trial) 7/03, Lancaster 11/03,
							Halifax 12/03, Northwich 8/04
Paul Brayson	10	5'06"	10 10	16/9/77	28	Newcastle	Newcastle, Swansea (3ML) 1/97, Reading £100,000 3/98, Cardiff (SL) 3/00,
							Cardiff 7/00 Rel c/s 02, Cheltenham 8/02 Rel 5/04, York C (Trial) 7/04,
							Northwich 8/04, Gateshead (L) 3/05
Michael Byrne	14	5'10"	11 06	14/5/85	21	Ashton-u-Lyne	Bolton (Trainee), Cardiff (Trial), Stockport 10/03, Leigh RMI (L), Northwich 2/05
Mark Sale	17	6'05"	13 08	27/2/72	34	Burton	Stoke Rel c/s 91, Yeovil 10/90 (L) (90/91 3,0), Cambridge U 5/91,
							Rocester 12/91, Birmingham 3/92 Rel c/s 92 Re-signed 8/92,
							Torquay £10,000 3/93, Preston £20,000 7/94, Mansfield £50,000 7/95,
							Colchester £20,000 3/97, Plymouth (SL) 3/99, Rushden & D £30,000
Kevin Townson	18	5'08"	10 03	19/4/83	23	Liverpool	Everton (Jnrs), Rochdale 7/00 Rel c/s 05, Scarborough (L) 9/04,
							Macclesfield (SL) 3/05, Macclesfield c/s 05 Rel 5/06 Northwich 6/06
Chris Williams	19	5'08"	9 00	2/2/85	21	Manchester	Stockport, Grimsby (L) 9/04, Leigh RMI (L) 12/05, Northwich (L) 2/06 (Perm) 3/05

LOANEES		HT	WT	DOB	AGE	POB	FROM - TO
None							

DEPARTURES		HT	WT	DOB	AGE	POB	FROM - TO
(D)Ben Chapman		5'06"	11 05	2/3/79	27	Scunthorpe	Alfreton 7/05 - Nuneaton 6/06
(D)Peter Handyside	21	6'01"	13 03	31/7/74	32	Dumfries	Barnsley 8/04 - Hucknall (L)8/06 (Perm) 8/06
(G)Kristian Rogers				2/10/80	25		Worksop 3/05 - Rel c/s 06
(M)Mark Devlin				8/1/73	33		ex Exeter 1/99 - Rel c/s 06

NORTHWICH VICTORIA

Ground Address: Victoria Stadium
Telephone: 01606 41555
Fax: 01606 41565
General email address: dnuttall@aol.com
Official website: www.nvfc.co.uk

SIMPLE DIRECTIONS: From Jct 19 M6 follow A556 towards Northwich for about three miles. Turn right onto
t the A559 towards Lostock (as the road becomes a dual carriageway).Turn right at
the t traffic lights immediately before the Slow & Easy pub. Turn left at the crossroads by
the Black Greyhound public house (signposted). Follow the road until the Renault
Garage on the left and turn left into Wincham Avenue. The ground ia at the bottom of
the road on the right.
By Rail: Nearest Railway Stations are Northwich (1mile) or Hartford (2 miles)
MATCH TICKETS:
Ticket office Telephone: 01606 41555
Midweek Home Matchday: Tuesday

CAPACITY: 5,300
Seats: 1.180
Covered: 3,700

Social Facilities Six Entertainmnent Boxes
Two Exeicutive Suits
Herriots Bar will be open to all fans
l Italian and Spanish sections in a large restaurant

Club Shop: Programmes and souvenirs available

MATCHDAY PROGRAMME
32 Pages £2.00
Editor: Dave Thonas(07798 564596(M)

Local Press: Northwich Guardian (Wed)
Northwich Chronicle (Wed) Daily Post,
Local radio:GMR (BBC Manchester), Picadilly
Radio and Signal Radio.

CLUB STATISTICS
RECORDS
Attendance: 11.290
v Witton Albion Cheshire LeagueGood Friday 1949
Victory 17-0
v Marple Association 1883

Defeat 3-10
v Port Vale 1931

Career Goalscorer: Peter Burns 160 1955 -1965

Career Apperances: Ken Jones 970 1969 -1985
Transfer Fee Paid: £12,000
to Hyde United for Malcolm O'Connor August 1988
Transfer Fee Received: £50,000
from Leyton Orient forGary Fletcher June 1921
from Chester City for Neil Morton October 1990
SENIOR HONOURS
Northern Premier League Runners-Up1976-77
F.A.Trophy Winners 1983-84
F.A.Trophy Runners-Up 1975-76
Welsh Cup R-Up (2) (7)
Cheshire Senior Cup (15) R-Up (13)
Staffordshire Senior Cup (3) R-Up (2)
PREVIOUS LEAGUES The Combination 1890-1892, Football League
Div 2 1892-94, The Combination 1894 1898 The Cheshire League: 1898-1900,
Manchester 1900-12, Lancashire 1912-1919, Cheshire County 1919-1968
and Northern Premier League 1968-79

OXFORD UNITED

Club Colours: Yellow with navy trim/Navy with yellow trim/Yellow with Navy trim
Change Colours: All White
Club Sponsor: Buildbase
Previous League: Football League
LAST SEASON
League: Division Two: 21st   **F.A. Cup:** 2nd Round
BEST PERFORMANCES
League: 12th Division One 1997-98
F.A. Cup: 6th Rd 1963-64

Re-Formed: 1893
Nickname: U's

CLUB PERSONNEL

Chairman:	Nick Merry
Directors:	Kelvin Thomas and Jim Smith
Secretary:	Mick Brown
	c/o club
Tel Nos:	07833 148883 (M)
	01685 337 555
	Fax: 01865 337 533
e-mail:	secretary@oufc.co.uk
Club Administrator:	
Commercial Manager:	Peter Corbett
	07748 743811
Press Officer:	Chris Williams
	01865 337523

MANAGEMENT TEAM

Manager:...Jim Smith

First Team Coach:....................................Andy Awford

Physiotherapist:.......................................Neil Sullivan

OXFORD UNITED

No.	Date	Comp	H/A	Opponents	Att:	Result	Goalscorers	Pos
1	Aug 6	FL2	A	Grimsby Town	4706	D 1 - 1		
2	10		H	Torquay United	4820	W 1 - 0		
3	13		H	Wycombe Wanderers	6364	D 2 - 2		
4	20		A	Lincoln City	3724	L 1 - 2		
5	23	LC 1	A	Gillingham	4149	L 0 - 1		
6	27	FL2	H	Stockport County	4329	D 1 - 1		
7	Sept 2		A	Shrewsbury Town	4073	L 0 - 2		
8	10		H	Rushden & Diamonds	4189	D 2 - 2		
9	13		A	Bristol Rovers	5098	D 1 - 1		
10	17		A	Darlington	4127	W 2 - 1		
11	24		H	Bury	4198	W 2 - 1		
12	27		A	Rochdale	2347	W 1 - 0		
13	Oct 1		A	Barnet	3272	D 0 - 0		
14	7		H	Carlisle United	5392	W 1 - 0		
15	14		A	Northampton Town	6802	L 0 - 1		
16	18	LDV (S)	A	Brentford	1785	D 1 - 1	(aet won 4-3 on pens)	
17	22	FL2	H	Boston United	5084	D 0 - 0		
18	29		A	Leyton Orient	5268	L 0 - 1		
19	Nov 5	FAC 1	A	Eastbourne Borough	3770	D 1 - 1		
20	12	FL2	H	Wrexham	4491	L 0 - 3		
21	16	FAC 1r	H	Eastbourne Borough	4396	W 3 - 0		
22	19	FL2	A	Carlisle United	6097	L 1 - 2		
23	23	LDV (S)	H	Leyton Orient	1521	W 1 - 0		
24	26	FL2	H	Grimsby Town	4323	L 2 - 3		
25	Dec 3	FAC 2	A	Cheltenham Town	4592	D 1 - 1		
26	6	FL2	A	Cheltenham Town	2852	W 2 - 1		
27	10		A	Torquay United	2678	D 3 - 3		
28	13	FAC 2r	H	Cheltenham Town	3455	L 1 - 2		
29	16	FL2	H	Lincoln City	3795	L 0 - 1		
30	20	LDV (S) QF	A	Cheltenham Town	1825	L 1 - 2		
31	26	FL2	H	Notts County	5626	W 3 - 0		
32	31		H	Mansfield Town	4005	L 1 - 2		
33	Jan 2		A	Chester City	2624	W 1 - 0		
34	7		H	Shrewsbury Town	3702	L 0 - 3		
35	10		A	Peterborough United	2926	D 0 - 0		
36	14		A	Macclesfield Town	1972	D 1 - 1		
37	21		H	Darlington	4204	L 0 - 2		
38	28		A	Rushden & Diamonds	3823	L 0 - 3		
39	Feb 4		H	Rochdale	3978	D 1 - 1		
40	15		H	Macclesfield Town	4331	D 1 - 1		
41	18		H	Cheltenham Town	5232	D 1 - 1		
42	25		A	Wycombe Wanderers	7016	L 1 - 2		
43	Mar 11		A	Stockport County	4424	L 1 - 2		
44	15		H	Bristol Rovers	6424	W 1 - 0		
45	18		A	Notts County	5265	D 0 - 0		
46	21		A	Bury	1882	D 1 - 1		
47	25		H	Peterborough United	7486	W 1 - 0		
48	April 1		A	Mansfield Town	3480	L 0 - 1		
49	8		H	Chester City	5754	L 0 - 1		
50	15		H	Barnet	6948	W 2 - 0		
51	17		A	Boston United	2313	L 0 - 1		
52	22		H	Northampton Town	8264	L 1 - 3		
53	29		A	Wrexham	4575	D 1 - 1		
54	May 6		H	Leyton Orient	12243	L 2 - 3		

Ave. League Home Attendance: 5443   **Goals** 52 64   **Top Goalscorer:** Steve Basham (13) ??

Best Position: 6th   **Worst:** 23rd

PLAYING SQUAD

CURRANT SQUAD AS OF BEGINING OF 2006-07 SEASON

GOALKEEPERS	SQ NO.	HT	WT	D.O.B	AGE	P.O.B	CAREER
Chris Tardif	1	5'11"	12 07	20/6/81	25	Guernsey	Portsmouth Rel c/s 04, Bournemouth (SL) 8/02, Havant & W (L) 10/03, Wycombe (Trial) 3/04, Oxford U 7/04
Billy Turley	23	6'04"	15 07	15/7/72	34	Wolverhampton	Evesham U, Northampton 7/95, Kettering (SL) 1/97, L.Orient (3ML) 2/98, Rushden & D £130,000 6/99 Rel 2/05, Oxford U 7/05

DEFENDERS							
Gavin Johnson	3	5'11"	11 07	10/10/70	35	Stowmarket	Ipswich Rel c/s 95, Luton 7/95, Wigan (2ML) 12/95 £15,000 2/96 Rel c/s 98, Dunfermline 7/98 Rel c/s 99, Colchester 11/99, Boston U 7/05, Northampton 8/05 Rel 5/06, Oxford U 7/06
Chris Willmott	5	6'02"	11 13	30/9/77	28	Bedford	Luton, Wimbledon £350,000 7/99 Rel c/s 03, Luton (4ML) 1/03, Northampton 7/03, Oxford U 7/05
Phil Gilchrist	6	5'11"	13 12	25/8/73	33	Stockton	Notts Forest, Middlesbrough 1/92, Hartlepool 11/92, Oxford U £100,000 2/95, Leicester £500,000 8/99, West Brom £500,000 3/01 Rel c/s 04, Rotherham (2ML) 3/04, Rotherham c/s 04 Rel 5/06, Oxford U 6/06
John Dempster	15	6'00"	11 07	1/4/83	23	Kettering	Rushden & D, Oxford U 1/06
Andrew Gunn	20			22/2/88	18		Oxford U
Matthew Day	21					Newbury	Portsmouth, Oxford U 8/06

MIDFIELDERS							
Eddie Anaclet	2	5'09"	10 00	31/8/85	21	Arusha, Tanzania	Southampton Rel 5/06, Chester (L) 12/04, Tamworth (3ML) 11/05, Oxford U 7/06
Barry Quinn	4	6'00"	12 02	9/5/79	27	Dublin	Coventry Rel c/s 04, Rushden & D (L) 1/04, Oxford U (2ML) 3/04, Oxford U 5/04
Carl Pettefer	7	5'07"	10 02	22/3/81	25	Taplow	Portsmouth Rel c/s 04, Exeter (SL) 10/02, Southend (2ML) 2/04, Southend 5/04, Oxford U 7/06
Eddie Hutchinson	8	6'01"	13 00	23/2/82	24	Kingston	Sutton U, Brentford £75,000 8/00, Oxford U 7/06
Chris Hargreaves	10	5'11"	12 02	12/5/72	34	Cleethorpes	Grimsby, Scarborough (L) 3/93, Hull C (2ML) 7/93 Undisc 9/93 Rel c/s 95, West Brom 7/95, Hereford (SL) 2/96, Hereford 8/96, Plymouth 7/98 Re c/s 00, Northampton 7/00, Brentford 7/04, Oxford U 7/05
Andy Burgess	11	6'02"	11 11	10/8/81	24	Bedford	Luton (Jun), Rushden & D, Oxford U 1/06
Josh Kennet	19			27/9/87	18		Oxford U

FORWARDS							
Steve Basham	9	5'11"	12 04	2/12/77	28	Southampton	Southampton, Wrexham (L) 2/98, Preston (SL) 2/99, Preston £200,000 7/99 Rel c/s 02, Oxford U 8/02
Yemi Odubade	12	5'07"	11 07	4/7/84	22	Lagos	Eastbourne T, Yeovil 7/04, Eastbourne B 2/05, Oxford U 1/06
Robert Duffy	14	6'01"	12 04	2/12/82	23	Swansea	Rushden & D Rel c/s 05, Stamford (L) 1/05, Peterborough (Trial) 7/05, Cambridge U 8/05, Kettering 9/05, Gainsborough 1/06, Stevenage 3/06 Rel 5/06, Oxford U 8/06
Billy Beechers	17			1/6/87	19	Oxford	Oxford U

LOANEES		HT	WT	DOB	AGE	POB	FROM - TO
None							

DEPARTURES		HT	WT	DOB	AGE	POB	FROM - TO
(D)Jon Ashton		6'02"	13 12	4/10/82	23	Nuneaton	Leicester (L) 8/03 (Perm) 9/03 - Rel 5/06, Bristol C (Trial) 5/06, Rushden & D 6/06
(G)Bradie Clarke		6'02"	13 08	26/5/86	20	Cambridge	Yth - Rel 5/06
(M)Jamie Brooks		5'10"	11 05	12/8/83	23	Oxford	Yth - Rel 5/06, Didcot 7/06
(D)Leo Roget		6'01"	13 06	1/8/77	29	Ilford	Rushden & D 7/04 - Rel 5/06
(M)Mark E'Beyer		5'11"	12 03	21/9/84	21	Stevenage	MK Dons (Sch) 7/04 - Rel 5/06, Crawley 8/06
(F)Eric Sabin		6'01"	12 05	22/1/75	31	Sarcelles (Fr)	Northampton 8/05 - Retired c/s 06
(D)Lee Mansell		5'10"	11 10	28/10/82	23	Gloucester	Luton 7/05 - Torquay 7/06
(M)Stuart Gray		6'00"	13 05	18/12/73	32	Harrogate	Rushden & D 7/05 - Rel c/s 06, Guiseley 8/06
Liam Smyth							Yth - Aylesbury 7/06
(F)Tim Sills		6'01"	14 00	10/9/79	26	Romsey	Aldershot 1/06 - Hereford 6/06
(M)Tom Winters	16	5'09"	10 10	11/12/85	20	Banbury	Yth - Brackley (L) 12/05, Rel 8/06, Brackley T 8/06
Ryan Brooks							Yth - Abingdon U 7/06
Terry Parker							Yth - Dorchester 8/06

OXFORD UNITED

Ground Address: The Kassam Stadium,Grenoble Road,Oxford OX4 4XP

Tel No: 01865 337500
Fax: 01865 337555
General email address: admin@oufc.co.uk
Capacity: 12,500
Official website: www.oufc.co.uk

SIMPLE DIRECTIONS
By road: The Kassam Stadium is clearly signposted on all makor approach roads to Oxford.
By Rail: Nearest Railway Station is Oxford (five miles from ground)

MATCH TICKETS
Ticket Office:
Match day prices: Adults £. U16, O.A.P. and Students £ and U12 £

Midweek Home Matchday: Tuesday
   Capacity: 12,500   **Seats:**   **Covered:**
Clubhouse: 'Priory & Question Mark' public house and nearby restaurants for pre match meets.
Refreshments: Bars around the ground.
Club Shop: Fully stocked.
Local Press: Oxford Mail.
Local Radio: BBC Radio Oxford.

MATCHDAY PROGRAMME
Pages: **Price:** £
Editor: Chris Wiliams
Tel.No: 01865 337523
07941 607842 (M)

CLUB STATISTICS

RECORDS

Attendance: 22,730
v P.N.E. 6th Rd F.A.Cup 1963-1964

Victory: 9-1
F.A.Cup First Round 1994-95 v Dorchester Town

Defeat: 0-7
Division One v Sunderland 1998-1999

Career Goalscorer: Graham Atkinson 771962-73

Career Appearances: John Shuker 478 1962-1977

Transfer Fee Paid: £475,000
to Aberdeen for Dean Windass
August 1998

Transfer Fee Received:
£1,600,000 from Leicester City for Matt Elliott Jan 1997

SENIOR HONOURS
Football League Cup Winners 1985-1986
FootballLerague Divison Two Champions1997098
Football League Division Two Runners-Up1995-96
Football League Division Three Champions 1967-8 83-84
Football League Promoted from Div 4 (4th) 1964-65

PREVIOUS

Names: 1893 Headington, 1894 -1960 Headington United

Recent Ground: Manor Ground 1925-2001

STEP 1
CONFERENCE

STEP 2 - P177
CONFERENCE Nth & Sth

STEP 3 - P269
NPL - SOUTHERN - ISTHMIAN PREV

STEP 4 - P269
NPL - SOUTHERN - ISTHMIAN

STEP 5/6 - P473

STEP 7 - P713

RUSHDEN & DIAMONDS

Club Colours: Al Red
Change Colours: All Blue or All White
Club Sponsor: MOTO
Previous League: Football League
LAST SEASON
League: 24th Football League Div 3   **F.A. Cup:** 2nd. Round
BEST PERFORMANCES
League: 22nd Football League Division 2 2003-2004
F.A. Cup: 3rd Rd 1999-2000   **F.A. Trophy:** Semi-Finalists 1993-94

Founded: 1992
Nickname: Diamonds

Rushden & Diamonds Football Club 2006/07

Back Row: Glenn Wilson - Jon Ashton - Michael Rankine - Lee Fortune-West - Greg Pearson - Wayne Hatswell - Daniel Chillingworth
Middle Row: Asst Manager Ian Bowyer - 1st Team Coach Ian Woan - Tom Shaw - Nicky Eyres - Scott Tynan - Daniel Crane - Marcus Kelly - Goalkeeper Coach Tony Godden - Physio Simon Parsell - Kit Manager Mark Stringer
Front Row: Daniel Grainger - Vernon Jackson - Andrew Rigby - Club Captain Dave Savage - Manager Paul Hart - Team Captain Chris Hope - Paul Watson - Tyrone Berry - Lee Tomlin

CLUB PERSONNEL

Chairperson:	Helen Thompson	**Commercial Manager:**	Rachel Roberts
			Tel: 01933 652000
Football Liaison Director :	Shaun Hodgkin		(M) 07915 640691
			e-mail: trustoffice@rdst.co.uk
Sales & Marketin g Director:	Nick Archer		
		Press Officer:	Fiona Palmer
Football Secretary:	Matt Wild		Tel No: 01933 652000
	Tel No:01933 65200		(M) 07989 964024
	Fax: 01933 650418		e-mail: press.office@rd-fc.co.uk
	(M) 07989 964024		
	e-mail: matt.wild@rd-fc.co.uk		

MANAGEMENT TEAM

Manager:	Paul Hart		
Assistant Manager:	Ian Bowyer	**Physio:**	Simon Parsell
Head of Youth Football:	Paul Driver	**Captain:**	Chris Hope

RUSHDEN & DIAMONDS

BEST LGE ATT.: **5,211** v Northampton Town
LOWEST: **2,216** v Carlisle United

No.	Date	Comp	H/A	Opponents	Att:	Result	Goalscorers	Pos
1	Aug 6	FL2	H	Darlington	2832	D 1 - 1		
2	9		A	Mansfield Town	3402	W 1 - 0		
3	20		H	Chester City	2682	D 1 - 1		
4	24	LC 1	H	Coventry City	3240	L 0 - 3		
5	27	FL2	H	Lincoln City	2860	D 1 - 1		
6	29		A	Grimsby Town	3774	L 0 - 2		
7	Sept 2		H	Peterborough	4403	L 0 - 2		
8	10		A	Oxford United	4189	D 2 - 2		
9	13		A	Macclesfield	2874	L 1 - 3		
10	17		H	Stockport County	2710	W 3 - 2		
11	24		A	Notts County	5142	D 0 - 0		
12	27		H	Northampton Town	5211	L 1 - 3		
13	Oct 1		A	Rochdale	2606	L 1 - 2		
14	7		H	Bury	2639	L 0 - 2		
15	15		A	Wycombe Wanderers	5231	D 0 - 0		
16	18	LDV (S)	H	Southend	1300	W 1 - 0		
17	22	FL2	H	Shrewsbury Town	2954	W 3 - 0		
18	29		A	Barnet	2564	L 1 - 2		
19	Nov 6	FAC 1	A	Halifax Town	2303	D 1 - 1		
20	11	FL2	H	Boston United	3205	W 1 - 0		
21	15	FAC 1r	H	Halifax Town	2133	D 0 - 0	(aet won 5-4 on pens)	
22	22	LDV (S)	A	Swansea City	5321	L 0 - 4		
23	26	FL2	A	Darlington	3209	D 1 - 1		
24	Dec 3	FAC 2	H	Leyton Orient	3245	L 0 - 1		
25	6	FL2	H	Carlisle United	2216	L 0 - 4		
26	10		H	Mansfield Town	2477	L 1 - 2		
27	17		A	Chester City	2265	W 2 - 1		
28	26		A	Leyton Orient	4558	L 1 - 5		
29	28		H	Cheltenham Town	2244	L 0 - 1		
30	31		A	Torquay United	2668	L 1 - 2		
31	Jan 2		H	Bristol Rovers	2720	L 2 - 3		
32	7		A	Peterborough United	4613	L 0 - 2		
33	14		H	Wrexham	2617	L 0 - 2		
34	21		A	Stockport County	4574	D 2 - 2		
35	28		H	Oxford United	3823	W 3 - 0		
36	Feb 4		A	Northampton Town	7036	L 0 - 2		
37	7		A	Bury	1777	D 1 - 1		
38	11		H	Notts County	3113	W 1 - 0		
39	14		A	Wrexham	3195	L 0 - 2		
40	18		A	Carlisle United	6922	L 0 - 5		
41	25		H	Macclesfield Town	2479	W 1 - 0		
42	Mar 4		H	Grimsby Town	3366	D 1 - 1		
43	11		A	Lincoln City	4383	D 2 - 2		
44	18		H	Leyton Orient	3679	W 1 - 0		
45	25		A	Cheltenham Town	3447	L 1 - 3		
46	April 1		H	Torquay United	3795	W 1 - 0		
47	8		A	Bristol Rovers	6432	W 1 - 0		
48	15		H	Rochdale	3135	D 1 - 1		
49	18		A	Shrewsbury Town	4239	L 1 - 4		
50	22		H	Wycombe Wanderers	3396	L 1 - 3		
51	29		A	Boston United	2489	L 0 - 2		
52	May 6		H	Barnet	4174	L 1 - 2		24
Ave. League Home Attendance:				3303	**Goals**	46 81		

STEP 1
CONFERENCE

STEP 2 - P177   STEP 3 - P269   STEP 4 - P269   STEP 5/6 - P473   STEP 7 - P713
CONFERENCE Nth & Sth   NPL - SOUTHERN - ISTHMIAN PREM   NPL - SOUTHERN - ISTHMIAN

PLAYING SQUAD

CURRANT SQUAD AS OF BEGINING OF 2006-07 SEASON

GOALKEEPERS	SQ NO.	HT	WT	D.O.B	AGE	P.O.B	CAREER
Nicky Eyre	1	5'10"	10 10	7/9/85	20	Braintree	Tottenham Rel c/s 05, Grays (L) 10/04, Grays 7/05 Rel 7/06, Rushden & D 8/06
Daniel Crane	13	6'03"	14 11	27/5/84	22	Birmingham	WBA Rel c/s 04, Burton 8/04, Moor Green (L) 10/05, Rushden & D 1/06
Scott Tynan	20	6'02"	13 03	27/11/83	22	Knowsley	Wigan (Sch), N.Forest Rel c/s 04, Telford (2ML) 12/03, Barnet 9/04, Rushden & D 1/06, Hereford (L) 8/06

DEFENDERS							
Glenn Wilson	2	6'01"	12 09	16/3/86	20	Lewisham	C.Palace Rel 5/06, Rushden & D 6/06
Paul Watson	3	5'08"	10 10	4/1/75	31	Hastings	Gillingham, Fulham £13,000 7/96, Brentford £50,000 12/97, Brighton £20,000 7/99 Rel c/s 05, Coventry 9/05, Woking 11/05, Rushden & D 6/06
Jon Ashton	4	6'02"	13 12	4/10/82	23	Nuneaton	Leicester, Notts County (L) 11/02, Notts County (Trial) 7/03, Oxford U (L) 8/03 (Perm) 9/03 Rel 5/06, Bristol C (Trial) 5/06, Rushden & D 6/06
Chris Hope	5	6'01"	13 01	14/11/72	33	Sheffield	Darlington (Jun), Notts Forest 8/90, Kettering (SL) 1/93, Scunthorpe £50,000 7/93, Gillingham 7/00 £250,000 Rel 5/06, Rushden & D 7/06
Wayne Hatswell	6	6'00"	13 10	8/2/75	31	Swindon	Cinderford T, Witney T, Cinderford, Forest Green 7/99, Oxford U £35,000 12/00 Rel 4/02, Chester Free 5/02, Kidderminster £15,000 10/03, Rushden & D 1/06
Daniel Grainger	19	5'10"	10 10	15/10/86	19	Thrapston	Peterborough (Jun), Rushden & D

MIDFIELDERS							
Dave Savage	7	6'01"	12 07	30/7/73	33	Dublin	Kilkenny C, Brighton 3/91 Rel c/s 92, Longford T 5/92, Millwall £15,000 5/94, Northampton £100,000 10/98, Oxford U 8/01 Rel c/s 03, Bristol R 7/03, Rushden & D 7/05
Marcus Kelly	11	5'07"	10 00	16/3/86	20	Kettering	Rushden & D
Andrew Rigby	17			19/1/87	19	Nottingham	Notts Forest, Rushden & D 7/06
Tom Shaw	18	6'00"	12 00	1/12/86	19		Notts Forest (Jun), Rushden & D (7/04)

FORWARDS							
Michael Rankine	8	6'01"	14 12	15/1/85	21	Doncaster	Armthorpe Welfare, Barrow 8/03, Scunthorpe 9/04, Barrow (L) 8/05, Lincoln C (Trial) 12/05, Alfreton 1/06, Rushden & D 7/06
Leo Fortune-West	9	6'04"	13 10	9/4/71	35	Stratford	Tiptree, B.Stortford, Dagenham, Dartford, B.Stortford, Hendon, B.Stortford, Stevenage 7/94, Gillingham £5,000 7/95, L.Orient (SL) 3/97, Lincoln C 7/98, Rotherham (L) 10/98, Brentford £60,000 11/98, Rotherham £35,000 2/99, Cardiff £300,000 9/00 Rel c/s 03,
Daniel Chillingworth	10	6'00"	12 06	13/9/81	24	Cambridge	Cambridge U, Cambridge C (SL) 3/01, Cambridge C (2ML) 8/01, Darlington (L) 11/01, Walsall (Trial) 11/04, L.Orient (L) 12/04, Rushden & D 7/05, Notts County (SL) 2/06
Simeon Jackson	12	5'10"	10 12	28/3/87	19	Kingston, Jam	Gillingham (Jun), Dulwich H (Jun), Rushden & D, Man Utd (Trial) 12/03
Lee Tomlin	14	5'11"	10 09	12/1/89	17		Leicester (Jun), Rushden & D 1/05, Liverpool (Trial) 4/06
Tyrone Berry	15	5'08"	10 02	11/3/87	19	London	C.Palace, Notts County (L) 9/05, Rushden & D (L) 1/06 Perm 1/06
Greg Pearson	16	6'00"	12 00	3/4/85	21	Birmingham	West Ham, Barnet (SL) 2/04, Lincoln C (L) 8/04, Grimsby (Trial) 11/04, Canvey Island (L) 12/04, Rushden & D 7/05, Hucknall (L) 2/06

LOANEES		HT	WT	DOB	AGE	POB	FROM - TO
None							

DEPARTURES		HT	WT	DOB	AGE	POB	FROM - TO
(M)Darren Caskey		5'08"	11 09	21/8/74	32	Basildon	Virginia Beach Mariners (USA) 1/06 -Kettering 5/06
(F)Drewe Broughton		6'02"	13 06	25/10/78	27	Hitchin	Southend 2/05 - Chester 6/06
(D)Graham Allen		6'01"	12 08	8/4/77	29	Bolton	Tranmere 6/04 - Chester 6/06
(M)Sean Ridgway		5'11"	12 02	10/12/86	19		Yth - Aldershot 6/06
(M)Ashley Nicholls		5'11"	11 11	30/10/81	24	Ipswich	Cambridge U 1/06 - Grays 8/06
(F)John Turner		5'10"	11 00	12/2/86	20	Harrow	Cambridge U 1/06 - Grays 8/06
(D)Philip Gulliver	23	6'02"	13 05	12/9/82	23	Bishop Auckland	Rushden & D, Hereford 8/06
(G)Ashley Jones							Yth - Basingstoke 8/06
(F)Magnus Okunghae							Yth - Aldershot 8/06
(M)Gary Mills							Yth - Crawley 8/06
(D)Rob Gier							Wimbledon 7/04 - Rel c/s 06
(D)Ronnie Bull							New Zealand Knights 1/06 - Rel c/s 06

RUSHDEN & DIAMONDS

Ground Address: Nene Park, Irthlingborough,Northants NN9 5QF
Telephone: 01933 652000
Fax: 01933 650418
Mobile: 07989 964024
e-mail: trustoffice@rdst.co.uk

Official website: therdiamondsfc.com
Office Opening Hours: 9.00am-5.0pm
SIMPLE DIRECTIONS:
By Road: **Nene Park is situated three qurters of a mile north of the A45/A6**
By Rail: Nearest Railway stationis Wellingborough (six miles)
MATCH TICKETS:

Ticket office Telephone: 01933 652936

Midweek Home Matchday: **Tuesday**

CAPACITY: 6,635   **Seats: 4,654**   **Covered: All four sides**

Clubhouse &
Refreshments: Social facilities open all day every day with full restaurant facilities

Club Shop: **Sells all types of memorabillia**

MATCHDAY PROGRAMME
Pages: **Price:**
Editor: Fiona Palmer
07989 964024
e-mail: press.office@rd-fc.co.uk

CLUB STATISTICS

RECORDS

Attendance:	6,431 v Leeds United
	F.A.Cup 3rd Rd1998-99
Record Victory:	8-0 v Desborough T
	County Cup 94-95
Career Goalscorer:	Darren Collins 153
Career Appearances:	Gary Butterworth 290
Transfer Fee Paid:	Undisclosed to Morecambe
	for Justin Jackson
Transfer Fee Received:	Undisclosed from Doncaster R
	for Justin Jackson

SENIOR HONOURS

Football League Division Three Champions	2002-2003
Conference Champions	2000-2001
Conference Championship Shield	2000-2001
Southern League Premier Champions	1995-1996
Southern League Midland Division Champions	1993-1994
Northants Huillier Senior Cup	1993-934 & 1998-99

PREVIOUS

Names: Irthlingborough Diamonds and Rushden Town
merged in 1992

Grounds: None
Leagues: Southern League1992-1996, Conference 1996-2001,
Football League 20012006

SOUTHPORT

Club Colours: All Yellow
Change Colours: White/blue/blue
Club Sponsor: Palace Products
Previous League: Conference North
LAST SEASON
Conference: 19th   **F.A.Cup:** 1st Round Replay   **F.A.Trophy:** 1st Round Replay
BEST PERFORMANCES
League: Football League Division Three, 23rd in 1973-74
F.A. Cup: 6th Rd 1930-31   **F.A. Trophy:** Runners -Up 1997-98

Founded: 1881
Nickname: The Sandgrounders

Top Row L to R: Dan Bromilow, Paul Harrison, Kevin Lee, Ryan Robinson, Chris Lane, John Bagnall, Dino Maamria. **Middle:** Barry Simms, Paul Martin, James Olsen, Robbie Booth, Lee Hoolickin, Liam Blakeman, Carl Baker, Mark Jackson, Joe Fowler, Mark Fairhurst. **Front:** Sean Clancy, Alex Smith, Mike Marsh, Mark Boyd, Paul Cook, Michael Powell, John Durnin, Stephen Rowlands, Francis Barry.

CLUB PERSONNEL

Chairman: Charles Clapham
Vice Chairman: S.Shrouder
Additional Directors: B.J.Hedley,A.Pope,
P.Abrams, T.Medcroft, S.Porter and G.Tait
Club & Company Secretary Ken Hilton,
34 Mill Lane, Burscough, Ormskirk L40 5TJ
Tel Nos: 01704 894504 (H) 07802 661906 (M)
Commercial Manager: Derek Hitchcock
Tel. Nos: 01704 380849 (H) 07976 555782(M)
e.mail: commercial@southportfc.net
Press Officer: Haydn Preece (07768 000818)

MANAGEMENT TEAM

Manager: Paul Cook
Coach: Joey Dunne
Physio: Mark Fairhurst
Captain: Steve Pickard

SOUTHPORT

No.	Date	Comp	H/A	Opponents	Att:	Result	Goalscorers	Pos
1	Aug 13	C	A	Dagenham & Redbridge	1265	L 1 - 3	**Daly** 32	18
2	16		H	York City	1646	L 1 - 4	**Daly** 6	20
3	20		H	Stevenage Borough	1007	W 3 - 2	Baker 24 (pen) Robinson 34,48	17
4	27		A	Kidderminster Harriers	1753	D 1 - 1	**Daly** 45	18
5	29		H	Burton Albion	1253	W 3 - 2	Robinson 16 66 Leadbetter 59	13
6	Sept 3		A	Gravesend & Northfleet	813	L 1 - 3	Leadbetter 34	14
7	10		A	Woking	1477	L 0 - 1		15
8	17		H	Exeter City	1423	L 0 - 3		19
9	20		H	Tamworth	1012	D 1 - 1	Baker 53	
10	24		A	Canvey Island	727	L 1 - 2	Ward (og) 34	20
11	27		A	Scarborough	1280	W 1 - 0	Leadbetter 27	16
12	Oct 1		H	Cambridge United	1204	D 2 - 2	Baker1 49	18
13	7		H	Forest Green Rovers	1087	W 3 - 1	Baker 9 10 **Daly** 24	15
14	15		A	Altrincham	1225	L 0 - 1		14
15	**22**	**FAC 4Q**	**H**	**Kidderminster Harriers**	**1108**	**W 1 - 0**	**Lane 69**	
16	29	C	H	Grays Athletic	1148	L 1 - 4	Rogan 59	17
17	**Nov 5**	**FAC1R**	**H**	**Woking**	**1417**	**D 1 - 1**	**Leadbetter 64**	
18	12	C	A	Crawley Town	2055	L 0 - 2		20
19	**15**	**FAC1R r**	**A**	**Woking**	**2298**	**L 0 - 1***		
20	19	C	H	Halifax Town	1402	L 0 - 2		21
21	26		A	Accrington Stanley	1630	L 0 - 4		21
22	Dec 10		A	Aldershot Town	2066	L 0 - 2		21
23	**17**	**FAT 1**	**A**	**Halifax Town**	**1101**	**D 0 - 0**		
24	**20**	**FAT 1r**	**H**	**Halifax Town**	**589**	**L 0 - 1**		
25	24	C	H	Morecambe	1807	L 0 - 3		22
26	Jan 2		A	Morecambe	2788	D 0 - 0		22
27	7		H	Dagenham & Redbridge	1002	L 1 - 2	Baker 48	22
28	14		H	Scarborough	1035	L 0 - 2		22
29	21		A	Stevenage Borough	2231	W 1 - 0	Robinson 61 (pen)	22
30	24		A	York City	2176	D 0 - 0		22
31	28		H	Kidderminster Harriers	1076	L 1 - 4	Robinson 3	22
32	Feb 11		H	Canvey Island	901	W 2 - 0	**Daly** 16 68	22
33	18		A	Cambridge United	2310	L 1 - 2	**Daly** 83	22
34	Mar 4		A	Exeter City	3485	L 0 - 5		22
35	11		A	Forest Gren Rovers	846	W 2 - 0	**Daly** 18 Blakeman 73	22
36	14		H	Hereford United	1057	L 1 - 2	Robinson 60 (pen)	22
37	18		H	Altrincham	1278	D 1 - 1	**Daly** 3	22
38	21		H	Accrington Stanley	1414	W 2 - 0	**Daly** 14 61	20
39	25		A	Tamworth	1442	D 0 - 0		21
40	April 1		H	Crawley Town	1308	L 0 - 2		21
41	8		A	Halifax Town	1791	L 1 - 2	Pickford 73	22
42	10		H	Woking	1054	W 1 - 0	Blakeman 22	20
43	15		H	Gravesend & Northfleet	1301	W 1 - 0	**Daly** 14	20
44	18		A	Burton Albion	1488	D 0 - 0		19
45	22		A	hereford United	2547	D 1 - 1	Blakeman 88	19
46	25		A	Grays Athletic	918	D 1 - 1	Pickford 67	19
47	29		H	Aldershot Town	1709	L 0 - 1		19

Ave. League Home Attendance: 1758   **Goals** 38 70   **Top Goalscorer:** Steve Daly (12)

Best Position: 13th   **Worst:** 22nd

	DICKINSON	LANE	KILBANE	DAVIS	FITZGERALD	PICKFORD	MORLEY	KRIEF	ROBINSON	FEARNS	DALY	LYNCH	BOOTH	BAKER	SPEARE	MCGINN	LEADBETTER	FITZHENRY	POWELL	KEARNEY	FIELD	EVANS	ROGAN	BROOKS	ROBERTS	BRASS	RIGOGLIOSO	BAILEY	STRINGFELLOW	BLAKEMAN	AGGREY	BRABIN	PRICE	JACKSON	
	1	19	12	6	3	2	10	18	8	9	11	14	21	5	15	20	7	4	16	23	24	22	9	24	25	27	26	30	28	17	26	18	26	9	
1	X	X	X	X	X	X	X	X	X	X	S	S	S	U	U																				1
2	X	X	X	X	X	X		U	X	X	S	S	X	U	S	X																			2
3	X	X	X	X	X	X		X	U	X	S	S	X	U	S	X																			3
4	X	X	X	X	X	X		X	X	S	X	S	U	X	S	X																			4
5	X	X	X	X	X	X		X	X	S	X	S	S	U	U	X																			5
6	X	X	X	X	X	X		X	U	X	S	S	X	U	S	X																			6
7	X	X	S	X	X	X		X	X	S	X	U		X	U	S	X	X																	7
8	X	X	U	X	X	X	X		X	X		X	X	S	S	X		X																	8
9	U	X	S	X	X	X	X	X		X	X			X	X	S	S	X	S	X			U												9
10	U	X	X	X	X	X	X			X	X	U	S	X	X	X	X	S		U															10
11	X	X	X		X	X	X				S	X	S	S	X	U	X	X		X	U														11
12	X	X	X		X		X				U	X	X	S	X	U	X	X		X	U	S													12
13	X	X	X	U		X					X	X	S	X	U	X	X	X		X			S	S											13
14	X	X	X	U	X		X		S		X	X	S	X	U	X	X	X	S																14
15	X	X	U	X		S	X		X		X	X	S	X	U	S	X	X	X																15
16	X	X	U	X			X		X	U	S	X	X	S	X	U	S	X	X	X			S												16
17	X		U	X	X			X	U	S	X	X	S	X	U	X	X	X	X																17
18	X	X	X		S				X		U	X	S	X	U	X	X	X	X				X	S											18
19	X		U	X	X	X	X	S		X	S		X	U	X	X	X	U																	19
20	X			X	X	X	X	S		X	U	U	X		X	X	X	S					S												20
21	X			X	U		X	X			S	S		U	S	X	X	X					X		X	X	X								21
22	X	X		X	X	X	X	X			X	X	U		U	S							S		X	X	X								22
23	X	X		X	X	X	X		S		X	X			U	U	X	U	S				X		X	X									23
24	X	X		X		X	S	X		S			X	U	U	X	X	U					X		X	X	X								24
25	X	X		X	X	X	X		S				X	U	S		U	S					X		X	X	X								25
26	X	X		X	S	X			X				X	U	X	S	U	X					U		X	X									26
27	X	X		X	U	X	S		X				X	U	X		S	X					S		X	X	X								27
28	X	X			S	X	X		X				X	U	X	X	X	U					S		X				X	S					28
29	X	X		X	X	X	X		X				X	U	S	X	X	U					S						U	X					29
30	X	X		X	X	X	X		X				X	U	U	X	X	S					S						U	X					30
31	X	X		X		X	X		X				X	U	X	X	X	S					S	U						X					31
32	X	X		X	X	X	X		X				X	U		S		U					U					S	X	X	S				32
33	X	X		X	X	X	X		X					U	U		U						U						X	X	U				33
34	X			X	X	X	X		X				X	U	S	X	X	S					U						X	X	S				34
35	X	X				X	X		X			X	U	U	U	U	S	X							X				X		X				35
36	X	X		X	S	X	X		X				S	X	U		S	U	X						X				X		X				36
37	X	X		X	S	X			X				U	X	U	X	S	U	X						X				X		X				37
38	X	X		X	X	X			X				S		U	X	S	U	X						X				X	S					38
39	X	X		X	X	X	X		X				U		U				U						X				X	U	X	S			39
40	X	X		X	X	X	X		X					S	U	S			U						X				X		X	S			40
41	X	X		X	X	X			S				S	X	U		U	X							X				X	S	X				41
42	X	X		S	X	X			X				X	X	U				U						X				X	S	X	S	S		42
43	X	X		S	X	X	X		S				X	X	U				U						X				X		X	X	S		43
44	X	X		X	X	X	X		X				S		U				U						X			S		X		X	X	U	44
45	X			X	X	X			S				X	X	U		U	S							X				X		X	X	X	S	45
46	X			X	X	X			X				X	X	U	U		U	S						X				X		X	X	X	S	46
47	X	X			X	X	X		S				X	S	U	U			S						X				X					X	47

Total Appearances (Conference)

	40	37	12	32	31	34	31	11	26	5	34	6	5	33	2	13	20	14	13	0	0	0	3	0	18	5	1	1	0	15	3	12	3	2	X
	0	0	2	2	5	0	1	0	6	4	2	9	18	3	0	14	7	2	10	0	2	1	8	1	0	0	0	1	1	1	0	2	3	6	S
	2	0	2	2	2	0	0	0	1	3	1	3	6	0	39	7	1	8	11	2	0	0	2	2	0	0	0	0	2	0	0	1	1	1	U

Cup Appearances

	5	3	0	5	3	3	4	1	2	0	4	3	0	4	0	2	5	4	2	0	0	0	2	0	2	1	0	0	0	0	0	0	0	0	X
	0	0	0	0	0	1	1	0	3	0	1	1	2	0	0	1	0	0	1	0	0	0	0	0	0	0	0	0	0	0	0	0	0	0	S
	0	0	3	0	0	0	0	0	1	0	0	0	0	5	2	0	1	2	0	0	0	0	0	0	0	0	0	0	0	0	0	0	0	0	U

SOUTHPORT

CURRANT SQUAD AS OF BEGINING OF 2006-07 SEASON

GOALKEEPERS	SQ NO.	HT	WT	D.O.B	AGE	P.O.B	CAREER	Apps	Gls
Ryan Robinson	1	6'02"	13 02	13/10/82	23	Tebay	Blackburn, Wigan (Trial) 9/02, Southend 7/03 Rel c/s 04, Wivenhoe (L) 10/03, Morecambe 9/04, Southport (L) 8/06		
John Bagnall	12	6'00"	12 00	23/11/73	32	Southport	Preston (Trainee), Chester, Wigan cc 94/95, Bury, Chester Rel c/s 96, Winsford, Southport (97/98 5,0, 98/99 2,0), Hyde U (L) 8/98, Radcliffe B, Winsford 11/98, Burscough, Bashley 8/02, St Helens 7/03, Burscough 10/03, Witton (L) 8/04, Southport 8/06		
Paul Harrison	21	5'10"	11 05	18/12/84	21	Liverpool	Liverpool Rel c/s 05, Leeds (L) 1/05, Accrington 8/05 Rel 8/05, Prescot Cables 8/05, Vauxhall Motors 9/05, Prescot Cables 9/05, Vauxhall Motors 10/05, Wolves 11/05, Chester 2/06 Rel 5/06, Hereford 8/06, Southport 8/06		

DEFENDERS

DEFENDERS	SQ NO.	HT	WT	D.O.B	AGE	P.O.B	CAREER	Apps	Gls
Chris Lane	2	6'00"	12 10	24/5/79	27	Liverpool	Everton Rel c/s 98, Hereford 6/98, Southport 1/01, Morecambe 5/03, Leigh RMI 1/04, Chester 2/04, Leigh RMI 6/04, Southport 5/05	37	0
Lee Hoolickin	3			30/10/82	23	Carlisle	Carlisle cc 01/02, Gretna (3ML) 9/01, Workington 8/02, Penrith 7/03, Leigh RMI 1/05, Penrith 2/05, Workington 8/05, Southport 7/06		
Kevin Lee	5	6'00"	11 10	4/11/85	20	Liverpool	Wigan, Accrington (L) 10/05, Blackpool (L) 3/06, Southport 7/06		
Steve Rowland	15	5'10"	12 04	2/11/81	24	Wrexham	Port Vale Rel 5/06, Southport 8/06		
Paul Martin	16	6'01"	13 05	29/10/85	20	Liverpool	Tranmere, Southport 7/06		
Alex Smith	17	5'09"	9 09	15/2/76	30	Liverpool	Everton, Swindon 1/96, Huddersfield 2/98 Rel c/s 98, Chester 7/98, Port Vale £75,000 3/99, Reading 7/01 Rel c/s 03, Shrewsbury (3ML) 12/02, Chester 11/03, Wrexham 7/04, Southport 8/06		
Dan Bromilow	24						Southport		

MIDFIELDERS

MIDFIELDERS	SQ NO.	HT	WT	D.O.B	AGE	P.O.B	CAREER	Apps	Gls
Mike Powell	4			11/9/85	20	Ormskirk	Southport	23	0
Marc Boyd	6	5'10"	12 04	22/10/81	24	Carlisle	Newcastle Rel c/s 02, Carlisle (Trial) 3/02, Port Vale 7/02, Carlisle 3/04 Rel c/s 04, Gretna 7/04 Rel 1/06, Macclesfield (SL) 1/05, Accrington 2/06, Southport 6/06		
Carl Baker	7			26/1/82	24	Whiston	Liverpool (Ass Sch), Prescot Cables, Southport 11/03	36	7
Liam Blakeman	8			6/9/82	23	Southport	Blackburn Rel c/s 02, Southport 7/02, Leigh RMI 11/02, St Helens 1/03, Burscough 7/03, Southport 1/06	16	3
James Olsen	11	5'10"	12 00	23/10/81	24	Bootle	Liverpool (Trainee), Tranmere 3/01, Macclesfield 3/04 Rel c/s 04, Vauxhall Motors 8/04, Altrincham 7/05 Rel 10/05, Vauxhall Motors 10/05, Barrow 2/05, Southport 7/06		
Robbie Booth	14	5'07"	11 08	30/12/85	20	Liverpool	Everton (Scholar), Chester (Sch) (Pro) 3/05 Rel c/s 05, Southport 7/05, Burscough (L) 1/06	23	0
Joe Fowler	19	5'08"	11 07	19/8/86	20	Liverpool	Tranmere, Southport 7/06		
Sean Clancy	20	5'08"	9 12	16/9/87	18	Liverpool	Blackpool, Southport 8/06		
Gary Brabin		5'11"	14 08	9/12/70	35	Liverpool	West Kirkby, Stockport cc 90/91, Gateshead 1/91, Runcorn 9/91, Doncaster £45,000 7/94, Bury £125,000 3/96, Blackpool £200,000 7/96, Lincoln C (L) 12/98, Hull C 1/99, Plymouth (Trial) 8/01, Dundee Utd (Trial) 9/01, Boston U 9/01, Torquay 10/01, Chester 1/0	14	0
Matty McGinn				27/6/83	23	Fazackerley	Southport, Runcorn 8/02, Southport 7/05	27	0
David Owens							Wigan (Scholar), Southport (L) 8/06		

FORWARDS

FORWARDS	SQ NO.	HT	WT	D.O.B	AGE	P.O.B	CAREER	Apps	Gls
Tony Gray	9			6/4/84	22	Newton	Bangor C 9/04, Burscough 7/05, Southport 6/06		
Dino Maamria	10	6'00"	12 02	18/2/74	32	Burnley	Glentoran, Ayr, Doncaster, Southport 7/00, Leigh RMI 7/01, Stevenage 5-fig AL 2/03, Charleston Batt 5/03 (USA), Stevenage 9/03, Charleston Battery (L) c/s 04, Southport 7/06		
Mark Jackson	18	5'11"	11 09	3/2/86	20	Preston	Preston Rel 5/06, Shrewsbury (2ML) 10/05, Southport (SL) 3/06, Southport 7/06	8	0
Francis Berry	23						Everton (Jun), Southport 7/06		
Stuart Barlow	26	5'10"	11 01	16/7/68	38	Liverpool	Sherwood Park, Everton 6/90, Rotherham (L) 1/92, Oldham £450,000 11/95, Wigan £45,000 3/98, Tranmere 7/00 Rel c/s 03, Stockport 8/03, Bury 7/05, Morecambe 1/06 Rel 6/06, Southport 8/06		

PLAYING SQUAD

LOANEES		HT	WT	DOB	AGE	POB	FROM - TO	APPS	GOA
(D)Ian Kearney							Clitheroe 9/05 - Radcliffe B AL 2/06	0	0
(D)Mark Roberts		6'01"	12 00	16/10/83	22	Northwich	Crewe (2M) 11/05 and 3/06 - Chester (L) 1/06, Halifax (5ML) 8/06	18	0
(M)Adriano Rigoglioso		6'01"	12 07	28/5/79	27	Liverpool	Doncaster 11/05 - Chester (Trial) 1/06, Rel 2/06, Morecambe 3/06	1	0
(D)Chris Brass		5'09"	12 06	24/7/75	31	Easington	York C (2M) 11/05 - Bury 1/06	5	0
(F)Matt Bailey		6'05"	11 06	12/3/86	20	Nantwich	Crewe 1/06 - Lancaster (L) 3/06	2	0
(M)Mike Stringfellow				9/10/81	24	Lancaster	Morecambe 1/06 - Lancaster (L) 2/06, Rel 5/06, Barrow 6/06	1	0
(D)Jimmy Aggrey		6'02"	12 13	26/10/78	27	London	Woking 2/06 - Rel c/s06	3	0
(M)Chris Price		5'09"	11 09	24/10/75	30	Liverpool	Stalybridge 3/06 - Burscough 6/06	6	0

DEPARTURES		HT	WT	DOB	AGE	POB	FROM - TO	APPS	GOA
(F)Terry Fearns		5'11"	10 12	24/10/77	28	Liverpool	Vauxhall Motors 5/04 - Droylsden 10/05	9	0
(M)Tom Field				2/8/85	21	Liverpool	Stalybridge 10/05 - Stalybridge 10/05, Witton 11/05, Vauxhall Motors 12/05	2	0
(D)Farrell Kilbane		6'00"	13 00	21/10/74	31	Preston	Lancaster 5/04 - Stalybridge AL 12/05, Rel 3/06, Burscough 6/06	14	0
(M)Kevin Lynch				1/5/75	31	Liverpool	Vauxhall Motors 5/04 - Droylsden 12/05	15	0
(M)Dominique Krief		5'09"	10 06	15/9/83	22	Leeds	Harrogate T 6/05 - Farsley Celtic 12/05	11	0
(F)Nick Rogan				15/10/83	22	Blackpool	Lancaster 10/05 - Barrow 2/06	11	1
(G)Jamie Speare		6'01"	13 00	5/11/76	29	Liverpool	Lancaster 3/05 - Barrow 5/06	2	0
(F)Liam Watson		5'11"	11 10	5/5/70	36	Liverpool	Runcorn (PL/Man) 10/03 - Resigned 5/06, Burscough (Man) 6/06		
(D)Jerome Fitzgerald				15/11/78	27	Darwen	Accrington 5/04 - Fleetwood 6/06	36	0
(M)Kevin Leadbetter				10/9/79	26	Liverpool	Runcorn 1/04 - Burscough 6/06	27	3
(M)Dominic Morley				7/6/77	29	Liverpool	Runcorn 5/04 - Burscough 6/06	32	0
(F)Neil Robinson		5'10"	13 07	18/11/79	26	Liverpool	Macclesfield (L) 12/03 (Perm) 2/04 - Burscough 6/06	32	7
(M)Steve Pickford				24/12/77	28	Ashton-under-Lyne	Stalybridge 5/02 - Hyde 6/06	34	2
(D)Neil Fitzhenry		6'00"	12 03	24/9/78	27	Wigan	Workington 8/04 - Burscough	16	0
(D)Earl Davis		6'01"	13 02	17/5/83	23	Manchester	Swansea 2/04 - Hyde U	34	0
(F)Steve Daly				10/12/81	24	Fazackerley	Runcorn 10/03 - Droylsden 8/06	36	12
(F)Tony Evans			4/1/86	20		Liverpool	Yth - Clitheroe (SL) 8/05 (Recalled 10/05), Rel c/s 06	1	0
(F)David Brooks			17/2/88	18		Southport	Yth - Rel c/s 06	1	0
(G)Steve Dickinson	1	6'01"	12 00	1/12/73	32	Leeds	Guiseley 7/99 - Guiseley 8/06	40	0

SOUTHPORT

Ground Address: Haig Avenue,Southport, Merseyside. PR8 6JZ
Telephone: 01704 533422
Fax: 01704 533455
General email address: dh001i1907@blueyonder.co.uk
Official website: www.southportfc.net
Commercial Office: Derek Hitchcock
Tel No: 01704 533422

SIMPLE DIRECTIONS:
By Road: Leave M6 at junction 26, join M58 to junction 3, join A570 signposted Southport and follow A570 through Ormskirk town centre following signs for Southport. At the big roundabout(McDonalds on left) take fourth exit and proceed with playing fields on your left. Retail Park on right and turn left before main traffic lights into Haig Avenue. Ground is on the left.

MATCH TICKETS:
Ticket office Telephone: 01704 533422
Midweek Home Matchday: Tuesday

Capacity: 6,008   **Seats:** 1,660   **Covered:** 2,760   **Floodlights:** Yes
Clubhouse: Open every evening and match days.
Tel No: 01704 530182
Refreshments: Snacks available

Club Shop: Fully stocked
Club Manager: Derek Hitchcock

Local Press: Southport Visitor,The Champion

Local Radio: Dune FM, Radio Merseyside, Radio Lancashire

£2.50   Southport v Tamworth - Tuesday, 20th September, 2005   *05
Southport Football Club
sandgrounder

MATCHDAY PROGRAMME
Pages: 48   **Price:** £2.00
Editor: Derek Hitchcock
Contact details: Tel No: 09066 555 875

CLUB STATISTICS

RECORDS
Attendance: 20,010 v Newcastke UNited F.A.Cup 1932
Victory: 8-1 v Nelson 01.01.31.
Defeat: 0-11 v Oldham Athletic 26.12.62

Career Goalscorer: Alan Spence 98

Career Appearances: Arthur Peat 401 (1962-1972)

Transfer Fee Paid: £20,000 to Macclesfield Town
for Martin McDonald
Transfer Fee Received: £25,000 from Rochdale
for Steve Whitehall 1991

SENIOR HONOURS   Football League Division Four 72-73
DIV 4 R-UP 66-67
NPL Champions 92-93
Liverpool Senior Cup(9)
Lancs Senior Cup1904-05 Lancs Junior Cup (4)
PREVIOUS
Leagues: Lancashire Combination, Football League, Northern Premier League, Conference
Grounds: Ash Lane
Names: Southport Central and Southport Vulcan

ST. ALBANS CITY

Club Colours: Yellow with blue diagonal band/Yellow/Yellow
Change Colours: Blue with yellow diagonal band/Blue/Blue
Club Sponsor: EBB Paper
Previous League: Conference South
LAST SEASON
League: 2nd Conference South **F.A. Cup:** 3rd Qualifying Round **F.A.Trophy** 2nd Round

BEST PERFORMANCES
League: 2nd Conference South **F.A. Cup:** 2nd Round Replay 1968-69 19890-81
F.A. Trophy: Semi-Final 1998-1999

Founded:1908
Nickname:
The Saints

Back Row (L-R): John Fenely (Kit Manager), Ram Marwa, Tom Davis, Gary Elphick, Ben Martin, Ricky Perks, Chris Seeby, Simon Martin, Ben Lewis, Lee Clarke, Dave Theobald, Dean Cracknell, Jason Laird (Physio).
Front: Adama Wilde, Matt Hann,Paul Hakim, Nick Roddis (Asst Manager), Colin Lippiatt (Manager), Rob Norris, Dane Harper, Lee Flynn.

CLUB PERSONNEL

Chairman: John Gibson

Vice Chairman: Steve Carroll

Other Directors Aladair McMillan, Karen Gibson, Steve Friend, Bill Chippington, Leigh Page and Greg Healey

Presidents: Cllr Malcolm McMillan

Football Secretary & Press Officer
Steve Eames
The Red House, High St, Redbourn, Herts AL3 7LE
Tel Nos: 01727 864296 (W) 07985 524942 (M)
e-mail:steveeames@sacfc.co.uk

MANAGEMENT TEAM

Manager: Colin Lippiatt

Assitant Manager: Nick Roddiis

Physio: Jason Laird

ST ALBANS CITY

No.	Date	Comp	H/A	Opponents	Att:	Result	Goalscorers	Pos
1	Aug 13	NS	A	Welling United	552	L 1 - 3	**Clarke** 36	16
2	16		H	Cambridge City	413	L 2 - 4	Cracknell 31 **Clarke** 87	22
3	20		H	Bognor Regis Town	311	W 2 - 0	**Clarke** 42 Martin 78	13
4	27		A	Basingstoke Town	440	D 1 - 1	**Clarke** 72	18
5	29		H	Weymouth	526	W 4 - 0	**Clarke** 32 (pen) 76 Hann 80 Sangare 90	8
6	Sept 3		A	Hayes	262	W 1 - 0	**Clarke** 49	5
7	10		H	Eastbourne Borough	405	W 5 - 0	Hann 3 (51 52 58) **Clarke** 62 70	5
8	17		A	Dorchester Town	506	W 4 - 1	Martin 31 72 **Clarke** 59 Hann 84	3
9	24	FAC 2Q	A	**Enfield Town**	525	D 1 - 1	**Martin** 88	
10	27	FAC 2Qr	H	**Enfield Town**	436	W 3 - 0	Seeby 57 Martin 73 Cracknell 90	
11	Oct 1	NS	H	Lewes	541	W 2 - 0	Hann 45 Martin 70	2
12	8	FAC 3Q	H	**Kettering Town**	882	D 0 - 0		
13	11	FAC 3Qr	A	**Kettering Town**	1220	L 0 - 4		
14	15	NS	A	Sutton United	640	L 0 - 4		3
15	17		A	Thurrock	281	L 1 - 2	Cracknell 1	4
16	22		H	Newport County	531	W 1 - 0	Hakim 90	3
17	29		A	Carshalton Athletic	367	W 2 - 0	Hakim 29 Nwanze 86 (og)	
18	Nov 5		H	Eastleigh	513	L 2 - 4	Hakim 45 84	3
19	8		H	Yeading	331	W 5 - 2	Hakim 8 Martin 64 **DAVIES** 3 (14 17 60 pen)	2
20	12		A	Maidennhead Unitted	326	W 4 - 0	Cracknell 7 Hann 13 47 Hakim 45	1
21	19		H	Farnborough Town	557	D 2 - 2	Hann 3 Cracknell 8	1
22	26	FAT 3Q	A	**Heybridge Swifts**	253	W 1 - 0	**Hakim** 10	
23	Dec 10	NS	A	Weston-s-Mare	260	L 1 - 3	Hakim 35	5
24	26		H	Bishop's Stortford	658	W 3 - 0	**Clarke** 49 Walshe 60 Hann 86	3
25	31		H	Havant & Waterlooville	560	W 2 - 0	**Clarke** 18 Martin 73	
26	Jan 2		A	Bishop's Stortford	512	W 3 - 1	**Clarke** 50 Cracknell 53 Hann 84	3
27	7		H	Welling United	576	W 3 - 1	Martin 9 Davis 28 Cracknell 35	2
28	11		A	Histon	494	W 5 - 0	Martin 13, Hann 28 54, **Clarke** 40 Walshe 80	1
29	14	FAT 2	A	**Tamworth**	705	L 0 - 1		
30	21	NS	A	Bognor Regis Town	402	L 1 - 2	**Clarke** 86	3
31	28		H	Basingstoke Town	526	W 3 - 1	**Clarke** 3 (4 18 56)	2
32	Feb 4		A	Lewes	555	W 2 - 0	Ada 32 Hann 68	2
33	11		H	Sutton United	639	W 3 - 1	Martin 16 **Clarke** 23 Marwa 74	2
34	14		A	Cambridge City	472	L 3 - 4	Marwa 6 8 Hakim 35	2
35	18		A	Newport County	665	W 3 - 1	Hann 3 Marwa 57 Walshe 64	2
36	21		H	Thurrock	354	W 3 - 2	Walshe 3 Marva 41 Martin 56	2
37	25		A	Eastbourne Borough	605	D 1 - 1	Seeby 44	2
38	Mar 4		H	Dorchester Town	647	W 2 - 0	Hakim 61 **Clarke** 90	2
39	7		A	Yeading	132	D 2 2 2	Marwa 23 Walshe 63	2
40	11		H	Carshalton ASthletic	562	W 3 - 0	Hann 46 **Clarke** 50 56	2
41	18		A	Eastleigh	357	W 2 - 0	Hakim 50 Elphick 85	2
42	25		H	Maidenhead UInited	835	W 4 - 0	Hann 7 Hakim 30 Marwa 58 **Clarke** 77	1
43	April 1		A	Farnborough Town	699	D 0 - 0		2
44	8		H	Histon	863	W 1 - 0	Marwa 87	2
45	15		H	Hayes	977	W 1 - 0	Walshe 73	2
46	17		A	Weymouth	5022	L 2 - 3	**Clarke** 29 Elphick 58	2
47	22		A	Havant & Waterlooville	502	W 1 - 0	**Clarke** 19	2
48	29		A	Weston-s-Mare	853	L 1 - 2	Hakim 68	2
49	**May 7**	Play Off F	H	**Histon**	3175	W 2 - 0	**Clarke** 7 Hakim 54	

Ave. League Home Attendance:		794		**Goals**	101 53	**Top Goalscorer:** Clarke (26)	
Best Position:	1st	**Worst:**	15th				

PLAYING SQUAD

CURRANT SQUAD AS OF BEGINING OF 2006-07 SEASON

GOALKEEPERS	SQ NO.	HT	WT	D.O.B	AGE	P.O.B	CAREER	APPS	GOA
Paul Bastock	1	5'11"	14 00	19/5/70	36	Leamington Spa	Coventry (Trainee), Cambridge Utd 3/88, Sabah (Mal) c/s 89, Kettering (L) 3/90, Kettering 7/90, Fisher (L) 10/90, Boston Utd 8/92, Scarborough 10/04, Dag & Red 10/04, St Albans 11/04		
Ricky Perks	13			6/3/82	24		St Albans, Harpenden (L) 9/05, Sandridge R 11/05, Walton & H Rel c/s 06, St Albans c/s 06		

DEFENDERS

DEFENDERS	SQ NO.	HT	WT	D.O.B	AGE	P.O.B	CAREER	APPS	GOA
Chris Seeby	2			20/11/84	21	St Albans	Watford (Jun), St Albans		
Scott Cousins	3	5'10"	11 06	12/7/83	23	Edgware	Chelsea Rel c/s 03, Hendon 8/03, Torquay (Trial) 9/03, Luton (Trial) c/s 04, St Albans 8/04		
Gary Elphick	5	6'01"	13 02	17/10/85	20	Brighton	Brighton, Eastbourne (L) 9/04, St Albans (SL) 12/04, Aldershot (2ML) 1/06, St Albans 3/06		
Ben Lewis	6			22/6/77	29	Chelmsford	Heybridge Swifts (Yth), Colchester Rel c/s 97, Southend 8/97 Rel c/s 98, Heybridge Swifts 6/98, Welling 10/98 Rel 11/98, Heybridge Swifts 11/98, Chelmsford 3/00, Grays 5/02, Ford U/Redbridge 12/02, B.Stortford 11/04, St Albans 1/06		
Lee Flynn	15	5'09"	11 05	4/9/73	32	Hampstead	Boreham Wood, Wingate & F, Romford, Hendon, Hayes 7/95, Barnet 1/01 £13,500, Stevenage 5/03 Rel 4/04, Dag & Red 5/04, St Albans (L) 10/05, Cambridge C (L) 12/05, St Albans (L) 1/06, St Albans 3/06		
Ben Martin	16	6'07"	13 08	25/11/82	23	Harpenden	Harpenden, Aylesbury 3/03, Swindon 8/03 Rel c/s 04, Lincoln C (L) 10/03, Farnborough (L) 1/04, St Albans 8/04		
David Theobald	17	6'02"	11 06	15/12/78	27	Cambridge	Cambridge U (Jun), Ipswich Rel c/s 99, Brentford 7/99 Rel c/s 02, Swansea 7/02 Rel 1/03, Cambridge U 2/03, Cambridge C (L) 3/03, Canvey Island 8/03, B.Stortford (L) 10/04, Kettering 10/05, St Albans 5/06		

MIDFIELDERS

MIDFIELDERS	SQ NO.	HT	WT	D.O.B	AGE	P.O.B	CAREER	APPS	GOA
Tom Davis	4	5'10"	11 07	17/2/84	22	Bromley	Fulham Rel c/s 04, Gravesend 9/04, St Albans (L) 11/04, St Albans 2/05		
Matthew Hann	7	5'09"	10 04	6/9/80	25	Saffron Walden	Cambridge U (Ass Sch), Peterborough, Stamford (L) 9/00, B.Stortford (L) 11/00, Cambridge C (L) 2/01 (Perm) 2/01, Dorchester 8/02, St Albans 7/04		
Rambir Marwa	8			10/1/80	26	Barkingside	L.Orient (Trainee), Erith & B 2/00, Ilford 7/00, Erith & B 1/01, Australia, L.Orient (Trial) 6/03, Grays 8/03, St Albans 8/04, Dag & Red 5/05, St Albans (L) 1/06 (Perm) 3/06		
Adam Wilde	11	5'10"	11 08	22/5/79	27	Southampton	Cambridge U, Wisbech (L) 97/98 Cambridge C, Kettering 3/99, Cambridge C 8/99, Worcester £7,500 10/02, Weymouth 5-fig 6/04, Salisbury 1/06, St Albans 5/06		
Dean Cracknell	12			12/10/83	22	Hitchin	Northampton Rel 2/04, Stevenage 3/04 Rel c/s 04, Aylesbury 7/04, Barnet 1/05, B.Stortford 2/05, St Albans 5/05		
Nick Roddis	19			18/2/73	33	Rotherham	N.Forest (Trainee), Boston T, Boston U, Yeading, Hayes c/s 96, Woking c/s 00, Rel c/s 01, Re-signed Woking, Margate 12/01, Aldershot 8/02 Rel 6/04, Crawley 6/04, AFC Wimbledon 9/04, St Albans (Pl/Coach) 11/04		
Dane Harper	20	5'10"		9/12/87	18	Boston	Boston U, St Albans 8/06		

FORWARDS

FORWARDS	SQ NO.	HT	WT	D.O.B	AGE	P.O.B	CAREER	APPS	GOA
Paul Hakim	9			18/6/82	24	London	Wingate & F, Cheshunt, Slough 11/02, Wingate & F 12/02, Dag & Red (Trial) c/s 04, B.Stortford 8/04, St Albans 7/05		
Lee Clarke	10	5'11"	10 08	28/7/83	23	Peterborough	Yaxley, Peterborough Undisc 10/01, Kettering (SL) 3/03, Kettering (2ML) 8/03, St Albans (SL) 1/04, St Albans 7/04		
Simon Martin	14			8/7/79	27	London	St Albans, Lincoln U, Hucknall, St Albans £5,000 c/s 01, Thurrock 1/04, St Albans 8/05		
Josh Sozzo	18			5/7/79	27	Bedford	Arsenal (Jun), Wycombe (Jun), Watford (Jun), Luton (Jun), Leighton T, Hemel Hempstead, Bedford c/s 00, Aylesbury 10/03, Hitchin 1/04, St Albans 5/06		
Robert Norris	21	5'09"	10 03	12/10/87	18	Radcliffe-on-Trent	Boston U, Alfreton (L) 1/06, St Albans 8/06		

LOANEES		HT	WT	DOB	AGE	POB	FROM - TO	APPS	GOA
None									

DEPARTURES		HT	WT	DOB	AGE	POB	FROM - TO	APPS	GOA
(D)Patrick Ada	16	6'00"		14/1/85	21		Barnet 7/05 - Rel 5/06, Exeter 7/06		
Ben Walshe				24/5/83	23		QPR 8/04 - Stage School c/s 06		
Mark Burgess							Hendon 12/05 - Maidenhead 7/06		
Andy Ross							Ricmond (Aus) 3/06 - Hitchin 8/06		

ST. ALBANS CITY

Ground Address: Clarence Park, York Road, St.Albans, Herts. AL1 4PL
Telephone: 01727 864296
Fax: 01727 866235
General email address: secretary@sacfc.co.uk
Official website: www.sacfc.co.uk

SIMPLE DIRECTIONS: Exit M25 jct 22 and follow A1081 towards St Albans, at 5th roundabout turn right into Alma Road. At the lights turn right into Stanhope Road and straight on at next lights into Clarence Road. Ground is 200 yards on left.

By Rail: Nearest Railwat Station is St Albans (300 metres from ground)

MATCH TICKETS:
Ticket office Telephone: 01727 864296
Midweek Home Matchday: Tuesday

CAPACITY: 6,000
Seats: 904
Covered: 1,900

Clubhouse: Open matchdays and open for functions

Refreshments: Available on matchdays

Club Shop: Fully stocked. Manager: Barry Hillard c/o club

MATCHDAY PROGRAMME
48 pages £ 2.00
Editor: Sreve Eames
steveeames@safc.co.uk
Local Press: St Albans Observer
Local radio: BBC Three Counties, Chiltern Radio

CLUB STATISTICS
RECORDS
Attendance: 9,757
v Ferryhill Athletic F.A.Amateur Cuo 1926

Victory 14-0
v Aylesbury United (H) Spartan League 19.10.12

Defeat 0-11
v Wimbledon (H) Isthmian League 1946

Career Goalscorer: W.H.(Billy) Minter 356
Top scorer for 12 consecutive seasonsf rom 1920 -1932
Career Apperances: Phil Wood 900 (1962-85
Transfer Fee Paid: £6,000
to Yeovil Town for Paul Turnert Auguat 1957?
Transfer Fee Received: £92,759
from Southend United for Dan Austin 1990

SENIOR HONOURS
Conference South Runners-Up 2005-2006
Isthmian Champions 23-24 26-27 27-28 R-Up 54-5 92-3
Athenian League Championms (2)
London Senior Cup 70-71 R-Up 69-70

PREVIOUS LEAGUES
Herts County 08-10 Spartan 08-20 Athenian 20-23

STAFFORD RANGERS

Club Colours: Black & white stripes/Black/Black
Change Colours: All Red
Club Sponsor: Kingdon Mortgages & Finance
Previous League: Conferenc North
LAST SEASON
League: 2nd Conference North **F.A. Cup:** 3rd Qualifying Rd Replay **F.A.Trophy** 2ndh Round

BEST PERFORMANCES
League: 2nd Conference North **F.A. Cup:** 2nd Round Replay 1968-69 19890-81
F.A. Trophy: Semi-Final 1998-1999

Founded:1876
Nickname:
Rangers

Back Row (L-R): Craig McAughtrie, Brian Quailey, Dean Williams, Neil Grayson, Richie Sutton, Danny Alcock, Wayne Daniel, Liam Murray. **Middle:** Chris Godwin (Medical), Guy Madjo, Ged Murphy, Nathan Talbott, John Hamnett (res Coach), Nathan Smith, Danny Edwards, Dolapo Olaoye, Simon Davies (Kit Manager).
Front: Alex Gibson, Kevin Street, Lee Downes, David Oldfield (Asst Manager), Phil Robinson (Manager), Craig Lovatt, Robin Gibson, Dave Walker.

CLUB PERSONNEL

Chairman: Jon Downing

Vice Chairman: Michael Hughes

Other Directors   C.S.Went, R.Tonnge, P.Bowers,

N.Oldfield, D.T.Montgomery (Managing Director)

Football Secretary   Michael Hughes

c/o Club

Tel Nos: 01785 254879 (H)) 07850 996386 (M)

e-mailsrfcmarston road2tiscali.co.uk

MANAGEMENT TEAM

Manager: Philip Robinson
Assitant Manager: David Oldfield
Coach: Chris Curtis

STAFFORD RANGERS

BEST LGE ATT.: **1,667** v Northwich Victoria
LOWEST: **552** v Vauxhall Motors

No.	Date	Comp	H/A	Opponents	Att:	Result	Goalscorers	Pos
1	Aug 13	CN	H	Hucknall Town	634	W 2 - 0	Downes 68 (pen) **Grayson** 72	2
2	16		A	Worksop Town	519	W 1 - 0	Lovatt 46	2
3	20		A	Hyde United	312	W 3 - 1	Thomas 43 Daniel 60 Street 75	1
4	27		H	Nuneatoon Borough	1.063	W 2 - 1	Groves 72 Thomson 81	1
5	29		A	Lancaster City	375	D 1 - 1	Street 60	2
6	Sept 3		H	Moor Green	729	L 1 - 3	Daniel 21	3
7	10		A	Kettering Town	966	W 1 - 0	Groves 89	2
8	17		H	Workington	737	D 2 - 2	Street 36 Powell 57 (pen)	3
9	**24**	**FAC 2Q**	**A**	**Kettering Town**	**971**	**L 0 - 1**		
10	Oct 1	CN	A	Hednesford Town	1452	W 2 - 0	Thomson 55 Smith 57	3
11	15		H	Redditch United	744	W 3 - 0	**Grayson** 25 Edwards 28 Talbot 30	3
12	18		H	Vauxhall Motors	552	W 3 - 0	Edwards 3 **Grayson** 7 Smith 27	3
13	22		A	Leigh RMI	301	W 3 - 1	Smith 28 **Grayson** 18 Thomson 55	2
14	29		H	Alfreton Town	913	W 1 - 0	Smith 86	1
15	Nov 5		A	Droylsden	473	L 1 - 2	Smith 21	1
16	8		A	Stalybridge Celtic	519	W 3 - 2	Street 18 Smith 60 77	1
17	12		H	Hinckley United	964	L 2 - 3	Piercewright 13 (pg) Thomson 76	2
18	19		A	Barrow	907	D 1 - 1	**Grayson** 61	2
19	**26**	**FAT 3Q**	**A**	**Leigh RMI**	**165**	**W 4 - 1**	**Talbot 22 82 Walker 26 Gibson 62**	
20	Dec 3	CN	H	Gainsborough Trinity	704	W 3 - 0	Smith 13 63 **Grayson** 63	1
21	10		A	Harrogate Town	505	W 2 - 0	Street 49 **Grayson** 69	1
22	**17**	**FAT 1**	**H**	**Lancaster City**	**646**	**W 4 - 2**	**Smith 17 Grayson 40 43 Walker 80**	
23	24	CN	A	Worcester City	1372	D 1 - 1	Clarke 82	1
24	31		H	Northwich Victoria	1677	W 2 - 0	**Grayson** 32 Smith 37	1
25	Jan 2		A	Worcester City	1228	D 1 - 1	McAughtrie 15	1
26	7		A	Hiucknall Town	601	W 2 - 0	**Grayson** 71 Street 84	1
27	**14**	**FAT 2**	**H**	**Morecambe**	**1121**	**W 1 - 0**	**Street 77**	
28	21	CN	H	Hyde united	935	W 1 - 0	Smith 27	1
29	28		A	Nuneaton Borough	2183	D 1 - 1	Groves 72	1
30	**Feb 4**	**FAT 3**	**H**	**Forest Green Rovers**	**1178**	**W 2 - 1**	**Lovatt 12 Grayson 54**	
31	11	CN	A	Redditch United	546	W 1 - 0	**Grayson** 21	1
32	14		H	Worksop Town	1045	W 3 - 2	Gibson 24 Thomson 53 Smith 65	1
33	18		H	Leigh RMI	1035	D 0 - 0		1
34	21		A	Vauxhall Motors	198	W 3 - 1	**Grayson** 33 Groves 54 Gibson 90	1
35	**25**	**FAT 4**	**A**	**Woking**	**2020**	**D 1 - 1**	**Grayson 38 (pen)**	
36	**28**	**FAT 4R**	**H**	**Woking**	**1781**	**L 2 - 4**	**Talbot 20 Thomson 66**	
37	Mar 7	CN	H	Stalybridge Celtic	561	W 1 - 0	Thomson 3	1
38	11		A	Alfreton Town	480	L 1 - 2	Groves 57	1
39	14		H	Hednesford Town	1519	D 1 - 1	Smith 39	1
40	18		H	Droylsden	785	D 0 - 0		1
41	25		A	Hinckley United	715	W 1 - 0	Daniel 86	1
42	28		H	Kettering Town	745	L 1 - 2	Gibson 50	2
43	April 1		H	Barrow	956	W 3 - 1	McAughtrie 28 Downes 47 Pope 90	1
44	8		A	Gainsborough Trinity	418	D 1 - 1	McMahon 80	2
45	11		A	Workington	495	L 1 - 0	**Grayson** 83	2
46	15		A	Moor Green	393	W 1 - 0	McMahon 84	2
47	17		H	Lancaster City	949	W 3 - 0	**Grayson** 25 73 Gibson 43	2
48	22		A	Northwich Victoria	3154	L 1 - 3	Gibson 24	2
49	29		H	Harrogate Town	806	L 0 - 1		2
50	**May 2**	**Play Off S-F**	**H**	**Harrogate Town**	**1665**	**W 1 - 0**	**Gibson 63**	
51	**6**	**Play Off Final**	**H**	**Droylsden**	**2704**	**D 1 - 1**	**Grayson 28 Won 5-3 after penalties**	
Ave. League Home Attendance:			891		**Goals**	77 44	Top Goalscorer: Grayson (19)	
Best Position:	1st	**Worst:**	3rd					

PLAYING SQUAD

CURRANT SQUAD AS OF BEGINING OF 2006-07 SEASON

GOALKEEPERS	SQ NO.	HT	WT	D.O.B	AGE	P.O.B	CAREER
Dean Williams	1	6'00"	12 07	5/1/72	34	Lichfield	Birmingham, Tamworth 3/92, Brentford £2,000 8/93, Doncaster 8/94, Huddersfield (L) 8/97, Gateshead 12/97, Telford 8/98, TNS 8/01, Aberystwyth 5/04, Forest Green 9/04, Stafford R 9/05
Danny Alcock	17	5'11"	11 03	15/2/84	22	Salford	Stoke, Barnsley 10/03 Rel c/s 04, Accrington 8/04 Rel 5/06, Stafford R 8/06

DEFENDERS

DEFENDERS							
Nathan Talbott	3	6'01"	13 00	21/10/84	21	Wolverhampton	Wolves (Scholar), Yeovil 3/04 Rel c/s 04, Stafford R 7/04
Craig McAughtrie	4	6'04"	13 10	3/3/81	25	Burton	Sheff Utd Rel c/s 00, Carlisle 8/00 Rel c/s 02, Stafford R 7/02
Wayne Daniel	5			12/12/76	29	Birmingham	St Gerards, Paget R 10/00, Boldmere St Michaels 5/02, Stafford R 6/02
Ritchie Sutton	26	6'00"	11 05	29/4/86	20	Stoke	Crewe, Leek T (2ML) 11/05, Stafford R (L) 3/06, Stafford R (L) 8/06
Liam Murray	30	6'03"	11 00	1/8/85	21	Stafford	Shrewsbury Rel c/s 05, Leigh RMI (L) 3/05, Stafford R 8/05

MIDFIELDERS

MIDFIELDERS							
Craig Lovatt	6			16/11/78	27	Stoke-on-Trent	Port Vale (Trainee), Eastwood Hanley, Kidsgrove A, Leek, Stafford R 10/00
Lee Downes	7	6'00"	12 00	27/2/83	23	Dudley	Wolves cc 00/01, Kidderminster, Stafford R 8/02
Kevin Street	8	5'10"	10 08	25/11/77	28	Crewe	Crewe Rel c/s 02, Luton (L) 11/01, Livingston (Trial) 5/02, Mansfield (Trial) 7/02, Northwich 8/02 (02/03 13,6), Bristol R 11/02, Shrewsbury 10/03 (03/04 28,2) Rel c/s 05, Stafford R 8/05
Robin Gibson	11	5'06"	10 07	15/11/79	26	Crewe	Crewe, Wrexham (Tr 7/96) Rel c/s 02, Stafford R 7/02
Danny Edwards	15			27/10/83	22	Shrewsbury	Shrewsbury, Stafford R (SL) 3/03, Stafford R c/s 03
Ged Murphy	27	5'10"	11 03	19/12/78	27	Manchester	Oldham Rel c/s 99, Norwich (Trial) 4/99, Altrincham (Trial) c/s 99, Barrow c/s 99 Rel 9/99, Stafford R 11/99, Nuneaton 11/99 Rel c/s 00, Hyde 9/00, Leigh RMI Rel 5/01, Stalybridge 8/01, Droylsden 8/02 Rel 11/05, Altrincham 11/05 Rel 6/06, Radcliffe B (L)
David Oldfield	28	6'01"	13 04	30/5/68	38	Perth (Aus)	Luton, Man City £600,000 3/89, Leicester £150,000 1/90, Millwall (SL) 2/95, Luton £150,000 7/95 Rel c/s 98, Stoke 7/98, Peterborough 3/00 Rel c/s 02, Oxford U (Pl/Coach) 8/02 Rel c/s 04, Oxford Utd (Ass Man), Brackley T 3/06, Stafford R 7/06 (Pl/Ass Man)
Phil Robinson	29	5'10"	11 07	6/1/67	39	Stafford	Aston Villa, Wolves £5,000 7/87, Notts County £67,500 8/89, Birmingham (SL) 3/91, Huddersfield (2ML) 9/92 £50,000 11/92, Northampton (3ML) 9/94, Chesterfield £15,000 12/94, Notts County £80,000 8/96, Stoke 6/98 Rel c/s 00, Hereford 7/00 (00/01 40,2), 01/02

FORWARDS

FORWARDS							
Neil Grayson	9	5'10"	12 09	1/11/64	41	York	Rowntree M, Doncaster 3/90, York 3/91 Rel c/s 91, Chesterfield 8/91 Rel c/s 92, Gateshead (SL) 2/92, Boston U 7/92, Northampton 6/94, Hereford 8/97, Cheltenham £15,000 3/98 Rel c/s 02, Forest Green 7/02, Stafford R Undis 3/04
Nathan Smith	10			26/3/85	21	Birmingham	Rushall O, Stafford R 8/05
Guy Madjo	12	6'00"	13 05	1/6/84	22	Cameroon	Petersfield 12/04, Millwall (Trial) 1/05, Aldershot (Trial) 2/05, Bristol C 9/05, Forest Green (L) 11/05 Perm 1/06 Rel 5/06, Stafford R 8/06
Dave Walker	14						Norton U, Stafford R
Brian Quailey	16	6'00"	13 04	21/3/78	28	Leicester	Deeping R, Nuneaton 7/96, WBA 9/97, Exeter (3ML) 12/98, Blackpool (L) 12/99, Scunthorpe 2/00, Carlisle (Trial) 1/01, Oxford U (Trial) 2/02, Rushden & D (Trial) 7/02, Doncaster 8/02, Halifax 9/02, Nuneaton 5/03, Tamworth 11/03, Stevenage 4/04, Nuneaton AL
Dolapo Olaoye	18	5'10"	12 04	17/10/82	23	Lagos, Nig	Port Vale, Mercer Univ (USA), Michigan Bucks (USA), Stafford R 8/06

LOANEES	SN	HT	WT	DOB	AGE	POB	FROM - TO
None							

DEPARTURES	SN	HT	WT	DOB	AGE	POB	FROM - TO
(F) Peter Thomson		6'03"	12 06	30/7/77	29	Crumpsall	Lancaster 7/05 - Altrincham 6/06
Matt Clarke							Redditch 12/05 - Redditch 6/06
Paul McMahon							Chasetown
Paul Groves							Portsmouth (Res Coach) 7/06

STAFFORD RANGERS

Ground Address: Marston Road,Stafford ST16 3BX
Telephone: 01785 602430
Fax: 01785 602431
General email address: srfcmarstonroad£tiscali.co.uk
Official website: www.sacfc.co.uk

SIMPLE DIRECTIONS: M6 Jct 14 A34 (Stone) to roundabout, straight over to Beaconside, then take third right into Common Road. Ground one mile ahead.**From** Town centre follow signs for B5066 (Sandon) turn left by new housing estate. Ground is two miles from BR.

By Rail: Nearest Railwat Station is Staffords (Two miles from ground)

MATCH TICKETS:
Ticket office Telephone: 01785 602430
Midweek Home Matchday: Tuesday

CAPACITY: 6,000
Seats: 4264
Covered: 3,500

Clubhouse: Open matchdayds and every evening.

Refreshments: Available on matchdays

Club Shop: Programmes and souvenirs available

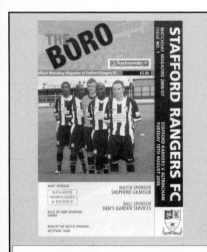

MATCHDAY PROGRAMME
48 Pages £2.00
Editor: Chris Bedford
chrisbedford@clara.co.uk
Local Press:
Local radio: Express & Star & Staffordshire Newsletter

CLUB STATISTICS
RECORDS

Attendance: 8,536
v Rotherham Utd F.A. Cuo3rd Rd 1975

Victory   14-0
v Kidsgrove Athletic Staffs.Senior Cup 2003

Defeat   0-12
v Burton TownBirmingham League 1930

Career Goalscorer: M.Cullerton 176

Career Apperances: Jim Sargent
Transfer Fee Paid: £13,000
to VS Rugby forS.Butterworth
Transfer Fee Received: £100,000
from Crystal Palace forStan Collymore

SENIOR HONOURS
Northern Premier League Champions 1971-72 1984-85
F.A.Trophy Winners 1971-72 1978-79
F.A.Trophy Runners-Up 1975-76
Staffordshire Senior Cup Winners (7)

PREVIOUS LEAGUES
Shropshire 1891-93 B'ham 1893-96 N.Staffs 1896-1900,
Cheshire 1900-01, B'ham Comb. 1900-12 46-52, Cheshire Co 52-69
N.P.L. 69-79 83-85 Alliance 79-83 Conf: 85-95

STEVENAGE BOROUGH

Club Colours: Red & white stripes/red/red
Change Colours: All Blue
Club Sponsor: CPM Omega
Previous League: Isthmian
BEST PERFORMANCES
League: Conference Champions 1995-96   **F.A. Cup:** 4th Rd replay 1997-98
F.A. Trophy: Runners -Uo 2001-2002
LAST SEASON
Conference: 6th   **F.A.Cup:** 3rd Round Teplay   **F.A.Trophy:**1st Round

Formed:
Nickname: Boro

CLUB PERSONNEL

Chairman: Phillip Wallace

Club Administrator: Roger Austin
Tel Nos: 01438 218072 (W) 07832 127839 (M)

Commercial Manager: Clive Abrey
Tel Nos: 01438 218073 (W) 07960 619314 (M)

Press Officer: Steve Watkins
Tel Nos: 01438 223223 (W) 07958 935182 (M)

MANAGEMENT TEAM

Manager: Mark Stimson
Assistant Manager: Graham Pearce
First Team Coach: :   Graham Benstead
Physio: Karl Ballard

STEVENAGE BOROUGH

BEST LGE ATT.: 3,463 v Stevenage Borough
LOWEST: 1,403 v Canvey Island

No.	Date	Comp	H/A	Opponents	Att:	Result	Goalscorers	Pos
1	Aug 13	C	H	Altincham	2008	W 3 - 0	Elding 15 Stamp 37 Maamria 73 (pen)	2
2	16		A	Woking	2592	L 2 - 3	Boyd 37 45	10
3	20		A	Southport	1007	L 2 - 3	Elding 54 Stamp 56 (pen)	14
4	27		H	Tamworth	1635	W 3 - 1	Boyd 41 Elding 64 Goodliffe 79	6
5	29		A	Crawley Town	2019	W 2 - 1	Stamps 23 (pen) Williams 83	3
6	Sept 3		H	Halifax Town	1682	W 1 - 0	Elding 23	3
7	10		H	Hereford United	2404	D 0 - 0		4
8	17		A	Aldershot Town	2563	D 2 - 2	Elding 29 Gregory 40	6
9	20		H	Exeter City	2445	W 2 - 0	Boyd 70 Bulman 88	5
10	24		A	Morecambe	1738	L 1 - 4	Nurse 60	6
11	27		A	Canvey Island	832	D 1 - 1	Berquez 63	8
12	Oct 5		H	Dagenham & Redbridge	24447	W 2 - 1	Vickers 34 (og) Boyd 90	6
13	8		A	Burton Albion	1319	L 1 - 3	Elding 51	6
14	15		H	Accrington Stanley	2141	W 3 - 1	Nurse 52 Maamria 60 (pen) Williams 80 (og)	5
15	18	LDV Vans T	A	**Swindon Town**	1771	L 0 - 2		
16	22	FAC 4Q	A	**Exeter City**	3421	W 1 - 0	Laker 57	
17	29	C	A	Gravesend & N	1372	W 2 - 0	Nurse 2 Boyd 70	5
18	Nov 5	FAC 1R	A	**Kettering Town**	4548	W 3 - 1	Stamp 8 Boyd 43 Elding 69	
19	12	C	H	Kidderminster Harriers	2207	W 3 - 1	Stamp 24 (pen) 69 (pen) Laker 26	
20	19		A	Scarborough	1152	D 1 - 1	Elding 73	4
21	26		H	Grays Athletic	2753	L 0 - 1		5
22	Dec 3	FAC 3R	H	**Northampton Town**	3937	D 2 - 2	Boyd 5 Elding 83	
23	10	C	H	Forest Green Rovers	1771	W 2 - 1	Nurse 55 Laker 74	
24	13	FAC 3R r	A	**Northampton Town**	4407	L 0 - 2		
25	17	FAT 1	H	**Crawley Town**	610	L 0 - 2		
26	24	C	A	Canbridge United	3697	L 0 - 1		6
27	31		A	Grays Athletic	1214	D 2 - 2	Maamria 77 Louis 88	6
28	Jan 2		H	Stevenage Borough	3463	W 3 - 1	Nurse 43 Louis 45 Boyd 55	6
29	7		A	Altrincham	914	D 1 - 1	Stamp 39	7
30	10		A	York City	2325	W 1 - 0	Louis 21	3
31	21		H	Southport	2231	L 0 - 1		6
32	24		H	Woking	2152	D 1 - 1	Stamp 62	6
33	28		A	Tamworth	1228	L 0 - 2		7
34	Feb 4		H	Aldershot Town	2010	W 2 - 1	Boyd 15 Maamria 76	
35	11		H	Morecambe	2068	W 1 - 0	Nurse 34	3
36	18		A	Dagenham & Redbridge	1427	D 2 - 2	Nurse 1 Maamria 5 (pen)	5
37	21		H	Canvey Island	1403	W 3 - 0	Maamria 16 Louis 54 Boyd 88	4
38	27		A	Hereford United	2394	L 0 - 2		4
39	Mar 11		H	Burton Albion	2081	L 2 - 3	Maamria 7 Stamp 45	7
40	14		A	Exeter City	3026	W 2 - 0	Stamp 38 Nurse 77	5
41	18		A	Accrington Stanley	2119	D 1 - 1	Stamp 1	5
42	25		H	Gravesend & Northfleet	1873	W 2 - 0	Nurse 35 Stamp 45	4
43	April 1		A	Kidderminster Harriers	1490	D 0 - 0		4
44	8		H	Scarborough	1861	W 2 - 0	Miller 10 Boyd 21	4
45	14		A	Halifax Town	2253	D 1 - 1	Stamp 85	5
46	17		H	Crawley Town	2410	W 2 - 1	Louis 3 80	6
47	22		H	York City	2701	D 1 - 1	Goodliffe 42	6
48	29		A	Forest Green Rovers	1510	L 0 - 2		6

| Ave. League Home Attendance: | | | | 3443 | | **Goals** 68 56 | **Top Goalscorer:** Darren Stamp (13) | |
| **Best Position:** 2nd **Worst:** 14th | | | | | | | | |

JULIAN 1	WARNER 2	GREGORY 3	GOODLIFFE 5	MAAMRIA 9	ELDING 10	BOYD 11	BULMAN 15	WEATHERSTONE 23	HENRY 25	STAMP 27	BERQUEZ 17	WILLIAMS 7	NURSE 20	GORE 31	HOCKING 14	FARROW 36	QUINN 4	PERPETUINI 18	LAKER 6	SULLIVAN 29	BROUGH 8	DEANE 19	LEWIS 32	SCHILLACHI 24	LOUIS 22	MILLER 10	OBINNA 8	OLIVER 21	DUFFY 12	#
X	X	X	X	X	X	X	X	X	X	S	S	S	U	U																1
	X	X	X	X	X	X			X	X	X	S	S	X	U	U	U													2
X	X	X	X		X	X	X	X	X	X	X			S	U	S		S	U											3
X	X	X	X		X	X	X	S		X	S	U	X	U	X		X	S												4
X	X	X	X		X	X	X	S		X	S	S	X	U	X		X	U												5
X	X	X			X	X	X	S	X	X	U	S	X	U	X		X		S											6
X	X	X			X	X	X	S	X	X	U	S	X	U	X		X		S											7
X	X	X			X	X	X	S		X	S	S	X	U	X		X	U	X											8
X	X	X	S	S	X	X	X	X			S	X	U	X			U													9
X	X	X	U	S	X	X	X	X	X		S		X	U	X		U													10
X	X		X	S	X	X	X	X		S	U	X	U	X			U													11
X		X		X	X	X	X	S	X		X	S	X	U	X		S		X	U										12
X	X	X			X	X	X	S		X	S	S	X	U	X		U		X											13
X	X				X		X	X	S	X	X	X		X	U		X	S	X		U	U								14
U				X	S	X	X	X	X	X		S	X		X	X		X	X		X	X	U		S					15
X	X			X	U	X	X		X	X	X		X	U		X	S	X	U	U										16
X	X			X		X	X		X	X		X	U		X	S	X	S	X		S	U								17
X	X	S			S	X	X		X	X		X	U		X	X	X	U	X		S									18
X	X	S			X	X	X	S		X	X		U		X	X	X		X		S	U								19
X	X	S		S	S	X	X	U		X	X		X	U		X	S	X		S										20
X	X	X		S	X	X	X	U		X	X		X	U		X	S	X		S										21
X	X	X	U		S	X	X	U		X	U	X	U		X	X	X		X											22
X	X	U	S		X	X	X		X	S		X	U		X	X	X		X		S									23
X	X	S	U		X	X	X		S	X	S	X	U		X	X	X		X											24
U	U	X	X		X	X	S	X	X		X		X	X		X		X	S		S									25
X	X	S		X		X	X	X	S	X	U	U		X	X	X		X		S										26
X	X	X		X		X	X	X	X		S	X	U	U		X	S		U				X							27
X	X	X		X		X	X	X	S	S		X		U	X		X	S					X							28
X	X			X		X	X		X	S		U	X		X	X	U	U		U	X									29
X	S			X		X	X		X	S	S	U	X	U	X		X				X									30
X	X	S			X	X		X	S		X	X	U	X		X	X	U		S		X								31
X		X			X	X		X		S	X	U	X		X	S	X		U			X	X	S						32
X	X	X			X	X		S		S	X	U		X	U	X					X	X	S	X						33
X	U			X		X	X		U	X	U	U		X				X	S	X										34
X	X	S	U	X	X	X		X	X	U		X	U		X	X					S	X								35
X	X	S	U	X	X	X		X		S	X		U		X	X					X	X	S							36
X	X	U	U	X	X	X		X	X	S			S		X	X					S	X	X							37
X		X	U	X	X	X	U	X	S	X		S		X	X						X	X	S							38
X			U	X	X	X	S	X	X	X		X	U		X	X					S	X		X						39
X			X	X	X	X	S	X	X	X		X	U	U		U		X			U		X							40
X	S			X	X	X	X		X	X	X		X	U		U		X			U	S	X							41
X	S			X	X	X	X	U	X		X	U		X					U	X	S	X								42
X	X	X	X		X	X		U	X	X		X	U		U					S	X		X	X	U					43
X	U	S	X	X		X	X		X	X		X	U		X						S	X				X				44
X	U			X	X	X	S	X	X	X		X	U				X				S	S	X							45
X	S	S	X	X		X	U	X	X	X		S	U					X	X		X		X							46
X	S	S	X	X		X	U	X	X	S		X	U					X	X		X		X							47
X	S	X		X		X	X		X		X	U		U			X	X	S	X	S									48

Total Appearances (Conference)

41	28	20	14	25	16	42	39	6	32	29	17	3	33	1	15	0	24	12	21	0	5	0	0	0	12	14	1	12	0	X
0	6	9	2	5	1	0	0	13	0	5	13	14	6	0	2	0	2	7	2	1	1	0	5	0	6	1	8	0	1	S
0	3	2	6	0	0	0	1	6	0	0	3	4	0	38	8	1	9	4	0	3	3	1	1	3	1	2	0	0	1	U

Cup Appearances

4	4	2	1	1	3	5	5	2	3	3	5	1	4	2	1	0	6	4	4	2	4	0	0	0	0	0	0	0	0	X
0	0	2	0	0	2	1	1	0	0	1	0	1	1	0	0	0	0	1	0	0	1	0	2	1	0	0	0	0	0	S
2	1	0	2	0	1	0	0	1	0	0	0	1	0	4	0	0	0	0	2	1	1	0	0	0	0	0	0	0	0	U

STEVENAGE BOROUGH

CURRANT SQUAD AS OF BEGINING OF 2006-07 SEASON

GOALKEEPERS	SQ NO.	HT	WT	D.O.B	AGE	P.O.B	CAREER	APPS	GOA
Alan Julian	1	6'01"	13 05	11/3/83	23	Ashford	Brentford Rel 2/05, Stevenage 2/05	41	0
Danny Potter	16	5'11"	13 00	18/3/79	27	Ipswich	Chelsea (Trainee), Colchester 10/97 Rel c/s 98,		
							Exeter 8/98 Rel c/s 00, Weymouth (L) 11,99, Salisbury (L) 1/00,		
							Weymouth 6/00, Chelmsford 2/02, Canvey Island 8/02,		
							Stevenage 6/06		

DEFENDERS

Barry Fuller	2	5'10"	11 10	25/8/84	22	Ashford	Charlton Rel 4/06, Barnet (SL) 1/06, Stevenage 7/06		
John Nutter	3	5'10"	11 09	13/6/82	24	Taplow	Blackburn (Sch), Wycombe Rel c/s 01, Aldershot 5/01,		
							Gravesend (L) 11/02, Grays (L) 1/03, Grays 6/04, Stevenage 5/06		
Luke Oliver	4	6'07"	14 05	1/5/84	22	Hammersmith	Brook House, Wycombe 7/02, Woking 2/04, Yeovil Undisc 5/05,		
							Woking (3ML) 8/05, Stevenage £15,000 1/06	12	0
Jason Goodliffe	5			7/3/74	32	Hillingdon	Brentford, Hayes 8/92, Stevenage 5/01	16	2
Santos Gaia	6	6'00"	12 04	8/9/78	27	Sao-Mateus-Es	AA Sao Mateus (Bra), Corinthians (Bra), Agrimiacao (Bra),		
							Exeter 7/02, Stevenage 6/06		
Ron Henry	25	5'11"	11 10	2/1/84	22	Hemel Hempstead	Tottenham Rel 11/03, Southend (L) 3/03, Fisher 2/04, Dublin C,		
							Stevenage 1/05	32	0

MIDFIELDERS

Dannie Bulman	7	5'09"	11 12	24/1/79	27	Ashford	Ashford T, Wycombe (Trial) 97/98, Wycombe £5,000 + 6/98 Rel c/s 04,		
							Stevenage 6/04	39	1
Adam Miller	10	5'11"	11 06	19/2/82	24	Hemel Hempstead	Ipswich (Scholar), Canvey Island 10/00, Southend (Trial),		
							Grays PE 8/02, Gravesend 9/03, Aldershot 10/03, QPR £50,000 11/04,		
							Peterborough (L) 9/05, Stevenage 1/06	15	1
George Boyd	11			2/10/85	20		Charlton (Sch), Stevenage 10/02, Chatham (L) 3/03	42	10
David Hicks	15	5'10"	10 08	13/11/85	20	Enfield	Tottenham (Scholar), Northampton 2/04, Hornchurch (L) 11/04,		
							Hitchin (2ML) 12/05, Hitchin 2/06, Stevenage 8/06		
Sam Hatton	17					St Albans	St Albans, Stevenage, Northwood (L) 4/06		
Chris Sullivan	18			26/9/87	18		Stevenage, Dunstable (L) 3/05, Chesham (3ML) 2/06	1	0
Steve Guppy	21	5'11"	12 00	29/3/69	37	Winchester	Southampton (Jun), Colden Common, Wycombe 9/89,		
							Newcastle £150,000 8/94, Port Vale £225,000 11/94,		
							Leicester £950,000 2/97, Celtic £350,000 8/01, Leicester 1/04 Rel c/s 04,		
							Leeds 8/04, Stoke 9/04, Wycombe 11/04, DC United (USA) 3/05, Stevenage 8/06		
Craig Dobson	22	5'06"	10 06	23/1/84	22	Chingford	C.Palace (Scholar), Cheltenham 7/03 Rel 5/04, Brentford (Trial),		
							Barnet 8/04 Rel 10/04, Waltham Forest 11/04, Lewes 12/04,		
							Cambridge C 7/05, Stevenage 4 fig 7/06		
Dale Binns	23					London	Hendon, Cambridge C 8/04, Stevenage 6/06		

FORWARDS

Tony Thorpe	8	5'09"	12 06	10/4/74	32	Leicester	Leicester (Trainee), Luton 8/92, Fulham £800,000 2/98,		
							Bristol C £1 million 6/98 Rel c/s 02, Reading (L) 2/99, Luton (L) 3/99,		
							Luton (2ML) 11/99, Luton 7/02, QPR £50,000 8/03, Rotherham (L) 3/05,		
							Swindon 7/05, Colchester 1/06 Rel 5/06, Stevenage 7/06		
Jon Nurse	9			1/3/81	25	London	Local, Sutton U 8/03, Stevenage 6/04, Lewes (L) 1/05	39	9
Hector Mackie	14				18		Welling, Stevenage 7/06		
Ieaun Lewis	19						Hitchin, Stevenage 10/05	5	0
Steve Morison	20	6'02"	12 00	28/8/83	23	London	Northampton, Bishops Stortford (L) 12/03, Bury (Trial) 10/04,		
							Bishops Stortford Nominal 10/04, Stevenage 5 fig 8/06		
Darryn Stamp	24	6'01"	11 10	21/9/78	27	Beverley	Hessle, Scunthorpe 7/97 Rel c/s 01, Halifax (L) 2/00,		
							Scarborough (L) 3/01, Scarborough 5/01, Northampton £30,000 5/02,		
							Chester 8/03, Kidderminster (L) 11/04, Stevenage 1/05	34	12

STEP 1
CONFERENCE

STEP 2 - P177
CONFERENCE Nth & Sth

STEP 3 - P269
NPL - SOUTHERN - ISTHMIAN PREM

STEP 4 - P269
NPL - SOUTHERN - ISTHMIAN

STEP 5/6 - P473

STEP 7 - P713

PLAYING SQUAD

LOANEES	HT	WT	DOB	AGE	POB	FROM - TO	APPS	GOA
None								

DEPARTURES	HT	WT	DOB	AGE	POB	FROM - TO	APPS	GOA
(M)Michael Brough	6'00"	11 07	1/8/81	25	Nottingham	Notts County 3/04 - Forest Green 1/06	6	0
(F)Anthony Elding	6'01"	13 10	16/4/82	24	Boston	Boston U 2/03 - Kettering Town £20,000 + 1/06, Boston U 5/06	17	7
(G)Lee Farrow						Yth -	0	0
(G)Shane Gore	6'01"	12 01	28/10/81	24	Ashford	Barnet 6/05 - Rel 5/06, Havant & W 6/06	1	0
(D)Michael Warner	5'09"	10 10	17/1/74	32	Harrogate	Farnborough 2/03 - Rel 5/06, Havant & W 6/06	34	0
(D)Justin Gregory			2/7/76	30	Sussex	Crawley 4 Fig 7/04 - Rel 5/06, Havant & W 5/06	29	1
(D)Barry Laker			3/11/73	32	Sutton	Farnborough 2/03 - Retired 5/06	23	2
(D)Matt Hocking	6'01"	12 02	30/1/78	28	Boston	Boston U 6/04 - Rel 5/06, Fisher 7/06	17	0
(D)Gary Schillachi						Yth - Aylesbury (L) 2/06, Rel 5/06	0	0
(D)Laurie Stewart						Yth - Rel 5/06		
(M)Rob Quinn	5'11"	11 02	8/11/76	29	Sidcup	Bristol R 5/04 - Rel 5/06, Gravesend 6/06	26	0
(M)Danny Williams	5'09"	10 01	2/3/81	25	Sheffield	Hereford 6/05 - Rel 5/06	17	1
(M)David Perpetuini	5'09"	10 07	26/9/79	26	Hitchin	Walsall 8/05 Rel 10/05, Re-signed 10/05 - Rel 5/06	19	0
(F)Eric Obinna	6'02"	13 03	10/6/81	25	Owerri	Reading 1/06 - Rel 5/06	9	0
(F)Dino Maamria	6'00"	12 02	18/2/74	32	Burnley	Charleston Battery (USA) 8/03 - Rel 5/06, Southport 7/06	30	7
(F)Robert Duffy	6'01"	12 04	2/12/82	23	Swansea	Gainsborough 3/06 - Rel 5/06, Oxford Utd 8/06	1	0
(F)Ollie Berquez					Essex	Canvey Island 6/05 - Rel 5/06, Woking 6/06	30	1
(F)Kieron Deane					Australia	ex Chester 10/05 - Aylesbury (L) 2/05, Northwood (L) 3/05, Rel 5/06	0	0
(F)Jefferson Louis	6'02"	13 00	22/2/79	27	Harrow	Worthing (NC) 12/05 - Rel 5/06, Eastleigh 7/06	18	6
(F)Simon Weatherstone	5'11"	11 00	26/1/80	26	Reading	Hornchurch 11/04 - Rel 5/06, Weymouth 6/06	19	0
Louis Lee						Yth - Arlesey 7/06		
Ricky Harding						Yth - Ware 8/06		

STEVENAGE BOROUGH

Ground Address: Stevenage Stadium, Broadhall Way, Stevenage, Herts SG2 8RH
Tel No: 01438 223223
Fax: 01438 743666
General email address: roger@stevenage borofc.com
Official website: http://www..stevenageborofc.com
SIMPLE DIRECTIONS
By Road: Stevenage South exit off A1(M) - ground on right at second roundabout.Spectators are however advised to go straight on at this roundabout and park inthe Showground opposite the stadium. The stadium is one mile from Stevenage BRstation. Buses SB4 and SB5

MATCH TICKETS
Ticket office Telephone: 01438 223223
Capacity: 7,107
Seats: 3,404
Covered: 3,703
Clubhouse: Tel.: 01438 218079. Clubhouse at ground open Monday to Friday 7 - 11pm, Saturday noon - 2.00 & 4.30 - 11pm, Sunday: All day from noon. Contact: Jenny Cairns
Club Shop: Mon - Sat 9-5.30. Broadhall Way, Stevenage. 01438 218061. Sells a complete range of club merchandise including a customising service. Mail Order, credit cards accepted, contact Tracey Levy (01438 218061)

Local Radio: Chiltern Radio, BBC Three Counties Radio and Hertbeat
Local Press: Stevenage Gazette, Comet, Stevenage Mercury, Herald

MATCHDAY PROGRAMME
Pages: 36   Price: £2.00
Editor: Stuart Govier
Tel No: 01438 210895
e-mail: stuandsteff@ntlworld.com

CLUB STATISTICS

RECORD
Attendance: 6,489
v Kidderminster H .Conf.25.01.97

Victory: 11-1 v British Timken Ath (H) UCL Div 1 1980-81

Defeat 0-7 v Southwick (h) Isthmian Div 1 1987-88

Career Goalscorer: Barry Hayles
Career Appearances: Martin Gittings
Transfer Fee Paid: £20,000
to Hereford United for Richard Leadbettert 1999
Transfer Fee Received: £300,000
from Bristol Rovers for Barry Hayles 1999
SENIOR HONOURS GM Vauxhall Conference 1995-96
Isthmian Premier Divison 1993-94I
Isthmian Division One 1991-92
Herts Senior Cup R-up 85-86 93-94
PREVIOUS LEAGUES Chiltern Youth 76-79, South
Combination ,Utd Co 80-84 and Isthmian League 1984-1994
U. Co.L 80-84 Isthmian 84-94
Grounds: King Georgs V Playing Field 1976-80

TAMWORTH

Club Colours: All Red
Change Colours: Yellow/Black/Black
Club Sponsor: Ocean Finance
Previous League: Southern
BEST PERFORMANCES
League: 15th Conference 2004-2005
F.A. Cup: 2nd Rd. 1969-70
F.A. Trophy: Runners Up 2002-03
F.A.Vase: Winners 1988-89

Formed: 1933
Nickname: The Lambs

Back Row (L-R): Dave Bampton, Graeme Law, Alan Neilson, Adie Smith (captain), John McGrath, Graham Ward, Lee Moore. **Middle:** Chris Leary (phyiso) Emmet Friars, Tom Kemp, James Dormand, Sean Bowles, Matthew Redmile, Kyle Storer, Buster Belford (Kit manager).
Front: Jon Stevenson, Richard Dryden (Asst Manager), Shaun Rigdway, Mark Cooper (Manager),Michael Tuohy, Derek Bond (Backroom Manager), Matthew Williams.

CLUB PERSONNEL

Chairman:	Bob Andrews	**Commercial Manager:**	Peter Cook
President:	Len Gendle	Tel. Nos: 01827 67595 (W) 07974 867823 (M)	
Secretary & General Manager:	Russell Moore	**Press Officer:**	David Clayton
97 Honeyboure, Belgrave,Tamworth, Staffs.B772JG		Tel Nos: 01827 65795 (W) and 07967 756918(M)	
Tel Nos:	07811 267304 (M)		

:

MANAGEMENT TEAM

Manager: Mark Cooper   **Assistant Manager:** Richard Dryden
Previous Clubs as a player: Bristl City, Birmingham City,Exeter City, Fulham, Hartlepools United and Forest Green Rovers

Physio: Chris Leary

.

TAMWORTH

No.	Date	Comp	H/A	Opponents	Att:	Result	Goalscorers	Pos
1	Aug 13	C	A	Aldershot Town	1012	W 2 - 0	Brown 16 Hollis 22	5
2	16		H	Forest Green Rovers	1258	D 0 - 0		7
3	20		H	Dagenham & Redbridge	1040	D 2 - 2	Whitman 48 Alsop 85	9
4	27		A	Stevenage Borough	1635	L 1 - 3	Redmile 58	12
5	29		H	Hererford United	1744	L 0 - 1		17
6	Sept 3		A	Morecambe	1413	D 0 - 0		16
7	10		A	Halifax Town	1453	L 0 - 4		19
8	17		H	Grays Athletic	1078	D 2 - 2	Stuart (og) 14 Mansaram 49	17
9	20		A	Southport	1012	D 1 - 1	Heggs 90	17
10	24		H	Woking	1021	L 0 - 1		18
11	27		H	York City	1005	L 0 - 3		19
12	Oct 1		A	Kiddermionster Harriers	1961	W 1 - 0	Heggs 39	18
13	7		A	Cambridge United	2606	L 1 - 2	Ward 53	22
14	15		H	Gravesend & Northfleet	1003	W 1 - 0	Bampton 58	17
15	22	FAC 4Q	H	Altrincham	801	W 3 - 1	Robinson 56 Edwards 84 88	
16	29	C	A	Exeter City	3369	L 0 - 3		19
17	Nov 5	FAC 1R	A	Bournemouth	4550	W 2 - 1	Ward 29 Storer 82	
18	12	C	H	Scarborough	1165	L 0 - 1		22
19	19		A	Canvey Island	646	W 2 - 1	Edwards 17 Jackson 64	17
20	26		A	Altrincham	824	L 0 - 2		19
21	Dec 3	FAC 2R	A	Hartlepool United	3786	W 2 - 1	Edwards 33 Redmile 48	
22	10	C	A	Crawley Town	1448	L 0 - 3		20
23	17	FAT 1	A	Halesowen Town	668	W 2 - 1	Ward 9 Ancelet 80	
24	24	C	H	Burton Albion	2151	D 1 - 1	Shaw 34	21
25	31		H	Altrincham	1064	D 1 - 1	Edwards 24	21
26	Jan 2		A	Burton Albion	2680	D 1 - 1	Edwards 3	21
27	9	FAC 3R	A	Stoke City	9366	D 0 - 0		
28	10		H	Accrington Stanley	1094	L 1 - 2	Edwards 39 (pen)	21
29	14	FAT 2	H	St Albans City	705	W 1 - 0	Davidson 39	
30	17	FAC 3Rr	H	Stoke City	3812	D 1 - 1	Jackson 41 Lost 4-5 after penalties	
31	21	C	A	Dagenham & redbridge	1352	L 1 - 2	Williams 41	21
32	24		A	Forest Green Rovers	788	W 3 - 1	Folkes 33 Davidson 78 Williams 81	20
33	28		H	Stevenage Borough	1228	W 2 - 0	Heggs 61 Williams 72	20
34	Feb 4	FAT 3	H	Dagenham & Redbridge	920	D 0 - 0		
35	7	FAT 3R	A	Dagenham & Redbridge	922	L 0 - 3		
36	11	C	A	Woking	2030	L 0 - 5		20
37	18		H	Kidderminster Harriers	1278	D 1 - 1	Williams 3	20
38	21		A	York City	2143	L 1 - 2	Williams 90 (pen)	20
39	25		H	Haliifax Town	1672	L 1 - 2	Heggs 68	20
40	Mar 4		A	Grays Athletic	1117	L 0 - 5		20
41	11		H	Cambridge United	1325	D 1 - 1	Neilson 12	21
42	18		A	Gravesned & Northfleet	841	L 0 - 2		21
43	25		H	Southport	1442	D 0 - 0		22
44	28		H	Exeter City	823	D 1 - 1	Cooper 18	22
45	April 4		H	Aldershot Town	914	W 2 - 1	Heggs 10 Johnson 50	20
46	8		H	Canvey Island	1156	W 1 - 0	Cooper 66	19
47	11		A	Scarborough	1648	D 0 - 0		19
48	15		H	Morecambe	1176	L 0 - 3		19
49	17		A	Hereford United	2809	L 0 - 1		19
50	22		A	Accrington Stanley	3014	L 1 - 2	Storer 90 (pen)	20
51	29		H	Crawley Athletic	1545	D 0 - 0		21

Ave. League Home Attendance: 1613 **Goals** 43 71 **Top Goalscorer:** Jake Edwards (7)

Best Position: 5th **Worst:** 22nd

	DORMAND 1	BAMPTON 4	REDMILE 5	BROWN 6	STAMPS 15	WARD 8	SMITH 2	HOLLIS 7	ALSOP 9	MCAULEY 11	WHITMAN 25	TURNER 23	TAYLOR 19	STORER 14	HEGGS 12	GAYLE 30	DOUGLAS 24	JACKSON 17	COOPER 16	CAMPBELL 10	MANSARAM 7	FRANCIS 20	DRYDEN 22	EDWARDS 21	BEVAN 34	ROBINSON 26	TOUHY 32	ANACLET 35	MELTON 6	NEILSON 27	RICKARDS 10	WRIGHT 11	DAVIDSON 9	WILLIAMS 7	FOLKES 3	BREEDON 34	BOWLES 40	ROMA 38	STAROSTA 39	SUMMERBEE 11	JOHNSON 21	REID 28	M
	X	X	X	X	X	X	X	X	X	X	X	S	S	S	U	U																											1
	X	X	X	X		X	X	X	X	X	X	X	X		S	U		S	U																								2
	X		X	X	X	X	X	X	S	X	X	X	X			U	U	U	U																								3
	X	X	X		X	X	X	X	X	X	X	X	S		S	U		S	U																								4
	X	U	X	X	X	X	S	X	X	S	S	X	X		U		X																										5
	X	X	X	X			X	S	X	X	X	X	S		U	U	S	X																									6
	X	X	X		X			X	X	X	X	S		U		U	X	S																									7
	X	X	X	X		X		X		X	X	S	S		U		U	X	X	S																							8
	X	X	X	X	U	X		X		X	X	S	U	S			X	X	S																								9
	X	X	X	X	X		X	X	U	S	U			S			X	X	X	U																							10
	X		X	X	X	X		X	X	S	S	X	U		S		X	X																									11
	X	X	X	X	X	X		S	S	X	X	X	U		S		S	X																									12
	X	X	X	X	X	X		S	X	X	X	U		S		S	U																										13
	X	X	X	X	X	X		X	S	X	X	U		U			S		X																								14
		X		X	X	X	X			S	S	S	X	X	X		U	U			X		X		X																		15
		X		X	X	X				X	X		X	X	U		S	U			S		S			X	X	U															16
		X		X	X	X				U	U		X	X	U		S	X			U		X	X	X	X																	17
		X	U	X	X	X	S						X	X	U		S	X			U		X	X	X	X																	18
		X	X	X		X	X					U	S	X	X	X		X			U		X		S	S	S	X															19
		X			X	X			S		S		X	X	U		X			U		X	X		X	X	X																20
		X	X			X	X						S		X	S	U		X	S		X	X			X	X		U	X	X												21
		X	X			X	X						S		X	U		X	X			S	U			X		U	X	X													22
		X				X	X						S		X		U		X	U		S			X	X		U	X	X	X												23
		X				X	X								X	X		U		S	U		S	U	X	X		X	X	X													24
			X		U	X	X							X				U	U			S			X	X		X	X	X	X		X										25
		X	X		U	X	X							X				S	S	U					X	X		X	X	X	X		X										26
		X	X		U	X	X							X				S	U	U			S			X	X		X	X	X		X			X							27
		X	X		S		X							X				U	U	U		S				X	X		X	X	X		X		X	X							28
		X			X	X	X							S				S	S	X		X	U					U	X	X	X		X			X	X						29
		X	X		S	X	X							S				X	U	X		X	U					X	X	X	X		X			X							30
		X	X			X	X							S				S	S	U			U					X	X	X			X			X		X	X				31
		X			U	X	X							U				X	S		X	S						X		X		X	S		X	X	X						32
		X	X			X	X							U				X	X		X	U						X		U	S	U		X	X	X							33
		X	X		U	X	X							S				X	X	X	U		S	U				X		X	X			X			X						34
		X	X		X									S				S	X	X	X		S					X			X			X	X	X							35
			X		X	X	X						X	X						X			S								S			X	X	X	X						36
					X	X	X											S		X			U								S			X	X	X	X	U	X	X	X		37
		X	X			X	X											S		S			U											X	X	X	X	U	X	X	X		38
		X	X		U	S	X											S													X			X	X	X	X	U	X	X	U	X	39
		X	X		S	X	X											X		X										X			S		U	X	X			X	X	40
		X			X	X								X	X			U				U									X			X		U	X	X	S	U	X	41
					X	X								S	X	X		S	U			S									X			X		U	X	X	X			X	42
		X			X									S	X	X		S	X			S									X			S		U	X	X			U	43
		X	X		X									X	X	X		S	X												X			S		U	X	X			U	44
		X			X	X	X							X	X	X	U					U									X			S			X	X		S	U		45
		X			X	X	X							S	X		U		X			U								U	X			X			X	X		X	U		46
		X			X	X	X							S	X			X				U					S			U	X			X			X	X		X	U		47
		X			X	X	X							X	X							U					S			X	X			X			X	X		X			48
		X			X	X		S						S	S	X	U		S			U								X	X			X			X	X		X			49
		X	U		X	X		S						S	S	X	U		S	X		X								X				X		X	X	X		X			50
		X	S		X	X		X						X	X		U		S	X		X								U				X		X		X	S				51

Total Appearances (Conference)

X	14	24	37	15	26	34	36	5	7	7	14	16	11	20	18	2	0	11	9	2	4	3	0	8	10	2	12	8	7	12	4	1	14	8	11	1	15	15	3	4	6	2	X
S	0	0	0	0	3	1	1	2	2	1	5	7	14	8	9	1	1	13	6	1	2	8	1	0	0	1	3	0	0	1	3	0	4	0	4	0	0	0	1	0	1	0	S
U	0	1	1	0	6	1	0	0	0	0	0	3	0	3	4	28	2	4	9	0	0	5	11	0	0	0	3	0	1	0	1	0	0	0	0	0	8	0	0	1	1	4	U

Cup Appearances

X	0	8	6	2	4	8	7	0	0	0	0	1	0	4	4	0	6	2	0	0	1	0	5	5	2	6	5	6	3	0	3	2	2	1	0	0	0	0	0	0	0	0	X
S	0	0	0	0	1	0	0	0	0	0	0	1	7	1	3	3	0	0	1	2	0	0	3	0	0	0	0	0	0	0	0	0	0	0	0	0	0	0	0	0	0	0	S
U	0	0	0	2	0	0	0	0	0	1	1	0	0	1	5	0	1	5	0	0	1	1	0	1	0	2	0	0	0	0	0	0	0	0	0	0	0	0	0	0	0	0	U

Also Played: Motteram(7): S(20) X(21,22,23). McConnnell(26): X(24,25) U(26). Lake(35): S(36). Brady(36): U(36). Ridgway(26): U(35,36). Merson(18): X(39) U(40). Belford(31): U(47)

TAMWORTH

GOALKEEPERS	SQ NO.	HT	WT	D.O.B	AGE	P.O.B	CAREER	APPS	GOA
James Dormand	1	6'01"	14 09	13/7/86	20	Birmingham	Birmingham Rel 5/06, Stafford R (L) 9/04, Tamworth (3ML) 8/05, Boston U (Trial) 7/06, Tamworth 7/06	14	0
Sean Bowles	13			28/4/83	23		Barwell, Coalville T, Tamworth 2/06	15	0
Tony Breedon							Sutton Coldfield, Tamworth 2/06, Stourport (Dual) 3/06	1	0

DEFENDERS									
Adie Smith	2	5'10"	12 00	11/8/73	33	Birmingham	Birmingahm C, Willenhall, Bromsgrove c/s 94, Coventry (Trial) (96/97), Kidderminster £19,000 6/97, Tamworth 2/04	37	0
Michael Touhy	3			6/6/87	19	Birmingham	Aston Villa, Ilford 9/05, Tamworth 10/05	15	0
David Bampton	4	5'08"	11 00	5/5/85	21	Swindon	Swindon, Tamworth 5/04	24	1
Matthew Redmile	5	6'04"	14 10	12/11/76	27	Nottingham	Notts County, Shrewsbury (2ML) 11/00 £30,000 1/01 Rel c/s 03, Scarborough 8/03, Barnet 2/04, Tamworth 7/04	37	1
Emmet Friars	6	6'01"	11 06	14/9/85	20	Derry	Notts County Rel 5/06, AFC Telford (2ML) 9/05, Alfreton (L) 3/06, Tamworth 6/06		
Graeme Law	14	5'10"	10 10	6/10/84	21	Kirkcaldy	York, Dundee 2/06, Tamworth 7/06		
Alan Neilson	15	5'11"	12 08	26/9/72	33	Wegburg, Ger	Newcastle, Southampton £500,000 6/95, Fulham £250,000 11/97, Grimsby 10/01, Luton 2/02 Rel c/s 05, Retired, Tamworth 12/05	13	1
Tom Kemp	21						Lincoln C, Tamworth (L) 8/06		
Richard Dryden	22	6'00"	13 04	14/6/69	37	Stroud	Bristol R, Exeter (L) 9/88, Exeter 3/89, Man City (L) 5/91, Notts County £250,000 8/91, Plymouth (L) 11/92, Birmingham £165,000 3/93, Bristol C £140,000 12/94, Southampton £150,000 8/96, Stoke (2ML) 11/99, Stoke (SL) 3/00, Northampton (2ML) 9/00, Swindon	1	0
Simon Weaver	23	6'01"	10 08	20/12/77	28	Doncaster	Sheff Wed Rel c/s 98, Doncaster (L) 2/97, Ilkeston, Grimsby (Trial) c/s 99, Nuneaton 2/00, Lincoln C 8/02, Macclesfield (2ML) 10/04, Kidderminster 12/04 Rel c/s 05, Scarborough 6/05 Rel 5/06, York C 8/06 Rel 8/06, Tamworth 8/06		

MIDFIELDERS									
Graham Ward	7	5'08"	11 09	25/2/83	23	Dublin	Wolves, Cambridge U (Trial) 3/03, Bournemouth (Trial) 4/03, Kidderminster Free 8/03 Rel c/s 04, Cheltenham 8/04, Rel c/s 05, Burton (L) 3/05, Tamworth 5/05	35	1
Kyle Storer	8			30/4/87	19	Nuneaton	Leicester (Jun), Bedworth 7/02, Tamworth 6/04, Hinckley U (L) 1/06	28	1
Mark Cooper	16	5'08"	11 04	18/12/68	37	Wakefield	Bristol C Rel c/s 89, Exeter 10/89, Southend (L) 3/90, Birmingham P/E 9/91, Fulham £40,000 11/92, Huddersfield (L) 3/93, Wycombe 1/94, Exeter 2/94 Rel c/s 96, Hartlepool 7/96, Macclesfield (2ML) 9/97, L.Orient 12/97, Rushden & D 1/98, Telford (L) 10/99, H	15	2
Shaun Ridgway	19			27/5/88	18		Tamworth	0	0
John McGrath	24	5'10"	10 04	27/3/80	26	Limerick	Belvedere, Aston Villa 9/99 Rel c/s 03, Southend (Trial) 7/02, Dag & Red (SL) 11/02, Doncaster 7/03, Shrewsbury (2ML) 8/04, Kidderminster 1/05 Rel c/s 05, Limerick 9/05, Weymouth 1/06, Tamworth 7/06		
Jamie Lake							Tamworth	1	0
Tom Brady							Tamworth	0	0

FORWARDS									
Jon Stevenson	10	5'06"	11 11	13/10/82	23	Leicester	Leicester Rel c/s 03, Swindon 7/03 Rel c/s 04, Cambridge C 6/04, Alfreton 8/05, Tamworth 5/06		
Lee Moore	18			9/11/85	20	Bathgate	Coventry (Jun), Bedworth 7/02, Tamworth 7/06		
Gary Birch	20	6'00"	12 13	8/10/81	24	Birmingham	Walsall, Exeter (L) 3/01, Exeter (3ML) 8/01, Nuneaton (L) 12/01 (01/02 5,3), Barnsley (SL) 3/04, Kidderminster 12/04 Rel c/s 05, Lincoln C 8/05, Tamworth (L) 8/06		
Steve Burton		6'01"	12 11	9/10/83	22	Doncaster	Ipswich Rel 1/03, Boston U (2ML) 8/02, Doncaster 3/03 Rel c/s 04, Scarborough 6/04, Leigh RMI (L) 10/04, Canvey Island (L) 2/05, Crawley 3/05, Tamworth 8/06		
James Francis				16/3/87	19		Rushall O, Tamworth, Moor Green (L) 1/06, Halesowen T (2ML) 3/06	11	0
Matthew Williams		5'08"	9 11	5/11/82	23	St Asaph	Man Utd, Notts County 3/04 Rel 5/06, Tamworth (SL) 1/06, Tamworth 5/06	8	5

PLAYING SQUAD

LOANEES 05/06	HT	WT	DOB	AGE	POB	FROM - TO	APPS	GOA
(M)Darren Campbell	5'07"	10 08	16/4/86	20	Huntingdon	Reading (1M) 9/05 - Rel 11/05, Staines 12/05, Colchester (Trial), Burnley (Trial), Inverness Caledonian 5/06	3	0
(F)Darren Mansaram	6'02"	11 07	25/6/84	22	Doncaster	Halifax (1M) 9/05 - Worksop (L) 12/05, Sligo R 1/06	6	1
(F)Jake Edwards	6'01"	12 08	11/5/76	30	Prestwich	Exeter (3M) 10/05 - Chester (SL) 3/06, Rel 5/06, Crawley 8/06	8	4
(M)Trevor Robinson	5'09"	12 11	20/8/84	22	St Catherines, Jam.	Millwall (M) 10/05 - Cambridge U (L) 1/06, Rel 5/06	3	0
(M)Eddie Anaclet	5'09"	10 00	31/8/85	21	Arusha, Tanzania	Southampton (3M) 11/05 - Rel 5/06, Oxford U 7/06	8	0
(M)Steve Melton	5'11"	10 11	3/10/78	27	Lincoln	Boston U (3M) 11/05 - Rel 5/06	7	1
(M)Carl Motteram	5'05"	9 11	3/9/84	21	Birmingham	Birmingham (1M) 11/05 - Rel 5/06, Torquay 7/06	2	0
(M)Nick Wright						Birmingham (1M) 1/06 -	1	0
(D)Dominic Roma	5'10"	11 11	29/11/85	20	Sheffield	Sheff Utd (SL) 2/06 -	15	0
(M)Ben Starosta						Sheff Utd (1M) 2/06 - Rel c/s 06	4	0
(F)Tommy Johnson	5'11"	12 04	15/1/71	35	Newcastle	Scunthorpe (SL) 3/06 -	7	1
(F)Craig Reid	5'10"	11 10	17/12/88	17	Coventry	Coventry (1M) 3/06 -	2	0
(G)Dale Belford			11/7/67	39	Birmingham	Sutton Coldfield (Cover) 4/06 -	0	0

DEPARTURES	HT	WT	DOB	AGE	POB	FROM - TO	APPS	GOA
(M)Simon Hollis			7/11/79	26	Birmingham	Redditch 5/05 - Redditch 9/05	7	1
(M)Hugh McAuley	5'10"	11 06	13/5/77	29	Plymouth	Forest Green 7/05 - Kettering (L) 10/05 (Perm) 12/05, Hucknall 3/06	8	0
(D)Richard Munday			24/8/87	19	Marston Green	Tamworth, Rushall O (L) 8/05, Loughborough Dynamo 12/05		
(F)Julian Alsop	6'04"	14 03	28/5/73	33	Nuneaton	Forest Green 7/05 - Forest Green (L) 10/05, Perm 1/06, Newport 7/06	9	1
(M)Barry McConnell	5'11"	10 03	1/1/77	29	Exeter	Bath C 12/05 - Rel 1/06, Forest Green 2/06, Tiverton 3/06	2	0
(D)Aaron Brown			23/6/83	23	Birmingham	Studley 7/04 - Reading (L) 11/05 (Perm) 1/06, Bournemouth (L) 2/06	15	1
(F)Scott Rickards	5'09"	12 00	3/11/81	24	Sutton Coldfield	Redditch 12/05 - Nuneaton 3/06	7	0
(F)Paul Merson	6'00"	13 02	20/3/68	38	Northolt	Walsall (Pl/Man) 2/06 - Retired 3/06	1	0
(M)Nicky Summerbee	5'08"	11 08	26/8/71	35	Altrincham	Tranmere Rel 11/05, 2/06 - Rel 3/06	4	0
(D)Jimmy Turner	5'11"	11 04	4/10/83	22	Derby	Farnborough 6/05 - AFC Telford (L) 2/06 (Perm) 3/06	23	0
Nicholas Green						Stouport 8/05, Tamworth 1/06 Rel		
(D)Scott Stamps	5'11"	11 09	20/3/75	31	Birmingham	Kidderminster 8/04 - Rel 5/06	29	0
(M)Nathan Jackson			26/8/86	20	Birmingham	Wednesfield c/s 05 - Stourport (L) 9/05, Rel 5/06, Hednesford 6/06	24	1
(F)Bob Taylor	5'11"	11 09	3/2/67	39	Easington	Cheltenham 8/04 - Rel 5/06	25	0
(F)Tris Whitman	5'07"	11 00	9/6/80	26	Nottingham	Scarborough 8/04 - Crawley (2ML) 11/05, Hinckley U (2ML) 2/06, Rel 5/06, Alfreton 6/06	19	1
(F)Danny Davidson	6'05"		23/10/79	26	Derby	Stafford R 1/06 - Rel 5/06, Moor Green 6/06	18	1
(D)Peter Folkes	6'00"	12 02	16/11/84	21	Birmingham	Lincoln C 1/06 - Rel 5/06	15	1
(F)Carl Heggs	6'01"	12 10	11/10/70	35	Leicester	ex Ilkeston 8/05 - Hinckley U 5/06	27	5
(G)Mark Gayle	6'02"	12 03	21/10/69	36	Bromsgrove	Halesowen T (Pl/Coach) 5/05 - Halesowen T 5/06	3	0
(G)Scott Bevan	6'06"	15 03	16/9/79	26	Southampton	MK Dons (3ML) 10/05 (Perm) 1/06 - Kidderminster 6/06	10	0
(D)Danny Douglas			25/3/88	18	Sutton Coldfield	Yth - Gresley R 8/06	1	0

TAMWORTH

Ground Address:	The Lamb Ground, Kettlebrook,Tamworth, Staffs. B77 1AA
Tel No:	01827 65798
Fax:	01827 62236
General email address:	russell@the lambs.co.uk
Official website:	www.the lambs.co.uk
SIMPLE DIRECTIONS	
By Road	Follow the signs for Town Centre/Snowdrome, then for Kettlebrook.
	Parking: The entrance to the ground and car park is in Kettlebrook Road, 50 yards from the traffic island by the railway viaduct.

MATCH TICKETS

Ticket office Telephone:	01827 65798
Capacity:	4,100
Seats:	518
Covered:	1,191
Clubhouse:	Open matchdays and training evenings
Refreshments:	On ground
Club Shop:	Yes .
Local Press:	Tamworth Herald and Tamworth Times
Local Radio:	Centre FM, Cpital Gold and Radio WM

MATCHDAY PROGRAMME
Pages: 44   Price: £2.00
Editor: Pete Cook
email: peter@thelambs.co.uk

CLUB STATISTICS

RECORDS

Attendance:	4,920
	v Atherstone Town, B'ham Comb. 1948
Victory:	14-4
	v Holbrook Institute (H) Bass Vase 193
Defeat:	0-11
	v Solihull (A) B'ham Comb. 1940
Career Goalscorer:	Graham Jessop 195
Career Appearances:	Dave Seedhouse 869
Transfer Fee Paid:	£7,500
	To Ilkeston Town for David Hemmings Dec.200
Transfer Fee Received:	£7,500
	from Telford United for Martin Myers 1990

SENIOR HONOURS   F.A.Trophy Runners-Up 2202-03
F.A.Vase Winners 1988-89
Birmingham Senior Cup (3) R-Up (3)
Southern League Premier Division 2002-03
Premier Divison R-Up 2001-02
Midland Division 1996-97

PREVIOUS
Leagues: Birmingham Combination 33-54, West Midlands
(originally B'ham League) 54-72 84-88, Southern 72-79
83-84.89-03 Northern Premier 1979-83
Ground: Jolly Sailor Ground 1933-34
:

WEYMOUTH

Club Colours: Maroon/Maroon/Sky Blue
Change Colours: Yellow/Green/Yellow
Club Sponsor: Brown/Black/Black.
Previous League: Conferenc South
LAST SEASON
League: Champions Conference South **F.A. Cup:** 1st Round Replay
F.A.Trophy 1st Round

BEST PERFORMANCES
League: 2nd Football Alliance **F.A. Cup:** 4th Round 1961-62 **F.A.Trophy** 5th Round 2000-1

Founded:1890
Nickname:
The Terras

WEYMOUTH FC 2006/07

CLUB PERSONNEL

Chairman: Martyn Harrison
Directors: Gary Calder and Faye Harrison
Chief Executive/Secretary   Gary Calder c/o club
9 Elounda Court,Benfleet, Essex SS7 5QA
Tel Nos: 01305 785558 (W) 07733 106505 (M)
e-mail: garycalder1@aol.com
Commercial Manager & Press Officer   Ken Wilde
Tel Nos: 01305 785558 (W) 07860 206466 (M)
Commercial Assistant   Jacqueline Williams
Company Secretary: Sara Redford

MANAGEMENT TEAM

Manager: Garry Hill

Assitant Manager: Kevin Hales

Physio: Roger Hoare

WEYMOUTH

No.	Date	Comp	H/A	Opponents	Att:	Result	Goalscorers	Pos
1	Aug 15	CS	H	Havant & Waterlooville	1521	W 1 - 0	Harris 70	11
2	17		A	Eastleigh	782	L 0 - 2		13
3	20		A	Histon	489	L 1 - 2	O'Brien 26	14
4	27		H	Carshalton Athletic	1370	W 4 - 0	Harris 4 Eribenne 16 Taggart 56 Purser 82	8
5	29		A	St.Albans City	526	L 0 - 4		15
6	Sept 3		H	Yeading	1.024	D 1 - 1	Eribenne 39	15
7	10		H	Thurrock	1.029	W 2 - 0	Purser 59 Wheeler 82	11
8	17		A	Newport County	724	W 3 - 0	Purser 14 Taggart 18 Jackson 52	7
9	24	FAC 2Q	A	Weston-s-Mare	744	D 2 - 2	Dutton 41 68	
10	27	FAC 2Qr	H	Weston-s-Mare	1003	W 1 - 0	Taggart 10	
11	Oct 1	NS	A	Maidenhead United	402	D 0 - 0		8
12	8	FAC 3Q	H	Bath City	1232	W 1 - 0	Bound 90	
13	15	NS	H	Eastbourne Borough	1252	W 2 - 1	Eribenne 24 49	8
14	22	FAC 4Q	H	Cambridge United	1652	W 2 - 1	Jackson 18 Purser 45	
15	29	NS	H	Sutton United	1703	W 3 - 1	Elam 3 Jackson 43 Bound 90	
16	Nov 5	FAC 1R	A	Nottingham Forest	10305	D 1 - 1	Harris 56	
17	8	NS	A	Basingstoke Town	557	W 3 - 0	Dutton 48 O'Connor 51 Bound (pen) 85	7
18	12		H	Welling United	1706	W 2 - 1	Dutton 39 Shipp 55	
19	14	FAC 1R r	H	Nottimgham Forest	6500	L 0 - 2		
20	26	FAT 3Q	H	Havant & Waterlooville	1018	W 2 - 1	Wilkinson 7 O'Connor 71	
21	29	NS	A	Cambridge City	429	W 3 - 1	Eribenne 3 (16 31 53)	5
22	Dec 3		H	Bognor Regis Town	1308	W 2 - 0	Elam 42 Bound 45	3
23	6		A	Weston-s-Mre	1221	W 2 - 1	Elam 30 Bound 62	1
24	10		A	Lewes	705	W 3 - 2	Eribenne 23 Bound 30 Wilkinson 51	1
25	17	FAT 1	H	Forest Green Rovers	1120	L 0 - 1		
26	26	NS	H	Dorchester Town	4029	W 1 - 0	Dutton 1	1
27	31		H	Bishop's Stortford	1452	W 3 - 1	Elam 22 Harris 39 Eribenne 81	1
28	Jan 2		A	Dorchester Town	3006	L 0 - 1		1
29	7		A	Havant & Waterlooville	1163	L 1 - 2	Eribenne 85	3
30	10		A	Farnborough Town	781	W 1 - 0	O'Brien 29	1
31	14		H	Eastleigh	1557	W 2 - 0	Harris 16 McGrath 45	1
32	21		H	Histon	1629	W 1 - 0	Jackson 73	1
33	24		H	Hayes	302	W 2 - 1	Harris 34 Collins (og) 59	1
34	28		A	Carshalton Athletic	513	L 1 - 2	Smith 69	1
35	Feb 4		H	Maidenhead United	1406	W 4 - 0	Smith 58 Nade 62 McGrath 78 Elam 82	1
36	11		A	Eastbourne Borough	802	W 2 - 0	Bound 58 (pen) McGrath 74	1
37	18		H	Farnborough Town	2058	L 1 - 2	Harris 27	1
38	22		A	Weston-s-Mare	613	W 3 - 1	Smith 20 Nade 35 Jackson 40	1
39	25		A	Thurrock	301	W 2 - 1	Clark 63 Nade 69	1
40	Mar 4		H	Newport County	2110	W 4 - 0	Nade 3 (11 44 81) Eribenne 77	1
41	11		A	Sutton United	668	W 3 - 0	Wilkinson 42 Clark 45 Nade 71	1
42	14		H	Basingstoke Town	1600	D 1 - 1	Nade 9	1
43	18		H	Cambridge City	1765	D 1 - 1	Nade 38	1
44	25		A	Welling United	905	L 0 - 1		2
45	April 1		H	Hayes	1727	W 5 - 1	Bound 10 (pen 54 (pen) Nade 23 63 Eribenne 75	1
46	8		A	Bognor Regis	802	W 2 - 0	Bound 27 (pen) Eribenne 28	1
47	15		A	Yeading	502	W 1 - 0	Wilkinson 57	1
48	17		H	St Albans City	5022	W 3 - 2	Nade 28 Bound 45 79	1
49	22		A	Bishop's Stortford	1016	W 2 - 0	Jackson 40 Elam 77	1
50	29		H	Lewes	4071	W 2 - 0	Nade 16 Jackson 25	1

Ave. League Home Attendance:	2354		**Goals**	89	41	**Top Goalscorer:** Eribenne & Nade (13)

Best Position: 1st **Worst:** 15th

PLAYING SQUAD

CURRANT SQUAD AS OF BEGINING OF 2006-07 SEASON

GOALKEEPERS	SQ NO.	HT	WT	D.O.B	AGE	P.O.B	CAREER
Arran Lee-Barrett	1	6'02"	12 10	28/2/84	22	Ipswich	Ipswich (Jun), Norwich, Cardiff 3/03,, Torquay (Trial) 3/05, Weymouth 7/05
Jason Matthews	17	6'00"	12 02	15/3/75	31	Paulton	Mangotsfield, Welton R, Westbury, Bath C, Paulton, Nuneaton, Taunton 8/98, Exeter 8/99 Rel c/s 00, Aberystwyth c/s 00, Cleveden 6/01, Weymouth 8/02

DEFENDERS

Steve Tully	2	5'09"	11 00	10/2/80	26	Paignton	Torquay Rel c/s 02, Bristol R (Trial) 4/02, Weymouth 8/02, Exeter 2/05, Weymouth 5/05
Trevor Challis	3	5'08"	11 06	23/10/75	30	Paddington	QPR, Bristol R 7/98 Rel c/s 03, Exeter (Trial) 7/03, Telford 8/03, Shrewsbury 3/04 Rel c/s 05, Weymouth 7/05
Roy O'Brien	4	6'01"	12 00	27/11/74	31	Cork	Arsenal Rel c/s 96, Wigan 8/96, Bournemouth 8/96 Rel 12/96, Dorchester T, Yeovil 8/00, Weymouth (2ML) 12/04, Weymouth (Pl/Coach) 2/05
Simon Downer	5	5'11"	12 08	19/10/81	24	Romford	L.Orient Rel 5/04, Newcastle (Trial) 2/01, Aldershot (SL) 3/04 (03/04 8,0), Retired, Hornchurch 11/04 Rel c/s 05, Weymouth 7/05
Ashley Vickers	14	6'03"	13 10	14/6/72	34	Sheffield	Sheff Utd, Worcester, Malvern T, 61 Club, Heybridge Swifts, Peterborough £5,000 12/97, St Albans 8/98, Dag & Red 3/00, Weymouth 5/06
Tony James	18	6'03"	14 02	27/6/76	30	Cardiff	WBA Rel c/s 98, Hereford 5/98 Rel 5/06, Weymouth 5/06
Abdelhalim El Kholti	23	5'10"	11 00	17/10/80	25	Annemasse (Fr)	Raja Casablanca (Mar), Yeovil 10/02 Rel c/s 04, Cambridge U 7/04 Rel c/s 05, Chester 7/05 Rel c/s 06, Weymouth 8/06

MIDFIELDERS

Andy Harris	6	5'10"	12 02	26/2/77	29	Springs, SA	Liverpool Rel c/s 96, Southend 7/96 Rel c/s 99, L.Orient 7/99 Rel c/s 03, Chester 6/03 Rel 5/05, Forest Green (3ML) 2/05, Weymouth 7/05
Nick Crittenden	7	5'08"	10 11	11/11/78	27	Ascot	Chelsea Rel 6/00, Plymouth (L) 11/98, Yeovil 8/00 Rel c/s 03 Re-signed, Rel c/s 04, Aldershot 6/04, Weymouth 5/06
Ben Smith	8	5'09"	11 09	23/11/78	27	Chelmsford	Arsenal (Trainee), Reading 4/97, Yeovil 3/98, Southend 6/01 Rel c/s 02, Hereford 6/02, Shrewsbury 6/04, Weymouth 1/06
Lee Elam	15	5'08"	10 12	24/9/76	29	Bradford	Guiseley, Southport 11/98, Morecambe 8/02, Halifax 5/03, Yeovil (L) 10/03 Perm 11/03, Chester (L) 3/04, Hornchurch 5/04, Burton 11/04, Morecambe 11/04 Rel 5/05, Crawley 7/05 Rel 9/05, Weymouth 9/05
Dean Howell	16	6'01"	12 05	29/11/80	25	Burton	N.County Rel c/s 00, Spalding (2ML) 12/99, Crewe 7/00 Rel c/s 01, Rochdale (L) 3/01, Southport Free 7/01, Morecambe 6/03, Halifax 7/04 Rel 4/05, Colchester 8/05, Halifax 2/06 Rel 5/06, Weymouth 6/06
Simon Weatherstone	19	5'11"	11 00	26/1/80	26	Reading	Oxford U, Boston U 2/01 (00/01 13,5, 01/02 34,12), Yeovil £15,000 1/04, Hornchurch Undisc 9/04, Stevenage 11/04 (04/05 21,2, 05/06 19,0) Rel 5/06, Weymouth 6/06
Shaun Wilkinson	20	5'07"	11 00	12/9/81	24	Portsmouth	Brighton, Havant & W (L) 12/01, Chesterfield (L) 11/02, Havant & W (2ML) 9/03 Perm 11/03, Weymouth £5,000 2/04, Havant & W 12/04, Weymouth
Jason Tindall	24	6'01"	12 01	15/11/77	28	Stepney	Charlton Rel c/s 98, Bournemouth 7/98 Rel 5/06, Weymouth 8/06

FORWARDS

Richard Logan	9	6'00"	12 05	4/1/82	24	Bury St Edmunds	Ipswich, Cambridge U (L) 1/01, Torquay (3ML) 12/01, Boston U (2ML) 11/02 (Perm) 1/03, Peterborough (3ML) 9/03, Peterborough 12/03, Shrewsbury (L) 9/04, Lincoln C (2ML) 11/05, Weymouth 6/06
Wayne Purser	10	5'09"	11 10	13/4/80	26	Basildon	QPR Rel c/s 00, Barnet 8/00, L.Orient £9,000 3/03, Hornchurch £15,000 8/04, Peterborough 11/04, Weymouth 7/05
Raphael Nade	11	6'00"	12 08	18/10/80	25	Touleplou, IVC	Le Havre (Fr), Troyes (Fr), QPR (Trial), Hampton & Richmond 8/01, Welling 7/02, Woking 11/02, Troyes (Fr) (Trial) 5/03, Carlisle £25,000 8/05, Weymouth (3ML) 1/06, Weymouth (SL) 7/06
Chukki Eribenne	12	5'10"	11 12	2/11/80	25	Westminster	Coventry Rel c/s 00, Bournemouth 7/00 Rel c/s 03, Hereford (L) 10/02, Northampton (Trial) 5/03, Havant & W 8/03, Weymouth 7/04, Aldershot (L) 12/04, Farnborough (L) 1/05
Marcus Richardson	22	6'02"	13 02	31/8/77	29	Reading	Slough, Cambridge U (Trial) 7/00, Reading (Trial) 8/00, Wycombe (Trial), Harrow 1/01, Cambridge U 3/01, Torquay (L) 9/01 £5,000 10/01, Hartlepool 10/02, Lincoln C (2ML) 8/03, Lincoln C (L) 12/03 Perm 1/04, Rochdale (L) 2/05, Yeovil 3/05 Rel c/s 05, Cheste

DEPARTURES	SN	HT	WT	DOB	AGE	POB	FROM - TO
Matt Bound							Oxford Utd c/s 04 - Eastleigh 5/06
Steve Clark							Dag & Red 3/05 - Fisher 5/06
Darren Wheeler							Godalming 1/05 - Eastleigh 5/06
Brian Dutton							Pickering T 7/05 - Eastleigh 5/06
Ian Hutchinson				7/11/72	33	Stockton	Halifax 7/95 - Dorchester 8/06
Kirk Jackson							Hornchurch 11/04 - Harrogate 6/06
Craig O'Connor						Slough	Thurrock 11/05 - Havant & W 6/06
(M)John McGrath		5'10"	10 04	27/3/80	26	Limerick	Limerick 1/06 - Tamworth 7/06
(F)Marcus Richardson	22	6'02"	13 02	31/8/77	29	Reading	Chester 7/06 - Cambridge U 8/06

WEYMOUTH

Ground Address: Wessex Stadium,Radipole Lane, Weymouth DT4 9XJ
Telephone: 01305 785558
Fax: 01305 766658
General email address: garycalder1@aol.com
Official website: www.theterras.co.uk

SIMPLE DIRECTIONS: Arriving from Dorchester on A354, turn right following signs for Granby Industrial estate at Safeway roundabout.Ground on right as you enter estate

By Rail: Nearest Railway Station is Weymouth (2 miles)
MATCH TICKETS:
Ticket office Telephone: 01305 785558
Midweek Home Matchday: Tuesday

CAPACITY: 6,600
Seats: 800
Covered: All Four Sides

Clubhouse: Matchdays and Functions
Refreshments: Two refreshment bars.
Club Shop: Matchdays Only

MATCHDAY PROGRAMME
64 pages £2.00
Editors: Liz Bell (07775 741077)
Iam White (07791 420211 (M)

Local Press: Dorset Evening Echo.
Local Radio:.Wessex F.M

CLUB STATISTICS
RECORDS
Attendance: 4,995
v Manchester United (ground opening)21.10.97
Victory

Defeat

Career Goalscorer: W 'Farmer' Haynes 275

Career Apperances: Tony Hobsons 1.076
Transfer Fee Paid: £15,000
to Northwich Victoria for Shaun Teal
Transfer Fee Received: £100,000
from Tottenham Hotspur forPeter Guthrie 1988

SENIOR HONOURS
Fooytball Alliance Runners-Up19769-80
Southern League Champions 1964-65 1965-66
Southern League Runners-Up 1954-55 1977-78 2003-2004
Dorset Senior Cup (27)

PREVIOUS LEAGUES
Dorset ,Western1907-23 28-49 Southern 23-28 49-79 Alliance Premier 79-89

STEP 1
CONFERENCE
STEP 2 - P177
CONFERENCE Nth & Sth
STEP 3 - P269
NPL - SOUTHERN - ISTHMIAN PREM
STEP 4 - P269
NPL - SOUTHERN - ISTHMIAN
STEP 5/6 - P473
STEP 7 - P713

WOKING

Club Colours: Red & white halves/ black/black
Change Colours: Sky blue & white stripes/white/white
Club Sponsor: Jako
Previous League: Isthmian
BEST PERFORMANCES :
League: Conference Runners Up 94-95 95-96   **F.A. Cup:** 4th Round 90-91
F.A. Trophy: Winners 93-94 95-94-95 96-97   **F.A.Amateur Cup:** Winners 1957-58
LAST SEASON
Conference: 11th   **F.A.Cup:** 2nd Round Replay   **F.A.Trophy:** Finalists

Formed: 1889
Nickname: 'The Cards'

Back row, left to right: Liam Cockerill, Craig McAllister, Karim El-Salahi, Shola Oyedelle, Tom Hutchinson and Matt Ruby. Middle Row: Malcolm Jobling, Ian Selley, DannyBunce, Steven Ferguson, Shwan Jalal, Karl Murray, Aaron Howe, Sam Cockerill, Giuseppe Sole, Steven Evans and Ron Rawling (Kit Man).
Front row: Simon Jackson, Graham Baker, (Head of Youth Development), Chris Sharpling, Gary MacDonald, Matt Crossley (Assistant Manager), Glen Cockerill (manager), Neil Smith, Ollie Berquez, Bobby Childs (physio) and Jerome Maledon.   Photo: Eric Marsh

CLUB PERSONNEL

Football Chairman: John Buchanan
Secretary, Press Officer: Phil Ledger J.P.
& Football Director
Tel Nos: 01483 772470 x 227 (club)
         01483 725295 (H)
         07831 271369 (M)
Correspondance to secretary at home.
19 Ainsdale Way, Woking, Surrey GU21 3PP
Directors: Phil Ledger, Peter Jordan and Bob Brown
Commercial/Managing Director: Mike Pay

MANAGEMENT TEAM

Manager: Glenn Cockerill   **Head of Youth Development**
Assistant Manager: Matt Crossley   **& Reserve Team Coach**   Graham Baker
Reserve Team Manager: Peter Johnson   **Youth Team Coach**:   Jimmy Dack
Sports Therapist: Bobby Childs

WOKING

BEST LGE ATT.: 3,244 v Aldershot Town
LOWEST: 890 v Forest Green Rovers

No.	Date	Comp	H/A	Opponents	Att:	Result	Goalscorers	Pos
1	Aug 13	C	A	Kidderminster Harriers	1926	L 1 - 2	**Richards** 54	14
2	16		H	Stevenage Borough	2592	W 3 - 2	Selley 10 (pen) MacDonald 51, Ferguson 88	11
3	20		H	Burton Albion	1692	D 2 - 2	McAllister 86 Selley 90 (pen)	10
4	27		A	York City	2302	L 1 - 2	**Richards** 58	16
5	29		H	Gravesend & Northfleet	1770	L 1 - 3	Selley 71	19
6	Sept 3		A	Accrington Stanley	959	L 1 - 2	Rawle 89	20
7	10		H	Southport	1477	W 1 - 0	**Richards** 90	14
8	17		A	Cambridge United	2345	W 2 - 0	McAllister 54 Murray 78	12
9	20		H	Canvey Islannd	1543	D 1 - 1	Chenery 45 (og)	12
10	24		A	Tamworth	1021	W 1 - 0	**Richards** 62	11
11	27		A	Exeter City	3082	D 1 - 1	Murray 76	10
12	Oct 1		H	Scarborough	1840	W 4 - 0	**Richards** 3 (4 17 pen 61) McAllister 45	8
13	8		H	Grays Athletic	1995	D 1 - 1	**Richards** 21	9
14	15		A	Forest Green Rovers	875	W 3 - 0	McAllister 1 Murray 12 **Richards** 28	8
15	18	LDV Vans T	H	**Nottingham Forest**	3127	W 3 - 2	Rawle 11 53 Richards 65	
16	22	FAC 4Q	H	**Thurrock**	1486	W 3 - 0	Oliver 68 Jackson 80 Ferguson 84	
17	29	C	H	Halifax Town	2054	D 2 - 2	Murray 21 Ferguson 62	8
18	Nov 5	FAC 1R	A	**Southport**	1417	D 1 - 1	Evans 32	
19	12		A	Hereford United	2498	L 0 - 4		9
20	15	FAC 1R r	H	**Southport**	2298	W 1 - 0*	**McAllister** 114	
21	19	C	H	Morecambe	2069	L 0 - 1		9
22	26		A	Dagenham & Redbridge	1138	W 3 - 1	**Richards** 4 Cockerill 7 McAllister 85	9
23	28	LDV Vans T2	H	**Cheltenham Town**	883	L 1 - 5*	Blackman 18	
24	Dec 3	FAC 3R	H	**Northwich Victoria**	2462	D 0 - 0		
25	10	C	A	Altrincham	825	W 4 - 0	**Richards** 2 53 Evans 41 Watson 61	9
26	13	FAC3Rr	A	**Northwich Victoria**	2302	L 1 - 2	Ferguson 45	
27	17	FAT 1	A	**Uxbridge**	471	W 2 - 1	McAllister 18 Rawle 56	
28	24	C	H	Crawley Town	2643	D 0 - 0		9
29	31		H	Dagenham & Redbridge	1806	D 0 - 0		8
30	Jan 2		A	Crawley Town	2073	D 2 - 2	**Richards** 32 Selley 79	9
31	7		H	Kidderminster Harriers	1514	L 0 - 1		9
32	14	FAT 2	H	**Northwich Victoria**	1071	D 1 - 1	Murray 22	
33	17	FAT 2r	A	**Northwich Victoria**	888	W 2 - 1*	Selley 44 (pen) Ferguson 110	
34	21	C	A	Burton Albion	2061	D 1 - 1	Murray 20	10
35	24		A	Stevenage Borough	2152	D 1 - 1	McAllister 57	
36	28		H	York City	1938	W 2 - 0	**Richards** 23 Ferguson 51	9
37	Feb 4	FAT 3	H	**Welling United**	1244	W 3 - 2	Sharpling 31 McAllister 65 Hutchinson 90	
38	11	C	H	Tamworth	2030	W 5 - 0	Evans 27 Sharpling 30 **Richards** 60 (pen) Watson 80 Ferguson 90	
39	18		A	Scarborough	1278	D 1 - 1	Ferguson 90	9
40	21		H	Exeter City	1536	W 1 - 0	**Richards** 81 (pen)	9
41	25	FAT 4	H	**Stafford Rangers**	2020	D 1 - 1	McAllister 68	
42	28	FAT 4R	A	**Stafford Rangers**	1781	W 4 - 2	McAllister 30 Daniel (og) 60 Smith 89 Ferguson 90	
43	Mar 4	C	H	Cambridge City	2066	L 0 - 1		9
44	11		A	Grays Athletic	1256	D 2 - 2	**Richards** 17 83	10
45	18	FAT S-F1	A	**Boreham Wood**	1511	W 1 - 0	Hutchinson 78	
46	21	C	H	Aldershot Town	3244	L 1 - 2	MacDonald 84	11
47	25	FAT S-F2	H	**Boreham Wood**	2080	W 2 - 0	Ferguson 19 90	
48	28	C	A	Halifax Town	1465	L 0 - 1		12
49	April 1		H	Hereford United	1929	D 1 - 1	McAllister 45	12
50	4		A	Canvey Island	358	W 2 - 0	Murray 8 Ferguson 37	11
51	8		A	Morecambe	1468	L 1 - 3	Ferguson 63	12
52	10		A	Southport	1054	L 0 - 1		12
53	15		H	Accrington Stanley	2665	L 0 - 1		13
54	17		A	Graveend & Northfleet	776	L 0 - 2		13
55	22		A	Aldershot Town	2704	D 1 - 1	**Richards** 6	13
56	25		H	Forest GreenRovers	890	W 2 - 1	Evans 15 **Richards** 55 (pen)	12
57	29		H	Altrincham	1650	W 3 - 1	McAllister 16 **Richards** 31 (pen) Watson 39	11
58	May 14	FAT Final	N	**Grays Athletic**	13997	L 0 - 2		

Ave. Home Attendance: 2385   **Goals** 84 61   **Top Goalscorer:** Justin Richards (22)
Best Position: 8th   **Worst:** 20th

STEP 1 — CONFERENCE
STEP 2 - P177 — CONFERENCE Nth & Sth
STEP 3 - P269 — NPL · SOUTHERN · ISTHMIAN PREV
STEP 4 - P269 — NPL · SOUTHERN · ISTHMIAN
STEP 5/6 - P473
STEP 7 - P713

#	JALAL 1	JACKSON 2	AGGREY 5	MACDONALD 6	L COCKERILL 11	BLACKMAN 10	SELLEY 7	MURRAY 8	S EVANS 16	RICHARDS 9	MCALLISTER 18	EL SALAHI 3	SHARPLING 14	SMITH 4	FERGUSON 15	DAVIES 21	FREED 17	RUBY 22	RAWLE 20	NETHERCOTT 19	OLIVER 24	COCKERILL 23	WATSON 17	SOLE ·	CROSSLEY ·	D EVANS ·	HUTCHINSON 25	OYEDELE 24	BUARI 27	TOWNSEND 26	HOWE ·
1	X	X	X	X	X	X	X	X	X	X	S			S	U	U	U														
2	X	X	X			S	X	X	X	X	U	X	X	S	X	U	X	U													
3	X	X		X	U	X	X		X	X	S	X		X	X	U	X	U	S												
4	X	X		X	S	X	X	X	X	X	S	X		U	X	U	X	U													
5	X	U		X	X	X	X	S	X	S	X			X	S	U	X		X												
6	X	S		X		X	X	X	X	X	X			U	S	U			S	X	X										
7	X	X	U	X			X	X	S	X	S	X		X	X	U	S		X	X	X										
8	X	X		X		S	X	X	S	X	U			X	X	U	S		X	X	X										
9	X	X	U	X	U	U	X	X	X	X	U			X	X	U				X	X										
10	X	X	U	X			S	X	X	X	X	U		X	X	U			S	X	X										
11	X	X	U	X			S	X	X	X	X	U		X	X	U			S	X	X										
12	X	X		X		S	S	X	X	X	U			X	X	U			S	X	X										
13	X	X		X		U	S	X	X	X	X	S		X	X	U			S	X	X										
14	X	X	U			X	S	X		X	X	U		X	X	U			S	X	X	S									
15	U	X	X		S	X	X	X		X			X		X	S	U	X	X		X		X	S							
16	X	X	U			S	X	X	X	X	X	X		X	X	U			S	X	X										
17	X	X	U		U	S	X		X	X	X	U		X	X	U			S	X	X										
18	X	X		U	U	U	X	X	X	X	X	U		X	X	U			S	X	X										
19	X	X		U	S	X	X	X	X	X	X	U		X	X	U			S	X	X										
20	X	X		U	S	X	X	X	U	X	S	X		X	X	U			X	X	X										
21	X	X		S	X	X	X	X	U	X	X			X	X	U			S	X	X										
22	X	X		X	S	S	X	U	X	X				X	X	U			U	X	X		X								
23	U	U	X		X	X	X	S	X	S	S	X				X		X	X			X	X								
24	X	X	U		X	S	U	X		X	X	X		X	X	U			U	X		X									
25	X	X	U		X	S			X	X	X	X		X	X	U			S	X		S	X								
26	X	X	U		X			S	X	S	X	X		X	X	U			S	X	X										
27	X		X		X			X	X		X	X	X		X	U			X	X		S	X	U	U	U					
28	X	X	X				U	X	X	X	X			X	U		U	U		U	X										
29	X	X	X				U	X	X	X	X			X	U		U	S	X		U	X									
30	X	X	X				S	X	X	X	X			X	U		U	X	X		S			X							
31	X	X	X					X	X	X	X	U	S	U			S					X				X					
32	X	X	U	U	X			X	S		X	U	X	X	U				X			X				X					
33	X	X		U	U		X		X	X	S	U	X	X	U				X			X				X					
34	X	X		U	U			U	X	X	X	X	U	U					X			X				X					
35	X	X			U			X	X	X	X	S	S	S	X	U			X			X				X					
36	X		U	S	U			X	X	S	X	X	X	X	X				X			X				X		U			
37	X		S				X	X	U	X	X	S	X	X	X				X			X				X	U				
38	X	U		S	S			X	X	X	X	X		X	U				X			X	S			X	X	S			
39	X	U		X	U			X	X	X	X	X	S	X	U				X			X	S			X	X	X			
40	X	U		X	U			X	X	X	X	X	S	X	U				X			X	X	X							
41	X	U		X	U		S	X	X		X	X	X	S					X			X	X	X	X	U					
42		X		X	U	S	X	X		X	S		X	X	X					S	X		X		U					U	
43	X	X		X	S	X	X	X	X		X	U		U				S		U	X		X				U	U			
44	X	S		X		S	X		X	X			X	X	U				X			X	X	U	U						
45	X	U		X		U	X	X		X	X	U		X	X	U			X		X		X	U	U						
46	X	X		X	S	X		X	X	X	S		S	X	U				X			X	U	X							
47	X	U		X	U	U	X	X	U	X	X		X	X	U				X			X		X							
48	X	X		X	X	U		S	X	X	X	X		X	X	U			X			X	U	S							
49	X	X		X	X	S		X	X		X	U		X	X	U			X	U			X	U							
50	X	X		X	X	S		X	X		X	U		X	X	U			X			X	S	U							
51	X			X	X	X		X	X		X	X	U		X	X	U			X		S	S	S							
52	X			X	X	X		X		S	S	X		S	X	U			X			X	X	X							
53	X	X		X	U	U			X	X	U		X	X	U				X			X	X	S							
54	X	X		X	U	X	U	X		X	X	X	U						X			X	X	S							
55	X	X		X	X	S			X	X	X	U		X					X	U			X	S							
56	X	X			X	U		X	X	X	U		X	X				S				X	U	S							
57	U	X		X	U	S		X	X	X	X	S		X			X					X	S	X							
58	X	X		X	S	S		X	X	X	X	U		X	X	U			X			X	S		X						

Total Appearances (Conference)

	JALAL	JACKSON	AGGREY	MACDONALD	L COCKERILL	BLACKMAN	SELLEY	MURRAY	S EVANS	RICHARDS	MCALLISTER	EL SALAHI	SHARPLING	SMITH	FERGUSON	DAVIES	FREED	RUBY	RAWLE	NETHERCOTT	OLIVER	COCKERILL	WATSON	SOLE	CROSSLEY	D EVANS	HUTCHINSON	OYEDELE	BUARI	TOWNSEND	HOWE	
X	41	33	5	27	10	11	18	39	31	35	33	17	5	27	35	1	4	0	4	32	13	0	14	0	0	0	19	6	2	0	0	X
S	0	2	0	3	5	16	5	0	3	3	6	5	3	6	2	1	2	0	13	1	0	4	1	0	0	0	1	5	4	0	0	S
U	1	4	8	1	12	7	0	0	2	0	2	13	0	5	1	40	0	6	2	0	0	8	1	0	0	0	0	4	2	0	0	U

Cup Appearances

	JALAL	JACKSON	AGGREY	MACDONALD	L COCKERILL	BLACKMAN	SELLEY	MURRAY	S EVANS	RICHARDS	MCALLISTER	EL SALAHI	SHARPLING	SMITH	FERGUSON	DAVIES	FREED	RUBY	RAWLE	NETHERCOTT	OLIVER	COCKERILL	WATSON	SOLE	CROSSLEY	D EVANS	HUTCHINSON	OYEDELE	BUARI	TOWNSEND	HOWE	
X	13	10	3	5	4	2	9	14	7	12	12	8	3	13	15	3	0	1	4	12	4	1	11	0	0	0	8	1	1	0	0	X
S	0	0	0	1	2	5	3	1	2	1	3	2	1	0	0	1	0	0	3	0	0	3	1	0	0	0	0	0	0	0	0	S
U	2	4	4	2	6	3	2	0	3	0	0	3	0	1	0	12	0	0	1	0	0	0	0	1	1	1	0	1	2	1		U

WOKING

GOALKEEPERS	SQ NO.	HT	WT	D.O.B	AGE	P.O.B	CAREER	APPS	GOA
Shwan Jalal	1	6'02"	14 02	14/8/83	23	Baghdad	Hastings U, Tottenham 6/01, Woking (L), Woking c/s 04	41	0
Aaron Howe	21						Woking	0	0

DEFENDERS									
Simon Jackson	2			4/4/85	21	Lewisham	Charlton (Scholar) Rel 03/04, Woking 8/04	35	0
Danny Bunce	3			30/4/86	20		West Ham Rel c/s 05, Cambridge U NC 11/05 Rel 5/06, Woking 7/06		
Tom Hutchinson	5	6'01"	12 06	23/2/82	24	Kingston	Sutton U, Fulham 8/98, Dundee 8/02, Woking 1/06	20	0
Gary MacDonald	6	6'01"	12 12	25/10/79	26	Iselone, Ger	Portsmouth Rel c/s 99, Havant & W 7/99, Peterborough Undisc 2/01,		
							Stevenage (L) 11/02, £10,000 12/02, Woking 7/03	30	2
Karim El-Salahi	17	6'02"	13 09	24/11/86	19	London	C.Palace Rel c/s 05, Woking 7/05	22	0
Shola Oyedele	20	5'11"	12 07	14/9/84	21	Kano. Nigeria	Wimbledon/MK Dons Rel c/s 06, Woking (SL) 2/06, Woking 8/06	11	0
Matt Ruby	22						Woking, Northwood (L) 10/05, Fleet T (L) 1/06, Basingstoke (L) 3/06	0	0
Matt Crossley							Woking (Ass Man)	0	0

MIDFIELDERS									
Neil Smith	4	5'09"	12 00	30/9/71	34	Lambeth	Tottenham, Gillingham (L) 10/91, Gillingham £40,000 11/91, Fulham 7/97,		
							Reading £100,000 8/99 Rel c/s 02, Bournemouth (Trial) 7/02,		
							Stevenage 8/02, Woking 10/02	33	0
Ian Selley	7	5'10"	10 09	14/6/74	32	Chertsey	Arsenal, Southend (L) 12/96, Fulham £500,000 10/97 Rel c/s 00,		
							Wimbledon 8/00 Rel c/s 03, Southend (SL) 2/02,		
							Southend (3ML) 8/02, Woking 8/03	23	4
Karl Murray	8	5'11"	12 06	26/8/82	24	London	Shrewsbury, Sheff Utd (Trial) 8/99, Northwich (L) 11/03, Woking 1/0439		6
Liam Cockerill	11						Gosport B, Woking 7/03, Lewes (L) 9/05	15	1
Stephen Evans	16	5'11"	11 02	25/9/80	25	Caerphilly	C.Palace, Swansea (3ML) 11/01, Brentford 3/02 Rel c/s 04, Woking 8/04	34	3
Goma Lambu	18	5'03"	9 08	10/11/84	21	Ghana	Millwall Rel c/s 03, Fisher c/s 03, Tooting & Mitcham 3/04, Southall,		
							Redbridge, Mansfield 1/05, Redbridge 3/05, Dulwich Hamlet, Woking 8/06		
Sam Cockerill	23						Woking, Fleet T (L) 1/06	4	0
Giuseppe Sole	24						Woking, Basingstoke (L) 3/06	0	0
Jerome Maledon	25						Woking		
Dan Evans							Woking	0	0

FORWARDS									
Craig McAllister	9					Hampshire	Eastleigh, Basingstoke 3/02, Stevenage 5/04, Gravesend (L) 12/04,		
							Eastleigh (L) 2/05, Woking 7/05	39	8
Chris Sharpling	10	5'11"	11 10	21/4/81	24	Bromley	C.Palace, Woking (3ML) 1/01, Woking £60,000 10/01	8	1
Ollie Berquez	14					Essex	Ipswich (Jun), Heybridge S, Chelmsford, St Albans, Chelmsford,		
							Dag & Red, Braintree, Canvey Island 12/02 (03/04 32,9),		
							Stevenage 6/05 Rel 5/06, Woking 6/06		
Steven Ferguson	15	5'11"	11 00	1/4/82	24	Dunfermline	Musselburgh Windsor U18s, East Fife, Tottenham 9/00 Rel c/s 03,		
							Motherwell (5ML) 8/02, Woking 8/03	37	7

PLAYING SQUAD

LOANEES	HT	WT	DOB	AGE	POB	FROM - TO	APPS	GOA
(D)Stephen Reed	5'08"	12 02	18/6/85	21	Barnstaple	Yeovil 8/05 - Aldershot (L) 9/05, Torquay (L) 3/06, Rel 5/06,		
						Torquay 5/06	6	0
(D)Stuart Nethercott	6'00"	13 08	21/3/73	33	Ilford	Wycombe (SL) 8/05 - Rel c/s 06	33	0
(D)Luke Oliver	6'07"	14 05	1/5/84	22	Hammersmith	Yeovil (3M) 8/05 - Stevenage 1/06	13	0
(F)Luke Townsend	6'00"	11 10	28/9/86	19	Guildford	QPR 2/06 - Crawley 8/06	0	0

DEPARTURES	HT	WT	DOB	AGE	POB	FROM - TO	APPS	GOA
(G)Clint Davies	6'03"	12 07	24/4/83	23	Perth (Aus)	Bristol C 8/05 - Rel 5/06	2	0
(M)Mark Rawle	5'11"	12 04	27/4/79	27	Leicester	Kidderminster 8/05 - Gravesend (SL) 1/06, Rel 5/06, Crawley 8/06	17	1
(M)Malik Buari	5'11"	11 11	21/1/84	22	Accra	Fulham 2/06 - Rel 5/06, New Zealand Knights	6	0
(F)Justin Richards	6'00"	11 10	16/10/80	25	Sandwell	Stevenage 5/04 - Peterborough 6/06	38	21
(F)Lloyd Blackman	6'00"	12 03	24/9/83	22	Ashford (Mx)	Farnborough 6/05 - Rel 6/06, Cambridge Utd (Trial) c/s 06	27	0
(D)Paul Watson	5'08"	10 10	4/1/75	31	Hastings	Coventry 11/05 - Rushden & D 6/06	15	3
(D)Jimmy Aggrey	6'02"	12 13	26/10/78	27	London	Bohemians c/s 05 - Southend (Trial) 1/06, Southport (L) 2/06, Rel c/s 06	5	0
Miles Jones						Yth - Hayes 8/06		

WOKING

Ground Address: Kingfield Stadium, Kingfield Road, Woking
Tel No: 01483 772470
Fax: 01483 888423
General email address: admin@wokingfc.co.uk
Official website: http: //www.wokingfc.co.uk
SIMPLE DIRECTIONS
By Road M25 exit 10 or 11, Woking FC signposted from outskirts of town wfc is opposite the well signposted Leisure Centre.
Parking: Big car park at Leisure Centre and a car park at the football club
MATCH TICKETS
Ticket office Telephone: 01483 772470
Capacity: 6,000
Seats: 2,500
Covered: 3,900
Clubhouse: Excellent clubhouse open on matchdays
Refreshments: Available on matchdays
Club Shop: Yes.

Local Radio: BBC Surrey Sussex, County Sound and BBC Southern Counties
Local Press: Woking News & Mail, Woking Herald, Surrey Advertiser.

MATCHDAY PROGRAMME
Co-ordinator: Sadie Gordon
(B) 01483 772 470
07718 627700 (M)
e-mail: commercial@woking.co.uk

CLUB STATISTICS
RECORD
Attendance: 6,000 v Swansea F.A. Cup 1978-79
v Coventry C F.A.Cup 1996-97
Victory: 17-4 v Farnham 1912-13

Defeat 0-16 v New Crusaders 1905-06

Career Goalscorer: Charlie Mortimore 331 1953-65

Career Appearances: Brian Finn 564 1962-74
Transfer Fee Paid: £60,000
paid to Crystall Palace forChris Sharpling

Transfer Fee Received: £150,000
from Bristol Rovers for Steve Foster
SENIOR HONOURS F.A.Trophy 93-94 94-95 96-97
F.A.Amateur Cup 1957-58
Conference R-Up 94-95 95-96
Isthmian Lg.91-92 R-Up 56-57
Surrey Senior Cup (9)
London Senior Cup R-Up 82-83
PREVIOUS
League: Isthmian 1911-92
Grounds: Wheatsheaf, Ive Lane (pre 19230)

YORK CITY

Club Colours: Red/White/Red

Change Colours: All Navy Blue

Club Sponsor: C.L.P. Industries

Previous League: Football League

BEST PERFORMANCES

League: 9th Division Two 1994-95

F.A. Cup: Semi-Final 1955 (when in Division Three)

F.A. Trophy: 3rd Round 2004-05

Formed: 1922

Nickname: Minstermen

CLUB PERSONNEL

Managing Director:	Jason McGill	**Commercial Manager**	Elliott Stroud
Financial Director:	Terry Doyle	**Press Officer:**	Sophie McGill
Commercial Director:	Peter Davis	**Tel Nos:**	01653 691500 (W) and 07734 172625
Additional Directors:	Ian McAndrew and Steve Beck		
Club Secretary:	Nigel Pleasants		
Tel No:	01904 624447		

:

MANAGEMENT TEAM

Manager:	Billy McEwan	**Club Playing Status**	Full Time
Reserve Team Coach: :	Colin Walker		
Physio:	Jeff MIller		

YORK CITY

BEST LGE ATT.: 4,921 v Scarborough
LOWEST: 1,768 v Kidderminster Harriers

No.	Date	Comp	H/A	Opponents	Att:	Result	Goalscorers	Pos
1	Aug 13	C	H	Crawley Town	2276	D 0 - 0		13
2	16		A	Southport	1646	W 4 - 1	O'Neill 3 (3 37 81) Convery 19	5
3	20		A	Grays Athletic	1272	D 1 - 1	**Bishop** 69	7
4	27		H	Woking	2302	W 2 - 1	**Bishop** 74 (pen) Dudgeon 78	4
5	29		A	Halifax Town	2078	L 0 - 1		7
6	Sept 2		H	Cambridge United	2666	W 1 - 0	Donaldson 53	4
7	10		A	Forest Green Rovers	889	W 2 - 1	Dudgeon 17 Convery 68	3
8	17		H	Altrincham	2634	W 5 - 0	O'Neill 25 Donaldson 38 Dudgeon 52 **Bishop** 62 Stewart 82	3
9	20		H	Dagenham & Redbridge	2927	D 1 - 1	**Bishop** 36	4
10	24		A	Aldershot Town	2470	L 1 - 2	Donaldson 64	5
11	27		A	Tamworth	1005	W 3 - 0	Donaldson 27 57 Convery 63	4
12	Oct 1		H	Exeter City	3503	W 4 - 2	**Bishop** 20 (pen) 90 Stewart 37 Donaldson 69	2
13	8		A	Gravesend & Northfleet	1133	D 2 - 2	Donaldson 9 **Bishop** 85	3
14	15		H	Canvey Island	3070	W 2 - 1	Convery 77 **Bishop** 88	2
15	**22**	**FAC 4Q**	**A**	**Gainsborough Trinity**	**1680**	**W 4 - 0**	**Bishop** 12 44 (pen) Donaldson 62 Convery 87	
16	29	C	A	Accrington Stanley	2193	L 1 - 2	**Bishop** 62	4
17	**Nov 5**	**FAC 1R**	**H**	**Grays Athletic**	**3586**	**L 0 - 3**		
18	12	C	H	Burton Albion	2411	L 0 - 1		5
19	19		A	Kidderminster Harriers	1768	D 0 - 0		6
20	26		A	Morecambe	1778	L 0 - 2		7
21	Dec 10		A	Hereford United	1950	L 0 - 1		8
22	**17**	**FAT 1**	**H**	**Northwich Victoria**	**1372**	**L 1 - 2**	**Bishop 29**	
23	24	C	H	Scarborough	4921	W 3 - 1	**Bishop** 45 Donaldson 57 McGurk 85	8
24	31		H	Morecambe	2712	D 1 - 1	Convery 41	7
25	Jan 2		A	Scarborough	4057	D 2 - 2	**Bishop** 38 72	8
26	7		A	Crawley Town	1514	W 1 - 0	Dudgeon 60	8
27	10		H	Stevenage Borough	2325	L 0 - 1		8
28	21		H	Grays Athletic	2461	L 1 - 2	O'Neill 4	8
29	24		H	Southport	2176	D 0 - 0		8
30	28		A	Woking	1938	L 0 - 2		8
31	Feb 12		H	Aldershot Town	2401	W 3 - 2	Convery 34 **Bishop** 49 Donaldson 52	8
32	18		H	Exter City	3381	W 3 - 1	Dudgeon 32 N.Bishop 47 A.**Bishop** 72	8
33	21		H	Tamworth	2153	W 2 - 1	**Bishop** 2 Donaldson 63	7
34	25		H	Forest Green Rovers	2314	W 5 - 1	**Bishop** 3 (14 (pen) 38 40) McGurk 23 Thomas 60	6
35	Mar 7		A	Dagenham & Redbridge	973	W 2 - 0	Donaldson 86 **Bishop** 90	
36	11		H	Gravesened & Northfleet	2902	W 1 - 0	Dudgeon 9	4
37	18		A	Canvey Island	754	D 1 - 1	Dunning 56	4
38	25		A	Accrington Stanley	3912	L 2 - 4	Donaldson 21 **Bishop** 40	5
39	April 1		A	Burton Albion	2605	D 0 - 0		6
40	4		A	Altrincham	1237	W 3 - 0	Donaldson 24 40 **Bishop** 33	5
41	9		H	KIdderminster Harriers	3376	D 2 - 2	**Bishop** 52 (pen) Donaldson 89	6
42	14		A	Cambridge United	3188	L 0 - 2		6
43	17		H	Halkifax Town	4084	L 0 - 2		7
44	22		A	Stevenage Borough	2701	D 1 - 1	Donaldson 36	8
45	29		H	Hererford United	2755	L 1 - 3	**Bishop** 56	8

Ave. League Home Attendance: 3191   **Goals** 68 53   **Top Goalscorer:** Andy Bishop (26)
Best Position: 2nd   **Worst:** 13th

Match	PORTER (1)	PRICE (2)	HOTTE (4)	MCGURK (5)	PEAT (3)	MALLON (21)	PANTHER (8)	CONVERY (7)	DUNNING (12)	DONALDSON (9)	MANSARAM (22)	A BISHOP (11)	STEWART (18)	DUDGEON (6)	MERRIS (15)	AFANDJYEV (26)	O'NEILL (10)	YALCIN (14)	WEBSTER (19)	STALEY (20)	PALMER (24)	STOCKDALE (13)	ANDREWS (22)	BERTOS (24)	BARWICK (25)	HORWOOD (26)	REID (25)	CRADDOCK (21)	NTOYA (22)	N BISHOP (16)	THOMAS (23)	RHODES (14)	KAMARA (21)
1	X	X	X	X	X	X	X	X	X	X	X	S	S	U	U	U																	
2	X	X	X	X	X	U	X	X	X	X	X	S	S		S	U	X																
3	X	X	X	X	X	U	X	X	X	X	X	S	U		S	U	X																
4	X	X		X	X		X	X	X	X	X	S	U	X	U	U	X	S															
5	X	X	X	X	X		X	X	X	X		X	S	U	U	U	X	S															
6	X	X	X	X	X		X	X	X	X	S	X	U	U		U	X	S															
7	X	X		X		S	X	X	X	X		X		X	X	U	X	S	S	U													
8	X	X	U	X			X	X	X	X		X	S	X	X	U	X	S			S												
9	X	X	U	X			X	X	X	X		X	U	X	U	X	U	X	U														
10	X	X	U	X			X	X	X	X		X	S	X	U	X	U	X	U			S											
11	X	X	U	X			X	X	X	X		X	X	X	U	X	S	U			S												
12	X	X	U	X			X	X	X	X		X	X	X	U	X	S	U	U														
13	X	X	S	X			X	X	X	X		X	S	X	U	X	U	X	U		U												
14	X	X	X	X	S		X	X	X	X		X	S	S	X		X			U	U												
15	X	X		X	X	S		X	X	X		X	S	X	S		X	X	U		U												
16	X	X		X		S		X	X	X		X	S	X	X		X	X	U	U	U												
17	X	X		X		S		X	X	X		X	S	X	X		X	X	S	U	U												
18	X	X		X		S		X	X	X		X	S		X		X	X	U	U	U												
19	X	X		X		S		X	X	X		X	S			U		X		U	X	X											
20	X	X		X				X	X	X		X			U	U		S	X	X	X	X											
21	U	U	U	X				S	X	X			S	X			X	X					X	X	X	X	X						
22	S		S	X			X	X	X		X		X		S	S			X	X	X	X	X										
23	X		X	X			S	X	X	X		X	S		X	S		X	U				X	X		X	X						
24	X		X	X				X	X	X		X	U	U	S		X	U					X	X		X							
25	X						X	X	X	X		X	U	X	X		X	S	U				X	S									
26	X		X				X	X	X	X		X	S	X	X		X		U				X	U		U	U						
27	X		X				X	X	X	X		X	S	X	X		X		U				X	S		U	U						
28	X		X		U		X	X	X	X		X			X	X		S	U					U				X	X				
29	X		X	U	S		X	X	X	X		S			X	X		X						U				X	X				
30	X		X	U	S		X	X	X	X		X			X	X		U						U				X	S				
31	X		U	X	X		X	X	X	X		X	S	X	U		U							U		X			X				
32	X		U	X	X		X	X	X	X		X	X	U			S		S					U					X	X			
33	X		U	X	X		X	X	X	X		X	S	X			S		U					U					X	X			
34	X		S	X	X		X	X	X	X		X	S	X			S		U					U					X	X			
35	X		X	X	X		X	X	X	X		X	U		U		U		U					U					X	X			
36	X		U	X	X		X	X	X	X		X		X	S		S		U					U					X	X			
37	X	S	U	X	X		X	X	X	X		X		X	S		U							U					X	X			
38	X	X	S	X	X		X	X	X	X		X		X	U	S								U					X	S			
39	X	X	U	X	X		X	X	X	X		X		X	U		U							U					X	S			
40	X		U	X	X		X	X	X	X		X		X			S							U					X	X	S	S	
41	X		U	X	X		X	X	X	X		X	S	X			S							U					X	X		U	
42	X		S	X	X		X	X	X	X		X	S	X			S		U					U					X	X			
43	X		X	X			X	S	X	X		X	S	X	X		X		U					U					U	X			
44	X	X	U	X	X		X	S		X		X		X			X	U			X			U					X	X			
45	X		U	X	X		X	S	X	X		X		X			S							U					X	X		S	

Total Appearances (Conference)

	PORTER	PRICE	HOTTE	MCGURK	PEAT	MALLON	PANTHER	CONVERY	DUNNING	DONALDSON	MANSARAM	A BISHOP	STEWART	DUDGEON	MERRIS	AFANDJYEV	O'NEILL	YALCIN	WEBSTER	STALEY	PALMER	STOCKDALE	ANDREWS	BERTOS	BARWICK	HORWOOD	REID	CRADDOCK	NTOYA	N BISHOP	THOMAS	RHODES	KAMARA	
X	41	21	16	36	20	1	36	38	41	42	4	35	2	30	18	0	25	4	0	0	0	1	9	3	3	4	0	4	2	14	12	0	0	X
S	0	1	4	0	3	4	1	4	0	0	1	5	19	1	7	0	12	7	3	0	3	1	0	2	0	0	0	0	1	0	2	1	2	S
U	1	1	16	2	1	2	0	0	0	0	0	0	7	6	10	13	4	8	14	4	3	7	0	3	0	2	20	0	0	1	0	0	1	U

Cup Appearances

	PORTER	PRICE	HOTTE	MCGURK	PEAT	MALLON	PANTHER	CONVERY	DUNNING	DONALDSON	MANSARAM	A BISHOP	STEWART	DUDGEON	MERRIS	AFANDJYEV	O'NEILL	YALCIN	WEBSTER	STALEY	PALMER	STOCKDALE	ANDREWS	BERTOS	BARWICK	HORWOOD	REID	CRADDOCK	NTOYA	N BISHOP	THOMAS	RHODES	KAMARA	
X	2	2	0	3	1	0	0	3	3	3	0	3	0	3	0	1	0	2	2	0	0	0	1	1	1	1	0	0	0	0	0	0	0	X
S	1	0	1	0	0	2	0	0	0	0	0	0	3	0	1	0	1	1	1	0	0	0	0	0	0	0	0	0	0	0	0	0	0	S
U	0	0	0	0	0	0	0	0	0	0	0	0	0	0	0	0	1	1	0	2	0	0	0	0	0	0	0	0	0	0	0	0	0	U

YORK CITY

CURRANT SQUAD AS OF BEGINING OF 2006-07 SEASON

GOALKEEPERS

GOALKEEPERS	SQ NO.	HT	WT	D.O.B	AGE	P.O.B	CAREER	APPS	GOA
Tommy Evans	1	6'00"	13 02	31/12/76	29	Doncaster	Sheff Utd, C.Palace 8/96 Rel c/s 97, Harrow (L) 8/96,		
							Coventry (L) 3/97, Scunthorpe 8/97 Rel 5/06, York C 7/06		
Arran Reid	18					York	York C	0	0

DEFENDERS

DEFENDERS	SQ NO.	HT	WT	D.O.B	AGE	P.O.B	CAREER	APPS	GOA
Darren Craddock	2	5'11"	12 02	23/2/85	21	Bishop Auckland	Hartlepool, Whitby (L) 1/04, York (L) 1/06 Rel 5/06, York C 5/06	4	0
Nathan Peat	3	5'09"	10 09	19/9/82	23	Hull	Hull C, Cambridge U (2ML) 12/03, Lincoln C (SL) 7/04, York 8/05	23	0
David McGurk	5	6'00"	11 10	30/9/82	23	Middlesbrough	Darlington, Bishop Auckland (L) 8/04, York (L) 9/04, York 6ML 8/05,		
							York (SL) 1/06, York 6/06	36	2
James Dudgeon	6	6'02"	12 04	19/3/81	25	Newcastle	Barnsley Rel c/s 03,Lincoln C (SL) 11/00, Scarborough 5/03 (03/04 1,0),		
							Halifax 9/03 (03/04 10,0) Rel 4/04, Worksop 7/04, York 6/05 (05/06 31,6) 31		6
Anthony Lloyd	12	5'07"	11 00	14/3/84	22	Taunton	Huddersfield, Torquay (2ML) 11/05 1/06 Rel 5/06, York C 7/06		
Ross Greenwood	14	5'11"	11 05	1/11/85	20	York	Sheff Wed, Stockport 7/05, York C 7/06		
Darren Hollingsworth	16					Stockton	York C		
Daniel Parslow	20	5'11"	12 05	11/9/85	20	Rhymney Valley	Cardiff Rel c/s 05, York C 8/05		
Michael Staley				19/6/87	19	Sheffield	York C	0	0
Nathan Kamara						York	York C	2	0

MIDFIELDERS

MIDFIELDERS	SQ NO.	HT	WT	D.O.B	AGE	P.O.B	CAREER	APPS	GOA
Neil Bishop	4	6'00"		7/8/81	25	Whitby	Middlesbrough (Jun), Billingham T, Gateshead c/s 02, Spennymoor 10/02,		
							Whitby c/s 04, Scarborough 3/05, York C 1/06	14	1
Mark Convery	7	5'06"	10 05	29/5/81	25	Newcastle	Sunderland, Hvidore FK (Den) (3ML) 7/00, Cardiff (Trial) 12/00,		
							Reading (Trial), Darlington 1/01 Rel c/s 05, York 6/05	42	6
Emmanuel Panther	8			11/5/84	22	Glasgow	St Johnstone, Partick T 6/03, Brechin (3ML) 2/05, York C 8/05	37	0
Steve Bowey	11			10/7/74	32	Durham	Bristol R, Forest Green, Gateshead, Q.o.South 2/02, York 6/06		
Byron Webster	15			31/3/87	19	Leeds	York C	3	0
Lewis McMahon				2/5/85	21	Doncaster	Sheff Wed, Notts County 7/05 Rel c/s 06, York C 8/06		

FORWARDS

FORWARDS	SQ NO.	HT	WT	D.O.B	AGE	P.O.B	CAREER	APPS	GOA
Clayton Donaldson	9	6'01"	11 07	7/2/84	22	Bradford	Hull C Rel c/s 05, Scarborough (L) 8/03, Halifax (L) 2/04,		
							Harrogate T (SL) 5/04, York 6/05	42	16
Craig Farrell	10	6'00"	12 11	5/12/82	23	Middlesbrough	Leeds, Carlisle (2ML) 10/02 (Undisc) 12/02 Rel 5/05,		
							Exeter c/s 05 Rel 5/06, York C 6/06		
Alex Rhodes	17						York C 10/05	1	0

PLAYING SQUAD

LOANEES	HT	WT	DOB	AGE	POB	FROM - TO	APPS	GOA
(F)Darren Mansaram	6'02"	11 07	25/6/84	22	Doncaster	Halifax 8/05 - Tamworth (L) 9/05, Worksop (L) 12/05, Sligo R 1/06	5	0
(F)Jermaine Palmer	6'01"	11 03	28/8/86	20	Nottingham	Grimsby 9/05 - Hinckley (3ML) 10/05, Kettering (L) 1/06, Alfreton 8/06	3	0
(D)Lee Andrews	6'01"	10 11	23/4/83	23	Carlisle	Carlisle (2M) 11/05 - Torquay (L) 3/06, Rel 5/06, Torquay 5/06	9	0
(M)Terry Barwick	5'11"	10 12	11/1/83	23	Sheffield	Grimsby 11/05 -	3	0
(D)Evan Horwood	6'00"	10 06	10/3/86	20	Hartlepool	Sheff Utd (2M) 11/05 - Chester (L) 1/06	4	0
(F)Tcham N'Toya	5'10"	12 08	3/11/83	22	Kinshasa	Chesterfield 1/06 - Oxford U (L) 3/06, Rel 5/06, Notts County 6/06	3	0

DEPARTURES	HT	WT	DOB	AGE	POB	FROM - TO	APPS	GOA
(G)Farhad Afandiyev			1/6/79	27	Baku	Rushden & D 8/05 - Wakefield & Emley (L) 10/05, Rel 11/05, Rugby Town 11/05	0	0
(M)David Pounder	5'08"	11 04	3/2/80	26	Newcastle	Scarborough 8/05 - Rel 1/06, Scarborough 1/06		
(D)Chris Brass	5'09"	12 06	24/7/75	31	Easington	Burnley 3/01 - Harrogate T (3ML) 9/05, Southport (L) 11/05, Rel 1/06, Bury 1/06		
(M)Ryan Mallon	5'09"	11 08	22/3/83	22	Sheffield	Halifax 8/05 - Gainsborough (L) 12/05 (Perm) 1/06,	5	0
(M)Leo Bertos	6'00"	12 06	20/12/81	24	Wellington (NZ)	Barrow 11/05 - Scarborough 2/06, Worksop 3/06	5	0
(D)Graeme Law	5'10"	10 10	6/10/84	21	Kircaldy	Youth - Rel 1/06, Dundee 2/06, Tamworth 7/06		
(F)Levent Yalcin	6'00"	12 02	25/3/85	21	Middlesbrough	Newcastle ??? - Rel 2/06, Whitby 3/06	11	0
(G)Chris Porter	6'02"	12 03	17/7/79	27	Middlesbrough	Darlington 7/03 - Rel 5/06	41	0
(G)David Stockdale	6'03"	13 04	20/9/85	20	Leeds	Huddersfield (Sch) - Wakefield & Emley (L) 9/05, Worksop (L) 3/06, Rel 5/06, Darlington 7/06	2	0
(D)Mark Hotte	5'11"	11 01	27/9/78	27	Bradford	Scarborough 6/05 - Rel 5/06, Scarborough 6/06	20	0
(D)Dave Merris	5'07"	10 06	13/10/80	25	Rotherham	Harrogate T 8/03 - Rel 5/06, Harrogate T 6/06	25	0
(M)Ashley Winn	5'10"	12 00	1/12/85	20	Stockton	Oldham 8/05 - Stalybridge (L) 3/06, Rel 5/06, Stalybridge 7/06		
(M)Steve Thomas	5'10"	11 12	23/6/79	27	Hartlepool	Darlington Rel 2/06, 2/06 - Rel 5/06, Durham C 7/06	14	1
(F)Joe O'Neill	6'00"	10 05	28/10/82	23	Blackburn	Preston 7/05 - Rel 5/06, Altrincham 6/06	37	5
(F)Andy Bishop	6'00"	10 10	19/10/82	23	Stone	Walsall 7/04 - Bury 5/06	40	23
Steve Baynes						Yth - Rel 5/06		
(D)Jamie Price	5'09"	11 00	27/10/81	24	Normanton	Doncaster 8/05 - Harrogate T 6/06	22	0
(M)Darren Dunning	5'06"	11 12	8/1/81	25	Scarborough	Blackburn 7/03 - Harrogate T 7/06	41	1
(M)Bryan Stewart	5'11"	11 00	13/9/85	20	Billingham	Yth - Rel c/s 06	21	2
(D)Simon Weaver	19	6'01"	10 08	20/12/77	28	Doncaster	Scarborough 8/06 - Rel 8/06, Tamworth 8/06	

YORK CITY

Ground Address:	Bootham Crescent , York YO30 7AQ
Tel No:	01904 624447
Fax:	01904 624447
General email address:	info@ycfc.net
Official website:	www.ycfc.net

SIMPLE DIRECTIONS

By Road From Tadcaster (A64) take left turning onto A1232 (outer ring road), continue for approx 5 miles to A19 then turn right into York and continue for justover a mile. Bootham Crescent is a turning on the left opposite the Crane Hotel

Parking:

MATCH TICKETS

Ticket office Telephone:	01904 624447
Capacity:	9,496
Seats:	1844
Covered:	7000
Clubhouse:	Open for supporters of both sides.
Refreshments:	Bars around the ground.
Club Shop:	Fully equipped with club merchandise.
Local Radio:	Radio York.
Local Press:	The Press.

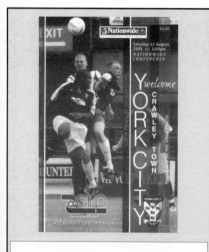

MATCHDAY PROGRAMME
Pages: 44   Price: £2.50
Editor: Terry Doyle
Tel No:01904 784400 (W)
07712 660359 (M)

CLUB STATISTICS

RECORDV

Attendance:	28,123
v Huddersfield Town F.A.Cup 6th Rd 1938	

Victory:	9-1
v Southport Div 3 (N) 1957	
Defeat	0-12
Chester City Div 3 (N) 1936	

Career Goalscorer:	Norman Wilkinson
Career Appearances:	Barry Jackson
Transfer Fee Paid:	£140,000
to Burnley for Adrian Randall Dec. 1995	

Transfer Fee Received:	£1,000,000
from Manchester United for Jonathon Greening March 1998	

SENIOR HONOURS

Football League Div 3 Promotion (3rd) 1973-74
Champions1983-84
1992-93 (play offs)
F.A.Cup Semi-Final 1955 when in Division Three

PREVIOUS

Grounds:	Fulfordgate 1922 -1932.

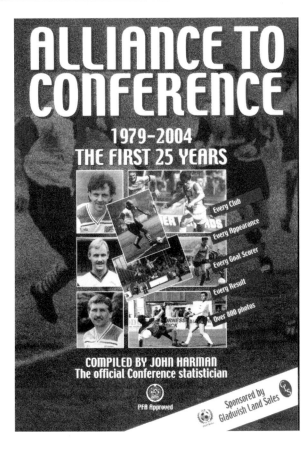

ACCRINGTON STANLEY

No.	Date	Comp	H/A	Opponents	Att:	Result	Goalscorers	Pos
1	Aug 13	C	H	Canvey Island	1012	W 1 - 0	Brown 68	7
2	16		A	Altrincham	1264	W 1 - 0	Welch 85	2
3	20		A	Cambridge United	2730	L 1 - 3	Mangan 83	4
4	27		H	Exeter City	1312	L 1 - 2	**Mullin** 58	9
5	29		A	Scarborough	1509	D 2 - 2	Jagielka 1 Cavanagh 15 (pen)	12
6	Sept 3		H	Woking	959	W 2 - 1	Brown 32 **Mullin** 62	9
7	10		A	Burton Albion	1374	W 2 - 0	Brown 9 Mangan 73	6
8	17		H	Crawley Town	1485	W 4 - 1	Craney 4 Jagielka 57 Roberts 77 Mangan 90	4
9	20		H	Aldershot Town	1114	W 3 2 2	Jagielka 35 D.Brown 41 Roberts 45	3
10	24		A	Dagenham & Redbridge	1331	W 2 - 1	Brown 49 Craney 59 (pen)	2
11	29		A	Morecambe	2162	L 2 - 3	Craney 45 Cavanagh 84 (pen)	3
12	Oct 1		H	Gravesned & Northfleet	1206	D 1 - 1	Craney 16	3
13	7		H	Hereford United	1603	W 2 - 1	Craney 9 Brown 55	2
14	15		A	Stevenage Borough	2141	L 1 - 3	Jagielka 26	4
15	18	LDV Vans T	A	**Rotherham United**	1888	D 3 - 3*	**Mangan 17 Williams 74 Brown 103 Lost 2-3 on pens**	
16	22	FAC 4Q	H	**Worcester City**	940	D 1 - 1	**Roberts 19**	
17	24	FAC4Qr	A	**Worcester City**	1431	L 2 - 3	**Roberts 10 Welch 14**	
18	29	C	H	York City	2193	W 2 - 1	Roberts 43 **Mullin** 67	3
19	Nov 12		A	Grays Athletic	1985	W 2 - 1	**Mullin** 37 Jagielka63	3
20	18		H	Forest Green Rovers	1506	W 2 - 0	Roberts 33 Jagielka 47	1
21	26		H	Southport	1630	W 4 - 0	Craney 32 Boco 36 **Mullin** 87 Mangan 90	2
22	Dec 3		H	Altrincham	1436	W 1 - 0	Roberts 62	1
23	10		H	Kidderminster Harriers	1366	W 2 - 0	Roberts 12 **Mullin** 77	1
24	17	FAT1	H	**Altrincham**	810	W 2 - 0	**Boco 3 Craney 34**	
25	26	C	A	Halifax Town	2688	D 2 - 2	Boco 27 Roberts 90	1
26	Jan 2		H	Halifax Town	3014	D 1 - 1	Cavanagh 80 (pen)	1
27	7		A	Canvey Island	962	W 2 - 0	Cavanagh 38 **Mullin** 66	1
28	10		A	Tamworth	1094	W 2 - 1	**Mullin** 3 Craney 56	1
29	14	FAT 2	A	**Carshalton Athletic**	618	D 2 - 2	**Craney 29 Mullin 90**	
30	17	FAT 2 R	H	**Carshalton Athletic**	556	W 2 - 0	**Mullin 41 68**	
31	21	C	H	Cambridge United	1837	W 1 - 0	Craney 77	1
32	30		A	Exeter City	4624	W 3 - 1	Roberts 12 68 Boco 53	1
33	Feb 4	FAT 3	H	**Worksop Town**	961	D 1 - 1	**Brown 60**	
34	7	FAT 3R	A	**Worksop Town**	773	D 1 - 1	**Craney 78 Lost 2-4 after penalties**	
35	11	C	H	Dagenham & Redbridge	1151	W 1 - 0	Boco 52	1
36	17		A	Gravesend & Northfleet	1616	W 3 - 1	Todd 35 **Mullin** 66 80	1
37	20		A	Morecambe	3041	W 2 - 0	Todd 25 **Mullin** 28	1
38	25		H	Burton Albion	1946	W 2 - 1	**Mullin** 9 90	1
39	Mar 4		A	Crawley Town	1361	W 1 - 0	Roberts 41	1
40	7		A	Aldershot Town	1645	W 4 - 1	Craney 48 Roberts 61 79 Mangan 67	1
41	11		A	Hereford United	4497	D 2 - 2	Brown 37 Mkandawire (og) 59	1
42	18		H	Stevenage Borough	2119	D 1 - 1	Todd 78	1
43	21		A	Southport	1414	L 0 - 2		1
44	25		A	York City	3912	W 4 - 2	**Mullin** 34 67 Brown 48 (pen) Craney 70	1
45	April 1		H	Grays Athletic	2642	L 2 - 3	Roberts 17 Craney 64	1
46	7		A	Forset Green Rovers	1187	D 1 - 1	Todd	1
47	15		A	Woking	2665	W 1 - 0	**Mullin** 37	1
48	17		H	Scarborough	3320	W 1 - 0	Todd 90	1
49	22		H	Tamworth	3014	W 2 - 1	Todd 62 Craney 67	1
50	29		A	Kidderminster Harriers	1934	L 0 - 2		1

Ave. League Home Attendance:	2067		**Goals**	89 52	**Top Goalscorer:** Paul Mullin (19)
Best Position: 1st	**Worst:**	12th			

JONES	WILLIAMS	WELCH	FLYNN	RICHARDSON	JAGIELKA	CRANEY	BARRY	ROBERTS A	MANGAN	MULLIN	CAVANAGH	D BROWN	A PROCTOR	ALCOCK	O'NEILL	BOSSU	HARRISON	RANDOLPH	BRANNAN	COOK	P BROWN	DIBBLE	BOCO	NAVARRO	BUTLER	VENTRE	EDWARDS	LEE	SMYTH	ELLIOT	TRETTON	FINCH	TODD	BOYD	#
1	4	3	27	16	7	8	19	21	9	10	2	30	6	12	20	22	23	25	14	17	11	29	26	31	28	15	11	31	14	25	5		14	22	
X	X	X	X	X	X	X	X	X	X	X	S		S	S	U	U																			1
X	X	X	X	X	X	X	X	X	X	X	S		S	U	U	U	S																		2
	X	X	U	X	S	X	X	X	S	X	X	X	X	S	X	U																			3
	X	U	X	S	X	X	X	X	X	X	X	S	X	S		X	U	U																	4
	S	X	X	X	X	X	X	S	S	X	X	X	X		X	U	U	U																	5
	X	U	X	X	X	X	X	S	X	X	X	X	U		X				S	U															6
	X	S	X	X	X	X	X	X	S	X	X	X			X				U		U	U													7
	X	U	X	X	X	X	X	X	S	X	X	X			X				S		S	U													8
	X	U	X	X	X	X	X	X	S	X	X	X			X				U		S	S													9
	X	U	X		X	X	X	S	X	X	X	X			X				X	U		U	X	U											10
	X	U	X		X	X	X	X	S	X	X	X			X				U		S	S	X												11
	X	U	X	X	X	X	X	X	S	X	X	X			X				U		S	S													12
	X	X	X	X	X	X	X	X	S	X	X	X			X	U		U		U		X	U												13
	X	X	U	X	X	X	X	S	X	X	X								S	X	S	U	X												14
X		**S**	**U**	**X**	**X**	**S**	**X**	**X**			**S**								**U**		**X**	**X**		**X**	**X**	**X**	**X**								15
X	**U**	**X**	**X**	**X**	**X**	**X**	**X**	**X**	**U**		**X**								**U**		**X**	**U**		**X**	**U**										16
																																			17
	X		X	X	X	X	S	X		X			U					X	U		U		X	X	U										18
X	X		X	X	X	X	X	S	X	X	X							X	S	U	U	U		X	X										19
X	X		X	X	X	X		X	U	X	U		U					X				S		U	X	U									20
X	X		X	X	X	X	X	S	X	S	U		U					X				X		U	X										21
X	X		X	X	X	X	X	S	X	U	U										U	X		U	X			X							22
X	X		X	X		X	X	S	X	U	X									U	U	X		U	X			X							23
X	**X**		**X**	**X**	**X**	**X**	**U**	**X**	**S**	**U**		**U**										**X**		**U**	**X**			**X**							24
X	X		X	X	X	X	X	S	X	S	S		U									X		U	X			X							25
X	X		X	X	X	X	X	S	X	S	S		S									X		U	X			X							26
X	X			X	X	X	U	X	X	S												X		U	X			X	U						27
X	X			X	X	X	X	X	S	X	U											X		U	X			X	U						28
X		**X**		**X**	**X**		**S**	**X**	**X**	**X**	**U**											**X**		**U**	**X**			**X**	**X**	**U**					29
X	**X**	**X**		**X**	**X**	**X**	**X**	**X**	**U**													**S**		**U**	**X**			**X**	**U**						30
X	X			X	X	X	X	X	X		U										U		X			U	X			X	U				31
X	X			X	X	X	X	S	X	X	U		U									X		U	X			X	S						32
X	**X**				**X**		**X**	**X**	**X**	**X**	**S**		**U**								**U**		**X**			**U**	**X**			**X**	**U**		**X**		33
																																			34
X	X		X		X		X	S	X		S			U							U		X			U	X		X	X	X		X		35
X	X		X		X		X	U	X		U		U								S		X			U	X		X	X	X		X		36
X	X		X		X		X	S	X	X	U		U								U		X			S			X	X	X				37
X	X		X		X		X	U	X		X										U		X			U	X		X	X	X		U		38
		X	U	X		X	S	X		X			X								U		X			X	X		X	X	X	U	U		39
	X		X	S	X		X	S	X		X										U		X			X	X		X		X	U	U		40
X	X			S	X		X	S	X		X										U		X			X	X		X		X	U	U		41
X	X		X	X	X		X	S	X		X									U	U	X				X			X	S	U				42
X	X		U	X		X	S	X	U	S		U									X				X	X	X							43
	X		S	X		X	S	X	X	U											X		X	X	U	X	S								44
X	X		X		X	S	X	X	X	U											X		S	X	X	U	X	S							45
	X		X	S	X	X	S	X	S	X								X			U	X	X	U	X					X					—

Total Appearances (Conference)

	JONES	WILLIAMS	WELCH	FLYNN	RICHARDSON	JAGIELKA	CRANEY	BARRY	ROBERTS A	MANGAN	MULLIN	CAVANAGH	D BROWN	A PROCTOR	ALCOCK	O'NEILL	BOSSU	HARRISON	RANDOLPH	BRANNAN	COOK	P BROWN	DIBBLE	BOCO	NAVARRO	BUTLER	VENTRE	EDWARDS	LEE	SMYTH	ELLIOT	TRETTON	FINCH	TODD	BOYD	
	2	35	32	12	33	22	38	26	40	5	40	19	26	3	1	0	1	0	14	0	1	1	24	0	3	10	27	0	0	23	6	0	13	4		X
	0	1	1	0	0	8	1	0	0	2	33	1	5	9	3	0	3	0	0	0	0	3	2	0	6	3	0	2	0	0	0	0	1	0	2	S
	0	0	8	2	0	3	0	0	0	3	0	4	7	2	24	2	0	1	0	2	12	3	8	4	4	1	18	0	1	1	6	0	0	0	6	U

Cup Appearances

	JONES	WILLIAMS	WELCH	FLYNN	RICHARDSON	JAGIELKA	CRANEY	BARRY	ROBERTS A	MANGAN	MULLIN	CAVANAGH	D BROWN	A PROCTOR	ALCOCK	O'NEILL	BOSSU	HARRISON	RANDOLPH	BRANNAN	COOK	P BROWN	DIBBLE	BOCO	NAVARRO	BUTLER	VENTRE	EDWARDS	LEE	SMYTH	ELLIOT	TRETTON	FINCH	TODD	BOYD	
	0	6	3	1	4	3	6	4	5	4	4	3	2	0	0	0	0	0	0	0	0	0	2	4	0	2	1	5	1	0	4	1	0	1	0	X
	0	0	0	1	0	0	0	1	0	1	0	1	2	0	0	0	0	0	0	0	0	0	0	1	0	0	0	0	0	0	0	0	0	0	0	S
	0	0	1	0	1	0	0	0	1	1	0	2	0	4	0	0	0	0	4	0	0	1	0	0	5	0	0	0	2	1	0	0				U

BEST LGE ATT.: 4,497 v Accrington Stanley
LOWEST: 19,50 v York City

No.	Date	Comp	H/A	Opponents	Att:	Result	Goalscorers	Pos
1	Aug 13	C	H	Scarborough	3105	W 4 - 0	Beckwith 64, Ipoua 69 Green 85 Carey-Bertram 90	1
2	16		A	Cambridge United	2924	L 1 - 2	Ipoua 62	9
3	20		A	CrawleyTown	1842	W 2 - 0	Ipoua 58 Mkandawire 83	2
4	27		H	Grays Athletic	2997	L 0 - 2		7
5	29		A	Tamworth	1744	W 1 - 0	Jeannin 20	4
6	Sept 3		H	Altrincham	2318	D 0 - 0		6
7	10		A	Stevenage Borough	2404	D 0 - 0		10
8	17		H	Morecambe	2422	W 1 - 0	Farrell 41	7
9	20		H	Gravesend & Northfleet	2396	D 1 - 1	Stanley 53	8
10	24		A	Halifax Town	1559	L 1 - 2	Carey-Bertram 8	9
11	27		A	Aldershot Town	2656	W 1 - 0	Carey-Bertram 2	7
12	Oct 1		H	Canvey Island	2500	D 1 - 1	Bailey 14	7
13	7		A	Accrington Town	1603	L 1 - 2	Carey-Bertram 46	9
14	15		H	Burton Albion	2493	W 2 - 0	Carey-Bertram 22 James 83 (pen)	9
15	18	LDV Vans T 1	A	Mansfield Town	1393	W 1 - 0	Day (og) 11	
16	22	FAC 4Q	H	Alfreton Town	1769	D 0 - 0		
17	25	FAC4Qr	A	Alfreton Town	740	D 1 - 1	Stanley 53 Won 4-3 after penalties	
18	29	C	A	Kidderminster Harriers	3241	D 1 - 1	Pitman 6	9
19	Nov 5	FAC 1R	A	Cambridge City	1116	W 1 - 0	Brady 70	
20	12	C	A	Woking	2498	W 4 - 0	Williams 28 Purdie 55 69 Ipoua 71	8
21	19		A	Dagenham & Redbridge	1294	W 1 - 0	Williams 11	8
22	22	LDV Vans T 2	H	Port Vale	1355	W 2 - 1*	Carey-Bertram 13 Mkandawire 102	
23	26	C	H	Exeter City	3754	L 0 - 2		8
24	Dec 3	FA CUP 3R	H	Stockport County	3620	L 0 - 2		
25	10	C	H	York City	1950	W 1 - 0	Stansfield 68	7
26	17	FAT 1	A	Bognor Regis Town	420	W 7 - 1	Williams 5 Stansfield 13 Purdie 63 (pen) 77 Ipoua 73 Stanley 75 Pitman 85	
27	20	LDV NQF	H	Scunthorpe United	1452	W 2 - 0	Stansfield 17 Mkandawire 44	
28	24	C	A	Forest Green Rovers	1957	D 2 - 2	Mkandawire 58 Jeannin 79	7
29	30		A	Exeter City	4433	W 2 - 1	Ipoua 29 Jeannin 42	
30	Jan 2		H	Forest Green Rovers	3507	D 1 - 1	Stansfield 29	
31	7		A	Scarborough	1582	W 1 - 0	Stansfield 10	5
32	14	FAT 2	A	Halifax Town	1220	W 1 - 0	Stansfield 20	
33	21	C	A	Crawley Town	2782	W 2 - 1	Williams 6 Ipoua 87	4
34	24	LDV N S-F	A	Macclesfield Town	1315	L 0 - 2		
35	28		A	Grays Athletic	1528	D 2 - 2	Mkandawire 70 Beckwith 81	6
36	31		H	Cambridge United	2142	W 3 - 0	Stansfield 34 Williams 42 50	3
37	Feb 4	FAT 3	H	Grays Athletic	1609	L 0 - 1		
38	11	C	H	Halifax Town	2555	W 1 - 0	Stansfield 77	2
39	18		A	Canvey Island	784	D 1 - 1	Fleetwood 14	3
40	21		H	Aldershot Town	2205	W 2 - 1	Williams 3 Fleetwood 29	2
41	27		A	Stevenage Borough	2394	W 2 - 0	Williams 45 Fleetwood 51	2
42	Mar 7		A	Gravesend & Northfleet	618	W 2 - 1	King 74 Williams 80	2
43	11		H	Accrington Stanley	4497	D 2 - 2	Fleetwood 73 Nicolau 90	2
44	14		A	Southport	1057	W 2 - 1	Mkandawire 10 Ferrell 43	2
45	18		A	Burton Albion	2512	W 1 - 0	Williams 39	2
46	25		H	Kidderminster Harriers	4223	L 0 - 1		2
47	April 1		A	Woking	1929	D 1 - 1	Mkandawire 90	2
48	4		H	Morecambe	1699	D 2 - 2	Carey-Bertram 49 78	2
49	8		H	Dagenham & Redbridge	2561	D 1 - 1	Purdie 77 (pen)	2
50	15		A	Altrincham	1251	W 1 - 0	Fleetwood 83	2
51	17		H	Tamworth	2809	W 1 - 0	Carey-Bertram 58	2
52	22		A	Southport	2547	D 1 - 1	Stansfield 75	2
53	29		A	York City	2755	W 3 - 1	Williams 12 Purdie 34 Ipoua 90	2
54	May 6	Play Off SF1	A	Morecambe	5208	D 1 - 1	Purdie (pen) 54	
55	11	Play Off SF2	H	Morecambe	6278	W 3 - 2*	Mkandawire 6 Williams 13 Ipoua 107	
56	20	Play Off Final	N	Halifax Town	15499	W 3 - 2*	Williams 34, Ipoua 80, Green 108	

Ave. League Home Attendance: 2392   **Goals** 73 37   **Top Goalscorer:** Andy Williams (13)
Best Position: 2nd   **Worst:** 10th

CONFERENCE Nth & Sth — NPL - SOUTHERN - ISTHMIAN PREM — NPL - SOUTHERN - ISTHMIAN

#	MAWSON 1/5	MKANDAWIRE 6	JAMES 28	BECKWITH 2	GREEN 4	COLDICOTT 7	BRADY 11	FERRELL 20	JEANNIN 9	STANSFIELD 10	IPOUA 21	PURDIE	CAREY-BERTRAM 18	STANLEY 15	BLEWITT 19	BROWN 14	EVANS 12	PITMAN 8	WILLIAMS 16	GWYNNE 17	BAILEY 22	KNUREK 35	LEWIS 35	TRAVIS 3	BAGNALL 35	TAYLOR 22	NICOLAU 12	FLEETWOOD 7	HALLIDAY 23	KING 24	TREWICK 25	Row
	X	X	X	X	X	X	X	X	X	X	S		S	S	U	U																1
	X	X	X	X	X	X	X	X	X	X	S		U	U	U																	2
	X	X	X	X	X	X	U	X	X	X	X		S	S	U	U	U															3
	X	X	X	X	X	X	U	X	X	X		S	S		U	U																4
	U		X	X	X	U	X	X	X	X	U	S	X	X	X	X	S															5
	U	U	X	X		S	X	X	X	X		X	X	X	X	X	S	U														6
	U	U	X	X		U	X	X	X	X		X	X	X	X	X	X	S	U													7
	U	S	X	X			X	X	X		X	X	X	X	X		X	S	U													8
	U	S	X	X	X		S	X	X		X	X	X	X	U	X	U															9
	U	S	X	X	X		X	S	X	X		X	S	X	X	X	X	U	S													10
	U	X	S		X		X	X	X		X	X	X	X	U	U	U		X													11
	U	X	S	U	X		X	X	X		X	X	X	X	S	U		X														12
	U	X	X	U	X		X	X	X		X	X	X	U	X		U	S	X													13
	U	X	X	U	X		X	X	X		X	X	X	U	X		S	S	X													14
	X	X	X	U	X		X	X	X			S	X		U			S	X	X		X		U								15
	X	X	X	U	X		X	X	X			S	X	X	U		U	X	S		X											16
	X	X	X	U			X	X	X			S	X	X	X	X		S	X	S		X										17
	U	X	X	S			X	X				S	X	X	X	X	X	U	X	S		X										18
	X	X	X	U	X		X	U	X			X	X	U	X		S	X	X			U										19
	X	X	X	U	X		X	S	X			X	X	S	X		U	S	X				U									20
	X	X	S	X			X	U	X			X	X	S	X		U	X	X				U									21
	X	X		X	X		X	U	X	S		X	X	X	X		S	X			U	S										22
	X	X	X	U			X	U	X			X	X	S	X		U	X	X		U	X										23
	X	X	X	U	X		S	U	X	S		X	X	X	X		X	X						U								24
	U	X	U	X			X	X	X			X		X	X	X	X	U	S				U									25
	X	X	U	X			X	X	X	X		X	S	S	X		S	S	X			X	U									26
	X	X	X	S			S	X	X	X	X	X		U		S	X	X			U	X										27
	X	X					U		X	X	X	X	U	X	X	U	U	X	X	U		X										28
	U	X		X			U		X	X	X	X	S	X	S	X	U	X	X			X										29
	U	X		X	S		S		X	X	X		X	X	U	X	X				X											30
	U	X		X	S		X	X		X	X	X		X	S	X	S	U			X		X									31
	X	X	X	U			X	X		X	X	S		X	S		U	X	X	U		X		X								32
	U	X	S	X			X	X	X	X	S	X		X	U	X					X											33
	X	X	U	X	U		X	X		X	S	X	X		S	X	X				U	X										34
	U	X	U	X	U		X	X	X	X	X	S	U		X						X			X								35
	U	X	U	X	U		X	X		X	X	U	X		X						X			X	S							36
	X	X	X	U	X	U		S	X	S		X	S	X		X					X			X	X	X						37
	U	X		X	X		X	X	X		U	X		X		X	U		S		S	X	X									38
	U	X		X	X		X	X	X	S		X		X		X	U		S		S	X	X									39
	U	X		X	X		X		S	U	X		X		X	U		X	X	X	X	U										40
	U	X		X	X		X		S	S	X		X		X	S		X	X	X	X	U										41
	U	X	U	X	X		X			X	U	X		X		X	U		X	X	U	X										42
	U	X	U	X	X		X			X	U	X		X		X	U		X	X	U	X										43
	U	X	X		X		X	X			S	X		S	X	U		X	X		X		U									44
	U	X	X	U			X	X			S	X		S	X	U		X	X		X		X									45
	U	X	X	U	X		X	X	S			X		X		X		X	U	X												46
	U	X	X	S	X			X	S	X		X		X		X		S	X	U	X		X									47
	U	X		X	X		X	X		X	X	X		X		X	S		S	X		S	U									48
	U	X		X			X	S		X	X	X		X		X	X	U	X		S	U										49
	U	X		X			X	X	U	S	X	X	X		U	X		X			U	X										50
	X	X		X			X	X	S	S	X	X	U		U	X	S		X		X	X										51
	U	X		X			X	X	S	X	X	X		S	X		U	X			X			U	X							52
	U	X	X				X	X	X	S	X		S	X			U	X			X			U	S							53
	U	X		X	X		X	X	X	S	X	U	X		X		X				X				S							54
	U	X		X	X		X	X	X	S	U	X		X		X		S	X		X				S							55
	U	X		X	X		X	X	X	S	X	U	X		X		X		S	X		X			S							56

Total Appearances (Conference)

	MAWSON	MKANDAWIRE	JAMES	BECKWITH	GREEN	COLDICOTT	BRADY	FERRELL	JEANNIN	STANSFIELD	IPOUA	PURDIE	CAREY-BERTRAM	STANLEY	BLEWITT	BROWN	EVANS	PITMAN	WILLIAMS	GWYNNE	BAILEY	KNUREK	LEWIS	TRAVIS	BAGNALL	TAYLOR	NICOLAU	FLEETWOOD	HALLIDAY	KING	TREWICK	
	9	36	20	29	25	4	18	30	37	17	13	33	18	35	10	33	2	14	23	0	5	0	0	15	0	8	10	13	0	5	0	X
	0	3	3	3	2	1	2	1	0	6	6	7	14	3	1	0	5	8	8	1	0	0	0	3	2	0	4	0	0	0	0	S
	33	2	5	7	2	2	2	4	0	1	1	0	5	4	5	7	11	7	3	11	0	0	2	0	0	5	0	4	2	1		U

Cup Appearances

	MAWSON	MKANDAWIRE	JAMES	BECKWITH	GREEN	COLDICOTT	BRADY	FERRELL	JEANNIN	STANSFIELD	IPOUA	PURDIE	CAREY-BERTRAM	STANLEY	BLEWITT	BROWN	EVANS	PITMAN	WILLIAMS	GWYNNE	BAILEY	KNUREK	LEWIS	TRAVIS	BAGNALL	TAYLOR	NICOLAU	FLEETWOOD	HALLIDAY	KING	TREWICK	
	11	14	7	7	9	0	5	10	14	6	6	13	5	10	0	3	0	9	11	0	3	0	0	7	0	2	1	1	0	0	0	X
	0	0	0	1	0	0	2	1	0	3	6	1	3	0	0	0	7	3	2	0	0	0	0	1	0	0	3	0	0	0	0	S
	3	0	2	6	2	1	0	3	0	0	0	0	4	3	1	0	2	1	0	1	0	1	4	0	2	0	0	0	0	0	0	U

FOOTBALL LEAGUE

STEP 1

FOOTBALL
CONFERENCE

STEP 2

| CONFERENCE NORTH | CONFERENCE SOUTH |

STEP 3

| SOUTHERN PREMIER | NORTHERN PREMIER | ISTHMIAN PREMIER |

STEP 4

| SOUTHERN DIVISION 1 SOUTH & WEST MIDLAND | NORTHERN PREMIER DIV. 1 | ISTHMIAN DIVISION 1 NORTH   SOUTH |

STEP 5/6

Combined Counties	Hellenic	Northern League	Spartan South Midlands	Wessex
Eastern Counties	Kent	Northern Counties East	Sussex County	Western
Essex Senior	Midland Alliance	North West Counties	United Counties	

STEP 7

Anglian Combination	Dorset County	Kent County	Midland Combination	Peterborough & District	West Cheshire
Bedford & District	Dorset Premier	Leicestershire Senior	Midland League	Reading League	West Lancashire
Brighton & Hove	East Sussex	Liverpool County	North Berkshire	Somerset County	West Midlands (reg)
Cambridgeshire County	Essex & Suffolk Border	Manchester Football	Northampton Town Lge	South Western	West Sussex
Central Midlands	Essex Intermediate	Mid Cheshire League	Northamptonshire Comb.	Suffolk & Ipswich	Wiltshire League
Crawley & District	Gloucesterhisre Co.	Mid Sussex	Northern Alliance	Teeside League	Worthing & District
Devon County	Herts Senior County	Middlesex County	Oxfordshire Senior	Wearside League	

CONFERENCE NORTH

		P	W	D	L	F	A	Pts
1.	Northwich Victoria	42	29	5	8	97	49	92
2.	Stafford Rangers*	42	25	10	7	68	34	85
3.	Nuneaton Borough	42	22	11	9	68	43	77
4.	Droylsden	42	20	12	10	80	56	72
5.	Harrogate Town	42	22	5	15	66	56	71
6.	Kettering Town	42	19	10	13	63	49	67
7.	Stalybridge Celtic	42	19	9	14	74	54	66
8.	Worcester City	42	16	14	12	58	46	62
9.	Moor Green	42	15	16	11	67	64	61
10.	Hinckley United	42	14	16	12	60	55	58
11.	Hyde United	42	15	11	16	68	61	56
12.	Hucknall Town	42	14	13	15	56	55	55
13.	Workington	42	14	13	15	60	62	55
14.	Barrow	42	12	11	19	62	67	47
15.	Lancaster City	42	12	11	19	52	66	47
16.	Gainsborough Trinity	42	11	13	18	45	65	46
17.	Alfreton Town	42	10	15	17	46	58	45
18.	Vauxhall Motors	42	12	7	23	50	71	43
19.	Worksop Town	42	10	11	21	46	71	41
20.	Redditch United	42	9	12	21	53	78	39
21.	Leigh RMI	42	9	13	20	45	79	39
22.	Hednesford Town	42	7	14	21	42	87	35

*Promted via play-offs.

		1	2	3	4	5	6	7	8	9	10	11	12	13	14	15	16	17	18	19	20	21	22
1	Alfreton Town		2-1	1-3	1-2	4-1	3-2	1-1	1-1	2-0	1-1	0-2	1-1	1-1	2-4	1-0	2-1	2-1	0-0	1-2	1-0	1-3	2-1
2	Barrow	2-2		2-0	3-1	3-1	3-1	2-5	2-0	2-2	0-1	1-4	3-1	2-2	1-1	0-3	1-1	1-1	4-2	0-2	0-2	6-1	1-0
3	Droylsden	1-0	2-2		1-2	2-1	1-1	3-1	2-3	1-0	3-1	6-1	4-1	3-0	4-3	2-2	2-1	2-1	1-0	4-0	3-0	2-3	3-1
4	Gainsborough T	2-2	3-2	2-2		0-2	1-1	1-2	3-2	0-3	0-2	1-0	2-1	2-2	1-2	1-2	2-2	1-1	1-0	1-1	0-1	0-0	2-0
5	Harrogate Town	1-0	2-1	1-1	2-0		2-3	2-1	1-0	1-0	1-1	3-1	3-0	3-0	0-2	2-0	1-1	0-2	1-0	2-1	4-1	1-1	2-0
6	Hednesford T.	1-0	0-3	0-1	1-1	0-4		3-4	1-1	0-2	2-0	1-0	1-3	1-2	1-4	0-0	1-1	0-2	1-1	0-1	0-0	0-0	2-1
7	Hinckley United	2-2	1-0	1-1	1-0	1-3	1-2		3-1	2-1	1-1	3-3	5-1	1-2	1-3	0-1	1-1	0-1	1-1	2-1	1-3	0-0	3-0
8	Hucknall Town	1-0	2-1	2-0	4-1	4-1	2-2	0-2		1-3	1-1	0-0	2-2	2-2	3-2	0-1	4-1	0-2	2-1	1-2	1-2	1-0	0-0
9	Hyde United	2-3	2-2	2-2	2-0	3-1	4-2	0-1	0-0		3-0	2-4	3-3	3-2	1-3	1-0	1-3	1-3	1-3	2-3	4-0	1-1	1-1
10	Kettering Town	1-0	1-3	1-0	1-2	0-2	4-0	2-2	0-0	3-2		2-0	4-0	0-3	2-0	3-0	4-0	0-1	4-1	1-0	2-1	2-1	1-0
11	Lancaster City	2-2	3-0	2-2	2-3	2-1	1-0	2-2	0-1	1-3	0-1		2-0	3-3	1-2	1-1	1-0	1-1	2-2	1-0	0-0	0-1	2-1
12	Leigh RMI	0-0	1-1	0-1	0-0	1-1	0-4		3-4	1-1	0-2	1-2		1-3	2-1	1-0	2-1	1-3	2-1	1-1	1-4	0-1	0-1
13	Moor Green	0-0	1-1	1-1	1-1	2-2	1-2	1-1	2-4	1-2	1-1	3-1	4-1		1-2	0-4	2-1	0-1	1-1	2-1	1-1	1-4	1-0
14	Northwich Vic.	1-1	2-0	2-1	2-0	3-0	8-0	2-0	2-0	1-2	3-1	3-2	1-0	1-1		2-2	5-1	3-1	1-0	3-1	0-1	4-1	4-1
15	Nuneaton Boro'	1-0	2-1	2-2	3-1	4-0	3-2	2-0	2-2	1-0	2-2	3-0	3-1	2-2	1-2		2-1	1-1	0-0	3-2	0-0	3-1	3-1
16	Redditch United	1-0	2-1	4-1	1-1	1-3	1-2	1-1	1-1	1-1	2-1	0-1	1-2	0-1	1-2	3-0		0-1	1-4	3-0	2-2	3-6	0-3
17	Stafford Rangers	1-0	3-1	0-0	3-0	0-1	1-1	2-3	2-0	1-0	1-3	3-0	0-0	1-3	2-0	2-0	3-0		1-0	3-0	1-1	2-2	4-2
18	Stalybridge C.	3-0	2-1	1-1	1-0	3-1	3-0	1-1	2-1	1-2	2-0	2-1	6-1	4-1	3-3	2-0	5-1	2-3		2-1	2-3	2-1	1-1
19	Vauxhall Motors	3-1	0-1	2-4	1-2	0-2	0-0	0-1	0-2	0-2	1-1	1-0	4-4	1-2	0-3	1-2	1-2	1-3	4-2		1-0	2-1	5-2
20	Worcester City	2-2	1-0	1-2	2-1	2-0	6-2	0-0	0-1	2-2	2-0	2-0	2-0	0-2	0-1	0-1	2-2	1-1	0-1	0-0		1-1	1-1
21	Workington	2-0	0-0	2-1	2-0	2-4	2-0	1-1	1-1	1-0	3-2	1-1	0-0	1-4	5-2	0-2	1-2	0-1	1-2	1-2	2-2		1-2
22	Worksop Town	1-1	2-1	3-2	1-1	1-0	3-3	0-0	2-1	1-1	2-1	2-0	3-3	0-2	1-2	0-4	1-1	0-1	2-1	1-1	0-3	1-2	

ALFRETON TOWN

Founded: 1959
Nickname: The Reds

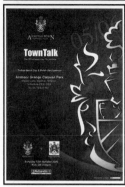

Manager: Gary Mills **Assistant Manager:** Darron Gee **Physio**: Doug Kyle
Club Colours: All Red
Change Colours: All White
Club Sponsors: Impact Marketing & Publicity Ltd.
Previous League: Northern Premier
Best Seasons: League: Conference North 14th 2004-2005
F.A. Cup: 1st Round 3rd Replay 69-70 **F.A.Trophy.:** 1st Round Proper 94-95
F.A.Vase : 5th Round 1999-2000
Ground address: Impact Arena, North Street, Alfreton, Derbys.
Tel No: 01773 830277 **Club Website:** alfretontownfc.com
Capacity: 5,000 **Seats**: 1,600 **Covered**: 2,600 **Floodlights**: Yes
Simple Directions: M1 jct 28 and A38 towards Derby for a mile then left onto B600. Right at main road to town centre and left after half a mile down North Street. Ground on right. Alfreton BR 1/2 mile. Buses 91,92,93 from Derby and Mansfield.

CLUB PERSONNEL

Chairman: Wayne Bradley
V-Chairman: Sean Egan
Secretary: Bryan Rudkin, 12 Crown Terrace, Bridge Street, Belper Derbys. DE56 1BD
Tel Nos:01773 825468(H)
01773 830277 (W)
Commercial Manager:
Donna Wheatley (0115 9392090)
Programme Editor:
Chris Tacey (01302722415)
e-mail: ctacey5087@aol.com
Programme
32 pages. Price: £2.00
Press Officer: Kev Miles
Tel No: 07957 721661(M)
2005-2006
Captain: David Robinson
Player of the Year: Ryan Clarke
Top Goalscorter: Jon Stevenson 15

Midweek Home Matchday: Tuesday
Clubhouse: Ground bar open matchdays. Supporters bar outside ground open daily
Club Shop: Yes. Contact: Brian Thorpe (01773 836251)
Local Press: Derbyshire Times, Derby Evening Telegraph
Local Radio: Radio Derby

CLUB STATISTICS

Record	**Attendance**: 5,023 v Matlock Town Central Alliance 1960
	Victory: 15-0 v Loughborough, Midland League 1969-70
	Defeat: 1-9 v Solihull F.A.T. 1997, 0-8 v Bridlington 1992
	Career Goalscorer:J.Harrison 303
	Career Appearances: J.Harrison 560 + 1
	Transfer Fee Paid: £2,000 to Worksop Town for Mick Goddard
	Received: £7,000 from Ilkeston Town for Paul Eshelby
Senior Honours:	N.Co.E Champions 84-85 2001-02 Derbyshire Senior Cup (7) R-up (8)
	N.P.L.Division 1 Champions 2002-03 R-up 95-96
Previous Leaguess:	Central Alliance (pre re-formation 21-25) 59-61 Midland Co: 25-27 61-82
	N.Co. East 82-87 NPL 87-99

Back row (L-R): Mark Barnard, Mark Turner, Lee Featherstone, Gary Sucharewycz, Emeka Nwadike, Dale Roberts, Anton Brown, Ryan Clarke, Craig Mitchell, Ashley Burbeary, Jermaine Palmer, Matt Worthington (physio).
Front: Alfie Ndyenge, Marcus Ebdon, Tristram Whitman, Darron Gee (assistant manager), Gary Mills (manager), Andy Tiday, Matt Glass, Damian Magee, Stuart Wall.
Not pictured: Stephen Melton and Chris Howard.

ALFRETON TOWN

BEST LGE ATT.: 575 v Kettering Town
LOWEST: 217 v Harrogate Town

No.	Date	Comp	H/A	Opponents	Att:	Result	Goalscorers	Pos
1	Aug 13	CN	H	Vauxhall Motors	283	L 1 - 2	White 53	15
2	15		A	Hednesford Town	640	L 0 - 1		22
3	20		A	Worksop Town	496	D 1 - 1	**Stevenson** 24	19
4	27		H	Northwich Victoria	385	L 2 - 4	Clarke 25 Robinson 55	21
5	29		A	Hyde United	433	W 3 - 2	White 40 78 Blount 90	18
6	Sept 3		H	Lancaster City	279	L 0 - 2		19
7	10		H	Redditch United	219	W 2 - 1	Duffield 9 White 58	16
8	17		A	Hinckley United	611	D 2 - 2	**Stevenson** 41 54	15
9	24	FAC 2Q	A	**St Helens Town**	142	W 2 - 0	**Stevenson** 45, 45	
10	Oct 1	CN	A	Droylsden	319	L 0 - 1		16
11	8	FAC 3Q	H	**Whitby Town**	231	W 2 - 1	**Stevenson** 1 Blount 6	
12	15	CN	H	Stalybridge Celtic	388	D 0 - 0		17
13	18		H	Leigh RMI	224	D 1 - 1	**Stevenson** 40	18
14	22	FAC 4Q	A	**Hereford United**	1769	D 0 - 0		
15	25	FAC4Qr	H	**Hereford United**	740	D 1 - 1	**Turner** 33 Lost 3-4 after penalties	
16	29	CN	A	Stafford Rangers	913	L 0 - 1		19
17	Nov 12		H	Moor Green	267	D 1 - 1	Ross 41	21
18	15		A	Barrow	712	D 2 - 2	Duffield 4 Turner 88	21
19	26	FAT 3Q	A	**Fleetwood Town**	552	W 3 - 1	**White** 2 Clarke 53 Stevenson 64	
20	Dec 6	CN	H	Kettering Town	575	D 1 - 1	Turner 90	20
21	10		A	Gainsborough Trinity	337	D 2 - 2	Duffield 55 66 (pen)	20
22	17	FAT 1	H	**Histon**	238	D 1 - 1	**Godber** 69	
23	21	FAT 1r	A	**Histon**	288	L 1 - 2	**Featherstone** 53	
24	26	CN	H	Hucknall Town	564	D 1 - 1	Bettney 76	20
25	Jan 2		A	Hucknall Town	909	L 0 - 1		22
26	7		A	Vauxhall Motors	197	L 1 - 3	Rankine 56	19
27	14		H	Hednesford Town	336	W 3 - 2	Hume 34 Turner 40 Adams 71 (og)	21
28	21		H	Worksop Town	367	W 2 1 1	Rankine 41 Godber 77	21
29	28		A	Northwich Victoria	1017	D 1 - 1	Clarke 89	22
30	31		A	Nuneaton Town	1108	L 0 - 1		22
31	Feb 4		H	Droylsden	271	L 1 - 3	Featherstone 71	22
32	7		H	Worcester City	250	W 1 - 0	Featherstone 38	20
33	11		A	Stalybridge Celtic	449	L 0 - 3		20
34	18		H	Barrow	287	W 2 - 1	Robinson 7 54	18
35	21		A	Leigh RMI	200	D 0 - 0		17
36	25		A	Redditch United	369	L 0 - 1		19
37	28		H	Harrogate Town	217	W 4 - 1	**Stevenson** 3 (18 62 74) Godber 51	
38	Mar 4		H	Hinckley United	344	D 1 - 1	Godber 90	16
39	11		H	Stafford Rangers	480	W 2 - 1	Daniel 40 (og) **Stevenson** 76	16
40	14		H	Workington	340	L 1 - 3	Clarke 7	16
41	18		A	Harrogate Town	468	L 0 - 1		16
42	25		A	Moor Green	226	D 0 - 0		16
43	April 1		A	Worcester City	860	D 2 - 2	Bettney 17 (pen) Nwadike 63	17
44	8		H	Nuneaton Borough	436	W 1 - 0	Rankine 90	16
45	11		A	Kettering Town	918	L 0 - 1		16
46	15		A	Lancaster City	254	D 2 - 2	**Stevenson** 1 50	16
47	17		H	Hyde United	281	W 2 - 0	Howard 64 Litchfield 85	16
48	22		A	Workington	380	L 0 2 2		15
49	29		H	Gainsborough Trinity	301	L 1 - 2	**Stevenson** 3	17

Ave. League Home Attendance: 1894   **Goals** 56 64   **Top Goalscorer:** Stevenson (15)
Best Position: 15th   **Worst:** 22nd

BARROW

Founded: 1901
Nickname: Bluebirds

Manager: Phil Wilson   **Physio**: Liam Enright

Club Colours: Blue&White/Blue/Blue

Change Colours: All Red

Club Sponsor: Chas Kendall Turf Accountants

Previous League: Conference

Best Seasons: League: 8th Conference 1981-1982 **F.A. Cup:** 3rd Round (9)

F.A.Trophy.: Winners 1989-90

Ground address: Holker Street Stadium, Wilkie Road, Barrow -in-Furness
Cumbria. **Tel No:** 01229 820346

Official website: www.barrowafc.com

Capacity: 4,500   **Seats:** 1,000   **Covered:** 2,200   **Floodlights:**Yes

Simple Directions: M6 to junction 36. A590 to Barrow. Enter the town on Park Road
and after two miles turn left into Wilkie Road

Midweek Home Matchday: Tuesday

Club Shop: A new shop is situated in main entrance to club and bar

Local Radio: BBC Radio Cumbria, Bay Radio

Local Press: North West evening Mail

CLUB PERSONNEL

Chairman: Brian Keen
President: Alan Dunn
Secretary: Russell Dodd, 9 Keswick Avenue, Barrow -in- Furness,
Cumbria LA14 4LL
07778700137 (M)
Commercial Manager: Jeff Keen
Press Officer: Phil Yelland
0131445 1010 (H)
Programme Editor: Bob Herbert
40 pages. Price £2.00

2005-2006
Captain: Stuart Howson
Player of the Year: Simon Bishop
Top Goalscore: Gavin Knight 20

CLUB STATISTICS

Record	**Attendance**: 16,854 v Swansea Town F.A.Cup 3rd Rd 1954
	Victory: 12-0 v Cleator F.A.Cup 1920
	Defeat: 1-10 v Hartlepool Utd. Football League Div 4 1959
	Appearances: Colin Cowperthwaite 704
	Career Goalscorer: Colin Cowperthwaite 282 Dec.1977 - December 1992
	Fee Paid: £9,000 to Ashton United for Andy Whittaker. July 94
:	**Fee Received**: £40,000 from Barnet for Kenny Lowe. Jan. 91
Senior Honours:	F.A.Trophy Winners 89-90 N.P.L. 97-8 88-89 83-4 Runners-Up 2002-03
	Lancs Senior Cup 54-55 Lancs Challenge Trophy 80-81
Previous Leagues:	Lancs Comb 01-21 Football Lg. 21-72 N.P.L. 72-79 83-84 86-89 92-98 99-04
	Conference: 79-83 84-86 89-92 98-99**Grounds**: Strawberry & Little Park,Roose

BackRow (L-R): Stuart Reynolds (physio); James Cotterill; Darren Edmondson; Jonathan Smith; Aron Wilford; Simon Bishop; Andy hill; Ben Morsby; Neil Tarrant; Dabe Mansergh; Guy heffernan; Mike Kewley; Graham Anthony.
Front: Stev Ridley; Danny Forde; Steve Flitcroft; Gavin Knight; Lee Turnbull (mgr); Brian keen (Chrmn); Paul Raven (AssMgr); Gareth Simpson; Dave Swarbrick; Mike Rushton; Scott Maxfield.

BARROW

BEST LGE ATT.: 1,308 v Workington
LOWEST: 630 v Vauxhall Motors

No.	Date	Comp	H/A	Opponents	Att:	Result	Goalscorers	Pos
1	Aug 13	CN	H	Hednesford Town	1031	W 3 - 1	Knight 29 55 Smith 35	1
2	16		A	Vauxhall Motors	305	W 1 - 0	Ridley 16	1
3	20		A	Northwich Victoria	724	L 0 - 2		6
4	27		H	Leigh RMI	1070	W 3 - 1	Tarrant 40 Rankine 84 Knight 90	4
5	29		A	Hucknall Town	551	L 1 - 2	Smith 70	5
6	Sept 3		H	Hyde United	920	D 2 - 2	Maxfield 70 (pen) Anthony 86	7
7	6		H	Workington	1308	W 6 - 1	Knight 12 43 Heffernan 30 58 Tarrant 34 Anthony 52	3
8	10		A	Droylsden	354	D 2 - 2	Knight 40 Rankine 90	5
9	17		H	Stalybridge Celtic	1057	W 4 - 2	Knight 3 (26 49 66) Tarrant 71	2
10	24	FAC 2Q	H	**Hebburn Town**	911	W 5 - 1	Tarrant 10 Smith 22 Flitcroft 27 Rogers 35 Knight 70	
11	Oct 1	CN	H	Hinckley United	981	L 2 - 5	Tarrant 36 Maxfield 67 (pen)	4
12	8	FAC 3Q	A	**Hyde United**	469	W 3 - 2	Anthony 71 88 Knight 81	
13	15	CN	A	Gainsborough Trinity	385	L 2 - 3	Rushton 39 53	6
14	18		A	Harrogate Town	425	L 1 - 2	Knight 3	7
15	22	FAC 4Q	A	**Northwich Victoria**	1116	L 1 - 4	Tarrant 4	
16	29	CN	A	Worcester City	913	L 0 - 1		12
17	Nov 5		H	Moor Green	714	D 2 - 2	Cowan 31 Taylor 20	12
18	12		A	Worksop Town	407	L 1 - 2	Rankine 80	13
19	15		H	Alfreton Town	712	D 2 - 2	Cowan 9 Knight 40	12
20	19		H	Stafford Rangers	907	D 1 - 1	Dawson 15	13
21	26	FAT 3Q	A	**Redditch United**	289	D 1 - 1	Flitcroft 23	
22	29	FAT 3Qr	H	**Redditch United**	756	W 2 - 0	Rushton 35 Tarrant 59	
23	Dec 3	CN	A	Kettering Town	1272	W 3 - 1	Tarrant 55 Cowan 89 Flitcroft 90	10
24	10		A	Redditch United	839	D 1 - 1	Ridley 37	10
25		FAT 1	H	**Clitheroe**	897	W 2 - 1	Ridlley Knight	
26	24	CN	A	Lancaster City	702	L 0 - 3		13
27	30		A	Nuneaton Borough	902	L 1 2	Wilkin 70 (pen)	15
28	Jan 2		H	Lancaster City	1301	L 1 - 4	Heffernan 78 (pen)	16
29	7		A	Hednesford Town	472	W 3 - 0	Tarrant 6 73 Wilson 25	14
30	14	FAT 2	H	**Cambridge City**	996	L 1 - 2	Rushton 71	
31	21	CN	H	Northwich Victoria	1007	D 1 - 1	Heffernan 74 (pen)	14
32	28		A	Leigh RMI	301	D 1 - 1	Heffernam 52 (pen)	14
33	Feb 4		A	Hinckley United	467	L 0 - 1		15
34	11		H	Gainsborough Trinity	852	W 3 - 1	Howson 11 Knight 35 Ridley79	15
35	18		A	Alfreton Town	287	L 1 - 2	Rushton 81	15
36	21		H	Harrogate Town	672	W 3 - 1	Rogers 45 Knight 24 59	15
37	25		H	Droylsden	892	W 2 - 0	Olsen 17 Rogan 86	14
38	Mar 7		A	Workington	542	D 0 - 0		13
39	11		H	Worcester City	932	L 0 - 2		15
40	18		H	Moor Green	187	D 1 - 1	Smith 23	15
41	25		H	Worksop Town	852	W 1 - 0	Knight 43	14
42	April 1		A	Stafford Rangers	956	L 1 - 3	Olsen 38	14
43	8		H	Kettering Town	801	L 0 - 1		15
44	11		H	Vauxhall Motors	630	L 0 - 2		15
45	14		A	Hyde UNited	503	D 2 - 2	Ridley 55 Knight 87	15
46	17		H	Hucknall Town	689	W 2 - 0	Flitcroft 35 Knight 90	14
47	22		H	Nuneaton Borough	752	L 0 - 3		13
48	25		A	Stalybridge Celtic	492	L 1 - 2	Ridley 70	14
49	29		A	Redditch United	751	L 1 - 2	Smith 5	14

Ave. League Home Attendance: 802   **Goals**   77   78   **Top Goalscorer:** Knight (20)
Best Position: 1st   **Worst:** 16th

BLYTH SPARTANS

Founded: 1899
Nickname: Spartans

Manager: Harry Dunn **Asst. Manager:** Graham Fenton **Physio:** Gary Newsham

Club Colours: Green & white stripes/black/black

Change Colours: White with Green trim

Club Sponsor: Drager Safety Ltd.

Previous League: Northern Premier League

Best Seasons: N.P.L. Champions 2005-2006 **F.A.Cup:** 5th Rd Replay 1977-78

F.A.Trophy.: 6th Rd 79-80 82-83 **F.A.Amateur Cup:** Semi-Final 1971-72

Ground address: Croft Park, Blyth, Northumberland.

Tel No: 01670 352373 **Fax:** 01670 545592

Website: www.blythspartansafc.co.uk

Capacity: 6,000 **Seats:** 300 **Covered:** 1,000 **Floodlights:** Yes

Simple Directions: From Tyne Tunnel heading North on A19 take Cramington turning A1061 follow signs for Newsham/Blyth. Right fork at railway gates in Newsham go down Plessey Rd. Ground is on left.

Midweek Home Matchday: Tuesday

Clubhouse:. Open every night plus lunchtimes at week ends.(01670 352373)

Club Shop: Fully stocked. Contact: Dereck Burdsey (01670 352373)

CLUB PERSONNEL

Chairman: Tommy Hedley
V-Chairman: Tony Platten
President: J.Coppinger
Secretary: Ian Evans c/o BSFC
Tel No: 01670 369308 (H)
07905 984308 (M)
Company Secretary: Colin Baxter
Press Officer: Brian Grey
General Manager: Ian Evans
Programme.Editor: Brian Grey
Tel No: 01912 656244(H)
0786 0 197250(M)
2005-2006
Captain: Richard Forster
Player of the Year: Robbie Dale &
Peter Snowden
Top Goalscorer: Robbie Dale 33

CLUB STATISTICS

Record	**Attendance:** (at Croft Park)10,186 v Hartlepools Utd.F.A.C. 8.12.56
	Victory: 18-0 v Gateshead Town N..Alliance 28.12.07
	Defeat: 0-10 v Darlington N E Lg,12.12.14. v Newcastle Res. Northumberland Cup 26.03.27 & v Middlesbrough Res.N.E.Lg.27.08 55
Goalscorer:	**Career Appearances:** Eddie Alder 605 (1965-1968)
	Goals in a Season: Tommy Orrick 54
	Goals in a Career: Brian Slane 294 19969-1977
Record Transfer Fee	**Paid:** Unknown
	Received: £30,000 from Hull City for Les Mutrie
Senior Honours:	Northern League (10) R-up (5) Northumberland Senior Cup (19)
Previous Leagues	Northumberland 01-07, Northern All 07-13 46-47 North Eastern (4)
	Northern Comb.: 45-46, Midland 58-60, Northern Co 60-62 and Northern 62-94

BLYTH SPARTANS

BEST LGE ATT.: 1,250 v Wakefield & Emley
LOWEST: **295** v Marine

No.	Date	Comp	H/A	Opponents	Att:	Result	Goalscorers	Pos
1	Aug 20	NP	A	Burscough	264	D 0 - 0		14
2	23		H	Farsley Celtic	322	L 0 - 1		17
3	27		H	Ashton United	313	W 2 - 0	Bell 16 Gildea A 25	10
4	29		A	Whitby Town	306	W 4 - 0	Bell 14 Fenton 31 **Dale** 45 57	
5	Sept 3		H	Marine	295	W 1 - 0	**Dale** 29 (pen)	5
6	6		A	Guiseley	282	W 2 - 0	Fenton 20 Bell 85	3
7	10	FAC 1Q	A	**Wakefield-Emley**	162	W 2 - 1	**Leeson 65 Gildea L 85**	2
8	13	NP	H	Frickley Athletic	351	W 1 - 0	Gildea L.70	2
9	17		A	Ilkeston Town	378	D 0 - 0		2
10	20		H	Whitby Town	460	W 1 - 0	**Dale** 60	1
11	24	FAC 2Q	H	**Prescot Cables**	484	W 1 - 0	**Dale 6**	
12	28	NP	A	Bradford PA	144	L 1 - 2	Bell 38	2
13	Oct 1		H	Leek Town	486	W 2 - 1	**Dale** 41 Bell 90	2
14	4		A	Frickley Athletic	392	L 2 - 3	Price 7 **Dale** 82 (pen)	3
15	8	FAC 3Q	A	**Rossendale United**	209	W 1 - 0	**Williams 43**	
16	11	NP	H	Runcorn FC Halton	352	D 0 - 0		4
17	15	FAT1Q	H	**Belper Town**	372	W 2 - 0	**Dale 13 (pen) Johnson 90**	
18	22	FAC4Q	H	**Chasetown**	926	D 2 - 2	**Snowdon 35 Dale 82 (pen)**	
19	25	FAC4Qr	A	**Chasetown**	2135	L 0 - 1		
20	29	NP	H	Matlock Town	430	D 2 - 2	**Dale** 28 51 (pen)	8
21	Nov 5		A	Wakefield-Emley	315	W 3 - 0	**Dale** 61 85 Williams 77	6
22	12	FAT 2Q	H	**Whitby Town**	501	W 2 - 0	**Leeson 75 McCabe 85**	
23	26	FAT 3Q	A	**Marine**	268	W 1 - 0	**Williams 60**	
24	Dec 3	NP	H	Lincoln United	314	L 0 - 1		10
25	10		A	AFC Telford	1388	D 1 - 1	Bell 88	9
26	17	FAT 1	A	**Warrington Town**	251	W 2 - 1	**Forster 45 (pen) Leeson 50**	
27	20	NP	A	Farsley Celtic	201	D 1 - 1	Forster 28	10
28	26		H	Gateshead	767	D 1 - 1	**Dale** 39	9
29	Jan 2		A	North Ferriby United	386	W 4 - 1	**Dale** 3 (33pen 45 89) McCabe 75	8
30	7			Ossett Town	359	D 4 - 4	Appleby 44 McCabe 47 **Dale** 52 78	
31	14	FAT 2	H	**Welling United**	784	L 1 - 3	**Rushton 71**	
32	21	NP	A	Lincoln United	135	W 1 - 0	Snowdon 89	6
33	28		H	Witton Albion	402	W 5 - 1	Bell 3 (12 24 52) **Dale** 55 70	6
34	Feb 4		A	Ashton United	180	W 3 - 2	Bell 3 (3 54 90)	5
35	15		A	Leek Town	235	W 3 - 0	Bell 29 Gildea L 36 Snowden 51	
36	18		H	AFC Telford	561	D 1 - 1	Gildea A	
37	22		H	Prescot Cables	132	W 3 - 1	McCabe 38 Snowden 64 Gildea A	4
38	25		H	Burscough	418	W 1 - 0	Bell 50	4
39	Mar 18		A	Marine	403	W 1 - 0	Snowden 61	4
40	21		A	Radcliffe Borough	188	W 3 - 0	**Dale** 3 (7 24 (pen) 67)	3
41	25		H	Prescot Cables	537	W 2 - 0	**Dale** 7 60	3
42	April 4		H	North Ferriby United		W 4 - 2	Leeson 23 **Dale** 24 51 Appleby 54	3
43	8		H	Ilkeston Town	592	D 1 - 1	McClen 44	4
44	11		A	Ossett Town	200	L 1 - 3	McCabe 85	4
45	14		A	Gateshead	715	W 2 - 1	Snowden 49 **Dale** 62	2
46	15		H	Radcliffe Borough	525	W 1 - 0	**Dale** 70	2
47	17		H	Bradford PA	658	W 2 - 0	Appleby 83 **Dale** 88 (pen)	1
48	19		A	Witton Albion	214	D 1 - 1	Leeson 38	1
49	22		A	Runcorn FC Halton	154	W 5 - 0	Appleby 18 Fenton 50 (pen) 74 Garaham 76 Roberts 90	1
50	25		A	Matlock Town	259	W 1 - 0	**Dale** 67	1
51	27		H	Guisley	1024	W 3 - 1	Bell 31 40 **Dale** 75	1
52	29		H	Wakefield -Emley	1250	W 3 - 0	Gildea 59 76 price 90	1

Ave. League Home Attendance: 489   **Goals**   91   39   **Top Goalscorer:** Dale (33)
Best Position: 1st   **Worst:** 17th

DROYLSDEN

Founded: 1892
Nickname: The Bloods

Manager: David Pace **Assistant Manager:** Aeon Lattie **Physio:** Alan Cross

Club Colours: Red/Black/Black

Change Colours: Royal Blue/Navy Blue/Royal Blue

Club Sponsor:

Previous League: Northern Premier League:

Best Seasons: League: 3rd Conference North 2004-2005

F.A. Cup: 2nd Round 1978-79

F.A.Trophy: 3rd Round. 1998-99

Ground address: The Butchers Arms Ground, Market Street, Droylsden, Manchester M43 7AY. **Tel No:** 0161 370 1426/8341 Fax: 0161 3708341

Capacity: 3,500 **Seats:** 500 **Covered:** 2,000 **Floodlights:**Yes

Simple Directions: Jct 23 M60 signed to Manchester. Join A635 (towards Manchester). Right at lights onto A662 to Droylsden. Turn right into Market Street after half a mile, then over lights and ground is on left.

Midweek Home Matchday: Monday

Clubhouse: Pub hours except match days **Club Shop:** Yes

Local Radio: BBC Manchester

Local Press: Tameside Reporter, Tameside Advertiser

CLUB PERSONNEL

Chairman: David Pace
Secretary: Alan Slater, 83 King Edward Rd., Hyde, Cheshire SK14 5JJ Tel & Fax: 0161 3683687 07989 024777 (M)
Commercial Manager: Stella Quimm
Tel No: 07850 369588 (M)
Programme Editor: Steve Jarvis
Tel No: 07775 701221 (M)

2005-2006
Captain: Garry Burke
Player of the Year: Jimmy Williams
Top Goalscorer: Terry Fearns 29

CLUB STATISTICS

Record	Attendance: 4,250 v Grimsby
	Victory: 13-2 v Lucas Sports Club
	Defeat: 2-1 v South Liverpool
Career Goalscorer:	E.Gillibrand 275 (1931-35)
Career Appearances:	Paul Phillips 326
Record Transfer Fee	Paid: For Terry Fearns 2005 (undisclosed)
	Received: £11,000 from Crewe Alexandra forTony Naylor 1990
Senior Honours:	NPL Premier Division R-up 2003-04, Division 1 1998-99 R-up 1989-90 Manchester Premier Cup: (3) Manchester Senior Cup (3)
Previous Leagues:	Manchester, Lancs Combination 36-39 50-68 Cheshire County: 39-50 68-82 N.W .Counties. 82-87 NPL 1986-2004

Backrow, left to right: B.Quinn,A.Lattie, D Cameron, P. Dogun, P.Phillips, G.Burke, C.Robinson, P.Howarth, G.Murphy, J.Worsnop, S.Halford,I Fitzpatrick, A.Cross and B.Harris. Front Row: M.Grose, L.Morris, D.Pace, N.Hall, J.Williams, J.Banim, S.Brodie, R.Talbot, S.Sturdy, K.Rapley and D.Warner.

DROYLSDEN

BEST LGE ATT.: 1,302 v Stalybridge Celtic
LOWEST: 260 v Workington

No.	Date	Comp	H/A	Opponents	Att:	Result	Goalscorers	Pos
1	Aug 13	CN	H	Nuneaton Borough	398	D 2 - 2	Banim 62 Morris 88	12
2	16		A	Leigh RMI	245	W 1 - 0	Banim 10	5
3	20		A	Moor Green	139	D 1 - 1	Talbot 16	9
4	27		H	Vauxhall Motors	275	W 4 - 0	Murphy 43 Williams 45 Talbot 55 Halford 73	5
5	29		A	Worcester City	816	W 2 - 1	Cameron 34 Banim 66	3
6	Sept 3		H	Hucknall Town	336	L 2 - 3	Rapley 43 (pen) 53 (pen)	5
7	10		H	Barrow	354	D 2 - 2	Talbot 20 Rapley 49	6
8	17		A	Redditch United	301	L 1 - 4	Banim 79	9
9	24	FAC 2Q	H	Burscough	316	L 1 - 2	Halford 53	
10	Oct 1	CN	H	Alfreton Town	319	W 1 - 0	Morris 69	8
11	8		H	Worksop Town	272	W 3 - 1	Robinson 71 Fearns 74 (pen) Talbot 80	4
12	15		A	Hinckley United	578	D 1 - 1	Talbot 3	4
13	17		A	Hyde United	633	D 2 - 2	Brodie 22 Phillips 73	4
14	29		A	Kettering Town	2060	L 0 - 1		7
15	Nov 5		H	Stafford Rangers	473	W 2 - 1	Rapley 36 Fearns 70	4
16	12		A	Harrogate Town	433	D 1 - 1	Denham 13	7
17	14		H	Gainsborough Trinity	320	L 1 - 2	Morris 42	7
18	26	FAT 3Q	H	Grantham Town	251	W 4 - 0	Robinson 24 Fearns 32 Brodie 47 Talbot 69	
19	Dec 4	CN	A	Lancaster City	271	D 2 - 2	Rapley 49 Fearns 83	9
20	10		A	Stalybridge Celtic	863	D 1 - 1	Fitzpatrick 89	8
21	12		H	Workington	260	L 2 - 3	O'Brien 79 Brodie 82	8
22	17	FAT 1	A	**Stalybridge Celtic**	598	L 0 - 1		
23	26	CN	H	Northwich Victoria	701	W 4 - 3	Fearns 23 (pen) Brodie 38 87 Cameron 54	8
24	31		A	Hedhesfoird Town	352	D 1 - 1	Rapley 47	7
25	Jan 2		A	Northwich Victoria	1106	L 1 - 2	Denham 48	10
26	14		H	Leigh RMI	370	W 4 - 1	FEARNS 3 (32 60 85) Talbot 90	7
27	21		H	Moor Green	342	W 3 - 0	Fearns 49 89 Denham 63	5
28	28		A	Vauxhall Motors	230	W 4 - 2	Denham 28 Fearns 30 85 McNulty 80 (og)	5
29	Feb 4		A	Alfreton Town	271	W 3 - 1	Talbot 40 47 Fearns 69	4
30	11		H	Hinckley United	397	W 3 1 1	Warner 2 Fearns 40 (pen) Denham 87	4
31	18		A	Gainsborough Trinity	300	D 2 - 2	Tandy 52 Fearns 75	4
32	20		H	Hyde United	761	W 1 - 0	Williams 62	4
33	25		A	Barrow	892	L 0 - 2		4
34	Mar 11		A	Kettering Town	419	W 3 - 1	Fearns 17 (pen) 57 Denham 47	5
35	14		A	Nuneaton Borough	900	D 2 - 2	Fearns 15 52	4
36	18		A	Stafford Rangers	785	D 0 - 0		4
37	21		H	Worksop Town	285	L 2 - 3	Fearns 1 Morris 49	4
38	25		H	Harrogate Town	382	W 2 - 1	Fearns 34 (pen) Talbot 86	5
39	April 1		A	Workington	414	L 1 - 2	Morris 7	5
40	3		H	Redditch United	279	W 2 - 1	Fearns 15 (pen) Talbot 66	4
41	8		H	Lancaster City	319	W 6 - 1	Talbot 16 Fearns 19 57 (pen) Morris 60 Fitzpatrick 87 89	4
42	15		A	Hucknall Town	356	L 0 - 2		4
43	17		H	Worcester City	468	W 3 - 0	Fearns 5 73 (Pen) Morris 25	4
44	22		A	Hednesford Town	434	W 1 - 0	Fitzpatrick 45	4
45	29		H	Stalybridge Celtic	1302	W 1 - 0	Burke 79	4
46	May 1	Play Off SF	A	**Nuneaton Borough**	2005	W 1 - 0	**Morris 2**	
47	6	Play Off Final	A	**Stafford Rangers**	2704	D 1 - 1	**Lost 3-5 after penalties**	
Ave. League Home Attendance:		433			**Goals**	87 60	**Top Goalscorer:** Fearns (26)	
Best Position:	3rd	**Worst:**	12th					

FARSLEY CELTIC

Founded: 1908
Nickname: Villagers

Manager: Lee Sinnott   **Assistant Manager:** John Deacy   **Physio:** Maria Kearns
Club Colours: Al Royal Blue
Change Colours: All Yellow
Club Sponsor: I.T.S.Turbos
Previous League: Northern Premier League
Best Seasons: 3rd NPL Premier 2004-05 and 5th 2005-2006 (Play off Winners)
F.A.Cup: 1st Round 74-75   **F.A.Vase** 6th Round 1987-1988
F.A.Trophy.: 3rd Rd Replay 2002-03   **F.A.Amateur Cup:** 3rd Rd 1934-35
Ground address: Throstle Nest, Newlands, Farsley, Pudsey, Leeds LS28 5BE
Tel No: 0113 2557292   **Website:** www.farsleyceltic.co.uk
e-mail:GRG LSL@aol.com
Capacity: 4,000   **Seats:** 300   **Covered:** 1,500   **Floodlights:** Yes
Simple Directions: From B6157 pass Police and Fire stations on the left, turn down New Street at Tradex warehouse before turning right into Newlands. Ground at bottom of road. One mile from Pudsey (BR)

Midweek Home Matchday: Tuesday
Clubhouse:. Open every evening and lunchtimes at week ends
Club Shop: Full range.Contact: Helen Shepherd or Martina Pearson 0113 256 1517
email: clubshop@vbreathemail.net

CLUB PERSONNEL
Chairman: Andrew Firbank
Managing Director: Terry Dighton
Additional Directors:
John Palmer, Paul Glover and Martin Carrington
Secretary: Keith Huggins, c/o Club
Tel Nos: 0113 2557292 (W)
07985 378326 (M)
Commercial Manager: John Boyd
Match Secretary: Josh Greaves
Programme Editor:
Howard Stevenson
Tel No: 07932 306556
Programme
32 Pages £1.00

2005-2006
Captain: Chris Stabb
Player of the Year: Carl Serrant
Top Goalscorer: KevinSanasay 14

CLUB STATISTICS	
Record	Attendance: 11,000 (at Elland Rd) v Tranmere Rovers F.A.Cup 1st Rd. 74
	Victory:
	Defeat:
	Goalscorer: Career Appearances:
	Record Transfer Fee Received:
	Received Paid:
Senior Honours:	West Riding Co. Cup (9) N.P.L. Cup and N.P.L. Play off Winners 2005-2006
	N.Co. East Premier League Runners -Up 1986-1987
Previous Leagues	West Riding Co Amateur, Leeds Red Triangle, Yorkshire, 49-82
	N.Co East 82-87
Grounds:	Red Lane Farsley, Calverley Lane Farsley prior to 1948

Back row (L-R): Andrew Jackson,Chris Thackray, Rob McQuarrie, Chis Jenkinson, James Knowles, Simon Parke, Amjad Iqbal, Gareth Grant, Danny Matthew, Nathan Hotte, James McDaid. **Middle:** Craig Midgeley,Kevin Ryan, Damian Reeves, Tom Morgan, Domonic Krief, Paul Cuss, Marin Pemberton, Kevin Sanasy, Roy Stamer. **Front:** Josh Greaves (matchday secretary), John Palmer (President), Terry Deighton (Managing Director),Paul Glover (Director), Gary Stokes (Coach), Lee Sinnot (Manager), Chris Stabb (Captain), John Deacey (Assistant Manager), Maria Kearns (Physio), Andy Firbank (Chairman), Matin Carrington (Director/ Company Secretary), Mark Bell (Sponsor ITS Turbos), Keith Huggins (Football Secretary). The Cups at the front are West Riding County Cup (left) and Unibond League Challenge Cup.

FARSLEY CELTIC

BEST LGE ATT.: 365 v Bradford Park Avenue
LOWEST: 151 v Ossett Town

No.	Date	Comp	H/A	Opponents	Att:	Result	Goalscorers	Pos
1	Aug 20	NP	H	Witton Albion	191	L 0 - 3		22
2	23		A	Blyth Spartans	322	W 1 - 0	Jackson 13	12
3	27		A	Ilkeston Town	331	D 1 - 1	McDaid 85	13
4	29		H	Guiseley	349	D 1 - 1	Bett 47	14
5	Sept 3		H	Leek Town	205	W 3 - 2	Shields 60 Bernard 63 71	10
6	6		A	Frickley Athletic	287	L 0 - 1		12
7	10	FAC 1Q	A	**Pickering Town**	147	W 2 - 1	**Duxbury 51 Bernard 63**	
8	13		H	Gateshead	178	W 4 - 2	Rowe 45 73 Jackson 56 59	9
9	17		A	Matlock Town	228	D 0 - 0		9
10	20		A	Bradford PA	365	W 3 - 2	Bissett 20 (og) Rickers 69 Jackson 71	8
11	24	FAC2Q	H	**Bradford PA**	403	W 2 - 0	**Rickers 36 Watson 69**	
12	Oct 1	NP	H	Burscough	200	L 2 - 4	Watson 82 Rowe 85	9
13	5		A	Bradford PA	287	L 3 - 4	Bernard 26 32 Duxbury 88	12
14	8	FAC 3Q	A	**Salford City**	195	W 1 - 0	**Iqbal 7**	
15	11	NP	H	Whitby Town	211	L 1 - 3	Rickers 80 (pen)	14
16	15	FAC1Q	H	**Runcorn FC Halton**	223	W 2 - 0	**Bambrook 12 35**	
17	18	NP	A	Lincoln United	85	W 1 - 0	Bernard 78	13
18	22	FAC 4Q	A	**Halifax Town**	1469	L 0 - 2		
19	29	NP	H	AFC Telford	279	W 2 - 0	Bambrook 44 52	13
20	Nov 5		H	North Ferriny	235	D 1 - 1	Iqbal 58	13
21	12	FAT 2Q	A	**Precot Cables**	214	W 2 - 1	**Bambrook 86 Sanasay 90**	
22	16		A	Whitby Town	206	D 1 - 1	**Sanasay** 77	11
23	19	NP	H	Prescot Cables	295	W 2 - 0	Bambrook 6 **Sanasay** 30	
24	26	FAT 3Q	H	**Nuneaton Borough**	271	W 3 - 1	**Sanasay 15 36 Knowles 27**	
25	Dec 3	NP	A	Radcliffe Borough	166	L 5 - 0	Shields 2 Bett 31 Iqbal 64 Knowles 79 **Sanasay** 80	
26	10		A	Burscough	526	W 3 - 0	**Sanasay** 3 (56 59 87)	6
27	17	FAT 1	A	**Kettering Town**	964	L 1 - 2	**Iqbal 9**	
28	20	NP	H	Blyth Spartans	201	D 1 - 1	Bett 38 (pen)	6
29	26		A	Guiseley	517	W 3 - 0	**Sanasay** 11 35 Bett 38	5
30	Jan 2		H	Frickley Athletic	335	L 0 - 1		5
31	14		H	Ossett Town	151	W 3 - 0	Bett 8 **Sanasay** 39 Shields 78	5
32	21		A	Ashton United	178	D 1 - 1	Bett 80	5
33	28		H	Radcliffe Borough	225	W 3 - 0	Stamer 58 Reeves 65 Bambrook 89	5
34	Feb 4		A	North Ferriby United	252	W 1 - 0	Stamer 67	4
35	14		A	Marine		L 0 - 1		
36	18		H	Ilkeston Town	221	D 1 - 1	Bett 33	5
37	21		H	Matlock Town	172	W 3 - 1	Bett 43 Reeve 58 Stamer 68	5
38	25		A	AFC Telford	1572	L 0 - 1		5
39	Mar 16		A	Gateshead		W 5 - 0	Watson 11 **Sanasay** 44 Shields 49 Stamer 51 Bambrook (pen) 82	
40	18		H	Ashton United	202	W 2 - 0	Bambrook 1 65 Knowles 58	5
41	21		H	Wakefield -Emley	79	W 1 - 0	Reeves 23	5
42	25		H	Ossett Town	175	W 1 - 0	Bambrook 88	5
43	28		H	Wakefield-Emley	176	W 6 - 1	Stamer 36 Reeves 40 81 **Sanasay** 49 Nesovic (og) 55 Watson 73	2
44	April 1		H	Lincoln United	295	W 3 - 0	Bambrook 41 (pen) Reeves 52 Watson 84	2
45	8		A	Leek Town	246	D 1 - 1	Reves 35	2
46	17		A	Witton Albion	255	W 1 - 0	Knowles 68	3
47	22		H	Marine	245	L 0 - 1		4
48	25		H	Runcorn FC Halton	202	W 5 - 0	Hanley (og) 1 Iqbal30 58 Watson 44 Bett 61	3
49	27		A	Runcorn FC Halton	101	W 7 - 0	Parke 28 Iqbal 46 Reeve 51 Krief 4 (64 68 70 72)	3
50	29		A	Prescot Cables	182	D 1 - 1	Reeves 31	4
51	**May 1**	Play Off SF	A	**Marine**	477	W 1 - 0	**Bambrook 87**	
52	6	Play Off Final	H	**North Ferriby United**	933	W 2 - 1	**Watson 5 Reeves 96**	

Ave. League Home Attendance:	212	**Goals**	94 41	**Top Goalscorer:** Sanasay (14)

Best Position:　2nd　　**Worst:**　22nd

GAINSBOROUGH TRINITY

Founded: 1873
Nickname: The Blues

Manager: Paul Mitchell   **Coach:** Steve Charles.

Club Colours: Blue/white/blue

Change Colours: All Yellow

Club Sponsor: T.Bland Welding

Previous League: Northern Premier

Best Seasons: League: 11th Conference North   **F.A.Trophy.:** 4th Rd. 2002-2003

F.A. Cup: 2nd Rd x 13 (including 8 times between 1927and 1939)1st Rd x 35

Ground address: Northolme, Bainsborough, Lincs. DN21 2QW

Tel No: 01427 613295(office) 613688 (club) 613295 (Fax)

Website: www.gainsboroughtrinity.com

Capacity: 4,340   **Seats:** 504   **Covered:** 2,500   **Floodlights:**Yes

Simple Directions: The Northolme is situated on the A159 Gainsborough to Scunthorpe road. Two miles from Lea Road.

Midweek Home Matchday: Tuesday   **Club Website:** www.gainsboroughtrinity.com

Clubhouse: Open on matchdays. Blues club open every evening

Shop Contacts: Wendy Godley (01427 611612) & Nigel Tasker (01522 542014)

Local Radio: BBC Radio Lincs and Linc FM

Local Press: Gainsborough Standard and Lincolnshire Echo

CLUB PERSONNEL

Chairman: Patrick Lobley
President: Ken Marsden
Commercial Director:
Geoff Holmes
Football Secretary: G.Lyner
Tel No: 01427 612791
Secretary & Press Officer:
Grahame Lyner, 2 Claremont Road, Gainsborough, Lincs.DN21 1QW
Tel No: 07789 950552 (M)§
Programme Editor :
Mark Southon (01302 7196140)
Programme 52 pages. Price: £1.50
2005-2006
Captain:
Player of the Year:
Top Goalscorer: Carl Smith 11

CLUB STATISTICS

Record	**Attendance:** 9,760 v Scunthorpe United Midland League 1948
Victory:	7-0 v Fleetwood Town and Great Harwood Town
Defeat:	1-7 V Stalybridge Celtic (N.P.L.) 2000-2001
	1-7 V Brentford F.A.Cup 03-04 & Stalybridge C NPL 00-01
Career Goalscorer:	
Career Appearances:	
Record Transfer Fee	**Paid:** £3,000 to Buxton for Stuart Lowe
	Received: £30,000 from Lincoln City for Tony James
Senior Honours:	Lincs Senior Cup (12)
Previous Leagues:	Midland Co. 1889-96 1912-60 61-68 Football League 1896-1912 Central Alliance 60-61 Northern Premier League 68-2004

Back Row (L-R): Luke Staton, Simon Bird, Ben Purkiss, Neil Allison, Jamie Sherlock, Jamie Holmshaw, Jason Maxwell, Adam Burley, Chris Hurst, Lee Ellington.
Front Row: Ryan Ford, Carl Smith, Ben Dixon, Danny Wood, Matty Caudwell.

STEP 1
CONFERENCE

STEP 2
CONFERENCE NORTH

STEP 3
NPL - SOUTHERN - ISTHMIAN PREM

STEP 4
NPL - SOUTHERN - ISTHMIAN

STEP 5/6

STEP 7

GAINSBOROUGH TRINITY

BEST LGE ATT.: **647** v Worksop Town
LOWEST: **255** v Northwich Victoria

No.	Date	Comp	H/A	Opponents	Att:	Result	Goalscorers	Pos
1	Aug 13	CN	H	Moor Green	317	D 2 - 2	Higgins 41 Marcelle 70	13
2	16		A	Northwich Victoria	669	L 0 - 2		20
3	20		A	Worcester City	738	L 1 - 2	Caudwell 85	21
4	27		H	Hednesford Town	362	D 1 - 1	Pell 75	20
5	29		A	Vauxhall Motors	155	W 2 - 1	Reeves 64 Pell 75	17
6	Sept 3		H	Leigh RMI	259	W 2 - 1	Reeves 51 (pen Pell 65	14
7	10		H	Hinckley United	363	L 1 - 2	Reeves 27	14
8	17		A	Hyde United	416	L 0 - 2		16
9	**24**	**FAC 2Q**	**H**	**Goole**	**423**	**D 2 - 2**	**Reeves 44 Rowan 68**	
10	**27**	**FAC 2Qr**	**A**	**Goole**	**298**	**W 2 - 1**	**Caudwell 53 Rowan 85**	
11	Oct 1	CN	A	Redditch United	332	D 1 - 1	Ellis 45	14
12	**8**	**FAC 3Q**	**A**	**Leigh RMI**	**165**	**D 1 - 1**	**Higgins 34**	
13	**11**	**FAC 3Qr**	**H**	**Leigh RMI**	**361**	**W 2 - 1**	**Udenkwor 5 Trout 13**	
14	15		H	Barrow	385	W 3 - 2	Trout 4 Ellis 65 Needham 82	12
15	18		H	Stalybridge Celtic	412	W 1 - 0	Pell 10	12
16	**22**	**FAC 4Q**	**H**	**York City**	**1680**	**L 0 - 4**		
17	29	CN	A	Workington	434	L 0 - 2		13
18	Nov 5		H	Hyde United	429	L 0 - 3		15
19	8		H	Harrogate Town	270	L 0 - 2		15
20	12		A	Hucknall Town	407	L 1 - 4	Needham 30	15
21	14		A	Droylsden	320	W 2 - 1	Trout 38 Steadman 80	14
22	19		H	Lancaster City	306	W 1 - 0	Hindley 41	12
23	**26**	**FAT 3Q**	**A**	**Kettering Town**	**1132**	**L 0 - 2**		
24	Dec 3	CN	A	Stafford Rangers	704	L 0 - 3		14
25	10		H	Alfreton Town	337	D 2 - 2	**Smith** 19 Mallon 27	14
26	17		H	Nuneaton Borough	373	L 1 - 2	**Smith** 28	
27	26		A	Worksop Town	615	D 1 - 1	Mallon 47	16
28	Jan 2		H	Worksop Town	647	W 2 - 0	Trout 50 Mallon 60	14
29	7		A	Moor Green	177	D 1 - 1	**Smith** 62	15
30	21		H	Worcester City	378	L 0 - 1		
31	28		A	Hednesford Town	472	D 1 - 1	Mallon 14	16
32	Feb 4		H	Redditch United	306	D 2 - 2	Parker 39 Trout 89	
33	11		A	Barrow	852	L 1 - 3	Mallon 27	17
34	18		H	Droylsden	300	D 2 - 2	Mallon 64 Parker 78	16
35	21		A	Stalybridge Celtic	327	L 0 - 1		16
36	25		A	Hinckley United	481	L 0 - 1		17
37	28		A	Kettering Town	906	W 2 - 1	**Smith** 17 60	17
38	Mar 11		H	Workington	337	D 0 - 0		17
39	14		H	Northwich Victoria	255	L 1 - 2	**Smith** 14	17
40	18		A	Nuneaton Borough	879	L 1 - 3	**Smith** 19	18
41	25		H	Hucknall Town	335	W 3 - 2	Mallon 5 **Smith** 50 Trout 88	17
42	April 1		A	Lancaster City	229	W 3 - 2	**Smith** 31 Graves 51 Perker 90	16
43	8		H	Stafford Rangers	318	D 1 - 1	**Smith** 53	17
44	11		A	Harrogate Town	376	L 0 - 2		17
45	15		A	Leiggh RMI	125	D 0 - 0		17
46	17		H	Vauxhall Motors	284	D 1 - 1	Caudwell 41	17
47	22		A	Kettering Town	457	L 0 - 2		17
48	29		A	Alfreton Town	301	W 2 - 1	**Smith** 28 Parker 82	16

Ave. League Home Attendance:		336			**Goals**	52 76	**Top Goalscorer:** Smith (11)	
Best Position: 1st	**Worst:** 16th							

HARROGATE TOWN

Founded: 1919
Nickname: Town

Manager: Neil Aspin   **Coach:** Lee Philpott

Club Colours: Sky Blue & White stripes/Blue/White

Club Sponsors: Jacuzzi UK

Previous League: Northern Premier

Best Seasons: League: 5th. Conference North 2005-2006

F.A. Cup: 1st Round Proper 2002-03 2004-05 **F.A.Vase:** 4th Round 1989-1990

F.A.Trophy.: 3rd Round Replay 99-00 01-02

Ground address: Wetherby Road, Harrogate. Tel No: 01423 880675 (Office & Fax) with Secretary and Admin on 01423 525341 **Website:** www.harrogatetownafc.co.uk

Capacity: 3,291   **Seats:** 502   **Covered:**1,300   **Floodlights:** Yes

Simple Directions: From A1 to towards Wetherby take A661 to Harrogate. On entering town go straight over roundabout and lights (Woodlands Pub). Gound is 500 yards on right.

Midweek Home Matchday: Tuesday

Clubhouse: Open every matchday (Tel No: 01423 883671)

Club Shop: Yes. (01423 885525) Open every day.

Local Press: Yorkshire Post Group and Harrogate Advertiser Series

Local Radio: BBC Radio Yorkshire and Stray FM.

CLUB PERSONNEL

Chairman: Bill Fotherby
Deputy Chairman: Andrew Thurkill
President: George Dunnington
Secretary: Dave Callaghan, c/o Club
Programme Editor: Bob Head
Tel No: 07799 834918(M)

2005-2006
Captain: Roy Hunter
Player of the Year: Danny Holland
Top Goalscore: Danny Holland

CLUB STATISTICS

Record	Attendance: 4,280 v Railway Athletic , Whitworth Cup Final 1950
Victory:	13-0 v Micklefield **Defeat:** 1-10 v Methley United 1956
Career Goalscorer:	Jimmy Hague 135 (1956-7 to 1957-8, 1961-2 to 193-74 & 1973-74 to 1975-76)
Career Appearances:	Paul Williamson 428 (1980-81 1982-83 to 1984-85 and 1986-87 to 1992-93)
Record Transfer Fee	**Paid:** for Mark Haran from Worksop T. and Lee Morris from Frickley A .2004-05
	Received: from York City for Dave Merris 2003-2004
Senior Honours:	NPL Div 1 Champions 2001-02 N.Co E Div1 (North) R-up 84-85
	W.Riding County Cup 62-63 72-73 85-86 W.Riding Challenge Cup (2)
Previous Leagues:	West Riding 1919-20, Yorkshire 20-21 22-31 57-82, Midland 21-22 Northern 31-32 Harrogate & Dist. 35-37 40-46 W.Riding Co Am.Lg 37-40 W.Yorks 46-57, N.Co East 82-87, N.P.L.87-2004

HARROGATE TOWN

BEST LGE ATT.: 602 v Nuneaton Borough
LOWEST: 301 v Moor Green

No.	Date	Comp	H/A	Opponents	Att:	Result	Goalscorers	Pos
1	Aug 13	CN	H	Hyde UNited	371	W 1 - 0	Lennon 70	7
2	16		A	Hucknall Town	520	L 1 - 4	Smith 65	12
3	20		A	Nuneaton Borough	724	L 0 - 4		16
4	27		H	Moor Green	301	W 3 - 0	**Holland** 25 (pen) 36 Hunter 84 (pen)	10
5	29		A	Worksop Town	342	L 0 - 1		13
6	Sept 3		H	Worcester City	319	W 4 - 1	**Holland** 21 61 Ellerker 74 Preston 66	10
7	10		A	Workington	475	W 4 - 2	Grant 3 (15 37 78) Ellerker 32	9
8	17		H	Kettering Town	437	D 1 - 1	**Holland** 52	7
9	24	FAC 2Q	H	**Great Harwood Town**	346	**W 3 - 0**	**Grant 7 84 Smith 11**	
10	Oct 1	CN	A	Stalybridge Celtic	647	L 1 - 3	**Holland** 12	11
11	8	FAC 3Q	H	**Witton Albion**	402	**W 2 - 0**	**Smith 25 90**	
12	15	CN	H	Vauxhall Motors	365	W 2 - 1	**Holland** 21 65	11
13	18		H	Barrow	425	W 2 - 1	Grant 7 Stoneman 12	6
14	22	FAC 4Q	H	**Scarborough**	1591	**W 1 - 0**	**Smith 48**	
15	29	CN	H	Hinckley United	432	W 2 - 1	**Holland** 33 66	7
16	Nov 5	FAC1R	A	**Torquay United**	2079	**D 1 - 1**	**Holland 20**	
17	8	CN	A	Gainsborough Trinity	270	W 2 - 0	Smith 51 65	4
18	12		H	Droylsden	433	D 1 - 1	**Holland** 82	5
19	15	FAC 1Rr	A	**Torquay United**	3317	**D 0 0 0**	**Lost 5-6 after penalties**	
20	19	CN	A	Hednesford Town	521	W 4 - 2	Smith 42 Philpott 46 Grant 60 **Holland** 71	4
21	26	FAT 3Q	A	**Solihull Borough**	199	**L 0 - 1**		
22	Dec 10	CN	H	Staford Rangers	505	L 0 - 2		5
23	17		A	Redditch United	226	W 3 - 1	Jones 5 Philpott 13 **Holland** 74	4
24	26		A	Leigh RMI	177	L 1 - 3	Hunter 72	5
25	Jan 2		H	Leigh RMI	428	W 3 - 0	Jones 1 21 Mallon 60	
26	7		H	Hyde UNited	404	L 1 - 3	Philpott 13	4
27	14		H	Hucknall Town	515	W 1 - 0	**Holland** 64	4
28	21		H	Nunneaton Borough	602	W 2 - 0	Jones 51 **Holland** 73	4
29	24		H	Northwich Victoria	502	L 0 - 2		4
30	28		A	Moor Green	192	D 2 - 2	Mason 27 Jones 44	4
31	Feb 11		A	Vauxhall Motors	1864	W 2 - 0	Brazier 38 (og) Smith 61	6
32	18		H	Redditch United	432	D 1 - 1	Jones 13	6
33	21		A	Barrow	672	L 1 - 3	**Holland** 3	6
34	25		H	Workington	433	D 1 - 1	**Holland** 35 (pen)	5
35	28		A	Alfreton Town	217	L 1 - 4	L.Wood 28	5
36	Mar 4		H	Kettering Town	1238	W 2 - 0	**Holland** 32 (pen) 77	4
37	11		A	Hinckley United	563	W 3 - 1	Dunning 65 **Holland** 70 (pen) Smith 76	4
38	18		H	Alfreton Town	468	W 1 - 0	**Holland** 60	4
39	21		H	Stalybridge Celtic	450	W 1 - 0	Smith 21	4
40	25		A	Droylsden	382	L 1 - 2	Grant 90	4
41	April 6		A	Lancaster City	192	L 1 - 2	McMahon 66 (og)	4
42	8		A	Northwich Victoria	1032	L 0 - 3		5
43	11		H	Gainsborough Trinity	376	W 2 - 0	Clark 45 Grant 54	5
44	15		A	Worcester City	923	L 0 - 2		5
45	17		H	Worksop Town	442	W 2 - 0	**Holland** 29 88	5
46	19		H	Hednesford Town	435	L 2 3 3	Timons 21 Philpott 72	5
47	22		H	Lancaster City	435	W 3 - 1	McMahon 26 (og) Grant 33 90	5
48	29		A	Stafford Rangers	806	W 1 - 0	**Holland** 38	5
49	May 2	Play Off SF	A	**Staffrord Rangers**	1665	**L 0 - 1**		

Ave. League Home Attendance: 434   **Goals** 73 59   **Top Goalscorer:** Holland (24)
Best Position: 4th   **Worst:** 16th

HINCKLEY UNITED

Founded: 1997
Nickname: United

Manager: Dean Thomas   **Coach:** Charlie Palmer   **Physio:** Julie Hayton
Club Colours: Royal blue with red side panel/Royal Blue/Red
Change Colours: Yellow/Black/Black
Club Sponsor: Wolverhampton Dudley Breweries
Previous League: Southern
Previous Name: Hinckley Town and Hinckley Athletic
Best Seasons: Lg: 10th Conference North 2005-2006
F.A. Cup: 2nd Rd Replay 2004-05
F.A.Trophy.: 4th Rd 98-99
Ground address: The Marstons Stadium, Leicester Road, Hinckley LE10 3DR
Tel.No: 01455 840088
Capacity: 4,329   **Seats:** 630   **Covered:** 2,695   **Floodlights:**Yes
Simple Directions: M6 Jct 2 then from M69 Jct 2 take A5 north
(Tamworth/Nuneaton) and at 3rd roundabout (Dodwells) take 2nd exit (A47 to Earl
Shilton). Marston Stadium just under two miles on right
Midweek Home Matchday: Monday
Clubhouse: Entrance outside the ground and open pub hours
Club Shop: Yes, off reception
Local Radio: BBC Radio Leicester, Fosseway Radio
Local Press: Heartland Evening News, Hinckley Times, Leicester Mercury,
Coventry Evening Telegraph.

CLUB PERSONNEL
Chairman: Kevin Downes
Vice-Chairman: Rob Mayne
Secretary: Ray Baggott, 37
Laneside Drive, Hinckley, Leics.
LE10 1TG Tel No: 01455 447278
**Programme Editor &
Press Officer:** Andy Gibbs
Tel No: 01455 617828

2005-2006
Captain: Carl Heeley
Player of the Year: Lee Jackson
Top Goalscorer: Andy Brown

CLUB STATISTICS

Record Attendance:	2,278 v Nuneaton Borough 10.12.05
Victory:	9-1 v Rocester (A) 28.08 2000
Defeat:	0-6 v Redditch United (a) 07.11.1988
Career Goalscorer:	Jamie Lenton 74
Career Appearances:	Jamie Lenton 280
Record Transfer Fee Paid:	£5,000 to Kidderminster Harriers for Matt Lewis .
Received:	£1,000 from Ilkeston Town for Justin Jenkins.
Senior Honours:	Southern League Western Division Champions 2000-01
Previous Leagues:	As United, Southern

Back Row (L-R): Dave Radburn(Kit Manager), Chris Nurse, Leigh Platnauer, Liam Castle, Danny Haystead, Russell Hitchen, Steve Marriner, Scott Machin(Reserve Team Manager). **Middle :** Andy Keeley(Physio) Andy Brown, Barry Woolley, Sam Shilton, Matt Gadsby, Jamie Lenton, Leon Kelly, Leon Jackson, Carl Heggs, Stuart Storer, Charlie Palmer(Ass. Manager). **Front:** Owen Story, Tom Manship, Michael Love, Dean Thomas(Manager), Richard Lavery, Neil Cartwright, Wayne Duik.

HINCKLEY UNITED

BEST LGE ATT.: **2,278** v Nuneaton Borough
LOWEST: **442** v Moor Green

No.	Date	Comp	H/A	Opponents	Att:	Result	Goalscorers	Pos
1	Aug 13	CN	H	Lancaster City	559	D 3 - 3	Winder 32 Shilton 36 Jackson 90	8
2	15		A	Worcester City	640	D 0 - 0		15
3	20		A	Hednesford Town	620	W 4 - 3	Colkin 15 Shilton 39 Heeley 42 **Brown** 51	8
4	27		H	Hucknall Town	617	W 3 - 1	Jackson 38 63 Lenton 75	6
5	29		A	Leigh RMI	232	L 0 - 1		9
6	Sept 3		H	Northwich Victoria	703	L 1 - 4	Lewis 34	12
7	10		A	Gainsborough Trinity	363	W 2 - 1	McGregor 2 47	10
8	17		H	Alfreton Town	611	D 2 - 2	Cluzel 46 Woolley 60	10
9	24	FAC 2Q	A	**Bromsgrove Rovers**	425	L 1 - 3	**McGregor 1**	
10	Oct 1	CN	A	Barrow	981	W 5 - 2	Cluzel 34 Shilton 45 **Brown** 72 Story 79 83	8
11	8		H	Moor Green	422	L 1 - 3	Cluzel 47	8
12	15		H	Droylsden	578	D 1 - 1	**Brown** 87	8
13	18		H	Redditch United	442	D 1 - 1	Woolley 33	8
14	22		A	Stalybridge Celtic	478	D 1 - 1	Palmer 35	10
15	29		A	Harrogate Town	432	L 1 - 2	Cartwright 74	11
16	Nov 5		H	Workington	429	D 0 - 0		11
17	12		A	Stafford Rangers	964	W 3 - 2	Colkin 45 Lenton 50 Storer 89	8
18	19		H	Hyde United	529	W 2 - 1	Piercewright 88 Shilton 90	
19	26	FAT 3Q	H	**Histon**	446	D 2 - 2	**Cluzel 15 Jackson 40**	
20	30	FAT 3Qr	A	**Histon**	218	L 1 - 2	**Story 40**	
21	Dec 3	CN	A	Worksop Town	376	D 0 - 0		8
22	10		H	Nuneaton Borough	2278	L 0 - 1		9
23	24	CN	A	Kettering Town	1444	D 2 - 2	Lavery 50 Palmer 84	9
24	31		A	Vauxhall Motors	174	W 1 - 0	**Brown** 18	8
25	Jan 2		H	Kettering Town	1322	D 1 - 1	Palmer 35	7
26	7		A	Lancaster City	264	D 2 - 2	**Brown** 23 Storer 45	9
27	21		H	Hednesford Town	719	L 1 - 2	**Brown** 15	12
28	24		H	Worcester City	470	L 1 - 3	Story 22	13
29	28		A	Hucknall Town	459	W 2 - 0	Story 70 Heeley 85	9
30	Feb 4		H	Barrow	467	W 1 - 0	Heeley 38	8
31	11		A	Droylsden	397	L 1 - 3	**Brown** 63	9
32	18		H	Stalybridge Celtic	506	D 1 - 1	Jackson 60	10
33	21		A	Redditch United	200	D 1 - 1	Storer 67	11
34	25		H	Gainsborough Trinity	481	W 1 - 0	Jackson 10	8
35	Mar 4		A	Alfreton Town	344	D 1 - 1	Lewis 31	7
36	11		H	Harrogate Town	563	L 1 - 3	**Brown** 90	11
37	18		A	Workington	475	D 1 - 1	Whitman 61	12
38	25		A	Stafford Rangers	715	L 0 - 1		12
39	April 1		A	Hyde United	402	W 1 - 0	Flynn 54 (og)	12
40	4		A	Moor Green	205	D 1 - 1	Kelly 16	11
41	8		H	Worksop Town	528	W 3 - 0	Kelly 46 Shilton 48 **Brown** 90	10
42	15		A	Northwich Victoria	1250	L 0 - 2		11
43	17		H	Leigh RMI	461	W 5 - 1	Jackson 28 Kelly 58 63 Lewis 65 **Brown** 75	10
44	22		H	Vauxhall Motors	651	W 2 - 1	Lenton 70 **Brown** 74	10
45	29		A	Nuneaton Borough	1301	L 0 - 2		10

Ave. League Home Attendance: 669   **Goals** 64 64   **Top Goalscorer:** Brown (11)
Best Position: 6th   **Worst:** 15th

HUCKNALL TOWN

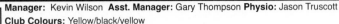

Manager: Kevin Wilson **Asst. Manager:** Gary Thompson **Physio:** Jason Truscott

Club Colours: Yellow/black/yellow

Change Colours: Sky blue/claret/sky blue

Club Sponsor: Daniel Stewart

Previous League: Unibond Northern Premier

Best Seasons: Lg: 10th Natonwide North 2004-05 **F.A.Trophy.:** Finalists 2004-05

F.A. Cup: 4th Qualifying Rd. 2000-02 and 2001-02 **F.A.Vase:** 6th Rd 1985-86

Ground address: Watnall Road, Hucknall, Notts NG15 6EY

Tel. No: 0115 956 1253 **Club Website:** www.hucknalltownfc.co.uk

Capacity: 3,013 **Seats:** 500 **Covered:** 900 **Floodlights:**Yes

Simple Directions: M1 Jct 27. A608 to lights, right onto A611 to Hucknall. Right at roundabout (new by-pass) over next roundabout and right into Watnall Road at next roundabout. Ground on right.

Midweek Home Matchday: Tuesday

Clubhouse: Open mid day and evenings daily

Club Shop: Yes. Contact: Lynne & Maurice Taylor and Lynda Lathall 0115 9630206

Local Press: Hucknall & Bulwell Dispatch, Nottingham Evening Post and Nottingham Football Post.

CLUB PERSONNEL

Chairman: Brian Holmes
Vice Chairman: David Gamble
President: Glen Lathall
Hon President: Andy Stewart
General Manager: David Green
Secretary: Brian Scothern, 95 Brookfield Avenue, Shortwood Estate, Hucknall, Notts. NG15 6FF
Tel No: 07801 976175(M)
Press Officer: Andy Donaldson

Programme Editor: Drew Baker
Tel No: 07811 117789
Programme: 32 Pages £ 2.00
2005-2006 Captain: Chris Timons
Top Goalscorer: Robert Gill

CLUB STATISTICS

Record	**Attendance:** 1,841 v Bishop's Stortford F.A.Trophy S-Final 2004-05
	Victory: 12-1 v Teversal Notts Sen. Cup 89-90
	Defeat:
Career Goalscorer:	Maurice Palethorpe approx. 400 (1980-90)
Career Appearances:	Dave McCarthy 282 Paul Tomlinson 240
Record Transfer Fee	**Paid:**
	Received: £10,000 from Brentford for Stuart Nelson 2003-2004
Senior Honours:	F.A.Trophy Runners Up 2004-2005, N.P.L. Champions 2003-2004, N.Co.E Champions 1997-1998, Lg Cup (3) N.Co East Div 1 R-up 91-92 Central Midland Lg 1989-90 1990-91 R-up 91-92 Central Midlands League Cup Winners (3) Notts Sen Cup (5) R-up (5)
Previous Leaguess:	Bulwell & Dist.46-59 60-65, Central Alliance: 59-60, Notts Spartan 65-70 , Central Midlands 89-92, Northern Counties East 92-97 and N.P.L. 97-2004

HUCKNALL TOWN

BEST LGE ATT.: 909 v Alfreton Town
LOWEST: **221** v Barrow

No.	Date	Comp	H/A	Opponents	Att:	Result	Goalscorers	Pos
1	Aug 13	CN	A	Stafford Rangers	634	L 0 - 2		22
2	16		H	Harrogate Town	520	W 4 - 0	Gill 50 80 Cooke 58 Groves 75	7
3	20		H	Workington	421	W 1 - 0	Smith 7	5
4	27		A	Hinckley United	617	L 1 - 3	Rowland 13	8
5	29		H	Barrow	221	W 2 - 1	McSweeney 17 Nangle 85	6
6	Sept 3		A	Droylsden	336	W 3 - 2	Palmer 28 McSweeney 61 (pen) 65	4
7	10		A	Worcester City	734	W 1 - 0	Smith 77	3
8	17		H	Nuneaton Borough	625	L 0 - 2		6
9	24	FAC 2Q	A	Nantwich Town	190	W 1 - 0	Gill 51	
10	Oct 1	CN	H	Moor Green	386	D 2 - 2	Ricketts 12 Gill 69	8
11	8	FAC 3Q	H	Cammell Laird	292	D 2 - 2	Ward 2 Gill 65	
12	11	FAC 3Qr	A	Cammell Laird	380	W 1 - 0	Nangle 67	
13	15	CN	A	Worksop Town	501	L 1 - 2	Nangle 66	10
14	18		A	Kettering Town	1067	D 0 - 0		10
15	22	FAC 4Q	H	Burscough	690	D 0 - 0		
16	25	FAC4Qr	A	Burscough	415	L 2 - 6	Timons 41 Gill 44	
17	29	CN	H	Northwich Victoria	620	W 3 - 2	Groves 3 (3 9 56)	
18	Nov 5		A	Vauxhall Motors	200	W 2 - 0	Brazier 5 (og) Gill 80	5
19	8		A	Hednesford Town	434	D 1 - 1	Ward 70	4
20	12		H	Gainsborough Trinity	407	W 4 - 1	Gill 45 60 (pen) Ward 26 Ricketts 82	4
21	19		A	Stalybridge Celtic	561	L 1 - 2	Ward 32	6
22	26	FAT 3Q	H	Northwich Victoria	439	D 0 - 0		
23	29	FAT 3Qr	A	Northwich Victoria	500	L 1 2	Sucharewycz 35	
24	Dec 3	CN	H	Redditch United	397	W 4 - 0	Necthorpe 12 70 Ward 20 65	
25	10		H	Lancaster City	404	D 0 - 0		4
26	17		H	Hyde United	337	L 1 - 3	Ward 47	5
27	26		A	Alfreton Town	564	D 1 - 1	Ricketts 90	4
28	30		A	Leigh RMI	181	L 1 2	Gill 60	4
29	Jan 2		H	Alfreton Town	909	W 1 - 0	Ricketts 78	5
30	7		H	Stafford Rangers	601	L 0 - 2		5
31	14		A	Harrogate Town	515	L 0 - 1		5
32	21		A	Workington	580	D 1 - 1	Rowland 2	6
33	28		H	Hinckley United	459	L 0 - 2		8
34	Feb 4		A	Moor Green	221	W 4 - 2	Gill 7 64 Morris 82 Groves 90	7
35	11		H	Worksop Town	480	D 0 - 0		7
36	18		H	Hyde United	501	D 0 - 0		8
37	21		H	Kettering Town	508	W 1 - 0	Harding 90	8
38	25		A	Worcester City	360	L 1 - 2	Pearson 45	11
39	Mar 4		A	Nuneaton Borough	1012	D 2 - 2	Morris 31 (pen) Francis 90	9
40	7		H	Hednrsford Town	281	D 2 - 2	Harding 45 Morris 74	7
41	11		A	Northwich Victoria	1020	L 0 - 2		10
42	18		H	Vauxhall Motors	271	L 1 2 2	Frew 6	13
43	25		A	Gainsborough Trinity	335	L 2 3 3	Frew 2 56	13
44	April 1		H	Stalybridge Celtic	394	W 2 - 1	Ricketts 51 Colkin 69 (pen)	13
45	8		A	Redditch United	323	D 1 - 1	Nangle 90	13
46	15		H	Droylsden	356	W 2 - 0	Nangle 21 Hollis 71	12
47	17		A	Barrow	689	L 0 - 2		12
48	22		H	Leigh RMI	304	D 2 - 2	Ricketts 80 90	13
49	29		A	Lancaster City	353	W 1 - 0	Ricketts 48	12

Ave. League Home Attendance: 411   **Goals** 63 63   **Top Goalscorer:** Gill (12)
Best Position: 3rd   **Worst:** 22nd

HYDE UNITED

Founded: 1919
Nickname: The Tigers

Manager: Steve Waywell   **Physio:** Gary Thompson
Club Groundsman: Charles Skatchell N.P.L.& National FA Groundsman of 2005
Club Colours: Red/white/red
Change Colours: Lime green/blue/lime green
Club Sponsor: A.T.S. Plumbing Supplies/Highwire
Previous League: Northern Premier League
Best Performances:League: N.P. L. Champions 2004-2005
League: F.A. Cup: 1st Rd 1954-5 1983-4 1994-5
F.A.Trophy.: Semi-Final 1988-9 1994-5 1995-6
Midweek Home Matchday: Monday
Ground address: Tameside Stadium, Ewen Fields,Walker Lane, Hyde
SK14 2SB Tel No: 0161 368 1031
Official website: www.hydeunited.co.uk
Capacity: 4,250   **Seats:** 660   **Covered:** 2,000   **Floodlights**: Yes
Simple Directions: On entering Hyde follow signs for Tameside Leisure Park. In
Walker Lane take second car park entrance near Leisure Pool and follow road
around pool. Quarter of a mile from Newton(BR).Train from Manchester(15min)
Club Shop: Full range of club accessories
Local Radio: Key 103 and BBC Radio Manchester
Local Press: Tameside Advertiser and Hyde Reporter

CLUB PERSONNEL
Chairman: Stephen Hartley
Secretary: Tony Beard,
30 Fishermans Close, Winterley,
Sandbach, Cheshire. CW11 4SW
Tel No.& Fax: 01270 212473
Commercial Manager:
Paul Harrop (0161 368 1031)
Public Relations Officer:
Frances Featherstone
Tel No: 0161 368 3252
Programme Editor: Mark Dring
Tel No: 0161 336 8076
Programme: 32 pages. Price: £1.00

2005-2006
Captain: M.Flynn
Player of the Year: M.Flynn
Top Goalscorer:D.Johnson

CLUB STATISTICS

Record	**Attendance**: 9,500 v Nelson F.A.Cup 1952
	Victory: 9-1 v South Liverpool
	Defeat: 0-26 v P.N.E. F.A..Cup as Hyde F.C.
	Career Goalscorer: P.O'Brien
	Career Appearances: S.Johnson 623
Record Transfer Fee	**Paid**: £8,000 to Mossley for Jim McCluskie 1989
	Received: £ 50,000 from Crewe Alexandra for Colin Little 1995
Senior Honours:	Champions N.P.L. 04-05, N.P.L. R-up (2), Lg Cup (3), N.I P. Div 1 Champions
	2003-2004, Cheshire Senior Cup (7), Manchester Premier Cup (5)
Previous Leagues:	Lancs & Cheshire 1919-21 Manchester 21-30 Cheshire County 30-68 70-82
	Northern Premier League 68-70 83-2004

Back row, left to right: Nicky Hill, Paul Jones, Matty McNeil, Chris Lynch, John O'Kane, Mark Westhead, Dale Johnson,Craig Dudley, Lincoln Adams and Steve Waywell (Manager). Front row: Phil Salt, Simon Garner, Steve Brackenridge, Gerry Harrison, Wayne Dean, Paul Armstrong and David Moore.

HYDE UNITED

BEST LGE ATT.: 1,087 v Stalybridge Celtic
LOWEST: 261 v Moor Green

No.	Date	Comp	H/A	Opponents	Att:	Result	Goalscorers	Pos
1	Aug 13	CN	A	Harrogate Town	371	L 0 - 1		20
2	15		H	Workington	422	D 1 - 1	Johnson 9	18
3	20		H	Stafford Rangers	412	L 1 - 3	Brackenbridge 36	22
4	27		A	Ketteriing Town	905	L 2 - 3	Johnson 6 McNeill 87	22
5	29		H	Alfreton Town	433	L 2 - 3	Salt 41 Brackenbridge 88	22
6	Sept 3		A	Barrow	920	D 2 - 2	O'Kane 89 McNeill 90	22
7	10		A	Worksop Town	276	D 1 - 1	Milligan 69	21
8	17		H	Gainsborough Trinity	416	W 2 - 0	Milligan 3 McNeil 55	18
9	24	FAC 2Q	H	Lancaster City	333	W 2 - 1	Johnson 10 Jones 20	
10	Oct 1	CN	A	Nuneaton Borough	1113	L 0 - 1		22
11	8	FAC 3Q	H	Barrow	469	L 2 - 3	Johnson 3 Clee 37	
12	15	CN	H	Lancaster City	351	L 2 - 4	McNeil 10 Johnson 30	22
13	17		H	Droylsden	633	D 2 - 2	Tolson 52 McNeill 54	20
14	22		H	Worksop Town	313	D 1 - 1	Adams 30	20
15	29		H	Redditch United	422	L 1 - 3	Brackenbridge 54	21
16	Nov 5		A	Gaimsborough Trinity	429	W 3 - 0	Tolson 65 Milligan 79 Adams 73	18
17	12		H	Leigh RMI	436	D 3 - 3	Tolson 7 64 McNeil 26	
18	19		A	Hinckley United	529	L 1 - 2	Harrison 79	20
19	26	FAT 3Q	H	Stalybridge Celtic	906	L 1 - 5	Lynch 89	
20	Dec 2	CN	H	Hednesford Town	334	W 4 - 2	Harrison 20 Johnson 43 90 Wharton 58	17
21	6		A	Vauxhall Motors	188	W 2 - 0	Wharton 30 Dean 60	16
22	10		A	Moor Green	177	W 2 - 1	Dean 67 Johnson 77	15
23	17		A	Hucknall Town	337	W 3 - 1	Wharton 45 Johnson 70 Dean 78	12
24	26		H	Stalybridge Celtic	1087	L 1 - 3	Johnson 63	14
25	31		H	Worcester City	401	W 4 - 0	Wharton 23 41 (pen) McNeil 87 Clee 90	10
26	Jan 2		A	Stalybridge Celtic	1243	W 2 - 1	McNeil 84 90	9
27	7		H	Harrogate Town	404	W 3 - 1	Clee 60 Johnson 74 Dean 77	6
28	14		A	Workington	491	L 0 - 1		8
29	21		A	Stafford Rangers	935	L 0 - 1		10
30	28		H	Kettering Town	520	W 3 - 0	Dean 18 Wharton 74 McNeil 83	6
31	Feb 4		H	Nuneaton Borough	507	W 1 - 0	Harrison 20	6
32	7		A	Northwich Victoria	850	W 2 - 1	Johnson 7 57	5
33	11		A	Lancaster City	352	W 3 - 1	Caldecott 25 Wharton 35 (pen) Johnson 60	5
34	18		H	Hucknall Town	501	D 0 - 0		5
35	20		A	Droylsden	761	L 0 - 1		5
36	Mar 6		H	Vauxhall Motors	301	L 2 - 3	Jones 64 Quayle 86	6
37	11		A	Redditch United	339	D 1 - 1	Jones 78	6
38	18		A	Northwich Victoria	667	L 1 - 3	Clee 36	8
39	25		A	Leigh RMI	195	D 1 - 1	Tolson 90	8
40	April 1		H	Hinckley United	402	L 0 - 1		11
41	8		A	Hednesford Town	362	W 2 - 0	Hanley 5 Tolson 58	11
42	14		H	Barrow	503	D 2 - 2	Tolson 35 44	10
43	17		A	Alfreton Town	281	L 0 - 2		11
44	22		A	Worcester City	803	D 2 - 2	Brackenbridge 12 Tolson 57	12
45	29		H	Moor Green	261	W 3 - 2	Harrison 18 Tolson 45 Quayle 66	11

Ave. League Home Attendance: 463   **Goals** 73 70   **Top Goalscorer:** Johnson (14)
Best Position: 5th   **Worst:** 22nd

KETTERING TOWN

Founded: 1872
Nickname: The Poppies

PRE-SEASON FRIENDLIES 2005 - 06

Manager: Morell Maison **Physio:** Chris Palmer and Kevin Grundy

Club Colours: Red/red/white

Change Colours: Yellow/blue/white

Club Sponsor: Weldon Plant Ltd.

Previous League: Conference League:

Best Performances: League: Runners-Up in Conference (4)

F.A. Cup: 4th Rd 1988-89   **F.A.Trophy.:** Runners-Up 78-9 99-00

Ground address: Rockingham Road, Kettering, Northants NN16 9AW

Tel Nos: 01536 83028 (club /410815 (office) 01536 412273 (Fax)

Official website: www.ketteringtownafc.co.uk

Capacity: 6,170 **Seats:** 1,800   **Covered:** 4,000   **Floodlights:**Yes

Simple Directions: A43 to Kettering from M1 jct 15. Use A14 to jct 7 follow A43 to Corby/Stamford to 1st roundabout, turn right onto A6003 and ground is half a mile. From North M1 or M6 use jct 19 then to A 14 jct 7 as above.

Midweek Home Matchday: Tuesday

Club Shop: Open before and after matches. Also Alex Elmore's in town centre

Local Radio: Northampton, Northants 96 Connect F.M.

Local Press: Evening Telegraph, Chronicle & Echo, Herald & Post & The Citizen

CLUB PERSONNEL

Chairman: Imraan Ladak
V-Chairman: Michael Leech
President: Syd Chapman
Managing Editor: Kevin Meikle
Commercial Manageress:
Nicky Harris
Secretary & Press Officer:
Mike Chase
Programme: 52 pages. Price £2.00

2005-2006
Captain: Craig McIlwain
Player of the Year: Mark Osborn
Top Goalscore: Christian Moore 12

CLUB STATISTICS

RECORD

Attendance: 11,536 v Peterborough F.A.Cup 1st Round Replay 1958-1959
Victory: 16-0 v Higham YMCI (F.A.Cup 1909)
Defeat: 0-13 v Mardy Southern Lg Div 2 1911-12
Career Goalscorer: Roy Clayton 171 (1972-810
Career Appearances: Roger Ashby
Record Transfer Fee Paid: £25,000 to Macclesfield for Carl Alford. in1994
Received: £150,000 from Newcastle United for Andy Hunt

Senior Honours: Premier Inter League Cup , F.A.Trophy R-up (2) Conference R-up (4)
Southern Lg Champions (4) Northants Senior Cup (28)

Previous Leagues: Northants League, Midland League, Birmingham League, Central Alliance
United Counties, Southern League, Conference 79-01 02-03
Grounds: North Park and Green Lane

Kettering Town FC 2005/06

Back Row L-R: Brett Selkhon,Rob Gould,Craig McIlwain,Mark Osborn,Rob McNey,Derek Brown,Daniel Thompson,Ian Robertson.
Middle Row: Misty (Coach),Ollie Burgess,James Gould,Junior McDougald,Wayne Diuk,Neil Midgley,Jonathan Bowers,Chris Palmer (Physio).

KETTERING TOWN

BEST LGE ATT.: 2,060 v Droylsden
LOWEST: 817 v Worksop Town

No.	Date	Comp	H/A	Opponents	Att:	Result	Goalscorers	Pos
1	Aug 13	CN	H	Worcester City	962	W 2 - 1	**Moore** 18 48	3
2	16		A	Moor Green	359	D 1 - 1	**Moore** 16	6
3	20		A	Lancaster City	317	W 1 - 0	Patterson 70	4
4	27		H	Hyde United	905	W 3 - 2	Burgess 24 **Moore** 45 61	3
5	29		A	Nuneaton Borough	1049	D 2 - 2	Midgley 12 Difante 90	2
6	Sept 3		H	Worksop Town	817	W 1 - 0	Hall 10	2
7	10		H	Stafford Rangers	966	L 0 - 1		2
8	17		A	Harrogate Town	437	D 1 - 1	**Moore** 73 (pen)	5
9	24	FAC 2Q	H	**Stafford Rangers**	971	W 1 - 0	Moore 68	
10	Oct 1	CN	A	Northwich Victoria	909	L 1 - 3	Burgess 70	9
11	8	FAC 3Q	A	**St.Albans City**	882	**D 0 - 0**		
12	11	FAC 3Qr	H	St Albans City	1220	W 4 - 0	**BURGESS 3 (20 48 70) Gould 25**	
13	15	CN	H	Leigh RMI	1211	W 4 - 0	Midgley 11 82 (pen) Burgess 65 (pen) Patterson 77	5
14	19		H	Hucknall Town	1067	D 0 - 0		5
15	22	FAC 4Q	H	**Gravesend & Northfleet**	1647	W 3 - 0	**Gould 58 Hall 65 Midgley 75**	
16	29	CN	H	Droylsden	2060	W 1 - 0	Moore 62	4
17	Nov 5	FAC 1R	H	**Stevenage Borough**	4548	L 1 - 3	Midgley 14	
18	12	CN	H	Stalybridge Celtic	1478	W 4 - 1	Gould 18 80 Theobald 30 Burgess 48	6
19	14		A	Hednesford Town	992	D 2 - 2	Morris 42 Gould 67	5
20	19		A	Vauxhall Motors	383	D 1 - 1	Duffy 14	5
21	22		A	Redditch United	752	L 1 - 2	Gould 89	5
22	Dec 3		H	Barrow	1272	L 1 - 3	**Moore** 71 (pen)	6
23	6		A	Alfreton Town	575	D 1 - 1	**Moore** 44	6
24	10		A	Workington	437	L 2 - 3	**Moore** 17 Nicoll 78	6
25	17	FAT 1	H	**Farsley Celtic**	964	W 2 - 1	Patterson 80 Moore 90 (pen)	
26	24	CN	H	Hinckley United	1444	D 2 - 2	Solkhon 64 Lewis 80	7
27	Jan 2		A	Hinckley United	1322	D 1 - 1	Midgley 86 (pen)	8
28	7		A	Worcester City	867	L 0 - 2		12
29	14	FAT 2	A	**Dagenham & Redbridge**	931	L 1 - 2	**Burgess 19**	
30	21	CN	H	Lancaster City	1592	W 2 1 1	Elding 12 Zico-Black 36	9
31	24		H	Moor Green	1108	L 0 - 3		11
32	28		A	Hyde United	520	L 0 - 3		13
33	Feb 4		H	Northwich Victoria	1154	W 2 - 0	Midgley 32 Elding 33	10
34	11		A	Leigh RMI	225	W 2 - 0	Midgley 25 Theobald 75	8
35	18		H	Hednesford Town	1282	W 4 - 0	Barrow54 (og) Theobald 56 77 Midgley 68	7
36	21		A	Hucknall Town	508	D 1 - 1	Timons (og) 15	7
37	28		H	Gainsborough Trinity	906	L 1 - 2	Midgley 12	7
38	Mar 4		H	Harogate Town	1238	L 0 - 2		7
39	11		A	Droylsden	419	L 1 - 3	Burgess 7	12
40	18		H	Redditch United	911	W 4 - 0	Midgley 44 Elding 58 King 63 (og) Black 84	9
41	25		A	Stalybridge Celtic	589	L 0 - 3		11
42	28		A	Stafford Rangers	745	W 3 - 1	Hall 42 Koo-Boothe 50 Black 87	8
43	April 1		H	Vauxhall Motors	1008	W 1 - 0	Solkhon 45	6
44	8		A	Barrow	801	W 1 - 0	Elding 18	7
45	11		H	Alfreton Town	918	W 1 - 0	Theobald 84	6
46	15		A	Worksop Town	468	L 1 - 2	Makofo 29	7
47	17		H	Nuneaton Borough	1205	W 3 - 0	Burgess 18 Okai 30 Lynch 67	6
48	22		A	Gainsborough trinity	457	W 2 - 0	Black 9 Koo-Boothe 63	6
49	29		H	Workinngton	974	W 2 - 1	Peters 8 Okai 31	6

Ave. League Home Attendance: 1166   **Goals** 75 57   **Top Goalscorer:** Moore (12)
Best Position: 2nd   **Worst:** 13th

LANCASTER CITY

Founded: 1905
Nickname: Dolly Blues

Manager: Gary Finlay   **Assistant Manager:** Mickey Melon   **Physios**: Wayne Gill
Club Colours: Royal Blue/White/Royal Blue
Change Colours: White/navy blue/white
Club Sponsors: Carling and Sports Direct UK
Previous League: Northern Premier
Best Seasons: League: 13th Conference North 2004-2005
F.A. Cup: 2nd Rd 46-47,72-73   **F.A.Trophy.:** 3rd Rd. 74-75 75-76
F.A.Vase : 2nd Rd 86-87 90-91
Ground address: Giant Axe, West Road, Lancaster LA1 5PE
Tel No: 01524 382238   **e-mail:** lancastercity @tiscali.co.uk
Capacity: 3,064   **Seats:** 513   **Covered:** 900   **Floodlights:** Yes
Simple Directions: M6 jct 33 follow into city, left at lights immediately after Waterstones bookshop. Second right past railway station on right, follow down hill and ground is first right.

Midweek Home Matchday: Tuesday

Clubhouse: The Dolly Blue Tavern just outside the ground. Manager:Lynne Upjohn
Club Shop: Yes
Local Press: Lancaster Guardian, Morecambe Visitor, Lancashire Evening Post and Lancaster Citizen.
Local Radio: Red Rose, Radio Lancaster and Bay Radio.

CLUB PERSONNEL
Chairman: Charles Moore
Vice Chairman: Andrew Page
President: Malcolm Woodhouse
Vice President: John Bagguley
Chief Executive: Michael Parkinson
Commercial Director:
Chris Niichols (0772706 2799)
Secretary: Barry Newsham
Tel No: 01524 32430
email:barry.newsham@tiscali.co.uk
Commercial Manager & Prog Ed.:
Les Taylor (01524 841710)
Club statistician: John Downham
Tel No: 01413001332
Programme
40pages. Price: £1.50
2005-2006
Player of the Year: Alex Taylor
Top Goalscorer: Alex Taylor 19

CLUB STATISTICS

Record	**Attendance**: 7,500 v Carlisle United F.A.Cup 1936
Victory:	8-0 v Leyland Motors(A) 83-84
Defeat:	0-10 v Matlock Town NPL Div 1 73-74
Career Goalscorer:	David Barnes 130
Career Appearances:	Edgar J.Parkinson 591
Record Transfer Fee	**Paid**: £6,000 to Droylsden for Jamie Tandy
	Received: £25.000 from Birmingham City for Chris Ward
Senior Honours:	N.P.L. Division One Champions 1995-96, Lancashire Junior Cup
	(ATS Challenge Trophy): 27-8 28-9 30-1 33-4 51-2 74-5 R-up (5)
Previous Leagues:	Lancs Comb. 05-70 NPL 70-82, NW Co 82-87 NPL 87-04

Back Row (L-R): Nick Rogan, Danny Mahoney, Andy Scott, Iain Swan, Anthony McMillan, Ryan Yeomans, Steve Jones, Joe McMahon, Tony Sullivan, Ian Dawes. **Front Row:** Ryan Elderton, Ryan-Zico Black, Gary Bauress, Peter Ward (Assist. Manager), Phil Wilson (Manager), Liam Enwright (Physio), Neil Uberschar, Alex Taylor, Mike Eckersley.

LANCASTER CITY

BEST LGE ATT.: 702 v Barrow
LOWEST: **192** v Harrogate Town

No.	Date	Comp	H/A	Opponents	Att:	Result	Goalscorers	Pos
1	Aug 13	NN	A	Hinckley United	559	D 3 - 3	Rogan 22 **Taylor** 54 Dawes 59 (pen)	9
2	16		H	Stalybridge Celtic	346	D 2 - 2	**Taylor** 21 63	13
3	20		H	Kettering Town	317	L 0 - 1		18
4	27		A	Redditch United	562	W 1 - 0	McMahon 19	12
5	29		H	Stafford Rangers	375	D 1 - 1	Rogan 61	12
6	Sept 3		A	Alfreton Town	279	W 2 - 0	Rogan 63 **Taylor** 85	8
7	10		A	Nuneaton Borough	716	L 0 - 3		12
8	17		H	Worksop Town	257	W 2 - 1	Morris 59 Elderton 64	11
9	24	FAC 2Q	A	Hyde United	333	L 1 - 2	Taylor 16	
10	Oct 1	NN	H	Worcester City	282	D 0 - 0		10
11	15		A	Hyde United	351	W 4 - 2	Black 43 51 Rogan 83 90	9
12	18		A	Workington	479	D 1 - 1	McMahon 34	9
13	22		H	Moor Green	293	D 3 - 3	**Taylor** 4 58 Black 15	7
14	29		H	Vauxhall Motors	281	W 1 - 0	**Taylor** 42	6
15	Nov 12		H	Northwich Victoria	513	L 1 - 2	Black 39	10
16	19		A	Gainsborough Trinity	306	L 0 - 1		11
17	26	FAT 3Q	H	Workington	206	D 0 - 0		
18	Dec 3	NN	H	Droylsden	271	D 2 - 2	McMahon 85 Pope 90	11
19	6	FAT 3Q r	A	Workington	328	W 2 - 1	Pope 61 Howson 79	
20	10	NN	A	Hucknall Town	404	D 0 - 0		12
21	17	FAT 1	A	Stafford Rangers	646	L 2 - 4	Taylor 6 Howson 64	
22	26	NN	H	Barrow	702	W 3 - 0	Pope 11 43 **Taylor** 78	10
23	Jan 2		A	Barrow	1301	W 4 - 1	Bond 9 **Taylor** 23 McMahon 74 Pope 87	12
24	7		H	Hinckley United	264	D 2 - 2	McMahon 85 **Taylor** 86	10
25	10		A	Leigh RMI	225	W 2 - 1	Pope 3 Bond 37	6
26	21		A	Kettering Town	1592	L 0 - 2		8
27	23		A	Hednesford Town	438	L 0 - 1		9
28	28		H	Redditch United	259	W 1 - 0	Taylor 69	7
29	Feb 4		A	Worcester City	745	L 0 - 2		9
30	11		H	Hyde United	352	L 1 - 3	Taylor 62	11
31	18		A	Moor Green	216	L 1 - 2	Bond 72	14
32	25		H	Nuneaton Borough	403	D 1 - 1	Taylor 68	15
33	Mar 7		H	Leigh RMI	246	W 2 - 0	Eckersley 5 Patterson 78	14
34	11		A	Vauxnhall Motors	220	L 0 - 1		14
35	18		H	Hednesford Town	259	W 1 - 0	Eckersley 62	14
36	25		A	Northwich Victoria	1027	L 2 - 3	Bond 58 **Taylor** 80	15
37	April 1		H	Gainsborough Trinity	229	L 2 - 3	**Taylor** 20 Bailey 67	15
38	6		H	Harrogate Town	192	W 2 - 1	**Taylor** 14 55	14
39	8		A	Droylsden	319	L 1 - 6	Brown 35	14
40	13		A	Stalybridge Celtic	308	L 1 - 2	Elderton 61	14
41	15		H	Alfreton Town	254	D 2 - 2	Bailey 82 Jones 86	14
42	17		A	Staffortd Rangers	949	L 0 - 3		15
43	20		A	Workington	265	L 0 - 1		15
44	22		A	Harrogate Town	435	L 1 - 3	Elderton 55 (pen)	15
45	25		A	Worksop Town	315	L 0 - 2		15
46	29		H	Hucknall Town	353	L 0 - 1		15

Ave. League Home Attendance: 320   **Goals** 57 72   **Top Goalscorer:** Taylor (19)
Best Position: 6th   **Worst:** 18th

LEIGH RMI

Founded:1896
Nickname: Railwaymen

Manager: Andy.Nelson   **Assistant Manager:** S.Humphrey   **Physio:** A.Bent
Club Colours: Red & white stripes/black/black
Change Colours: All Yellow
Club Sponsor: VC Betts.co.uk
Previous League: Conference
Previous Grounds: Grundy Hill, Horwich until 1994
Best Seasons: League: 5th Conference 2000-01   **F.A.Trophy.:** 6th Rd 90-91
F.A. Cup: 1st Rd 28-29 82-83 98-99 00-01
Ground address: Hilton Park, Kirkhall Lane, Leigh WN7 1RN
Tel No: 01942 743743   Fax: 01942 768856
Website: http://www.leigh-rmi.co.uk
Capacity: 8,000   **Seats:** 2,000   **Covered:** 4,000   **Floodlights:** Yes
Simple Directions: At traffic lights with Asda on left in Leigh town centre, turn right
and right again into Glebe Street. Then right into Chadwick Street and ground is
straight ahead.
Midweek Home Matchday: Tuesday

CLUB PERSONNEL
Chairman: William Taylor
V-Chairman: Alan Leach
Directors: L.Berry, K Freer,
M.Peck, S.Walker, A.Hogan,
G.Culshaw and P.Lowe
Secretary: Alan Robinson, 55
Janice Drive, Fulwood, Preston,
Lancs PR2 9TY
Tel No: 01772 719266 (H)
07974 651231 (M)
Press Officer: Secretary
Programme Editor: Secretary

2005-2006
Captain: R.Roscoe
Player of the Year:
Top Goalscorer: C.Simm

Clubhouse: Open matchdays and pre match meals can be ordered
Club Shop: At the ground
Local Radio: Radio Lancs, Red Rose Radio and G.M. R.
Local Press: Bolton Evening News

CLUB STATISTICS

Record	**Attendance:** 8,500 v Wigan Athletic, Lancs Jnr.Cup 1954
	Victory: 19-1 Nelson. Lancs Comb. 1964
	Defeat: 1-9 v Brandon United F.A.Cup
Career Goalscorer:	Neil McLachlan
Career Appearances:	Neil McLachlan
Record Transfer Fee	**Paid:** £6,000 to Prescot Cables for Peter Cumiskey
	Received: £75,000 from Crewe Alexandra for Steve Jones
Senior Honours:	N.P.L. Champions 1999-2000, N.P.L. League Cup 99-00,
	Div 1 R-Up 96-97, Lancs F.A.Cup 84-85 and Lancs Trophy 02-03
Previous Leagues:	Lancs Alliance 1891-97, Lancs Lg 1897-1900, Lancs Comb., 17-18 19-39
	46- 68, Cheshire Co 68-82, N.W.Co 82-83 N.P.L. 83-2000

Back Row (L-R): Asst. Kit Man, Kit Man, C Gaunt, M Moran, B Ashmole, N Smith, D Morton, I Martin, C Simm,
C Lane, K Rose, B Miller, Physio, Asst. Physio.
Front Row: G Tench, G Holmes, S Smith, G Stoker, P Starbuck (Manager), G Kelly (Asst. Manager), A Meechan, W
Peyton, C Mitchell, C Adams.

LEIGH RMI

BEST LGE ATT.: 801 v Workington
LOWEST: **125** v Gainsborough Trinity

No.	Date	Comp	H/A	Opponents	Att:	Result	Goalscorers	Pos
1	Aug 13	CN	A	Redditch United	316	W 2 - 1	Simm 44 56	4
2	16		H	Droylsden	245	L 0 - 1		8
3	20		H	Stalybridge Celtic	317	W 2 - 1	Roscoe 90 Smith 90	7
4	27		A	Barrow	107	L 1 - 3	McDowell 23	9
5	29		H	Hinckley United	232	W 1 - 0	Stoker 70	7
6	Sept 3		A	Gainsborough Trinity	259	L 1 - 2	Roscoe 12	11
7	10		A	Vauxhall Mtors	155	D 4 - 4	Shillito 20 Smith 26 Coybne 35 McDowell 73	11
8	17		H	Hednesford Town	301	D 0 - 0		12
9	24	FAC 2Q	A	**Chester le Street**	193	W 3 - 1	Simm 23 N.Smith 71 Thompson 90	
10	Oct 1	CN	H	Workington	801	W 0 - 1		12
11	8	FAC 3Q	H	**Gainsborough Trinity**	165	D 1 - 1	Smith 25	
12	11	FAC 3Qr	A	**Gainsborough Trinity**	361	L 1 - 2	Smith	
13	15	CN	A	Kettering Town	1211	L 0 - 4		15
14	18		A	Alfreton Town	224	D 1 - 1	Coyne 31	14
15	22		H	Stafford Rangers	301	L 1 - 3	Simm 46	16
16	29		A	Moor Green	170	L 1 - 4	Midworth 41 (og)	17
17	Nov 5		H	Worksop Town	186	L 0 - 1		17
18	12		A	Hyde United	436	D 3 - 3	Simm 12 80 McDowell 65	
19	26	FAT 3Q	H	**Stafford Rangers**	165	L 1 - 4	Simm 23	
20	Dec 10	CN	A	Northwich Victoria	755	L 0 - 1		21
21	26		H	Harrogate Town	177	W 3 - 1	Simm 3 (75 pen 88 pen 90)	19
22	30		H	Hucknall Town	181	W 2 1	Willis 34 43	17
23	Jan 2		A	Harrogate Town	428	L 0 - 3		17
24	7		H	Redditch United	178	W 2 - 1	Willis 19 45	17
25	10		H	Lancaster City	225	L 1 - 2	Simm	18
26	14		A	Droylsden	370	L 1 - 4	McDowell 83	18
27	21		A	Stalybridge Celtic	560	L 1 - 6	Willis 19	20
28	24		H	Nuneaton Town	201	W 1 - 0	Willis 50	19
29	28		H	Barrow	301	D 1 - 1	Simm 50	18
30	Feb 4		A	Workington	502	D 0 - 0		18
31	11		H	Kettering Town	225	L 0 - 2		18
32	13		A	Worcester City	818	L 0 - 2		18
33	18		A	Stafford Rangers	1035	D 0 - 0		19
34	21		H	Alfreton Town	200	D 0 - 0		19
35	24		H	Vauxhall Motors	185	D 1 - 1	Hay 47	18
36	Mar 7		A	Lancaster City	246	L 0 - 2		19
37	11		A	Moor Green	175	L 1 - 3	Wilkinson 73	20
38	18		A	Worksop Town	296	D 3 - 3	Simm 56 (pen) 80 Williams 72	20
39	25		H	Hyde United	195	D 1 - 1	Roscoe 72	21
40	April 1		A	Nuneaton Borough	1082	L 1 - 3	Williams 52	21
41	3		A	Hednesford Town	492	W 3 - 1	Willis 31Smith 38 Roscoe 80	20
42	8		H	Worcester City	185	L 1 - 4	Smith 4	21
43	15		H	Gainsborough Trinity	125	D 0 - 0		21
44	17		A	Hinckley United	461	L 1 - 5	Williams 85	21
45	22		A	Hucknall Town	304	D 2 - 2	McGrath 32 Smith 40	20
46	29		H	Northwich Victoria	629	W 2 - 1	Willis 30 Simm 65	20

Ave. League Home Attendance: 265   **Goals** 51 87   **Top Goalscorer:** Simm (15)
Best Position: 4th   **Worst:** 21st

MOOR GREEN

Founded: 1901
Nickname: The Moors

Manager: Bob Faulkner   **Asst.Manager:** John Frain   **Coach:** Rob Elmes

Club Colours: Navy Blue with sky blue band

Change Colours: Yellow & Green

Club Sponsors: Alexander Forbes Insurance

Previous League: Southern

Best Seasons: League: 9th Conference North 2005-2006

F.A. Cup: 1st Round 79-80., 02-03   **F.A.Trophy:** 1st Round 90-91 96-97

Coaches: John Frain & Rob Elms   **Physio:** Peter Denham & Steve Shipway

Ground address: Ground Sharing with Solihull Borough for season 2005-2006 So match day telephone number is: 01217056770

Capacity: 3,250   **Seats:** 250   **Covered:** 1,200   **Floodlights:** Yes

Simple Directions: Sherwood Road is off Highfield Road which is the A34 Birmingham - Stratford road

Midweek Home Matchday: Tuesday

Clubhouse: Two bars open nightly and at mid day week ends

Club Shop: Yes, sells scarves, mugs, stickers and programmes.

Local Press: Solihull News, Solihull Times, Birmingham Post & Mail, Express & Star

Local Radio: Radio W.M. BRMB

CLUB PERSONNEL

Chairman: Ian Childs
V-Chairman: John Basford
Directors: Nigel Collins & Geoff Hood
Secretary: Nigel Collins,
7 The Morelands, West Heath,
Birmingham, B31 3HA
Tel No: 0121476 49454(H)
07801248211(M)01216830701(Fax)
Commercial Manager:
Chris Hooper
Prog Ed: Martin North
Tel No: 0121 603 7357
Programme
40 pages. Price: £1.50
Press Officer: Geoff Hood

2004-2005 Captain:
Player of the Year:
Top Goalscorer: Gary McPhee 15

CLUB STATISTICS

Record	Attendance: 5,000 v Romford F.A.Amateur Cup 1951	
	Victory:	Defeat:
	Career Goalscorer: Phil Davies 221	
	Career Appearances: Michael Hawkins 800	
Record Transfer Fee	Paid: £1,000 to Alvechurch for Adrian O'Dowd	
	Received: £90,000 from Port Vale for Ian Taylor	
Senior Honours:	Southern League Midland Div R-up 87-88 Midland Comb 80-81 Birmingham Senior Cup 57-58 2000-01 Worcs. Sen. Cup 2000-01 B'ham. Junior Cup 66-67 Worcs. Junior Cup 85-86AFA Senior Cup 26-27 35-36	
Previous	Leagues: Friendlies only 1901-21, Birmingham & Dist A.F.A. 1908-1936 Central Amateur 36-39 B'ham Comb 45-54, West Mids 54-65 Midland Comb. 65-83, Southern Lg. 1983-2004	
Grounds:	Moor Green Lane 1901-02 Many 02-22 Windemere Rd 10-30	

MOOR GREEN

BEST LGE ATT.: 530 v Nuneaton Borough
LOWEST: **139** v Droylsden

No.	Date	Comp	H/A	Opponents	Att:	Result	Goalscorers	Pos
1	Aug 13	CN	A	Gainsborough Trinity	317	L 2 - 2	Middleton 69 Pell 83 (og)	14
2	16		H	Kettering Town	359	D 1 - 1	English 89	16
3	20		H	Droylsden	139	D 1 - 1	Middleton 67	12
4	27		A	Harrogate Townn	301	L 0 - 3		17
5	29		H	Workington	230	L 1 - 4	Penny 79	19
6	Sept 3		A	Stafford Rangers	729	W 3 - 1	Morrison 29 Sanders 45 Middleton 69	16
7	10		A	Staybridge Celtic	385	L 1 - 4	Middleton 48 (pen)	17
8	17		H	Worcester City	311	D 1 - 1	Lyttle 80 (og)	17
9	**24**	**FAC 2Q**	**A**	**Hednesford Town**	**491**	**L 0 - 2**		
10	Oct 1	CN	A	Hucknall Town	386	D 2 - 2	McPhee 50 Scott 72	18
11	8		A	Hinckley United	422	W 2 - 1	Trainer 50 Dowdall 77	
12	15		H	Nuneaton Borough	530	L 0 - 4		16
13	18		H	Hednesford Town	233	L 1 - 2	Midworth 30	17
14	22		A	Lancaster City	293	D 3 - 3	Trainer 38 75 Penny 63	17
15	29		H	Leigh RMI	170	W 4 - 1	Trainer 44 Dowdall 83 Collins 89 McPhee 90	14
16	Nov 5		A	Barrow	714	D 2 - 2	Faulds 4 Middleton 10	
17	12		A	Alfreton Town	267	D 1 - 1	Faulds 31	14
18	19		A	Northwich Victoria	737	D 1 - 1	McPhee 3	15
19	Dec 3		H	Vauxhall Motors	202	W 2 - 1	McPhee 17 Trainer 85	13
20	**6**	**FAT 3R**	**A**	**Hednesford Town**	**254**	**D 1 - 1**	**McPhee 17**	
21	10	CN	H	Hinckley United	177	L 1 - 2	Trainer 39	16
22	**13**	**FAT 3R r**	**H**	**Hednesford Town**	**192**	**L 2 - 4**	**Trainer 61 68**	
23	26	CN	A	Redditch United	406	W 1 - 0	Nurse 16	15
24	30		H	Worksop Town	284	W 2 - 0	English 5 Faulds 80	11
25	Jan 2		H	Redditch United	171	W 2 - 1	McPhee 66 Francis 84	
26	7		H	Gainsborough Trinity	177	D 1 - 1	Collins 25	9
27	21		A	Droysden	342	L 0 - 3		13
28	24		A	Kettering Town	1108	W 3 - 0	Morrison 2 Dowdall 43 Scott 68	8
29	28		H	Harrogate Town	192	D 2 - 2	McPhee 47 Middleton 84	10
30	Feb 4		H	Hucknall Town	221	L 2 - 4	McPhee 27 54	12
31	11		A	Nuneaton Borough	1118	D 2 - 2	McPhee 17 Trainer 30	13
32	18		H	Lancaster City	216	W 3 - 1	Faulds 7 Penny 22 Middleton 59	11
33	20		A	Hednesford Town	454	W 2 - 1	Middleton 35 McPhee 76	9
34	25		H	Stalybridge Celtic	193	D 1 - 1	Dowdall 82	9
35	Mar 11		A	Leigh RMI	175	W 3 - 1	McPhee 45 Collins 50 Trainer 70	6
36	13		A	Worcester City	969	W 2 - 0	Morrison 83 Trainer 87	6
37	18		H	Barrow	187	D 1 - 1	McPhee 68	6
38	25		A	Alfreton Town	226	D 0 - 0		7
39	April 1		H	Northwich Victoria	384	L 1 - 2	Anderson 7	8
40	4		H	Hinckley United	205	D 1 - 1	Middleton 42	7
41	8		A	Vauxhall Motors	168	W 2 - 1	Morrison 51 Faulds 82	8
42	15		H	Stafford Rangers	393	L 0 - 1		9
43	17		A	Workington	392	W 4 - 1	Collins 2 Scott 63 Middleton 64 McPhee 90	9
44	22		H	Worksop Town	210	W 1 - 0	Nurse 76	8
45	29		A	Hyde United	261	L 2 - 3	McPhee 57 (pen) Middleton 84	9

Ave. League Home Attendance: 258   **Goals**   70   71   **Top Goalscorer:** Gary McPhee (15)
Best Position: 6th   **Worst:**   19th

NUNEATON BOROUGH

Founded: 1937
Nickname: The Boro

NUNEATON BOROUGH vs HARROGATE TOWN

Manager: Roger Ashby   **Assistant Manager:** Kevin Wilkin

Physio: Paul Egan & Richie Norman   **Youth Team Manager:** Terry Angus

Club Colours: Blue shirts with white shorts

Change Colours: White shirts and blue shorts

Club Sponsor: Bloor Homes

Previous League: Conference North

Beat Seasons: League: Conference Runners-Up 83-84 84-85

F.A. Cup: 3rd Rd Replay   **F.A.Trophy.:** Quarter Final 76-77

Ground address: Manor Park, Beaumont Road, Nuneaton, Warwicks CV11 5HD

Tel No: 02476 385738 Fax 02476 342690   **Clubcall:** 09066 555 848

Official website: www.nbafc.net

Capacity: 6,500   **Seats:** 520   **Covered:** 3,000   **Floodlights:**Yes

Simple Directions: A444 to Nuneaton from M6 jct 3. Take 2nd exit at 1st r'about, 2nd exit at 2nd roundabout and left at the third. Then take 2nd right into Greenmoor Rd and right at the end. Ground on left, one mile from Nuneaton Trent Valley (BR)

Midweek Home Matchday: Tuesday   **Programme Shop:** Manager Andy Pace

Souvenir Shop: Full range of club accessories. Managers: Celia and Kelly

Local Radio: Mercia Sound, BBC CWR

Local Press: Nuneaton Telegraph & Weekly Tribune

CLUB PERSONNEL

Chairman: Roger Stanford
Managing Director: Clair Finnigan
Secretary: Paul Lewis, 7 Garfitt Road, Kirby Muxloe, Leics.
Tel No: 0116 2394981 (H) 07711 410642 (M)
Commercial Department:
Josie Moore,Mandy Williams & Graham Wilson
Press Officer & Prog Ed:
Dave Riche 02476 738385 (W)
Programme: Pages 40. Price £2.00

2005-2006
Top Goalscorer: Gez Murphy 20

CLUB STATISTICS

Record	**Attendance :**22,114 v Rotherham United F.A.Cup 3rd Rd 1967
	Victory: 11-1 45-46 & 55-56 **Defeat:** 1-8 55-56 & 68-69
	Career Goalscorer: Paul Culpin 201 (Career) 55 (Season 92-93)
	Career Appearances: Alan Jones 545 (62-74)
	Fee Paid: £35,000 to Forest Green Rovers for Marc McGregor 2000
	Fee Received: £80,000 from Kidderminster H for Andy Ducross 2000
Senior Honours:	Alliance Runners-up 83-4-84-5 Southern Premier 98-99 R-up 66-7 74-75
	Midland Div 81-2 92-3 Birmingham Senior Cup (7)
Previous Leagues:	Central Amateur, 37-8 B'ham Comb. 38-52 West Mids 52-58 Southern 58-79
	81-2 88-9, Conference 79-81 82-88 99-03

Back Row (L-R): Martin Reeves, Gez Murphy, Derek Brown, Darren Acton, Dave Clarke, Scott Rickards, Duane Darby, Mark Noon.
Middle: Dave Lee (Director), Richie Norman (Physio), Ian Weaving (Youth/Community Coach), Rob Oddy, Oliver Burgess, Matty Collins, Tom Breward, Gary McPhee, Gary Fitzpatrick, Brian Qualiey (departed), Alan Cooper (Kitman), Graham Wilson (Secretary/Youth Manager), Roger Stanford (Chairman), Dave Riche (Sales/Media Manager). **Front:** David Blenkinsopp, Kevin Wilkin (player/assistant manager), Neil Moore (captain), Roger Ashby (Manager), David Staff, James Ellis (Conditioning coach), Ben Chapman. Not pictured: Daryl Burgess, Paul Egan (Physio).

NUNEATON BOROUGH

BEST LGE ATT.: 2,183 v Stafford Rangers
LOWEST: 629 v Droylsden

No.	Date	Comp	H/A	Opponents	Att:	Result	Goalscorers	Pos
1	Aug 13	CN	A	Droylsden	398	D 2 - 2	Quailey 37 Whittaker 53	15
2	19		H	Redditch United	920	W 2 - 1	Moore 11 Murphy 76	4
3	20		H	Harrogate Town	724	W 4 - 0	Frew 25 Quailey 60 (pen) Angus 79 Wilkin 88	2
4	27		A	Stafford Rangers	1063	L 0 - 2		7
5	29		H	Kettering Town	1049	D 2 - 2	Frew 26 88	7
6	Sept 3		A	Workington	611	W 2 - 0	Frew 70 Murphy 73 (pen)	6
7	10		H	Lacnaster City	716	W 3 - 0	Wilkin 4 Moore 6 Reeves 35	4
8	17		A	Hucknall Town	625	W 1 - 0	Frew 61	3
9	24	FAC2Q	H	**AFC Telford United**	1174	W 3 - 1	Frew 16 Collins 71 Staff 79	
10	Oct 1	CN	H	Hyde United	1113	W 1 - 0	Quailey 84	2
11	8	FAC 3Q	H	**Chelmsford City**	915	D 1 - 1	Quailey 31	
12	12	FAC 3Qr	A	**Chelmsford City**	379	W 2 - 1*	Noon 89 Murphy 120	
13	15	CN	A	Moor Green	530	W 4 - 0	Frew 13 Noon 43 Murphy 51 (pen) 54	2
14	17		A	Worcester City	922	W 1 0 0	Murphy 32	2
15	22	FAC 4Q	H	**Tiverton Town**	1237	D 0 - 0		
16	25	FAC4Qr	A	**Tiverton Town**	880	W 1 - 0	Quailey 88	
17	29	CN	A	Stalybridge Celtic	818	D 0 - 0		3
18	Nov 5	FAC 1R	H	**Ramsgate**	2153	W 2 - 0	Oddy 15 Staff 34	
19	8	CN	A	Norhwich Victoria	1119	D 2 - 2	Fitzpatrick 25 Wilkin 79	3
20	12		H	Vauxhall Motors	810	W 3 - 2	Staff 23 84 Murphy 90 (pen)	3
21	26	FAT 3Q	A	**Farsley Celtic**	271	L 1 - 3	Quinlan 49 (pen)	
22	Dec 3	FAC 3R	H	**Histon**	3366	D 2 - 2	Collins 35 Quailey 52 (pen)	
23	6	CN	A	Worksop Town	820	W 3 - 1	Quailey 37 (pen) 55 Foster 84	3
24	10		A	Hinckley United	2278	W 1 - 0	Quailey 80	3
25	14	FAC2r	A	**Histon**	3000	W 2 - 1	Oddy 34 Angus 90	
26	17	CN	A	Gainsborough Trinity	373	W 2 - 1	Staff 60 Quailey 79	
27	26		H	Hednesford Town	1254	W 3 - 2	Murphy 3 (39 50 59)	2
28	30		H	Barrow	902	W 2 - 1	Murphy 35 Staff 80	2
29	Jan 2		A	Hednesford Town	1011	D 0 - 0		2
30	7	FAC 3R	H	**Middlesbrough**	6000	D 1 - 1	Murphy 90 (pen)	
31	14	CN	A	Redditch United	644	L 0 - 3		2
32	17	FAC 3R r	A	**Middlesbrough**	26255	L 2 - 5	Murphy 70 85 (pen)	
33	21	CN	A	Harrogate Town	602	L 0 - 2		2
34	24		A	Leugh RMI	201	L 0 - 1		2
35	28		H	Stafford Rangers	2183	D 1 - 1	Taylor 5	2
36	31		H	Alfrteon Town	1108	W 1 - 0	Murphy 90 (pen)	2
37	Feb 4		A	Hyde United	507	L 0 - 1		2
38	11		H	Moor Green	1118	D 2 - 2	Moore 52 Darby 69	2
39	18		A	Worksop Town	476	W 4 - 0	Whittaker 1 (pen) Darby 71 Murphy 72 Noon 84	2
40	21		H	Worcester City	801	D 0 - 0		2
41	25		A	Lancaster City	403	D 1 - 1	Darby 6	2
42	Mar 4		H	Hucknall Town	1012	D 2 - 2	Collins 20 Reeves 39	2
43	11		A	Stalybridge Celtic	572	L 0 - 2		3
44	14		H	Droylsden	629	D 2 - 2	Murphy 12 Acton 90	3
45	18		H	Gainsborough Trinity	879	W 3 - 1	Foster 37 77 (pen) Moore 86	3
46	25		A	Vauxhall Motors	234	W 2 - 1	Murphy 44 Fitzpatrick 70	3
47	April 1		H	Leigh RMI	1082	W 3 - 1	Rickards 57 67 Staff 71	3
48	8		A	Alfrteon Town	436	L 0 - 1		3
49	11		H	Northwich Victoria	1296	L 1 - 2	Richards 25 (pen)	3
50	15		H	Workington	1003	W 3 - 1	Moore 11 Murphy 35 Brown 56	3
51	17		A	Kettering Town	1205	L 0 - 3		3
52	22		A	Barrow	752	W 2 - 1	Rickards 11 Staff 29 Wilkin 53	3
53	29		H	Hinckley Athletic	1301	W 2 - 0	Murphy 40 Foster 80	3
54	May 1	Play Off SF	H	**Droylsden**	2005	L 0 - 1		

Ave. League Home Attendance: 947   **Goals** 83 53   **Top Goalscorer:** Gez Murphy (20)

Best Position: 2nd   **Worst:** 15th

REDDITCH UNITED

Founded: 1891
Nickname: The Reds

The official matchday programme of Redditch United Football Club

REDS

Redditch United v Scarborough FC

Nationwide ISSUE ONE £1.80
Saturday 2 September 2006, Kick-off 3.00pm

Manager: Gary Whild   **Assistant Manager/Coach:** Kim Casey.

Physio: Peter James & Malcolm Cowell

Club Colours: Red with white trim

Change Colours: All Blue

Club Sponsors: Prudden Road Surfacing

Previous League: Southern   **Previous Name:** Redditch Town

Previous Ground: HDA Sports Ground ,Millsborough Rd

Best Seasons: League: 9th. Conference North 2004-2005

F.A. Cup: 1st Round Replay 71-72   **F.A.Trophy:** 4th Round 98-99

Ground address: Valley Stadium, Bromsgrove Road, Redditch B97 4RN

Tel No: 01527 67450

Capacity: 5,000   **Seats:** 400   **Covered:** 2,000   **Floodlights:** Yes

Simple Directions: Access 7 on town ring road takes you into Bromsgrove Road (via Unicorn Hill). Ground entrance is 400 yards past traffic lights on right.

Midweek Home Matchday: Tuesday

Clubhouse: Open matchdays and private hire.

Club Shop: Yes

Local Press: Redditch Advertiser, Birmingham Evening Mail and Redditch Standard

Local Radio: BBC Hereford & Worcester & The Bear radio FM102

CLUB PERSONNEL

Chairman & Press Officer:
Steve Rossiter (07773421076)
President: Major JiM Gilllespie MBE
Secretary: Robin Lamb, 14 Regal Close, Two Gates, Tamworth,Staffs B77 1GT
Commercial Manager
Jeoff Sharpe (07788917115)
Prog Ed: Malcolm Cowell

2005-2006
Captain: Mark Taylor.
Player of the Year: Carl Palmer.
Top Goalscorer: Craig Wilding.

CLUB STATISTICS

Record	**Attendance:** 5,500 v Bromsgrove Rovers. League 54-55	
	Victory:	**Defeat:**
Career Goalscorer:		
Career Appearances:		
Record Transfer Fee	**Paid:** £3,000 to Halesowen Town for Paul Joinson	
	Received: £40,000 from Aston Villa for David Farrell	
Senior Honours:	Southern Lg Div 1 North 1975-76 Staffs Senior Cup 90-91	
	Birmingham Senior Cup 24-2531-32 38-39 76-77 Worcs Senior Cup (4)	
	R-up (4) Worcs Junior Cup 90-91	
Previous Leagues:	B'ham Comb 05-21 29-39 46-53 West Midlands 21-29 53-72 Southern 72-79	
	Alliance 79-80 Southern 81-2004	

Back Row (L-R): M.Cowell (Physio), J.Foxon, D.Thomas, B.Petty, F.Francis, R.Cornelius, R.Anstiss, J.Clarke, R.Softley, M.Clarke, R.Robinson, R.Taylor, J.Knott, P.James (Physio). **Middle:** S.Rea, D.Willetts, L.Prudden (Sponsor), D.Chatwin (Director), S.Rossiter (Chairman), K.Casey (Coach), G.Whild (Manager), K.Rae (Director), A.Ellis (Sponsor), C.Palmer, E.Geohaghan. **Front:** S.Hollis, D.Whitcombe, C.Murphy, D.Reece.

REDDITCH UNITED

BEST LGE ATT.: 752 v Kettering Town
LOWEST: **200** v Hinckley United

No.	Date	Comp	H/A	Opponents	Att:	Result	Goalscorers	Pos
1	Aug 13	CN	H	Leigh RMI	316	L 1 - 2	Moore 13	17
2	16		A	Nuneation Borough	920	L 1 - 3	Murphy 13	21
3	20		A	Vauxhall Motors	724	W 2 - 1	Palmer 22 Brazier 90 (og)	13
4	27		H	Lancaster City	562	L 0 - 1		16
5	29		A	Northwich Victoria	784	L 1 - 5	Williams 61	20
6	Sept 3		H	Hednesford Town	381	L 1 - 2	Charlton 20	20
7	10		A	Alfreton Town	219	L 1 - 2	Moore 84	22
8	17		H	Droylsden	301	W 4 - 1	Broad 1 49 Rickards 61 Taylor 90	19
9	24	FAC 2Q	H	Woodford United	316	D 1 - 1	Jenkins 83	
10	27	FAC 2Qr	A	Woodford United	207	D 2 - 2	Rickards 4 Wilding 96 Woodford won 10-9 after pens	
11	Oct 1	CN	H	Gainsborough Trinity	332	D 1 - 1	Rickards 8	20
12	15		A	Stafford Rangers	744	L 0 - 3		21
13	18		A	Hinckley United	442	D 1 - 1	**Hollis** 15	19
14	22		H	Workington	281	L 3 - 6	Wilding 20 Crighton 49 Flynn 75	19
15	29		A	Hyde United	422	W 3 - 1	Wilding 71 Flynn 30 **Hollis** 47	18
16	Nov 5		H	Stalybridge Celtic	354	L 1 - 4	Rickards 12	19
17	12		A	Workington	487	W 2 - 1	Wilding 18 Charlton73	
18	19		H	Worksop Town	332	L 0 - 3		17
19	22		H	Kettering Town	752	W 2 - 1	Rickards 26 Clarke 36	16
20	26	FAT 3Q	H	Barrow	289	D 1 - 1	Rickards 7 (pen)	
21	29	FAT 3Qr	A	Barrow	756	L 0 - 2		
22	Dec 3	CN	A	Hucknall Town	397	L 0 - 4		16
23	10		A	Barrow	839	D 1 - 1	Clarke 25	17
24	17		H	Harrogate Town	226	L 1 - 3	Field 81	17
25	20		H	Worcester City	451	D 2 - 2	Field 16 Moore 25	17
26	26		H	Moor Green	406	L 0 - 1		17
27	Jan 2		A	Moor Green	171	L 1 - 2	Doyle 11	18
28	7		A	Leigh RMI	178	L 1 - 2	**Hollis** 70	20
29	14		H	Nuneaton Borough	644	W 3 - 0	Taylor 43 Wilding 68 82	
30	21		H	Vauxhall Motors	365	W 3 - 0	Palmer 20 Clarke 22 Field 22	17
31	28		A	Lancaster City	249	L 0 - 1		19
32	Feb 4		A	Gainsborough Trinity	306	D 2 - 2	Palmer 15 **Hollis** 47	19
33	11		A	Stafford Rangers	546	L 0 - 1		19
34	18		A	Harrogate Town	432	D 1 - 1	Wilding 52	20
35	21		H	Hinckley United	200	D 1 - 1	Platnaurer (og) 90	20
36	25		H	AlfretonTown	369	W 1 - 0	**Hollis** 5	16
37	Mar 6		A	Worcester City	1060	D 2 - 2	**Hollis** 52 Palmer 63	18
38	10		A	Hyde United	339	D 1 - 1	Rea 90	18
39	18		A	Kettering Town	911	L 0 - 4		19
40	April 1		A	Worksop Town	370	D 1 - 1	King 35	20
41	3		A	Droylsden	279	L 1 - 2	**Hollis** 55	20
42	8		H	Hucknall Town	323	D 1 - 1	Palmer 89	18
43	15		A	Hedhesford Town	552	D 1 - 1	Clarke 80	20
44	17		H	Northwich Victoria	703	L 1 - 2	**Hollis** 23	20
45	22		A	Stalybridge Celtic	521	L 1 - 5	Murphy 77	21
46	29		H	Barrow	751	W 2 - 1	Wilding 31 Palmer 62	20

Ave. League Home Attendance: 425   **Goals**   56   85   **Top Goalscorer:** Hollis (8)
Best Position: 13th   **Worst:**   22nd

SCARBOROUGH

Founded: 1879
Nickname: Seadogs or The Boro

Head Coach: Mark Patterson   **Physio:** Martin Woodmansey

Club Colours: All Red

Change Colours: All Blue

Club Shirt Sponsor: Crest Teamwear

Previous League: Conference

BEST PERFORMANCES. League: 5th Football League Divison Four

F.A. Cup: 4th Round Replay 2003-2004

F.A.Trophy.: Winners: 1972-73 1975-76 1976-77

Ground address: McCain Stadium, Seamer Road, Scarborough, N.Yorkshire
YO 12 4HF Tel No: 01723 375094 Fax: 01723 366211

Simple Directions: The stadium is situated on the main Scarborough to York Road about half a mile beyond B& Q on the left as you drive towards Scarborough.

Club Website:www.scarboroughfc.co.uk

Capacity: 5,900   **Seats:** 3,500   **Covered:**1,000   **Floodlights:** Yes

Midweek Home Matchday: Tuesday

Clubhouse: Open matchdays & refreshments on ground   **Club Shop:** Yes

Local Radio: Radio York and Yorkshire Coast Radio

Local Press: Scarborough Evening News and Yorkshire Post

CLUB PERSONNEL
Chairman: Ian Scobie
President: John Birley
Secretary: Derek Megginson
C/o Club
Tel Nos: 01723 375094
and 07866 291877
Programme Editors:
Nick Clarke & Richard Speight
Tel No: 01723 375094
36 Pages £2.00

2005-2006
Captain: Steve Baker
Player of the Year:
Michael Coulson
Top Goalscorer: Michael Coulson

CLUB STATISTICS

Record	**Attendance:** 11,162 v Luton Town F.A.Cup 3rd Round 1938
	Career Goalscorer: 'Ocky 'Johnson 245 1905-1923
	Career Appearances: Harry Dunn 901 1965-1986
Record Transfer Fee	**Paid:** £100,000 to Leicester City for Martin Russell 1987
	Received: £350,000 from Nottds County for Craig Short 1992
	Victory: 16-1 v Leeds Amateurs (H) F.A.Amateur Cup 1907
	Defeat: 1-13 v Darlington (A) F.A.Cup 1891
Senior Honours:	F.A.Trophy Winners 72-73 75-76 76-77 Vauxhall Conference: 1986-87 East Riding Sen Cup (8) & North Riding Sen Cup (17)
Previous Leagues:	Northern 1898-1910,14-26,Yorks Comb.10-14 ,Yorkshire 26-27 Midland 27-40 46-60 63-68Scarborough & Dist. 45-46, N.Co.East 60-62, N.Eastern 62-63, N.P. L. 68-79, and the Football League 87-99 Alliance Premier/ Conference 79-87 1999-2006

Back row (L-R): Tony Hackworth, Matt Perry, Michael Byron, Jamie Vermiglio, Curtis Aspden, Jimmy Beadle, Darren Thornton, Ged Dalton, Carl Cook
Front: Ashley Lyth, Jason Blunt, Mark Hotte, Martin Woodmansey (physio), Denny Ingram (captain), Mark Patterson (head coach), Ryan Blott, Lee Whittington, Lee Cartwright.

SCARBOROUGH

BEST LGE ATT.: 4,057 v York City
LOWEST: 1,152 v Stevenage Borough

No.	Date	Comp	H/A	Opponents	Att:	Result	Goalscorers	Pos
1	Aug 13	C	A	Hereford United	3105	L 0 - 4		22
2	16		H	Morecambe	1759	L 0 - 1		21
3	20		H	Kidderminster H	1401	D 1 - 1	Foot 90	22
4	27		A	Dagenham & Redbridge	1074	W 2 - 0	Speight 85 Wake 90	17
5	29		H	Accrington Stanley	1509	D 2 - 2	Quayle 45 Speight 76	18
6	Sept 3		A	Burton Albion	1336	L 1 - 2	Wake 50	19
7	10		H	Gravesend & Northfleet	1207	W 3 - 1	Wake 32 McCarthy 38 (og) Nicholson 43	13
8	17		A	Canvey Island	744	L 0 - 1		16
9	20		A	Altrincham	862	D 1 - 1	**Coulson** 87	16
10	24		H	Forest Green Rovers	1341	W 1 - 0	Redfearn 61 (pen)	14
11	27		H	Southport	1280	L 0 - 1		14
12	Oct 1		A	Woking	1840	L 0 - 4		16
13	8		H	Crawley Town	1257	L 1 - 2	**Coulson** 45	20
14	15		A	Grays Athletic	1515	L 0 - 5		22
15	**22**	**FAC 4Q**	**A**	**Harrogate Town**	**1591**	**L 0 - 1**		
16	29	C	H	Aldershot Town	1682	D 2 - 2	Quayle 55 **Coulson** 56	21
17	Nov 12		A	Tamworth	1165	W 1 - 0	Quayle 42	19
18	19		H	Stevenage Borough	1152	D 1 - 1	Nicholson 43	18
19	26		H	Halifax Town	1843	W 2 - 0	Fowler 47 Clark 73 (pen)	17
20	Dec 3		A	Cambridge United	2809	L 1 - 2	Hackworth 63	17
21	10		H	Exeter City	1428	L 0 - 1		19
22	**17**	**FAT 1**	**A**	**Kidderminster Harriers**	**957**	**L 0 - 4**		
23	24	C	A	York City	4921	L 1 - 3	Wake 21	19
24	30		A	Halifax Town		L 0 - 1		
25	Jan 2		H	York City	4057	D 2 - 2	Wake 42 Hughes 90	20
26	7		H	Hereford United	1582	L 0 - 1		20
27	14		A	Southport	1035	W 2 - 0	McNiven 2 Fowler 18	18
28	21		A	Kidderminster Harriers	1740	L 1 - 2	McNiven 72	19
29	24		A	Morecambe	1478	W 3 - 0	McNiven 19 Hughes 27 Fowler 87	17
30	28		H	Dagenmham & Redbridge	1505	L 0 - 1		18
31	Feb 4		H	Altrincham	1405	L 1 - 2	McNiven 74	18
32	11		A	Forest Green Rovers	732	L 1 - 5	McNiven 85	19
33	18		H	Woking	1278	D 1 - 1	**Coulson** 8	19
34	25		A	Gravesend & Northfleet	930	D 0 - 0		19
35	Mar 11		A	Crawley Town	1181	L 0 - 2		20
36	21		H	Canvey Island	1153	L 1 - 2	**Coulson** 84	21
37	25		A	Aldershot Town	2245	W 1 - 0	**Coulson** 23	21
38	April 8		A	Stevenage Borough	1861	L 0 - 2		21
39	11		H	Tamworth	1648	D 0 - 0		22
40	15		H	Burton Albion	1808	W 3 - 0	Redfearn 34 (pen) Hackworth 71 **Coulson** 80	21
41	17		A	Accrington Stanley	3320	L 0 - 1		21
42	19		H	Grays Athletic	1560	L 2 - 7	McNiven 55 Weaver 61	21
43	22		A	Cambridge United	1831	L 1 - 2	Redfearn 35	21
44	29		A	Exeter City	3382	D 1 - 1	Hackworth 90	22

Ave. League Home Attendance: 1604 　　　**Goals** 40　71　**Top Goalscorer:** Michael Coulson (7)
Best Position: 13th 　**Worst:** 22nd

STALYBRIDGE CELTIC

Founded: 1909
Nickname: Celtic

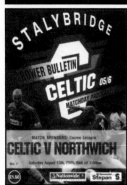

Club Colours: All Blue.
Change Colours: Tangerine/Black/Black
Club Sponsor: Tameside Stepan
Previous League: Conference
Best Seasons: **League:** 12th (Conference) 1992-93
F.A. Cup: 2nd Rd 93-94
F.A.Trophy.: 6th Rd 2001-02
Manager: John Reed **Assistant Manager:** Mark Atkins
Sports Therapist: David Pover
Ground address: Bower Fold, Mottram Road, Stalybridge Cheshire SK15 2RT
Tel No: 0161 338 2828 Fax: 0161 338 8256
Official website: www.stalybridgeceltic.co.uk
Capacity: 6,108 **Seats:** 1,200 **Cover** 2,400: **Floodlights:** Yes
Simple Directions: From Stockport and South M60, M67 to end of motorway through large roundabout to traffic lights. Then left to mini roundabout and left again into Mottram Road. Follow signs to Stalybridge, down hill and ground is on left by Hare & Hounds pub and F.X.Leisure Gym.
Midweek Home Matchday: Tuesday
Clubhouse: Open Matchdays Club Shop: Contact Bob Rhodes Tel: 01457 76044
Local Radio: G.M.R. (BBC Manchester) 96.2 The Revolution
Local Press: Manchester Evening News, Saturday News Pink, Ashton Reporter Ashton Advertiser

CLUB PERSONNEL
Chairman: Peter Dennerly
V-Chairman: Dorothy Norton
President: Roy Oldham
Directors: B.McCallum, G.Crossley, G.Greenwood, J. Dillon, R.Gorski S.White, D.Norton & P.Donnelly
Commercial Manager: John Hall Tel: 07813 864492(M)
Secretary: Martyn Torr Tel No: 07860 841765
Press Officer: KeithTrudgeon 0161205 7631 (W) 01613048934(H) 07767 404642
Programme Editor: Nick Shaw Tel No: 0161 633 1117
2005-2006 Captain: Mark Haran
Player of the Year: Paul Sykes
Top Goalscorer: Lee Ellington
40 pages Price £2.00

CLUB STATISTICS

Record	Attendance :9,753 v W.B.A. F.A.Cup Replay 1922-23	
	Victory:	16-2 v Manchester NE 1.5.26 & Nantwich 22.10.32
	Defeat:	1-10 V Wellington Town 9.3.46.
Career Goalscorer	In Career:	Harry Dennison 215 **in Season:** Cecil Smith 77 1931-32
Career Appearances:	In Career:	Kevan Keelan 395
Record Transfer Fee	Paid:	£15,000 to Kettering Town for Ian Arnold 1995
	Received:	£16,000 from Southport for Lee Trundle
Senior Honours:	NPL Prem 1991-92 2000-01 Cheshire Sen.Cup (2) Manchester Sen. Cup 22-3	
Previous Leagues:	Lancs Comb. 11-12, Central Lg 12-21, Southern 1914-15, Football Lg 21-23, Cheshire Co., 23-82 N.W.Co 82-87 NPL 87-92 Conference: 92-98 01-02	

Back row (L-R): Dave Pover, sports therapist; Rebecca Webb, assistant physio; Lee Ellington; Hugh McAuley; Garry Kharras; Scott Maxfield; Grant Black; Barrie Keeling; Lee Morris; Ashley Winn; Paul Pettinger; Danny Whitworth; Nick Buxton; Paul Sykes; Kevin Parr; Mark Hume; Ronnie Kirkham; Roy Barker; Kay Morgan, assistant physio.**Front:** Danny Forde; Steve Garvey; Jamie Kay; Peter Dennerley, Chairman; Mark Haran, Captain; John Reed, Manager; James Turley; Nicky Platt; Ian Snodin; Ben Smith.**Inset** Steve Brodie.

STALYBRIDGE CELTIC

BEST LGE ATT.: 1,243 v Hyde United
LOWEST: **308** v Lancaster City

No.	Date	Comp	H/A	Opponents	Att:	Result	Goalscorers	Pos
1	Aug 13	CN	H	Northwich Victoria	533	D 3 - 3	Prince 27 (pen) 35 **Ellington** 69	11
2	16		A	Lancaster City	346	D 2 - 2	Prince 75 88 (pen)	15
3	20		A	Leigh RMI	304	L 1 - 2	**Ellington** 68	17
4	27		H	Worksop Town	576	W 2 - 1	Sykes 67 **Ellington** 70	11
5	29		A	Hednesford Town	816	D 1 - 1	Sykes 12	11
6	Sept 3		H	Vauxhall Motors	417	W 2 - 1	**Ellington** 17 Sykes 90	9
7	10		H	Moor Green	385	W 4 - 1	**Ellington** 3 (34 51 71) Price 83	8
8	17		A	Barrow	1057	L 2 - 4	Sykes 40 Prince 45	8
9	24	FAC2Q	H	**Workington**	448	D 0 - 0		
10	27	FAC 2Qr	A	**Workington**	315	L 1 - 2*	Price 51	
11	Oct 1	CN	H	Harrogate Town	647	W 3 - 1	Haran 39 **Ellington** 44 72	7
12	15		A	Alfreton Town	388	D 0 - 0		7
13	18		A	Gainsborough Trinty	412	L 0 - 1		11
14	22		H	Hinckley United	478	D 1 - 1	**Ellington** 76	9
15	29		A	Nuneaton Borough	818	D 0 - 0		10
16	Nov 5		A	Redditch United	354	W 4 - 1	Garvey 11 **Ellington** 17 Banim 38 Eastwood 85	8
17	8		H	Stafford Rangers	519	L 2 3 3	**Ellington** 11 45	8
18	12		A	Lancaster City	1478	L 1 - 4	Price 52	9
19	19		H	Hucknall Town	561	W 2 - 1	Prince2 Sykes 62	9
20	26	FAT 3Q	A	**Hyde United**	906	W 5 - 1	**Prince 3 (20 26 28) Ellington 51 62**	
21	Dec 3	CN	A	Workington	458	W 2 - 1	Price 8 Sykes 54	7
22	10		H	Droylsden	863	D 1 - 1	Haran 74	7
23	17	FAT 1	H	**Droylsden**	598	W 1 - 0	Eastwood 50	
24	26	CN	A	Hyde United	1087	W 3 - 1	**Ellington** 41 55 Keeling 76	
25	Jan 2		H	Hyde United	1243	L 1 - 2	Prince 8	6
26	14	FAT 2	H	**Solihull Borough**	612	W 1 - 0	Eastwood 71	
27	21	CN	H	Leigh RMI	560	W 6 - 1	Sykes 8 87 **Ellington** 37 Garvey 55 Haran 57 Eastwood 74	7
28	28		A	Worksop Town	506	L 1 - 2	Eastwood 31	11
29	Feb 4	FAT 3	A	**Salisbury City**	1533	D 0 - 0		
30	7	FAT 3R	H	**Salisbury City**	704	L 0 - 1		
31	11	CN	H	Alfreton Town	449	W 3 - 0	**Ellington** 6 11 Sykes 17	10
32	18		A	Hinckley United	506	D 1 - 1	Eastwood 81	12
33	21		A	Gainsborough Trinity	327	W 1 - 0	Prince 16	10
34	25		A	Moor Green	193	D 1 - 1	Garvey 18	10
35	28		A	Northwich Victoria	834	L 0 - 1		10
36	Mar 7		H	Stafford Rangers	561	L 0 - 1		11
37	11		H	Nuneaton Borough	572	W 2 - 0	Prince 10 14	8
38	18		H	Worcester City	742	W 1 - 0	**Ellington** 90	7
39	21		H	Harrogate Town	450	L 0 - 1		7
40	25		H	Kettering Town	589	W 2 - 0	**Ellington** 53 Sykes 82	6
41	April 1		A	Hucknall Town	394	L 1 - 2	Eastwood 62	7
42	4		H	Worcester City	380	L 2 - 3	**Ellington** 75 Parr 80	8
43	8		A	Workington	423	W 2 - 1	Turley 6 **Ellington** 70	9
44	13		A	Lancaster City	308	W 2 - 1	**Ellington** 20 Turley 84	7
45	15		A	Vauxhall Motors	262	L 2 - 4	**Ellington** 49 80 (pen)	8
46	17		H	Hednesford Town	511	W 3 - 0	**Ellington** 19 90 Prince 41	7
47	22		H	Redditch United	521	W 5 - 1	Turley 25 Parr 49 Sykes 74 Eastwod 78 90	7
48	25		H	Barrow	492	W 2 - 1	Banim 27 **Ellington** (pen) 31	7
49	29		A	Droylsden	1302	L 0 - 1		7

Ave. League Home Attendance: 541 **Goals** 82 56 **Top Goalscorer:** Ellington (30)
Best Position: 6th **Worst:** 17th

VAUXHALL MOTORS

Founded: 1963
Nickname: The Motormen

Player/Manager: Carl Macauley   **Player/Assistant Manager:** Carl Spellman

Player/Caretaker Coach: Brian McGorry

Club Colours: White/navy blue/white

Change Colours: All Sky Blue

Club Sponsor: Lookers Wirral

Previous League: Northern Premier League.

Best Seasons: **League:** 15th Conference North 04-05

               F.A. Cup: 2nd Round 2003-4

               F.A.Trophy.: 4th Round 2001-2

Ground address: Vauxhall Sports Ground, Rivacre Road, Ellesmere Port, South Wirrall CH66 1NJ Tel & Fax: 0151 328 1114

Official website: www.vmfc.com

Capacity: 2,500   Seats: 300   Covered: 1,000   Floodlights: Yes

Simple Directions: M53 Jct 5 take A41 to Chester. First lights left to Hooton Green. Left at T junction to the end, turn right at T junction into Rivacre Road. Ground on rt

Midweek Home Matchday: Tuesday

Clubhouse: Yes   **Club Shop:** Yes Contact Ian Cowell 01516257491

CLUB PERSONNEL

Chairman: Alan Bartlam
V-Chairman: Len Jones
Secretary: Carole Paisey, 31 South Road, West Kirby, Wirral CH48 3HG
Tel No: 01516256936
Website Manager: Andy Wilson
Tel No: 0774 3895006
Press Officer: Chairman
Programme Editor:
Mike Harper
Tel No: 07817 400202
Programme: 36 Pages

2005-2006
Captain: Sreve McNulty
Player of the Year: Brian Moogan
Top Goalscorer: Peter Cumiskey

CLUB STATISTICS

Record	**Attendance** : 1,500 F.A.X1 Fixture 1987
	Career Goalscorer: Terry Fearrns 111
	Career Apearances: Carl Jesbitt 509
	Transfer Fee Paid: Undisclosed
	Transfer Fee Received: Undisclosed
Senior Honours:	Northern Premier League Premier R-up 2002-2003
	Northern Premier League Division 1 R-up 2001-2002
	Cheshire Amateur Cup R-up 1987,1994,2000,2005
	Wirral Senior Cup 1987
Previous Leagues:	Ellesmere Port, Wirral Combination, West Cheshire 66-87, 92-95
	North West Counties 87-92 95-2000
Names:	Vauxhall Motors 63-87 Vauxhall GM 95-99

2005-2006 Back row left to right: Steve McNulty, Peter Cumiskey, Robbie Lawton (Captain), Tim Dittmer, Phil Brazier, Brian Moogan and Owen Brown (Manager). Front row: Carl Spellman, Lee Woodyatt, Wayne McDermott, Leighton McGivern, MIke Duffy and Mike Garrity.

STEP 1
CONFERENCE

STEP 2
CONFERENCE NORTH

STEP 3
NPL · SOUTHERN · STHMIAN PREM

STEP 4
NPL · SOUTHERN · ISTHMIAN

STEP 5/6

STEP 7

VAUXHALL MOTORS

BEST LGE ATT.: 529 v Northwich Victoria
LOWEST: 155 v Leigh RMI & Gainsboro'T

No.	Date	Comp	H/A	Opponents	Att:	Result	Goalscorers	Pos
1	Aug 13	CN	A	Alfreton Town	283	W 2 - 1	McGivern 2 McNulty 75	5
2	16		H	Barrow	305	L 0 - 1		9
3	20		H	Redditch United	186	L 1 - 2	Cumiskey 53	14
4	27		A	Droylsden	275	L 0 - 4		18
5	29		H	Gainsborough Trinity	155	L 1 - 2	Cumiskey 83	21
6	Sept 3		A	Stalybridge Celtic	417	L 1 - 2	Cumiskey 36	21
7	10		H	Leigh RMI	155	D 4 - 4	Cumiskey 23 Woodyatt 25 Addo 40 Lawton 87	20
8	17		A	Northwich Victoria	778	L 1 - 3	McGivern 77	22
9	24	FAC 2Q	H	Ramsbottom United	109	W 2 - 0	Rooney 9 Moogan 38	
10	Oct 1	CN	H	Worksop Town	201	W 5 - 2	Cumiskey 14 28 Willis 66 Rooney 68 McGivern 85	21
11	8	FAC 3Q	H	Skelmersdale United	243	W 4 - 3	Cumiskey 4 (27 49 pen 68 78)	
12	15	CN	A	Harrogate Town	365	L 1 - 2	Stoneman 12	20
13	18		H	Stafford Rangers	552	L 0 - 3		22
14	22	FAC 4Q	A	Hednesford Town	628	L 0 - 3		
15	29	CN	A	Lancaster City	281	L 0 - 1		22
16	Nov 5		H	Hucknall Town	200	L 0 - 2		22
17	12		A	Nuneaton Borough	810	L 2 - 3	Rooney 30 56	22
18	19		H	Kettering Town	383	D 1 - 1	Lawton 80	22
19	26	FAT 3Q	H	Mossley	151	W 2 - 1	Rooney 16 McGivern 44	
20	Dec 3	CN	A	Moor Green	202	L 1 - 2	Willis 26	22
21	6		H	Hyde United	188	L 0 - 2		22
22	10		A	Hednesford Town	397	W 1 - 0	O'Donnell 10	22
23	17	FAT 1	H	Morecambe	322	L 0 - 4		
24	26	CN	H	Workington	180	W 2 - 1	Cumiskey 51 78	22
25	31		H	Hinckley United	174	L 0 - 1		22
26	Jan 2		A	Workington	562	W 2 - 1	O'Donnell 58·90	20
27	7		H	Alfreton Town	197	W 3 - 1	Field 2 Cumiskey 5 O'Donnell 32	19
28	10		A	Worcester City	186	W 1 - 0	O'Donnell 31	17
29	21		A	Redditch United	365	L 0 - 3		19
30	28		H	Droysden	230	L 2 - 4	Olsen 39 Cumiskey 78	21
31	Feb 11		H	Harrogate Town	164	L 0 - 2		22
32	18		H	Worcester City	905	D 0 - 0		22
33	21		H	Stafford Rangers	198	L 1 - 3	Rooney (pen) 44	22
34	24		A	Leighg RMi	185	D 1 - 1	O'Donnell 20	21
35	Mar 6		A	Hyde United	301	W 3 - 2	Moogan 39 O'Donnell 55 Garrity 83	21
36	11		H	Lancaster City	220	W 1 - 0	Field 20	19
37	14		A	Worksop Town	316	D 1 - 1	McNulty 66 (pen)	19
38	18		H	Hucknall Town	271	W 2 - 1	Furlong 48 Garrity 54	17
39	25		H	Nuneaton Borough	234	L 1 - 2	Furlong 60	17
40	April 1		A	Kettering Town	1006	L 0 - 1		19
41	4		H	Northwich Victoria	529	L 0 - 3		19
42	8		H	Moor Green	168	L 1 - 2	McNulty 66 (pen)	20
43	11		A	Barrow	630	W 2 - 0	Field 17 Furlong 32	20
44	15		H	Stalybridge Celtic	262	W 4 - 2	O'Donnell 6 Martindale 18 40 Field 90	18
45	17		A	Gainsborough Trinity	284	D 1 - 1	Martindale 65	18
46	22		H	Hinckley United	651	L 1 - 2	Furlong 78	18
47	29		A	Hdnesford Town	316	D 0 - 0		18

Ave. League Home Attendance: 230   **Goals** 58 82   **Top Goalscorer:** Cumiskey (14)

Best Position: 5th   **Worst:** 22nd

WORCESTER CITY

Founded: 1902
Nickname: City

Player-Manager: Andy Preece
Assistant Manager/Coach: Andy Morrison   **Physio:** Ben Schiffmann
Club Colours: Blue& White/Blue/White
Change Colours: Red & Black/black/black
Club Sponsor: M. Pinches Transport
Previous League: Southern
Best Seasons: **League:** 3rd Conference 1979-80
    F.A. Cup: 4th Round 58-59
    F.A.Trophy.: 6th Round (4)
Ground address: St George's Lane, Barbourne, Worcester WR1 1QT
Tel No: 01905 23003 Fax: 26668   **Newsline:** 09066 555810
Website: www.worcestercitywfc.co.uk
Capacity: 4.004   Seats: 1,125   Covered: 2,000   Floodlights:Yes
Simple Directions: M5 Jct 6 (Worcester North) follow signs for Worcester and turn
right at first lights. St George's Lane is 3rd left. One mile from Foregate Station BR
Midweek Home Matchday: Monday
Clubhouse: Open every evening and all day at week ends.   **Club Shops:** Two
Local Radio: Radio Wyvern,Classic Hits, BBC Hereford & Worcester
Local Press: Worcester Standard , Worcester Evening News

CLUB PERSONNEL
Chairman: Dave Boddy
V-Chairman: Laurie Brown
Secretary: Graham Hill, 8 Dawson
Close, Lower Wick, Worcester WR2
4DL.01905 428853 (H)
07786 992272 (M)
Press Officer &
Programme Editor: Secretary

2005-2006
Captain: Des Lyttle
Player of the Year: Des Lyttle
Top Goalscorer: Adam Webster

CLUB STATISTICS

Record	Attendance:	17,042 v Sheffield United F.A.Cup 4th Rd 24.0159
	Victory:	18-1 v Bilston, Birmingham League 21.11.31
	Defeat:	0-10 v Wellington, Birmingham League 29.08.20
Career Goalscorer:		John Inglis 189 (1970-77)
Career Appearances:	In Career:	Bobby McEwan 596 (1959-75)
Record Transfer Fee	Paid:	£8,500 to Telford United for Jim Williams 1981
	Received:	£27,000 from Everton for John Barton
Senior Honours:		Southern League Champions78-79, Southern League Cup
		Winners (2) Worcs Sen Cup (26) and B'ham Sen.Cup 75-76
Previous	Leagues:	West Mids, 1902-38 Southern 38-79 Alliance 79-85 Southern
		1985-2004
	Grounds:	Severn Terrace, Thorneloe, Flagge Meadow.

Back Row (L-R): Geoff Ashby, Nick Colley, Shabir Khan, Chris Smithy, Justin Thompson, Adam Webster,
Craig Wilding, Dennis Pearce, Danny Hodnett, Ben Schiffmann. **Middle:** Martin Obrey, Troy Wood, Dale Watkins,
Danny McDonnell, James Coates, Nat Bulmer, Gary Wlker, Ray Woods. **Front:** Tom Warmer, Adam Burley,
George Clegg, Andy Preece, Andy Morrison, Des Lyttle, Jai Stanley, Jay Sztybel.

WORCESTER CITY

BEST LGE ATT.: 1,278 v Hednesford Town
LOWEST: 734 v Hucknall Town

No.	Date	Comp	H/A	Opponents	Att:	Result	Goalscorers	Pos
1	Aug 13	CN	A	Kettering Town	962	L 1 - 2	Woolley	18
2	15		H	Hinckley United	1064	D 0 - 0		19
3	20		H	GainsboroughTrinty	738	W 2 - 1	Smith 8 Hyde 32	10
4	27		A	Workington	503	D 2 - 2	Smith 62 Stanley 90	13
5	29		H	Droylsden	816	L 1 - 2	Hines 36	15
6	Sept 3		A	Harrogate Town	319	L 1 - 4	Webster 5	17
7	10		H	Hucknall Town	734	L 0 - 1		18
8	17		A	Moor Green	311	D 1 - 1	Webster 11	20
9	24	FAC 2Q	H	Bemerton Heath Harlequins	579	W 7 - 0	McDonald 13 Colley 32 Webster 45 53 Kelly 5 60 Wedgbury 66	
10	Oct 1	CN	A	Lancaster City	282	D 0 - 0		19
11	8	FAC 3Q	H	Tonbridge Angels	684	W 3 - 0	Kelly 24 Webster 79 Hyde 88	
12	15	CN	H	Northwich Victoria	951	L 0 - 1		19
13	17		H	Nuneaton Borough	922	L 0 - 1		19
14	22	FAC 4Q	A	Accrington Stanley	940	D 1 - 1	Kelly 42	
15	24	FAC4Qr	H	Accrington Stanley	1431	W 3 - 2	Smith 39 Webster 74 Warmer 87	
16	29	CN	H	Barrow	1019	W 1 - 0	Lyttle 36	20
17	Nov 5	FAC 1R	A	Chippenham Town	2815	D 1 - 1	Webster 6	
18	12	CN	H	Hednesford Town	1278	W 6 - 2	Clegg 7 Kelly 3 (10 36 79) Webster 30 Hines 74 (pen)	18
19	14	FAC 1r	H	Chippenham Town	4015	W 1 - 0	Webster 76	
20	26	FAT 3Q	H	Kendal Town	973	W 1 - 0	Webster 68	
21	Dec 4	FAC 3R	H	Huddersfield Town	4163	L 0 - 1		
22	10	NN	H	Worksop Town	806	D 1 - 1	Webster 20	19
23	17	FAT 1	H	Hayes	677	W 1 - 0	Clegg 77	
24	20	NN	A	Redditch United	451	D 2 - 2	Colley 13 Smith 58	18
25	26		A	Satfford Rangers	1372	D 1 - 1	Lyttle 33	
26	31		A	Hyde United	401	L 0 - 4		19
27	Jan 2		H	Stafford Rangers	1228	D 1 - 1	Webster 48	19
28	7		H	Kettering Town	867	W 2 - 0	Wood 72 Kelly 87	19
29	10		A	Vauxhall Motors	186	L 0 - 1		
30	17	FAT 2	A	Crawley Town	878	L 1 - 3	Preece 90	
31	21	NN	A	Gainsborough Trinity	378	W 1 - 0	Webster 90	18
32	24		A	Hinckley United	470	W 3 - 1	Webster 44 Danks 50 90	16
33	28		H	Workington	931	D 1 - 1	Danks 37	17
34	Feb 4		H	Lancaster City	745	W 2 - 0	Danks 32 Webster 78	14
35	7		A	Alfreton Town	250	L 0 - 1		14
36	11		A	Northwich Victoria	1062	W 1 - 0	Thompson 45	14
37	13		H	Leihj RMI	818	W 2 - 0	Colley 38 Danks 45	12
38	18		A	Vauxhall Motors	905	D 0 - 0		13
39	21		A	Nuneaton Borough	801	D 0 - 0		13
40	25		H	Hucknall Town	360	W 2 - 1	Danks 10 Kelly 56	12
41	Mar 6		H	Redditch United	1060	D 2 - 2	Danks 9 Colley 16	12
42	11		A	Barrow	932	W 2 - 0	Danks 38 (pen) 60	9
43	13		H	Moor Green	969	L 0 - 2		9
44	18		H	Stalybridge Celtic	742	L 0 - 1		11
45	25		A	Hednesford Town	510	W 4 - 0	Webster 11 46 Clegg 15 Kelly 47	9
46	April 1		H	Alfreton Town	860	D 2 - 2	Wood 23 Preece 81	9
47	4		A	Stalybridge Celtic	380	W 3 - 2	Seddon 60 Webster 65 Preece 89	7
48	8		A	Leigh RMI	185	W 4 - 1	Webster 15 23 Clegg 47 60	6
49	15		H	Harriogate Town	923	W 2 - 0	Webster 18 Danks 72	6
50	17		A	Droylsden	468	L 0 - 3		8
51	22		H	Hyde United	803	D 2 - 2	Webster 8 Wood 20	9
52	29		A	Worksop Town	390	W 3 - 0	Webster 3(39 (pen 53 82)	8

Ave. League Home Attendance:		827		**Goals**	74 49	**Top Goalscorer:** Webster (25)		

Best Position: 6th **Worst:** 20th

WORKINGTON

Manager: Tommy Cassidy   **Assistant Manager:** Tony Elliott

Physio: Alan Currie

Club Colours: All red

Change Colours: All white

Club Sponsor: Crest Sportswear

Previous League: Northern Premier League

Best Seasons: 5th Football Lg. Div 3 1965-66   **F.A. Cup:** 4th Rd 1933-34

F.A.Trophy.: 6th Rd 1999-2000

Ground address: Borough Park, Workington, Cumbria CA14 2DT

Tel. No: 01900 602871

Official website: www.workingtonredsafc.co.uk

Capacity: 2,500   Seats: 500   Covered: 1,000   Floodlights: Yes

Simple Directions: A66 into town. Right at T junction, follow A596 for 3/4 mile. Ground is signposted and visible.

Midweek Home Matchday: Tuesday

Clubhouse: Open matchdays and for private functions

Club Shop: Yes **Contact:** John Crook 01946 832710

Local Radio: BBC Radio Cumbria , C.F.M.

Local Press: Evening News & Star, Times & Star

CLUB PERSONNEL
Chairman: Dale Brotherton
V-Chairman: Humphrey Dobie
Secretary: Dale Brotherton, Lime House, Holm Hill, Dalston,Carlisle CA5 7BX Tel. No: 07977 759903
Press Officer & Programme.Editor:
Steve Durham 01946 61380
Programme
50 pages £1.50

2005-2006
Captain: Steve Birks
Player of the Year: Carl May
Top Goalscorer:: Craig Johnston 10

CLUB STATISTICS

Record	**Attendance**: 21,000 v Manchester United F.A.Cup 3rd Rd 04.01.58
	Victory: 17-1 v Cockermouth Crusaders , Cumberland Sen.Lg. 19.01.01
	Defeat: 0-9 v Chorley (A) NPL Premier 10.11.87
	Career Goalscorer: Billy Charlton 193
	Career Appearances: Bobby Brown 419
Record Transfer Fee	**Paid:** £6,000 for Ken Chisolm from Sunderland 1956
	Received: £33,000 from Liverpool for Ian McDonald 1974
Senior Honours:	Cumberland County Cup (23) N.P.L. Premier R-up 2004-05
Previous Leagues:	Cumberland Assoc. 1890-94, Cumberland Senior League 94-1901, 03-04, Lancs Lg., 1901-03, Lancs Comb, 04-10, North Eastern10-11 21-51 F.Lg 51-77
Previous Grounds:	Various 1884-1921 LonsdalePark 1921-37

Back row,left to right: Gareth Arnison, Kyle May, Lee Hoolickin, Adam Collin, Greg Goodall, Steve Birks, Darren Edmondson and Matt Henney. Front Row: Marc Green, Alan Gray, Tom Cowan, Craig Johnston, Dan Dillon and Graham Goulding.   Photo: Steve Durham

WORKINGTON

BEST LGE ATT.: 611 v Nuneaton Borough
LOWEST: 380 v Alfreton Town

No.	Date	Comp	H/A	Opponents	Att:	Result	Goalscorers	Pos
1	Aug 13	CN	H	Worksop Town	517	L 1 - 2	Goulding 66	19
2	15		A	Hyde United	422	D 1 - 1	Hooper 90	17
3	20		A	Hucknall Town	421	L 0 - 1		20
4	27		H	Worcester City	503	D 2 - 2	Arnold 17 Goulding 42	19
5	29		A	Moor Green	230	W 4 - 1	Henson 41 Arnold 48 (pen) Dillon 82 Hoolickin 90	14
6	Sept 3		H	Nuneaton Borough	611	L 0 - 2		17
7	6		A	Barrow	1308	L 1 - 6	Henney 65	18
8	10		H	Harrogate Town	475	L 2 - 4	Dillon 33 **Johnstone** 34 (pen)	19
9	17		A	Stafford Rangers	737	D 2 - 2	Street 36 Powell 57 (pen)	21
10	24	FAC 2Q	A	Stalybridge Celtic	448	D 0 - 0		
11	27	FAC 2Qr	H	Stalybridge Celtic	315	W 2 - 1*	**Johnstone** 42 Keeling 117 (og)	
12	Oct 1	CN	A	Leigh RMI	801	W 1 - 0	**Johnstone** 57	15
13	8	FAC 3Q	A	Burscough	303	L 0 - 2		
14	15	CN	H	Hednesford Town	385	W 2 - 0	Birks 44 Henney 67	13
15	18		H	Lancaster City	479	D 1 - 1	Heiniger 15	13
16	22		A	Redditch United	281	W 6 - 3	Henney 6 Arnold 28(pen) 57 (pen) Dillon 47 **Johnstone** 76 90	12
17	29		H	Gainsborough Trinity	434	W 2 - 0	Birks 3 Arnold 74	9
18	Nov 5		A	Hinckley United	567	D 0 - 0		10
19	12		H	Redditch United	487	L 1 - 2	Heiniger 47	11
20	26	FAT 3Q	A	Lancaster City	206	D 0 - 0		
21	Dec 3	CN	H	Stalybridge Celtic	458	L 1 - 3	Heiniger 55	15
22	6	FAT 3Qr	H	Lancaster City	326	L 1 - 2	Arnold 88	
23	10	CN	H	Kettering Town	437	W 3 - 2	Arnold 13 (pen) Hewson 30 86	13
24	12		A	Droylsden	246	W 3 - 2	Hoolicken 59 Gordon 72 78	10
25	26		A	Vauxhall Motors	180	L 1 - 2	Heineger 36	11
26	Jan 2		H	Vauxhall Motors	562	L 1 - 2	Hoolickin 84	13
27	7		A	Worksop Town	315	W 2 - 1	**Johnstone** 74 86	13
28	14		H	Hyde United	491	W 1 - 0	Hewson 26	10
29	21		H	Hucknall Town	580	D 1 - 1	Gordon 78	11
30	28		A	Worcester City	931	D 1 - 1	Henney 69	12
31	Feb 4		H	Leigh RMI	502	D 0 - 0		11
32	11		A	Hednesford Town	438	D 0 - 0		12
33	18		H	Northwich Victoria	476	W 5 - 2	Berkeley 3 (5 45 59) Hoolickin 81 Arnison 86	9
34	25		A	Harrogate Town	433	D 1 - 1	**Johnstone** 26	13
35	Mar 7		H	Barrow	542	D 0 - 0		
36	11		A	Gainsborough Trinity	337	D 0 - 0		13
37	14		A	Alfreton Town	257	W 3 - 1	Henney 3 (12 22 75)	9
38	18		H	Hinckley United	475	D 1 - 1	Arnison 85	10
39	28		A	Northwich Victoria	729	L 1 - 4	Berkeley 1	11
40	April 1		H	Draylsden	414	W 2 - 1	**Johnstone** 38 (pen) Henney 66	10
41	8		A	Stalybridge Celtic	423	L 1 - 2	**Johnstone** 72	12
42	11		H	Stafford Rangers	495	L 0 - 1		12
43	15		A	NuneatonBorough	1003	L 1 - 3	Hewson 41	13
44	17		H	Moor Green	392	L 1 - 4	Birks 45	13
45	20		A	Lancaster City	265	W 1 - 0	Hoolicken 62	11
46	22	41	H	Alfreton Town	380	W 2 - 0	Cowan 18 Heeney 65	11
47	29		A	Kettering Town	974	L 1 - 2	Birks 85	13

Ave. League Home Attendance: 481 　　**Goals** 63 67 　**Top Goalscorer:** Johnstone (10)
Best Position: 9th 　**Worst:** 21st

WORKSOP TOWN

Founded: 1861
Nickname: Tigers

Manager: Ronnie Glavin **Assistant Manager:** Peter Price **Physio:** Ian Peirce

Club Colours: BLack/Amber/Black

Change Colours: Green & White

Club Sponsors: Greencore

Previous League: Northern Premier

Best Seasons: League: 17th, Conference North 2004-2005

F.A. Cup: 3rd Rd 07-08, 21-22, 22-23 and 55-56 **F.A.Trophy:** 6th Rd 2000-01

Ground address: Babbage Way, off Sandy Lane, Worksop, Notts. S80 1UJ

Tel No: 01909 501911

Capacity: 3,000 **Seats:** 1,000 **Covered:**1,000 **Floodlights:** Yes

Simple Directions: M1 jct 31 (from north) and jct 30 (from South) towards Worksop sign. Then join A57 and follow signs for Sandy Lane Industrial Estate.Ground on left.

Midweek Home Matchday: Tuesday

Clubhouse: Bar, restaurant and sportsmans bar.

Club Shop: Yes, contact Steve Jarvis.

Local Press: Worksop Guardian, Worksop Star, Nottingham Football Post

Local Radio: Radio Sheffield, Radio Hallam, Radio Lincoln Trax FM

CLUB PERSONNEL

Chairman : Keith Illett
Secretary: Frank Nicholson, 9 North St., Morton, Gainsborough, Lincs. DN21 3AS
Company Sec & Press Officer: Janice Hepworth
Press Officer: Samantha Medlam
Prog Ed: Steve Jarvis
Programme 28-40 pages £2.00
2005-2006
Captain:
Player of the Year: K.Davies
Top Goalscorer: Saunders 10

CLUB STATISTICS

Record	**Attendance:** 2,100 v Chris Waddle XI for Linden Whitehead's testimonial 2001
Victory:	20-0 v Staveley 01.09.84
Defeat:	1-11 v Hull City Reserves 55-56
Career Goalscorer:	Kenny Clark 287 **Career Appearances:** Kenny Clark 347
Record Transfer Fee	**Paid:** £5,000 to Grantham Town for Kirk Jackson
	Received: £47,000 from Sunderland for Jon Kennedy 2000
Senior Honours:	NPL Prem Div R-up 98-99, NPL Div 1 R-up 97-98, Sheff & Hallamshire Senior Cup (9)
Previous Leagues:	Midland Counties 1896--98 1900-30 49-60 61-68 69-74 Sheff Association 1898-99 1931-33, Central Combination 33-35, Yorkshire 35-39 and Central Alliance 47-49 60-61 NPl 68-69 74-2004

Back Row (L-R): Ian Park (Physio), Adam Oldham, Kevin Dawson, Ben Saunders, Michael Simpkins, Tony Crane, Steve Wilson, Antony Jackson, Glen Downey, Kevin Davies, Jamie Harwood, Chrissy Christie (Assistant Physio).
Front Row: Steve Nicholson, Steve Robinson, Gregg Archer, John Hepworth (Director), Ronnie Glavin (Manager), Shaun Hird (Coach), Keith Ilett (Chairman), Steve Owens, Andrew Parton, Karl Everett

WORKSOP TOWN

BEST LGE ATT.: 615 v Gainsborough Trinity
LOWEST: 276 v Hyde United

No.	Date	Comp	H/A	Opponents	Att:	Result	Goalscorers	Pos
1	Aug 13	CN	A	Workington	517	W 2 - 1	Wilson 28 Carrington 72	6
2	16		H	Stafford Rangers	519	L 0 - 1		10
3	20		H	Alfreton Town	496	D 1 - 1	Jackson 8	11
4	27		A	Stalybridge Celtic	576	L 1 - 2	Jackson 33	14
5	29		H	Harrogate Town	342	W 1 - 0	Hurst 86	10
6	Sept 3		A	Kettering Town	817	L 0 - 1		15
7	10		H	Hyde United	276	D 1 - 1	Jackson 90	13
8	17		A	Worksop Town	257	L 1 - 2	Wilson 39	14
9	24	FAC 2Q	H	Witton Albion	348	L 0 - 1		
10	Oct 1	CN	A	Vauxhall Motors	201	L 2 - 5	Robnson 62 Wilson 86	16
11	8		A	Droylsden	272	L 1 - 3	Owens 69	18
12	15		H	Hucknall Town	501	W 2 - 1	**Saunders** 5 Oldham 30	14
13	18		H	Worksop Town	446	D 1 - 1	Oldham 26	16
14	22		A	Hyde United	313	D 1 - 1	Carrington 84	14
15	29		H	Hednesford Town	446	D 3 - 3	**Saunders** 55 88 Carrington 74	15
16	Nov 5		A	Leigh RMi	186	W 1 - 0	Dempsey 31	13
17	12		H	Barrow	407	W 2 - 1	Robinson 29 Jackson 55	
18	19		A	Redditch United	332	W 3 - 0	Jackson 54 **Saunders** 71 79	10
19	26	FAT 3Q	H	**AFC Telford**	416	D 1 - 1	**Jackson 51**	
20	29	FAT 3Qr	A	**AFC Telford**	952	W 2 - 1	**Saunders 36 83**	
21	Dec 3	CN	H	Hinckley United	376	D 0 - 0		8
22	6		A	Nuneaton Borough	820	L 1 - 3	Wilson 67	11
23	10		A	Worcester City	806	D 1 - 1	Kirkwood 29	11
24	17	FAT 1	A	**Burton Albion**	1359	W 1 - 0	**Saunders 90**	
25	26	CN	H	Gainsborough Trinity	615	D 1 - 1	Dempsey 58	12
26	30		H	Moor Green	284	L 0 - 2		14
27	Jan 2		A	Gainsborough Trinity	647	L 0 - 2		15
28	7		H	Workington	315	L 1 - 2	Crane 3	16
29	14	FAT2	A	**Weston-s-Mare**	366	D 1 - 1	**Crane 25**	
30	17	FAT2r	H	**Weston-s-Mare**	369	W 2 - 1	**Norton 8 Wilson 42**	
31	21	CN	A	Alfreton Town	367	L 1 - 2	Dempsey 30	16
32	28		H	Stalybridge Celtic	506	W 2 - 1	**Saunders** 7 Crane 14	15
33	Feb 4	FAT 3	A	**Accrington Stanley**	961	D 1 - 1	**Norton 49 (pen)**	
34	7	FAT 3R	H	**Accrington Stanley**	773	D 1 - 1	**Norton 76 Worksop won 4-2 after penalties**	
35	11	CN	H	Hucknall Town	480	D 0 - 0		16
36	14		A	Stafford Rangers	1045	L 2 - 3	Grayson (og) 59 Wilson 84	16
37	18		H	Nunerton Borough	476	L 0 - 4		17
38	21		H	Norwich Victoria	479	L 1 - 4	Owens 81	18
39	25	FAT 4	H	**Boreham Wood**	1006	L 0 - 1		
40	Mar 11	CN	A	Hednesford Town	478	L 1 - 2	Owens 21	21
41	14		H	Vauxhall Motors	318	D 1 - 1	Owens 19	20
42	18		H	Leigh RMI	296	D 3 - 3	Owens 7 **Saunders** 32 Bertos 41	20
43	21		D	Droylsden	285	W 3 - 2	Wilson 10 Davies 26 Crane (pen~) 77	18
44	25		A	Barrow	852	L 0 - 1		19
45	April 1		H	Redditch United	370	D 1 - 1	Owns 9	18
46	8		A	Hinckley United	528	L 0 - 3		19
47	15		H	Kettering Town	468	W 2 - 1	Crane 44 Bertos 58	19
48	17		H	Harrogate Town	442	L 0 - 2		19
49	22		A	Moor Green	210	L 0 - 1		19
50	25		H	Lancaster City	315	W 2 - 0	Owens 9 Crane 49	19
51	29		H	Worcester City	380	L 0 - 3		19

Ave. League Home Attendance: 375   **Goals**   55   77   **Top Goalscorer:** Saunders (10)
Best Position: 9th   **Worst:** 21st

FOOTBALL LEAGUE

STEP 1

FOOTBALL
CONFERENCE

STEP 2

| CONFERENCE NORTH | **CONFERENCE SOUTH** |

STEP 3

| SOUTHERN PREMIER | NORTHERN PREMIER | ISTHMIAN PREMIER |

STEP 4

| SOUTHERN DIVISION 1 SOUTH &WEST MIDLAND | NORTHERN PREMIER DIV.1 | ISTHMIAN DIVISION 1 NORTH   SOUTH |

STEP 5/6

Combined Counties	Hellenic	Northern League	Spartan South Midlands	Wessex
Eastern Counties	Kent	Northern Counties East	Sussex County	Western
Essex Senior	Midland Alliance	North West Counties	United Counties	

STEP 7

Anglian Combination	Dorset County	Kent County	Midland Combination	Peterborough & District	West Cheshire
Bedford & District	Dorset Premier	Leicestershire Senior	Midland League	Reading League	West Lancashire
Brighton & Hove	East Sussex	Liverpool County	North Berkshire	Somerset County	West Midlands (reg)
Cambridgeshire County	Essex & Suffolk Border	Manchester Football	Northampton Town Lge	South Western	West Sussex
Central Midlands	Essex Intermediate	Mid Cheshire League	Northamptonshire Comb.	Suffolk & Ipswich	Wiltshire League
Crawley & District	Gloucesterhisre Co.	Mid Sussex	Northern Alliance	Teeside League	Worthing & District
Devon County	Herts Senior County	Middlesex County	Oxfordshire Senior	Wearside League	

CONFERENCE SOUTH

		P	W	D	L	F	A	Pts
1.	Weymouth	42	30	4	8	80	34	90
2.	St Albans City*	42	27	5	10	94	47	86
3.	Farnborough Town	42	23	9	10	65	41	78
4.	Lewes	42	21	10	11	78	57	73
5.	Histon	42	21	8	13	70	56	71
6.	Havant & Waterlooville	42	21	10	11	64	48	70
7.	Cambridge City	42	20	10	12	78	46	67
8.	Eastleigh	42	21	3	18	65	58	66
9.	Welling United	42	16	17	9	58	44	65
10.	Thurrock	42	16	10	16	60	60	58
11.	Dorchester Town	42	16	7	19	60	72	55
12.	Bognor Regis Town	42	12	13	17	54	55	49
13.	Sutton United	42	13	10	19	48	61	49
14.	Weston-super-Mare	42	14	7	21	57	88	49
15.	Bishop's Stortford	42	11	15	16	55	63	48
16.	Yeading	42	13	8	21	47	62	47
17.	Eastbourne Borough	42	10	16	16	51	61	46
18.	Newport County	42	12	8	22	50	67	44
19.	Basingstoke Town	42	12	8	22	47	72	44
20.	Hayes	42	11	9	22	47	60	42
21.	Carshalton Athletic	42	8	16	18	42	68	40
22.	Maidenhead United	42	8	9	25	49	99	31

*Promoted via the play-offs.

		1	2	3	4	5	6	7	8	9	10	11	12	13	14	15	16	17	18	19	20	21	22
1	Basingstoke Town		1-1	2-3	0-5	2-1	2-0	2-2	0-1	0-1	2-1	1-1	0-1	1-5	0-1	1-0	1-1	2-0	0-3	2-2	2-1	0-3	0-4
2	Bishop's Stortford	1-1		2-1	1-3	3-3	5-2	0-1	4-1	1-1	1-3	1-0	5-0	0-3	1-0	0-1	1-3	2-1	2-2	1-1	2-3	0-2	2-1
3	Bognor Regis Town	2-1	2-2		4-2	1-1	1-1	2-1	2-0	0-1	0-1	1-1	3-1	2-2	8-1	1-1	2-1	0-0	0-1	0-0	0-1	0-2	0-2
4	Cambridge City	1-0	1-1	2-0		0-0	1-2	2-3	2-1	0-2	0-0	3-1	3-1	0-2	3-0	0-2	4-3	3-0	6-0	0-0	3-0	1-3	0-2
5	Carshalton Athletic	1-2	0-0	1-1	0-2		3-1	2-2	1-3	2-2	1-3	1-2	0-0	2-2	0-1	1-0	0-2	0-0	0-0	1-0	1-1	2-1	2-2
6	Dorchester Town	2-1	1-3	3-5	1-0	2-0		3-0	1-3	1-1	1-1	2-2	0-3	2-2	1-3	2-2	1-4	0-5	2-0	0-3	1-2	2-0	4-0
7	Eastbourne Borough	2-3	1-1	0-0	1-1	1-1	1-1		0-1	0-1	2-2	0-0	1-1	3-1	3-3	2-0	1-1	2-1	0-0	1-1	1-3	0-2	2-1
8	Eastleigh	0-3	0-1	1-0	1-1	3-1	1-2	2-1		2-0	2-6	2-1	1-2	2-0	2-1	2-0	0-2	2-0	3-0	1-3	4-1	2-0	0-3
9	Farnborough Town	1-0	2-1	0-3	4-0	0-1	2-3	1-0		4-1	0-0	0-2	2-2	3-1	2-1	0-0	2-1	0-0	1-0	5-0	0-1	1-0	
10	Havant-&-W'ville'	2-0	2-2	1-0	1-1	1-1	1-0	1-0	2-1	1-0		1-1	3-1	1-0	2-1	1-2	1-0	0-1	1-2	0-0	3-2	2-1	3-0
11	Hayes	1-2	2-0	1-2	2-0	1-2	0-1	1-0	0-2	1-0	0-1		2-1	2-2	2-2	3-2	0-1	2-1	0-1	1-3	4-1	1-2	0-1
12	Histon	2-0	3-2	2-2	1-0	0-1	4-1	3-1	1-0	3-6	3-1	2-3		1-1	3-0	2-3	0-5	3-0	3-1	1-1	1-1	2-1	1-0
13	Lewes	3-0	2-1	1-1	2-2	2-1	3-2	1-0	1-2	6-2	0-2	2-1	0-3		2-2	1-0	0-2	2-0	0-0	2-1	5-2	2-3	1-0
14	Maidenhead Utd	0-0	2-2	1-2	0-5	0-2	2-3	2-6	2-2	1-2	3-1	2-1	1-4	0-1		1-1	0-4	2-0	1-3	2-4	2-4	0-0	1-2
15	Newport County	2-0	1-0	1-0	0-2	4-1	0-2	1-1	0-2	1-2	2-3	1-0	0-1	2-3	3-0		1-3	1-0	3-4	2-2	2-2	0-3	1-3
16	St Albans City	3-1	3-0	2-0	2-4	3-0	2-0	5-0	2-4	2-2	2-0	1-0	1-0	2-0	4-0	1-0		3-1	3-2	3-1	1-2	4-0	5-2
17	Sutton United	0-1	1-1	1-0	3-2	1-1	1-0	2-0	0-3	1-0	1-1	2-1	1-1	1-5	4-1	1-1	4-0		1-1	2-1	1-2	0-3	0-0
18	Thurrock	4-1	2-1	3-0	0-3	2-1	0-1	1-0	3-1	0-2	0-2	1-1	1-2	2-3	1-2	4-2	2-1	5-3		1-1	0-1	1-2	0-1
19	Welling United	3-2	0-0	2-0	1-1	2-0	4-3	1-2	2-1	1-0	2-2	1-0	1-1	2-1	3-3	1-1	3-1	0-0	1-1		1-0	1-0	0-1
20	Weston-super-Mare	4-3	0-1	2-2	1-3	2-0	0-4	1-0	1-4	1-1	1-3	1-1	1-4	1-2	1-1	2-1	3-1	2-3	0-5	0-1		1-3	0-3
21	Weymouth	1-1	3-1	2-0	1-1	4-0	1-0	2-1	2-0	1-2	1-0	5-1	1-0	2-0	4-0	4-0	3-2	3-1	2-0	2-1	2-1		1-1
22	Yeading	0-4	0-0	0-3	1-2	3-4	0-1	1-1	2-2	0-3	2-0	2-3	1-0	0-3	0-2	1-2	2-2	0-2	1-1	1-0	1-2	0-1	

BASINGSTOKE TOWN

Founded: 1896
Nickname: Dragons

Manager: Francis Vines   **Assistant Manager:** Steve Richardson

Club Colours: Blue & Yellow stripes/blue/blue

Change Colours: Red/black/black

Club Sponsor: Centerprise International

Previous League: Isthmian

Best Seasons: Conference South 6th 2004-05   **F.A. Cup:** 2nd Rd Replay 97-98

F.A.Trophy.: 3rd Round 98-99

Physio: Mark Randall

Ground address: Camrose Road, Western Way, Basingstoke RG22 6EZ

Tel No: 01256 327575   **E-mail:** info@btfc.co.uk

Official website: www.btfc.co.uk

Capacity: 6,000   **Seats:** 651   **Covered:** 2,000   **Floodlights:**Yes

Simple Directions: Exit 6 off M3 and follow A30 west.Ground off Winchester Road. Two miles from bus and rail stations

Midweek Home Matchday: Tuesday

Reserves League: Suburban Premier Division

Clubhouse: Open daily including lunchtimes   **Club Shop:** Open Daily

Local Radio: Radio 210 and Kestral Radio

Local Press: Basingstoke Gazette

CLUB PERSONNEL

Chairman: T.B.A.
Patron: Charles Foyle
President: Rafi Razzack
Secretary: Richard Trodd, 5 Lehar Close, Brighton Hill, Basingstoke RG22 4HT
Company Sec: Mrs Linda Murfitt
Commercial Manager: Steve Duly
Press Officer: Steve Duly
Programme Editor:
Linda Murfitt (07795 617314)
Programme
24 Pages Price: £1.50

2005-2006
Captain: Jason Bristow
Player of the Year: Ben Surey
Top Goalscorer: Lewis Cook

CLUB STATISTICS

Record	Attendance:	5,085 v Wycombe Wanderers FAC 1st Rd replay 97-8
	Victory:	10-1 v Chichester City (H) F.A. Cup 1st Qual 1976
	Defeat:	0-8 v Aylesbury United Southern League April 1979
	Career Goalscorer:	Paul Coombs 159 (91-99)
	Career Appearances:	Billy Coomb
Record Transfer Fee	**Paid:**	£4,750 to Gosport Borough for Steve Ingham
	Received:	Undisclosed from Wycombe Wanderers for Sergio Torres
Senior Honours:		Southern League Southern Division Champions 84-85 , Isthmian League Division 1 Runners-Up 1996-97 1998-99 and Hants Senior Cup (3) R-Up (6)
Previous Leagues:		Hants 1900-40 45-71 Southern 71-87 Isthmian 87-2004
Grounds:		Castle Field 1896-1947

Back row,left to right: Francis Vines (Manager), Joe Harris, Joe Dolan, Ben Wright, Danny Brown, Stuart Searle, Andrew Smallpiece, Ashley Jones, James Taylor, Jason Bristow, Ade Olayinka, Ben Surey, Andrew Ottley and Mark Randall (Physio) Front Row: Francis Quarm, Neville Roach, Mark Peters, David Ray, Matthew Warner, Scott Kirkwood, Matthew Ottley, Justyn McKay and Steve Richardson (Assistant Manager).

BASINGSTOKE TOWN

BEST LGE ATT.: 3,900 v Hayes
LOWEST: 202 v Welling United

No.	Date	Comp	H/A	Opponents	Att:	Result	Goalscorers	Pos
1	Aug 13	CS	H	Dorchester Town	388	W 2 - 0	Torres 48 **Peters** 90	6
2	17		A	Weston-s-Mare	309	L 3 - 4	Cook 30 Torres 44 **Peters** 87 (pen)	9
3	20		A	Eastbourne Borough	704	W 3 - 2	**Peters** 31 39 Whiddett 47	7
4	27		H	St Albans City	440	D 1 - 1	Webber 50	6
5	29		A	Histon	441	L 0 - 2		7
6	Sept 3		H	Carshalton Athletic	304	W 2 - 1	**Peters** 7 Whiddett 13	7
7	10		A	Cambridge City	433	L 0 - 1		9
8	17		H	Farnborough Town	706	L 0 - 1		15
9	24	FAC 2Q	A	**Bognor Regis Town**	552	D 1 - 1	McKay 55	
10	27	FAC 2Qr	H	**Bognor Regis Town**	315	W 2 1 1	Cook 11 Ray 47	
11	Oct 1	CS	H	Sutton United	437	W 2 - 0	Ray 26 54	12
12	8	FAC 3Q	A	**Worthing**	577	W 4 - 2	Whiddett 29 Cook 73 Peters 75 78	
13	15	CS	A	Bishop Stortford	340	D 1 - 1	**Peters** 78	12
14	17		A	Havant & Waterlooville	410	L 0 - 2		12
15	22	FAC 4Q	H	**Chippenham Town**	1072	L 0 - 1		
16	29	CS	A	Lewes	448	L 0 - 3		17
17	Nov 5		H	Newport County	471	W 1 - 0	Dolan 82	15
18	8		H	Weymouth	557	L 0 - 3		17
19	12		A	Thurrock	187	L 1 - 4	Holgate 26	18
20	19		H	Yeading	285	L 0 - 4		18
21	22		H	Welling United	202	D 2 - 2	Taylor 7 Surey 9	18
22	26	FAT 3Q	H	**Welling United**	313	L 0 - 2		
23	Dec 10	CS	H	Bognor Regis Town	287	L 2 - 3	Morgan 38 87	18
24	17		H	Havant & Waterlooville	298	W 2 - 1	Morgan 46 Cook 66	18
25	26		A	Eastleigh	506	W 3 - 0	McKay 6 64 Ray 54	16
26	31		A	Hayes	213	W 2 - 1	Ray 37 Surey 74	
27	Jan 2		H	Eastleigh	507	L 0 - 1		14
28	7		A	Dorchester Town	521	L 1 - 2	Morgan 43	15
29	21		H	Eastbourne Borough	346	D 2 - 2	Whiddett 35 Taylor 44	15
30	28		A	St Albans City	526	L 1 - 3	Taylor 89	17
31	31		A	Maidenhead United	395	D 0 - 0		17
32	Feb 4		A	Sutton United	453	W 1 - 0	McKay 28	15
33	11		H	Bishop's Stortford	320	D 1 - 1	Cook 23	15
34	14		A	Weston-s-Mare	224	W 2 - 1	Ray 59 Cook 74	12
35	18		A	Welling United	537	L 2 - 3	Pedroiti 60 Surey 84	14
36	25		H	Cambridge City	301	L 0 - 5		16
37	Mar 4		A	Farnborough Town	619	L 0 - 1		17
38	11		H	Lewes	280	L 1 - 5	Basualdo 61	17
39	14		A	Weymouth	1802	D 1 - 1	Basualdo (pen) 33	17
40	18		A	Newport County	504	L 0 - 2		17
41	25		H	Thurrock	268	L 0 - 3		17
42	April 1		A	Yeading	191	W 4 - 0	Taylor 32 40 Ray 44 Sole 48	17
43	8		H	Maidenhaed United	345	L 0 - 1		17
44	15		A	Carshalton Athletic	386	W 2 1 1	Sole 3 Taylor 49	17
45	17		A	Histon	293	L 0 - 1		17
46	22		H	Hayes	3900	D 1 - 1	Cook 90 (pen)	19
47	29		A	Bognor Regis Town	329	L 1 - 2	Wright 71	19

Ave. League Home Attendance: 531   **Goals** 54 79   **Top Goalscorer:** Peters (8)
Best Position: 6th   **Worst:** 19th

BEDFORD TOWN

Founded: 1908
Reformed 1989
Nickname: The Eagles

Manager: Nick Platnauer **Asst.Manager:** Dave Randall **Physio:** Brendon Skinner

Club Colours: Blue with white and gold trim

Change Colours: White with blue trim

Club Sponsor: Turner's Carpets

Previous League: Southern

Best Seasons: League: Southern League Champions 1958-59

F.A. Cup: 4th Rd 63-64 65-66 **F.A.Trophy.:** Semi-Final 1974-75

Ground address: The Eyrie, Meadow Lane, Cardington, Bedford MK44 3SB

Tel No: 01234 831558 Fax: 01234 831990

Supporters Website: www.bedfordeagles.net

Capacity: 3,000 **Seats:** 300 **Covered:** 1,000 **Floodlights:**Yes

Simple Directions: From the A1 at the Sandy roundabout take A603 through Moggerhanger and Willington and the ground is situated just before the Bedford by-pass on the right.

Midweek Home Matchday: Tuesday

Clubhouse: Large function room with bar and food.

Club Shop: Well stocked.**Contact:** Gerry Edmonds 01234 381213

Local Radio: Chiltern Radio and Three Counties.

Local Press: Beds Times and Beds on Sunday

CLUB PERSONNEL

Chairman: David Howell
Directors: Dave Redman,Tony Luff
Gerry Edmunds, Dave Swallow and
Michael Hooker
Secretary: Dave Swallow, c/o club
Commercial Manager:
Mick Hooker
Press Offiicer:
Dave Swallow
Programme Editor: Dave Swallow
Programme
40 pages £1.50
2005-006
Captain: Lee Howarth
Player of the Year:
Derwayne Stupple
Top Scorer: Rene Howe

SOUTHERN CLUB STATISTICS

Record	**Attendance** :3,000 v Peterborough United Ground opening 06.08.93
	Victory: 9-0 v Ickleford and v Cardington
	Defeat: 0-5 v Hendon
	Career Goalscorer: Jason Reed
	Career Appearances: Eddie Lawley
Senior Honours:	Southern League Play Off Winners 2005-2006, Isthmian Div 1 R-up 00-01 Div 2 98-909 Bedfordshire Senior Cup 94-95
Previous Leagues:	South Midlands: 91-94, Predecessors: Utd Co.1908-39, Southern 46-82, Isthmian 94-2004 and Southern 200 5-2006
Grounds:	Allen Park, Queens Park, Bedford Park Pitch 1991-93 (for predecessors): London Rd., Gasworks, Queens Park, The Eyrie, Raleigh St

Back row,left to right: Nick Platnauer (Manager), Dave Randall (Assistant Manager), Gavin Hoyte, Rene Howe, Ian Brown, Lee Howarrth (Captain), Chris Dillon, Matt Childs and Brendon Skinner (physio). Front row: Jason James, Jonathon Woolf, Craig Rydeheard, Rob Miller, Derwayne Stupple, Carl Williams and Eddie Lawley.

BEDFORD TOWN

BEST LGE ATT.: 556 v Aylesbury United
LOWEST: **357** v Yate Town

No.	Date	Comp	H/A	Opponents	Att:	Result	Goalscorers	Pos
1	Aug 13	SP	A	Salisbury City	571	L 0 - 1		17
2	16		H	Chesham United	407	L 2 - 3	Rydeheard 86 Dillon 90	18
3	20		H	Yate Town	357	W 2 - 0	Hatch 11 **Howe** 34	13
4	23		A	Northwood	159	W 3 - 2	**Howe** 56 60 Hatch 90	8
5	27		H	Banmbury United	474	W 3 - 2	**Howe** 29 37 Hatch 49	5
6	29		A	King's Lynn	835	L 0 - 1		10
7	Sept 3		A	Tiverton Town	416	W 1 - 0	Dillon 57	7
8	10	FAC 1Q	H	**AFC Sudbury**	460	D 2 - 2	**Rydeheard 42 Howarth 84**	
9	13	FAC 1Qr	A	**AFC Sudbury**	441	L 1 - 2*	**Miller 13**	
10	17	SP	H	Bath City	399	W 1 - 0	Miller 69	6
11	24		H	King's Lynn	439	W 3 - 2	Dillon 3 (55 70 86)	4
12	27		A	Grantham Town	263	L 0 - 3		5
13	Oct 1		H	Gloucester City	472	W 5 - 3	Miller 34 Dillon 76 87 **Howe** 43 79	2
14	4		A	Cheshunt	167	W 3 - 0	Hatch 24 Rydeheard 44 Dillon 88	2
15	15	FAT1Q	H	**Bracknell Town**	420	**W 3 - 0**	**Blake 25 Howe 57 63**	
16	22	SP	A	Evesham United	235	D 1 - 1	Hatch 30	2
17	29		H	Team Bath	439	D 1 - 1	Phillips 89	4
18	Nov 5		A	Rugby Town	304	L 2 - 5	McElroy 73 76	4
19	8		H	Mangotsfield Town	372	W 1 - 0	Hatch 74	3
20	12	FAT 2R	A	**Hitchin Town**	603	**W 2 - 1**	**Dillon 7 88**	
21	19	SP	H	Halesowen Town	505	D 0 - 0		3
22	26	FAT 3Q	A	**Weston-s-Mare**	221	**L 0 - 4**		
23	Dec 3	SP	A	Chippenham Town	632	W 2 - 1	Dillon 20 **Howe** 65	2
24	10		H	Cheshunt	453	D 1 - 1	Howarth 63 (pen)	4
25	13		A	Chesham United	241	W 3 - 0	**Howe** 29 33 Howarth 67 (pen)	3
26	17		A	Merthyr Tydfil	395	W 3 - 1	**Howe** 6 Dillon 83 Rydeheard 86	1
27	31		H	Grantham Town	517	D 1 - 1	Dillon 67	4
28	Jan 2		A	Aylesbury United	493	W 2 - 1	Phillips 43 Miller 64	3
29	7		A	Bath City	661	D 1 - 1	Priestnall 73	3
30	14		H	Merthyr Tydfil	501	L 0 - 1		3
31	21		A	Yate Town	215	L 0 - 4		4
32	28		H	Tiverton Town	387	W 3 - 0	Howarth 34 (pen) Hoyte 75 Gould 84 (og)	4
33	31		A	Hitchin Town	480	L 0 - 2		4
34	Feb 4		A	Team Bath	98	W 2 - 1	Hoyte 21 Wiliams 64	3
35	11		H	Northwood	463	W 4 - 0	Draycott 30 47 Williams 43 **Howe** 44	3
36	18		H	Evesham United	489	D 1 - 1	**Howe** 86	5
37	25		A	Banbury United	454	L 2 - 3	Williams 44 Lawley 52	
38	Mar 4		A	Chippenham Town	550	W 2 - 1	**Howe** 45 Bonner 65	5
39	11		A	Cirencester Town	166	L 1 - 5	**Howe** 44	5
40	18		H	Salisbury City	479	W 1 - 0	**Howe** 90	5
41	25		A	Mangotsfield United	209	W 2 - 0	**Howe** 15 Howarth 35 (pen)	5
42	April 1		A	Gloucester City	384	D 0 - 0		5
43	8		H	Citrencester Town	452	W 2 - 1	**Howe** 43 Draycott 90	5
44	15		A	Aylesbury United	556	W 2 - 1	Dillon 21 Bonner 56	5
45	17		A	Hitchin Town	508	W 4 - 1	Dillon 2 Williams 47 **Howe** 51 61	5
46	22		A	Halesowen Town	355	D 1 - 1	**Howe** 34	5
47	29		H	Rugby Town	482	D 1 - 1	Draycott 46	5
48	May 1	Play Off SF	A	**Bath City**	1691	**W 1 - 0**	**Howe** 4	
49	6	Play Off Final	A	**Chippenham Town**	2029	**W 3 - 2**	**Bonner 10 90 Howe 33**	

Ave. League Home Attendance: 461   **Goals**   81 62   **Top Goalscorer:** Howe (25)
Best Position: 1st   **Worst:**   18th

BISHOP'S STORTFORD

Founded: 1874
Nickname: Blues or Bishops

Manager: Martin Hayes   **Asst.Manager/Coach:** Paul Joynes

Physios: David Jude, Peter Fox and ColinTaylor

Club Colours: Blue & white stripes/blue/blue

Change Colours: All yellow

Club Sponsor: Servebase

Previous League: Isthmian

Best Seasons: League: Conference South 10th **F.A. Cup:** 3rd Rd replay 82-83

F.A.Trophy.: Winners 1980-81   **F.A.Amateur Cup:** Winners 73-74

Ground address: Woodside Park, Dunmow Road, Bishop's Stortford

Tel No: 08700 339900   Website: www.bsfc.co.uk

Capacity: 4,000   **Seats:** 298   **Covered:** 700   **Floodlights:** Yes

Simple Directions: M11 Jct 8 A1250 towards town centre. Left at first roundabout. Woodside is first on right opposite Golf Club

Midweek Home Matchday: Tuesday

Clubhouse: extensive bars and function rooms. Open lunchtimes, evening and matchdays Mick Wheeler c/o club **Shop:** Full stock**. Contact:** Adam Sydesvia.

Local Radio: Essex FM Breeze AM Mercury FM Three Counties.

Local Press: Bishops Stortford Citizen, Herts & Essex Observer and The Herald.

CLUB PERSONNEL
Chairman: Luigu Del Basso
Chief Executive & Director of Football: John Goodwin
Vice President: Graham Kelly
Football Secretary & Press Off.: Ian Kettridge, 25 Cox Ley, Hatfield Heath, Bishop's Stortford , Herts. CM22 7ER
Tel No: 07904 169017 (M)
Commercial Manager: Liz Farr
Programme Editor: Neil Archer: 01279 832566 (H)

CLUB STATISTICS

Record	**Attendance:** 6,000 F.A.Cup 2nd Rd 1972 and 2 nd Rd repl;ay 1983
Victory:	11-0 v Nettleswell & Buntwill, Herst Jun Cup 1911
Defeat:	0-13 v Cheshunt (H) Herts Sen. Cup 1926
Career Goalscorer:	Since 1929. Jimmy Badcock 123 **Career Appearances:** Phil Hopkins 543
Record Transfer Fee	**Paid:** Undisclosed to Grays Athletic for Vinnie John 1999
	Received: Undisclosed from Dagenham & Redbridge for Glen Southam
Senior Honours:	F.A.Trophy 80-1 F.A.Amateur Cup 73-4 Prem Inter Lg.Cup 89-90 Isthmian Div 1 80-1 Athenian 69-70 London Senior Cup 73-4 Herts Sen.Cup (9)
Previous Leagues:	Stansted & Dist 06-19, Saffron Walden & District, East Herts 1896-97 02-06 19-21 Herts Co 21-5 27-9, Herts & Essex Border: 25-27 Spartan 29-51 Delphian 51-63 Athenian 63-73 Isthmian 74-2004

Back row – left to right David Jude(physio),Daryl Bourgeois,Duane Jackman, Darren Williams, James Hussey, Ben Lewis,Andy Young, Rob Gillman,Steve Morison,Gareth Gwillim,Jack Midson and Colin Taylor(physio)
Front row – Matt Jones,Leon Green,Bob Thanda, Martin Hayes(player/manager), David Rainford (Captain), Paul Joynes, Alex Martin, Richard Howell andTim Langer.

BISHOP'S STORTFORD

BEST LGE ATT.: 1,016 v Weymouth
LOWEST: **267** v Dorchester Town

No.	Date	Comp	H/A	Opponents	Att:	Result	Goalscorers	Pos
1	Aug 13	CS	H	Eastbourne Borough	307	L 0 - 1		13
2	16		A	Carshalton Athletic	326	D 0 - 0		16
3	20		A	Dorchetser Town	472	W 3 - 1	Jackman 44 83 Brown 72 (og)	10
4	27		H	St Albans City	440	D 1 - 1	Webber 50	15
5	29		A	Eastleigh	386	W 1 - 0	Midson 33	11
6	Sept 3		H	Farnborough Town	363	D 1 - 1	Howells 28	11
7	10		A	Hayes	202	L 0 - 2		15
8	17		H	Sutton United	305	W 2 - 1	Hodges 31 Jackman 56	14
9	24	FAC 2Q	A	**Fleet Town**	201	W 2 - 0	Rainford 5 (pen) Edwards 48	
10	Oct 1	CS	A	Cambridge United	1052	D 1 - 1	Jackman 58	15
11	8	FAC 3Q	A	**Hayes**	231	L 0 - 2		
12	15	CS	H	Basingstoke Town	340	D 1 - 1	Rainford 88	14
13	18		H	Maidenhead United	310	W 1 - 0	Gillman 5	13
14	22		A	Bognor Regis Town	326	D 2 - 2	Howell 34 Rainford 70	11
15	29		A	Thurrock	294	L 1 - 2	Evans 60	14
16	Nov 5		H	Lewes	312	L 0 - 3		16
17	12		A	Newport County	649	L 0 - 1		17
18	15		H	Histon	342	W 5 - 0	Morison 3 (3 8 52) Midson 30 Jackman 72	15
19	19		H	Havant & Waterlooville	307	L 1 - 3	Martion 27	16
20	26	FAT 3Q	A	**Maidenhead United**	165	D 2 - 2	Essandoh 22 Forbes 55	
21	29	FAT 3Qr	H	**Maidenhead United**	171	W 2 - 1*	Essandoh (2)	
22	Dec 3	CS	A	Yeading	169	D 0 - 0		16
23	10		H	Welling United	309	D 1 - 1	Rainford 48	17
24	18	FAT 1	A	**Exeter City**	1807	L 1 - 2	Essandoh 43	
25	26		A	St.Albans City	658	L 0 - 3		18
26	31		A	Weymouth	1452	L 1 - 3	Rainford (pen) 72	
27	Jan 2		H	St Albans City	512	L 1 - 3	**Morison** 5	18
28	7		A	Eastbourne Borough	538	L 1 - 3	**Morison** 58	18
29	21		H	Dorchester Town	267	W 5 - 2	Rainford 32 (pen) Ward 33 Essandoh 56 85 **Morison** 66	18
30	28		A	Weston-s-Mare	186	W 1 - 0	Rainford 31 (pen)	16
31	Feb 1		A	Basingstoke Town	320	D 1 - 1	**Morison** 21	16
32	15		H	Carshalton Athletic	289	D 3 - 3	Dolman 8 Mason 12 Essandoh 28	16
33	18		H	Bognor Regis Town	330	W 2 - 1	**Morison** 20 Essendoh 61	16
34	21		A	Maidenhead United	183	D 2 - 2	Essendoh 75 Gillman 87	16
35	25		H	Hayes	314	W 1 - 0	Maxwell 34	13
36	Mar 4		A	Sutton United	487	D 1 - 1	**Morison** 50	12
37	11		H	Thurrock	320	D 2 - 2	**Morison** 30 42	12
38	14		H	Cambridge City	384	L 1 - 3	**Morison** 33	13
39	18		A	Lewes	395	L 1 - 2	Mason 74	13
40	25		H	Newport County	370	L 0 - 1		14
41	April 1		A	Havant & Waterlooville	428	D 2 - 2	Jackman 51 Mason 61	13
42	8		H	Yeading	302	W 2 - 1	Rainford 57 **Morison** 66	14
43	14		A	Farnborough Town	698	L 0 - 3		14
44	17		H	Eastleigh	270	W 4 - 1	**Morison** 1 80 Rainford 70 pen Evans 75	13
45	22		H	Weymouth	1016	L 0 - 2		13
46	26		A	Histon	691	L 2 - 3	Gwilliam 49 87	13
47	29		A	Weling United	512	D 0 - 0		15

Ave. League Home Attendance: 367   **Goals**   61 67   **Top Goalscorer:** Morison (15)
Best Position: 10th   **Worst:** 18th

BOGNOR REGIS TOWN

Founded: 1883
Nickname: The Rocks

Manager: Jack Pearce **Assistant Manager:** Michael Birmingham
Coaches: Colin Hunwick and Derrin Kilpatrick
Club Colours: White with green trim/green/white
Change Colours: All Azure
Club Sponsors: T.B.A.
Previous League: Isthmian
Best Seasons: League: 9th Conference South 2004-05
F.A. Cup: 2nd Round (4) **F.A.Trophy:** 3rd Rd 95-96 **F.A.Amateur Cup**: 1st Rd 71-2
Coach: Colin Hunwick
Physio: Mel Henry
Ground address: Nyewood Lane, Bognor Regis PO21
Tel No: 01243 822325   Website: www.therocks.co.uk
Capacity: 4,100   **Seats:** 350   **Covered:** 2,600   **Floodlights**: Yes
Simple Directions:. West along sea front from pier past Aldwick shopping centre
then turn right into Nyewood Lane.
Midweek Home Matchday: Tuesday
Clubhouse: Open matchdays and Sunday lunchtimes.
Club Shop: Yes
Local Press: Bognor Regis Guardian, Bognor Regis Observer, Brighton Argus and
Portsmouth Evening News
Local Radio: Radio Sussex,Ocean Sound, Radio Solent,Southern Sound &Spirit FM

CLUB PERSONNEL

Chairman: D.Reynolds
Secretary: Simon Cook, c/o the club. Tel No: 07974 229405 or 01243 864237
Press Officer & General Manager: Jack Pearce
Prog Ed: Nigel.Folland & Rob Garforth
Tel Nos: 01243 826622 (W)
07802 206194 (M)
Programme: 36 Pages £1.50

2005-2006
Captain: David Piper
Player of the Year: Ben Watson
Top Goalscorer: Ben Watson 23

CLUB STATISTICS

Record	**Attendance**: 3,642 v Swansea City 1st Rd replay F.A.C 1984
	Victory: 24-0 v Littlhampton W.Sussex Lg. 1913-14
	Defeat: 0-19 v Shoreham W.Sussex Lg 1906-07
Career Goalscorer:	Kevin Clements 206 **Career Appearances**: Mick Pullen 967 (20 seasons
Record Transfer Fee	**Paid**: £2,000 for Guy Rutherford 95-96
	Received: £10,500 from Brighton & Hove for John Crumplin and Geoff Cooper and from Crystal Palace for Simon Rodger
Senior Honours:	Isthmian Div 1 R-Up 81-82 Southern Lg R-up 80-81 Sussex Senior Cup (9) R-up (4) Sussex Professional Cup: 73-74 Sussex RUR Cup 71-72
Previous Leaguess:	West Sussex 1896-1926, Brighton & Hove & Dist. 26-27, Sussex Co 27-72 Southern Lg 72-81 Isthmian 82-2004

Back row, left to right: G Rutherford, M Russell, D Wright, K Murphy, R Sansom, C Foster, C Stoner,
P Lawrence, D Beck, J Rowland, T White, R Brown.
Front Row: R Hudson, J Howell, D Birmingham, L Savage, M Birmingham, S Sargent, J Price, D Piper.

BOGNOR REGIS

BEST LGE ATT.: **486** v Farnborough Town
LOWEST: **220** v Histon

No.	Date	Comp	H/A	Opponents	Att:	Result	Goalscorers	Pos
1	Aug 15	CS	H	Yeading	358	L 0 - 2		17
2	16		A	Dorchester Town	488	W 5 - 3	**Watson** 1 73 Nightingale 3 (28 57 90)	11
3	20		A	St Albans City	311	L 0 - 2		12
4	27		H	Eastbourne Borough	481	W 2 - 1	Piper 29 Nightingale 47	10
5	29		A	Carshalton Athletic	297	D 1 - 1	Balfe 34	12
6	Sept 3		H	Eastleigh	340	W 2 - 0	Nightingale 3 90	8
7	10		A	Sutton United	536	L 0 - 1		10
8	17		H	Cambridge City	417	W 4 - 2	**Watson** 43 56 Nightingale 53 Russell 83	8
9	24	FAC 2Q	H	Basingstoke Town	552	D 1 - 1	Watson 59	
10	27	FAC 2Qr	A	Basingstoke Town	315	L 1 - 2	Watson 7	
11	Oct 1	CS	H	Welling United	442	D 0 - 0		9
12	15		A	Hayes	215	W 2 - 1	Nightingale 19 (pen) **Watson** 77	9
13	19		A	Lewes	580	D 1 - 1	**Watson** 19	8
14	22		H	Bishop's Stortford	326	D 2 - 2	**Watson** 45 Nightingale 68	6
15	29		A	Newport County	604	L 0 - 1		10
16	Nov 5		H	Farnborough Town	486	L 0 - 1		12
17	8		H	Maidenhead United	312	W 8 - 1	Nightingale 3 (20 38pen 72 pen) Hudson 27 **Watson** 4 (43 57 79 84)	10
18	12		A	Histon	489	D 2 - 2	Nightingale 43 **Watson** 90	11
19	19		H	Thurrock	360	L 0 - 1		14
20	26	FAT3Q	A	Ashford Town (Mdx)	140	W 3 - 2	Battams 4 (og) Hudson 54 Watson 86	
21	Dec 3	CS	A	Weymouth	1308	L 0 - 2		14
22	10		A	Basingstoke Town	287	W 3 - 2	Piper 8 Beck 35 **Watson** 79	12
23	17	FAT 1	H	Hereford United	624	L 1 - 7	Beck 16	
24	26	CS	H	Havant & Waterlooville	481	L 0 - 1		12
25	Jan 2		A	Havant & Waterlooville	757	L 0 - 1		16
26	7		A	Yeading	177	W 3 - 0	Elphick 35 **Watson** 53 77	13
27	21		H	St Albans City	402	W 2 - 0	**Watson** 26 (pen) 39	13
28	28		A	Eastbourne Borough	704	D 0 - 0		12
29	31		H	Dorchester Town	385	D 1 - 1	**Watson** 9	12
30	Feb 7		A	Welling United	417	L 0 - 2		12
31	11		H	Hayes	341	D 1 - 1	Hudson 37	12
32	18		A	Bishop's Stortford	330	L 1 - 2	**Watson** 9	15
33	21		H	Lewes	341	D 2 - 2	**Watson** 63 Beck 68	14
34	25		H	Sutton United	331	D 0 - 0		15
35	Mar 4		A	Cambridge City	628	L 0 - 2		15
36	11		H	Newport County	425	D 1 - 1	Nightingale 47	15
37	14		H	Weston-s-Mare	248	L 0 - 1		16
38	18		A	Farnborough Town	465	L 1 - 2	Fraser 42	16
39	25		H	Histon	220	W 3 - 1	Nightingale 11 59 **Watson** 40	13
40	April 1		A	Thurrock	193	L 0 - 3		13
41	4		A	Maidenhead United	165	W 2 - 1	Murphy 50 Mightingale 63	13
42	8		A	Weymouth	802	L 0 - 2		13
43	15		A	Eastleigh	525	L 0 - 1		13
44	17		H	Carshalton Athletic	305	D 1 - 1	Chamberlain 83	15
45	22		A	Weston-S_Mare	245	D 2 - 2	Kirkwood 85 **Watson** 90	14
46	29		H	Basingstoke Town	329	W 2 - 1	Nightingale 65 69	

Ave. League Home Attendance: 349   **Goals** 60 66   **Top Goalscorer:** Watson (25)
Best Position: 6th   **Worst:** 17th

BRAINTREE TOWN

Founded: 1898
Nickname: The Iron

Manager: George Borg **Coach:** Ollie Asedeji **Physio:** Kirk Bowye
Club Colours: All Yellow
Change Colours: All Sky Blue
Club Sponsor: Westdrive
Previous League: Ryman Premier
Previous Grounds: The Fair Field 1898-1903, Spaldings Meadow & Panfield Lane
Best Seasons: League: Champions Isthmian Premier 2005-2006
F.A. Cup: 1st Round 2005-2006 **F.A.Trophy**: 5th Round 2001-2002
Ground address: Cressing Road Stadium, Clockhouse Way, Braintree , Essex
Tel No: 01376 345617   **Website:** www.braintreetownnfc.org.uk
Capacity: 3,600   **Seats:** 294   **Covered:** 1,848   Floodlights: Yes
Simple Directions: From Braintree by-pass, turn into Braintree at the Galleys Corner roundabout. Ground is signposted and three quarters of a mile on left. Entrance in Clockhouse Way.
Midweek Home Matchday: Tuesday
Clubhouse: Open evenings and mid day at week ends
Club Shop: Yes. Contact Gordon Humphries
Local Radio: BBC Essex and Essex Radio

CLUB PERSONNEL
Chairman: Lee Harding
V-Chairman: Barry Shepherd
President: Ron Webb
Secretary: T.A.Woodley, 19a Bailey Bridge Rd., Braintree, Essex CM7 5TT Tel No: 01376 326234
Press Officer & Prog. Ed: Lee Harding

2005-2006
Captain: Alex Revell
Player of the Year: Paul Lorraine
Top Scorer: AlexRevell

CLUB STATISTICS

Record	**Attendance**: 4,000 v Spurs Testimonial May 1952
	Victory: 12-0 v Thetford (Eastern League) 1935-3
	Defeat :0-14 V Chelmsford City (A) N. Essex Lg.1923
	Goalscorer: Career: Chris Guy 211 1963-90 **Season** Gary Bennett 57 97-98
	Career Appearances: Paul Young 524 (1966-77)
	Transfer Fee Paid: to Hornchurch for Danny Gay.
	Received: £10,000 from Brentford for Matt Metcalf and from Colchester United for John Cheesewright
Senior Honours:	Isthmian Champions 05-06, Div 2 R-up 97-98 Eastern Co (3) R-Up (4)
	E.Anglian Cup (3) Essex Senior Cup 95-96 R-Up 96-97 Previous Leagues:
Previous Leagues:	N.Essex 1898-1925, Essex & Suffolk Border,25-29 55-64, Spartan 28-35 Eastern Co. 35-37 38-39 52-55 70-91 Essex Co: 37-38 London 45-52 Gtr London 64-66 Metropolitan 66-70 and Southern 91-96 Isthmian 96-05

Champions 2005-2006 Braintree Town FC

230

BRAINTREE

BEST LGE ATT.: 1,916 v AFC Wimbledon
LOWEST: 316 v Windsor & Eton

No.	Date	Comp	H/A	Opponents	Att:	Result	Goalscorers	Pos
1	Aug 20	IP	H	Hendon	317	W 1 - 0	**Revell** 55	8
2	23		A	East Thurrock	165	W 3 - 1	Riddle 4 **Revell** 42 Porter 68	4
3	27		A	Worthing	369	L 0 - 2		9
4	29		H	Maldon Town	406	D 1 - 1	Griffiths 34	8
5	Sept 3		A	Slough Town	260	L 1 - 2	**Revell** 75	10
6	6		A	Heybridge Swifts	326	W 3 - 0	Griffiths 44 **Revell** 45 81	7
7	10	FAC 1Q	A	Cheshunt	160	W 2 - 1	**Revell** 2 **Burgess** 73	
8	17	IP	H	Redbridge	322	W 2 - 0	Griffiths 10 57	5
9	20		H	Leyton	318	D 1 - 1	Riddle 16	7
10	24	FAC 2Q	H	Didcot Town	306	W 2 - 0	**Lorraine** 69 Revell 90	
11	Oct 1	IP	A	Wealdstone	305	W 3 - 2	Griffiths 32 Porter 50 **Revell** 61	5
12	4		H	Hampton & Richmond B	422	W 2 1 1	Griffiths 11 Hawes 26	4
13	8	FAC 3Q	A	Heybridge Swifts	362	D 1 - 1	Griffiths 38	
14	11	FAC 3Q	H	Heybridge Swifts	479	W 3 - 1	Riddle 55 Griffiths 77 84	
15	15	FAT 1Q	H	Great Wakering R	210	W 4 - 2	Revell 31 (pen) 86 (pen) Ofori 53 55	
16	22	FAC 4Q	A	Crawley Town	970	W 1 - 0	Ofori	
17	25	IP	H	Heybridge Swifts	487	W 3 - 1	Grifiths 3 Ofori 16 **Revell** (pen) 90	5
18	29		H	Margate	478	W 1 - 0	**Revell** 8 (pen)	5
19	Nov 5	FAC 1R	A	Shrewsbury Town	2969	L 1 - 4	Quinton 78	
20	12	FAT 2Q	A	Chelmsford Town	436	W 2 - 0	Baker 44 65	
21	19	IP	H	Folkestone Invivta	413	W 3 - 0	Ofori 9 24 Hawes 75	5
22	22		A	Leyton	115	W 1 - 0	Griffiths	4
23	26	FAT 3Q	H	Hayes	228	L 0 - 1		
24	Dec 3	IP	H	Fisher Athletic	510	W 3 - 2	Ofori 20 50 **Revell** 23	5
25	6		A	Harrow Borough	111	L 0 - 1		5
26	10		H	Windsor & Eton	316	W 3 - 0	Baker 27 Ofori 36 Griffiths 83	5
27	13		A	Billericay Town	371	D 1 - 1	Ofori 45	
28	17		A	Walton & Hersham	159	L 2 - 3	Quinton 41 76	5
29	26		H	Chelmsford City	967	W 2 - 1	Lorraine 44 Baker 90	5
30	Jan 2		A	Maoldon Town	404	W 3 - 2	**Revell** 15 30 Baker 68	3
31	7		A	Hendon	222	W 2 - 1	Quinton 86 90	4
32	10		H	Bromley	409	W 3 - 1	Baker 3 (48, 90,90)	1
33	14		A	East Thurrock	504	W 1 - 0	Porter 40	
34	21		A	Redbridge	168	W 1 - 0	**Revell** 53 (pen)	1
35	24		A	Staines Town	284	D 1 - 1	Lorraine 45	1
36	28		H	Worthing	557	W 4 - 2	**Revell** 11 Griffiths 22 Quinton 46 Lorraine 79	1
37	Feb 4		A	Fisher Athletic	378	D 1 - 1	Riddle 75	1
38	7		A	AFC Wimbledon	2615	D 1 - 1	Lorraine 89	1
39	11		H	Staines Town	517	W 3 - 1	Griffiths 47 **Revell** 48 Ofori 51	1
40	18		A	Margate	678	D 1 - 1	**Revell** 87	1
41	25		H	Billericay Townn	703	W 2 - 0	Porter 38 **Revell** 42	1
42	Mar 4		H	AFC Wimbledon	1916	D 0 - 0		1
43	11		A	Folkestone Invicta	370	D 0 - 0		1
44	18		H	Wealdstone	503	W 2 - 0	Hawes 23 Ofori 60	1
45	25		A	Hampton & Richmond B	439	W 1 - 0	J.Hawes 79	1
46	April 1		H	Harrow Borough	510	W 3 - 0	**Revell** 24 Quinton 43 59	1
47	8		A	Broml;ey	431	D 1 - 1	Griffiths 90	1
48	14		H	Slough Town	875	W 2 - 1	**Revell** 52 70	1
49	17		A	Chelmsford Town	1495	W 2 - 0	Hawes 28 Ofori 29	1
50	22		A	Windsor & Eton	147	W 1 - 0	**Revell** 10	1
51	29		H	Walton & Hersham	961	W 3 - 1	Ofori 30 Martion 82 **Revell** 88	1

Ave. League Home Attendance: 576 **Goals** 87 42 **Top Goalscorer:** Revell (25)
Best Position: 1st **Worst:** 10th

CAMBRIDGE CITY

Founded: 1908
Nickname: Lilywhites

Cambridge City Football Club

City v Tiverton Town

Manager: Gary Roberts

Club Colours: White/black/white

Change Colours: All Sky Blue

Club Sponsor:

Previous League: Southern

Best Performances:

League: 2nd Conference South 2004-2005   **F.A. Cup:** 2nd Round 2004-2005

F.A.Trophy.: 5th Rd 2004-2005   **F.A. Amateur Cup:** Semi-Final 1927-1928

Ground address: City Ground, Milton Road,Cambridge CB4 1UY

Tel No: 01223 357973   **Website:** cambridgecityfc.com

Official website: www.cambridgecityfc.com

Capacity: 2,000   **Seats:** 533   **Covered:**1,400   **Floodlights:**Yes

Simple Directions: On A1309 (Cambridge to Ely) at beginning of road behind Westbrook centre.

Midweek Home Matchday: Tuesday

Club Shop: Sells all club accessories

Local Press: Cambridge Evening News

Local Radio: BBC Radio Cambridge

CLUB PERSONNEL

Chairman: Kevin Setchell
President: Sir Neil Westbrook
Secretary: Andy Dewey, 50 Doggett Road, Cambridge,CB1 9LF
Tel No: 01223 245694
Commercial Man: Robert Arbon
Press Officer: Nick Austin
e-mail: info@cambridgecityfc.comf
Programme.Editors:
Keith Harris & Chris Farrington
e-mail: editor.ccfc@ntlworld.com
Shop Manager: Sue Townley
Tel No: 01223235991
2005-2006
Captain: Glen Fuff
Player of the Year: Glen Fuff
Top Goalscorer: Paul Booth

CLUB STATISTICS

Record	Attendance : 12,058 v Leytonstone F.A.Amateur Cup 1st Rd 1949-50
	Career Goalscorer: Gary Grogan
	Appearances in career: Mal Keenan
Record Transfer Fee	Paid : £ 8,000 to Rushden & Diamonds for Paul Coe
	Received : £100,000 from Millwall for Neil Harris 1998
Senior Honours:	Southern Lg 62-3 R-up 70-71 , Southern Div 85-6 R-up 69-70
	Southern Lg Cup R-up 98-9 Suffolk Sen Cup (09-10) East Anglian Cup (9)
Previous	**Leagues:** Bury & Dist.,08-13 19-20 E Anglian 08-10 Southern Olympian 11-14
	Southern Amateur 13--35 Spartan 35-50 Athenian 50-58 Southern 58-2004
	Name : Cambridge Town 1908-1951

Back row (L-R): Gary Roberts (manager), Ben Bowditch, Darren Lynch, Glen Fuff, Alan Calton, Danny Naisbitt, Darren Coe, Lee Chaffey, Danny Blanchett, Barry Green (coaching assistant). **Front:** Lewis Baillie, Mark Graham, Greg Lincoln, Sam Reed, Craig Pope, Kalam Mooniaruck, Stuart Sinclair, Lee Roache. Photo: Ian Pettengell.

CAMBRIDGE CITY

BEST ATT.: 737 v St. Albans City
LOWEST: 254 v Thurrock

Date	Competition	Venue	Opponents	Att.	Result		Goalscorers	Pos.
Aug 14	CS	A	Weymouth	1,568	W	2-1	Gash 21, **Sadler** 70	5
18	CS	H	Bishop's Stortford	539	W	3-2	Gash 46,Chaffey 51, Scott (pen) 85	3
21	CS	H	Weston-s-Mare	373	L	1-2	**Sadler** 63	7
24	CS	A	Welling United	492	W	2-0	Scott 49 (pen), Brown (og) 52	5
28	CS	A	Hayes	241	L	0-4		8
30	CS	H	Margate	353	W	2-1	Stevenson 18,73	4
Sept 4	CS	A	Havant & Waterlooville	496	W	2-0	Stevenson 57, Simpson 90	3
11	CS	H	Grays Athletic	361	L	0-2		6
14	CS	H	Hornchurch	330	L	0-3		8
18	CS	A	Newport County	803	W	1-0	Simpson 74	7
21	CS	H	Redbridge	439	W	2-1	**Sadler** 35, 64	5
25	CS	A	Bognor Regis Town	393	W	2-1	**Sadler** 2, Stevenson 70	4
Oct 2	**FAC 2Q**	**A**	**Worcester City**	753	W	3-1	Stevenson 59, Simpson 64, **Sadler** 87	
9	CS	H	Dorchester Town	367	D	2-2	**Sadler** 19, Fuff 59	4
16	**FAC 3Q**	**A**	**Tooting & Mitcham**	401	W	4-2	Stevenson 13, 73 Miller 8, Thomas 75 (pen)	
23	CS	A	Thurrock	331	W	1-0	Simpson 3	3
26	CS	A	Basingstole Town	393	L	1-2	Williams 8	4
30	**FAC 4Q**	**A**	**Bromley**	732	W	3-0	Binns 7,90 Langston 86	
Nov 6	**FAT 1**	**A**	**Cinderford Town**	148	D	1-1	Simpson 30	
9	**FAT 1r**	**H**	**Cinderford Town**	185	W	3-1	Gash 22,Williams 53, Miller 67	
13	**FAC 1**	**H**	**Leigh RMI**	930	W	2-1	**Sadler** 58, Stevenson 90	
20	CS	A	Maidenhead United	205	W	5-1	**Sadler** 17, 63 Simpson 18,70 Williams 32	5
27	**FAT 2**	**H**	**Hornchurch**	390	D	1-1	Simpson 22	
30	**FAT 2R**	**A**	**Hornchurch**	290	W	4-0	**Sadler** 33 Philip 50 (og) Fuff 52 Fiddes 85	
Dec 3	**FAC 2**	**H**	**MK Dons**	2,000	L	0-1		
7	CS	A	Hornchurch	263	W	1-0	**Sadler** (pen) 80	5
11	CS	H	Havant & Waterlooville	350	W	2-0	Simpson 75 **Sadler** 82	4
14	CS	H	Lewes	343	L	2-3	Stevenson 72 80 (pen)	5
18	CS	A	Grays Athletic	566	W	2-1	Binns 31 **Sadler** 64	4
26	CS	H	St Albans City	**737**	L	0-2		5
Jan 1	CS	A	St Albans City	522	L	0-1		6
8	CS	H	Newport County	430	W	2-0	Simpson 60 Langston 71	4
15	**FAT 3**	**A**	**Redbridge**	154	W	5-1	Williams 24 J.Simpson 29 R Simpson 44 Langston 83 Scott 90(pen)	
18	CS	A	Sutton United	420	W	3-0	Robinson 12 71 (pen) Stone 46	3
22	CS	H	Bognor Regis Town	436	W	1-0	Scott 60	2
25	CS	H	CarshaltonAthletic	331	W	3-0	**Sadler** 42 Simpson 55 80	2
29	CS	A	Redbridge	152	D	0-0		2
Feb 5	**FAT 4**	**H**	**Crawley Town**	698	D	3-3	Simpson 4 Langston 23 Stevenson 67	
8	**FAT 4R**	**A**	**Crawley Town**	936	W	2-1	Williams 31 Robinson 38	
12	CS	A	Dorchester Town	501	D	0-0		2
15	CS	H	Eastbourne Borough	434	D	2-2	**Sadler** 4 Chaffey 44	2
19	CS*	H	Basingstoke Town	491	W	2-1	Langston 37 Robinson 57	2
22	CS	H	Thurrock	**254**	D	0-0		2
26	**FAC 5**	**H**	**Hucknall Town**	684	L	0-1		
Mar 5	CS	H	Maidenhead United	456	L	0-1		2
12	CS	A	Eastbourne Borough	928	W	2-1	**Sadler** 14 Binns 24	2
15	CS	A	Lewes	451	D	2-2	**Sadler** 49 56	2
19	CS	A	Bishops Stortford	439	L	0-3		2
26	CS	H	Welling United	428	L	0-1		2
28	CS	H	Margate	227	W	2-0	Miller 38 Shipley 75	2
April 2	CS	A	Weymouth	537	W	4-1	Binns 54 **Sadler** 72 (pen) Robinson 77 Fiskin 82	2
9	CS	A	Weston-s-Mare	314	L	1-2	Gash 82	2
16	CS	H	Hayes	703	W	1-0	Fisken 55	2
23	CS	A	Carshalton Athletic	376	W	2-0	Stevenson 42 Gash 77	2
30	CS	H	Sutton United	520	L	0-1		**2**
May 7	**Play Off F**	**H**	**Eastbourne Borough**	1.106	L	0-1		

Matches: **56**　Average Home League Attendance: **439**　　Goals:**91-59**　Top Goalscorer: **David Sadler 20** (17 + 2FAC + 1FAT)
Best position to Lowest position: **2nd-8th**

DORCHESTER TOWN

Founded:1880
Nickname: The Magpies

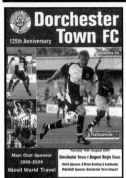

Dorchester Town FC
125th Anniversary

Manager: Mark Morris   **Asst. Man.:** Brian Benjafield   **Physio:** Geoff Dine

Club Colours: Black & white quarters/black/black

Change Colours: All Yellow

Club Sponsor: Loders Motor Group

Previous Leagues: Southern

Best Seasons: League: 8th Conference South   **F.A. Cup:** 2nd Rd Replay

F.A.Trophy.: 3rd Rd replay 71-72 96-97

Ground address: Avenue Stadium , Weymouth Avenue, Dorchester DT1 2RY

Tel No: 01305 262451   **Website:** www.the-magpies.net

Capacity: 5,009   Seats: 697   Covered: 2,846   Floodlights:Yes

Simple Directions: Situated at the junction of the town by-pass(A35) and the Weymouth road (A354)

Midweek Home Matchday: Tuesday

Clubhouse: Dorchester Lounge Club- access via main entrance to stadium

Club Shop: Fully Stocked

Local Radio: Radio Solent and Wessex FM

Local Press: Dorset Evening Echo, Western Gazette and Western Daily Press

CLUB PERSONNEL

Chairman: E.C.G.Belt
V-Chairman: A.E.Miller
Secretary: David Martin, 21 Diggory Crescent, Dorchester
Tel. No: 01305 262345
Commercial Manager: Keith Kellaway c/o club
Press Officer: Rob Hodder (07971 2259100)
Programme.Editor: Melvin Cross (01305 848365)
2004-2005
Captain: Alex Browne
Player of the Year: Matt Groves
Top Goalscorer: Matt Groves

Programme: 32 Pages £1.50

CLUB STATISTICS

Record	**Attendance:**	4,159 v Weymouth, Southern Premier 1999
	Career Goalscorer:	Denis Cheney 61 (in one season)
	Career Appearances:	Derek 'Dinkie' Curtis 458 1950-66
Record	**Transfer Fee Paid:**	£12,000 to Gloucester City for Chris Townsend 1990
	Received:	£35,000 from Portsmouth for Trevor Senior
	Victory:	7-0 v Canterbury (A)Southern Lg.Southern Div 86-87
	Defeat:	0-13 v Welton Rovers (A) Western League 1966
Senior Honours:		Southern League 85-86 R-up 79-80 Div One South R-up 91-92
		Western League 54-55 R-up 60-61 Dorset Senior Cup (7)
Previous	**Leagues:**	Dorset, Western 1947-72
	Grounds:	Council recreation Ground, Weymouth Avenue 19880-1929,The Avenue Ground, Weymouth Avenue 1929--1990

Back row, left to right: Simon Radcliffe, Mike Taylor, Scott Morgan, Mark Robinson, Jamie Brown, Ryan Hill, Richard Martin, Jamie Gleeson, Michael,Walker, Justin Keeler, Liam Horsted, Guy Lopez, Warren Byerley, Glenn Howes, Alex Browne (captain), and Mark Jermyn. **Front row:** Matt Groves, Geoff Dine (Physio), Brian Benjafield (coach), Mick Jenkins, (Manager), Steve Johnson (coach), Derek Taylor (Kit Manager) and Terry Parker (Assistant Physio).

DORCHESTER TOWN

BEST LGE ATT.: 3,006 v Weymouth
LOWEST: **345** v Havent & Waterlooville

No.	Date	Comp	H/A	Opponents	Att:	Result	Goalscorers	Pos
1	Aug 13	CS	A	Basingstoke Town	388	L 0 - 2		18
2	16		H	Bognor Regis Town	488	L 3 - 5	**Keeler** 31 (pen) Byerley 36 Groves 90	21
3	20		H	Bishop's Stortford	472	L 1 - 3	Howes 63	22
4	27		A	Cambridge City	411	W 2 - 1	Groves 13 31	19
5	29		H	Sutton United	482	L 0 - 5		21
6	Sept 3		A	Welling United	447	L 3 - 4	Keeping 39 Brown 52 **Keeler** 62	21
7	10		A	Weston-s-Mare	373	W 4 - 0	Howes 19 **Keeler** 51 (pen) 69 Brown 63	19
8	17		H	St Albans City	506	L 1 - 4	**Keeler** 1	19
9	24	FAC 2Q	H	Team Bath	317	W 4 - 2	**Keeler** 2 Brown 21 26 Groves 45	
10	Oct 1	CS	H	Hayes	426	D 2 - 2	Groves 16 Jermyn 67	19
11	8	FAC 3Q	A	Yeading	151	D 1 - 1	Howes 18	
12	11	FAC 3Qr	H	Yeading	500	W 3 - 2	Groves 40 63 Keeler 87	
13	15	CS	A	Thurrock	221	W 1 - 0	Brown 51	19
14	19		A	Newport County	587	W 2 - 0	Brown 26 (pen) Robinson 50	17
15	22	FAC 4Q	H	Welling United	533	L 1 - 2	Browne 2	
16	29	CS	A	Yeading	132	W 1 - 0	Browne 5	16
17	Nov 1		H	Lewes	380	D 2 - 2	Browne 14 **Keeler** 23	16
18	5		H	Maidenhead United	459	L 1 - 3	**Keeler** 45 (pen)	17
19	8		H	Havant & Waterlooville	345	D 1 - 1	**Keeler** 61	14
20	12		A	Farnborough Town	604	W 1 - 0	Jermyn 83	14
21	19		H	Carshalton Athletic	428	W 2 - 0	Browne 45 Groves 51	13
22	26	FAT 3Q	A	Lewes	364	D 2 - 2	Browne 61 Keeler 74	
23	29	FAT 3Qr	H	Lewes	235	W 3 - 1	Keeler (2 -1pen) Groves	
24	Dec 3	CS	A	Eastleigh	352	W 2 - 1	Groves 1 Moss 89 (pen)	9
25	10		H	Eastbourne Borough	522	W 3 - 0	Browne 10 J.Brown 29 Groves 81	7
26	17	FAT 1	H	Cambridge United	426	W 3 - 2	**Keeler** 21 Brown 37 Robinson 57	
27	26	CS	A	Weymouth	4029	L 0 - 1		9
28	31		A	Histon	548	L 1 - 4	**Keeler** 85 (pen)	
29	Jan 2		H	Weymouth	3006	W 2 - 0	Howes 27 **Keeler** 57	9
30	7		H	Basingstoke Town	521	W 2 - 1	**Keeler** 85 Robinson 89	9
31	14	FAT 2	A	Forest Green Rovers	861	L 1 - 3	Groves 45	
32	21	CS	A	Bishop's Stortford	267	L 2 - 5	Midson 18 (og) Morgan 37	10
33	28		H	Cambridge City	465	W 1 - 0	Jermyn 9	9
34	31		A	Bognor Regis Town	385	D 1 - 1	Moss 76	9
35	Feb 4		A	Hayes	160	W 1 - 0	**Keeler** 90	6
36	11		H	Thurrock	452	W 2 - 0	Groves 8 Jermyn 75	6
37	18		A	Lewes	405	L 2 - 3	Jermyn 24 Groves 27	9
38	21		H	Newport County	452	D 2 - 2	Robinson 11 Brown 85	9
39	25		H	Weston-s-Mare	453	L 1 - 2	Browne 1	9
40	Mar 4		A	St Albans City	647	L 0 - 2		10
41	6		A	Havant & Waterlooville	399	L 0 - 1		10
42	11		H	Yeading	402	W 4 - 0	**Keeler** 34 Groves 53 Mekchiche 72 Brown 73	10
43	18		A	Maidenhead United	285	W 3 - 2	Groves 28 42 Mekchiche 48	9
44	April 1		A	Carshalton Athletic	348	L 1 - 3	**Keeler** 53	10
45	4		H	Farnborough Town	429	D 1 - 1	Howes 18	10
46	8		H	Eastleigh	461	L 1 - 3	Groves 23	10
47	15		H	Welling United	526	L 0 - 3		10
48	17		A	Sutton United	502	L 0 - 1		10
49	22		H	Histon	417	L 0 - 3		11
50	29		A	Eastbourne Borough	578	D 1 - 1	Groves 42	11

Ave. League Home Attendance: 576 **Goals** 78 87 **Top Goalscorer:** Keeler (20)
Best Position: 6th **Worst:** 22nd

EASTBOURNE BOROUGH

Founded: 1966
Nickname: Borough

Manager: Garry Wilson **Coach:** Nick Greenwood
Club Colours: Al red
Change Colours: All Yellow
Club Sponsors: T.B.N.
Previous League: Southern
Previous Name: Langney Sports
Best Seasons: League: 5th Conference South & losing Play off Finalists 04-05
F.A. Cup: 1st Round 2006-2007 **F.A.Trophy.:** 3rd Round 2001-2002 2002-2003
F.A.Vase : (As Langney Sports) 2nd Round Replay 1991-1992
Physio: Ray Tuppen
Ground address: Langney Sports Club, Priory Avenue, Eastbourne, E.Sussex
Tel No: 01323 743561 **email:** info@eastbourneboroughfc.com
Website: www.eastbourneboroughfc.co.uk **Clubcall:** 09066 555894
Capacity: 3,000 **Seats:** 542s **Covered:** 2,500 **Floodlights**: Yes
Simple Directions: A22 to Polegate A27 and at junction of A27/A22new by-pass,
follow signs to crematorium, then first right to Priory Lane.
Midweek Home Matchday: Tuesday
Clubhouse: Open every evening and lunchtime
Club Shop: Yes
Local Press: Eastbourne Gazette & Herald
Local Radio: Sovereign Radio & BBC South Counties

CLUB PERSONNEL
Chairman: Len Smith
President: J.Stonestreet
Chief Executive: Mike Spooner
Secretary: Mrs Myra Stephens,
9 Gwent Court, St James Rd
Eastbourne,BN227BX
Tel & F: 01323 642834 or
07754174406 (M)
email: myra-ebfc@uwclub.net
Commercial Man: Lorna Gosling
Tel No: 01323 743561
Prog Ed: Mike Spooner
Tel No: 07793 558635 (M)
Programme
76 pages £2.00

2005-2006
Captain: Stuart Tuck
Player of the Year: Stuart Tuck
Top Goalscorer: Scott Ramsay

CLUB STATISTICS

RECORD	
Attendance:	3,770 v Oxford United F.A.Cup 1st Round 2006-2007
Victory:	10-1 v Haywards Heath Town Sussex Co. Div 1 91-92
Defeat:	0-8 v Sheppey United (A) F.A.Vase 09.10.93
	0-8 v Peacehaven & Telscombe (A) Sussex Co Div 1 09.11.93
Career Goalscorer:	Nigel Hole 146
Career Appearances:	Darren Baker 689
Transfer Fee Paid:	£1,800 to Yeovil Town for Yemi Odoubade
Received:	£15,000 from Oxford United for Yemi Odoubade
Senior Honours:	Conference South Play oFf Finalists Sussex Co Champions 99-00
	2002-03 Sussex Senior Cup 2001-2002 Southern Lg Eastern Div R-up 02-03
Previous Leagues:	Eastbourne & Hastings, Sussex County, Southern

EASTBOURNE BOROUGH

BEST LGE ATT.: 1,066 v Lewes
LOWEST: **434** v Hayes

No.	Date	Comp	H/A	Opponents	Att:	Result	Goalscorers	Pos
1	Aug 13	CS	A	Bishop's Stortford	307	W 1 - 0	Odubade 34	9
2	16		H	Thurrock	711	D 0 - 0		7
3	20		H	Basingstole Town	704	L 2 - 3	Odubade 29 **Ramsay** 51	11
4	27		A	Bognoer Regis Toiwn	481	L 1 - 2	Tuck 51	16
5	29		H	Weklling United	674	D 1 - 1	**Ramsay** 8	17
6	Sept 3		A	Cambridge City	386	W 3 - 2	Crabbe 13 **Ramsay** 67 80	13
7	10		A	St.Albans City	405	L 0 - 5		17
8	17		H	Weston -s - Mare	555	L 1 - 2	Odubade 48	17
9	24	FAC 2Q	A	Redbridge	113	D 2 - 2	Rowland 38 (pen) Tuck 86	
10	27	FAC 2Qr	H	Redbridge	359	W 5 - 2	Rowland 39 (pen) 72 Smart 47 88 Tuck 69	
11	Oct 1	CS	H	Newport County	580	W 2 - 0	Simmonds 34 Smart 57	17
12	8	FAC 3Q	A	Metropolitan Police	201	D 3 - 3	Ramsay 14 Storey 44 Odubade 81	
13	11	FAC 3Qr	H	Metropolitan Police	601	W 3 - 2	Rowland 15 44 (pen) Odubade 20	
14	15	CS	A	Weymouth	1252	L 1 - 2	Rowland 90	17
15	18		A	Sutton United	493	L 0 - 2		19
16	22	FAC 4Q	A	Bishop's Cleeve	625	W 1 - 0	Ramsay 40	
17	29	CS	A	Eastleigh	409	L 1 - 2	Rowland 1	19
18	Nov 5	FAC 1R	H	Oxford United	3770	D 1 - 1	Rowland 90 (pen)	
19	8	CS	H	Carshalton Athletic	547	D 1 - 1	Odubade 38	19
20	12		A	Havant & Waterlooville	474	L 0 - 1		19
21	16	FAC 1R r	A	Oxford United	4396	L 0 - 3		
22	19	CS	H	Histon	603	D 1 - 1	**Ramsay** 22	19
23	22		H	Hayes	434	D 0 - 0		
24	26	FAT 3Q	H	Thurrock	368	L 0 - 3		
25	Dec 3	CS	A	Farnborough Town	524	W 3 - 2	Odubade 6 Simmonds 22 Marney 57	
26	10		A	Dorchester Town	522	L 0 - 3		19
27	20		A	Yeading	133	D 1 - 1	Storey (pen) 35	19
28	26		H	Lewes	1066	W 3 - 1	Storey 45 (pen) Keenan 53 67	
29	31		H	Maidenhead United	676	D 3 - 3	**Ramsay** 10 Storey 24 (pen) Marney 82	
30	Jan 2		A	Lewes	1193	L 0 - 1		19
31	7		H	Bishop's Stortford	538	D 1 - 1	Storey 59	19
32	14		A	Thurrock	235	L 0 - 1		19
33	21		A	Basingstoke Town	346	D 2 - 2	**Ramsay** 19 Corneille 71	19
34	28		H	Bognor RegisTown	704	D 0 - 0		19
35	Feb 4		A	Newport County	548	D 1 - 1	Newman 40	19
36	11		H	Weymouth	802	L 0 - 2		19
37	18		A	Hayes	205	W 2 - 0	Storey 73 (pen) Fazackerley 86	19
38	25		H	St Albans City	605	D 1 - 1	Storey 10 (pen)	19
39	Mar 4		A	Weston-super-Mare	236	L 0 - 1		19
40	7		A	Carshalton Athletic	350	D 2 - 2	Newman 44 55	18
41	11		H	Eastleigh	503	L 0 - 1		19
42	18		H	Yeading	435	W 2 - 1	Storey 66 **Ramsay** 68	19
43	25		H	Havant & Waterlooville	447	D 2 - 2	**Ramsay** 24 86	18
44	April 1		A	Histon	571	L 1 - 3	Storey 29 (pen)	19
45	5		N	Sutton United	458	W 2 - 1	Fazackerley Parr 84	18
46	8		H	Farnborough Town	512	L 0 - 1		18
47	15		H	Cambridge City	538	D 1 - 1	Tuck 88	19
48	17		H	Welling United	603	W 2 - 1	Smart 30 **Ramsay** 84	18
49	22		A	Maidenhead United	217	W 6 - 2	Tuck 13 Atkinn 3 (39 75 77) Crabb 42 Warner 58	17
50	29		H	Dorchester Town	578	D 1 - 1	Newman 88	17

Ave. League Home Attendance: 603   **Goals**   66   76   **Top Goalscorer:** Ramsay (13)
Best Position: 7th   **Worst:**   19th

EASTLEIGH

Manager: Paul Doswell **Coaches:** David Hughes, Mark Dennis & Mark Blake.
Physio: Daniel Ray
Club Colours: White & Navy/Navy/White & Navy
Change Colours: All Red
Club Sponsors: Silverlake Autoparts
Previous League: Isthmian
Best Seasons: League: 8th Conference South 2005-2006
F.A. Cup: 3rd Qualifying Round 1981-82 2004-05
F.A.Trophy.: 2nd Rd 2003-2004 **F.A.Vase** : 4th Rd. 82-83 90-91
Ground address: Silverlake Stadium 'Ten Acres', Stoneham Lane, North Stoneham,
Eastleigh SO50 9HT Tel No: 02380-613361
Website: www.eastleighfc.net
Capacity: 2,300   **Seats**: 175   **Covered**: 385 **Floodlights**: Yes
Simple Directions: M27 Jct 5 to roundabout exit marked Stoneham Lane. Carry on
to next roundabout and drive down Stoneham Lane, turning right opposite Concord
Club. Ground 400 yards on left.
Midweek Home Matchday: Tuesday
Clubhouse: 11-11 Mon-Sat plus mid day Sundays
Club Shop: Yes

CLUB PERSONNEL
Chairman: Paul Murray
President: Derik Brooks
Corporate Managers:
Mark Dennis and Stuart Douglas.
Secretary: Ray Murphy, 21 Villette
Close,Christchurch,Dorset. BH23
2NR. **Tel Nos:** 01202 482067 (H)
07801 638158 (M)
Press Officer: Malcolm Clarke
Commercial Man: Stuart Douglas &
Mark Dennis
Programme Editors:
Mike Denning
Captains:
Nick Burton & Martin Thomas
Player of the Year: Ryan Ashford
Top Goalscorer: Andy Forbes
Programme
32 pages with admission

CLUB STATISTICS

RECORD	**Attendance:** 2,589 V Southampton July 2005
Victory:	12-1 v Hythe & Dibden (H) 11.12.48
Defeat:	0-11 v Austin Sports (A) 01.01.47
Career Goalscorer:	Johnnie Williams 177
Career Appearances:	Ian Knight 611
Record Transfer Fee	**Paid**: £10,000 to Newport (I.O.W.) for Colin Matthews
	Received: Undisclosed
Senior Honours:	Play Off Winners Isthmian Premier 2004-05
Previous Leagues:	Southampton Jnr & Snr 46-59 Hampshire 50-86 Wessex 86-2003
	Isthmian Premier 2004-2005
Names:	Swaythling Athletic 1946-59 Swaythling 73-80

Back Row (L-R): John Dunn (Club Secretary), Kevin Dixon (Kit Man), Ray Murphy (Football Secretary), Lee Pragnell (Physio), Bob Beattie (Fitness Coach), Ashley Jarvis, Rob Marshall, Chris Collins, Brian Dutton, Luke Douglas, Wayne Shaw, Paul Musselwhite, Steve Forbes, Matt Bound, Ryan Ashford, Andy Puckett, Jason Dodd, Justin Bennett, Steve Beck (Scout), Mick Geddes (Vice Chairman). **Front:** David Malone (Director), Martin Thomas, Ben Ngwa, Richard Hodgson, Adam James, Ian Oliver, Mark Dennis, Mark Blake, Paul Murray (Chairman), Paul Doswell (Manager), David Hughes, Danny Smith, Andy Forbes, Darren Wheeler, Jack Smith, Adam Roberts, Dave Town, Derik Brooks (President).

EASTLEIGH

BEST LGE ATT.: 782 v Weymouth
LOWEST: **257** v Sutton United

No.	Date	Comp	H/A	Opponents	Att:	Result	Goalscorers	Pos
1	Aug 13	CS	A	Hayes	229	L 0 - 1		14
2	17		H	Weymouth	782	W 2 - 0	Ashford 39 73	10
3	20		H	Newport County	578	W 2 - 0	**A.Forbes** 16 (pen) 23	6
4	27		A	Thurrock	227	L 1 - 3	**A.Forbes** 54 (pen)	9
5	29		H	Bishop's Stortford	386	L 0 - 1		14
6	Sept 3		A	Bognor Regis Town	340	L 0 - 2		17
7	10		H	Welling United	287	L 1 - 3	Hughes 73	18
8	17		A	Histon	424	L 0 - 1		18
9	24	FAC 2Q	H	Havant & Waterlooville	470	D 0 - 0		
10	26	FAC 2Qr	A	Havant & Waterlooville	329	L 1 - 4	S.Forbes 37	
11	Oct 1	CS	A	Yeading	143	D 2 - 2	**A.Forbes** 39 65	18
12	15		H	Carshalton Athletic	343	W 3 - 1	Smith 23 S. Forbes 57 **A.Forbes** 83 (pen)	18
13	19		H	Farnborough	360	W 2 - 0	Roach 11 **A.Forbes** 48 (pen)	
14	22		A	Maidenhead United	315	D 2 - 2	Roach 62 Wilde 83	15
15	29		H	Eastbourne Borough	409	W 2 - 1	Roach 47 **A.Forbes** 65	13
16	Nov 5		A	St Albans City	513	W 4 - 2	Roach 3 Bowers 52 Thomas 67 Peters 87	10
17	9		A	Weston-s-Mare	252	W 4 - 1	Robinson 30 Smith 52 Roach 85 **A.Forbes** 84	8
18	12		A	Sutton United	513	W 2 - 0	**A.Forbes** 89 90	6
19	19		A	Cambridge City	525	L 1 - 2	Stavroulakis16	6
20	26	FAT 3Q	A	Leighton Town	145	D 1 - 1	**Thomas 90 (pen)**	
21	30	FAT3Qr	H	Leighton Town	186	L 1 - 2	**Town**	
22	Dec 3	CS	H	Dorchester Town	352	L 1 - 2	Town 26	10
23	10		A	Havant & Waterlooville	668	L 1 - 2	S.Forbes 57	13
24	26		H	Basingstoke Town	506	L 0 - 3		14
25	Jan 2		A	Basingstoke Town	507	W 1 - 0	Hughes 10	12
26	7		H	Hayes	356	W 2 - 1	Smith 23 Ashford 64	11
27	14		A	Weymouth	1557	L 0 - 2		12
28	21		A	Newport County	675	W 2 - 0	Town 26 90	11
29	28		H	Thurrock	312	W 3 - 0	Town 42 Smith 53 **A.Forbes** 64	10
30	Feb 1		H	Lewes		W 2 - 0	Smith Town	10
31	4		H	Yeading	312	L 0 - 3		10
32	11		A	Carshalton Athletic	388	W 3 - 1	Smith 32 S.Forbes 53 Roach 85	9
33	18		H	Maidenhead United	368	W 2 - 1	Roach 61 Douglas 77	8
34	21		A	Farnborough	377	L 0 - 1		8
35	25		A	Welling United	523	L 1 - 2	Town 65	8
36	Mar 4		H	Histon	356	L 1 - 2	Douglas 9	9
37	11		A	Eastbourne Borough	503	W 1 - 0	**A.Forbes** 50	8
38	18		H	St Albans City	357	L 0 - 2		10
39	25		A	Sutton United	482	W 3 - 0	S.Forbes 9 **A.Forbes** 27 Town 72	9
40	April 4		H	Sutton United	257	W 4 - 1	Town 4 **A.Forbes** 11 82 Smith 25	8
41	8		A	Dorchester Town	461	W 3 - 1	S.Forbes 2 4 **A.Forbes** 68	8
42	11		H	Cambridge City	364	D 1 - 1	Douglas 2	8
43	15		A	Bognor Regis Town	525	W 1 - 0	Town 14	8
44	17		A	Bishop's Stortford	270	L 1 - 4	Hodgson 56	8
45	22		A	Kewes	435	W 2 - 0	Hodgson 67 Marshall 86	6
46	29		H	Havant & Waterlooville	652	L 2 - 6	Town 8 **A.Forbes** 79	8

Ave. League Home Attendance: 382   **Goals** 68 64   **Top Goalscorer:** A. Forbes (18)
Best Position: 6th   **Worst:** 18th

FARNBOROUGH TOWN

Founded:1967
Nickname: Boro or Town

Manager: Ian McDonald   **Coach:** Ernie Howe   **Physio:** Dave Spratt
Club Colours: Red & white
Change Colours: Yellow & Blue
Club Sponsor: World Wide Carpets
Previous League: Conference
Previous Grounds: Queens Rd. Farnborough
Best Seasons: League: Conference   **F.A. Cup:** 4th Rd v Arsenal 2002-03
F.A.Trophy.: 6th Rd 92-93 02-03
Ground address: Cherrywood Road, Farnborough, Hants. GU14 8UD
Tel No:01252 541469 Fax: 01252 372640
Clubcall: 09068 440088   **Website**: www.farnboroughtownfc.com
Capacity: 4,163   **Seats:** 627   **Covered:** 1,350   **Floodlights:** Yes
Simple Directions: From M3 exit 4. Take A325 towards Farnborough, right into Prospect Avenue (club is signposted). Second right into Cherrywood Road and ground is on the right.
Midweek Home Matchday: Tuesday
Clubhouse: Open daily.
Club Shop: All types of leisurewear Contact: 01252 691129
Local Radio: BBC Southern Counties and County Sound
Local Press: Farnborough News

CLUB PERSONNEL
Chairman:
V-Chairman:
Director: Ron Higgins
President: Charlie Mortimer
Secretary: Vince Williams,c/o club
Tel No: 01252 541469
Press Officer: Secretary
Programme Editor: T.B.A.
2005-2006
Captain: Mark Rooney
Player of the Year: Steve Laidler
Top Goalscorer: Warrenm Bean

CLUB STATISTICS

Record

Attendance: 3,581 v Brentford F.A.Cup22.01.95
Victory: 11-0 v Chertsey Town (H) Spartan League 72-73
Defeat: 2-10 v Worpleston (H) Surrey Senior Lg Div 1 68-69
Career Goalscorer: Simon Read 209 1986-1994
Career Appearances: Brian Broome 529 1980-1994
Transfer Fee Paid: Undisclosed
Received: £50,000 from Dover Athletic for David Leworthy August 1993

Senior Honours: Southern League Prem Div 90-91 93-94 Isthmian Prem 00-01 R-Up 88-89 Div 1 84-85 Hampshire Senior Cup 74-75 81-82 83-84 85-86 90-91 03-04

Previous Leagues: Surrey Senior 68-72 Spartan 72-76 Athenian 76-77 Isthmian 77-89 99-01 Alliance Premier /Conference 89-90 91-93 94-99 Southern 90-91 93-94

240

FARNBOROUGH TOWN

BEST LGE ATT.: 781 v Weymouth
LOWEST: 377 v Eastleigh

No.	Date	Comp	H/A	Opponents	Att:	Result	Goalscorers	Pos
1	Aug 13	CS	A	Lewes	620	L 2 - 6	Townsend 48 **Gibbs** 77	22
2	16		H	Hayes	669	D 0 - 0		19
3	20		H	Thurrock	480	D 0 - 0		19
4	27		A	Sutton United	693	L 0 - 1		20
5	29		H	Newport County	610	W 2 - 1	Charles 34 McBean 68	18
6	Sept 3		A	Bishop's Stortford	363	D 1 - 1	Smith 6	18
7	10		H	Carshalton Athletic	484	W 4 - 0	T.Smith 14 Harkness 16 McBean 78 83	14
8	17		A	Basingstoke Town	706	W 1 - 0	Gibbs 35	13
9	24	FAC 2Q	H	**Berkhamsted Town**	456	W 3 - 0	**McBean 44 Gibbs 79 90**	
10	Oct 1	CS	H	Havant & Waterlooville	566	W 4 - 1	Sestanovich 21 Theo 24 **Gibbs** 26 Laidler 85	10
11	8	FAC 3Q	A	**Leatherhead**	1017	W 2 - 0	**Harkness 15 McBean 41**	
12	15	CS	A	Histon	791	W 6 - 3	**Gibbs** 4 (4 30 39 84) Jackman 17 (og) Canham 88	7
13	19		A	Eastleigh	360	L 0 - 2		
14	22	FAC 4Q	A	**Merthyr Tydfil**	1019	L 0 - 2		
15	29	CS	H	Weston-s-Mare	528	W 5 - 0	McBean 11 67 **Gibbs** 27 Laidler 41 Warner 45	6
16	Nov 5		A	Bognor Regis Town	486	W 1 - 0	McBean 23	4
17	8		A	Welling United	726	L 0 - 1		4
18	12		H	Dorchester Town	604	L 0 - 1		8
19	19		A	St Albans City	557	D 2 - 2	Pattison 29 Gasson 88	9
20	26	FAT 3Q	H	**Banbury United**	466	W 2 - 0	**Gibbs 20 Harkness 40**	
21	Dec 3	CS	H	Eastbourne Borough	524	L 2 - 3	Sestanovitch 20 (pen) McBean 25	12
22	10		A	Cambridge City	709	W 2 - 0	Warner 35 Canham 52	10
23	17	FAT 1	H	**Cambridge City**	377	L 0 - 2		
24	26		H	Maidenhead United	610	W 3 - 1	Harkness 31 33 Pattison 51	8
25	31		H	Yeading	504	W 1 - 0	McBean 14	4
26	Jan 2		A	Maidenhead United	411	W 2 - 1	Sestanovich 77 Charles 78	4
27	7		H	Lewes	566	D 2 - 2	Hankin 44 McBean 65	4
28	10		H	Weymouth	781	L 0 - 1		4
29	14		A	Hayes	244	W 1 - 0	Warner 40	4
30	21		A	Thurrock	294	W 2 - 0	Laidler 71 **Gibbs** 74	4
31	28		H	Sutton United	540	W 2 - 1	Sestanovich 63 Charles 78	4
32	Feb 4		A	Havant & Watreloouville	602	L 0 - 1		4
33	11		H	Histon	484	L 0 - 2		4
34	18		A	Weymouth	2058	W 2 - 1	Sestanovitch 30 Laidler 55	4
35	21		H	Eastleigh	377	W 1 - 0	Harkness 37	3
36	25		A	Carshalton Athletic	402	D 2 - 2	Canham 3 **Gibbs** 42	
37	Mar 4		H	Basingstoke Town	619	W 1 - 0	Charles 64	3
38	11		A	Weston-s-Mare	317	D 1 - 1	Canham 8	5
39	18		H	Bognor Regis Town	465	W 2 - 1	Charles 57 Pattison 78	3
40	21		H	Welling United	383	W 1 - 0	McBean 84	3
41	April 1		A	St Albans City	699	D 0 - 0		4
42	4		A	Doprchester Town	429	D 1 - 1	Sestanovich 61	4
43	8		A	Eastbourne Borough	512	W 1 - 0	Hankin 82	4
44	14		H	Bishop's Stortford	696	W 3 - 0	McBean 3 **Gibbs** 51 Warner 58	3
45	17		A	Newport County	1059	W 2 - 1	Gasson 47 Sestanovich 59 (pen)	3
46	22		A	Yeading	258	W 3 - 0	Harkness 43 70 Charles 51	3
47	29		A	Cambridge City	510	L 0 - 3		3
48	May 1	Play Off SF	H	Histon	1081	L 0 - 3		

Ave. League Home Attendance: 609   **Goals**   72   48   **Top Goalscorer:** Gibbs (14)

Best Position: 3rd   **Worst:** 22nd

FISHER ATHLETIC

Founded: 1908
Nickname: The Fish

The Official Programme of Fisher Athletic (London) FC

Manager: Justin Edinburgh

Club Colours: Black & white stripes/black/black

Change Colours: All red

Previous League: Ryman

Previous Name: Fisher Athletic 08-93 Fisher 93 93-96

Best Seasons: League: 15th Conference 87-88   **F.A. Cup:** 1st Rd 84-85 88-89

F.A.Trophy.: 3rd Rd Replay 87-88

Ground address: Ground Share with Dulwich Hamlet

Capacity: 3,000   **Seats:** 500   **Covered:** 1,000   **Floodlights:** Yes

Simple Directions: As for Dulwich Hamlet (Isthmian Division One)

Website: www.fisherathletic.co.uk

Midweek Home Matchday: Monday

Clubhouse: open for all matchdays   **Club Shop:** No

Local Radio: Capital & Capital Gold

Local Press: South London Press

CLUB PERSONNEL
Chairman: Eren Muduroglu
President:
Secretary: John Leyden, 148 Sachfield Drive, Chafford Hundred, Grays, Essex
Tel No:07835 850167 (M)
Programme Editor:
& Press Officer: Joe Aris

2005-2006
Captain: S.Piper
Player of the Year:
Top Goalscorer: Steve Watts

CLUB STATISTICS

Record	**Attendance:** 4,283 v Barnet GMV Conference 04.05.91
	Victory: 7-0 v Lewes F.A.Cup Sept. 95 **Defeat:** 1-8 v Clevedon (a) 10.03.01
	Career Goalscorer: Paul Shinners 205
	Career Appearances: Dennis Sharpe 720
	Transfer Fee Paid: £2,500 to Sittingbourne for Ben Taylor
	Received: £ 45,000 from Charlton Athletic for Paul Gorman
Senior Honours:	Southern Lg Champions 86-87 R-up 83-84 Southern Div 82-83
	London Senior Cup (5) Kent Senior Cup 83-84 Kent Senior Trophy (2)
	Ryman League Cup 2005-2006
Previous Leagues:	Parthenon, West Kent, Kent Amateur, London Spartan 76-82 Southern 82-7
	GMV Conference: 87-91, Southern 91-2005 Ryman 2005-06

Back row, left to right: Steve Watts,Tim Clancey, Mark Warren, James Pullen, Nick Davis,Hamid Barr and Charlie Taylor. **Front Row:** Damien Scannel, Ahmed Deen, Anthony Riviere, Charlie Hearn and Lenny Piper. **Missing** : Chris Piper (Captain).

FISHER ATHLETIC

BEST LGE ATT.: 1,036 v AFC Wimbledon
LOWEST: 112 v Leyton

No.	Date	Comp	H/A	Opponents	Att:	Result	Goalscorers	Pos
1	Aug 20	IP	H	Redbridge	120	W 3 - 1	Griffiths 31 L.Piper 41 Riviere 88	3
2	23		A	Hendon	216	W 2 - 1	Griffiths 18 C.Piper 39	3
3	27		A	Maldon Town	104	W 3 - 0	C.Piper 76 Scannell 80 Reilly 85	2
4	29		H	Worthing	206	D 2 - 2	Griffiths 26 75	3
5	Sept 3		A	Staines Town	219	L 0 - 2		4
6	6		A	Margate	112	D 1 - 1	Watts 68	4
7	10	FAC 1Q	H	Tooting & Mitcham U	159	W 6 - 1	Griffiths 5 38 Watts 41 57 Barr 45 Riviere 65	
8	17	IP	H	Harrow Borough	134	W 4 - 1	Riviere 29 Barr 70 (pen) L.Piper 86 90	3
9	19		H	Hampton & Richmond B	234	W 4 - 3	Griffiths 20 57 Barr 60 Watts 83	2
10	24	FAC 2Q	H	Tonbridge Angels	257	L 2 - 3	Barr 5 Watts 70	
11	Oct 1	IP	A	Billericay Town	511	W 3 - 1	Griffiths 10 19 Riviere 85	3
12	3		H	Heybridge Swifts	184	W 2 - 0	Watts 58 78	3
13	15	FAT1Q	H	Hendon	189	W 4 - 2	Clancey 13 Walshe 35 Watts 41 51	
14	22	IP	A	AFC Wimbledon	2745	L 0 - 1		3
15	24		H	Margate	192	W 2 - 1	Griffiths 11 Barr 87 (pen)	2
16	29		H	Folkestone Invicta	152	D 0 - 0		3
17	Nov 5		A	Leyton	112	W 4 - 3	Watts 36 89 L.Piper 59 79	2
18	12	FAT 2Q	H	Uxbridge	123	L 1 - 2	C.Piper 80	
19	19	IP	H	Slough Town	160	L 1 - 2	Martin 3	4
20	22		A	Hampton & Richmond B	376	W 3 - 0	Scannell Watts Griffiths	3
21	26		H	Windsor & Eton	116	W 2 - 0	Lovell 4 Watts 8	2
22	29		H	Wealdstone	170	W 2 - 1	Watts 26 Clancy 65	
23	Dec 3		A	Braintree Town	510	L 2 - 3	Watts 21 Barr 65 (pen)	
24	10		H	Walton & Hersham	144	W 2 - 0	C.Piper 55 Griffiths 90	2
25	17		A	Chelmsford City	401	W 2 - 0	Watts 27 Barr 79	1
26	26		A	East Thurrock United	138	L 1 - 2	Watts	2
27	Jan 2		A	Worthing	765	L 0 - 4		4
28	7		A	Redbridge	140	W 5 - 0	Hearn 44 88 West 52 Griffiths 65 L.Piper 71	3
29	14		H	Hendon	170	L 0 - 1		4
30	17		A	Bromley	510	W 2 - 1	C.Piper 43 Barr 79 (pen)	2
31	21		A	Harrow Borough	150	W 2 - 0	Watts 34 (pen) Duku 82	2
32	28		H	Maldon Town	116	D 1 - 1	L.Piper 29	2
33	Feb 4		H	Braintree Rown	378	D 1 - 1	Riviere 54	2
34	11		A	Windsor & Eton	128	W 4 - 1	Watts 48 51 Taylor 90 C.Piper 90 (pen)	2
35	18		A	Folkestone Invicta	427	W 1 - 0	Watts 43	2
36	25		H	AFC Wimbledon	1036	L 0 - 1		2
37	Mar 4		H	Leytpn	112	W 4 - 1	Scannell 19 45 Watts 60 L.Piper 81	2
38	11		A	Slough Town	293	W 4 - 0	Watts 7 24 Smith 53 Riviere 75	2
39	18		H	Billericay Town	208	L 0 - 2		2
40	25		A	Heybridge Swifts	269	W 2 - 1	Taylor 80 87	2
41	April 1		H	Bromley	246	D 0 - 0		2
42	8		A	Wealdstone	302	W 2 - 1	L. Piper 51 Barr 60	2
43	15		A	Staines Ton	139	W 2 - 1	Watts 42 West 77	2
44	17		H	East Thurrock	124	W 5 - 2	Barr 11 70 Watts 22 44 Riviere 42	2
45	22		A	Walton & Hersham	138	W 1 - 0	Richards 56	2
46	29		H	Chelmsford City	208	D 3 - 3	Barr 18 Richards 50 Watts 54 (pen)	3
47	May 2	Play Off SF	H	AFC Wimbledon	2274	W 2 - 1	Griffithe 20 Watts 68	
48	6	Play Off Final	H	Hampton & Richmond	900	W 3 - 0	Watts 7 Barr 63 C.Piper 70	

Ave. League Home Attendance: 217   **Goals** 102 55   **Top Goalscorer:** Watts (30)
Best Position: 1st   **Worst:** 4th

HAVANT & WATERLOOVILLE

Founded: 1998
Nickname: Hawks

The Hawks

31st July 2006 - Kick Off 7:45pm
Versus Portsmouth F.C.
Pre Season Friendly Match

Club Colours: All white with yellow & blue trim/white & blue/white
Change Colours: All yellow
Club Sponsors: Carlsberg UK Ltd.
Previous League: Southern
Previous Names: Havant Town & Waterlooville merged in1998
Best Seasons: League: 6th Conference South 2005-06
F.A. Cup: 1st Round Proper 2000-01 01-02   **F.A.Trophy.:** Semi-Final 2002-03
Manager: Ian Baird   **Assistant Manager:** Shaun Gale   **Physio:** Luke Brady
Ground address: Westleigh Park, Martin Road, West Leigh, Havant PO9 5TH
Tel No: 02392 787822 **Fax:** 02392 262367 **Website:** havantandwaterlooville.net
Capacity: 4,800   **Seats**: 562   **Covered**:3,500 **Floodlights**: Yes
Simple Directions: Take B2149 to Havant off the A27 (or B2149 to Petersfield if leaving Havant) second turning off dual carriageway into Bartons Road then first right into Martins Road.

Midweek Home Matchday: Monday
Clubhouse: Open every day with function rooms for hire.
Club Shop: Yes, fully stocked.
Local Press: The News (Portsmouth)
Local Radio: BBC Radio Solent, Power FM and The Quay

CLUB PERSONNEL
Chairman: Peter Demott
Presidents:
Maurice Hibberd & Arthur Sitch
Directors: Trevor Brock, Ray Jones, Drek Pope, John Carter, Ian Beard & Kevin Moore
Secretary & Press Officer: Trevor Brock, 2 Betula Close, Waterlooville, Hampshire
PO7 8EJ Tel No: 02392 267276
Prog Ed: Simon Lynch
Tel No: 07913 700497 (M)
Programme: Pages 48 £2.00

2005-2006: **Captain:** Tom Jordan
Player of the Year: Rocky Baptiste
Top Goalscorer: Rocky Baptiste 30

CLUB STATISTICS

RECORD	**Attendance:** 1,331 v Tamworth F.A.Trophy S-Final 12.04.03
	Victory: 9-0 v Moneyfields, Hants. 23.10.01 Senior Cup
	Defeat: 0-5 v Worcester City Southern Premier 20.03.04
	Career Goalscorer: James Taylor 138
	Career Appearances: James Taylor 254 + 41 as sub
	Transfer Fee Paid: £5,000 to Bashley for John Wilson
	Received: £15,000 from Peterborough United for Gary McDonald
Senior Honours:	Southern Lg Southern Division Champions1998-99. Russell Coates Cup Winners 2003-2004 Hampshire Senior Cup R-up 2000-01 01-02
Previous Leagues:	Portsmouth 58-71,Hampshire 71-86 Wessex 86-91 Southern 98-2004

Back row (L-R): Justin Gregory, Mickey Warner, Darren Annon, Shea Saunders, Shane Gore, Tom Taylor, Gareth Howells, Tony Taggart, Craig Watkins, Ludovic Quistin. **Middle:** Kevin Moore (Referee Liaison Officer), Derek Pope (Director), Brett Poate, Jamie Collins, Luke Byles, Carl Wilson-Denis, Tom Jordan, Matt Gray, Neil Sharp, Neil Davis, Rocky Baptiste, Richard Pacquette, Peter Demott (Chairman), Trevor Brock (Secretary/Director). **Front:** Dave Topliss (Chief Scout), Neil Champion, Fitzroy Simpson, Adie Aymes (Fitness Coach), Ian Baird (Manager), Shaun Gale (Asst Manager), Robin Ilott (Goalkeeping Coach), Craig O'Connor, Mo Harkin, Luke Brady (Physio). Photo: Dave Haines.

HAVANT & WATERLOOVILLE

BEST LGE ATT.: 1,163 v Weymouth
LOWEST: **349** v Hayes

No.	Date	Comp	H/A	Opponents	Att:	Result	Goalscorers	Pos
1	Aug 13	CS	A	Weymouth	1521	L 0 - 1		15
2	15		H	Sutton U ited	500	L 0 - 1		20
3	20		H	Hayes	349	D 1 - 1	Davis 72	20
4	27		A	Newport County	720	W 3 - 2	Poate 32 86 Town 39	17
5	29		H	Lewes	411	W 1 - 0	**Baptiste** 14	11
6	Sept 3		A	Thurrock	250	W 2 - 0	Poate 38 **Baptiste** 82	6
7	10		H	Histon	418	W 3 - 1	Collins 24 **Baptiste** 57 81	6
8	17		A	Yeading	199	L 0 - 2		9
9	24	FAC 2Q	A	Eastleigh	470	D 0 - 0		
10	26	FAC 2Qr	H	Eastleigh	329	W 4 - 1	**Baptiste** 2 29 Town 47 Davis 85	
11	Oct 1	CS	A	Farnborough Town	566	L 1 - 4	Davis 43	10
12	8	FAC 3Q	A	Cirencester Town	278	L 1 - 2	Harrison 85	
13	15	CS	H	Maidenhead United	453	W 2 - 1	Powell 29 Poate 53	10
14	17		H	Basingstoke Town	410	W 2 - 0	**Baptiste** 12 70	5
15	22		A	Carshalton Athletic	342	W 3 - 1	Byles 7 Powell 60 **Baptiste** 88	4
16	29		H	Cambridge City	474	D 1 - 1	**Baptiste** 61	4
17	Nov 8		A	Dorchester Town	345	D 1 - 1	**Baptiste** 62	6
18	12		H	Eastbourne Borough	474	L 0 - 1		9
19	19		A	Bishop's Stortford	307	W 3 - 1	Poate 8 64 **Baptiste** 56	3
20	26	FAT 3Q	A	Weymouth	1018	L 1 - 2	Harrison 63	
21	Dec 3	CS	H	Weston -s-Mare	370	W 3 - 2	**Baptiste** 42 Wilson-Dennis 50 Saunders 81	1
22	10		H	Eastleigh	668	W 2 - 1	**Baptiste** 19 Wilson-Dennis 50	2
23	13		A	Weling United	520	D 2 - 2	Wilson-Dennis 3 Byles 68	2
24	17	CS	A	Basinstoke Town	298	L 1 - 2	Saunders 50	2
25	26		A	Bognor Regis Town	481	W 1 - 0	Wilson-Dennis 78	2
26	31		A	St Albans City	560	L 0 - 2		
27	Jan 2		H	Bognor Regis Town	757	W 1 - 0	**Baptiste** 38	2
28	7		H	Weymouth	1163	W 2 - 1	Wilson-Denis 7 Sharp 66	1
29	14		A	Sutton United	536	D 1 - 1	**Baptiste** 5	3
30	21		A	Hayes	184	W 2 - 1	**Baptiste** 14 Taggart 24	2
31	28		H	Newport County	524	L 1 - 2	Wilson-Denis 16	3
32	Feb 4		H	Farnborough Town	602	W 1 - 0	**Baptiste** 42	3
33	11		A	Maidenhead United	251	L 1 - 3	**Baptiste** 63	3
34	25		A	Histon	552	L 1 - 3	Jordan 55	6
35	Mar 4		H	Yeading	401	W 3 - 0	**Baptiste** 42 (pen) Saunders 54 Watkins 77	5
36	6		H	Dorchester Town	399	W 1 - 0	**Baptiste** 73	4
37	18		H	Welling United	494	D 0 - 0		6
38	25		A	Eastbourne Borough	447	D 2 - 2	**Baptiste** 5 Pacquette 90	5
39	April 1		H	Bishop's Stortford	428	D 2 - 2	**Baptiste** 28 38	5
40	8		A	Weston-s-Mare	240	W 3 - 1	Taggart 2 **Baptiste** 20 88 (pen)	5
41	10		H	Carshalton Athletic	407	D 1 - 1	**Baptiste** 4	5
42	15		H	Thurrock	377	L 1 - 2	Wilson-Denis 68	5
43	17		A	Lewes	527	W 2 - 0	**Baptiste** 10 (pen) Pacquette 82	5
44	22		H	St Albans City	502	L 0 - 1		5
45	25		A	Cambridge City	245	D 0 - 0		5
46	29		A	Eastleigh	652	W 6 - 2	Poate 39 Pacquette 40 Thomas 45 (og) **Baptiste** 81 Sharp 86 Jordan 89	6

Ave. League Home Attendance: 504   **Goals**   69   54   **Top Goalscorer:** Baptiste (29)

Best Position: 1st   **Worst:**   20th

HAYES

Manager: Kevin Hill   **Physio**: Steve Hockham

Club Colours: Red and white stripes/black/black

Change Colours: Light & dark blue stripes/black/black

Club Sponsors: Taylor Woodrow

Previous League: Isthmian

Best Seasons: 12th Conference South 2004-05

F.A. Cup: 2nd Rd Replay 1972-73   **F.A.Trophy.:** 6th Rd 1978-79

Ground address: Townfield House, Church Road, Hayes, Middlesex.

Tel No: 0208 573 2075   **Website: www.hayesfc.net**

Capacity: 6,500   **Seats**: 450   **Covered** 2,450   **Floodlights**: Yes

Simple Directions: M25, M4 A312 (Hayes by-pass) Take A4020 (Uxbridge Rd) and Church Road is on the left.

Midweek Home Matchday: Tuesday

Clubhouse: Open from lunchtime at week ends and mid week evenings

Club Shop: Yes. Contact Lee Hermitage c/o club.

Local Press: Hayes Gazette

Local Radio: Capital Radio

CLUB PERSONNEL

Chairman: Derek Goodall
Vice Chairman: Trevor Griffith
Club Patron: Les Ferdinand MBE
President: Les Lovering
Directors: D.Goodall, C.Porter, E.Stevens, T.Griffith, C.Hanlon, S.East J.Bond Sen., J.Bond jun., N.Griffith and T.Gorman and D.Matthews
Football Secretary: John Bond Jnr. 57 Austin Road, Hayes, Middx UB3 3DG. Tel No:0208 5818938
Commercial Manager: Willie Wordsworth c/o club
Press Officer: Kevin Watts
Programme (Ray Peploe) 32 pages £1.50
2005-2006:Captain:
Player of the Year:
Top Goalscorer:

CLUB STATISTICS

RECORD

Attendance: 15,370 v Bromley F.A.Amateur Cup 10.02.51

Victory: 12-1 v Newbury Town F.A.Cup 1946-1947

12-1 v AEC Southall Middlesex Senior Cup 1937-1938

Defeat: 0-12 v Arsenal London Challenge Cup 1937-1938

Career Goalscorer: Unknown   **Career Appearances**: Reg Leather 701

Record Transfer Fee   **Paid:** £6,000 to Hendon for Gary Keen & to Enfield for Joe Francis

Received: £30,000 from Q.P.R. for Les Ferdinand

Senior Honours: Isthmian Champions 95-96 Athenian Champions 56-57, London Senior Cup 31-32 80-81 Middlesex Senior Cup (10)

Previous Leagues: Local football 1909-14 G.Western Suburban 19-22 , London 22-24 Spartan 24-30 Athenian 30-71, Isthmian 71-96, Conference 96-02 & Isthmian 02-04

Back Row (L-R): Tobi Jinadu, Shaun McAuley, Marvin Bartley, Liam Feeney, Ryan Ashe, Adam Logie, Michael Bartley. **Middle:** Jackie Matthews (Kit Manager), Stafforde Palmer, Mark Nicholls, Ryan Tackley, Reece Kirk, Kevin Davies, Adam Thomson, Orlando Jeffrey, Jon Dyer, Daniel Dyer, Derek Matthews (Youth Development Officer).**Front:** Pauline Beaven (Physio), Gilbert Nuako, Peter Collins, Kieran Knight, Phil Gridelet (Asst Manager), Derek Goodall (Chairman), Kevin Hill (Manager), Miles Jones, Mark Boyce, Damon Ming, Colin Davis (Reserve Team Manager).

HAYES

BEST LGE ATT.: 417 v Yeading
LOWEST: 160 v Dorchester Town

No.	Date	Comp	H/A	Opponents	Att:	Result	Goalscorers	Pos
1	Aug 13	CS	H	Eastleigh	229	W 1 - 0	McKenna 15	10
2	16		A	Farnborough Town	669	D 0 - 0		8
3	20		A	Havant & Waterlooville	349	D 1 - 1	Marvin Bartley 32	8
4	27		H	Maidenhead United	243	W 2 - 1	Goodall 58 Hill 90	4
5	29		A	Weston-s-Mare	201	D 1 - 1	Knight 37	4
6	Sept 3		H	St Albans City	262	L 0 - 1		10
7	10		H	Bishop's Stortford	202	W 2 - 0	Scott 68 Michael Bartley 82	7
8	17		A	Welling United	572	L 0 - 1		12
9	24	FAC2Q	H	Brook House	406	D 1 - 1	Warner 25	
10	27	FAC2Qr	A	Brook House	342	W 4 - 0	Knight 31 Warner 43 Scott 65 McAvery 85	
11	Oct 1	CS	A	Dorchester Town	426	D 2 - 2	Goulding 25 5 6	12
12	8	FAC 3Q	H	Bishops Stortford	231	W 2 - 0	Goulding 35 McAvery 80	
13	15	CS	H	Bognor Regis Town	215	L 1 - 2	Scott 45	14
14	18		H	Cambridge City	209	W 2 - 0	Warner 28 Knight 82	12
15	22	FAC4Q	A	Histon	588	L 1 - 3	Scott 41 (pen)	
16	29	CS	A	Histon	453	D 3 - 3	Warner 85 Goulding 86 90	9
17	Nov 5		H	Thurrock	192	L 0 - 1		11
18	8		H	Newport County	264	W 3 - 2	Saulsbury (pen) 72 Scott (pen) 82 Michael Bartley 89	11
19	12		A	Carshalton Athletic	313	W 2 - 1	Ellis 3 Michael Bartley 18	9
20	22		A	Eastbourne United	434	D 0 - 0		9
21	29	FAT 3Q	A	Braintree Town	228	W 1 - 0	Michael Bartley 62	
22	Dec 10	CS	A	Sutton United	494	L 1 - 2	Jeffries	12
23	17	FAT 1	A	Worcester City	677	L 0 - 1		
24	20	CS	A	Lewes	356	L 1 - 2	Scott 17	15
25	26		H	Yeading	417	L 0 - 1		13
26	31		H	Basingstoke Town	213	L 1 - 2	Goulding 6	
27	Jan 2		A	Yeading	601	W 3 - 2	Goulding 2 62 Knight 45	13
28	7		A	Eastleigh	356	L 1 - 2	Feeney 73	14
29	9		H	Farnborough Town	244	L 0 - 1		14
30	21		H	Havant & Waterlooville	184	L 1 - 2	Michael Bartley 90	14
31	24		H	Weymouth	302	L 1 - 2	Jordan 54	14
32	28		A	Maidenhead United	315	L 1 - 2	Knight 65	15
33	Feb 4		H	Dorchester Town	160	L 0 - 1		18
34	11		A	Bognor Regis Town	341	D 1 - 1	Marvin Bartley 62	17
35	18		H	Eastbourne United	205	L 0 - 1		18
36	21		A	Cambridge City	279	L 1 - 2	McKenna 42	18
37	25		A	Bishop's Stortford	314	L 0 - 1		18
38	Mar 4		H	Welling United	214	L 1 - 3	Knight 11	18
39	11		H	Histon	190	W 2 - 1	Knight 64 (pen) Warner 88	18
40	18		A	Thurrock	159	D 1 - 1	Goulding 51	18
41	25		H	Carshalton Athletic	203	L 1 - 2	Knight 7	19
42	April 1		A	weymouth	1727	L 1 - 5	Knight 51	20
43	5		A	Newport County	702	L 0 - 1		21
44	8		H	Lewes	167	D 2 - 2	Osbourne 85 90	21
45	15		A	St Albans City	977	L 0 - 1		21
46	22		A	Basingstoke Town	3900	D 1 - 1	Knight 86 (pen)	21
47	25		H	Weston-s-Mare	174	W 4 - 1	Knight 5 78 Warner 28 Michael Bartley 43	20
48	29		H	Sutton United	389	W 2 - 1	Williams 47 Mi Bartley 89	20

Ave. League Home Attendance: 232 **Goals** 56 65 **Top Goalscorer:** Knight (12)
Best Position: 4th **Worst:** 21st

HISTON

Founded: 1904
Nickname: The Stutes

Manager: Steve Fallon   **Coach:** John Beck
Physio: Lee Petrucci
Club Colours: Red/black/black
Change Colours: Sky & navy navy/navy
Club Sponsor: Glass World and Websters Hill Residential
Previous League: Southern   **Previous Name:** Histon Institute 1904-1951
Best Seasons: Lg: 5th Conference South 2005-2006 **F.A.Vase:** 4th Rd 96-97 87-98
F.A. Cup: 2nd Rd 2003-2004 2004-2005 **F.A.Trophy.:** 4th Round 2000-01, 2004-05
Ground address: The Glassworld Stadium, Bridge Rd, Impington, Cambs. CB4 9PH
Tel No: 01223 237373   Fax 01223 237373 (matchdays)
Official website: www.histonfc.co.uk
Capacity: 3,250   Seats: 450   Covered: 1,800   Floodlights:Yes
Simple Directions: Leave A14 northern Cambridge bypass on B1049 (signposted Histon and Cottenham) Ground half a mile on right. Cambridge BR 4miles Bus:104
Midweek Home Matchday: Tuesday
Clubhouse: Open daily hot & cold food. **Club Shop:** Yes
Local Radio: BBC Radio Cambridgeshire, Q103 and Star FM
Local Press: Cambridge Evening News and Histon& IImpington Crier

B PERSONNEL
Chairman: Gareth Baldwin
V-Chairman: John Webster
Secretary: Lisa Baldwin,
Tanglewood, 5 Caxton Lane, Foxton,
Cambs. CB2 6SR
Tel No: 01223 872 989 email:
lisa.baldwin@my.intervivo.com
Mobile: 07721 763 418
Press Officer: Graham Eales
Tel No: 07977 471023 (M)
Programme.Editor:
Stuart Hamilton 077535 64980
email stuart.hamilton10@tesco.net
Programme 32 Pages £1.50

2005-2006
Captain: Neil Andrews
Player of the Year: Jamie Barker
Top goalscorer: Jamie Barker (16)

CLUB STATISTICS

Record	**Attendance** : 6,400 v Kings Lynn F.A.Cup 1956
	Recent best: 2,6 54 v Yeovil Town F.A.Cup 2nd Rd. Nov.2004
	Victory: 11-0 v March Town Cambs Invitation Cup 15.02.2001.
	Defeat:1-8 v Ely City Eastern Counties Div.1 1994.
Career Goalscorer:	Neil Kennedy (292)
Career Appearances:	Neil Andrews and Neil Kennedy
Record Transfer Fee	**Paid:** £6000 to Chelmsford City for Ian Cambridge, 2000.
	Received: £30,000 from Manchester United for Guiliano Maiorana.
Senior Honours:	Southern Premier Champions 2004-05 Southern Eastern Div R-up 03-04
Previous Leagues:	Cambs 1904-1948,Spartan 48-60 Delphian 60-63 Eastern Co 66-2000 Southern 2000-2005 Eastern Co Champions 99-00 Div 1 R-up 96-97 Camb Prof Cup: 2001-2-3-4 Camb Inv.Cup (6)

Back Row (L-R): Drew Roberts, Robbie Nightingale, Jamie Barker, Steve Jackman, Matt Langston, Lance Key, Nathaniel Knight - Percival, Neil Kennedy, Ian Cambridge.
Front: Neil Andrews, Junior McDougald, Danny Bloomfield, John Kennedy, Matty Haniver, Erkan Okay, Adrian Cambridge.

HISTON

BEST LGE ATT.: 1,711 v Cambridge City
LOWEST: 261 v Thurrock

No.	Date	Comp	H/A	Opponents	Att:	Result	Goalscorers	Pos
1	Aug 13	CS	A	Thurrock	278	W 2 - 1	Collis 3 (og) Kennedy 45	8
2	17		H	Welling United	367	D 1 - 1	Goddard 90	6
3	20		H	Weymouth	489	W 2 - 1	Andrews 54 Vowden 58	5
4	27		A	Lewes	478	W 3 - 0	Watts 26 (og) Kenndy 26 Hanvier 45	2
5	29		H	Basingstoke Town	441	W 2 - 0	**Barker** 53 Kennedy 66	2
6	Sept 4		A	Newport County	604	W 1 - 0	A.Cambridge 22	1
7	10		A	Havant & Waterlooville	418	L 1 - 3	Knight-Percival 43	2
8	17		H	Eastleigh	424	W 1 - 0	**Barker** 59	1
9	24	FAC 2Q	A	**Malvern Town**	196	W 4 - 1	**Haniver 6 Kennedy 45 Andrews 77 Humphries 90**	
10	Oct 1	CS	A	Carshalton Athletic	212	D 0 - 0		1
11	8	FAC 3Q	H	**Welwyn Garden City**	373	W 2 - 1	**Nightingale 55 64**	
12	15	CS	A	Farnborough Town	791	L 3 - 6	Jackman 51 Kennedy 62 Nightingale 65	2
13	18		H	Yeading	440	W 1 - 0	Kennedy 86	2
14	22	FAC 4Q	H	**Hayes**	588	W 3 - 0	**Gutzmore 75 Barker 78 85**	
15	29	CS	H	Hayes	453	L 2 - 3	Williams 4 (og) **Barker** 45	
16	Nov 5	FAC 1R	H	**Hednesford Town**	1080	W 4 - 0	**Jackman 10 58 I.Cambridge 50 Nightingale 84**	
17	12	CS	H	Bognor Regis Town	489	D 2 - 2	Jackman 50 Vowden 63	10
18	15		A	Bishop's Stortford	342	L 0 - 5		10
19	19		A	Eastbourne Borough	603	D 1 - 1	**Barker** 50	12
20	23		A	Weston-s-Mare	180	W 4 - 1	Roberts 21 36 Gutzmore 52A. A. Cambridge 86	5
21	26	FAT 3Q	A	**Hinckley United**	446	D 2 - 2	**I Cambridge 26 Haniver 78**	
22	30	FAT3Qr	H	**Hinckley United**	218	W 2 - 1	**Haniver 45 Storer 45**	
23	Dec 3	FAC 3R	A	**Nuneaton Borough**	3366	D 2 - 2	**Barker 36 Knight-Percival 44**	
24	10	CS	A	Maidenhead United	235	W 4 - 1	Haniver 1 **Barker** 29 Andrews 63 Hipperson 79	6
25	14	FAC 3Rr	H	**Nuneaton Borough**	3000	L 1 - 2	**Vowden 61**	
26	17	FAT 1	A	**Alfrteon Town**	238	D 1 - 1	**Vowden 80**	
27	21	FAT 1r	H	**Alfreton Town**	288	W 2 - 1	**Barker 17 68**	
28	26	CS	H	Cambridge City	1711	W 1 - 0	Farrington 31	6
29	31		H	Dorchester Town	548	W 4 - 1	**Barker** 58 Andrews 84 89 Haniver 86	
30	Jan 2		A	Cambridge City	1542	L 1 - 3	Hipperson 81	5
31	11		H	St Albans City	494	L 0 - 5		6
32	14	FAT 2	A	**Exeter City**	2103	L 2 - 3	**I.Cambridge 45 54**	
33	21	CS	A	Weymouth	1629	L 0 - 1		9
34	28		H	Lewes	425	D 1 1 1	**Barker** 81	11
35	Feb 4		H	Carshalton Athletic	454	L 0 - 1		11
36	7		A	Sutton United	420	D 1 - 1	Nightingale 28 (pen)	
37	11		A	Farnborough Town	484	W 2 - 0	Bloomfield 37 39	10
38	18		A	Weston-s-Mare	438	D 1 - 1	I Cambridge 11	10
39	21		A	Yeading	102	L 0 - 1		10
40	25		H	Havant & Waterlooville	552	W 3 - 1	Nightingale 3 4 Kennedy 47	10
41	28		A	Welling United	500	D 1 - 1	A.Cambridge 72	
42	Mar 4		A	Eastleigh	356	W 2 - 1	Andrews 69 **Barker** 81	8
43	11		A	Hayes	190	L 1 - 2	Kennnedy 51	9
44	15		H	Thurrock	261	W 3 - 1	Jackman 70 Bloomfield 81 **Barker** 86	8
45	18		H	Sutton United	409	W 3 - 0	Bloomfield 20 A.Cambridge 54 Andrews 82	8
46	25		A	Bognor Regis Town	220	L 1 - 3	**Barker** 62	8
47	April 1		H	Eastbourne Borough	571	W 3 - 1	**Barker** 8 Bloomfield 24 Andrews 37	8
48	8		A	St Albans City	863	L 0 - 1		9
49	15		H	Newport County	1092	L 2 - 3	Bloomfield 4 Nightingale 36 (pen)	9
50	17		A	Basingstoke Town	293	W 1 - 0	Bloomfield 64	9
51	22		A	Dorchester Town	417	W 3 - 0	Hanvier 24 Bloomfield 71 Knight-Percival 74	7
52	26		H	Bishop's Stortford	691	W 3 - 2	Bloomfield 71 60 Mitchell-King 65	6
53	29		H	Maidenhead United	893	W 3 - 0	Andrews 14 Kennedy 65 A.Cambridge 79	
54	May 1	Play Off SF	A	**Farnborough Town**	1081	W 3 - 0	**Kennedy 3 (15 37 69)**	
55	7	Play Off Final	A	**St Albans City**	3175	L 0 - 2		
Ave. League Home Attendance:					**530**			
Goals						89 66	**Top Goalscorer:** Barker (16)	

Best Position: 1st   **Worst:** 12th

LEWES

Founded: 1885
Nickname: Rooks

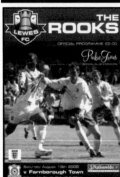

THE ROOKS

Club Colours: Red& black/Black/Black

Change Colours: Orange/White & Orange/ Black

Club Sponsor: Icon Live Ltd.

Previous Leagues: Athenian and Isthmian.

Best Seasons: Lg: 4th Nationwide South 2004-05 & 2005-2006

F.A. Cup: 1st Rd 2001-02

F.A.Trophy.: 3rd Round 02-03 03-04

F.A.Vase: Quarter FInal 2001-02   **F.A.Amateur Cup**: 2nd Round 67-68

Manager: Steven King   **Asst Manager/Coach**: Stuart Cash **Physio:** Mark Davis

Ground address: The Dripping Pan, Mountfield Road, Lewes BN7 1XN

Tel No: 01273 472100   **Website:** www.lewesfc.com

Capacity: 3,000   **Seats:** 400 **Covered:** 1,400   **Floodlights:** Yes

Simple Directions: Two minutes walk from Lewes BR. Turn left out of station and left again into Mountfield Road. Ground 30 yards on right.

Midweek Home Matchday: Wednesday

Clubhouse: Bar and tea bar. Tel No: 01273 472100   **Club Shop:** Yes

Local Radio: Southern F.M. BBC Southern Counties

Local Press: Evening Argus,Southern Express and Sussex Express

CLUB PERSONNEL

Chairman: Terry Parris

Secretary: Carole Bailey, Lewes F.C., Westgate Street, Lewes , East Sussex. BN7 1YR

Tel No: 07793 404140

Commercial Manager:
Steve White: 07967 806930 (W)
01273 473804 (H)

Programme Editor: Sean Trendall

2005-2006
Captain: Paul Kennett
Player of the Year:
Jean Michel Sigere
& Steve Robinson
Top Goalscorer: S

CLUB STATISTICS

Record	Attendance: 2,500 v Newhaven Sussex County Lg.26.12.47
Victory:	
Defeat:	
Career Goalscorer:	'Pip' Parris 350
Career Appearances:	Terry Parris 662
Record Transfer Fee	**Paid**: £ 2,000 for Matt Allen
	Received: £2,500 from Brighton for Grant Horscroft
Senior Honours:	Isthmian Div 1 South Champions and Play Off winners for Conference South 2003-2004
Previous Leagues:	Mid Sussex 1886 1920 Sussex County 20-65 Athenian 65-77 Isthmian 77-03

Back row, left to right: Ray Bugg (Kit Man), Paul Booth, Steve Elliott, Lewis Hamilton, Jay Saunders, Leon Legge, Jack Stern, Paul Wilkerson, Aaron France, Steve Robinson, Pau lKennett (Captain) Andy Drury, Max Ellison-Hustwick, Jean-Michel Sigere and Gary Holloway. Front row: Ryan Bradley, Lewis Cook, Simon Wormull, Dean Hooper, Mark Davis (Physio), Steve King (Manager), Stuart Cash Assistant Manager/Coach), Lee Farrel, Anthony Srorey, Jamie Cade and Karl Beckford.

LEWES

BEST LGE ATT.: 1,193 v Eastbourne Borough
LOWEST: **305** v Sutton United

No.	Date	Comp	H/A	Opponents	Att:	Result	Goalscorers	Pos
1	Aug 13	CS	H	Farnborough Town	620	W 6 - 2	Kennett 16 90 Beckford 28 89 (pen) Robinson 67 Holligan 80	1
2	16		A	Yeading	230	W 3 - 0	Beckford 18 **Sigere** 20 Harvey 50	1
3	20		A	Carshalton Athletic	336	D 2 - 2	Sigere 47 90	3
4	27		H	Histon	478	L 0 - 3		5
5	29		A	Havant & Waterlooville	411	L 0 - 1		7
6	Sept 4		H	Maidenhead United	485	D 2 - 2	Beckford 41 **Sigere** 74	11
7	10		H	Newport County	485	W 1 - 0	**Sigere** 79	8
8	17		A	Rhurrock	289	W 3 - 2	Legge 13 **Sigere** 41 Beckford 62	6
9	24	FAC 2Q	A	Leyton	162	W 1 - 0	Beckford 41	
10	Oct 1	CS	A	St Albans City	541	L 0 - 2		7
11	8	FAC 3Q	H	Dulwich Hamlet	539	W 1 - 0	Beckford 19 (pen)	
12	15	CS	H	Weston-s-Mare	459	W 5 - 2	Foyewa 57 Sangare 67 Holligan 75 84 **Sigere** 79	7
13	19		H	Bognor Regis Town	612	D 1 - 1	Watts 44	7
14	22	FAC 4Q	A	Cambridge City	588	L 1 - 2	Watts 32	
15	29	CS	H	Basingstoke Town	448	W 3 - 0	Holligan 22 37 Legge 57	
16	Nov 1		A	Dorchester Town	380	D 2 - 2	Brennan 49 79	6
17	5		A	Bishop's Stortford	312	W 3 - 0	Lewis 51 (og) **Sigere** 77 (pen) 90	
18	8		A	Sutton United	628	W 5 - 1	Sigere 4 (1 8 18 59) Kennett 41	1
19	12		H	Cambridge City	586	D 2 - 2	Foyewa 14 **Sigere** 57	2
20	19		A	Welling United	713	L 1 - 2	Legge 73	4
21	26	FAT 3Q	H	Dorchester Town	364	D 2 - 2	Holligan 2 Sigere 68	
22	29	FAT 3Qr	A	Dorchester Town	235	L 1 - 3	Sigere (pen)	
23	Dec 10	CS	H	Weymouth	705	L 2 - 3	Sigere 34 (pen) 78	8
24	20		H	Hayes	356	W 2 - 1	**Sigere** 18 Ellis (og) 69	5
25	26		A	Eastbourne Borough	1066	L 1 - 3		7
26	Jan 2		H	Eastbourne Borough	1193	W 1 - 0	Legge 73	7
27	7		A	Farnborough Town	566	D 2 - 2	Gomis 29 Lovett 83	7
28	14		H	Yeading	449	W 1 - 0	Cade 69	5
29	21		A	Carshalton Athletic	553	W 2 - 1	**Sigere** 34 Graves 53 (og)	5
30	28		A	Histon	425	D 1 - 1	Cade 80	5
31	Feb 4		H	St Albans City	555	L 0 - 2		5
32	11		A	Weston-s-Mare	261	W 2 - 1	Cade 35 Harkin 90 (pen)	5
33	18		A	Dorchester Town	405	W 3 - 2	Robinson 13 **Sigere** 54 (pen) Middleton 61 (og)	5
34	21		A	Bognor Regis Town	341	D 2 - 2	Beckford 21 Howell 81	6
35	25		H	Newport County	534	W 3 - 2	Fontana 27 Kennett 45 Beckford 64	5
36	Mar 4		H	Thurrock	452	D 0 - 0		7
37	8		H	Sutton United	305	W 2 - 0	Beckford 3 **Sigere** 86	5
38	11		A	Basingstoke Town	280	W 5 - 1	Cade 25 70 **Sigere** 36 39 Beckford 77	3
39	18		H	Bishop's Stortford	395	W 2 - 1	**Sigere** 38 Beckford 42	3
40	25		A	Cambridge City	585	W 2 - 0	Robinson 31 **Sigere** 83	3
41	April 1		H	Welling United	660	W 2 - 1	Cade 15 Beckford 85	3
42	8		A	Hayes	167	D 2 - 2	Elsegood 4(og) Cade 69	3
43	15		A	Maidenhead United	307	W 1 - 0	Kennett 55	3
44	17		H	Havant & Waterlooville	527	L 0 - 2		4
45	22		H	Eastleigh	435	L 0 - 2		4
46	29		A	Weymouth	4071	L 0 - 2		4

Ave. League Home Attendance: 532   **Goals**   83   62   **Top Goalscorer:** Sigere (26)
Best Position: 1st   **Worst:**   11th

NEWPORT COUNTY

Manager: Peter Beadle **Assistant Manager:** Scott Young **Physio:** Tommy Cosh
Club Colours: Amber and Black
Change Colours: Red& Blue stripes
Club Sponsor: Acorn Recruitment & Training
Previous League: Southern
Best Seasons: Lg: 18th Conference South **F.A. Cup:** 1st Rd 2001-02
F.A.Trophy.: 3rd Rd 99-00 00-01 02-03
Ground address: Newport International Sports Village, Newport Stadium, Spytty Park, Newport NP19 4PT **Tel No:** 01633 662262
Official website: www.newport-county.co.uk **Academy Director:** Glyn Jones
Capacity: 4,300 Seats: 1,236 Covered: 3,236 Floodlights: Yes
Simple Directions: From Severn Bridge on M4 take first exit signed Newport (jct 24) tand follow sigms to Newport International Sports Village. Turn left into Langland Way (Carcraft)and take next left into stadium car park.
Midweek Home Matchday: Wednesday
Clubhouse: Open matchdays offering comprehensive meal menu and Sky Sports.
Club Shop: Open matchdays. (Duncan Jardine & Neil Evans)
Local Radio: Red Dragon, Real Radio and BBC Wales.
Local Press: South Wales Argus and South Wales Echo

CLUB PERSONNEL

Chairman: Chris Blight
Secretary:
Mike Everett, 13 Dale Rd., Newport, Gwent NP 19 9DZ
Tel No: 01633 292130
Press Officer
Colin Everett 07867 553757
Programme Editor:
Ray Taylor: 40 pages £1.50

2005-2006
Captain: John Brough
Player of the Year: Ian Hillier
Top Scorers: Hughes 11

CLUB STATISTICS

Record	**Attendance**: 4,300 v Manchester United (friendly) 31.03.04	
	v Blackpool F.A.Cup 1st Rd. Replay 2001-02	
	Victory: 9-0 v Pontlottyn Blast Furnance (A) Welsh Cup 01.09.90	
	Defeat: 1-6 v Stafford Rangers (A) 06.01.96	
	Career Goalscorer: Chris Lillygreen 93	
	Career Appearances: Mark Price 275 (222 lg +53 Cup)	
	Transfer Fee Paid: £5,000 to Forest Green Rovers for Shaun Chapple	
	Received: £5,000 from Merthyr Tydfil for Craig Lima	
Senior Honours:	Hellenic Premier Division Champions 89-90 Glos Sen Cup 93-94	
	Southern League Midland Div Champions 94-95 Gwent F.A.Senior Cup (7) F.A.Wales Premier Cup R-up 2002-2003	
Previous	**Leagues:** Hellenic 89-90 Southern 90-2004	
	Names: Newport AFC after demise of Newport County in 88-89 Change back again in 1999.	

Back Row (L-R): Tony Gilbert (Kit Manager), Matthew Prosser, Tyrone Toppar, Matt Green, Andrew Thomas, Sam O'Sullivan, Tony Pennock, Jacob Giles, Mark Ovendale, Nathan Davies, Stuart Edwards, Ashley Williams, Kris Leek, Gareth Mouncher, Russell Jones (Assistant Physio).
Front: Bobby Morris (Assistant), Jason Bowen, Lee Collier, Ian Hillier, Damon Searle, Scott Young (Assistant Manager), Peter Beadle (Manager), John Brough, Lee Jenkins, Julian Alsop, Craig Hughes, Tommy Cosh (Physio).

NEWPORT COUNTY

BEST LGE ATT.: 1,148 v Thurrock
LOWEST: 504 v Basingstoke Town

No.	Date	Comp	H/A	Opponents	Att:	Result	Goalscorers	Pos
1	Aug 13	CS	H	Cambridge City	886	W 4 - 1	Corbisierso 32 Harrhy 36 Bowen 64 Draycott 84	2
2	16		A	Maidenhead United	434	D 1 - 1	O'Sullivan 41	4
3	20		A	Eastleigh	578	L 0 - 2		9
4	27		H	Havant & Waterlooville	720	L 2 - 3	O'Sullivan 9 Corbisierso 85	14
5	29		A	Farnborough Town	610	L 1 - 2	Thomas 47	19
6	Sept 4		H	Histon	604	L 0 - 1		19
7	10		A	Lewes	485	L 0 - 1		20
8	17		H	Weymouth	724	L 0 - 3		21
9	24	FAC 2Q	A	**Chippenham Town**	949	**L 0 - 4**		
10	Oct 1	CS	A	Eastbourne Borough	580	L 0 - 2		21
11	15		H	Yeading	703	L 1 - 3	Thomas 83	21
12	19		H	Dorchester Town	587	L 0 - 2		21
13	22		A	St Albans City	531	L 0 - 1		21
14	29		H	Bognor Regis Town	604	W 1 - 0	Draycott 20	20
15	Nov 5		A	Basingstoke Topwn	471	L 0 - 1		21
16	8		A	Hayes	264	L 2 - 3	**Hughes** 30 Bowen 63	21
17	12		H	Bishop's Stortford	649	W 1 - 0	Brown 63 (pen)	20
18	19		A	Sutton United	581	D 1 - 1	Belle 55	20
19	26	FAT 3Q	A	**Salisbury City**	806	**L 0 - 3**		
20	Dec 10	CS	A	Thurrock	231	L 2 - 4	O'Sullivan 6 Belle 78	20
21	26		H	Weston-s-Mare	754	D 2 - 2	Jenkins 11 **Hughes** 19	20
22	Jan 2		A	Weston-s-Mare	680	L 1 - 2	Toppar 24	20
23	7		A	Carshalton Athletic	431	L 0 - 1		22
24	14		H	Maidenhead United	625	W 3 - 0	J.Bowen 32 **Hughes** 51 Davies 58	20
25	18		H	Welling United	602	D 2 - 2	Green 18 Ashby 75	20
26	21		H	Eastleigh	675	L 0 - 2		20
27	28		A	Haant & Waterlooville	524	W 2 - 1	**Hughes** 27 Fisken 44	20
28	Feb 4		H	Eastbourne Borough	548	D 1 - 1	Green 59	20
29	7		H	Cambridge City	522	L 0 - 2		20
30	11		A	Yeading	201	W 2 - 1	Fisken 11 **Hughes** 34	20
31	18		H	St.Albans City	665	L 1 - 3	Green 38	20
32	21		A	Dorchester Town	452	D 2 - 2	**Hughes** 2 Green 42	20
33	25		H	Lewes	534	L 2 - 3	O'Sullivan 61 **Hughes** 90	22
34	Mar 4		A	Weymouth	2110	L 0 - 4		22
35	11		A	Bognor Regis Town	425	D 1 1 1	Hillier 90 (pen)	22
36	18		H	Basingstoke Town	504	W 2 - 0	Bowen 15 **Hughes** 32	21
37	25		A	Bishop's Stortford	370	W 1 - 0	**Hughes** 19	21
38	April 1		H	Sutton United	632	W 1 - 0	Bowen 45	21
39	5		A	Hayes	702	W 1 - 0	Cochin 53	18
40	8		A	welling United	629	D 1 - 1	Bowen 15	19
41	11		A	Histon	1092	W 3 - 2	Cochlin 58 Fisken 64 Thomas 69	18
42	17		H	Farnborough Town	1059	L 1 - 2	Bowen 82 (pen)	19
43	22		A	Cambridge City	507	W 2 - 0	**Hughes** 30 Fisken 32	18
44	29		H	Thurrock	1148	L 3 - 4	**Hughes** 9 Prosser 37 Davies 75	18

Ave. League Home Attendance: 688   **Goals**   50   74   **Top Goalscorer:** Hughes (11)
Best Position: 2nd   **Worst:**   22nd

SALISBURY CITY

Founded: 1947
Nickname: The Whites

Club Manager: Nick Holmes **Coach:** Tom Widdrington **Chief Scout:** Graham Daish
Assistant Manager: Barry Blankley **Reserve Team Manager:** Mitch Blake
Club Colours: White/Black/White
Change Colours: Sky BLue/white/white
Club Sponsor: In-Excess
Previous League: Southern League
Best Performances:
League: Southern League Champions 1994-95 2005-2006
F.A. Cup: 2nd Rd 1959-60 **F.A.Trophy.:** 2nd Rd 1996-97
Physio and Trainer: Conrad Parrott and Kevin Bushby
Reserve League: Suburban
Ground address: Raymond McEnhill Stadium, Partridge Way, Old Sarum, Salisbury
Wiltshire. SP4 6PU **Tel No:** 01722 326454 **Fax No:** 01722 323100
Official website: www.salisburyjournal.co.uk/sport/salisburycityfc
Capacity: 3,740 **Seats:** 457 **Covered:** 2,247 **Hospitality Boxes** 5(12 seats)
Simple Directions: The ground is on northern edge of the city and is well signposted
off the A345 main Salisbury to Amesbury road.
Midweek Home Matchday: Tuesday
Clubhouse: On ground with hot and cold snacks.
Club Shop: Open all week and matchdays.
Local Press: Salisbury Journal,Western Daily Press and Evening(Sports) Echo
Local Radio: BBC Radio Wiltshire

CLUB PERSONNEL
Chairman: Neville Beal
Other Directors: Stuart McGlashan, Peter Yeldon and Paul Orsborne
Secretary: Alec Hayter, 37 Lackford Avenue, Totton, Soton. SO40 9BS
Tel Nos: 0788 4477168(M)
02380 867195 (H)
Commercial Department:
Val Knight &Trevor Cross
Press Officer: Mike Turner
Tel No: 07977 886291
Programme Editor: Paul Orsborne
Programme
44pages £2.00
Club Manageress:
Lynn Robinson
2005-2006
Captain: Aaron Cook
Player of the Year: AaronCook
Top Goalscorer: Matthew Tubbs

CLUB STATISTICS

RECORD	**Attendance:** At present ground: 2,570 v Hull City FAC 14.11.98
	Victory: 11-1 v RAF Colerne (H) Western Lg Div 2 1948
	Defeat: 0-7 v Minehead (A) Southern League 1975
	Career Goalscorer: Royston Watts 180 (1959-1965)
	Career Appearances: Barry Fitch 713 (1963-1975)
Transfer Fees:	**Paid:** £15,000 for Craig Davis (Bashley)
	Received: £20,000 Adrian Randall (Forest Green Rovers)
SENIOR HONOURS:	Southern Champions 1994-5, 2005-2006 R-Up 1985-86 92-93.
	Western League Champions 57-8 60-1 R-up 58-9 59-60 61-62 67-8
PREVIOUS	**Names:** Salisbury F.C.
	Leagues: Western League 47-68 and Southern 1968-2004 Isthmian 2004-2005

SALISBURY CITY

BEST LGE ATT.: 1,907 v Chippenham Town
LOWEST: 494 v Banbury United

No.	Date	Comp	H/A	Opponents	Att:	Result	Goalscorers	Pos
1	Aug 13	SP	H	Bedford Town	571	W 1 - 0	Tubbs 17	8
2	16		A	Mangotsfield United	395	D 0 - 0		9
3	20		A	Evesham United	238	D 2 - 2	**Sales** 45 Tubbs 71	7
4	23		H	Cirencester Town	506	W 3 - 0	**Sales** 26 57 Tubbs 45	4
5	27		A	Bath City	787	W 2 - 0	Widdrington 32 Tubbs 46	2
6	29		H	Merthyr Tydfil	761	W 2 - 0	Davis 73 (pen) Matthews 81	1
7	Sept 2		H	Yate Town	800	W 3 - 1	Browne 14 Tubbs 55 Davis 86 (pen)	1
8	10	FAC 1Q	A	Clevedon Town	264	D 1 - 1	Tubbs 21	
9	13	FAC1Qr	H	Clevedon Town	506	W 4 - 2	Tubbs 24 90 Turk 35 Whitcombe (og) 78	
10	17	SP	A	Halesowen Town	401	W 1 - 0	**Sales** 66	1
11	24	FAC 2Q	A	Yate Town	371	W 2 - 0	Widdrington 39 Tubbs 67	
12	27	SP	A	Chesham United	252	W 4 - 1	Tubbs 9 Davis 33 (pen) **Sales** 70 Haddow 83	1
13	Oct 1		H	Grantham Town	875	W 3 - 0	**Sales** 43 45 Tubbs 53	1
14	8	FAC 3Q	H	Merthyr Tydfil	615	L 1 - 2	Tubbs 56	
15	11	SP	A	Chippenham Town	851	L 1 - 2	Turk 4	1
16	15	FAT1Q	A	Paulton Rovers	285	D 1 - 1	**Sales** 15	
17	18	FAT1Qr	H	Paulton Rovers	336	W 3 - 1	Haddow 43 Heath 102 106	
18	22	SP	H	Rugby Town	587	W 3 - 0	Tubbs 45 **Sales** 50 67	1
19	29		H	King's Lynn	922	W 1 - 0	Tubbs 76 (pen)	1
20	Nov 5		A	Yate Town	320	L 0 - 1		1
21	12	FAT 2R	H	Clevedon Town	552	W 2 - 0	Davis 27 Tubbs 45	
22	26	FAT 3Q	H	Newport County	806	W 3 - 0	Haddow 1 Sales 27 Widdrington 81	
23	Dec 3	SP	A	Grantham Town	282	L 0 - 1		3
24	10		H	Chesham United	557	W 6 - 0	**Sales** 3 (27 45 78) Haddow 33 Tubbs 62 87	1
25	13		A	Merthyr Tydfil	394	W 1 - 0	Tubbs 45	1
26	17	FAT 1	H	Harlow Town	731	W 1 - 0	Tubbs 44 (pen)	
27	27	SP	H	Tiverton Town	980	W 1 - 0	**Sales** 21	1
28	31		H	Northwood	759	W 3 - 0	Tubbs 30 42 Davis 60	1
29	Jan 2		A	Gloucester City	551	D 2 - 2	Davis 26 Turk 67	1
30	7		H	Aylesbury United	763	W 3 - 0	Matthews 20 24 Heath 82	1
31	10		A	Cheshunt	136	W 1 - 0	Cook 75	1
32	14	FAT 2	A	Canvey Island	534	W 1 - 0	Haddow 69	
33	21	SP	A	Hitchin Town	388	W 3 - 0	Matthews 3 (10 17 71)	1
34	28		H	Team Bath	690	L 0 - 1		1
35	Feb 4	FAT 3	H	Stalybridge Celtic	1533	D 0 - 0		
36	7	FAT 3R	A	Stalybridge Celtic	704	W 1 - 0	Tubbs 24	
37	11	SP	H	Chippenham Town	1907	W 2 - 1	Tubbs 57 (pen) **Sales** 63	1
38	18		A	Northwood	234	D 2 - 2	Turk 24 Widdrington 87	1
39	21		H	Banbury United	494	L 1 - 3	Turk 45	1
40	25	FAT 4	A	Exeter City	3653	L 1 - 3	Matthews 79	
41	Mar 4	SP	H	Halesowen Town	787	L 0 - 1		4
42	7		A	Cirencester Town	188	W 5 - 2	Ferrett 10 Haddow 26 **Sales** 45 64 Wilde 85	2
43	11		H	Mangotsfield United	826	D 2 - 2	Turk 10 Mattews 73	2
44	18		A	Bedford Town	479	L 0 - 1		4
45	21		A	Aylesbury United	214	W 3 - 1	**Sales** 19 88 Haddow 48	2
46	25		H	Evesham United	774	W 1 - 0	Regis 28	1
47	28		H	Bath City	1478	D 0 - 0		1
48	April 1		A	Banbury United	588	W 2 - 1	Prince 31 Matthews 89	1
49	4		A	King's Lynn	1821	W 3 - 1	Turk 5 51 Holgate 28	1
50	8		H	Hitchin Town	978	W 3 - 0	Prince 32 Turk 71 Matthews 81	1
51	11		A	Rugby Town	262	W 3 - 1	Prince 5 **Sales** 26 33	1
52	15		H	Gloucester City	978	W 3 - 1	Prince 32 Turk 71 Matthews 81	1
53	17		A	Tiverton Town	629	W 1 - 0	Tubbs 19	1
54	22		H	Cheshunt	1327	W 5 - 0	Turk 2 89 Bond 9 A.Cook 16 Tubbs 34	1
55	29		A	Team Bath	337	W 2 - 1	**Sales** 45 Tubbs 80	1
Ave. League Home Attendance:			785		**Goals**	102 37	**Top Goalscorer:** Sales (23)	
Best Position: 1st	**Worst:** 9th							

SUTTON UNITED

Founded: 1898
Nickname: The U's

Manager: Ian Hazel   **Coach:** Paul Harford   **Captain:** John Brough
Club Colours: Amber and Chocolate quarters/chocolate/amber
Change Colours: Green & white quarters/black/black
Club Sponsor: Group 4 Securicor
Previous League: Isthmian Premier
League: 15th Conference South **F.A. Cup:** 4th Rd 69-70 88-89
F.A.Trophy.: Runners -Up 1980-81 F.A.Amateur Cup: Runners-Up 62-63 68-69
Physio: Sarah Capewell
Reserve League: Suburban
Ground address: Borough Sports Ground, Gander Green Lane, Sutton, Surrey
SM1 2EY. **Tel No:** 0208 644 4440 **Fax:** 0208 6445120
Official website: www.suttonunited.net
Capacity: 7,032   **Seats:** 765   **Covered:** 1,250   **Floodlights:**Yes
Simple Directions: Gander Green Lane runs between A232 (Cheam Road - turn by
Sutton Cricket club) and A217 (Oldfields Road - turn at The Gander Public House).
Ground opposite The Plough 50 yards from W.Sutton BR. Bus: No 413
Midweek Home Matchday: Tuesday
Club Shop: All club accessories on matchdays Contact: Tony Cove c/o club.
Local Press: Sutton Advertiser,Sutton Guardian, Sutton Independent and S.Comet
Local Radio: Radio Jackie

CLUB PERSONNEL

Chairman: Bruce Elliott
President: Andrew Letts
Secretary: Dave Farebrother,
C/o Club Tel: 07734 719936 (M)
Advertising & Promotions:
Barry Alpin 01737 362038 (W
07957 812363 (M)
Press Officer: Tony Dolbear
Tel 07966 507023 (M) or
PR@suttonunited.net
Programme.Editor:
Lyall Reynolds
suttoneditor@hotmail.com
2005-2006
Captain: Ryan Palmer
Player of the Year:
John Scarborough
Top Goalscorer: Matt Gray 12

CLUB STATISTICS

Record	**Attendance:** 14,000 v Leeds United F.A.Cup 4th Rd 24.01.70
	Victory: 11-1 v Clapton 1966 & Leatherhead 82-83 Isthmian League
	Defeat: 0-13 V Barking Athenian League1925-26
	Career Goalscorer: Paul McKinnon 279
	Career Appearances:: Larry Pritchard 781 (65-84)
	Transfer Fee Paid: Undisclosed to Malmo for Paul McKinnon in 1983
	Fee Received: 100,000 from Bournemouth for Efan Ekoku in 1990
Senior Honours:	Anglo Italian Semi-Pro Cup 1979 R-Up 80-+ 82 Isthmian Champions (3)
	R-up (4) Athenian Champions (3) R-Up (1) London Senior Cup (2) Surrey
	Senior Cup (15) London Senior Cup (2) F.A.Trophy and F.A.Am. Cup as above.
Previous Leagues:	Sutton Jnr,Southern Sub.,Athenian 21-63, Isthmian 63-86 91-99 Conf.99-00
Grounds:	Western Rd, Manor Lane, London Rd and The Find

Back Row (L-R): Paul Harford (Assistant Manager), Peter Fear, Paul Honey, Lewis Gonsalves, Ryan Palmer,
Richard Harris, Phil Wilson,Mohamed Maan, Neil Lampton, Steve Douglas, John Scarborough,
Ian Hazel (Manager).
Front: Sarah Francis (Team Physio), Matt Gray, Michael Johnson, Carl Gibbs, Glenn Boosey, Michael Gordon, Zak
Graham, Eddie Akuamoah, Ben Garner, Richard Blackwell, Lee Southernwood (Team Fitness Coach).

SUTTON UNITED

BEST LGE ATT.: 950 v Carshalton Athletic
LOWEST: 420 v Histon

No.	Date	Comp	H/A	Opponents	Att:	Result	Goalscorers	Pos
1	Aug 13	CS	H	Maidenhead United	510	W 4 - 1	CORNWALL 3 (7 8 18) Quinton 80	3
2	15		A	Havant & Waterlooville	500	W 1 - 0	Cornwall	3
3	20		A	Yeading	225	W 2 - 0	Behzadi 20 (og) Cornwall 90	2
4	27		H	Farnborough Town	693	W 1 - 0	Mackie 29	1
5	29		A	Dorchester Town	482	W 5 - 0	Douglas 45 Mackie 70 Akuamoah 76 **Gray** 77 (pen) 81	1
6	Sept 3		H	Weston-s-Mare	562	L 1 - 2	Pitcher 87	2
7	10		H	Bognor Regis Town	536	W 1 - 0	**Gray** 15 (pen)	1
8	17		A	Bishop's Stortford	305	L 1 - 2	Castledine 49	2
9	**24**	**FAC 2Q**	**H**	**Maldon Town**	**402**	**W 2 - 0**	**Cornwall 20 Castledine 57**	
10	Oct 1	CS	A	Basingstoke Town	437	L 0 - 2		3
11	**8**	**FAC 3Q**	**A**	**Chippenham Town**	**727**	**L 0 - 1**		
12	15	CS	H	St Albans City	640	W 4 - 0	Quinton 6 23 Akuamoah 54 Cornwall 77	1
13	18		H	Eastbourne Borough	493	W 2 - 0	Akuamoah 17 Cornwall 30	1
14	29		A	Weymouth	1703	L 1 - 3	Watkins 46	3
15	Nov 5		H	Lewes	628	L 1 - 5	Gonsalves 88	5
16	12		A	Eastleigh	513	L 0 - 2		9
17	19		H	Newport County	581	D 1 - 1	Jones 85 (og)	10
18	**26**	**FAT 3Q**	**A**	**Uxbridge**	**204**	**D 2 - 2**	**Elliot 21 Castledine 90**	
19	**29**	**FAT 3Qr**	**H**	**Uxbridge**	**253**	**L 0 - 1**		
20	Dec 3	CS	A	Thurrock	276	L 3 - 5	Akuamoah 18 Gray 83 (pen) 90 (pen)	13
21	10		H	Hayes	494	W 2 - 1	**Gray** 11 Akuamoah 16	11
22	26		A	Carshalton Athgletic	1056	D 0 - 0		10
23	31		A	Welling United	718	D 0 - 0		
24	Jan 2		H	Carshalton Athletic	950	D 1 - 1	Graves 39 (og)	11
25	7		A	Maidmenhead United	322	L 0 - 2		12
26	14		H	Havant & Waterlooville	536	D 1 - 1	Fear 27	11
27	17		A	Cambridge City	379	L 0 - 3		12
28	21		H	Yeading	502	D 0 - 0		12
29	28		A	Farnborough Town	540	L 1 - 2	Douglas 60	13
30	Feb 4		H	Basingstoke Town	453	L 0 - 1		13
31	7		H	Histon	420	D 1 - 1	Gonsalves 17	13
32	11		A	ST Albans City	639	L 1 - 3	Watson 18	13
33	18		H	Cambridge City	518	W 3 - 2	Douglas 19 Scarbrough 84 **Gray** 89	12
34	25		A	Bognor Regis Town	331	D 0 - 0		14
35	Mar 4		H	Bishop's Stortford	487	D 1 - 1	**Gray** 86 (pen)	13
36	8		A	Lewes	305	L 0 - 2		14
37	11		H	Weymouth	668	L 0 - 3		14
38	18		A	Histon	409	L 0 - 3		15
39	25		H	Eastleigh	482	L 0 - 3		16
40	April 1		H	Newport County	632	L 0 - 1		17
41	4		A	Eastbourne Borough	458	L 1 - 2	Gray 45 (pen)17	17
42	8		H	Thurrock	517	D 1 - 1	Scarbrough 62	15
43	15		A	Weston-s-Mare	231	W 3 - 2	**Gray** 26 Gordon 72 Cornwall 64	15
44	17		A	Dorchester Town	502	W 1 - 0	**Gray** 27(pen)	14
45	22		H	Welling United	525	W 2 - 1	Cornwall 10 **Gray** 70 (pen)	12
46	29		A	Hayes	389	L 1 - 2	Scarbrough 78	13

Ave. League Home Attendance: 587   **Goals** 52 65   **Top Goalscorer:** Gray (13)
Best Position: 1st   **Worst:** 17th

THURROCK

Founded: 1985
Nickname: Fleet

2005/2006

THURROCK V HEMEL HEMPSTEAD TOWN
FA CUP SECOND QUALIFYING ROUND
Saturday 10th September 2005 Kick Off 3.00pm
In memory of Mr. KENNETH FOREMAN
(Groundsman) by Mrs. Gladys Butler (Daughter)

Home kit Sponsor: CORRINGHAM TYRE SERVICES
Away kit Sponsor: LAKESIDE SHOPPING CENTRE

Manager: Hakan Ramis-Hayrettin   **Assistant Manager:** Hassan Oktay
Coach: Jimmy Gilligan   **Physio**: Steve Taylor
Club Colours: Yellow & Green/green/yellow & green
Change Colours: All white
Club Sponsor: Lakeside Shopping Centre
Previous League: Isthmian
Previous Name: Purfleet
Best Seasons: League: 3rd. Conference South   **F.A. Cup:** 1st Rd Replay 2003-2004 **F.A.Trophy.:** 2nd Rd 1995-96
Coach: Jason Broome & Ronnie Hanley   **Physio**: Michelle Sheehan
Ground address: Thurrock Hotel, Ship Lane, Grays, Essex
Tel No: 01708 865492 FAX: 01708 868863   **Website**: www.thurrockfc.co.uk
Capacity: 4,500   **Seats**: 300 **Covered**: 1,000   **Floodlights**:Yes
Simple Directions: M25 or A13 to Dartford tunnel roundabout. Ground is fifty yards on right down Ship Lane.
Midweek Home Matchday: Monday
Club Shop: Yes Tommy South
Clubhouse: Hotel facilities. Steward Tommy South (01708 868901)
LocalRadio: BBC Essex Essex Radio
Local Press: Romford,Thurrock Recorder & Thurrock Gazette

CLUB PERSONNEL
Chairman:
V-Chairman/ Chief Executive:
Tommy South
Committeemen: George Brooks, Wiliam Wiseman & Mark Nevill
Secretary, Press Officer & Prog.Ed: Norman Posner, 1 Chase House Gardens, Hornchurch,Essex RM11 2PJ Tel No: 01708 458301
Programme 60 pages £1.50
Commercial Manager:
Graham Beechey:

2005-2006
Captain: Jimmy McFarlane
Player of the Year: John Purdie
Top Goalscorer: Steve Harper 14

CLUB STATISTICS

Record Attendance:	2,572 v West Ham United Friendly 1998
Victory:	10-0 v Stansted (h) 86-7 v East Ham U 87-8 (A) both Essex Sen Lg
Defeat:	0-6 v St Leonards Stamco (A) F.A.Trophy 96-7 and Sutton U (H) 97-8 Isth
Career Goalscorer: George Georgiou 106	
Career Appearances: Jimmy McFarlane 632	
Transfer Fees Paid:	
Received:	
Senior Honours:	Isthmian Div 2 91-92 R-up 93-94Div 2 North R-up 88-89
	Essex Senior Cup 2003-2004 2005-2006 R-up 97-98 99-00
Previous Leagues:	Essex Senior 85-89 Isthmian 1989-2004

Back Row (L-R): Gary Redmond, David Collis, John O'Brien, Danny Lye, Steve Heffer, Michael Basham, Tresor Kandol, Martyn Lawrence, Cliff Akurang, Kris Lee, Danny Greaves, Mark Goodfellow. **Front Row:** Lee Allen, Gary Howard, Chris Harvey, John Purdie, Paul Gothard, Paul Linger, Terry Bowes. **Inset:** Jimmy McFarlane.

THURROCK

BEST LGE ATT.: 422 v Welling United
LOWEST: **159** v Hayes

No.	Date	Comp	H/A	Opponents	Att:	Result	Goalscorers	Pos
1	Aug 13	CS	H	Histon	278	L 1 - 2	O'Connor 4	12
2	16		A	Eastbourne Borough	711	D 0 - 0		15
3	20		A	Farnborough Town	480	D 0 - 0		17
4	27		H	Eastleigh	227	W 3 - 1	Lee 31 58 O'Connor 45	13
5	29		A	Maidenhead United	223	W 3 - 1	Hodges 2 90 (pen) Bowes 37	5
6	Sept 3		H	Havant & Waterlooville	250	L 0 - 2		12
7	10		A	Weymouth	1029	L 0 - 2		16
8	17		H	Lewes	289	L 2 - 3	O'Connor 24 57 (pen)	16
9	24	FAC 2Q	H	Hemel Hempstaed Town	93	W 3 - 2	**Harper** 45 **McFarlane** 62 O'Connor 73	
10	Oct 1	CS	A	Weston-s-Mare	271	W 5 - 0	Jarman 41 (og) O'Connnor 44 McFarlane 75 **Harper** 83 Cross 90	14
11	8	FAC 3Q	H	Solihull Borough	126	W 1 - 0	O'Connor 78	
12	15	CS	H	Dorchester Town	221	L 0 - 1		16
13	17		H	St Albans City	281	W 2 - 0	**Harper** 11 48	14
14	22	FAC 4Q	A	Woking	1486	L 0 - 3		
15	29	CS	H	Bishop's Stortford	294	W 2 - 1	Carthy 79 83	16
16	Nov 5		A	Hayes	192	W 1 - 0	**Harper** 68	9
17	8		A	Cambridge City	427	L 0 - 6		13
18	12		H	Basingstoke Town	187	W 4 - 1	Cross 8 **Harper** 30 McFarlane 55 Goddard 62	
19	19		A	Bognor Regis Town	360	W 1 - 0	Carthy 20	7
20	22		A	Yeading	140	D 1 - 1	Collins 88	6
21	26	FAT 3Q	A	Eastbourne Borough	368	W 3 - 0	**Harper** 44 54 Hodges 45(pen)	
22	Dec 3	CS	H	Sutton United	276	W 5 - 3	Janney 28 Cross 52 80 Goddard 68 89	5
23	10		H	Newport County	231	W 4 - 2	**Harper** 14 79 Carthy 77 90	4
24	17	FAT 1	A	Dagenham & Redbridge	797	L 0 - 2		
25	26	CS	A	Welling United	705	D 1 - 1	**Harper** 78 (pen)	5
26	31		A	Carshalton Athletic	299	D 0 - 0		
27	Jan 3		H	Welling United	422	D 1 - 1	Carthy 74	
28	14		H	Eastbourne Borough	235	W 1 - 0	Cross 42	6
29	21		A	Farnborough TGown	294	L 0 - 2		8
30	28		A	Eastleigh	312	L 0 - 3		8
31	Feb 4		H	Weston-s-Mare	182	L 0 - 1		10
32	11		A	Dorchester Town	452	L 0 - 2		11
33	18		H	Yeading	165	L 0 - 1		11
34	21		A	St Albans City	354	L 2 - 3	Lee 61 89	12
35	25		H	Weymoutth	301	L 1 - 2	Lee 90	11
36	Mar 4		A	Lewes	452	D 0 - 0		11
37	6		H	Cambridge City	218	L 0 - 3		11
38	11		A	Bishop's Stirtford	320	D 2 - 2	Fletcher 25 **Harper** 64	11
39	16		A	Histon	261	L 1 - 3	**Harper** 22	11
40	18		H	Hayes	159	D 1 - 1	Cross 80	11
41	25		A	Basingstoke Town	268	W 3 - 0	Cross 7 McFarlane 9 Lee 19	11
42	April 1		H	Bognor Regis Town	193	W 3 - 0	Sloma 17 82 Moore 44	10
43	8		A	Sutton United	517	D 1 - 1	Janney 85 (pen)	11
44	15		H	Havant & Waterlooville	377	W 2 - 1	Champion 24 (og) Cross 55	11
45	17		H	Maidenhead United	184	L 1 - 2	Moore 12 (Pen)	11
46	22		H	Carshalton Athletic	187	W 2 - 1	Parker 37 Sloma 83	10
47	29		A	Newport County	1148	W 4 - 3	Moore 19 Lee 34 Parker 83 85	10

Ave. League Home Attendance: 217   **Goals** 67 66   **Top Goalscorer:** Harper (13)
Best Position: 4th   **Worst:** 17th

WELLING UNITED

Founded:1963
Nickname: The Wings

Manager: Adrian Pennock   **Asst. Manager** Phil Handford   **Physio:** Peter Green
Club Colours: Red/Red/White
Change Colours: All Blue
Club Sponsor: E.Coomes, Bookmakers
Previous League: Southern Premier
Previous Grounds: Butterfly Lane Eltham 1963-78
Best Seasons: **League:** 6th (Conference) 1989-90
                          F.A. Cup: 3rd Rd 1988-89
                          F.A.Trophy.: 6th Rd. 1988-89
Ground address: Park View Road Ground, Welling, Kent DA16 1SY
Tel No: 0208 301 1196 Fax 0208 301 5676 **e-mail:** info@wellingunited.com
Newsline: Welling Wingsline: 09068 8006 54
Website: www.welling united.com
Capacity: 4,000   Seats: 1,070   Covered: 1,500   Floodlights: Yes
Simple Directions: M25 then A2 towards London. Take Welling turn off and ground is one mile. Welling BR 3/4 mile.
Midweek Home Matchday: Tuesday
Clubhouse: Open on match days
Club Shop: Fully stocked. Manager: Peter Mason
Local Radio: Radio Kent Radio Invicta R.T.M.
Local Press: Kentish Times, Kent Messenger, Bexleyheath & Welling Mercury

CLUB PERSONNEL
Chairman: Paul Websdale
V-Chairman: Steven Pain
President: Eric Brackstone
General Manager:
Graham Hobbins
Secretary: Barrie Hobbins
0208 3011196 (W)
07904201177 (M)
Press Officer: Paul Carter c/o club
Tel No: 0208 301 1196
Fax: 0208 301 5676
Commercial Manager:
Barry Wallis: 07803 355990 (M)
Programme Editor: Paul Pettet
Mobile 07834 518215
email:pdpettet@ntlworld.com
Programme:40pages £1.20

2005-2006
Captain: Chris Moore
Top Goalscorer: Danny: Kedwell 23

CLUB STATISTICS

Record	**Attendance**: 4,100 v Gillingham F.A.Cup
	Victory: 7-1 v Dorking 1985-86
	Defeat: 0-7 v Welwyn Garden City 1972-73
Career Goalscorer:	John Bartley 533
Career Appearances:	Nigel Ransom 1,066 & Ray Burgess 1,44
Record Transfer Fee	**Paid**: £30,000 to Enfield for Gary Abbott
	Received: £95,000 from Birmingham City for Steve Finnan 1995
Senior Honours:	Southern League Champions 1985-86 Kent Senior Cup 85-86 98-99
	London Senior Cup 1989-90 London Challenge Cup 91-92 R-Up 93-94
Previous Leagues:	Eltham & Dist.1963-71. London Spartan 1971-77, Athenian 77-79
	Southern 79- 86 2001-04 Conference 86-2000

Back row (L-R): Barry Hobbins (Kit Manager), Luke Holmes, Mark Lovell, Andrew Sam, Joe Vines, Jamie Turner, Paul Hyde, Chris Moore, John Guest, Steve Perkins, Danny Kedwell, Neil Withington (Fitness Coach).
Front: Dave Lawson, keith Rowland, Des Boateng, Matt Bodkin, Che Stadhart, Adrian Pennock (Manager), Phil Handford (Assistant Manager), Ronayne Benjamin, Akwasi Edusei, Jamie Day, Leon Solomon.

WELLING UNITED

BEST LGE ATT.: 905 v Weymouth
LOWEST: **417** v Bognor Regis Town

No.	Date	Comp	H/A	Opponents	Att:	Result	Goalscorers	Pos
1	Aug 13	CS	H	St.Albans City	552	W 3 - 1	**Kedwell** 45 87 Carruthers 52	5
2	17		A	Histon	367	D 1 - 1	Pinnock 52	5
3	20		A	Weston-S-Mare	315	W 1 - 0	Carruthers 26	4
4	27		H	Yeading	566	L 0 - 1		7
5	29		A	Eastbourne United	674	D 1 - 1	Owen 74	6
6	Sept 3		H	Dorchester Town	447	W 4 - 3	Perkins 6 Clarke 11 **Kedwell** 30 84	5
7	10		A	Eastleigh	287	W 3 - 1	Owen 26 36 Moore 38	4
8	17		H	Hayes	572	W 1 - 0	Perkins 87	
9	24	FAC 2Q	A	Boreham Wood	267	W 2 - 0	Parkins 37 Pinnock 45	
10	Oct 1	CS	A	Bognor Regis Town	442	D 0 - 0		4
11	8	FAC 3Q	A	Harrow Borough	258	W 1 - 0	Bodkin 89	
12	15	CS	H	Cambridge City	811	D 1 - 1	Kedwell 89	4
13	18		H	Carshalton Athletic	462	W 2 - 0	Perkins 11 **Kedwell** 82 (pen)	3
14	22	FAC 4Q	A	Dorchester Town	533	W 2 - 1	Bodkin 62 Kedwell 81	
15	29	CS	A	Maidenhead United	306	W 4 - 2	Stadhart 28 Owen 47 **Kedwell** 83 (pen) 90	2
16	Nov 5	FAC 1R	A	Huddersfield Town	5518	L 1 - 4	Moore 82	
17	8	CS	H	Farnborough Town	726	W 1 - 0	**Kedwell** (pen) 30	3
18	12		A	Weymouth	1706	L 1 - 2	Carruthers 72	3
19	19		H	Lewes	713	W 2 - 1	**Kedwell** 30 Moore 80	2
20	22		A	Basingstoke Town	202	D 2 - 2	Shearer 29 Stadhart 40	2
21	26	FAT 3Q	A	Basingstoke Town	313	W 2 - 0	Perkins 45 (og) Day 60	
22	Dec 10	CS	A	Bishop's Stortford	309	D 1 - 1	Stadhart 89	3
23	13		H	Havant &Waterlooville	520	D 2 - 2	**Kedwell** 29 (pen) Clarke 38	3
24	18	FAT 1	H	Redbridge	415	W 4 1 1	**Stadhart** 13 25 Kedwell 35 Day 90	
25	26	CS	H	Thurrock	705	D 1 - 1	Kedwell 6	4
26	31		H	Sutton United	718	D 0 - 0		
27	Jan 3		A	Thurrock	422	D 1 - 1	Kedwell 28 (pen)	5
28	7		A	St Albans City	576	L 1 - 3	Day 24	6
29	14	FAT 2	A	Blyth Spartans	784	W 3 - 1	Day 35 Kedwell 45 Owen 49	5
30	18		A	Newport County	602	D 2 - 2	Day 67 90	7
31	21		H	Weston-s-Mare	671	W 1 - 0	Kedwell 77	6
32	28		A	Yeading	189	L 0 - 1		6
33	Feb 4	FAT 3	A	Woking	1244	L 2 - 3	Stadhart 17 Kedwell 30	
34	7	CS	H	Bognor Regis Town	417	W 2 - 0	Bodkin 6 Perkins 83	5
35	11		A	Cambridge City	542	D 0 - 0		7
36	18		H	Basingstole Town	537	W 3 - 2	Kedwell 51 Stadhart 54 790	6
37	21		A	Carshalton Athletic	236	L 0 - 1		7
38	25		H	Eastleigh	523	W 2 - 1	**Kedwell** 25 87 (pen)	7
39	28		A	Histon	500	D 1 - 1	Stadhart 1	
40	Mar 4		A	Hayes	214	W 3 - 1	Bodkin 9 Day 36 **Kedwell** 62	6
41	11		H	Maidenhead United	646	D 3 - 3	Stadhart 6 80 **Kedwell** 73 (pen)	7
42	18		A	Havant & Waterlooville	494	D 0 - 0		7
43	21		A	Farnborough Town	383	L 0 - 1		7
44	25		H	Weymouth	905	W 1 - 0	Moore 15	7
45	April 1		A	Lewes	660	L 1 - 2	Robinson 5 (og)	7
46	8		H	Newport County	629	D 1 - 1	Carthy 21	7
47	15		A	Dorchester Town	526	W 3 - 0	Carthy 3 (38 40 82)	6
48	17		H	Eastbourne Borough	603	L 1 - 2	Bodkin 11	6
49	22		A	Sutton United	525	L 1 - 2	Carthy 75	8
50	29		H	Bishop"s Stortford	512	D 0 - 0		9

Ave. League Home Attendance: 606   **Goals**   75 54   **Top Goalscorer:** Kedwell (23)
Best Position: 2nd   **Worst:**   9th

WESTON-SUPER-MARE

Founded: 1899
Nickname: Seagulls

Club Colours: White/blue/blue
Change Colours: All Yellow
Club Sponsor:
Previous Leagues: Western **Premier**
Previous Name: Borough of Weston-super-Mare
Best Seasons: Lg: 11th Conference South **F.A. Cup:** 2nd Rd Proper 2003-4
F.A.Trophy.: 4th Round 98-99 03-04
Manager: Frank Gregan **Assistant Manager:** David Lee **Physio:** Dave Evans
Ground address: Woodspring Stadium, Winterstoke Road,Weston-super-Mare
BS24 9AA. Tel No: 01934 621618 FAX: 01934 622704
Website: www.westonsupermarefc.co.uk
Capacity:3,000 **Seats:** 278 **Covered:** 2,000 **Floodlights:** Yes
Simple Directions: From Junction 21 of the M5 take A370 along dual carriageway
to 4th roundabout and follow Winterstoke Road.

Midweek Home Matchday: Wednesday
Clubhouse: Open daily Mid week evenings (Steward Dave Wiliams)
Club Shop: Yes (Manager: Brian Graver)
Local Radio: Somerset Sound and Radio Bristol
Local Press: Bristol Evening Post and Western Daily press

CLUB PERSONNEL
Chairman: Paul Bliss
President: Dennis Usher
Secretary/Groundsman:
Bob Flaskell c/o club.
Tel Nos: 01934 621618 (W)
Commercial Manager:
Wayne Entwhistle(07909 791104)
Press Officer: Russell Wintle
07967 644959 (M)
Programme Editors:
Phil Sheridan 07963 166031(M)
01934 822467 (H)

2005-2006
Top Scorer: Brown 18
Programme: 32 pages £1.00

CLUB STATISTICS

Record	**Attendance:** 2,623 v Woking F.A.Cup 1st Rd Replay 23.11.93
	Victory: 11-0 v Paulton Rovers
	Defeat: 1-12 v Yeovil Town Reserves
	Career Goalscorer: Matt Lazenby 180
	Career Appearances: Harry Thomas 740
	Transfer Fee Paid: None
	Received: £20,000 from Sheffield Wednesday for Stuart Jones
Senior Honours:	Western League Champions: 91-92 Somerset Senior Cup 1923-24 1926-27
	Somerset Premier Cup Runners-Up 1990-1991
Previous Leagues:	Somerset Senior League and Western League

Back row,left to right: Mike Kilgour (Assistant Manager),Sam Bailey, Craig Mountford, Lee Jarman, Craig Rand, Ryan Northmore, John Williams, Matt Rose (captain), Darren Hawkins, Craig Herrod, Lee Smart and Frank Gregan (Manager). **Front row:** Andy Crawford, Matt Fisher, Craig Loxron, Marvin Brown, Scott Walker,Gary Thorne and Mike Hudson.

WESTON-SUPER-MARE

BEST LGE ATT.: 680 v Newport County
LOWEST: 149 v Yeading

No.	Date	Comp	H/A	Opponents	Att:	Result	Goalscorers	Pos
1	Aug 13	CS	A	Cambridge City	387	L 0 - 3		21
2	17		H	Basingstoke Town	309	W 4 - 3	Hogg 15 40 French 30 Lewis 50	14
3	20		H	Welling United	315	L 0 - 1		15
4	27		A	Bishop's Stortford	267	W 3 - 2	French 22 **Brown** 61 Hogg 83	11
5	29		H	Hayes	389	D 1 - 1	French 39 (pen)	11
6	Sept 3		A	Sutton United	562	W 2 - 1	Hogg 20 24	9
7	10		H	Dorchester Town	373	L 0 - 4		13
8	17		A	Eastbourne Borough	555	W 2 - 1	Rawlings 49 **Brown** 90 (pen)	11
9	24	FAC 2Q	H	Weymouth	744	D 2 - 2	**Evans 30 French 46**	
10	27	FAC 2Qr	A	Weymouth	1003	L 0 - 1		
11	Oct 1	CS	H	Thurrock	271	L 0 - 5		14
12	15		A	Lewes	459	L 2 - 5	**Brown** 14 Hawkins 82	15
13	29		A	Farnborough Town	526	L 0 - 5		18
14	Nov 5		H	Carshalton Athletic	229	W 2 - 0	French 31 Walker 85	18
15	9		H	Eastleigh	252	L 1 - 4	French 61 (pen)	18
16	12		A	Yeading	135	W 2 - 1	**Brown** 25 67	18
17	19		H	Maidenhead United	237	D 1 - 1	McKeevor 75	17
18	23		H	Histon	180	L 1 - 4	Walker 64	17
19	26	FAT 3Q	H	Bedford Town	221	W 4 - 0	**Rogers 2 89 Walker 33 Brown 75**	
20	Dec 3	CS	A	Havant & Waterlooville	370	L 2 - 3	Rawlins 36 **Brown** 60	18
21	6		A	Weymouth	1221	L 1 - 2	Rand 60	
22	10		H	St Albans City	260	W 3 - 1	Rogers 10 **Brown** 17 Rose 42	15
23	17	FAT 1	H	Barking & East Ham	243	W 3 - 2	**French 42 (pen) 50 Brown 43**	
24	26	CS	A	Newport County	754	D 2 - 2	Hopgg 37 Rawlins 52	17
25	Jan 2		H	Newport County	680	W 2 - 1	French 26 (pen) McKeever 84	15
26	7		H	Cambridge City	276	H 1 - 3	Holland 90	16
27	14	FAT 2	H	Worksop Town	366	D 1 - 1	**Walker 12**	
28	17	FAT 2r	A	Worksop Town	369	L 1 - 2	**Rose 40**	
29	21	CS	A	Welling United	671	L 0 - 1		17
30	28		H	Bishop's Stortford	186	L 0 - 1		18
31	Feb 4		A	Thurrock	182	W 1 - 0	Hogg 5	16
32	11		H	Lewes	261	L 1 - 2	Walker 90 (pen)	17
33	14		A	Basingstoke Town	224	L 1 - 2	Walker 39	18
34	18		A	Histon	438	D 1 - 1	Walker 33	17
35	22		H	Weymouth	613	L 1 - 3	**Brown** 45	17
36	25		A	Dorchester Town	453	W 2 - 1	Jarman 36 McKeever 90	17
37	Mar 4		H	Eastbourne Borough	236	W 1 - 0	**Brown** 3	16
38	11		H	Farnborough Town	317	D 1 - 1	**Brown** 12	16
39	14		A	Bognor Regis Town	248	W 1 - 0	**Brown** 51	12
40	18		A	Carshalton Athletic	266	D 1 - 1	**Brown** 55	12
41	April 1		A	Maidenhead United	208	W 4 - 2	**Brown** 14 32 Pritchard 63 Williams 69	12
42	4		A	Eastleigh	257	L 1 - 4	Bailey 28	12
43	8		H	Havant & Waterlooville	240	L 1 - 3	Byles 58 (og)	12
44	12		H	Yeading	149	L 0 - 3		12
45	15		H	Sutton United	231	L 2 - 3	Walker 40 (pen) Roberston 51	14
46	22		H	Bognor Regis Town	245	D 2 - 2	**Brown** 33 Balfe 71 (og)	16
47	25		A	Hayes	174	L 1 - 4	Williams 31	16
48	29		A	St Albans City	853	W 2 - 1	Williams 60 **Brown** 72	14

Ave. League Home Attendance: 298   **Goals** 67 96   **Top Goalscorer:** Brown (18)
Best Position: 9th   **Worst:** 21st

YEADING

Founded: 1965
Nickname: The Ding

Manager: Johnson Hyppolyte   **Assistant Manager:** Dereck Brown
Club Colours: Red & black stripes/black/black
Change Colours: Yellow/blue/blue
Club Sponsors: T.B.A.
Previous League: Isthmian Premier
Website: www.yeadingfc.com or yeading @ yeadingfc.co.uk
Best Seasons: League: Isthmian Champions 2004-2005
F.A. Cup: 3rd Round 2004-2005   **F.A.Trophy:** 2nd Rd 97-898-900-01 01-02
F.A.Vase: Winners 1989-99
Coaches: David Gumbs & Erskine Smart **Physio:** Chris James
Ground address: The Warren, Beaconsfield Road, Hayes, Middlesex UB4 0SL
Tel NO: 02088487362 (Ground) 020 8756 1200 (Office & Fax)
Capacity: 3,500   **Seats:** 250   **Covered:** 100   **Floodlights:** Yes
Simple Directions: From Hayes by pass A312, The Parkwa, take signpost towards
Southall and Uxbridge. At top of slip road take exit to Southall, get into far right hand
lane immediately and turn right into Springfield Rd at next lights. Past Technicolour
Sports on the right. Road bears left into Beaconsfield Rd and YFC 100 yards on right.
Midweek Home Matchday: Tuesday 7.30
Club Shop: Yes with badges available. (Contact: Steve Powell)
Clubhouse: Open pub hours with Warren banqueting suite for hire.
Local Press: Hayes & Harlington Gazette, Hillingdon Times.
Local Radio: UK Gold Circular, BBC London

CLUB PERSONNEL

Chairman: Phillip Spurden
Director of Football:
Tony O'Driscoll
Secretary: Bill Gritt, Fourwinds,
182 Cherry Tree Road,
Beaconsfield, Bucks. HP9 1BA
Tel No: 01494 674188 (H)
07710102004 (M)
Commercial Manager:
Bill Perryman (020 8756 1200)
Programme Editor: Tim Fuell
Press Officer: Tim Fuell

2005-2006
Captain: Darti Brown
Player of the Year: Bobby Behzadi
Top Goalscorer: Telemaque 13

CLUB STATISTICS

Record	**Attendance:** 3,000 v Hythe Town F.A.Vase S-Final 1990
	10,824 v Newcastle United F.A.Cup 3rd Rd
	Victory: **Defeat:**
Career Goalscorer:	Dave Burt 327 goals in 285 games. (Inc: 1x10, 2x7,4x6, 3x5 7x4 & 17x3)
Career Appearances:	Norman Frape 457
Record Transfer Fee	**Paid:** £3,000 to Hucknall Town for Matt Edwards
	Received: £45,000 from QPR for Andrew Impey
Senior Honours:	F.A.Vase Winners 90, Isthmian Champions 04-05 Div 1 N champs 03-04
	Middx Sen.Cup 3 R-Up (2) Middx Charity Cup 2005 Middx Co.Prem Cup 1981
Previous Leagues:	Uxbridge & Dist., 65-67, W.Middx Comb 67-68,S.W.Middx. 68-74,Middx Co.74-
	84 Spartan 84-87 and Isthmian 1987-2005

Back Row (l-r) Dereck Brown (Asst Man), Max Banger (Physio), Nicky Greene, Darti Brown, Davis Haule, Jeff Goulding, Fouahde Belaid,
Delroy Preddie, Nevin Saroya, Marvin Morgan, Nathan Bowden-Haase, Richard Goddard, Bradley Quamina, Johnson Hippolyte (Manager)
Front Row David Clarke (Coach), Ben Hudell, Luke Blackmore, Richard Bouton, Michael Barima, Bobby Behzadi,
Marlon Patersson, Danny Allen-Page, Liam Collins, Adam Everitt

YEADING

BEST LGE ATT.: 601 v Hayes
LOWEST: **102** v Histon

No.	Date	Comp	H/A	Opponents	Att:	Result	Goalscorers	Pos
1	Aug 13	CS	A	Bognor Regis Town	358	W 2 - 0	Morgan 41 Cox 72	7
2	16		H	Lewes	230	L 0 - 2		12
3	20		H	Sutton United	225	L 0 - 1		16
4	27		A	Welling United	566	W 1 - 0	Clarke 74	12
5	29		H	Cambridge City	201	L 1 - 2	**Telemaque** 41	16
6	Sept 3		A	Weymouth	1024	D 1 - 1	Johnson 56	16
7	10		A	Maidenhead United	284	W 2 - 1	Johnson 20 **Telemaque** 58	12
8	17		H	Havant & Waterlooviile	199	W 2 - 0	Williams 74 Blackmore 86	10
9	**24**	**FAC 2Q**	**H**	**Maidenhead United**	**185**	**W 3 - 0**	**Telemaque 38 Williams 76 Saroya 84 (pen)**	
10	Oct 1	CS	H	Eastleigh	143	D 2 - 2	**Telemaque** 3 Haule 59	10
11	**8**	**FAC 3Q**	**H**	**Dorchester Town**	**151**	**D 1 - 1**	**Williams 32**	
12	**11**	**FAC 3Qr**	**A**	**Dorchester Town**	**500**	**L 2 - 3**	**Mapes 60 Wiliams 90**	
13	15	CS	A	Newport County	703	W 3 - 1	Williams 18 Protain 45 Morgen 71	10
14	18		A	Histon	440	L 0 - 1		11
15	29		H	Dorchester Town	132	L 0 - 1		15
16	Nov 5		A	St Albans City	331	L 2 - 5	**Telemaque** 74 Williams	15
17	12		H	Weston-s-Mare	135	L 1 - 2	Saroya (pen)	16
18	19		A	Basingstole Town	285	W 4 - 0	**Telemaque** 22 85 Wiliams 25 78	15
19	22		H	Thurrock	140	D 1 - 1	Collins 88	15
20	**26**	**FAT 3Q**	**A**	**Bath City**	**383**	**W 2 - 1**	**Telemaque 20 75**	
21	Dec 3	CS	H	Bishop's Stortford	169	D 0 - 0		15
22	10		H	Carshalton Athletic	146	L 3 - 4	Saroya 25 (pen) 41 Morgan 60	16
23	**17**	**FAT 1**	**H**	**Carshalton Athletic**	**120**	**L 1 - 2**	**Saroya 71**	
24	20	CS	H	Eastbourne Borough	133	D 1 - 1	Williams 49	15
25	26		H	Hayes	417	W 1 - 0	Williams 67	15
26	31		A	Farnborough Town	504	L 0 - 1		
27	Jan 2		H	Hayes	601	L 2 - 3	Morgan 16 23	17
28	7		H	Bognor Regis Town	177	L 0 - 2		17
29	14		A	Lewes	449	L 0 - 1		17
30	21		A	Sutton United	502	D 0 - 0		16
31	28		H	Welling United	189	W 1 - 0	Roache 43	14
32	Feb 4		A	Eastleigh	312	W 3 - 0	Yeboah 38 Morgan 72 89	14
33	11		H	Newport County	201	L 1 - 2	Morgan 43	14
34	18		A	Thurrock	165	W 1 - 0	Morgan 54	13
35	21		H	Histon	102	W 1 - 0	Clarke 20	11
36	25		H	Maidenhead United	189	L 0 - 2		12
37	Mar 4		A	Havant & Waterlooville	401	L 0 - 3		14
38	7		H	St Albans City	132	D 2 - 2	Roache 81 Barima 83	12
39	11		A	Dorchester Town	402	L 0 - 4		13
40	18		A	Eastbourne Borough	435	D 1 - 1	Morgan 48	14
41	April 1		H	Basingstoke Town	191	L 0 - 4		15
42	8		A	Bishop's Stortford	302	L 1 - 2	Morgan 80	16
43	12		A	Weston-s-Mare	149	W 3 - 0	Behzadi 8 **Telemaque** 80 Morgan 81	13
44	15		H	Weymouth	502	L 0 - 1		16
45	17		A	Cambridge City	370	W 2 - 0	**Telemaque** 8 32	13
46	22		H	Farnborough Town	258	L 0 - 3		15
47	29		A	Carshalton ASthletic	474	D 2 - 2	Sartoya 70 (pen) **Telemaque** 74	16

Ave. League Home Attendance: 209   **Goals**   56   65   **Top Goalscorer:** Telemaque (13)
Best Position: 7th   **Worst:**   17th

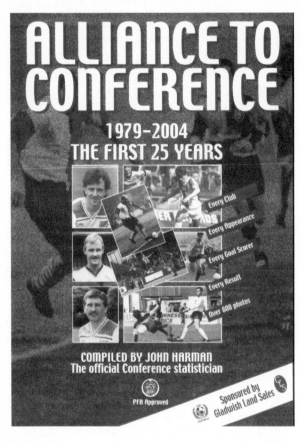

FOOTBALL LEAGUE

STEP 1

FOOTBALL
CONFERENCE

STEP 2

| CONFERENCE NORTH | CONFERENCE SOUTH |

STEP 3

| SOUTHERN PREMIER | **NORTHERN PREMIER** | ISTHMIAN PREMIER |

STEP 4

| SOUTHERN DIVISION 1 SOUTH & WEST MIDLAND | NORTHERN PREMIER DIV. 1 | ISTHMIAN DIVISION 1 NORTH SOUTH |

STEP 5/6

Combined Counties	Hellenic	Northern League	Spartan South Midlands	Wessex
Eastern Counties	Kent	Northern Counties East	Sussex County	Western
Essex Senior	Midland Alliance	North West Counties	United Counties	

STEP 7

Anglian Combination	Dorset County	Kent County	Midland Combination	Peterborough & District	West Cheshire
Bedford & District	Dorset Premier	Leicestershire Senior	Midland League	Reading League	West Lancashire
Brighton & Hove	East Sussex	Liverpool County	North Berkshire	Somerset County	West Midlands (reg)
Cambridgeshire County	Essex & Suffolk Border	Manchester Football	Northampton Town Lge	South Western	West Sussex
Central Midlands	Essex Intermediate	Mid Cheshire League	Northamptonshire Comb.	Suffolk & Ipswich	Wiltshire League
Crawley & District	Gloucesterhisre Co.	Mid Sussex	Northern Alliance	Teeside League	Worthing & District
Devon County	Herts Senior County	Middlesex County	Oxfordshire Senior	Wearside League	

NORTHERN PREMIER LEAGUE

SPONSORED BY: **UNIBOND**
President: N White F.S.C.A. **Chairman:** Peter Maude
Vice Chairman: Tom Culshaw **Chief Executive:** Duncan Bayley
Secretary & Treasurer: R D Bayley, 22 Woburn Drive, Hale, Altrincham, Cheshire WA15 8LZ Tel: 0161 980 7007 Fax: 0161 904 8850
Press Secretary: P Bradley, 7 Guest Road, Prestwich, Manchester M25 7DJ Tel: 0161 798 5198 Fax: 0161 773 0930

PREMIER DIVISION		P	W	D	L	F	A	Pts
1.	Blyth Spartans	42	26	11	5	79	32	89
2.	Frickley Athletic	42	26	8	8	72	36	86
3.	Marine	42	23	12	7	61	25	81
4.	Farsley Celtic*	42	23	10	9	84	34	79
5.	North Ferriby United	42	21	10	11	77	54	73
6.	Whitby Town	42	18	10	14	60	59	64
7.	Burscough	42	19	6	17	64	64	63
8.	Witton Albion	42	17	9	16	68	55	60
9.	Matlock Town	42	16	11	15	60	55	59
10.	AFC Telford United	42	14	17	11	54	52	59
11.	Ossett Town	42	17	7	18	57	61	58
12.	Leek Town	42	14	14	14	50	53	56
13.	Prescot Cables	42	15	8	19	49	60	53
14.	Guiseley	42	14	9	19	45	58	51
15.	Ashton United	42	13	10	19	62	63	49
16.	Ilkeston Town	42	12	13	17	48	51	49
17.	Gateshead	42	12	10	20	52	77	46
18.	Radcliffe Borough	42	12	8	22	54	62	44
19.	Lincoln United	42	10	14	18	44	64	44
20.	Wakefield Emley	42	11	9	22	38	69	42
21.	Bradford Park Avenue	42	10	9	23	64	86	39
22.	Runcorn FC Halton	42	6	11	25	36	108	29

*Promoted via the play-offs.

		1	2	3	4	5	6	7	8	9	10	11	12	13	14	15	16	17	18	19	20	21	22
1	AFC Telford U.		2-1	1-1	3-6	0-1	1-0	1-3	1-1	0-0	0-0	1-0	2-0	1-1	2-1	2-1	1-1	3-2	2-1	3-1	2-3	3-1	2-2
2	Ashton United	0-0		2-3	3-0	1-3	1-1	0-1	3-1	2-2	2-2	3-1	3-0	1-2	1-1	2-4	0-3	1-3	3-0	6-0	4-0	4-2	0-2
3	Blyth Spartans	1-1	2-0		2-0	1-0	0-1	1-0	1-1	3-1	1-1	2-1	0-1	1-0	2-2	4-2	4-4	2-0	1-0	0-0	3-0	1-0	5-1
4	Bradford P.A.	0-1	1-1	2-1		3-4	4-3	1-4	0-1	1-3	2-2	0-0	1-1	1-3	1-2	0-4	2-0	1-0	1-2	8-0	2-1	0-0	2-3
5	Burscough	0-1	3-0	0-0	0-1		0-3	0-1	2-3	3-2	2-1	1-2	1-1	0-3	1-1	3-2	4-1	2-3	3-0	2-2	3-2	2-1	1-1
6	Farsley Celtic	2-0	3-0	1-1	3-0	2-4		0-1	4-2	1-1	1-1	3-2	3-0	0-1	3-1	1-1	3-0	2-0	3-0	5-0	6-1	1-3	0-3
7	Frickley Athletic	1-0	2-2	3-2	6-2	4-1	1-0		1-2	2-1	2-0	2-1	2-2	0-0	1-0	1-1	1-0	0-1	0-2	1-0	0-0	3-0	2-0
8	Gateshead	1-1	3-2	1-2	2-1	2-0	0-5	2-2		0-2	1-2	2-0	1-1	0-1	1-5	2-3	2-1	0-3	0-0	2-4	3-2	3-2	3-2
9	Guiseley	1-0	1-3	0-2	0-3	3-1	0-3	2-0	1-0		2-2	1-1	1-2	1-0	1-0	0-2	0-2	2-5	3-2	1-1	0-1	0-2	3-1
10	Ilkeston Town	2-0	2-0	0-0	2-0	2-1	1-1	0-2	3-1	0-1		2-2	1-2	1-0	0-1	1-1	0-1	0-2	3-1	2-0	2-0	0-0	2-0
11	Leek Town	1-1	1-0	0-3	3-0	3-1	0-1	0-2	0-3		1-0		1-1	1-1	0-0	1-1	1-1	1-0	2-3	0-0	3-0	2-2	
12	Lincoln United	1-2	0-0	0-1	3-2	0-1	0-1	3-7	2-2	1-0	2-2	3-3		1-1	0-1	0-0	0-2	1-1	0-0	1-2	2-0	1-2	
13	Marine	1-1	2-2	0-1	3-1	2-1	1-0	1-0	0-0	2-0	4-2	1-2	5-1		0-0	1-0	4-0	1-0	3-0	2-0	0-0	0-0	0-1
14	Matlock Town	1-1	0-0	0-1	1-0	3-0	0-0	1-2	1-2	1-1	1-0	2-0	0-2	0-3	2-5		1-1	1-0	3-1	1-1	2-1	0-1	4-1	0-4
15	North Ferriby U.	1-0	1-0	1-4	5-2	0-1	1-2	1-2	2-1	4-0	0-0	0-0	0-2	3-2		3-0	2-1	3-1	3-3	0-0	5-1	
16	Ossett Town	1-1	3-2	3-1	3-0	1-1	0-1	2-4	3-1	1-0	1-0	0-1	1-3	0-2	4-4	2-3		3-1	2-0	2-1	2-0	2-3	1-0
17	Prescot Cables	0-0	2-1	1-3	2-2	1-2	1-1	0-2	2-1	0-2	0-0	0-2	1-3	0-1	2-1	0-2	2-1		1-0	0-0	2-0	5-1	1-1
18	Radcliffe Boro'	2-2	1-2	0-3	1-0	0-2	0-5	0-3	4-0	0-0	3-1	2-3	4-0	2-0	0-1	1-2	0-1	4-0		8-1	3-0	0-1	1-3
19	Runcorn FC H.	0-7	1-2	0-5	2-2	1-3	0-7	1-1	2-1	0-0	2-1	0-2	0-1	0-0	0-4	2-4	0-2	5-1	2-2		2-1	1-1	0-4
20	Wakefield Emley	1-1	0-1	0-3	1-1	2-1	1-0	0-0	1-0	1-3	1-0	1-3	1-1	0-2	2-3	1-0	0-1	1-0	0-0	2-0		2-3	0-2
21	Whitby Town	4-1	2-0	0-4	3-3	1-2	1-1	2-0	2-0	1-0	2-0	1-0	2-1	1-1	2-1	4-2	2-1	0-1	1-1	4-0	4-2		0-2
22	Witton Albion	4-0	0-1	1-1	2-3	2-3	0-1	1-0	2-2	4-0	3-1	0-1	0-3	0-2	2-4	2-2	2-0	0-0	0-1	2-0	1-2	0-0	

STEP 1   STEP 2   **STEP 3**   STEP 4   STEP 5/6   STEP 7

CONFERENCE   CONFERENCE NORTH/SOUTH   **NORTHERN PREMIER LEAGUE PREM.**   NORTHERN PREMIER LEAGUE DIV.1.

Northern Premier League Goalscorers 2005-2006

(Minimum ten goals from League F.A.Cup and F.A. Trophy matches)

		Lge	FAC	FAT	Total	
Strike force of Three						
Burscough	Gray	20	4	5	29	
	Eaton	7	3		10	49
	Gedman	8	1	1	10	
Matlock Town	Cropper	11	3	1	15	
	Clarke				12	38
	Barraclough				11	
North Ferriby United	Bradshaw	14	3		17	
	Fothergill	9	1	1	11	38
	Wainman				10	
Twin Strikers						
Blyth Spartans	Dale	30	2	1	33	49
	Bell				16	
Ossett Town	Walshaw	16	10	2	28	46
	Hayward	15	2	1	18	
Leek Town	Naggington	16	4	1	21	32
	MacPherson				11	
Frickley Athletic	Callery	16	1		17	30
	Woolford	12		1	13	
Whitby Town	Brunskill				16	30
	Wilford	9	1	4	14	
Witton Albion	Moseley	15	1		16	30
	Jones	13		1	14	
AFC Telford	Reynolds	8	3	3	14	26
	Hamilton	11		1	12	
Farsley Celtic	Sanasay	10	1	3	14	26
	Bambrook	10	2		12	
Marine	Young	10	2		12	22
	Byrne				10	
Single Strikers						
Ashton United	Kilheeney	19		1	20	
Gateshead	Johnston	16		1	17	
Bradford PA	Greaves	13		1	14	
Prescot Cables	Massie				10	
Radcliffe Borough	Ward	15		1	16	

No player from Guiseley, Ilkeston Town, Lincoln United, Runcorn FC Halton or Wakefield &-Emley scored ten goals last season

A.F.C.TELFORD UNITED

Founded: 2004
Nickname: The Bucks

Manager: Rob Smith   **Asst. Manager:** Larry Chambers   **Coach:** Steve Wynn
Physios: Brin May & R oddy Farquarson
Goalkeeping Coach: Paul Mellings
Club Colours: White/black/black
Change Colours: All Red
Club Sponsor: Cappemini
Previous Leagues: Predecessors - Conference
Previous Name: Telford United   **website**:www.telfordutd.co.uk
Best Seasons: League: 3rd NPL Div 1   **F.A. Cup:** Extra Preliminary Round
F.A.Trophy.: Preliminary Round
Ground address: The New Bucks Head Stadium, Watling Street, Wellington
Telford TF1 2TU
Capacity: 6,380   **Seats:**2,004   **Covered:** 5,000   **Floodlights:**Yes
Simple Directions: Leave M54 at Jct6 take A 5223 signposted Wellington.Take
second exit at second roundabout and left at third. First right after railway bridge. Car
park entrance on left. Officials make way to hotel car park by ground.
Midweek Home Matchday: Tuesday
Clubhouse: Hotel   **Club Shop Manager:** Ann Wellings
Local Radio: BBC Radio Shropshire, Beacon Radio,Telford FM and WABC
Local Press: Shropshire Star and Wellington News

CLUB PERSONNEL

Chairman: Lee Carter
Directors: L.ee Carter,Wyn Pryce,
Ian Dosser and David.Topping
The Supporters Trust
14 Members
Company Secretary: Ian Tyrer
Secretary: Sharon Lawley
c/o club 01952 640064 (Office)
07970 040106 (M)
Commercial Managers: Lee
Carter& Bridget Glaxebrook
Programme Editor: James Baylis
Tel No: 07977481185
48 Pages Price £2.00

2005-2006
Captain: Sean Parrish
Player of the Year: Stuart Brook
Top Goalscorer: Luke Reynolds

CLUB STATISTICS

Record	Attendance: 4,215 v Kendal Town N.P.L. Play off Final	
Victory:	7-0 v Runcorn (a) N.P.L. Div 1 2005-2006	
Defeat:	3-6 v Bradford (P.A.) (H) N.P.L. 2005-2006	
Career Goalscorer:	Kyle Perry	
Career Appearances:		
Record Transfer Fee	Paid: £3,000	
	Received: £25,000	
Senior Honours:	N.P.L. Div 1 Play Off Winners 2004-2005	
Previous Leagues:	Predecessors: Birmingham, Cheshire, Southern and Conference	

Back row, left to right: Paul Mellings, Ben Twigger, Richard Beale, Steve Palmer, Andy Jones, Indy Khela, Steve Foster and Steve Wynn. Middle row: Derek Wellings, Karl Brown, Jimmy Turner, Stuart Brock, Carl Rodgers, Damien Stevens, Gary Hay, Justin Marsden and Brin May. Front row: Dave Woodvine, Lee Vaughan, Larry Chambers, Steve Pope, Rob Smith, Glenn Tolley and Dean Perrow.

AFC TELFORD UNITED

BEST LGE ATT.: 2,323 v North Ferriby United
LOWEST: **233** v Marine

No.	Date	Comp	H/A	Opponents	Att:	Result	Goalscorers	Pos
1	Aug 20	NP	A	Ossett Town	440	D 1 - 1	Briggs 4 (og)	8
2	23		H	Burscough	1686	L 0 - 1		15
3	27		H	Radcliffe Borough	1471	W 2 - 1	Perry 42 Hamilton 43	11
4	29		A	Leek Town	615	D 1 - 1	Perry 12	11
5	Sept 3		H	Bradford PA	1385	L 3 - 6	Tolley 2 Jordan 53 Hamilton 86	16
6	6		A	Ilkeston Town	513	L 0 - 2		18
7	10	FAC1Q	H	**Rugby United**	1065	D 1 - 1	**Reynolds 11**	
8	13	FAC 1Qr	A	**Rugby United**	265	W 3 - 2	**Reynolds 9 43 Charie 76**	
9	17	NP	A	Gateshead	289	D 1 - 1	Alexander 71	20
10	20		H	Marine	233	D 1 - 1	**Reynolds 50**	19
11	24	FAC 2Q	A	**Nuneaton Borough**	1174	L 1 - 3	**Love 53 (og)**	
12	27	NP	A	Burscough	305	W 1 - 0	Cudworth 17	17
13	Oct 1		H	Frickley Athletic	1627	L 1 - 3	**Reynolds 16**	19
14	4		A	Marione	364	D 1 - 1	**Reynolds 85**	19
15	8		H	Wakefield-Emley	357	L 2 - 3	Hamilton 11 32	19
16	11		H	Leek Town	1250	W 1 - 0	Hamilton 24	16
17	15	FAT1Q	A	**Witton Albion**	404	D 1 - 1	**Charie 80**	
18	18	FAT1Qr	H	**Witton Albion**	843	W 2 - 1	**Reynolds 16 Hamilton 67**	
19	22	NP	H	Prescot Cables	1564	W 3 - 2	Hamilton 49 73 **Reynolds 84**	15
20	25		H	Ilkeston Town	1629	D 0 - 0		15
21	29		A	Farsley Celtic	279	L 0 - 2		15
22	Nov 1		H	Runcorn FC Halton	1342	W 3 - 1	Hamilton 7 Craven 16 **Reynolds** 26	14
23	5		A	Whitby Town	386	L 1 - 4	**Reynolds 78**	14
24	12	FAT 2R	H	**Goole**	990	D 1 - 1	**Reynolds 59**	
25	15	FAT 2Rr	A	**Goole**	330	W 1 - 0	**Curtis 75**	
26	26	FAT 3Q	A	**Worksop Town**	416	D 1 - 1	**Reynolds 81**	
27	Dec 3	NP	H	Matlock Town	1192	W 2 - 1	**Reynolds** 57 Craven 64	15
28	10		H	Blyth Spartans	1388	L 0 - 1	Perry 76	15
29	17		A	North Ferriby United	333	L 0 - 1		15
30	26		A	Witton Albion	617	L 0 - 4		16
31	Jan 2		H	Witton Albion	1782	D 2 - 2	McNally 23 Ryan 65	16
32	14		A	Frickley Athletic	460	L 0 - 1		18
33	21		A	Guiseley	363	L 0 - 1		21
34	28		H	Gateshead	1601	D 1 - 1	**Reynolds 70**	20
35	Feb 4		H	Ossett Town	1451	D 1 - 1	Jones 17	20
36	18		A	Blyth Spartans	560	D 1 - 1	Perry 88	19
37	25		H	Farsley Celtic	1572	W 1 - 0	Hamilton 73 (pen)	17
38	Mar 4		H	Lincoln United	1556	W 2 - 0	Khela 47 Brown 64 (og)	15
39	11		A	Lincoln United	266	W 2 - 1	Palmer 56 Perry 90	13
40	14		A	Prescott Cables	335	D 0 - 0		13
41	18		A	Matlock Town	559	D 1 - 1	Challender 33	13
42	25		H	WHitby Town	1835	W 3 - 1	Palmer 59 Beale 62 Hay 76	13
43	April 1		A	Ashton United	442	D 0 - 0		13
44	8		A	Guiseley	1556	D 0 - 0		13
45	14		H	Ashton United	1720	W 2 - 1	Beale 17 Alexander 73	12
46	17		A	Runcorn FC Halton	349	W 7 - 0	Turner 12 Perrow 27 Hamilton 34 86 Perry 3(70 71 75)	10
47	19		A	Radcliffe Borough	303	D 2 - 2	Pope 11 (pen) Perry 45	10
48	22		A	Bradford PA	423	W 1 - 0	Twigger 36	10
49	24		A	Wakefield-Emley	159	D 1 - 1	Pope 75	10
50	29		H	North Ferriby United	2323	W 2 - 1	Khera 2 Hay 27	10

Ave. League Home Attendance: 1453   **Goals** 65 62   **Top Goalscorer:** Reynolds (14)
Best Position: 8th   **Worst:** 21st

ASHTON UNITED

Founded: 1878
Nickname: Robins

ASHTON UNITED FOOTBALL CLUB
SEASON 2006 - 2007

Manager: Scott Green **Asst Manager:** Darren Bowman **Physio:** Kerry Wilkinson
Club Colours: Red & white halves/black/red
Change Colours: Sky/maroon/maroon
Club Sponsor: Rol-Lite Blinds
Previous League: Conference North
Best Seasons: 21st Conference North   **F.A.Cup:** 1st Rd Replay 52-53
F.A.Trophy.: 6th Rd 96-97
Ground address: Hurst Cross, Surrey Street, Ashton-u-Lyne 0L68DY
Tel No: 0161339 4158 (office) 01613 301511 (Social Club) 0161 339 4158 (Fax)
e-mail:ashtonunited@tiscali.co.uk
Official Website: www.ashtonunited.com
Capacity: 4,500   **Seats:** 250   **Covered:** 750   **Floodlights:** Yes
Simple Directions: From M62 jct 20 take A627 to Oldham. Keep to right and leave at Ashton sign, take A627 at next island then keep to left and take slip road to Ashton. At island follow Stalybridge/Park road sign straight for three miles to ground at Hurst Cross
Midweek Home Matchday: Monday
Clubhouse: Open 11am -11 pm Snacks on matchdays
Club Shop: Yes. Contact: Ken Lee (0161330 9800)

CLUB PERSONNEL
Chairman: John Milne
V-Chairman: Terry Hollis
President: Ronnie Thomasson
Secretary: Bryan Marshall,330 Manchester Road East, Little Hutton, Worsley, Mnachester M38 9WH Tel No: 0161 950 3167 (H) 07944 032362 (M)
Programme Editor: Ken Lee Tel No: 0161 330 9800

2005-2006
Captain: Danny White
Player of the Year: Phil Cooney
Top Goalscorer: Ciaran Kilheeney

CLUB STATISTICS

Record	**Attendance**: 11,000 v Halifax Town, F.A.Cup 1st Rd.1952	
	Victory:	11-3 v Stalybridge Celtic, Manchester Intermediate Cup 1955
	Defeat:	1-11 Wellington Town , Cheshire League 1946-47
Goalscorer:	**Career Appearances**: Micky Boyle 462	
Record Transfer Fee	**Paid**:	£9,000 to Netherfield for Andy Whittaker 1994
	Received:	£15,000 from Rotherham United for Karl Marginson 1993
Senior Honours:	N.P.L. Div 1 Cup 94-95 Manchester Senior Cup (4) Manchester Prem Cup (5) Manchester Challange Shield 92-93 Manchester Junior Cup: (3)	
Previous Leagues:	Manchester, Lancs Comb 12-33 48-64 66-68, Midland 64-66 Cheshire County 23-48 68-82 N.W.Co82-92	
Name:	Hurst 1878-1947 **Ground:** Rose Hill 1878-1912	

Back row, left to right: A.Jones, A.Kirk, P.Garvey, L.Adams, D.Trueman, D.White, A.Connor, D.Johnson, J.Mitten, A.Johnston (Assistant Manager) and G.Quinn (Manager). **Front row:** M.Grose (Physio), S.Smith, A,Bailey, C.Fleury, A.Thackeray, P.Cooney, P.Carty, N.Clee and M.Allison.

ASHTON UNITED

BEST LGE ATT.: 442 v AFC Telford United
LOWEST: **120** v North Ferriby United

No.	Date	Comp	H/A	Opponents	Att:	Result	Goalscorers	Pos
1	Aug 20	NP	H	North Ferriby United	120	L 2 - 4	Denham 37 Garvey 49	18
2	23		A	Prescot Cables	138	L 1 - 2	Thurston 90 (pen)	21
3	27		A	Blyth Spartans	313	L 0 - 2		21
4	29		H	Matlock Town	202	D 1 - 1	Denham 45 (pen)	22
5	Sept 2		H	Frickley Athletic	230	L 0 - 1		22
6	6		A	Runcorn FC Halton	181	W 2 - 1	Bowker 44 Denham 77	19
7	10	FAC 1Q	A	**Burscough**	187	L 2 - 3	**Denham 72 Connelly 88**	
8	12		H	Burscough	250	L 1 - 3	Denham 14	21
9	17	NP	A	Bradford PA	191	D 1 - 1	**Kilheeney** 45	22
10	19		H	Leek Town	233	W 3 - 1	Denham 71 Garvey 82 **Kilheeney** 45	17
11	24		H	Lincoln United	172	W 3 - 0	Denham 3 Garvey 61 **Kilheeney** 67	13
12	Oct 1		H	Ilkeston Town	210	D 2 - 2	**Kilheeney** 44 Green 73	15
13	4		A	Witton Albion	240	W 1 - 0	Bowker 90	13
14	8		A	Marine	218	D 2 - 2	**Kilheeney** 44 Denham 66	11
15	10		H	Gateshead	214	W 3 - 1	Cooney 45 **Kilheeney** 61 Denham 71	10
16	15	FAT 1Q	A	**Kidsgrove Athletic**	178	L 1 - 3	**Kilheeney** 19	
17	22		A	Gateshead	144	L 2 - 3	**Kilheeney** 27 44	10
18	29		A	Whitby Town	296	L 0 - 2		14
19	Nov 1		A	Burscough	236	L 0 - 3		15
20	5		H	Guiseley	227	D 2 - 2	**Kilheeney** 9 Smith 45	15
21	12		A	North Ferriby United	226	L 0 - 1		16
22	Dec 10		H	Prescot Cables	172	L 1 - 3	Bowker 86	18
23	17		A	Lincoln United	138	D 0 - 0		19
24	26		A	Radcliffe Borough	213	W 2 - 1	Smith 5 Dudley 59	17
25	Jan 2		H	Marine	223	L 1 - 2	German 84	18
26	14		A	Wakefield & Emley	99	W 1 - 0	White 84	17
27	21		H	Farsley Celtic	178	D 1 - 1	**Kilheeney** 21	17
28	28		A	Ossett Town	164	L 2 - 3	Smith 33 39	18
29	Feb 4		H	Blyth Spartans	180	L 2 - 3	**Kilheeney** 35 Green 81	18
30	7		A	Guiseley	151	W 3 - 1	Bjork 18 63 Bowker 58	15
31	18		A	Matlock Town	273	D 0 - 0		15
32	25		H	Whitby Town	178	W 4 - 2	**Kilheeney** 34 45 Bowker 11 Smith 63	14
33	28		A	Frickley Athletic	334	D 2 - 2	Naylor 37 pen 54 pen)	14
34	Mar 4		A	Ilkeston Town	352	L 0 - 2		14
35	13		H	Ossett Town		L 0 - 3		
36	18		A	Farsley Celtic	202	L 0 - 3		16
37	20		H	Bradford Park Avenue	151	W 3 - 0	Benn (og) **Kilheeney** Bjork	15
38	25		H	Wakefield-Emley	151	W 4 - 0	Bjork 16 45 Curtis 79 (og) Royle 88	14
39	April 1		H	AFC Telford	442	D 0 - 0		14
40	8		A	Witton Albion	164	L 0 - 2		14
41	14		A	AFC Telford U	1720	L 1 - 2	Taylor 85	14
42	17		H	Radcliffe Borough	207	W 3 - 0	Holden 80 Rowe 83 **Kilheeney** 90	14
43	22		A	Leek Town	297	L 0 - 1		16
44	29		H	Runcorn FC Halton	202	W 6 - 0	Smith 4 69 **Kilheeney** 4 (53 56 59 62)	

Ave. League Home Attendance: 205   **Goals** 65 69   **Top Goalscorer:** Kilheeney (20)
Best Position: 10th   **Worst:** 22nd

BURSCOUGH

Founded: 1946
Nickname: Linnets

Manager: Liam Watson **Asst Manager:** Joey Dunne **Physio:** Mel Singleton
Club Colours: White with green panel/white/white
Change Colours: Al Green
Club Sponsor: Glenroyd Developments
Previous League: North West Counties
Best Seasons: League: 6th Northern Premier League 2004-05
F.A.Cup: 2nd Rd 2005-06 v Burton Albion   **F.A.Trophy.:** Winners 2002-2003
Ground address: Victoria Park, Bobby Langton Way, Mart Lane, Burscough, Lancs.
L40 0SD. **Tel No**: 01704 893237
Website: www.burscoughfc.co.uk
Capacity: 2,500   **Seats:** 270   **Covered:** 1,000   **Floodlights:** Yes
Simple Directions: M6 Jct 27 follow signs through Parbold A5209, right into Junction
Lane (signed Burscough & Martin Mere) to lights, right into A59 to Burscough village.
Then second left over canal bridge into Mart Lane to ground. Only 200 yards from
Burscough (BR).
Midweek Home Matchday: Tuesday
Clubhouse:.Barons Club outside ground. No food.
Club Shop: Yes Contact: Sue Berry (01772 724996)

CLUB PERSONNEL
Chairman: Chris Lloyd
President: Rod Cottam:
Company Sec: Dave McIlwain
Secretary: Keith Maguire, 218
Bescar Lane, Scarisbrick, Lancs.
Tel Nos: 01704 880587 (H)
07970 030588 (M)
Press Officer: Neil Leatherbarrow
Tel No: 07855 701512 (M)
Programme Editor:
Secretary
Programme
44 Pages £1.50
2005-2006
Captain: Ryan Bowen
Player of the Year: Tony Gray
Top Goalscorer: Tony Gray

CLUB STATISTICS

Record	Attendance: 4,798 v Wigan Athletic F.A.Cup 3rd Qualifying Round 1950-51
	Victory: 10-0 V Cromptons Rec 1947 & Nelson 1948-49 both Lancs.Comb.
	Defeat: 0-9 v Earltown, Liverpool Co Comb. 1948-49
	Goalscorer in a Game : Louis Bimpson 7 Season: Johnny Vincent 60 1953-64
	Career: Wes Bridge 188
	Career Appearances:
Transfer Fees	Paid: £2,,500 to Skelmersdale United for Stuart Rudd 2000-01
	Received: £20,000 to Rochdale for Lee McEvilly 2001-02
Senior Honours:	F.A.Trophy Winners 2002-03 Liverpool Challenge Cup (3) Lancashire
	Junior Cup 4) Liverpool Non-League Senior Cup (2) R-up (3)
Previous Leagues	Liverpool Co.Comb.46-53 Lancs Comb. 53-70 Cheshire Co 70-82 N.W.Co 82-9

Back Row left to right, Mal Liptrott(coach), Farrell Kilbane, Neil Fitzhenry, Dominic Morley, Mike Tomlinson, Tony McMillan, Paul Gedman, Ryan Bowen, Mel Singleton(physio).
Front Row left to right, Kevin Leadbeater, Joey Dunne(coach), Chris Price(captain), Liam Watson(manager), Steve McEwan, Neil Robinson, Own Rimmer (mascot).

BURSCOUGH

BEST LGE ATT.: 702 v North Ferriby United
LOWEST: **172** v Ossett Town

No.	Date	Comp	H/A	Opponents	Att:	Result	Goalscorers	Pos
1	Aug 20	NP	H	Blyth Spartans	264	D 0 - 0		15
2	23		A	AFC Telford	1686	W 1 - 0	Blakeman 14	6
3	27		A	Guisley	198	L 1 - 3	Eaton 4	12
4	29		H	Witton Albion	349	D 1 - 1	Blakeman 90	13
5	Sept 3		A	Lincoln United	128	W 1 - 0	Bell 44	9
6	6		H	Radcliffe Borough	215	W 3 - 0	**Gray** 20 Gedman 61 Eaton 75	7
7	10	FAC 1Q	H	**Ashton United**	187	W 3 - 2	**Byrne 9 Parry 12 Tong 80**	
8	12	NP	A	Ashton United	250	W 3 - 1	**Gray** 5 Parry 8 Tong 88	3
9	17	NP	H	North Ferriby United	702	W 3 - 2	Blakeman 34 Tong 69 Gedman 80	3
10	20		A	Radcliffe Borough	188	W 2 - 0	Byrne 24 Barlow 28	2
11	24	FAC 2Q	A	**Droylsden**	316	W 2 - 1	**Blakeman 77 Eaton 82**	
12	27	NP	H	AFC Telford	305	L 0 - 1		3
13	Oct 1		A	Farsley Celtic	200	W 4 - 2	Tong 21 Bell 42 (pen) **Gray** 38 73	3
14	4		A	Runcorn FC Halton	173	W 3 - 1	Eaton 46 **Gray** 60 62	2
15	8	FAC 3Q	H	**Workington**	303	W 2 - 0	**Parry 57 Gray 80**	
16	15	FAT 1Q	H	**Leek Town**	212	D 3 - 3	**Gedman 10 Gray 35 41**	
17	18	FAT1Qr	A	**Leek Town**	175	W 3 - 1	**Gray 70 82 Bell 78 (pen)**	
18	22	FAC4Q	A	**Hucknall Town**	690	D 0 - 0		
19	25	FAC4Qr	H	**Hucknall Town**	415	W 6 - 2	**Hussey 22 Gray 3 (23 31 78) Eaton 50 Gedman 66**	
20	29	NP	H	Bradford PA	355	L 0 - 1		6
21	Nov 1		H	Ashton United	236	W 3 - 0	**Gray** 11 Tong 48 Parry 76	4
22	5	FAC 1R	H	**Gillingham**	1927	W 3 - 2	**Bell 10 Cox 89 (og) Rowan 90**	
23	8	NP	H	Runcorn FC Halton	350	D 2 - 2	Blakeman26 Parry 59	4
24	12	FAT 2Q	H	**Fleetwood Town**	438	L 1 - 2	**Gray 50**	
25	19	NP	A	Whitby Town	265	W 2 - 1	Crowder 31 **Gray** 70	4
26	26		H	Ilkeston Town	231	W 2 - 1	Blakeman 26 Eaton 46	3
27	Dec 6	FAC 2R	A	**Burton Albion**	4499	L 1 - 4	**Eaton 60**	
28	10	NP	H	Farsley Celtic	528	L 0 - 3		5
29	17		A	Wakefield-Emley	245	L 1 - 2	**Gray** 61	5
30	26		A	Marine	452	L 1 - 2	Gagham 86	6
31	Jan 2		H	Prescot Cables	443	L 2 - 3	Blakeman 68 90	6
32	14		A	Matlock Town	221	L 0 - 3		6
33	21		H	Gateshead	252	L 2 - 3	**Gray** 27 77	9
34	28		A	Wakefield -Emley	224	W 3 - 2	Gedman 13 **Gray** 61 66	7
35	Feb 4		A	Bradford PA	216	W 4 - 3	Booth 33 61 Bowen 75 Gedman 80	7
36	18		H	Kincoln City	258	D 1 - 1	**Gray** 1	7
37	21		A	Leek Town	173	L 0 - 3		7
38	25		H	Blyth Spartans	413	L 0 - 1		9
39	Mar 7		H	Leek Town	187	L 1 - 2	Gedman 2	10
40	11		A	Witton Albion	237	W 3 - 2	Eaton 17 **Gray** 52 74	7
41	18		H	Guiseley	240	W 3 - 2	Gedman 42 **Gray** 43 58	7
42	25		H	Ilkeston Town	412	L 1 - 2	Gedman 17	7
43	28		H	Ossett Town	172	W 4 - 1	Gedman 31 Eaton 72 75 Bowen 88	7
44	April 1		A	Gateshead	120	L 0 - 2		7
45	4		H	Frickley Athletic	193	L 0 - 1		7
46	8		H	Matlock Town	218	D 1 - 1	Armstrong 5	7
47	11		A	North Ferrioby United	200	W 1 - 0	Crowder 8 (pen)	7
48	14		A	Prescot Cables	304	W 2 - 1	**Gray** 31 Hussey 59	7
49	17		A	Marine	387	L 0 - 3		7
50	22		H	Whitby Town	195	W 2 - 1	Hussey 54 Bowen 84	6
51	25		A	Ossett Town	54	D 0 - 0		6
52	29		A	Frickley Athletic	407	L 1 - 4	**Gray** 1 (pen)	7

Ave. League Home Attendance:	288		**Goals**	87 81	**Top Goalscorer:** Gray (29)

Best Position: 2nd   **Worst:**   15th

FLEETWOOD TOWN

Founded: 1908
Nickname:
The Fishermen

CLUB PERSONNEL
Chairman: Andrew Pilley
Directors: Terry Poole, Phil Brown, Kevin Pennington, Ian Cassford, Dave Mackie and Roger Smith
Secretary: Kevin Pennnington, 1Carlisle Avenue, Fleetwood, Lancs. FY7 8ILP **Tel .No:** 01253-771602(H) (M) 07967 192843
General Manager: Les Taylor
Programme
Editor: Phil Brown
Tel No: 01253 701280
2005-2006
Captain: Steve Macauley
Player of the Year: Nathon Pond
Top Goalscorer: Richie Alllen

Manager: Tony Greenwood   **Assistant Manager:** Steve Edwards
Coach: Steve Macauley **Physio**: Danny Moore
Colours: Red with white trim/white/white.
Change Colours: All White
Club Sponsor: E.T.Knagg & Co Insurance Brokers
Previous League: N.W.Counties
Best Seasons: F.A. Cup: 1st Round 1949-50 1965-66
F.A.Vase: Finalists 1984-1985
Ground address: Highbury Stadium, Park Avenue, Fleetwood, Lancs
Tel Nos: 01253 770702 (club) 07967 192843 (for club bookings)
Club Website: www.fleetwoodtownfc.co.uk
Capacity: 3,00   **Seats**: 250   **Covered**:1,200   **Floodlights**: Yes
Simple Directions: from M55 junction 3 follow signs to Fleetwood on A585 for about eleven miles then turn left at Nautical College traffic island (campus on left) at second island take sixth exit into into Hatfield Avenue. Ground is 3/4 mile on left.
Midweek Home Matchday: Tuesday
Clubhouse: Smart refurbished club room with bar, dance floor and Sky TV can be booked. Contact: 01253 7700702 or 07948 876002
Club Shop: Full range of products
Local Radio: Radio Lancashire
Local Press: Fleetwood Weekly News & Chronicle and Blackpool Evening Gazette

CLUB STATISTICS

Record
Attendance: 7,900 v Liverpool F.C. 12 August 2003
Career Goalscorer:
Career Appearances:
Transfer Fee Paid:
Transfer Fee Received:
Senior Honours: N.P.L. Div 1 R-up 2005-2006 N.West Co. Div 1 Champions 2004-20005
Div 2 Champions 1998-1999
Previous: **Names** Fleetwood 1908 Fleetwood Wanderers 1997 then in the same year reverted to Fleetwood Freeport and Fleetwood Town in 2002

Back row,left to right: Danny Moore(physio), Phil Robinson, Matthew Gilston, Stuart Beech, Andy Banks, Kevin Barnes, Richard Allen,Paul Cook, Andy Gouck and Gary McGonnell. Front row: Jimmy Hone, Joe Booth, Sean Lawler, Darryl Avery, Jamie Hastings, Jamie Nay and Ricky Singleton.

AFFORDABLE SEATING FOR SALE

Take a Seat!

with The Arena Sports Stand & Sports Shelter

From 50 to 50,000... Arena Seating have the solution

Designed for Sports Arenas requiring substantial covered grandstand accommodation, this popular product provides a flexible modular cantilevered roof cover in conjunction with the proven Arena tiered seating system.

The Arena Sports Shelter is a smaller lightweight 4-row version of the Sports Stand with all the flexibility of seating configuration inherent in the Arena system.

Contact us to see how we can enhance your venue.

WWW.ARENASEATING.COM

Arena Seating
Arena House Membury Lambourn Woodlands Hungerford Berkshire RG17 7TQ
T. 01488 67 48 00   **W.** www.arenaseating.com   **E.** info@arenaseating.com

PART OF THE ARENA GROUP

FRICKLEY ATHLETIC

Founded: 1910
Nickname: The Blues

Manager: Gary Marrow   **Assistant Manager:** Mark Ogley
Club Coach: Alan Ogley   **Sports Therapist:** Mick Gilbert
Club Colours: Royal blue /white/blue.
Change Colours: White & Black
Club Sponsor: Millennium Worldwide
Previous Leagues: Conference
Previous Name: Frickley Colliery
Best Seasons: League: Alliance (Conference) Runners-up 85-86
F.A. Cup: 3rd Round 85-6   **F.A.Trophy.:** Quarter-Finals 84-85
Ground address: G.M.B. Stadium, Westfield Lane, South Elmsall, Pontefract. **Tel No/Fax:** 01977 642460 **email:** steve@frickleyafc.co.uk
Official Website: www.frickleyafc.co.uk
Capacity: 6,000   **Seats:** 800 **Covered:** 2,500   **Floodlights:**Yes
Simple Directions: From A1and A638. Left at superdrug warehouse, right at T junction and left up Westfield Lane. Left into Oxford Road opposite Westfield Hotel. Ground at bottom on right.
Midweek Home Matchday: Tuesday
Clubhouse: On ground, open matchdays
Club Shop: Yes. Contact: Bryan Pennock (01302 832042)
Local Radio: Radio Sheffield, Radio Hallam, Radio Leeds and Ridings F.M.
Local Press: South Yorks Times, Hemsworth & South Elmsall Express.

CLUB PERSONNEL
Chairman: Peter Bywater
President: Peter Naylor.:
Finance Sec: A.Steel
0114 2460218
Secretary: Steve Pennock, 3 KIngsley Crescent,Armthorpe, Doncaster DN3 3JG
01302 835956(H) 07985 291074(M)
Commercial Manager: Tom Grindel
Marketing Manager: Jamie McIntyre
Programme Editor: Darren Haynes (01924 366462)
Programme
Pages 40 Price 1.50

2005-2006 P.o.Y.: Garry Ingham
Captain: Steve Kennedy
Top Goalscorer: Alex Callery 17

CLUB STATISTICS

Record

Attendance: 6,500 v Rotherham United F.A.Cup 1st Rd 1971
Career Goalscorer: K.Whiteley
Career Appearances:
Transfer Fee Paid: £1,800
Transfer Fee Received: £12,500 from Boston United for Paul Shirtliff
                    &   £12,500 from Northampton Town for Russ Wilcox

Senior Honours: Alliance Runners-up 1985-86 Midland Co Lg R-up 72-73
                  Hallamshire Senior Cup (10)
Previous Leagues: Sheffield, Yorkshire 22-24, Midland Counties, 24-33 34-60 70-76,
                  Cheshire Co. 60-70,   NPL 76-80, and Conference 80-87

Back Row (L-R): Rebecca Henry-Brown (Physio), Steve Robinson, Lee Pugh, Mark Ward, Calum Selby, Ritchie Butler, Martyn Woolford, Mick Gilbert (Physio), Gary Ingham, Andy Evans, Rob Pell, Mark Crossfield, Matt Daly, Lee Stratford, Steve Heath, Pete Bywater (Chairman). **Front:** Richard Tracey, Chris Adam, Alex Callery, Steve Kennedy, Neil Ashley, Simon Collins, Gary Marrow (Manager), Alan Ogley (Coach). All celebrating after receiving the NPL Divison One runners-up trophy.

FRICKLEY ATHLETIC

BEST LGE ATT.: 908 v North Ferriby United
LOWEST: 212 v Prescot Cables

No.	Date	Comp	H/A	Opponents	Att:	Result	Goalscorers	Pos
1	Aug 20	NP	A	Runcorn FC Halton	147	D 1 - 1	Chambers 61	9
2	23		H	Whitby Town	220	W 3 - 0	Scothern 7 **Callery** 54 60	5
3	27		H	Leek Town	331	W 2 - 1	Scothern 34 76	4
4	29		A	Gateshead	201	D 2 - 2	**Callery** 48 (pen) 65 (pen)	5
5	Sept 2		A	Ashton United	230	W 1 - 0	Selby 68	4
6	6		H	Farsley Celtic	287	W 1 - 0	Evans 18	2
7	10	FAC 1Q	H	Chadderton	214	W 2 - 0	Scothern 20 Evans 32	
8	13		A	Blyth Spartans	351	L 0 - 1		4
9	17	NP	H	Prescott Cables	212	L 0 - 1		6
10	20		A	North Ferriby United	251	W 2 - 1	Woolford 3 **Callery** 44	4
11	24	FAC 2Q	H	Northwich Victoria	392	L 1 - 4	Callery 3	
12	Oct 1	NP	A	AFC Telford	1627	W 3 - 1	Pell 42 55 **Callery** 84	4
13	4	NP	H	Blyth Spartans	392	W 3 - 2	Smith (og) 45 **Callery** 53 (pen) 57	4
14	8		H	Lincoln United	357	D 2 - 2	**Callery** 11 Selby 90	3
15	11		A	Ossett Town	280	W 4 - 2	Woolford 3 (35 38 77) **Callery** 45	2
16	15	FAT1Q	A	Warrington Town	132	D 1 - 1	Woolford 6	
17	18	FAT1Qr	H	Warrington Town	265	D 1 - 1*	Latham 81 Lost 4-5 after penalties)	
18	22	NP	H	Marine	299	D 0 - 0		6
19	26		A	Bradford PA	320	W 4 - 1	**Callery** 14 Evans 3 (35 65 81)	2
20	29		H	Ilkeston Town	310	W 2 - 0	Woolford 62 **Callery** 77 (pen)	2
21	Nov 5		A	Marine	354	L 0 - 1		2
22	12		A	Witton Albion	301	L 0 - 1		2
23	19		H	Witton Albion	263	W 2 - 0	Chambers 42 73	2
24	26		H	Radcliffe Borough	246	L 0 - 2		2
25	Dec 10		A	Guiseley	274	L 0 - 2		3
26	17		H	Ossett Town	244	W 1 - 0	Morris 39	2
27	26		H	Wakefield-Emley	348	D 0 - 0		4
28	Jan 2		A	Farsley Celtic	335	W 1 - 0	**Callery** 90	3
29	14		H	AFC Telford	460	W 1 - 0	**Callery** 63	3
30	21		A	Prescot Cables	190	W 2 - 0	Collins 48 Pell 71	2
31	28		H	Bradford PA	454	W 6 - 2	Pell 4 Collins 7 Evans 20 Woolford 35 49 Adam 71	
32	Feb 18		H	Runcorn FC Halton	319	W 1 - 0	Woolford 81	2
33	25		A	Radcliffe Borough	239	W 3 - 0	Kennedy 19 Woolford 52 83	2
34	28		H	Ashton United	334	D 2 - 2	Daly 25 Adam 27	1
35	Mar 18		H	Gateshead	251	L 1 - 2	Duffield 61	3
36	21		H	Guisley	230	W 2 - 1	Daly 37 89	2
37	25		A	Leek Town	323	W 2 - 0	Pell 4 Duffield 21	1
38	April 1		H	Matlock Town	324	W 1 - 0	Daly 65	1
39	4		A	Burscough	193	W 1 - 0	Adam 20	1
40	7		A	Lincoln United	167	W 7 - 3	Daly 3 25 Ward 28 48 Duffield 53 67 Evans 90	1
41	14		H	North Ferriby United	908	D 1 - 1	**Callery** 23	1
42	18		A	Wakefield-Emley	289	D 0 - 0		1
43	22		A	Frickley Athetic	393	W 2 - 0	**Callery** 18 Pugh 65	2
44	24		A	Matlock Town	265	W 2 - 1	Pugh 39 Evans 89	1
45	26		A	Whitby Town	272	L 0 - 2		2
46	29		H	Burscough	407	W 4 - 1	Daly 19 (pen) Woolford 62 72 Evans 78	2
47	May 1	Play Off SF	H	North Ferriby United	593	D 0 - 0*	North Ferriby United won 4-2 after penalties	

Ave. League Home Attendance: 343   **Goals**   77   41   **Top Goalscorer:** Callery (17)

Best Position: 1st   **Worst:** 9th

GATESHEAD

Founded: 1930
Nickname: Tynesiders

Matchday Programme £1.50 Members of the UniBond
Match Sponsors: League Premier Division
ORANGE INTERIORS 2005/06
Gateshead v Guiseley

Manager: Tony Lee

Asst Manager: Alan Radford   **Coach:** Dave Clark   **Physio:** Bev Dougherty

Club Colours: White/black/white

Change Colours: Red with white sleeves/white/red

Club Sponsor: Veritas

Previous League: Conference

Best Seasons: **League:** 5th (Conference) 1995-96

    F.A.Cup: 6th Rd 1952-53

    F.A.Trophy.: 6th Rd 19192-93

Ground address: International Stadium, Neilson Rd, Gateshead NE10 0EF

Tel No: 0191 478 3883   **FAX:** 0191 427 5211

Website: www.gateshead-fc.com

Capacity: 11,795   **Seats:** 11,795   **Covered:** 3,300   **Floodlights:** Yes

Simple Directions: From South follow A1(M) to Granada services (Birtley) take right hand fork marked A194(M)(Tyne Tunnel, South Shields) follow A194 to first roundabout, turn left into A184- then three miles to Stadium.

Midweek Home Matchday: Monday

Clubhouse: Bar inside Tyne & Wear stand open on matchdays.

Club Shop: Full range of souvenirs etc. **Contact:** Mick Thornton: 07913 646451

CLUB PERSONNEL

Chairman: Derek Bell

Club & Match Secretary:
Margaret Lloyd, 4 The Hawthirns, Eighton Banks, Gateshgead, Tyne & Wear NE9 1LF 0191 487 3143 (H) 0191478 3883

Tel No: 07726 790971 (M)

Commercial Manager:
Douglas Kennedy C/o Club

Press Officer& Prog.Ed.:
Dean Ranyard
Tel No: 0191 2377430 (H)

2005-2006
Top Goalscorer: Johnston 17

CLUB STATISTICS

Record	**Attendance:** 11,750 v Newcastle United Friendly 7th August 1995
Victory:	8-0 v Netherfield, N.P.L.
Defeat:	0-9 v Sutton United Conference 22.09.90
Goalscorer:	Bob Topping
Career Appearances:	Simon Smith 450 1985-94
Record Transfer Fee	**Paid:** £9,000 to Dagenham & Redbridge for Paul Cavell
Received:	Undisclosed from Rushden & Diamonds for Kenny Cramman
Senior Honours:	Football League Div 3N R-up 31-2 49-50 NPL Champs 8-83 85-86 R-up 89-90
Previous Leagues	Football League 1930-60 N.Co E 60-62 North Regional 62-68 NPL 68-70 73-83 85-86 87-90 Wearside 70-71 Midland 71-72 Alliance/Conference 83-85 86-87 90-98 **Ground:** Redheugh Park 1930-1971

Back row left to right: Bev Doughty (Physio), David Colvin, Richard Flynn, Stephen Harrison, Paul Thompson, Peter Keen, Darren Horrigan, James Curtis, Sonny Parker, Kevin Henderson, Tom Doleman (KIt Man) and Mark Walton (Asst.Kit Man) Front row: James Huntley, Robert Huntley, Liam Bell, Adam Smith, Chris Laws, Eric Tait (Club Coach), Derek Bell (Chairman) , Tom Wade (Manager), Sreven Richardson, Chris Feasey, Paul Buzzo, Gareth Mc Alindon and Mark Atkinson.

GATESHEAD

BEST LGE ATT.: 715 v Blyth Spartans
LOWEST:　　87 v Farsley Celtic

No.	Date	Comp	H/A	Opponents	Att:	Result	Goalscorers	Pos
1	Aug 20	NP	H	Lincoln United	136	D 1 - 1	Henderson 64	10
2	23		A	Guiseley	231	L 0 - 1		16
3	27		A	Marine	267	D 0 - 0		17
4	29		H	Frickley Athletic	201	D 2 - 2	Thompson 29 (pen) Curtis 77	17
5	Sept 3		A	Witton Albion	214	D 2 - 2	Colvin 17 Thompson 20	17
6	7		H	Wakefield -Emley	121	W 3 - 2	Flynn 8 Richardson 14 Feasey 34	13
7	11	FAC1Q	H	**Warrington Town**	235	W 4 - 0	**Henderson 65 80 (pen) Feasey 73 R.Huntley 90**	
8	13	NP	A	Farsley Celtic	178	L 2 - 4	Laws 11 Pemberton (og) 69	14
9	17	NP	H	AFC Telford	289	D 1 - 1	Henderson 6	6
10	20		A	Wakefield & Emley	115	L 0 - 1		16
11	24	FAC 2Q	A	**Salford City**	213	L 0 - 1		
12	28	NP	H	Presct Cables	118	W 2 - 1	Henderson 54 57	15
13	Oct 1		A	North Ferribby United	262	L 0 - 1		16
14	5		H	Guiseley	137	L 0 - 2		18
15	8		H	Prescot Cables	126	L 0 - 3		20
16	10		A	Ashton United	214	L 1 - 3	Thompson 16 (pen)	21
17	15	FAT 1Q	A	**Bradford PA**	191	D 1 - 1	**Laws 90**	
18	18	FAT1Qr	H	**Bradford PA**	130	W 4 - 3*	**Johnston 4 Walsh (og) 54 Thompson 90 Taylor 114**	
19	22	NP	H	Ashton United	144	W 3 - 2	Thompson 7 (pen) Taylor 23 Parker 57	17
20	29		H	Leek Town	153	W 2 - 0	**Johnston 54 Reay 87**	17
21	Nov 5		A	Ilkeston Town	368	L 1 - 3	Taylor 63	18
22	12	FAT 2R	H	**Kidsgrove Athletic**	127	W 1 - 0	**Thompson 72**	
23	19	NP	A	Runcorn FC Halton	73	L 1 - 2	**Johnston 21**	19
24	26	FAT 3Q	A	**Warrington Town**	121	L 0 - 4		
25	Dec 3	NP	H	Runcorn FC Halton	113	L 2 - 4	Flynn 50 Radfold 83	20
26	10		A	Matlock Town	215	W 2 - 1	**Johnston 8 82**	
27	17		H	Radcliffe Borough	130	D 0 - 0		21
28	26		A	Blyth Spartans	767	D 1 - 1	**Johnston 48**	20
29	Jan 2		H	Whitby Town	194	W 3 - 2	Thompson 1 41 (pen) **Johnston** 82	17
30	14		H	Bradford PA	200	W 2 - 1	Thompson 70 (pen) Taylor 73	
31	21		A	Burscough	252	W 3 - 2	**Johnston** 53 86 Curtis 58	14
32	28		A	AFC Telford	1601	D 1 - 1	**Johnston 11**	13
33	Feb 4		H	Matlock Town	184	L 1 - 5	Selby 4	14
34	11		A	Prescot Cables	132	L 1 - 2	**Johnston 26**	14
35	18		A	Leek Town	253	D 0 - 0		15
36	Mar 11		H	North Ferriby United	126	L 2 - 3	Harrattt 37 White 41	20
37	15		H	Farsley Celtic	87	L 0 - 5		
38	18		A	Frickley Athletic	251	W 2 - 1	Graydon 25 Okike 63	17
39	22		A	Whitby Town	145	L 0 - 2		19
40	29		A	Bradford PA	177	W 1 - 0	Okike 30	17
41	April 1		H	Burscough	120	W 2 - 0	Okike 3 **Johnston** 85	14
42	4		A	Radcliffe Borough	123	L 0 - 4		16
43	14		H	Blyth Spartans	715	L 1 - 2	**Johnston 45**	16
44	17		A	Ossett Town	114	L 1 - 3	Briggs (og) 88	16
45	22		A	Lincoln United	115	D 2 - 2	**Johnston 15 30**	17
46	24		H	Witton Albion	103	W 3 - 2	**Johnston** 57 70 Curtis 85	17
47	26		H	Marine	102	L 0 - 1		17
48	29		H	Ilkeston Town	194	L 1 - 2	Okike 20	17

Ave. League Home Attendance:	176	**Goals**	62　83	**Top Goalscorer:** Johnston (17)

Best Position:　6th　　**Worst:**　21st

GRANTHAM TOWN

Founded: 1874
Nickname: Gingerbreads

Manager: Lee Glover   **Assistant Manager:** Phil Turner   **Physio:** Nigel Marshall

Club Colours: Black & white stripes/Black/Black

Change Colours: Yellow & Black or white & yellow

Club Sponsor: Downtown (Home) Gladwish Landsales (Away)

Previous League: Northern Premier

Best Seasons: League: Southern League Runners-Up 1973-74

F.A.Cup: 3rd Rd 1883-83 86-87 1973-74

F.A.Trophy.: 6th Rd 1971-72 1997-98

Ground address: South Kesteven Sports Stadium, Trent Rd, Grantham, Lincs.

Tel No:01476 402224   **Website:** www.granthamtownfc.co.uk

Capacity: 7,500   **Seats:**750   **Covered:**1,950   **Floodlights:**Yes

Simple Directions: Midway between A1 and A52 on edge of Earlsfield Industrial
Estate from A1take A607 to Earlsfield Industrial Estate and continue into Trebt Rd.

Midweek Home Matchday: Tuesday

Clubhouse: Open evenings and week ends (01476 402225)

Club Shop: Wide range of products.Contact: John Gilbert (07966 920021)

CLUB PERSONNEL
Chairman: Roger Booth
President: George Freeston
Secretary: Pat Nixon,
72 Huntingtower Rd., Grantham,
Lincs. NG31 7AU
Tel No: 01476 419391
Programme Editor: Mike Koranski
Tel No: 01476 562104

CLUB STATISTICS

Record	**Attendance:** 3,695 v Southport F.A.Trophy 97-98
	Victory: 13-0 v Rufford Colliery (H) F.A.Cup 15.09.34
	Defeat: 0-16 v Notts County Rovers(A) Midland Am.Alliance 22.101892
	Goalscorer: Jack McCartney 416
	Career Appearances: Chris Gardner 664
Record Transfer Fee	**Paid:** Undisclosed for Mario Ziccari
	Received: £20,000 from Nottingham Forest for Gary Crosby
Senior Honours:	Southern Lg R-up 90-91 Mid Div Champions 97-98 Eastern Div R-up 2001-02, Lincs Senior Cup (20 R-up (5) Linc Co Sen Cup(2) R-up 80-81
Previous Leagues	Mid Am Alliance, Central Al l11-25 59-61 Midland Co. 25-59 61-72 Southern 72-79 NPL 79-85

GRANTHAM TOWN

BEST LGE ATT.: 523 v King's Lynn
LOWEST: 212 v Cirencester Town

No.	Date	Comp	H/A	Opponents	Att:	Result	Goalscorers	Pos
1	Aug 13	SP	H	Bath City	472	L 0 - 3		21
2	16		A	Banbury United	352	D 1 - 1	Brown 14	17
3	20		A	Cirencester Town	208	W 1 - 0	Glover 10	12
4	23		H	Hitchin Town	264	D 1 - 1	Smith 10 (pen)	14
5	27		H	Northwood	266	W 2 - 0	Sneddon 49 Evans 64	10
6	29		A	Evesham United	245	W 2 - 0	Carruthers 19 61	5
7	Sept 2		H	Halesowen Town	270	D 1 - 1	Sneddon 78	8
8	**10**	**FAC 1Q**	**H**	**Lincoln United**	**413**	**W 4 - 0**	**Smith 41 (pen) Carruthers 60 Sturgess 68 Pell 77**	
9	17	SP	A	Aylesbury United	349	W 2 - 0	Smith 1 Carruthers 61	5
10	**24**	**FAC 2Q**	**A**	**Leek Town**	**347**	**L 0 - 1**		
11	27	SP	H	Bedford Town	263	W 3 - 0	Pell 70 Murray 75 Francis 87	3
12	Oct 1		A	Salisbury City	875	L 0 - 3		7
13	8		A	Chesham United	283	D 2 - 2	Sturgess 4 Pell 12	6
14	11		H	Banbury United	298	L 2 - 3	Brown 45 Evans 49	7
15	**15**	**FAT1Q**	**A**	**Bamber Bridge**	**162**	**D 2 - 2**	**Francis 79 Julien 84**	
16	**18**	**FAT1Qr**	**H**	**Bamber Bridge**	**230**	**W 3 - 0**	**Smith 15 Carruthers 84 Popple 89**	
17	22	SP	H	Cheshunt	272	L 0 - 1		7
18	25		A	Halesowen Town	291	W 2 - 0	Glover 23 Sneddon 35	6
19	29		A	Merthyr Tydfil	541	L 1 - 2	Turner 85	6
20	Nov 5		H	Mangotsfield United	319	D I - 2	Weale 30	9
21	**12**	**FAT 2Q**	**H**	**Lincoln United**	**308**	**W 2 - 1**	**White 16 Sturgess 53**	
22	19	SP	A	Tiverton Town	408	L 1 - 3	Popple 4	9
23	**26**	**FAT 3Q**	**A**	**Droylsden**	**251**	**L 0 - 4**		
24	Dec 3	SP	H	Salisbury City	282	W 1 - 0	Turner 47	8
25	10		A	Bath City	490	L 0 - 2		9
26	17		H	Yate Town	277	W 2 - 0	Sneddon 18 Julien 52	8
27	27		A	King's Lynn	1118	L 1 - 3	Turner 8	10
28	31		A	Bedford Town	517	D 1 - 1	Smith 74	12
29	Jan 2		H	Rugby Town	398	D 2 - 2	Sneddon 2 Turner 58	12
30	7		A	Chippenham Town	626	L 0 - 1		15
31	14		H	Gloucester City	366	W 2 - 1	Brown 27 Sneddon 73	16
32	17		H	Evesham United	236	D 1 - 1	Bacon 85	11
33	21		A	Northwood	201	W 2 - 0	Sneddon 21 Brown 29	10
34	28		H	Chesham United	271	D 0 - 0		11
35	Feb 4		A	Cheshunt	117	L 2 - 3	Smith 6 75	14
36	11		H	Aylesbury United	248	W 2 - 0	Turner 13 24	11
37	18		A	Gloucester City	339	L 1 - 4	Turner 23	13
38	25		H	Tiverton Town	234	D 1 - 1	Turner 73	14
39	Mar 4		A	Team Bath	101	W 2 - 1	Turner 67 Canham 86 (og)	10
40	11		H	Merthyr Tydfil	241	D 0 - 0		10
41	18		H	Cirencester Town	212	L 0 - 1		10
42	25		A	Hitchin Town	268	W 2 - 0	Robinson 25 Brown 39	10
43	April 1		H	Team Bath	266	L 0 - 1		10
44	8		A	Yate Town	154	L 1 - 3	Jefferies 75 (og)	11
45	15		A	Rugby Town	265	W 2 - 0	Brown 37 Turner 53	11
46	17		H	King's lynn	523	L 0 - 1		11
47	22		H	Chippenham Town	232	D 1 - 1	McEnteggart 59 (og)	11
48	29		A	Mangotsfield United	190	W 1 - 0	Matthews 83	11

Ave. League Home Attendance: 296 | | | | | **Goals** 59 57 | **Top Goalscorer:** Turner (10) |

Best Position: 3rd **Worst:** 21st

GUISELEY

Founded: 1909

Manager: Neil Parsley   **Assistant Manager:** Trevor Storton
Physio: Ian McCreadie
Club Colours: White/with navy trim/navy/navy
Change Colours: Yellow & Navy
Club Sponsors: Previous League: N.Co East
Best Seasons: League:
F.A. Cup: 1st Round 94-95 99-00 **F.A.Trophy.:** S-F 94-95 **F.A.Vase** :Winners 90-91
Ground address: Nethermoor Park, Otley Road, Guiseley, Leeds LS20 8BT
Tel No: 01943 873223
Official Website: www.guiseleyafc.co.uk
Capacity: 3,000   **Seats**:427   **Covered:** 1,040 **Floodlights**: Yes
Simple Directions: Via M1 to M62 jct 28 follow airport signs to junction of A65 at Horsforth.Turn left at roundabout onto A65 through Rawdon to Guisley centre. Ground a quarter of mile past traffic lights on the right. Entrance on A65 opposite Silver Cross factory.

Midweek Home Matchday: Tuesday
Clubhouse: Open before and after all games. Tel No: 01943 872872
Club Shop: Yes full range: Contact: Jennifer Rogerson 01943 879236
Local Press: Yorkshire Evening Post, Bradford Telegraph & Argus, Airedale & Wharfdale Observer and Wharfe Valley Times

CLUB PERSONNEL
Chairman: Philip Rogerson
Directors: S.Allan & R.Northfieldt:
Secretary: Bruce Speller, 71 Oxford Avenue, Guiseley, Leeds. LS20 9BY Tel. No: 01943 874534 e-mail: bruce.speller@virgin.net
Prog Ed: Rachel O'Connor
Programme
40 pages £1.50

2005-2006
Captain:
Player of theYear:
op Goalscorer:

CLUB STATISTICS

RECORD	
Attendance:	2,486 v Bridlington Town F.A.Vase S-F 1st Leg 89-90
Victory:	
Defeat:	
Career Goalscorer:	
Career Appearances:	
Transfer Fee Paid:	
Received:	
Senior Honours:	F.A.Vase Winners 1990-91 R-up 91-92 , F.A.Trophy S-F 1994-95
Previous Leagues:	West Riding Co.Amateur, West Yorks, Yorkshire 68-82 N.Co's East 82-91

Back Row(L to R) Mark Stuart,Danny Ellis,Sam Denton,Chris Clarke,Lee Connor,Roy Stamer,Matty Smithard, Simon Parke, Neil Parley(Mgr). Front.David Henry,Nathan Hay,Chris Coupe,Jez Illingworth,Steven Ball, Craig Smith,Matt Taylor. Photo: Bruce Speller.

GUISELEY

BEST LGE ATT.: 517 v Farsley Celtic
LOWEST: 93 v Whitby Town

No.	Date	Comp	H/A	Opponents	Att:	Result	Goalscorers	Pos
1	Aug 20	NP	A	Leek Town	248	W 2 - 0	**Henry** 26 Connor 75	3
2	23		H	Gateshead	231	W 1 - 0	**Henry** 5	4
3	27		H	Burscough	198	W 3 - 1	Connor 3 Stammer 33 **Henry** 50	2
4	29		A	Farsley Celtic	576	D 1 - 1	Clarke 77	1
5	Sept 2		A	Prescot Cables	210	W 2 - 0	Clarke 20 Connor 48	1
6	6		H	Blyth Spartans	282	L 0 - 2		4
7	10	FAC 1Q	H	Salford City	192	L 0 - 1		
8	13	NP	A	Lincoln United	117	L 0 - 1		5
9	17		H	Radcliffe Borough	252	W 3 - 2	Clarke 30 Stammer 60 Coupe 75	4
10	20		A	Ossett Town	191	L 0 - 1		5
11	24		A	Radcliffe Borough	228	D 0 - 0		6
12	27		H	North Ferriby United	223	L 0 - 2		6
13	Oct 1		A	Wakefield-Emley	216	W 3 1	**Henry** 23 79 **Cooke** 89	5
14	5		A	Gateshead	137	W 2 - 0	Stammer 58 79 (pen)	5
15	11		H	Bradford PA	473	L 0 - 3		6
16	15	FAT1Q	H	Chorley	182	W 3 - 1	**Parke** 4 **Illingworth** 8 **Cooke** 61	
17	22	NP	A	Ilkeston Town	323	W 1 - 0	Parke 1	
18	29		H	Runcorn FC Halton	295	D 1 - 1	Lee 27	5
19	Nov 5		A	Ashton United	227	D 2 - 2	Ellis 18 Hay 62	7
20	12	FAT 2R	H	Kendal Town	228	D 2 - 2	**Connor** 15 **Stuart** 19	
21	15	FAT 2Rr	A	Kendal Town	183	L 0 - 4		
22	26	NP	H	Leek Town	215	D 1 - 1	Parke 41	7
23	Dec 10		H	Frickley Athletic	274	H 2 - 0	Tracey 5 (og) **Stuart** 75	
24	17		H	Witton Albion	245	L 0 - 4		7
25	26		H	Farsley Celtic	517	L 0 - 3		8
26	Jan 2		A	Bradford PA	370	W 3 - 1	Marsden 45 Ball 69 Grayson 83	7
27	14		A	Marine	353	L 0 - 2		
28	21		H	AFC Telford	363	W 1 - 0	**Stuart** 15	7
29	28		A	Tlkeston Town	238	D 2 - 2	Jackson 32 Lee 46	8
30	Feb 4		A	RuncornFC Halton	154	D 0 - 0		9
31	7		H	Ashton United	151	L 1 - 3	**Stuart** 3	9
32	11		H	Wakefoeld -Emley	212	L 0 - 1		9
33	18		H	Witton Albion	213	W 3 - 1	**Stuart** 63 Forrest 69 Smithard 72	8
34	25		A	North Ferriby United	194	D 2 - 2	Jackson 2 Wood 49 (og)	8
35	28		H	Ossett Town	113	L 0 - 2		8
36	Mar 18		A	Burscough	240	L 2 - 3	Hay 89 Grayston 90	7
37	21		A	Frickley Athletic	230	L 1 - 2	Jackson 39 (pen)	12
38	25		H	Matlock Town	200	W 1 - 0	**Cooke** 32	8
39	April 8		A	AFC Telford U	1556	D 0 - 0		11
40	14		A	Whitby Town	355	L 0 - 1		11
41	15		H	Marine	225	W 1 - 0	Smithard 6	10
42	17		H	Prescot Cables	205	L 2 - 5	**Cooke** 70 90	10
43	19		H	Whitby Town	93	L 0 - 2		10
44	22		A	Matlock Town	204	L 0 - 1		14
45	27		A	Blyth Spartans	1024	L 1 - 4	Jackson 58	18
46	29		H	Lincoln United	145	L 1 - 2	Smithard 60	14

Ave. League Home Attendance: 244 **Goals** 50 67 **Top Goalscorer:** Cooke, Henry & Stuart (5)
Best Position: 1st **Worst:** 18th

HEDNESFORD TOWN

Founded: 1880
Nickname:THe Pitmen

Manager: Phil Starbuck
Assistant Manager: John Ramshaw
Club Colours: All White
Change Colours: All Red
Club Sponsor: Extra Personnel
Previous League: Conference North
BEST PERFORMANCES
League: Conference   **F.A. Cup:** 4th Rd 1996-97 v Middlesbrough (A) 2-3
F.A.Trophy.: Winners 2003-2004
Physio: Don Drakeley
Reserve League: Central Conference
Ground Address: Keys Park, Park Road, Hednesford, Cannock, Staffordshire.
Tel/Fax: 01543 422870/ 428180   **e-mail:** contact@hednesford town.fsnet.co.uk
Official website: www.hednesfordtown.com
CAPACITY: 6,039   **Seats:** 1,010   **Covered:** 5,334   **Floodlights: Yes**
SIMPLE DIRECTIONS:M6 Jct.11 to Cannock (or M6 toll jct T7). Follow signs for A460 (Rugeley). After crossing A5 at Churchbridge Island continue to follow A460 (Rugeley) over five islands and pick up signs for HTFC, Keys Park.
Midweek Home Matchday: Monday   **Clubcall:** 09066 555 880 (60p per min)
Clubhouse: Open matchdays evening (Julie Jones-Functions & Conferences)
Club Shop: Open throughout the week **Manager:** Dave Derry
Local Press: Express & Star, Sporting Star, Chase Post, Cannock Mercury, Evening Mail & Birmingham Post **Local Radio:** Radio WM

CLUB PERSONNEL
Chairman: Steve Price
Managing Director:
Terry Brumpton
Other Director Carole Price
Secretary:
Rod Hadley, 30 Godolphin, Riverside, Tamworth, StaffsB797UF
01827 66786 (H) 07971013714(M)
Press Officer:
 Neil Holden
Commercial Manager:
Terry Brumpton
Programme. Editor:
Terry Brumpton
2005-2006
Captain: Lee Barrow
Player of the Year:
Richard Teesdale
Top Goalscorer: Paul McMahon

CLUB STATISTICS

RECORD   **Attendance:** At Keys Park: 3,169 v York City F.A.Cup 3rd Rd 13.01 97
Victory: 12-1 v Redditch U. B'ham Comb. 52-53.
Defeat: 0-15 v Burton B'ham Comb. 52-53
Career Goalscorer: Joe O'Connor (post war) 230 in 430 games
Career Apps: Kevin Foster 463
Transfer Fee Paid: £12,000 to Macclesfield Town for Steve Burr
Transfer Fee Received: £50,000 from Blackpool for Kevin Russell
SENIOR HONOURS: F.A.Trophy 2004. Welsh Cup R-up 91-92. Southern Prem.94-95 Lg Cup R-Up 86-87. Southern Midland Div 1 R-up 91-92. Staffs Senior Cup (2). B'ham Senior Cup 35-36.
PREVIOUS Leagues: Walsall & Dist, B'ham Comb. 06-15,45-53. West Midlands 19-39, 53-72,74-84 Midland Counties 72-74. Southern 84-95 Conference 95-01. Southern 01-05 **Names:** None

STEP 1   STEP 2   **STEP 3**   STEP 4   STEP 5/6   STEP 7

CONFERENCE   CONFERENCE NORTH/SOUTH   **NORTHERN PREMIER LEAGUE PREM.**   NORTHERN PREMIER LEAGUE DIV 1.

HEDNESFORD TOWN

BEST LGE ATT.: 1,452 v Stafford Rangers
LOWEST: 362 v Hyde United

No.	Date	Comp	H/A	Opponents	Att:	Result	Goalscorers	Pos
1	Aug 13	NC	A	Barrow	1.031	L 1 - 3	Barrow 72	21
2	15		H	Alfreton Town	640	W 1 - 0	Bell 50	11
3	20		H	Hinckley United	620	L 3 - 4	Heath 11 **McMahon** 52 65	15
4	27		A	Gainsborough Trinity	362	D 1 - 1	Barrow 84 (pen)	15
5	29		H	Stalybridge Celtic	816	D 1 - 1	**McMahon** 83	16
6	Sept 3		A	Redditch United	381	W 2 - 1	Hunter 34 **McMahon** 57	13
7	10		H	Northwich Victoria	660	L 1 - 4	**McMahon** 73	15
8	17		A	Leigh RMI	301	D 0 - 0		13
9	24	FAC 2Q	H	**Moor Green**	491	W 2 - 0	**Anthrabus 61 Bell 72**	
10	Oct 1	CN	H	Stafford Rangers	1452	L 0 - 2		14
11	8	FAC 3Q	A	**Banbury United**	1005	W 4 - 3	**Hunter 18 58 Bell 32 46**	
12	15	CN	A	Workington	385	L 0 - 2		18
13	18		A	Moor Green	233	W 2 - 1	Williams 72 Coollins (og) 78	15
14	22	FAC4Q	H	**Vauxhall Motors**	628	W 3 - 0	**Heath 38 Bell 43 McMahon 90**	
15	29	CN	A	WorksopTown	446	D 3 - 3	Brannan 3 (5 78 85)	
16	Nov 5	FAC 1R	A	**Histon**	1080	**L 0 - 4**		
17	7	CN	H	Hucknall Town	434	D 1 - 1	Brindley 50	16
18	12		A	Worcester City	1278	L 2 - 6	Hunter 45 Heath 61	17
19	14		H	Kettering Town	992	D 2 - 2	Heath 1 Scheppel 21	16
20	19		H	Harrogate Town	521	L 0 - 4		16
21	Dec 3		A	Hyde United	334	L 2 - 4	Hunter 41 Heath 50	18
22	6	FAT 2R	H	**Moor Green**	254	D 1 - 1	**Bell 19**	
23	10	CN	H	Vauxhall Motors	397	L 0 - 1		18
24	13	FAT 2R r	A	**Moor Green**	192	W 4 - 2	**Brannen 53 77 Marshall 71 Dyer 90**	
25	17	FAT 1	A	**Solihull Borough**	306	L 1 - 2	**McMahon 77**	
26	26	CN	A	Nuneaton Borough	1254	L 2 - 3	Platt 76 (pen) **McMahon** 90	21
27	31		A	Droylsden	352	D 1 - 1	**McMahon** 85	20
28	Jan 2		H	Nuneaton Borough	1011	D 0 - 0		21
29	7		H	Barrow	472	L 0 - 3		21
30	14		A	Alfreton Town	336	L 2 - 3	Bell 63 McSweeney 81	22
31	21		A	Hinckley United	719	W 2 - 1	Hunter 13 Bell 69	22
32	23		H	Lancaster City	438	W 1 - 0	Dyer 63	21
33	28		H	Gainsborough Trinity	472	D 1 - 1	Teesdale 19	20
34	Feb 11		H	Workington	438	D 0 - 0		21
35	18		A	Kettering Town	1282	L 0 - 4		21
36	20		H	Moor Green	454	L 1 - 2	Wright 78	21
37	25		A	Northwich Victoria	855	L 0 - 8		22
38	Mar 7		A	Hucknall Town	281	D 2 - 2	McSweeney 2 Williams 79	22
39	11		A	Worsop Town	478	W 2 - 1	Hunter 46 Lamey 65	22
40	14		A	Stafford Rangers	1519	D 1 - 1	McSweeney 90	22
41	18		A	Lancaster City	259	L 0 - 1		22
42	25		H	Worcester City	510	L 0 - 4		22
43	April 3		H	Leigh RMI	492	L 1 - 3	Anthrobus 10	22
44	8		H	Hyde United	362	L 0 - 2		22
45	15		H	Redditch United	552	D 1 - 1	Teesdale 8	22
46	17		A	Stalybridge Celtic	511	L 0 - 3		22
47	19		H	Harrogate Town	435	W 3 - 2	Heard (og) 25 Hunter 40 Hadland 86	22
48	22		H	Droylsden	434	L 0 - 1		22
49	29		A	Vauxhall Motors	316	D 0 - 0		22

Ave. League Home Attendance: 673   **Goals** 57 99   **Top Goalscorer:** McMahon (9)
Best Position: 11th   **Worst:** 22nd

ILKESTON TOWN

Founded: 1945
Nickname: The Robins

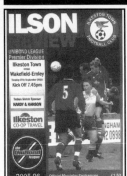

Manager: Nigel Jemson
Reserves' Manager: Andy Worrall
Club Colours: All Red
Change Colours: Yellow/Black/Black
Club Sponsor: Ilkeston Co-op Travel
Previous League: Southern League
Previous Ground: New Manor Ground, Awsworth Road , Ilkeston, Derbys.
Tel No: 07887 832125
Best Seasons: League: 12nd N.P.L. 2004-2005 **F.A.Cup:** 2nd Rd 1997-98 1999-00
F.A.Trophy: 3rd Rd 82-83 94-95   **F.A.Vase:** 4th Rd 88-89
Ground address: New Manor Ground, Awsworth Road, Ilkeston, Derbyshire.
Tel No: 0115 932 4094
Official Website: www.whiteballproject.co.uk
Capacity: 3,029   **Seats:** 550   **Covered:** 2,000   Floodlights: Yes
Simple Directions: M42 toM1 jct 23A continue on M1 to jct 26, exit left onto A610
towards Ripley, take first exit (to Awsworth) and Ilkeston (A6096) follow bypass
signed Ilkeston A6096. Turn right after half a mile (signed Cotmanhay). Ground 200
yards on left.

Asst Manager: Ernie Oliver
Physio: Mike Ainsley

Midweek Home Matchday: Tuesday
Clubhouse: Open Wed - Sun and Monday and Tuesday if there are matches.
Snacks on maych days with additional large snack bar
Club Shop: Wide range of souvenirs etc. Contact: Craig Lamont (0115 8774486)

CLUB PERSONNEL

Chairman: Paul Millership
Secretary: Keith Burnand,
2 Woodland Grove,Clowne,
Chesterfield S43 4AT
Tel No: 01246 811063 (H)
07887 832125 (M)
Commercial Executive: Sarah
Morgan
Programme Editor: Mic Capill
40 pages £1.50
Editors : Mic Capill,John Shiels &
Duncan Payne

2005-2006
Player of the Year: Ben Scott
Top Goalscorer: Mick Goddard 9

CLUB STATISTICS

Record	**Attendance**: 2,504 v Boston United F.A.Cup 1st Rd 97-98
Victory:	14-2 v Codnor M.W. 46-47
Defeat:	1-11 v Grantham Town 47-48 0-10 v VS Rugby 85-86
Goalscorer:	Jackie Ward 141 **Career Appearances:** Terry Swincoe 377
Record Transfer Fee	**Paid:** £ 7,500 to Southport for Justin O'Reilly 1998
Received:	£25,000 from Peterborough United for Francis Green
Senior Honours:	N.P.L. R-up 04-05 Southern Lg. Midland Division 94-95 R-up 97-98
	Derbyshire Senior Cup (9) and R-up 2003-04
Previous Leagues	Midland 1894-1902 25-58 61-71 Notts & Derby 1945-47 Central Alli: 47- 62
	Midland Co: 1961-71 73-82 Southern 1971-73 N.Co East 82-86 Cent Midls 86-90 W.Mid (Reg) 90-94 Southern League 1995-2004

Back row,left to right: Ritchie Butler, Gareth Holmes, Mark Smith, Ben Scott, Leon McSweeney, Chris Adam, Craig Swinscoe and Joel Hodgkinson. Middle Row: Mike Ainsley (Physio), Adam Muller, Adam Walker, Martin Murray, Paul Robinson, Glenn Kirkwood, Rick Brewer, Martin Carruthers, Alistair Asher, Andy Worrall (Reserve Manager). Front Row: Robert Gill, Nigel Jemson (Manager), Keith Burnand (Secretary), Craig Gaunt and Barry Miller.

ILKESTON TOWN

BEST LGE ATT.: 513 v AFC Telford United
LOWEST: **265** v Wakefield-Emley

No.	Date	Comp	H/A	Opponents	Att:	Result	Goalscorers	Pos
1	Aug 20	NP	A	Whitby Town	318	L 0 - 2		19
2	23		H	Leek Town	397	D 2 - 2	Jenkins 4 Swinscoe 4	18
3	27		H	Farsley Celtic	331	D 1 - 1	Townsend 30	18
4	29		A	Ossett Town	97	L 0 - 1		20
5	Sept 2		A	Wakefield -Emley	159	L 0 - 1		20
6	6		H	AFC Telford	513	W 2 - 0	Burns 15 Holmes 30	17
7	10	FAC1Q	H	**Coalville Town**	336	**W 1 - 0**	**Swinscoe 57**	
8	14	NP	A	North Ferriby United	188	L 1 - 2	Jenkins 72	19
9	17		H	Blyth Spartans	378	D 0 - 0		18
10	20		A	Witton Albion	225	L 1 - 3	Jenkins 68	21
11	24	FAC 2Q	A	**Solihull Borough**	237	**L 0 - 3**		
12	27	NP	H	Wakefield-Emley	265	W 2 - 0	**Goddard** 13 46	19
13	Oct 1		A	Ashton United	210	D 2 - 2	**Goddard** 18 (pen) 28	17
14	4		H	Prescot Cables	348	L 0 - 2		20
15	8		H	Radcliffe Borough	357	W 3 - 1	Jervis 4 Jenkins 47 Gaunt 81	15
16	15	FAT1Q	A	**Gresley Rovers**	320	**D 2 - 2**	**Burns 45 Clifford 52**	
17	18	FAT1Qr	H	**Gresley Rovers**	349	**L 2 - 3**	**Jenkins 52 Jemson 89**	
18	22	NP	H	Guiseley	323	L 0 - 1		18
19	25		A	AFC Telford United	1629	D 0 - 0		17
20	29		A	Frickley Athletic	310	L 0 - 1		19
21	Nov 5		H	Gateshead	368	W 3 - 1	Adam 35 56 Smith 73	17
22	12		A	Bradford PA	235	D 2 - 2	Townsend 4 40	17
23	19		H	North Ferriby United	373	D 1 - 1	Adam 47	
24	26		A	Burscough	231	L 1 - 2	Hodgkinson 52	17
25	Dec 3		A	Marine	490	L 2 - 4	Towmsend 10 Smith 49	18
26	10		A	Runcorn FC Halton	104	L 1 - 2	Hoyle 77	20
27	17		H	Bradford PA	332	W 2 - 0	**Goddard** 51 Jemson 60	17
28	26		A	Matlock Town	541	L 0 - 2		18
29	Jan 2		H	Lincoln United	442	L 1 - 2	Muller 66	21
30	14		A	Leek Town	317	W 3 - 0	Muller 14 (pen) **Goddard** 70 Clifford 84	19
31	21		H	Runcorn	378	W 2 - 0	Clifford 69 Carruthers 78	16
32	28		A	Guisleley	238	D 2 - 2	Kirkwood 31 89	16
33	Feb 4		H	Whitby Town	395	D 0 - 0		18
34	18		A	Farsley Celtic	221	D 1 - 1	Carruthers 83	18
35	25		H	Ossett Town	313	L 0 - 1		19
36	Mar 4		H	Ashton United	352	W 2 - 0	Carruthers 10 Gill 44	16
37	18		A	Prescot Cables	150	D 0 - 0		18
38	21		H	Matione	293	W 1 - 0	M.Smith 90	16
39	25		H	Burscough	412	W 2 - 1	Gaunt 44 Muklker 88	15
40	April 1		A	Radcliffe Borough	217	L 1 - 3	Muller 33	16
41	8		A	Blyth Spartans	592	D 1 - 1	Gill 71	15
42	14		A	Lincoln United	193	D 2 - 2	Hoyle 54 Muller 62	15
43	17		H	Matlock Town	470	L 0 - 1		15
44	20		A	Witton Albion	279	W 2 - 0	Giull 11 66	15
45	22		H	Frickley Athletic	393	L 0 - 2		15
46	29		A	Gateshead	194	W 2 - 1	Ludlam 66 (pen) Gaunt 71	16

Ave. League Home Attendance: 367　　**Goals** 53 58　　**Top Goalscorer:** Goddard (6)
Best Position: 15th　　**Worst:** 21st

KENDAL TOWN

Founded: 1920
Nickname: Town

Club Colours: Black & White stripes/White/White
Change Colours: All Yellow
Club Sponsor: Staintons Olympic Coaches
Previous League: Northern Counties East
Best Seasons: F.A. Cup: 2nd Round Replay 1963-1964
F.A.Trophy.: 2nd Round 1980-1981   **F.A.Vase:** 3rd Round 1989-1990
Manager: Tony Hesketh   **Assistant Manager:** Barry Stimpson
Physio: Christian Chow
Ground address: Parkside Road, Kendal, Cumbria
Club Website: www.kendaltownfc.co.uk
Capacity: 2,490   **Seats:**450   **Covered:** 1000   **Floodlights:** Yes
Simple Directions:
M6 junction 36, follow signs for Kendal (South), right at lights, left at roundabout to Kendal'Village -
Parkside Road on right opposite factory main offices - ground 400 yds. Mile & a half from
Oxenholme (BR) station - bus service to Kendal, Nos 41 or 41A

CLUB PERSONNEL
Chairman: David Willan
Secretary: Craig Campbell, 22
Hanesmead Drive, Kendall, Cumbria
LA 9 5HD
Tel Nos: 01539722593(H)
07980 660428 (M)
Press Officer: John Wharton

**Programme
Editor:** Peter Hartley
32 Pages £1.00

**2006-2007
Captain:** Stuart Cuff
Player of the Year: Ian Kilford
Top Goalscorer: Lee Ashcroft

Midweek Home Matchday: Tuesday **Club Shop: Contact:** Graham O'Callaghan
Clubhouse: Open matchdays. Pies and pasties available
Local Press: Westmorland Gazette & Lancaster Evening Post
Local Radio: Cumbria, the Bay & Lakeland.

CLUB STATISTICS

Record	**Attendance:** 5,184 v Grimsby Town F.A.Cup1st Round 1955	
	Career Goalscorer: Tom Brownlee	
	Career Appearances:	
Record Transfer Fee	**Paid:** Undisclosed to Bradford City for Tom Brownlee 1966	
	Received: £10,250 from Manchester City for Andy Milner 1995	
	Victory: 11-0 v Great Harwood 22.3.47.	
	Defeat: 0-10 v Stalybridge Celtic 1.9.84.	
Senior Honours:	Westmorland Senior Cup (12) Lancashire Senior Cup: 2002-2003	
Previous Leagues:	Westmorland; North Lancs; Lancs Combination 45-68; Northern Premier 68-83;	
	North West Counties 83-87	

Back row (L-R): Paul sparrow,Ricky mercer,Andy hill,Ben hinchcliffe,ian Milford,Kieran Malmsey.
Front: Ged Smith,Paul Rigby,Paul Osborne,lee ashcroft,Dave foster
Photographers: Westmorland Gazette.

Soccer Speaker

a new brand of sports speaker

Soccer Speaker helps clubs up and down the country raise much needed cash for various things including kits, new posts, mini buses, new changing rooms etc, over the past two years we have raised thousands of pounds for grass roots football. We don't just supply you with the speaker, we will also help you to organise your event, advertising, raffle prizes, ticket printing etc.

No job is too small, we organise things for small clubs, pie & a pint with 50 guests and a speaker right up to your bigger events with a 5 course meal, speaker, comedian & compare. Auction items are also available, all come with a photo of the piece being signed along with a double your money back certificate of authenticity.

Soccer Speaker are Neil Razor Ruddock's official agents for all his sportsman's dinners, Neil is one of the best speakers on the circuit, his stories from the jungle and his footballing career are hilarious, other names available include Ronnie Whelan, Mike Summerbee, John Aldridge, Ron Chopper Harris, Frank Bruno, Jeff Winter, Peter Osgood, John McGovern, Duncan McKenzie, Tommy Docherty, Henry Cooper and many more (see website for details)
See **www.soccerspeaker.com**

LEEK TOWN

Founded: 1946
Nickname: The Blues

Manager: Mark Cartwright
Physio: Ann Marie Jones
Club Colours: Blue/Blue/White
Change Colours: All Yellow
Club Sponsor: Kerrygold
Previous League: Conference
Best Seasons: Conference 19th 1998-99
F.A.Cup: 2nd Round Replay 90-91
F.A.Trophy.: Runners-up 89-90
Ground address: Harrison Park, Macclesfield, Leek, Cheshire ST13 8LD
Tel No: 01538 399278 Fax: 01538 399278
Official Website: www.leektown.co.uk
Capacity: 3,600   **Seats:** 625   **Covered:** 2,675   **Floodlights:**Yes
Simple Directions: Opposite Coutaulds Chemical works on A523 Macclesfield to Buxton road half a mile out of Leek heading towards Macclesfield.
Midweek Home Matchday: Tuesday
Clubhouse: Open matchdays Functions by request (01538 383734)
Club Shop: Yes. Contact: Mark Graham at club on 01538 398341

CLUB PERSONNEL
Chairman: Paul Burston
Directors: Alan Clarke, Andy Wain Dennis Bates, Ray Bettany & Stan Trafford (Co.Sec.)
Secretary: Brian Wain c/o Club
Press Officer: Mike Cope
Programme Editors:
Steve & Tracy Reynolds
Tel Nos: 01782 269040 (M))
Commercial Manager: Paul Ogden
Press Officer: Mike Cope

2005-2006
Top Scorer: Alan Nagington 21

CLUB STATISTICS	
Record	**Attendance:** 5,312 v Macclesfield Town F.A.Cup 1973-74
Victory:	Not Known
Defeat:	Not Known
Goalscorer:	Dave Sutton 144
Career Appearances:	Gary Pearce 447
Record Transfer Fee	**Paid:** £2,000 to Sutton Town for Simon Snow
Received:	£30,000 from Barnsley for Tony Bullock
Senior Honours:	F.A.Trophy R-up 89-90 NPL 96-97 R-up 93-94 Staffs Sen. Cup 95-96 R-up (3)
Previous Leagues	Staffs Co, Manchester 51-54 57-73, W.Mids (B'ham) 54-56, Cheshire Co 73-82, N.W.Co 82-87, NPL 87-94 95-97, Southern 94-95 and Conrference 97-99

Back Row - L to R - Kingsley Marshall, Danny Smith, Lee Barrow, Simon Eldershaw, Martin Kearney, David MacPherson, Paul Booth, Dan Booth, Sam Wood.
Front Row - L to R - Ken Ashford (Kitman), Adam Yates, Anthony Danylyk, Ashley Woolliscroft, Mark Cartwright (Manager), Mark Devlin, Alan Nagington, Robrt Hawthorne, Jordan Johnson, David Tickle.

LEEK TOWN

BEST LGE ATT.: 615 v AFC Telford United
LOWEST: **173** v Burscough

No.	Date	Comp	H/A	Opponents	Att:	Result	Goalscorers	Pos
1	Aug 20	NP	H	Guiseley	248	L 0 - 2		20
2	23		A	Ilkestoon Town	397	D 2 - 2	Brown 8 MacPhersoon 59	19
3	27		A	Frickley Athletic	197	L 1 - 2	MacPherson 19	19
4	29		H	AFC Telford	615	D 1 - 1	**Nagington** 42	20
5	Sept 3		A	Farsley Celtic	205	L 2 - 3	**Nagington** 57 MacPherson 74	19
6	6		H	Witton Albion	286	D 2 - 2	MacPherson 33 **Nagington** 59	20
7	10	FAC 1S	H	**Long Eaton United**	193	**W 7 - 0**	Nagington 16 30 Kinsey 3 (23 44 82) Brown 39 Eldershaw 68	
8	13	NP	A	Prescot Cables	132	W 2 - 0	**Nagington** 64 Clarke (og) 85	16
9	17	NP	H	Ossett Town	269	D 1 - 1	Eldershaw 10	
10	19		A	Ashton United		L 1 - 3	MacPherson 86	18
11	24	FAC 2Q	H	**Grantham Town**	347	**W 1 - 0**	**Nagington** 68	
12	27	NP	H	Radcliffe Borough	200	L 0 - 3		21
13	Oct 1		A	Blyth Spartans	486	L 1 - 2	Brown 32	22
14	4		H	Wakefield & Emley	243	D 0 - 0		22
15	8	FAC 3Q	H	**Thornaby**	211	**W 2 - 1**	**Whittaker 73 Nagington 82**	
16	11	NP	A	AFC Telford	1250	L 0 - 1		22
17	15	FAT1Q	A	**Burscough**	212	**D 3 - 3**	**Nagington** 5 Hadrell 27 Whittaker 49 (pen)	
18	18	FAT1Qr	H	**Burscough**	175	**L 1 - 3**	Blakeman 75 (og)	
19	22	FAC 4Q	A	**Burton Albion**	1467	**L 0 - 2**		
20	29	NP	A	Gateshead	153	L 0 - 2		22
21	Nov 5		H	Prescot Cables	256	D 1 - 1	**Nagington** 10	22
22	12		H	RuncoenFC Halton	247	L 2 - 3	Brown 5 **Nagington** 50	22
23	26		A	Guiseley	215	D 1 - 1	Whittaker 75	22
24	Dec 10		A	Bradford PA	278	D 0 - 0		22
25	27		A	Lincoln United	134	D 3 - 3	Wooliscroft 66 75 Eldershaw 80	22
26	Jan 2		H	Matlock Town	394	D 1 - 1	Varnes 18	22
27	14		H	Ilkeston Town	317	L 0 - 3		22
28	21		A	North Ferriby United	286	L 0 - 4		22
29	28		H	Marine	231	D 1 - 1	Hawthorne 69	22
30	31		A	Witton Albion	282	W 1 - 0	**Nagington** 40	22
31	Feb 4		A	Radcliffe Borugh	230	W 3 - 2	**Nagington** 45 MacPherson 63 Eldershaw 86	22
32	15		H	Blyth Spartans	235	L 0 - 3		22
33	18		H	Gateshead	253	D 0 - 0		22
34	21		H	Burscough	173	W 3 - 0	Donylyk 17 Wooliscroft 20 (pen) Booth 34	22
35	25		A	Wakefield-Emley	84	W 3 - 1	Dodgeson 7 88 McPherson 32	21
36	Mar 4		A	Marine	387	W 2 - 1	**Nagington** 47 89	20
37	7		A	Burscough	187	W 2 - 1	MacPherson 16 **Nagington** 29	19
38	18		H	Bradford PA	293	W 3 - 0	Yates 39 **Nagington** 48 Eldershaw 83	15
39	25		A	Frickley Athletic	323	L 0 - 2		17
40	April 4		A	Runcorn FC Halton		W 2 - 0	**Nagington** 34 Booth 60	17
41	8		H	Farsley Celtic	246	D 1 - 1	Tickle 28	17
42	15		A	Matlock Town	404	W 2 - 0	Byrne 5 **Nagington** 23	15
43	17		H	Lincoln United	206	W 1 - 0	McPherson 76	14
44	19		A	Ossett Town		W 1 - 0	**Nagington** 35	13
45	22		H	Ashton United	297	W 1 - 0	**Nagington** 30	12
46	24		H	WhitbyTown	209	W 3 - 0	Wooliscroft 35 McPherson 52 63	11
47	26		A	North Ferriby United	232	D 0 - 0		11
48	29		A	Whitby Town	315	L 0 - 1		12

Ave. League Home Attendance: 275   **Goals** 64   62   **Top Goalscorer:** Naggington (21)
Best Position: 11th   **Worst:** 22nd

293

LINCOLN UNITED

Founded: 1938
Nickname: United

Manager: John Wilkinson   **Coach:** Mick Hogg   **Physio :** Steve Churcher

Club Colours: All white

Change Colours: All light blue

Previous League: Central Midlands

Previous Name: Lincoln Amateurs until 1954.

Best Seasons: Lg: F.A. Cup: 1st Rd 91-92, 97-98 **F.A.Trophy.:** 3rd Rd

Ground address: Ashby Avenue, Hatsholme, Lincoln

Tel No: 01522 690674

Website: www.comeonyouwhites.co.uk

Capacity: 2,714   **Seats:** 400 **Covered:** 1,084   **Floodlights:**Yes

Simple Directions: From A46 onto Lincoln relief road (A446) right at second round-about for Birchwood (Skellingham Road). Then first right after 30mph sign into Ashby Avenue. Ground in 200 yards opposite old peoples' home.

Midweek Home Matchday: Tuesday

Clubhouse: Open daily   **Club Shop:** Manager : Graham Wallhead

Local Press: Lincolnshire Echo and Lincoln Standard

CLUB PERSONNEL
Chairman: Robin Taylor
President: Phil Morley
Directors: P.Doyle, T.Hill, G.Forbes, M.Bull C.Geeson & P Addinall
Secretary & Press Officer:
Tom Hill, 4 Westwood Derive, Swanpool, Lincoln LN6 0HJ
Tel No:07885 020797
or 01522 683630 (H)
Programme Editor :
Gary Lines (01522 873973)
2005-2006
Captain: Brendan McDaid
Player of the Year:
Stuart Reddington
Top Goalscorers: Matt Roche

CLUB STATISTICS

Record	**Attendance**: 2,000 v Crook Town F.A.Amateur Cup 1st Round 1968
	Victory: 12-0 v Pontefract Colls 95
	Defeat: 0-7 v Huddersfield Town F.A.Cup 1st Rd 16.11.91
	Career Goalscorer: Tony Simmons 215
	Career Appearances: Steve Carter 447
Record Transfer Fee	**Paid:** 1,000 to Hucknall Town for Paul Tomlinson Dec. 2000
	Received: 3,000 from Charlton Athletic for Dean Dye july 1991
Senior Honours:	N.Co.East Prem Champions 94-95 Div 1 92-93 Lincs Sen Cup R-up 97-8
Previous Leagues:	Lincs 45-38, 60-67, Lincoln 46-60, Yorks 67-82,N.Co East 82-86 92-95
	Central Midlands: 82-92
	Grounds: Skew Bridge (40s), Co-op Sports Ground to mid 60s) Hartsholme Cricket Club (to 82)

LINCOLN UNITED

BEST LGE ATT.: 266 v AFC Telford United
LOWEST: **83** v Marine

No.	Date	Comp	H/A	Opponents	Att:	Result	Goalscorers	Pos
1	Aug 20	NP	A	Gateshead	136	D 1 - 1	**Roche** 90	11
2	23		H	Ossett Town	135	D 0 - 0		13
3	27		H	Whitby Town	142	W 2 - 0	**Roche** 37 64	9
4	29		A	Bradford PA	213	D 1 - 1	Hone 12	9
5	Sept 3		H	Burscough	128	L 0 - 1		13
6	6		A	Matlock Town	265	W 3 - 0	Walters 17 **Wilkinson** 47 53	9
7	10	FAC 1Q	A	**Grantham Town**	413	**L 0 - 4**		
8	13	NP	H	Guiseley	117	W 1 - 0	Brown 67	6
9	17		A	Marine	440	L 1 - 5	Brooks 82	8
10	20		H	Matlock Town	140	L 0 - 1		11
11	24		A	Ashton United	172	L 0 - 3		12
12	Oct 1		H	Runcorn FC Halton	135	D 0 - 0		13
13	4		H	North Ferriby United	175	L 0 - 1		15
14	8		A	Frickley Athletic	357	D 2 - 2	**McDaid** 54 Miller 56	14
15	11		A	Wakefield -Emley	147	D 1 - 1	**Roche** 62	15
16	15	FAT1Q	H	**Colwyn Bay**	113	**W 2 - 1**	Miller 29 Wilkinson 51	
17	18	NP	H	Farsley Celtic	85	L 0 - 1		15
18	22		A	Witton Albion	206	L 0 - 3		16
19	25		A	Ossett Town	43	W 3 - 1	Brown 60 68 **McDaid** 74	16
20	29		H	Witton Albion	135	L 1 - 2	**Roche** 49	16
21	Nov 8		H	Bradford PA	115	W 3 - 2	**Wilkinson** 65 Walters 73 Wilkins 84	14
22	12	FAT 2Q	A	**Grantham**	308	**L 1 - 2**	Hawley 75 (pen)	
23	26		H	Wakefield-Emley	92	L 1 - 2	Bell 89	14
24	Dec 3		A	Blyth Spartans	314	W 1 - 0	**Wilkinson** 75	14
25	10		A	Radcliffe Borough	153	L 0 - 4		16
26	17		H	Ashton United	136	D 0 - 0		16
27	27		H	Leek Town	134	D 3 - 3	**Roche** 27 Hawley 40 (pen) Minett 64	15
28	Jan 2		A	Ilkeston Town	442	W 2 - 1	**McDaid** 73 **Roche** 78	14
29	14		A	Whitby Town	291	L 1 - 2	**Roche** 56	14
30	21		H	Blyth Soartans	135	L 0 - 1		15
31	28		A	Prescot Cables	133	W 3 - 1	**Wilkinson** 65 83 Cann 90	
32	Feb 4		H	Marine	83	D 1 - 1	Reddington 5	13
33	18		H	Burscough	218	D 1 - 1	Hawley 5 (pen)	13
34	25		H	Prescot Cabbles	101	L 0 - 2		15
35	Mar 4		A	AFC Telford	1556	L 0 - 2		17
36	11		H	AFC Telford	266	L 1 - 2	Reddington 44	17
37	18		H	Radcliffe Borough	102	D 1 - 1	Carshedi 43	19
38	21		A	North Ferriby United	230	D 0 - 0		18
39	April 1		A	Farsley Celtic	295	L 0 - 3		19
40	8		H	Frickley Athletic	167	L 3 - 7	Brooks 27 **McDaid** 32 Butler 40 (og)	19
41	10		A	Runcorn FC Halton		W 1 - 0	**McDaid** 82	19
42	14		H	Ilkeston Town	193	D 2 - 2	Carchedi 14 **McDaid** 45	18
43	17		A	Leek Town	306	L 0 - 1		18
44	22		H	Gateshead	115	D 2 - 2	Talbot 61 (og) **McDaid** 85	18
45	29		A	Guisley	145	W 2 - 1	**Wilkinson** 58 **McDaid** 84	19

Ave. League Home Attendance: 135   **Goals**   47 71   **Top Goalscorer:** Roche, McDaid & Wilkinson (8)
Best Position: 6th   **Worst:** 19th

MARINE

Manager: Alvin McDonald
Asst Manager/Coach: Dave Thompson
Club Colours: White/black/black
Change Colours: Yellow/green/green
Club Sponsor: Ascot Property Group Ltd.
Previous League: Cheshire County
Previous Name: Waterloo Melville
Previous Ground: Waterloo Park(1894-1903)
Best Seasons: League: NPL Champions 93-94 094-95
F.A.Cup: 3rd Round 92-93   **F.A.Amateur Cup:** Runners Up 31-32
F.A.Trophy.: Semi-Final 83-84 91-92
Ground address: Arriva Stadium, College Road, Crosby, Liverpool L23 3AS
Tel No: 0151 924 1743.4046
Club Website: www.marinefc.com
Capacity: 3,185   **Seats:** 400   **Covered:** 1,400   **Floodlights:**Yes)
Simple Directions: College Road is off the main A565 (Liverpool-Southport road) in Crosby. Ground is ten minutes walk from Crosby & Blundellsands (Mersey Rail). Bus: No 92
Midweek Home Matchday: Tuesday
Clubhouse: Open daily with concert hall (250 seats) and members lounge (100).
Club Shop: Full range of products. Contact: Joanne Cross (0151 929 3616)

CLUB PERSONNEL

Chairman: Paul Leary
President: Dave Wutherspoon
Directors: Chairman, Secretary, President,G.Kewley,M.Prescott, D.Rannard, B.Lawler, S.Rimmer,J Hall, DMcMillan, P Bassett and P Eustace.
Secretary: John Wildman, 4 Ashbourne Avenue, Blundell-sands, Liverpool. L23 8TX
Tel No: 0151 928 9722
Programme Editor: Dave Rannard
Tel No: 0151 4749848
Programme
40 page £1.50
2005-2006
Captain: James Connolly
PLayer of the Year: Andy Ralph
Top Goalscorer: Nicky Young

CLUB STATISTICS

Record Attendance:	4,000 v Nigeria Friendly 1949
Victory:	14-2 v Rossendale United (A) Cheshire Co. 25.02.78
Defeat:	2-11 v Shrewsbury Town F.A.Cup 1st Rd 1995
Goalscorer:	Paul Meachin 200
Career Appearances:	Peter Smith 952
Record Transfer Fee	**Paid:** £6,000 to Southport for Jon Penman Oct.1985
	Received: £20,000 from Crewe Alexandra for Richard Norris 1996
Senior Honours:	F.A.Amateur Cup R-up 31-32, NPL Champions 93-94 94-95 R-Up 85-86 91-92, Lancashire Trophy (3), Lancashire Junior Cup 78-79, Lancs Amateur Cup (5), Lancs Sen Cup (6), Liverpool Non-Lg Cup (3) and Liverpool Challenge Cup (3)
Previous Leagues	Liverpool Zingari, Liverpool Co.Comb, Lancs. Comb.35-39 46-69 Cheshire Co. 69-79

Marine 2005-06

MARINE

BEST LGE ATT.: 642 v Ossett Town
LOWEST: 218 v Ashton United

No.	Date	Comp	H/A	Opponents	Att:	Result	Goalscorers	Pos
1	Aug 20	NP	A	Wakefiekld -Emley	107	W 2 - 0	Parle 7 Byrne 88	4
2	23		H	Radcliffe Borough	261	W 3 - 0	McGuire 30 (og), Nesbitt 41 Brookfield 90	2
3	27		H	Gateshead	267	D 0 - 0		3
4	29		A	Runcorn FC Halton	203	D 0 - 0		4
5	Sept 3		A	Blyth Spartans	295	L 0 - 1		7
6	6		H	Prescott Cables	270	W 1 - 0	Townley 52	6
7	10	FAC 1Q	H	**Cheadlke Town**	191	**W 4 - 0**	**Young 44 70 Connelly 53 Rendell 72**	
8	13	NP	A	Radcliffe Borough	145	L 0 - 2		8
9 ·	17		H	Lincoln United	440	W 5 - 1	Byrne 45 Brookfield 54 Rey 86 89 Dawes 90	5
10	20		A	AFC Telford	1424	D 1 - 1	Byrne 6	7
11	24	FAC 2Q	H	**Cammell Laird**	358	**D 1 - 1**	**Mullin 42**	
12	28	FAC 2Qr	A	**Cammell laird**	205	**L 1 - 3**	**Rendell 80**	
13	Oct 1	NP	A	Ossett Town	112	W 2 - 0	Allison 64 (og) Rey 90	6
14	4		H	AFCTelford United	364	D 1 - 1	Rey 26 (pen)	6
15	8		H	Ashton United	218	D 2 - 2	**Young** 9 Brookfield 65	7
16	11		A	Prescott Cables	320	W 1 - 0	Rey 43	5
17	15	FAT1Q	A	**Radcliffe Borough**	173	**W 2 - 1**	**Nesbitt 9 Parle 85**	
18	18	NP	H	Runcorn FC Halton	273	W 2 - 0	Brookfield 25 Dawes 86	3
19	22		A	Frickley Athletic	299	D 0 - 0		3
20	29		A	North Ferriby United	279	W 2 - 0	Brookfield 26 **Young** 33	3
21	Nov 5		H	Frickley Athletic	354	W 1 - 0	Courtney 34	3
22	12	FAT 2R	H	**Matlock Town**	239	**W 2 - 1**	**Nesbitt 69 Connelly 85**	
23	26	FAT 3Q	H	**Blyth Spartans**	268	**L 0 - 1**		
24	Dec 3	NP	H	Ilkeston Town	490	W 4 - 2	Latham 58 Byrne 81 Parle 83 Kay 90	3
25	10		H	Whitby Town	232	D 1 - 1	Rey 66	2
26	17		H	Matlock Town	246	D 0 - 0		4
27	26		H	Burscough	452	W 2 - 1	Lathem 6 **Young** 59	3
28	Jan 2		A	Ashton United	223	W 2 - 1	Lynch19 Byrne 36 (pen)	2
29	14		H	Guiseley	353	W 2 - 0	Byrne 51 **Young** 58	2
30	21		H	Whitby Town	355	D 0 - 0		3
31	28		A	Leek Town	231	D 1 - 1	Farley 51	3
32	Feb 4		A	Lincoln United	83	D 1 - 1	Byrne 47	3
33	14		H	Farsley Celtic		W 1 - 0	Byrne 11	3
34	18		H	Wakefild-Emley	285	D 0 - 0		3
35	21		A	Witton Albion	196	W 2 - 0	**Young** 45 88	2
36	Mar 4		H	Leek Town	387	L 1 - 2	Byrne 24	3
37	16		A	Bradford P.A.	169	W 3 - 1	**Young** 26 Jensen 38 Benn (og) 52	
38	18		H	Blyth Spartans	403	L 0 - 1		2
39	21		A	Ilkeston Town	293	L 0 - 1		5
40	25		H	North Ferriby United	337	W 1 - 0	Jensen 8	5
41	April 4		A	Matlock Town	231	W 5 - 2	**Young** 5 53 Flood 24 47 Cumiskey 42	4
42	8		H	Bradford PA	303	W 3 - 1	Lynch 74 **Young** 80 Brookfield 90	3
43	14		H	Wittion Albion	394	L 0 - 1		4
44	15		A	Guiseley	225	L 0 - 1		4
45	17		A	Burscough	387	W 3 - 0	Cumiskey 13 41 Mulhaney90	4
46	22		A	Farsley Celtic	245	W 1 - 0	Cumiskey 73	3
47	26		A	Gateshead	102	W 1 - 0	Farley 56	3
48	29		H	Ossett Town	642	W 4 - 0	Cumiskey 25 Byrne 53 Lynch 85 90	3
49	May 1	Play Off SF	H	Farsley Celtic	477	L 0 - 1		

Ave. League Home Attendance: 355 **Goals** 71 33 **Top Goalscorer:** Young (12)
Best Position: 2nd **Worst:** 8th

MATLOCK TOWN

Founded: 1885
Nickname: The Gladiators

Joint Player-Managers: Phil Brown & Gareth Williams

Physio: Michael Cunningham

Club Colours: All Royal Blue with Red trim/Blue/Blue

Change Colours: Lime Green/Navy Blue/Lime Green

Club Sponsor: Matlock Spa @ R.L.Partnerships

Previous League: Midland Counties

Best Seasons: League: N.P.L. Runners Up 1983-84

F.A.Cup: 3rd Rd 1976-77

F.A.Trophy.: Winners 1974-75

Ground address: Causeway Lane, Matlock, Derbyshire.DE4 3AR

Tel No & Fax: 01629 5838866

Official Website: www.matlocktownfc.co.uk

Capacity: 5,500   **Seats:** 560   **Covered:** 1,200   **Floodlights:** Yes

Simple Directions: On A615, ground is 500 yds from town centre and Matlock (BR)

Midweek Home Matchday: Tuesday

Clubhouse: Gladiators Social Club on ground.

Club Shop: Yes. Contact: Sue Tomlinson (01629 583866)

CLUB PERSONNEL

Chairman: Darrell Holmes
President: Cliff Britland
V-Chairman: Tom Wright:
Chief Executive: Keith Brown
Barncroft, 1 Malvern Gardens,
Matlock, Derbys. DE4 3JH
Tel NO: 01629 584231 (H)
07831 311427 (M)
Press Officer & Prog Ed:
Mike Tomlinson
Tel No: 01629 583866
Commercial Manager:
Tom Wright
2005-06
Top Goalscorer:
Simon Barraclough
Player of the Year: James Lukic
Captain: James Lukic

CLUB STATISTICS

Record	**Attendance:** 5,123 v Burton Albion F.A.Trophy 1975
	Victory: 10-0 v Lancaster City (A) 1974
	Defeat: 0-8 v Chorley (A) 1971
	Goalscorer: Peter Scott
	Career Appearances: Mick Fenoughty
	Transfer Fee Paid: £2,000 for Kenny Clark 1996
	Received: £10,000 from York City for Ian Helliwell
Senior Honours:	F.A.Trophy Winners 1974-75 NPL R-up 83-84 Div1 R-up 03-04
	Derbys.Senior Cup (7) R-up (10) Anglo Italian Non-League Cup 1979
Previous Leagues	Mid.Co 1894-96, Matlock & Dist., Derbys.Sen , Central Alliance 24-25 47-61,
	Central Comb. 34-35, Chesterfield & Dist. 46-47 & Midland Counties 61-69

Back row, left to right: Phil Brown (joint manager), Steve Taylor, Charlie Cresswell (Goalkeeping Coach), Ben Rach, Damien Snelston, James Lukic (Captain), Andy Richmond, Jamie Ironside, Danny Bostock, RichardTaylor, Dave Mc Nicholas, Michael Cunningham (Physio) and Gareth Williams (joint manager). Front row: Kyle Johnson, Mark Stuart, Nick Baker, Ryan Davis, Simon Barraclough, Gary Webster, Steve Circuit, Kris Bowler and Ian Clarke.

Photo: Lindsay Colbourne, Matlock Mercury.

MATLOCK TOWN

BEST LGE ATT.: **559** v AFC Telford United
LOWEST: **185** v Prescot Cables

No.	Date	Comp	H/A	Opponents	Att:	Result	Goalscorers	Pos
1	Aug 20	NP	A	Radcliffe Borough	230	W 1 - 0	Lukic 67	7
2	23		H	Wakefield-Emley	295	L 0 - 1		8
3	27		H	Bradford PA	280	W 1 - 0	Clarke 78 (pen)	7
4	29		A	Ashton United	202	D 1 - 1	Clarke 66 (pen)	8
5	Sept 3		A	Whitby Town	264	L 1 - 2	Clarke 87	12
6	6		H	Lincoln United	265	L 0 - 3		14
7	10	FAC 1Q	H	**Pegasus Juniors**	160	W 4 - 0	**Warne 4 77 Cropper 53 Webster 89**	
8	13	NP	A	Ossett Town	103	D 4 - 4	Allison (og) 71 Clarke (pen) 84 **Cropper** 89,90	13
9	17		H	Farsley Celtic	228	D 0 - 0		13
10	20		A	Lincoln United	140	W 1 - 0	**Cropper** 16	12
11	24	FAC 2Q	H	**Corby Town**	333	W 2 - 0	**Cropper 52 Riley 56**	
12	27	NP	H	Runcorn FC Halton	234	W 2 - 1	Webster 19 **Cropper** 59	10
13	Oct 1		A	Prescot Cables	187	L 1 - 2	**Cropper** 42	11
14	4		H	Radcliffe Borough	294	D 1 - 1	Clarke 9 (pen)	
15	8	FAC 3Q	H	**Ossett Town**	332	L 3 - 6	**Webster 1 35 Cropper 27**	
16	11	NP	A	North Ferriby United	248	L 2 - 3	Riley 21 **Cropper** 45	12
17	15	FAT1Q	A	**Brigg Town**	214	W 1 - 0	**Warne 40**	
18	22	NP	H	Whitby Town	276	W 4 - 1	**Cropper** 10 Warne 13 Clarke 47 (pen) Barraclough 79	11
19	25		A	Wakefield-Emley	138	W 3 - 2	**Cropper** 23 Webster 25 Riley 60	10
20	29		A	Blyth Spartans	430	D 2 - 2	Webster 7 McNicholas 33	9
21	Nov 5		H	Witton Albion	315	L 0 - 4		10
22	12	FAT 2Q	A	**Marine**	239	L 1 - 2	**Cropper** 67	
23	26	NP	H	Ossett Town	186	W 1 - 0	Bowler 84	
24	Dec 3		A	AFC Telford United	1192	L 1 - 2	Riley 11	
25	10		H	Gateshead	215	L 1 - 2	Circuit 90	13
26	17		A	Marine	246	D 0 - 0		13
27	26		H	Ilkeston Town	541	W 2 - 0	Barraclough 29 (pen) Davie 40 ?	12
28	Jan 2		A	Leek Town	394	D 1 - 1	Taylor 79	11
29	14		H	Burscough	221	W 3 - 0	Taylor 17 **Cropper** 45 48 (pen)	9
30	21		A	Bradford PA	246	W 2 - 1	Taylor 20 Barraclough 41	8
31	28		H	North Ferriby United	402	D 1 - 1	**Cropper** 88	9
32	Feb 4		A	Gateshead	184	W 5 - 1	Barraclough 3 (3 40 76 pen) Warne 44 Lukic 63	8
33	18		H	Ashton United	273	D 0 - 0		9
34	21		A	Farsley Celtic	172	L 1 - 3	Barraclough 55 (pen)	9
35	25		A	Runcorn FC Halton	142	W 4 - 0	Clarke 13 89 Webster 62 Lukic 71	7
36	Mar 8		H	AFC Telford	559	D 1 - 1	Clarke 58 (pen)	8
37	25		A	Guiseley	200	L 0 - 1		9
38	April 1		A	Frickley Arthletic	324	L 0 - 1		11
39	4		H	Marine	231	L 2 - 5	Warne 29 Barraclough 36	11
40	8		A	Burscough	218	D 1 - 1	Taylor 48	12
41	15		H	Leek Town	404	L 0 - 2		13
42	17		A	Ilkeston Town	470	W 1 - 0	Lukic 90 (pen)	13
43	22		H	Guisley	204	W 1 - 0	Taylor 24	11
44	24		H	Frickley Athletic	265	L 1 - 2	Barraclough 27	12
45	25		A	Blyth Spartans	259	L 0 - 1		12
46	27		H	Prescot Cables	185	W 3 - 1	Clarke 3 (15 32 89)	11
47	29		A	Witton Albion	260	W 4 - 2	Barrowclough 37 54 Bowler 44 76	9

Ave. League Home Attendance: 292   **Goals** 71 63   **Top Goalscorer:** Cropper (15)
Best Position: 7th   **Worst:** 14th

MOSSLEY

Founded:1903
Nickname:
Lilywhites

Manager: Jason Beckford   **Coach:**   **Physio:**
Club Colours: White with black trim/Black/Black
Change Colours: Yellow/Blue/Blue
Club Sponsor:
Previous League: North.West Counties
Best Seasons: League: NPL ?   **F.A. Cup:** 2nd Round Replay 1949-1950
F.A.Trophy.: Finalists 1979-1980   **F.A.Vase:** 6th Round, 1996-1997 1999-2000
Ground address: Seel Park, Market Street, Mossley, Lancs.
Tel No: 01457 832369
Club Website:
Capacity: 4,500   **Seats:** 200   **Covered:**1,500   **Floodlights:** Yes
Simple Directions:
From north; M60 J.23, then A635 to Ashton-U-Lyne, A670 Mossley to town centre .Ground behind market place. From south: M6 Junc 19, A556, M56 to Junc3, A5103 to M'chester, then Mancunian Way (A57M) to A635. Follow Ashton signs 5m, the Mossley signs via A670 to town centre.
Rail: Mossley BR. Buses 153 from Manchester, 343 from Oldham, 350 from Ashton
Midweek Home Matchday: Tuesday
Clubhouse: Open evenings and matchdays.
Club Shop: Manager: Mike Chamley 01457 833736
Local Radio: BBC GMR (Key 103) 96.2 Revolution
Local Press: Oldham Evening Chronicle, Mossley & Saddleworth Reporter, Manchester Evening News, Tameside Advertiser and Pink Final.

CLUB PERSONNEL
Chairman: Sam Rigby
President: J.Wharmby
Secretary: David Buckley, 18 Chellow Drive, Mossley, Ashton under Lyme, Lancs. OL5 0NB
Tel No: 01457 835089

Programme Editor: John Cawthorne
28 Pages £1.00

CLUB STATISTICS

Record	**Attendance:** 7,000 v Stalybridge Celtic 1950
	Career Goalscorer:
	Career Appearances:
Record Transfer Fee	**Paid:** £2,300
	Received: 30025,000 from Everton for Eamonn O'Keefe.
Senior Honours:	FA Trophy Runners-up 1979-80; Northern Premier League 1978-79 79-80
	R-up (3), Challenge Cup 19 78-79;
Previous	**Leagues:** Ashton; South East Lancs; Lancs Comb. 18-19;
	Cheshire County 19-72; Northen Premier, N.West Counties..
	Names: Park Villa 03-04; Mossley Juniors 04-0

Back Row (L-R): Rhodri Giggs, Paul Challinor, Phil Denney, Karl Vernon, Jordan Goodeve, Lee Bracey, Danny Meadowcroft, Steve Shail and Chris Downey.. Front Row: Joe Shaw, Christian Cooke, Nicky Thompson, Maccot, Andy Thackeray and Adam Morning.

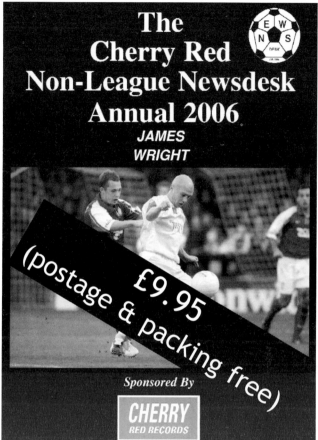

NORTH FERRIBY UNITED

Founded: 1934
Nickname: United

Manager: Brian France   **Assistant Manager:** Paul Olsson

Physios: Ben Neves & Paul Bradford

Club Colours: White shirts with green trim and green shorts.

Change Colours: Yellow shirts and black shorts

Club Sponsor: Dransfield Developments

Previous League: N.Co East

Best Seasons:

F.A.Cup: 3rd Qualifying Rd   **.F.A.Trophy.:** 4th Round 2001-02

F.A.Vase: Runners-Up 96-97

Ground address: Grange Lane, Church Rd., N.Ferriby, East Yorks.HU14 3AA

Tel No: 01482 634601   **Website:** www.northferribyunited.co.uk

Capacity: 3,000   **Seats:** 250   **Covered:** 1,000   **Floodlights:** Yes

Simple Directions: Main Leed-Hull road A630 M62. North Ferriby is 8 miles west of Hull. Go through N-F pass Duke of Cumberland Hotel, right down Church Road Ground half a mile on left.One mile from North Ferriby BR

Midweek Home Matchday: Tuesday

Clubhouse: Open every evening.

Club Shop: Yes Contact: Alan Beadle: (01482 634601)

CLUB PERSONNEL

Chairman: Les Hare
President: Brian Thacker
Directors: Les Hare,Steve Tather, Dave Simmons,David Searby, Albert Hoyle, Mike Bonwell and Steve Wells
Secretary: Stephen Tather, 39 Northfielld,North Ferriby, E.Yorks.HU13 0NY
Tel No: 01482 634444 (H)
Prog Editor: Dave Simmons
Tel No: 01482632502
Programme: 40 Pages £1.20
2005-2006
Captain: Chris Bolder
Player of the Year:
Andy Thompson
Top Goalscorer: Gary Bradshaw 18

CLUB STATISTICS

Record

Attendance: 1,927 v Hull City Charity Game 2005

Victory: 9-0 v Hatfield Main N.Co.East 1997-98

Defeat: 1-7 v North Shields N.C.E. 1991

Goalscorer: Andy Flounders 50 (season) 1998-99

Goalscoring in Career: Mark Tennison 161

Appearances: Paul Sharp 497 (1996-2006)

Transfer Fee Paid: Not Known

Received: £60,000 from Hull City for Dean Windass

Senior Honours: F.A.Vase Finalists 1996-97 N.Co.East Champions 99-00 R-up 97-98 E.Riding Senior Cup: (11) Unibond Div 1 Champions 2004-05

Previous Leagues   East Riding Church, East Riding Amateur, Yorks 69-82, N.Co.East

Back Row (L-R): Brian France (manager), Leon Wainman, Jamie Waltham, Antoni Pecora, Neil Allison, Paul Foot, Paul Olsson (Assistant Manager). **Front row:** Luke Moulds, Andy Thompson, Chris Bolder, Gary Bradshaw (and Mascot Harvey Bradshaw), Michael Price and Danny Moore.

NORTH FERRIBY UNITED

BEST LGE ATT.: 386 v Blyth Spartans
LOWEST: **118** v Runcorn FC Halton

No.	Date	Comp	H/A	Opponents	Att:	Result	Goalscorers	Pos
1	Aug 20	NP	A	Ashton United	120	W 4 - 2	Wainman 52 Hockness 58 Hartley 82 **Bradshaw** 90	2
2	23		H	Bradford PA	212	W 5 - 2	**Bradshaw** 3 (12 42 44) Wainman 19 Hockness 25	1
3	27		H	Runcorn FC Halton	118	W 3 - 1	**Bradshaw** 53 63 Hartley 78	1
4	29		A	Wakefield -Emley	144	L 0 - 1		2
5	Sept 3		A	Radcliffe Borough	160	W 2 - 1	**Bradshaw**7 89 (pen)	2
6	6		H	Ossett Town	231	W 2 - 1	**Bradshaw** 51 83	1
7	10	FAC 1Q	H	**Brigg Town**	213	W 3 - 1	Farley 46 Bradshaw 63 80	
8	14	NP	H	Ilkeston Town		W 2 - 1	**Bradshaw** 22 Waltham 56	1
9	17		A	Burscough	702	L 2 - 3	Hartley 65 Hockness 86	1
10	20		H	Frickley Athletic	251	L 1 - 2	Wainman 55	3
11	24	FAC 2Q	A	**Billingham Synthonia**	183	W 3 - 0	**Fothergill** 55 (pen) 76 Bradshaw 63	
12	27	NP	A	Guisley	223	W 2 - 0	Fothergill 50 Hartley 90	
13	Oct 1		H	Gateshead	262	W 1 - 0	Lightowler 14	
14	4		A	Lincoln United		W 1 - 0	Hocknes	
15	8	FAC 3Q	A	**Northwich Victoria**	684	L 0 - 1		
16	11	NP	H	Matlock Town	248	W 3 - 2	Bostick (og) 48 Wainman 67 Hartley 83	1
17	15	FAT 1Q	H	**Prescot Cables**	188	D 1 - 1	Hartley 13	
18	18	FAT1Qr	A	**Prescot Cables**	192	D 2 - 2*	Fothergill 7 (pen) Lightowler 88 P.Cables won 4-3 after pens	
19	22	NP	A	Runcorn FC Halton	116	W 4 - 2	Coupe 3 69 Hartley 7 Lightowler 60	1
20	25		H	Prescott Cables	216	W 3 - 0	Butcher 1 Flynn (og) 31 Cowen 71	1
21	29		H	Marine	279	L 0 - 2		1
22	Nov 5		A	Farsley Celtic	235	D 1 - 1	Hartley 37	1
23	12		H	Ashton United	226	W 1 - 0	Botham 67	1
24	19		A	Ilkeston Town	373	D 1 - 1	Fothergill 63	1
25	26		A	Witton Albion	257	D 2 - 2	Thompson 81 Wainman 88	1
26	Dec 3		H	Wakefield-Emley	153	D 3 - 3	Farley 51 Fothergill 75 Lightowler 77	
27	10		A	Ossett Town	81	W 3 - 2	Boulder 22 Lightowler 60 Thompson 70	1
28	17		H	AFC Telford	333	W 1 - 0	Dewhurst 33	1
29	26		H	Whitby Town	386	L 2 - 4	Boulder 69 Botham 78	1
30	Jan 2		H	Blyth Spartans	386	L 1 - 4	Botham 58	1
31	14		H	Radcliff Borough	169	W 2 - 1	Botham 43 Fothergill 48	1
32	21		H	Leek Town	286	W 4 - 0	Connor 24 Fothergill 64 73 (pen) Wainman 83	1
33	28		A	Matlock Town	402	D 1 - 1	Wainman 1	1
34	Feb 4		H	Farsley Celtic	252	L 0 - 1		1
35	18		A	Prescot Cables	145	W 2 - 0	Botham 25 Connor 67	1
36	25		H	Guiseley	194	D 2 - 2	Connor 30 Hotte 61	1
37	Mar 11		A	Gateshead	126	W 3 - 2	**Bradshaw** 20 83 Morley 26	1
38	21		H	Lincoln United	230	D 0 - 0		1
39	25		A	Marine	337	L 0 - 1		2
40	April 4		A	Blyth Spartans	659	L 2 - 4	Fothergill 15 **Bradshaw** 57	2
41	11		H	Burscough	201	L 0 - 1		5
42	14		A	Frickley Athletic	908	D 1 - 1	Allison 65	5
43	17		H	Whitby Town	255	D 0 - 0		5
44	19		A	Bradford PA	215	W 4 - 0	Morley40 Smith 44 Fothergill 65 Wainman 68	4
45	22		H	Witton Albion	171	W 5 - 1	Morley 16 Allison 27 Wainman 53 72 Wood 83	5
46	26		A	Leek Town	232	D 0 - 0		5
47	29		A	AFC Telford	323	L 1 - 2	Allison 45	5
48	May 1	Play Off SF	A	**Frickley Athletic**	593	D 0 - 0	Won 4-2 after penalties	
49	6	Play Off Final	A	**Farsley Celtic**	933	L 1 - 2	Bradshaw 79	

Ave. League Home Attendance: 234   **Goals** 87 59   **Top Goalscorer:** Bradshaw (18)
Best Position: 1st   **Worst:** 5th

OSSETT TOWN

Founded: 1936
Nickname: Town

Manager: Steve Richards **Asst Manager:** Steve Kittrick **Physio:** John Kent.

CLUB PERSONNEL
Chairman: Graham Firth
Vice-Chairman: Tim Astbury
President: Paul Jarvis
Vice-President: Ray Ward
Football Executive:
Phil Thompson
Football Secretary: Trevor Jowett
21 Thirlmere Avenue, Wyke,
Bradford, West Yorkshire BD12 9DS
01274 675303 (H)
07770 266115 (M)
Commercial Manager: Richard Kelly
Programme Editor:
Graham Rickett: (01924 456587 (H)
2005-2006
Captain: Andy Haywood
Player of the Year: James Walshaw
Top Goalscorer: James Walshaw 29

Club Colours: All Red with white trim

Change Colours: All Sky Blue

Club Sponsor: United Co-Operative

Previous League: Northern Counties East

Best Seasons:

F.A.Cup: 4th Qualifying Round 2005-06

F.A.Trophy.: 2nd Round 1999-2000 **F.A.Vase:** 5th Round 1988-1989

Ground address: Ingfield, Prospect Road, Ossett, Wakefield, WF5 8AN

Tel No: 01924 272960 **Website:** www.ossett-town.com

Capacity: 4,000 **Seats:** 360 **Covered:** 1,000 **Floodlights:** Yes

Simple Directions: M1 jct 40 B6129 to Ossett. Left into Dale Street, left again at lights opposite bus station on ring road. Ground is on left

Midweek Home Matchday: Tuesday

Clubhouse: Open every evening plus Friday lunchtimes and all day Saturdays

Club Shop: Yes Contact: 01924456587 (Mrs Helen Rickett)

CLUB STATISTICS

Record	**Attendance:** 2,600 v Manchester United friendly 1988
Victory:	10-1 v Harrogate RA (H) N.Co.E. 27.04.93
Defeat:	0-7 v Easington Colliery F.A.Vase 08.10..83
Goalscorer:	Dave Leadbetter
Career Appearances:	Steve Worsfold
Record Transfer Fee	**Paid:** Not Known
	Received: £1,350 from Swansea Town for Dereck Blackburn
Senior Honours:	West Riding County Cup 58-59 81-82 N.Co.East R-Up 98-99 (promotion)
Previous Leagues	Leeds 36-39, Yorkshire 45-82 and Northern Counties East 83-99

Back Row (L-R): John Hood, John Kent (Physio), Paul Stansfield, Andy Hayward (Assistant Manager), James Walshaw, Neil Bennett, Matt Daley (Captain), James Riorden, Phil Lindley, Daniel Davidson, Kirk Wheeler, Aiden Savory, Richard Marchant.
Front: Rob O'Brien, James Calcutt, Robert Tonks, James Coubrough, Steve Kittrick (Manager), Carl Fothergill, David Briggs, Paul Rickers, Wayne Benn, Mark Hancock.

OSSETT TOWN

BEST LGE ATT.: 440 v AFC Telford United
LOWEST: 43 v Lincoln United

No.	Date	Comp	H/A	Opponents	Att:	Result	Goalscorers	Pos
1	Aug 20	NP	H	AFC Telford	440	D 1 - 1	**Walshaw** 83	12
2	23		A	Lincoln United	135	D 0 - 0		14
3	27		A	Prescott Cables	156	L 1 - 2	Hayward 10	16
4	29		H	Ilkeston Town	97	W 1 - 0	**Walshaw** 55	12
5	Sept 3		H	Runcorn FC Halton	78	W 2 - 1	Pell 8 Williamson 65	8
6	6		A	North Ferriby United	231	L 1 - 2	Wheeler 66	11
7	10	FAC 1Q	A	**Stocksbridge P.S.**	104	W 3 - 1	**Gaughan 29 (og) Walshaw 70 75**	
8	13	NP	H	Matlock Town	103	D 4 - 4	**Walshaw** 7 81 Williamson 14 Briggs 65	11
9	17		A	LeekTown	269	D 1 - 1	Haywood 79	11
10	20		H	Guiseley	191	W 1 - 0	**Walshaw** 52	10
11	24	FAC 2Q	A	**Consett**	166	W 5 - 1	**Hayward 41 80 Allison 52 Walshaw 65 69**	
12	28	NP	A	Gateshead	118	L 1 - 2	Hayward 41 (pen)	11
13	Oct 1		H	Marine	112	L 0 - 2		12
14	5		A	Whitby Town	82	L 1 - 2	**Walshaw** 69	14
15	8	FAC 3Q	A	**Matlock Town**	332	W 6 - 3	**Walshaw 4 (24 57 77 90) Staton 71 Briggs 76**	
16	11		H	Frickley Athletic	280	L 2 - 4	Briggs 7 Collins (og) 55	18
17	15	FAT1Q	H	**Stocksbridge PS**	109	D 1 - 1	**Walshaw 44**	
18	18	FAT1Qr	A	**Stocksbridge PS**	103	D 2 - 2*	**Walshaw 7 Arthur 100 Won 4-1 after penalties**	
19	22	FAC4Q	H	**Leamington**	900	L 2 - 4	**Walshaw 12 90 (pen)**	
20	25	NP	H	Lincoln United	43	L 1 - 3	Rowan 47	19
21	29		A	Radcliffe Borough	160	W 1 - 0	**Walshaw** 57	18
22	Nov 12	FAT 2R	H	**Clitheroe**	108	D 2 - 2	**O.Brien 13 Hayward 84**	
23	15	FAT 2Rr	A	**Clitheroe**	188	D 1 - 1	**Hansen 82 Lost 4-5 after penalties**	
24	26	NP	A	Matlock Town	186	L 0 - 1		21
25	Dec 10		H	North Ferriny United	81	L 2 - 3	Price 28 Wheeler 80	21
26	17		A	Frickley Athletic	244	L 0 - 1		21
27	26		H	Bradford PA	256	W 3 - 2	Briggs 9 **Walshaw** 22 89	21
28	Jan 2		A	Wakefield-Emley	212	W 1 - 0	Hayward 12	20
29	7		A	Blyth Spartans	359	D 4 - 4	Hayward 37 **Walshaw** 82 89 Scothern 90	20
30	14		A	Farsley Celtic	151	L 0 - 3		21
31	21		H	Witton Albion	178	W 1 - 0	Staton 36	20
32	28		A	Ashton United	164	W 3 - 2	Haywood 45 52 **Walshaw** 50	17
33	Feb 4		A	AFC Telford United	1345	D 1 - 1	Hayward 3	17
34	18		H	Radcliffe Borough	122	W 2 - 0	Scothern 34 53	14
35	24		A	Ilkeston Town	313	W 1 - 0	O'Brien 5	13
36	28		A	Guiseley	113	W 2 - 0	Wheeler 5 Hayward 52	13
37	Mar 4		H	Prescot Cables	151	W 3 - 1	Hayward 24 82 (pen) Marchant 60	11
38	13		A	Ashton United		W 3 - 0	Walsh 48 Scothan 51 **Walshaw** 74	
39	18		A	Witton Albion	193	L 0 - 2		10
40	25		H	Farsley Celtic	175	L 0 - 1		12
41	28		A	Burscough	172	L 1 - 4	Hayward 34	12
42	April 4		H	Whitby Town	82	L 2 - 3	Hayward 37 **Walshaw** 47	12
43	8		A	Runcorn FC Halton	79	W 2 - 0	Hayward 34 Staton 61	10
44	11		H	Blyth Spartans	200	W 3 - 1	Briggs 80 **Walshaw** 88 Davidson 89	9
45	14		A	Bradford PA	244	L 0 - 2		9
46	17		H	Gateshead	114	W 3 - 1	Coughborough 15 Hayward 52 **Walshaw** 59	9
47	19		H	Leek Town	82	L 0 - 1		9
48	22		H	Wakefield - Emley	135	W 2 - 0	Watts 55 (og) Marchant 79	9
49	25		A	Burscough	54	D 0 - 0		8
50	29		A	Marine	642	L 0 - 4		11

Ave. League Home Attendance:	642	**Goals**	79 74	**Top Goalscorer:** Walshaw (28)

Best Position: 8th   **Worst:** 21st

PRESCOT CABLES

Founded: 1866
Nickname: Tigers

Manager: Andy Gray   **Assistant Manager:** Karl Connelly

Club Colours: Gold/black/black

Change Colours: All Blue

Club Sponsor: Belvoir Lettings

Previous League: North West Counties

Best Seasons: 5th Unibond Premier 2004-2005

F.A.Cup: 1st Round 1957-58 59-60

F.A.Trophy.: 3rd Qualifying Round 1981-82

F.A.Vase: 5th Round 1975-76 1977-78 2002-03

Ground address: Valerie Park, Eaton Street, Prescot. L34 6HD

Tel No:0151 430 0507

email: prescotcables@hotmail.com **Website:** www.prescotcablesfc.co.uk

Capacity: 3,000   **Seats:** 500   **Covered:** 600   **Floodlights:** Yes

Simple Directions: M62 Jct 7 A57 to Prescot. Take 3rd exit at roundabout after two and half miles. Turn right after another half mile. Right at Hope & Anchor pub, into Hope Street.

Midweek Home Matchday: Tuesday

Clubhouse: Open matchdays with refreshments.

Club Shop: Fully stocked.. Orders can be made from website above

CLUB PERSONNEL

Chairman: Anthony Zeverona
President: Georg.Hayward
Commercial Manager:
David Williams
Secretary: Dennis Bellairs, 13
P.O.Box 169, Prescot, Merseyside
L34 2WT. **Tel No**: 0151 292 5074
01512925074 (M)
Programme Editor: Paul Watkinson
(0151 426 4593)

2005-2006
Captain: Adam Flynn
Player of the Year: Mark Duffy
Top Goalscorer: Dean Thurston &
Jason Massie

CLUB STATISTICS

Record	**Attendance:**	8,122 v Ashton National 1932
	Victory:	18-3 v Great Harwood 1954-55
	Defeat:	1-12 v Morecambe 1936-37
	Goalscorer:	Freddie Crampton
	Career Appearances:	Harry Grisedale
	Transfer Fee Paid: N/A	**Received:** N/A
Senior Honours:	N.W.Co Champions 2002-03 Liverpool Non-League Cup (4)
	Liverpool Challenge Cup (6) Lane's Combination Champions 1956-57
	N.W.Co.Cup Winners 1947-48
Previous Leagues	Liverpool Co Comb., Lancs Comb.1897-98 18-20 27-33 36-37,
	Mid Cheshire 1977-78 Cheshire County 1978-82 N.W.Co.1982-2003

PRESCOT CABLES

BEST LGE ATT.: 335 v AFC Telford United
LOWEST: **132** v Burscough

No.	Date	Comp	H/A	Opponents	Att:	Result	Goalscorers	Pos
1	Aug 20	NP	A	Bradford PA	244	L 0 - 1		16
2	23		H	Ashton United	138	W 2 - 1	Garforth 32 O'Donnell 67	7
3	27		H	Ossett Town	156	W 2 - 1	**Massie** 48 O'Donnell 78	6
4	29		A	Radcliffe Borough	189	L 0 - 4		10
5	Sept 2		H	Guiseley	210	L 0 - 2		14
6	6		A	Marine	270	L 0 - 1		16
7	10	FAC 1Q	A	**Woodley Sports**	71	**W 4 - 2**	O'Donnell 26 Prescot 3 (38 71 86)	18
8	13	NP	H	Leek Town	132	L 0 - 2		18
9	17		A	Frickley Athletic	212	W 1 - 0	Flynn 19 (pen)	
10	20		A	Runcorn FC Halton	244	L 1 - 5	Tuck 79	14
11	24	FAC 2Q	A	**Blyth Spartans**	484	**L 0 - 1**		
12	27	NP	H	Witton Albion	186	D 1 - 1	Connelly 82	18
13	Oct 1		H	Matlock Town	187	W 2 - 1	**Massie** 64 Davis 86 (og)	
14	4		A	Ilkeston Town	348	W 2 - 0	McEwan 32 **Massie** 87	11
15	8		A	Gateshead	126	W 3 - 0	Feeny 34 Connoly 37 Molyneaux 58	
16	11		H	Marine	320	L 0 - 1		11
17	15	FAT 1Q	A	**North Ferriby United**	188	**D 1 - 1**	Feeney 89	
18	18	FAT1Qr	H	**North Ferriby United**	192	**D 2 - 2**	McKewan 1 Flynn 68 (pen)Won 4-3 after penalties	
19	22	NP	A	AFC Telford United	1564	L 2 - 3	Garforth 37 Duffy 51	13
20	25		A	North Ferriby United	216	L 0 - 3		13
21	29		H	Wakefield-Emley	165	W 2 - 0	Garforth 10 Connolly 48	12
22	Nov 5		A	Leek Town	256	D 1 - 1	Flynn 63	11
23	12	FAT 2R	H	**Farsley Celtic**	214	**L 1 - 2**	Duffy 46	
24	19	NP	A	Farsley Celtic	295	L 0 - 2		13
25	26		H	Whitby Town	165	W 5 - 1	THURSTON 3 (13 62 72) Garforth 40 Duffy 64	12
26	Dec 10		A	Ashton United	172	W 3 - 1	**Massie** 6 Thurston 62 Prescott 66	10
27	26		H	Runcorn FC Halton	227	D 0 - 0		13
28	Jan 2		A	Burscough	443	W 3 - 2	Rendell 26 30 Connolly 36	9
29	14		A	Witton Albion	296	D 0 - 0		10
30	21		H	Frickley Athletic	190	L 0 - 2		11
31	28		H	Lincoln United	133	L 1 - 3	McEwan 11	11
32	Feb 4		A	Wakefield -Emley	98	L 0 - 1		12
33	11		H	Gateshead	132	W 2 - 1	Thurston 65 **Massie** 73	12
34	18		H	North Ferriby United	145	L 0 - 4		12
35	22		H	Blyth Spartans	132	L 1 - 3	Thurston	12
36	25		A	Lincoln United	101	W 2 - 0	Thurston 75 (pen) Duffy 79	11
37	28		A	Radcliffe Borough	152	W 1 - 0	Thurston 27	10
38	Mar 4		A	Ossett Town	151	L 1 - 3	Milson 90	10
39	6		H	Bradford PA	167	D 2 - 2	Garforth 10 73	9
40	14		H	AFC Telford	335	D 0 - 0		9
41	18		H	Ilkeston Town	150	D 0 - 0		9
42	25		A	Blyth Sparatans	537	L 0 - 2		11
43	29		A	Whitby Town	271	W 1 - 0	Rendell 85	8
44	April 4		H	Burscough	304	L 0 - 1		10
45	17		H	Guiseley	205	W 5 - 2	**Massie** 3 (40 55 76) Connelly 50 Thurston 83 (pen)	8
46	27		A	Matlock Town	185	L 1 - 3	**Massie** 36	13
47	29		A	Farsley Celtic	182	D 1 - 1	**Massie** 11	13

Ave. League Home Attendance: 188   **Goals**   56   67   **Top Goalscorer:** Massie (10)
Best Position: 6th   **Worst:**   18th

RADCLIFFE BOROUGH

Founded: 1949
Nickname: Boro

Manager: Andy Johnson **Coach:** Ronnie Evans **Physio:** Roy Davies

Club Colours: Blue/Blue/White

Change Colours: Red& black stripes/Black/Red

Club Sponsor: West-Tec

Previous League: N.W.Co.

Best Seasons: League: N.P.L. Premier ?   **F.A. Cup:** 1st Round 00-01

F.A.Trophy.: 3rd Round 1995-96 **F.A.Vase:** 4th Round v Boston Town

Ground address: The 'Inn2Gether' Stadium,Stainton Park Pilkington Rd, Radcliffe, Lancs. M26 3PE **Tel No:** 0161 724 5937 (club) 0161 724 8346 (office)

Club Website: www.radcliffeborough.com

Capacity: 3,000   **Seats:** 350   **Covered:** 1,000   **Floodlights:** Yes

Simple Directions: M62 Jct 17 follow signs for Whitefield and Bury. Take A665 to Radcliffe, through town centre. Right into Unsworth Street (opposite Turf Hotel). Ground half a mile on left.

Midweek Home Matchday: Tuesday

Clubhouse: On ground-food available (0161 724 5937)

Club Shop: Yes. Contact David Greenhough

Local Radio: GMR, Piccadilly Tower and F.M. Bolton

Local Press: Radcliffe Times, Bolton Evening News & Manchester Evening News.

CLUB PERSONNEL

Chairman: Bernard Manning (Jnr))
President: Bernard Manning (Snr)
Secretary: Graham Fieldingc/o club
Directors: D.Murgatroyd,
M.Darlington, K.Glendon,
B.Hampson, G.Fielding (Co Sec)
Programme Editor :
Roy Swinbank (7946 543674)
Programme
28 pages 80p

2005-2006
Top Goalscorer: Foster 16

CLUB STATISTICS

Record	**Attendance:** 2,495 v York City F.A.Cup 1st Rd 2000-01
Career Goalscorer:	Ian Lunt
Career Appearances:	Chris Lilley
Record Transfer Fee	**Paid:** £5,000 to Buxton for Gary Walker 1991
	Received: £20,000 from Shrewsbury Town for Jody Banim 2003
Senior Honours:	N.P.L. Div One Champions 96-97 N.W.Co 84-85
	Manchester Premier Cup R-up 97-98
Previous Leagues:	S.E. Lancs, Manchester 53-63 Lancs Combination 63-71
	Cheshire Co.. 71-82 N.W.Co 82-87

Back Row (L-R): Kevin Glendon (Manager), Ronnie Evans (Asst. Manager), Simon Garden, Simon Kelly, Danny Hurst, Richard Landon, David Bean, Karl Marginson, Davy Luker, David Felgate, Roy Davies (physio).
Front Row: Tony Whealing, Steven Spencer, Richard Battersby, Jody Banim, Bernard Manning Jnr. (Chairman), Chris Denham, James Price, Jason Astley, Gary Simpson.

RADCLIFFE BOROUGH

BEST LGE ATT.: 366 v Bradford Park Avenue
LOWEST: **123** v Gateshead

No.	Date	Comp	H/A	Opponents	Att:	Result	Goalscorers	Pos
1	Aug 20	NP	H	Matlock Town	230	L 0 - 1		17
2	23		A	Marine	261	L 0 - 3		22
3	27		A	AFC Telford	1471	L 1 - 2	Sampson 35	22
4	29		H	Prescot Cables	189	W 4 - 0	Wilson 50 **Foster** 59 61 Sampson 70	16
5	Sept 3		H	North Ferriby United	160	L 1 - 2	Lomax 11	18
6	6		A	Burscough	215	L 0 - 3		21
7	10	FAC 1Q	A	**Canmmell Laird**	175	L 1 - 2	**Wilson 67**	
8	13	NP	H	Marine	145	W 2 - 0	Whealing 6 Sampson 30	17
9	17		A	Guiseley	252	L 2 - 3	Lomax 9 67	19
10	20		H	Burscough	188	L 0 - 2		22
11	24		H	Guiseley	228	D 0 - 0		20
12	27		A	Lekk Town	200	W 3 - 0	Whealing 18 **Foster** 52 Lomax 77	16
13	Oct 1		H	Whitby Town	209	L 0 - 1		18
14	4		A	Matlock Town	294	D 1 - 1	**Foster** 64	17
15	8		A	Ilkeston Town	258	L 1 - 3	O'Neill 62	18
16	11		H	Witton Albion	220	L 1 - 3	Lomax 45	20
17	15	FAT1Q	H	**Marine**	173	L 1 - 2	**Foster** 90	
18	29	NP	H	Ossett Town	160	L 0 - 1		21
19	Nov 5		A	Bradford PA	287	W 2 - 1	McGuire 31 Sampson 37	20
20	19		A	Wakefield-Emley	104	D 0 - 0		21
21	26		A	Frickley Athletic	246	W 2 - 1	**Foster** 59 63	17
22	Dec 3		H	Farsley Celtic	166	L 0 - 5		19
23	10		H	Lincoln United	153	W 4 - 0	**Foster** 68 Wilson 84 Forrest 89 Heald 90	17
24	11		A	Gateshead	130	D 0 - 0		18
25	26		H	Ashton United	213	L 1 - 2	**Foster** 20	19
26	Jan 2		A	Runcorn FC Halton	166	D 2 - 2	**Foster** 51 Duffy 88	19
27	14		A	North Ferriby United	169	L 1 - 2	Forrest 52	20
28	21		H	Wakefield-Emley	167	W 3 - 0	O'Neill 53 **Foster** 59 Kelly 74	19
29	28		A	Farsley Celtic	225	L 0 - 3		21
30	Feb 4		H	Leek Town	230	L 2 - 3	Smith 27 Wilson 88	21
31	18		A	Ossett Ttown	122	L 0 - 1		21
32	25		H	Frickley Athletic	239	L 0 - 3		22
33	28		A	Prescot Cabls	152	L 0 - 1		22
34	Mar 18		A	Lincoln United	102	D 1 - 1	Banim 52	22
35	21		H	Blyth Spartans	188	L 0 - 3		22
36	April 1		H	Ilkeston Town	217	W 3 - 1	Banim 29 64 O'Neill 45	21
37	4		H	Gateshead	123	W 4 - 0	Wilson 7 Banim 27 Forrest 30 Heald 86	20
38	8		A	Whitby Town	264	D 1 - 1	Kelly 14	21
39	14		H	Runcorn FC Halton	253	W 8 - 1	Banim 4 (22 37 57 78) **Foster** 13 (pen) 75 Forrest 52 Flanagan 83	21
40	15		A	Blyth Spartans	525	L 0 - 1		21
41	17		A	Ashton United	207	L 0 - 3		21
42	19		H	AFC Telford United	303	D 2 - 2	**Foster** 50 90	21
43	26		A	Witton Albion	184	W 1 - 0	O'Neill 61	19
44	29		H	Bradford PA	366	W 1 - 0	**Foster** 90	18

Ave. League Home Attendance: 207   **Goals**   56   67   **Top Goalscorer:** Foster (16)
Best Position: 16th   **Worst:**   22nd

WHITBY TOWN

Founded: 1926
Nickname: Seasiders

Manager: David Logan **Coach:** Graham Robinson **Physio:** Steve Collins

Club Colours: Royal Blue hoops with black,red & white shirts /royal blue/royal blue

Change Colours: All white

Club Sponsor: Crest Teamware

Previous League: Northern

Previous Name: Whitby United (pre 1950)

Best Seasons: League: **F.A. Cup:** 2nd Round 1983-84

F.A.Trophy.: Quarter Finals 83-4

F.A.Vase: Winners 1997-98

Ground address: Turnbull Ground, Upgang Lane, Whitby, NorthYorks.

Tel No: 01947 604847 **Fax:** 01947 603779

Website: www.whitby-town.com

Capacity: 2,680 **Seats:** 622 **Covered:** 1,372 **Floodlights:**Yes

Simple Directions: Take A174 road from town centre.

Midweek Home Matchday: Wednesday

Clubhouse: Open every evening and w/e lunchtimes

Club Shop: Yes. Contact Alan McCloy 01947 603781

Local Radio: Yorkshire Coast Radio

Local Press: Whitby Gazette & Northern Echo

CLUB PERSONNEL

Chairman: Graham Manser
President: Brooks Mileson
Secretary & Press Officer:
Mike Green,14 Linden Close,
Briggsworth, Whitby, N.Yorks YO21
!RA Tel 01947 811704
Programme Edito: Alison Booth
Tel No: 07968 188587 (M)
Programme
Pages 40 Price £1.50

2005-2006
Captain: Scott Nicholson
Player of the Year:
Danny Brunskill
Top Goalscorer: Danny Brunskill 16

CLUB STATISTICS

Record	**Attendance:** 4,000 v Scarborough North Riding Cup 18.04 65	
	Victory: 11-2 v Cargo Fleet Works 1950	
	Defeat: 3-13 v Willington 24.03.28	
	Career Goalscorer: Paul Pitman 382	
	Career Appearances: Paul Pitman 468	
Record Transfer Fee	**Paid:** £2,500 to Newcastle Blue Star for John Grady 1990	
	Received: £5,000 from Gateshead for Graham Robinson 1997	
Senior Honours:	F.A.Vase Winners 96-97 F.A.Amateur Cup Finalists: 64-65 NPL Div 1 97-98	
	Northern Lg 92-93 96-97 R-up (5) Rothmans National Cup 75-76 77-78	
	N.Riding Senior Cup (5)	
Previous Leagues:	Northern League 1926-97	

Back row,left to right: Denis Wheeler (Coach), Danny Farthing, Paul Atkinson, Chris Hudson, Scott Nicholson, David Campbell, Graham Robinson, Andrew Brown, Tom Burke and David Logan (Manager). Front row: Anthony Ormorod, Tom Raw, Craig Veart, Karl Richards, Nick Scaife, David McTiernan and David Wells.

WHITBY TOWN

BEST LGE ATT.: 386 v North Ferriby United
LOWEST: **82** v Ossett Town

No.	Date	Comp	H/A	Opponents	Att:	Result	Goalscorers	Pos
1	Aug 20	NP	H	Ilkeston Town	318	W 2 - 0	Nicholson 23 Ormorod 87	5
2	23		A	Frickley Athletic	220	L 0 - 3		9
3	27		A	Lincoln United	142	L 0 - 2		15
4	29		H	Blyth Spartans	306	L 0 - 4		18
5	Sept 3		H	Matlock Town	264	W 2 - 1	Raw 2 Brown 86	15
6	5		A	Bradford PA	236	D 0 - 0		15
7	10	FAC 1Q	H	**Newcastle Blue Star**	208	**W 2 - 1**	**Veart 45 Atkinson 50**	
8	17	NP	H	Witton Albion	271	L 0 - 2		17
9	20		A	Blyth Spartans	460	L 0 - 1		20
10	24	FAC 2Q	A	**Trafford**	164	**D 1 - 1**	**Raw 59**	
11	27	FAC 2Qr	H	**Trafford**	196	**W 6 - 0**	**Raw 3 Veart 50 Brown 3 (53 74 79) Wilford 86**	
12	Oct 1	NP	A	Radcliffe Borough	187	W 1 - 0	Brown 58	20
13	5		H	Ossett Town	82	W 2 - 1	Wilford 60 Veart 66 (pen)	16
14	8	FAC 3Q	A	**Alfreton Town**	231	**L 1 - 2**	**McTiernan 43**	
15	11	NP	A	Farsley Celtic	211	W 3 - 1	Raw 15 Brown 82 83	13
16	15	FAT1Q	H	**Eastwood Town**	228	**W 4 - 2**	**Wilford 4 (40 60 69 pen 70)**	
17	18	NP	A	Wakefield-Emley	256	W 4 - 2	Wilford 3 (11 14 64) Nicholson 17	11
18	22		A	Matlock Town	278	L 1 - 4	Veart 88 (pen)	12
19	29		H	Ashton United	296	W 2 - 1	Nicholson 79 Wilford 89	
20	Nov 5		H	AFC Telford	386	W 4 - 1	Wilford 21 Ormerod 28 Hudson 55 Nicholson 62	9
21	12	FAT 2R	A	**Blyth Spartans**	501	**L 0 - 2**		
22	16	NP	H	Farsley Celtic	206	D 1 - 1	Raw 49	9
23	19	NP	H	Burscough	265	L 1 - 2	Richards 71	10
24	26		A	Prescot Cables	165	L 1 - 5	Veart 44	
25	Dec 3		A	Witton Albion	243	D 0 - 0		11
26	10		H	Marine	232	D 1 - 1	Nicholson 17	12
27	26		H	North Ferriby United	386	W 4 - 2	Wilford 3 Brunskill 3 (45 82 89)	11
28	Jan 2		A	Gateshead	194	L 2 - 3	**Brunskill** 43 45	12
29	14		H	Lincoln United	291	W 2 - 1	Eccles 41 Farthing 55	11
30	21		A	Marine	355	D 0 - 0		10
31	28		H	Runcorn FC Halton	286	W 4 - 0	**Brunskill** 3 (5 31 48) Ormorod 78	10
32	Feb 4		A	Ilkeston Town	395	D 0 - 0		10
33	18		H	Bradford Pa	337	D 3 - 3	**Brunskill** 14 Ormorod 43 Veart 48	10
34	25		A	Ashton United	178	L 2 - 4	**Brunskill** 39 Nicholson 74	10
35	Mar 18		A	Wakefield -Emley	91	W 3 - 2	Wilford 44 Nicholson 52 **Brunskill** 70	12
36	22		H	Gateshead	262	W 2 - 0	Greening 2 **Brunskill** 13	9
37	25		A	AFC Telford	1835	L 1 - 3	**Brunskill** 81	10
38	29		H	Prscot Cables	271	L 0 - 1		11
39	April 1		A	Runcorn FC Halton	115	D 1 - 1	**Brunskill** 19	9
40	4		A	Ossett Town	82	W 3 - 2	Ormorod 3 35 Nicholson 16	8
41	8		H	Radcliffe Borough	264	D 1 - 1	**Brunskill** 90	8
42	14		A	Guiseley	355	W 1 - 0	Clarke (og) 6	8
43	17		A	North Ferriby United	255	D 0 - 0		8
44	19		A	Guiseley	93	W 2 - 0	Wilford 32 **Brunskill** 90	7
45	22		A	Burscough	195	L 1 - 2	Nicholson 62	8
46	24		A	Leek Town	209	L 0 - 3		8
47	26		H	Frickley Athletic	272	W 2 - 0	Ormorod 56 Yalcin 90	7
48	29		H	Leek Town	315	W 1 - 0	McTiernan 68	6

Ave. League Home Attendance: 282   **Goals**   74   68   **Top Goalscorer:** Brunskill (16)

Best Position: 5th   **Worst:**   20th

WITTON ALBION

Manager: Jim Vince   **Asst Manager:** Benny Phillips   **Physio:** T.B.A.
Club Colours: Red & white stripes/red/white
Change Colours: Yellow shirts, blue shorts.
Club Sponsor: Len Cooke Financial Consultants
Previous League: Conference
Best Seasons: League 10th (Conference) 1991-92
                        F.A.Cup: 2nd Round 1991-92
                        F.A.Trophy.: Runners Up 1991-92
Ground address: Btitannia Carpets Stadium, Wincham Park, Chapel Street,
Wincham, Northwich. Tel No: /Fax: 01606 43008
Website: wittonalbion.co.uk
Capacity: 4,500 **Seats:** 650 **Covered:** 2,300   **Floodlights:** Yes
Simple Directions: M6 jct 19 Take A556 towards Northwich. After 3 miles turn onto
A559 at beginning of dual carriageway . After 3/4 mile turn left opposite Black
Greyhound Inn. Ground 1/2 mile on left after crossing canal bridge.
Midweek Home Matchday: Tuesday
Clubhouse: Concert Room and Vice Presidents club open matchdays, Tuesdays,
Thursdays and Friday evenings. Contact: Dermot Curran
Club Shop: Yes Contact: Neil Wilson(07951 192195)

CLUB PERSONNEL

Chairman: Mike Worthington
President: David Leather
Directors: Graham Edgeley, Paul Worthington & Wayne Peach
Commercial Manager: Bennty Phillips
Secretary: Graham Edgeley, 61 Haris Road, Lostock, Gralam, Northwich, CW9 7PE
Tel No: 01606 41549 (H)
07834 813533 (M)
Football Secretary: Ohil Chadwick
Programme Editor: Mark Harris
2005-2006
Captain: Tom Spearitt
Player of the Year: Steve Connors
Top Goalscorer: Mike Molesey 16

CLUB STATISTICS

Record		
	Attendance:	3,940 V Kidderminster Harriers F.A.Trophy Semi-Final
		13.04.91at Wincham Road
	Victory:	13-0 v Middlewich (H)
	Defeat:	0-9 v Macclesfield Town (A) 18.09.65
	Goalscorer:	Frank Fidler 175 (1947-1950)
	Career Appearances:	Alf Ashley 556 (1946-1958)
Record Transfer Fee	**Paid:**	£12,500 to Hyde United for Jim McCluskie 1991
	Received:	£11,500 from Chester City for Peter Henderson
Senior Honours:		N.P.L. Champions 1990-91 Cheshire County Senior Cup (7)
		F.A.Trophy Runners-Up 91-92
Previous Leagues		Lancashire Comb., Cheshire Co.>79, N.P.L.79-91 & Conf 91-94

Back Row: (L-R) Anthony Marshall; Keiron Haughton; Tom Spearritt (Capt); Jon Worsnop; Gary Furnival; Brian Pritchard; Tony Barras.
Middle: Triston Hendricks-Hamilton; Alastair Brown; Mark Jones; Steve Connors; Michael Moseley; Darren Hockenhull; Alex Brown; Carl Frost.
Front Liam Brownhill; Shaun Whalley; Jim Vince (Manager); Mike Worthington (Chairman); Benny Phillips (Assistant Manager); Chris Gaghan;
Adam Foy. The Trophy is the Cheshire Senior Cup which Witton won last March against Stalybridge Celtic (2-0).

WITTON ALBION

BEST LGE ATT.: 617 v AFC Telford United
LOWEST: **184** v Radcliffe Borough

No.	Date	Comp	H/A	Opponents	Att:	Result	Goalscorers	Pos
1	Aug 20	NP	A	Farsley Athletic	191	W 3 - 0	**Moseley** 6 Jones 14 Maguire 61	1
2	23		H	Runcorn FC Halton	309	W 2 - 0	Byrne 21 Lathem 48	3
3	27		H	Wakefield-Emley	258	L 1 - 2	Lathem 90	5
4	29		A	Burscough	349	D 1 - 1	Barlow 45 (og)	7
5	Sept 3		H	Gateshead	214	D 2 - 2	**Moseley** 42 Byrne 64	6
6	6		A	Leek Town	286	D 2 - 2	Lee 74 (pen) Peers 90	8
7	10	FAC 1Q	A	**Kendal Town**	163	W 3 - 2	**Peers** 6 Jones 27 Moseley 60	
8	17	NP	H	Whitby Town	271	W 2 - 0	**Moseley** 28 Jones 46	
9	20		H	Ilkeston Town	225	W 3 - 1	Hoyle 7 (og) Peers 44 Jones 56	6
10	24	FAC 2Q	A	**Worksop Town**	348	W 1 - 0	**Jones** 75	
11	27	NP	A	Prescot Cables	186	D 1 - 1	King 89	7
12	Oct 1		H	Bradford PA	303	L 2 - 3	**Moseley** 32 Pritchard 60	8
13	4		H	Ashton United	246	L 0 - 1		9
14	8	FAC 3Q	A	**Harrogate Town**	402	L 0 - 2		
15	11	NP	A	Radcliffe Borough	220	W 3 - 1	Jones 18 80 **Moseley** 37	9
16	15	FAT1Q	H	**AFC Telford**	404	D 1 - 1	**Jones** 62	
17	22	NP	H	Lincoln United	206	W 3 - 0	Jones 60 90 (pen) **Moseley** 86 (pen)	9
18	29		A	Lincoln United	135	W 2 - 1	Spearritt 25 Gaghan 46	7
19	Nov 5		A	Matlock Town	315	W 4 - 0	Jones 23 42 **Moseley** 64 Gaghan 66	5
20	12		H	Frickley Athletic	301	W 1 - 0	Jones 52	4
21	19		A	Frickley Athletic	263	L 0 - 2		5
22	26		H	North Ferriby United	257	D 2 - 2	Connors 12 (pen) Lloyd 41	
23	Dec 3		H	Whitby Town	243	D 0 - 0		5
24	10		A	Wakefield -Emley	127	W 2 - 0	Peers 28 Jones 44	4
25	17		H	Guiseley	245	W 4 - 0	Spearitt 11 Pritchard 34 **Moseley** 83 Maynard 90	
26	26		H	AFC Telford	617	W 4 - 0	Connors 56 **Moseley** 77 King 88 Lloyd 90	2
27	Jan 2		A	AFC Telford	1782	D 2 - 2	**Moseley** 3 Lloyd 74	4
28	14		H	Prescot Cables	296	D 0 - 0		4
29	21		A	Ossett Town	178	L 0 - 1		4
30	28		A	Blyth Spartans	402	L 1 - 5	Spearitt 35	4
31	31		H	Leek Town	282	L 0 - 1		4
32	Feb 18		A	Guisley	213	L 1 - 3	Peers 67	6
33	21		H	Marine	196	L 0 - 2		6
34	25		A	Bradford PA	261	W 3 - 2	Whittaker 9 Thomspon 14 (og) **Moseley** 45	6
35	Mar 11		H	Burscough	237	L 2 - 3	Brownhill 3 (pen) 73 (pen)	6
36	18		H	Ossett Albion	193	W 2 - 0	Peers 18 **Moseley** 82	6
37	22		A	Runcorn FC Halton	145	W 4 - 0	**Moseley** 3 (13 20 90) Whalley 72	6
38	April 8		A	Ashton United	164	W 2 - 0	Whittaker 11 Whalley 55	6
39	14		A	Marine	394	W 1 - 0	Whittaker 12	6
40	17		H	Farsley Celtic	255	L 0 - 1		6
41	19		H	Blyth Sparatans	214	D 1 - 1	Brownhill (pen) 14	6
42	20		A	Ilkeston Town	279	L 0 - 2		7
43	22		A	North Ferriby United	171	L 1 - 5	Whalley 15	7
44	24		A	Gateshead	103	L 2 - 3	Whalley 6 Peers 39	7
45	26		H	Radcliffe Borough	184	L 0 - 1		8
46	29		H	Matlock Town	260	L 2 - 4	Ness 89 Peers 90	8

Ave. League Home Attendance: 264　　**Goals** 73 60　**Top Goalscorer:** Moseley (16)
Best Position: 1st　　**Worst:** 9th

FOOTBALL LEAGUE

STEP 1

FOOTBALL
CONFERENCE

STEP 2

| CONFERENCE NORTH | CONFERENCE SOUTH |

STEP 3

| SOUTHERN PREMIER | NORTHERN PREMIER | ISTHMIAN PREMIER |

STEP 4

| SOUTHERN DIVISION 1 SOUTH &WEST MIDLAND | NORTHERN PREMIER DIV.1 | ISTHMIAN DIVISION 1 NORTH   SOUTH |

STEP 5/6

Combined Counties	Hellenic	Northern League	Spartan South Midlands	Wessex
Eastern Counties	Kent	Northern Counties East	Sussex County	Western
Essex Senior	Midland Alliance	North West Counties	United Counties	

STEP 7

Anglian Combination	Dorset County	Kent County	Midland Combination	Peterborough & District	West Cheshire
Bedford & District	Dorset Premier	Leicestershire Senior	Midland League	Reading League	West Lancashire
Brighton & Hove	East Sussex	Liverpool County	North Berkshire	Somerset County	West Midlands (reg)
Cambridgeshire County	Essex & Suffolk Border	Manchester Football	Northampton Town Lge	South Western	West Sussex
Central Midlands	Essex Intermediate	Mid Cheshire League	Northamptonshire Comb.	Suffolk & Ipswich	Wiltshire League
Crawley & Disrict	Gloucesterhisre Co.	Mid Sussex	Northern Alliance	Teeside League	Worthing & District
Devon County	Herts Senior County	Middlesex County	Oxfordshire Senior	Wearside League	

NORTHERN PREMIER LEAGUE DIVISION ONE

DIVISION ONE		P	W	D	L	F	A	Pts
1.	Mossley	42	23	9	10	83	55	78
2.	Fleetwood Town	42	22	10	10	72	48	76
3.	Kendal Town*	42	22	10	10	81	58	76
4.	Woodley Sports	42	22	8	12	85	53	74
5.	Gresley Rovers	42	20	10	12	79	64	70
6.	Stocksbridge PS	42	17	16	9	66	43	67
7.	Eastwood Town	42	16	14	12	66	58	62
8.	Brigg Town	42	16	14	12	70	64	62
9.	Belper Town	42	17	8	17	53	56	59
10.	Shepshed Dynamo	42	15	13	14	57	56	58
11.	Bridlington Town	42	16	10	16	61	68	58
12.	Colwyn Bay	42	15	11	16	56	53	56
13.	Bamber Bridge	42	13	15	14	65	59	54
14.	Ossett Albion	42	15	9	18	54	64	54
15.	Rossendale United	42	12	17	13	58	61	53
16.	Clitheroe	42	15	8	19	54	73	53
17.	Kidsgrove Athletic	42	14	9	19	66	69	51
18.	Chorley	42	14	8	20	58	59	50
19.	Warrington Town	42	11	15	16	62	74	48
20.	Spalding United	42	10	15	17	49	70	45
21.	Goole (-1)	42	11	11	20	55	85	43
22.	Bishop Auckland	42	3	6	33	39	99	15

*Promoted via the play-offs.

DIVISION ONE	1	2	3	4	5	6	7	8	9	10	11	12	13	14	15	16	17	18	19	20	21	22
1 Bamber Bridge		0-1	7-2	1-1	3-4	3-1	2-2	2-1	3-1	2-1	1-0	1-1	0-5	2-4	1-2	0-0	0-1	2-1	4-0	1-1	2-1	1-1
2 Belper Town	1-0		2-1	2-3	1-1	3-1	2-0	2-1	2-1	1-4	2-0	2-1	3-4	0-0	4-0	1-4	0-1	0-1	2-2	0-1	1-1	1-0
3 Bishop Auck	1-1	1-3		2-1	0-3	1-4	1-2	0-1	0-1	1-3	0-2	1-2	2-2	2-1	1-2	1-2	1-1	0-4	0-2	1-4	2-3	0-3
4 Bridlington T	2-0	2-1	1-0		3-1	4-1	1-0	0-0	2-3	1-1	3-1	2-2	1-2	1-1	2-1	1-2	1-0	1-1	1-1	0-2		
5 Brigg Town	3-2	1-2	2-0	3-2		1-0	2-2	1-1	2-2	3-1	1-0	2-1	2-1	2-3	0-1	2-3	2-2	0-1	3-1	0-0	3-2	1-2
6 Chorley	0-1	1-0	2-1	2-2	1-2		1-2	1-1	0-1	1-1	0-1	2-2	1-1	1-2	3-0	2-3	1-2	1-1	1-1	3-0	1-4	
7 Clitheroe	1-0	0-2	4-1	2-0	2-2	0-1		1-0	0-3	1-0	1-0	3-3	0-3	2-2	3-2	4-2	2-0	1-1	2-1	0-1	2-3	3-2
8 Colwyn Bay	1-1	0-1	2-0	1-3	0-0	1-2	0-0		0-0	2-0	4-1	6-0	0-1	4-3	3-0	2-0	0-4	2-0	3-0	1-1	3-0	2-1
9 Eastwood Town	1-1	2-0	2-0	0-3	2-0	0-4	3-1	4-1		0-1	3-3	2-3	3-2	2-1	2-2	3-2	4-0	1-1	0-0	1-1	3-3	4-0
10 Fleetwood Town	0-0	3-2	2-3	5-1	2-1	4-0	2-1	3-2	0-1		1-1	1-2	0-2	1-1	2-2	2-2	2-1	2-1	1-1	1-0	2-0	
11 Goole	3-3	1-0	1-0	2-2	2-2	2-2	1-0	3-0	0-3	3-3		2-3	2-4	1-1	0-0	1-4	1-1	0-5	1-6	0-4	2-3	1-4
12 Gresley Rovers	3-1	3-1	3-1	2-1	3-2	2-1	3-1	3-2	2-0	0-2	4-0		0-1	0-0	3-1	3-1	1-1	0-0	3-0	1-1	2-3	2-5
13 Kendal Town	2-0	2-2	3-3	2-1	1-4	1-2	1-4	0-0	1-1	2-1	3-1	0-3		4-0	1-1	0-1	4-0	1-2	3-0	1-1	3-1	2-1
14 Kidsgrove Ath	0-2	1-0	3-0	3-2	1-4	1-0	5-0	6-0	0-0	0-3	3-3	0-1	0-2		2-3	1-3	2-1	2-3	3-0	0-3	3-3	2-1
15 Mossley	1-1	4-2	2-1	6-1	1-0	2-1	1-0	1-2	4-0	0-1	3-0	3-1	5-2	2-1		7-0	2-1	2-3	3-1	2-0	1-1	2-2
16 Ossett Albion	3-2	0-2	2-2	5-2	1-2	1-2	2-1	1-0	0-0	1-2	0-1	2-1	1-2	0-1	0-2		1-0	1-1	1-2	1-0	1-1	2-1
17 Rossendale Utd	1-1	2-2	3-0	5-0	1-1	0-1	2-1	2-1	1-0	0-1	2-2	1-4	3-2	1-1	0-0	0-1		2-4	3-3	0-0	2-2	2-3
18 Shepshed D.	0-5	0-1	0-0	0-0	1-1	1-0	5-0	0-0	0-2	4-0	0-4	1-2	0-3	2-1	2-1	1-1	2-2		0-0	0-1	2-1	1-2
19 Spalding United	1-1	0-0	2-1	2-0	1-1	1-2	1-2	2-3	0-0	0-4	0-2	4-3	3-0	2-1	0-4	1-1	0-0	2-2		2-2	2-2	1-0
20 Stocksbridge PS	1-1	4-1	4-2	1-0	3-0	1-3	4-0	1-1	3-1	1-2	1-2	2-1	0-1	2-0	2-3	1-0	2-3	3-1	0-0		2-1	0-0
21 Warrington T.	0-3	0-0	4-2	3-0	1-1	2-1	1-0	1-2	1-2	2-4	2-1	0-0	0-1	3-2	1-1	2-0	0-0	2-2	1-2	2-2		1-3
22 Woodley Sports	3-1	3-0	0-2	1-2	2-2	0-2	2-1	2-1	4-1	0-0	2-1	2-1	2-2	2-1	5-0	0-0	2-0	5-1	3-0	4-2	4-1	

ALSAGER TOWN

Founded: 1968
Nickname: The Bullets

CLUB PERSONNEL
Chairman: Peter Clegg
Vice-Chairman:
President:
Secretary: Pauline Mattews
43 Ellgreave Street,
Dalehall,Stoke on Trent ST6 4DJ
Tel No: 01782 834296
Programme
Editor:
Pages/Price

2005-2006
Captain: Wayne Brotherton
Top Scorerr: Richard Mitchell 29
Players of the Year: Dean Stokes
& Wayne Brotherton

Managers: Greg Clowes and Dorrian Garner
Club Colours: Black and White/ Black/Black
Change Colours: All White
Club Sponsor: Doveys Stationers
Previous League: North West Counties
Best Seasons: League: 3rd North West Co 2005-2006 **F.A.Trophy.:** N/A
F.A.Cup: Ist Qualifying Round 2004-2005 **F.A.Vase:**1st Qualifying Round 2003-004
Ground address: Town Ground, Wood Park, Woodland Court, Alsager, Staffordshire
ST7 2DP **Tel No:** 01270 882336
Club Website: www.alsagertown.co.uk
Capacity: 3,000 **Seats:** 250 **Covered:** 1,000 **Floodlights:** Yes
Simple Directions: From junction16 off M6 follow signs to Alsager (Little Chef and BurgerKing on left).Go over level crossing and turn right at T junction. Proceed to centre of Alsager and over traffic lights in centre (civic buildings on left). Take 2nd left into Shady Grove and first left into West Grove. Take opening on right to enter Town Ground. Match day parking in side streets.
Midweek Home Matchday: Tuesday
Clubhouse: Yes
Local Radio: Radio Stoke
Local Press: Stoke Centinal

CLUB STATISTICS

Record

Attendance: 450 v Crewe Alexandra (Friendly) 2004

Career Goalscorer: Gareth Rowe **Career Appearances:** Wayne Brotherton.

Transfer Fee Paid: N/A **Received:** N/A

Senior Honours Mid Cheshire Runners-Up 1985-1986, Springbank Vending League Runners-Up 1998-1999

Previous Names: Alsager F.C. (A merger of Alsager Institute and Alsager United) in 1965 Became Alsager Town in 2002-2001

Leagues: Crewe League 1968- 1971, Mid Cheshire 1971 - 1988 . A years rest . Junior Football for two years, Crewe Premier League, Mid Cheshire League Div 2 1991, Springbank Vending Lg. / North West Counties League1999-2006

Back Row (L-R): Chris Budrys, Andrew Parkinson, Ryan Dicker, Danny Smith, Phil McGing (keeper), John Sheldon, Steve Grocott, Karl Espley, Stuart Tulloch, Glynn Blackhurst.
Front: Karl Robinson, Paul Macari, Danny Brown, Greg Clowes (Manager), Dorian Garner (Assistant Manager), Lee Madin, Joe Gibiluru, Peter Heler.

BAMBER BRIDGE

Re-formed 1952
Nickname : Brig

Manager: Andy Whittaker   **Assistant Manager:** Phil Entwistle   **Physio:** Andy Jones

CLUB PERSONNNEL
Chairman: Nigel Webster
President: Dennis Allen
Directors: Nigel Webster, Dave Spencer, Dennis Allen, Gerry Lawson, Brian Gitty and Mike Boardman
Secretary: George Halliwell, Irongate, Brownedge Road,, Bamber Bridge, Preston PR5 6UX
Tel Nos: 01772 454762 (H)
07929 231945 (M)
Commercial Manager: Geoff Wright
Programme Editor: Dave Rowland
Tel No: 01772 312987
Pages: 36   Price: £1.00
2005-2006
Top Goalscorer: Alex Potter 15
2006-0-2007Captain: Steve Macauley

Colours: White/black/black
Change colours: All Red

Club Sponsor: Sheet Piling (UK) Ltd.

Previous League: North West Counties.
Best Seasons: League:N.P.L. Champions 1995-1996 **F.A.Cup:** 2nd Round 1999-2000

F.A.Trophy: 2nd Rd. 1994-95 96-97 98-99 1999-2000   **F.A.Vase:** Semi-Final 1991-1992
Ground: Irongate Ground, Brownedge Road, Bamber Bridge, Preston, Lancs. PR5 6UX
Tel.No: Club Office: 01772 909690 Social Club : 01772 909695 Fax: 01772 909691
Website: www.bamberbridgefc.co.uk
Capacity: 3,000 **Seats:** 554   **Cover:** 800   **Floodlights:** Yes
Directions:.M6 jct 29 then A6 (Bamber Bridge bypass) towards Walton-le-Vale to roundabout. A6 London Road to next roundabout, third exit marked Bamber Bridge (Brownedge Road) and first right. Ground 100 yards on left at end of road.

Midweek Home Matches: Tuesday
Clubhouse: .Open all day matchdays, every evening and Sunday lunchtime.Hot and cold snacks on sale in refreshments cabin on matchdays.Contact: Sandra Perry c/o 01772 909695

Club Shop: Contact: Joe Marchant Tel No: 01253 402533

CLUB STATISTICS
RECORDS: **Attendance:** 2,300 v Czech Rep[ublic, Pre Euro 96 Friendly
   Victory: 8-0 v Curzon Ashton N.W.Co. 94-95 **Defeat:** Unknown
   Transfer Fee Paid: £10,000 to Horwich RMI for Mark Edwards
   Fee Received: £15,000 from Wigan Athletic for Tony Black 1995
Senior Honours: NPL Premier Champions 95-96, Div 1 R-up 94-95, NPL Challenge Cup 95-96
   ATDC Lancs Trophy 94-95 N.W.Co R-up 92-9
PREVIOUS   **Leagues:** Preston & Disrict 52-90 and North West Counties 90-93
   Grounds: King George V Ground, Higher Wallton1952-86

Back Row: (L-R) P Entwistle (Assistant Manager), A Fleming, R Salmon, J Squires, D Stevenson, R Bain, G Bennett, N Spencer, D Mahoney, J King, N Reynolds.
Front: M Boardman (Physio), D Woodruff, S Brown, R Myres, M Fletcher, G Brickell, L Clitheroe, T Ince, J Sheppard, A Whittaker (Manager).

BELPER TOWN

Formed: 1883
Nickname: Nailers

Manager: Ernie Moss   **Assistant Manager:** Sean O'Neil
Colours: Yellow/black/black & yellow
Change colours: All white
Sponsor: The Dunmar Group
Best Seasons: League: 9th N.P.L. 2005-2006
F.A.Cup: 1st Rd Proper 1887-88 4th Qual. Rd 1957-58 00-01 ,01-02)
F.A.Trophy: 3rd Qualifying Round 1997-1998
F.A.Vase: Semi-Final 1994-1995
Ground Address: Christchurch Meadow, Bridge Street, Belper DE56 1BA (01773825549).
Tel No: 01773 825549
Directions: From M1 North, Jnct 28 onto A38 towards Derby, turn off at A 610 (Ripley/Nottingham), then fourth exit at roundabout towards Ambergate. At junction with A6 (Hurt Arms Hotel) left to Belper. Ground on right past traffic lights. 400 yards from Belper (BR)
Capacity: 2,560   **Seats:** 500   **Cover:**850   **Floodlights:** Yes
Website: www.belpertownfc.co.uk
Previous League: Northern Counties East
Midweek home matchday: Tuesday
Clubhouse: Open matchdays and for functions with bar and hot and cold food available.
Shop Manager: Paul Bennett (01773 å823946)
Local Press: Belper News, Derby Evening Telegraph, Belper Express
Local Radio: BBC Radio Derby:

CLUB PERSONNEL

Chairman: Phil Varney
Vice Presidents: Arthur Sims & Eric Allen
Director of Football: Andy Carter.
Additional Directors: Chris Balls, Rex Barker, Andrew Benfield, John Harrington, David & Neil Laughlin.
Secretary: David Laughlin.
Tel No: 01773 856556 or 07768 010604
Press Officer: Nigel Oldrini
Pages:36 Price £1.20
Programme Editor: Dave Laughlin
Tel No:01773 856556
36 Pages £1.50
2005-2006
Player of the Year: Danny Hudson
Top Goalscorer: Andy Rushbury
Captain: Danny Hudson

CIUB STATISTICS

RECORD	**Attendance:** 3,200 v Ilkeston Town, 1955
	Goalscorer: Mick Lakin 231
	Appearances: Gil Rhodes
	Fee Received: £2,000 for Craig Smith from Hinckley United
	Fee Paid: £2,000 to Ilkeston Town for Jamie Eaton. 2001
	Victory: 15-2 v Nottingham Forest 'A'1956
	Defeat: 0-12 v Goole Town 1965
Senior Honours	Northern Counties East Lge 84-85, Midland Counties Lg 79-80; Central Alliance Lge 58-59; Derbys Senior Cup 58-59 60-61 62-63 79-80
Previous	**Leagues:** Central Alliance 57-61; Midland Co's 61-82, Northern Counies East 1982-97
	Grounds: Acorn Ground prior to 1951

Back Row (L-R): Bob Elliott (Physio), Andy Freeman (Asst. Manager), Steve Kennedy, Jordan, Lambert, Anthony Tansley, Gary Ingham, Micky Allsop, Dominic Crookes, Tim Hogg, Gary Hayward (Manager). **Front Row:** Wayne Thornhill, Paul Hurrell, Matt Moran, Sean Gummer, Richie Butler, Lee Stratford, Paul Bennett (Kit Man), Neil Ashley.

BRADFORD (P.A.)

Founded: 1907 Reformed 1988
Nickname: Avenue

Manager: Gary Brook   **Asst Manager:** Brian Crowther   **Physio:** Ray Killick

Club Colours: All White

Change Colours: All Sky Blue

Club Sponsor: Bakes & Lord

Previous League: N.W. Counties

Best Seasons: 2nd Football League 2nd Division 1913-1914

F.A.Trophy.: 3rd Round 98-99

F.A.Cup: 6th Round. 1945-1946 and old 4th Round: 1912-13 1919-20

Ground address: Horsfall Stadium, Cemetery Rd, Bradford, West Yorks BD6 2NG

Tel No: 01274 604578

e-mail:Capacity: 5,000   **Seats:** 1,247   **Covered:** 2,000   **Floodlights:** Yes.

Simple Directions: M62 Jct 26 Along A6036 (Halifax).Then in approx one mile turn left into Cemetery Road (by Kings Head Pub). Ground is 150 yards on left.

Midweek Home Matchday: Wednesday

Clubhouse:.Yes

Club Shop: Yes. Contact: Dave Storey (c/o Ground or 01535 670441)

CLUB PERSONNEL

Chairman: Dr.John Dean
V-Chairman: Steve Wright
President: Charlie Atkinson
Director of Football: Alan Hirst
Commercial Director: Paul Grayson
Tel NoI 07720 419279
Secretary: Steven Burnett,21
Edward Turner Close, Low Moor,
Bradford BD12 0AS
Tel No: 01274 608344 (H)
07866 076220(M)
Programme.Editor: Ian Smith
email: ian.smith@bpafc.com
Programme
36pages £1.20

CLUB STATISTICS

Record	**Attendance**: 1,007 v Bradford City 97 (Centenary Challenge)
Victory:	11-0 v Derby Dale F.A.Cup 1908 **Defeat**: 0-7 v Barnsley 1911
Goalscorer:	Len Shackleton 171 1940-46 **Career Appearances**: Tommy Farr 542 1934-50
Record Transfer Fee	**Paid**: £24,500 to Derby County for Leon Leuty 1950
	Received: £34,000 from Derby County for Kevin Hector1966
Senior Honours:	Div 2 R-up 1914 3rd Div N Champions 1928 West Riding Senior Cup(9)
	West Riding Co.Cupo (2) N.W.Co Champs 94-95 NPI Div 1 Champions 00-01
Previous Leagues	Southern 07-08 Football League 08-70 NPL 70-74 W.Riding Co Am. 88-89
	Central Midlands 89--90 N.W.Co 90-95
Grounds:	Park Avenue 07-73 Valley Parade: 73-74 Manningham Mills 88-89
	Bramley RLFC McLaren Field 85-93 Batley 93-96

Back row (L-R): J Illingworth, A Shuttleworth, M Hoyle, A Jeffrey, P Allen, G Shaw, N Ross,N Kamara,P Mumbley.
Front: C Smith, T Greaves, L Connor(Captain), P Sharpe(Manager),C Freeman Asst Manager), R Chattoe,
N Redfearn, L Tuck, L Flynn, D Wilson(Kit Man).

BRIDLINGTON TOWN

Formed: 1894
Nickname: Seasiders

Manager: Peter Smurthwaite **Asst. Managers**:Wayne Lewis & Shaum Baker
Coach: Gavin Kelly **Physio**: Ken Knight

Club Colours: All red
Change Colours: All White

Previous League: Northern Conties East
Best Seasons: **League**: 20th N.P.L. 2005-2206
F.A.Trophy ?
F.A.Cup: 4th Qualifying Rd 2002-2003 **F.A.Vase** Winners 2992-2993
Ground address: Queensgate Stadium, Queensgate,
Bridlington, YO16 7LN   **Tel. No**: 01262 606879
Club Website: www.bridtownafc.freeserve.co.uk
Capacity: 3,000   **Seats:** 533   **Covered:** 500   **Floodlights**: Yes
Simple Directions: From South: on A165 pass golf course and go over
lights, turn right at B &Q roundabout then left at next lights and over railway
bridge. At roundabout,, bare left and then straight on up Quay Road. After
lights turn right into Queensgate and ground is 800 yards on right.
Midweek Home Matchday: Tuesday
Clubhouse: Open every evening and all day weekends
Club Shop: Matchdays

Local Radio: **Local Press:**

CLUB OFFICIALS

Chairman: Pete Smurthwaite

President: Barrie Garton

Club Secretary & Press Office:
Gavin Branton, 4 Constable Way,
Flamborough,East Yorks. YO15 1LZ
Tel No: 01262 851387 (H) 078708 65438 (M)
e-mail: gavinbranton@yahoo.co.uk
Programme Editor: Justin Choat

2005-2006
Captain: Shaun Baker
Player of the Year: Carl Giblin
Top Goalscorer: Ben Eastwood

CLUB STATISTICS

Record	**Attendance** : 432 for an F.A.Sunday Cup semi-final 03.03.2000
	Victory: 15-1 v Rudstoon (A) Driffield Lg Cup 94-95
	Career Goalscorer: Neil Rimson
	Career Appearances: Neil Grimson 200+ (87-97)
Senior Honours:	E.Riding Senior Cup (13)
	N.Co.East Premier Champions 02-03
Previous	**Names:** Bridlington Town disbanded after 93-94 season then in
	September 1994 a new club played as Grays Inn and the new
	Bridlington Town was formed when Greyhound FC took over the
club,	changing its nameback to a new version of Bridlington
Town and	played at the Queensgate Stadium.
	Leagues: Yorkshire League, Driffield & District, East Riding County
	Northern Counties East. :

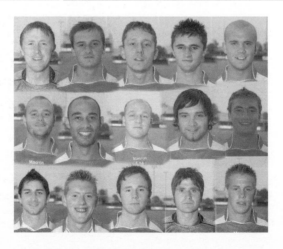

320

BRIGG TOWN

Formed: 1864
Nickname: Zebras

CLUB PERSONNEL

Chairman: Mike Harness 01724 869893 (H)
President: Gordon Ringrose
Secretary: John Martin, Kingfisher Lodge,The Old Stackyard,Wrawby, Brigg, N.Lincs DN208RH
Tel Nos:01652 654526 (H) 07812 108195 (M)
Programme: 28 pages
Editors:simon & Tim Harris
Tel No:01482 492049/01482 574357

2005-2006
Pllayer of the Year:Lee Cochrane
Top Goalscorer: Several on 8
Captain: Steve Housham

Manager: Dave McLean
Colours: Black & white stripes/black/red
Change colours: Sky Blue/Maroon
Club Sponsor:Paul Wiseman Electrical
Previous League: Northern Counties East
Best Seasons: **League**: 8th N.P.L. Div 1 2004-05 2005-06 **F.A.Cup**:1st Round 2000-2001
F.A.Vase: Winners 1995-1996 2002-2003 **F.A.Trophy**: ?
Ground: The Hawthorns, Hawthorn Avenue, Brigg (01652 652767) Office: 01652 651605
Capacity: 2,500 **Seats**: 370 **Cover**: 2 Stands **Floodlights**: Yes
Directions: From M180 Junc 4 Scunthorpe East, A18 through Brigg leaving on Wrawby Rd, left into recreation ground and follow road into BTFC.
Website: www.briggtownfc.co.uk
Clubhouse: Licensed club open matchdays **Shop**: Contact: Kiron Brown (01652 656189)
Midweek Matchday: Wednesday
Local Radio: Radio Humberside
Local Press: Scunthorpe Evening Telegraph

CLUB STATISTICS

RECORD
Attendance: 2,000 v Boston U. 1953 (at Brocklesby Ox)
Goalscorer::
Appearances:
Victory:
Defeat:

HONOURS
F.A. Challenge Vase 95-96 02-03; NCE (Premier) 00-01,Northern Co's East Lg Presidents Cup R-up 91-92 92-93, R-up 95-96; Lincs Lg Champions (8) ,
Lg Cup (5);Midland Counties League Champions 1977-78
Lincs `A' Snr Cup (4) Lincs `B' Snr Cup (5),

PREVIOUS
Leagues: Lindsey; Lincs 48-76; Midland Counties 76-82
Grounds: Old Manor House Convent, Station Rd (pre1939); Brocklesby Ox 1939-59

Back Row L-R: John Eyre, Jason Maxwell, Lee Warren, Damien Steer, Dan Hope, Lee Cochrane, Alex Allen, Craig Stones.
Front Row L-R: Tommy Spall, Nathan Ireland, Helen Redgrift (Physio) Simon Roach, Dave McLean (Manager), Steve Housham (Capt.) Dave Andrews (Asst. Mgr.) Karl Slack, Paul Grimes.

BUXTON

Founded: 1912
Nickname: Broddy

CLUB PERSONNEL
Chairman: Tony Tomlinson
Secretary: David Belfield, 20 Hereford Rord, Buxton,Derbyshire SK17 9BG
Tel No:0129826033

Programme
Editor: Mike Barton
36 Pages £1.00
2005-2006
Captain:
Players of the Year:
Mark Reed (supporters) and Scott Healy (Players)
Top Goalscorer: Mark Reed 42

Manager: Nicky Law   **Assistant Manager:** Chris Marples: **Physio:** Paul Smith
Club Colours: Royal Blue and White/blue/blue
Change Colours: Amber & Black
Club Sponsor: Paintmaster
Previous League: Northern Premier League
Best Seasons: League: 4th Northern Premier League 1980-1981
F.A.Trophy.: Quarter Final 70-71 71-72   **F.A.Vase:** 3rd Round Replay 2003-2004
F.A. Cup: 3rd Round 1951-52
Ground address: The Silverlands, Buxton, Derbyshire. SK17 6QH
Tel.No: 01298 23197
Club Website: www.buxtonfc.co.uk
Capacity: 4,000   **Seats:** 490   **Covered:** 2,500   **Floodlights:** Yes
Simple Directions: 200 yeads off Buxton market place opposite County Police HQ
Midweek Home Matchday: Wednesday
Clubhouse: Open match Days and Friday evenings   **Club Shop:**
Manager:Chris Brindley
Local Radio: High Peak radio
Local Press: Buxton Advertiser

CLUB STATISTICS

Record Attendance: 6,000 v Barrow F.A.Cup 1st Round 1951-1952
Career Goalscorer:: Dave Herbert 104 in 263 games
Career Appearances: David Bainbridge 635
Record Transfer Fee **Paid:** £5,000 to Hyde United for Gary Walker
         Received: £3,000 from Rotherham United for Ally Pickering
Senior Honours: Derbyshire Senior Cup (9) Northern Premier League Cup R-Up 1990-1991
         Presidents Cup 1980-1981, Manchester League 1931-32 Cheshire League   1971-72 R-Up 62-
63 Northern Counties East Champions 2005-06   N.Co.Presidents Cup 2005-06
Previous Leagues: Combination 1891-99 Manchester League 1899 Northern Premier League

David Reeves scores Buxton's first goal against Shirebrook. Photo: Bill Wheatcroft.

322

CAMMELL LAIRD

Founded: 1907
Nickname: Lairds

CAMMELL LAIRD FOOTBALL CLUB
Official matchday magazine of Cammell Laird FC 2006 - 07

TODAY'S GAME
LAIRDS v TRANMERE ROVERS
Pre-season Friendly
Tuesday, 11th July, 2006
Kick off 7.00 p.m.

£1.50

MATCH SPONSOR: Messenage Restaurant

Manager: Ian Doran   **Coach**: Paul Conboy & Ian Kerr
Physio: Ged Peacock
Club Colours: All Blue
Change Colours: Yellow/Green/Yellow
Club Sponsor: Cralsberg
Previous League: North West Counties
Best Seasons: League: Champions N.W.Co. 2005-2006   **F.A. Trophy:** N/A
F.A.Cup: 3rd Qualifying Round 2004-05 2005-06   **F.A.Vase:** Semi-Final 2205-2006
Ground address: Kirklands, St Peter's Road, Rock Ferry, Birkenhead, Merseyside
CH42 1PY 0789 1962 150.   FAX: 0151 644 7354
Club Website: www.camelllairdfc.co.uk
Capacity: 2,000   **Seats**: 150   **Covered**: Yes   **Floodlights**: Yes
Simple Directions: From M6 take M56 towards Chester and then M53 towards Birkenhead.
Exit jct 5 towards Birkenhead on A4. After aprox.4 miles take B 5136 signposted New Ferry.
After a mile turn right into Procter Road. Club is at bottom of the road on the left.
Midweek Home Matchday: Tuesday
Clubhouse: Yes **Tel Nos**: 0151 645 3121/5991   **Club Shop:**
Yes (matchdays and online) Manager: Julie Doran (07891 962150)
Local Radio: Radio Merseyside
Local Press: Wirral Globe

CLUB PERSONNEL

Chairman: John Lynch
President: Roy Williams
Secretary: Paul Mcloughlan,c/o 3 Shenley Close, Bebington, Wirral CH63 7QU
Tel Nos& e-mail: 07852 141169 (M) & 0151 644 8588
glocko1@cammelllairdfc.co.uk
Programme
Editor: Mark McKean
E-Mail: mark.mckean@ntlworld,com
32Pages £1.00
2005-2006
Captain: Derek Ward
Player of the Year: Jamie McGuire
Top Goalscorer: Ronnie Morgam
Jamie McGuire 42

CLUB STATISTICS

Record	**Attendance:** 1,700 v Harwich & Parkeston 5th Round F.A.Vase 1990-91
	Career Goalscorer:
	Career Appearances:
Record Transfer Fee	**Paid:** N/A
	Received: N/A
Senior Honours:	N.W.Counties Champions 2005-2006 Div 2 League Cup & Trophy Treble
	2004-2005 West Cheshire Champions (19)Cheshire Amateur Cup (11) and
	Wirral Senior CUp
Previous Leagues:	West Cheshire, North West Counties

Lairds celebrate with the North West Counties League Championship trophy

CHORLEY

Manager: Shaun Teale

Colours: White & black stripes/black/black
Change colours: All red

Sponsors: KC Couriers (North West) Ltd.
Previous League: GMV Conference

Best Seasons: League: 18th Conference 1988-1989
F.A.Cup: 2nd Round 1986-1987,19901991
F.A.Trophy: Semi-Final; 1995-1996

Ground address: Victory Park, Duke Street, Chorley, Lancs PR7 3DU   Tel: 01257 263406
Directions: From jct 6 of M61 to Chorley turm left into Pilling Lane after Yarrow BridgeHotel. First right into Ashley Street.Ground is second left.
Official Website: www.chorleyfc.com
Capacity: 4,100   Cover: 2,800   Seats: 900
Clubhouse: 01257 275662. Open matchdays and other evenings by arrangement
Club Shop: Yes
Midweek matchday: Tuesday.
Local Press: Lancs Evening Post, Chorley Guardian, Chorley Citizen & LancashireTelegraph
Local Radio: BBC Radio Lancashire

CLUB PERSONNEL

Chairman: Ken Wright

Commercial Manager: T.B.A.

Secretary / Press Officer:
Mick Wearmouth
6 Avondale Rd, Chorley, Lancs. PR7 2ED
Tel: 01257 271395(H) 07889 119588 (M)

Editor: John Newman(07939 877204)
Pages: 40 Price: £1.50

2005-2005
Captain: Ian Leather.
Player of the Year: Phil Priestley
Top Goalscorer: Peter Wright 22

CLUB STATISTICS	
CLUB RECORDS	**Attendance:** 9,679 v Darwen, F.A.Cup 1931-32.
	Goalscorer: Peter Watson. 371 (1958-1966)
	Fee Paid: £16,000 to Marine for Brian Ross 1995.
	Fee Received: £30,000 from Newxastle U for David Eatock 1996
HONOURS	Northern Premier Lg 87-88, Cheshire Co. Lg 75-76 76-77 81-82,
	Lancs F.A.Trophy Winners (14) R-Up(16) Lancs Comb. (11) R-up 6.,
	League Cup (3), Lancs Lg 1896-97 98-99
	, Lancs Alliance 1892-93 (R-Up 94-95), Lanc s Junior (14)
PREVIOUS	**Leagues:**Lancs Alliance 1890-94; Lancs18 94-1903; Lancs Comb1903-68
	69-70; Northern Premier 68-69, 70-72, 82-88; Cheshire County 70-82;
	GMV Conference 88-90.
	Grounds: Dole Lane 1883-1901; Rangletts Park 01-05;
	St George's Park 05-20

Back row (L-R): Steven Fisher (goalkeeping coach), Danny Self, James Mullineux, Daryl Allen, Phil Priestley, Ian Callaghan, Adam Roscoe, Joe Gibbons, Martin Clark, Chris Thompson. **Front:** Franny Barry, John Bluck, Michael Bromham, Peter Wright, Shaun Teale (player-manager), Ray Stafford (assistant-manager), Graham Tench, Jamie Vermiglio.

CLITHEROE

Formed: 1877
Nickname:The Blues

Colours: Al Royal ll Blue
Change colours: All yellow
Website: www.clitheroefc.co.uk
GROUND   Shawbridge, off Pendle Road,Clitheroe Lancashire BB7 1DZ
    Tel No: & Fax: 01200 423 344
Directions   M6 jct 31. A59 to Clitheroe (17 miles) at fifth roundabout turn left after half a
    mile at Pendle Road. Ground is one mile behind Bridge Inn on the right.
Capacity: 2,400   **Seats**: 250   **Cover** 1,400   **Floodlights** Yes
Clubhouse: Open on match days, Snacks available. Club Tel No: 01200 423344

Midweek matchday: Tuesday
Reserves' Lge: N.W.C.L

Pages: Price:
Editor: Tim Lees (01204 520406)

Official Website: ww.clitheroefc.co.uk

Tuesday 4th October 2005
Clitheroe FC v Woodley Sports
UniBond League Division One
MATCH SPONSORS - RUFUS CARR LTD
Match Ball Sponsor - Keith Wilkinson

www.clitheroefc.co.uk

CLUB PERSONNEL

President: Mr J E R Aspinall
Chairman: CarlGarner
Vice Chairman: Mark Gidlow

Secretary: Colin Wilson, 4 Moss Street,
Clitheroe, Lancs BB7 1DP
Tel/Fax: 01200 424 370
Mobile: 0771 438 2232

Commercial Manager: Mark Gidlow

FOOTBALL MANAGEMENT TEAM
Manager: Mike Smitheringale
Physio: Colin Edwards
Captain: James McIlvogue

CLUB STATISTICS

CLUB RECORDS   **Attendance:** 2,050 v Mangotsfield .F.A.Vase Seimi-Final 95-96.
    Goalscorer: Don Francis   **Appearances:** Lindsey Wallace

BEST SEASON   **FA Vase:** Runners-Up 1995-96
    F.A Cup:

SENIOR HONOURS   F.A.Vase Runners-Up 1995-96 Lancs Challenge Tropphy 84-85
    N.W.Co. Lge 84-85 East Lancs Floodlit Trophy 94-95

PREVIOUS   Leagues: Blackburn& District , Lancs Combination 03-04 05-10 25-82
    Grounds:

Back Row (L-R): Ian Cairney, Tom Hardwick, Mike Wolstenholme, Peter Collinge, Paul Stansfield, Tony Evans, Chris Nestor.
Front: Ben Johnson, Craig Sargeson, Ryan Parr, Gary Jackson, Neil Reynolds, Russel Clark, Sean White.

COLWYN BAY

Manager: **Assistant Man:**   **Coach:**
Sports Therapist: Colin Edwards
Club Colours: Sky Blue & White halves/sky blue
Change Colours: All Tangerine
Club Sponsor: gap personnel
Previous League: North West Counties
Best Seasons: League: N.P.L. Premier 1992 +   **F.A. Cup:** 2nd Round 1995-1996
F.A.Trophy.:   Quarter Finals 1996-1997   **F.A.Vase:**
Ground address: Llanelian Road, OLd Colwyn, North Wales LL29 8UN
Tel No.01492 514581
Club Website: www.cbfc .co.uk
Capacity: 2,500   **Seats:** 250   **Covered**: 700   **Floodlights**: Yes
Simple Directions: Take A55 North Wales Expressway. Exit Jct.22 signposted to
Hen Golwyn/Old Colwyn. At end of slip road turn left then straight on at roundabout
and into Llanelian Road. Ground half a mile on left.
Midweek Home Matchday: Tuesday
Clubhouse: Open Matchdays Only. **Contact:** Nicola Kingston
Club Shop: Yes. **Contacts:** Eryl & Shaila Jones
Local Radio:
Local Press:

CLUB PERSONNEL
Chairman: Bob Paton
Vice Chairman: A.Owens
President: G.Owens
Vice President: Dr.D.R. Williams
Patron: John Martin
Secretary: Mike Roberts, 18
Belgrave Road, Colwyn Bay,
N.Wales. Tel No: 01492 534724
(M) 07887 782565
Commercial Manager:
Carol Beard
Prog. Editor: Dave Jones
Pages/Price

CLUB STATISTICS

Record	**Attendance:** 5,000 v Boorough United at Eirias Park 1964	
	Career Goalscorer: Peter Donnelly	
	Career Appearances: Bryn A. Jones	
Record Transfer Fee	Paid:	
	Received:	
Senior Honours:	N.P.L.Div 1 1991-1992, N.W.Co R-Up 90-91	
Previous Leagues:	N.Wales Coast 1901-21 33-35, Welsh National 21-30 N.Wales Comb. 30-31	
	Welsh Lg. (North) 45-84. N.W. Co 84-91	

Back row (L-R): Peter Davenport (manager), Shaun Tierney, Neil Black, Chris Adamson, Ryan Brookfield, Tim Brandreth, Paul Roberts, Huw Griffiths (ass Manager / coach). **Front:** James Foran, Lewis Callaghan, Robbie Williams, Darren Wright, John Boardman, Kenny Burgess, Chris Hogg, Rob Whyte.

EASTWOOD TOWN

Founded: 1953
Nickname:
The Badgers

Manager: Paul Cox   **Asistant Manager:** Andy Miller   **Physio:**Fred Kirk
Club Colours: White with black trim/black/black
Change Colours: Gold/gold/black
Club Sponsor: Eurocell
Previous League: Northern Counties East
Best Seasons: League: 6th N.P.L. Div 1 2004-2005 **F.A. Cup:** 1st Rd.1999-2000
F.A.Trophy.: 5th Round 2004-2005
F.A.Vase: 6th Round 2003-2004
Ground address: Coronation Park, Eastwood, Notts. **Tel No:** 01773 715823
Club Website: www.eastwoodtownfc.com:
Capacity: 5,500   **Seats:**650   **Covered:**1,150   **Floodlights**: Yes
Simple Directions: From North: M1 jct 27 follow Heanor signs via Brinsley to lights in Eastwood. Turn left then first right after fire station- ground on Chewton Street.
From South: M1 jct 26. Take A610 to Ripley, leave at first exit (B60100) towards Eastwood. Left at lights and first left at 'Man in Space', ground entrance on Chewton Street.
Midweek Home Matchday: Tuesday
Clubhouse: Social club open normal licensing hours (Sat 11am-11pm, midweek matches 6.30-11pm). Hot & cold food available. Steward; Jane Rowley
Club Shop: Programmes, mugs, scarves, badges etc. Contact: GlenysStorer - 0115 9199596
Local Radio: BBC Nottingham and Radio Trent
Local Press: Eastwood & Kilberly Advertiser

CLUB PERSONNEL
Chairman: Keith Smith
Vice Chairman: Roy Cheatle
President: George Belshaw
Secretary: Paddy Farrell, 7 Primrose Rise, Newthorpe, Notts. NG16 2BB Tel No: 01773 786186
Programme Editor: P.Farrell
50 Pages £1.50
2005-2006
Captain: Paul Gover
Player of the Year:
Richard Cooper
Top Goalscorer: Peter Knox

CLUB STATISTICS

Record   **Attendance:** 2,723 v Enfield F.A.Amateur Cup Frbruary 1965
Career Goalscorer: Martin Wreight 147
Career Appearances: Arthur Rowley pover 800 games (no bookings) 1955-76
Record Transfer Fee Paid: £500 several times
Record Transfer Fee Received: £80,000 for Richard liburd
Senior Honours: Northern Co. East Lg R-up 82-83 84-85 79-80; Notts Senior Cup x 9 R-up x 5.
Previous **Leagues:** Notts Alliance 53-61; Central Alliance 61-67; East Mids 67-71; Midland Counties 71-82; N.C.E. 82-88; N.P.L. 88-03

327

GOOLE A.F.C.

Founded: 1997
Nickname:

Caretaker Manager: Nigel Darby   **Coach:**   **Physio:**

Club Colours: Red/white/red

Change Colours: Yellow and Blue.

Club Sponsor:

Previous League: Northern Counties East.

Best Seasons: League: 20th Div 1 NPL 2005-2006

F.A. Cup: 2nd Qualifying 2001-2002   **F.A.Trophy.:**

F.A.Vase: 4th Round 1998-1999

Ground address: Victoria Plaesure Gardens, Marcus Road, Goole DN14 6AR

Club Website: www.gooleafc.co.uk

Capacity: 3,000   **Seats:**200   **Covered:**800   **Floodlights:** Yes

Simple Directions: M62 to jct 36 then follow signs to town centre. Right at 2nd lights into Boothferry Road, after 300 yards turn right into Carter St.Ground at end.

Clubhouse: Matchdays only

Midweek Home Matchday: Tuesday

Clubhouse: Matchdays Only **Club Shop:** Manager: Eric Lawton

Local Radio:

Local Press:

CLUB PERSONNEL
Chairman: Desmond O'Hearne
President:
Secretary: Terrence Redhall
c/o the club

Programme
Editor: Andrew Lawson
Tel No: 0430457333
Pages/Price

2006-2007
Captain: Nigel Danby

CLUB STATISTICS

Record	**Attendance:** 964 v Leeds UNited 1999	
	Career Goalscorer: Kevin Severn (1997-2001)	
	Career Appearances: Phil Dobson 187 1999-2001	
Record Transfer Fee	**Paid:**	
	Received:	
Senior Honours:	N.Co.East Champions 2003-2004 N.Co. East Division One 1999-2000	
	Central Midlands 2997-2998	
Previous Leagues:	Central MIdlands 1997-1998 Northern Counties East 2000-2004	

Back row, left to right: Ian McClean, Kenny Gormley (Kitman), Mark Willoughby, DeanWilson, David Watts, Chris Hill, Phil Walker, Neil Harrison, Graham Whitehead and Steve Robinson. **Front row:** Tony Wetherall, Adam Walker, Jimmy Gore, Paul Marshall(manager), Steve Davey, Mark Smitheringale (Asst.Manager), Ben Eastwood, Craig Gorman and Colin Naylor (Physio)

GRESLEY ROVERS

Founded: 1882
Nickname:
The Moatman

UniBond League Division One
Gresley Rovers v Stocksbridge Park Steels
Monday, 17th April 2006
Official Matchday Programme
£1.00

Manager: Gary Norton   **Assistant Manager::**Mick Curry **Coach:** Raffaele Long
Physio: Harry Takhar
Club Colours: Red/white/red   **Change Colours:** White/black/white
Club Sponsor: Ashfield Healthcare
Previous League: Southern
Best Seasons: League: Southern/NPL?   **F.A. Cup:** 1st Round 1930-331 1994-95
F.A.Trophy.: Quarter Finals 1995-1996   **F.A.Vase:** Finalists 1990-1991
Ground address: Moat Ground, Moat Street, Church Gresley, Swadlincote,
Derbyshire. DE11 9RE **Tel No:** 01283 216315
Club Website: wwww.gresleyrovers.com
Capacity: 2,000   **Seats** 400:   **Covered:** 1,200   **Floodlights**: Yes
Simple Directions: To A444 via either the A5, A38, A5121 or M42 , Junction 11. On reaching
A444 head for Castle Gresley. At large island turn to Church Gresley, at next island second exit
(Church St), then second left (School St &1st left into Moat St. 5 miles Burton-on-Trent (BR). Buses
from Swadlincote & Burton.
Midweek Home Matchday: Tuesday
Clubhouse: Inside Ground OpenThursday evenings and matchdays (Harry & Kath
Southern) **Club Shop:** Yes, with full range of merchandise.Contact:Secretary
Local Radio: BBC Radio Derby
Local Press: Derby Evening Tel.,Burton Mail, Burton Trader & Swadlincote Times

CLUB PERSONNEL

Chairman: Mark Evans
Vice-Chairman: George Stutton
President: Gordon Duggins
Secretary & Press Odfficer:
Tony Kirkland,40 HUrst Drive,
Stretton, Burton on Trent, Staffs.
DE13 0ED

Programme
Editor: Chairman
32 Pages £1.00

2005-2006
Captain: A.Simpson
Player of the Year: A.O'Connor
Top Goalscorer: A O'Connor

CLUB STATISTICS	
Record	**Attendance:** 3,950 v Burton Albion Birmingham Lg. (now West Mids) 57-58
	Career Goalscorer: Gordon Duggins 306
	Appearances: Dennis King 579
Record Transfer Fee	**Paid:** £2,500 to Ilkeston Town for David Robinson
	Received: £30,000 from Port Vale for Justin O'Reilly 1996
Senior Honours:	The F.A.Vase Runners -Up 1990-1991, Southern League Champions 1996-97
	Lg Cup R-Up 93-94, Southern League Midland Division R-Up 1992-1993
	Derbys Senior Cup (8) R-Up (4), Dr..Martens South League Cup R-Up 93--94
	West Midlands League (2) R-Up (2)
Previous Leagues:	**Leagues:** Burton Lge 1892-95 97-01 09-10 43-45, Derbyshire Sen 1895-97 02-
	03,Leics Sen 1930-91 98-99 08-09 10-12 15-16 35-42 45-49, Notts 01-02,
	Miidland 03-06, Central All 11-15 19-25 49-53 59-67, Birmingham Comb 25-33
	53-54, Birmingham (now West Mids) 54-59 75-92, Central Comb 33-35,
	East Mids 67-75

Back row (l-r): Chris Mawbey, Martin Rowntree, Steve Gomm, Matt Millns, Chris White, Sebastian Kalinowski, Nicky Carter, Ravi Sangha, Lewis Gadsby, Dan Douglas. **Middle:** Matt Dingley (Kit manager), Alan Titterton (Chief Scout), Richard Lonsdale, David Holmes, Jamie Barrett, Steve Harris, Paul Edwards, Andy Spencer, Tom Betteridge, George Sutton (Vice Chairman), Tony Kirkland (Secretary). **Front:** Aaron O'Connor, Colin Hoyle, Gary Norton (Manager), Mark Evans (Chairman), Mick Curry (Assistant Manager), Andy Simpson, Carl Slater.

HARROGATE RAILWAY

Founded: 1935
Nickname: The Rail

CLUB PERSONNEL
Chairman: Dennis Bentley
Secretary: Stuart Lloyd,61 Jesmond Road, Harrogate HG2 7NP
Tel No: 07884 012797
Press Officer: Ken Welford
Tel No: 01423 889186
Programme Editor: Gordon Ward
Tel No: 01423 880423
Pages/Price

2005-2006
Captain: Scott Baistow
Manager's PoY: Graham Marchant
Supporter's PoY: Scott Ryan
Top scorer: Graham Marchant

Manager: Martin Haresign   **Assistant Manager:** Ian Blackstone

Physio: David Roach

Club Colours: Red/green/red

Change Colours: White/black/white

Club Sponsor: John Smiths

Previous League: Northern Counties East

Best Seasons: League: 3rd N.Co.East Champions 2005-06

F.A. Cup: 2nd Round 2002-2003 **F.A.Vase:** 4th Round Replay 1988-1989

F.A.Amateur Cup: 3rd Round 1952-63

Ground address: Station View, Starbeck, Harrogate, North Yorks. HG2 7JA

Tel Nos: 01423 885539 and 01423 883104 (Fax)

Club Website: www.harrogaterailway.com

Capacity: 3,500   **Seats:** 800   **Covered:** 600   **Floodlights:** Yes:

Simple Directions: A59 Harrogate to Knaresborough Road. Turn left after one and a half miles just before railway level crossing. Ground is 150 yards up the lane.

Midweek Home Matchday: Tuesday

Clubhouse: Full facilities available   **Shop:** No. But club merchandise available.

CLUB STATISTICS

Record   **Attendance:** 3,500 v Bristol City F.A.Cup 2nd Round 2002-2003

Career Goalscorer: Unknown

Career Appearances: Unknown

Record Transfer Fee   **Paid:** n/a

Received: £1,000 from Guiseley for Colin Hunter.

Senior Honours: N.Co.East Div 1 1989-1999 Div 2 North Lg & Cup 1983-84

Previous Leagues: West Yorks., Harrogate & District, Yorkshire 55-73 80-82 N.Co East 82-06

Harrogate Railway Athletic F.C. 2006-2007
Back row: Martin Haresign (Manager), Danny Budge, Steve Jones, Damian Henderson, Will Witford, Graham Marchant, Chris Howarth, Rob Morgan, Nathan James, Vince Brockie
Front row: Jonny McLaughlin, David Conway, Ryan Haigh, Scott Ryan, Liam Gray, Phil Turner, Lyle Hillier, David Roach

KIDSGROVE ATHLETIC

Founded: 19952
Nickname:
The Grove

Managers: Peter Ward & Paul Ogden   **Physio**: Graham Plant
Club Colours: All Royal Blue with white trim/ White/ White
Change Colours: All Yellow
Club Sponsor:
Previous League: North West Counties
Best Seasons: Lg: 10th NPL Div 1 2004-2005
F.A. Cup: 1st Qualifying Round 1995
F.A.Trophy.: 1st Round.   **F.A.Vase:** Semi-Final 1997-1998
Ground address: Stan Brown Stadium, Hollinswood Road, Kidsgrove, Stoke on Trent. Staffs. Telk No: 01782 782412
Club Website:www.kidsgroveathletic.com
Capacity: 4,500   **Seats:** 1,000   **Covered:** 800   **Floodlights**: Yes
Simple Directions: From M6 Jct 16 take A500 towards Stoke then second junction onto A34 towards Manchester. Turn right at first lights down hill and right at lights into Cedar Rd. Take second right into Lower Ash Rd and third left into Hollinwood Rd and ground. BR Kidsgrove (5mins)
Midweek Home Matchday: Monday
Clubhouse: Yes with food matchdays Hall to seas 180 with Sky TV
Club Shop: Yes . Manager: Ray Green 01782 7736
Local Radio: Radio Stoke, Signal Radio
Local Press: Staffordshire Evening Sentinel

CLUB PERSONNEL

Chairman: Stan Brown
Vice-Chairman: Arthur Duckworth
President: Ernie Langford
Secretary: Alan Thompson,
7 Sandown Road, Crewe,
Cheshire
Tel Nos: 01270 256588 (H)
07712 956400(M)
Programme Editor:
John Naisbett
32 Pages £1.00

2005-2006
Captain: Anthony Kielthy
Player of the Year:
Top Goalscorer: Matt Rhead

CLUB STATISTICS

Record	**Attendance:** 1,903 v Tiverton Town F.A.Vase Semi-Final 1998
	Career Goalscorer: Scott Dunndas 53 1997-1998
	Career Appearances:
	Transfer Fee Received: `£3,000 for Richard Mitchell 2001-2002 Paid ?:
	Victory: 23-0 v Cross Heath W.M.C. Staffs Cup 1965
	Defeat:: 2-7 v Glossop N.E. NSCo.L DDiv 1 1993-94
Senior Honours:	NWC Div. 1 97-98, 01-02; NWC Chall. Cup 97-98; Mid Cheshire Lg (4), R-up (2); Lg Cup (3), R-up (2)
revious Leagues:	**Leagues:** Burslem & Tunstall 1953-63, Staffordshire County 63-66, Mid Cheshire Lge. 66-90, North West Counties 90-2002.
	Ground: Vickers & Goodwin 1953-60

Back row, left to right: Graham Plant (Physio), Darren Twigg (Joint Manager), Phil Bostock, Chris Holmes (Coach), Matt Rhead, Wayne Johnson, Mark Fitton, and Anthony Buckle (Joint Manager). Front row: Andy Thomas, Richard Eyre, John Paul Jones, Ben Matthews, Anthony Keilthy, Ashley MIller, Neil Sargent and Andy Bostock

OSSETT ALBION

Manager: Eric Gilchrist   **Assistant Manager:** Tony Passmore
Club Colours: All Old Gold
Change Colours: All White
Club Sponsor: TASCA Tankers
Previous League: Northern Counties East
Best Seasons: League: 12th NPL Div 1 2004-2005
F.A. Cup: 4th Qualifying Round 2003-2004
F.A.Trophy.:   **F.A.Vase:** 4th Round 2nd Replay 1995-1996
Coach: Nigel Yarrow   **Physio:**Nicky Davies
Ground address: Queens Terrace, Dimple Wells, Ossett, Yorkshire.
Tel Nos: 01924 273618 (club office) 01924 280450 (Ground)
Club Website: www.ossettalbion.bravehost.com
Capacity: 3,000   **Seats:**2   **Covered:** 750   **Floodlights:** Yes
Simple Directions:
M1 jct 40. Take Wakefield road, right at Post House Hotel down Queens Drive. Right at end then second left down Southdale Rd. Right at end, then first left into Dimple Wells (cars only). Coaches take second left following the road for 200yds bearing left twice. Four miles from both Wakefield and Dewsbury BR stations. Buses 116 and 117

Midweek Home Matchday: Wednesday
Clubhouse: Three bars & catering facilities. Open seven days a week
Club Shop: Full range of souvenirs. **Contact:** David Reilly
Local Radio: Radio Leeds and Ridings Radio
Local Press: Wakefield Express

CLUB PERSONNEL

Chairman: Neville Wigglesworth
President: Miss Helen Worth
Secretary: David Chambers, 109 South Parade, Ossett, Wakefield WF5 0BE Tel No: 01924 276004

**Programme
Editor:** Chairman
44 Pages £1.50

**2005-2006
Captain:** Dominic Riordan
Player of the Year:
Danny Toronczak
Top Goalscorer: Rob Edwrads

CLUB STATISTICS

Record	**Attendance:** 1,200 v Leeds United Opening of flodlights 1986
	Career Goalscorer: John Balmer
	Career Appearances:: Peter Eaton 800+ (22years)
Record	**Victory:** 12-0 v Britiosh Ropes (H0 Yorks League 2 6/5/59
	Defeat: 2-11 v Swillington (A) W.Yorkds Lge Div 1 25/4/56
Senior Honours:	N.C.E. PremierChampions: 98-99 03-04 Div. R-up 00-01,
	League Cup R-Up: 95-96 President's Cup R-Up: 97-98 00-01 Div 1 86-87
	Lg Cup 83-84;02-03 Yorks Lg 74-75 R-up (4), Lg Cup (2);
	W. Riding County Cup (4)
Previous Leagues:	Heavy Woollen Area 44-49; West Riding Co. Amtr 49-50;
	West Yorks 50-57 Yorks 57-82. **Ground:** Fearn House

Back Row (L-R): T.Passmore (Asst.Manager), D. Riordan, D Toronczak, N.Handley, N.Clark, J.Wordsworth, D.Syers, A.Mackay, and E.Gilchrist (Manager)
Front Row: R.Edwrads, G.Duffty, M.Senior, J.Gaughan, A.Shuttleworth, S.Wright amd S.Downes. Insets N.Yarrow (Goalkeeping coach) and N.Davies (Physio)

ROSSENDALE UNITED

Founded: 1898
Nickname:
The Stags

UNITED REVIEW
The Official Match Magazine of Rossendale United Football Club

Saturday 15th October 2005
FA Trophy Preliminary Round
v Woodley Sports
Season 2005/06   Programme Price £1.50

Manager: Derek Egan   **Assistant Manager::** Wayne Goodison
Club Colours: Blue & white/blue/blue
Change Colours: All Red
Club Sponsor: Swinburne James Insurance
Previous League: North West Counties
Best Seasons: League: 15th NPL Division 1 2004-2005
F.A. Cup: 2nd Round 1971-1972   **F.A.Trophy.:** 2nd Round 1981-1982
F.A.Vase: 5th Round 1985-1986 1988-1989
Physio: Cath Fitton
Ground address: Dark Lane, Staghills Road, Newchurch, Rossendale
Club Website: www.the-stags.co.uk
Capacity: 2,500   **Seats**:500   **Covered**:Yes   **Floodlights**:Yes
Simple Directions: M60 Junc 18, M66 north following signs for Burnley, then A682 to
Rawstenstall, take 2nd exit sign Burnley A682, at 1st lights turn right into Newchurch Rd, 1.5 miles
turn right into Staghills Rd. Ground is 800 yards right.
Midweek Home Matchday: Tuesday
Clubhouse: Evenings and Matchdays. Hot Snacks. Sky TV, Pool and hall.
Club Shop: Yes. Contact: Dave Rudge 01706 213296
Local Radio: Red Rose Radio Lancashire.
Local Press: Lancs Evening Telegraph & Rossendale Free Press.

CLUB PERSONNEL

Chairman: Declan Callan
President & V-Chair : David White
Secretary & Pres Officer:
Kevin Proctor, 5 Booth Street,
Wtaerfoot, Rossebdale, Lancs. BB4
9AL
Tel No: 01706 223405
Programme
Editor: David Hawortth
28 Pages £1.50

2005-2006
Captain: Bill Robertson
Player of the Year: Bill Robertson
Top Goalscorer: Neil Zarat

CLUB STATISTICS

Record	**Attendance:** 12,000 v Bolton Wanderers F.A.Cup 2nd Round 1971
	Career Goalscorer: Bob Scott: 230
	Career Appearances:: Johhny Clark 770 1947-65
Record Transfer Fee	**Paid**: £3,000 to Buxton for Jimmy Clarke 1992
	Received: £1,500 from Huddersfield Town for Dave O'Neill 1974
	Victory: 17-0 v Ashton Town Lancs. Comb. 1911-12
	Defeat: 0-14 v Morecambe Lancs. Comb. 1967-1968
Senior Honours:	N.W.Co League DIV.1 1988-1989 2000-2001 R-UP 1987-88 1993-94
Previous Leagues:	N.E.Lancs. Combination, Lancs Cobination1898-1899 1901-1970, Central
	Lancs 1899-1901, Cheshire County 1970-1982 and North West Counties
	1982-89 1993-2001

Taken before their friendly match v's Blackburn Rovers on Tuesday 20th July 2004. Rossendale Utd are wearing their
change strip of all red as a gesture to the Premier League Club.

SHEPSHED DYNAMO

Founded: 1994
Nickname: Dynamo

Shepshed Dynamo FC
Sponsored By :
Coalville Paint & Decorating Supplies

UniBond Premier Northern League (Div 1)
SHEPSHED DYNAMO FC
versus
KIDSGROVE ATHLETIC
Wednesday, 14 September 2005, k.o. 7.45pm
Matchday Programme £1.20

Manager: Peter McGurck **Coach:** Adam Stevens **Physio:** Ian Davies

Club Colours: Black & white stripes/black/black

Change Colours: All Yellow

Club Sponsor: Coalville Paints

Previous League: MIdland Alliance

Best Seasons: League: 10th NPL **F.A. Cup:** 1st Round 1982-1983

F.A.Trophy.: 3rd Round Replay 1998-1999 **F.A.Vase:** Semi-Final Replay 1978-79

Ground address: The Dovecote, Butthole Lane, Shepshed, Leicestershire.

Tel No: 01509 650992

Club Website: www.shepsheddyname.co.uk

Capacity: 5,000 **Seats:** 1,500 **Covered:** 400 **Floodlights:** Yes

Simple Directions: M1 J 23, A512 towards Ashby, right at first lights, right at garage in Forest Street, right into Butthole Lane opposite Black Swan. Five miles from Loughborough (BR)

Midweek Home Matchday: Wednesday

Clubhouse: Yes **Club Shop:** Yes. Managers Steve Straw & Alan Gibson

Local Radio: Radio Leicester, Oak F.M.

Local Press: Loughborough Echo, Leicester Mercury, Coalville Times

CLUB PERSONNEL

Chairman: Peter Bull
Vice-Chairman: Shaun Taylor
President: Paul Mitchell.
Secretary: Dave Wheatley, 9 Holcombe Close, Whitwick, Leics. LE67 5BR. **Tel No:** 01530814959
Commercial Manager: John Squires (0785 9030110)
Press Officer: John Brindley
Tel NO: 07971 339105
Programme Editor: Ben Reed
40Pages £1.20
2005-2006
Captain: Andy Bourne
Player of the Year: Jordan Lambert
Top Goalscorer: Darryl Thomas

CLUB STATISTICS

Record	**Attendance:** 2,500 v Leicester City (friendly) 1996--1997
	Career Goalscorer: Jeff Lissaman 104 (1981-1986)
	Career Appearances: Austin Straker 300
Record Transfer Fee	**Paid:** £ 2,000 for Doug Newton
	Received: £10,000 from Birmingham City for John Deakin
Senior Honours:	Southern Lge Midland Div. R-up 83-84, N.C.E. Lge 82-83, Lge Cup 82-83;
(7);;	Midland Counties Lge 81-82, Lge Cup 81- 82; Leicestershire Senior Cup
	Midland Alliance Winners 95-96
Previous Leagues:	Leicestershire Senior 07-16 19-27 46-50 51-81, Midland Counties 81-82,
93,	Northern Counties (East) 82-83, Southern 83-88, Northern Premier 88-93, Midland Combination 93-94, Midland Alliance 94-96

SKELMERSDALE UNITED

Founded: 1882
Nickname: Skem

Manager: Tommy Lawson   **Coaches**   Paul McNally & Brian Richardson

Club Colours: All Blue

Change Colours: Gold/Black/Black

Club Sponsor: Ashley Travel Limited

Previous League: North West Counties.

Best Seasons: League: 11th N.P.L. 1971-72   **F.A. Cup:** 1st Rd 67-68 68-69 71-72

F.A.Amateur Cup: Winners 19701971 **F.A.Vase:** 4th Round 1999-2000 2004-2005

Ground address: Ashley Travel Stadium, Selby Place, off Stathem Road, Stanley Industrial Estate, Skelmersdale, Lancs.WN8 8EF **Tel No:** 01695 722123

Club Website: www.skelmersdaleutdfc.com

Capacity: 2,300   **Seats:** 240   **Covered:** 500   **Floodlights:** Yes

Simple Directions: M58 Jct 4 to Skem. Over roundabout into Glenburn Road, left into Neverstitch Rd. at roundabout and then first right at next two roundabouts into Staveley Road. Sharp left into Stathem Rd with ground 500 yds on left in Selby Place.

Midweek Home Matchday: Tuesday

Clubhouse: Matchdays.   **Club Shop:** Yes

Local Radio: Radio Merseyside

Local Press: Advertiser/Champion

CLUB PERSONNEL

Chairman: Frank Hughes
President:
Managing Director: Arthur Gore
Secretary: Bryn Jones, 34 Bromiloe Road, Skelmersdale Lancs, WN8 8TU. Tel No: 01695 724647 (H) 07904 911234 (M)

Programme Editor: Frank Hughes
40 Pages £1.20

2005-2006
Captain: Steve Rimmer
Player of Year: Michael Douglas
Top Goalscorer: Stuart Rudd 47

CLUB STATISTICS

Record

Attendance: 7,000 v Slough Town F.A.Amateur Cup Semi-Final 1967

Career Goalscorer: Stuart Rudd 230

Career Appearances: Robbie Holcroft 422 including 398 consecutive

Transfer Fee Paid:

Transfer Fee Received:

Senior Honours: F.A.Amateur Cup Winners 1970-71, R-Up 1966-67 Lancs Junior Cup (2) Barassi Anglo-Italioan Cup 1970-1971, Lancs Non-League Cup (2)

Previous Leagues: Liverpool Co.Comb., Lancs. Comb. 1891-93 1903-07 21-24 55-56 76-78 Cheshire County: 1968-1971 1978-1982 N.P.L. 1971-1976 N.W.Co. 1983-2006

Back Row (L-R): Ari Ubido, Andy Barlow, Tim Mullock (Goalkeeper) Peter Owens, Ian Price.
Middle: Brian Richardson (Coach) Tom Hardwick, Paul McNally (Assistant Manager), Frank Hughes (Chairman) Steve Rimmer, Michael Douglas (Captain) Nicola Pye (Physio).
Front: Adam Birchall, Phil Holland, John Cass, Tommy Lawson (Manager) Sean Wright, Carl Osman, Ryan Wallace.

STOCKSBRIDGE PARK STEELS

Founded: 1986
Nickname: Steels

Manager: Peter Rinkcavage **Assistant Manager::** Paul Bradshaw
Physio: John Megson

Club Colours: Yellow/Blue/Yellow

Change Colours: All Blue

Club Sponsor: John Crawshaw (Butchers)

Previous League: Northern Counties East

Best Seasons: League: NPL **F.A. Cup:** 3rd Qualifying Rd 2003-2004
F.A.Trophy.: 3rd Qualifying Round 1996-1997 **F.A.Vase:** 4th Round 1951-1952

Ground address: Bracken Moor Lane, Stocksbridge, Sheffield.
Tel No: 0114 288 2045
Club Website: www.spsfc.com
Capacity: 3,500 **Seats:** 400 **Covered:**1,500 **Floodlights:** Yes
Simple Directions: M1 jct 35a (from S), 36 (from N), A616 to Stocksbridge.On arrival in Stocksbridge turn left into Nanny Hill under the Clock Tower and continue up the hill for about 500 yds - ground on left
Midweek Home Matchday: Tuesday
Clubhouse: Open every day lunchtime & evenings . No food but spearate food **bar** for matchdays. **Club Shop:** Full range of products . Contact: Mrs Janet Cartledge 01226 759023
Local Radio:
Local Press: Look Local, The Green Un & The Star.

CLUB PERSONNEL
Chairman: Allen Bethel
President: J.Newton
Vice Chairman: Michael Grimmer
Secretary: Michael Grimmer, 48 Hole House Lane, Stocksbridge, Sheffield. S36 1BT
Tel No: 0114 288 6470

Programme
Editor: Eddie O'Sullivan
28 Pages £1.00

2005-2006
Captain: Gary Middleton
Player of the Year: Stefan Zoll
Top Goalscorer:

CLUB STATISTICS

Record	**Attendance:** 2,000 v Sheffield Wednesday Opening Floodlights,October 19991
	Career Goalscorer: Trevor Jones 145
	Match: Paul Jackson 10 v Oldham Town 2002-2003 (F.A. Cup Record).
	Career Appearances:
Record Transfer Fee	**Received:** £15,000 from Wolverhampton Wanderers for Lee MIlls
	Victory: 17-1 v Oldham Town F.A.Cup. 2002-2003
	Defeat: 2-7 v Witton Albion 2001-2002.
Senior Honours:	Northern Co's East Prem Div 93-94, R-up 95-96, Div 1 91-92, Lg Cup 94-95; Sheffield Snr Cup 1951-52 92-93 95-96,98-99.
Previous Leagues:	**Leagues:** Sheffield Amateur/ Sheffield Association/Yorkshire 49-82
	Ground: Stonemoor 49-51 52-53
	Names: Stocksbridge Works & Oxley Park merged in 1986

Back row, left to right: Peter Rincavage (Manager), Jason Maybury (coach), Paul Lavender, Wayne Bullimore, Andy Ring, Simon Brown, Steve Hodgson, Gary Middleton, Scott Lowe, Stefan Zoll, Steve Gaughan and John Megson.
Front row: Alvin Riley, Chris Dolby, Ben Walker, Darren Schofield, Andy Smith, Ross Hannah, Duncan Richards and James Colliver.

WAKEFIELD F.C.

Re-Formed: 2006
Nickname:

Manager: Paul David　　**Physio:** Martin Loughran
Club Colours: Blue with Yellow trim/Blue
Change Colours: Yellow/Black/Yellow
Club Sponsor: Plumbase
Previous Leagues: N.Co.East
Previous Name: Emley F.C. 1903-2002
Previous Ground: Emley Welfare Sports Ground Wakefield-Emley 2002-05
Best Seasons: League: N.P.L. Divison 1　　**F.A. Cup:** 3rd Round Proper 97-98
F.A.Trophy: 6th Round 98-99　　　　　　**F.A.Vase:** Finalists 87-88
F.A.Amateur Cup: 3rd Round 69-70
Ground address:　College Grove,Eastmoor Road,Wakefield WF1 3RR
Tel No: 01924 365007 (office) 01484 661780 (Fax)
Website: www.wakefield-emley.co.uk
Capacity: 2,500　　**Seats:** 460　　**Covered:** 700　　**Floodlights:**Yes
Simple Directions: From M1 Juction 41 take A650(Wakefield) then at third round-
about takeA642 (Garforth). After fuirst roundabout take first right (North Avenue).
Then left at T Junction and ground is 80 yards on the right.
Midweek Home Matchday: Tuesday
Clubhouse: Yes
Club Shop: Yes　**Contact:** David Richardson　01924 211611
Local Radio: Radio Leeds, Radio Sheffield,Pulse FM,
Huddersfield FM & Ridings FM.
Local Press: Huddersfield Examiner, Huddersfleld,field & Dist Chronicle,
Wakefield Express

CLUB PERSONNEL
Chairman: Alan Blackman
President: Peter Maude
Secretary: Peter Matthews,
Hillandale, Slant Gate, Highburton,
Huddersfield HD 8 0QN Tel No:
01484 603629
& Fax: 01484 603629
Programme Editor: Neil Thorpe
Tel No: 08703 339994
Programme
Pages 34 Price £1.00

2005-2006
Captain: Paul Stoneman
Player of the Year: Richard Chattor
Top Goalscorer: Damien Reeves

CLUB STATISTICS

Record	**Attendance:** 5,134 v Barking Amateur Cup 3rd proper 01.02.69
	18,000 at West Ham for F.A.Cup 3rd Rd 03.01.99
	Victory: 12-0 v Ecclesfield Red Rose 09.06.97
	Defeat: 1--7 v Altrincham 25.04.98
	Career Goalscorer: Mick Pamment 305
	Career Appearances: Ray Dennis 762
Record Transfer Fee	**Paid:**
	Received: £60,000 for Michael Reynolds (Ayr United 98)
Senior Honours:	F.A.Vase R-up 87-88 NPL Div 1 R-up 90-91 N.Co E 87-88 88-89 R-up 85-86
	Sheffield & Hallamshire Senior Cup (8)
Previous Leagues:	Huddersfield, Yorkshire 69-82, Northern Counties East 82-89

WARRINGTON TOWN

Founded: 1948
Nickname:
The Town

Warrington Town AFC

The official match day programme of Warrington Town AFC

Official Kit Sponsors
Clockwork Orange Ltd
IT and Internet Solutions Provider

Associate Sponsors
DJ Hughes Construction
Murrayland Construction

Manager: Glenn Walker **Assistant. Manager:** Derek Brownbill
Coach: Steve Pennington
Club Colours: Blue & Yellow/Blye/Blue
Change Colours: Orange/Black/Black
Club Sponsor: D.J.Hughes Construction & Billy Murray Construction
Previous League: North West Counties
Best Seasons: League : NPL ? **F.A. Cup:** 4th Qualifying Round 1994-1995
F.A.Trophy.: Quarter Finals 1992-1993 **F.A.Vase:** Finalists 1986-1987
Ground address: Cantilever Park, Common Lane, Latchford, Warrington WA4 2RS
Tel No: 01925 631932 (Club) 01925 653044 (Office)
Club Website: www.townafc.co.uk
Capacity: 2,000 **Seats:** 350 **Covered:** 650 **Floodlights:** Yes
Simple Directions: M6 junction 20, then A50 towards Warrington. After 2 miles turn left immediately after swing bridge into Station Road, ground 600yds on left. From town centre travel 1 mile south on A49, left at lights into Loushers Lane, ground quarter mile on right. Two miles from Warrington Bank Quay (BR)
Midweek Home Matchday: Tuesday **Club Shop:** Yes.
Clubhouse: Weekdays 1-11pm, Sat.12-11pm, Sun. 12-11pm Bar food on matchdays
Local Radio: Wire Radio and Hospital Radio
Local Press: Warrington Guardian

CLUB PERSONNEL

Chairman: Dave Huighes
President: Eric Shaw
Secretary: Barry Thorpe, 46 Greenheys, Road, Little Hulton, Manchester M38 9TP
Tel No: 0161 7901490
Press Officer: Colin Serjent
Programme Editor: Paul Roach(07740 430190) 46-60Pages £1.00

2005-2006
Captain: Douglas Pitts
Player of the Year: Paul Mitchell
Top Goalscorer: Graeme Mitchell

CLUB STATISTICS

Record	**Attendance:** 2,600 v Halesowen Town F.A.Vase Semi-Final 1st Leg 1985-86
	Career Goalscorer: Steve Hughes 167
	Career Appearances: Neil Whalley
Record Transfer Fee	**Paid:** #50,000 from P.N.E. for Liam Watson
	Received: £60,000 from Preston North End for Liam Watson
Senior Honours:	F.A. Vase R-up 86-87; N.W.C. Lge 89-90 Lg Cup 85-86 87-88 88-89 (R-up 89-90), Div 2 00-01R-up 86-87, Div 3 R-up 82-83;
Previous Leagues:	**Leagues:** Warrington & Dist. 49-52; Mid-Cheshire 52-78; Cheshire Co. 78-82; N.W.C. 82-90; N.P.L. 90-97.
	Name: Stockton Heath 1949-62.

(L-R): Clint Burton, Steve Akrigg, Ian Lowe, Douglas Pitts (C), Chris Fitzsimmons, Steve Latham, Graeme Mitchell, Darren Kinsey, Danny salt, Dave Tickle, Andy Potter.

WOODLEY SPORTS

Founded: 1970
Nickname: Sports

Manager: Ally Pickering **Asst. Manager:** Ian Nevison: **Physio:** Darrin Whitaker

Club Colours: Royal Blue & Red stripes/White/White

Change Colours: Yellow

Club Sponsor:

Previous League: North West Counties

Best Seasons: League: 4th NPL Division 1 2005-2006

F.A. Cup: 1st Qualifying Round 1999-2000

F.A.Trophy.: 1st Round 2004-2005   **F.A.Vase:** 1st Round 1998-1999

Ground address: Lambeth Grove Stadium, Lambeth Grove, Woodley, Stockport

Tel No: 0161 406 6896

Club Website: www.woodleysports.co.uk

Capacity: **Seats:**   **Covered:**   **Floodlights:** Yes

Simple Directions: M60 Jct 25, follow signs (A560) Bredbury, take left filter at lights which brings you onto A560 Stockport Road for approx 1 mile, turn left at Lowes Arms into Mill Street which goes into Mill Lane. Second right over bridge into Woodlands Avenue, then first left into Lambeth Grove. Ground 200 yards ahead.

Midweek Home Matchday: Tuesday

CLUB PERSONNEL

Chairman: Ian Campbell
Vice Chairman: John Flanagan
Secretary: Rod Haslem,62 Marina Drive,Bredbury,Stockport,SK6 2P. Tel Nos: 01613552407(H) 07855 445636

Programme
Editor: 48 Pages £1.50

2005-2006
Captain: Carlos Meakin

CLUB STATISTICS

Record	**Attendance:** 1,500 v Stockport County
	Career Goalscorer:
	Career Appearances:
	Record Transfer Fee Paid:
	Record Transfer Fee Received:
Senior Honours:	NWC Div 2 99-00. Cheshgire Senior Cup 2003-04, N.P.L. Chairman's Cup R-up 2004-2005
Previous Leagues:	Lancashire & Cheshire, Manchester , North West Counties.

Back Row (L-R): Neil Light - Physio, Gary Gee, Chris Curley, Mark Phillips, Carlos Meakin, Liam Higginbotham, Rob Parsonage, Gavin Salmon, Adam Morning.
Front row: Mark Haslam, Danny Queeley, Luke Horrocks, Ally Pickering - Manager, Chris Young - Captain, Ian Nevison - Coach, Daniel Douglas-Pringle, Russell Headley, Mario-Sergio Daniel.

arena
SEATING

Take a Seat!
with The Arena LT Grandstand & LT Super Grandstand

From 50 to 50,000... Arena Seating have the solution

The LT and LT Super grandstand provide the perfect solution for smaller local clubs looking to enhance their seating facilities on sometimes very limited budgets as they move up the Leagues, without the need for expensive construction work.

This prefabricated tiered covered grandstand arrives on site fully assembled and is placed on the prepared foundations by a lorry-mounted crane. It can be added to as funds allow.

Contact us to see how we can enhance your venue.

WWW.ARENASEATING.COM

Arena Seating
Arena House Membury Lambourn Woodlands Hungerford Berkshire RG17 7TQ
T. 01488 67 48 00   W. www.arenaseating.com   E. info@arenaseating.com

PART OF THE ARENA GROUP

STEP 1 - P26
CONFERENCE

STEP 2 - P128
CONFERENCE NORTH/SOUTH

STEP 3
SOUTHERN LEAGUE PREMIER

STEP 4
SOUTHERN DIV 1 MID/STH&WEST

STEP 5/6 - P473

STEP 7 - P713

FOOTBALL LEAGUE

STEP 1

| FOOTBALL |
| CONFERENCE |

STEP 2

| CONFERENCE NORTH | CONFERENCE SOUTH |

STEP 3

| SOUTHERN PREMIER | NORTHERN PREMIER | ISTHMIAN PREMIER |

STEP 4

| SOUTHERN DIVISION 1 SOUTH &WEST MIDLAND | NORTHERN PREMIER DIV.1 | ISTHMIAN DIVISION 1 NORTH SOUTH |

STEP 5/6

Combined Counties	Hellenic	Northern League	Spartan South Midlands	Wessex
Eastern Counties	Kent	Northern Counties East	Sussex County	Western
Essex Senior	Midland Alliance	North West Counties	United Counties	

STEP 7

Anglian Combination	Dorset County	Kent County	Midland Combination	Peterborough & District	West Cheshire
Bedford & District	Dorset Premier	Leicestershire Senior	Midland League	Reading League	West Lancashire
Brighton & Hove	East Sussex	Liverpool County	North Berkshire	Somerset County	West Midlands (reg)
Cambridgeshire County	Essex & Suffolk Border	Manchester Football	Northampton Town Lge	South Western	West Sussex
Central Midlands	Essex Intermediate	Mid Cheshire League	Northamptonshire Comb.	Suffolk & Ipswich	Wiltshire League
Crawley & Disrict	Gloucesterhisre Co.	Mid Sussex	Northern Alliance	Teeside League	Worthing & District
Devon County	Herts Senior County	Middlesex County	Oxfordshire Senior	Wearside League	

SOUTHERN LEAGUE

SPONSORED BY: BRITISH GAS BUSINESS

Chairman: Ken Turner
Secretary: Dennis Strudwick
PO Box 90, Worcester WR3 8RX   Tel: 01905 757509

PREMIER DIVISION		P	W	D	L	F	A	Pts
1.	Salisbury City	42	30	5	7	83	27	95
2.	Bath City	42	25	8	9	66	33	83
3.	King's Lynn	42	25	7	10	73	41	82
4.	Chippenham Town	42	22	11	9	69	45	77
5.	Bedford Town*	42	22	10	10	69	53	76
6.	Yate Town (2nd Div.1W 04-05)	42	21	5	16	78	74	68
7.	Banbury United	42	17	11	14	66	61	62
8.	Halesowen Town	42	15	15	12	54	45	60
9.	Merthyr Tydfil	42	17	9	16	62	58	60
10.	Mangotsfield United (1st Div.1W 04-05)	42	15	13	14	67	67	58
11.	Grantham Town	42	15	11	16	49	49	56
12.	Tiverton Town	42	14	10	18	69	65	52
13.	Gloucester City	42	14	10	18	57	60	52
14.	Hitchin Town	42	13	12	17	59	76	51
15.	Rugby Town	42	13	11	18	58	66	50
16.	Cheshunt (T)	42	13	9	20	57	70	48
17.	Team Bath	42	14	6	22	55	68	48
18.	Cirencester Town	42	14	4	24	49	68	46
19.	Northwood (T)	42	12	6	24	53	88	42
20.	Evesham United (3rd Div.1W 04-05)	42	9	14	19	46	58	41
21.	Aylesbury United	42	9	12	21	43	69	39
22.	Chesham United	42	9	9	24	43	84	36

*Promoted via the play-offs.

	1	2	3	4	5	6	7	8	9	10	11	12	13	14	15	16	17	18	19	20	21	22
1 Aylesbury Utd		2-0	1-5	1-2	0-1	1-0	1-1	1-0	2-2	0-1	0-2	2-1	1-3	1-0	1-1	0-2	3-0	1-1	1-3	1-2	0-5	3-0
2 Banbury United	2-1		2-3	3-2	0-1	1-1	4-2	2-1	3-2	1-0	1-1	1-0	2-2	4-2	2-4	4-2	0-1	2-1	1-2	1-1	3-1	1-1
3 Bath City	3-2	0-3		1-1	2-0	2-0	0-2	3-0	2-0	0-0	2-0	0-0	2-1	1-1	1-2	2-0	3-0	1-0	0-2	3-1	1-0	1-2
4 Bedford Town	2-1	3-2	1-0		2-3	1-1	2-1	2-1	1-1	5-3	1-1	0-0	0-2	3-2	1-0	0-1	4-0	1-1	1-0	1-1	3-0	2-0
5 Chesham Utd	1-1	1-1	0-1	0-3		4-2	0-1	0-2	0-2	0-2	2-2	0-2	0-0	1-0	2-2	3-1	1-2	1-4	0-2	3-3		2-5
6 Cheshunt	0-1	2-0	1-0	0-3	4-1		1-1	1-2	1-0	1-1	3-2	2-3	1-2	0-1	2-2	3-3	5-2	2-3	0-1	2-1	1-0	2-3
7 Chippenham T.	1-1	1-0	2-0	1-2	3-0	1-1		2-0	2-0	3-0	1-0	0-0	2-2	1-1	3-1	2-1	3-1	4-0	2-1	4-2	0-1	4-2
8 Cirencester T.	2-1	1-3	1-2	5-1	0-1	0-2	1-1		0-1	0-1	0-1	2-1	2-1	0-2	0-3	1-1	0-0	1-2	2-5	1-0	2-1	1-3
9 Evesham Utd	0-0	0-1	0-2	1-2	0-4	0-1	0-2	0-4		0-0	0-2	1-1	2-0	1-1	2-3	1-2	4-0	3-0	2-2	0-1	1-1	0-1
10 Gloucester City	1-1	1-1	0-2	0-0	3-1	3-2	0-1	0-1	1-1		4-1	1-0	1-0	1-2	1-3	1-1	4-1	5-2	1-2	3-0	4-5	2-0
11 Grantham Town	2-0	2-3	0-3	3-0	0-0	0-1	1-1	0-1	1-1	2-1		1-1	1-1	0-1	1-2	0-0	2-0	2-2	1-0	0-1	1-1	2-0
12 Halesowen T.	1-1	2-2	2-1	1-1	1-0	1-1	1-2	1-1	2-0	1-0	0-2		1-1	0-0	2-0	1-3	4-1	3-2	0-1	1-3	4-2	7-2
13 Hitchin Town	3-2	3-0	2-2	1-4	1-1	4-1	3-3	1-3	2-2	2-2	0-2	1-0		0-5	0-0	1-2	4-2	1-0	0-3	2-1	3-2	4-3
14 King's Lynn	1-1	2-0	0-2	1-0	2-0	2-0	3-1	2-1	2-1	4-0	3-1	0-1	3-0		1-1	0-3	3-2	1-1	1-3	4-2	4-1	1-0
15 Mangotsfield U.	0-0	1-2	0-2	0-2	4-3	2-1	1-2	3-0	2-2	5-4	0-1	1-1	1-0	1-3		3-0	1-3	0-0	3-3	1-1	0-3	
16 Merthyr Tydfil	2-4	1-0	0-0	1-3	1-4	2-0	4-0	3-1	3-0	2-2	2-1	2-3	1-2	0-1	1-0		0-1	1-1	0-1	1-0	1-1	3-0
17 Northwood	2-1	2-1	0-3	2-3	1-1	3-1	2-1	3-0	1-2	0-1	0-2	3-0	0-0	0-1	3-5	2-3		0-0	2-2	1-1	2-4	3-2
18 Rugby Town	4-0	3-0	1-2	5-2	3-0	1-5	0-0	1-2	1-3	0-1	0-2	0-0	4-1	0-3	2-2	1-0	1-2		1-3	1-0	3-1	0-0
19 Salisbury City	3-0	1-3	0-0	1-0	6-0	5-0	2-1	3-0	1-0	2-0	3-0	0-1	3-0	1-0	2-2	2-0	3-0	3-0		0-1	1-0	3-1
20 Team Bath	1-1	2-2	0-4	1-2	2-0	0-1	2-0	4-2	2-1	1-0	1-2	0-2	1-0	1-3	0-1	2-3	2-3	1-3	1-2		0-2	5-3
21 Tiverton Town	1-1	0-0	1-2	0-1	4-0	1-1	0-2	0-4	3-0	1-0	3-1	0-0	6-2	1-2	2-3	2-0	4-1	2-2	0-1	2-0		3-2
22 Yate Town	3-0	0-3	1-1	4-0	5-2	4-1	1-2	3-1	1-1	3-1	3-1	2-1	2-1	3-2	2-2	3-2	1-0	1-0	1-0	0-3	2-1	

Southern Premier League Goalscorers 2005-2006

(Minimum ten goals from League, F.A.Cup and F.A. Trophy matches)

		Lge	FAC	FAT	Total		
Strike Force of Four							
Salisbury City	Tubbs	18	5	3	26		
	Sales	21		2	23	Total	72
	Turk	11	1		12		
	Matthews	10		1	11		
Bath City	Partridge	20			20		
	Bird	9	3	4	16	Total	57
	Walsh	9		2	11		
	Holloway	6	1	3	10		
Strike Force of Three							
Chippenham Town	Gilroy	25	3	1	29	Total	51
	Herring	11			11	(+ 2 in Play offs)	
	Constable	7	4		11		
Banbury United	Baird	15	3	2	20		
	Fuller	11		1	12	Total	43
	Gardner	7	4		11		
HalesowenTown	Lamey	12	1	3	16		
	Forinton	9	4	1	14	Total	42
	Forsdick	8	1	3	12		
King's Lynn	Bloomfield	15			15		
	Nolan	14			14	Total	41
	Defty	12			12		
Mangotsfield Utd.	Claridge	16	1		17		
	Seal	9	4		13	Total	41
	Paul	11			11		
Merthyr Tydfil	Shepherd	15	1		16		
	Steins	11	2		13	Total	40
	Walsh	10	1		11		
Twin Strikers							
Bedford Town	Howe	21		2	23	(+ 2 in Play offs)	
	Dillon	13		2	15	Total	38
Merthyr Tydfil	Steins	20 (inc 1 PO)			20	Total	32
	Shepherd	8	3	1	12		
Tiverton Town	Mudge	18	2	1	21	Total	32
	Pears	10	1		11		
Cheshunt	Opara	15	1		16	Total	27
	Clark	11			11		
Rugby Town	Stone	13	2		15	Total	26
	Gordon	11			11		
Northwood	Clark	13		1	14	Total	25
	Dean	11			11		
Single Strikers							
Hitchin Town	Sosso	21	1		22		
Yate Town	Edwards	21	1		22		
Evesham United	Ball	19			19		
Team Bath	Canham	17	2		19		
Cirencester Town	Hopkins	11	2	1	14		
Gloucester City	Corbett	12			12		
Aylesbury United	Gutzmore	10			10		
Grantham Town	Turner	10			10		

No player with **Chesham United** scored ten goals in the above competitions last season.

BANBURY UNITED

Founded: 1933
Re-Formed: 1965
Nickname: Puritans

Manager: Kevin Brock   **Physio:** Wally Hastie

Club Colours: Red & gold/gold/red

Change Colours: All white

Club Sponsor: Alex Lawrie Factors

Previous League: Hellenic

Best Seasons: League: Southern Premier 2004-05

F. A. Cup: 1st Round Replay 73-74

F.A.Trophy.: 3rd Round 1970-71 1973-74

Ground address: Spencer Stadium, off Station Road, Banbury, Oxon. OX16 5TA

Tel No: 01295 263354

Official website: www.banbury-united cityside.com

Capacity: 6,500   Seats: 250   Covered: 50   Floodlights:Yes

Simple Directions: M40 jct11 follow signs for Banbury then to BR station at eastern end of town. Turn right down narrow lane just before station forecourt

Midweek Home Matchday: Tuesday

Reserves League: Hellenic Div 1 East

Clubhouse: Open matchdays and week-ends. Hot & Cold food.**Club Shop:** Yes

CLUB PERSONNEL

Chairman: David Bennett
President: David Jesson
Secretary: Barry.Worsley, c/o Sol Systems, Unit 4, Mallorie House, Beaumont Road, Banbury, Oxon. OX161RH
Tel Nos: 01295 265638(H)
07941 267567 (M)
Commercial Manager: Dave Bennett
Programme Editor: David Shadbolt (01295 253533
Programme
Pages 48 Price £1.50

2005-2006
Captain:
Player of the Year: Andy Baird
Top Goalscorer: Anndy Baird 20

CLUB STATISTICS

Record	**Attendance:** 7,160 v Oxford City F.A.Cup 3rd Qualifying Road 30.10.48
	Victory: 12-0 v RNAS CULHAM Oxon. Senior Cup 45-46
	Defeat: 2-11 v W.B.A. 'A' Birmingham Combination 38-39
Career Goalscorer:	Dick Pike (1935-48) Tony Jacques (65-76) both 222
Career Appearances:	In Career: Jody McKay 576
Record Transfer Fee	**Paid:** £2,000 to Oxford United for Phil Emsden
	Received: £20,000 from Derby County for Kevin Wilson 1979
Senior Honours:	Hellenic Premier 99-00, Oxford Senior Cup 78-9 87-8 03-04 R-up (7) and Birmingham Senior Cup R-up 48-9 59-60
Previous	**Leagues:** Banbury Jnr 33-34, Oxon. Sen. 34-35 Birmingham Comb. 35-54 West Mids 54-66 Southern 66-90 Hellenic 91-2000
	Name: Banbury Spencer

Back Row (L-R): Kevin Brock (Manager), Paul Lamb, Howard Forinton, George Redknap, Matt Hayward, Alan Foster, Andy Baird, Darren Pond, Tommy Kinch, Wayne Blossom, Daniel Szczukiewics, Brian Robinson (Assistant Manager). **Front Row:** Les Robinson, Jon Gardner, Murray Nicholls, Ollie Stanbridge, Milan Barisic, Kieran Sullivan (Captain) Ady Fuller, Stuart Bridges, Neil Lazarus.

BANBURY UNITED

BEST LGE ATT.: 588 v Salisbury City
LOWEST: 333 v Hitchin Town

No.	Date	Comp	H/A	Opponents	Att:	Result	Goalscorers	Pos
1	Aug 13	SP	A	Yate Town	210	W 3 - 0	Stanbridge 29 Jeffries 33 (og) **Baird** 37	1
2	16		H	Grantham Town	352	D 1 - 1	Fuller 41 (pen)	4
3	20		H	Tiverton Town	380	W 3 - 1	Redknap 21 Gardner 32 **Baird** 37	2
4	23		A	Halesowen Town	416	D 2 - 2	Kinch 85 Potter 90	2
5	27		A	Bedford Town	474	L 2 - 3	Stanbridge 15 Gardner 27	8
6	29		H	Cheshunt	425	D 1 - 1	Gardner 21	9
7	Sept 2		A	Bath City	718	W 3 - 0	Gardner 42 **Baird** 46 McKay 90	6
8	10	FAC 1Q	H	King's Lynn	549	W 2 - 1	**Lamb** 44 Baird 60	
9	17	SP	A	Chesham United	444	L 0 - 1		10
10	24	FAC 2Q	A	Brackley Town	680	D 1 - 1	**Gardner** 45 (pen)	10
11	27	FAC 2Qr	H	Brackley Town	960	W 5 - 2	**Gardner** 20 65 Fuller 40 48 (pen) Gooderick 60	9
12	Oct 1		A	Mangotsfield United	413	W 2 - 1	Gooderick 18 Lamb 78	9
13	8	FAC 3Q	H	Hednesford Town	1005	L 3 - 4	**Gardner** 69 Baird 84 90 (pen)	
14	11	SP	A	Grantham Town	298	W 3 - 2	Gardner 9 (pen) Gooderick 21 Pond 29	9
15	15	FAT1Q	A	Brackley Town	494	D 1 - 1	**Bridges** 87	
16	18	FAT1Qr	H	Brackley Town	479	W 3 - 0	**Blossom** 11 Lamb 22 Potter 65	
17	22	SP	A	Hitchin Town	367	L 0 - 3		10
18	25		H	Aylesbury United	418	W 2 - 1	**Baird** 31 Lamb 68	7
19	29		H	Northwood	389	L 0 - 1		9
20	Nov 1		H	Chippenham Town	411	W 4 - 2	Gooderick 20 G.Thorne 22 (og) Gardner 31 **Baird** 69	5
21	5		A	Gloucester City	341	D 1 - 1	Lamb 58	5
22	8		H	Evesham United	346	W 3 - 2	**Baird** 31 Fuller 64 (pen) Knurck 86 (og)	5
23	12	FAT 2Q	H	Cirencester Town	990	D 2 - 2	**Fuller** 29 McKay 89	
24	15	FAT 2Qr	A	Cirencester Town	186	W 4 - 3	**Baird** 38 55 Reknapp 43 Blossom 95	
25	19	SP	H	Yate Town	411	D 1 - 1	Wyatt 76 (og)	4
26	26	FAT 3Q	A	Farnborough Town	466	L 0 - 2		
27	Dec 3	SP	H	Cirencester Town	341	W 2 - 1	McKay 2 Nichiolls 5	4
28	10		A	Evesham United	303	D 0 - 0		5
29	17		H	Team Bath	419	D 1 - 1	Fuller 26 (pen)	5
30	27		H	Rugby Town	505	L 0 - 3		6
31	31		A	Chesham United	320	D 1 - 1	Fuller 31(pen)	6
32	Jan 2		H	Kings Lynn	543	W 4 - 2	**Baird** 3 8 Blossom 45 Gooderick 71	5
33	7		A	Merthyr Tydfil	420	L 0 - 1		5
34	14		H	Hitchin Town	333	D 2 - 2	Godderick 17 Kilmartin 43	5
35	21		A	Cheshunt	149	L 0 - 2		6
36	28		H	Merthyur Tydfil	371	W 4 - 2	Fuller 15 **Baird** 20 78 Redknapp 73	6
37	Feb 4		A	Halesowen Town	418	W 1 - 0	Redknap 20	6
38	11		A	Tiverton Town	549	D 0 - 0		6
39	18		H	Mangotsfield United	372	L 2 - 4	Fuller 25 Sullivan 45	6
40	21		A	Salisbury City	494	W 3 - 1	**Baird** 11 55 Gooderick 87	6
41	25		H	Bedford Town	454	W 3 - 2	Lazarus 8 **Baird** 55 Fuller 88 (pen)	6
42	Mar 4		A	Aylesbury United	432	L 0 - 2		6
43	11		H	Bath City	508	L 2 - 3	Blossom 4 Fuller 36	6
44	21		A	Cirencester Town	148	W 3 - 1	**Baird** 29 Fuller 45 (pen) Redknap 54	6
45	25		A	Chippenham Town	601	L 0 - 1		6
46	April 1		H	Salisbury City	588	L 1 - 2	Pond 83	7
47	8		A	Team Bath	117	D 2 - 2	Stanbridge 2 **Baird** 11	8
48	15		A	King's Lynn	841	L 0 - 2		9
49	17		H	Rugby Town	356	W 2 - 1	Gardner 42 Pond 65	7
50	25		A	Northwood	171	L 1 - 2	Stanbridge 35	8
51	29		H	Gloucester City	426	W 1 - 0	Stanbridge 89	7

Ave. League Home Attendance: 380   **Goals**   86   77   **Top Goalscorer:** Baird (20)
Best Position: 1st   **Worst:**   10th

BATH CITY

Founded: 1889
Nickname: The Romans

Manager: John Relish
Physio: Dave Lukins
Club Colours: Black & white stripes/Black/Black
Change Colours: Blue/White/Blue
Club Sponsor: www.JohnCrick.com
Previous League: Conference
Best Seasons: **League:** 4th (Conference) 1984-85
              F.A. Cup: 3rd Rd.Replay 1963-64 & 1993-94
              F.A.Trophy.: 4th Rd.1989-90
Ground address: Twerton Park, Twerton,Bath, North East Somerset BA2 1DB
Tel No: 01225 423087/313247 **Fax:** 01225481391
E-mail: mail@bathcityfootballclub.co.uk
Unofficial website: www.bathcityfc.com
Capacity: 8,840   Seats: 1,017   Covered: 4,800   Floodlights:Yes
Simple Directions: Twerton Park is situated off the A4/A36 Lower Bristol Road on the Bristol side of Bath
Midweek Home Matchday: Tuesday
Clubhouse: Several Bars open all week
Club Shop: Contact Martin Brush Tel. Nos: 01225 420613 (H) 07881728689 (M)

CLUB PERSONNEL
Chairman: Geoff Todd
Directors: G.Todd, P. Weaver, M.Hughes, P.Williams, A.Pierce, J.Reynolds & A.Pridham
Managing Director: Paul Williams
Secretary: Quentin Edwards c/o club Tel Nos: 01225 423087(W) 07785 795532 (M)
Press Officer: Secretary
Programme.Editor:
Philip Weaver 01225 832003 (H) 07867 546088 (M))
e-mail:
philip@weaver1234.freeserve.co.uk
Programme
48 pages £1.50
2005-2006
Player of the Year: Gethin Jones
Top Scorer: Scott Partrisge 23
2006-2007Captain: Jim Rollo

CLUB STATISTICS

Record	Attendance:18,020 v Brighton & Hove Albion F.A.Cup
	Victory: 8-0 v Boston United 1998-99
	Defeat: 0-9 v Yeovil Town 1946-47
	Career Goalscorer: Paul Randall 106
	Career Appearance: David Mogg 530
	Transfer Fee Paid: £15,000 to Bristol City for Micky Tanner
	Received: £80,000 from Southampton for Jason Dodd
Senior Honours:	Southern League Champions 59-60 77-78 R-up 29-30 32-33 61-2 89-90 05-06
	Somerset Premier Cup (16) Anglo-Italian Cup R-Up 76-77 77-78
Previous Leagues:	Southern League, Conference
Grounds:	The Belvoir Ground, Lambridge 1889-1932

BATH CITY

BEST LGE ATT.: 2,268 v Chippenham Town
LOWEST: 405 v Aylesbury United

No.	Date	Comp	H/A	Opponents	Att:	Result	Goalscorers	Pos
1	Aug 13	SP	A	Grantham Town	472	W 3 - 0	Partridge 29 44 Sykes 55	2
2	16		H	Tiverton Town	800	W 1 - 0	Sendell 74	2
3	20		H	Chesham United	617	W 1 - 0	Partridge 23	1
4	23		A	Yate Town	575	D 1 - 1	Partridge 61	1
5	27		H	Salisbury City	787	L 0 - 2		4
6	29		A	Team Bath	632	W 4 - 0	Partridge 6 78 Walsh 65 Sandell 88	2
7	Sept 2		H	Banbury United	718	L 0 - 3		3
8	10	FAC 1Q	H	Cinderford Town	404	W 1 - 0	Bird 86	
9	17	SP	A	Bedford Town	399	L 0 - 1		7
10	24	FAC2Q	A	Gosport Borough	440	W 4 - 3	Bird 13 84 Holloway 33 Holland 41	
11	27	SP	H	Mangotsfield United	618	L 1 - 2	Jones 72	9
12	Oct 1		A	Rugby Town	246	W 2 - 1	Bird 11 Holloway 75	8
13	8	FAC 3Q	A	Weymouth	1232	L 0 - 1		
14	11	SP	A	Cirencester Town	417	W 3 - 0	Holloway 35 Partridge 38 86	6
15	15	FAT1Q	A	Dunstable Town	122	D 2 - 2	Bird 86 Walsh 90	
16	18	FAT1Qr	H	Dunstable Town	241	W 5 - 0	Walsh 11 Bird 29 36 Holloway 40 44	
17	22	SP	H	Halesowen Town	580	D 0 - 0		6
18	29		H	Gloucester City	583	D 0 - 0		8
19	Nov 5		A	Northwood	222	W 3 - 0	Holloway 18 Sandell 71 Harris 74	6
20	12	FAT 2R	H	Bromsgrove Rovers	423	W 2 - 0	Bird 10 Holloway 45	
21	26	FAT 3Q	H	Yeading	383	L 1 - 2	Rollo 14	
22	Dec 3	SP	A	Hitchin Town	282	D 2 - 2	Sandell 22 59	7
23	10		H	Grantham Town	490	W 2 - 0	Partridge 74 76	7
24	17		H	Cheshunt	561	W 2 - 0	Walsh 45 Davidge 90	
25	27		A	Chippenham Town	1612	L 0 - 2		7
26	31		A	Helesowen Town	403	L 1 - 2	Walsh 80	7
27	Jan 2		H	Evesham United	585	W 2 - 0	Jones 39 Partridge 75	7
28	7		H	Bedford Town	661	D 1 - 1	Bird 36	7
29	14		A	Mangotsfield United	661	W 2 - 0	Bird 32 Walsh 70	6
30	17		A	Merthyr Tydfil	467	D 0 - 0		5
31	21		A	Gloucester City	521	W 2 - 0	Sykes 22 Partridge 27	5
32	28		H	King's Lynn	631	D 1 - 1	Harris 74	5
33	Feb 4		A	Chesham United	304	W 1 - 0	Walsh 36	5
34	11		A	Hitchin Town	588	W 2 - 1	Bird 1 Partridge 74	5
35	14		H	Aylesbury United	405	W 3 - 2	Partridge 27 Bird 58 68	5
36	18		A	Cirencester Town	325	W 2 - 1	Bird 52 (Pen) Partridge 65	4
37	25		H	Merthyr Tydfil	643	W 2 - 0	Holloway 22 Sandell 49	4
38	Mar 4		A	Tiverton Town	649	W 2 - 1	Walsh 18 Rollo 82	3
39	7		H	Team Bath	579	W 3 - 1	Partridge 24 S.Jones 28 Holloway 89	1
40	11		A	Banbury United	508	W 3 - 2	Partridge 3 (46 55 90)	1
41	18		A	Northwood	718	W 3 - 0	Harris 6 Partridge 38 Sandell 74	1
42	25		H	Yate Town	960	L 1 - 2	Davidge 77	3
43	28		A	Salisbury City	1478	D 0 - 0		2
44	April 1		H	Rugby Town	773	W 1 - 0	Walsh 71	2
45	8		A	Cheshunt	220	L 0 - 1		2
46	15		A	Evesham UNited	396	W 2 - 1	Walsh 20 Sykes 56	2
47	17		H	Chippenham Town	2268	L 0 - 2		3
48	22		A	Aylesbury United	301	W 5 - 1	Rogers 27 Bird 56 Holloway 60 Sandell 71 Davidge 90	3
49	29		H	King's Lynn	1079	W 2 - 0	Rogers 7 Walsh 60	2
50	May 1	Play Off SF	H	Bedford Town	1691	L 0 - 1		

Ave. League Home Attendance:	713	**Goals**	81 42	**Top Goalscorer:** Partridge (20)

Best Position: 1st   **Worst:** 9th

CHESHUNT

Founded: 1946
Nickname: Ambers

"Ambers hope to return to winning ways"

Manager: Tom Loizou
Asst Manager: John Meakes   **Coaches:** Kevin Mudd & Gavin Berry
Club Colours: All Amber & Black
Change Colours: All Sky Blue
Club Sponsor: Falcon Coaches
Previous League: Isthmian
Best Seasons: League: 16th Southern Premier 2005-2006
F.A.Cup: 4th Qualifying Round (4)   **F.A.Trophy.:** 3rd Round Replay 2004-2005
F.A.Vase: 6th Rd 1981-82   **F.A.Amateur Cup:** 3rd Round 1949-50 1969-70
Ground address: The Stadium, Theobalds Lane, Cheshunt, Herts.
Tel No: 01992 626752   **Website:** www.cheshuntfc.com
e-mail: rob@brassett.net
Capacity: 3,500   **Seats:** 424   **Covered:** 600   **Floodlights:** Yes
Simple Directions: M25 Jct 25 Take A10 north towards Hertford. Third exit at roundabout towards Waltham Cross A121. Then left at next one under railway bridge, turn left and ground is 400 yards on left.
Midweek Home Matchday: Tuesday
Clubhouse: Bar and Function Hall   **Club Shop:** No
Local Press: Herts Mercury, Enfield Gazette, Herald (free), Welwyn & Hatfield Times and Lee Valley Star (free).

CLUB PERSONNEL
Chairman: Vince Satori
V-Chairman: Rex Dory
President: Paul Phillips
Secretary: Neil Harrison
Tel No: 01992 301324(H)
07931 537141 (M)
Press Officer: As Secretary
Programme Editor: Alex Kalinic
Tel No: 01992 424653
Programme
56 pages £1.50

2005-2006
Captain: Mick Gyoury
Player of the Year: Michael Kalli
Top Goalscorer: Lloyd Opara

CLUB STATISTICS

Record	**Attendance:** 5,000 v Bromley F.A.Amateur Cup 2nd Rd 28.01.50
	Victory: 11-0 v Royal Ordinance Factories (A) 1946-47 London League Div 1
	Defeat: 0-10 v Eton Manor, London League 17.04..56
	Goalscorer: Eddie Sedgwick 128
	Career Appearances: John Poole 526
Record Transfer Fee	**Paid:**
	Received: £10,000 from Peterborough United for Lloyd Opara
Senior Honours:	Athenian League Champions 75-76 R-Up 73-74
	Herts Senior Cup 23-24 R-Up (6) E.Anglian Cup 74-75
Previous Leagues	London 46-51 Delphian 51-55 Aetolian 59-62 Spartan 62-64 Athenian 64-77 Isthmian 77-87 94-05

Back Row L to R. Sarah Stimpson (Physio) Danny Gibson (Coaching Staff) Michael Deane, Steve Magona, Liam Patrick, Ryan Bernard, Martin Peat, Nicky Gyoury, Michael Kalli, Dave Reddington, Anthony Fenton, Steve Obeng, George Gregorio, Vince Sartori (Chairman) Alex Kalinic (Committee Member).
Front Row L to R Anton Smith, Lee Allen, Bobby Highton, Ross White, Glen Parry, Tom Loizou (Manager) Paul McGiven (Coach), Dean Fenton, Tommy Morgan, Emmanuel Sackey, Rob Tungatt.

CHESHUNT

BEST LGE ATT.: 227 v Chesham United
LOWEST: 100 v Hitchin Town

No.	Date	Comp	H/A	Opponents	Att:	Result	Goalscorers	Pos
1	Aug 13	SP	A	Team Bath	85	W 1 - 0	Gregoriou 68	7
2	16		H	Aylesbury United	138	L 0 - 1		11
3	20		H	Gloucester City	110	D 1 - 1	Gregoriou 49	11
4	23		A	Chesham United	209	L 2 - 4	Gregoriou 8 Highton 27	17
5	27		H	Evesham United	107	W 1 - 0	Gregoriou 83	13
6	29		A	Banbury United	425	D 1 - 1	Tungatt 89	14
7	Sept 3		H	King's Lynn	115	L 0 - 1		15
8	10	**FAC 1Q**	**H**	**Braintree Town**	160	**L 1 - 2**	**Opara** 34	
9	17	SP	A	Rugby Town	225	W 5 - 1	Gregoriou 13 Clark 37 64 **Opara** 39 Bernard 76	11
10	Oct 1		H	Merthyr Tydfil	115	D 3 - 3	Deane 15 Clark 52 Gregoriou 63	13
11	4		H	Bedfont Town	167	L 0 - 3		15
12	8		A	Yate Town	167	L 1 - 4	Clark 80	15
13	15	**FAT 1Q**	**A**	**Tonbridge**	430	**L 0 - 1**		
14	22	SP	A	Grantham Town	272	W 1 - 0	**Opara** 2	11
15	25		H	Hitchin Town	100	L 1 - 2	**Opara** 89	14
16	29		H	Halesowen Town	149	L 2 - 3	Clark 24 Allen 55	15
17	Nov 5		A	Tiverton Town	521	D 1 - 1	Bernard 54	15
18	15		A	Aylesbury United	187	L 0 - 1		17
19	26		A	Gloucester City	234	L 2 - 3	D.Fenton 26 Deane 48	
20	Dec 3		H	Rugby Town	114	L 2 - 3	Gregoriou 33 40	20
21	10		A	Bedford Town	453	D 1 - 1	Deane 23	20
22	17		A	Bath City	591	L 0 - 2		21
23	31		H	Cirencester Town	119	L 1 - 2	**Opara** 59	21
24	Jan 2		A	Hitchin Town	278	L 1 - 4	**Opara** 44 (pen)	21
25	7		H	Mangotsfield United	114	D 2 - 2	**Opara** 63 Gregoriou 85	22
26	10		H	Salisbury City	136	L 0 - 1		22
27	14		H	King's Lynn	820	L 0 - 2		22
28	21		H	Banbury United	148	W 2 - 0	Clark 74 **Opara** 86	22
29	28		A	Cirencester Town	127	W 2 - 0	**Opara** 26 Highton 83	20
30	Feb 4		H	Grantham Town	117	W 3 - 2	**Opara** 3 (35 48 54)	18
31	11		A	Evesham United	184	W 1 - 0	Bernard 64	16
32	18		H	Tiverton Town	145	W 1 - 0	Clark 29	16
33	21		H	Northwood	114	W 5 - 2	Deane 40 43 **Opara** 7 55 Clark 67	16
34	25		H	Tean Bath	135	W 2 - 1	**Opara** 23 78	16
35	Mar 4		A	Mangotsfield United	196	L 1 - 2	Deane 15	16
36	11		A	Halesowen Town	347	D 1 - 1	Deane 73	16
37	18		H	Chippenham Town	128	D 1 - 1	Herring 85 (og)	16
38	April 1		A	Chippenham Town	578	D 1 - 1	Fenton 39	17
39	8		H	Bath City	220	W 1 - 0	Deane 90	17
40	15		A	Northwood	132	L 1 - 3	Wattley 18	17
41	17		H	Chesham United	227	W 4 - 1	Clark 38 63 A.Fenton 44 Deane 73	14
42	22		A	Salisbury City	1327	L 0 - 5		15
43	29		H	Yate Town	155	L 2 - 3	Oben 14 Clark 38	16

Ave. League Home Attendance: 137 | **Goals** 58 71 | **Top Goalscorer:** Opara (16)

Best Position: 7th   **Worst:** 22nd

CHIPPENHAM TOWN

Founded: 1873
Nickname: The Bluebirds

Manager: Darren Perrin **Assistant Manager:** Adie Mings **Physio:** Paul Watts

Club Colours: Royal Blue/royal blue/white

Change Colours: All Yellow

Club Sponsors: Wiltshire Gazette & Herald, Specsavers, and Shoestrings.

Previous League: Western

Best Seasons: League: Runners-Up Southern Premier 2004-2005

F.A. Cup: 1st Round 1951-1952 2005-2006 **F.A.Trophy.:** 2nd Round 2003-04

F.A.Vase: Finalists 1999-2000

Ground address: Hardenhuish Park, Bristol Road, Chippenham SN 14 6LR

Capacity: 3,000 **Seats:**300 **Covered:** 1,000 **Floodlights:** Yes

Simple Directions: M4 Jct 17. A 350 into Chippenham. Follow signs for Trowbridge and Bath to Bumpers Farm roundabout. Then left onto A420 towards town. Ground 800 yds on left.

Midweek Home Matchday: Tuesday

Clubhouse: Matchdays Managers- Peter & Barbara Jefferies

Club Shop: Yes. Contact- Roger Lewis

Local Press: Chippenham News, Wilts Gazette and Wiltshire Chronicle

CLUB PERSONNEL

Chairman: Sandie Webb
President: Doug Webb
Secretary: Chris Blake, 28 Sadlers Mead, Chippenham, Wilts. SN15 3PB
Tel Nos: 01249658212 (H&W) 07713502116 (M)
Programme Editor : Gary Lawrence
Press Officer: Chris Blake

2005-2006
Captain: Ian Herring
Player of the Year: Ross Adams
Top Goalscorer: Dave Gilroy

CLUB STATISTICS

Record	**Attendance:** 4,800 v Chippenham United. Western League 1951
	Victory: 9-0 v Dawlish Town (H) Western League
	Defeat: 0-10 v Tiverton Town (A) Western League
	Career Goalscorer: Dave Ferris
	Career Appearances: Ian Monnery
Senior Honours:	Southern League Premier R-Up 2004-05,F.A.Vase R-Up 99-00
	Western League 51-52 R-Up 00-01 Wiltshire Senior Cup
	and Wiltshire Senior Shield (4)
Previous Leagues:	Hellenic, Wiltshire Senior, Wiltshire Premier, Western.

Back row.left to right: Scott Garraway (Asst.Kit Manager), Nick Stanley, Sean Seavill, Ian Harvey, Matt Rawlings, Adam Gardner, Alan Griffin, Ross Adams, Steve Perrin, Paul Milsom, Steve Jenkins, Kevin Halliday, Kye Holly, Josh Jefferies, Paul Watts (Physio), Dave Tyrrell (Physio) and Clive Garraway (Kit Manager). Front Row: Danny Maye, Simon Charity, Sam Allison, Ian Herring, Adie Mings (Asst.Manager), Darren Perrin (Manager), Dave Gilroy, Mark Badman, Alex Stanley and Andy Riobinson

CHIPPENHAM TOWN

BEST LGE ATT.: 1,612 v Bath City
LOWEST: 384 v Team Bath

No.	Date	Comp	H/A	Opponents	Att:	Result	Goalscorers	Pos
1	Aug 13	SP	A	Aylesbury United	333	D 1 - 1	**Gilroy** 90 (pen)	12
2	16		H	Gloucester CIty	605	W 3 - 0	Constable 18 Thorne 40 Thompson 43 (og)	5
3	20		H	Northwood	550	W 3 - 1	**Gilroy** 3 (8 55 74)	3
4	22		A	Team Bath	417	L 0 - 2		7
5	27		A	Merthyr Tydfil	466	L 0 - 4		12
6	29		H	Cirencester Town	651	W 2 - 0	Constable 26 Viveash 70 (og)	8
7	Sept 2		A	Chesham United	333	W 1 - 0	Herring 54	5
8	10	FAC 1Q	H	**Falmouth Town**	443	**W 4 - 0**	**Constable 20 29 Gilroy 23 77**	
9	17	SP	H	Evesham United	522	W 2 - 0	Thorne 13 Constable 90	4
10	24	FAC 2Q	H	**Newport County**	949	**W 4 - 0**	**Constable 11 33 Gilroy 45 Adams 80**	
11	Oct 1	SP	H	Yate Town	633	W 4 - 2	Herring 8 Harvey 11 Constable 17 **Gilroy** 74	5
12	8	FAC 3Q	H	**Sutton United**	727	**W 1 - 0**	**Allison 2**	
13	11	SP	H	Salisbury City	851	W 2 - 1	**Gilroy** 5 36	3
14	15	FAT 1Q	A	**Cinderford Town**	197	**D 1 - 1**	**Allison 79**	
15	18	FAT1Qr	H	**Cinderford Town**	309	**W 3 - 1**	**Jefferies 28 De Francescantonio 55 Griffin 57**	
16	22	FAC 4Q	A	**Basingstoke Town**	1072	**W 1 - 0**	**Harvey 84**	
17	25	SP	H	Merthyr Tydfil	743	W 2 - 1	Herring 29 (pen) Constable 73	3
18	29		H	Rugby Town	734	W 4 - 0	Harvey 2 Constable 30 Herring 34 **Gilroy** 49	2
19	Nov 1		A	Banbury United	411	L 2 - 4	Herring 12 Constable 90	2
20	5	FAC 1 Rd	H	**Worcester City**	2815	**D 1 - 1**	**Harvey 47**	
21	12	FAT 2R	A	**Hemel Hempstaed Town**	226	**W 3 - 2**	**Adams 6 Tego 15 Gilroy 79**	
22	22	SP	A	Hitchin Town	146	D 3 - 3	Allison 29 **Gilroy** 69 Thorne 75	4
23	26	FAT 3Q	H	**Carshalton Athletic**	510	**L 0 - 2**		
24	Dec 3	SP	H	Bedford Town	632	L 1 - 2	Bunyard 24	5
25	6		A	Gloucester City	261	W 1 - 0	Herring 46	
26	10		A	Yate Town	380	W 2 - 1	**Gilroy** 10 58	2
27	17		A	Cirencester Town	394	D 1 - 1	**Gilroy** 52 (pen)	3
28	27		H	Bath City	1612	W 2 - 0	Herring 62 (pen) Badman 82	3
29	31		H	Mangotsfield United	663	W 3 - 1	**Gilroy** 77 Adams 80 Seavill 90	2
30	Jan 2		A	Tiverton Town	796	W 2 - 0	Herring 45 (pen) Allison 66	2
31	9		A	Grantham Town	626	W 1 - 0	Herring 68	2
32	14		A	Halesowen Town	463	W 2 - 1	**Gilroy** 12 Kirk 60	2
33	17		A	Northwood	215	L 1 - 2	**Gilroy** 68	2
34	21		A	Aylesbury United	652	D 1 - 1	Allison 88	2
35	28		A	Mangotsfield UNited	569	W 2 - 1	Griffin 35 **Gilroy** 49	2
36	Feb 4		H	King's Lynn	568	D 1 - 1	**Gilroy** 76	2
37	11		A	Salisbury City	1907	L 1 - 2	Bartlett 37 (og)	2
38	18		H	Chesham United	543	W 3 - 0	Rawlins15 32 **Gilroy** 76	2
39	21		H	King's Lynn	810	L 1 - 3	G.Thorne 74	2
40	25		A	Evesham United	304	W 2 - 0	**Gilroy** 2 Kirk 46	1
41	Mar 4		A	Bedford Town	550	L 1 - 2	**Gilroy** 10	1
42	11		H	Hitchin Town	548	D 2 - 2	Allison 13 **Gilroy**73	4
43	14		H	Team Bath	384	W 4 - 2	Wheeler 7 Herring 23 (pen) 51 (pen) Allison 35	2
44	18		A	Cheshunt	128	D 1 - 1	Allison 31	3
45	25		H	Banbury United	601	W 1 - 0	Griffin 62	4
46	April 1		H	Cheshunt	578	D 1 - 1	**Gilroy**	4
47	8		A	Rugby Town	256	D 0 - 0		4
48	15		H	Tiverton Town	662	L 0 - 1		4
49	17		A	Bath City	2268	W 2 - 0	**Gilroy** 51 64	4
50	22		A	Grantham Town	232	D 1 - 1	**Gilroy**17	4
51	29		H	Halesowen Town	610	D 0 - 0		4
52	May 1	Play Off SF	A	**King's Lynn**	1065	**W 3 - 1**	**Herring 18 (pen) Harvey 40 Carey 53**	
53	6	Play Off FInal	H	**Bedford Town**	2029	**L 2 - 3**	**Herring 42 (pen) Griffin 47**	

Ave. League Home Attendance: 665   **Goals** 88 52   **Top Goalscorer:** Gilroy (29)

Best Position: 1st   **Worst:** 12th

CIRENCESTER TOWN

Founded: 1889
Nickname: Centurions

CIRENCESTER TOWN
V
BEDFORD TOWN
Saturday 11th March 2006
Kick Off 3:00pm

MATCHDAY PROGRAMME
Printed and Sponsored by
SWIFTPRINT.biz

Manager: Neil Hards **Asst. Man/Coach:** Martin Blackler **Physio/Coach:** Tony Dunne
Club Colours: Red & black/black/red
Change Colours: Blue & white
Club Sponsor:.Sports Solutions GB
Previous League: Hellenic
Best Seasons: League: 7th Southern Premier 2004-05
F.A.Cup: 4th Qualifying Round 2001-02
F.A.Trophy.: 3rd Qualifying Round 1999-2000
F.A.Vase: 3rd Round Replay 1975-1976
Coaches: Tony Dunne, Steve Tapp and Martin Blackler
Physio: Ceri Roberts
Ground address: Corinium Stadium, Kingshill Lane, Cirencester
Tel. No: 01285 654543
e-mail: jim@ lynn16wanadoo.co.uk   **Website:** www.cirentownfc..com
Capacity: 4,500   **Seats:** 550   **Covered:** 1250   **Floodlights:** Yes
Simple Directions: Leave North South bypass(A417(T)/A419)T) at Stow in the Wold
turn off. Turn towards Stow. Right at lights then right again at next junction, London
Road and first left onto Kingshill Lane. Ground about a mile on right.
Midweek Home Matchday: Tuesday 7.30p.m.
Clubhouse: Open seven days a week. Two bars, function rooms. Catering available,
food bar on matchdays. Also Indoor full size **Training Arena**
Club Shop: at the bar.
Local Press: Wilts & Glos Standard and Swindon Advertiser.

CLUB PERSONNEL
Chairman: Steven Abbley
President: Alan Sykes
Press Officer:
Ian Stewart (0117 9402319)
e-mail: ian60@blueyonder.co.uk
Secretary/Business Manager:
c/o Club **Tel No:** 01285 654543
Caroline Carter **email:** caroline
carter@cirentowndc.plus.com
Programme Ed: Robert Saunders
e-mail:rosaunders@btinternet.com
079770694935(M)
01666577579(H)
Programme
32 pages £1.50

2005-2006
Captain: Neil Arndale
Player of the Year: Lee Smith
Top Goalscorer: Gareth Hopkins

CLUB STATISTICS

Record	Attendance: 2,600 v Fareham Town 1969	
	Victory:	
	Defeat:	
	Goalscorer:	
	Career Appearances:	
Record Transfer Fee	Paid: £4,000 to Gloucester City for Lee Smith	
	Received:	
Senior Honours:	Glos. Senior Amateur Cup 89-90 Hellenic Lg.Premier Champions 95-96	
	Glos. County Cup 95-96	
Previous League Ground:	Hellenic	
	Smithfield Stadium	

sports
solutions GB
01793 842088

Back Row (L-R): Eddie Leather (kit Man), Phil Hall, Matt Jones, Gareth Hopkins, Alex Hards, Marc Richards, Steve Lee, Matt Smith, Matt Bicknell, Neil Hards (Manager). **Front:** Mike Symons, Steve Cowe, Joe Dorey, Ian McSherry, Scott griffin, Michael Jackson (Captain), Lee Molyneaux, Lee Smith, Matt Young.
Missing are Rene Regis, and Martin Blackler (coach) and Tony Dunn (physio).

CIRENCESTER TOWN

BEST LGE ATT.: 394 v Chippenham Town
LOWEST: 127 v Cheshunt

No.	Date	Comp	H/A	Opponents	Att:	Result	Goalscorers	Pos
1	Aug 13	SP	A	Chesham United	249	W 2 - 0	Cowe 27 **Hopkins** 90	4
2	16		H	Halesowen Town	253	W 2 - 1	**Hopkins** 9 Wimble 76 (pen)	3
3	20		H	Grantham Town	208	L 0 - 1		6
4	23		A	Salisbury City	506	L 0 - 3		12
5	27		H	Team Batth	174	W 1 - 0	Horgan 26	7
6	29		A	Chippenham Town	651	L 0 - 2		13
7	Sept 2		A	Merthyr Tydfil	432	L 1 - 3	Hunt 83	14
8	10	FAC 1Q	H	**Wimborne Town**	147	W 5 - 3	**Hopkins 25 54 Richards 62 65 Horgan 71**	
9	17	SP	H	Mangotsfield United	239	L 0 - 2		16
10	24	FAC 2Q	A	**Christchurch**	165	W 2 - 0	**Cowe 3 83**	
11	27	SP	A	Gloucester City	329	W 1 - 0	Arndale 51 (pen)	12
12	Oct 1		H	Hitchin Town	186	W 2 - 1	Halliday 37 Fuller 81	10
13	8	FAC 3Q	H	**Havant & Waterlooville**	278	W 2 - 1	**Halliday 1 Richards 52**	
14	11	SP	A	Bath City	417	L 0 - 3		11
15	15	FAT1Q	H	**Gloucester City**	322	W 2 - 0	**Halliday 26 Crowe 58**	
16	22	FAC 4Q	A	**Ramsgate**	697	L 0 - 3		
17	25	SP	H	Rugby Town	168	L 1 - 2	Jackson 33	15
18	29		H	Chesham United	196	L 0 - 1		16
19	Nov 5		A	Halesowen Town	367	D 1 - 1	Halliday 45	16
20	12	FAT 2Q	A	**Banbury United**	404	D 2 - 2	**Halliday 55 Griffin 90**	
21	15	FAT 2Qr	H	**Banbury United**	186	L 3 - 4*	**Stanley15 Horgan 21 Hopkins15**	
22	19	SP	H	Gloucester City	230	L 0 - 1		20
23	22		A	Aylesbury United	168	L 0 - 1		20
24	27		A	Team Bath	83	L 2 - 4	Richards 8 **Hopkins** 73	21
25	Dec 3		A	Banbury United	341	L 1 - 2	Jackson 88	21
26	10		H	Merthyr Tydfil	202	D 1 - 1	**Hopkins** 76	21
27	17		H	Chippenham Town	394	D 1 - 1	Danks 80	20
28	20		H	King's Lynn	171	L 0 - 2		
29	27		A	Evesham Uited	270	W 4 - 0	Danks 3(20 70 84) **Hopkins** 60	21
30	31		A	Cheshunt	119	W 2 - 1	**Hopkins** 18 58	21
31	Jan 2		H	Yate Town	276	L 1 - 3	Halliday 32	17
32	7		A	Northwood	151	L 0 - 3		17
33	21		A	Tiverton Town	731	W 4 - 0	Smith 6 Richards 9 Griffin 49 Arndale 81 (pen)	16
34	28		H	Cheshunt	127	L 0 - 2		17
35	Feb 4		H	Aylesbury Town	140	W 2 - 1	Wimble 45 Smith 78	16
36	11		A	Mangotsfield United	243	L 0 - 3		17
37	18		H	Bath City	325	L 1 - 2	Arndale 24 (pen)	17
38	25		A	Rugby United	212	W 2 - 1	Richards 17 **Hopkins** 73	17
39	Mar 4		H	Hitchin Town	270	W 3 - 1	**Hopkins** 10 59 Cowe 15	17
40	7		H	Salisbury City	188	L 2 - 5	Hanley 22 Richards 75	17
41	11		H	Bedford Town	166	W 5 - 1	Halliday 10 Griffin 53 64 Fuller 60 **Hopkins** 81	16
42	18		A	Grantham Town	212	W 1 - 0	Smith 89	15
43	21		H	Banbury United	148	L 1 - 3	Griffin 57	15
44	April 1		A	Tiverton Town	201	W 2 - 1	Griffin 11 Smith 86	16
45	8		A	Bedford Town	452	L 1 - 2	Jackson 87	18
46	15		A	Yate Town	2790	L 1 - 3	Jackson 28	18
47	17		H	Evesham United	239	L 0 - 1		18
48	22		A	King's Lynn	787	L 1 - 2	Griffin 17	18
49	29		H	Northwood	158	D 0 - 0		18

Ave. League Home Attendance: 198   **Goals**   65 76   **Top Goalscorer:** Hopkins (14)
Best Position: 3rd   **Worst:**   21st

CLEVEDON TOWN

Founded: 1880
Nickname:
Seasiders

Manager: Billy Clark   **Coach:** Jason Eaton: **Physio:**Paul Dighton
Club Colours: Blue & whitestripes/blue/blue
Change Colours: All yellow or all green.
Club Sponsor: Errea
Previous League: Western
Best Seasons: League: Southern League Premier?
F.A. Cup: 3rd Qualifying Round 2nd Replay 1992-1993
F.A.Trophy.: 2nd Round 1998-1999   **F.A.Vase:** 6th Round 1987-1988
Ground Address: Hand Stadium, Davis Lane, Clevedon
Club Website:www.clevedontownafc.co.uk
Capacity: 3,650   **Seats:** 300   **Covered:** 1,600   **Floodlights:**Yes
Simple Directions: M5 Jct 20 - follow signs for Hand Stadium; first left into Central Way (at island just after motorway), 1st left at mini-roundabout into Kenn Rd, 2nd left Davis Lane; ground half mile on right. Or from Bristol (B3130) left into Court Lane (opposite Clevedon Court), turn right after one mile, ground on left. Nearest BR station: Nailsea & Backwell. Buses from Bristol.
Midweek Home Matchday: Tuesday
Clubhouse: Open every day and evening. Separate function suite & lounge bar. Hot food available. Matchday refreshment bar within ground sells confectionary, teas & hot food
Club Shop: Sells all types of souvenirs, programmes and replica kit. Exchanges welcome. Contact: Steve Small (steve.small@blueyonder.co.uk)
Local Radio: Radio Bristol, Star 107.,7 FM
Local Press: Clevedon Mercury, Evening Post and Western Daily Press

CLUB PERSONNEL
Chairman: John Croft
Secretary: Steve Battt, Sutley Hoouse, Pilton, Nr.Shepton Mallet,Somerset BA4 4BL
Tel Nos: 01749 890762 (H)
07817 397677 (M)
Commercial Manager:
Gary Bradshaw (07768 270718)
Programme
Editor: Steve Small
(stevesmall@blueyonder.co.uk)
34 pages £1.30
2005-2006
Captain: Alex Watson
Player of the Year:
Top Goalscorer

CLUB STATISTICS

Record	**Attendance:** 1,600 v Bristol City (Friendly) 27.07.98
	at Teignmouth Road, 2,300 v Billingham Synthonia , F.A.Amateur Cup 1952-53
	Career Goalscorer: **Career Appearances:**
Record	**Victory::** 18-0 v Dawlish Town (H) Western Premier Division 24.04.93
	Defeat: 3-13 v Yate YMCA (A) Bristol Combination 1967-1968
Senior Honours:	Southern League, Midland Division 98-99, Western League 92-93 (R-up 91-92), League Cup (R-up 92-93), Somerset Senior Cup 01-02 04-05 28-29 , 00-01,01-02 , Somerset Prem Cup (4)Somerset Junior Cup 1897-98,
Previous Leagues:	**Leagues:** Weston & District, Somerset Senior, Bristol Charity, Bristol & District, Bristol Suburban, Western 74-93
	Grounds: Dial Hill (until early 1890's); Teignmouth Road (until 1991)
	Names: Clevedon FC, Ashtonians (clubs merged in 1974)

Back row, left to right: Paul Pocock (Physio), Billy Clarke, James Zabek, Mike Trought, Ray Johnstone, Richard Fey, Tom Jacobs, Kris Whitcombe, Danny Haines and Andy Eisentrager (Coach).
Front row: Andy Hates, Steve Lester, Mike Barr, Jack Pitcher, Leon Hapgood, Peter Sheppard, Rob Scott, RyanScott, Ryan Harvard and Mitchel Page.   Photo: Courtesy of Bob Bowen

CORBY TOWN

Founded: 1948
Nickname:
The Steelmen

Manager: Rob Dunion   **Asst.Manager:** Des Elliott
Physio: Neil Berrett & Gordon Kyle
Club Colours: White/Black/Black
Change Colours: Yellow/Blue/Blue
Club Sponsor: English Partnerships and Corus Tubes
Previous League: United Counties League
Best Seasons: League: 3rd Southen Premier   **F.A. Cup:** 3rd Round 1965-1966
F.A.Trophy.: 3rd Round 1986-1987   **F.A.Vase:**
Ground address: Rockingham Triangle Stadium, Rockingham Road,Corby
Tel No: 01536 406640
Club Website: www.corbytownfc.com
Capacity: 3,000   **Seats:**960   **Covered:** 1,150   **Floodlights:**Yes
Simple Directions: On Northern outskirts of town at junction of A6003 and A6116
opposite entrance to RockinghamCastle grounds.
Clubhouse: Trackside bar open on matchdays and during week for hot snacks.
Midweek Home Matchday: Wednesday

CLUB PERSONNEL

Chairman: James Kane C.B.E.
Company Secretary: Myles Rhinds
Secretary: Gerry Lucas, 8 Richmond Avenue, Kettering, Northants. NN15 5JG
Tel Nos: 01536 513507 (H)
07932 633343 (M)
Commercial Manager: Mary Masson
Press Officer: Chuck Middleton
Programme Editor: David Tilley
Tel No: 01536 403667
2005-2006
Captain: Bobby White
Player of the Year: Darren Watts
Top Goalscorer: Kevin Byrne 22

Clubhouse: Trackside bar open on matchdays and during week for hot snacks.
Club Shop: Full range. Contact: C.Wolmer (01536 260900)
Local Radio: BBC Radio Northampton,Northants 96, Connect FM and Corby Radio.
Local Press: Northampton Evening Telegraph, Herald & Post and The Citizen

CLUB STATISTICS

Record	**Attendance:** 2,240 v Watford (friendly) 1986-1987
	Career Goalscorer: David Holbauer 159 1984-1995
	Career Appearances: Derek Walker 601 1979-1920
Record Transfer Fee	**Paid:** £2,700 to Barnet for Elwun Edwards 1981
	Received: £20,000 from Oxford United for Matt Murphy 1993
Senior Honours:	Southern League Midland Division Runners -Up 1990-1991
	Northants Senior Cup (6) United Counties Champions (3)
Previous Leagues:	United Counties League 1935-1952 Midland League 1952-1958

Back Row (L-R): Carl Holmes, Gordon Kyle (Physio), Brett Darby, Zac Nedimovic, Mark Burrows, Stewart Marshall, Darren Watts, Jamie Clarke, Glyn Turner, Rob Dunion (Manager) and Des Elliott (Asistant Manager).
Front Row: Kevin Byrne, Mark Forbes, Chris Goodman, Bobby White (Captain), Danny Marlow, Gary Kennedy and Domonic Hallows
Photo: David Tilley

GLOUCESTER CITY

Founded:1889
Nickname: The Tigers

Manager: Tim Harris **Assistant Manager:** David Mehew
Club Colours: Yellow & Black stripe/black/black& yellow
Change Colours: Red & White
Club Sponsor: Keyway
Previous Leagues: Birmingham Combination
Previous Name: Gloucester Y.M.C.A.
Best Seasons: Lg: Southern Premier R-Up 1990-91 **F.A. Cup:** 2nd Rd 1989-90
F.A.Trophy.: Semi-final 1996-97
Ground address: Meadow Park, Sudmeadow Road, Hempsted, Gloucester
GL2 6HS **Tel No:** 01452 421400
Capacity: 3,500 **Seats:** 560 **Covered:** 2,500 **Floodlights:** Yes
Simple Directions: A40 then A4301 towards city centre and Historic docks. Right
into Severn Rd, over swing bridge then right into Llanthony Road/Hempsted Lane
and right into Sudmeadow Road.
Midweek Home Matchday: Tuesday
Clubhouse: Meadow Park Sports and social club in ground.Normal hours.
Club Shop: Yes
Local Radio: Severn Sound and BBC Radio Gloucestershire
Local Press: Gloucester Citizen and Western Daily Press

CLUB PERSONNEL
Chairman: Chris Hill
President: R.F.Etheridge
Commercial Team: Stuart Pike, Nigel Hughes, Shelley Roffey & Tim Harris
Secretary: Jason Mills, 18 Terry Ruck Close, Gloucester GL51 0KR
Tel No: 07768 750590 (M)
Programme Editor & Press Officer: Mike Dunstan
Tel No:01242 701662

2005-2006
Captain: Tom Webb
Player of the Year: Tom Webb
Top Goalscorer: Luke Corbett

CLUB STATISTICS

Record	**Attendance**: 4,000 v Dagenham & Redbridge F.A.Trophy Semi-Final12.04.97	
	Victory: 10-1 v Sudbury Town (H) F.A.Cup 3rd Q. Rd 17.10 98	
	Defeat: 1-12 v Gillingham 09.11.46	
Career Goalscorer:	Reg Weaver 250	
Career Appearances:	Stan Myers & Frank Tredgett in 1950s	
Record Transfer Fee	**Paid:**£ 25,000 to Worcester City for S.Ferguson & to Gresley R for D.Holmes	
	Received: £25,000 from AFC Bournemouth for Ian Hedges 1990	
Senior Honours:	Southern Premier R-up 90-91 Midland Div: 88-89 Glos Sen Cup:(13)	
Previous Leagues:	Bristol & Dist. (now Western),1893-96, Gloucester & Dist. 97-1907	
	North Glos. 1907-10 Glos. North Senior 1920-34 Birmingham Comb.1935-39	

Back row, left to right: Ken Blackburn (Coach), Jamie Reid, Dan Avery, Chris Burns (Player-manager), Chris Thompson, Andy Hoskins*, Matt Bath, Marvin Thompson, Dave Wikkinson, Lyndon Tomkins and Ade Tandy (Physio) **Front row:** Jimmy Cox, Keith Knight (player-Asst.Manager), Tom Webb, Neil Griffiths, Neil Mustoe (captain) Lee Smith*, Adie Harris and Lee Davis.   * denotes a player who has left the club.

GLOUCESTER CITY

BEST LGE ATT.: 551 v Salisbury City
LOWEST: **223** v Rugby Town

No.	Date	Comp	H/A	Opponents	Att:	Result	Goalscorers	Pos
1	Aug 13	SP	H	King's Lynn	372	L 1 - 2	Bath 5	16
2	16		A	Chippenham Town	605	L 0 - 3		20
3	20		A	Cheshunt	110	D 1 - 1	Davis 23	20
4	23		H	Merthyr Tydfil	355	D 1 - 1	Davis 39	20
5	27		A	Tiverton Town	471	L 0 - 1		20
6	29		H	Mangotsfield Town	425	L 1 - 3	Mustoe 18 (pen)	20
7	Sept 2		H	Rugby Town	223	W 5 - 2	Webb 3 Harris 9 Mustoe 27 (pen) Davis 42 Thompson 71	20
8	10	FAC 1Q	H	**Christchurch**	280	**D 0 - 0**		
9	13	FAC 1Qr	A	**Christchurch**	103	**L 0 - 3**		
10	17	SP	A	Team Bath	114	L 0 - 1		21
11	27		H	Cirencester Town	329	L 0 - 1		21
12	Oct 1		A	Bedford Town	472	L 3 - 5	Webb 20 Addis 51 Kear 59	21
13	8		H	Northwood	264	W 4 - 1	Reid 29 Davis 33 Kear 38 Wilkinson 66	19
14	11		A	Evesham United	219	D 0 - 0		20
15	15	FAT1Q	A	**Cirencester Town**	322	**L 0 - 2**		
16	25	SP	A	Mangotdfield United	332	L 4 - 5	**Corbett** 1 49 Reid 43 Wilkinson 80	21
17	29		A	Bath City	583	D 0 - 0		20
18	Nov 5		H	Banbury United	341	D 1 - 1	Webb 33	21
19	12		A	King's Lynn	690	L 0 - 4		21
20	19		A	Cirencester Town	230	W 1 - 0	Mustoe 35 (pen)	21
21	26		H	Cheshunt	234	W 3 - 2	Addis 27 **Corbett** 41 Mustoe 80 (pen)	
22	Dec 3		H	Aylesbury United	299	D 1 - 1	Wilkinson 64	18
23	6		H	Chippenham Town	261	L 0 - 1		
24	10		A	Rugby Town	214	W 1 - 0	**Corbett** 17	17
25	17		A	Chesham United	223	W 2 - 0	**Corbett** 26 (pen) 69	14
26	27		A	Halesowen Town	468	L 0 - 1		16
27	31		A	Yate Town	340	L 1 - 2	**Corbett** 30	16
28	Jan 2		H	Salisbury Vity	551	L 1 - 2	Wilkinson 32	16
29	7		H	Tiverton Town	392	L 4 - 5	**Corbett** 42 (pen) Mansell 73 Wilkinson 74 Addis 79	
30	14		A	Grantham Town	366	L 1 - 2	Harris 12	16
31	21		H	Bath City	521	L 0 - 2		19
32	Feb 4		H	Evesham United	340	D 1 - 1	**Corbett** 63	20
33	11		A	Mertyr Tydfil	411	D 2 - 2	Stonehouse 30 Whittington 63	20
34	18		A	Grantham Town	339	W 4 - 1	Bevan 31 Whittington 45 80 Wilkinson 78	18
35	25		A	Hitchin Town	338	D 2 - 2	Miller 11 Whittington 78	19
36	Mar 4		A	Northwood	182	W 1 - 0	Whittington 50	18
37	11		H	TeamBath	347	W 3 - 0	Webb 20 Bevan 26 **Corbett** 83	18
38	21		H	Yate Town	366	W 2 - 0	Whittington 12 52	18
39	25		A	Aylesbury United	267	W 1 - 0	Wilkinson 80	15
40	April 1		H	Bedford Town	384	D 0 - 0		17
41	8		H	Chesham United	338	W 3 - 1	Holland 9 McKevor 51 **Corbett** 55	15
42	15		A	Salisbury City	978	L 0 - 3		15
43	17		H	Halesowen Town	471	W 1 - 0	Bevan 70	13
44	22		H	Hitchin Town	391	W 1 - 0	**Corbett** 77	13
45	29		A	Banbury United	426	L 0 - 1		13

Ave. League Home Attendance: 359   **Goals** 57 65   **Top Goalscorer:** Corbett (12)
Best Position: 13th   **Worst:** 21st

HALESOWEN TOWN

Founded: 1873
Nickname: Yeltz

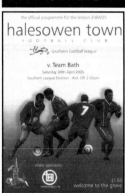

Manager: Paul Holleran   **Assistant Manager:**Chris Brindley
Club Colours: Blue with white trim
Change Colours: White/White/Whitek
Club Sponsor: Cradtcare Construction Ltd.
Previous League: West Midlands (Regional)
Best Seasons: League: Southern Premier Runners -up 1996 **F.A. Cup:** 1st Rd (10)
F.A.Trophy.: 3rd Rd Proper 1994-95
Coaches: Nick Amos & Robin Judd   **Physio:** Graham Jones
Ground address: The Grove, Old Hawne Lane, Halesowen, West Midlands
B63 3TB **Tel No:** 0121 550 2179 **or Fax :** 01902 714221
Capacity: 3150   **Seats:** 525   **Covered** 930   **Floodlights:** Yes
Simple Directions: M5 jct 3 A456 (signed to Kidderminster) then turn right at first
island (signed A459 Dudley). Left at next island (signed A458 Stourbridge) then at
next island take third left into Grammar School Lane, then Old Hawne Lane.
Midweek Home Matchday: Tuesday
Clubhouse: Open every day   **Club Shop:** Yes
Local Radio: BBC West Midlands,B.R.M.B., Beacon.
Local Press: Sports Argus, Express & Star,Birmingham Mail, Halesowen News
Stourbridge & Halesowen Chronicle.

CLUB PERSONNEL

Chairman: Nigel Pitt
Secretary: Stewart Tildesley, 83 Bloomfield Street,Halesowen B63 3RF Tel No: 0121 5508443(H) 07710 434708 (M)
General Manager & Press Officer: Colin Brookes
Programme Editor: Bob Pepper

2005-2006
Captain: Niki Preston
Player of the Year: Simon Forsdick
Top Goalscorer: Lathan Lamey

CLUB STATISTICS

Record	**Attendance**: 5,000 v Hendon F.A.Cup 1st Rd Proper 1954
	Victory: 13-1 v Coventry Amateurs ,Birmingham Senior Cup 1956
	Defeat: 0-8 v Bilston, West Midlands League 07.04.62
	Career Goalscorer: Paul Joinson 369 **Appearances:** Paul Joinson 608
	Record Transfer Fee Paid: £ 7,250 to Gresley Rovers for Stuart Evans
	Received: £40,000 from Rushden & Diamonds for Jim Rodwell
Senior Honours:	Southern Premier League R-up 1996 Midland Div 89-90
	Western Div 2001-02 Birmingham Sen Cup 83-4 97-8 R-up (2)
	Staffs Sen Cup 88-89 R-up 83-4 FA.Vase 84-85 85-86 R-up 83-3
	Worcs Sen Cup 51-52 61-62 02-03 04-05 R-up 2005-06
Previous Leagues:	West Mids.1892-1905 06-11 46-86 Birmingham Comb. 1911-1939

Back row (L-R): Graham Jones (Physio), Bob Warner, Nick Smith, Paul Szewczyk, Stuart Pierpoint, Dan Woodhall, Matt Lewis, Dan Thompson, Sean Dowdell, Aaron Drakeley, Ryan Robinson (Kit man).
Front: Roger Lucas (Director), Jason Powell, Ian Cooper, Alex Cowley, Nick Amos (Player coach), Nigel Pitt (Chairman), Paul Holleran (Manager), Mark Serrell (Director), Nick Preston, Lee Williams, Dave Haywood, Grant Beckett, Colin Brookes (General manager).

HALESOWEN TOWN

BEST LGE ATT.: 468 v Gloucester City
LOWEST: 216 v Mangotsfield Town

No.	Date	Comp	H/A	Opponents	Att:	Result	Goalscorers	Pos
1	Aug 13	SP	H	Hitchin Town	371	D 1 - 1	Pope 50 (pen)	13
2	16		A	Cirencester Town	253	L 1 - 2	Farmer 3	16
3	20		A	King's Lynn	801	W 1 - 0	Lamey 65	9
4	23		H	Banbury United	416	D 2 - 2	Lamey 51 Farmer 87	13
5	27		A	Mangotsfield United	309	D 1 - 1	Lamey 78	16
6	29		H	Rugby Town	375	W 3 - 1	Cowley 28 Amos 55 Smith 61	11
7	Sept 2		A	Grantham Town	270	D 1 - 1	Lamey 56	10
8	**10**	**FAC 1Q**	**H**	**South Normanton**	**279**	**W 5 - 3**	**Forinton 4 (19 21 26 77) Lamey 70**	
9	17	SP	H	Salisbury City	401	L 0 - 1		13
10	**24**	**FAC 2Q**	**A**	**Glapwell**	**171**	**W 1 - 0**	**Forsdick 71**	
11	27	SP	A	Evesham United	200	D 1 - 1	Forinton 74	14
12	Oct 1		H	Chesham United	386	W 1 - 0	Forinton 41	11
13	**8**	**FAC 3Q**	**H**	**Bromsgrove Rovers**	**757**	**L 0 - 2**		
14	11	SP	A	Yate Town	243	W 7 - 2	N.Smith 1 41 Forinton 20 26 Lamey 3 (45 56 59)	10
15	**15**	**FAT 1Q**	**H**	**Willenhall**	**326**	**D 0 - 0**		
16	**18**	**FAT1Qr**	**A**	**Willenhall**	**210**	**W 3 - 2***	**Amos 18 Forsdick 89 Preston 113**	
17	22	SP	A	Bath City	580	D 0 - 0		9
18	25		H	Grantham Town	291	L 0 - 2		10
19	29		A	Cheshunt	149	W 3 - 2	Lamey 3 (3 34 52)	10
20	Nov 5		H	Cirencester Town	367	D 1 - 1	Forsdick 67	8
21	**12**	**FAT 2Q**	**H**	**Aylesbury United**	**374**	**W 2 - 0**	**Lamey 64 Forsdick 82**	
22	19	SP	A	Bedford Town	505	D 0 - 0		8
23	**26**	**FAT 3Q**	**A**	**Sutton Coldfield T**	**278**	**D 1 - 1**	**Forinton 16**	
24	Dec 3	SP	H	King'sLynn	360	D 0 - 0		9
25	**6**	**FAT 3Qr**	**H**	**Sutton Coldfield Town**	**130**	**W 3 - 0**	**Forsdick 43 Lamey 76 Pope 84**	
26	10	SP	A	Northwood	182	L 0 - 3		11
27	**17**	**FAT 1**	**H**	**Tamworth**	**668**	**L 1 - 2**	**Lamey 7**	
28	27	SP	H	Gloucester City	468	W 1 - 0	Forinton 50	13
29	31		H	Bath City	403	W 2 - 1	Forinton 2 Pope 87	11
30	Jan 2		A	Merthyr Tydfil	512	W 3 - 2	Forsdick 15 51 Skidmore 72	8
31	7		A	Hitchin Town	293	L 0 - 1		10
32	14		H	Chippenham Town	463	L 1 - 2	Cowley 26	11
33	21		A	Chesham United	308	W 2 - 0	Pope 26 Forsdick 36	
34	28		H	Evesham United	402	W 2 - 0	Lamey 11 Forinton 65	7
35	30		A	Team Bath	82	W 2 - 0	Lamey 43 Forsdick 74	6
36	Feb 4		A	Banbury United	418	L 0 - 1		7
37	11		H	Team Bath	343	L 1 - 3	Pope 86	8
38	15		A	Tiverton Towm	359	D 0 - 0		7
39	18		A	Yate Town	270	L 1 - 2	Pope 87	8
40	25		H	Aylesbury United	309	D 1 - 1	Haywood 3	9
41	Mar 4		A	Salisbury City	787	W 1 - 0	Smith 58	9
42	11		H	Cheshunt	347	D 1 - 1	Amos 28	9
43	18		H	Mangotsfield Town	216	W 2 - 0	Amos 10 Forsdick 46	8
44	21		A	Rugby Town	207	D 0 - 0		8
45	28		H	Tiverton Town	288	W 4 - 2	Francis 7 24 Preston 14 Forinton 45	6
46	April 1		A	Aylesbury United	287	L 1 - 2	Myers 28	6
47	8		H	Northwood	301	W 4 - 1	Forsdick 4 Myers 34 Francis 35 C.Smith 63	6
48	15		H	Merthyr Tydfil	349	L 1 - 3	Forsdick 88	7
49	17		A	Gloucester City	471	L 0 - 1		7
50	22		H	Bedford Town	355	D 1 - 1	Forinton 30	7
51	29		A	Chippenham Town	610	D 0 - 0		8

Ave. League Home Attendance: 337   **Goals**   68   49   **Top Goalscorer:** Lamey (16)

Best Position: 6th   **Worst:** 16th

HEMEL HEMPSTEAD

Founded: 1885
Nickname: The Tudors

Manager: Steve Bateman   **Physio:** Tyrone Matthews
Club Colours: All Red
Change Colours: Yellow/Black/Yellow
Club Sponsor: Henkel/Coors
Previous League: Isthmian
Best Seasons: League: Southern Premier 03-04
F.A. Cup: 3rd Qualifying Round 1962-1963
F.A.Trophy.: 1st Round 2002-2003   **F.A.Vase:** 4th Round 1998-1999
Ground address: Vauxhall Ground, Adeyfield Road, Hemel Hempstead HP2 4 HW
Tel No: 01442 259777
Club Website: www.hemelhempsteadtownfc.com
Capacity: 3,152   **Seats:** 300   **Covered:** 900   **Floodlights:** Yes
Simple Directions: Leave MI at junction 8 and follow dual carriageway over two roundabouts. From outside lane take first right then left at mini roundabout.Take third turning right at next large roundabout intio ground car park.
Midweek Home Matchday: Tuesday
Clubhouse: Open 7-11 pmweekdays 12-11pm weekends & bank holidays
Tea bar with hot snacks open on matchdays. **Club Shop:** No
Local Radio: Local Radio, Sports Talk, Chiltern and Three Counties Radio.
Local Press: Hemel Gazette and The Herald

UB PERSONNEL
Chairman: David Boggins
President: Brendan Glynn
Secretary: Laurie McParland, 95 The Myrke, Datchet, Slough, Berks.Tel No: 01753 527 394 97836 265105
Programme Editor: Chris Walker
48 Pages 80p

2005-2006
Captain: Grant Carney
Players of the Year: Steve Smith & Paul Edgeworth
Top Scorer: Anthony Thomas 40

CLUB STATISTICS

Record	Attendance:	2,000 vWatford 1985
		at Crabtree Lane 3,500 v Tooting & Mitcham U Amateur Cup 1962
	Career Goalscorer: Dai Price	
	Career Appearances: John Wallace 1012	
Record Transfer Fee	**Paid:** **Received**	
Senior Honours:	Ryman League Division 3 1998-1999 Herts Senior Cup (7)	
	Herts Charity Cup (6) Athenian League Diov 1 R-Up 64-65	
Previous Leagues:	Spartan 22-52 Delphian 52-63 Athenian 63-77 Isthmian 77-04	
Name:	Crabtree Lane >	

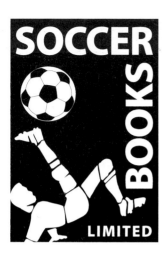

HITCHIN TOWN

Founded: 1865
Re-formed: 1928
Nickname: Canaries

Manager: Darren Salton   **Assistant Manager:** Ken Gillard

Club Colours: Yellow/green/yellow

Change Colours: White/Black

Club Sponsor: Alma Engineering

Previous League: Isthmian

Best Seasons: League: Isthmian League Runners-up 1968-69

F.A. Cup: 2nd Round 1973-74 1976-77 1994-95 1995-96

F.A.Trophy.: 5th Round 1976-77 1980-81 1998-99

Physio: T.B.A.i

Ground address: Top Field, Fishponds Road, Hitchin, SG5 1NU

Tel No: 01462 459028 (matchdays only)

Official website: www.hitchintownfc.co.uk

Capacity: 5,000   Seats: 500   Covered:1,250   Floodlights: Yes

Simple Directions: On A505 near town centre opposite a large green. One mile from Hitchin BR

Midweek Home Matchday: Tuesday

Clubhouse: Open every day   **Club Shop:** Yes

Local Radio: Chiltern, BBC Three Counties

Local Press: Hitchin Comet, Herts on Sunday

CLUB PERSONNEL

Chairman: Terry Barratt
Secretary: Roy Izzard, 2 Bedford Road, Ickleford, Hitchin,Herts
Tel No: 01462 433171
Media Officer & Prog Ed:
Neil Jensen 01462 454678 (H)
0798 498 2034 (M)
e-mail: neil.jensen@ntlworld.com
2004-2005
Captain: Josh Sozzo
Player o.t. Year: Josh Sozzo
Top Goalscorer: Josh Sozzo 31

CLUB STATISTICS

Record	Attendance :	7,878 v Wycombe Wanderers. F.A.Amateur Cup 3rd Rd 8.02.56
	Victory:	13-0 v Cowley 0 and v R.A.F.Uxbridge both Spartan Lg.1929-30
	Defeat:	0-10 v Kingstonian (A) 65-66 and v Slough Town (A) 79-80
	Career Goalscorer:	Paul Giggle 214
	Career Appearances: In Career:	Paul Giggle 769 (68-86)
Record Transfer Fee	Paid:	£2,000 To Potton United for Ray Seeking
	Received:	£30,000 from Cambridge United for Zema Abbey. Jan 2000
Senior Honours:		Isthmian R-up 68-69, Div 1 92-93 R-up 98-99, A.F.A.Senior Cup 31-32,
		Herts Senior Cup (19-a record) and London Senior Cup 69-70 R-up 72-73
Previous Leagues:		Spartan 28-39, Herts & Middx. 39-45 Athenian 45-63 & Isthmian1964-2004

Back row, left to right: Terry Barrett (Chairman), Ken Gillard, Richard Wilmott, Gavin Jaggard, Daniel French, Liam Folds, Aaron Cavill, James Ayres, Tommy Hayes, Tony Huckle (President) and Darren Salton (Manager).
Front row: Stuart Hammonds,David Hicks, David Deeney, Josh Sozzo, Neil Puck, Glen Lamacraft, Mark Duckett, Wayne Mills and Stuart Lockhead

HITCHIN TOWN

BEST LGE ATT.: **508** v Bedford Town
LOWEST: **146** v Chippenham Town

No.	Date	Comp	H/A	Opponents	Att:	Result	Goalscorers	Pos
1	Aug 13	SP	A	Halesowen Town	371	D 1 - 1	McMenamin 65	14
2	16		H	Northwood	257	W 4 - 2	HAYES 3 (22 38 61) **Sozzo** 90	6
3	20		H	Team Bath	231	W 2 - 1	Cavill 19 French 52	5
4	23		A	Grantham Town	264	D 1 - 1	McCulloch 76	5
5	27		A	Rugby Town	302	L 1 - 4	McMenamin 60	9
6	29		H	Chesham United	336	D 1 - 1	French 5	12
7	Sept 2		A	Mangotsfield United	251	L 0 - 1		13
8	10	FAC 1Q	H	Waltham Forest	168	W 4 - 1	**Ayres** 9 **Sozzo** 37 **Bridge** 61 **Cavill** 90	
9	17	SP	H	Merthyr Tydfil	333	L 1 - 2	Ayres 19	15
10	24	FAC 2	A	Deal Town	211	W 3 - 1	Hammond 48 (og) Hayes 51 63	
11	27		H	Kings Lynn	223	L 0 - 5		16
12	Oct 1		A	Cirencester Town	186	L 1 - 2	**Sozzo** 20 (pen)	
13	8	FAC 3Q	A	Cambridge City	461	L 1 - 4	French 16	
14	11		A	Northwood	209	D 0 - 0		17
15	15	FAT 1Q	A	Team Bath	86	W 1 - 0	Cavill 9	
16	22	SP	H	Banbury United	367	W 3 - 0	French 44 **Sozzo** 45 Mills 86	15
17	25		A	Cheshunt	100	W 2 - 1	**Sozzo** 28 Phelan 34	13
18	29		H	Aylesbury United	349	W 3 - 2	Phelen 2 64 **Sozzo** 15	
19	Nov 5		A	Team Bath	108	L 0 - 1		13
20	12	FAT 2R	H	Bedford Town	603	L 1 - 2	W.Mills 30	
21	19	SP	H	Rugby Town	249	W 1 - 0	French 10	10
22	22		H	Chippenham Town	146	D 3 - 3	**Sozzo** 27 Bridge 71 French 74 (pen)	9
23	26		A	Yate Town	175	L 1 - 2	**Sozzo** 45	9
24	Dec 3		H	Bath City	282	D 2 - 2	Lamacraft 65 **Sozzo** 66	11
25	10		A	Tiverton Town	442	L 2 - 6	Cavill 37 **Sozzo** 40	12
26	17		H	Evesham United	222	D 2 - 2	French 22 Hicks 72	12
27	31		A	King's Lynn	928	L 0 - 3		15
28	Jan 2		H	Cheshunt	278	W 4 - 1	**Sozzo** 3 (24 58 67) Jaggard 32	15
29	7		A	Halesowen Town	293	W 1 - 0	Jaggard 63	14
30	14		A	Banbury United	333	D 2 - 2	Cavill 15 **Sozzo** 69	15
31	21		H	Salisbury City	388	L 0 - 3		15
32	28		A	Aylesbury United	313	W 3 - 1	French 16 Hicks 26 **Sozzo** 45	15
33	31		A	Bedford Town	480	W 2 - 0	**Sozzo** 44 Jaggard 61	12
34	Feb 4		H	Mangotsfield United	249	D 0 - 0		12
35	11		A	Bath City	588	L 1 - 2	Hayes 65	14
36	18		A	Merthyr Tydfil	408	W 2 - 1	Pugh 50 Cavill 85	12
37	25		H	Gloucester City	338	D 2 - 2	Hayes 34 76	13
38	Mar 4		A	Cirencester Townn	270	L 1 - 3	**Sozzo** 90	14
39	11		A	Chippenham Town	548	D 2 - 2	Hayes 25 **Sozzo** 38	13
40	18		A	Evesham United	201	L 0 - 2		14
41	25		H	Grantham Town	268	L 0 - 2		14
42	April 1		H	Yate Tiwn	237	W 4 - 3	**Sozzo** 7 (pen) 41 Folds 9 Lochead 35	12
43	8		A	Salisbury City	978	L 0 - 3		13
44	15		A	Chesham United	367	D 0 - 0		14
45	17		H	Bedford Town	508	L 1 - 4	Jaggard 54	16
46	22		A	Gloucester City	391	L 0 - 1		17
47	29		H	Tiverton Town	307	W 3 - 2	**Sozzo** 4 65 Duckett 13	141

Ave. League Home Attendance: 276   **Goals** 69 84   **Top Goalscorer:** Sozzo (22)
Best Position: 5th   **Worst:** 17th

KING'S LYNN

Founded: 1879
Nickname: Linnets

Manager: Tommy Taylor
Physio: Dave Spratt
Club Colours: Yellow with Blue Trim/Yellow/Yellow
Change Colours: Orange/Black/Black
Club Sponsor: Lynn News
Previous Name: Lynn Town
Previous League: Northern Premier
Best Seasons: League: Southern League Runners -Up 1984-85
F.A.Cup: 3rd Rd 61-62 **F.A.Trophy.:** 4th Round 2000-01
F.A.Vase: 5th Rd 94-95 **F.A.Amateur Cup:** Runners-Up 1900-01
Ground address: The Walks Stadium, Tennyson Road, King's Lynn PE30 5PB
Tel No: 01553 760060 E-mail: commercial.klfc@virgin.net
Capacity: 8,200 **Seats:** 1,200 **Covered:** 5,000 **Floodlights:** Yes
Simple Directions: At mini roundabout arriving from A10/A47 take Vancouver Avenue. Ground on left after half a mile
Midweek Home Matchday: Tuesday
Clubhouse: Normal licensing hours with extensions on matchdays.
Club Shop: Full range of merchandise.

CLUB PERSONNEL
Chairman: K.Bobbins
Director of Football: Kevin Booth
President: Jim Chamdler
Secretary: Nigel Link, 58 Hall Lane, West Winch, King's Lynn
Tel No: 01553 841089(H)
07885 144039 (M)
Programme Editor: M.Davis
e-mail: villa.man@btinternet.com
Programme
48 Pages £1.50
2004-2005
Captains: Jack Defty & Sam McMahon
Player of the Year: Adam Smith
Top Goalscorer:
Danny Bloomfield 16

CLUB STATISTICS

Record	**Attendance**:	12,937 v Exeter City F.A.Cup 1st Rd.1950-51
	Victory:	17-0 v Beccles 1929-30
	Defeat:	0-11 v Aston Villa F.A.Cup 1905-06
	Goalscorer:	Malcolm Lindsey 321
	Career Appearances:	Mick Wright 1,152 (British Record)
Record Transfer Fee	**Paid:**	£5,000 to Halesowen Towen for Lyndon Rowland Nov. 1999
	Received:	£60,000 from Southampton for Mark Paul 1998-99
Senior Honours:		F.A.Amateur Cup R-up 1900-01 Southern Lg. R-Up 84-85 Southern Lg Cup 04-05 Norfolk Sen. Cup (19) Norfolk Prem Cup (2) E. Anglain Cup (4) R-up (3)
Previous Leagues		Norfolk & suffolk, Eastern Cos 35-39 48 -54 UCL 46-48 Midland Co's 54-58 NPL 80-8

Back row, left to right: Rob Norris, Mark Warren, Matt Nolan, Jack Defty, Lee Hyde, Michael Frew and Luke Fell.
Centre Row:Howard Bailey, Grant Cooper, Sam McMahon, Shaun Marshall, Charlie Defty, Ashley Nicholls and Luke Kennedy.
Front Row: Shaun Carey, Stephen Harvey, Dean West, Mark Camm, Matt O'Halloran, Louis Blois and Adam Smith

KING'S LYNN

BEST LGE ATT.: 1,821 v Salisbury City
LOWEST: 690 v Gloucester City

No.	Date	Comp	H/A	Opponents	Att:	Result	Goalscorers	Pos
1	Aug 13	SP	A	Gloucester City	372	W 2 - 1	Anselin 32 **Bloomfield** 44	6
2	16		H	Rugby Town	889	D 1 - 1	Defty 38	7
3	20		H	Halesowen Town	801	L 0 - 1		10
4	23		A	Aylesbury United	307	L 0 - 1		15
5	27		A	Chesham United	258	L 0 - 1		18
6	29		H	Bedford Town	835	W 1 - 0	**Bloomfield** 10	15
7	Sept 2		A	Cheshunt	115	W 1 - 0	**Bloomfield** 40	12
8	10	FAC 1Q	A	**Banbury United**	548	**L 1 - 2**	Jones 53	
9	17	SP	H	Tiverton Town	710	W 4 - 1	Harris 63 McMahon 79, **Bloomfield** 85 O'Halloran 90	8
10	24		A	Bedford Town	439	L 2 - 3	Anselin 3 **Bloomfield** 15	8
11	27		A	Hitchin Town	223	W 5 - 0	**Bloomfield** 16, 64 Defty 53 O'Halloran 80 Bunn 85 (pen)	6
12	Oct 1		H	Evesham United	771	W 2 - 1	McMahon 50 **Bloomfield** 80	6
13	15	FAT1Q	A	**AFC Wimbledon**	1720	**L 0 - 1**		
14	22	SP	H	Team Bath	734	W 4 - 2	**Bloomfield** 9 O'Halloran 34 Defty 56 74	3
15	29		A	Salisbury City	922	L 0 - 1		5
16	Nov 5		H	Aylesbury United	759	D 1 - 1	**Bloomfield** 74	7
17	12		H	Gloucester City	690	W 4 - 0	**Bloomfield** 5 79 Hammond 31 Smith 48	6
18	26		A	Evesham United	180	D 1 - 1	Hammond 85	6
19	Dec 3		A	Halesowen Town	360	D 0 - 0		6
20	10		H	Mangotsfield United	832	D 1 - 1	**Bloomfield** 3	6
21	17		A	Northwood	202	W 1 - 0	Smith 75	6
22	20		A	Cirencester Town	171	W 2 - 0	O'Halloran 30 58	
23	27		H	Grantham Town	1118	W 3 - 1	**Bloomfield** 36 Defty 75 90	4
24	31		H	Hitchin Town	928	W 3 - 0	**Bloomfield** 2 Nolan 78 Defty 22	3
25	Jan 2		A	Bamnbury United	543	L 2 - 4	Carey 52 West 66	4
26	7		A	Yate Town	210	L 2 - 3	West 80 Smith 88	4
27	14		H	Cheshunt	820	W 2 - 0	Nolan 30 40	4
28	21		A	Merthyr Tydfil	442	W 1 - 0	Nolan 29	3
29	28		H	Bath City	631	D 1 - 1	Nolan 3	3
30	Feb 4		A	Chippenham Town	568	D 1 - 1	West 90	4
31	11		H	Yate Town	868	W 1 - 0	Nolan 30	4
32	18		A	Team Bath	287	W 3 - 1	O'Halloran 19 Nolan 52 67	3
33	21		H	Chippenham Town	810	W 3 - 1	Cooper 7 Defty 23 77	3
34	Mar 4		H	Chesham United	871	W 2 - 0	McMahon 45 O'Halloran 86	2
35	11		A	Rugby Town	293	W 3 - 0	West 60 McMahaon 70 Defty 73	3
36	18		A	Tiverton Town	351	W 2 - 1	Nolan 9 51	2
37	25		A	Northwood	1026	W 3 - 2	Cooper 35 O'Halloran 46 Nolan 48	2
38	April 1		A	Mangotsfield United	303	W 3 - 1	Cooper 2 Nolan 49 McMahon 56	3
39	4		H	Salisbury City	1821	L 1 - 3	Nolan 8	3
40	8		H	Merthyr Tydfil	843	L 0 - 3		3
41	15		H	Banbury United	841	W 2 - 0	Defty 19 75	3
42	17		A	Grantham Town	523	W 1 - 0	Ziccardi 24 (og)	2
43	22		H	Cirencester Town	787	W 2 - 1	O'Halloran 8 Nolan 48	2
44	29		H	Bath City	1079	L 0 - 2		3
45	May 1	Play Off SF	H	**Chippenham Town**	1065	**L 1 - 3**	**Cooper** 2 (pen)	

Ave. League Home Attendance: 845 **Goals** 75 46 **Top Goalscorer:** Bloomfield (15)
Best Position: 2nd **Worst:** 18th

MAIDENHEAD UNITED

Founded: 1870
Nickname: Magpies

Manager: Carl Taylor   **Assistant Manager:** Phil Heggi
Physios: Lisa Goodenough & John Urry
Club Colours: Black& white stripes/white/white
Change Colours: Yellow/green/green
Club Sponsor: Pharmalink Consulting
Previous League: Conference South
Previous Name: Maidenhead F.C. and Maidenhead Norfolkians.
Best Seasons: Lg: 20th, Conference South **F.A.Trophy.:** 6th Rd 2003-04
F.A. Cup: Quarter FInals 1872-73 73-74 **74-75** **F.A.Amateur Cup:** S-Final 35-36
Ground address: York Road, Maidenhead, Berks SL6 1SF
Tel NOs; 01628 624 624739 or 636314
Capacity: 4,500   **Seats**: 400   **Covered**: 2,000   **Floodlights:**Yes
Simple Directions: From Maidenhead BR drive eastwards down Bell St. Ground is 500 yards. Ground is 5 miles from Jct 7 on the M4
Midweek Home Matchday: Tuesday
Reserve League: Capitol.

CLUB PERSONNEL
Chairman: Una Loughrey
President: Jim Parsons
Secretary: Ken Chandler c/o Club
Commercial manager:
Paul Carney
Programme Editor: Steve JInman (07909 655409)
Programme: 32 Pages Price 2.50
Press Officer: Steve Jinman

2005-2006
Captain: Nathan Bunce
Player of the Year:
Scott Tarr
Top Goalscorer:
Stephen Hughes 14

Clubhouse: Open week day evenings and matchdays
Club Shop: Yes. Contact: Mark Smith (01753 854674)
Local Radio: Star FM. Thames Valley F.M & BBC Radio Berkshire
Local Press: Maidenhead Advertiser and Maidenhead Express.

CLUB STATISTICS

Record Attendance:	7,920 v Southall F.A.Amateur Cup Q/F 07.03.36
Victory:	14-1 v Buckingham Town F.A.Amateur Cup 06.09.52
Defeat:	0-14 v Chesham United (a) Spartan Lg 31.03.23
Career Goalscorer:	George Copas 270 1924-35
Career Appearances:	Bert Randall 532 1950-64
Record Transfer Fee	**Paid**: Undisclosed
	Received: 5,000 from Norwich City for Alan Cordice 1979
Senior Honours:	Promotion to Isthmian Premier 99-00 Berks & Bucks Senior Cup (19)
Previous Leagues:	Southern 1894-1902, West Berks 02-04, Gt West Suburban1904-22 . Spartan 22-39, Gt West Comb. 39-45, Corinthian 45-63, Athenian 63-73 . Isthmian 1973-2004 Conference South 2004-2006

Back Row L-R): Matt Gore (Coach), Nathan Bunce, Dominic Sterling, Mark Nisbet, Yashwa Romeo, Dwain Clarke, Brian Haul, Chico Ramos.
Front: Adie Allen, Danny Burnell, Ashley Smith, Craig Lewington, Ryan Parsons, Eric Kwakye. Photo: Nigel Keene.

MAIDENHEAD UNITED

BEST LGE ATT.: 434 v Newport County
LOWEST: **165** v Bognor Regis Town

No.	Date	Comp	H/A	Opponents	Att:	Result	Goalscorers	Pos
1	Aug 13	CS	A	Sutton United	510	L 1 - 4	**Hughes** 71	20
2	16		H	Newport County	434	D 1 - 1	Traynor 32	17
3	20		H	Cambridge City	309	L 0 - 5		21
4	27		A	Hayes	243	L 1 - 2	Bacon 86	22
5	29		H	Thurrock	223	L 1 - 3	**Hughes** 45	22
6	Sept 4		A	Lewes	604	D 2 - 2	Ogeleabi 70 **Hughes** 85	22
7	10		H	Yeading	284	L 1 - 2	**Hughes** 42 (pen)	22
8	17		A	Carshalton Athletic	278	W 1 - 0	Bacon 45	20
9	24	FAC 2Q	A	Yeading	185	L 0 - 3		
10	Oct 1	CS	H	Weymouth	402	D 0 - 0		20
11	15		A	Havant & Waterlooville	453	L 1 - 2	Traynor 45	20
12	18		A	Bishop's Stortford	310	L 0 - 1		20
13	22		H	Eastleigh	315	D 2 - 2	Newman 65 Saeed-Osman 87	20
14	29		H	Welling United	305	L 2 - 4	Newman 54 **Hughes** 60	21
15	Nov 5		A	Dorchester Town	459	W 3 - 1	**Hughes** 54 Newman 68 83	20
16	8		A	Bognor Regis Town	312	L 1 - 8	**Hughes** 58	20
17	12		H	St Albans Citty	328	L 0 - 4		21
18	19		A	Weston-s-Mare	237	D 1 - 1	Glynn 38 (pen)	21
19	26	FAT 3Q	H	Bishop's Stortford	165	D 2 - 2	**Newman** 28 **Badu** 40	
20	29	FAT 3Qr	A	Bishop's Stortford	171	L 1 - 2	**Newman** 107	
21	Dec 10	CS	H	Histon	235	L 1 - 4	Whiteman 81	21
22	26		A	FarnboroughTown	610	L 1 - 3	Bradshaw 77	21
23	31		A	Eastboune Borough	676	D 3 - 3	Newman 11 Ashe 69 **Hughes** 72	
24	Jan 2		H	Farnborough Town	411	L 1 - 2	Newman 11	21
25	7		A	Sutton United	322	W 2 - 0	**Hughes** 9 Whiteman 59	20
26	14		A	Newport County	625	L 0 - 3		21
27	21		A	Cambridge City	535	L 0 - 3		21
28	28		H	Hayes	315	W 2 - 1	**Hughes** 45 73	21
29	31		H	Basingstoke Town	395	D 0 - 0		21
30	Feb 4		A	Weymouth	1406	L 0 - 4		22
31	11		H	Havant & Waterlooville	251	W 3 - 1	**Hughes** 35 90 Bradshaw 49	21
32	18		A	Eastleigh	368	L 1 - 2	Glynn 89	21
33	21		H	Bishop's Stortford	183	D 2 - 2	Romeo 37 **Hughes** 81	22
34	25		A	Yeadiong	189	W 2 - 0	Wild 12 Bunce 58	20
35	Mar 4		H	Carshalton Athletic	405	L 0 - 2		21
36	11		A	Welling United	646	D 3 - 3	Bradshaw 35 Wild 48 Romeo 90	
37	18		H	Dorchester Town	285	L 2 - 3	Ashe 55 76	22
38	25		A	St Albans City	835	L 0 - 4		22
39	April 1		A	Weston-s-Mare	208	L 2 - 4	Roach 29 74	22
40	4		H	Bognor Regis Town	165	L 1 - 2	Johnson 68	22
41	8		A	Basingstoke Town	345	W 1 - 0	Ashe 89	22
42	11		H	Lewews	307	L 0 - 1		22
43	17		A	Thurrock	184	W 2 - 1	Roach 19 Badu 31	22
44	22		H	Eastbourne Borough	217	L 2 - 6	Roach 56 70 (pen)	22
45	29		A	Histon	893	L 0 - 3		22

Ave. League Home Attendance: 300   **Goals** 52 106   **Top Goalscorer:** Hughes (14)
Best Position: 17th   **Worst:** 22nd

MANGOTSFIELD UNITED

Formed:1950
Nickname : The Field

Manager: Lee Howells
Assistant Manager: Nigel Webb
Club Colours: Sky/maroon/maroon
Change Colours: White/black/black
Club Sponsor: Shield
Previous League: Western
Best Seasons: League: Champions Southern Div 1West 2004-2005
F.A.Vase: Semi-Final 95-96 **F.A.Trophy.:** 4th Round 2001-2002
F.A. Cup: 4th Qualifying Round Replay 2001-2002
Ground address: Cossham Street, Mangotsfield, Bristol BS16 9EN
Tel No: 0117 956 0119
Capacity: 2,500 Seats: 300 Covered: 800 Floodlights:Yes
Simple Directions: M4 Jct 19 A4174 marked Downend. Follow signs to
Mangotsfield. Left by church towards Pucklechurch. Ground quarter of mile on right.
Midweek Home Matchday: Tuesday
Clubhouse: Open 12-11 Snacks hot food on matchdays . Lounge bar for functions.
Club Shop: Yes

CLUB PERSONNEL
Chairman: Mike Richardson
Vice-Chairman: Len Street
Secretary: Steve Porter, 40 Colliers Break, Emersons Green, Bristol BS16 7EE
Tel No: 0117 3308742
or 07812608605
Programme. Editor: Bob Smale
email: bob_smale@yahoo.co.uk
Programme
32 Pages Price £1.50

2005-2006
Captain: Rob Cousins
Player of the Year: Rob Claridge
Top Goalscorer: Rob Claridge 20

CLUB STATISTICS

Record	**Attendance** : 1,253 v Bath City F.A.Cup 1974
	Victory: 17-0 v Hanham Sports (H) 1953 Bristol & District League
	Defeat: 3-13 v Bristol City United (Bristol & District Div 1)
	Career Goalscorer: John Hill
	Career Appearances: In Career: John Hill 600+
Senior Honours:	Southern Lg Div 1 West Champions 2004-205, Western League Champions 90- 91 R-up 99-00, Somerset Prem. Cup: 87-8, Glos.Sen.Cup: 68-9 75-6 02-03 Glos F.A.Trophy (6), and Rothmans National Cup R-up 77-78
Previous Leagues:	Bristol & District 50-67, Avon Premier Comb. 67-72 and Western 1972-2000

Back Row (L-R): Tom Gould, Alex Ball, Tom Warren, Gary Horgan, Rob Claridge, Danny Greaves, Ollie Price, Matt Lock, Matt Denton, Ross Casey, Papa Diepe, Rob Cousins.
Front: Lee Williams (Physio), Aaron Cornwall, Neil Arndale, Jack Allward, Paul Fowler, Lee Davis, Ellis Wilmot, Michael Meaker, Guy Cox.

MANGOTSFIELD TOWN

BEST LGE ATT.: 661 v Bath City
LOWEST: 190 v Grantham Town

No.	Date	Comp	H/A	Opponents	Att:	Result	Goalscorers	Pos
1	Aug 13	SP	A	Rugby Town	327	D 2 - 2	Lane 15 **Claridge** 73	9
2	16		H	Salisbury City	395	D 0 - 0		15
3	20		H	Aylesbury United	315	D 0 - 0		16
4	24		A	Tiverton Town	456	W 3 - 2	Prince 57 Zabek 72 Ball 83	9
5	27		H	Halesowen Town	309	D 1 - 1	**Claridge** 81	11
6	29		A	Gloucester City	425	W 3 - 1	Shore 25 (pen) Wilmott 37, **Claridge** 45	6
7	Sept 2		H	Hitchin Town	251	W 1 - 0	Corbett 31	4
8	10	FAC 1Q	A	Bournemouth	130	D 1 - 1	Corbett 17	
9	13	FAC 1Qr	H	Bournemouth	197	W 7 - 0	Prince 32 Seal 3 (43 46 55) Claridge Lane Corbett	
10	17	SP	A	Cirencester Town	239	W 3 - 0	Seal 50 55 **Claridge** 75	3
11	24	FAC 2Q	H	Swindon Spermarine	278	W 4 - 2	Price 17 Seal 18 Ball 44 Casey 52	
12	27	SP	A	Bath City	618	W 2 - 1	**Claridge** 4 35	2
13	Oct 1		H	Banbury United	413	L 1 - 2	**Claridge** 16	4
14	8	FAC 3Q	A	Bromley	488	D 0 - 0		
15	11	FAC 3Qr	H	Bromley	403	L 0 - 1		
16	15	FAT1Q	A	Tiverton Town	564	D 0 - 0		
17	18	FAT1Qr	H	Tiverton Town	294	L 1 - 2	Casey 31	
18	22	SP	A	Northwood	183	W 5 - 3	Seal 2 65 Shore 38 (pen) 55 (pen) Warren 77	4
19	25		H	Gloucester City	332	W 5 - 4	Claridge 11 G.Warren 16 Amyimah 41 Seal 65 Shore 70 (pen)	2
20	29		H	Tiverton Town	434	D 1 - 1	Price 31	3
21	Nov 5		A	Grantham Town	319	W 2 - 1	Casey 2 Summers 86	2
22	8		A	Bedford Town	372	L 0 - 1		2
23	19		H	Chesham United	242	W 4 - 3	**Claridge** 10 35 Casey 49 Seal 51	2
24	26		A	Aylesbury United	281	D 1 - 1	Seal 81	1
25	Dec 10		A	King's Lynn	832	D 1 - 1	Anyinsah 68	3
26	17		H	Rugby Town	300	L 1 - 3	Casey 90	4
27	27		A	Yate Town	710	D 2 - 2	**Claridge** 44 85	5
28	31		A	Chippenham Town	663	L 1 - 3	Paul 87	5
29	Jan 2		H	Team Bath	324	D 3 - 3	Ball 7 Metitiri 83 (og) Paul 90	6
30	7		A	Cheshunt	114	D 2 - 2	**Claridge** 50 Shore 90	6
31	14		H	Bath City	661	L 0 - 2		8
32	21		H	Evesham United	269	D 2 - 2	Paul 3 Anyinsah 52	9
33	28		H	Chippenham Town	569	L 1 - 2	Paul 72	10
34	Feb 4		A	Hitchin Town	249	D 0 - 0		10
35	11		H	Cirencester Town	243	W 3 - 0	Zabek 51 Thomas 61 Anyinsah 65	7
36	18		A	Banbury United	372	W 4 - 2	Paul 2 13 **Claridge** 18 90	7
37	21		A	Merthyr Tydfill	251	L 0 - 1		7
38	25		H	Northwood	225	L 1 - 3	Paul 26	8
39	Mar 4		A	Cheshunt	196	W 2 - 1	**Claridge** 8 Lane 33	8
40	11		A	Salisbury City	826	D 2 - 2	Paul 75 Seal 84	7
41	18		A	Halesowen Town	216	L 0 - 2		9
42	25		H	Bedford Town	209	L 0 - 2		9
43	April 1		H	King's Lynn	303	L 1 - 3	Casey 85	9
44	8		A	Evesham United	195	W 3 - 2	Casey 24 Paul 38 65	9
45	11		A	Merthyr Tydfil	199	W 3 - 0	Lock 7 Paul 58 (pen) Seal 82	9
46	15		A	Team Bath	154	W 1 - 0	Casey 49	8
47	17		H	Yate Town	421	L 0 - 3		9
48	22		A	Chesham United	269	L 0 - 2		9
49	29		H	Grantham Town	190	L 0 - 1		10

Ave. League Home Attendance: 324   **Goals** 80 73   **Top Goalscorer:** Claridge (17)

Best Position: 1st   **Worst:** 16th

MERTHYR TYDFIL

Founded: 1945
Nickname: The Martyrs

Manager: Paul Sugrue   **Assistant Manager:** John Lewis
Coaches: Jason Murphy and David Hughes
Club Colours: Black & white stripes/black/black
Change Colours: Red with yellow trim
Club Sponso: Rainbow Print
Previous League: Conference
Best Seasons: **League:** 4th (Conference) 1991-92
                     F.A.Cup: 2nd Rd (6)
                     Welsh F.A.Cup: Winners 48-9 50-1 86-7
                     F.A.Trophy.: 3rd Rd 1995-96
Ground address: Penndarren Park, Merthyr Tydfil, Mid Glamorgan.
Tel No: 01685 384102
emai: pughy@tinyonline.co.uk
Capacity: 10,000   **Seats:** 1,500   **Covered:** 5,000   **Floodlights:** Yes
Simple Directions: From South: A470 Express Way to Merthyr Centre to Pontmorlais (traffic lights) turn left then right. First right at Catholic Church and right again into Park Terrace.
Midweek Home Matchday: Tuesday
Clubhouse: Daily from 6,30-11,00pm. Two club cafes on matchdays for hot food
Club Shop: Fully stocked. Contact: Mel Jenkins: 01443 692336

CLUB PERSONNEL

Chairman: Wyn Holloway
Vice Chairman: Paul Sugrue
Football Secretary:
Anthony Hughes. 4 Brynmorlais,
Penydarren, Merthyr Tydfil
CF479YE
Tel No: 01685 359921 (H & Fax)
07958 006911 (M)
Prog Ed: Mike Donovan
Tel No: 07788 185149 (M)

2005-2006
Captain: Mike Fowler
Player of the Year: Craig Steins
Top Goalscorer: Craig Steins

CLUB STATISTICS

Record	Attendance: 21,000 v Reading F.A.Cup 2nd Rd 1949-50
	Victory: 11-0 v Rushden 1987
	Defeat: 2-9 v Altrincham 1993
	Goalscorer:
	Career Appearances:
Record Transfer Fee	Paid: £10,000 to Cardiff City for Robbie James 1992
	Received: £12,000 from Exeter City for Ray Pratt 1981
Senior Honours:	Welsh F.A.Cup (3) Southern League (5) Midland Div 87-8
	Premier Div Champions 1988-89
Previous Leagues	Southern Lg. 46-49,and Conference 89-95

Back Row - Les Barlow (Youth Team - Head Coach), Paul Evans (Assistant Manager), Dale Griffiths, Mike Symons, Lee Idzi, Lewis Sommers, Ashley Morris, Jeff Eckhardt, Craig Steins, Tim Harris (Manager) Jane Price (Physio).
Middle Row - Adrian Needs, Garry Shephard, Paul Keddle, Mike Fowler (Captain), Richard Ingram, Dane Williams, Chris Thomas, Steve Williams. Front Row - Dean Clarke, Carl Jenkins, Jamie Hammonds, Jason Davies.

MERTHYR TYDFIL

BEST LGE ATT.: 541 v Grantham Town
LOWEST: **251** v Mangotsfield United

No.	Date	Comp	H/A	Opponents	Att:	Result	Goalscorers	Pos
1	Aug 13	SP	A	Northwood	227	W 3 - 2	Ingram 74 Fowler 88 (pen) Welsh 90	5
2	16		H	Yate Town	321	W 3 - 0	Ingram 3 Steins 26 28	1
3	20		H	Rugby Town	412	D 1 - 1	D.Williams 88	4
4	22		A	Gloucester City	355	D 1 - 1	D.Williams 90	3
5	27		H	Chippenham Town	466	W 4 - 0	Welsh 17 Steins 41 78 **Shepherd** 82	1
6	29		A	Salisbury City	761	L 0 - 2		3
7	Sept 2		H	Cirencester Town	432	W 3 - 1	Steins 41 **Shepherd** 58 Welsh 71	2
8	10	FAC 1Q	H	St.Blazey	407	W 3 - 2	**Shepherd 30 D.Williams 60 Fowler 67**	
9	17	SP	A	Hitchin Town	333	W 2 - 1	Steins 30 Welsh 57	2
10	24	FAC 2Q	A	Taunton Town	414	D 1 - 1	**Fowler 78**	
11	27	FAC 2Qr	H	Taunton Town	370	W 2 - 1	**Griffiths 44 Welsh 68**	
12	Oct 1	SP	A	Cheshunt	115	D 3 - 3	Welsh 13 9 Steins 81	6
13	8	FAC 3Q	H	Salisbury City	615	W 2 - 1	**Steins 48 Sommers 88**	
14	15	FAT1Q	H	Rushall Olympic	403	L 0 - 3		
15	22	FAC 4Q	H	Farnborough Town	1019	W 2 - 0	**Fowler 43 Steins 75**	
16	25	SP	A	Chippenham Town	743	L 1 - 2	**Shepherd** 89	9
17	29		H	Grantham Town	541	W 2 - 1	Steins 61 D Williams 69	7
18	Nov 5	FAC 1R	H	Walsall	3046	L 1 - 2	**S.Williams** 29	
19	26	SP	A	Rugby Town	295	L 0 - 1		12
20	Dec 3		H	Northwood	405	L 0 - 1		14
21	10		A	Cirencester Town	202	D 1 - 1	**Shepherd** 77	14
22	13		H	Salisbury City	394	L 0 - 1		
23	17		H	Bedford Town	385	L 1 - 3	**Shepherd** 30	16
24	20		A	Aylesbury United	241	W 2 - 0	D.Williams 68 Welsh 88	
25	27		A	Tean Bath	196	W 3 - 2	Fowler 25 Welsh 27 Elliott 75	8
26	31		A	Evesham United	226	W 2 - 1	Welsh 14 **Shepherd** 20	8
27	Jan 2		H	Halesowen Town	512	L 2 - 3	Fowler 3 D Williams 35	10
28	7		H	Banbury United	420	W 1 - 0	Moses 39	8
29	14		A	Bedford Town	501	W 1 - 0	D.Williams 26	7
30	17		H	Bath City	467	D 0 - 0		7
31	21		H	King's Lynn	442	L 0 - 2		8
32	28		A	Banbury United	371	L 2 - 4	O'Sullivan 27 Dorrian 36	9
33	Feb 4		A	Yate Town	220	L 2 - 3	**Shepherd** 50 Steins 71	13
34	7		A	Tiverton Town	343	D 1 - 1	Fowler 61	
35	11		H	Gloucester City	411	D 2 - 2	D.Williams 44 48	12
36	18		H	Hitchin Town	408	L 1 - 2	**Shepherd** 90 (pen)	14
37	21		H	Mangotsfield Unired	251	W 1 - 0	**Shepherd** (pen) 74	8
38	25		A	Bath City	643	L 0 - 2		11
39	Mar 11		A	Grantham Town	241	D 0 - 0		12
40	18		A	Chesham United	333	D 2 - 2	Colvin 67 Moses 82	11
41	April 1	H		Chesham United	387	L 1 - 4	**Shepherd** 35 (pen)	14
42	4		A	Evesham United	310	W 3 - 0	**Shepherd 20 Fowler 40 Dimond 46**	11
43	8		A	King's Lynn	843	W 3 - 0	**Shepherd** 12 75 Keddle 77	10
44	11		A	M<angotsfield United	199	L 0 - 3		10
45	15		A	Halesowen Town	349	W 3 - 1	Welsh 10 Steins 15 Kweddle 27	10
46	17		H	Team Bath	336	W 1 - 0	**Shepherd** 15	10
47	22		A	TivertonTown	422	L 0 - 2		10
48	29		H	Aylesbury United	402	L 2 - 4	**Shepherd** 5 Stein 32	9

Ave. League Home Attendance: 383   **Goals** 71 69   **Top Goalscorer:** Shepherd (16)
Best Position: 1st   **Worst:** 16th

NORTHWOOD

Founded: 1899
Nickname: Woods

Manager: Colin Payne
Coaches: Gary Farrell and John Toogood   **Physio:** George Price
Club Colours: All red
Change Colours: All Yellow
Club Sponsor: Don Bruce Bookmakers
Previous League: Isthmian
Previous Name: Northwood Town
Best Seasons: League Isthmian Premier
F.A.Cup: 4th Qualifying Round 2000-01
F.A.Trophy.: 3rd Rd 2000-01   **F.A.Vase:** 6th Round 96-97
Ground address: Northwood Park, Chestnut Avenue, Northwood, Middx.
Tel No: 01923 827148
Capacity: 3,075   **Seats** 307   **Covered**: 932   **Floodlights:** Yes
Simple Directions: A404 (Pinner-Rickmansorth) Chestnut Avenue, A third of a mile from Northwood Hill station (Metropolitan Line). Right out of station to roundabout , left into Pinner Road, left into Chestnut Avenue after 300 yards.
Midweek Home Matchday: Tuesday
Clubhouse: Week-ends and most week days. Hot food available.
Club Shop: No

CLUB PERSONNEL

Chairman: Ken Green
Vice-Chairman: Pat Byrne
President: Lothar Hahn
Secretary: Alan Evans, 48 Webster Gardens, Ealing, W5 5ND Tel NO: 07960 744349
Programme Editor: Secretary
Programme
60 pages £1.20

2005-2006
Captain: Wayne Carter
Player of the Year: Kevin Hart
Top Goalscorer: Dean Clark 14

CLUB STATISTICS

Record	**Attendance**: 1,642 v Chelsea. Friendly July 1997
	Victory: 15-0 v Dateline (H) Middlesex Intermediate Cup 1973
	Defeat: 0-8 v Bedfont Middx. Lg 1975
	Goalscorer: (season) Lawrence Yaku 61 (99-00)
	Career Appearances: Chris Gell 493 + ?
Senior Honours:	Middlesex Premier Cup 94-95 R-Up 99-00 01-02, Isthmain Lg Div 1
	North Champions 2002-03 Isthmian Charity Shield Winners 2002
Previous Leagues	Harrow & Wembley 32-69, Middlesex 69-78 , Hellenic 79-84
	London Spartan 84-92

Back Row (L-R): Lee Carroll, Wayne Carter, Ryan Kirkland, Luke Evans, Dean Lindsay, Rob Bixby, Harry Howell, Max Howell, Terry Back, Fergus Moore. Front Row: Peter Dean, Gavin Hart, Chris Gell, Dave Nolan, Shayne Demetrious, Richard Gell, Richard McDonagh.

NORTHWOOD

BEST LGE ATT.: 253 v Chesham United
LOWEST: 127 v Team Bath

No.	Date	Comp	H/A	Opponents	Att:	Result	Goalscorers	Pos
1	Aug 13	SP	H	Merthyr Tydfil	227	L 2 - 3	Demetrious 10 Dean 24	14
2	16		A	Hitchin Town	257	L 2 - 4	Dean 11 Demetrious 80 (pen)	21
3	20		A	Chippenham Town	550	L 1 - 3	Kirkland 72	21
4	23		H	Bedford Town	159	L 2 - 3	Howelll 75 Kirkland 89	22
5	27		A	Gtrantham Town	266	L 0 - 2		22
6	30		H	Aylesbury United	243	W 2 - 0	Hart 15 Dean 37	21
7	Sept 3		H	Team Bath	127	D 1 - 1	Dean 79	21
8	10	FAC 1Q	H	March Town	141	W 3 - 0	Kirkland 10 Moore 79 83	
9	17	SP	A	Yate Town	220	L 0 - 1		22
10	24	FAC 2Q	H	Aylesbury United	249	D 0 - 0		
11	27	FAC 2Qr	A	Aylesbury United	262	L 0 - 2		
12	Oct 1	SP	A	Tiverton Town	475	L 1 - 4	Clark 3	22
13	8		A	Gloucester City	264	L 1 - 4	Kirkland 58	22
14	11		H	Hitchin Town	209	D 0 - 0		22
15	15	FAT1Q	H	Ramsgate	152	L 2 - 4	Kirkland 32 Clark 76	
16	22	SP	H	Mangotsfield United	183	L 3 - 5	Clark 62 64 (pen) Heselton 90	22
17	25		A	Chesham United	243	L 1 - 3	Dean 31	22
18	29		A	Banbury United	389	W 1 - 0	Heselton 84	22
19	Nov 5		H	Bath City	222	L 0 - 3		22
20	12		H	Rugby Town	162	D 0 - 0		22
21	19		A	Evesham United	196	L 0 - 4		22
22	Dec 3		A	Merthyr Tydfil	405	W 1 - 0	Garrard 46	22
23	10		H	Halesowen Town	182	W 3 - 0	Clark 22 Heselton 74 Dean 81	22
24	17		H	King's Lynn	202	L 0 - 2		22
25	31		A	Salisbury City	759	L 0 - 3		22
26	Jan 2		H	Chesham United	253	D 1 - 1	Clark 89	22
27	7		H	Cirencester Town	151	W 3 - 0	Garrard 8 Grieves 14 Dean 17	21
28	14		A	Team Bath	83	W 3 - 2	Clark 36 54 (pen) Heselton 58	21
29	17		A	Chippenham Town	215	W 2 - 1	Meakin 27 Clark 33	16
30	21		H	Grantham Town	201	L 0 - 2		18
31	28		A	Rugby Town	208	W 2 - 1	Clark 21 Garrard 75	16
32	Feb 4		H	Tiverton Town	193	L 2 - 4	Davies 10 (og) Hart 59	17
33	11		A	Bedford Town	463	L 0 - 4		18
34	18		H	Salisbury City	234	D 2 - 2	Dean 52 Demetrious 90	19
35	21		A	Cheshunt	114	L 2 - 5	Dean Shipperley	19
36	25		A	Mangotsfield Town	225	W 3 - 1	Hesselton 47 Demetrious 67 Clark 76	18
37	Mar 4		H	Gloucester City	182	L 0 - 1		19
38	11		H	Yate Town	138	W 3 - 2	Heselton 35 Dean 47 Courtnage 75	19
39	18		A	Bath City	718	L 0 - 3		19
40	25		A	King's Lynn	1026	L 2 - 3	Shipperley 41 Clark 67	19
41	April 1		H	Evesham, United	178	L 1 - 2	Hart 47	19
42	8		A	Halesowen Town	301	L 1 - 4	Hart 37	19
43	15		H	Cheshunt	132	W 3 - 1	Clark 39 Dean 47 Hatton 90	19
44	17		A	Aylesbury United	268	L 0 - 3		19
45	22		H	Banbury United	171	W 2 - 1	Moore 72 Clark 76 (pen)	19
46	29		A	Cirencester Town	158	D 0 - 0		19

Ave. League Home Attendance: 189   **Goals** 58 94   **Top Goalscorer:** Clark (14)
Best Position: 14th   **Worst:** 22nd

RUGBY TOWN

Formed: 1956
Nickname: Town

Manager: Billy Jeffrey
Asst Manager: Steve Shea   **Assistant Manager**: Kenny Mist
Physio: Bob Gardner
Club Colours: Sky blue/white/white
Change Colours: Tangerine/Black/Black
Club Sponsor: Rugby Telegraph and Melbros Ltd
Previous League: West Midlands
Previous Names: Valley Sports, Valley Sports Rugby, V.S.Rugby, Rugby United
Best Seasons: F.A.Cup: 2nd Rd 1987-88
F.A.Vase: Winners: 1982-83   **F.A.Trophy.:** 2nd Round 2004-2005
Ground address: Butlin Road, Rugby, Warwicks. CV21 3ST
Tel No: 01788 844806   **Club call** No: 09066 555971
Club Website: www.rugbytownfc.co.uk
Capacity: 6,000   **Seats:** 750   **Covered:** 1,000 **Floodlights:** Yes
Simple Directions: Ground is off Clifton (B5414) on the north side of Rugby. One mile from Rugby station.
Midweek Home Matchday: Tuesday
Clubhouse: Open every evening and week end lunchtimes
Club Shop Manager: Carl Barnes

CLUB PERSONNEL

Chairman: Brian Melvin,
President: Dr.Pete Kilvert
Directors: Mike Yeats, Les Leeson, Danny Lordon, Lisa Melvin, Jim Melvin and Darren Knapp.
Secretary: Doug Wilkins, 298 Rocky Lane, Great Barr, Birmingham, B42 1NQ
Tel NO: 0121 6t811544 (H)
Programme Editor: Neil Melvin
Tel No: 01788 567717

2005-2006
Captain: Craig Herbert
Player of the Year:Delroy Gordon
Top Goalscorer: Dave Stone

CLUB STATISTICS

Record	**Attendance:** 3,961 v Northampton Town F.A.Cup 1964	
	Victory: 10-0 v Ilkeston Town F.A.Trophy 04.09.85	
	Defeat: 1-11 v Ilkeston Town (A) 18.04.98	
	Goalscorer: Danny Conway 124	
	Career Appearances: Danny Conway 374	
Record Transfer Fee	**Paid:** £3,500 for R. Smith, I. Crawley and G.Bradder	
	Received: £15,000 from Northampton Town for T.Angus.	
Senior Honours:	F.A.Vase Winners 82-83 Southern League Midland Division 86-87	
	Birmingham Senior Cup: 88-89 91-92	
Previous Leagues	Rugby & District, 56-63 Coventry & Partnership, North Warwicks 63-69	
	United Counties 69-75 and West Midlands 75-83	

Back Row (L-R): Billy Jeffrey (Manager), Bob Gardner (Physio), Steve Townsend (Coach), Simon Lynn, Matt Wells, Mike Feely, Jason Taylor, Delroy Gordon, Craig Herbert, David Stone, Ross Harris, Farhad Afandiyev, Mark Shackleton (Coach). **Front:** Chris Tullin, David Kolodynski, Ryan Byrne, Danny Hall, Aaron Stringfellow, Willis Francis, Matt Gearing, Tom Breward, Kenny Mist (Assistant Manager).

RUGBY TOWN

BEST LGE ATT.: 505 v Banbury United
LOWEST: **202** v Tiverton Town

No.	Date	Comp	H/A	Opponents	Att:	Result	Goalscorers	Pos
1	Aug 13	SP	H	Mangotsfield United	327	D 2 - 2	**Stone** 60 Gould 67	10
2	16		A	King's Lynn	889	D 1 - 1	Squire 87	14
3	20		A	Merthyr Tydfil	412	D 1 - 1	**Stone** 77	14
4	23		H	Evesham United	259	L 1 - 3	Tully 17	19
5	27		H	Hitchin Town	302	W 4 - 1	Slinn 33 **Stone** 37 Cross 54 Maddox 88	13
6	29		A	Halesowen Town	375	L 2 - 3	Squire 60 Slinn 76	16
7	Sept 3		A	Gloucester City	223	L 2 - 5	Squire 7 **Stone** 52	19
8	10	FAC 1Q	A	**AFC Telford**	1065	D 1 - 1	**Slinn** 76	
9	13	FAC1Qr	H	**AFC Telford**	265	L 2 - 3	**Stone** 40 66	
10	17	SP	H	Cheshunt	225	L 1 - 5	Gordon 2	20
11	Oct 1		H	Bath City	246	L 1 - 2	Maddox 3	20
12	11		H	Chesham United	247	W 3 - 0	Bowden-Hasse 12 (og) Gordon 51 **Stone** 57	19
13	15	FAT1Q	A	**Leighton Town**	134	L 1 - 2	**Squire** 52	
14	22		A	Salisbury City	587	L 0 - 3		21
15	25		A	Cirnecester Town	168	W 2 - 1	Tully 2 **Stone** 75	19
16	29		A	ChippenhamTown	734	L 0 - 4		19
17	Nov 5		H	Bedford Town	304	W 5 - 2	Slinn 3 (20 pen 25 49) Gordon 64 **Stone** 84	
18	12		A	Northwood	162	D 0 - 0		16
19	19		A	Hitchin Town	249	L 0 - 1		19
20	26		H	Merthyr Tydfil	295	W 1 - 0	**Stone** 78	17
21	Dec 3		H	Cheshunt	114	W 3 - 2	Gordon 43 Slinn 68 Stoke 77	
22	10		H	Gloucester City	214	L 0 - 1		15
23	17		A	Mangotsfield United	300	W 3 - 1	Gordon 36 Tullen 80 **Stone** 85	11
24	27		H	Banbury United	505	W 3 - 0	Evans 31 Tullen 59 Beard 75	11
25	31		A	Aylesbury United	354	W 4 - 0	Beard 20 Francis 56 **Stone** 69 84 (pen)	9
26	Jan 2		A	Grantham Town	398	D 2 - 2	Gordon 14 **Stone** 44	9
27	7		A	Evesham United	179	L 0 - 3		13
28	14		H	Yate Town	233	D 0 - 0		13
29	17		H	Tiverton Town	202	W 3 - 1	Gardner 10 (og) Gordon 54 Beard 70	10
30	21		A	Team Bath	102	W 3 - 1	Slinn 45 Gordon 54 Green 63	
31	28		H	Northwood	208	L 1 - 2	Wooding 15	8
32	Feb 11		A	Chesham United	223	W 2 - 1	**Stone** 44 Slinn 90	9
33	18		A	Aylesbury United	272	D 1 - 1	Beard 3	9
34	25		H	Cirencester Town	212	L 1 - 2	Beard 7	12
35	Mar 4		A	Yate Town	207	L 0 - 1		13
36	11		H	King's Lynn	293	L 0 - 3		14
37	21		H	Halesowen Town	207	D 0 - 0		13
38	25		A	Tiverton Town	372	D 2 - 2	Gordon 2 Evans 7	13
39	April 1		A	Bath City	773	L 0 - 1		15
40	8		H	Chippenham Town	256	D 0 - 0		16
41	11		H	Salisbury City	262	L 1 - 3	Gordon 57	16
42	15		H	Grantham Town	265	L 0 - 2		16
43	17		A	Banbury United	356	L 1 - 2	Gordon 49	17
44	22		H	Ream Bath	204	W 1 - 0	Wells 64	14
45	29		A	Bedford Town	482	D 1 - 1	Tullen 89	15

Ave. League Home Attendance: 268   **Goals** 62 72   **Top Goalscorer:** Stone (15)
Best Position: 8th   **Worst:** 21st

STAMFORD

Founded: 1896
Nickname:
The Daniels

Manager: Graham Drury   **Coach:** Andy Drummond   **Physio:** Becky Toone
Change Colours: All Blue
Club Sponsor: V.Couzens (Stamford) Ltd., Newflame and H.P.C. (Homes) Ltd.
Previous League: United Counties
Best Seasons: Lg: F.A. Cup: 5th Qualifying Round 1912-1913
F.A.Trophy.: 5th Round 2004-2005
F.A.Vase: Winners 1979-1980
Ground address: Vic Couzens Stadium, Kettering Road,Stamford Lincs.PE9 2JR
Tel No: 01780 763079 (clubhouse)
Club Website: www.stamfordafc.moorfruit.co.uk
Capacity: 2,000   **Seats:** 250   **Covered:** 1,250   **Floodlights:** Yes
Simple Directions: Off A43 Kettering Rd, one mile east of A1. 200 yards from station.
Midweek Home Matchday: Tuesday
Clubhouse: Open matchdays and for functions
Club Shop: Full range of products
Local Radio: Rutland Radio, BBC Radio Lincolnshire & BBC Radio Cambridgeshire
Local Press: Stamford Mercury, Peterborough Evening Telegraph, Herald & Post and Rutland Times.

CLUB PERSONNEL

Chairman: Ken Joynson
President: Vick Charlton
Secretary: Jeremy Biggs,The Essendine, Bourne Road, Essendine, Stamford, Lincs. PE9 4LD **Tel Nos:** 01780 763048 (W) 01958 288464 (M)
Programme
Editor: John Burrows
44 pages £1.50
2005-2006
Captain: Jim Neil
Player of the Year:
Graham Bowater & Lee Marshall
Top Goalscorer: Martin Wormall 25

CLUB STATISTICS

Record	**Attendance:** 4,200 v Kettering Town F.A.Cup 3rd Qualifying Round 1953
	Career Goalscorer: Bert Knighton 248
	Career Appearances: Dick Kwiatkowski 462
Record	**Victory::** 13-0 v Peterborough Reserves, Northants League 1929-1930
	Defeat: 0-17 Rothwell F.A.Cup 1927-1928
Senior Honours:	F,.A.Vase Winners 1979-80, United Co. Champions (7), Lincolnshire Senior Cup (3), Lincs Senior B Cup (2),
Previous Leagues:	Peterborough, Northants (UCL) 08-55, Central Alliance 55-61, Mld Co 61-72 UCL 72-98

The Daniels celebrate promotion after winning last season's Southern League Division One East play-off.
Back row (L-R): Becky Toone, Pete Foskett, Lee Marshall, Elton Holmes, Ayden Duffy, Stuart King, Danny George, Martin Wormall, Graham Bowater, Mark Angel, Dennis Rhule, Garath Pritchard, Ian Pledger, Dave Toone.
Front: Mark Lovelace, Mark Foster, assistant manager Andy Drummond, Jim Neil, Scott Taylor, manager Graham Drury.   Photograph courtesy of Rutland & Stamford Mercury.

TEAM BATH

Founded: 2000
Nickname:

Manager: Ged Roddy   **Coach:** Andy Tillson   **Physio:** Ian Andrews

Club Colours: Yellow & Blue/blue/yellow

Change Colours: All White

Club Sponsor: Kukri, Ted Baker and Mowbray Woodwards

Previous League: Western

Best Seasons: League 13th Southern Premier 2004-2005

F.A.Cup: 1st Rd. 2002-03

F.A.Trophy: 3rd Round 2004-05   **F.A.Vase:** 3rd Rd 2001-02

Ground address: Groundsharing with Bath City at Twerton Park, Twerton, Bath, Somerset. BA2 1DB   **Tel No:** 01225 423087

Capacity: 8,840   **Seats** 1.017   **Covered:**4,800   **Floodlights:**Yes

Simple Directions: Twerton Park is situated off the A4/A36 Lower Bristol Road on the Bristol side of Bath

Midweek Home Matchday: Monday

Clubhouse: Bath City facilities open on matchdays.

Club Shop: No

CLUB PERSONNEL
Chairman: John Lacock
Secretary: Phil Searle
email: phil@matchtight.co.uk
Programme Editor: Secretary

2005-2006
Captain: Neil Saunders
Top Goalscorer: Sean Canham

CLUB STATISTICS

Record	**Attendance**: 5,469 v Mansfield Town F.A.Cup 1st Rd. 02-03
	Victory: 13-0 v Bath City Reserves (a) **Defeat:** 0-5 v King's L:ynn (A)
	Goalscorer and **Career Appearances**: not known
Record Transfer Fee	**Paid:** None
	Received: None
Senior Honours:	Southern Lg Div West 03-04, Western Lg Prem Division 02-03, Div 1 00-01
Previous Leagues	Western 2000-2003

Back row, left to right: Ade Adams, Jake Reid, Sami Elab, David Bailey, Steve Abbott and Matt Taylor **Second row**: Andrew Reilly, Josh Llewelyn, Neil Saunders (Captain),Alax Leaman,Darren Chitty, Richard de Villiers, Simon Cooper, Dan Dillon and Alex Frost. **Third row**: Joe Long, Ryan Jerwood,Matt Towneley, Blake Newbold, Adam Green, Matt Williams, Joe Arnold, Pete Ball and Matt Hale. **Front Row:** Kes Metitiri, Ian Andrews (Physio) Brian Parkin (Academy Coach), Ivor Powell (Asst Coach), John Laycock (Chairman), Ged Roddy (Manager), Andy Tilson (Head Coach) and Martin Graham.

TEAM BATH

BEST LGE ATT.: 632 v Bath City
LOWEST: 48 v Yate Town

No.	Date	Comp	H/A	Opponents	Att:	Result	Goalscorers	Pos
1	Aug 13	SP	H	Cheshunt	85	L 0 - 1		18
2	16		A	Evesham United	223	W 1 - 0	Long 40	12
3	20		A	Hitchin Town	231	L 1 - 2	Jaukovic 36 (pen)	17
4	22		H	Chippenham Town	417	W 2 - 0	**Canham** 33 Cook 35	10
5	27		A	Cirencester Town	174	L 0 - 1		17
6	29		H	Bath City	632	L 0 - 4		18
7	Sept 3		A	Northwood	127	D 1 - 1	Smith 38	17
8	10	FAC 1Q	A	**Hamworthy United**	145	W 2 - 0	**Canham** 45 **Adams** 80	
9	17	SP	H	Gloucester City	114	W 1 - 0	**Canham** 75	14
10	24	FAC 2Q	A	**Dorchester Town**	317	L 2 - 4	**Canham** 32 Tisdale 62 (pen)	
11	27	SP	A	Yate Town	165	W 3 - 0	Hudson 3 **Canham** 14 15	
12	Oct 1		H	Aylesbury Town	102	D 1 - 1	**Canham** 76	12
13	11		A	Tiverton Town	334	L 0 - 2		12
14	15	FAT1Q	H	**Hitchin Town**	86	L 0 - 1		
15	22	SP	A	King's Lynn	734	L 2 - 4	Reid 85 90	13
16	24		H	Evesham United	84	W 2 - 1	Smith 2 Tisdale 79 (pen)	11
17	29		A	Bedford Town	439	D 1 - 1	Maye 42	
18	Nov 5		H	Hitchin Town	108	W 1 - 0	Davies 47	11
19	21		H	Yate Town	48	W 4 - 1	Reid 8 63 Coppard 34 Adams 38	8
20	Dec 10		A	Aylesbury United	254	W 2 - 1	Cozic 28 46	8
21	17		A	Banbury United	419	D 1 - 1	**Canham** 61	9
22	27		H	Merthyr Tydfil	196	L 2 - 3	**Canham** 45 Jones 85	9
23	31		H	Tiverton Town	161	L 0 - 2		13
24	Jan 2		A	Mangotsfield United	324	D 3 - 3	Maye 4 59 **Canham** 72	14
25	7		A	Chesham United	195	W 2 - 0	Jones 13 Coppard 90	12
26	14		H	Northwood	83	L 2 - 3	Reid 77 Tisdale 78	14
27	21		H	Rugby Town	102	L 1 - 3	Jaukovic 85	14
28	28		A	Salisbury City	690	W 1 - 0	Cozic 85	14
29	30		H	Halesowen Town	82	L 0 - 2		15
30	Feb 4		H	Bedford Town	96	L 1 - 2	Long 89	15
31	11		A	Halesowen Town	343	W 3 - 1	Jaukovic 52 **Canham** 75 90	15
32	18		H	King's Lynn	287	L 1 - 3	Adams 64	15
33	20		H	Yate Town	145	W 5 - 3	**Canham** 6 90 Adams 41 76 Townley 42	15
34	25		A	Cheshunt	135	L 1 - 2	Reid 88	15
35	Mar 4		H	GranthamTown	101	L 1 - 2	**Canham** 31	15
36	7		A	Bath City	579	L 1 - 3	**Canham** 80	15
37	11		A	Gloucester City	347	L 0 - 3		15
38	14		A	Chippenham Town	384	L 2 - 4	Adams 87 Maye 89	15
39	28		H	Chesham United	141	W 2 - 0	**Canham** 60 Cooper 87	12
40	April 1		A	Grantham Town	266	W 1 - 0	Adams 26	11
41	8		H	Banbury United	117	D 2 - 2	**Canham** 37 Reid 73	12
42	15		H	Mangotsfield United	154	L 0 - 1		13
43	17		A	Merthyr Tydfil	336	L 0 - 1		13
44	22		A	Rugby Town	204	L 0 - 1		16
45	29		H	Salisbury City	337	L 1 - 2	**Canham** 53	173

Ave. League Home Attendance: 171 | **Goals** 59 72 | **Top Goalscorer:** Canham (19)
Best Position: 8th **Worst:** 18th

TIVERTON TOWN

Founded: 1920
Nickname: Tivvy

Manager: Martyn Rogers   **Player Coaches**: Steve Flack and Chris Vinniecombe

Physio: Mike Perry

Club Colours: All Yellow

Change Colours: All white

Club Sponsor: Market Carpets of Devon

Previous League: Western

Best Seasons: 8th Southern Premier 2004-2005

F.A.Cup: 1st Rd 1990-91 91-92 94-95 97-98 2004-05

F.A.Trophy.: 5th Round 2000-2001   **F.A.Vase:** Winners: 97-87 98-99

Ground address: Ladysmead, Bolham Road, Tiverton, Devon EX16 6SG

Tel No:01884 252397   **Fax:** 01884 258840

Capacity: 3,500   **Seats** 520   **Covered:** 2,300   **Floodlights:** Yes

Simple Directions: Leave M5 at jct 27. Take second Tiverton turning off A361 at end of dual carriageway. Turn left then over new roundabout and left at next roundabout. Ground is now on you right.

Midweek Home Matchday: Wednesday

Clubhouse: Two large bars with hot and cold food

Club Shop: Yes, fully stocked.

CLUB PERSONNEL

Chairman: Dave Wright
President: Dr Gavin Haig FRCS
Other Directors: Pete Buxton, Ramsey Findlay, John Smith and Kimm Smith
Secretary: Ramsey Findlay, 35 Park Road, Tiverton, Devon EX16 6AY T **Tel Nos:** 01884 256341 01884 254949 (W)
Treasurer: Kimm Smith c/o club
Commercial Manager: Martyn Rogers (01884 252397)
Programme Editor: Alan Reidy
Tel Nos: 01884 235947 (H) 07719 585560 (M)

2005-2006
Captain: Nathan Rudge
Player of the Year: Mark Ovendale
Top Goalscorer: Jamie Mudge

CLUB STATISTICS

Record	**Attendance**: 3,00 v Leyton Orient F.A.Cup First Round Proper 1994-95
	Victory: 7-1 v Cirencester Town (Southern League) 2001
	Defeat: 2-6 v Stafford Rangers (A) Southern League 2001-2002
	Career Goalscorer: Phil Everett
	Career Appearances:
	Transfer Fee Paid: to Clevedon for Steve Peters
	Transfer Fee Received: from Coventry City for Jason Smith
Senior Honours:	F.A.Vase Winners (2) Western League Champions (4) R-up 3)
	Devon Senior Cup 55-56 65-6 East Devon Senior Cup ((7)
Previous Leagues	Devon & Exeter and Western.

Back row,left to right: Chris Vinnicombe,Tom Beddow, Barry McConnell,Tom Gardner, Mark Rock, Steve Flack,Nat Pepperell, Danny Harris and Liam Raybould. Front row: Adam Kelly, Jamie Skinner, Kwame Ampadu, Nathan Rudge, Chris Bale, Mike Booth, Shaun Bowden and Richard Lammacraft.

Photo: Courtesey Nigel Chanter/www.sportactionphotos.co.uk

TIVERTON TOWN

BEST LGE ATT.: 796 v Chippenham Town
LOWEST: **334** v Team Bath

No.	Date	Comp	H/A	Opponents	Att:	Result	Goalscorers	Pos
1	Aug 13	SP	H	Evesham United	584	W 3 - 0	Friend 26 Yetton 33 Winter 44 (pen)	3
2	16		A	Bath City	800	L 0 - 1		10
3	20		A	Banbury United	380	L 1 - 3	Yetton	15
4	24		H	Mangotsfield United	456	L 2 - 3	Milsom 39 Yetton 63	18
5	27		H	Gloucester City	471	W 1 - 0	Winter 45 (pen)	15
6	29		A	Yate Town	295	L 1 - 2	Moor 27	17
7	Sept 3		H	Bedford Town	416	L 0 - 1		18
8	10	FAC 1Q	H	**Evesham United**	392	D 1 - 1	**Yetton 20**	
9	13	FAC 1Qr	A	**Evesham United**	130	W 1 - 0	Bale 50	
10	17	SP	A	King's Lynn	710	L 1 - 4	Yetton 80	19
11	24	FAC 2Q	A	**Highworth Town**	284	W 7 - 1	Booth 3 (1 22 69) Yetton 24 Daley 57 Mudge 63 Winter 83 (pen)	
12	Oct 1	SP	H	Northwood	475	W 4 - 1	**Mudge** 22 Pears 3 (38 56 87)	16
13	8	FAC 3Q	H	**Windsor & Eton**	531	W 2 - 1	**Yetton 32 Mudge 70**	
14	11	SP	H	Team Bath	334	W 2 - 0	Mudge 69 90	14
15	15	FAT1Q	H	**Mangotsfield United**	564	D 0 - 0		
16	18	FAT1Qr	A	**Mangotsfield United**	294	W 2 - 1	**Daley 44 Mudge 87**	
17	22	FAC 4Q	A	**Nuneaton Borough**	1237	D 0 - 0		
18	25	FAC4Qr	H	**Nuneaton Borough**	885	L 0 - 1		
19	29	SP	A	Mangotsfield United	434	D 1 - 1	Hutchinson 13	17
20	Nov 5		H	Cheshunt	521	D 1 - 1	Davies 47	18
21	12	FAT 2Q	A	**Solihull Borough**	204	L 1 - 3	Pears 46	
22	15	SP	H	Yate Town	380	W 3 - 2	Pears 6 Brice 70 (og) Nogan 74	15
23	19		H	Grantham Town	408	W 3 - 1	Pears 23 Nogan 41 **Mudge** 71	13
24	Dec 3		A	Chesham United	253	D 3 - 3	Bale 73 78 **Mudge** 77	15
25	10		H	Hitchin Town	442	W 6 - 2	**Mudge** 3 (16 57 78) Nogan 30 Holloway 62 87	10
26	17		A	Aylesbury United	270	W 5 - 0	**Mudge** 24 Booth 48 Bale 56 Davies 59 Pears 72	10
27	27		A	Salisbury City	980	L 0 - 1		12
28	31		A	Team Bath	161	W 2 - 0	Bale 30 Davies 43	10
29	Jan 2		H	Chippenham Town	796	L 0 - 2		11
30	7		A	Gloucester City	392	W 5 - 4	**Mudge** 10 18 Bale 46 87 Bath 83 (og)	9
31	14		H	Chesham United	536	W 4 - 0	Stamp 7 (og) **Mudge** 26 Davies 30 Gardner 43	9
32	17		A	Rugby Town	202	L 1 - 3	Nogan 73	9
33	21		H	Cirencester Town	731	L 0 - 4		12
34	28		A	Bedford Town	387	L 0 - 3		13
35	Feb 4		A	Northwood	193	W 4 - 2	**Mudge** 46 60 Clay 55 Winter 78 (pen)	9
36	7		A	Merthyr Tydfil	343	D 1 - 1	Holloway 5	
37	11		H	Banbury United	549	D 0 - 0		10
38	15		H	Halesowen Town	359	D 0 - 0		8
39	18		A	Cheshunt	145	L 0 - 1		11
40	25		A	Grantham Town	234	D 1 - 1	Davies 60	10
41	Mar 4		H	Bath City	649	L 1 - 2	Winter (pen) 90	11
42	11		A	Evesham United	269	D 1 - 1	Milsom 86	11
43	18		H	King's Lynn	351	L 1 - 2	Holloway 86	12
44	25		H	Rugby Town	372	D 2 - 2	**Mudge** 23 Pears 40	11
45	28		A	Halesowen Town	288	L 2 - 4	Hambley 19 Davies 34	11
46	April 1		A	Cirencester Town	201	L 1 - 2	Pears 8	13
47	8		H	Aylesbury United	387	D 1 - 1	Pears 30	14
48	15		A	Chippenham Town	662	W 1 - 0	Pears 31	12
49	17		H	Salisbury City	629	L 0 - 1		12
50	22		H	Merthyr Tydfil	422	W 2 - 0	**Mudge** 55 90	12
51	29		A	Hitchin Town	307	L 2 - 3	Davies 9 **Mudge** 61	12

Ave. League Home Attendance: 461   **Goals** 81 69   **Top Goalscorer:** Mudge (21)
Best Position: 3rd   **Worst:** 19th

WEALDSTONE

Founded: 1899
Nickname: The Stones

Manager: Gordon Bartlett **Assistant Manager:** Leo Morris   **Coach:** Mark Gill
Physio: Richard Crook & James Smith
Cllub Colours: Blue & white quarters/blue/blue & white.
Change Colours: Navy & Yellow quarters/navy
Club Sponsor: T.B.A.
Previous League: Isthmian
Best Performances: Conference Champions 1984-1985 **F.A. Cup:** 3rd Rd 77-8
F.A.Trophy.: Winners 1984-85
Ground address: (Sharing with Northwood F.C.) Chestnut Avenue, Northwood
e-mail: office @wealdstonefc.co.uk
Wealdstone F.C. Information Line: 09062 892011
Official website: http://www.come-to-wealdstonefc.co.uk
Capacity: 3.075   **Seats:** 307   **Covered:** 932   **Floodlights: Yes**
Simple Directions: A404)(Pinner-Rickmansworth) and Chestnut Avenue is on left by
a large grey iron railway bridge. A third of a mile from Northwood Hills station
(Metropolitan Line. Buses 282 and H11 pass end of Chestnut Avenue)
Midweek Home Matchday: Tuesday
Clubhouse: Northwood F.C. clubhouse open matchdays.
Local Press: Harrow Observer, Harrow Times
Local Radio: None give reports   **Clubcall Line:** 0901 5607001

CLUB PERSONNEL
Chairman: Nick Symmons
Vice Chairman: T.B.A.
Secretary: Mick Fishman
c/o 31 Jersey Avenue,Stanmore,
Middx HA7 2JG Tel.0208863 2120
Company Sec: Trevor Davies
Commercial Director:
Howard Krais
Press Officer:
Steve Paull
Programme. Editor:
Terry Dolman
2005-2006
Captain: Robin Tucker
Player of the Year;
Jermaine Beckford
Top Goalscorer: Jermaine Beckford

CLUB STATISTICS

Record	**Attendance**: 13,504 v Leytonstone, 4th Rd.F.A. Amateur Cup 05.03.49 (at Lower Mead Stadium) **Victory:** 22-0 v The 12th London Regiment (The Rangers) F.A.Amateur Cup 13.10.23 **Defeat:**0-14 v Edgware Town (A) London Senior Cup 09.12.44 **Career Goalscorer**: George Duck 251 **Career Appearances**: Charlie Townsend 514 **Transfer FeesPaid**: £15,000 to Barnet for David Gipp **Transfer Fee Received:**Undisclosed from Coventry for Jermaine Beckford
Senior Honours:	F.A.Trophy Winners 84-85 F.A.Amateur Cup 65-66 Conference 84-85 Isthmian Div 3 96-97 Southern Lg Southern Div 81-82 Div 1 South 73-4 Athenian Lg 51-2 London Sen Cup 61-2 Middx Sen Cup 11
Previous Leagues:	Willesden & Dist. 1899-1906 08-13 London 1911 -22 Middx 13-22 Spartan 22-28 Athenian 28-64 Isthmian 64-71 95-06 Southern 71-79 ,81-82 88-95 Conference 79-81 82-88

Back row (L-R): James Smith (physio), Mark Gill, (coach) Stuart Bamford, Chris Oleary, Gavin Bamford, Kevin Swift, Fergus Moore, Graham Montgomery, Julian Edwards, Billy Sentance, Chris Zoricich, Leo Morris (ass mgr) Gordon Bartlett (manager)
Front: Carl Martin, Dean Papali, Stuart Goodhall, Lee Carroll, Matt Gooderick, Lee Holland, John Christian.

WEALDSTONE

BEST LGE ATT.: 1,009 v AFC Wimbledon
LOWEST: 227 v Heybridge Swifts

No.	Date	Comp	H/A	Opponents	Att:	Result	Goalscorers	Pos
1	Aug 20	IP	H	Worthing	315	W 2 - 1	**Beckford** 41 (pen) Jolly 58	7
2	23		A	Redbridge	162	W 3 - 2	**Beckford** 12 Adolphe 17 Jolly	7
3	27		A	Chelmsford City	360	D 0 - 0		4
4	31		H	Hendon	412	L 4 - 5	Harris 6 (pen) Jolly 20 44 Adolphe 31	7
5	Sept 3		A	Maldon Town	196	W 4 - 2	Jolly 43 73 Harding 75 **Beckford** 78	6
6	6		A	Hampton & Richmond B	373	L 0 - 3		9
7	10	FAC 1Q	A	**Stanway Rovers**	170	**D 0 - 0**		
8	13	FAC1Qr	H	**Stanway Rovers**	179	**W 3 - 0**	Ryan 24 Beckford 24 Jolly 67	
9	17	IP	H	East Thurrock	327	L 0 - 2		11
10	20		H	Heybridge Swifts	227	L 3 - 4	**Beckford** 3 (44 pen 47 80 pen)	13
11	24	FAC 2Q	A	**Banstead Athletic**	164	**W 4 - 1**	Jolly 2 Cooper 7 Harris 22 (pen) 77	
12	Oct 1	IP	H	Braintree Town	305	L 1 - 3	**Beckford** 41 (pen) Baptiste 70	15
13	4		A	AFC Wimbledon	2464	D 1 - 1	**Beckford** 51	15
14	8	FAC 3Q	H	**Burnham**	247	**L 2 - 4**	Beckford 10 36	
15	10	IP	H	Windsor & Eton	243	W 4 - 2	D.Cox 3 (49 62 89) Jolly 83	13
16	15	FAT1Q	A	**Tooting & Mitcham U**	312	**W 2 - 1**	Ryan 50 Tucker 76	
17	22	IP	A	Margate	708	L 0 - 1		14
18	25		H	Hampton & Richmond B	253	L 1 - 2	Jolly 90	15
19	29		H	Slough Town	380	D 2 - 2	**Beckford** 9 50	14
20	Nov 5		A	Billericay Town	472	L 0 - 2		16
21	12	FAT 2Q	A	**Folkestone Invicta**	316	**L 3 - 5**	Beckford 42 Jolly 45 (pen) Montgomery 80	
22	22	IP	A	Heybridge Swifts	143	W 3 - 1	**Beckford** 50 Burrell 72 Jolly 80 (pen)	15
23	26		A	Leyton	150	W 2 - 1	**Beckford** 15 Ursell 57	14
24	29		A	Fisher Athletic	170	L 1 - 2	Jolly 84	
25	Dec 3		H	Staines Town	265	L 1 - 2	**Beckford** 48	14
26	9		H	Folkestone Invicta	251	L 1 - 2	**Beckford** 12	19
27	17		A	Bromley	374	D 1 - 1	**Beckford** 78	18
28	26		H	Harrow Borough	469	W 4 - 1	Jolly 45 65 **Beckford** 58 88	15
29	Jan 2		A	Hendon	380	W 3 - 0	Jolly 4 **Beckford** 63 (pen) Burell 86	13
30	7		A	Worthing	602	L 1 - 3	**Beckford** 23	14
31	10		H	Walton & Hersham	274	L 1 - 3	**Beckford** 87	14
32	14		H	Redbridge	308	W 6 - 1	Ryan 4 Burrell 34 **Beckford** 41 58 Cooper 66 Jolly 78	13
33	21		A	East Thurrock	162	L 0 - 2		14
34	28		H	Chelmsford City	344	L 1 - 2	Turner 87	
35	Feb 4		A	Staines Town	315	W 3 - 1	**Beckford** 26 89 Turner 90	14
36	11		H	Leyton	238	W 1 - 0	**Beckford**	12
37	18		A	Slough Town	412	L 2 - 3	**Beckford** 46 Remy 62	16
38	25		A	Margate	280	L 0 - 4		18
39	Mar 11		A	Walton & Hersham	229	L 0 - 1		18
40	18		A	Braintree Town	503	L 0 - 2		18
41	25		H	AFC Wimbledon	1009	L 1 - 5	Miller 35	18
42	April 1		A	Woindsor & Eton	210	W 3 - 0	Francis 1 62 Burrell 65	17
43	4		H	Billericay Town	255	D 1 - 1	Cooper 88	17
44	8		H	Fisher Athgletic	302	L 1 - 2	Ryan 13	18
45	14		H	Maldon Town	311	L 0 - 2		18
46	18		A	Harrow Borough	547	W 2 - 1	Zoricich 25 Holland 61	17
47	22		A	Folkestone Invicta	384	L 2 - 5	Cooper 47 Alexander 51	18
48	29		H	Bromley	307	L 1 - 2	Alexander 35	18

Ave. League Home Attendance: 337   **Goals**   81   93   **Top Goalscorer:** Beckford (30)
Best Position: 4th   **Worst:** 19th

YATE TOWN

Founded: 1946
Nickname: The Bluebells

YATE TOWN
Football Club

GFA SENIOR CHALLENGE CUP FINAL
YATE TOWN v CHELTENHAM TOWN
Wednesday 26th April 2006 Kick off 7.45pm
Programme £1.50

Manager: Richard Thompson **Assistant Manager:** Lee Barlass
Physio: Steven Carter
Club Colours: White/navy/white
Change Colours: All Yellow
Club Sponsor: E.R.P. (?)
Previous League: Hellenic
Previous Name: Yate YMCA 1946-70
Previous Grounds: Yate Airfield 50-54 Newmans Field 54-60 Sunnyside Lane 60-84
Best Seasons: Lg: Southern Div 1 West Runners-Up 2004-2005
F.A. Cup: 2nd Qualifying Round 2005-2006 ? F.A.Vase 5th Rd 1991-92.
F.A.Trophy; 3rd Round 2004-2005
Ground address: Lodge Road, Yate, Bristol BS37 7LE
Tel No: 01454 228103
Capacity: 2,000 **Seats:** 236 **Covered:** 400 **Floodlights:** Yes
Simple Directions: M4 jct 18 A46 towards Stroud then A432 to Yate. Turn right at Green Goose Way and at first roundabout into link road and Yate shopping centre. Turn right at third main traffic lights into North Road, then first left into Lodge Road.
Midweek Home Matchday: Tuesday
Clubhouse: Open every evening and lunchtimes at week-ends **Club Shop:** Yes

CLUB PERSONNEL
Chairman: Peter Jackson
President: Roger Hawkins
Secretary: Terry Tansley, 1 Tyning Close, Yate, Bristol BS37 5PN
Tel No: 01454 324305
Programme Editor: Secretary
Press Officer: Secretary
Programme
Pages 40 Price £1.50

2005-2006
Captain: Lee Jefferies
Player of the Year: Scott Brice
Top Goalscorer: Darren Efwrads

CLUB STATISTICS

Record	**Attendance:**	2,000 v Bristol R v Rovers Past Vaughan Jones Testimonial 1990
	Victory:	13-3 Clevedon, Bristol Premier Combination 1967-68
	Defeat:	Not Known
	Career Goalscorer:	Kevin Thaws
	Career Appearances:	Gary Hewlett
Record Transfer Fee	**Paid:**	£2,000 to Chippenham Town for Matt Rawlings 2003
	Received:	#15,000 from Bristol Rovers for Mike Davis
Senior Honours:		Hellenic League (2), Glos. F.A.Senior Cup 2004-2005 & 2005-06 R-Up (3), Dr Martens Fairplay Awards 98-99 99-00
Previous Leagues:		Glos. County 68-83 and Hellenic 83-89 00-03

Back row.left to right: Darren Edwards, Andy Neal, Scott Brice, Dave Elsey, Lee Bridson, Sam Jones*, Tony Court, Gareth Loydon, Jason Wood, Jacob Guy* Mike Wyatt, Christian Sylvester, Aaron Blakemore & Steve Carter (Physio). Front row:Jimmy Cox, Lee Vickerman, Adam Sims, Richard Thompson (Manager), LereJefferies (Captain),Lee Barlass (Assistant Manager), Paul Chenoweth (Player Coach), Adam Mayo, Dave Seal and Mark Summers.*Not now with club

YATE TOWN

BEST LGE ATT.: 710 v Mangotsfield United
LOWEST: **154** v Grantham Town

No.	Date	Comp	H/A	Opponents	Att:	Result	Goalscorers	Pos
1	Aug 13	SP	H	Banbury United	210	L 0 - 3		22
2	16		A	Merthyr Tydfil	321	L 0 - 3		22
3	20		A	Bedford Town	357	L 0 - 2		22
4	23		H	Bath City	575	D 1 - 1	Pritchard 45	21
5	27		A	Aylesbury United	294	L 0 - 3		21
6	29		H	Tiverton Town	295	W 2 - 1	Pritchard 45 (pen) Sims 79	20
7	Sept 2		A	Salisbury City	800	L 1 - 3	Sims 5	22
8	**10**	**FAC 1Q**	**H**	**Bodmin Town**	**170**	**W 2 - 0**	**Stone 75 Edwards 88**	
9	17	SP	H	Northwood	220	W 1 - 0	Wyatt 73	18
10	**24**	**FAC 2Q**	**H**	**Salisbury City**	**371**	**L 0 - 2**		
11	27	SP	H	Team Bath	165	L 0 - 3		18
12	Oct 1		A	Chippenham Town	633	L 2 - 4	McEnteggart 43 (og) Wood 58	19
13	8		H	Cheshunt	167	W 4 - 1	Elsey 43 Campbell 47 Wood 68 Sims 74	16
14	11		A	Halesowen Town	243	L 2 - 7	Edwards 33 Stonehouse 84	18
15	**15**	**FAT1Q**	**A**	**Burnham**	**75**	**L 0 - 2**		
16	22	SP	H	Chesham United	262	W 5 - 2	Wood 10 Neal 43 Edwards 85 Stonehouse 87 Wyatt 90	16
17	29		A	Evesham United	199	W 1 - 0	Elsey 45	14
18	Nov 5		H	Salisbury City	320	W 1 - 0	Neal 16	14
19	16		A	Tiverton Town	380	L 2 - 3	Wood 80 Wyatt 85	14
20	19		A	Banbury United	411	D 1 - 1	Edwards 55	15
21	26		H	Hitchin Town	175	W 2 - 1	Edwards 5 Neal 74	10
22	Dec 10		H	Chippenham Town	380	L 1 - 2	Edwards 63	13
23	17		A	Grantham Ttown	277	L 0 - 2		15
24	27		H	Mangotsfield Town	710	D 2 - 2	Neal 3 Sims 47	16
25	31		H	Gloucester City	340	W 3 - 1	Wood 18 Campbell 25 Edwards 64	14
26	Jan 2		A	Cirencester Town	276	W 3 - 1	Pritchard 18 Sims 19 Sylvester 90	13
27	7		H	King's Lynn	210	W 3 - 2	Sims 13 Elsey 20 Pritchard 52	11
28	14		A	Rugby Town	233	D 0 - 0		10
29	21		H	Bedford Town	215	W 4 - 0	Jefferies 8 Brice 22 Edwards 56 Cox 86	11
30	Feb 4		A	Merthyr Tydfil	220	W 3 - 2	Edwards 43 89 Metheringham 86	8
31	11		A	King's Lynn	868	L 0 - 1		13
32	18		H	Halesowen Town	270	W 2 - 1	Chenoweth 15 Edwards 27	10
33	20		A	Tream Bath	145	L 3 - 5	Metheringham 72 Rutter 73 (og) Sims 87	11
34	25		A	Chesham United	295	W 5 - 2	Edwards 22 29 Wyatt 37 Wood 52 Cox 75	7
35	Mar 4		H	Rugby Town	207	W 1 - 0	Jefferies 80	7
36	11		A	Northwood	138	L 2 - 3	Edwards 5 60	8
37	18		H	Aylesbury United	220	W 3 - 0	Edwards 41 45 Sims 85	7
38	21		A	Gloucester City	366	L 0 - 2		7
39	25		A	Bath City	960	W 2 - 1	Edwards 10 Wyatt 59	7
40	April 1		A	Hitchin Town	237	L 3 - 4	Wilmot 60 Cox 67 Brice 78	8
41	8		H	Grantham Town	154	W 3 - 1	Sims 52 Cox 58 70	7
42	15		H	Cirencester Town	270	W 3 - 1	EDWARDS 3 (2 (pen 23 47)	6
43	17		A	Mangotsfield United	421	W 3 - 0	Bryce 4 16 Wyatt 34	6
44	22		A	Evesham United	222	D 1 - 1	Edwards 40	6
45	29		H	Cheshunt	155	W 3 - 2	Cox 10 50 Jefferies 75	6

Ave. League Home Attendance: 277   **Goals**   80 78   **Top Goalscorer:** Edwards (22)
Best Position: 6th   **Worst:** 22nd

FOOTBALL LEAGUE

STEP 1

FOOTBALL
CONFERENCE

STEP 2

| CONFERENCE NORTH | CONFERENCE SOUTH |

STEP 3

| SOUTHERN PREMIER | NORTHERN PREMIER | ISTHMIAN PREMIER |

STEP 4

| **SOUTHERN DIVISION 1** **SOUTH &WEST MIDLAND** | NORTHERN PREMIER DIV.1 | ISTHMIAN DIVISION 1 NORTH   SOUTH |

STEP 5/6

Combined Counties	Hellenic	Northern League	Spartan South Midlands	Wessex
Eastern Counties	Kent	Northern Counties East	Sussex County	Western
Essex Senior	Midland Alliance	North West Counties	United Counties	

STEP 7

Anglian Combination	Dorset County	Kent County	Midland Combination	Peterborough & District	West Cheshire
Bedford & District	Dorset Premier	Leicestershire Senior	Midland League	Reading League	West Lancashire
Brighton & Hove	East Sussex	Liverpool County	North Berkshire	Somerset County	West Midlands (reg)
Cambridgeshire County	Essex & Suffolk Border	Manchester Football	Northampton Town Lge	South Western	West Sussex
Central Midlands	Essex Intermediate	Mid Cheshire League	Northamptonshire Comb.	Suffolk & Ipswich	Wiltshire League
Crawley & Disrict	Gloucesterhisre Co.	Mid Sussex	Northern Alliance	Teeside League	Worthing & District
Devon County	Herts Senior County	Middlesex County	Oxfordshire Senior	Wearside League	

SOUTHERN LEAGUE DIVISION ONE WEST

DIVISION ONE WEST		P	W	D	L	F	A	Pts
1.	Clevedon Town	42	28	6	8	86	45	90
2.	Ashford Town (Mx)	42	24	8	10	84	50	80
3.	Brackley Town	42	23	9	10	71	34	78
4.	Hemel Hempstead Town*	42	22	9	11	86	47	75
5.	Swindon Supermarine	42	22	9	11	70	47	75
6.	Marlow	42	22	6	14	62	59	72
7.	Sutton Coldfield Town	42	21	6	15	91	62	69
8.	Leighton Town	42	19	8	15	55	48	65
9.	Willenhall Town	42	17	12	13	78	61	63
10.	Rushall Olympic	42	17	11	14	73	57	62
11.	Bromsgrove Rovers	42	17	11	14	65	50	62
12.	Solihull Borough	42	15	13	14	50	51	58
13.	Beaconsfield SYCOB	42	14	13	15	60	66	55
14.	Burnham	42	16	5	21	58	71	53
15.	Cinderford Town	42	14	9	19	71	79	51
16.	Bedworth United	42	14	9	19	46	57	51
17.	Paulton Rovers	42	12	10	20	55	76	46
18.	Taunton Town	42	12	9	21	67	81	45
19.	Bracknell Town	42	12	6	24	53	77	42
20.	Stourport Swifts	42	9	14	19	55	80	41
21.	Dunstable Town	42	8	12	22	45	91	36
22.	Thame United	42	4	5	33	30	122	17

*Promoted via the play-offs.

DIV. ONE WEST	1	2	3	4	5	6	7	8	9	10	11	12	13	14	15	16	17	18	19	20	21	22
1 Ashford Town (Mx)		3-1	2-0	1-0	0-2	1-1	2-0	0-1	3-0	1-1	1-1	1-0	1-0	4-2	2-1	1-2	4-0	1-2	1-0	5-1	5-0	2-2
2 Beaconsfield SYCOB	0-2		1-1	0-2	2-1	1-2	3-0	2-0	2-4	3-0	0-5	1-1	2-2	2-2	1-1	0-0	1-1	2-1	1-3	3-2	1-0	2-1
3 Bedworth United	1-2	1-2		2-1	1-0	1-1	1-3	0-3	0-2	1-2	0-1	1-1	1-2	1-1	2-1	1-1	0-1	1-0	1-0	0-4	4-0	2-0
4 Brackley Town	0-1	5-0	0-0		2-0	1-0	5-2	2-2	2-0	0-0	1-0	3-0	2-1	1-0	0-2	0-1	5-0	0-1	1-2	1-0	5-0	1-1
5 Bracknell Town	2-1	0-0	0-4	1-3		1-2	2-1	3-1	0-2	4-4	0-3	1-3	3-1	0-1	0-2	1-5	2-0	1-5	1-1	6-0	3-0	
6 Bromsgrove Rovers	1-3	2-0	1-2	1-1	0-0		2-0	6-2	3-0	4-0	0-2	0-2	2-0	4-1	0-0	2-1	3-6	0-2	1-2	4-0	1-4	
7 Burnham	0-4	1-1	2-0	2-4	0-2	1-2		1-1	1-3	1-1	0-3	2-0	3-1	1-0	0-2	0-1	0-1	3-2	4-2	1-0	2-1	
8 Cinderford Town	3-1	3-4	1-2	1-1	2-0	1-3	2-4		0-2	3-1	1-2	0-1	0-1	4-2	3-2	1-3	0-1	2-0	4-0	1-1	2-1	1-4
9 Clevedon Town	3-1	1-0	3-0	0-1	2-1	2-0	3-2	5-1		2-1	2-3	1-0	0-1	3-0	3-3	4-0	3-1	0-0	3-2	3-1	4-1	2-5
10 Dunstable Town	2-5	0-3	1-1	3-2	2-4	0-4	0-3	0-0	0-1		1-0	1-1	0-0	2-0	1-1	1-0	0-1	0-1	1-1	5-4	4-2	1-1
11 Hemel Hempstead T.	1-1	1-1	1-1	1-3	2-3	1-1	5-1	0-0	5-0			6-2	1-1	0-1	1-3	1-1	2-0	0-1	2-1	4-2	3-0	3-2
12 Leighton Town	1-4	3-0	2-0	0-2	2-1	1-1	0-1	0-1	1-2	2-1	2-1		1-2	1-0	3-1	1-0	1-1	1-0	0-1	3-0	1-2	1-0
13 Marlow	2-0	4-3	1-3	1-2	2-1	0-0	1-3	3-3	1-0	4-0	0-4	0-2		0-2	0-4	1-0	2-1	3-2	0-2	2-1	2-0	1-2
14 Paulton Rovers	1-2	4-0	2-1	0-0	0-0	0-2	2-2	1-4	2-2	2-0	2-1	1-1	1-3		2-0	0-1	3-1	1-3	1-3	2-2	3-0	2-3
15 Rushall Olympic	1-2	2-1	2-0	0-0	3-0	1-1	3-1	1-1	1-3	4-0	0-2	2-1	3-3	1-1		3-1	2-0	0-3	0-1	3-0	5-0	2-2
16 Solihull Borough	2-1	0-0	0-1	1-1	6-1	1-1	2-0	2-0	2-2	4-0	1-3	1-2	1-2	2-0	0-0		0-3	2-1	0-0	2-0	2-2	2-0
17 Stourport Swifts	4-0	1-5	1-0	0-2	2-2	1-1	0-0	3-0	0-3	5-1	1-3	1-1	1-2	2-3	1-3	1-1		3-3	0-0	3-3	1-2	2-2
18 Sutton Coldfield T.	2-2	1-4	3-1	4-0	2-1	1-1	3-2	1-1	1-4	2-4	1-1	1-3	2-3	7-1	4-1	2-0	4-0		2-3	2-0	8-0	3-1
19 Swindon Supermarine	1-3	1-0	2-2	1-2	3-0	1-0	1-0	1-2	2-2	3-1	0-0	2-2	0-2	3-0	2-0	2-2	1-0	4-2		1-1	2-1	0-0
20 Taunton Town	1-1	0-0	1-2	0-2	2-0	0-1	1-3	6-4	0-2	3-2	3-0	0-3	1-0	1-3	2-2	2-0	4-0	1-5	2-3		4-0	1-2
21 Thame United	2-2	1-4	0-2	0-5	0-2	0-4	1-3	1-4	0-1	0-0	4-4	1-2	0-1	2-2	3-1	1-3	1-3	2-1	0-3	1-3		1-1
22 Willenhall Town	3-3	1-1	3-1	2-0	1-0	2-1	0-2	3-1	0-2	3-1	0-3	0-1	3-1	4-1	0-0	5-0	4-4	3-0	0-2	1-2	4-0	

ABINGDON UNITED

Founded: 1946
Nickname: The U's

Manager: Andy Slater **Coach:**Nigel Shepherd **Physio:** Chris James

Club Colours: Yellow & Blue/Blue/Yellow

Change Colours: All Red

Club Sponsor: Abbey Press

Previous League: Hellenic League

Best Seasons: League: Hellenic R-Up 1996-97 **F.A. Cup:** 2nd Qual Rd 2000-2001

F.A.Vase: 3rd Round 1988 -1989

Ground address: The North Court, Northcourt Road, Abingdon,Oxon. OX14 1PL

Club Website: www.abingdonunitedfc.couk

Capacity: 2,000 **Seats:**158 **Covered:**258 **Floodlights**: Yes

Simple Directions: Take A4183 main road towards Oxford from town centre. Ground is on left after one mile.

Midweek Home Matchday: Tuesday

Clubhouse: . Open evening pub hours every night and week end lunchtimes.with lounge bar and function room.

Local Radio: BBC Radio Oxford and FOX FM

Local Press: Oxford Mail

CLUB PERSONNEL
Chairman: Derek Turner
Vice -Chairman: Alf White
President: Pat Evans
Vice President: Shirley Evans
Secretary: John Blackmore, 91 Gainsborough Green, Abingdon, Berks OX14 5JL
Tel No: 01235 203167(W& 07747 615691 (M)
Press Officer&
Programme Editor: Bill Fletcher
e-mail: billfletcher@fsbdial.co.uk
Price £1.00
2005-2006
Captain: Richard Pierson
Player of the Year: Mike Herbert
Top Goalscorer: Mark Simms 27

CLUB STATISTICS		
Record	**Attendance:** 1,500 v Oxford United Friiendly 1994	
	Career Goalscorer: Not Known	
	Career Appearances: Not Known	
Senior Honours:	Hellenic R-Up 1996-1997 Prem Cup R-up 89-90	
	Hellenic Lg Div 1Cup 65-66, Div 1 Champions 1981-82	
	Berks & Bucks Sen. Cup R-Up 83-84 04-05 Berks & Bucks Senior Trophy (2)	
Previous Leagues:	North Berks and Hellenic	

Back row (L-R): Chris Janes (Physio) Chris Hooper, Scott Davis, Luke Holden, Andy Ballard, Richard Peirson (Player Assistant Manager) Nathan Woodley, Leeyon Phelan, Jermaine-Ferreira, Nigel Shepherd. (Coach).
Front: Ryan Brooks, Mark Simms, Ryan Curtin, Micheas Herbert, Simon Tricker, Julian McCalmon, Dean Moss, James Organ.

ANDOVER

Re-Formed 1983
Nickname: The Lions

CLUB PERSONNEL
Chairman: Alan Mussell
Vice Chairman: Geoff Yates
President: Bill Maynard
Directors: George Underwood, Martin Mitty, Geoff Randall, P.Vear
Secretary: Chris Jeremy, 75 Galahad Close, Andover, Hants. SP10 3LF
Tel Nos: 01264 350097 & 07962019896
Company Secretary: Laurie Noble
Commercial Manager: Ray Bulpitt
Prog Ed: Graham Cousins
Tel No: 07784 575214 (M)
Programme 50 Pages £1,00
2005-2006
Captain: Glen Damon
Player of the Year: Justin Bennett
Top Goalscorer:

Manager: Adie Burfield   **Assistant Managers:** Ray Cozze: and Graham Knight

Club Colours: Red & Black Stripes/Black/Black

Change Colours: All White with sky blue trim

Club Sponsor: Sydenhams

Previous League: Wessex

Best Seasons: League: 6th Southern League   **F.A. Cup:** 1st Round 1962-1963

F.A.Trophy.: 3rd Qualifying Round 1969-1970 1970-1971 **F.A.Vase:** 6th Rd.2003-4

First Team Coach: Russ Bennett   **Physio:** Kim Beckett

Ground address: The Portway Stadium, West Portway Industrial Estate, Andover, Hants SP10 3LF Tel No: 01264 351302

Club Website: www.andover-fc.co.uk

Capacity: 3,000   **Seats:** 250   **Covered:** 250   **Floodlights:** Yes

Simple Directions: Situated on the western outskirts of the club. Follow signs to Portway Industrial Estate two miles from Andover BR.

Midweek Home Matchday: Tuesday

Clubhouse: Matchdays and Private Functions   **Club Shop:** No

Local Radio: Radio Spire F.M.

Local Press: Andover Asdvertiser

CLUB STATISTICS

Record	**Attendance:** 1,100 v Leicester City . Ground Opening.
	Career Goalscorer: Tommy Muchalls
	Career Appearances:: Pete Pollard
Record Transfer Fee	**Paid:**
	Received:
Senior Honours:	Wessex League Champions 2001 & 2002 Runners-Up 1994 &1998 Cup 2002
	Western <eague Runners-Up (2) Hants Senior Cup (5) N. Hants Sen Cup (6)
Previous Leagues:	Salisbury & Dist, Hants 1896-98 1899-1901 2002-2062 Southern Lg: 1898-99, 1971-93 1998-99 Western 1962-71
	Wessex 193-98 99-2006

Back Row (L-R): Kieron Hall; Bobby Swayne; Lee Chudy; Matt Davies; Simon Arthur: Dave Tasker: Tom Willoughby;Craig Martin; Matt Styles; Ashley Vine
Front: Phil Andrews (Player/Coach; Adam Heath; Dave Asker; Mark Keogh; Andy Puckett; Jack Smith; Paul Hunt; Danny Taylor; Adam Roberts.

BASHLEY

Founded: 1947
Nickname:
The Bash

Manager: Steve Riley   **Assistant Manager:** Eddie Harper   **Physio:**John Edwards

Club Colours: Gold/Black/Black

Change Colours: All Green

CLUB PERSONNEL

Chairman: Ray Pinney
President: Trevor Adams
Secretary: Pete Millard,3 Winsford Close,Highcliffe, Christchurch,Dorset BH24 4PT (07855 580232)
Programme Editor: Richard Milbery
36 Pages £1.00

2006-2007
Captain: PaulGazzard
Player of the Year: Matt Parnell
Top Goalscorer: Richard Gillespie

Club Sponsor: KEY111

Previous League: Southern

Best Seasons: League: 4th Southern Premier **F.A. Cup:** 2nd Round 1994-1995 **F.A.Trophy.:** 3rd Round 1996-1997 **F.A.Vase:** Semi-Fianl 1987-1988

Ground address: Bashley Road Ground, Bashley Road, New MIlton Hampshire. BH25 5RY **Tel No**: 01425 620280

Club Website: www.bashleyfc.co.uk

Capacity: 4,250   **Seats**: 300   **Covered**:1,200   **Floodlights**: Yes

Simple Directions: A35 Lyndhurst towards Christchurch, turn left down B3058 towards New Milton, ground on left in Bashley village. Half hour walk from New Milton (BR) station. New Cargo Bus service C32 (New Milton-Lymington)

Midweek Home Matchday: Tuesday

Clubhouse: Usual; Licensing Hours with food available. **Club Shop:** Matchdays

Local Radio: 2CR FM   & BBC Radio Solent

Local Press: Bournemouth Echo, Southern Pink & New MIlton Advertiser Southampron Echo.

CLUB STATISTICS

Record   **Attendance:** 3,500 v Emley F.A.Vase S-Final 1st Leg 1987-1988

Career Goalscorer: Colin Cummings 128

Career Appearances: John Bone 829

Record Transfer Fee   **Paid**: £7,500 to Newport (IOW)for Danny Gibbons and to Dorchester Town for & David Elm

Received: £15,000 from Salisbury City for Craig Davis,from Eastleigh for Paul Sales and from AFC Bournemouth foir Wade Elliott

Victory: 21-1 v Co-Operative (A) Bournemoutth League1964

Defeat: 2-20 v Air Special (A) Bournemouth League 1957

Senior Honours: Southern Lg Southern Division 89-90 , Wessex Lg 86-87 87-88 88-89

Previous Leagues: Bournemouth 53-83 Hants 83-86 Wessex 86-89 Southern 89-04 Isthmian 04-06

Back Row (L-R): Martin Doolan (coach), Eddie Harper (Assistant Manager), Phil Archbold, Zeke Rink, Craig Davis, Stacey Harper, Danny Neville, David Elm, Gareth Keeping, Richie Hayter, Steele Saunders and John Edwards (Physio).
Front Row: Chris Ferrett, Mark Preston, Richard Gillespie, Neil Morant, Steve Riley (Player-Manager), Dave Wakefield, Paul Gazzard, Pat Blackmore and Ashley Wilson.

BEACONSFIELD SYCOB

Founded: 1994
Nickname:
The Rams

Manager: Simon Delahunty   **Assistant Manager:** Nick Wells
Head Coach: Peter Scott   **Physio:** Phil Gray
Club Colours: Red & white quarters/Black/Black
Change Colours: All yellow
Club Sponsor: Perfect Sports. **Shirt Sponsor:** Zecker & Co Solictors
Previous League: Spartan South Midlands
Best Seasons: League: 13th 2005/06 - Southern League Division One West
F.A. Cup: 3rd Qualifying Round 1998-1999   **F.A.Trophy.:** ?
F.A.Vase: 1st Round 1983-1984 85-86 87-88
Ground address: Holloway's Park, A355 (old Slough Road), Beaconsfield, Bucks.
HP9 2SG.
Tel No: 01494 676868
Club Website: www.intheteam.com
Capacity: 3,000   **Seats:** 201   **Covered:**400   **Floodlights** Yes:
Simple Directions: M 40 (Jct 2), 1st exit to A355. Club 100yds on right. 1.5 miles
fromoBeaconsfield BR Bus 441Slough/ High Wycombe
Midweek Home Matchday: Monday
Clubhouse: Open evenings and matchdays. Full facilities for bookings.
Local Radio: Mix107 (107.4 FM) and Star FM (106.6 FM)
Local Press: Beaconsfield Advertsier, Bucks Free Press, Slough Express,
Slough Observer.

CLUB PERSONNEL
Chairman: John McCaw
President: Dave Piercey
Secretary: Robin Woolman,13 East Crescent,Windsor, Berkshire SL4 5LD Tel Nos: 01753 853607 (H)

Programme
Editor: RecognitioN Express
24 Pages £1.00
2005-2006
Captain: Allan Arthur & Nick Leach
Manager's Player of the Year:
Terry Gibbs
Player's PoY: Kieron Gradwell
Top Goalscorer: Allan Arthur

CLUB STATISTICS

Record	**Attendance:** 300 v Chesham United Berks & Bucks Senior Cup 1985
	Career Goalscorer: Allan Arthur
	Career Appearances: Allan Arthur
	Record Transfer Fee Paid: N/A
	Record Transfer Fee Received: N/A
Senior Honours:	**As Beaconsfield SYCOB:** Champions Spartan South Midlands 2000-01,03-04
	Berks & Bucks Sen Trophy 2003-04
Previous Leagues:	**Beaconsfield Utd:** Wycombe & District; Maidenhead. **Slough YCOB:** Windsor,
	Slough & District; East Berks; Chiltonian (pre 1994)Spartan South Midlands.
Names:	SloughYCOB & Beaconsfield United merged 1994

Back row (L-R): Allan Arthur, Daniel Willment, Lee Canavan, Kieron Gradwell, Julian Taylor, Finlay Doney, Roy Gumbs.
Front: Jack Jeffries, Terry Gibbs, Kevin Cotton, Adrian Sear, Jason Griffiths, Jason Bowler, Daniel Russell*.
* Daniel Russell was not a registered Southern League player (but did pre-match training with the first team on the day of the photo-shoot).

BRACKNELL TOWN

Founded: 1896
Nickname:
The Robins

Manager: Alan Taylor   **Assistant Manager:** Jon Underwood
Club Colours: Red & white trim/White/White
Change Colours: All Blue
Club Sponsor: DGAME (www.game.uk.com)
Previous League: Isthmian
Best Seasons: League: 19th Southern League Divison 1 West 2005-2006
F.A.Trophy.: 2nd Qualifying Round 1986-1987
F.A.Vase: 5th Round 1975-1976 1982-1983   **F.A. Cup:** 1st Round 2000-2001
Ground address: Larges Lane, Bracknell, Berks. RG12 9AN.
Tel No: 01344 412305 (club) 01344 300933 (office)
Club Website: www.robins.org.uk/
Capacity: 2,500   **Seats:** 190   **Covered:** 400   **Floodlights:** Yes
Simple Directions: Off A329 just before Met Office r'bout by Bracknell College, ground 200
yards. From Bracknell (BR)/bus station - right out of station, follow pathover bridge, left down steps
and follow cycle path ahead, after 300yds follow curve over footbridge, right and follow lane to end,
left and ground on leftafter bend
Midweek Home Matchday: Tuesday
Clubhouse: Members Bar open 11am-11 pm Mon-Sat: &12-3 & 7-10.30 pm Sunday.
Club Shop: Yes with full range of products
Local Radio: Radio Berkshire
Local Press: Bracknell News and Bracknell Times

CLUB PERSONNEL
Chairman: Chris Nixon
President: Jack Quinton
Secretary: Malcolm Hutt,
3 Livingstone Gardens, Woodley,
Reading **Tel No:** 07977 822148 (M)

Programme
Editor: Robert Scully
498 Page £1.00
2005-2006
Captain: Neil Baker
Player of the Year: John Dyer
Top Goalscorer:

CLUB STATISTICS

Record

Attendance: 2,500 v Newquay F.A.Amateur Cup 1971

Career Goalscorer: Justin Day

Career Appearances:: James Woodcock

Transfer Fee Paid: N/A

Transfer Fee Received: N/A

Senior Honours: Isthmian Lg Div 3 93-94; Berks & Bucks Senior Cup Runners-up 2003-04

Previous Leagues: Great Western Combination.; Surrey Senior 63-70; London Spartan 70-75 and
Isthmian 1984-2004

Back Row (L-R): Chris Nixon (chairman), Mark Tallentire (assistant-manager), Scott Taylor, Stuart Hammonds, Ben
Edwards, Andrew Poyser, David Fenton, Jon Underwood, Neil Baker, Mike Cook, Steve French, Mike Savage
(goalkeeping coach), Alan Taylor (manager). **Front row:** Eddie Carpenter (physio), John Dyer, Jon Palmer, Stuart
Tanfield, Jim Griffin, Neil Selby, Gavin Taylor, Danny Hayward, Paul Frame (coach). Not pictured: Gavin Smith,
Jorden Oldham, Chris Andrews. Picture: Robins Photography.

BROOK HOUSE

Founded: 1974
Nickname: The Brook

BROOK HOUSE FC
FIRST XI 2004 - 5

Ryman
football league
Division 2

April 23 Brook House v Abingdon Town

Manager: Joe Mitchell **Assistant Manager:** C.Murphy

Club Colours: Blue & White Stripes/Blue/Blue

Change Colours: Red/Black/Red

Club Sponsor: Cove & Bracket Ltd. ??

Previous League: Ryman League Division Two.

Best Seasons: League: 3rd Ryman Div 2 2004-2005 2005-2006

F.A. Cup: 2nd Qualifying Round 2005-2006 **F.A.Vase:** 5th Round 2004-2005

Ground address: Farm Park, Kingshill Avenue, Hayes, Middlesex.

Tel No: 02088421448

Club Website: www.brookhousefc.com

Capacity: 2,000 **Seats:** 150 **Covered:** 200 **Floodlights:** Yes

Simple Directions: From North Circular Road take A40 Western Avenue then left at the Target Roundabout towards Hayes. Turn right at traffic lights into Kingshill Avenue and the Ground is one mile on right.

Midweek Home Matchday: Tuesday **Club Shop:** No

Clubhouse: Open Week days 7-11pm and Week Ends 12noon-11pm.

Local Radio:

Local Press: Hayes Gazette

CLUB PERSONNEL
Chairman: Mick Ralph
President: Victor Kirby
Secretary: Barry Crump,
19 Bradenham Road, Hayes,
Mifddlesex. 0208 8413959 (H)
07966 468029 (W)
Press Officer: Lawrie Watts
Programme Editor: Dave Swan
28 Pages/with enmtry (£3.00)

2005-2006
Captain: Chris Fermie
Player of the Year: Chris Owens
Top Goalscorer: Dean Papali 32

CLUB STATISTICS

Record	Attendance:
	Career Goalscorer:
	Career Appearances:
Record Transfer Fee	Paid:
	Received:
Senior Honours:	Spartan South Midlands Premier South 1997-1998 and Premier Division Runners-Up 1999-2000 and 2003-2004
Previous Leagues:	Spartan South Midlands and Ryman Division Two.

Ryman League Associate Members Trophy Winners

BURNHAM

Founded: 1878
Nickname:

Manager: David Mudge **Asst.Man:** Paul Brett **Coach**: Calvin Maye**Physio**: Jo Smith

Club Colours: Blue & white quarters /Blue/White
Change Colours: Red & Black Quarters/Red/Red

Club Sponsor:

Previous League: Hellenic
Best Seasons: League: Southern ? **F.A. Cup:** 1st Round 2005-2006
F.A.Trophy.: 4th Round Replay 1999-2000 **F.A.Vase:** Semi-Final 1982-1983

Ground address: The Gore, Wymers Wood Road, Burnham, Slough. SL1 8JB

Tel No: 01628 602 467 **Club Website**: www.burnham-fc.co.uk

Capacity: 2,500 **Seats**: **Covered**: **Floodlights**:

Simple Directions: North west of village centre, two miles from Burnham BR station, two miles from M4 junction 7 & 5 miles from M40 junction 2,100yds north of Gore crossroads - fork right into Wymers Wood Rd and ground is immediately on right
Midweek Home Matchday: Tuesday

Clubhouse: Open every evening and lunch times at week-emds. **Club Shop:** Yes:

CLUB PERSONNEL
Chairman: Malcolm Higton
Vice Chairman: Rod Saunders
Secretary: Trevor Saunders, 51 Disraeli Crescent,High Wycombe, Bucks. HP13 5EW
Tel No: 01494 447604 (H) 07711 856780 (M)
Programme Editor: Cliff Sparkes
32 Pagese

2005-2006
Captain: Paul Brett
Player of the Year:
Top Goalscorer:

Local Radio: Star FM, BBC THames Valley and Swan F.M.
Local Press: Slough Observer and Buckingham Advertiser

CLUB STATISTICS	
Record	**Attendance:** 2,380 v Halesowen Town F.A.Vase 2.4.83.
Career	**Goalscorer:** Fraser Hughes 65 1969-1970
Career	**Appearances**:
Record	**Victory:** 18-0 v High Duty Alloys 1970-1971
	Received: 1-10 v Ernest Turner Sports 1963-1964
Senior Honours:	Athenian Lg R-up (2) , Hellenic Lg 75-76 98-99 Div 1 R-up 72-73, Lg Cup 75-76 98-99, Div 1 Cup 71-72,
Previous Leagues:	**Leagues:** Hellenic 71-77; Athenian 77-84; London Spartan 84-85; Southern 85-95; Hellenic 95-99
	Name: Burnham & Hillingdon 1985-87 **Ground:** Baldwin Meadow (until 20's)

CHESHAM UNITED

Founded: 1917
Nickname: The Generals

Manager: Luther Blissett   **Asst.Manager:** Keith Scott   **Physio:** John Burt

Club Colours: All Sky Blue with claret trim
Change Colours: All Yellow with black trim
Club Sponsor: Synxspeed
Previous League: Isthmian
Best Seasons: Isthmian League Champions 1992-93
F.A.Cup: 3rd Rd 1979-80   **F.A.Amateur Cup:** Finalists 1967-68
F.A.Trophy.: 3rd Rd 1992-93
Ground: The Meadow, Amy Lane, Amersham Rd, Chesham, Bucks. HP5 1NE
Website: www.cheshamunitedfc.co.uk (Harrison Gould)
Tel No: 91494 783964   **Fax:** 01494 782456
Capacity: 5,000   **Seats:** 284   **Covered:** 2,500   **Floodlights:** Yes
Simple Directions: M25 Jct 18 to Amersham. A416 to Chesham go down to roundabout at foot of AmershamHill then sharp left.
Midweek Home Matchday: Tuesday
Clubhouse: Open every evening and matchdays. Available for hire.
Club Shop: Open matchdays (Craig Knowles)

CLUB PERSONNEL
Chairman: Charles Manchester
President: Bill Wells
Directors: Phil Morgan,Brian McCarthy, Mike Dragisic
Secretary: David Stanley, 17 Old Vicarage Gardens, Markyate , St.Albans, Herts AL3 8PW
Tel No: 01582 840707 (H)
07766 761862
Press Officer: Alan Calder
Programme Editor: Alan Calder
Tel No: 01442 230420

2005-2006
Captain: Shaun Byrne
Player of the Year: Nathen Bowden
Top Scorer: Sippetts 9

CLUB STATISTICS

Record — **Attendance:** 5,000 v Cambridge United 3rd Rd F.A.Cup 05.12.79
Victory:
Defeat:
Goalscorer: John Willis
Career Appearances: Martin Baguley 600+
Record Transfer Fee — **Paid:** Undisclosed
Received: £22,000 from Oldham Athletic for Fitz Hall
Senior Honours: F.A.Amateur Cup R- Up 1967-68 Isthmian League Champions 1992-93 Div 1 86-87 96-97 Berks & Bucks Senior Cup (12) R-up (2)
Previous Leagues Spartan 17-47 Corinthian 47-63 Athenian 63-73 Isthmian 73-2004

Photo: BUCKINGHAMSHIRE EXAMINER

DIDCOT TOWN

Founded: 1907
Nickname: Railwaymen

Manager: Stuart Peace   **Coach:** Paul Noble   **Physio**: Mark Roberts

Club Colours: Red with White trim/White/Red

Change Colours: Yellow/Blue/Yellow

Club Sponsor: Bellingers

Previous League: Hellenic League

Best Seasons: League: Hellenic Champions 2005-2006

F.A. Cup: 2nd Qual. Rd. 2004-05 2005-06   **F.A.Vase:** Winners 2004-2005

Ground address: Npower Loop Meadow Stadium, Bowmont Water, Didcot OX11 7GA

Tel No: 01235 813138

Club Website: www.didcottownfc.com

Capacity: 5,000   **Seats:** 250   **Covered:** 200   **Floodlights:** Yes

Simple Directions: from A34 take Milton interchange on Didcot road for a mile. At roundabout take perimeter road and cross three roundabouts before turning right at Avon Way.

Midweek Home Matchday: Tuesday   **Club Shop:** Yes

Clubhouse: Full faciliites available every evening and from mid day at week-ends and holidays. Function rooms available..

Local Radio: Fox FM

Local Press: Oxford Mail & Didcot Herald

CLUB PERSONNEL

Chairman: John Bailey
Vice Chairman: Michael Cox
President: Ed Vaisey M.P.
Secretary: Simon Kelly c/o club.
Tel No: 01235 816352

Programme Editor: Steve Clare
32 Pages £1.00

2005-2006
Captain: J.Heapy
Player of the Year: D.Campbell
Top Goalscorer: I.Concanon

CLUB STATISTICS

Record	**Attendance:** 1,512 v Jarrow Roofing F.A.Vase S-Final 2005
	Career Goalscorer: I. Concanon
	Career Appearances:
Record Transfer Fee	**Paid:** N/A
	Received: N/A
Senior Honours:	F.A.Vase Winners 2004-2005 Hellenic Champions 1953-54 2005-2006
	Hellenic Cup Winners (6) Division One Champions 1976-77 1987-88
	Runners Up 2004-05 Berks & Bucks Senior Trophy 2001-02 2002-03 2005-6
	Hellenic League Cup (6)
Previous Leagues:	Metroploitan 1957-1963 Hellenic 1963-2006

Back Row (L-R): Paul Noble (Asst. Manager), Billy Warner, Adam Learoyd, Jack King, Paul Bedwell, Andy Parrott, Chris Webb, Sean Purcell, Dave Green, Andy Wallbridge, Matty Jack, Mark Roberts (Physio).
Front Row: Paul Hannigan, Grant Goodal, Ian Cancannon, Chris Hogan, Jamie Heapy, Stuart Peace (Manager), Danny Campbell, Stuart Beavon, Paul Powell, Jamie Brooks, Ross Weatherstone.

HANWELL TOWN

Founded: 1948
Nickname: Magpies

Joint Managers: Pat Gavin & Danny Vincent

Club Colours: Black & White Stripes/Black/Black

Change Colours: Yellow/Blue/White.

Club Sponsor: Gowing & Pursey Ltd.

Previous League: Runners -Up Spartan South Midlands 2004-2005

Best Seasons: League: 3rd Spartan South Midlands 2005-2006

F.A. Cup: 3rd Qual.Rd 1987-98   **F.A.Vase:** 3rd Round 1985-1986

Ground address: Reynolds Field, Perivale Lane, Perivale, Greenford, Middlessex.

Tel No: 0208 9981701

Club Website: www.hanwellfooty.co.uk

Capacity: 1,250   **Seats:**175   **Covered:**600   **Floodlights:** Yes

Simple Directions: A40 (M) west from London. Leave opposite Hoover building (B456 for Ealing) and turn left into Argyle Road and left into Perivale Lane. Ground 500 yards on left.

Midweek Home Matchday: Tuesday

Clubhouse: Saturday matchdays and training evenins   **Club Shop:** No.

Local Radio: Capital Radio

Local Press: Ealing Gazette

CLUB PERSONNEL

Chairman: Bob Fisher
President: Dave Iddiols
Patron: Stephen Pound MP
Secretary: Phil Scott,129 Sutton Court Rd. Hillingdon, Middlesex UB 10 8HT Tel No: 07958 633183
Press Officer: Chairman bob.fisher@hanwelltfc.plur.com
Programme Editor: Bob Fisher
16 Pages/ withh entry

2005-2006
Captain: Chris Mills
Player of the Year: Jason Tucker
Top Goalscorer: Luke Sheekey

CLUB STATISTICS

Record	**Attendance:**	600 v Spurs (first floodlit match).
	Career Goalscorer: Keith Rowlands	
	Career Appearances: Phil Player 617 (20 seasons)	
Record Transfer Fee	**Paid:** N/A	
	Received: N/A	
Senior Honours:	Spartan Senior Runners-Up (3) London Senior Cup 1991-92 92--93	
	R-Up 93-94 Middlesex Charity Cup R-Up 1992-93 1999-2000	
Previous Leagues:	Dauntless League, Wembley & District League, Middlesex League and Spartan South Midlands	

Back Row (L-R): Bob Fisher (Chairman), Danny Vincent (Joint Manager), Danny Gavin, Adam Jaso, Gary Brown, Ricky Pither, Jason Tucker, Matt Pollard, Warren Clarke, Ashley Anjarin, Dean Harper, Pat Gavin (Joint Manager) and Phil Scott (Secretary)
Front Row: Sean James, Luke Sheekey, Mark Sroka, Chris Mills, Antony Rowlands and Victor Osubo.

HILLINGDON BOROUGH(1900)

Re-Formed: 1990
Nickname: Boro

Manager: Steve Ringrose   **Assistant Managers:** Ray Daley and Boysie Wise
Club Colours: White with Blure stripe/Blue/Blue
Change Colours: Orange/Black/Black
Club Sponsor:
Previous League: Spartan South Midlands
Best Seasons: League: 2nd S.S.Mids. 2004-2005 **F.A.Vase:** Finalists 2005-2006
F.A. Cup: Since re-formed 2nd Quallifying Round. Previously 3rd Rd Replay 69-70
Physio: Dave Pook
Ground address: Middlesex Stadium, Breakspear Road, Ruislip, Middlesex HA4 7SB Tel No: 01895 639544
Club Website: www.hillingdonboroughfc.co.uk
Capacity: 1,500   **Seats:** 150   **Covered:**150   **Floodlights:**Yes
Simple Directions: From A40 take B467 (signed Ickenham), left at second round-about into Breakspear Road South, then right after a mile by the Breakspear pub. Ground is half a mile on the left.
Midweek Home Matchday: Tuesday
Clubhouse: Open Daily   **Club Shop:** ?
Local Radio:
Local Press:

CLUB PERSONNEL
Chairman: Gamdoor Dhaliwal
Vice Chairman: Alan Taylor
Life President: John Mason
Company Secretary: Mrs D Dhand
Directors: Dave Pook, KenTaylor and Nick Buckingham.
Secretary: Chris Potter, 23 Lyndhurst, Avenue, Southall, Middlesex UB1 2UN
Tel NO: 0208866 8480 (H)
07903 743821 (M)
Marketing Manager:
Darren O'Sullivan
Programme Editor:
Nick Buckingham
Programme: 20 pages

CLUB STATISTICS

Record	Attendance:
	Career Goalscorer:
	Career Appearances:
	Victory: 12-0 Hanwell Town (H) SSM Premier 1997-98
	Defeat: 1-11 v St Albans City (A) F.A.Cup 1994-1995
Record Transfer Fee	Paid:
	Received: £1,000 from Weadstone for Craig Johnson
Senior Honours:	Spartan League R-Up 1995-96 96-97 S.S.M Cup 1996-97Chalenge Trophy Winners 2004-2005 London Senior Cup R-Up 1996-1997
Previous Names::	Yiewsley , Bromley Park Rangers & Hillingdon Borough

Back Row (L-R): Joe Lyons, Chris Phillips, Mark Kirby, Matt Kidson (Team Captain), BenHarris, Michael Murray,
Front Row: Sam Byfield, Nick Rundell, James Duncan, Blaise O'Brien, Gavin Brown.
Squad members not in picture: Danny Tilbury, Leon Nelson, Chris Hibbs

LYMINGTON & NEW MILTON

Founded: 1998
Nickname: Linnets

Manager: Ian Robinson **Asst.Manager:** Richie Phippard **Coach:** John Waldock

Club Colours: Maroon & Blue Stripes/Blue/Maroon

Change Colours: Yellow/Green/Yellow

Club Sponsor: T.B.A.

Previous League: isthmian

Best Seasons: League: 16th Isthmian div 1 **F.A.Vase:** Quarter Finals 1998-1999

F.A. Cup: 4th Qualifying Round Replay 2004-2005 **F.A.Trophy.:** Prelim Rd. 05-06

Ground address: Fawcetts Field, Christchurch Road, New Milton, Hants.bh25 6qb

Tel No: 01425 628191

Club Website: www.lnmfc.net

Capacity: 3,000   **Seats:** 262   **Covered:** 262   **Floodlights:** Yes

Simple Directions: M27 Jct 1 follow A337 to Lyndhurst one way system (A35) towards Christchurch. Left in Hinton Admiral at Cat & Fiddle. Follow Ringwood road then left at A337 roundabout to New MIlton. Ground one mile on left.

Midweek Home Matchday: Wednesday

Clubhouse: Open seven days a week 11a.m. to 11p.m. **Club Shop: no**

Local Radio: Radio Solent

Local Press: Bournemouth Evening Echo. Lymington Echo and Lymington Times

CLUB PERSONNEL

Chairman:t T.B.A.
President: Jack Holliday
Secretary: Mrs Pat Drake, Kingfishers, Bowling Green, Sway Road, Lymington SO41 8LQ
Tel No: 01590 675647
Press Officer: Tony Baker
Tel No: 01202 424222

Programme
Editor: John Mills
48 Pages £1.50
2005-2006
Player of the Year: Adam Lang
Top Goalscorer: Kevin James 15
2006-2007:
Captain: Tommy McCormick

CLUB STATISTICS

Record	**Attendance:** 1,500 v Aldershot Town 1999-2000 at Southampton Road 2,900. Karen MIlls memorial match	
	Career Goalscorer: Darren Pitter 197 **Career Apps:** Graham Kemp 500 +	
Record	**Victory:** 11-1 v Romsey Towen (H) 1991-1992	
	Defeat : 0-8 v Basingstoke Town (A) 1989-1990	
Senior Honours:	Wessex League 92-3 96-7 97-8 98-9 04-05 & Hants Senior Cup R-Up 89-90	
Previous	**Names:** Lymington Town (until 1988 merged with Wellworthy Ath AFC Lymington 1988-89 (merged with New Milton Town)	
	League Wessex	
	Grounds: Ampress Ground (Wellworthy Ath), Recreation Ground, and Southampton Road Lymington until 1997	

Back Row (L-R): Ian Robinson (manager), Jimmy Sheppard (Coach), Danny Gibbons, Martin Beck, Dan Cann, John Waldock, Dave Allen, Mark Clothier, Dan Turner, Mark Watson, Matt Bowley, Richie Phippard (Ass manager).
Front: Louise Wood (Physio), James Stokoe, Danny Neville, James Ford, Kevin James, Tommy Mccormick, Sam Carter, Adam Lang, Toby Redwood.

MARLOW

Manager: Kevin Stone **Assistant Manager:** Graham Bressington
Coach: Jim Melvin **Physio:** Mark Skoyles:
Club Colours: Royal Blue with white trim/Blue/Blue
Change Colours: All red with white trim
Club Sponsor: North West Estates Plc.
Previous League: Isthmian
Best Seasons: Lg: Isthmian Premier ?   **F.A.Trophy.:** 4th Round 2003-2004
F.A. Cup: Semi-final 1882 3rd Round 1994-1995 1992-1993
F.A.Vase: 5th Rd.Replay 1974-1975
Ground address: Alfred Davies Memorial Ground, Oak Tree Road, Marlow SL7
3ED **Tel No**: 01628 483970 **Information Line**: 01932 710215
Club Website: www.marlowfc.co.uk
Capacity: 3,000   **Seats:**250   **Covered:**600   **Floodlights**: Yes
Simple Directions: A404 to Marlow (from M4 or M40), then A4155 towards town centre.Turn right
into Maple Rise (by ESSO garage), ground in road opposite (Oak Tree Rd).1/2 mile from Marlow (BR).
1/4 mile from Chapel Street bus stops
Midweek Home Matchday: Tuesday
Clubhouse: Open matchdays and most evenings. Smack bar on matchdays.
Club Shop:
Local Radio: Radio Berkshire & Thames Valley Radio
Local Press: Bucks Free Press, Maidenhead Advertiser and Evening Post.

CLUB PERSONNEL
Chairman: Terry Staines
Secretary: Paul Burdell, 69
Wycpombe Road, Marlow, SL7 3HZ
Tel No: 01628 890540
Programme
Editor: Terry Staines
40 Pages £1.00

2006-2007
Captain: John Beale
Player of the Year:
Top Goalscorer: jJerrmaine Roche

CLUB STATISTICS

Record	**Attendance:** 3,000 v Oxford United F.A.Cup 1st Round 1994	
Career Goalscorer:	Kevin Stone	
Career Appearances:	Mick McKeown 500+	
Record Transfer Fee	**Paid**: £5,000 to Sutton United for Richard Evans	
	Received: £8,000 from Slough Town for David Lay	
Senior Honours:	Isthmian Lg Div 1 87-88, Div 2 South R-up 86-87, Lg Cup 92-93, Berks & Bucks Sen Cup (11)	
Previous	**Leagues:** Reading & Dist.; Spartan 1908-10 28-65; Great Western Suburban; Athenian 65-84	
	Name: Great Marlow	
	Grounds: Crown Ground 1870-1919); Star Meadow 19-24	

Back Row (L-R): Jemaine Roche, Aaron Couch, Colin Simpson, Matt Pollard, Jeff Lamb, Ian MacTaggart,
John Beale, Michael Watkins, Johnny Isaac, Seb Neptune, Jack Smillie, Callum Coull, Mark Skoyles (Physio).
Front: Stuart MacLellan, James Flint, Simon Herbert, Adam Dickens, Sam Shepherd, Johnny Gray, Scott Webb,
Micky Floyd, Adam Harman.

NEWPORT (Isle of Wight)

Founded: 1888
Nickname:
The Port

Manager: Hughie Lewis **Assistant Manager:** Steve Brougham
Coach: Steve Greening **Physio:** Tony Harris
Club Colours: Yellow/Blue/Yellow
Change Colours: All Green
Club Sponsor: Wightlink
Previous League: Wessex
Best Seasons: League: ? **F.A. Cup:** 2nd Round 1935-1936 1945-1946
F.A.Trophy.: 4th Road 1999-2000 **F.A.Vase:** 5th Round 1991-1992 1992-1993
Ground address: St.George's Park, St George's Way, Newport, I.O.W.
Club Website: www.newport-fc.co.uk
Capacity: 5,000 **Seats:** 300 **Covered:** :1,000 **Floodlights:** Yes
Simple Directions: Roads from all ferry ports lead to Coppins Bridge roundabout at eastern end of town. Take Sandown/Ventnor exit, go to small roundabout, St George's Way is first exit. Ground is on left five minutes walk from Newport bus station along Church Litten (past old ground) turn left then right at roundabout.
Midweek Home Matchday: Wednesday
Clubhouse: Open every evening & weekend lunchtimes. Two bars & full range of hot and cold at food bar in club and in ground.
Club Shop: Full range of products. **Contact:** Roger Sanders (01983 825925)
Local Radio: Solent, Isle of Wight Radio & Ocean Sound.
Local Press: Portsmouth Evening News I.o.W. County Press & Southampton Evening Echo.

CLUB PERSONNEL
Chairman: Alan Phillips
President: Hilton Bunday
Directors: Alan Phillips & David Bartlett
Secretary: David Bartlett, 10 Eastcliff, Court, Crescent Rd., Shanklin I.O.W.
Company Secretary: Martyn Appel
General Manager: Karen Rogers
Programme
Editor: Alan Phillips
28 Pages £1.30

CLUB STATISTICS		
Record	**Attendance:** 2,270 v Portsmouth (friendly) 7th July 2001	
	2,,217 v Aylesbury United F.A.Cup 1st Rd. November 1994	
	Career Goalscorer: Roy Gilfillan 220 1951-1957	
	Goalcsorer in a Season: Frank Harrison 62 1929-1930	
	Career Appearances:: Jeff Austin 540 (1969-1987)	
Record Transfer Fee	**Paid:** £5,000 to Bognor Regis Town for Colin Matthews.	
	Received: £2,250 from Havant & Waterlooville for Mick Jenkins 1992-1993	
	Victory: 14-1 v Thornycroft Ath (Hants) 45-46 **Defeat** 1-11 v Emsworth 26-27	
Senior Honours:	Southern League Eastern Division 2000-2001 Wessex R-Up 89-90	
	Hants Senior Cup (8) I.o.W. Cup (34)	
Previous Leagues:	I.o.W. 1896-1928 Hants 1928-1986 Wessex 1986-1990	

Back Row Left to Right
M. McEnery, D. Greening, R. Hardwell, T. White, P. Jones, B. Simpkins,J. McCormack, L. Wood, O. Dedegbe,J. Dunk, S. Pilcher, L. Forrest
Front Row Left to Right
T. Harris, G. Snow, N. Betts, G. Keogh, S. Greening, F. Quirke, J. Holmes, S. Leigh.(manager), S. Brougham (Asst Manager), T. Scovell, A. Wright

OXFORD CITY

Founded: 1882
Nickname: CITY

CLUB PERSONNEL

Chairman: Brian Cox

Vice-Chairman: Paul Cotterell

Managing Director: Colin Taylor

Director of Development: Andy Sinott

Secretary: John Shepherd,20 Howe Close,Wheatley, Oxford OX33 1SS
Tel No: 01865 872181 (H)
07748 628911 (M)

Prog Ed: ColinTaylor(07764 386658)
60 Pages £1.00

Manager: Andy Lyne   **Assistant Manager:** Justin Merrit

Club Colours: Blue & white hoops /Blue/Blue

Change Colours: All yellow

Club Sponsor: S.M.C.

Previous League: Spartan South Midlands

Best Seasons: League: Isthmian Runners Up 1934-35 45-46

F.A. Cup: 2nd Round 1969-70   **F.A.Vase:** Runners Up 1994-95

F.A.Trophy.: 2nd Round   **F.A.Amateur Cup:** Winners 1905-1906

Coach: Paul Spittle   **Goalkeeping Coach** Jon Maskell **Physio:** Neil Greig

Ground address: Court Place Farm, Marsh :L:ane, Marston, Oxford OX3 0NQ

Club Website: www.oxfordcityfc.co.uk

Capacity: 3,000   **Seats:** 300   **Covered:** 400   **Floodlights:** Yes

Simple Directions: From London M40 or A40 take ring road to North of Oxford . then first slip road and follow signs to John Radcliffe Hospital and Court Farm Stadium. Ground on left aftyer leaving flyover.

Midweek Home Matchday: Tuesday

Clubhouse: Open matchdays with snacks. **Club Shop:** Yes

CLUB STATISTICS

Record	**Attendance:** 9,500 v Leytonstone F.A.Amateur Cup 1950(White House)
	Career Goalscorer: John Woodley
	Career Appearances: John Woodley
Record Transfer Fee	**Paid:** £3,000 to Woking for S.Adams
	Received: £15,000 from Yeovil Town for Howard Forintopn
Senior Honours:	F.A.Amateur Cup 1905-06 F.A.Vase R-Up 1994-95 Oxford Sen. Cup (31)
	Isthmian Runners-Up 1934-35 1945-46
Previous Leagues:	Spartan S. Midlands 2005-06, Isthmian1907-88 94-2005 South Midlands 90-93.
Grounds:	The White House 1882-1988 Cuttleslowe Park 1990-91 Pressed Steel 91-93

Photo: Andrew Fitzsimons

402

PAULTON ROVERS

**Founded: 1881
Nickname: Rovers**

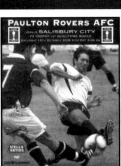

Manager: Andy Jones   **Player Assistant Manager:** Mike Kilgour   **Physio:**
Club Colours: White /Maroon/Maroon
Change Colours: Yellow/Navy/Navy
Club Sponsor: Barons Propertry Centre & Bass Breweries
Previous League: Western
Best Seasons: League:
F.A. Cup: 4th Qualifying Round 1906-1907 2003-2004
F.A.Vase: 5th Round Replay 1989-90
Ground address: Athletic Ground, Winterfield Road, Paulton, Somerset
BS39 7RF **Tel No:** 01761 412907
Club Website: www.paultonroversafc.co.uk
Capacity: 5,000   **Seats:** 253   **Covered:** 2,500   **Floodlights:** Yes
Simple Directions: From A39 at Farrington Gurney, follow A 362 marked Radstock for
two miles. Turn left at roundabout, take B3355 to Paulton and ground is on right.
Midweek Home Matchday: Monday
Clubhouse: Three bars with full social facilities to hire. Lounge, skittle alley and
dancehall available to hire. **Social Club Chairman:** Paul Reynolds
Club Shop: Contact: Chairman 07793 908616 (M)
Local Radio:
Local Press: Bath Evening Chronicle, Bristoil Evening Post, Western Daily Press
and Somerset Gaurdian.

CLUB PERSONNEL
Chairman: David Bissex
President: L.Rogers
Secretary: Tracy Curtis, 12 Linden Close, Waterford Park, Westfield, Radstock BA3 3EJ
Tel Nos: 01761 420659 (H) 07760 377302 (M)
Press Officers:
Matt Bissex & Tony Walsh

Programme Editor: Chairman
20 Pages £1.00
2006-2007
Captain: Richard Perry
Player of the Year:
Top Goalscorer:

CLUB STATISTICS

Record	**Attendance:** 2,000 v Crewe Alexandra F.A.Cup 1906-1907
	Career Goalscorer: Graham Colbourne
	Career Appearances: Steve Tovey
Record Transfer Fee	**Paid:**
	Received:
Senior Honours:	Western League Premier Division Runners-Up 2003-2004
	Div 2 R-Up 1900-01 Somerset Senior Cup (12)
Previous Leagues:	Wiltshire Premier, Somerset Senior, Western
Grounds:	Chapel Field, Cricket Ground and Recreation Ground.

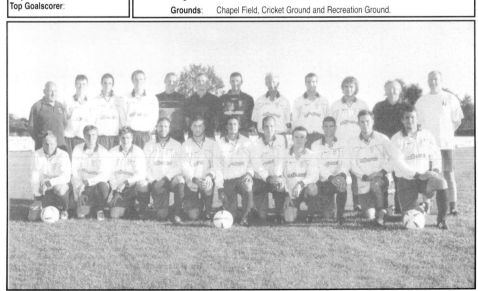

SWINDON SUPERMARINE

Founded: 1992
Nickname: Marine

Club Colours: Blue & white hoops /Blue/Blue

Change Colours: Red & white/Red/Red

Club Sponsor: Profile Shopfitting

Previous League: Hellenic

Best Seasons: **F.A. Cup:** 2nd Qualifying Round 2005-2006

F.A.Trophy.: 1st Round 2002-03 **F.A.Vase:** 2nd Round 1998-1999 1999-2000

Manager: Mark Collier **Coach:**Ian Howell **Physio:**Wayne Roberts

Ground address: Hunts Copse, South Marston, Swindon, Wilts.

Tel No: 01793 828778

Club Website:

Capacity: 3,000 **Seats:** 300 **Covered:** 300 **Floodlights:** Yes

Simple Directions: On A361 Swindon/Highworth road, adjoining South Marston Ind. Estate.Six miles from Swindon (BR) - buses in direction of Highworth, Fairford & Lechdale. If lost ask for Honda!

Midweek Home Matchday: Tuesday

Clubhouse: Yes **Club Shop: Contact:** Andy Garrett

Local Radio: BBC Wiltshire Sound G.W.R.F.M.

Local Press: Swindon Advertiser

CLUB PERSONNEL

Chairman: Mick Parsons
Vice Chairman: Steve Moore
President: Cliff Puffett
Secretary & Press Officer: Judi Moore, Chardon Rise, Bell Lane, Liddington, Swindon SN4 0HH
Tel NO: 01793 790685

Programme
Editor: Keith Yeomans
40 Pages/.00
2006-2007
Captain: Steve Davis
Player of the Year: Steve Bennett
Top Goalscorer: Matt Pratley

CLUB STATISTICS

Record	**Attendance:** 1,550 v Aston Villa
	Career Goalscorer: Damon York 136
	Career Appearances: Damon York 298 + 16 1990-1998
Record Transfer Fee	**Paid:** £1,000 to Hungerford Town for Lee Hartson
	Received: N/A,
Senior Honours:	Hellenic Lge - Premier Div. 97-98, 00-01, R-up 95-96 98-99; Div. One 85-86 86-87;
	Hellenic Challenge Cup 96-97, 99/00.Wiltshire Senior Cup 82-83, 86-87, 89-90.
Previous Leagues:	**Leagues:** Wiltshire Lge., Hellenic League to 2001
	Names: Vickers Armstrong 46-81,Supermarine 82-91 (merged 1992),
	Penhill Youth Centre 70-84, Swindon Athletic 84-89 (merged)
	Grounds: Supermarine: Vickers Airfield (until mid-1960s);
	Swindon Ath.: Merton 70-84; `Southbrook', Pinehurst Road 84-92

Back Row L to R: David Pratt, Matt Pratley, Tom King, Steve Davies, Neil Dix, Roman Ronchinsky, Dave Slattery, Jimmy Griffin, **Middle:** Gus Fraser, Giles Harris, Danny Allen, Steve Campbell, Steve Bennett, JP Mills, Bradley Newman, Steve Jenkins, Jeremy Newton, Robbie Burns (Kit Man). **Front:** Kate Cady (Sports Therapist) Roger Emms (Coach), Judi Moore (Football Secretary) Mark Collier (Manager), Cliff Puffett (Chairman), Ian Howell (Assistant Manager), Katy Henley, (Sports Therapist).

TAUNTON TOWN

Founded: 1947
Nickname:
Peacocks

Home of
The Peacocks
in the heart of
Somerset

Official Match Day Programme £1.50

Southern League Division 1 West 2005/2006

Main Sponsor

Ashwood

Programme Sponsor

KONICA MINOLTA

Manager: Gary Domone   **Therapist:**Graham Webster

Club Colours: All Sky Blue
Change Colours: All Gold

Club Sponsor: RAM Scaffolding
Previous League: Western

Best Seasons: League: Southern 9th   **F.A. Cup:** 1st Round 1981-1982
F.A.Trophy.: 1st Round 1980-1981   **F.A.Vase:** Winners 2000-2001

Ground address: Wordsworth Drive, Taunton, Somerset TA1 2HG
Tel No: 01823 278191   **Newsline:** 09066 555 849
Club Website: www.tauntontown.com
Capacity: 4,000   **Seats:** 400   **Covered:**1,000   **Floodlights:** Yes

Simple Directions: Leave M5 Jct 25, follow signs to town centre. At traffic lights bear left and then straight on through through second lights into Wordsworth Drive; ground on left. 25 mins walk from Taunton (BR); turn left out of station and follow road right through town centre bearing left into East Reach. Follow road down and turn right into Wordsworth Drive shortly after Victoria pub

CLUB PERSONNEL

Chairman: Tom Harris
Directors: Harold Needs, Martin Dongworth, Desmond Badcock, Richard Newman, John Eastment and Clive Perrott.
Secretary & Press Officer:
Martin Dongworth: c/o club
Tel Nos: 01823 322850 (H)
07791 948686 (M)
Commercial Managers:
Sue Draper & Tom Rooks.
Prog.Editor: Secretary
48 Pages £1.50
2005-2006
Captain: Gary Fisher
Player of the Year: Gary Fisher
Top Goalscorer: Aron Blackmore

Midweek Home Matchday: Wednesday
Clubhouse: Social club to accomodate 300 with full bar facilities. Plus separate bar and hallfor private functions.. Hot snacls also always on sale matchdays.
Club Shop: Yes
Local Radio: Orchard FM & Radio Bristol
Local Press: Somerset County Gazette and Taunton Times

CLUB STATISTICS

Record	**Attendance:** 3,284 v Tiverton Town F.A.Vase Semi-Final1999
	Career Goalscorer: Tony Payne
	Goalscorer in a Season: Reg Oram 67
	Career Appearances:: Tony Payne
Record	**Victory:** 12-0 v Dawlish Town (a) F.A.Cup Preliminary Round 28.8.93
	Received: 0-8 v Cheltenham Town (A) F.A.Cup 2nd Qualifying Round 28.9.91
Senior Honours:	FA Vase Winners 00-01 R-up 93-94, Western Lg Champions 68-69 89-90,95-6, 98-9,99-00, 00-01 R-up (2) Somerset Prem.Cup Winners 02-03, 05-06.
	R-up 82-83 89-90 92-93 98-99.
Previous	**Leagues:**: Western 1954 -1977 Southern 1977-1983 Western 1983-2002

Back row, left to right: Graham Webster (physio), Neil Ward, Jak Martin, Charlie Welsh, Tom Buckler, Alexis Piper, Gary McCauley, Pete Monks and Danny Phillips (Coach). **Front row:** Chris Wright, Dan Kiely, Steve Hint, Sam Duggan, Loris Gaglia, Sono, Sam Jones and Dean Copard.

Photo courtesy of Philip Waite

THATCHAM TOWN

Founded: 1895
Nickname:

THATCHAM TOWN FC
AN FA CHARTER STANDARD COMMUNITY CLUB
WWW.THATCHAMTOWNFC.CO.UK

British Gas
Football League

MATCHDAY MAGAZINE SPONSORED BY GARDNER LEAGUE) £1.00
SOUTHERN LEAGUE DIVISION ONE (S & W)

TONIGHT'S VISITORS:
TAUNTON TOWN
SOUTHERN LEAGUE
DIV ONE (S & W)
AUG 22ND 2006 KO: 7.45 PM

Manager: Jason Braidwood   **Coach:**   **Physio:**

Club Colours: Blue & white stripes/ Blue/Blue

Change Colours: Red/Black/Red

Club Sponsor: Lakeside Sperbowl

Previous League: Wessex League

Best Seasons: League: Wessex League Champions 1995-1996

F.A. Cup: 4th Qualifying Round 1996-1997   **F.A.Vase:** 6th Round 1987-1988

Ground address: Waterside Park, Crookham Hill, Thatcham, Berks. RG19 4PA

Club Website: www.thatchamtowntc.co.uk

Capacity: 3,000   **Seats:** 300   **Covered:** 300   **Floodlights:** Yes

Simple Directions: From M4 jct 13 take A34 to Newbury. Left onto A4 towards
Reading and turn right in Thatcham following signs to the B.R. station. Ground is on
left before the station.

Midweek Home Matchday: Tuesday

Clubhouse: Open every evening and iunchtimes   **Club Shop:** Yes

Local Radio:

Local Press:

CLUB PERSONNEL
Chairman& Press Officer:
Phil Holdway
Director of Football:
Steve Melledew
Secretary: Peter Woodage, 5 Elm
Grove Yjaychham, Berkshire RG 18
3PJ Tel No: 01635 867803
General Secretary: Tony Lawson
**Programme
Editor:** Edward Houghton
28 Page £1.00

2005-2006
Captain:
Player of the Year:
Top Goalscorer:

CLUB STATISTICS		
Record	**Attendance:**	1,400 v Aldershot F.A.Vase
	Career Goalscorer:	
	Career Appearances:	
Record Transfer Fee	Paid:	
	Received:	
Senior Honours:	Wessex League Champions 95-96 Runners Upo 1996-97 2005-06	
	Hellenic Honours?	
Previous Leagues:	Hellenic League , Wessex League	
Previous Grounds:	Station Road 1946-1952 Lancaster Close 1952-1992	

Back Row (L-R): Campion, Taplin, Green M, Green J, Allaway, Mattingley, Strudley, Witt, Cook, Perry, Thomas,
Sullivan.
Front: Gooding, Rees, Nurse, Worsfold,Melledew S, Goddard, Braidwood (Mgr), Tillen, Blackford, Davies, McClay,
Melledew T.

UXBRIDGE

Founded: 1871
Nickname:
The Reds

Manager: Tony Choules **Assistant Manager:** Scott Tarr
Coach: Gary Farrell **Physio:** Paul Donnell
Club Colours: Red/White/Red
Change Colours: Old Giold/Black/Black
Club Sponsor:
Previous League: Isthmian
Best Seasons: League: 4th Southern League Div 1 East 2004-2005
F.A. Cup: 2nd Round 1873-1874 **F.A.Trophy.:** 2nd Round 1998-99 99-00 00-01
F.A.Vase: 4th Round 1983-1984
F.A.Amateur Cup: Runners-Up 1897-1898
Ground address: Honeycroft, Horton Road, West Drayton, Middlesex UB7 8HX
Tel No: 01895 443557
Club Website: www.uxbridgefc.co.uk
Capacity: 3,770 **Seats:** 339 **Covered:** 760 **Floodlights:** Yes
Simple Directions: From West Drayton (BR) turn right then1st right (Horton Road).Ground one
mile on left. From Uxbridge (LT) take 222 or U3 bus to West Drayton station, then follow as above.
By road, ground 1 mile north of M4 jct 4 taking road to Uxbridge and leaving by first junction and
turning left into Horton Rd- ground 500yds on right. Nearest Railway station is West Drayton.
Midweek Home Matchday: Tuesday 7.45
Clubhouse: Open every evening and week end & bank holiday lunchtimes
Tel No: 01895 443557
Club Shop:
Local Radio: Capital, G.L.R. and Star F.M.
Local Press: Uxbridge Gazette & Leader and Uxbridge Recorder.

CLUB PERSONNEL

Chairman: Alan Holloway
President: Alan Odell
Secretary: Roger Stevens,
9 Bourne Avenue, Hillingdon,
Middlesex. UB8 3AR
Tel No: 01895 236879
Commercial Manager:
Derek Marshall
Press Officer: David Gill

Programme
Editor: BB Publications
44 Pages £1.00
2005-2006
Captain: Stuart Bamford
Player of the Year: John Peacock
Top Goalscorer: Mark Nicholls

CLUB STATISTICS

Record	**Attendance:** 1,000 v Arsenal opening of floodlights 1981
	Career Goalscorer: Phil Duff 153
	Career Appearances:: Roger Nicholls 1054
Record Transfer Fees	**Paid:**
	Received:
Senior Honours:	F.A Amateur Cup R-up 1897-98; London Chall. Cup 93-94 96-97 98-99,
	R-up 97-98; IsthLge Div 2 S. R-up 84-85; Athenian Lge Cup R-up 81-82,
	Middx Sen.Cup 1893-94 95-96 1950-51, 2000-01 R-up 97-98;
Previous	**Leagues:** Southern 1894-99; Gt Western Suburban 1906-19, 20-23; Athenian
	1919-20, 24-37, 63-82; Spartan 37-38; London 38-46; Gt Western Comb.
	39-45;Corinthian 46-63 **Name:** Uxbridge Town 23-45
	Grounds: RAF Stadium 23-48 and Cleveland Road 48-78

Back Row (L to R): Charlie Hill, Billy Matthews, Jonathan Ashwood, John Swift, Mark Weedon, John Peacock, Harry Howell,
Matt Stamp. **Middle:** Phil Granville (Reserve Team Manager), Tristan Lewis, Liam Parrington, Dean Peltohaka, Ryan Spencer, Greg Kirkpatrick,
Darren Whittock, Danny Yeoman, Stuart Everley (Physio). **Front:** Richard McDonagh, Sean Kelleher, Ian Dickens, Scott Tarr (Assistant Manager),
Tony Choules (Manager), Gary Farrell (Coach), Danny Hawkesworth, Daryl King, Nathan Stamp. **Seated in Front:** Blake Farrell (Kit Man)

WINCHESTER CITY

Founded: 1884
Nickname: City

Manager: Steve Moss   **Physio**: Scott Rickard

Club Colours: Red & Black stripes/Black/Black

Change Colours: Yellow & BLue

Club Sponsor: Denplan

Previous League: Wessex League

Best Seasons: League: Southern League   **F.A. Cup:** 4th Qualifying Rd 1954-55

F.A.Trophy.: 2nd Qualifying Round 1972-1973   **F.A.Vase:** Winners 2003-2004

Ground address: Denplan City Stadium, Hillier Way, Abbots Barton, Winchester, Hants. SO23 7SR Tel NO: 01962 810200

Club Website: www.winchestercityfc.com

Capacity: 2,500   **Seats**: 200   **Covered**: 275   **Floodlights**: Yes

Simple Directions: M3 jct 9 take A33/A34 for a mile, then A33 for another mile anot first left into Kings Worthy. After three miles take second left after 30 mph sign , then first right and first left into Hilliers Road.

Midweek Home Matchday: Tuesday

Clubhouse: Open on Matchdays. **Club Shop:** Open match days

Local Radio: RadioSolent and Win F.M

Local Press: Hampshire Chronicle

CLUB PERSONNEL

Chairman: Martin Moody
President: Richard Newsome
Secretary: John Moody,13 Tadfield Crescent, Romsey, Hampshire SO51 5AN
Tel Nos :1794 500672 (H)
07879 816898 (M)

Programme
Editor: Derek Caws
50Pages £1.00

2005-2006
Captain: Matt Bricknell
Player of the Year: Ian Mancey
Top Goalscorer: Ian Mancey

CLUB STATISTICS

Record	Attendance: 1,818 v Taunton town S-Final FA.Vase
	Career Goalscorer:Andy Forbes
	Career Appearances: Ian Mancey
	Transfer Fee Paid N/A Received: N/A
Senior Honours:	F.A.Vase 2004, Hants.Sen.Cup 1932 2005, Hants Lg. Cnampions 2003,
	Wessex Lg 2003-4 2005-6 R-Up 2005 Southampton Sen. Cup 2000-2001
Previous Leagues:	Hampshire 1898-1971 1973-2003 Southern 1971-1973 Wessex 2003-2006

WINDSOR & ETON

Founded:1892
Nickname: Royalists

Club Colours: All red with greentrim

Change Colours: All blue

Club Sponsor: Commonwealth Coaches

Previous League: Athenian

Best Seasons: 5th Isthmian Premier Division   **F.A. Cup:** 2nd Rd Replay

F.A.Trophy.: 3rd Rd 68-69   **F.A.Vase:** Semi-Final 80-81

Manager: Dave Carroll   **Asst.Manager:** Paul Holsgrove

           Ground address: Stag Meadow, St Leonards Rd., Windsoor, Berkshire,

SL4 3DR Tel No: 01753 860656

Capacity: 4,500   **Seats:** 400   **Covered: 550**   Floodlights: Yes

Simple Directions: A332 from M4 Jct. Third left at roundabout then into

St L eonards Rd at light at T junction. Ground 500 yards on right on B3022 oppo-

site Stag & Hounds pub.

Midweek Home Matchday: Tuesday

Clubhouse: Yes **Club Shop:** Yes

LocalRadio: BBC Radio Berkshire and Star FM

Local Press: Windsor & Eton Express and Windsor Observer

CLUB PERSONNEL

Chairman: Peter Simpson
President: Barry Davies
V-Chairman: Kevin Stott
Secretary: Steve Rowland
C/o Club
Tel No: 07887 779630 (M)
Press Officer: Secretary
Programme.Editors:
 Michael Gedd & Dan Gomm
Programme
32 pages £1.50

2005-2006
Captain: Jamie Jarvis
Player of the Year: Kieron Drake
Top Goalscorer: Adam Wallace

CLUB STATISTICS

Record	**Attendance**: 8,500 (Charity Match)
	Career Appearances: Kevin Mitchell
Record Transfer Fee	**Paid**: 9,000 to Slough Town for Keith White
	Received: 45,000 from Barnet for Michael Banton & Michael Barnes
Senior Honours:	Isthmian Div 1 83-84 Div 2 R-up 21-22 Athenian Lg 79-80 80-81 Berks & Bucks Senior Cup (11) R-up (6)
Previous Leagues:	Southern, West Berks, Great Western Suburban, Athenian 22-29 63-81 Spartan 29-32 Gt Western Comb., Corinthian 45-50 Metropolitan 50-60 Delphian 60-63 Athenian
Ground:	Ballon Meadow 1892-1912

Back Row (L-R): Iain Gardiner, Jez Weeks, David Tilbury, Mark Cooper, Paul Coyne, Mark Davidson.
Middle: Omar Maqsood, Matt Seedel, James Edgerley, Daniel Sacha, Jamie Furmage, Paul Reed, Michael Chennels, Ricci Dolan, Angela Di Benedetto (Sports Therapist). **Front**: Stuart Tanfield, Terry O'Connor, Jon Case, Simon Lane (Manager), Chris Cahill, Ben Porter, Daniel Blatchford.

FOOTBALL LEAGUE

STEP 1

FOOTBALL
CONFERENCE

STEP 2

| CONFERENCE NORTH | CONFERENCE SOUTH |

STEP 3

| SOUTHERN PREMIER | NORTHERN PREMIER | ISTHMIAN PREMIER |

STEP 4

| SOUTHERN DIVISION 1 SOUTH &WEST MIDLAND | NORTHERN PREMIER DIV.1 | ISTHMIAN DIVISION 1 NORTH SOUTH |

STEP 5/6

Combined Counties	Hellenic	Northern League	Spartan South Midlands	Wessex
Eastern Counties	Kent	Northern Counties East	Sussex County	Western
Essex Senior	Midland Alliance	North West Counties	United Counties	

STEP 7

Anglian Combination	Dorset County	Kent County	Midland Combination	Peterborough & District	West Cheshire
Bedford & District	Dorset Premier	Leicestershire Senior	Midland League	Reading League	West Lancashire
Brighton & Hove	East Sussex	Liverpool County	North Berkshire	Somerset County	West Midlands (reg)
Cambridgeshire County	Essex & Suffolk Border	Manchester Football	Northampton Town Lge	South Western	West Sussex
Central Midlands	Essex Intermediate	Mid Cheshire League	Northamptonshire Comb.	Suffolk & Ipswich	Wiltshire League
Crawley & Disrict	Gloucesterhisre Co.	Mid Sussex	Northern Alliance	Teeside League	Worthing & District
Devon County	Herts Senior County	Middlesex County	Oxfordshire Senior	Wearside League	

SOUTHERN LEAGUE DIVISION ONE EAST

DIVISION ONE EAST		P	W	D	L	F	A	Pts
1.	Boreham Wood	42	24	12	6	84	41	84
2.	Corby Town	42	25	9	8	63	33	84
3.	Enfield Town	42	24	9	9	75	43	81
4.	Stamford*	42	20	10	12	73	53	70
5.	Barking & East Ham United	42	20	10	12	63	47	70
6.	Wivenhoe Town	42	17	11	14	56	54	62
7.	Dartford	42	16	13	13	65	57	61
8.	Waltham Forest	42	17	8	17	64	66	59
9.	Harlow Town	42	14	16	12	57	56	58
10.	Arlesey Town	42	15	11	16	58	65	56
11.	Rothwell Town	42	13	14	15	48	53	53
12.	Wingate & Finchley	42	13	14	15	57	64	53
13.	Great Wakering Rovers	42	13	12	17	65	67	51
14.	Uxbridge	42	13	11	18	62	64	50
15.	Potters Bar Town	42	13	11	18	60	66	50
16.	Enfield	42	13	11	18	52	64	50
17.	Chatham Town	42	13	10	19	51	57	49
18.	Sittingbourne	42	12	12	18	53	69	48
19.	Barton Rovers	42	13	8	21	59	73	47
20.	Aveley	42	11	13	18	51	70	46
21.	Ilford	42	8	17	17	35	59	41
22.	Berkhamsted Town	42	8	12	22	51	81	36

*Promoted via the play-offs.

DIV. ONE EAST	1	2	3	4	5	6	7	8	9	10	11	12	13	14	15	16	17	18	19	20	21	22
1 Arlesey Town		1-0	1-3	2-2	2-0	0-2	0-1	0-1	0-1	1-0	2-4	2-5	0-2	3-3	4-0	1-0	1-3	2-2	2-1	1-0	1-1	2-0
2 Aveley	1-2		0-1	1-0	1-0	0-2	2-2	3-0	1-3	1-1	0-0	1-1	2-0	1-0	0-2	1-0	2-2	0-3	2-0	1-4	2-1	1-1
3 Barking&E.H.U.	4-2	2-1		2-0	1-0	0-0	1-1	0-1	2-2	2-1	1-2	2-0	2-1	3-1	1-0	1-2	0-1	2-3	1-1	2-1	2-1	2-1
4 Barton Rovers	3-0	1-1	0-0		3-2	0-1	1-0	0-3	0-2	0-1	1-2	1-2	2-2	2-3	1-2	4-1	0-2	2-1	1-1	1-0	3-1	0-0
5 Berkhamsted T.	2-2	2-1	0-7	1-6		1-2	1-0	2-2	3-1	0-1	1-2	2-2	1-1	1-1	2-3	2-2	1-3	3-1	2-0	0-2	0-2	1-1
6 Boreham Wood	1-3	7-3	3-0	2-2	2-0		3-0	2-1	3-1	1-1	1-0	0-0	1-1	4-2	3-1	1-1	2-0	5-0	1-1	6-1	1-2	4-0
7 Chatham Town	0-1	3-2	1-1	3-2	3-0	2-0		0-0	1-0	3-0	0-2	3-2	1-1	1-2	3-2	3-1	2-3	0-1	1-2	0-1	3-1	2-2
8 Corby Town	1-2	1-0	3-1	5-0	2-1	2-0	2-0		4-1	3-0	1-0	1-1	2-1	1-1	1-3	1-0	2-1	1-0	0-0	1-0	1-0	3-0
9 Dartford	0-0	5-1	2-2	2-1	1-1	2-2	3-1	1-1		4-2	0-1	3-2	1-1	3-1	1-2	0-1	0-0	2-1	1-2	1-1	2-1	3-0
10 Enfield	1-0	1-2	1-0	3-0	1-2	1-2	0-2	2-1	2-2		1-2	0-0	2-3	1-1	3-2	1-3	4-3	0-1	2-2	2-1	0-0	0-0
11 Enfield Town	4-1	0-0	3-0	3-2	0-2	0-2	2-1	0-1	0-1	2-2		1-0	1-2	1-0	2-0	1-2	1-1	4-2	2-2	2-0	1-1	2-1
12 Great W. R.	2-1	2-2	3-1	5-1	2-1	0-1	2-0	1-3	0-1	6-1	0-5		2-3	1-0	3-2	1-0	2-0	2-1	1-2	2-3	2-2	2-2
13 Harlow Town	1-1	2-2	0-2	3-0	3-2	2-1	1-1	0-0	1-1	0-1	1-5	1-1		3-2	2-0	2-1	1-0	4-1	2-2	2-0	1-2	2-2
14 Ilford	1-1	0-0	0-1	0-2	0-0	1-4	0-0	1-0	0-2	0-1	0-0	1-0	2-0		1-1	2-2	1-1	1-0	0-0	1-3	0-0	1-0
15 Potters Bar T.	1-1	4-1	0-1	3-1	4-2	1-1	1-1	0-1	1-4	0-0	4-2	2-1	0-0	2-2		0-0	4-4	1-0	2-3	1-2	2-0	1-2
16 Rothwell Town	2-2	0-0	1-5	0-0	2-2	1-1	1-2	0-0	3-0	2-0	2-2	3-3	3-2	2-1	1-0		1-0	1-0	1-4	1-1	0-2	1-0
17 Sittingbourne	0-1	0-4	1-1	2-4	3-1	1-1	2-1	0-0	1-0	1-0	2-4	2-1	1-1	0-0	1-1	1-0		4-2	1-3	1-1	0-0	0-2
18 Stamford	3-1	2-2	1-1	3-0	2-2	2-2	1-1	2-0	2-0	2-1	0-0	2-0	1-0	5-0	1-0	6-2		3-1	4-0	2-2	4-2	
19 Uxbridge	1-3	1-1	4-1	1-2	0-0	2-3	0-1	0-1	3-1	2-5	1-2	4-0	1-1	3-0	0-2	0-3	3-0	1-1		0-1	0-1	1-2
20 Waltham Forest	2-2	6-2	1-0	0-4	1-0	0-1	3-1	4-5	2-2	3-1	0-1	1-1	1-2	4-0	1-1	3-1	4-2	0-1	1-0		3-2	0-3
21 Wingate & F.	3-1	1-3	1-1	3-3	1-4	0-2	2-0	0-3	3-2	0-3	1-4	1-1	2-0	2-2	2-0	0-0	2-1	2-2	4-2	4-2		1-2
22 Wivenhoe Town	1-3	3-0	0-1	2-0	5-1	3-1	1-0	3-1	1-1	2-2	1-3	2-1	1-0	0-0	2-1	0-2	1-0	1-3	2-1	2-0	0-0	

411

AYLESBURY UNITED

Founded: 1897
Nickname: The Ducks

Manager: Ian Franklin
Physio: Gareth Styles
Club Colours: Green & white/white/white
Change Colours: Amber& black/black/amber
Club Sponsor: A.P.S.Mortgages
Previous League: Isthmian
Best Seasons: Southern Premier League Champions 1987-88
F.A. Cup: 3rd Rd 1995   **F.A.Trophy.:** Semi-Final 2002-2003
Ground address: The Stadium, Buckingham Road, Aylesbury HP20 2AQ
Tel No: 01296 436350 Fax: 01296 395667
Official website: www.aylesburyunited.co.uk (Luke Brown)
Capacity: 4,000   Seats: 500   Covered: 1,000   Floodlights:Yes
Simple Directions: On A413 to Buckingham just off ring road opposite Horse & Jockeys Pub.
Midweek Home Matchday: Tuesday
Clubhouse: Pub hours. Bar snacks available (Mick Read)   **Club Shop:** Yes
Local Radio: BBC Three Counties Mix96
Local Press: Bucks Herald and Bucks Advertiser

CLUB PERSONNEL

Chairman: BillCarroll
Director: Graha.Reed
Commercial Director:R.Shepherd
Secretary: Chris Damm, 72 Hilton Avenue, Aylesbury,Bucks, HP 20 2HF Tel No: 07890 524397 (M)
Press Officer: P.Ash
Programme Editor: Luke Brown

2005-2006
Captain: Enzo Silvestri
Player of the Year: Matt Hayward
Top Goalscorer:

CLUB STATISTICS

Record Attendance :	6,000 v England 1988
Career Goalscorer:	Cliff Hercules 301
Career Appearances:	Cliff Hercules 651+18
Record Transfer Fee	**Paid:** £15,000 to Northampton Town for Glenville Donegal 1990
	Received: Undisclosed fee for Jermaine Darlington from Q.P.R. 1999
Senior Honours:	Southern League 87-88 Mids Div R-up 84-85 Southern Div R-up 79-80
	Isthmian R-up 1998-99 Berks & Bucks Sen Cup (4) Isth Cup 94-95
Previous Leagues:	Bucks Contiguous 1897-1903, South Eastern 03-07 Spartan 07-51 Delphian
51-	63 Athenian 63-76, Southern 76-88 GMV Conference 88-89 Conference
88-99	Isthmian 89-2004
Grounds:	Printing Works Ground 1897-1903 Wendover Rd /The Stadium Turnfurlong Rd
	35-85 (same ground -name changed). Shared grounds 85-86

Back row, I to r: Gareth Styles (Sports Therapist), Kieron Schmidt, Justin Gordon, Aston Goss, Ron Schmidt (Kit Man). **MIddle Row:** John Newman (Director), Bartex Mozczski, Dean Powles, Sam Styles, Matt Hayward, Jack Rashid, Liam Folds, Jamie Kearns, Gavin Jaggard and Jamie Nicholls. **Front row:** GaryCrawshaw, Daniel Mead, Drew Roberts, Danny Nicholls (Manager), Kevin England (Asst.Manager), Neil Lazarus and Greg Williams.

BARTON ROVERS

Founded: 1898
Nickname: Rovers

Manager: Gordon Taylor   **Assistant Manager:** Tony McNaly
Coach: Neil Rodney   **Physio:** Mick Clark
Club Colours: All Royal Blue with White trim
Change Colours: All Yellow
Club Sponsor: Hanover Consulting
Previous League: Isthmian
Best Seasons: League: 8th Southern Div 1 East 2004-05,12th Isthmian Div 1 99-00
F.A.Vase: Finalists:77-78
F.A. Cup: 1st Round 1980-1981   **F.A.Trophy.:** 3rd Round 2000-2001
Ground address: Sharpenhoe Road, Barton-le-Clay, Bedford, MK45 4SD
Tel No: 01582 707772
Club Website: www.bartonrovers.co.uk
Capacity: 4,000   **Seats:**160   **Covered** 1,120:   **Floodlights:** Yes
Simple Directions: M1 Jct 12, from London exit turn right, take 2nd right through Harlington and Sharpenhoe. Entrance to ground 44 yds on right down concrete drive entering village. 4.5 miles from Harlington (BR), 6 miles from Luton (BR), good bus or taxis service from Luton
Midweek Home Matchday: Tuesday
Clubhouse: Noon-3pm weekends (no football), noon-11pm (matchdays), 7-11pm weekdays. Real ale, hot & cold snacks, pool, darts, gaming machines available.
Club Shop: Yes Contact: 01582 751013
Local Radio: Radio Chiltern, Radio Beds & Three Counties Radio.
Local Press: Luton News, The Herald and Beds on Sunday

CLUB PERSONNEL
Chairman: Malcolm Bright
Vice Chairman: Mick Brooks
President: Pat Howarth
General Secretary: Owen Clark, C/o club
Tel No: 01582 882398
Football Secretary: Chris Sterry
Press Officer: Nick Rhodes

Programme
Editor: Nick Rhodes & Owen Clark
64 pages £1.30

2005-2006
Captain: James Gray
Player of the Year: Andy Reed
Top Goalscorer: Paul Barnes 27

CLUB STATISTICS

Record

Attendance: 1,900 v Nuneation Borough 4th. Q.Rd F.A.Cup 1976

Career Goalscorer: Richard Camp 152 1989-1998

Career Appearances: Tony McNally 598 (1988-2005)

Record Transfer Fee   **Paid:** £1,000 to Hitchin Town for for B.Baldry 1980

Received: £1,000 from Bishop's Stortford for B.Baldry 1981

Senior Honours: Isthmian Lge Div 2 R-Up 94-95South Midlands League (8) ;

Beds Senior Cup (7), R-up (5); Beds Premier Cup 95-96, R-up (5)

Previous Leagues: Luton # District 1947-1954 South Midlands 1954-1979 Isthmian1979-2004

Back row, left to right: Mick Clark (physio), Jackson Gash, Ricky Case, Chris Cutmore, Neil Morgan, Ben Boorman, Mark Paradise, Eliot Thomas, Paul Getley, James Hatch, Graham Clark and Owen Clark(Secretary). **Front row:** Andy Reid, Paul Barnes, Gordon Taylor (Manager), James Gray (Captain), Tony McNally (Asst.Manager), David Bounds and Matt Tlbbs. Mascots: Aaron Davison-Williams and Anthony Rhodes.

BEDWORTH UNITED

Founded: 1896
Nickname:
Greenbacks

Manager: Martin Sockett   **Asst.Manager:** John Scott
Coach: Carl Adams   **Physio:** Catherine Tonks **Groundsman:** Colin Brown
Club Colours: Green& White/White/White

CLUB PERSONNEL
Chairperson: Suzanne Harrison
Vice Chairman: Bill Haywood
Secretary: Graham Bloxham, 43 Mount Pleasant Road, Bedworth, Warwicks. CV 12 8EX
Press Officer: Bob Howe
Tel No: 07748 8107736 (M)
02476 731160 (H)
e-mail: bobhowe6@yahoo.co.uk
Programme
Editors: Ron Kemp & Mick Harrison
60 pages £1.20
2005-2006
Captain: Lee Darlison
Player of the Year: Leon Doughty
Top Goalscorer: Jon Douglas

Change Colours: Yellow/Green/Yellow
Club Sponsor: Thomson Holidays
Previous League: West Midlands
Best Seasons: League: 15th Southern Div 1 West 2004-2005
F.A. Cup: 4th Qualifying Round 1982-1983 1988-1989 1989-1990
F.A.Trophy.: 2nd Round 19801981
Ground address: The Oval, Miners Welfare Park, Coventry Road, Bedworth CV12 8NN **Tel No:** 02476 314302
Website: www.bedworthunited.fwsi.com(Bob Howe,Ron Kemp & Mick Harrison)
Capacity: 7,000   **Seats:**300   **Covered:** 300   **Floodlights:**Yes
Simple Directions: M6 jct 3, into Bedworth on B4113 Coventry to Bedworth road, ground 200yds past Bedworth Leisure Centre on this road.Coaches should park at the Leisure Centre. Buses from Coventry and Nuneaton pass ground. Nerarest BR is Bedworth (5 mins walk)
Midweek Home Matchday: Tuesday
Clubhouse: Social club open every day 7.30-11pm & w/e noon-3pm. Hot and cold bar food
Club Shop: Full range of souvenirs & programmes. Contact : Ron Kemp   02476 318014
Local Radio: Mercia Sound BBC CWR
Local Press: Heartland Evening News, Weekly TribuneBedworth Echo and Coventry Evening Telegraph

CLUB STATISTICS

Record
Attendance: 5,127 v Nuneatyon Boro.Southern Lg. Midland Div   23.02.82
Career Goalscorer: Peter Spacey 1949-1969
Career Appearances: Peter Spacey
Record Transfer Fee   **Paid:** £1,750 to Hinckley Town for Colin Taylor 1991-1992
Received: £30,000 from Plymouuth Argyle for Richard Landon
Senior Honours: Birmingham Comb.(2) 48-50, Birmingham Snr Cup(3) 78-79 80-82, Midland Floodlit Cup 81-82 92-93
Previous   **Leagues:** Birmingham Comb. 47-54; West Mids (at first Birmingham) Lg 54-72
Name: Bedworth Town 47-68
Ground: British Queen Ground 11-39

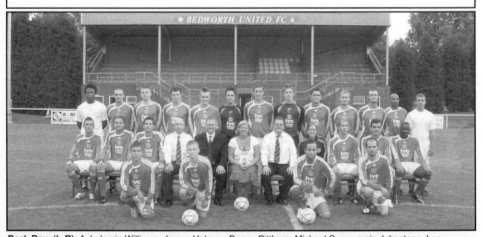

Back Row (L-R): A,J. Jamie Williams, James Holmes, Danny Pittham, Micheal Swan, craig Johnstone, Lee Greenway, Andrew Kemp, Guy Barnett, Richard Kavanagh, Pete Barry, Jae Martin, Nick Harrison.
Middle Row: Scott Rowe, Pete Spacey, Lee Darlison, Martin Sockett, Wayne Harris, Sue Harrison, John Scott, Cat Tonks, Paul Spacey, adam Kinder, Jason Ramsey. **Front:** Luke Baker, Danny Harris, Liam O'Neil, Darren Beckett.

BERKHAMSTED TOWN

Founded: 1919
Nickname:
Lilywhites

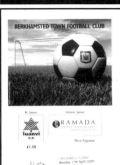

Manager: Guillermo Ganet   **Asst Manager**: Ashu Besong **Physio** Miss Sam Petch

Club Colours: White/Black/Black

Change Colours: All Gold

Club Sponsor:

Previous League: Isthmian

Best Seasons: League:18th Southern Lg. Div 1 East 2004-2005

F.A. Cup: 3rd Qualifying Round v Barnet 1987-1988 91-92 92-93 2001-02

F.A.Trophy.: 1st Round 1997-1998   **F.A.Vase:** Finalists 2000-2001

Ground address: Broadwater,Lower Kings Road,Berkhamsted Herts HP4 2AA

Tel No: 01442 862815

Club Website:www.berkhamstedfc.co.uk

Capacity: 2,500   **Seats:** 170   **Covered:** 350   **Floodlights:** Yes

Simple Directions: Adjacent to Berkhamsted station (Euston-Birmingham line). A41 toBerkhamsted town centre traffic lights, left into Lower Kings Road

Midweek Home Matchday: Tuesday

Clubhouse: Open seven days a week. Pool & Darts plua a big screen.

Club Shop: Contact: Doug Peacey

Local Radio: Chiltern Radio, Mix '96' and Three Counties Radio.

Local Press: Berkhamsted Herald and Berkhamsted Gazette

CLUB PERSONNEL

Chairman: Guillermo Ganet
President:
Secretary: Keith Hicks, 24 Holy Drive, Berkhamsted, Herts HP4 2JR. Tel No: 01442 863216 (H) 07767 430087 (M)
Press Officer: Grant Hasty

Programme
Editor: Grant Hastie
64 Pages £1.00
2005-2006
Captain: Sam Chapman
Player of the Year: Henry Thomas
Top Scorer: John Paul Marner 18

CLUB STATISTICS

Record	Attendance: 1,732 v Bedlington Terriers F.A.Vase Semi-Final 2nd Leg 2001
	Career Goalscorer:
	Career Appearances: Ray Jeffrey 612
Record	Victory 14-0 v ?
	Defeat: 2-12v ?
Senior Honours:	Herts Senior Cup 52-53; London Spartan Lge 79-80 (Div 2 26-27);Herts Charity Cup: 2001-02
Previous Leagues:	Leagues: Herts Co. 1895-1922; Herts Co: 1921,Spartan 22-51, 66-75; Delphian 51-63; Athenian 63-66, 83-84; London Spartan 75-83
	Grounds: Sunnyside Enclosure 1895-1919, Sports Ground 1919-83
	Name: Bekhamsted Comrades 1919-22

Berkhamsted Town Football Club

BISHOP'S CLEEVE

Founded: 1892
Nickname: The Skinners

Manager: Paul Collicutt   **Assistant Manager**: Tim Bayliffe

Club Colours: Royal Blue & Black/Blue/White

Change Colours: Yellow & Blue/Blue/White

Club Sponsor: B and W Electronics

Previous League: Hellenic

Best Seasons: League: 2nd Hellenic 2005-2006 **F.A.Vase:** 2nd Rd 2003-2004

F.A. Cup: 3rd Qualifying Round 2004-2005

Coach: Andy Tucker **Physio**: Susie Jones

Ground address: Kayte Lane, Bishop's Cleeve, Cheltenham , Glos. GL52 3PD

Tel No: 07969 680984

Club Website: bishopscleevefc.co.uk

Capacity: 1,500 **Seats**: 50 **Covered**: 50 **Floodlights**: Yes

Simple Directions: Pass Racecourse North of Cheltenham on the A534 then turn right at Traffic lights and left into Kayte Lane. Ground is half a mile on left.

Midweek Home Matchday: Wednesday

Clubhouse: Full facilities including bar, dance floor, television,etc. **Club Shop:** Yes

Local Radio: BBC Radio Gloucestershire and Severn Sound

Local Press: Gloucestershire Echo and Western Daily Press

CLUB PERSONNEL

Chairman: David Walker
President: John Davies
Secretary: Phil Tustain,36 Hardy Road, Bishops Cleeve, Cheltenham GL52 4BN01242 697281 (H) 07719991134 (M)
Press Officer: John Pickup
Programme Editor: Andy Tucker
30 pages 1.50
2005-2006
Captain: Andy Tucker
Player of the Year: Nick Williams
Top Goalscorer: Kacey Johnstone

CLUB STATISTICS

Record	**Attendance:** 1,300 v Cheltenham Town July 2006
	Career Goalscorer: Kevin Slack
	Career Appearances: John Skeen
	Record Transfer Fee Paid N/A **Received:** N/A
Senior Honours:	Glos. Jumior Cup North, Glos Sen.Amateur Cup North (3)
	Hellenic League Div 1 86-87 PremLg Cup 888 Div 1 West R-up 00-01
	Hellenic Premier Runners Up 2005-2006
Previous Leagues:	Cheltenham, North Gloucestershire and Hellenic 1983-2006
Grounds:	Stoke Road and ground sharing with Moreton Town F.C., Wollen Sports F.C. Highworth F.C. & Forest Green Rovers F.C.

Back Row (L-R): James Veresci, Mike Rhodes, Nick Williams, John Curtis, Jon Skeen, Sam Avery, Dan Avery, Steve Cleal, Jon Hills.
Front Row: James Bayliffe, Richard Mansell, Andy Tucker (capt), Kevin Slack, Matt Collins, KevinLee, Gary Cornwall.

BRACKLEY TOWN

Founded: 1890
Nickname: Saints

Brackley Town F.C.
Season 2005 - 2006

Members of The Southern Football League

Manager: Phil Lines   **Assistant Manager:** Andy Sinnott   **Physio:** Ian Maskell

Club Colours: Red& White Hoops/Red/Red

Change Colours: Yellow/Black/Yellow

Club Sponsor: Moto Service Stations

Previous League: Hellenic

Best Seasons: League: 3rd Southern Lg. Southern Div 1 West 2005-2006

F.A. Cup: 2nd Qualifying Round 1997-1998   **F.A.Trophy.:** 1st Qual Round 97-98

F.A.Vase: 3rd Round 1987-1988

Ground address: St James Park, Churchill Way, Brackley, Northants NN13 7EJ

Tel No: 01280 704077

Club Website: www.brackleytownfc.co.uk

Capacity: 3,500   **Seats:**300   **Covered:**1,500   **Floodlights:** Yes

Simple Directions: Churchill Way, east off A 43, south end of town

Midweek Home Matchday: Tuesday

Clubhouse: Fully licensed. Lounge & main hall. Food available. Open all week.

Club Shop: Yes, selling club merchandise,programmes and badges etc

Local Press: Brackley Advertiser, Banbury Guardian and Herald & Post

Local Radio: Fox F.M., Touch FM & Radio Northampton

CLUB PERSONNEL
Chairman: Sara Crannage
Managing Director: Sara Crannage
President: Mike Bosher
Secretary: Pat Ashby,
2 Barrington Court, Ward Road,
Brackley, NN13 7LE
Tel No: 07969 825636

Programme
Editor: Brian Martin
/Price: £1.00

2005-2006
Captain: Andy Williams
Player of the Year: Martin Brown
Top Goalscorer: Matt Murphy

CLUB STATISTICS

Record	**Attendance:** 960 v Banbury United, F.A. 2005-2006
	Career Goalscorer: Paul Warrington 320
	Career Appearances: Terry Muckelberg 350
	Transfer Fee Paid: N/A
	Received: £2,000 from Oxford City for Phil Mason 1998
Senior Honours:	United Counties R-up 88-89 (Div 1 83-84); Northants Snr Cup R-up 88-89;
	Hellenic Lg Prem 96-97, 2003-04 Div 1 Cup 82-83.
Previous	**Leagues:**Banbury & District; North Bucks; Hellenic 77-83; United Co. 83-94;
	Hellenic 94-97,Southern 97-99
	Ground: Banbury Road, Manor Road, Buckingham Road (up to 1974)

Back Row: Andy Sinnott (asst Manager) Leon Gutzmore, Guy Hadland, Andy Williams, Matt Murphy, Martn Brown, Richard Knight, Elliott Sandy, Stuart Smeathers, James Saulsbury, Anthony Fontanelle, Ian Maskell (physio) Phil Lines (Manger).
Front Row: Phil Miurpy, Craig Farley, Les Hines, Robbie Beard, Fazal Koryia, Tom Winters.

BROMSGROVE ROVERS

Founded: 1885
Nickname: Rovers or Greens

THE ROVERS
Official Matchday Programme for Bromsgrove Rovers

Bromsgrove Rovers
versus
Paulton Rovers
Southern League Division One West
Saturday 14th January 2006
£1.30
3.00pm Kick Off

Manager: Rod Brown   **Physio:** Steve Ball
Club Colours: Green & White stripes/Black/White
Change Colours: Blue & Yellow/Blue/Blue
Club Sponsor: Banks's Brewery
Previous League: Midland Alliance
Best Seasons: League: Conference Runners-Up 1992-1993
F.A. Cup: 3rd Round 1993-1994   **F.A.Vase:** 3rd Round 2001-2002
F.A.Trophy.: Quarter Final Replay 1975-1976
Ground address: Victoria Ground, Birmingham Rd, Bromsgrove, Worcs. B61 0DR
Tel No: 01527 876949
Club Website: www.bromsgroveroversfc.co.uk
Capacity: 4,893   **Seats:**394   **Covered:** 1,344   **Floodlights:**Yes
Simple Directions: Ground is situated on the north side of Bromsgrove on the Birmingham Road, off the A38 Bromsgrove by pass. The M5 and M42 join theA38 to the north of the town making it easy to get to the ground without havingto go into town.
Midweek Home Matchday: Tuesday
Clubhouse: Victoria Club (01527 878260) - Serves hot & cold food. Big screenTV, pool table & darts. Open matchdays and week-day evenings.
Club Shop: Selling replica clothing & souvenirs. Contact Tracy Kite (01527 876949)
Local Radio: Radio Wyvern
Local Press: Bromsgrove Advertiser and Bromsgrove Standard

CLUB PERSONNEL

Chairman: Tom Herbert
President: Charles Poole
Secretary: Geoff Bayley,14 Orchard Road, Bromsgrove B61 8HZ
Tel No: 01527 877559 (H)
Fixture Secretary: Brian Hewings
Tel NO; 01527 831182 (H)

Programme
Editors: Helen & Andy Jones
40 Pages £1.30

2005-2006
Captain: Steve Hillman
Player of the Year: Joe Williams
Top Goalscorer:

CLUB STATISTICS

Record	**Attendance:** 7,389 v Worcester City 1957
	Career Goalscorer: Chris Hanks 238 1983-1984
	Career Appearances: Shaun O'Meara 763 1975-1994
Record Transfer Fee	**Paid:** £3,000 to Solihull Borough for Recky Carter
	Received: Undisclosed from Peterbrough United for Scott Cooksey Dec 93
Senior Honours:	Vauxhall Conference R-up 92-93, Lge Cup 94-95 95-96; Southern Lge Prem 91-92, R-up 86-87, Cup 92-93, R-up 86-8 Midland Div 85-86, Worcester Sen Cup (8), R-up (10); Birmingham Sen Cup 46-47, R-up (2)
Previous Leagues:	**Leagues:** Birmingham Lge 1898-08 53-65, Birmingham Comb. 1908-53, West Midlands 65-72, Southern Lge - Northern Div, 73-79, Midland Div. 79-86, Premier Div. 86-92, GMVC 92-97, Southern 97-01, Midland Alliance 01-02
	Grounds: Old Station Road 1885-87, Recreation Ground 87-88, Churchfields 88-97,Well Lane 1897-1910.

Back Row (L-R): James Smith, Mark Benbow, Wayne Dyer, Chris McHale, Neil Davis, Joe Williams, Chris Taylor, Tim Clarke, Dean Coleman, Daire Doyle, Carl Heeley, Riad Erraji, Kevin Banner, Nigel Clement (Coach).
Front Row: Ron Mellor (Coach), John Snape (Player / Coach), Liam McDonald, Delton Francis, Nathan Lamey, Tom Herbert (Chairman), Rod Brown (Manager), Mark Taylor (Captain), Richard Burgess, Paul Carty, Paul Lloyd, Steve Ball (Physio).

CHASETOWN

Founded: 1954
Nickname: The Scholars

Club Colours: Royal blue/royal/white
Change Colours: All Red
Club Sponsor: Virgin Holidays.
Previous League: Midland Alliance
Best Seasons: League: Champions Midland Alliance 2005-2006
F.A. Cup: 1st Round Replay 2005-2006　**F.A.Vase:** 5th Round 1999-2000
Manager: Charlie Blakemore　**Assistant Manager:** Paul Jones
Coach: Kevin Sweeney. **Physios:** Mick Andrews & Gary McHale.
Ground address: The Scholars, Church Street, Chasetown, Walsall WS7 8QL
Club Website: www.chasetownfc.com
Capacity: 2,000　**Seats:** 151　**Covered:** 220　**Floodlights:** Yes
Simple Directions: M6 toll road, exit Jct 6 Burntwood, left at first island, left at second island onto B5011, over toll road bridge, left at island at bottom of road, continue up the hill Highfields Road, cross over mini island at top into Church Street, pass Church on left and School on right, ground on left at the end of the street. **A5** from Tamworth, turn right at main traffic lights, Brownhills and continue on B5011 as above. As from **M6 Jct 11**/Cannock, turn left at lights at Brownhills and continue as above.

CLUB PERSONNEL
Chairman: John Donnelly
President: Brian Baker
Chief Exec/Secretary:
Michael Joiner.
5 Windermere Place, Cannock,
Staffs. WS11 18DU
Tel No: 01543 502358
Pres Officer: Paul Mullins
**Programme
Editor:** Loz Hawkes
loz@lhawkes.freeserve.co.uk
26 Pages £1.00

2005-2006
Captain: Craig 'Chopper' Harris
Player of the Year: Chris Slater
Top Goalscorer: Lee Bullimore (34)

Midweek Home Matchday: Tuesday
Clubhouse: Open Daily　**Club Shop:** Yes.
Local Radio: BBC Radio W.M.
Local Press: Express & Star, Burntwood Mercury/Burntwood Post.

CLUB STATISTICS		
Record	**Attendance:** 2,134 v Blyth Spartans 4th Q..Rd F.A.Cup 2005-2006	
	Career Goalscorer: Tony Dixon 197	
	Career Appearances: 469 +15 subs	
Record Transfer Fee	**Paid:** N/A **Received:** £200 fromTelford United for Chris Aullet	
	Victory: 14-1 v Hanford, Walsall Senior Cup 1991-1992	
	Defeat: 1-8 V Telford United Res, W.Mids Lg.	
Senior Honours:	W.Mids Champions 1978, Lg.Cup (2) Walsall Senior Cup (2)	
	Staffs Senior Cup R-Up 91-92 Midland Alliance Champions 2005-06	
Previous Leagues:	Cannock Youth 54-54 Lichfield & District 58-61 Staffs.Co. 61-72	
	West Mids.72-94 Midland Alliance 199420-06	
Previous Name:	Chase Terrace Old Scholars 54-72 **Previous Ground:** Burntwood Rec.	

Back Row (L-R): Simon Bryan, Lee Parsons, Gavin Stone, Ian Wright, Lee Bullimore, Andy Turner.
Front Row: Chris Slater, John Branch, Paul McMahon, Dave Egan, Ben Steane.

CINDERFORD TOWN

Founded: 1922
Nickname: Town

Manager: Mike Cook   **Asst.Man/Coach:**Paul Davies   **Physio:** Roger Loader

Club Colours: Black & White stripes/Black/Black

Change Colours: Green & White stripes/White/White

Club Sponsor: The Forester

Previous League: Hellenic

Best Seasons: League: 15th Southern Div 1 West 2005-2006

F.A. Cup: 2nd Round 1995-1996   **F.A.Trophy.:** 2nd Qualifying Round

F.A.Vase: 2nd Round 1991-1992

Ground address: The Causeway, Hildene, Cinderford, Glos.

Tel No: 01594 827147 or 822039

Capacity: 2,500   **Seats:**250   **Covered:**1,000   **Floodlights:**Yes

Simple Directions: From Gloucester take A40 to Ross-on-Wye, then A48 - Chepstow. In 8miles turn right at Elton garage onto A4151 signed Cinderford, thru Littledean, up steep hill, right at cross-roads, second left into Latimer Rd. Ground 5 minswalk from town centre

Midweek Home Matchday: Tuesday

Clubhouse: Open daily 2 bars, kitchen, 2 skittle alleys, darts, dancehall,committee room

Club Shop: Souvenirs, club badges, ties, mugs , scarves and pennants (Contact: Dave Gettings)

Local Radio: Radio Gloucester and Severn Sound

Local Press: The Forester, Gloucester Citizen and Western Dail;y Press

CLUB PERSONNEL
Chairman: Ashley Saunders
President: S.Watkins
Secretary: Chris Warren, 9c Tusculum Way,Mitcheldean, Glos. GL17 0HZ.
Tel Nlo: 01594 543065 (H)
e-mail: warro@tusc.wanadoo.co.uk
Programme
Editor: Dave Roberts
50 Pages £1.00e

2005-2006
Captain: Quentin Townsend
Player of the Year: Mike Green
Top Goalscorer: Richard Kear

CLUB STATISTICS

Record	**Attendance:** 4,850 v Minehead , Western League 1955-1956
	Career Goalscorer:
	Career Appearances: Russel Bowles 528
Record	**Victory:** 13-0 v Cam Mills 1938-1939
	Defeat: 0-10 v Sutton Coldfield 1978-1979
Senior Honours:	Hellenic Lg Premier Champions 94-95, Premier Lg.Cup 94-95, Glos Snr Amtr Cup (Nth) (6), R-up (3); Western Lg Div 2 56-57; Glos Jnr Cup (Nth) 80-81; Midland Comb. 81-82; Glos.Sen Cup Winners 00-01
Previous	**Leagues:** Glos Northern Snr 22-39 60-62, Western 46-59, Warwickshire Comb 63-64,West Midlands 65-69, Gloucestershire County 70-73 85-89, Midland Comb. 74-84,Hellenic 90-95
	Grounds: Mousel Lane, Royal Oak.

DUNSTABLE TOWN

Re-formed: 1998
Nickname:
The Blues

Manager: Paul Reeves & Kerry Dixon   **Coach:**   **Physio:** John Bell

Club Colours: All Navy Blue

Change Colours: Red & Black

Club Sponsor:

Previous League: Isthmian

Best Seasons: League: Southern ?   **F.A. Cup:** 1st Round 1956-1957

F.A.Trophy.:

F.A.Vase: 2nd Round Replay 1992-1993

Ground address: Creasey Park Stadium, Dunstable, Bedfordshire. LU6 1DNN

Tel No: 01582 667555

Club Website:

Capacity: 2,400   **Seats:**240   **Covered:** 1000   **Floodlights:**Yes

Simple Directions: Travel north on A5, through centre of Dunstable, then left at traffic lights into Brewers Hill Road and straight over mini roundabout. Ground is on the right.

Midweek Home Matchday: Tuesday

Clubhouse: Open six days a week and may be used by away supporters in match days. Snack also in ground on match days for all supporters with refreshments available.

Club Shop:

Local Radio:

Local Press:

CLUB PERSONNEL

Chairman: Roger Dance
President: Barry Fry
Secretary: Malcolm Aubrey, 25 Copperfields Close, Houghton Regis, Dunstable Beds. LU5 5TE
Tel No: 01582 864916 (H)
Press Officer: Derek Tripney

Programme
Editor: Derek Tripney

2005-2006
Captain:
Player of the Year:
Top Goalscorer:

CLUB STATISTICS

Record	Attendance:
	Career Goalscorer:
	Career Appearances:
Record Transfer Fee	Paid:
	Received:
Senior Honours:	S.S.M. Champions 2002-03 & Beds Sen Cup 03-04 Beds Senior Cup Runners-up 2000-01 S.Mid Div 1 Champions 99-00,
Previous	Leagues: Spartan South Midlands 1998-2003 & Isthmian 2003-2004.

EVESHAM UNITED

Founded: 1945
Nickname: The Robins

Manager: Paul West   **Physio:** Ted Thomas

Club Colours: Red& white stripes/white/red

Change Colours: All sky blue

Club Sponsors: Jewson & Banks's

Previous League: West Midlands

Best Seasons: Lg: 3rd Southern Div 1 West 04-05   **F.A. Cup:** 2nd Qual.Rd 96-97

F.A.Trophy.: 3rd Qualifying Rd. 96-97   **F.A.Amateur Cup:** Finalists 1923-24

Ground address: Sharing with Worcester City at St George's Lane, Worcester, WR1 1QT **Tel No:** 01905 23003

Capacity: 2,000   **Seats:** 350   **Covered:** 600   **Floodlights:**Yes

Simple Directions: M5 Jct 6 (Worcester North) follow signs for Worcester and turn right at first lights. St George's Lane is 3rd left. One mile from Foregate Station BR

Midweek Matchday: Wednesday

Clubhouse: Worcester City's facilities are available on matchdays.

Club Shop: Contact: John Hawkins (01905 28794)

Local Radio: Classic Gold, BBC Hereford & Worcs, FM102 The Bear

Local Press: Evesham Journal, Worcester Evening News, Gloucester Echo.

CLUB PERSONNEL

Chairman: Jim Cockerton
V-Chairman: Steve Lane
President: M.E.H.Davis
Secretary/Press Officer:
Michael Peplow, 2 College Mews, Somers Road,Malvern, Worcs. WR14 1JD;
Tel Nos: 01684 561770(H)

Programme Editor: T.B.A.
Programme
58 Page £1.20

20054-2006
Capts: Gavin O'Toole
Player of the Year:. Richard Ball
Top Scorer: Richard Ball

CLUB STATISTICS

Record	**Attendance**: 2,338 v W.B.A. friendly 18.07.92	
	Victory: 11-3 v West Heath United	
	Defeat: 1-8 v Ilkeston Town	
	Career Goalscorer: Sid Brain	
	Career Appearances: Rob Candy	
	Record Transfer Fee **Paid:** £1,500 to Hayes for Colin Day 1992	
	Received: £5,000 from Cheltenham Town for Simon Brain.	
Senior Honours:	F.A.Amateur Cup R-up 23-24, Worcs. Senior Urn (2) R-up 90-1	
Previous Leagues:	Worcester, Birmingham Comb., Midland Combination 51-55 65-92 West Midlands Regional 55-62	
Grounds:	The Crown Meadow (pre-1968) Common Road (1968-2006)	

Evesham United celebrate promotion. Back row, left to right: Paul West (Asst. Manager), David Busst (Manager), Lee Knight, Gavin o'Toole, Tom Clarke, Simon Fitter, Neil O'Sullivan, Jermaine Clarke, Steve Duncan, Steve Hands, Karl Lewis, Matthew Hall and Richard Ball. Front row: Leon Blake, Grant Pinkney, Marc Burrow, Anthony Watson, Simeon Williams, Danny Williams and Stuart Hamilton   Photo: Worcester Evening News.

LEIGHTON TOWN

Founded: 1885
Nickname: Reds

Manager: Paul Burgess **Assistant Manager:** Paul Copson
Physios: George Lathwell & Eddie Kerr
Club Colours: Red & White stripes/Red/Red
Change Colours: Amber/Black/Amber
Club Sponsor: Buttles
Previous League: Isthmian
Best Seasons: League: 8th Southern League Div 1West
F.A. Cup: 3rd Qualifying Round 1970-1971   **F.A.Vase:** 5th Round 2003-2004
F.A.Trophy.:
Ground address: Bell Close, Lake Street,Leighton Buzzard, Beds.
Club Website: www.leightontownfc.co.uk
Capacity: 2,800   **Seats:**155   **Covered**: 300   **Floodlights**: Yes
Simple Directions: From bypass (A505) take A4146 (Billington Rd) towards Leighton Buzzard, straight overfirst roundabout then straight over mini-r'bout .After aprox 50 yards take first left into car park which is opposite the Morrisons petrol stattion.Half a mile from Leighton Buzzard (BR) station. Buses from Luton, Aylesbury and Milton Keynes
Midweek Home Matchday: Tuesday
Clubhouse: Normal licensing hours.Snack bar on matchdays - full range of hot snacks & drinks
Club Shop: No
Local Radio: Chiltern, Mix 96
Local Press: Leighton Buzzard Observer, The Citizen

CLUB PERSONNEL
Chairman: Iain McGregor
President: M.Hide
Secretary: Roy Parker c/o club
Press Officer: Chairman

Programme
Editor: James Ullyett
Price: £1.00

2005-2006
Captain: Peter Clifford
Player of the Year: Peter Clifford
Top Goalscorer: Michael Chennels

CLUB STATISTICS

Record	Attendance: 1,522 v Aldershot Town Isthmian Div 3 30.01.93
	Career Goalscorer:
	Career Appearances:
Record Transfer Fee	Paid: Received:
	Victory: 1-0 v Met Railway 1925-26 (H) Spartan League
	Defeat: 0-12 v Headington United (A) 18.10.47 Spartan Lreague.
Senior Honours:	Isthmian Lge Div 2 Champions 03-04 Div 3 R-up 95-96; Sth Midlands Lg 66-67 91-92, Beds Snr Cup 26-27 67-68 68-69 69-70 92-93;
Previous Leagues:	Leagues: Leighton & Dist; South Midlands 22-24 26-29 46-54 55-56 76-92; Spartan 22-53 67-74; United Counties 74-76
	Name: Leighton United 1922-63
	Ground: Wayside

Back row,left to right:Andy Fagan, Andy Hughes, Lee Clark,Wes Lewis, Mark Burfoot, Andy Peek,Paul Burgess (Manager)
Front row: Matt Myatt, Alex Kinsley, Enzo Silvestri, Srteve Stanson and Michael Chennells.

MALVERN TOWN

Founded: 1947
Nickname:

Manager: Paul Malloy **Coach**: Pete Boyle

Club Colours: Sky Blue /Claret/Claret

Change Colours: Claret/Sky Blue/Sky Blue

Club Sponsor: E & E Engineering Limited

Previous League: Midland Football Alliance

Best Seasons: League: 3rd Midland Alliance **F.A.Vase:** 3rd Round

F.A. Cup: 3rd Qualifying Round 1981-1982 1996-1997

Ground address: Langland Stadium, Lagland Avenue, Malvern, Worcs.

Tel No: 01684 574068

Capacity: 2,500 **Seats**:150 **Covered**: 310 **Floodlights**: Yes

Simple Directions: From Worcester take A449 to Malvern. Left at roundabout signposted B4208 to Welland. Left at light into Pickersleigh Rd. Left at Longford Arms Pub into Maddesfield Rd. Second left into Langland Avenue. Ground 100 yards on right.

Midweek Home Matchday: Tuesday

Clubhouse: Two bars and a tea bar open on mtachdays **Club Shop:** By order

Local Radio: BBC Hereford and Worcester.

Local Press: Malvern Gazette

CLUB PERSONNEL
Chairman: Paul Pallet
President: Reg Fox
General Manager: Paul Molloy
Secretary: Marg Scott, 20 Nixon Court, Callow End, Worcester WR2 4UU
Tel No: 01905 831327H)

Programme Editor: Marg Scott
28 Pages £1.50

2005-2006
Captain: Nathan Jukes
Player of the Year:
Craig Humphries
Top Goalscorer: Mark Owen

CLUB STATISTICS

Record	**Attendance:** 1,221 v Worcester City F.A.Cup
	Career Goalscorer: Graham Buffery.
	Career Appearances: Nick Clayton
Record Transfer Fee	**Paid**: £800 to Westfields for Duncan Preedy.
	Received: £1,000 + further £10,000 from knock on transfers for Darren Bullock from Nuneaton.
Senior Honours:	Worcestershire Senior Urn (7)
Previous Leagues:	

Back Row (L-R): Dave Oakley (Youth), Martin Stephens (Assistant Manager), Luke Whittington, Lee Tompkins, Dave Cannon, Craig Humphries, Richard Tompkins, Wes Joyce, Rik Halion, Duncan Preedy, Paul Molloy (Manager).
Front Row: Joe Rawle (Scout), Richard Jones, Tom Coley, Bryan Craven, Dan Finnegan, Phil Preedy, Neil Gardiner, Dean Roberts, Jamie Hyde.

ROTHWELL TOWN

Founded: 1895
Nickname:
The Bones

Rothwell Town
Football Club 2004/2005

Manager: Dave Williams   **Coach:** Frank Benjamin   **Physio:**Pete Lake
Club Colours: All Blue & White
Change Colours: POrange/Black/Black
Club Sponsor: Springfir Country Homes
Previous League: United Counties
Best Seasons: League: 10th Southern Div 1 West 2004-2005
F.A. Cup: 4th Qualifying Round 1999-2000   **F.A.Trophy.:** 2nd Round 1994-1995
F.A.Vase: 5th Round 1992-1993
Ground address: Home Close, Cecil Street, Rothwell, Northants. NN14 2EZ
Tel No: 01536 710694
Club Website: www.rothwelltownfc.com
Capacity: 3,500   **Seats:**264   **Covered:**1,264   **Floodlights:** Yes
Simple Directions: A14/A6 to Rothwell. At town centre r'about turn into BridgeStreet (right if northbound, left if southbound), take 3rd left into TreshamStreet, ground is at top on left. 3 miles from Kettering (BR); Rothwell is served by Kettering to Market Harborough buses
Midweek Home Matchday: Tuesday
Clubhouse: Rowellian Social Club, open evenings and weekend lunchtimes.Crisps and rolls available on matchdays (hot food and drinks in ground). 'Top of the Town Ballroom'for 200.
Club Shop: Sells various souvenirs incl. metal badges.
Local Radio: BBC Radio Northants and KCBC.
Local Press: Northants EveningTelegraph, Chronicle & Echo and Herald & Post

CLUB PERSONNEL
Chairman: Peter Bradley
Vice Chairman: Dick Goode
President: Stuart Andrews
Secretary: Roger Barnett,18 Norton Street, Rothwell, Northants. NN14 6DL **Tel No:** 01536 507744

Programme
Editor: David Rudkin
48 Pages £1.00

CLUB STATISTICS

Record	**Attendance:** 2,508 v Irthlingborough Diamonds , Utd.Co. 1971
	Career Goalscorer:
	Career Appearances:
Record Transfer Fee	**Paid:** Undisclosed for Andy Wright (Aylesbury United) 1992
	Received: Undisclosed for Matty Watts (CharltonAthletic) 1990
Senior Honours:	Northants Snr Cup 1899-1900 23-24 59-60 88-89 95-96 01-02 R-Up (3)
	United Counties Lg 92-93 94-95 R-Up (5)
Previous Leagues:	**Leagues:** Northants 1896-1911 21-33, Kettering Amateur 11-21 33-48, 02-03Leics.Senior 48-50, United Counties 50-56 61-94Central Alliance 56-61
	Grounds: Harrington Rd, Castle Hill
	Name: Rothwell Town Swifts

Back row, left to right:
Danny Potter, Carl Lake, Reece Lester, Kevin Brooks, Danny Spencer, Paul Rice, John Hughes.

Front Row:
Martin Flanagan, Lee Quincy, Jonathan Mitchell, Joe Hanney.

Photo: Alan Coomes

RUSHALL OLYMPIC

Founded: 1951
Nickname:
The Pics

Manager: Kevin Hadley   **Assistant Manager**: Dave Beesley

Physio: Gary McHale & Mick Andrews

Club Colours: Old Gold/Black/Black

Change Colours: White and Black/White/White

Club Sponsor: Williams Bookmakers

Previous League: Midland Alliance

Best Seasons: League: 10th Southern Div 1 West 2005-2006

F.A. Cup: 3rd Qualifying Round 1992-1993

F.A.Trophy.:   **F.A.Vase:** 5th Round 2000-2001

Ground address: Dales Lane off Daw End Lane, Rushall, Nr. Walsall

Tel No: 01922 641021

Club Website: www.rofc.co.uk

Capacity: 2,500   **Seats**:200   **Covered**: 200   **Floodlights**: Yes

Simple Directions: From Rushall cemtre (A461) take B4154 signed Aldridge. Approx one mile on right opposite Royal Oak Public house in Daw End Lane.

Midweek Home Matchday: Tuesday

Clubhouse: **Club Shop:**

Local Radio:

Local Press:

CLUB PERSONNEL

Chairman: Bob Hubble
Vice-Chairman: Nick Allen
President: Brian Greenwood
Secretary: Peter Athersmith,46 Blakenall Lane, Leamore,Walsall. West Midlands WS3 1HG
Tel No: 07909 792422
Commercial Manager: Jeff Husted

Programme
Editor: Darren Stockall
60 pages £1.00

2005-2006
Captain:
Player of the Year:
Top Goalscorer:

CLUB STATISTICS

Record	**Attendance:** 2,000 v Leed United Ex Players
	Career Goalscorer: Graham Wiggin
	Career Appearances: Alan Dawson 400+:
Record Transfer Fee	**Paid**:
	Received:
Senior Honours:	Midland Alliance R-Up 00-01 02-03 West Midlands Champions 1979-80
Previous	**Leagues:** Walsall Amateur 52-55 Staffs Co (South) 56-78 W. Mids 78-94
	Grounds: Rowley Place 51-75 and Aston University 76-79

Rushall Olympic taken at The Britannia Stadium, Stoke-on-Trent in April 2006 after the club won the Staffordshire Senior Cup for the first time in their history with an impressive 1-0 victory over Stoke City.

SOLIHULL BOROUGH

Founded: 1953
Nickname: Boro

Manager: Micky Moore   **Assistant Manager:** Duncan Riddle
Physio: Leona McCarron
Club Colours: Red/White/Red
Change Colours: White/Black/Black
Club Sponsor: Intersport & Carling
Previous League: Midland Combination
Best Seasons: League: 6th Southern Premier 1992-93
F.A. Cup: 1st Round, 1992-93 1997-1998
F.A.Trophy.: 4th Round 1997-1998 **F.A.Vase:** 5th Round 1974-1975
Ground address: Damson Park, Solihull, West Midlands. B91 2PP
Tel No: 0121 705 6770
Club Website: www.solihullborough-fc.co.uk
Capacity: 3,050   **Seats:** 280   **Covered:** 1,000   **Floodlights:** Yes
Simple Directions: Leave M42 at Jnct 6. A45 for 2 miles towards B'ham.Past Honda Garage
and opp Forte Posthouse Hotel, left at filter to traffic lights into Damson Parkway.(Signpost
Landrover/ Damsonwwod) Go round roundabout, down other side of dual crriageway for 100 jds
.Ground on left. From Coventry use A45 to Posthouse. Solihull,A41 into Hampton Lane and Yew
Tree LaneLane.
Midweek Home Matchday: Wednesday
Clubhouse: Country Club facilities and all type of functions can be booked.(0121 705 6770)
Club Shop: Merchandise in clubhouse
Local Radio: Radio WM & BRMB
Local Press: Solihull Times,Solihull News,Sunday Mercury & Sports Argus

CLUB PERSONNEL

Chairman: Trevor Stevens
President: Joe McGorian
Secretary: Joe Murphy, 2 Wilford Grove, Solihull, West Midlands. B91 2FP**Tel No**; 079711 89952
Commercial Director: Oscar Singh

Programme
Editor: Paul Carter
44 pages £1.50

2005-2006
Captain: Danny Hall
Players of the Year:
Martin Hier & Gary Moran
Top Goalscorer: Justin Marsden

CLUB STATISTICS

Record	**Attendance:** 2,000 v Birmingham City Friendly 2002-2003
	Career Goalscorer: Joe Dowling 138
	Career Appearances: Darrel Houghton 360
Record Transfer Fee	**Paid**: £15,000 to Kettering Town for Recky Carter
	Received: £30,000 fromCoventry City for Andy Williams
	Victory: 9-0 v Glossop North End (H) F.A.Cup 1st Q.Rd. 2002-2003
	Defeat: 1-6 v Tiverton Town (S) Southern League (Western Division) 1999-00
Senior Honours:	Southern League Midland Div 91-92; Midland Comb. R-up 84-8590-91,
	Worcs Sen.Cup R-up 92-93 96-97 97-98; 99-00 Birmingham Sen.Cup 94-95
Previous Leagues:	**Leagues:** Mercian; Midland Combination 69-91
	Name: Lincoln FC
	Grounds: Widney Stadium, Solihull 65-88,Moor Green 88-98,Redditch 98-00

Back row (L-R): Simon Williams, Dave Egan, Rob Taylor, Matt Hawker, Dean Wellington, Justin Bray,
Simon Owen (Golkeeping coach), Brett Clowes, Morton Titterton, Craig Dutton, Martin Crowley and Craig Herbert.
Front row: Paul Carter (Kit attendant), Bary Moran, Danny Hall, John Grady, Tony Dobson, (Manager),
Steve Shea (Assistant Manager), Justin Marsden, Martin Hier, Pete Barry and Leona McCarren (Physio).

SPALDING UNITED

Founded: 1921
Nickname: Tulips

Spalding United Football Club

Tulips' magazine
Official match programme
2005/06 £1.20

Kendal Town

Manager: Phil Hubbard **Asst.Man:** Mark Hone **Physio:**Trish Wintersgill
Club Colours: Royal Blue/White/Blue
Change Colours: Yellow/Blue./Yellow
Club Sponsor: T.B.A.
Previous League: Southern League
Best Seasons: League: ? **F.A. Cup:** 1st Round 1957-1958 1964-1965
F.A.Trophy.: 3rd Round 1999-2000 **F.A.Vase:** Quarter Finals 1989-1990
Ground address: Sir Halley Stewart Playing Field, Winfrey Avenue, Spalding.
Tel No: 01775 713328 **E-mail:** Tulips@uk.net
Club Website: www.spaldingutdfc.co.uk
Capacity: 2,700 **Seats:**300 **Covered:**500 **Floodlights:**Yes
Simple Directions: Town centre off A16, adjacent to bus station. 250 yds from Spalding(BR) station
Midweek Home Matchday: Tuesday
Clubhouse: Open matchdays and functions
Club Shop: Contact: Andy Gay 01775 710081
Local Radio: Radio Lincolnshire
Local Press: Lincolnshire Free P{ress, Spalding Target and Spalding Guardian

CLUB PERSONNEL
Chairman: Chris Toynton
President: Graham Chappell
Secretary: R.P.Lawton, 24 Regent Street, Spalding, Lincs. PE11 2YT
Tel No: 01775 722269
Programme
Editor: Ray Tucker
36 pages 4281.00

2005-2006
Captain:
Player of the Year:
Top Goalscorer:

CLUB STATISTICS

Record	**Attendance:** 6,972 v Peterborough F.A.Cup 1982
	Career Goalscorer:
	Career Appearances:
Record Transfer Fee	**Paid:**
	Received:
Senior Honours:	Utd Counties Lg 54-55 74-75 87-88 98-99 R-up 50-53(x3) 72-73 75-76 96-97; N.C.E.Lg 83-84; Lincs Snr Cup 52-53;
Previous Leagues:	**Leagues:** Peterborough; U.C.L. 31-55 68-78 86-88 91-99; 03-04 Eastern Co's 55-60; Central Alliance 60-61;Midland Co's 61-68; N.C.E.F.L. 82-86; Southern 88-91, 99-03, N.P.L. Div 1 2004-05

Back Row (L-R): Phil Hubbard (Manager), Danny Hussey (Captain), Gary Pawson, Simon Daniels, Mark Hone (Assistant Manager), Daniel P{awson, Sam Wadieh, Dave Frecklington, and Trish Wintersgill.
Front Row: Johnny Bell, Danny Hargreaves, Nathan ILey, Luke Forbes, Sanele Hlengwa, Lee Hudson and Ben Garrick.

STOURBRIDGE

Founded: 1876
Nickname: The Glassboys

CLUB PERSONNEL
Chairman: Stephen Hyde
President: Hugh Clark
Secretary: Hugh Clark, 10 Burnt Oak Drive, Stourbridge, West Mids. DY8 1HL Tel No: 01384 392975
Press Officer: Nigel Gregg

Programme Editors: Hugh Clark & Nigel Gregg 32 Pages £1.20

2005-2006
Captain: Morgan Brookes
Player of the Year: Mark Bellingham
Top Goalscorer: Mark Bellingham 61

Manager: Gary Hackett   **Coach:**   **Physio:** Richard Drewitt
Club Colours: Red & White Stripes with Red shorts
Change Colours: Yellow and Green
Club Sponsor: Caterers Club
Previous League: Midland Alliance
Best Seasons: League: 14th 1982-83 Southern League Premier Division
F.A.Vase: 6th Round 2004-2005
F.A. Cup: 4th Qualifying Round 67-8 84-5 85-6 98-99 **F.A.Trophy:** Q-Final 1970-71
Ground address: War Memorial Athletic Ground, High Street, Amblecote, Stourbridge, W.Mids.. DY8 4HN Tel No: 01384 394040
Club Website: www.stourbridgefc.com
Capacity: 2,000   **Seats:** 250   **Covered:** 750   **Floodlights:** Yes
Simple Directions: From Stourbridge ringroad, take A491 signposted Wolverhampton, and ground is 300 yards on left opposite Royal Oak pub. Buses 311 and 246 from Dudlley and 256 from Wolverhampton pass the ground.
Midweek Home Matchday: Tuesday
Clubhouse: Open matchdays and training evenings. **Club Shop:** Yes
Local Radio: Beacon Radio
Local Press: Stourbridge News and Express & Star

CLUB STATISTICS

Record
Attendance: 5,726 v Cardiff City Welsh Cup Final 1st Leg 1974
Career Goalscorer: Ron Page 269
Career Appearances: Ron Page 427

Record Transfer Fee
Paid: None
Received: £20,000 From Lincoln City for Tony Cunningham 1979

Senior Honours: Welsh Cup R-Up 73-74, Southern League Mid.Div. 90-91, Lg Cup 92-93,
Div 1 North 73-74, Mid Alliance 01-02 02-03, B'ham Senior Cup (3) R-Up (4), Worcs Senior Cup (9)
Hereford Sen. Cup 54-55 and Worcs Junior Cup 27-28   **Previous Name:** Stourbidge Standard

Previous Leagues: West Midlands (ex Birmingham League.) 1892-1939,54-71
Birminghamham Comb.ination 45-53 and Southern League 19 71-2000

STOURPORT SWIFTS

Founded: 1882
Nickname: Swifts

Manager: Roy Pencher **Assistant Manager:** Jake Findlay **Physio:** Lee Rhodes
Club Colours: All Yellow
Change Colours: All White
Club Sponsor: Reyniolds of Rushock
Previous League: Midland Aliance
Best Seasons: League: 14th Southern Div 1 West ?
 F.A. Cup: 3rd Qualifying Round 2001-2002   **F.A.Trophy.:** 2nd Round ?
F.A.Vase: 6th Round 2000-2001
Ground address: Walshes Meadow, Harold Davis Drive, Stourport on Severn
Tell No: 01299 825188
Club Website: www.stourportswifts.co.uk
Capacity: 2,000   **Seats:**250   **Covered:** 150   **Floodlights:**Yes
Simple Directions: Follow one-way system through Stourport sign posted Sports Centre.Go over River Severn Bridge, turn left into Harold Davie Drive. Ground is at rear of Sports Centre. Nearest rail station is Kidderminster.

Midweek Home Matchday: Tuesday
Clubhouse: Open matchdays. Hot snacks available   **Club Shop:** Yes
Local Radio: Hereford & Worcester
Local Press: Kidderminster Shuttle

CLUB PERSONNEL
Chairman: Chris Reynolds
President: Roy Crowe
Secretary: John McDonald, 65 Princess Way, Stourport, Worcs. DY13 0EL
Tel No: 01299 822088

Programme
Editor: Leighton Jones
68 pages 4301.50
2005-2006
Captain: Craig Webb
Player of the Year: Craig Webb
Top Goalscorer: Richard Burgess

CLUB STATISTICS

Record	**Attendance:** 2,000
	Career Goalscorer: Gary Crowther
	Career Appearances: Ian Johnson
Record Transfer Fee	**Paid:** N/A
	Received: N/A
	Victory: 10-0 **Defeat:** 1-7
Senior Honours:	Midland A lliance 2000-01, West Mids Prem Div R-Up 94-95 96-97 97-98, Lg Div 1 R-up 87-88
Previous Leagues:	**Leagues:** Kidderminster/ Worcester/ West Midland Regional, Midland Football Alliance 1998-2001
	Grounds: Bewdley Rd; Moor Hall Park; Feathers Farm; Olive Grove; Hawthorns.

Back Row (L-R): John Reeves,Mark Swann, Craig Jenkins, Paul Fryer, Lee Knight, (Captain), Carl Lewis, Daniel Harvey, Andy Hodgetts, Craig Webb and Kevin Brookes
Front Row: Matt Webb, Stuart Rencher, Andy Burgess, Marcus Jackson, Matt Graham, Peter Taylor, Adam Robinson, Tim Jackson and Shaun Findlay

SUTTON COLDFIELD TOWN

Founded: 1897
Nickname: Royals

Manager: Chris Keogh   **Assistant Manager::**Brian Kenning   **Physio:** Ed Judge

Club Colours: All Blue

Change Colours: All Yellow

Club Sponsor:

Previous League: Midland Combination

Best Seasons: League: Southern Premier ?   **F.A. Cup:** 1st Rd.1980-81 1992-93

F.A.Trophy.: 1st Round Replay   **F.A.Amateur Cup :** 2nd Round 1970-1971

Ground address: Central Ground, Coles Lane, Sutton Coldfield B721NL

Tel No: 0121 354 2997 or 0121 355 5475

Club Website:

Capacity: 4,500   **Seats:**200   **Covered:** 500   **Floodlights:** Yes

Simple Directions: A 5127 into Sutton, right at Odeon cinema (Holland Rd), then first right into Coles Lane - ground 150 yds on left. 10 mins walk from SuttonColdfield (BR), bus 104 from B'ham.

Midweek Home Matchday: Monday**Clubhouse:** Fully carpeted brick built lounge & concert room Open daily, food available

Club Shop: Selling metal badges, scarves, hats, pens, rosettes, progs. Contact: Bill Portman

Local Radio: BRMB and Radio WM

Local Press: Sutton Coldfield News, Sutton Observer and Sports Argus.

CLUB PERSONNEL
Chairman: Tom Keogh
President:
Secretary: Alan Fleming, 28 Manor Road, Sreetly,W.Mids. B74 3NG
Tel Nos: 0121 353 5383 (H) 07970 573638 (M)

Programme
Editor: Terry Coley
28 pages 4311.20

2005-2006
Captain:
Player of the Year:
Top Goalscorer:

CLUB STATISTICS

Record	**Attendance:** 2,029 v Doncaster Rovers F.A.Cup 1980-1981
	Career Goalscorer: Eddie Hewitt 288
	Career Appearances: Andy Ling 550
Record Transfer Fee	**Paid:** £1,500 to Gloucester C for Lance Morrison , to Burton Albion for Micky Clarke and to Atherstone United for Steve Farmer 1991
	Received: £25,000 from W.B.A. for Barry Cowrill 1979
Senior Honours:	Southern League Midland Div R-up 82-83, West Midlands Lg 79-80 Midland Comb.(2) (R-up(2), Staffs Sen. Cup R-up 89-90, Worcs Sen. Cup SF 88-89,
Previous Leagues:	**Leagues:** Central Birmingham, Walsall Sen., Staffs Co., BirminghamComb. 50-54, West Mids (Regional) 54-65 79-82, Midlands Comb. 65-79
	Name: Sutton Coldfield FC 1879-1921
	Grounds: Meadow Plat 1879-89/ Coles Lane 90-1919

WILLENHALL TOWN

Founded: 1953
Nickname:

Manager: Robert Smith   **Assistant Manager::** Larry Chambers
Cioach: Steve Wynn **Physio:**Gary McHale
Club Colours: AllRed
Change Colours: Yellow/Blue/Yellow
Club Sponsor: Aspray Transport Ltd.
Previous League: Northern Premier League
Best Seasons: League: ? **F.A. Cup:** 1st Round 1981-1982
F.A.Trophy.: 3rd Round 2004-2005 **F.A.Vase:** Finalists 19801981
Ground address: Noose Lane, Willenhall, West Midlands WV13 3BB
Tel No: 01902 605132
Club Website: www.willenhalltownfc.com
Capacity: 5,000   **Seats:**324   **Covered:** 500   **Floodlights:**Yes
Simple Directions: M6 jct 10 follow 'new' Black Country route then 'Keyway'. Onl eaving
'Keyway' follow signs to Wolverhampton (A454). At Neachells Publivc House turn right into
Neachells Lane and first right again into Watery Lane. At island turn left into Noose Lane and
ground is 200 yards on left.
Midweek Home Matchday: Tuesday
Clubhouse: Club Shop: Full rangeof products
Local Radio:
Local Press:

CLUB PERSONNEL
President/Chairman:
Jack Williams
Secretary: Simon Haynes
,6 Ingledew Close, Briarsleigh,
Walsall W.Midlands. WS2 0NF
Tel Nos:01902411758 or
07906 561750

Programme
Editor: Russ Brown
46 pages £1.00

CLUB STATISTICS

Record	**Attendance:** 3,454 V Crewe Alexandra F.A.Cup 1st Round 1981
	Career Goalscorer: Gary Matthews
	Career Appearances: Gary Matthews
Record	**Victory:** 11-1 v Bridgnorth Town 2001-2002:
	Defeat::
Senior Honours:	
Previous Leagues:	**League:** Wolverhampton Amateur/ Staffs County/ West Midland 1975-8 and 991-94 Midkland Allliance 1994-2004 Unibond Div 1 2004-05 Southern League: 1982-1991, 2005-

Back Row (L-R): Rob Smith, Indypaul Khala, Gary Hay, Aaron Bishop, Danny Tipton, Dave Woodvens, Larry Chambers, John Quilt.
Front Row: Craign Holland, Dean Perrow, Martin Myers, Nicky Campbell, Paul Danks, Domininc Reece.

Photo: Marshall's Sports Service (01384 274 877).

WOODFORD UNITED

Founded: 1946
Nickname: Reds

Manager: Phil Mason   **Physio:** Trudy Thornton

Club Colours: All Red

CLUB PERSONNEL

Change Colours: All Blue

Chairman: Andrew Worrall
Vice Chairman: R.Adams

Club Sponsor: Woodford Halse Social

Secretary: A.J.Worrall, 30 Townsend,Woodford Halse, Daventry, Northants NN11 3QL
Tel NOs: 07787 126636 (M) 013277 263365 (H)

Previous League: United Counties

Best Seasons: League: Champions United Counties 2005-2006

Programme (24 Pages)
Editor: Richard Usher
Tel No: 07976 112004

F.A. Cup: 3rd Qualifying Round   2005-2006

F.A.Vase: 3rd Round 2004-2005

Ground address: Bygate Road, Woodford Halse, Daventry, Northants.

Club Website: www.wufc.net

2005-2006
Captain: Arron Parkinson
Player of the Year: Ben Milner
Top Goalscorer:
Russell Dunkley 44

Capacity: 3,000   **Seats:**252   **Covered:** 252   **Floodlights:**Yes

Simple Directions: Off A361 Daventry to Banbury road the ground is on Woodford road out of Byfield.

Midweek Home Matchday: Monday

Clubhouse: Yes ,full facilities.   **Club Shop:** No

Local Radio:

Local Press:

CLUB STATISTICS

Record   **Attendance:** 1,500 v Stockport County

Career Goalscorer:

Career Appearances:

Record Transfer Fee   Paid:

Received:

Senior Honours: United Counties Champions 2005-2006 Div 2 1973-1974

Previous Leagues: Central Northants Combination 1946-1970 United Counties 1971-2006

Woodford UnitedEagle Bitter United Counties League Premier Division Champions 2005/2006
Back Row (L-R): Trudy Thornton, Ben Milner, Carl Standen, Tony Burt, Tom Fountain, Matt Finlay, Jason Burnham, Russell Dunkley, Kai Ridley, Neil King, Roger Ashford. **Front:** Craig pearman, Terry Fitton, Aaron Parkinson, James Foote (Asst Mgr), Phil Mason (Mgr), Nicky Gordon, Lewis Travers, Sammy Ibrahim.

FOOTBALL LEAGUE

STEP 1

FOOTBALL
CONFERENCE

STEP 2

CONFERENCE NORTH	CONFERENCE SOUTH

STEP 3

SOUTHERN PREMIER	NORTHERN PREMIER	**ISTHMIAN PREMIER**

STEP 4

SOUTHERN DIVISION 1 SOUTH & WEST MIDLAND	NORTHERN PREMIER DIV.1	ISTHMIAN DIVISION 1 NORTH SOUTH

STEP 5/6

Combined Counties	Hellenic	Northern League	Spartan South Midlands	Wessex
Eastern Counties	Kent	Northern Counties East	Sussex County	Western
Essex Senior	Midland Alliance	North West Counties	United Counties	

STEP 7

Anglian Combination	Dorset County	Kent County	Midland Combination	Peterborough & District	West Cheshire
Bedford & District	Dorset Premier	Leicestershire Senior	Midland League	Reading League	West Lancashire
Brighton & Hove	East Sussex	Liverpool County	North Berkshire	Somerset County	West Midlands (reg)
Cambridgeshire County	Essex & Suffolk Border	Manchester Football	Northampton Town Lge	South Western	West Sussex
Central Midlands	Essex Intermediate	Mid Cheshire League	Northamptonshire Comb.	Suffolk & Ipswich	Wiltshire League
Crawley & District	Gloucesterhisre Co.	Mid Sussex	Northern Alliance	Teeside League	Worthing & District
Devon County	Herts Senior County	Middlesex County	Oxfordshire Senior	Wearside League	

ISTHMIAN LEAGUE

SPONSORED BY: RYMAN
Chairman: A C F Turvey, MCIM
Competition Secretary: Bruce Badcock
18 Calford Drive, Hanchett Village, Haverhill Suffolk CB9 7WQ
Tel/Fax: 01440 708064 Email: bruce.badcock@btinternet.com

PREMIER DIVISION		P	W	D	L	F	A	Pts
1.	Braintree Town	42	28	10	4	74	32	94
2.	Heybridge Swifts	42	28	3	11	70	46	87
3.	Fisher Athletic *	42	26	7	9	84	46	85
4.	AFC Wimbledon	42	22	11	9	67	36	77
5.	Hampton & Richmond	42	24	3	15	73	54	75
6.	Staines Town	42	20	10	12	74	56	70
7.	Billericay Town	42	19	12	11	69	45	69
8.	Worthing	42	19	10	13	71	60	67
9.	Walton & Hersham	42	19	7	16	55	50	64
10.	Chelmsford City	42	18	10	14	57	62	64
11.	Bromley	42	16	14	12	57	49	62
12.	East Thurrock United	42	18	5	19	60	60	59
13.	Folkestone Invicta	42	16	10	16	47	51	58
14.	Margate	42	11	17	14	49	55	50
15.	Leyton	42	13	9	20	58	61	48
16.	Harrow Borough	42	13	9	20	56	73	48
17.	Slough Town	42	13	8	21	63	75	47
18.	Wealdstone	42	13	5	24	68	82	44
19.	Hendon	42	9	12	21	44	64	39
20.	Maldon Town	42	8	11	23	41	73	35
21.	Windsor & Eton	42	8	8	26	37	75	32
22.	Redbridge	42	3	5	34	28	97	14

*Promoted via the play-offs.

		1	2	3	4	5	6	7	8	9	10	11	12	13	14	15	16	17	18	19	20	21	22
1	AFC Wimbledon		1-1	1-1	1-1	0-1	3-2	1-0	4-1	0-4	2-1	2-1	1-0	0-0	3-0	1-2	5-0	2-2	1-1	2-1	1-1	1-1	1-2
2	Billericay Town	2-1		1-1	2-2	4-2	1-3	1-3	2-0	1-2	3-1	1-0	1-2	2-2	2-3	4-1	1-0	3-1	1-1	0-2	2-0	3-0	1-1
3	Braintree Town	0-0	2-0		3-1	2-1	1-0	3-2	3-0	2-1	3-0	1-0	3-0	1-1	1-1	1-0	2-0	2-1	3-1	3-1	2-0	3-0	4-2
4	Bromley	2-0	1-0	1-1		1-1	1-1	1-2	3-3	2-0	1-1	3-1	2-1	1-2	2-1	2-2	1-0	2-3	1-1	1-0	1-1	4-1	1-2
5	Chelmsford City	1-0	2-1	0-2	3-2		2-4	0-2	0-1	3-3	3-0	3-0	0-2	1-1	1-2	1-0	2-1	2-0	4-4	1-1	0-0	2-1	1-0
6	East Thurrock	1-1	0-3	1-3	1-0	3-0		2-5	0-2	1-2	3-2	3-0	0-4	1-3	1-1	3-1	2-0	3-2	0-2	1-0	2-0	0-2	5-1
7	Fisher Athletic	0-1	0-2	1-1	0-0	3-3	1-2		0-0	4-3	4-1	0-1	2-0	4-1	1-1	2-1	3-1	1-2	2-1	2-0	2-1	2-0	2-2
8	Folkestone Inv	0-1	1-0	0-0	1-0	1-1	1-0	0-1		1-2	2-1	1-2	0-2	2-2	2-0	1-1	1-0	3-0	0-2	3-1	5-2	1-0	1-2
9	Hampton-&-R.	2-1	0-1	0-1	0-0	3-0	1-0	0-3	3-1		1-3	3-1	0-5	4-2	1-2	0-1	3-1	2-2	2-1	2-0	3-0	4-0	1-2
10	Harrow Boro'	1-2	1-1	1-0	2-0	2-1	5-4	0-2	5-0	0-2		1-1	1-2	3-3	1-1	0-0	0-0	2-1	1-4	1-2	1-2	2-1	2-2
11	Hendon	0-1	2-2	1-2	2-1	0-0	0-0	1-2	0-0	0-2	2-1		0-1	4-0	1-1	1-2	2-0	1-1	1-2	1-1	0-3	1-2	2-2
12	Heybridge Swifts	1-1	0-0	0-3	1-0	2-0	0-1	1-2	2-0	2-1	2-1	3-0		1-0	2-0	2-0	2-0	1-0	4-2	2-1	1-3	2-0	1-1
11	Leyton	1-2	1-3	0-1	0-1	5-1	1-2	3-4	1-1	1-1	0-1	2-0	0-1		4-2	0-2	4-0	1-2	0-2	0-1	1-2	1-2	1-0
12	Maldon Town	0-2	0-2	2-3	0-2	0-1	3-2	0-3	1-0	1-2	1-4	2-2	0-1	0-2		1-1	2-1	0-2	2-2	1-2	2-4	1-2	2-0
13	Margate	0-1	1-1	1-1	1-1	0-1	2-1	1-1	1-1	3-2	0-0	4-2	1-2	0-1	1-0		0-0	2-2	2-5	2-4	1-0	1-1	0-0
14	Redbridge	0-3	0-5	0-1	3-2	1-2	0-1	0-5	0-2	0-2	0-1	0-0	1-2	0-4	0-0	3-1		1-4	1-2	1-3	2-3	1-1	3-2
15	Slough Town	0-2	0-2	2-1	2-2	0-1	1-2	0-4	2-0	0-1	5-2	0-2	1-2	0-0	4-1	2-2	3-2		1-2	0-2	3-2	3-3	0-3
16	Staines Town	0-3	1-2	1-1	1-2	3-0	1-0	2-0	2-2	0-1	2-0	5-1	2-3	1-1	2-1	2-2	2-1	2-1		2-1	1-3	1-0	0-1
17	Walton & H.	0-2	0-0	3-2	0-1	2-2	1-0	0-1	0-3	2-0	3-1	1-0	2-1	2-0	3-0	1-1	2-1	0-1	0-2		1-0	3-2	2-3
18	Wealdstone	1-5	1-1	2-3	1-2	1-2	1-2	1-2	1-2	4-1	4-5	3-4	1-0	0-2	0-4	6-1	2-2	1-2	1-3		4-2	2-1	
19	Windsor & Eton	0-4	1-0	0-1	0-1	1-2	0-0	1-4	1-0	1-3	0-1	1-1	3-4	2-0	0-0	0-1	1-0	0-3	1-2	1-1	0-3		2-1
20	Worthing	0-2	2-4	2-0	1-2	1-3	1-0	4-0	1-0	2-1	3-0	1-1	4-1	0-1	3-0	1-1	0-3	1-1	5-1	4-2	0-0	3-1	

DIVISION ONE

		P	W	D	L	F	A	Pts
1.	Ramsgate	44	24	14	6	84	38	86
2.	Horsham	44	25	11	8	94	55	86
3.	Tonbridge Angels*	44	24	8	12	71	48	80
4.	Metropolitan Police	44	24	7	13	72	46	79
5.	Dover Athletic	44	21	14	9	69	46	77
6.	Tooting & Mitcham United	44	22	9	13	93	62	75
7.	Kingstonian	44	20	14	10	82	56	74
8.	Croydon Athletic	44	20	13	11	56	41	73
9.	Bashley	44	20	10	14	63	61	70
10.	Leatherhead	44	18	14	12	64	50	68
11.	Cray Wanderers	44	20	8	16	80	74	68
12.	Hastings United	44	19	10	15	65	58	67
13.	Dulwich Hamlet	44	19	8	17	55	43	65
14.	Fleet Town	44	13	19	12	50	56	58
15.	Walton Casuals	44	16	10	18	68	75	58
16.	Lymington & New Milton	44	12	11	21	61	80	47
17.	Molesey	44	12	10	22	56	79	46
18.	Whyteleafe	44	10	14	20	50	66	44
19.	Burgess Hill Town	44	10	10	24	57	83	40
20.	Banstead Athletic	44	8	13	23	43	71	37
21.	Ashford Town	44	8	11	25	41	81	35
22.	Newport IOW	44	6	11	27	38	97	29
23.	Corinthian-Casuals	44	6	9	29	39	85	27

*Promoted via the play-offs.

	1	2	3	4	5	6	7	8	9	10	11	12	13	14	15	16	17	18	19	20	21	22	23
1 Ashford T.		1-1	2-0	1-0	3-1	0-3	0-1	3-2	1-2	0-2	2-2	0-7	2-1	0-0	0-5	1-2	1-3	0-1	0-3	2-3	0-2	1-1	1-2
2 Banstead A.	0-1		1-2	1-0	2-1	0-2	2-0	2-1	1-1	1-1	1-2	0-3	0-4	1-2	0-1	1-0	0-0	3-0	2-2	0-2	0-4	3-3	1-1
3 Bashley	1-1	3-1		2-1	3-1	3-2	3-1	0-2	0-3	0-5	0-0	1-1	3-2	0-1	2-1	3-4	2-1	3-0	0-1	0-0	1-2	5-2	1-0
4 Burgess Hill	5-0	2-2	0-1		1-3	1-4	1-1	0-1	2-0	3-2	1-2	0-3	1-3	2-2	3-0	0-3	3-1	5-0	1-2	1-2	2-1	3-3	1-0
5 Corinthian C.	0-1	0-0	1-3	0-1		1-2	0-3	0-5	1-4	3-1	0-2	0-1	0-0	3-0	1-2	0-0	2-0	1-1	0-1	1-1	1-5	3-4	3-0
6 Cray W.	2-0	2-1	2-2	3-0	3-2		2-2	3-1	2-1	0-2	0-2	2-1	1-3	3-3	2-5	2-1	3-3	0-3	0-1	2-0	3-3	1-0	3-1
7 Croydon Ath.	2-0	1-0	0-1	0-0	0-0	2-1		0-0	3-0	1-1	0-1	1-1	3-1	1-1	1-1	2-1	2-0	1-0	0-3	3-2	3-0	3-1	1-1
8 Dover Ath	1-0	1-0	2-1	3-3	4-0	2-1	1-1		2-1	1-1	2-3	0-0	1-1	1-0	5-1	0-3	1-0	1-0	1-1	0-0	4-0	2-1	4-1
9 Dulwich H.	2-0	3-1	0-1	3-0	2-0	1-0	1-0	0-0		0-1	2-0	2-2	0-1	0-1	0-0	1-2	0-1	1-2	3-3	1-3	2-0	1-0	
10 Fleet Town	1-0	1-0	1-1	1-1	1-0	3-3	1-3	1-2	1-0		1-0	1-0	3-3	1-1	2-0	1-1	1-1	1-2	0-0	1-0	0-4	0-2	0-0
11 Hastings U.	2-0	3-5	0-2	2-1	3-0	4-0	1-0	4-0	1-4	0-0		2-3	3-3	1-1	0-1	2-1	3-0	0-1	1-1	0-3	3-2	3-4	3-1
12 Horsham	3-3	2-0	7-1	3-3	1-0	3-0	1-1	2-3	2-1	4-1	0-0		2-2	2-1	4-0	1-3	5-0	2-1	2-1	1-0	1-6	3-1	2-1
13 Kingstonian	2-4	0-0	1-0	3-2	2-2	2-2	2-0	2-2	1-2	1-3	2-0	1-2		2-1	5-0	2-0	2-1	0-1	1-1	1-2	2-2	4-0	3-1
14 Leatherhead	1-1	4-0	1-0	2-0	3-2	3-0	2-1	0-0	0-1	0-0	1-2	2-4	0-0		1-1	2-0	5-4	1-0	1-2	4-1	0-3	2-1	2-1
15 Lymington&N	2-1	3-0	0-1	3-0	2-0	0-3	0-2	1-1	0-1	1-1	0-0	3-1	2-4	0-1		0-3	0-3	4-0	0-3	1-2	1-1	3-3	1-2
16 Met.Police	2-1	4-3	2-1	3-0	3-1	1-0	2-0	1-2	1-0	3-0	0-0	4-1	0-0	2-1	1-1		0-1	5-1	1-0	2-3	0-1	1-0	3-1
17 Molesey	1-1	2-1	2-0	1-1	1-1	0-2	0-1	2-1	1-1	3-1	0-1	1-3	2-3	0-1	2-7	3-2		3-0	0-2	1-1	0-1	5-1	0-0
18 NewportIOW	1-1	0-2	1-1	0-2	0-0	2-6	1-2	1-1	2-4	2-2	2-2	0-1	1-3	2-2	3-3	0-0	0-1		0-0	0-1	1-2	2-5	0-1
19 Ramsgate	0-0	1-1	2-4	1-0	3-1	2-0	0-0	3-2	0-0	2-0	2-1	1-0	3-3	0-0	5-0	4-1	7-1	6-0		3-3	3-2	0-1	5-1
20 Tonbridge A.	3-1	1-0	1-1	2-1	3-1	1-0	2-1	0-0	2-0	1-1	1-0	0-1	1-0	1-4	3-1	0-1	2-0	7-0	2-1		2-3	1-2	0-2
21 Tooting A.	2-2	1-1	2-1	2-2	6-0	3-4	1-2	2-0	0-2	4-0	4-1	2-3	0-1	2-1	3-2	1-1	4-3	3-1	1-1	0-2		3-0	1-1
22 Walton Cas.	1-0	2-2	1-1	5-1	1-0	0-1	1-2	0-2	1-0	2-2	2-3	2-0	1-1	0-3	2-0	1-0	1-1	4-1	0-1	3-1	2-1		0-0
23 Whyteleafe	3-2	1-0	1-1	6-0	1-2	3-3	1-1	0-2	1-1	0-0	0-2	1-1	0-2	1-1	2-2	1-2	3-1	3-2	0-1	0-3	0-1	1-2	

DIVISION TWO		P	W	D	L	F	A	Pts
1.	Ware	30	19	4	7	77	36	61
2.	Witham Town	30	17	7	6	61	30	58
3.	Brook House	30	17	7	6	63	33	58
4.	Flackwell Heath	30	15	7	8	54	49	52
5.	Egham Town	30	15	5	10	39	36	50
6.	Chertsey Town	30	14	7	9	47	37	49
7.	Edgware Town	30	13	5	12	46	41	44
8.	Chalfont St Peter	30	13	2	15	50	53	41
9.	Dorking	30	11	8	11	48	51	41
10.	Croydon	30	11	7	12	43	43	40
11.	Wembley	30	11	6	13	44	43	39
12.	Kingsbury Town	30	9	10	11	32	37	37
13.	Hertford Town	30	7	10	13	35	54	31
14.	Camberley Town	30	5	8	17	31	57	23
15.	Epsom & Ewell	30	5	6	19	32	64	21
16.	Clapton	30	4	9	17	33	71	16

		1	2	3	4	5	6	7	8	9	10	11	12	13	14	15	16
1	Brook House		2-0	4-2	2-0	2-0	2-0	4-1	1-2	0-2	2-0	7-1	6-1	1-1	2-6	2-1	1-0
2	Camberley Town	0-3		1-2	1-3	2-2	1-0	0-0	2-1	3-0	0-0	1-3	2-2	1-1	2-4	1-3	0-3
3	Chalfont St Peter	3-2	2-0		2-0	3-1	2-3	0-2	1-1	3-0	2-3	1-2	1-0	0-3	3-1	2-1	0-2
4	Chertsey Town	3-1	3-1	3-2		3-0	2-1	0-2	2-1	0-1	2-2	1-3	3-0	2-2	3-1	3-0	0-0
5	Clapton	1-3	3-0	2-2	0-0		1-0	0-3	0-2	1-4	1-3	2-2	0-0	2-0	0-6	1-6	0-3
6	Croydon	1-1	1-1	0-1	3-0	8-5		2-1	0-3	0-0	3-0	1-2	2-2	1-0	1-1	1-4	1-2
7	Dorking	0-1	1-2	1-0	2-2	3-3	1-0		2-1	4-1	4-3	1-1	2-2	1-2	2-5	2-2	1-5
8	Edgware Town	1-1	1-0	6-2	1-1	0-2	1-4	3-0		0-0	1-0	4-1	2-4	0-1	0-2	3-1	2-1
9	Egham Town	1-2	5-1	3-2	2-1	2-1	1-1	1-0	0-1		0-2	0-1	2-1	1-1	1-0	2-0	2-1
10	Epsom & Ewell	2-2	0-4	0-4	4-2	2-2	0-1	2-2	0-1	0-1		2-3	0-2	1-1	1-2	1-3	1-0
11	Flackwell Heath	1-1	3-2	3-2	0-2	2-2	1-2	0-1	3-2	4-2	2-0		2-1	1-0	0-2	4-0	5-2
12	Hertford Town	0-4	0-0	3-2	0-2	0-0	0-0	1-0	3-5	2-1	2-0	1-1		0-1	1-2	2-1	0-2
13	Kingsbury Town	1-1	1-1	1-3	1-2	2-0	0-1	1-3	1-0	0-1	1-0	3-0	1-1		1-0	0-4	2-2
14	Ware	0-2	2-1	3-0	2-1	4-1	5-2	2-3	3-1	2-0	7-0	1-1	3-3	4-1		4-0	0-2
15	Wembley	1-1	2-0	0-1	0-1	1-0	0-2	2-0	0-0	1-2	4-2	0-0	1-0	2-2	0-2		2-2
16	Witham Town	1-0	4-1	2-0	0-0	3-0	3-1	3-3	3-0	1-1	3-1	3-2	6-1	1-0	1-1	0-2	

STEP 1
CONFERENCE

STEP 2
CONFERENCE NORTH/SOUTH

STEP 3
ISTHMIAN LEAGUE PREMIER

STEP 4
ISTHMIAN LEAGUE DIV.1

STEP 5/6

STEP 7

Ryman Premier League Goalscorers 2005-2006

(Minimum ten goals from League F.A.Cup and F.A.Trophy matches)

		Lge	FAC	FAT	Total	
Strike Force of Three						
Braintree Toiwn	Revell	21	2	2	25	
	Griffiths	12	3		15	Total 54
	Ofori	11	1	2	14	
Fisher Athletic	Watts	23	3	2	28	
	Griffiths	12	2		14	Total 54
	Ofori	11	1	2	14	
Worthing	Browne	23	3	2	28	
	Francis	9	4		13	Total 52
	Pacquette	12	1		13	
Twin Strikers						
Wealdstone	Beckord	26	3	1	30	Total 47
	Jolly	15	1	1	17	
AFC Wimbledon	R.Butler	15	1	4	20	Total 35
	Sanathy	14		1	15	
Hampton & Richmond B	Yaku	17	2		19	Total 32
	Godfrey	13			13	
Billericay Town	Elder	14			14	Total 25
	Hunter	11			11	
Heybridge Swifts	Akurang	14			14	Total 25
	Jolly	11			11	
Chelmsford City	Richards	10		2	12	Total 23
	Halle	10	1		11	
Single Strikers						
Slough Town	Hodges	21		1	22	
Bromley	McDonnell	17	2	1	20	
Folkestone Invicta	Dryden	11	4	3	18	
Hockton	Margate	16			16	
Leyton	Bajada	15	1		16	
Staines Town	Chaaban	16			16	
Harrow Borough	Onochie	11	3	1	15	
Windsor & Eton	Wallace	12	1	1	14	
Walton & Hersham	Traynor	12	1		13	
East Thurrock United	West	9	0	1	10	

No player with Hendon, Malden Town or Redbridge scored ten goals during the season.

AFC WIMBLEDON

Founded: 2002
Nickname: Dons

Manager: Dave Anderson   **Assistant Manager:** John Turner

Coach: Warren Kelly   **Physio:** Mike Raynor

Club Colours: All Blue with Yellow Trim

Change Colours: All Red with Black Trim

Club Sponsor: St Games

Previous League: Combined Counties

Best Seasons: League Champions Isthmian Division One 2004-2005
                 F.A.Cup: 3rd Qualifying Rd 2004-2005
                 F.A.Trophy.: 1st Round 2005-2006
                 F.A.Vase: 4th Rd 2003-2004

Ground address: The Fans' Stadium, Kingsmeadow Stadium, Jack Goodchild Way, 422A Kingston Rd., Kingston upon Thames, Surrey KT1 3PB

Tel No: 0208 547 3528   **Website:** www.afcwimbledon.co.uk

Capacity: 4,500   **Seats** 1,047   **Covered Terrace** :2,700   **Floodlights:** Yes

Simple Directions: From town centre Cambridge Rd on to Kingston Rd (A2043) to Maiden Road. From A3 turn off at New Malden and then left onto A2043. Ground one mile on left.

Midweek Home Matchday: Tuesday

Clubhouse: Open matchdays and evenings. Two function rooms for hire.

Club Shop: Yes, fully stocked

CLUB PERSONNEL

Chairman: Kris Stewart
President: Dickie Guy
Finance Director: Eric Samuelson
Commercial Director: Ivor Heller
Secretary: Trevor Williams, 110B Cavendish Road, Colliers Wood, SW19 2EZ (M) 07817 480 505 (W) 0208 547 3528 e-mail: trevor.williams@afcwimbledon.co.uk
Youth & Community Director: Nigel Higgs
Press Officer & Programme Editor: Secretary
Club Statistician: Rob Dale
2005-2006
Captain: Steve Butler
Player of the Year: Andy Little
Top Goalscorer: Richard Butler

CLUB STATISTICS

Record	
	Attendance: 4,563 v Chipstead Co.Co Lg 2002
	Victory: **Defeat:**
	Goalscorer: Kevin Cooper
	Career Appearances: Anthony Howard 108
Record Transfer Fee	**Paid**: Undisclosed for: Michael Haswell (CHelmsford C) , Richard Butler (Ashfprd Town Middlx),Paul Barnes (Bristol Rovers), Simon Sweeney (Chesham U) & Steves Wals (Yeading)
	Received: Undisclosed from Halifax Town for for Shane Smeltz
Senior Honours:	Combined Counties League & Cup winners 2003-04 Isthmian Division 1 Champions 2004-05 Surrey Senior Cup 2004-05
Previous Leagues	Combined Counties.

Back row(standing) Simon Bassey (coach) Mike Rayner(physio) Steve Watson, Luke Garrard, Steve Wales, Simon Sweeney, Paul Smith, Josh Lennie, Andy Little, Darren Grieves, Antony Howard, Mark Rooney, Michael Haswell, Jon Boswell, Stephen Goddard, John Morris (Reserve manager) Steve West(kit man)
Front row (seated) Byron Bubb, Wes Daly, Simon Sobihy, Paul Barnes, Lee Kersey, Dave Anderson (manager) Jon Turner(assistant manager) Steve Butler, Chris Gell, Joe Paris, Roscoe Dsane, Richard Butler

AFC WIMBLEDON

BEST LGE ATT.: 3,315 v Hampton & Rich. B.
LOWEST: 2,093 v Redbridge

No.	Date	Comp	H/A	Opponents	Att:	Result	Goalscorers	Pos
1	Aug 20	IP	H	Folkestoine Invicta	3002	W 4 - 1	Smeltz 12 69 **R.Butler** 49 York 67	1
2	23		A	Maldon Town	528	W 2 - 0	**R.Butler** 70 80	1
3	27		A	Slough Town	1264	W 2 - 0	Smeltz 20 Moore 90	1
4	29		H	Staines Town	2734	D 1 - 1	Smeltz 6	2
5	Sept 3		A	East Thurrock	778	D 1 - 1	Howard 61	2
6	6		H	Bromley	2563	D 1 - 1	Smeltz 73	3
7	10	FAC 1Q	H	Ashford Town(Middx)	1619	D 2 - 2	Daly 32 S.Butler 46	
8	13	FAC 1Qr	A	Ashford Town (Middx)	720	W 2 - 0	**R.Butler** 11 Moore 88	
9	17	IP	H	Worthing	2642	L 1 - 2	Moore 77	7
10	20		A	Redbridge	489	W 3 - 0	Smeltz 7 36 Moore 29	4
11	24	FAC 2Q	H	**Walton & Hersham**	1930	L 0 - 3		
12	Oct 1	IP	A	Heybridge Swifts	816	D 1 - 1	**R.Butler** 89	6
13	4		H	Wealdstone	2464	D 1 - 1	Daly 48	6
14	8		H	Billericay Town	2445	D 1 - 1	Moore 46	
15	11		A	Hampton & Richmond B	2520	L 1 - 2	Daly 27	7
16	15	FAT 1Q	H	**Kings Lynn**	1720	W 1 - 0	Howard 77	
17	22	IP	H	Fisher Athletic	2745	W 1 - 0	Fowler 42	5
18	25		A	Bromley	1235	L 0 - 2		7
19	29		A	Windsor & Eton	1012	W 4 - 0	York 8 **R.Butler** 26 56 Plummer 27 (pen)	6
20	Nov 5		H	Maldon Town	2528	W 3 - 0	**R.Butler** 40 81 Smeltz 79	5
21	12	FAT 2QR	A	**Ramsgate**	1047	D 1 - 1	**R.Butler** 57	
22	15	FAT 2QRr	H	**Ramsgate**	1140	W 2 - 1	**R.Butler** 43 Smeltz 77 (pen)	
23	19	IP	A	Chelmsford City	878	L 0 - 1		6
24	22		H	Redbridge	2093	W 5 - 0	Gell 19 Harvey 45 71 Howard 47 Smeltz 55	6
25	26	FAT 3Q	A	**Dartford**	1082	D 0 - 0		
26	29	FAT 3Qr	H	**Dartford**	1068	W 2 - 0	**R.Butler** 87 Moore 88	
27	Dec 3	IP	H	Leyton	2470	D 0 - 0		7
28	10		H	Hendon	2693	W 2 - 1	Harvey 7 **R.Butler** 30	6
29	17	FAT 1	H	**St Albans City**	1953	L 2 - 3	**R.Butler** 25 Sargeant 53 (pen)	
30	26		H	Walton & Hersham	2969	W 2 - 1	S.Butler 23 Smeltz 44	6
31	Jan 2		A	Staines Town	2285	W 3 - 0	Ursell 8 Sargent 51 (pen) **R.Butler** 61	6
32	7		A	Folkestone Invicta	1048	L 0 - 1		8
33	21		A	Worthing	2253	W 2 - 0	Howard 54 **R.Butler** 57	8
34	28		H	Slough Town	2859	D 2 - 2	Smeltz 42 **R.Butler** 51	8
35	Feb 4		A	Leyton	718	W 2 - 1	**R.Butler** 1 George 61	8
36	7		H	Braintree Town	2615	D 1 - 1	S.Butler 90	7
37	11		H	Margate	2543	L 1 - 2	Carthy 26	7
38	18		H	Windsor & Eton	3158	D 1 - 1	Plummer 71	8
39	25		A	Fisher Athletic	1036	W 1 - 0	Daly 67	7
40	Mar 4		A	Braintree Town	1916	D 0 - 0		7
41	7		A	Margate	776	W 1 - 0	Plummer 73	6
42	11		H	Chelmsford City	2762	L 0 - 1		7
43	18		H	Heybridge Swifts	2455	W 1 - 0	Plummer 45	7
44	21		A	Harrow Borough	611	W 2 - 1	Smeltz 3 Daly 67	5
45	25		A	Wealdstone	1009	W 5 - 1	Barnes 3 (7 23 72) Howard 47 Smeltz 75	4
46	April 1		H	Hampton & Richmond B.	3315	L 0 - 4		7
47	8		A	Billericay Town	1180	L 1 - 2	Barnes 9	7
48	15		H	East Thurrock	2706	W 3 - 2	Sargeant 15 Smeltz 19 Howard 90	6
49	17		A	Walton & Hersham	1975	W 2 - 0	Barnes **R.Butler**	5
50	22		H	Hendon	1444	W 1 - 0	**R.Butler** 59	4
51	29		H	Harrow Borough	3044	W 2 - 1	Battersby 61 Barnes 72	4
52	May 2	Play Off SF	A	**Fisher Athletic**	1174	L 1 - 2	Howard 76	

Ave. League Home Attendance: 2306   **Goals**   77   46   **Top Goalscorer:** R.Butler (20)

Best Position: 1st   **Worst:**   8th

ASHFORD TOWN (Middlesex)

Founded:1964
Nickname:
Ash Trees

ASHFORD TOWN
(Middlesex)
Football Club

Manager: Mark Butler   **Asst.Manager**: Rory Gleeson   **Coach:**Gary Ross

Club Colours: Tangerine & white stripes/black/tangerine

Change Colours: All Blue

Club Sponsor:

Previous League: Southern

Best Seasons: League Runners-Up Southern Division 1 West 2005-2006

F.A. Cup: 4th Qualifying Round 2004-2005   **F.A.Trophy.:**   **F.A.Vase:**

Ground address: Short Lane, Stanwell, Staines, Middlesex

Tel No: 01784 245908

Club Website:www.ashfordtownmxfootballclub.co.uk

Capacity: 2,550   **Seats:**150   **Covered:** 300   **Floodlights:** Yes

Simple Directions: M25 jct 13, A30 towards London, third left at footbridge after Ashford Hospital crossroads - ground signposted after 1/4 a mile on right down Short Lane.two miles from Ashford (BR) & Hatton Cross (tube) stations.

Midweek Home Matchday: Tuesday

Clubhouse: Open seven days a week with refreshments always available

Club Shop: No

Local Radio:

Local Press:

CLUB PERSONNEL

Chairman: Robert Parker
Vice-Chairman: John Ellis
Secretary: Alan Connstable, 3 Craigwell Close, Chertsey Lane, Staines, Middlesex.TW18 3NP
Tel Nos: 01784 440613 (H) 07956 930719(M)
Press Secretary: Terry Ryan
Commercial Manager:
Eamonn Chandiram
Programme
Editor: Secretary
40 Paes £1.50
2005-2006
Captain: Steve Battams
Player of the Year:
Top Goalscorer:

CLUB STATISTICS

Record	**Attendance:** 750 v Brentford friendly 29.07.86	
	Career Goalscorer: Andy Smith	
	Career Appearances: Alan Constable 650	
Record Transfer Fee	**Paid:**	
	Received:	
Senior Honours:	Combined Counties League Champions 94-95, 95-96, 96-97, 97-8, 99-00;	
	Middx Prem. Cup R-up 89-90;, Middsx Charity Cup 2000-01	
Previous :	**Leagues:** Hounslow & Dist. 64-68; Surrey Intermediate 68-82; Surrey Premier	
	82-90 Combined Counties League 90-00 Isthmian 2000-01 - 03-4	
	Ground: Clockhouse Lane Rec	

Back Row (L-R): Aaron Jones, Mark Todd, Paul Johnson, Shane Graham, Stewart Lake, Gavin Smith, Damien Smith, Ricky Wellard, Leon Canning, Russ Canderton, Ben Lauderdy-Dykes, Pat Munns (Goal Keeping Coach), Tony Wells, John Hamsher, Lee Passmore, Jacob Mingle, Jon Palmer, Dean Pitcher, Mihail Polakov, Mick Cook, Andy Tomkins (Physio).
Front: Glynn Stephens (Reserve Team Manager), Jason Chewins, Scott Harris, Scott Todd, Darren Deegan, Gary Ross (1st Team Coach). Mark Butler (Manager), Rory Gleeson (Assistant Manager), Brett Cooper, Anthony Joseph, Simon Langley, Steve Battams (Club Captain). **Inset:** Paul Burgess.

arena
SEATING

Take a Seat!
with The LT Portastand

From 50 to 50,000... Arena Seating have the solution

Our very latest development, the LT Portastand is an uncovered 50-seater grandstand, which arrives fully assembled and can be fork lifted into position from a truck, providing the most economical grandstand on the market today.

To the base of each seating unit are 8 adjustable height ground plates which spread the load over reasonably level ground, without the need for concrete foundations.

Contact us to see how we can enhance your venue.

WWW.ARENASEATING.COM

Arena Seating
Arena House Membury Lambourn Woodlands Hungerford Berkshire RG17 7TQ
T. 01488 67 48 00   **W.** www.arenaseating.com   **E.** info@arenaseating.com

PART OF THE ARENA GROUP

BILLERICAY TOWN

Founded:1880
Nickname: The Town

Manager: Matt Jones **Assistant Manager:** Jason Broom
Physio: Gary Lynn
Club Colours: Royal Blue/white/royal blue
Change Colours: White/ Royal Blue/White
Club Sponsor: Glasslam.
Previous League: Athenian
Previous Grounds: Laindon Road (pre 1971)
Best Seasons: F.A. Cup: 1st Rd 97-98 04-05 **F.A.Trophy.:** 5th Rd 2000-01
Ground address: New Lodge, Blunts Wall Road, Billericay CM12 9SA
Tel No:Newsline: 01277 652188
Capacity: 3,500 **Seats:** 424 **Covered:** 2,000 **Floodlights:** Yes
Simple Directions: From Shenfield (A129)right at first lights then 2nd right. From Basildon (A129) over first lights in town, then left at next lights and second right.
Midweek Home Matchday: Tuesday
Clubhouse: Open every evening except Mondays and open weekend lunchtime.
Club Shop: Open matchdays. Contact: Andrew Turner 01277 631476
Local Radio: BBC Radio Essex, Essex Radio and Essex FM
Local Press: Evening Echo, Billericay Gazette and Billericay Recorder.

CLUB PERSONNEL
Chairman: Steve Kent
V-Chairman:
President: Jim Hall
Secretary: Ian Ansell c/o BTFC
Tel No: 07958 978154 (M)
Press Officer & Prog.Ed:
Simon Williams
Programme
32 pages £1.50

2004-2005
Captain: Jamie Dormer
Player of the Year: Pat Sappleton
Top Goalscorer: Nathan Elder

CLUB STATISTICS

Record	**Attendance**: 3,841 v West Ham Utd. Opening Floodlights 1977
	3,193 v Farnborough T. F.A.Vase SF 1976
	Victory: 11-0 v Stansted (A) Essex Senior .League. 05.05.76
	Defeat: 3-10 v Chelmsford City (A) Essex Senior Cup 04.01.93
	Career Goalscorer: Freddie Claydon 273 **Season**: Leon Gutzmore 51 (97-8)
	Career Appearances: J.Pullen 418
	Transfer Fee Paid: Undisclosed
	Received: £22,500 + from W.H.U. for Steve Jones Nov. 1992
Senior Honours:	F.A.Vase Winners 75-76 76-77 78-79, Isthmian Div 1 R-up 80-81 97-98
	Arthenian Lg 78-79 Essex Senior Cup 75-76 R-up (4) Essex Sen Trophy (2)
Previous Leagues:	Romford & Dist. 1890-1914, Mid Essex 18-47, S.Essex Comb. 47-66 Essex
	Olympian 66-71 Essex Senior 71-77 and Athenian 77-79

BILLERICAY TOWN

BEST LGE ATT.: 1,160 v AFC Wimbledon
LOWEST: **241** v Windsor & Eton

No.	Date	Comp	H/A	Opponents	Att:	Result	Goalscorers	Pos
1	Aug 20	IP	H	Slough Town	522	W 3 - 1	Lay 7 Cousins 47 Hockton 53	2
2	27		A	Staines Town	301	W 2 - 1	Thomas 5 Dormer 9	5
3	29		H	Chelmsford City	980	W 4 - 2	**Elder** 30 Wareham 71 Stapleton 84 Hockton 90	4
4	Sept 3		A	Harrow Borough	144	D 1 - 1	Hockton 44	3
5	6		H	Maldon Town	524	L 2 - 3	Hockton 17 Hunter 44	6
6	**10**	**FAC 1Q**	**A**	**St.Margaretsbury**	**224**	**D 0 - 0**		
7	**13**	**FAC 1Qr**	**H**	**St Margaretsbury**	**302**	**L 2 - 3***	**Turner 8 (og) Hockton 45**	
8	17	IP	H	Walton & Hersham	484	L 0 - 2		10
9	24		A	East Thurrock	258	W 3 - 0	**Elder** 22 90 Hunter 74 (pen)	10
10	26		A	Folkestone Invicta	242	L 0 - 1		10
11	Oct 1		H	Fisher Athletic	511	L 1 - 3	**Elder** 28	12
12	4		A	Margate	294	D 1 - 1	Hockton 26	12
13	8		A	AFC Wimbledon	2445	D 1 - 1	McSweeney 12	
14	11		H	Leyton	368	D 2 - 2	**Elder** 30 Parker 37	10
15	**15**	**FAT 1Q**	**H**	**Wingate & Finchley**	**317**	**W 1 - 0**	**Poole 24**	
16	25	IP	A	Maldon Town	201	W 2 - 0	Hunter 29 Poole 59	9
17	29		A	Hendon	248	D 2 - 2	Wareham 15 Poole 23	9
18	Nov 5		H	Wealdstone	472	W 2 - 0	Hunter 54 (pen) Hockton 78	8
19	**12**	**FAT 2Q**	**A**	**Heybridge Swifts**	**326**	**L 1 - 2**	**Barber 50 (og)**	
20	19	IP	A	Bromley	403	L 0 - 1		10
21	22		H	Windsor & Eton	241	W 3 - 0	Ryan 70 Game 72 Hockton 88	7
22	26		H	Worthing	421	D 1 - 1	Trott 84	8
23	Dec 3		A	Heybridge Swifts	261	D 0 - 0		9
24	10		H	East Thurrock	458	L 1 - 3	Hockton 76	10
25	13		H	Braintree Town	371	D 1 - 1	Game 77	
26	17		A	Hampton & Richmond B	302	W 1 - 0	**Elder** 73	8
27	26		H	Redbridge	461	W 1 - 0	Hunter 90	7
28	Jan 2		A	Chelmsford City	2998	L 1 - 2	Game 80	9
29	7		A	Slough Town	308	W 2 - 0	**Elder** 41 Dormer 48	9
30	14		H	Folkestone Invicta	513	W 2 - 0	Poole 47 Game 55	8
31	21		A	Walton & Hersham	302	D 0 - 0		9
32	28		H	Staines Town	423	D 1 - 1	Hunter 65	9
33	Feb 4		A	Heybridge Swifts	540	L 1 - 2	Hunter 52 (pen)	9
34	11		A	Worthing	502	W 4 - 2	Flack 22 Henty 48 Hunter 53 Poole 54	9
35	18		H	Hendon	447	W 1 - 0	Hunter 8	9
36	25		A	Braintree Town	703	L 0 - 3		9
37	Mar 11		H	Bromley	503	D 2 - 2	Flack 23 Brown 53	10
38	18		A	Fisher Athletic	208	W 2 - 0	Hunter 36 (pen) **Elder** 89	9
39	25		H	Margate	512	W 4 - 1	**Elder** 31 Hedges 58 Henty 79 Poole 82	9
40	28		A	Windsor & Eton	124	L 0 - 1		9
41	April 1		A	Leyton	135	W 3 - 1	**Elder** 45 Flack 46 71	9
42	4		A	Wealdstone	255	D 1 - 1	Game 90	9
43	8		H	AFC Wimbledon	1160	W 2 - 1	**Elder** 22 Finnie 34 (og)	8
44	15		H	Harrow Borough	422	W 3 - 1	Ryan 1 Hunter 27 (pen) **Elder** 29	8
45	17		A	Redbridge	204	W 5 - 0	Hodges 38 Flack 56 73 Collins 68 **Elder** 76	6
46	29		H	Hampton & Richmond B	1020	L 1 - 2	**Elder** 21	7

Ave. League Home Attendance: 541   **Goals**   73 48   **Top Goalscorer:** Elder (14)
Best Position: 2nd   **Worst:**   12th

BOREHAM WOOD

Founded: 1948
Nickname:
The Wood

Manager: Steve Cook   **Asst. Manager**: Mickey Engwell: **Physio**:Joe Miller
Club Colours: White/Black/Black
Change Colours: Sky Blue/White/White
Club Sponsor: Cardiff Pinnacle Group & BNP Barbas Group
Previous League: Isthmian
Best Seasons: Isthmian League Premier Division Runners Up 1997-1998
F.A. Cup: 2nd Round 1996-97 1997-98   **F.A.Vase:**
F.A.Trophy.: Semi-Final 2005 -1006
Ground address: Meadow Park, Broughinge Road, Boreham Wood, Herts.
Tel No: 0208 953 5097
Club Website: www.web-teams.co.uk/borehamwoodfc
Capacity: 4,502   **Seats**: 600   **Covered**: 1,568   **Floodlights**: Yes
Simple Directions: A1 towards London from M25, 1st turn for Boreham Wood, head for town-centre, into Brook Road at roundabout before town centre, Broughinge Rd is first right. 1 mile from Elstree & Boreham Wood station (Thameslink), or bus 292 or107 to McDonalds (5 minutes walk)
Midweek Home Matchday: Monday
Clubhouse: Open norman licemsing hours with snacks available. Function Room (250) for hire. **Club Shop:** Full selection of products. Contact: Jeff Weston
Local Radio: Chiltern Radio
Local Press: Boreham Wood Times, Watford Observer and Herts Advertiser.

CLUB OFFICIIALS
Chairman: Danny Hunter
President: Bill O'Neill
Secretary: Bob Nicholson, 56 Newcombe Road, Shenley, Radlett, Herts WD7 9EJ
Tel No: 01923 856077 (H)
07768 172400 (M)
Press Officer: John Gill
Tel No: 0795 627 5111 (M)
Programme
Editor: Mark Kettlety
MK Publications
54 Pages £2.00
2006-2007
Captain: Mark Smith
Player of the Year: Marvin Samuel
Top Goalscorer: :eon Archer 31

CLUB STATISTICS

Record	**Attendance:** 4,030 v Arsenal (Friendly) 13.07.01
	Career Goalscorer: Mickey Jackson
	Career Appearances: Dave Hatchett 714
Record Transfer Fee	**Paid**:
	Received: £5,000 from Daganham & redbridge for Steve Heffer
Senior Honours:	Southern League Diov 1 East Champions 2005-2006 Isthmian Lg.Prem Div R-Up 97-98 Div I 94-95, 00-01 Isthmian Lg Div 2 76-77 Athenian Lg 73-74 , Herts Senior Cup 71-72 ,98-99 01-02 R-up (8), London Challenge Cup 97-98
Previous :	**Leagues:** Mid Herts 48-52, Parthenon 52-57, Spartan 56-66, Athenian 66-74
	Ground: Eldon Avenue 1948-63
	Names: Boreham Wood Rovers and Royal Retournez, amalgamated in 1948

Back Row: Micky Engwell (Asst. Manager), Steve Cook (Team Manager), Joe Miller (Physio.), Elvis Balic, Bradley Hewitt, Chris Bangura, Callum Horton, Noel Imber, Ryan Moran, Jon Stevenson, Matthew Corbould, Darrell Cox, Paul Burrows, Ken Baker (Coach), Danny Hunter (Chairman), Daniel Hunter (Kit Manager).   FRONT ROW: Greg Morgan, Joe O'Brien, Danny Hart, Jamie Hazell, Kieren Adams, Mark Smith (Captain), Marvin Samuel, Leon Archer, Tommy Williams, Chris Watters, Ian Cooper, Michael Black.   Photo: John D. Gill

Soccer Speaker
a new brand of sports speaker

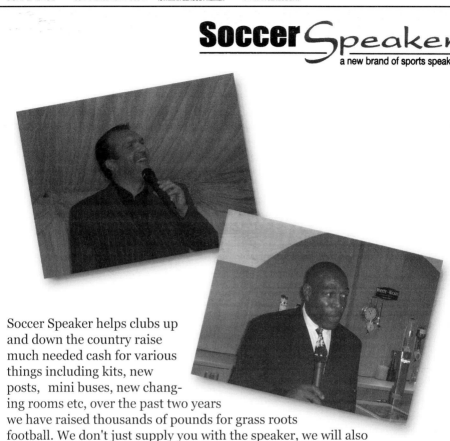

Soccer Speaker helps clubs up and down the country raise much needed cash for various things including kits, new posts, mini buses, new changing rooms etc, over the past two years we have raised thousands of pounds for grass roots football. We don't just supply you with the speaker, we will also help you to organise your event, advertising, raffle prizes, ticket printing etc.

No job is too small, we organise things for small clubs, pie & a pint with 50 guests and a speaker right up to your bigger events with a 5 course meal, speaker, comedian & compare. Auction items are also available, all come with a photo of the piece being signed along with a double your money back certificate of authenticity.

Soccer Speaker are Neil Razor Ruddock's official agents for all his sportsman's dinners, Neil is one of the best speakers on the circuit, his stories from the jungle and his footballing career are hilarious, other names available include Ronnie Whelan, Mike Summerbee, John Aldridge, Ron Chopper Harris, Frank Bruno, Jeff Winter, Peter Osgood, John McGovern, Duncan McKenzie, Tommy Docherty, Henry Cooper and many more (see website for details)
See **www.soccerspeaker.com**

BROMLEY

Founded:1892
Nickname: The Lillywhites

BROMLEY FOOTBALL CLUB

2005-2006 SEASON £1.50

John Ullman Kent Senior Cup 1st Round
BROMLEY vs ASHFORD TOWN
Tuesday 15th November 2005
Kick Off 7.45pm

Managers: Mark Goldberg   **Assistant Manager:** Murray Jones

Club Colours: White/black/black

Change Colours: All Red

Club Sponsor: Sycamore Group

Previous Leagues: Athenian

Best Seasons: League: Isthmian Champions (4)   **F.A. Cup:** 2nd Round Replay

F.A.Trophy.: 2nd Round 91-92

Ground address: The Stadium, Hayes Lane, Bromley, Kent BR2 9EF

Tel No: 020 8460 5291 and Fax 020 83183992

Official website: www.bromleyfc.net

Capacity: 4,900   **Seats:** 1,300   **Covered:** 2,500   **Floodlights:** Yes

Simple Directions: M25 Jct4 then A21 towards London

Midweek Home Matchday: Tuesday

Clubhouse: Open Matchdays   **Club Shop:**Yes. Contact Jim Brown

Local Radio: Radio Kent, Bromley Local Radio

Local Press: Bromley Times, South London Press.

CLUB PERSONNEL

Chairman: Jerry Dolke
Secretary: Colin Russell, c/o B.F.C.
email info@bromleyfc.net
Programme Editor & Press Officer:
Iona Bartlett
Programme
Pages 32 Price £1.50

2005-2006
Captain: Mark Willy
Player of the Year: Sam Wood
Top Goalscorer: Nic McDonnell

CLUB STATISTICS

Record	**Attendance** : 12,000 v Nigeria 1950
	Victory: 13-1 v Redhill Athenian Lg. 1945-46
	Defeat: 1-11 v Barking Athenian Lg. 1933-34
	Career Goalscorer: George Brown 570 (1938-61)
	Career Appearances: George Brown
	Record Transfer Fee Paid: Unknown
	Record Transfer Fee Received: £ 50,000 from Millwall for John Goodman.
Senior Honours:	Isthmian Champions 08-10 53-54 60-61 R-up (3) Div 1 R0-up (3) Athenian Lg. 22-3 48-9 50-1 Kent Sen Cup (5) Kent Am.Cup (12) London Senior Cup (4)
Previous Leagues:	S.London, Southern, London, W.Kent,S.Suburban,Kent, Spartan1907-08 Isthmian1908-11 Athenian 1919-1952

THE JOHN FIORINI STAND

Back Row (L-R): Junior Kadi, Lee Fieldwick, Adrian Stone, Gary Drewett, Nathan Simpson, Tony Boot, Alex Tiesse.
Middle: Mark Corneille, Sam Wood, Bobby Bowry (Player/Coach), Andy Walker, Barry Moore, Kirk Watts,
Donal O'Sulivan, Peter Adeniyi. **Front:** Michael Power, Jerrome Sobers, Tutu Henriques, Mark Goldberg (Manager),
Jerry Dolke (Chairman), Francis Duku, Nic McDonnell. Inset - Murray Jones (Assistant Manager).
Standing on the left - Derek Parnham (Goalkeeping Coach), standing on the right - Andre Vincent (Physio).

BROMLEY

BEST LGE ATT.: 1,235 v AFC Wimbledon
LOWEST: 203 v Hampton & Rich. B.

No.	Date	Comp	H/A	Opponents	Att:	Result	Goalscorers	Pos
1	Aug 20	IP	H	Chelmsford City	499	D 1 - 1	**McDonnell** 36	10
2	23		A	Walton & Hersham	175	W 1 - 0	Gardner 61	8
3	27		A	East Thurrock	162	L 0 - 1		10
4	29		H	Folkestone Invicta	409	D 3 - 3	Logan 60 **McDonnell** 62 Willey 90	11
5	Sept 3		A	Hendon	179	L 1 - 2	**McDonnell** 78	14
6	6		A	AFC Wimbledon	2563	D 1 - 1	Gardner 2	15
7	10	FAC1Q	A	**Bedfont**	128	**W 4 - 1**	**Amoako 1 McDonnell 57 Boateng 70 Logan 90**	
8	17	IP	H	Maldon Town	205	W 2 - 1	Logan 23 **McDonnell** 45	12
9	20		H	Margate	362	D 2 - 2	Henriques 25 Boating 66	
10	24	FAC 2Q	H	**Chipstead**	407	**W 2 - 1**	**McDonnell 32 Vines 52**	
11	Oct 1	IP	H	Windsor & Eton	344	W 4 - 1	**McDonnell** 3 (18 37 78 pen) Vines 54	10
12	4		A	Leyton	142	W 1 - 0	Tompkins 78	9
13	8	FAC 3Q	H	**Mangotsfield United**	488	**D 0 - 0**		
14	11	FAC 3Qr	A	**Mangotsfield United**	403	**W 1 - 0**	**Stone 85**	
15	15	FAT1Q	A	**Ashford Town**	251	**W 2 - 0**	**Logan 28 Locke 41**	
16	22	FAC 4Q	H	**Aldershot Town**	1454	**L 0 - 1**		
17	25	IP	H	AFC Wimbledon	1235	W 2 - 0	**McDonnell** 43 Wood 46	9
18	29		H	Staines Town	402	D 1 - 1	Stone 25	9
19	Nov 5		A	Heybridge Swifts	213	L 0 - 1		11
20	12	FAT 2Q	A	**Boreham Wood**	195	**L 1 - 4**	**McDonnell 60**	
21	19	IP	H	Billericay Town	403	W 1 - 0	Anuah 7	9
22	22		A	Margate	401	D 1 - 1	**McDonnell** 72 (pen)	11
23	Dec 3		H	Slough Town	378	L 2 - 3	George 35 Awuah 43	11
24	6		A	Hampton & Richmond B	203	D 0 - 0		11
25	10		A	Redbridge	117	L 2 - 3	Aquah 31 80	12
26	17		H	Wealdstone	374	D 1 - 1	**McDonnell** 90	12
27	27		H	Worthing	480	L 1 - 2	**McDonnell** 80	14
28	Jan 2		A	Folkestone Invicta	369	L 0 - 1		15
29	7		A	Chelmsford City	1663	L 2 - 3	**McDonnell** 26 Carew 82	
30	10		A	Braintree Town	409	L 1 - 3	Carroll	16
31	14		H	Walton & Hersham	363	W 1 - 0	Luckett 42 (pen)	14
32	17		H	Fisher Athletic	510	L 1 - 2	C.Piper 20 (og)	15
33	21		A	Maldon Town	133	W 2 - 0	Remy 51 Wood 81	13
34	24		A	Harrow Borough	113	L 0 - 2		13
35	28		H	East Thurrock	345	D 1 - 1	Stone 10	13
36	Feb 4		A	Slough Town	294	D 2 - 2	Wood 58 Willy 85	15
37	11		H	Harrow Borough	321	D 1 - 1	Stone 22	16
38	18		A	Staines Town	251	W 2 - 1	Drewett 46 Remy 62	15
39	25		H	Hampton & Richmond B	312	W 2 - 0	Henriques 52 Remy 90	13
40	Mar 4		H	Heybridge Swifts	322	W 2 - 1	Stone 59 Mitchell 90	12
41	11		A	Billericay Town	503	D 2 - 2	**McDonnell** 80 Wood 89	12
42	18		A	Windsor & Eton	132	W 1 - 0	Greenway 59	12
43	25		H	Leyton	331	L 1 - 2	O'Sullivan 53	13
44	April 1		A	Fisher Athletic	246	D 0 - 0		13
45	8		H	Braintree Town	431	D 1 - 1	**McDonnell** 20	13
46	15		H	Hendon	272	W 3 - 1	**McDonnell** 47 70 Mitchell 73	12
47	17		A	Worthing	532	W 2 - 1	Stone **McDonnell**	11
48	22		H	Redbridge	268	W 1 - 0	Wood 19	11
49	29		A	Wealdstone	307	W 2 - 1	Stone 13 Wood 63	11

Ave. League Home Attendance: 418   **Goals** 67 56   **Top Goalscorer:** McDonnell (20)
Best Position: 8th   **Worst:** 16th

CARSHALTON ATHLETIC

Founded: 1905
Nickname: Robins

Manager: Dave Garland **Assistant Manager:** Peter Burdett

Physio: John Franks

Club Colours: All Maroon

Change: Maroon

Club Sponsors: BDS Fire and Security

Previous League: Isthmian League

Best Seasons: League: 19th Conference South 2004-2005

F.A. Cup: 2nd Rd 82-83   **F.A.Trophy:** 3rd Rd 95-96

Ground: War Memorial Sports Ground, Colston Avenue, Carshalton, SM5 2PW

Tel No: 0208 642 8658

Capacity: 8,000   **Seats**: 240   **Covered**: 4,500   **Floodlights**: Yes

Simple Directions: Turn right out of Carshalton BR and Colston Ave. is first left.

Midweek Home Matchday: Tuesday

Clubhouse: Open daily evenings and midday.Bookings taken 0181 642 8658

Club Shop: Yes

Local Press: Sutton Comet and Sutton Herald

Local Radio: BBC Southern Counties

CLUB PERSONNEL

Chairman: Harry Driver
President: John Carpentiere
Secretary: Vic Thompson,
11 Poulton Avenue, Sutton, Surrey
SM5 3ET (H) 02086446402
(W) 0208 643 0999
Press Officer: Peter Randell
Tel No 0208 642 1109 (H)
Prog.Ed: Richard Jeacock
Tel No: 07949 028528 (M)
Programme
20 Pages £2.00

2005-2006
Player of the Year: Craig Dundas
Top Goalscorer:

CLUB STATISTICS

Record	**Attendance**: 7,800 v Wimbledon London Senior Cup
	Victory: 13-0 v Worthing Lg Cup 28.02.91
	Defeat:
	Career Goalscorer: Jimmy Bolton 242
	Career Appearances: Jon Warden 504
Record Transfer Fee	**Paid**: £15,000 to Enfield for Curtis Warmington
	Received: £30,000 from Crystal Palace for Ian Cox
Senior Honours:	Surrey Senior Cup (3) Runners-Up (5) Surrey Senior Shield 75-76 R-Up (2)
	London Challenge Cup 91-92
Previous Leagues:	Southern Suburban (pre 1911) Surrey Senior 22-23 London 23-46
	Corinthian 46-56 Athenian 56-73

CARSHALTON ATHLETIC

BEST LGE ATT.: 1,056 v Sutton United
LOWEST:　　**212** v Histon

No.	Date	Comp	H/A	Opponents	Att:	Result	Goalscorers	Pos
1	Aug 13	CS	A	Newport County	886	L 1 - 4	Haki 73	19
2	16		H	Bishop's Stortford	326	D 0 - 0		18
3	20		H	Lewes	336	D 2 - 2	Hunt 8 62	18
4	27		A	Weymouth	1370	L 0 - 4		21
5	29		H	Bognor Regis Town	297	D 1 - 1	Hooper 13	20
6	Sept 3		A	Basingstoke Town	304	L 1 - 2	Pritchard 52	20
7	10		A	Farnborough Town	484	L 0 - 4		21
8	17		H	Maidenhead United	278	L 0 - 1		22
9	24	FAC 2Q	A	**Margate**	773	L 0 - 1		
10	Oct 1	CS	H	Histon	212	D 0 - 0		22
11	15		A	Eastleigh	343	L 1 - 3	Patterson 29 (pen)	22
12	18		A	Welling United	462	L 0 - 2		22
13	22		H	Havant & Waterlooville	342	L 1 - 3	Patterson 47	
14	29		H	St. Albans City	367	L 0 - 2		22
15	Nov 5		A	Weston-s-Mare	229	L 0 - 2		22
16	8		A	Eastbourne Borough	547	D 1 - 1	**Fontana** 62	22
17	12		H	Hayes	313	L 1 - 2	**Fontana** 65	22
18	19		A	Dorchester Town	428	L 0 - 2		22
19	26	FAT 3Q	A	**Chippenham Town**	510	W 2 - 0	**Fontana 20 Dundas 89**	
20	Dec 3	CS	H	Cambridge City	297	L 0 - 2		22
21	10		A	Yeading	146	W 4 - 3	**Fontana** 3 (29 38 89) Patterson 79 ~(pen)	22
22	17	FAT 1	A	**Yeading**	120	W 2 - 1	**Fontana 57 61**	
23	26		H	Sutton United	1056	D 0 - 0		22
24	31		H	Thurrock	299	D 0 0		22
25	Jan 2		A	Sutton United	950	D 1 - 1	Nwanze 14	22
26	7		H	Newport County	431	W 1 - 0	Dundas 24	21
27	14	FAT 2	H	**Accrington Stanley**	618	D 2 - 2	**Tchakounte 8 Johnson 80**	
28	17	FAT 2r	A	**Accrington Stanley**	556	L 0 - 2		
29	21	CS	A	Lewes	553	L 1 - 2	Johnson 5	22
30	28		H	Weymouth	513	W 2 - 1	Dundas 77 Fowler 79	22
31	Feb 4		A	Histon	454	W 1 - 0	Johnson 83	21
32	11		H	Eastleigh	388	L 1 - 3	Patterson 70 (pen)	22
33	15		A	Bishop's Stortford	289	D 3 - 3	Quniton 33 38 Dundas 63	22
34	21		H	Welling United	236	W 1 - 0	Quinton 18	21
35	25		A	Farnborough Town	402	D 2 - 2	Johnson 14 Nwanze 85	21
36	Mar 4		A	Maidenhead United	405	W 2 - 0	Johnson 57 Patterson 74 (pen)	20
37	7		H	Eastbourne Borough	350	D 2 - 2	Dundas 11 Fowler 52	20
38	11		A	St Albans City	562	L 0 3		20
39	18		H	Weston-s-Mare	266	D 1 - 1	Marshall 12	20
40	25		A	Hayes	203	W 2 - 1	Fowler 43 Armal 82	20
41	April 1		H	Dorchester Town	348	W 3 - 1	Dundas 59 Graves 78 Fowler 80	18
42	8		A	Cambridge City	504	D 0 - 0		20
43	10		A	Havant & Waterlooville	407	D 1 - 1	Quinton 12	20
44	15		A	Basingstoke Town	386	L 1 - 2	Graves 84	20
45	17		A	Bognor Regis Town	305	D 1 - 1	York 14	20
46	22		A	Thurrock	187	L 1 - 2	Patel 90	20
47	29		H	Yeading	474	D 2 - 2	Yeboah 19 (og) Dundas 7	21

Ave. League Home Attendance:　377　　　　　**Goals**　　48 74　　**Top Goalscorer:** Fontana (8)
Best Position:　18th　　**Worst:**　22nd

CHELMSFORD CITY

Founded: 1938
Nickname: City or Clarets

Manager: Jeff King   **Coach:** Glenn Pannyfather   **Physio:** Tony Steeles

Club Colours: All claret with white trim/white/white

Change Colours: All sky blue with claret trim

Club Sponsor: LOF Futures

Previous League: Southern

Best Seasons: League: Southern League Champions (3)

F.A. Cup: 4th Rd. 1938-39   **F.A.Trophy.:** Semi-Final 69-70

Ground address: Chelmsford Sport and Athletic Centre., Salerno Way, Chelmsford, Essex. CM1 2EH **Tel No:** 01245 290959

Club Website: www.chelmsfordcityfc.com

Capacity: 3,800   **Seats:** 1,400   **Covered:** 400   **Floodlights:** Yes.

Simple Directions:

Midweek Home Matchday: Monday

Clubhouse: Open weekends and evenings except Mondays.

Club Shop: Fully stocked. Contact: Sharon Chantryvia

Local Radio: Essex Radio, Breeze AM , BBC Essex & Chelner FM

Local Press: Essex Chronicle,Chelmsford Weekly News, E.Anglian Daily Times and Evening Gazette

CLUB PERSONNEL

Chairman: Paul Hopkins
V-Chairman: Stuart Collard
President: Don Walker
Secretary: David Selby.
34 Paddock Drive,Chelmsford,
Essex CM1 6SS (H) 01245 464922
(M) 0780 1908441
Company Secrtary: Trevor Smith
Commercial Manager: Gary Mixture
Press Officer: Chris Evans
Tel No: 0779 903 0669 (M)
Programme Editor: Mandy Smith
Programme: 64 pages £2.00
2005-2006
Captain: Russell Edwards
Playe rof the Year: Michael Haswell
Top Goalscorer: Jamie Richards

CLUB STATISTICS

Record	**Attendance:** 16,807 v Colchester United, Southern League 10.09.49
	Victory: 10-1 v Bashley (H) Southern League 26.04.2000
	Defeat: 2-10 v Barking (A) F.A.Trophy 11.11.78
Career Goalscorer:	Tony Butcher 287 (1957-71)
Career Appearances:	Derek Tiffin 550 (1950-63)
Record Transfer Fee	**Paid:** £10,000 to Dover Athletic for Tony Rogers 1992
	Received: £50,000 from Peterborough United for David Morrison
Senior Honours:	Southern League.Champions 45-6 67-8 71-2 R-Up: (4) Southern Division 88-89
	R-up 97-98 Essex Pro Cup (5) Essex Senior Cup (4) Essex Floodlit Cup (6)
	Non-League Champions Cup 1971-72
Previous Grounds:	New Writtle Street 1938-97 Maldon Town 97-98 Billericay Town 1998-2005

Back Row (L-R) -Kezie Ibe, Jerrome Sobers, Ben Chennery, Richard McKinney, Lucas Debski, Peter Smith, Tony Battersby, Glenn Pennyfather (Coach). **Front Row:** Jay Conroy, Mitchell Lowes, Liam Hopkins, Ricky Holmes, Jeff King (Manager), Paul Hopkins (Chairman), Jason Hallett, Chris Duffy, Stuart Ainsley, Gavin Heeroo.

CHELMSFORD CITY

BEST LGE ATT.: 2,998 v Billericay Town
LOWEST:　　282 v Walton & Hersham

No.	Date	Comp	H/A	Opponents	Att:	Result	Goalscorers	Pos
1	Aug 20	IP	A	Bromley	499	D 1 - 1	Moralee 90	11
2	22		H	Heybridge Swifts	515	L 0 - 2		13
3	27		H	Wealdstone	360	D 0 - 0		16
4	29		A	Billericay Town	980	L 2 - 4	McSweeney 4 (og) J.Edwards 8	20
5	Sept 3		H	Windsor & Eton	316	W 2 - 1	**Richards** 20 Summercales 28	16
6	6		A	Staines Town	264	L 0 - 3		17
7	10	**FAC 1Q**	**H**	**Harlow Town**	**301**	**D 1 - 1**	**Halle 45**	
8	13	**FAC1Qr**		**Harlow Town**	**206**	**W 1 - 0**	**Lincoln 89**	
9	17	IP	A	Leyton	150	L 1 - 5	Halle 64	18
10	19		H	Folkestone Invicta	286	L 0 - 1		19
11	24	**FAC 2Q**	**H**	**Dover Athletic**	**404**	**W 1 - 0**	**Baldez 5**	
12	Oct 1	IP	A	East Thurrock	246	L 0 - 3		19
13	3		A	Walton & Hersham	282	D 1 - 1	R Edwards 3	20
14	8	**FAC 3Q**	**A**	**Nuneaton Borough**	**915**	**D 1 - 1**	**R.Edwards 23**	
15	12	**FAC3Qr**	**H**	**Nuneaton Borough**	**379**	**L 1 - 2***	**Allen 67**	
16	16	**FAT1Q**	**H**	**Horsham**	**358**	**W 6 - 0**	**Halle 26 Fiddes 31 Linolln 37 (pen) 90 Richards 54 88**	
17	22	IP	A	Slough Town	340	W 1 - 0	Allen 21	20
18	24		H	Staines Town	350	D 4 - 4	**Richards** 15 Allen 19 C. Edwards 42 Halle 89	20
19	29		H	Harrow Borough	418	W 3 - 0	Lincoln 33 C.Edwards 48 Halle 60	18
20	Nov 5		A	Margate	759	W 1 - 0	J.Edwards 3	14
21	12	**FAT 2Q**	**H**	**Braintree Town**	**436**	**L 0 - 2**		
22	19	IP	H	AFC Wimbledon	403	W 1 - 0	C.Edwards 41	12
23	21		A	Folkestone Invicta	304	D 1 - 1	Smith 15	13
24	26		A	Maldon Town	403	W 1 - 0	Halle 56	12
25	Dec 3		H	Hampton & Richmond B	392	D 3 - 3	**Richards** 19 83 Lincoln 71 (pen)	15
26	10		A	Worthing	504	W 3 - 1	Fiddes 17 Allen 47 **Richards** 68	11
27	17		H	Fisher Athrletic	401	L 0 - 2		11
28	26		A	Braintree Town	967	L 1 - 2	Allen 25	13
29	Jan 2		H	Billericay Town	2998	W 2 - 1	**Richards** 21 60	12
30	7		H	Bromley	1663	W 3 - 2	**Richards** 34 Boot 65 Holmes 80	10
31	14		A	Heybridge Swifts	604	L 0 - 2		12
32	21		H	Leyton	1485	D 1 - 1	Fiddes 90	12
33	28		A	Wealdstone	344	W 2 - 1	Moralee 47 Boot 90	11
34	Feb 4		A	Hampron & Richmond B	357	L 0 - 3		11
35	11		H	Maldon Town	1238	L 1 - 2	Boot 60 (pen)	13
36	14		A	Redbridge	184	W 2 - 1	Boot 53 Moralee 81	11
37	18		A	Harrow Borough	193	L 1 - 2	Boot 39 (pen)	
38	25		H	Slough Town	1006	W 2 - 0	Halle 11 46	11
39	Mar 3		H	Margate	853	W 1 - 0	**Richards** 35	10
40	8		H	Hendon	502	W 3 - 0	Halle 8 90 Boot 25	10
41	11		A	AFC Wimbledob	2762	W 1 - 0	Allen 58	9
42	18		H	East Thurrock	757	L 2 - 4	Palmer 46 **Richards** 62	11
43	25		A	Walton & Hersham	219	D 2 - 2	Palmer 32 45	10
44	April 1		A	Redbridge	748	W 2 - 1	Boot 13 Palmer 90	10
45	8		A	Hendon	265	D 0 - 0		10
46	15		A	Windsor & Eton	136	W 2 - 1	Halle 64 Boot 80	10
47	17		H	Braintree Town	1495	L 0 - 2		10
48	22		H	Worthinmg	611	W 1 - 0	Boot 55 (pen)	10
49	29		A	Fisher Athletic	208	D 3 - 3	Allen 29 63 Fiddes 74	10

Ave. League Home Attendance: 754　　　　**Goals** 68 66　　**Top Goalscorer:** Richards (12)
Best Position: 9th　　**Worst:** 20th

EAST THURROCK UNITED

Founded: 1969
Nickname: Rocks

Manager: Lee Patterson
Coach: John Coventry **Physio:** Steve Gracie
Club Colours: Amber& Black/black/black
Change Colours: Blue/white/white
Club Sponsor:
Previous League: Southern Division One East
Previous Name: Corringham Social (pre 1969 Sunday side)
Previous Grounds: Billet,Stanford-le-Hope 70-73 74-76 Grays Athletic 73-74, Tilbury F.C. 77-82 New Thames Club 82-84
Best Seasons: Lg: 2nd Southern Div 1 East **F.A. Cup:** 4th Q Rd 03-04
F.A.Trophy.: **F.A. Vase:** 5th Round 1988-1989
Ground address: Rookery Hill, Corringham, Essex SS17 9LB
TelNo: 01375 644166
Capacity: 4,000 **Seats:** 160 **Covered:** 1,000 **Floodlights:** Yes
Simple Directions: From A13 London -Southend road, take A1014 at Stanford -le-Hope for two and a half miles. Ground on left. Two miles from Basildon & S-le-H BR
Midweek Home Matchday: Tuesday
Clubhouse: Open all day seven days a week.
Club Shop: No
Local Radio: BBC Essex
Local Press: Thurrock Gazette and Thurrock Recorder.

CLUB PERSONNEL
Chairman: Wayne Bennett
Secretary: Mick Stephens,39 NewPark Road, Benfleet, Essex SS75URTel No: 01268 458571(H)
07979 214350 (W)
Press Officer: Mike Bakewell
Programme Editor: Neil Speight

2005-2006
Captain:
Player of the Year:
Top Goalscorer: West 10

CLUB STATISTICS

Record	**Attendance**: 1,215 v Woking F.A.Cup 2003
	Victory: 7-0 v Coggeshall (H) 1984 Essex Senior League
	Defeat: 0-9 v Eton Manor (A) 1982 Essex Senior League
Career Goalscorer:	Graham Stewart 102
Career Appearances:	Glen Case 600+
Record Transfer Fee	**Paid:**
	Received: £22,000 from Leyton Orient for Greg Berry
Senior Honours:	Essex Senior Trophy R-up 91-92 95-96 Isthmian Div 3 99-00
	E.Anglian Cup 0203 Southern League Division One East R-up 2004-2005
Previous Leagues:	South Essex Comb. Greater London, Metroplitan 72-75 London
	Spartan 75- 79 Essex Senior 79-92 Isthmian 92-2004

Back row,left to right: John Coventry (Coach), Scott Holding, Darren Grieves, Gary Wotton, Jamie Riley, Kevin Mully, Elliott Gresham, Danny Dafter and Lee Patterson (Manager).
Front row: Danny Harris, Shaun Batt, Steve Harrison, John Turnbull, Danny Hayzeldean, Wes Faulkner, Lee Burns and Martin Tuohy. Photo: Alan Coomes

EAST THURROCK

BEST LGE ATT.: 778 v AFC Wimbledon
LOWEST: **84** v Redbridge

No.	Date	Comp	H/A	Opponents	Att:	Result	Goalscorers	Pos
1	Aug 20	IP	A	Windsor & Eton	131	D 0 - 0		12
2	23		H	Braintree Town	165	L 1 - 3	West 79	14
3	27		H	Bromley	162	W 1 - 0	Holding 80 (pen)	12
4	29		A	Heybridge Swifts	188	W 1 - 0	Hazelden 86	9
5	Sept 3		H	AFC Wiumbledon	778	D 1 - 1	Daly 2 (og)	9
6	6		A	Harrow Borough	130	L 4 - 5	West 28 Boot 45 Turnbull 51 Burns 52	11
7	10	FAC 1Q	H	Harrow Borough	96	L 1 - 2	Harris 84	
8	17	IP	A	Wealdstone	327	W 2 - 0	Boot 40 West 51	9
9	20		H	Slough Town	175	W 3 - 2	West 8 Daly 41 (og) Boot 71	
10	24		H	Billericay Town	258	L 0 - 3		9
11	Oct 1		H	Chelmsford City	246	W 3 - 0	Turnbull 2 Boot 3 Harris 54	5
12	3		A	Folkestone Invicta	251	L 0 - 1		8
13	8		A	Maldon Town	120	L 2 - 3	Harris 55 Palmer 80	
14	11		H	Worthing	132	W 5 - 1	Palmer Boot (2) Thomas West	5
15	15	FAT1Q	A	Leatherhead	141	W 1 - 0	Boot 41	
16	22	IP	A	Walton & Hersham	147	L 0 - 1		7
17	25		H	Harrow Borough	125	W 3 - 2	Boot 47 86 Burns 51	6
18	29		H	Hampton & Richmond B	158	L 1 - 2	Harris 59	7
19	Nov 5		A	Staines Town	220	L 0 - 1		9
20	12	FAT 2Q	H	Leyton	109	W 2 - 1	West 71 Harris 88	
21	19	IP	H	Leyton	103	L 1 - 3	Hazeldon 73	11
22	22		A	Slough Town	191	W 2 - 1	West 40 Harris	9
23	26	FAT 3Q	A	Tonbridge Angels	288	D 0 - 0		
24	Dec 3	IP	H	Margate	161	W 3 - 1	West 2 Harris 7 Tuohy 67	8
25	6	FAT3Qr	H	Tonbridge Angels	130	W 3 - 0	Harris 16 Tuohy 56 Hayzelden 63	
26	10	IP	A	BillericayTown	458	W 3 - 1	Burns 62 West 69 Wotton 80	7
27	17	FAT 1	H	Gravesend & Northfleet	381	L 0 - 2		
28	26	IP	A	Fisher Athletic	138	W 2 - 1	Turnbull 51 West 82	8
29	Jan 2		H	Heybridge Swifts	179	L 0 - 4		10
30	14		A	Btraintree Town	504	L 0 - 1		10
31	21		H	Wealdstone	162	W 2 - 0	Batt 25 Turnbull 54	10
32	24		A	Hendon	134	D 0 - 0		10
33	28		A	Bromley	345	D 1 - 1	Batt 1	10
34	31		H	Redbridge	84	W 2 - 0	Batt 7 Harrison 18	10
35	Feb 4		A	Margate	491	L 1 - 2	Harrison 82	10
36	11		H	Hendon	148	W 3 - 0	Turnbull 42 Hazeldene 0 Harrison 84	10
37	14		H	Windsor & Eton	95	L 0 - 2		10
38	18		A	Hampton & Richmond B	228	L 0 - 2		10
39	Mar 4		A	Staines Town	114	L 0 - 2		10
40	11		A	Leyton	35	W 2 - 1	Burns 45 Edwards 51	12
41	18		A	Chelmsford City	757	W 4 - 2	Edwards 43 Burns 59 Mully 66 Grieves 83	10
42	25		H	Folkestone Invicta	151	L 0 - 2		11
43	28		H	Walton & Hersham	91	W 1 - 0	Harrison 15	10
44	April 1		A	Worthing	459	L 0 - 1		12
45	8		H	Maldon Town	107	D 1 - 1	Harrison 85	11
46	15		A	AFC Wmbledon	2706	L 2 - 3	Grieves 27 Ferns 28	11
47	17		H	Fisher Athletic	124	L 2 - 5	Burns 83 90	12
48	29		A	Redbridge	65	W 1 - 0	Greaves 64	12

Ave. League Home Attendance: 177   **Goals**   67   64   **Top Goalscorer:** West (10)
Best Position: 5th   **Worst:**   14th

FOLKESTONE INVICTA

Founded: 1936
Nickname: The Seasiders

Manager: Neil Cugley   **Assistant Manager:** Scott Lindsey **Physio:** Dave Williams
Club Colours: Amber & black stripes/black/amber
Change Colours: All blue
Club Sponsor: Buzzlines
Previous League: Southern Premier
BEST PERFORMANCES
League: 14th Ryman Premier   **F.A. Cup:** 1st Rd 2005-06
F.A.Trophy: 3rd Round (x3)
F.A.Vase 5th Rd 98
Ground Address: The Buzzlines Stadium, The New Pavilion, Cheriton Road, Folkestone, Kent CT19 5JU
Telephone & Fax: 01303 257461   **Official website:** www.folkestoneinvicta.co.uk
Capacity 6,500   **Seats:** 900   **Covered:** 3,500   **Floodlights:** Yes
Simple Directions: On the A20 behind Morisons Foodstore, midway between Folkestone Central and West B.R. stations.
Midweek Home Matchday: Monday
Clubhouse: Stripes Club & Invicta Club
Club Shop: Yes (01303 257266)
Local Press: Folkestone Herald
Local Radio: K.M.F.M. Invicta Radio & Radio Kent

CLUB PERSONNEL

Chairman: Bob Dix
President: Bill Hewson
Secretary: Neil Pilcher, 4 Sea View Close, Capel-le-Ferne. Folkestone, Kent CT18 7JW
Tel: 01303 245066
Commercial Manager:
Name (Tel)
Prog. Editor & Press Officer:
Richard Murril (07810864228)

2005-2006
Captain: Adam Flanagan
Player of the Year: Adam Flanagan
Top Goalscorer: Jimmy Dryden

CLUB STATISTICS

RECORD	**Attendance**: 2,332 v West Ham United (friendly) November 1996
	Ground record 7,881 v Margate . Kent Senior Cup 1958
	Victory: 13-0 v Faversham Town Kent League Division 1
	Defeat: 1-7 v Crockenhill Kent League Division 1
	Transfer Fee Paid: N/A
	Transfer Fee Received: N/A
SENIOR HONOURS:	Southern League, Eastern Divisdion R-Up
PREVIOUS	**Ground:** South Rd, Hythe (pre 1991) County Lg.matches on council pitches
	League: Kent County (pre 1991-92)

Back Row (L-R): Mark Patterson (Assistant Manager), Mick Dix (Reserve Team Manager), Simon Rainbow, Ben Sly, Joe Neilson, James Everitt, Gary Towse (Goalkeeping Coach) & Dave Williams (Physio).
Middle: Bill Hewson (President), William Webb (Stadium Manager), Dayne Southern, Rob Knott, Lee Shearer, Matt Carruthers, Kieron Mann, Tony Kessell, Liam Friend, Micheal Everitt, Martin Chandler, Neil Pilcher (Club Secretary), Roy Seidenbird (Kit Manager) & Brian. **Front:** Stuart Mayall, Steve Norman, Paul Lamb, Alan Flanagan (Club Captain), Neil Cugley (Manager), Mark Saunders (Player/Coach), Kevin Watson, Paul Jones & Walid Matata.

FOLKSTONE INVICTA

BEST LGE ATT.: 1,048 v AFC Wimbledon
LOWEST: **239** v Hendon

No.	Date	Comp	H/A	Opponents	Att:	Result	Goalscorers	Pos
1	Aug 20	IP	A	Wimbledon	3002	L 1 - 4	Jones 45	22
2	27		H	Leyton	286	D 2 - 2	Elpsewood 28 (og) Flanaghan 55	19
3	29		A	Bromley	409	D 3 - 3	**Dryden** 3 (22 32 53)	17
4	Sept 3		H	Heybridge Swifts	256	L 0 - 2		19
5	5		H	Worthing	241	L 1 - 2	Glover 84	21
6	**10**	**FAC 1Q**	**H**	**Egham Town**	**212**	**W 3 - 1**	**Guest 18 Glover 37 Dryden 88**	
7	17	IP	A	Hampton & Richmon B	292	L 1 - 3	Myall 50	21
8	19		A	Chelmsford City	286	W 1 - 0	Myall 82	
9	**24**	**FAC 2Q**	**A**	**St.Margaretsbury**	**212**	**W 1 - 0**	**M.Everitt 73**	
10	26	TP	H	Billericay Town	242	W 1 - 0	Glover 70	16
10	Oct 1	IP	A	Harrow Borough	147	L 0 - 5		16
11	3		H	East Thurrock United	251	W 1 - 0	**Dryden** 46	16
12	**8**	**FAC 3Q**	**H**	**Staines Town**	**337**	**W 2 - 0**	**Flanagan 22 Jones 45**	
13	11	IP	A	Walton & Hersham	173	W 3 - 0	Jones (2) **Dryden**	14
14	**15**	**FAT 1Q**	**H**	**Whyteleafe**	**165**	**D 1 - 1**	**Dryden 82**	
15	**17**	**FAT1Qr**	**A**	**Whyteleafe**	**103**	**W 2 - 1**	**Jones 5 Dryden 15**	
16	**22**	**FAC4Q**	**A**	**Aylesbury United**	**646**	**W 2 - 0**	**Dryden 17 81**	
17	25	IP	A	Worthing	408	L 0 - 1		16
18	29		A	Fisher Athletic	152	D 0 - 0		15
19	**Nov 5**	**FAC 1R**	**A**	**Chester City**	**2503**	**L 1 - 2**	**Flanagan 10**	
20	**12**	**FAT 2Q**	**H**	**Wealdstone**	**316**	**W 5 - 3**	**Myall 15 Dryden 23 77 Guest 38 Flanaghan 61**	
21	19	IP	A	Braintre Town	413	L 0 - 3		19
22	21		H	Chelmsford City	304	D 1 - 1	Jones 77	19
23	**26**	**FAT 3Q**	**A**	**Harlow Town**	**184**	**L 1 - 2**	**Norman 86**	
24	29	IP	H	Slough Town	263	W 3 - 0	**Dryden** 3 (18 66 69)	
25	Dec 3		A	Windsor & Eton	100	L 0 - 1		19
26	5		H	Hendon	239	L 1 - 2	**Dryden** 90	19
27	9		A	Wealdstone	251	W 2 - 1	**Dryden** 39 77	17
28	17		H	Staines Town	263	L 0 - 2		19
29	26		A	Margate	902	D 1 - 1	Matata 88	19
30	Jan 2		H	Bromley	369	W 1 - 0	Matata 12	16
32	7		H	AFC Wimbledon	1048	W 1 - 0	Myall 38	13
33	14		A	Billericay Town	513	L 0 - 2		16
34	21		H	Hampton & Richmond B	405	L 1 - 2	Saunders 32	16
35	28		A	Leyton	84	D 1 - 1	Matata 61	17
36	30		H	Maldon Town	248	W 2 - 0	Fraser 30 Matafa 40	14
37	Feb 4		H	Windsor & Eton	417	W 1 - 0	Watson 59 (pen)	12
38	11		A	Redbridge	93	W 2 - 0	Norman 26 36	11
39	18		H	Fisher Atrhletic	427	L 0 - 1		13
40	25		A	Hendon	157	D 0 - 0		14
41	27		H	Redbridge	274	W 1 - 0	Norman 74	11
42	Mar 4		A	Maldon Town	175	L 0 - 1		13
43	11		H	Braintree Town	370	D 0 - 0		13
44	18		H	Harrow Borough	346	W 2 - 1	Saunders 45 88	13
45	25		A	East Thurrock United	151	W 2 - 0	Saunders 45 Norman 53	12
46	April 1		H	Walton & Hersham	405	W 3 - 1	Watson 45 (pen) Saunders 58 Carruthers 70	12
47	8		A	Slough Town	289	L 0 - 2		12
48	14		A	Heybridge Swifts	312	L 0 - 2		12
49	17		H	Margate	574	D 1 - 1	Matata 90 ?	12
50	22		H	Wealdstone	384	W 5 - 2	Carruthers 3 Knott 27 38 J.Everett 36 Chandler 79	12
	29		A	Staines Town	226	D 2 - 2	Watson 68 (pen) Knott 72	13

Ave. League Home Attendance: 349   **Goals**   65   61   **Top Goalscorer:** Dryden (18)
Best Position: 11th   **Worst:** 22nd

HAMPTON & RICHMOND BOROUGH

Founded: 1921
Nickname: Beavers/Borough

Hampton & Richmond Borough FC

The Beveree Review
2003-2004 Season

Manager: Alan Devonshire　　　**Coach:** Mick House

Club Colours: Red & Blue/Red &Blue /Red

Change Colours: White/Red/ Blue

Club Sponsor: M.M.Cox Properties Ltd.

Previous Leagues: Athenian

Best Seasons: League: 5th Isthmian Premier 2005-2006

F.A. Cup: 1st Round 2000-01　**F.A.Trophy.:** 4th Round 2001-02

F.A.Vase: 3rd Round 1991-92　　　**F.A.Amateur Cup:** 1st Round Proper 73-74

Ground address: MEM Beveree Stadium, Beavor Close, off Station Road, Hampton TW12 2BX **Tel No:** 0208 9422838 (Matchdays) 0208 9792456 (Club)

Official website: www.hrbfc.co.uk

Capacity: 3,000　　　**Seats:** 300　　　Covered: 800　　　**Floodlights:**Yes

Simple Directions: From Hampton Court Bridge onto A 308, after a mile right into Church St (A3110) and left after White Hart pub into High St. Station Rd is on right.

Midweek Home Matchday: Tuesday

Clubhouse: Matchdays & training nights. Function hall for hire.(0208 9792456)

Club Shop: Yes. Contact Adrian Mann (0208 7730858)

Local Press: Middlesex Chronicle,Surrey Comet, Richmond & Twickenham Times and The Informer.

CLUB PERSONNEL

Chairman: David Cole
President: Alan Simpson OBE
Club Secretary:
Nick Hornsey, C/o club
Tel NO: 0776 8861446 (M)
Football Secretary:
Adrian Mann
0208 773 0858
Press Officer: Les Rance
Programme.Editor: Stefan Rance

2005-2006
Captain: Dean Wells
Player of the Year: Dean Wells
Top Goalscorer: Yaku 20

CLUB STATISTICS

Record	**Attendance** : 2,500 v AFC Wimbledon	
	Victory:	11-1 v Eastbourne United , Isthmian Div 2 (S) 91--92
	Defeat:	0-13 v Hounslow Town Middx Sen Cup 62-3
Career Goalscorer:		Peter Allen 176 1964-73
Career Appearances:		Tim Hollands 750 1977-95
Record Transfer Fee	**Paid:**	£3,000 to Chesham United for Matt Flitter June 2000
	Received:	£40,000 from Q.P.R. for Leroy Phillips
Senior Honours:		London Senior Cup (2) Spartan Lg (4), Midd. Senior Cup R-up (4),
		Isthmian promotion from Div. 1 1997-98
Previous Leagues:		Kingston & Dist., S.W. Middx, Surrey Senior 59-64, Spartan 64-71 & Athenian

Back row, left to right: Tom Crossland, Graham Harper, Dean Wells, Orlando Jeffrey, Alan Inns, Kieron Drake, Luke Fontana, Marcello Fernandes and Abby Nsubuga. Front row: Elliott Godfrey, Dudley Gardner, Matt Elverson, Andy Morley, Ryan Ashe and Obinna Vlasi. Mascots Bradley Rance and Ryan Downes.

HAMPTON & RICHMOND BORO'

BEST LGE ATT.: 2,520 v AFC Wimbledon
LOWEST: 203 v Bromley

No.	Date	Comp	H/A	Opponents	Att:	Result	Goalscorers	Pos
1	Aug 20	IP	H	Walton & Hersham	291	W 2 - 0	Yaku 65 Fontana 85	4
2	23		A	Harrow Borough	165	W 2 - 0	Godfrey 27 Paris 32	2
3	27		A	Hendon	261	W 2 - 0	McGrath 12 (og) Elverson 31	3
4	29		H	Slough Town	303	W 3 - 2	Morley 2 Godfrey 8 Yaku 21	1
5	Sept 3		A	Redbridge	60	W 2 - 0	Quarm 15 Harris 25	1
6	6		H	Wealdstone	373	W 3 - 0	Paris 17 Godfrey 33 Quarm 48	1
7	**10**	**FAC 1Q**	**H**	**Witham Town**	**226**	**W 3 - 0**	**Paris 16 Yaku 26 41**	
8	17	IP	H	Folkstone Invicta	292	W 3 - 1	Harper 68 Henry-Hayden 85 Fontana 90	1
9	19		A	Fisher Athletic	234	L 3 - 4	Yaku 12 McIntosh 54 Gardner 81	2
10	**24**	**FAC 2Q**	**H**	**Leatherhead**	**357**	**D 1 - 1**	**Fontana 2**	
11	**27**	**FAC 2Qr**	**A**	**Leatherhead**	**273**	**L 1 - 2**	**Harper 54**	
12	Oct 1	IP	H	Leyton	222	W 4 - 2	Godfrey 20 (pen) Wells 78 Boosey 79 Fontana 85	1
13	4		A	Braintree Town	422	L 1 - 2	Fontana	1
14	11		H	AFC Wimbledon	2520	W 2 - 1	Paris 49 Godfrey 65	1
15	**15**	**FAT 1Q**	**H**	**Newport (IOW)**	**293**	**L 0 - 2**		
16	22	IP	H	Hendon	287	W 3 - 1	Sodje 21 Yaku 61 80	
17	25		A	Wealdstone	253	W 2 - 1	Yaku 28 49	1
18	29		A	East Thurrock	158	W 2 - 1	Godfrey 28 Yaku 84	
19	Nov 5		H	Windsor & Eton	308	W 4 - 0	Elverson 24 Godfrey 75 Morley 80 Henry-Hayden 85	1
20	19		A	Worthing	640	L 1 - 2	Yaku 27	1
21	22		H	Fisher Athletic	376	L 0 - 3		1
22	26		A	Margate	505	L 2 - 3	Yaku 42 Godfrey 71 (pen)	1
23	Dec 3		A	Chelmsford City	392	D 3 - 3	Yuku 15 Inns 53 Morley 62	
24	6		H	Bromley	203	D 0 - 0		1
25	10		A	Malden Town	140	W 2 - 1	Yaku 2 Inns 4	1
26	17		H	Billericay Town	302	L 0 - 1		2
27	26		H	Staines Town	463	W 2 - 1	Godfrey Inns	1
28	Jan 2		A	Slough Town	448	W 1 - 0	Godfrey 63 (pen)	1
29	7		A	Walton & Hersham	301	L 0 - 2		2
30	14		H	Harrow Borough	291	L 1 - 3	Fernandes 44	3
31	21		H	Folkstone Invicta	405	W 2 - 1	Olayinka 39 Wells 55	
32	Feb 4		H	Chelmsford Cioty	357	W 3 - 0	Yaku 3 90 Olayinka 18	3
33	11		A	Heybridge SWifts	237	L 1 - 2	Fernandes 84	3
34	19		H	East Thurrock U	228	W 1 - 0	Quarm 54 (pen)	3
35	25		A	Bromley	312	A 0 - 2		4
36	Mar 4		A	Windsor & Eton	169	W 3 - 1	Lake 48 Inns 58 Paris 78	3
37	11		H	Worthing	291	L 1 - 2	Yaku 18	4
38	18		A	Leyton	56	D 1 - 1	Godfrey 19	3
39	25		H	Braintree Town	430	L 0 - 1		6
40	April 1		A	AFC Wimbledon	3315	W 4 - 0	Yaku 23 Quarm 34 Godfrey 48 Lake 55	4
41	4		H	Heybridge Swifts	303	L 0 - 5		5
42	8		H	Margate	320	L 0 - 1		6
43	11		A	Staines	588	W 1 - 0	Godfrey 70	5
44	15		H	Redbriudge	273	W 3 - 1	Yaku 17 Elvirson 44 Quarm 52 (pen)	4
45	22		H	Maldon Town	295	L 1 - 2	Quarm 72 (pen)	5
46	29		A	Billericay Town	1020	W 2 - 1	Matthews 77 Henry-Hayden 85	5
47	**May 1**	**Play Off SF**	**A**	**Heybridge Swifts**	**589**	**D 1 - 1**	Yaku 68　　Won 4-2 after penalties	
48	**6**	**Play Off Final**	**A**	**Fisher Athletic**	**900**	**L 0 - 3**		

Ave. League Home Attendance: 416 　　**Goals** 79 63 　**Top Goalscorer:** Yaku (19)
Best Position: 1st 　**Worst:** 6th

HARROW BOROUGH

Founded: 1933
Nickname: Boro

Manager: David Howell   **Assistant Manager:** Ken Charlery
Club Colours: Red with white trim/red/red+white hoops
Change Colours: White/white/navy blue
Club Sponsor: T.B.A.
Previous League: Athenian
BEST PERFORMANCES
League: Champions 1983-1984   **F.A. Cup:** 2nd Rd 83-84 v Newport Co 1-3
F.A.Trophy.: Semi-Final 1982-83
Physio: Jenny Mullen
Ground Address: Earlsmead, Carlyon Avenue,South Harrow, Middl'x HA2 8SS
Telephone: 0870 6091959 Fax: 0208 4230159
Official website: www.harrowboro.com
CAPACITY: 3,070   **Seats:** 350   **Covered:** 1,000   **Floodlights:** Yes
SIMPLE DIRECTIONS: Underground to Northolt Central and140 bus to Northolt Park
BR or South Harrow (Piccadilly Line) then 114 or H10 to King Rd junction. By road
leave A40 at MacDonalds roundabout towards Northolt station (A312 north) left at
lights right at Eastcote Arms pub. Ground 5th turning on right.
Midweek Home Matchday: Tuesday
Clubhouse: Open daily normal pub hours.
Club Shop: Yes contact c/o club
Local Press: Harrow Observer & Harrow Times
Local Radio:

CLUB PERSONNEL

Chairman: Peter Rogers
President: Jim Ripley
Secretary: Peter Rogers,
21 Ludlow Close,South Harrow,
Middlesex HA2 8SR
Tel : 0208 248 8003 (H)
    0208 4230157 (W)
Commercial Manager:
Bill Duffy c/o Club
Press Officer &
Programme Editor:
Paul Carter (07971 848385)
paul@harrowboro.com
(Prog 40pages £2,00)
2005-2006
Captain: Watne Walters
Player of the Year: Wayne Walters
Top Goalscorer: Elliot Onochie 20

CLUB STATISTICS

RECORD	
Attendance:	3,000 v Wealdstone F.A.C.1st Qualifying Round 1946
Victory:	13-0 v Handley Page (A) 18.10.41
Defeat:	0-8 on five occasions
Career Goalscorer:	Dave Pearce 153
Career Appearances:	Steve Emmanuel 522 Colin Payne 557 Les Currell 582

SENIOR HONOURS: Isthmian Champions 1983-84 Athenian Div 2 R-Up 63-64 Middx Sen Cup 82-83 92-93 Middx Premier Cup 81-82 Middx Sen. Charity Cup 79-80 92-93 05-06

PREVIOUS   **Names:** Roxonian 1933-38 Harrow Town 38-66
Leagues: Harrow & District 1933-34 Spartan 34-40 45-58 W.Middx Comb 40-1
Middlesex SeniorCU. 41-45 Delphian 56-63 Athenian 63-75

Back Row: (L-R): Danny Norris, Leon Morris, Jonathan Constant, Junior Adeoye, Gary Ross, Keita Karamoko, Craig Nicholson, Kieran Jimmy, Danny McGonigle, Elliot Onochie, Dean Marney. **Middle:** Mick Martin (Kit Manager)
Stuart Crawford (Asst Reserve Team Coach) Kwasi Frempong, Nico Coleman, Mobi Oparku, Bradley Brown, Adam Gotting, Dean Sylvester, Kevin Wynter, Rob Sterry, Kai Williams, Mark Henry, Rob Parillon,Rickey Brown,
Peter Grant (Reserve Team Coach). **Front:** Martin Grant, Rickey Roberts, Lee White, Albert Adomah, Danny Leech, Dave Howell (Manager) Wayne Walters, Daniel Nielsen, Gary Meakin, James Bent,Aaron Ferdinand. Photo by Stuart Emmerson.

HARROW BOROUGH

BEST LGE ATT.: 611 v AFC Wimbledon
LOWEST: 94 v Maldon Town

No.	Date	Comp	H/A	Opponents	Att:	Result	Goalscorers	Pos
1	Aug 20	IP	A	Heybridge Swifts	185	L 1 - 2	Onochie 17	14
2	23		H	Hampton & Richmond B	165	L 0 - 2		20
3	27		H	Margate	212	D 0 - 0		19
4	29		A	Leyton	178	W 1 - 0	Onochie 87	14
5	Sept 3		H	Billericay Town	144	D 1 - 1	Asonbang 5	15
6	6		H	East Thurrock	130	W 5 - 4	Bent 2 Le Roux 6 27 Lamb 62 Asonbang 75 (pen)	12
7	10	FAC 1Q	A	East Thurrock	96	W 2 - 1	Asombang 6 Onochie 75	
8	17	IP	A	Fisher Athletic	134	L 1 - 4	Fitzimmons 48	15
9	20		A	Maldon Town	186	W 4 - 1	Fitzsimmons 6 Bent 55 Onochie 65 85	10
10	24	FAC 2Q	H	Burnham Ramblers	140	W 2 - 1	Onochie 45 90	
11	Oct 1	IP	H	Folkestone Invicta	147	W 5 0 0	Asombang 42 Bent 45 Constant 3(49 55 81)	9
12	4		A	Staines Town	343	W 1 - 0	Asombang	7
13	8	FAC 3Q	H	Welling United	258	L 0 - 1		
14	22	IP	H	Redbridge	163	D 0 - 0		10
15	25		A	East Thurrock	125	L 2 - 3	Onochie 32 Newtown 73	12
16	29		A	Chelmsford City	418	L 0 - 3		12
17	Nov 5		H	Worthing	185	D 2 - 2	Asombang 45 56	12
18	12	FAT 2Q	H	Met Police	126	W 4 - 2	Le Roux 18 Haule 68 Onochie 90 Leech 90	
19	19	IP	A	Hendon	210	L 1 - 2	Le Roux 18	13
20	22		H	Maldon Town	94	D 1 - 1	Asombang 76	12
21	26	FAT 3Q	A	Redbridge	94	D 1 - 1	Le Roux 85	
22	29	FAT 3Qr	H	Redbridge	101	L 2 - 3*	Fitzimmons 37 Le Roux 42	
23	Dec 3	IP	A	Walton & Hersham	160	L 1 - 3	Haule 90	17
24	6		H	Braintree Town	111	W 1 - 0	Dyer 90	15
25	10		A	Slough Town	333	L 2 - 5	Onochie 49 84	15
26	26		A	Wealdstone	469	L 1 - 4	McGonicle 3	17
27	Jan 2		H	Leyton	144	D 3 - 3	Bent 16 64 Leech 81	18
28	7		H	Heybridge Swifts	140	L 1 - 2	Onochie 80	18
29	14		A	Hampton & Richmond B	291	W 3 - 1	Haule 26 McConigle 37 Harper 57 (og)	
30	21		H	Fisher Athletic	150	L 0 - 2		17
31	24		H	Bromley	113	W 2 - 0	Bent 51 Onochie 90	16
32	28		A	Margate	535	D 0 - 0		17
33	Feb 4		H	Walton & Hersham	158	L 1 - 2	Le Roux 47	17
34	11		A	Bromley	321	D 1 - 1	Leech 90	18
35	18		H	Chelmsford City	193	W 2 - 1	Leech 41 82	17
36	25		A	Redbridge	53	W 1 - 0	Bent 13	17
37	Mar 11		H	Hendon	190	D 1 - 1	Walters 12	16
38	14		A	Windsor & Eton	85	W 1 - 0	Asombang 65	14
39	18		H	Folkestone IUnvicta	346	L 1 - 2	Haule 34	16
40	21		H	AFC Wimbledon	611	L 1 - 2	Haule 71	16
41	25		H	Staines Town	137	L 1 - 4	Nuefille 75	16
42	28		A	Worthing	227	L 0 - 3		16
43	April 1		A	Braintree Town	510	L 0 - 3		16
44	8		H	Windsor & Eton	141	W 2 - 1	Haule 26 (pen) Dogbe 43	16
45	14		A	Billericay Town	422	L 1 - 3	Onochie 87	16
46	18		H	Wealdstone	547	L 1 - 2	Haule 17 (pen)	16
47	22		H	Slough Town	220	W 2 - 1	Onochie 34 (pen) Leech 45	14
48	29		A	AFC Wimbledon	3044	L 1 - 2	Newton 48	16

Ave. League Home Attendance: 195　　**Goals** 67 79　**Top Goalscorer:** Onochie (15)
Best Position: 7th　**Worst:** 20th

HENDON

Manager: Gary McCann
Assistant Manager: Freddie Hyatt   **Player/Coach:** Iain Duncan
Club Colours: Green/white/white
Change Colours: White/Green/Green
Club Sponsor: UK Packaging
Previous League: Athenian
BEST PERFORMANCES
League: Champions 64-5 72-3   **F.A. Cup:** 3rd Round Replay 1973-74
F.A.Trophy.: 5th Rd 98-99
Medical and Fitness Consultant: Gary Anderson
Reserve League: Capital Football League
Ground address: Claremont Road, Brent Cross, London NW2 1AE
Tel: 0208 2019494 **Fax:** 0208 9055966
Official website: www.hendonfc.net
Capacity: 3,029   **Seats:** 329 **Covered:** 601
Floodlights: Yes **Simple Directions:** From Brent Cross station (Northern Line) to the east take first left after flyover on North Circular-Claremont Road is then left at 4th mini roundabout. Buses 102, 210 226 and C11pass ground.
Midweek Home Matchday: Monday
Clubhouse (0208 4559185): Two banqueting suites and conference centre for hire. Restaurant and bars open normal licensing hours every day
Club Shop:
Local Press: Hendon Times,Willesden & Highgate Express
Local Radio: Capital, GLR LBC.

CLUB PERSONNEL
Chairman: T.B.A.
Secretary: Graham Etchell, c/o Hendon FC 02082 019494
Marketing Manager: T.B.A.,
Press Officer: David Balheimer
Programme. Editor: Club Secretary
Programme Prog 40 pages 1.50
Club Shop Manager: Chris Rogers
2005-2006:
Captain: Mark Cooper
Player of the Year: James Parker
Top Goalscorer John Frendo

CLUB STATISTICS

RECORD	
Attendance:	9,000 v Northampton Town F.A.Cup 1st Rd 1952
Victory:	13-1 v Wingate Middlessex County Cup 2.2.57
Defeat:	2-11 v Walthamstowe Avenue. Athenian League 9.11.35
Career Goalscorer:	Freddie Evans 176 (1929-35)
Career Appearances:	Bill Fisher 787 (1940-1964)
Senior Honours:	European Amateur Champions 1972-73. F.A.Amateur Cup Winners 59-60 64-65 71-72 R-up 54-5 65-6 Isthmian League 64-5 72-3 Premier Inter League Cup R-up 86-7Athenian Lg (3)London Senior Cup 63-4 68-9 Middx Sen Cup (14)
Previous Names:	Christ Church Hampstead to 1908 Hampstead Town to 1933 Golders Green to 1946 Leagues:Finchley & District 08-11 Middlesex League 1910-11 London League 1911-14 Athenian 14-63

BackRow (L-R): Richard Wilmot, Dwane Williams, Dean Thomas, Craig Vargas, Rakatahr Hudson, Ryan Wharton, Nas Richardson, Lee O'Leary, Adilson Lopes, Ricky Pattenden, Anthony O'Connor.
Middle: Josh Hunte, Danny Edwards, Gary McCann (manager), James Burgess, Freddie Hyatt (assistant manager), Rene Street, Leon Maloney.
Front: Takumi Ake, Francois Gabbidon, Jamie Busby, Hussain Karas, Greg Deacon, Wayne O'Sullivan, Franklyn Morris.

HENDON

BEST LGE ATT.: 1,444 v AFC Wimbledon
LOWEST: **120** v Redbridge

No.	Date	Comp	H/A	Opponents	Att:	Result	Goalscorers	Pos
1	Aug 20	IP	A	Braintree Town	317	L 0 - 1		16
2	23		H	Fisher Athletic	216	L 1 - 2	**Frendo** 21	17
3	27		H	Hampton & Richmond B	167	L 0 - 2		21
4	31		A	Wealdstone	412	W 5 - 4	Aiteouakrim 11 Ofori 45 80 **Frendo** 65 Murphy 82	16
5	Sept 3		H	Bromley	179	W 2 - 1	Julienne18 **Frendo** 29	13
6	6		A	Walton & Hersham	192	L 0 - 1		16
7	10	FAC1Q	H	**Biggleswade United**	116	W 6 - 0	Frendo 3 (28 39 73) Pickett 56 Nabil 66 M.Burgess 68	
8	17	IP	A	Heybridge Swifts	188	L 0 - 3		16
9	20		H	Staines Town	141	L 1 - 2	Street 90	
10	24	FAC 2Q	H	**Metropolitan Police**	155	D 0 - 0		
11	27	FAC 2Qr	A	**Metropolitan Police**	104	L 0 - 1		
12	Oct 1	IP	H	Worthing	191	D 2 - 2	Street 38 Pickett 87	16
13	4		A	Windsor & Eton	135	L 1 - 2	Crace 33	17
14	11		H	Maldon Town	151	D 1 - 1	Campbell 80	18
15	15	FAT1Q	A	**Fisher Athletic**	189	L 2 - 4	Cook 11 **Frendo** 75	
16	22	IP	A	Hampton & Richmond B	287	L 1 - 3	**Frendo** 70	19
17	25		H	Walton & Hersham	180	D 1 - 1	Pickett 69 (pen)	19
18	19		H	Billericay Town	248	D 2 - 2	Froud 80 (pen) Hunt 89	
19	Nov 5		A	Slough Town	291	W 2 0 0	Crace 16 Hunt 50	19
20	19		H	Harrow Borough	210	W 2 - 1	Crace 43 Cooper 67	17
21	22		A	Staines Town	401	L 0 - 2		18
22	Dec 3		A	Redbridge	94	W 2 - 0	Hudell 30 Crace 75	18
23	5		A	Folkestone Invicta	239	W 2 - 1	O'Brien 33 Crace 65	14
24	10		A	AFC Wimbledon	2693	L 1 - 2	O'Brien 54	16
25	17		H	Margate	221	L 1 - 2	Hudell 48	17
26	26		A	Leyton	128	L 0 - 2		18
27	Jan 2		H	Wealdstone	380	L 0 - 3		19
28	7		H	Braintree Town	140	L 1 - 2	O'Brien 17	19
29	14		A	Fisher Athletic	170	W 1 - 0	Cook 66	19
30	21		H	Heybridge Swifts	202	L 0 - 1		19
31	24		A	East Thurock United	134	D 0 - 0		19
32	Feb 4		H	Redbridge	120	W 2 - 0	Watson 38 Cooper 47	19
33	11		A	East Thurrock	148	L 0 - 3		19
34	18		H	Billericay Town	447	L 0 - 1		19
35	25		H	Folkestone Invicta	157	D 0 - 0		19
36	Mar 4		H	Slough Town	241	D 1 - 1	Hunt 69	19
37	8		A	Chelmdford City	502	L 0 - 3		19
38	11		A	Harrowe Borough	190	D 1 - 1	Mapes 80	19
39	18		A	worthing	394	D 1 - 1	Cable 21 (og)	19
40	25		H	Windsor & Eton	235	L 1 - 2	O.Brien 25 (pen)	19
41	April 1		A	Maldon Town	107	D 2 - 2	O'Brien 69 Pickett 84	19
42	8		H	Chelmsford City	265	D 0 - 0		19
43	15		A	Bromley	272	L 1 - 3	Pickett 37	19
44	17		H	Leyton	195	W 4 - 0	Campbell Hunt Cook Pickett	19
45	22		H	AFC Wimbledon	1444	L 0 - 1		19
46	29		A	Margate	701	L 2 - 4	Busby 8 Crace 38	19

Ave. League Home Attendance: 249   **Goals** 52 70   **Top Goalscorer:** Frendo (8)
Best Position: 13th   **Worst:** 21st

HEYBRIDGE SWIFTS

Founded: 1880
Nickname: Swifts

Manager: Brian Stathem   **Assistant Manager**: Barry Lakin

Sports Therapist: Steve Spencer

Club Colours: Black & white stripes/black/black

Change Colours: All red or amber & white

Club Sponsor: Michael Ward Associates

Previous League: Essex Senior

Best Seasons: League: Isthmian Premier Runners-Up **F.A.Cup**:1st Round 94-95

F.A.Trophy.: Quarter Final v Woking 1996-97   **F.A. Vase:** 5th Round1986-1987

Ground address: Scraley Road, Heybridge, Maldon, Essex CM9 8JA

Tel No: 01621 852978

Club Website: www.heybridgeswifts.com

Capacity: 3,000   **Seats:** 550   **Covered:** 1,200   **Floodlights:** Yes

Simple Directions: Leave Maldon on the main road to Colchester, pass through Heybridge then turn right at sign to Tolleshunt Major (Scraley Road). The ground is on the right.

Midweek Home Matchday: Tuesday

Clubhouse: Two bars open every evening

Club Shop: Open matchdays.

CLUB PERSONNEL

Chairman: Andrew Barber
V-Chairman: Michael Gibson
President:
Secretary: Liz Creasey c/o club
Tel No: 0794 173 3439 (M)
Prog.Editors:
Tony Foster & MK Publications
Press Officer: Tony Foster
07931 330756 (M)01621 858171(H)

2005-2006
Captain: Ian Cousins
Player of the Year: Ian Wiles
Top Goalscorer: Cliff Akurang

CLUB STATISTICS

Record	**Attendance**: 2,477 v Woking F.A.Trophy 1997
Career Goalscorer:	Julian Lamb 115 (post war) Dave Matthews 112 (Isthmian)
Career Appearances:	Hec Askew 500+ John Pollard 496
Record Transfer Fee	**Paid:** £1,000 for Dave Rainford and for Lee kersey
	Received: £35,000 from Southend United for Simon Royce
Senior Honours:	Isthmian Div 1 R-Up 95-96 Div 2 North 89-90 Essex Senior Lg (3)
	E.Anglian Cup 93-94 94-95 Essex Junior Cup 31-32
Previous Leaguess:	Essex & Suffolk Border , North Essex, South Essex & Essex Senior 1971-84

Back Row (L-R): Steve Spencer (sports therapist), Ross Statham (kit man), Gavin Bensley, Erdem Artun, Paul O'Donoghue, Sean Marks, Ian Cousins, Ian Wiles, Danny Hill, Pat Alexander (physio).
Front: Cliff Akurang, Dean Bradshaw, Paul Abbott, Danny Barber, Barry Lakin (assistant manager), Brian Statham (manager), Kris Lee, Simon Glover, Adam Gillespie, Mike Shinn.

HEYBRIDGE SWIFTS

BEST LGE ATT.: 816 v AFC Wimbledon
LOWEST: 141 v Margate

No.	Date	Comp	H/A	Opponents	Att:	Result	Goalscorers	Pos
1	Aug 20	IP	H	Harrow Borough	185	W 2 - 1	O'Donoghue 24 Abbott 72	6
2	22		A	Chelmsford City	515	W 2 - 0	**Akurang** 66 89	5
3	27		A	Walton & Hersham	126	L 1 - 2	**Akurang** 37	6
4	29		H	East Thurrock	188	L 0 - 1		10
5	Sept 3		A	Folkestone Invicta	256	W 2 - 0	**Akurang** 4 Nichols 90 (pen)	7
6	6		H	Braintree Town	326	L 0 - 3		10
7	10	FAC 1Q	H	**Arlesey Town**	169	**W 1 - 0**	**Artun 72**	
8	17	IP	H	Hendon	188	W 3 - 0	**Akurang** 26 64 Marks 59	8
9	20		A	Wealdstone	227	W 4 - 3	**Akurang** 3 (10 51 90) Lee 81	6
10	24	FAC 2Q	A	**Wivenhoe Town**	241	**W 4 - 1**	**Janney 15 Shinn 33 Lee 88 Gillespie 90**	
11	Oct 1	IP	H	AFC Wimbledon	816	D 1 - 1	**Akurang** 57	8
12	3		A	Fisher Athletic	184	L 0 - 2		11
13	8	FAC 3Q	H	**Braintree Town**	360	**D 1 - 1**	**Lee 29**	
14	11	FAC 3Q	A	**Braintree Town**	479	**L 1 - 3**	**Lee 70**	
15	15	FAT 1Q	H	**Walton & Hersham**	202	**W 3 - 0**	**Glover 6 Hill 16 Bradshaw 89**	
16	22	IP	H	Windsor & Eton	199	W 2 - 0	Hill 14 **Akurang** 40	8
17	25		A	Braintree Town	487	L 0 - 3		11
18	29		A	Worthing	451	L 1 - 4	**Akurang** 46	11
19	Nov 5		H	Bromley	213	W 1 - 0	Lee 32	10
20	12	FAT 2Q	H	**Billericay Town**	326	**W 2 - 0**	**Lee 6 64**	
21	19	IP	A	Redbridge	75	W 2 - 1	Tedder 23 (og) Perkins 76 (og)	
22	22		H	Wealdstone	143	L 1 - 3	Lee 49	10
23	26	FAT 3Q	H	**St Albans City**	253	**L 0 - 1**		
24	Dec 3	IP	H	Billericay Town	281	D 0 - 0		10
25	6		H	Margate	141	W 2 - 0	Marks 57 Artun 80	9
26	10		A	Staines Town	173	L 1 - 5	Marks 47	9
27	17		H	Slough Town	201	W 1 - 0	Marks 15	10
28	26		H	Maldon Town	529	W 2 - 0	Marks 38 Shinn 42	10
29	Jan 2		A	East Thurrock United	179	W 4 - 0	Shinn 7 Gillespie 57 Francis 80 90	8
30	7		A	Harrow Borough	140	W 2 - 1	Marks 32 Glover 54	7
31	14		H	Chelmsford City	604	W 2 - 0	**Akurang** 20 (pen) 80 (pen)	7
32	21		H	Hendon	202	W 1 - 0	Marks 4	6
33	Feb 4		A	Billericay Town	540	W 2 - 1	Wiles 67 Francis 90	6
34	11		H	Hampton & Richmond	237	W 2 - 1	Jolly 53 Glover 75	5
35	18		H	Worthing	246	D 1 - 1	Jolly 51 (pen)	5
36	21		A	Leyton	59	W 1 - 0	Jolly 41	4
37	25		A	Windsor & Eton	122	W 4 - 3	Glover 49 Marks 58 Artun 83 Jolly 90	3
38	Mar 4		A	Bromley	322	L 1 - 2	Glover 73	4
39	11		H	Redbridge	264	W 2 - 0	Jolly 34 Francis 82	3
40	18		A	AFC Wimbledion	2455	L 0 - 1		4
41	21		H	Walton & Hersham	175	W 2 - 1	Jolly 3 Keevill 49	3
42	25		H	Fisher Athletic	269	L 1 - 2	N.Cousins 90	3
43	April 1		A	Margate	557	W 2 - 1	Holdsworth 67 69 (pen)	3
44	4		A	Hampton & Richmond B	303	W 5 - 0	Jolly 28 43 Francis 68 Holdsworth 77 87	3
45	8		H	Leytpon	260	W 1 - 0	Wiles 90	3
46	14		H	Folkestone Invicta	312	W 2 - 0	Shinn 34 Jolly 75	3
47	17		A	Maldon Town	360	W 1 - 0	Holdsorth 35	3
48	22		H	Staines Town	227	W 4 - 2	N.Cousins 1 61 Jolly 22 Francis 90	3
49	29		A	Slough Town	274	W 2 - 1	Abbott 41 Jolly 88	2
50	May 1	Play Off SF	H	Hampton & Richmond B	589	D 1 - 1	Jolly 44	

Ave. League Home Attendance: 286   **Goals** 83 53   **Top Goalscorer:** Akurang (14)
Best Position: 2nd   **Worst:** 11th

HORSHAM

Manager: John Maggs **Asst.Man./Coach:**Tom Warrilow **Physio:** Geoff Brittain
Club Colours: Amber & Lincoln Green
Change Colours: Maroon & Lincoln Green
Club Sponsor: Sunley Homes
Previous League: Athenian
Best Seasons: League: Runners-Up Isthmian Division One 2005-2006
F.A. Cup: 1st Round 1947-1948 1966-1967 **F.A.Vase** 4th Round Replay 1985-86
F.A.Trophy.: 1st Round Replay 1976-1977
Ground address: Atspeed Stadium, Queen Street, Horsham, Sussex RH13 5AD
Tel NO: 01403 52310
Club Website: www.horshamfc.co.uk
Capacity: 2,500 **Seats**: 300 **Covered**:1,100 **Floodlights**: Yes
Simple Directions:
From the station turn left into North Street. Pass the Arts Centre to lights and turn left. At lights (200 yards) turn left again into East Street. East St. becomes Queen Street after the Iron Bridge and the ground lies opposite Queens Head pub.

Midweek Home Matchday: Tuesday
Clubhouse: Matchdays only. Hot and cold food and dance hall facilities.
Club Shop: Yes.
Local Radio: BBC Southern Counties Radio and Radio Mercury
Local Press: West Sussex County Times

CLUB PERSONNEL
Chairman & President:
Frank King

Secretary & Pres Officer:
Jeff Barrett, 3 Bunting Close,
Horsham, West Sussex RH13 5PA
Tel No: 01403 267730

Programme
Editor: Jeff Barrett
80 Page £1.50
2006-2007
Captain: Eddie French
Player of the Year:
Mark Hawthorne
Top Goalscorer: Jamie Taylor 28

CLUB STATISTICS	
Record	**Attendance:** 8,000 v Swindon F.A.Cip 1st Round November 1966
	Career Goalscorer: Mick Browning
	Career Appearances: Mark Stepney
Record	**Victory:** 16-1 v Southwick Sussex Co. League 1945-1946
	Defeat: 1-11 v Worthing ,Sussex Senioe Cup 1913-1914:
Senior Honours:	Athenian League Div 1 72-73 Isthmian Div 1 R-Up 2005-06
	Sussex Senior Cup (7)
Previous	**Leagues:** W Sussex Sen; Sussex County 26-51; Metropolitan 51-57;
	Corinthian 57-63; Athenian 63-73
	Grounds: Horsham Park, Hurst Park, Springfield Park

Back Row (L-R): Tom Graves, Andy Howard, Eddie French (Captain), Andy Walker and Owen Botting.
Midle Row: Darren Etheridge (Kit Man), Carl Rook, Alan Mansfield, Lewis Taylor, Gareth Williams, Nigel Brake, and Geoff Britain (Sports Injury Specialist). Front row: Rob Frankland (Goalkeeping Coach), John Westcott, Ian Payne, Jamie Taylor, John Maggs (Manager), Matt Geard, Lee Carney, Gary Charman, and Tom Warrilow (Assistant Manager).

STEP 1
CONFERENCE

STEP 2
CONFERENCE NORTH/SOUTH

STEP 3
ISTHMIAN LEAGUE PREMIER

STEP 4
ISTHMIAN LEAGUE DIV 1

STEP 5/6

STEP 7

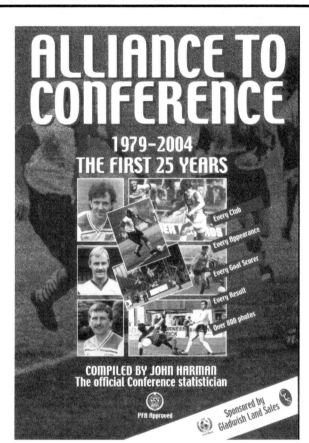

LEYTON

Founded: 1868
Nickname: Lilywhites

Manager: Costas Sophocleous   **Assistant Manager:** Stuart Hibberd

Coach: Alan Payne   **Physio:** Simon Purton

Club Colours: White/blue/white

Change Colours: Blue/white/blue

Club Sponsor:

Previous League: Essex Senior

Best Seasons: League: 5th Isthmian Premier & Play offs   **F.A.Cup:** 1st Rd 84-85

F.A.Trophy.:   **F.A.Amateur Cup:** Winners 26-27 27-28

F.A. Vase: 2nd Round 2002-2003   (as Leyton Wingate 6th Rd 1983-84)

Ground address: Leyton Stadium, 282 Lea Bridge Road, Leyton, E10 7LD

Tel No: 0208 539 5405

e-mail: enquiries@leytonfc.co.uk

Capacity: 2,500   **Seats:** Yes   **Covered:** Yes   **Floodlights:** Yes

Simple Directions: Lea Bridge Road is the A 104 and ground is next to Hare & Hounds pub.. Leyton (Central Line) then bus 58 or158 to Lea Bridge Rd.

Midweek Home Matchday: Tuesday

Clubhouse:.Open every evening and week ends at lunchtinme

Club Shop: Yes Contact: Tony Hampford 020 8539 5405

CLUB PERSONNEL

Chairman: Costas Sophocleous
Hon Life President: Doug Digby
Secretary:
Tony Hampford, 282 Lea Bridge Rd.,
Leyton, London E10 7LD
Press Officer: Steve Bellanoff
Tel No: 0778 8421172 (M)
Programme Editor:
Alan McPherson

CLUB STATISTICS

Record	Attendance:
	Career Goalscorer:
	Career Appearances:
	Victory:
	Defeat:
	Transfer Fee Paid:
	Transfer Fee Received:

Senior Honours: F.A.Amateur Cup Winners 1926-27 27-28 and Runners Up 1951-52 when 100,000 watched their Final with Walthamstow Avenue at Wembley

Previous Leagues: Essex Intermediate, Essex Senior and London Spartan.

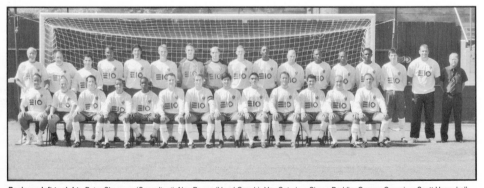

Back row left to right: Peter Shreeves (Consultant) Alan Payne (Head Coach), Vas Soteriou, Simon Peddie, George Georgiou, Scott Honeyball, James Hasell, James Courtnage, Scott Curley, Chris Bangura, Danny Jones, Des Thomas, Trevor Paul, Victor Renner, Paul Golby, Stuart Hibberd (Asst. First Team Manager), Rowly Cray (Director of Football).

Front row left to right: Lee Taylor (Club Physiotherapist), Alan Hyde (Matchday physio), Ian Bass, Troy Braham, Manny Williams, Paul Armstrong, Ben Wood (Captain), Mark Sophocleous, Leli Bajada, Roy Parkyn, Brett Freeman, Danny Honeyball, George Gregoriou.

LEYTON

BEST LGE ATT.: 718 v AFC Wimbledon
LOWEST: **35** v East Thurrock

No.	Date	Comp	H/A	Opponents	Att:	Result	Goalscorers	Pos
1	Aug 20	IP	H	Staines Town	204	L 0 - 2		20
2	23		A	Slough Town	246	D 0 - 0		16
3	27		A	Folkestone Invicta	286	D 2 - 2	**Bajada** 10 Ashe 14	15
4	29		H	Harrow Borough	178	L 0 - 1		19
5	Sept 3		A	Walton & Hersham	126	L 0 - 2		21
6	10	FAC 1Q	A	Leyton	110	W 1 - 0	Bajada 45	
7	17	IP	H	Chelmsford City	150	W 5 - 0	Shipp 3 (7 42 90) Ashe 21 Knight 45	17
8	20		A	Braintree Town	318	D 1 - 1	**Bajada** 62	16
9	24	FAC 2Q	H	Lewes	162	L 0 - 1		
10	Oct 1	IP	A	Hampton & Richmond B	222	L 2 - 4	**Bajada** 3 Ashe 25	
11	4		H	Bromley	142	L 0 - 1		19
12	11		A	Billericay Town	368	D 2 - 2	Chadder Curley	19
13	15	FAT 1Q	H	**Arlesey Town**	73	W 1 - 0	**S.Curley** 90	
14	18	IP	H	Windsor & Eton	50	W 1 - 0	**Bajada** 21 S.Curley 78	17
15	22		H	Maldon Town	78	W 4 - 2	Howard 60 (og) **Bajada** 36 68 Batt 52	16
16	25		A	Windsor & Eton	104	L 0 - 2		17
17	Nov 1		A	Redbridge	94	W 4 - 0	S.Curley 3 2 **Bajada** 34 Correia 66	13
18	5		H	Fisher Athletic	112	L 3 - 4	**Bajada** 7 14 (pen) Clancy 75 (og)	13
19	12	FAT 2Q	A	**East Thurrock**	109	L 1 - 2	**Correio** 1	
20	19	IP	A	East Thurrock	103	W 3 - 1	Curley 37 Thomas 68 Batt 75	12
21	22		H	Braintree Town	115	L 0 - 1		14
22	26		H	Wealdstone	150	L 1 - 2	F.Curley 85	16
23	Dec 3		A	AFC Wimbledon	2470	D 0 - 0		16
24	10		A	Margate	505	W 1 - 0	Thomas 73	14
25	17		H	Worthing	78	W 1 - 0	Knight 32	13
26	26		H	Hendon	128	W 2 - 0	Bunn 39 Corriera 60	11
27	Jan 2		A	Harrow Borough	144	D 3 - 3	Chandler 11 **Bajada** 65 85	11
28	7		A	Staines Town	178	W 3 - 2	Temkorang 2 Peddie 26 **Bajada** 40	
29	14		H	Slough Town	137	L 1 - 2	**Bajada** 32	11
30	21		A	Chelmsford City	1485	D 1 - 1	**Bajada** 61	11
31	26		H	Folkestone Invicta	84	D 1 - 1	**Bajada** 31 (pen)	12
32	Feb 4		H	AFC Wimbledon	718	L 1 - 2	Warner 26 (pen)	13
33	11		A	Wealdstone	238	L 0 - 1		15
34	18		H	Redbridge	88	W 4 - 0	Aldertonn 15 Brady 30 62 S.Curley 34	14
35	21		H	Heybridge	59	L 0 - 1		14
36	25		A	Maldon Town	123	W 2 - 0	James Bunn 9 Knight 83	12
37	Mar 4		A	Fisher Athletic	112	L 1 - 4	Bunn 35	14
38	11		H	East Thurrock	35	L 1 - 2	Tenkorank 90	14
39	18		H	Hampton & Richmond B	56	D 1 - 1	Godfrey 19	15
40	25		A	Bromley	331	W 2 - 1	Bunn 46 A.Thomas 51	14
41	April 1		H	Billericay Town	135	L 1 - 2	Soteriou 90	14
42	8		A	Heybridge Swifts	260	L 0 - 1		15
43	15		H	Walton & Hersham	79	L 0 - 1		15
44	17		A	Hendion	195	L 0 - 4		15
45	22		H	Margate	104	L 0 - 2		17
46	29		A	worthing	346	W 3 - 0	Honeyball 38 Bunn 46 66 (pen)	15

Ave. League Home Attendance: 137   **Goals**   60   61   **Top Goalscorer:** Bajada (16)
Best Position: 11th   **Worst:**   21st

MARGATE

Founded: 1896
Nickname: The Gate

Manager: Robin Trott   **Asst Manager:** Mike Flanigan   **Physio:** Liam Taylor

Club Colours: Royal Blue/Royal blue/white

Change Colours: Green & white/white/green

Club Sponsor: Active

Previous League: Conference South

Best Seasons: **League:** 8th (Conference) 2001-02

                F.A.Cup: 3rd Rd 72-73 and 36-37

                F.A.Trophy.: 6th Round 2001-2002

Ground address: Hartsdown Park, Hartsdown Road, Margate, Kent CT9 5QZ

Tel No: 01843 221 769   **Website:** www.margate-fc.com

Capacity: 3,000   **Seats:** 350   **Covered:** 1750   **Flooodlights:** Yes

Simple Directions:

Midweek Home Matchday: Tuesday

Clubhouse:

Club Shop: Yes . Contacts: Dave and Debra Canham (01843 221769)

CLUB PERSONNEL
Chairman: Malcolm Rowlett
V-Chairman: Keith Piper
President: Gordon Wallis
Secretary: Ken Tomlinson, 65 Nash Road, Margate, Kent CT94BT Tel No:07710033566 (M)
Press Officer: Keith Piper
Programme.Editor: Steve Ball

2005-2006
Captain: Lee Protheroe
Player of the Year: Bill Edwards
Top Goalscorer:

CLUB STATISTICS	
Record	Attendance: 14,500 v Spurs F.A.Cup 3rd Rd 1973
	Victory: 8-0 v Stalybridge Celtic (H) 2001-02 V Tunbridge Wells(H) 66-7
	v Chatham Town (H) 87-88
	Defeat: 0-11 v AFC Bournemouth (A) F.A.Cup 20.11.71
Goalscorer:	(Season) Jack Paletrhorpe 66 1929-30 **Career Appearances:** Bob Harrop
Record Transfer Fee	Paid: £5,000 to Dover Athletic for Steve Cuggy
	Received: Undisclosed from St Johnstone for Martin Buglione
Senior Honours:	Southern League 35-36 2000-02 Div 1 62-63 RT-up 66-67
	Div 1 South 77- 78 R-up 98-99 Eastern Div 1 R-up 33-34
Previous Leagues:	Kent 11-23 24-28 29-33 37-38 46-59 Southern 33-37 59-2001 Conference 01-04

Back Row (L-R): Aaron Barnett, Bill Edwards, Rocky Baptiste, Nejdet Hussen, Scott Ward, Greg Oates, Pat Gradley, Adrian Clarke, Mark Green. **Front Row:** John Keister, Che Stadhart, Peter Benevides, Darron Annon, Moses Jurju, Ian Pulman, Tamba Ngongou.

MARGATE

BEST LGE ATT.: 1,280 v Maldon Town
LOWEST: **401** v Bromley

No.	Date	Comp	H/A	Opponents	Att:	Result	Goalscorers	Pos
1	Aug 20	IP	H	Maldon Town	1280	W 1 - 0	Braithwaite	9
2	23		A	Staines Town	314	L 1 - 2	Brown 89	11
3	27		A	Harrow Borough	212	D 0 - 0		11
4	29		H	Redbridge	1010	D 0 - 0		12
5	Sept 3		A	Worthing	404	D 1 - 1	Brayley 17	12
6	6		H	Fisher Athletic	812	D 1 - 1	Remy 33	13
7	10	FAC 1Q	A	**Cowes Sports**	672	W 4 - 0	**Hilaire 20 Watson 44 Brown 51 Remy 80**	
8	17	IP	H	Slough Town	871	D 2 - 2	Remy 2 Hilaire 22 (pen)	13
9	20		A	Bromley	362	D 2 - 2	Sacha 73 McGowan 90	13
10	24	FAC 2Q	H	**Carshalton Town**	773	W 1 - 0	**Remy 4**	
11	Oct 1	IP	A	Walton & Hersham	262	D 1 - 1	Sacha 39	14
12	4		H	Billericay Town	807	D 1 - 1	McGowan 52	13
13	8	FAC 3Q	H	**Cray Wanderers**	807	L 0 - 3		
14	15	FAT 1Q	A	**Bashley**	95	W 3 - 0	**Braithwaite 21 36 (pen) Amoako 71**	
15	22	IP	H	Wealdstone	708	W 1 - 0	Amoako	13
16	24		A	Fisher Athletic	192	L 1 - 2	Remy 50	13
17	29		A	Braintree Town	478	L 0 - 1		16
18	Nov 5		H	Chelmsford City	759	L 0 - 1		18
19	12	FAT 2Q	H	**Dartford**	549	L 0 - 1		
20	19	IP	A	Windsor & Eton	154	W 1 - 0	Amoaku	14
21	22		H	Bromley	401	D 1 - 1	Edwards 74	15
22	26		H	Hampton & Richmond B	505	W 3 - 2	Edwards 21 Amoako 55 Taylor 67	13
23	Dec 3		A	East Thurrock	161	L 1 - 3	Deen 75	13
24	6		A	Heybridge Swifts	141	L 0 - 2		15
25	10		H	Leyton	505	L 0 - 1		18
26	17		A	Hendon	221	W 2 - 1	Brayley 24 82 (pen)	14
27	26		H	Folkestone Invicta	902	D 1 - 1	Hilaire 84	16
28	Jan 2		A	Redbridge	154	L 1 - 3	Taylor 23	17
29	7		A	Maldon Town	131	D 1 - 1	Hillaire 34	17
30	14		H	Staines Town	593	L 2 - 5	**Hockton** 40 (pen) Charalambous 89	18
31	21		A	Slough Town	346	D 2 - 2	Avery 10 (og) Brayley 62	18
32	28		H	Harrow Borough	535	D 0 - 0		18
33	Feb 4		H	East Thurrock	491	W 2 - 1	Deen 20 Yiga 28	18
34	11		A	AFC Wimbledon	2542	W 2 - 1	**Hockton** 15 48	17
35	18		H	Braintre Town	678	D 1 - 1	**Hockton** 52	18
36	25		A	Wealdstone	280	W 4 - 0	Yiga 23 **Hockton** 44 69 Brayley 67	16
37	Mar 3		A	Chelmsford ~City	853	L 0 - 1		16
38	7		H	AFC Wimbledon	776	L 0 - 1		17
39	18		H	Walton & Hersham	508	L 2 - 4	Hilaire 13 **Hockton** 47	17
40	21		A	Billericay Town	512	L 1 - 4	**Hockton** 71	17
41	April 1		H	Heybridge Swifts	557	L 1 - 2	**Hockton** 89	18
42	4		A	Windsor & Eton	456	D 1 - 1	**Hockton** 44	18
43	8		A	Hampton & Richmond B	320	W 1 - 0	**Hockton** 86	17
44	15		H	Worthing	528	D 0 - 0		17
45	17		A	Folkestone Invicta	574	D 1 - 1	**Hockton** 52	17
46	22		A	Leyton	104	W 2 - 0	**Hockton** 70 75	15
47	29		H	Hendon	701	W 4 - 2	**Hockton** 59 61 Knight 66 Protheroe 90	14

Ave. League Home Attendance: 685 **Goals** 57 59 **Top Goalscorer:** Hockton (16)
Best Position: 9th **Worst:** 18th

RAMSGATE

Founded: 1945
Nickname: Rams

WELCOME TO SOUTHWOOD FOOTBALL STADIUM
Lymington & New Milton

Manager: Jim Ward   **Assistant Manager:** Danny Ward: **Physio:**Adrian Hubbard

Club Colours: All Red

Change Colours: All Green

Club Sponsor: J.McCarthy Contractors

Previous League: Ryman

Best Seasons: League: Southern Premier 1972-1973

F.A.Trophy.: 3rd Qualifying Round 1969-70 1970-71 1975-76

F.A. Cup: 1st Round 1955-1956 2005-2006   **F.A.Vase:** 4th Rd Replay 1999-2000

Ground address: Southwood Stadium, Prices Avenue, Ramgate, Kent. CT11 0AN

Tel No: 01843 591662

Club Website: www.ramsgate-fc.co.uk

Capacity: 5,000   **Seats:**400   **Covered:** 600   **Floodlights:** yes

Simple Directions: A229 from London then A253 to Ramsgate. Left into Metherhill at roundabout then right into Ashburnham Road and right again into Southwood Rd.

Midweek Home Matchday: Tuesday

Clubhouse: Open five nights aweek plus week-ends. Hot & cold food available.

Club Shop: Yes. Open on first team match days.

Local Radio: Radio Kent & KMFM

Local Press: hanet Times & Kent Mesenger

CLUB PERSONNEL

Chairman: Richard Lawson
Vice Chairman: Paul Jefcoate
President: Lord Pendry
Secretary: Martin Able, 1 Parkside Villas, Tivoli Road, Margate, Kent CT 9 5PZ **Tel No:** 01843 290272
Commercial Manager: Vic Todd Tel No; 07837 817266
Press Officer: Arran Ayers Tel No: 07817 774945
Programme Editor: Steve Redford
28 Pages £1.00
2006-2007
Player of the Year: Ollie Schulz
Top Goalscorer: Shaun Welford
2006-07 Captain: Mark Munday

CLUB STATISTICS

Record	**Attendance:** 5,200 v Margate 1956-19657
	Career Goalscorer: Mick Williamson
	Career Appearances:
Record	**Victory:** 11-0 & 12-1 v Canterbury City Kent League 2000-2001
	Defeat:
Senior Honours:	Isthmian Div 1 Champions 05-06 Kent Senior Cup 1963-1964,
	Kent League (5) Kent Lg Cup (6) Kent Senior Trophy (3)
Previous Leagues:	Southern 1959-1975 Kent Senior.>2005

Back Row (L-R): Danny Ward, Liam Morris, David Cory, Warren Schulz, Edd Vahid, Steffan Ball, Jack Crawford, Jurgen Wild, Ben Laslett, Ollie Schulz, Michael Cassar, Stuart Vahid, Shaun Welford, Jim Ward
Front Row (L-R): Adran Hubbard, Luke Williams, Kieran Morris, Emlyn Taylor, Kenny Pratt, Alex Bond, Michael Yianni, Dean Hill, Simon Pettit, Shane Suter, Richard Sinden, Robbie Summers
Not Pictured: James Gregory, Mark Harrop, Mark Munday, Graham Taylor, Danny Twyman

SLOUGH TOWN

Founded: 1890
Nickname: The Rebels

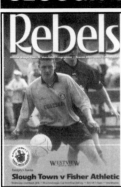

Manager: Eddie Denton

Coach: Mark West

Club Colours: Amber/navy blue/amber

Change Colours: All white

Club Sponsor:

Previous League: Conference

Best Seasons: **League** : 5th (Conference) 1992-93
            F.A.Cup: 2nd Rd (4)
            F.A.Trophy.: Semi-Final 76-77, 97-98

Ground address: Ground sharing with Windsor & Eton

Tel No:01753 860656   **Website**: www.sloughtownfc.com

Capacity: 4,500   **Seats** 400   **Covered:** 650 **Floodlights:** Yes

Simple Directions: A332 from M4 jct 6 .Third left at roundabout , left into St Leonards Road at lights on T junction. Ground 500 yards on right on B 3022.

Midweek Home Matchday: Tuesday

Clubhouse: Yes

Club Shop: Yes

CLUB PERSONNEL

Chairman: Bernard Devine

Secretary/Press Officer:
Roy Merryweather c/o club
Tel NOs: 01753 860656 (ground)
01753 554833 (W)
01189722871 (H)
01753 533949(Fax)
Press Officer: John Tebbitt
Programme Editor: Glen Riley

2005-2006
Captain: Steve Daly
Player of the Year: Ian Hodges
Top Goalscorer: Ian Hodges

CLUB STATISTICS

Record	**Attendance:** At Slough: 8,000 Schoolboys Slough v Liverpool 1976
	Victory: 17-0 v RailwayClearing House 1921-22
	Defeat: 1-11 v Chesham Town 1909-1910
	Goalscorer: Tory Norris 84 1925-26
	Career Appearances: Terry Raeerdon 458 1964-81
Record Transfer Fee	**Paid:** £18,000 from Farnborough Town for Colin Fielder
	Received: £22,000 from Wycombe Wanderers for Steve Thompson
Senior Honours:	F.A.Amateur Cup R-Up 1972-73 Isthmian League Champions 80-81 89-90
	Athenian League (3) Berks & Bucks Senior Cup: (10)
Previous Leagues:	Southern Alliance 1892-93, Berks & Bucks 1901-05, Gt Western Subebian 1906 19 Spartan 1920-39 Herts & Middx 1940-45, Corinthiian 46-63, Athenian 63-73 Isthmian 73-90 94-95 Conference 90-94

Back Row (L-R): Alex Gibson, Matt Glynn, Mark Bartley, Marc Leach, Kieron Drake, Jamie Jarvis, Leon Woodruffe, Ian Lovegrove, Daryl Harris. **Middle:** Kevin McGoldrick (Physio), Darron Wilkinson (Player/Coach), Rav Braith, Adam Wallace, Ancalet Odhiambo, Iain Duncan, Carl Marsh (Coach), Paul Lillywhite (Kit Man). **Front:** Gareth McCleary, Leigh Mason, Steve Daly (Club Captain), Eddie Denton (Manager), Mark West (Asst. Mgr.), Michael Alexis, George Moleski, Steve Dell.

SLOUGH TOWN

BEST LGE ATT.: 1,264 v AFC Wimbledon
LOWEST: **191** v East Thurrock

No.	Date	Comp	H/A	Opponents	Att:	Result	Goalscorers	Pos
1	Aug 20	IP	A	Billericay Town	522	L 1 - 3	**Hodges**19	19
2	23		H	Leyton	246	D 0 - 0		15
3	27		H	AFC Wimbledon	1264	L 0 - 2		20
4	29		A	Hampton & Richmond B	303	L 2 - 3	Seedall 55 **Hodges** 63	21
5	Sept 3		H	Braintree Town	260	W 2 - 1	Ballard 36 Alexis 90	17
6	6		H	Redbridge	248	W 3 - 2	**Hodges** 23 Harris 32 Brooks 45	14
7	10	FAC 1Q	H	**Oxford City**	312	**W 4 - 1**	**Harris 8 Carbon 56 86 Alexis 76**	
8	17	IP	A	Margate	871	D 2 - 2	Carbon 26 Daly 66	14
9	20		A	East Thurrock	275	L 2 - 3	Daly 57 Alexis 66	16
10	**24**	FAC 2Q	A	**Wroxham**	**251**	**L 0 - 2**		
11	Oct 1	IP	H	Maldon Town	303	W 4 - 1	Ballard 49 Daly 70 Millar 76 84	13
12	4		A	Worthing	436	L 2 - 4	**Hodges** 9 Mason 44	14
13	11		H	Staines Town	274	L 1 - 2	**Hodges** 74	16
14	**16**	FAT1Q	H	**Croydon Athletic**	**286**	**L 1 - 3**	**Hodges** 57	
15	22	IP	H	Chelmsford City	340	L 0 - 1		17
16	25		A	Redbridge	201	W 4 - 1	Mason 29 **Hodges** 44 47 Alexis 84	14
17	29		A	Wealdstone	380	D 2 - 2	West 82 Evans 90 (og)	13
18	Nov 5		H	Hendon	291	L 0 - 2		15
19	19		A	Fisher Atrhletic	160	W 2 - 1	**Hodges** 6 57	15
20	22		H	East Thurrock	191	L 1 - 2	Harris 75	17
21	26		H	Walton & Hersham	311	L 0 - 2		17
22	29		A	Folkestone Invicta	263	L 0 - 3		
23	Dec 3		A	Bromley	378	W 3 - 2	Mousinho 58 Carbon 75 **Hodges** 90	15
24	10		H	Harrow Borough	333	W 5 - 2	Carbon 22 McCleary 43 Mason 53 **Hodges** 73 90	13
25	17		A	Heybridge Swifts	201	L 0 - 1		15
26	26		H	Windsor & Eton	609	W 3 - 0	**Hodges** 6 47 (pen) Jarvie (og) 45	12
27	Jan 2		H	Hampton & Richmond B	448	L 0 - 1		14
28	7		H	Billericay Town	308	L 0 - 2		15
29	14		A	Leyton	137	W 2 - 1	Ballard 16 Carbon 90	14
30	21		H	Margate	346	D 2 - 2	McCleary 23 51	15
31	28		A	AFC Wimbledon	2859	D 2 - 2	McCleary 60 **Hodges** 67	14
32	Feb 4		H	Bromley	294	D 2 - 2	**Hodges** 13 48 (pen)	16
33	11		A	Walton & Hersham	275	W 1 - 0	Harris 36	14
34	18		H	Wealdstone	412	W 3 - 2	**Hodges** 43 Harris 48 Mason 79	12
35	25		A	Chelmsford City	1006	L 0 - 2		15
36	Mar 4		A	Hendon	241	D 1 - 1	McCleary 72	15
37	11		H	Fisher Athletic	293	L 0 - 4		15
38	18		A	Maldon Town	119	W 2 - 0	Woodruffe 6 **Hodges** 90	14
39	25		A	Worthing	258	L 0 - 3		15
40	April 1		A	Staines Town	376	L 1 - 2	Daly 28	15
41	8		H	Folkestone Invicta	289	W 2 - 0	Ide 21 Alexis 71	14
42	14		H	Braintree Town	875	L 1 - 2	Harris 16	14
43	17		H	Windsor & Eton	508	D 3 - 3	**Hodges** 9 60 Harris 44	14
44	22		A	Harrow Borough	220	L 1 - 2	Mason 62	16
45	29		H	Hetbridge Swifts	274	L 1 - 2	McCleary 64	17

Ave. League Home Attendance: 357   **Goals** 68 81   **Top Goalscorer:** Hodges (22)
Best Position: 12th   **Worst:** 21st

STAINES TOWN

Manager: Steve Cordery
Assistant Manager: Craig Maskell
Physio: Gareth Workman
Club Colours: Old Gold(blue trim)/royal blue/royal blue and gold
Change Colours: All white
Club Sponsor: Gilmour Quinn Mortgage Services (GQMS)
Previous League: Athenian
Best Performances:
League: 4th Isthmian Premier 81-82   **F.A. Cup:** 1st Rd 84-85 v Burton Albion
F.A.Trophy.: 2nd Rd Replay 1976-77 & 2003-04
Ground address: Wheatsheaf Park, Wheatsheaf Lane, Staines, Middlesex.TW18
2PD **Tel.No.:** 01784 225943
Official website: www.stainesmassive.co.uk/www.stainestownwfc.co.uk
Capacity: 3,000   **Seats:** 300   **Covered:** 850   **Floodlights:** Yes
Simple Directions: Ground is located at the Thames Club. Turn left off B376
(Lakeham Road) approx. one mile from town centre, bus and railway stations.
Midweek Home Matchday: Tuesday (7.45)
Clubhouse: All facilities plus modern sports bar
Club Shop: All souvenirs available.Contact Ray Moore c/o club
Local Press: Staines & Ashford News, Middx Chronicle,Informer + Staines Guardian
Local Radio: County Sound, GLR,Capital and Radio Wey

CLUB PERSONNEL
Chairman: Alan Boon
Secretary: Steve Parsons,3 Birch Green, Staines, Middlesex TW18 4HA (01784 450420)
Press Officer: Stuart Moore (07803 207661)
Programme Editors: Secretary & Press Officer
Programme 44 pages £1.50
2005-2006
Captain: Matt Flitter
Player of the Year: Jake Newton
Top Goalscorer: Ali Chaaban 18

CLUB STATISTICS

RECORD

Attendance: 2,750 v Banco di Roma, Barassi Cup 1975
(70,000 watched the second leg)
Victory: 14-0 v Croydon (A) Isthmian Div 1 19.03.94
Defeat: 1-18 v Wycombe Wanderers (A) Gt. Western Suburban.Lg. 27.12.09
Career Goalscorer: Alan Gregory 122
Career Appearances: Dickie Watmore 840

SENIOR HONOURS: Isthmian Div 1 74-75 88-89, Athenian Lg. Div. 2 71-72, Spartan Lg.59-60 Middx Sen Cup (7) R-up (4) Isthmian Full Members Cup 94-95 Barssi Cup 1976

PREVIOUS **Names:**Staines Albany & St Peters Institute merged in 1895, Staines 05-18, Staines Lagonda 1918-25, Staines Vale (Second World War)
Leagues:(since 1920) Hounslow & Dist 1919-1920, Spartan 24-35,58-71, Middx Sen 43-52, Parthenon 52-53, Hellenic 53-58 and Athenian 71-73

Back-row: Steve Cordery (Manager) Julian Sills*, Elliot Onochie*, Jacob Mingle*, Samuel Kola Okikiolu*, Leon Gordon, Mark Jones*, Jon Henry-Hayden*, Matt Lovett, Danny Gordon, Richard Gell, Danny Thomas*, Andy Poyser*, Darren Deegan*, Matt Hodson*, Roni Joe* Paul Ellis*, Gareth Risbridger, Trent Phillips (Coach,) Michael Webb, Peter Barnsby, Nick Taylor (kit-man,) Craig Maskell (player-coach.)
Front-row: Matt Flitter, Kevin George*, Micheal Harper*, Andre Delisser, Gavin Tomlin*, Jon McDonald.

STAINES TOWN

BEST LGE ATT.: 2,285 v AFC Wimbledon
LOWEST: 173 v Heybridge Swifts

No.	Date	Comp	H/A	Opponents	Att:	Result	Goalscorers	Pos
1	Aug 20	IP	A	Leyton	204	W 2 - 0	Plummer 21 Currie 37	5
2	23		H	Margate	314	W 2 - 1	James 54 Maskell 87 (pen)	6
3	27		H	Billericay Town	301	L 1 - 2	De Lisser 13	7
4	29		A	AFC Wimbledon	2754	D 1 - 1	Hunter 45	6
5	Sept 3		H	Fisher Athletic	219	W 2 - 0	Hunter 20 48	5
6	6		H	Chelmsford City	364	W 3 - 0	Manuella 4 Currie 24 Plummer 52	2
7	10	FAC 1Q	H	**Dunstable Town**	174	D 1 - 1	Hunter 55	
8	13	FAC 1Qr	A	**Dunstable Town**	118	W 1 - 0*	James 115	
9	17	IP	A	Windsor & Eton	180	W 2 - 1	Nabil 43 Murphy 83	2
10	20		A	Hendon	141	W 2 - 1	Duncan 56 (og) Hunter 78	2
11	24	FAC 2Q	H	**Croydon**	251	D 1 - 1	**Plummer71**	
12	28	FAC 2QR	A	**Croydon**	82	W 2 - 1	**Popovic 15 Newton 54**	
13	Oct 1	IP	A	Redbridge	41	W 2 - 1	Popovic 4 Currie 12	2
14	4		H	Harrow Borough	343	L 0 - 1		3
15	11		A	Slough Town	274	W 2 - 1	Manuella 8 Nabil 55	2
16	15	FAT 1Q	A	**Wivenhoe Town**	201	W 2 - 0	**Newton 27 Nabil 86**	
17	22	IP	H	Worthing	280	L 0 - 1		2
18	24		A	Chelmsford City	350	D 4 - 4	Currie 4 Guy 65 DeLisser 69 Popovic 85	3
19	29		A	Bromley	402	D 1 - 1	Manuella 89	
20	Nov 6		H	East Thurrock	220	W 1 - 0	King 14	3
21	12	FAT 2Q	A	**Cray Wanderers**	131	L 2 - 4	**Maskell 8 Hunter 45 Delisser 86**	
22	19	IP	A	Maldon Town	115	D 2 - 2	Hunter 70 Flitter 76	3
23	22		H	Hendon	176	W 2 - 0	Hunter 2 Currie 78	2
24	Dec 3		A	Wealdstone	265	W 2 - 1	King 74 Guy 85	3
25	10		H	Heybridge Swifts	173	W 5 - 1	Sippetts 33 61 Murphy 39 Guy 52 67	3
26	17		A	Folkestone Unvicta	201	W 2 - 0	Guy 69 Scarlett 90	3
27	26		A	Hampton & Richmond B	463	L 1 - 2	Manuella 29	4
28	Jan 2		H	AFC Wimbledon	2285	L 0 - 3		5
29	7		H	Leyton	178	L 2 - 3	Guy 3 De Lisser 25	5
30	14		A	Margate	593	W 5 - 2	Esdwards 4 (og), Ifura 7, **Chaaban** 30 Guy 60 74	
31	21		H	Windsor & Eton	289	W 1 - 0	Currie 90	5
32	24		H	Braintree Town	284	D 1 - 1	**Chaaban** 42 (pen)	5
33	28		A	Billericay Town	423	D 1 - 1	Currie 86	4
34	Feb 4		H	Wealdstone	315	L 1 - 3	Green 84	4
35	7		H	Walton & Hersham	412	W 2 - 1	Green 6 **Chaaban** 16	4
36	11		A	Braintree town	517	L 1 - 3	Scarlett 5	4
37	18		H	Bromley United	251	L 1 - 2	Green 10	4
38	25		A	Worthing	411	D 2 - 2	Nwokeji 38 Murphy 62	5
39	Mar 4		A	East Thurrock	114	W 2 - 0	Green 76 **Chaaban** 90 (pen)	5
40	11		H	Maldon Town	207	D 1 - 1	**Chaaban** 30	5
41	18		H	Redbridge	191	D 2 - 2	**Chaaban** 5 54	5
42	25		A	Harrow Borough	137	W 4 - 1	**Chaaban** 3 (25 65 90) De Lisser 78	5
43	April 1		H	Slough Town	376	W 2 - 1	**Chaaban** 8 (pen) Nwokeji 45	4
44	7		A	Walton & Hersham	401	W 2 - 0	**Chaaban** 70 Scarlett 89	4
45	11		H	Hampton & Richmond B	588	L 0 - 1		5
46	15		A	Fisher Athletic	139	L 1 - 2	Green 29	5
47	22	41	A	Heybridge Swifts	227	L 2 - 4	**Chaaban** 55 79	7
48	29		H	Folkesteone Invicta	226	D 2 - 2	**Chaaban** 14 75	6

Ave. League Home Attendance:	381		**Goals**	83 63	**Top Goalscorer:** Chaaban (16)
Best Position: 2nd	**Worst:** 7th				

TONBRIDGE ANGELS

Manager: Tony Dolby   **Assistant Manager:** Mike Rutherford
Physios: Melvin Slight &Chris Dunk
Club Colours: Royal Blue with white trim
Change Colours: Red & Black/Black/Black
Club Sponsor: Betterview Windows
Previous League: Isthmian
Best Seasons: League: 3rd Isthmian Div 1 East 2003-2004
 F.A.Vase: 3rd Round 1993-1994
F.A. Cup: 1st Round 50-51 51-52 52-53 67-68 72-73   **F.A.Trophy.:**
Ground address: Longmead Stadium. Darenth Avenue, Tonbridge, Kent.
TN10 3JW **Tel No**: 01732 352417
Club Website: www.tonbridgeangels.co.uk
Capacity: 5,000   **Seats:**202   **Covered**: 400   **Floodlights**: Yes
Simple Directions: From Tonbridge BR through High Street, then north up
Shipbourne Rd (A227 Gravesend road) to 2nd mini roundabout (The Pinnacles Pub),
left into Darenth Avenue and ground is at bottom on far side of car park.
Midweek Home Matchday: Tuesday
Clubhouse: Mon-Sat evenings and Sunday lunchtimes.. Hot foor on matchdays
from Burger Bar. **Club Shop:** Yes full range of products. Tel No: 01732 3562417
Local Radio: Mercury, Radio Kent and K.F.M.**Local Press:** Kent Messenger,
Ciourier and Sevenoaks Leader.

CLUB PERSONNEL
Chairman: Nick Sullivan
Vice Chairman: Paul Dainty
President: Colin Fry
Secretary & Press Officer: Charlie Cole, 30 Faraday Ride, Tonbridge. Kent TN10 4RL
Tel No: 01732 354985

Editors:
Dan Couldridge & Geoff Curtis
38 Pages £1.50
2005-2006
Captain: Steve Aris
Player of the Year: Ray Powell
Top Goalscorer: Ray Powell

CLUB STATISTICS		
Record	**Attendance**: 1,853 v Dover Athletic Ryman League Div 1 Play Off 06.05.06	
	Career Goalscorer:	
	Career Appearances:: Mark Giham	
Record Transfer Fee	**Paid**:	
	Received: £7,000 from Charlton Athletic for Paul Emblem	
	Victory: 11-1 v Worthing F.A.Cup 1951	
	Defeat: 2-11 v Folkestone Kent Senior Cup 1949	
Senior Honours:	Southern League Cup R-Up (2) Kent Senior Cup 64-65 74-75	
Previous Leagues:	Southern 48-80 Kent 1989-1993 Southern 1993-2004	
	Grounds: The Angel 1948-1980 (Record Att. 8,236 v Aldershot F.A.Cup 1951)	
	Names: Tonbridge Angels, Tonbridge F.C. Tonbridge A.F.C.	

Back Row (L-R): Bob Gott (KIt Mnager), Chris Dunk (Trainer), Danny Lye, Mike Rutherford, John Beales, Alex O'Brien, Nick Barnes, Lew Watts, Fraser Logan, Jon Main, Steve Aris, Jay May
Front Row: Michal Czanner, Jerome John, Mike Cramp, Adam O'Neill, Luke Piscina, Ray Powell, Tony Dolby and Drew Watkins.

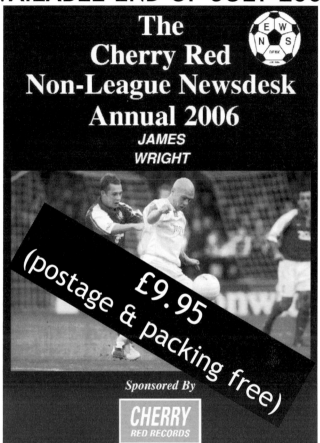

WALTON & HERSHAM

Manager: Alan Dowson   **Assistant Manager:** Lloyd Wye

Club Colours: All Red

Change Colours: Yellow/blue/yellow

Club Sponsor: Beales

Previous League: Athenian

Best Seasons: League Isthmian League Runners -Up 1972-73

F.A.Cup: 2nd Round 1972-73, 1973-74

F.A.Trophy.: 4th Round 1999-2000

F.A.Amateur Cup: Winners 1972-73

Ground address: Sports Ground, Stompond Lane, Walton-on-Thames

Tel No: 01932 244967   **Website:** www.waltonandhershamfc.org.uk

Capacity: 5,000   **Seats** 400   **Covered:** 2,500   **Floodlights:** Yes

Simple Directions: From Walton Bridge. Go over and along New Zealand Avenue,down one way street and up A244 Hersham road. Ground second on right.

Midweek Home Matchday: Tuesday

Clubhouse: Open every evening (01932 244967)

Club Shop: Open matchdays. Contact: Richard Olds c/o club.

CLUB PERSONNEL
Chairman: Alan Smith
President: Allen Batsford
Secretary: Michael Groom,
15 Windsor Walk, Weybridge,
Surrey. Tel No: 01932 842982
Programme Editor:
Mark Massingham
Tel No: 01932 885814
Programme
36 pages £1.50
Press Officer:
Mervyn Rees (01932 245756)

2005-2006
Captain:
Player of the Year: Wes Goggin
Top Goalscorer: Bobby Traynor

CLUB STATISTICS

Record	**Attendance**: 10,000 v Crook Town F.A.Amateur Cup 6th Rd 1951-52
	Victory: 10-0 v Clevedon F.A.Amateur Cup 1960
	Defeat: 3-11 v Kingstonian, Surrey Shield 1958
	Goalscorer: Reg Sentance 220 in 11 seasons.
	Career Appearances: Terry Keen 449 in 11 seasons.
Record Transfer Fee	**Paid:** £6,000
	Received: £150,000 from Bristol Rovers for Nathan Ellington 1999
Senior Honours:	F.A.Amateur Cup 72-73, Isthmian League Runners-Up 1972-73, Barassi Cup 73-74, Athenian League 68-69 R-up (3), Surrey Senior Cup (6) R-up (6) and London Senior Cup
Previous Leagues	Surrey Senior, Corinthian 45-50 and Athenian 50-71

Back row, left to right: Alan Dowson (Manager), Jason Rose, Jamie Reive, Scott Edgar, Ricky Perks, Simon Huckle, Gavin Cartwright, Jloyd Wye (Assistant Manager). Front row: Tristan Frontin, Wes Goggin, Rob George, Steve McNamara and Bobby Traynor.

WALTON & HERSHAM

BEST LGE ATT.: 1,975 v AFC Wimbledon
LOWEST: **126** v Leyton

No.	Date	Comp	H/A	Opponents	Att:	Result	Goalscorers	Pos
1	Aug 20	IP	A	Hampton & Richmond B	291	L 0 - 2		21
2	23		H	Bromley	175	L 0 - 1		22
3	27		H	Heybridge Swifts	126	W 2 - 1	Haylock 5 Charman 67	13
4	29		A	Windsor & Eton	144	D 1 - 1	Edgar 70	13
5	Sept 3		H	Leyton	126	W 2 - 0	Savage 21 Keevill 26	11
6	6		H	Hendon	192	W 1 - 0	Edgar 28	8
7	10	FAC 1Q	A	**Burgess Hill Town**	**169**	**W 4 - 0**	**Haylock 23 28 Edgar 60 85**	
8	17	IP	A	Billericay Town	484	L 1 - 2	Lampton 49 Nwokejl 81	
9	20		A	Worthing	408	D 0 - 0		8
10	24	FAC 2Q	A	**AFC Wimbledon**	**1930**	**W 3 - 0**	**Nwokeji 10 Keevil 30 Cartwright 89**	
11	Oct 1	IP	H	Margate	262	D 1 - 1	Nwokeji 89	9
12	3		A	Folkestone Invicta	251	L 0 - 1		10
13	8	FAC 3Q	A	**Ramsgate**	**301**	**L 0 - 1**		
14	11	IP	H	Folkestone Invicta	173	L 0 - 3		12
15	15	FAT1Q	A	**Heybridge Swifts**	**202**	**L 0 - 3**		
16	22	IP	H	East Thurrock United	147	W 1 - 0	Riddell 90	8
17	25		A	Hendon	180	D 1 - 1	Riddell 45	8
18	29		A	Maldon Town	174	W 2 - 1	Keevill 44 Lampton 88	8
19	Nov 5		H	Redbridge	156	W 2 - 1	Nwokeji 3 Edgar 87	
20	26		A	Slough Town	311	W 2 - 0	Nwokeji 62 **Traynor** 72	7
21	Dec 3		H	Harrow Borough	160	W 3 - 1	Jenkins 45 Nwokeji 64 84	6
22	10		A	Fisher Athletic	144	L 0 - 2		8
23	13		H	Worthing	182	L 2 - 3	Edgar 25 Morrison 90	
24	17		H	Braintree Town	159	W 3 - 2	**Traynor** 48 Keevill 68 78	
25	26		A	AFC Wiumbledon	2969	L 1 - 2	Fontin 90	9
26	Jan 2		H	Windsor & Eton	220	W 3 - 2	Nwokeji 33 **Traynor** 48 73	7
27	7		H	Hampton & Richmond B	301	W 2 - 0	**Traynor** 2 88	6
28	10		A	Wealdstone	274	W 3 - 1	**Traynor** 2 Lampton 30 Jenkins 49	5
29	14		A	Bromley	363	L 0 - 1		6
30	21		H	Billericay Town	302	D 0 - 0		7
31	Feb 4		A	Harrow Borough	158	W 2 - 1	Lampton 50 Thorne 77	7
32	7		S	Staines Town	412	L 1 - 2	Lampton 41 (pen)	8
33	11		H	Slough Town	275	L 0 - 1		8
34	18		H	Maldon Town	151	W 3 - 0	Healy11 12 Stroncin 28	7
35	Mar 4		A	Redbridge	84	W 3 - 1	**Traynor** 27 Healy 48 Green 65	6
36	11		H	Wealdstone	229	W 1 - 0	George 52	6
37	18		A	Margate	508	W 4 - 2	Lampton 52 (pen) Healy 67 George 88 Thorne 90	6
38	21		A	Heybridge Swifts	175	L 1 - 2	**Traynor** 73	7
39	25		H	Chelmsford City	219	D 2 - 2	**Traynor** 22 82 (pen)	7
40	28		A	East Thurrock United	91	L 0 - 1		7
41	April 1		A	Folkestone Invicta	405	L 1 - 3	George 13	8
42	7		H	Staines Town	401	L 0 - 2		8
43	15		A	Leyton	79	W 1 - 0	Frontin 57	9
44	17		H	AFC Wimbledon	1975	L 0 - 2		9
45	22		H	Fisher Athletic	138	L 0 - 1		9
46	29		A	Braintree Town	961	L 1 - 3	**Traynor** 51	9

Ave. League Home Attendance: 289   **Goals**   61 54   **Top Goalscorer:** Traynor (12)
Best Position: 5th   **Worst:** 22nd

WORTHING

Joint Managers: Alan Pook and Danny Bloor
Sports Therapists: Alan Robertson, Ian Stevens and Peter Knee
Club Colours: Red with white trim/red/red.
Change Colours: All Light Blue
Club Sponsor:
Previous League: Athenian
Best Performances: Isthmian Premier R-up 83-85 **F.A. Cup:** 2nd Rd 82-83
F.A.Trophy.: 3rd Rs Replay 85-86 **F.A.Amateur Cup:** Quarter Final replay 1907-08
Ground address: Victor Gladwish Stadium, Woodside Road, Worthing,
West Sussex.BN14 7HQ Tel No: 01903 239575 Club e-mail:contact@worthingfc.com
Official website: www.worthingfc.com
Capacity: 3,650 **Seats:**500 **Covered:**1,500 **Floodlights:** Yes
Simple Directions: A24 or A27 to Grove Lodge roundabout. A24 (Town centre exit)
and right into South Farm Rd. Over 5 roundabouts take last on right (Pavilion Road)
before level crossing. Woodside Rd on right. ground on left. 1/2 mile from BR.

CLUB PERSONNEL
Chairman: Ray Smith
President: Morty Hollis
Secretary: Paul Damper, 19 Fletcher Road, Worthing, West Sussex BN14 8EX
Tel: 01903 210290
Press Officer:
Danny Bloor
Programme. Editor:
Alistair McKail
01903 694127 (H)
Programme
44 pages 1.50
2005-2006
Captain:
Player of the Year:
Top Scorer:

Midweek Home Matchday: Tuesday
Clubhouse: Open two hours before kick-off until 11.0 p.m.
Local Press: Evening Argus, Worthing Herald
Local Radio: Southern FM, Splash FM & Southern Counties Radio

CLUB STATISTICS

Record	**Attendance**: 3,600 v Wimbledon F.A..Cup 14th November 1936
	Victory: 25-0 V Littlehampton (H) West Sussex League 1911-12
	Defeat: 0-14 v Southwick (A) Sussex County League 1946-47
Career Goalscorer:	Mick Edmonds 276 **Career Appearances:** David Bloom 397
Transfer Fees:	**Paid:** Undisclosed for Marc Rice (Havant & Waterlooville) 1998
	Received: 7,500 for Tim Read from Woking 1990
Senior Honours:	Isthmian Prem R-Up 83-84,84-85. Div1 82-83 Div 2 81-82, 92-93
	Sussex Sen Cup (21) Isth Full Membs C. R-up 98-9 Athenian 2 R-up 63-4
Previous Leagues:	West Sussex 1896-1904 05-14 19-20 Brighton Hove & Dist 19-20
	Sussex County 1920-1940 1945-48 Corinthian 48-63 and Athenian 63-77

WORTHING

BEST LGE ATT.: 2,253 v AFC Wimbledon
LOWEST: 227 v Harrow Borough

No.	Date	Comp	H/A	Opponents	Att:	Result	Goalscorers	Pos
1	Aug 20	IP	A	Wealdstone	315	L 1 - 2	**Browne** 90	15
2	23		H	Windsor & Eton	346	W 2 - 1	**Browne** 37 Pacquette 68	10
3	27		H	Braintree Town	369	W 2 - 0	**Browne** 23 Alexander 90	8
4	29		A	Fisher Athletic	206	D 2 - 2	**Browne** 34 (pen) M.Watson 67	5
5	Sept 3		H	Margate	404	D 1 - 1	Brotherton	8
6	5		A	Folkestone Invicta	241	W 2 - 1	Collins 2 Grice 53	5
7	10	FAC 1Q	A	**Wick**	303	W 4 - 0	**Browne 21 40 Francis 85 89**	
8	17	IP	A	AFC Wimbledon	2645	W 2 - 1	Cable 17 Francis 89	4
9	20		H	Walton & Hersham	408	D 0 - 0		5
10	24	FAC 2Q	A	**AFC Hornchurch**	544	W 4 - 1	**Francis 10 49 Browne 14 (Pen) Knee 80**	
11	Oct 1	IP	A	Hendon	191	D 2 - 2	Francis 56 Cable 61	6
12	4		H	Slough Town	436	W 4 - 2	Pacquette 47 75 **Browne** 58 (pen) Francis 82	5
13	8	FAC 3Q	H	**Basingstoke Town**	577	L 2 - 4	**Browne** 37 Cable 51	
14	11		A	East Thurrock United	132	L 1 - 5	Francis 60	6
15	15	FAT1Q	A	**Lymington & N.M.**	179	W 4 - 1	**Browne** 3 (2 36 45) Pacquette 35	
16	22		A	Staines Town	280	W 1 - 0	Pacquette 17	4
17	25		H	Folkestone Invicta	408	W 1 - 0	Pacquette 78	4
18	29		H	Heybridge Swifts	451	W 4 - 1	Pacquette 14 **Browne** 24 86 (pen) Wiles 82 (og)	2
19	Nov 5		A	Harrow Borough	185	D 2 - 2	**Browne** 48 Pacquette 50	4
20	12	FAT 2Q	H	**Stamford**	427	D 1 - 1	**Browne 20 (pen)**	
21	15	FAT 2Qr	A	**Stamford**	203	L 0 - 2		
22	19	IP	H	Hampton & Richmond B	640	W 2 - 1	**Browne** 30 (pen) 79	2
23	26		A	Billericay Town	421	D 1 - 1	Pacquette 27	4
24	Dec 3		H	Maldon Town	414	W 2 - 0	Davis 45 Alexander 53	4
25	6		H	Redbridge	260	W 5 - 1	Louis 1 **Browne** 16 Pacquette 25 75 Alexander 89	3
26	10		H	Chelmsford City	504	L 1 - 3	Francis 84	4
27	13		A	Walton & Hersham	182	W 3 - 2	**Browne** 27 (pen) Francis 75 Pacquette 88	
28	17		A	Leyton	78	L 0 - 1		4
29	27		A	Bromley	480	W 2 - 1	Knee 3 82	3
30	Jan 2		H	Fisher Athletic	765	W 4 - 0	Alexander 11 Holmes 24 (pen) Francis 36 Knee 82	2
31	7		H	Wealdstone	602	W 3 - 1	Alexander 13 Davies 56 Francis 62	1
32	14		A	Windsor & Eton	173	L 1 - 2	Pacquette 62	2
33	21		H	AFC Wimbledon	2253	L 0 - 2		4
34	28		A	Braintree Town	557	L 2 - 4	Marney 33 39	5
35	Feb 4		A	Maldon Town	121	L 0 - 2		5
36	11		H	Billericay Town	502	L 2 - 4	**Browne** 12 68	6
37	18		A	Heybridge Swifts	246	D 1 - 1	**Browne** 25	6
38	25		H	Staines Town	411	D 2 - 2	Knee 21 Rents 28	6
39	Mar 11		A	Hampton & Richmond B	291	W 2 - 1	Rents 28 Alexander 73	8
40	18		H	Hendon	394	D 1 - 1	Davis 54	8
41	25		A	Slough Town	258	W 3 - 0	Knee 45 **Browne** 80 Francis 86	8
42	28		H	Harrow Borough	227	W 3 - 0	Cable 37 Davis 43 **Browne** 60	7
43	April 1		H	East Thurrrock	459	W 1 - 0	Knee 80	5
44	8		A	Redbridge	101	L 2 - 3	**Browne** 27 Ray 58 (og)	5
45	15		A	Margate	628	D 0 - 0		7
46	17		H	Bromley	532	L 1 - 2	Knee 39	8
47	22		A	Chelmsford City	611	L 0 - 1		8
48	29		H	Leyton	346	L 0 - 3		8

Ave. League Home Attendance: 530   **Goals** 86 68   **Top Goalscorer:** Browne (26)
Best Position: 1st   **Worst:** 15th

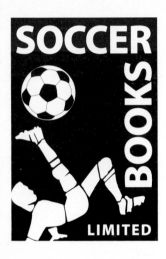

SOCCER BOOKS LIMITED

72 ST. PETERS AVENUE (Dept. NLD)
CLEETHORPES
N.E. LINCOLNSHIRE
DN35 8HU
ENGLAND

Tel. 01472 696226   Fax 01472 698546

Web site   www.soccer-books.co.uk
e-mail   info@soccer-books.co.uk

Established in 1982, Soccer Books Limited has one of the largest ranges of English-Language soccer books available. We continue to expand our stocks even further to include many new titles including German, French, Spanish, Italian and other foreign-language books.

With well over 100,000 satisfied customers already, we supply books to virtually every country in the world but have maintained the friendliness and accessibility associated with a small family-run business. The range of titles we sell includes:

YEARBOOKS – All major yearbooks including many editions of the Sky Sports Football Yearbook (previously Rothmans), Supporters' Guides, Playfair Annuals, North & Latin American Guides, Non-League Directories and European Football Yearbooks.

CLUB HISTORIES – Complete Statistical Records, Official Histories, Definitive Histories plus many more.

WORLD FOOTBALL – World Cup books, International Line-up & Statistics Series, European Championships History, International and European Club Cup competition Statistical Histories and much more.

BIOGRAPHIES & WHO'S WHOS – of managers and players plus Who's Whos etc.

ENCYCLOPEDIAS & GENERAL TITLES – Books on stadia, hooligan and sociological studies, histories and hundreds of others, including the weird and wonderful!

DVDs – Season's highlights, histories, big games, World Cup, player profiles, a selection of over 40 F.A. Cup Finals with many more titles becoming available all the time.

For a current printed listing containing a selection of our titles, please contact us using the details at the top of this page. Alternatively, our web site offers a secure ordering system for credit and debit card holders and lists our full range of over 1,300 books and 250 DVDs.

FOOTBALL LEAGUE

STEP 1

FOOTBALL
CONFERENCE

STEP 2

| CONFERENCE NORTH | CONFERENCE SOUTH |

STEP 3

| SOUTHERN PREMIER | NORTHERN PREMIER | ISTHMIAN PREMIER |

STEP 4

| SOUTHERN DIVISION 1 SOUTH &WEST MIDLAND | NORTHERN PREMIER DIV.1 | **ISTHMIAN DIVISION 1 NORTH   SOUTH** |

STEP 5/6

Combined Counties	Hellenic	Northern League	Spartan South Midlands	Wessex
Eastern Counties	Kent	Northern Counties East	Sussex County	Western
Essex Senior	Midland Alliance	North West Counties	United Counties	

STEP 7

Anglian Combination	Dorset County	Kent County	Midland Combination	Peterborough & District	West Cheshire
Bedford & District	Dorset Premier	Leicestershire Senior	Midland League	Reading League	West Lancashire
Brighton & Hove	East Sussex	Liverpool County	North Berkshire	Somerset County	West Midlands (reg)
Cambridgeshire County	Essex & Suffolk Border	Manchester Football	Northampton Town Lge	South Western	West Sussex
Central Midlands	Essex Intermediate	Mid Cheshire League	Northamptonshire Comb.	Suffolk & Ipswich	Wiltshire League
Crawley & Disrict	Gloucesterhisre Co.	Mid Sussex	Northern Alliance	Teeside League	Worthing & District
Devon County	Herts Senior County	Middlesex County	Oxfordshire Senior	Wearside League	

A.F.C.HORNCHURCH

Re-Formed 2003:
Nickname: Urchins

£1.50

main sponsor - accused
tuesday 22nd august 2006
v GREAT WAKERING ROVERS ko 7.45pm

Manager: Colin McBride   **Physios:** Richard Harper & Del Edkins

Assistant Managers: Ronnie Hanley, Jimmy McFarlane,and Bioll Lapage

Change Colours: Blue & white/Blue/Blue

Club Sponsor:

Previous League: Essex Senior

Best Seasons: League: 17th Conference South 2003-2004 **F.A. Cup:** 2nd Round 2003-2004   **F.A.Trophy.:** 2nd Round 2004-2005   **F.A.Vase:** 5th Round 1974-1975

Physio: Del Edkins

Ground address: Hornchurch Stadium, Bridge Avenue, Upminster, Essex.

Tel Nos: 01708 220080 (clubhouse) 01708 250501 (Office) 01708 227931 (FAX)

Club Website: www.afchornchurch.com

Capacity: 3,500   **Seats:** 800   **Covered:** 1,400   **Floodlights:** Yes

Simple Directions: Bridge Avenue is off A124 between Hornchurch and Upminster

Nearest BR Station: Upminster **Underground Station:** Upminster Bridge (District)

Midweek Home Matchday: Tuesday

Clubhouse: Open Daily **Club Shop:** Yes

Local Radio: Essex Radio , Time FM

Local Press: Romford Recorder

CLUB PERSONNEL

Managing Director: Jon Smith
President: Del Edkins
Directors:
Jon Smith, Jennifer Smith, Ben Williams and Wayne Slade
Secretary: Jennifer Cliff, c/o Club
Press Officer: Ian Walmsley
Programme Editor: Secretary
40 Pages £1.50

2005-2006
Captains:
Jordan Bostock & Nicky Cowley
Player of the Year: Danny Cowley
Top Goalscorer: Billy Holland

CLUB STATISTICS	
Record	**Attendance:** 3,500 v Tranmere Rovers 2nd Rd F.A.Cup 2003-2004
	Career Goalscorer:
	Career Appearances:
Record Transfer Fee	**Paid:**
	Received:
Senior Honours:	Since club was re-formed. Essex League Champions 2005-2006 (Record points total 64) and League Cup and Memorial Trophy winners
Previous Leagues:	Athenian, Istthmian, Conference South, Essex Senior

486

A.F.C.SUDBURY

Founded: 1999
Nickname:

CLUB PERSONNEL

Chairmen: Keith Morris
President: Les Bolitho
Vice Chairman: Keith Morris
General Manager: Mick Mills
Secretary: Davis Webb, 6 Melford Road, Sudbury, Suffolk CO10 1WG
Tel No: 01787 372352(H)
e-mail: dave-afc@supanet.com
Sponsorship Manager: Mark Pearman
Programme Editor: Barry Moult bjm@btinternet.com
48 Pages 31.00

2005-2006
Captain: Brett Girling
Player of the Year:
Top Goalscorer: Ommu Noble
2006-07 Captain:: David Head

Manager: Mark Morsley **Coach:** Paul Skingley **Physio:** Ian Vernau

Club Colours: Yellow/Blue/Yellow

Change Colours: All Red

Club Sponsor: Mel Aviation (Oxygen) Ltd.

Previous League: Eastern Counties

Best Seasons: League: Champions Eastern Co.(6) **F.A. Cup:** 1st Round 2000-01

F.A.Vase: Finalists 2002-03-04-05

Ground address: Kingsmarsh Stadium, Brundon Lane, Sudbury, Suffolk CO10 1WQ Tel No: 01787 376213

Club Website: www.afcsudbury.com

Capacity: 2,500 **Seats:** 200 **Covered:** 150 **Floodlights:** Yes

Simple Directions: Follow Halstead/Chelmsford road from Sudbury centre for a mile. Then first right after railway bridge at foot of steep hill and first right again after left hand bend.

Midweek Home Matchday: Tuesday

Clubhouse: Match days and Training Evenings **Club Shop:** Yes

Local Radio: BBC Suffolk Radio

Local Press: Suffolk Free Press East Anglian Daily Times

CLUB STATISTICS

Record	Attendance: 1,800
	Career Goalscorer: Gary Bennett
	Career Appearances: Paul Betson
Record Transfer Fee	Paid: N/A
	Received: N/A
Senior Honours:	F.A.Vase Runners-Up (4) Champions of Eastern Counties League (5)
	Suffolk Premier Cup 2002-03-04
	Previous Leagues: Essex & Suffolk Border, Suffolk & Ipswich, Eastern Co, Southern 1991-91
	Names: Sudbury Town (1874) and Sudbury Wanderers (1958) merged in 1999

Back Row (L-R): Mark Morsley (manager), Shane Wardley, Paul Abrahams, John Pollard, Andrew Claydon, Nathan Munson, Kevin Hughes, Paul Betson, David Head (capt), Tommy Noble, Terry Rayner, Ian Vernau (physio), Dwayne Clarke, Paul Skingley (coach). **Front Row:** Luke Hammond, Brett Girling, Darren Bethell, Pip Boyland, James Rowe, Tommy Bradlaugh, Neil Calver, Chris Howlett.

ARLESEY TOWN

Manager: Jon Taylor   **Coach**: Scott Houghton **Assistant**: Mike Brooks
Physio: Eric Turner
Club Colours: Sky and Navy Blue Quarters/Blue/Blue
Change Colours: All White
Club Sponsor: RAJ Villa
Previous League: Southern
Best Seasons: League: 10th Southern Div 1 East 2005-2006
F.A. Cup: 4th Qualifying Round 2003-2004   **F.A.Trophy.:**
F.A.Vase: Winners 1994-1995
Ground address: Hitchin Road, Arlesey,Beds. SG15 6RS
Club Website:www.arleseyfc.co.uk
Capacity: 2,920   **Seats**:150   **Covered**: 600   **Floodlights**: Yes
Simple Directions: A1 take A507 to Shefford, at 3rd roundabout turn left, 1st left follow road through village, ground 1.5 miles on left.
 Midweek Home Matchday: Tuesday
Clubhouse: Open daily 7- 11.00, Sat 12p.m.-11.30, Sun 12-2.30 7-11.30
                    Members bar ,wide screen for Sky TV, function suite and hot food available.
Club Shop: Yes. Old programmes, leisure wear, replica shirts and various souvenirs
Local Radio:
Local Press:

CLUB PERSONNEL
Chairman: Bryan Ellis
President: Mautice Crouch
Se: Keith Broughton, 9 Davis Row, Arlesey, Beds. SG15 6RB
e-mail:
secretary@arleseytown.co.uk

Programme
Editor: Dave Brabrook
Pages/Price

CLUB STATISTICS

Record	Attendance: 2,000 v Luton TownReserves Beds Senior Cup 1906
	Career Goalscorer:
	Career Appearances: Gary Marshall
Record Transfer Fee	**Paid**:
	Received:
Senior Honours:	FA Vase Winners 1994-5; Isthmian League (Ryman) Div 3 Champions 00-01, Beds Sen Cup 65-6 78-9 96-7, S Mids Prem Div (5) Utd Co Prem Div 84-85,
Previous Leagues:	**Leagues**: Biggleswade & Dist.; Beds. Co. (S. Mids) 22-26 ,27-28; Parthenon; London 58-60; Utd Co's 33-36 82-92. Spartan South Midlands 92-99

Back row,left to right: Scott Houghton, Eric Turner, Bobby Dance, Dave Hatchett, Bratt Donnelly, Nick Bussy, Stuart Beevor, Martin Patching, Damien Mathews, Michael Cox, Mike Brooks and Jon Taylor (Manager). Front row: James Dillnut, Jordan Houghton, Ozzie Foster, Martin Williams, Barrington Belgrave, Ivan Finch, Charile Henry, Lee Tekell, Paul Bloss, Ryan Nichol and Craig Reynolds.

AVELEY

Founded: 1927
Nickname:
The Millers

A V E L E Y F.C.

Manager: Steve Brown   **Assistant Manager::** Lee Harvey   **Physio:** Kevin Head

Club Colours: All Royal Blue

Change Colours: All Red

Club Sponsor: Elite Direct .com

Previous League: Southern

Best Seasons: League: 17th Southern League 2004-2005

F.A. Cup: 1st Round 1970--1971   **F.A.Trophy.:** 3rd Qual. Rd Replay 1974-1975

F.A.Vase: 3rd Round 1989-1990 **F.A.Amateur Cup:** Quarter Final 1970-1971

Ground address: Mill Field, Mill Road, Aveley Essex RM15 4TR

Tel No: 01708 865940

Club Website: www.aveleyfc.net

Capacity: 4,000   **Seats:** 400   **Covered:** 400   **Floodlights:** Yes

Simple Directions: London - Southend A1306, turn into Sandy Lane at Aveley. Rainham or Purfleet BR stations then bus No. 723 to the ground. Bus from Rainham No 324

Midweek Home Matchday: Monday

Clubhouse: Normal pub hours. Bar snacks and hot food available. **Club Shop:** No

Local Radio: Radio Essex and Essex Radio !

Local Press: Thurrock Gazette and Romford Recorder

CLUB PERSONNEL

Chairman: Graham Gennings
President: Ken Clay
Secretary: Craig Johnston, 10 San Jaun Drive, Chalford Hundfred, Grays, Essex. RM16 6LQ
Tel No: 07946 438540(M)
Match Secretary: Terry King

Programme
Editor: Secretary
Tel No: 01375 650220
48 Pages £1.00
2005-2006
Captain: Steve Dickinson
Player of the Year:
Bradley Stevens
Top Goalscorer: Gary Dixon 10

CLUB STATISTICS

Record	**Attendance:** 3,741 v Slough Town F.A.Amateur Cup 27.02.71
	Career Goalscorer: Jotty Wilks 214
	Career Appearances: Ken Riley 422
Record	**Victory:** 1-1 v Histon 24.08.63
	Defeat: 0-8 v Orient Essex Thameside Trophy 11.04.85
Senior Honours:	Isthmian Lg Div 2 (North) R-up 89-90, Athenian Lg 70-71 (Div 2 R-up 68-69), Essex Senior Cup Finalists 2002/03 03-04
Previous Leagues:	**Leagues:** Thurrock Com 46-49; London 49-57; Delphian 57-63; Athenian 63-73 Isthmian 1973-2004 Southern 2004-2006

Standing (L-R):- Lee Harvey (Asst Manager) Shayne Mangodza, Ricky Dobson, Bradley Stevens, Danny O'Sullivan, Marc Palmer, Robert Port, Sam Adejokun, Daryl Bourgeois, Linor Kransiqi, Kevin Head (Physio).
Seated:- Stuart Strange, Ryan Sammons, Daniel Francis, Tom Davey (Captain), Steve Browne (Manager), Gary Dixon, Jake Gibson, Abul Hussain.

BURY TOWN

Founded: 1872
Nickname: The Blues

CLUB PERSONNEL

Chairman: Russell Ward
Vice Chairman: Adrian Lewis
President: Colin Hurley
General Manager: Ron Kent
Director of Football: Trevor Collins
Additional Directors: Wendy and
Bernard Turner, David Scarfe , Chris
Ward and William Angus.
Secretary: Mrs Wendy Turner, 64
Winthrop Road, Bury St.Edmunds,
Suffolk. IP3 3UF
Tel No: 01284 753688
Programme Editor: Chris Ward
£1,20
2005-2006
Captain: Richard Skelly
Player of the Year: Ian Miller
Top Goalscorer:

Manager: Richard Wilkins **Coach:** John Zdrenka **Physio:**Alan Isted
Club Colours: Blue with Red Trim/Blue/Blue
Change Colours: All red
Club Sponsor: Gary Taylor Construction
Previous League: Eastern Counties
Best Seasons: League: 9th Southern League 1988
F.A. Cup: 1st Round Replay 1968-1969   **F.A.Vase:** Semi-Final 2005-2006
F.A.Trophy: 2nd Round 1970-1971
Ground address: Ram Meadow, Cotton Lane, Bury St.Edmunds, Suffolk IP33 1XP
Tel No: 01284 754721
Club Website: www.burytownfc.co.uk
Capacity: 3,500   **Seats:** 300   **Covered:** 1,500   **Floodlights:** Yes
Simple Directions: Follow signs to town centre from A14. At second roundabout take first
left into Northgate Street then left into Mustow Street at T junction at lights and left again into
Cotton Lane. Ground is 350 yards on right.
Midweek Home Matchday: Tuesday
Clubhouse: Match days and training nights **Club Shop:** Yes
Local Radio: BBC Suffilk or SGR FM
Local Press: East Anglian Daily Times, Bury Fre Press and The Green Un.

CLUB STATISTICS

Record	**Attendance:** 2,500 v Enfiled F.A.Cup 1986	
	Career Goalscorer: Doug Tooley	
	Career Appearances: Doug Tooley	
Record Transfer Fee	**Paid:** £1,500 to Chelmsford City for Mel Springett	
	Received: £5,500 from Ipswich Town for Simon MIlton	
Senior Honours:	Eastern Counties Champions 1963-1964 R-Up 2004-05 2005-06	
	Suffolk Premier Cup (9)	
Previous Leagues:	Norfolk & Suffolk Border, Essex & Suffolk Border,	
	Eastern Co. 35-64 76-87 97-05 Metropolitan 64-71 Southern 71-76 87-97	
Names:	Bury St.Edmunds 1895-1902 Bury United 1902-1906 Bury Town (1995) Ltd	

Back Row (L-R): Lee Smith, Ian Miller, Paul Barber, Tom Bullard and Richard Skelly (Captain)   Front Row: James Tatham, Daniel
Cunningham, Scott Field, Carl Murkin, Craig Parker and Steve McGavin Mascots: Matthew Collins, Scott and Brett McGavin

CANVEY ISLAND

Founded: 1926
Nickname:
The Gulls

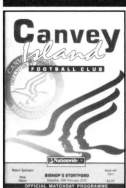

Manager: John Batch   **Coach:** Garry Britnell   **Physio:** Dale Corbell
Club Colours: Yellow/White/White
Change Colours: White/Sky Blue/Sky Blue
Club Sponsor: Frost Financial Services
Previous League: Conference
Best Seasons: League: 5th Conference 2003-2004   **F.A.Vase:** Semi-Final 1992-93
F.A. Cup: 3rd Round 2001-2002   **F.A.Trophy.** Winners 2000-2001
Ground address: Park lane, Canvey Island, Essex SS8 7PX
Tel No: 01268 511888
Club Website: www.canveyislandfc.com
Capacity: 4,100   **Seats:**500   **Covered:**827   **Floodlights:** Yes
Simple Directions:
  By Road: A130 from A13 or A127 at Sadlers Farm roundabout.One mile through
town centre, first right past old bus garage..
  By Rail: Nearest statio:Benfleet (BR). Three miles from ground on Fenchurch St
line from London.Then bus 3 or151 to the stop after the Admiral Jellicoe pub.
Midweek Home Matchday: Tuesday
Clubhouse: Open Tuesday & Thursday evenings, matchdays and private functions.
Club Shop: Sells full range of club products.
Local Radio: BBC Essex & Essex FM
Local Press: Evening Echo

CLUB PERSONNEL
Chairman: Dennis Rugg
President: Dr. Bob Spink M.P.
Secretary: Gary Sutton, 58 Lottem Road, Canvey Island,Essex SS8 7HX
Tel Nos; 01268 696863 (H) 07790 25828 (M)
Programme
Editor: Keith Johnson
Tel No: 07773 959 125
40 pages £1.50
2005-2006
Captain: Ben Chenery
Player of the Year:
Ben Sedgemore
Top Goalscorer: Lee Boylan

CLUB STATISTICS

Record	**Attendance:** 3,553 v Aldershot Town Isthmian League 2002-2003	
	Career Goalscorer: Andy Jones	
	Season's Top Scorer: Lee Boylan	
	Career Appearances: Steve Ward	
Record Transfer Fee	**Paid:** £5,000 to Northwich Victoria for Chris Duffy	
	Received: £4,500 to Farnborough Town for Brian Horne	
Senior Honours:	F.A.Trophy Winners 2000-2001 R-Up 2001-2002 Isthmian Champions 2003-04	
	Isthmian Divison 1 Champions 1993-1994 Essex Sen. Cup 98-99 00-01 01-02	
Previous Leagues:	Southend & District, Thurrock & Thamesid Combination,	
	Parthenon, Metropolitan, Greater London 64-71 Essex Senior	
	71-95 Isthmian 95-04 Conference 2004-2006	

Back row (L-R): Leon Gordon, Dave Kreyling, Kevin Dobinson, Ricky Wiseman, Glen Johnson, Matt Reade, Jay Curran.**Middle:** John Batch (manager), Dale Corbell (physio), Stuart Batch, George Blewer, Andrew West, Lee Jay, Steve Corbell, Danny Lamb, Matt Grocott, Jon Stuart, Tony West (assistant). **Front:** Clyde Roberts, Chris Bourne, Nicky Rugg, Ryan Edgar, Adam Holmes, Craig Davidson.

ENFIELD

Founded: 183
Nickname:
The E's

Manager: Paul Wildman **Coach:** **Physio:** Joe Miller

Club Colours: White/Blue/White **Change Colours:** Yellow & Blue

Club Sponsor: DBS Desira **Previous League:** Southern

Best Seasons: League: Alliance Champions 1982-83 1985-86

F.A. Cup: 4th Round 1980-1981 **F.A.Trophy.:** Winners1981-82 1987-88

F.A.Vase: 5th Round 2004-2005

Ground address: Groundshare with Ware F.C.

Club Website: www.enfieldfc.co.uk

Capacity: 3,300 **Seats:**312 **Covered:**500 **Floodlights:** Yes

Simple Directions: Leave A10 at juction of A602 & B101 (Ware North) turn right at roundabout after 300 yards and follow Ware sign past Rank factory. Turn left at main roundabout onto A1170 (Wadesmill Road). Stadium on right after 3/4 mile

Midweek Home Matchday: Tuesday

Clubhouse: Bar open for E.F.C. on matchdays **Club Shop: Yes**

Local Radio:

Local Press: Enfield Gazette, Enfield Advertiser and Enfield Independant.

CLUB PERSONNEL
Chairman: S.Whittington
President: R.Prosser
Secretary: Mark Wiggs, 1 Trumper
Road, Stevenage, HertsSG1 5JZ
Tel No: 07957 647820 (M)

Programme
Editor: Mark Kettlety
40 page s£.50

CLUB STATISTICS

Record	**Attendance:** 10,000 v Spurs (Floodlight opening at Southbury Rd.)10.10.62
	Career Goalscorer: Tommy Lawrence 191 (1959-1964)
	Career Appearances: Andy Pape 643 (1985-92 93-99)
Record Transfer Fee	**Paid:** Undisclosed from Barnet for Gary Abbott
	Received: Undisclosed from Coventry City for Paul Furlong
	Victory: 18-0 v Stevenage F.A.Cup Qualifying Round. 22.01.27
	Defeat: 0-12 v Woolwich Poly London League Division 2 27.04.04
Senior Honours:	Alliance Championship 82-3 85-6 R-up 81-82 Isthmian Lg (8)

Senior Honours: Alliance Championship 82-3 85-6 R-up 81-82 Isthmian Lg (8) R-up (2) Athenian Lg (2) R-up 34-5 Middlesex Senior Cup (9) R-up (10) London Sen.Cup (5) R-up (3) European Amateur Cup winners 1969-70

Previous Leagues: Tottenham & Dist. 1894-95, North Middx 1896-1903 London 03-13 Athenian 12-14 21-39 45-63, Herts & Middx Comb 39-42 Isthmian 63-81 Alliance/Conference 81-90

Back row.left to right: Precious Koko, Danny Jones, Jeff Jackson, Sanny Alleyne, Greg Howell, Anthony Anseed, Nick Christoph, Michael Collier, Jamie Richards, Ronnie Watson, Owen Beale and Mark Whittington.
Front row: Jimmy Faulkner, Payul Wildman, Jeff Hammond, Dave McDonald, James Bunn, Jamie Andrews, Craig Chad wick, Al-James Hannigam and Michael Pattick..

ENFIELD TOWN

Founded: 2001
Nickname:
' ET's or Towners

Manager: Jim Chandler   **Coach:**   **Physio:**

Club Colours: White/VBliue/White

Change Colours: All Yellow

Club Sponsor: Direct Boot & Embroidery

Previous League: Southern

Best Seasons: League:3rd Southern Division 1 East

F.A. Cup: 2nd Qualifying Round Replay 2004-2005

F.A.Trophy.:   **F.A.Vase:** 3rd Round 2003-2004 2004-2005

Ground address: Groundsharing with Brimsdown Rovers at Brimsdown Soocial Club, Goldstone Ground, Enfield. Tel No: 0208 8045491

Club Website: www.etfc.co.fc

Capacity: 2,300   **Seats:** 250   **Covered:**300   **Floodlights:** Yes

Simple Directions: Off Green Street which is off Hertford Road (A1010) Buses 191 or 307 or Liverpool Street to Brimsdown (BR) or Southbury Rd

Midweek Home Matchday: Tuesday

Clubhouse: Yes **Club Shop:** No

Local Radio:

Local Press: Enfield Gazette, Enfield Advertiser and Enfield Independant

CLUB PERSONNEL

Chairman: David Bryant
President:
Secretary: Peter Coath, 33 Ashford Crescent, Enfield,Midd'x EN3 7HX **Tel No:** 07949 378931

Programme Editor & Press Officer: Ciaron Glennon
32 Pages £1.50

CLUB STATISTICS		
Record	**Attendance:** 562 v Enfield, Middlesex Charity Cup 2002-2003	
	Career Goalscorer: Dan Clarke 68	
	Career Appearances: Stuart Snowden 147	
Record	**Victory:** 7-0 v Ilford (a) 29.04.03	
	Received:	
Senior Honours:	Essex Senior Champions 2002-2003 Runners -Up 2001-2002	
	Middlesex Senior Cup Runners-Up 2002-2003	
Previous	**Leagues:** Essex Senior League and Isthmian League	
	Name: Broke awy fromEnfield F.C. in 2001	

Back Row (L-R): Peter Hammatt, Phil Snowden, (Coaches), Russell Penn, David Allen, Steve Magona, Andy Hall, Jim Chandler (Manager)Adam Gant, Paul Campbell, Steve Baldwin, Graeme Hall, Roy Austin (Physio), Bradley Brotherton. **Front:** Lee Smith,Kieron Woodward, Matt Negus, Bryan Hammatt, Trevor Paul, Niall Ritchie, John Morgan, Rudi Hall.

FLACKWELL HEATH

Founded: 1907
Nickname: Heath

Manager: Byron Walton   **Assistant Manager:** Mark Tallentine
Coach: Tony Calvert   **Physio:** Richard Lansiquot
Club Colours: All Red
Change Colours: All Gold
Club Sponsor: Thakar Coombs (Solicitors)
Previous League: Hellenic
Best Seasons: League : 3rd Isthmian Div 2
F.A. Cup: 4th Qualifying Round 2002-03 2004-05
F.A.Vase: 3rd Round 1986-1987
Ground address: Wilks Park, Heath End Road, Flackwell Heath, High Wycombe HP 10 9EA Tel No: 01628 523892
Club Website: www.flackwellheathfc.co.uk
Capacity: 2,000   **Seats:** 150   **Covered:** Yes   **Floodlights:** Yes
Simple Directions: From Junction 3 (Wycombe East) off the M40, follow signs to Flackwell Heath left up Treadwell Hill and right at roundabout at top of hill. Ground is 800 yards on right at rear of Magpie pub.
Midweek Home Matchday: Tuesday
Clubhouse: Open every evening   **Club Shop:** No
Local Radio: Thames Valley FM
Local Press: Maidenhead Advertiser

CLUB PERSONNEL
Chairman: Terry Glynn
President: Ken Crook
Vice Chairman: G.Turner
Secretary: Mrs Christine Hobbs, 23 Southfield Road,Flackwell Heath, Bucks.HP10 9BT
Tel No: 01628 521051(H)
07929 216264(M)
Press Officer & Prog Ed:
Geoff Turner
Programme Editor:
18 Pages £1.00
2005-2006
Captain: Gordon Hill
Player of the Year: Gordon Hill
Top Goalscorer: Gordon Hill

CLUB STATISTICS

Record

Attendance: 4,500 v Oxford United (Charity Game 1966)

Career Goalscorer: Tony Wood

Career Appearances: Lee Elliott

Victory 6-0 v Clapton (A) & Petersfield United (A):

Defeat: 0-7 v Aveley

Senior Honours: Hellenic League Divisoon 1 Runners-Up 76-77

Wycombe Senior Cup Winners (12)

Previous Leagues: Great Western Combination and Hellenic.

Back Row (L-R): Byron Walton (Manager) James Roake, Richie Glynn, James Clarke, Nick Hart.
Matt Rolfe (captain) Neil Hanson, Danny Oliphant, Renee Fontaine.
Front: James Cox, Rory Jenkins, Dean Thomas, Tony Calvert (Asst) Barry McCoy, Mark Tallentire (Asst)
Derek Payne, Callum Coull.

GREAT WAKERING ROVERS

Founded: 1919
Nickname:Rovers

£1.50

t**Manager:** Ian O'Connell   **Assistant Manager:** Dave Patien: **Physio:** Clive Taylor
Club Colours: Green & White Stripes/White/Green
Change Colours: Red/Blue/red
Club Sponsor: I.M.S.
Previous League: Southern
Best Seasons: League: 13th Southern Div 1 East   **F.A.Trophy.:**
F.A. Cup: 2nd Qualifying Round 1998-1999
F.A.Vase: 5th Round 1997-8 2001-2
Ground address: Burroughs Park, Little Wakering Hall Lane, Gt.Wakering,
Southend, Essex SS3 0HQ Tel No: 01702 217812
Club Website:www.greatwakeringroversfc.co.uk
Capacity: 2,500   **Seats:** 150   **Covered:**300   **Floodlights:** Yes
Simple Directions: A127 towards Southend and follow signs for Shoeburyness for
about four miles.. Turnleft to Gt Wakering onn B1017 at Bournes Green. Go down
High Street for half a mile and ground is on the left.
Clubhouse: Open every evening, Sat 11-11, Sun 12-3 & 7.30-10.30p.m.
Hot meals, snacks etc matchdays only
Club Shop: No
Local Radio: Essex F.M.
Local Press: Evening News

CLUB PERSONNEL
Chairman: Roy Ketteridge
President: Roger Burroughs
Secretary: Roger Sampson,
37 Lee Lotts,Gt.Wakering,Esssex
SS3 0HA **Tel No:** 01702218794
Press Officer: Nobby Johnson

Programme
Editor: Nobby Johnson
24-32 Pages £1.30

2005-2006
Captain: John Heffer
Player of the Year: Nicki Beale
Top Goalscorer: Neil Richmond

CLUB STATISTICS

Record	**Attendance:** 1,150 v Southend United (Friendly) 19.07.06
	Career Goalscorer:
	Career Appearances:
Record	**Victory:** 9-0 v Eton Manor 27.12.931:
	Defeat: 1-7 v Bowers United ,Essex Senior 01.04.98
Senior Honours:	Isthmian League Div. 3 R-up 99-00; Essex Snr Lg. 94-95,
	(Wirral Programme Essex Sen. Lg. Award 92-93 94-95)
Previous Leagues:	**Leagues:** Southend & Dist. 19-81, Southend All. 81-89, Essex I'mediate 89-92,
	Essex Senior 1992-1999, Isthmian 1999-2004 Southern 2004-2005
	Ground: Gt Wakering Rec

Back Row (L-R): Keith Wilson, Joel Ettienne-Clark, Dave Burnie, Michael Begg, Joe Brandon, Kevin Cole.
Middle: David Hey (Res. Manager), John Simmons, Gary Howard, Nikki Beale, Neil Richmond, Elliott Gresham, James White,
Cleve Taylor (Physio). **Front Row:** Ryan Wilkinson, Steve Butterworth, Ashley Harrison, Roger Burroughs (President),
Iain O'Connell (Manager), Louis Green, John Heffer, Dave Patient (Asst. Manager).

HARLOW TOWN

Founded: 1879
Nickname: Hawks

Manager: Tom Cunningham **Coaches:** Paul Wickenden and Tan Green

Club Colours: Red & White/White/White

Change Colours: White/Black/Black

Club Sponsor: BritSec International.Ltd.

Previous League: Southern

Best Seasons: League: 9th Southern Div 1East 2005-2006

F.A. Cup: 4th Round 1979-1980   **F.A.Trophy.:** 2nd Rd 1980-81 1981-82

F.A.Vase: 3rd Round 1988-1989

Ground address: Harlow Sports Centre,Hammarskold Road,Harlow CM20 2JF

Tel No: 01279 445319

Club Website: www.harlowtown.co.uk

Capacity: 10,000   **Seats:** 400   **Covered:** 500   **Floodlights:** Yes

Simple Directions: Near town centre, 10 mins walk from Harlow Town (BR) station

Midweek Home Matchday: Wednesday

Clubhouse: Club Shop: Yes

Local Radio: Essex Radio, BBC Essex,Ten 17

Local Press: Harlow Citizen, Harlow Star and Harlow Herald & Post

CLUB PERSONNEL

Chairman: Steve Ray
President: Ron Bruce
Secretary: Martin Haines, 23 Wood Hill, Harlow,Essex,CM12 0XA
Tel No: 07729 967876(M)

Programme Editor: Mark Kettley
36pages £1.00

2005-2006
Captain: Gary Wraight
Player of the Year:
Top Goalscorer: Sammy Winstone

CLUB STATISTICS

Record | **Attendance:** 9,723 v Leicester City F.A.Cup 3rd Round Replay 08.01.80
Goalscore in a Season: Jeff Wood 45 in 1988-1989
Career Appearances: Norman Gladwin 646 (1949-1970)

Record | **Victory:** 12-0 v Hertford Athletic (H) E.Herts Lg. 05.10.29
Defeat: 0-11 v Ware(A) Spartan Div 1 (East) 06.03.48

Senior Honours: Isthmian League Div 1 78-79 R-up 82-83, Div 2 North 88-89, Athenian Lg Div 1 71-72, Essex Snr Cup 78-79,

Previous Leagues: **Leagues:** East Herts (pre-1932); Spartan 32-39 46-54; London 54-61; Delphian 61-63; Athenian 63-73; Isthmian 73-92; Inactive 92-93
Grounds: Marigolds 1919-22; Green Man Field 22-60

Back Row (L-R): Ryan Oliva, Danny Chapman, Viegbe Ganyo, Theo Daniels, Oliver Monksfield, Gregg Williams. **Middle:** Paul Wickenden (coach), Kevin Warren, Neil Moore, Stephen Mensah, Glenn Jackson, Charlie Hasler, Gabriel Fanibuyan, Tobi Ositola, Adam Dangerfield, Ian Green (coach). **Front Row:** Marvin Hong, Mark Taylor, Marc Salmon, Tommy Cunningham (Manager), Leon Lalite, Ricky Goldblatt, Jon Renaut.

ILFORD

Re-Formed: 1987
Nickname:
The Foxes

Manager: Allan Fenn   **Assistant Manager:** Chris Woods:

Club Colours: Blue & White Hoops/White/Whites

Change Colours: Red & White

Club Sponsor: T.B.A.

Previous League: Southern

Best Seasons: League: 21st Southern Div 1 East **F.A. Cup:** 2nd Round 1973-1974

F.A.Trophy.: 1st Round 2005-06   **F.A.Vase:** 2nd Round 1999-2000

Ground address: Cricklefield Stadium,High Road, Ilford, Essex. 1GI 1UB

Tel No: 0181 5140019

Club Website: www.ilfordfootballclub.co.uk

Capacity: 5,000   **Seats:** 216   **Covered**: Yes   **Floodlights**: Yes

Simple Directions: Five minures walk from Seven Kings Station, opposite 'The Cauliflower' pub. Or 86 Bus.

Midweek Home Matchday: Wednesday

Clubhouse: Open lunchtimes and evenings every day. Snacks available.

Club Shop: No

Local Radio: Time F.M.and BBC Essex

Local Press: Ilford Recorder

CLUB PERSONNEL

Chairman: George Hogarth

Vice-Chairman: Melvin Attwell

President:
Lord John Taylor of Warwick

Secretary: Roger Chivers: 50 Harrow Road, Barking, Essex IG11 7RA**Tel No**: 07710 285571

Programme
Editor: Len Llewellyn
Tel No: 01277 363103

2005-2006
Captain: Ray Taylor
Player of the Year:
Top Goalscorer: Declan Perkins 8

CLUB STATISTICS	
Record	**Attendance:** 17,000 Ilford Boys v Swansea Boys (Schools Trophy Final)
	Career Goalscorer:
	Career Appearances:
	Transfer Fee Paid:
	Transfer Fee Received:
Senior Honours:	FA Amateur Cup: 28-29 29-30, R-up 35-36 57-58 1973-74
	Isthmian League Champions 06-07 20-21 21-22 Runners-up (6)
	Essex Senior Cup x 14 (record number of wins), R-up x5;
	London Senio. Cup x 7 R-up x 5
Previous Leagues:	Isthmian. Spartan, Essex Senior, Isthmian, Southern

MALDON TOWN

Founded: 1946
Nickname: Blues

Manager: Colin Wallington   **Asst.Man.**: NIck Smith   **Coach:** Glen Churchett
Goalkeeptng Coach: Ian Huttley   **Physio:** Ian Jenkins
Club Colours: Blue & white hoops/blue/blue
Change Colours: Red & Black
Club Sponsor: Maddison Heights
Previous League: Southern Division One East.
Previous Ground: Fambridge Road (pre 1994)
Best Seasons: League:3rd Southern Div 1 East and won play-offs.
F.A.Cup: 3rd Qualifying Round 2000-01   **F.A.Trophy.:**   2nd Qual. Rd.
F.A.Vase: Semi-Final 2003
 Ground address: Wallace Binder Ground, Park Drive, Maldon CM9 5XX
Tel No: 01621 853762
e-mail: robbophil@hotmail.com
Website: http:// www.maldontownfc.co.uk
Capacity: 2,800   **Seats:** 155   **Covered:** 300   **Floodlights:** Yes
Simple Directions: From M25 jct.28 travel north on A12 until A414 to Maldon. Turn right at Safeways roundabout, then over next two roundabouts. Ground on right.
Midweek Home Matchday: Tuesday
Clubhouse:.Open to visitors on matchh days with variety of food.
Club Shop:

CLUB PERSONNEL
Chairman: Mike Kirkham
President: Bob Large
Secretary: Phil Robinson,
9 Lyndhurst Drive, Bicknacre, Essex
CN3 4XL
01245 222633 (H)
07759 066636 (M)
Programme Editor: Lisa Noble
Press Officer: Vernon Stitch
Commercial Department:
Mike Kirkham & Dave Buckby

CLUB STATISTICS

Record	**Attendance**: 1,163 v AFC Sudbury .F.A.Vase Semi-Final April 2003
	Victory: 10-1 v Dartford (a)
	Defeat:
	Career Goalscorer:
	Career Appearances: Jack Judd
	Transfer Fee Paid: **Received:** £5,000 from Millwall for Neil Harris
Senior Honours:	Essex Senior League 84-85 Eastern Co.Div 1 96-97
Previous Leagues:	Mid Essex, N.Essex, Essex & Suffolk Border, Essex Senior.

Back row, left to right: Neal Shade, Chris Whelpdale, Sean Bell, Simon Overland, Gary Howard, Craig Huttley.
Front row: Nicky Rugg, Paul Sammons, Simon Parker, Dean Parratt and Judd Cole.   Photo Alan Coomes

POTTERS BAR TOWN

Founded: 1960
Nickname: Grace or Scholars

Manager: Andy Leese   **Coach:** Steve Hurd: **Physio:** Carly Wells
Club Colours: Red & Royal Blue Stripes/Blue/Blue
Change Colours: All Yellow with Blue trim
Club Sponsor: Dagenham Motors
Previous League: Spartan South Midlands
Best Seasons: League: 15th Southern League Division 1 East 2005-2006
F.A. Cup: Preliminary Round 2004-2005   **F.A.Trophy.:**
F.A.Vase: 6th Round 1997-1998
Ground address: Parkfield, Watkins Rise, off The Walk, Potters Bar, Herts.
EN6 1QN **Tel No:** 01707 654833
Club Website: www.pottersbartown.co.uk
Capacity: 2,000   **Seats:** 150   **Covered:** 250   **Floodlights:** Yes
Simple Directions: M25 Jct 24 enter Potters Bar along Southgate Road (A111) turn right into High Street at first lights (A1000) then left into The Walk after half a mile. Ground 200 yards on right.(opposite Potters Bar cricket club)
Midweek Home Matchday: Tuesday
Clubhouse: Training Nights, Matchdays and week-ends.
Club Shop: Contact Jeff Barnes (01707 662399) for details of club badges, pennants, car stickers etc.
Local Radio:
Local Press: Welwyn & Hatfield Times (Potters VBar edition)

CLUB PERSONNEL

Chairman: Peter Waller
Vice Chairman: JohnRobinson:
General Manager: Les Eason
Secretary: KevinWilmot,83 Mandeville Court, Lower Hall Lane, Chingford, London
Tel No: 0208 5298475

Programme
Editor: Kevin Wilmot
44 Pages £1.50

2005-2006
Captain: Ryan Harris
Player of the Year: James Dickie
Top Goalscorer: Richard Howard

CLUB STATISTICS

Record	**Attendance:** 4,000 Charity Match.1997 268 for club v Wealdstone FACup 98
Career Goalscorer:	
Career Appearances:	
Record Transfer Fee	**Paid:**
	Received:
Senior Honours:	Spartan South Midlands Champions 04-05 R-up 98-99
	Prem ier Divison North R-up 97-98
	South Midlands League Premier Division 1996-97,
Previous Leagues:	Barnet & Dist.1960-65 N.London Comb. 1965-68 Herts Senior County League 1968-91 Spartan and Spartan South Midlands 1991-2005 Southern 2005-2006

Back row (L-R): Andy Martin, Dave Blower, Richard Hayward, Gabriel Fanibuyan, Sam Ledger, Carl Ashton, Nicky Winger, James Dickie, Luke Smith.
Front: Tony Burke, Josh Cooper, Dean Harding, Kieron Woodward, Michael Sharman, Richard Howard, Daniel Talbot

REDBRIDGE

Re-Formed: 2004
Nickname: Motormen

THE OFFICIAL MATCHDAY PROGRAMME OF REDBRIDGE F.C.

THE motormen
AT OAKSIDE STADIUM   V ILFORD
K.O. 3.00pm   SATURDAY 26th AUGUST 2006

2006/07 Season Kicks Off

RYMAN DIVISION ONE NORTH   Ryman

Manager: Jim Stannard

Coach: Lyndon Lynch   **Asst. Coach:** John Froskett

Club Colours: All Blue

Change Colours: Red/white/red

Club Sponsor: Sky Sports

Previous League: Conference South

Best Seasons: Highest League Position: 22nd Conference South 2004-05

F.A.Cup: 1st Rd 98-99 1st Rd replay 03-04

F.A.Amateur Cup: S-Final 1953-54

F.A.Trophy.: 3rd Rd 2004-05   **F.A.Vase:** 5th Rd 98-99

Ground address: Oakside Stadium, Station Rd., Barkingside, Ilford, Essex.

Tel No: 0208 5503611

Capacity: 3,000 **Seats:** 316 **Covered:** 1,000   **Floodlights:** Yes

Simple Directions: A12 from London. Turn left off Eastern Ave into Horns Rd, Barkingside (Greengate). Right into Craven Gardens, right again into Carlton Drive and left into Station Road. Go over bridge and ground is on right.

Midweek Home Matchday: Tuesday

Clubhouse: Large bar open very day.

Club Shop: Yes

CLUB PERSONNEL

Chairman: Jimmy Chapman
President: Nick Scheeler
Chief Executives: John Rowe & George Adams
Secretary: Mark Gallon
email:markgallon@redbridgefc.com
Prog. Ed.: Mike Stephenson
Tel No: 01268 684638 (H & Fax)

CLUB STATISTICS

Record	
Attendance:	F.A.Amateur Cup Semi-Final v Bishop Auckland 58.000 at St James Park, Newcastle.
Goalscorer:	Jeff Wood 196
Career Appearances:	Roger Bird

Senior Honours: London Senior Cup (5) Essex Senior Trophy (3) EsseX Senior Cup(5) Promoted from Isthmian Div 3 98-99, Div2 99-00 and Premier 01-02

Previous Leagues Spartan, Aetolian, Metropolitan, Essex Senior and Isthmian

500

TILBURY

Founded: 1900
Nickname:
The Dockers

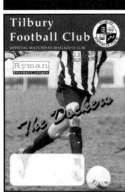

Gary heywoodManager: Tony Cross   **Coach:**   **Physio**: Steve Tyalorwww.portoflondon.co.uk

Club Colours: Black & White Stripes/Black/Black

Change Colours: Red& White Stripes/White/White

Club Sponsor:

Previous League: Essex Senior

Best Seasons: League: Isthmian Premier 76?

F.A. Cup: 3rd Round 1977-1978   **F.A.Trophy.:**

F.A.Vase: 4th Round 1999-2000   **F.A.Amateur Cup:** 6th Round1946-1947

Ground address: Chadfields, St.Chads Road, Tilbury, Essex RM18 8NL

Tel No: 01375 843093

Club Website:

Capacity: 4,000   **Seats**:350   **Covered**:1,000   **Floodlights**:Yes

Simple Directions: A 13 Southend bound go left at Chadwell St Mary's turning, then right after 400 metres and right again at roundabout (signed Tilbury). Right into St Chads Road after five miles. First right into Chadfields for ground.

Midweek Home Matchday: Tuesday

Clubhouse: Open Daily

Club Shop: No.

Local Radio:

Local Press:

CLUB PERSONNEL

Chairman: Robin Nash

Vice Chairman: Daniel Nash

Secretary & Pres Officer:

Mark Southgate, 93 Falcon Avenue, Grays. RM17 6SB

Tel No: 01375 377215 (H)

07979 525117 (M)

Programme

Editor: Secretary

40 pages £1.50

2005-2006

Captain: Terry Harris

Player of the Year: Paul Cobb

Top Goalscorer: Paul Cobb 32

CLUB STATISTICS	
Record	**Attendance:** 5,500 v Gorleston F.A.Cup 1949
	Career Goalscorer: Ross Livermore 282 in 305 games
	Career Appearances: Nicky Smith 424 (1975-1985)
Record Transfer Fee	**Paid**:
	Received: £2,000 from Grays Athlwetic for Tony Macklin 1990 and from Dartford for Steve Connor (1985)
Senior Honours:	Isthmian Division One 1975-11976, Athenian League 1968-1969 and Essex SeniorCup (4) Runners-Up (5)
Previous Leagues:	Grays & Dist, also South Essex, Kent 27-31, London, South Essex Comb.(war time) Corinthian 50-57, Delphian 62-63, Athenian 6-73 Isthmian73-2004 Essex Senior 2004-2005

WALTHAM ABBEY

Founded: 1946
Nickname:
The Abbotts

Manager: Bob Ballard   **Coach:** Lee Johnson   **Physio:** T.B.A.

Club Colours: Green & White Hoops/White/White

Change Colours: Red & Black Hoops/Black/Red

Club Sponsor: Ems Group

Previous League: Essex Senior

Best Seasons: League: Runners Up Essex Senior 2005-2006

F.A. Cup: 2nd Qualifying Round   **F.A.Trophy.:** N/A

F.A.Vase: 2nd Round 1997-1998

Ground address: Capershotts, Sewardstone Road,Waltham Abbey, Essex.

Tel No: 01992 711287

Club Website: www.wafc.net

Capacity: 2,000   **Seats:** 300   **Covered:** 500   **Floodlights:** Yes

Simple Directions:

Midweek Home Matchday: Tuesday

Clubhouse: Yes   **Club Shop:** no

Local Radio:

Local Press:

CLUB PERSONNEL

Chairman: Joe Collins
President: R.Waite
Secretary: Dave Hodges, 13 Rosebank, WalthamAbbey ,Essex EN9 3DE
Tel No: 07956 570408 (M)

Programme
Editor: Derek Bird
Tel No: 01992 711287
44 Pages £1.20

2005-2006
Captain: Lee White
Player of the Year: Lee White
Top Goalscorer: Harry Elmes

CLUB STATISTICS

Record	Attendance:
	Career Goalscorer:
	Career Appearances:
	Transfer Fee Paid:
	Transfer Fee Received:
Senior Honours:	Essex Junior Cup 1975-1976 Essex Senior Cup 2004-005
	Essex Senior League Runners-Up 2005-2006 London Senior Cup 1999
Previous Leagues:	Spartan, Esex & Herts Border League, Essex Senior
Names:	Abbey Sports and amalgamated with Beechfields Sports in 1974 to form
	Beechfield. Renamed tas Waltham Abbey in 1976

Back Row (LR) Albert Bostock, Harry Elmes, Marc Sontag, Luke Power, John Hickman, Lee White, Wesley Forde, Westley Rutherford, Tony Tillbrook
Front Row (LR) Daniel Page, Nicky Burt, James Elmes, Russell Williamson, Lee Mitchell, Harry Hayes

WALTHAM FOREST

Founded: 1995
Nickname:Lilywhites

Manager: Coach: Physio: Mike Gordon
Club Colours: White/Black/White
Change Colours: Yellow/Blue/Blue
Club Sponsor: Eds Transport Sercvices
Previous League: Essex Senior
Best Seasons: League: 8th Southern Divison 1 East
F.A. Cup: 2nd Qualifying round 2004-2005　　**F.A.Trophy.:**
F.A.Vase:
Ground address: Wadham Lodge Sports Ground, Kitchener Road, Walthamstowe, London E17 **Tel No:** 0208 527 2444
Club Website:
Capacity: 2,000　　**Seats**:200　　**Covered**: 600　　**Floodlights**: Yes
Simple Directions: Take the North Circular Road to The Crooked Billet,then turn right into Chingford Road and into Brookscroft Road , ground is in Kitchener Road first on left .Walthamstowe Central (Victoria Line tube) is one mile away then buses W21 or 256

Midweek Home Matchday: Tuesday
Clubhouse: Club Shop:
Local Radio:
Local Press:

CLUB PERSONNEL
Chairman: Harry Ramis
Vice-Chairman: Altan Kemal
Secretary: Andy Perkins, 4 Chestnit Drive, Wanstead . London E11 2TA
Tel No: 0208 5304551
Programme
Editor & Press Officer:
Andy Perkins
32 pages 31.00

CLUB STATISTICS

Record	Attendance:
	Career Goalscorer:
	Career Appearances:
Record Transfer Fee	Paid:
	Received:
Senior Honours:	London Challenge Cup Runners-Up 1995-96, 1996-97
	Essex Senior League Runners Up 2005-2006
Previous	Leagues:
	Name: Walthamstow Pennant (64-95), Leyton Pannant (1995-2003)

Back Row (L-R): Cevdet Ezel. Dave Salmon. Altan Kemal, Dave Crabb, David Field, Simon Tickler, Rick Brown, Ian Barnes, Peter Goodman, Gavin King, Paul Salmon. Robert Carter, Liam Baptiste. John Lawford, Andy Perkins, Tony Brazior, George Gross, Harry Ramis.
Middle Row: Billy Reid, Jay devereax. Tony Samuels. Kemi Kemal, Hakan Ramis, Wayne Brown, Onder Acil, John Morgan, SAS.
Front Row: Hasan Oktay, Ryan Lee, Warren Ryan, Paul Adolphe, Chris Cashman, I SOS, Ryan Fishendon, Warren Hackett.

WARE

Founded: 1892
Nickname: Blues

Manager: Glen Alzapiedi   **Assistant Manager**: Barry Mason
Physio: Lisa Corallini
Club Colours: Blue & White Stripes/Blue/Blue
Change Colours: Amber & Black
Club Sponsor: M.C.Plumbing
Previous League: Isthmian
Best Seasons: League: Isthmian Div 2 Champions 2005-2006
F.A. Cup: 1st Round 1968-1969   **F.A.Trophy.:**
F.A.Vase: 4th Round 2002-2003
Ground address: Woodsmill Park, Wadesmill Road, Ware, Herts. SG12 0HZ
Tel No: 01920 463247
Club Website: www.ware.intheteam.com
Capacity: 3,300   **Seats**:500   **Covered**:312   **Floodlights**: Yes
Simple Directions: A10 off Jct A602 & B1001 turn right at roundabout after 300 yards and follow Ware sign, past Rank factory. Turn left at main road onto A1170 (Wadesmill Rd.) Stadium on right after 3/4 mile.
Midweek Home Matchday: Tuesday
Clubhouse: Open Matchdays   **Club Shop:** Yes
Local Radio: Heartbeat F.M.
Local Press: Hertfordshire Mercury

CLUB PERSONNEL
Chairman: Aiden Mynott
Secretary: Ian Bush, 42 Burnett Square, Hertford, SG14 2HG
Tel No: 01992 587334

Programme Editor: K.Mynott
24pages 50p

2005-2006
Captain: Matt Allen
Player of the Year: Joe Stevens
Top Goalscorer: John Frendo

CLUB STATISTICS

Record	**Attendance:** 3,800 v Hendon F.A.Amateur Cup 1956-1957
	Career Goalscorer:M.Hibbert 229
	Goalscorer in a Season: Geirge Dearman 98 1926-1927
	Career Appearances: Gary Riddle 654
Record	**Victory:** 10-1 v Wood Green Town
	Defeat: 0-11 v Barnet
Senior Honours:	Isthmian Divison 2 Champions 2005-2006 Herts Senior Cup (5) East Anglian Cup 1973-1974
Previous	**Leagues:** East Herts, North Middx 07-08, Herts Co. 08-25, Spartan 25-55 Delphian 55-63, Athenian 63-75 **Grounds:** Highfields, Canons Park, London Road, Presdales Lower Park 1921-26

Back Row (L-R): Kai Ramshaw, Lee Chappell, Daryl Hanson, Sam Berry, Terry Gritton, Ali Waldron, Adam Spenceley, Russell Ling, Joe Stevens, Bradley Stamp, Steve Horsey, Sam Rose, Ricky HArding, Paul Burton, Lennie Mason.**Front:** Andy Crawford, Ashley D`Silva, Jimmy Martin, John Frendo, Danny Wolf, Barry Mason (Asst Manager), Glen Alzapiedi (Manager), Matt Allen (Coach), Ilyas Cil, Danny Spaul, Chris Ellerbeck, Gormen Dogan.

WINGATE & FINCHLEY

Founded: 1991
Nickname: Blues

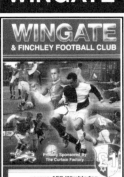

Manager: Adam Lee   **Coach:** Michael Stone   **Physio:**

Club Colours: Blue/White/White
Change Colours: All Yellow

Club Sponsor:
Previous League: Southern

Best Seasons: League: Isthmian Div 2 ?   **F.A.Vase:** Quarter Final 1974-1975
F.A. Cup: 2nd Qualifying Round 2003-2004   **F.A.Trophy.:**

Ground address: The Abrahams Stadium, Sunners Lane, Finchley,
London N12 0PO **Tel No:** 0208 446 2217

Club Website:
Capacity: 8,500   **Seats:** 500   **Covered:** 500   **Floodlights:** Yes
Simple Directions: North Circular (A406) to junction with High Road Finchley (A1000).
Go north and Summers Lane is 200 yds on right - parking for 80 cars. Bus 382 passes ground
Tube: to East Finchley (Northern Line) and then 263 bus to Summers Lane towards North Finchley
Midweek Home Matchday: Tuesday

Clubhouse: Open on match days plus a tea-bar. **Club Shop:** No.

Local Radio: **Local Press:**

CLUB PERSONNEL
Chairman: Mark Martyn
Presidents:
David Pleat & Harvey Ackerman
Secretary: Alan Evans c/o club
Tel Nos: 0208446 2217 (club)
07833632965 (M)

Programme
Editor: Peter Rebak
32 pages £1,50

CLUB STATISTICS

Record	**Attendance:** 9,555 Finchley v Bishop Auckland F.A.Amateur Cup 1949-1950
	Career Goalscorer: Marc Morris 578
	Career Appearances: Marc Morris 587 91975-1985)
Record	**Victory::**9-0 v Sarrett Herts Co. 20.04 85
	Defeat: 0-9 v Edgware Istthmian Div 2 15.01.2000
Senior Honours:	**As Finchley:** Isthmian League Div. 3 R-up 98-99, Promoted (7th) 2001-02,
	London Senior Cup winners 94-95
	As Wingate: Middx SnrCup SF, Athenian Lg Div 2 69-70, Sth Midlands League
	Div 1 R-up 89-90, London Sen Cup 79-80
Previous Leagues:	**Leagues:** (as Wingate & Finchley) South Mids 89-95Finchley: London 02-12
	14-15 23-25 30-39; Athenian 12-14 29-30 45-73; Isthmian73-91Wingate: Middx
	46-52; London 52-62; Delphian 62-63; Athenian 63-75; Barnet Yth,Hendon &
	Dist. Sunday 75-84; Herts 84-89 Isthmian 94-04, Southern 05-06
	Names: Wingate (founded 46), Finchley (founded late 1800s) merged in 91

WITHAM TOWN

Founded: 1947
Nickname: Town

Manager: Russell Tanner **Asst.Manager/ Coach**: Ken Varney
Club Colours: White/Black/Black
Change Colours: Red & Black/Black/Black
Club Sponsor: Specsavers
Previous League: Isthmian
Best Seasons: League: 2nd Isthmian Div 2 2005-2006
F.A. Cup: 2nd Qualifying Round 1988-89 1989-90
F.A.Vase: 5th Rd 1985-86
Ground address: Spa Road, Witham, Essex CM8 1UN
Tel No: 01376 511198 (Lounge) 520996 (Boardroom)
Club Website: www.withamtownfc.co.uk
Capacity: 2,500 **Seats**: 157 **Covered**:780 **Floodlights**: Yes
Simple Directions: From Witham BR (network SE) through pub car park and follow road to Faulkbourne at main roundabout turn left and ground is on the right, or if driving off A12 at Witham sign, take left at first lights (Spinks Lane) follow road under railway bridge and ground is 100 yards on left
Midweek Home Matchday: Tuesday
Clubhouse: Open every evening with hot snacks available. **Club Shop:** No
Local Radio: BBC Essex and Dream F.M.
Local Press: Witham & Braintree Times

CLUB PERSONNEL

Chairman: Tony Last
Secretary: Ron Macey, 36 Saxon Drive, Witham, Essex CM8 2HL
Tel No: 01376 511697 (H)
07711 959231 (M)
Programme
Editor: Nigel Dudley
35 pages £1.50
2005-2006
Captain: Justin Pearce
Player of the Year: Nicky Smith
Top Goalscorer: Kevin Budge

CLUB STATISTICS

Record	**Attendance:**	800 v Billericay Town Essex Senior League May 1976
	Career Goalscorer:	Colin Mitchell
	Career Appearances:	Keith Dent
Record Transfer Fee	**Paid:**	N/A
	Received:	Undisclosed from Southend United for Steve Tilson
	Victory:	7-0 v Banstead 1994
	Defeat:	0-9 v Collier Row 1995
Senior Honours:		Isthmian Div 2 Runners Up 2005-2006 Essex Senior Lg 70-71 85-86
Previous		**Leagues:** Mid Essex, Essex & Suffolk Border, Essex Senior 71-87
		Ground: Spa Road

Back Row (L to R) : Tony Last (Chairman), Ken Varney (Assistant Manager), Simon Turnnidge, Kevin Hawes, Stuart Crumpen, Kaan Hawes, Tony Walkin, Glen Revell, Justin Pearce (capt.), Ben Fuller, Alan Sampson, Russell Tanner (Manager), Jim Maunton (Safety Officer), Ron Macey (Football Secretary)
Front: Lance Forrester, David Hawes, Paul Rippingale, Cody McDonald, Nicky Smith, Gary Bennett, Danny Rowell, Gino Defeo, 2 mascots

WIVENHOE TOWN

Founded: 1925
Nickname:
The Dragons

Manager: Steve Pitt   **Assistant Manager:** Steve Wignall   **Physio:**
Club Colours: Royal Blue/White/White
Change Colours: Orange/Black/Black
Club Sponsor:
Previous League: Southern
Best Seasons: League: Isthmian Premier 90-91 ?
F.A. Cup: 4th Qualifyting Round 1989-1990 1994-1995
F.A.Trophy.: 2nd Round Replay 1989-1990
F.A.Vase: 5th Round 1982-1983
Ground address: Broad Lane Ground, Elmstead Road, Wivenhoe CO7 7HA
Tel No: 01206 825380
Club Website: www.wivenhoetownfc.co.uk
Capacity: 3,000   **Seats:** 250   **Covered:**1,300   **Floodlights:** Yes
Simple Directions: Leave Colchester towards Clacton take first turning (right) towards
Wivenhoe & 1st left. Ground is on the right at the cross-roads one mile from Wivenhoe (BR)
Midweek Home Matchday: Tuesday
Clubhouse: Open normal pub hours. Tel No: 01206 825380
Club Shop: A full range of souvenirs etc.
Local Radio: BBC Radio Essex and S.G.R.
Local Press: East Anglian Daily Times, Colchester Evening Gazette

CLUB PERSONNEL
Chairman: Phil Reeve
President:
Secretary/ Press Officer:
Mike Doyle, 15 Daniell Drive,
Colchester Essex
Tel No: 01206 573223

Programme
Editor: M.Boyle
Pages/Price

CLUB STATISTICS	
Record	**Attendance:** 1,912 v Runcorn F.A.Trophy 1st Round Feb. 1990
	Career Goalscorer: PaulHarrison 258 in 350 games
	Career Appearances: Keith Bain 538
Record Transfer Fee	**Paid:**
	Received: £5,875 for BobbyMayes (Redbridge Forest)
	Victory: 18-0 v Nayland
	Defeat: 0-8 v Carshalltton Athletic (*H) Isthmian League 28.08.93
Senior Honours:	IsthmianLeague Div 1 89-90 (Div 2 North 87-88); Essex Senior League R-up (3)
	Essex Senior Trophy 1987-88,. Essex Junior Cup R-up 55-56 78-79;
Previous Leagues:	**Leagues:** Brighlingsea & District 1927-50; Colchester & East Essex 50-71;
	Essex & Suffolk Border 71-79; Essex Senior 79-86 **Name:** Wivenhoe Rangers
	Grounds: Spion Kop; Broomfield (twice); Claude Watcham's Meadow; Vine
	Farm; King George V Playing Fields; Essex University

ASHFORD TOWN

Joint Managers: Tim Thorogood & John Cumberbatch **Physio:** Owen Jenner

Club Colours: Green/nNavy Blue/Green
Change Colours: All Yellow

Club Sponsor: Redrow

Previous League: Kent

Best Performances:
League: Southern Lg Southern Div R-up 1986-7,1995-6
F.A.Trophy.: Semi-Final 1972-3
F.A. Cup: 2nd Round 1961-62 v QPR (H) 1966-7 v Swindon T (A)

Ground address: The Homelands, Ashford Road, Kingsnorth, Ashford, Kent. TN26 1NJ Tel NO: 01233 611838
Simple Directions: Jct 10 off M20 onto A2070 towards Breneitt & Lydd Airport. Dual carriageway to junction of old A2070.Ground one mile on left through Kingsnorth four miles south of Ashford.
Capacity: 3,200   **Seats:** 500   **Covered:**1,250 **Floodlights:** Yes

Chairman: Tim Thorogood
President: Ashley Batt
Secretary: & Press Officer:
Elaine Osbourne, The Homelands, Ashford Rd., Kingsnorth, Ashford, Kent TH26 1NJ **Tel** 01233646713 (H) 07759891852 (M)
Commercial Manager:
Peter Young c/o Club

Progrtamme
Editor: Shelley Jenner

2005-2006
Captain: Ian Ross
Players of the Year: Tom Adlington
Top Goalscorer: Joby Thorogood

Official website: www.ashfordtownnfc.co.uk

Midweek Home Matchday: Tuesday
Clubhouse: Open matchdays and for special functions.
Local Press: Kentish Express & Adscene
Local Radio: Radio Kent,Invicta Radio & KMFM

CLUB STATISTICS

Record Attendance :	3,363 v Fulham F.A.Cup 1st Rd 1994 (at present ground.)
Victory:	10-1 v Bury Town February 1964
Defeat:	0-8 v Crawley Town Nov ember 1964
Career Goalscorer:	Dave Arter 197 **Career Appearances:** Peter McRobert 765
Transfer Fees:Paid:	£7,000 for Jeff Ross & Dave Arter to Sittingbourne 1994
Received:	£25,000 for Jeff Ross & Dave Arter from Hythe Town
	for an individual: £20,000 from Sittingbourne for Lee McRobert
Senior Honours:	Kent League 1948-49 Kent Senior Cup (4)
Previous Leagues:	Kent 1930-59
Ground:	Essella Park (6,525 v C.Palace FAC 1959)

Back row, left to right: Jason Long, Rajinder Sooch, Matt Curnock, Aiden Pursglove, Jamie Moxton, Paul Farmer, David Bourne, Sean Glover, Jani Seitsonen, Tim Russell, Terry Hawkey, Shane Simms, Andrew Raffle, Richard Vidler, Barry Cunningham, Sherlone Spooner and Joff Thorogood. **Middle Row**: Lynval Duncan, Ian Ross, Owen Jenner (Physio), Ray Risley, John Cumberbatch, Tim Thorogood, Mike Delaney, Martin Larkin, Mike Robbins, Shaun Bradshaw, and Eddie Achoko.**Front Row:** Steve Humphreys, Richard Boorman, Ken Elliott, Soloman Henry, Joby Thorogood, John-Paul Collier, Tery McCann, Anthony Pace, Mark Banks, Jahzeel Bonaparte, Tom Adlington, Marc Cumberbatch and Fabian Bolange.

BURGESS HILL TOWN

Founded: 1882
Nickname: Hillians

BURGESS HILL TOWN
FOOTBALL CLUB

Division 1

The
Leylands
Review

Season 2005/2006

Versus
Banstead Athletic
Monday 29th
August 2005

MAIN CLUB SPONSOR

TIME 24

Manager: Gary Croydon   **Coach:** Jim Thompson   **Physio:** Becky Morrison

Club Colours: Yellow & Black Quarters/Black/Yellow

Change Colours: White/Green/White

Club Sponsor: Time 24

Previous League: Southern

Best Seasons: League: 10th Isthmian Div 1 2004-2005

F.A. Cup: 4th Qualifying Round 1999-2000   **F.A.Trophy.:** 2nd Round 2003-2004

F.A.Vase: Quarter Finals 2001-2002

Ground address: Leylands Park, Maple Drive, Burgess Hill, West Sussex

Tel No: 01444 242429

Club Website: www.bhtfc.co.uk

Capacity: 2,250   **Seats:** 307   **Covered:** Yes   **Floodlights:** Yes

Simple Directions: Turn east from A273 London Road into Leylands Road, take 4th left
signposted Leyland Park. Nearest station Wivelsfield

Midweek Home Matchday: Wednesday

Clubhouse: Bar & Social Facilities plus tea bar.   **Club Shop:** Yes, full range.

Local Radio: Bright F.M. Southern F.M.

Local Press: Mid Sussex Times and The Argus

CLUB PERSONNEL

Chairman: Gary Croydon
Patron: Jack Lake
Chief Executive : Gary Croydon
Secretary: Tim Spencer, 30 Condor Way, Burgess Hill, RH15 9QA
Tel No: 07812 642498
Commercial Manager:
Dave Bradbury I
Programme
Editor & Press Officer:
Gary Newton
60 Pages £1.00
2005-2006
Captain: Mark Pulling
Player of the Year: Luke Gedling
Top Goalscorer: Luke Gedling

CLUB STATISTICS

Record	**Attendance:** 2,005 v AFC Wimbledon Isthmian Div 1 2004-2005
	Career Goalscorer: Ashley Carr 208
	Career Appearances: Paul Williams 499
Record	**Transfer Fee Paid:** N/A
	Fee Received: Undisclose four figure fee from Thurrock for Steve Harper
Senior Honours:	Sussex County League Championship (6) Sussex Senior Cup: 1883-84 184-85
	1885-86 Runners-Up 1997-98 Sussex RUR Charity Cup 91-92;
Previous Leagues:	**Leagues:** Mid Sussex League, Sussex County >03, Southern League 2003-04

Back row, left to right: Nick Bridle, Kevin Townsend, Darin Killpatrick, Shaheen Sadough, Ben Andrews, Steve Harper, Mattt Hurley, John Sullivan, Chris White (assistant manager) and Pat Gannon. **Front row:** Sean Edwards, Nicky Sullivan, Darren Smith, Lloyd Cotton, Adie Downey (Captain), Alex Robinson, Jack Holdroyd, Matt Stares and Matt Geard.

CHATHAM TOWN

Founded: 1882
Nickname: Chats

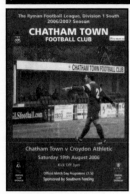

The Ryman Football League, Division 1 South 2006/2007 Season
CHATHAM TOWN FOOTBALL CLUB

Chatham Town v Croydon Athletic
Saturday 19th August 2006
Kick Off 3pm

Manager: Phil Miles   **Assistant Manager:** Steve Best   **Physio:** Andy Hyland

Club Colours: Red/Black/Black

Change Colours: All Blue

Club Sponsor: Ward Homes

Previous League: Kent

Best Seasons: League: 17th Southern Divison One East 2005-2006

F.A. Cup: Quarter Final 1888-1889   **F.A.Trophy.:** 3rd Round 1970-1971

F.A.Vase: 2nd Round 1996-97 1997-98 1999-2000

Ground address: Maidstone Road Sports Ground, Maidstone Road,Chatham, Kent.

ME4 6LR**Tel No:** 01634 812194

Club Website: www.chathamtownfc.net

Capacity: 5,000   **Seats:**500   **Covered 1,000:**   **Floodlights:** Yes

Simple Directions: M2, A229 Chatham turn-off, follow signs to Chatham, ground one and a half miles on right opposite garage. 1 mile from Chatham (BR).

Midweek Home Matchday: Tuesday 7.45

Clubhouse: Matchdays and functions   **Club Shop:** Yes

CLUB PERSONNEL
Chairman: Jeff Talbot
Vice Chairman: Barry Adams
Secretary: Brian Burcombe, 4 Hallwood Close, Parkwood, Rainham, Kent ME8 9NT
Tel No: 01634 363 419 (H)
Programme
Editor: John Crow
56 pages £1.50

2005-2006
Captain: Steve Best
Player of the Year: Steve Best
Top Goalscorer: Rob Denness

CLUB STATISTICS

Record	**Attendance:** 5,000 v Gillingham 1980	
	Career Goalscorer:	
	Career Appearances:	
Record Transfer Fee	**Paid:** N/A	
	Received: £500	
Senior Honours:	Kent Lg (9) Kent Snr Cup 1888-89 1904-05 10-11 18-19, Kent Snr Shield 19-2	
Previous	**Leagues:** Southern (several spells); Aetolian 59-64; Metropolitan 64-68; Kent (Several spells),	
	Names: Chatham FC; Medway FC (1970s)	
	Ground: Great Lines, Chatham 1882-90	

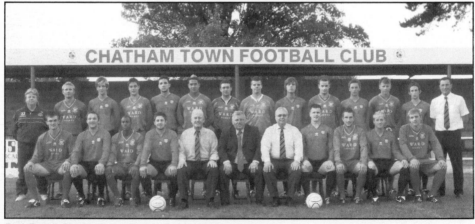

Back Row (L-R): Alan Collins (Coach), Searle, Botterill, Douglas, Denness, Goodyear, Whitehouse, Smith, Whitnall, Larkin, Davey, Lyons, Smith, Phil Miles (Manager).
Front Row: Harvey, Boyle, Brookes, Binks (Captain), Barry Adams (Vice Chairman), Chris Sparks (Sponsor), Jeff Talbot (Chairman), Best (Player Coahc), Finn, Pullman, Mortimor.

CORINTHIAN CASUALS

Founded: 1939
Nickname:
Casuals

Corinthian - Casuals F.C.
2005/06

Ryman
Ryman League Division One

Match ball sponsor:
Peter Haworth

Manager: Brian Adamson **Asst.Manager:** Lyndon Buckwell **Physio:** Paul Midwinter

Club Colours: Chocolate & Pink Halves/Navy Blue/White

Change Colours: White/Navy Blue/White

Club Sponsor: Bright Hygiene Management (London) Ltd.

Previous League: Combined Counties

Best Seasons: League: 5th Isthmian 1953-54 1959-60

F.A. Cup: 1st Round Replay 1985-1986 **F.A.Trophy.:** 2nd Round 2002-2003

F.A.Vase: 5th Round 1983-1984

Ground address: King George's Field,Queen Mary Close, Hook Rise South, Tolworth Surrey.KT6 7NA **Tel No:** 0208 397 3368

Club Website: www.corinthian-casuals.com

Capacity: 2,000 **Seats:**161 **Covered:**700 **Floodlights:** Yes

Simple Directions: A3 to Tolworth (Charrington Bowl) roundabout. Hook Rise is the slip road immediately past the Toby Jug pub. Left under railway bridge after quarter of a mile and ground is on right. Half mile from Tolworth BR.

Midweek Home Matchday: Tuesday

Clubhouse: Evenings and Matchdays plus functions **Club Shop:**

Local Radio:

Local Press: South London Press and Surrey Comet

CLUB PERSONNEL
Chairman: T.B.A.
Vice Chairman: David Harrison
President: Jimmy Hill
Secretary: B.Vandervilt c/o club

Programme
Editor: Nick Overend
32 pages £1.50

2005-2006
Captain: Simon Shergold
Player of the Year: Gareth Williams
Top Goalscorer: SimonMoore 14

CLUB STATISTICS	
Record	**Attendance:**
	Career Goalscorer: Cliff West 219
	Career Appearances: Simon Shergold 526
Record Transfer Fee	**Paid:** N/A **Received** N/A
Senior Honours:	F.A.Amateur Cup R-Up 1955-56
	London Spartan R-up 92-3 Co.Counties R-up 96-97
	As Casuals: F.A.Amateur Cup Winners 1935-36 Isthmian League R-Up 1935-6
	London Senior Cup r-up (4) London Charity Cup (6) Surrey Sen. Cup 1929-3
Previous Leagues:	Isthmian 39-84 Spartan 84-96 Combined Counties 96-97
Grounds:	Kennington Oval and shared with Kingstonian and Dulwich Hamlet
Names:	Casuals and Corinthians combined in 1939

Back Row (L-R) : Brian Adamson (Manager),   Luke Gaye, James Moran, Alex Rodrigues, Chris Horwood, Ryan Hillary, Michael Corbett, Colin Harris, Steve Broad, Ben Ward, Matt Howard (Coach).
Front : Matt Smith, Danny Green, Rico Morris, Terry Fenassey, Cain Sergent, Craig Dunne, Jamie Byatt, Lyndon Buckwell (Asst Manager).

CRAY WANDERERS

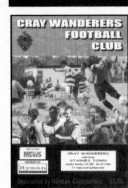

Manager: Ian Jenkins   **Coach:** Joe Francis   **Physio:** John de Palma

Club Colours: Amber & Black

Change Colours: All Blue

Club Sponsor:
Previous League: London Spartan

Best Seasons: League: 6th Isthmian Div 1 2004-2005   **F.A.Trophy.:**

F.A. Cup: 1st Round 1954-1955   **F.A.Vase:** Quarter Finals 1979-1980

Ground address: c/o Bromley F.C. Hayes Lane, Bromley, Kent
Tel No: 0181 4605291 or 0181 313 3992
Club Website: www.craywands.co.uk

Capacity: 5,000   **Seats:** 1,300   **Covered:** 2,500   **Floodlights:** Yes

Simple Directions: One mile from Bromley South (BR). Buses 316, 146 and 119 pass the ground. Junction 4 off M25 then A21 towards London.

Midweek Home Matchday: Tuesday

Clubhouse: Open Matchdays **Club Shop:** Yes

Local Radio: Radio Kent

CLUB PERSONNEL
Chairman: Gary Hillman
President: Bill Faulkner
Secretary: John de Palma, c/o Club
Pres Officer: Greg Mann
Programme
Editor: Greg Mann
32 pages 50p
2005-2006
Captain: Ian Rawlins
Player of the Year:
Top Goalscorer: Steve Northwood

CLUB STATISTICS

Record	**Attendance:** 1,523 v Stamford F.A.Vase 6th Round 1979-1980
	Career Goalscorer: Ken Collishaw 274
	Career Appearances: John Dorey 500 1961-1972
Record	**Victory :** 15-0 v Sevenoaks 1894-1895
	Defeat : 1-11 v Bromley 1920-1921
Senior Honours:	Kent Senior Trophy 92-93 03-04 Kent Amateur Cup (4) Kent Lg (5)
Previous Leagues:	**Previous Leagues:** Kent (4 spells) latest 34-38, W.Kent, London, Kent Amateur, S.London All., Aetolian 59-64, Gtr London 64-66, Metropolitan 66-71, Lon Metropolitan 71-75 London Spartan 75-78
Grounds:	Star Lane, Tothills, Twysden, Fordcroft, Grassmeade and St Mary Cray.

Back Row (L-R): Joe Francis, Ian Jenkins, Ross Lover, James Taylor, Gary Abbott, Michael Power, Tony Russell, Dean Mann, Ian Rawlings, Danny Bower, David Gray, Richard Dimmock, Jon Main, Ricky Bennett.
Front Row: John de Palma, Danny Harris, Leigh Bremner, Jamie Wood, Steve Northwood, Dean Morris, Drew Watkins, Gary Ward, Adam Heaslewood, Mark Hanscombe.

CROYDON ATHLETIC

Founded: 1947
Nickname:
The Rams

Manager: Brian Sparrow **Asst.Manager:** Peter Thomas **Coach:** Jerry Scola
Physio: Mick Reed
Club Colours: Maroon & White/Maroon/Maroon
Change Colours: Yellow/Royal Blue
Club Sponsor:
Previous League: London Spartan
Best Seasons: League: 8th Isthmian Division One
F.A. Cup: 3rd Qualifying Round 2003-2004
F.A.Vase: 4th Round 2000-2001
Ground address: The Keith Tuckey Stadium, off Mayfield Road, Thornton Heath,
Surrey CR7 6DN
Tel No: 0208 6648343
Club Website: wwwcroydonathletic.co.uk
Capacity: 3.000 **Seats:** 163 **Covered:** 660 **Floodlights:** Yes
Simple Directions: Follow A23 from London & continue on A23 into Thornton Road.After round-
about take !st on right into Silverleigh Road, left fork into Trafford Road which continues into Mayfield
Road. To end and turn leftand follow narrow road to ground. 1 mile from Norbury (BR). Buses 109, 60
Midweek Home Matchday: Tuesday
Clubhouse: Open every evening and match days. **Club Shop:** Yes
Local Radio:
Local Press: Croydon Advertiser

CLUB PERSONNEL
Chairman: Dean Fisher
Vice Chairman/Press Officer:
Clive Thompson
**Secretary, Press Officer &
Programme Editor:** Rob Cavallini,
8 Rutland House,Pyne Road,
Surbitoin, Surrey. KT6 7BW
Tel NO: 07940 317292
52 pages £1.50
2005-2006
Captain: James Gibson
Player of the Year:
Mark Waters & James Gibson
Top Goalscorer: Eben Allen

CLUB STATISTICS

Record	Attendance: 1,372 v AFC Wimbledon 2004-2005
	Career Goalscorer:
	Career Appearances: James Gibson 300
Record Transfer Fee	Paid:
	Received:
Senior Honours:	London Spartan Lg 94-95, R-up 88-89 93-94, (Reserve Div 88-89,
	R-up (88-89); London Snr Cup R-up 91-92; Isthmian League Div 3 2001-02
Previous	**Leagues**: Wandsworth Parthenon 1960-1964 Surrey Senior 1964-1977
	London Spartan 1977-1979 Isthmian 1997-
	Nmaes: Wandsworth & Norwood amalgamated in 1986 and changed their
	name to Croydon Amateurs in 1990

Back Row (L-R): Peter Thomas (Asst Manager), Dave Garland (Coach), Joe Sheerin, Aaron Cole-Bolt, Leon McDowall, Luke Garrard, Danny Cecil, Dave Hyatt, Adiran Toppin, Gavin Bolger, Micky Beale, Hayden Bird (Manager). **Front Row:** Mark Waters, James Cecil, Barry Stevens, Steve Gibson, James Evans, Jon Waite, Eben Allen.

DARTFORD

Founded: 1888
Nickname:
The Darts

Manager: Tony Burman **Asst.Man./Coach:** Steve Robinson & Paul Sawyer
Physio: Dave Phillips
Club Colours: White & Black/ Black/Black
Change Colours: All Yellow
Club Sponsor: Direct Metals
Previous League: Ryman Div.1 South
Best Seasons: League: Alliance
F.A. Cup: 3rd Round 1935-36 1936-37 **F.A.Trophy.:** Finalists 1973-1974
F.A.Vase: 2nd Qualifying Round 19951996
Ground address: Princes Park Stadium, Grassbanks, Darenth Road,
Dartford DA1 1RT (From 11/11/2006)
Club Website: www.dartfordfc.co.uk
Capacity: 4,100 **Seats:** 1000 **Covered:** 3100 **Floodlights:** Yes
Simple Directions: 1) Fast track bus route from Dartford Town Centre to Princes Park bus stop outside ground. **2)** Ten minute walk from Dartford Town Centre. **3) By Car:** From Dartford Town Centre leave by A226 (Lowfield Street), up to junction with Princes Road controlled by traffic lights. Turn left into Princes Road, up to next traffic lights and junction with Darenth Road, turn right and entrance to gound is second road on the left.
Email Address: info@dartfordfc.co.uk
Midweek Home Matchday: Tuesday
Clubhouse: Opening hours T.B.C. **Club Shop:** At ground.
Local Radio: Radio Kent. **Local Press:** Dartford Times and Dartford Messenger.

CLUB PERSONNEL
Co-Chairman: David Skinner
Co-Chairman: Bill Archer
President: Fred Leach
Secretary: Peter Martin. 10 Pembroke Place, Sutton-at-Hone, Dartford, Kent DA4 9HR
Tel No: 01322 864038

Programme
Editor: Tony Jaglo
40 pages £1.50

2005-06
Captain: Tommy Osborne.
Player of the Year: Dave Martin.
Top Goalscorer: Ryan Hayes.

CLUB STATISTICS

Record	**Attendance:** 11,004 v Leyton Orient F.A.Cup 1948
	Career Appearances:: Steve Robinson 692
Record Transfer Fee	**Paid:** £6,000 to Chelmsford City for John Bartley
	Received: £25,000 from Redbridge Forest for Andy Hessenthaler
Senior Honours:	Southern Lg 1930-31, 31-32, 73-74, 83-84, R-up 87-88, 88-89, Eastern Div 30-31,31-32, Southern Div 80-81, Southern Lg Div 2 1896-97, Lg Cup 76-77, 87-88, 88-89, Championship Shield 83-84, 87-88, 88-89, Kent Lg 1995-96, Lg Cup 24-25,Kent Snr Cup 29-30, 34-35, 38-39, 69-70, ;FA Trophy R-up 1974
Previous Leagues:	**Leagues:** Kent League 1894-96 1897-98 1899-1902 1909-14 21-26 93-96; Southern League 1996-2006
	Grounds: The Brent/ Westgate House, Potters Meadow, Engleys Meadow, Summers Meadow, Watling St, then groundshares with Cray Wanderers, Erith & Belvedere, Purfleet, Gravesend & Northfleet and Thurrock.

Back Row (L-R): Tony Burman (Manager); Tommy Osborne (Captain); Danny White; Brad Potter; Jay May; James Tedder; Kevin Hudson; Anthony Henry; Richard Avery; John Farley; Glenn Billenness; Eddie McClements; Paul Sawyer (Asst.Manager/Coach); Dave Phillips (Physio).**Front:** Tommy Olson; Ryan Hayes; Craig Maguire; Ryan Briggs; Ted Ansell; Steve Hafner; Dave Martin, Brendon Cass.

DOVER ATHLETIC

Founded: 1983
Nickname:
The Whites

Manager: Clive Walker   **Asst.Manager:** Steve Nolan   **Physio:** Frank Clarke
Club Colours: White/Black/White
Change Colours: Yellow/Blue/Yellow
Club Sponsor: Paul Brown of Dover
Previous League: Southern
Best Seasons: League: 6th Conference 199-2000
F.A. Cup: 2nd Round 1975-1976   **F.A.Trophy.:** Sem-Final 1997-1998
Ground address: Crabble Athletic Ground, Lewisham, Dover, Kent CT17 0PA
Tel No: 01304 822373
Club Website: www.dover-athletic.co.uk
Capacity: 6,500   **Seats:**1,000   **Covered:**4,900   **Floodlights:** Yes
Simple Directions: Follow A2 from Canterbury until you pass the Forte Post House
on left and approach a roundabout with MacDonalds and petrol station on the left.
Turn right to 'town centre' and follow down hill.
Midweek Home Matchday: Tuesday
Clubhouse: Open seven days a week. Meals available. Gavin Hughes

CLUB PERSONNEL
Chairman: Jim Parmenter
Directors: R.Knight, C.Oakley and S.Wiliams, D.Weber & B Wetzel
Secretary: Frank Clarke,c/o club.
Tel No 07813 888320 (M)
Commercial Manager:
R.Knight c/o club

Programme
Editor: Jim Parmenter
38 pages £1.50
2005-2006
Captain: Lee Spiller
Player of the Year: Craig Cloke
Top Goalscorer: Craig Wilkens

Tel No:01304 822306 or 01304 822373
Club Shop: Manager: Contact: 01304 822373
Local Radio: Radio Kent, Invicta amd FM KFM Radio
Local Press: Dover Express and Dover Mercury

CLUB STATISTICS

Record	**Attendance:** 4,186 v Oxford United FAC 1st Round November 2002
	Career Goalscorer: Lennie Lee 160
	Career Appearances: Jason Bartlett 359
Record Transfer Fee	**Paid:** £50,000 to Farnborough Town for David Leworthy August 1993
	Received: £50,000 from Brentford for Ricky Reina 1997
	Victory: :7-0 v Weymouth 03.04.90
	Defeat: 1-7 v Poole Town :
Senior Honours:	Southern Premier Champions 89-90 92-93 Southern Division 87-88 Premier Inter League Cup 90-91 Kent Senior Cup 90-91
Previous	**Leagues:** Kent, Southern, Conference, Southern
	Name:: Dover F.C.

Back row (L-R): Matt Bourne, Tommy Tyne, Craig Wilkins, Glen Knight, Darren Smith, Craig Wilkins, Bradley Spice, Craig Cloke. **Middle:** Robin Hastie (Kit Manager), Sam Vallance, Anthony Hogg, Shane Hamshare, James Rogers, Frank Clarke (Physio).**Front:** Byron Walker, Lee Spiller, Clive Walker (Manager), Steve Nolan (Assistant Manager), Tony Browne, Chris Chase.

DULWICH HAMLET

Manager: Wayne Burnett   **Physio:** Peter Green
Club Colours: Navy blue & pink/navyblue/navy blue
Change Colours: Gren & White/Green/Green
Club Sponsor: H.R.Jennings for Insurance
Previous League: Spartan
Best Seasons: League: Isthmian Champions 1919-20 1925-26 1932-33 1948-49
F.A. Cup: 1st Round Replay 1930-31 1933-34 **F.A.Trophy.:** 6th Rd 1979-80
F.A.Amateur Cup Winners: 1919-20 1931-32 1933-34 1936-37
Ground address: Champion Hill Stadium, Edgar Kail Way, East Dulwich,
London.SE22 8BD **Tel No:** 0207 274 8707
Club Website: www.dulwichhamletfc.com
Capacity: 3,000   **Seats:**500   **Covered:** 1,000   **Floodlights:** Yes
Simple Directions: East Dulwich station, 200yds. Denmark Hill station, 10 mins walk. Herne
Hill station then bus 37 stops near grd. Buses 40 & 176 from Elephant & Castle, 185 from Victoria
Midweek Home Matchday: Tuesday
Clubhouse: Open 7 days a week. Function rooms & meeting room available for hire Health
Club, Gymnasium, Squash courts (020 7274 8707)
Club Shop: Sells programmes, pennants, badges, scarves, caps, replica shirts (by order only).
Local Press: South London Press and Southwark News

CLUB PERSONNEL
Chairman: Martin Eede
President: Tommy Jover
Secretary: John Leahy,
58 Newquay House, Black Prince
Road, Kenninfgton, London SE11
6HL **Tel No:** 0207 582 9296

Programme
Editor: John Lawrence
48 pages £1.50
2005-2006
Captains:
Alex O'Brien & Jamie Coyle
Player of the Year: Jamie Coyle
Top Goalscorer: Richard Brady 8

STATISTICS

Record	**Attendance:** 20,744 for F.A.Amateur Cup Final 1933 (Kingstonian v Stockton)
	At refurbished ground: 1,835 v Southport F.A.Cup 1998-1999
	Career Goalscorer: Edgar Keil 427 (1919-1933)
	Career Appearances: Reg Merritt 576 (1950-1966)
Record Transfer Fee	**Paid:** Undisclosed for T.Eames (Wimbledon) and G.Allen (Carshalton Ath) 80
	Received: Undisclosed from Luton Town for E.Nwajiobi 1983
Senior Honours:	Isthmian League (4) (R-up (7) Div 1 77-78; London Senior Cup (5) R-up(5);
	Surrey Senior Cup (16) R-up (16); London Chal. Cup 98-9 R-up(2)
Previous Leagues:	**Leagues:** Camberwell 1894-97; S/thern Sub 1897-1900 01-07; Dulwich 00-01;
	Spartan 07-08
	Grounds: Woodwarde Rd 1893-95; College Farm 95-96; Sunray Avenue 96-
	1902; Freeman's Ground, Champion Hill 02-12; Champion Hill (old ground)
	1912-92; Sandy Lane (groundshare with Tooting & Mitcham F.C.) 91-92

Back Row (L-R): Jason Turley, Lewis Tozer; Jamie Coyle (Capt); James Pullen; Daniel Nwanze; Chris Dickson
Front: Carlton Murray-Price; Nicolas Plumain; David Moore; Phil Williams; Kenny Beaney

FLEET TOWN

**Re-Formed: 1947
Nickname:
The Blues**

Manager: Andy Sinton   **Assistant Manager:** Steve Mellor
Coaches: Jesse Bone & Mervyn Griffiths   **Physio:**David Keir
Club Colours: Navy & Sky blue stripes/sky blue/navy and sky blue
Change Colours: Red & Black/black/red & black
Club Sponsor: Erif (UK) Ltd
Previous League: Wessex
Best Seasons: League: Southern or Isthmian 1 ?   **F.A. Cup:** 2nd Qualifying Round
1997-1998   **F.A.Trophy.:** 2nd Round 1997-1998   **F.A.Vase:** 3rd Round 1994-1995
Ground address: Calthorpe Park, Crookham Road, Fleet, Hants.
Tel No: 01252 623804
Club Website: www.fleettownfc.co.uk
Capacity: 2,000   **Seats:**200   **Covered:** 250   **Floodlights:** Yes
Simple Directions: Leave the M3 at Junction 4A. Follow signs to Fleet via A3013. At 5th round
about (a T-junction), turn left over railway bridge. Carry on past `Oatsheaf' pub on the right - ground
is 1/4 mile further on right.

Midweek Home Matchday: Tuesday
Clubhouse: Yes, hot & cold food available   **Club Shop:** Yes
Local Radio:
Local Press:

CLUB PERSONNEL
Chairman: Graham Smith
Vice Chairman: Jon Goodyear
President: Tony Frost
Secretary: John Goodyear,25
Velmead Road, Fleet, Hants. GU52
7LJ **Tel. No** 07966 895210(M)
Press Officer: Steve Cantle

Programme
Editor: Steve Cordingley
20pages £1.00

CLUB STATISTICS

Record	**Attendance:** 1.050 v Coventry City (Pre season Friendly 1995)
	Career Goalscorer: Mark Frampton 428
	Career Appearances: Mark Frampton 250
Record Transfer Fee	**Paid:** £3,000 to Aldershot for MarkRussell
	Received:
	Victory: 15-0 v Petersfield 26.12.94
	Defeat: 0-6 vMargate 1999
Senior Honours:	Wessex Lg 94-95 Runners-Up 01-02, Lg Cup R-up 92-93, 01-02;
Previous Leagues:	**Leagues:** Hampsire 61-77, Athenian, Combined Co's, Chiltonian, Wessex 89-95, Southern 95-00, Wessex 00-02

January 2004 - Back Row (L-R): Bruce Kendall (Asst. Manager), Ed Hare, Craig Anstey, Dan Jeffrey, Calvin Sparshatt, Anthony Millerick, Steve Black, Ian Saunders (Capt.), Mick Catlin (Manager). **Front Row:** Steve Whitcher, Nick Clark, Jamie Proctor, Ben Buckland, Shea Saunders. Not in picture: Shaun Hale. Photo: Steve Cantle.

GODALMING TOWN

Founded: 1950

Club Colours: Yellow/Green/Yellow

Change Colours: All blue

Club Sponsor: Beeline Cars

Previous League: Combined Counties

Best Seasons: Leagueg : Champions Combined Counties 1983-1984 2005-2006

F.A. Cup: 2nd Round Qualifying   **F.A.Vase:** 2nd Rd 1987-1988

Manager: Roger Steer. **Assistant Manager:** Hugh Doyle. **Physio**: Martin Rochefort

Ground address: Weycourt, Meadrow, Guildford, Surrey Tel No: 01483 417520

Club Website:

Capacity: 3,000   **Seats**::200   **Covered**:200   **Floodlights**: Yes

Simple Directions:

Midweek Home Matchday: Tuesday

Clubhouse: Club Shop:

Local Radio: Radio Southern Counties and County Sound Radio.

Local Press: Surrey Advertiser.

CLUB PERSONNEL

Chairman: Kevin Young

President: Bill Kyte

Secretary: Mrs Jane Phillips, 135 Manor Road, Stoughton, Guildford

Programme Editor: digital@zapdigitalprint.co.uk
Price: £1.50

2005-06
Captain: Jamie Laister.
Player of the Year: Jamie Laister.
Top Goalscorer: Danny Newman.

CLUB STATISTICS		
Record	Attendance:	
Career Goalscorer:		
Career Appearances:		
Record Transfer Fee	Paid:	
	Received:	
Senior Honours:	Combined Counties Champions 1983-1984, 2005-2006	
Previous Leagues:	Combined Counties	
Names:	Godalming & Farncombe United, Godalming & Guildford	

Photo: Eric Marsh.

518

HASTINGS UNITED

Founded: 1898
Nickname : YM's

Managers: Nigel Kane **Coach:** Ryan Light **Physio:** Carl Milton

Club Colours: Claret & Blue

Change Colours: Gold & Black

Club Sponsor: The London Trader

Previous League: Southern

Best Seasons: League: 5th Southern Premier 1998-1999

F.A. Cup: 1st Round 2002 -2003 **F.A.Trophy.:** 3rd Round 1998-199 **F.A.Vase:**

Ground address: The PIlot Field, Elphinstone Road, Hastings TN34 2EZ

Tel No: 01424 444635

Club Website: www.hastingsunitedfc.co.uk

Capacity: 4,050 **Seats:**800 **Covered:** 1,750 **Floodlights:** Yes

Simple Directions: From A1 turn left at 3rd mini roundabout into St Helens Rd..
Then left after one mile into St Helens Park Rd. leading into Downs Rd. Turn left at
T junction at end of road. Ground is 200yds on right.

Midweek Home Matchday: Tuesday

Clubhouse: Open matchdays **Club Shop:** Sells full range of club products

Local Radio: BBC SouthernCounties, Southern Sound and Arrow F.M.

Local Press: Hastings Observer and The Argus.

CLUB PERSONNEL

Chairman: David Walters
President: Mick Maplesden
Secretary r: R.A.Cosens, 22
Baldslow Road,Hastings. TN34 2EZ
Tel NO: 0771 2634288 (M)
Press Office: SeanAdams
Programme
Editor: Simon Rudkins
Tell No: 01424 719146
2005-2006
Captain: Sean Ray
Player of the Year: Jimmy Elford
Top Goalscorer: Sam Adams 15

CLUB STATISTICS

Record	**Attendance:** 4,888 v Nottingham Forest (Friendly) 23.06.96
	Goalscorer in a Season: :Terry White 33 199-2000
	Career Appearances:
Record Transfer Fee	**Paid**: £8,000 to Ashfor Town for Nicky Dent
	Received: £30,000 from Nott'm Forest for Paul Smith
Senior Honours:	Southern Lg.Cup 94-95 Southern Div 1 91-92 Div 2 R-Up 08-09
Previous Leagues:	South Eastern 04-05 Southern 05-10 Sussex County 21-27 52- 85
	Southern Amateur 27-46 Corinthian 46-48
	Ground: Bulverhythe Recreation (pre 76)
	Name: Hastings & St Leonards Amateurs,Hastings Town>2002

BackRow (L-R): Richard Wilmot, Dwane Williams, Dean Thomas, Craig Vargas, Rakatahr Hudson,
Ryan Wharton, Nas Richardson, Lee O'Leary, Adilson Lopes, Ricky Pattenden, Anthony O'Connor.
Middle: Josh Hunte, Danny Edwards, Gary McCann (manager), James Burgess, Freddie Hyatt (assistant manager), Rene Street, Leon Maloney.
Front: Takumi Ake, Francois Gabbidon, Jamie Busby, Hussain Karas, Greg Deacon, Wayne O'Sullivan,
Franklyn Morris.

HORSHAM YMCA

Founded: 1898
Nickname : YM's

Manager: John Suter   **Coach:** Tommy Sampson   **Therapist:** Robin Bishop

Club Colours: White with red trim/White/White
Change Colours: All Blue

Club Sponsor: GlsFootball.com

Previous League: Sussex County

Best Seasons: League: Sussex Champions   **F.A. Cup:** 4th Qual. Rd. 1999-2000
F.A.Vase: 3rd Qualifying Round 1976-77 1977-78

Ground address: Gorings Mead, Horsham,West Sussex RH13 5BP

Club Website: www.horshamymcafc.com

Capacity: 1,575   **Seats:** 150   **Covered:** 200   **Floodlights:** Yes

Simple Directions: From the east, take A281 (Brighton Road) and the ground is on the left and signposted opposite Gorings Mead.

Midweek Home Matchday: Tuesday

Chairman: Mick Browning
Vice Chairman: J.Birch
President:
Secretary: Bob Brading, 16 Hazelhurst Crescent, Horsham, Werst Sussex
Tel Nos: 01403 250270 (H)
07788 183746 (M)

Programme
Editor: Bob Brading
24 Pages £1.00
2005-2006
Captain: Matt Duffield
Player of the Year: Dean Carden
Top Goalscorer: Matt Russell 20

Clubhouse: Open matchdays and functions

Club Shop: No but souvenirs on sale from Secretary
Local Radio: Southern Counties
Local Press: West Sussex County Times

CLUB STATISTICS

Record

Attendance: 950 v Chelmsford City F.A. Cup 2000
Career Goalscorer: Danny Cherryman
Career Appearances: Gerry Marsh, Peter Durrant & Jason Dumbrill all 500+
Transfer Fee P aid: N/A   **Received:**   N/A
Victory: 21-1 v Litttlehampton (Nick Flint 10) October 2003
Senior Honours: Sussex League Champions 2004-2005 2005-2006
Sussex RuR Cup Wunners 2000-2001
Previous Leagues:: Horsham & District, Brighton& Hove, , Mid Sussex and Sussex County

Back Row (L-R): Robin Bishop (Therapist), Scott Bidwell, Wayne Potter, Matt Russell, Glen Woodburn, Ellis Hooper, Ian Chatfield, Tom Carter, Joel O'Hara, Barrie Westgate, Dave Gellatly, Adam O'Corroll, Alex Suter (Kit).
Front: Nick Levett, John Suter (Manager), Matt Duffield (Capt), Tommy Sampson (Coach), James Grant, James Bird.

Photo: Clive Turner

KINGSTONIAN

Founded: 1886
Nickname: The K's

Ryman League Premier Division 2004-05

Official Matchday Programme £1-50

Kingstonian
V
Folkestone Invicta
Saturday 30th April
K.O. 3pm

Ryman

Manager: Coach: Physio: Chris Cornish
Club Colours: Red & White hoops/white/white
Change Colours: Yellow/light blue/white
Previous League: Conference   **Club Sponsor:** Anderson Coaches
Best Seasons: League: 5th Conference 1999-2000
F.A. Cup: 4th Round Replay v Bristol City 2000-2001
F.A.Trophy.: Winners 1998-99 1999-2000
Ground address: Kingsmead Stadium,Kingston Road, Kingston upon Thames,
Surrey KT1 3PB **Tel No;** 0208 8547 3528 **Club Website:** www.kingstonian.net
Capacity: 4,262 **Seats:** 1,080 **Covered:** 2,538 **Floodlights:** Yes
Simple Directions: Take Cambridge Rd. from town centre (A2043) to Malden Rd.
From A3 turn off at New Malden and turn left onto A2043. Ground is 1 mile on left
which is half a mile from Norbiton (BR) .
Midweek Home Matchday: Monday
Clubhouse: Three Bars. Capacity 400 with a banqueting centre available daily.
Club Shop: Sandra & Gary Winters
Local Radio: County Sound,1566 MW,BBC Southern Counties,SCR 104.8 FM, 95.3
FM and Radio Jackie 107.8 FM.
Local Press: Surrey Comet, Kingston Informer, Kingston Guardian, Esher News &
Mail and Kingston, Surbiton and New Malden Times.

CLUB PERSONNEL
Chairman: Jimmy Cochrane
President:
Secretary & Press Officer:
Gerry Pettit, 149 Bridge Road,
Chessington, Surrey KT9 2RT
Tel Nos: 0208 397 0433 (H)
or 07764 834659 (M)
Commercial Manager:
Gary Anstead 07774 267502 (M)

Programme
Editor: Robert Wooldrige

2005-2006
Player of the Year: Julian Sills

CLUB STATISTICS

Record	**Attendance:** 4,582 v Chelsea (Friendly)
	Career Goalscorer: Johnnie Wing 296
	Career Appearances: <Micky Preston 555
Record Transfer Fee	**Paid:** £18,000 to Rushden & Diamonds for David Leworthy 1997
	Received: £150,000 from West Ham United for Gavin Holligam1999
	Victory: 10-1 V Hitchin Town(H) Isthmian Lg. 19.03.66
	Defeat: 0-11 v Ilford Isthmian 13.02.37
Senior Honours:	F.A.Trophy Winners 98-99 99-00 F.A.Am Cup Winners 32-33 R-up 59-60
	Isthmian Champions 33-34 36-37 97-98 R-up (2), Athenian Lg. (2)
	London Senior Cup (3) Surrey Sen Cup (3)
Previous Leagues:	Kingston & Dist., West Surrey, Southern Suburban, Athenian 1919-29
	Isthmian 29-98 Conference 98-01
	Grounds: Several to 1921 Richmond Rd21-89
	Names: Kingston & Suburton YMCA 85-87 Saxons 87 -90
	Kingston Wanderers 1893-1904 Old Kingstonians 1908-1919

Back row,left to right: Julian Sills, Michael Brady, Stuart Reeks, Chuck Martini, Scott Corbett and Scott Bennetts.
Front row: Bashiro Alimi, Damian Panter, Martin Lee, Tony Reid and Brahim Elouman. Photo: Alan Coomes

521

LEATHERHEAD

Founded: 1946
Nickname:
The Tanners

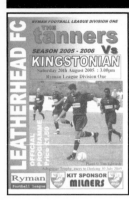

Managers: Dave Harlow & Barry Barnes **Physio**: Steve Young

Club Colours: Green&White/Green/Green

Change Colours: Blue & White

Club Sponsor: Milners

Previous League: Athenian

Best Seasons: League: Isthmian ?

F.A. Cup: 4th Round 1974-1975   **F.A.Trophy.:** Finalists 1977-1978

F.A.Vase: 2nd Roujhd 1992-93 1994-95

Ground address: Fetcham Grove, Guilford Road,Leatherhead, Surrey. KT22 9AS

Tel No: 01372 360151

Club Website: www.leatherheadfc-online.co.uk

Capacity: 3,400   **Seats**: 200   **Covered**:45   **Floodlights**: Yes

Simple Directions: M25 jct 9 to Leatherhead; follow signs to Leisure Centre, ground adjacent.

Half mile from Leatherhead (BR)

Midweek Home Matchday: Tuesday

Clubhouse: Bar open 12.11pm matchdays. Full catering. Tel No : 01372 360151

Club Shop: Tel No: 01372 362705

Local Radio: County Sound

Local Press: Leatrherhead Advertiser and Surrey Advertiser

CLUB PERSONNEL

Chairman: Tim Edwrads

President:

Secretary: Gerald Darby, Ranmore, 31 Hariots Lane, Ashtead, Surrey KT21 2QG

Tel No:01372 273260

Press Offver/Commercial Manager: Steve Dennis

Programme Editor: Dave Pope

Page 40 £1,40

2005-2006

Captain: Ian Hendry

Player of the Year: Jamie Beer

Top Goalscorer: Dave Stephens

CLUB STATISTICS

Record	**Attendance:** 5,500 v Wimbledon 1976	
	Goalscorer in a Season: Steve Lunn 46 1996-1997	
	Career Appearances: P.Caswell 200	
Record Transfer Fee	**Paid:** £1,500 to Croydon for B.Salkeld	
	Received: £1,500 fromCroydon for B.Salkeld	
	Victory: 13-1 v Leyland Motors 1946-1947 Surrey Senior League	
	Defeat: 1-11 v Sutton United	
Senior Honours:	FA Trophy R-up 77-78; Isthmian League Cup 77-78; ; Athenian Lg Div 1 63-64; Surrey Snr Cup 68-69 R-up (4); London Senior Cup R-Up 1974-75 1977-78	
Previous	**Leagues:** Surrey Snr 46-50; Metropolitan 50-51; Delphian 51-58; Corinthian 58-63; Athenian 63-72	

Back Row (L-R): Matt Bennett, Marc Charles-Smith, Tommy Moorhouse, Iain Hendry, Tommy Dunn, Lee Doherty, Adam Gray, Muhammed Cisse and Hibert Noah. Front Row: Dean Carpenter, Steve Sargent, Jamie Beer, Dante Alighieri, Dave Stevens, Julian Thompson, Paul Wetherall and Lee Dooley.

MAIDSTONE UNITED

Re-Formed 1992:
Nickname: The Stones

Managers: Alan Walker & Lloyd Hume **Coach:** Mal Watkins
Physio: Simon Kavanagh

Club Colours: Amber/Black/Gold
Change Colours: All White

Club Sponsor: Britelite Windows
Previous League: Kent

Best Seasons: League: Kent League Champions 2001-02 2005-06
F.A. Cup: 3rd Qualifying Round 2004-2005
F.A.Vase: 2nd Round 2001-02 2004-05

Ground address: c/o Sittingbourne Football Club

Club Office Telephone Number: 01732 222125

Website: www.maidstoneunited.co.uk

Capacity: 3,000   **Seats:** 300   **Covered:** 600   **Floodlights:** Yes

Simple Directions: The club is clearly and regularly signposted through Sittingbourne on main A2 from East or West. One mile from Sittingbourne BR

Midweek Home Matchday: Tuesday

Local Press: Kent Messenger

CLUB PERSONNEL
Chairman: Paul Bowden-Brown
V-Chair: Richard Bowden-Brown
Life President: George Gray
Secretary: Darren Lovell,
573 Lordswood Road, Chatham,
Kent. ME5 8NP
Tel Nos: 01634 672086
07773 745577 (M)
General Manager: Bill Williams
Programme
Editor: Ian Tucker
24 Pages £1.50

2005-2006
Captain: Jimmy Strouts
Player of the Year: Mario Celaire
Top Goalscorer: Mo Takaloo 44

CLUB STATISTICS		
Record	**Attendance:** 1,589 v Gillingham (friendly)	
	Career Goalscorer:	
	Career Appearances:	
Record	**Victory:** 12-1 v Aykesford, Kent League 1993-1994	
	Defeat: 2-8 v Scott Sports 1995-1996	
Senior Honours:	Kent League Champions 2001-2002 League & Cup 2005-2006	
	Kent Senior Trophy 2002-2003	
Previous Leagues:	Kent County League, and Kent League	
Grounds:	London Road 1992-2001 Central Park 2001-2002	

Back Row (L-R): Nathan Paul, Mario McNish, Lynden Rowland, Sam Tydeman, Neil Miller, Aaron Lacy, Simon Austin, Jason Batt.
Front: Nick Hegley, Mo Takalobighashi, Michal Czanner, Jim Strouts, Kane Rice.

METROPOLITAN POLICE

Founded: 1919
Nickname:
The Blues

Management: Jim Cooper, Gavin MacPherson and John Nicholson
Physio: Dick Pierce
Club Colours: All Blue
Change Colours: All Yellow
Club Sponsor: Chatterbox.(mobile telephones)
Previous League: Southern
Best Seasons: League: 4th Isthmian Div 1 2005-2006
F.A. Cup: 1st Round 1932-1933   **F.A.Vase:** 6th Round 1994-1995
F.A.Trophy.: 3rd Qualifying Round 1974-75 1979-80 1982-83 1989-90
Ground address: Imber Court, East Molesey, Surrey. **Tel No:** 0208 398 7358
Club Website: www.metpolicefc.co.uk
Capacity: 3,000   **Seats:** 297   **Covered:** 1,800   **Floodlights:** Yes
Simple Directions: From London A3 take A309 towards Scilly Isles roundabout then right into Hampton Court Way. Left at 1st roundabout into Imber Court Rd. Ground faces in 300 yards.
Midweek Home Matchday: Tuesday
Clubhouse: Four Bars, Dance Hal, Cafeteria open 9a.m. - 11p.m. **Club Shop:** No
Local Radio: County Sounds
Local Press: Surrey Comet & Surrey Herald

CLUB PERSONNEL

Chairman: Des Flanders
President: JSir Ian Blair
Secretary: Tony Brooking, 15 Westmoreland Avenue, Hornchurch, EssexRM11 2EJ
Tel No; 07961 334523 (M)
01708 450715 (H)
Press Officer & Programme Editor:: Cliff Travis
e-mail: cliffordtravis@hotmail.com:

2005-2006
Captain: Paul Barrowcliff
Players of the Year:
Stuart Mackenzie & Stuart Hart
Top Goalscorer: Kevib Cooper

CLUB STATISTICS

Record	**Attendance:** 4,500 v Kingstonian F.A.Cup 1934
	Career Goalscorer: Mario Russo
	Career Appearances: Pat Robert
Record	**Victory:** 10-1 v Tilbury 1995
	Defeat: 1-11 v Wimbledon 1956
Senior Honours:	Isthmian Lg. Div. 2 R-up Spartan Lg (7) Middlesex Senior Cup 27-28
	Surrey Senior Cup: 32-33 London Senior Cup : R-Up: 34-35 40-41
Previous Leagues:	Spartan 28-60 Metropolitan 60-71 Southern 71-78

Back row, left to right: Kori Davis, Nigel Edwards, Danny Bolt, Dave Newman, Jon Daly(Captain), Chrise Rose, Rob Haworth, Stuart Mackenzie, Michaell Miso, Danny Baillie, Ian Batten, John Nicholson and Gavin McPherson.
Front row: Craig Brown, Andy Oxby, Micky Parma, Jim Cooper(manager), Paul Barrowcliff, StuartHarte, Paul Sears and Rob Tarrant.

MOLESEY

Founded: 1952
Nickname:
The Moles

Manager: Steve Beeks   **Asst.Manager/Coach:**Dave Skilton   **Physio:**
Club Colours: White/Black/Black
Change Colours: All Yellow
Club Sponsor:
Previous League: Athenian
Best Seasons: League: Isthmian Premier 93?
F.A. Cup: 1st Round 1994-1995   **F.A.Trophy.:**1st Round Replay 1990-1991
F.A.Vase: 6th Round 1981-1982
Ground address: 412 Walton Road, West Molesey, surrey KT8 0JG
Tel Nos: 0181 941 7989 (boardroom) 0181 979 4823 (clubhouse)
Club Website:
Capacity: 4,000   **Seats:**400   **Covered:**600   **Floodlights:** Yes
Simple Directions: A3 from London to Hook, thenA309 to Marquis of Granby pub, right to
Hampton Court station, turn left forWest Molesey, ground one mile on left
Midweek Home Matchday: Tuesday
Clubhouse: Open every evening and weekend lunchtimes 2 bars, discos, live artists, darts,
bingo, pool. Steward: John Chambers
Club Shop: Contact John Chambers
Local Radio: Thames 107.8 FM, Hospital Radio, County Sound, Three Counties
and Star FM.
Local Press: Surrey Comet, Surrey Herald and Molesey News.

CLUB PERSONNEL
Chairman: Keith Knight
President:
Secretary: Fiona Bowers, 104
Carlton Road, Walton on Thames,
Surrey KT22 9LU
Tel No: 07710603430 (M0

Programme (28 pages £1.20)
Editor & Press Officer:
Pete Bowers

CLUB STATISTICS

Record	**Attendance:** 1,255 v Sutton United Surrey Senior Cup S-FInal 1966
	Career Goalscorer: Michael Rose 139
	Career Appearances: Frank Hanley 453:
Record Transfer Fee	**Paid:** £500 to Leatherhead for Chris Vidal 1988
	Received: £5,000 from Hythe Town for Chris Bidal 1989
Senior Honours:	Isthmian Lg Div 1 R-up 92-93, Div 2 South R-up 89-90, Lg Cup R-up 92-93, Surrey Senior Lg 57-58,
Previous Leagues:	**Leagues:** Surrey Intermediate 53-56; Surrey Snr 56-59; Spartan 59-72; Athenian72-77
	Name: Molesey St Pauls 1950-53.

Back Row (L-R): Stan Brabon, John Murphy, Phil Caughter, Steve Brown, Phil Ruggles, Chuck Martini, Clark Gooding, Brahim Eloumani ,Youssef Metwali, Warren Burton, Chris Antoine, Merv Griffiths and Steve Beeks.
Front Row: Jerome Elroy, Jay Richardson , Chris Wales, Aaron Nowacki , Wayne Noads , Lee Richardson Jamie Lee Smithers, Sam Lampard.

SITTINGBOURNE

Founded:1881
Nickname:
Brickies

Manager: Steve Lovatt   **Coach:**   **Physio**: Gary Wisdom
Club Colours: Red with black trim/red/black
Change Colours: All Blue
Club Sponsor:
Previous League: Kent
Best Seasons: League: Southern Prem?
F.A. Cup: 2nd Round 1925-1926   **F.A.Vase:** 4th Round 199192 1992-93
F.A.Trophy.:
Ground address: Bourne Park, Central Park Stadium, Eurolink,Sittingbourne, Kent.
ME10 3SB Tel No: 01795 435077 or 420444
Club Website:
Capacity: 3,000   **Seats**:300   **Covered**: 600   **Floodlights**: Yes
Simple Directions: Through Sittingbourne on main A2, club signposted clearly and regularly
from both east and west. 1 mile from Sittingbourne BR station
Midweek Home Matchday: Tuesday
Clubhouse: Tel No: 01795 435077
Club Shop: Wide variety of souvenirs etc. Contact: Ann Morrison(01795 664436)
Local Radio: BBC Radio and KMFM
Local Press: East Kent Gazette, Kent Messenger and Kent on Sunday

CLUB PERSONNEL
Chairman: Andy Spice
President: Jim Clarke
Secretary: John Pitts, 4 Silverdale
Grove, Sittingbourne, Kent. ME10
1UY **Tel No:** 01795 476809
Commercial Manager: John Cooper

Programme
Editor: John Pitts
44 pages £1.50

CLUB STATISTICS

Record	**Attendance:** 5,951 v Tottenham Hotspur. Friendly 26.01.93
	Career Goalscorer:
	Career Appearances:
Record Transfer Fee	**Paid:** £20,000 to Ashford Town for Lee McRobert 1993
	Received: £210,000 from Millwall for Neil Emblen and Micharle Harle. 1993
Senior Honours:	Southern Lg Southern Div 92-93 95-96; Kent Lg (7) Lg Cup (4), Kent Senior Cup 01-02 28-29 29-30 57-58;
Previous:	**Leagues:** Kent 1894-1905 09-27 30-39 46-59 68-91, South Eastern 05-09, Southern 27-30 59-67
	Grounds: SittingbourneRec. Ground 1881-90, Gore Court Cricket Ground 90-92, The Bull Ground1892-1990
	Names: Sittingbourne United 1881-86

2005-06 - Back Row (L-R): Peter Taylor, Dan Tanner, Paul Ainsworth, Bradley Spice, Kevin Fewell, Steve Williams, Lee Friend, Kieran Marsh, Darren Hare, Richard Styles. **Front Row:** Ricky Spiller, Mark Lovell, Lee Browning, Joe Dowley, Clint Gooding, Toby Ashmore, Jon Neal.

TOOTING MITCHAM UNITED

Founded: 1932
Nickname:
The Terrors

Manager: Richard Cadette　**Coach:**Keith Jones　**Physio:** Dennis Lawton

Club Colours: Black & White stripes/Black/Black

Change Colours: Red/White/White

Club Sponsor: London Interspace

Previous League: Athenian

Best Seasons: League: IsthmianLeague Champions 1957-1958 1959-1960

F.A. Cup: 4th Round 1975-1976　　**F.A.Trophy.:**

F.A.Vase: 6th Round 2000-2001

Ground address: Imperial Fields, Bishopsford Road, Morden, Surrey SM4 6BF

Tel No: 0208 648 3248　**Special Facilities:**Allweather pitches for football, hockey, touch rugby+ quick cricket plus gym and facilities for the disabled.

Club Website:

Capacity: 3,500　　**Seats:** 600　　**Covered:**3,500　　**Floodlights:**Yes

Simple Directions: Ground is on A217 between Mitcham and Rose Hill. Buses 118 (Streatham to Morden) and 280 (Tooting to Sutton). Morden tube

Midweek Home Matchday: Tuesday

Clubhouse: Cafe/Bar open daily and family friendly facilties

Club Shop: Open Matchdays.

Local Radio: Capital

Local Press: South London Press,Wimbledon News , Wandsworth Borough News

CLUB PERSONNEL

Chairman: John Buffoni
Vice Chairman: Alan Simpson
President: Chris Jackson
Secretary: Les Roberts, 92 Fernlea Road, Mitcham, Surrey, CR4 2HG
Tel No: 07939127997(M)

Programme
Editor: Steve Taylor
32 pages £1.50
2005-2006
Captains:
Craig Turner & Steve Kinch
Player of the Year: Aaron Day
Top Goalscorer: John Hastings

CLUB STATISTICS

Record	**Attendance:** 17,500 v Q.P.R. FAC 2nd Round 1956-1957 (At Sandy Lane)
	Career Goalscorer:
	Career Appearances: Danny Godwin 470
Record Transfer Fee	**Paid:** £9,000 to Enfield for David Flint
	Received: £10,000 from Luton Townn for Herbie Smith
	Victory: 11-0 v Welton Rovers F.A.Amateur Cup 1962-1963
	Defeat: 1-8 v Kingstonian Surrey Senior Cup 1966-1967
Senior Honours:	Isthmian Champions(2) Div 2 Champions 00-01 Full Members Cup 92-3
	Lg Champions (2) LondonSen Cup (8 R-up (3)
Previous Leagues:	London 32-37 Athenian 37-56
	Ground: Sandy Lane Mitcham.

Back Row (L-R): Peter Smith (Goalkeeping Coach), Jamie Findlay, Denis Lawton (Physio), Tyran James, James Lasbrey, John Hastings, Paul Borg, Adam Broomfield, Scott Kinch, Paul Scott, Vernon Francis, Aaron Day, Mikael Munday, Scott Simpson, Keith Dublin (Coach) and Ryan Adams. **Front Row:** Richard Cadette (Manager), Shelkh Ceesay, Ted Hart, Jason Pinnnock, Craig Tanner, Ryan Gray, Jason Haniff, Benson Kpaka and Charlie Smith.

WALTON CASUALS

Founded: 1948
Nickname:
Casuals

Manager: Spencer Coillins **Coach:** **Physio:**

Club Colours: Tangerine /Black/Black

Change Colours: All Blue

Club Sponsor: Antler Homes

Previous League: Combined Counties

Best Seasons: League: 15th Isthmian Division 1

F.A. Cup: 1st Qualifying Round 2003-2004 **F.A.Trophy.:**

F.A.Vase: 1st Round 199-2000 2001-2002

Ground address: Franklyn Road Sports Ground, Watersdie Drive, Walton-on-Thames, Surrey. KT12 2JP Tel No: 01932 787749

Club Website: www.waltoncasuals.co.uk

Capacity: 1,320 **Seats:** 153 **Covered:**403 **Floodlights:** Yes

Simple Directions: Left off Terrace Roa at first major roundabout out of Walton centre. Ground is next to Elmbridge Leisure Centre.,

Midweek Home Matchday: Tuesday

Clubhouse: Open matchdays only. Hot food available. **Club Shop:** No

Local Radio:

Local Press:

CLUB PERSONNEL
Chairman: Graham James
President: Bob Mott
Director of Football: Tony Gale
Secretary: Maureen Cayford
c/o club
General Manager: David Symonds

Programme Editor & Press Off.:
Stuart Roberts
28 pages £1.00

CLUB STATISTICS

Record	**Attendance:** 1,748 v AFC Wimbledon Combined Counties League 12.04.04
	Career Goalscorer:
	Career Appearances:
Record Transfer Fee	Paid:
	Received:
Senior Honours:	Combined Counties League Champions 2004-2005
Previous Leagues:	Surrey Intermediate, Surrey Senior, Suburban, Surrey Premier, & Co.Counties.

Back row,left to right: Dick Errington (physio), James Pearson, Michael Cobden, Bradley Collins, James Crowe, Danny Andrews, John Ambridge, Michael Cayford, Michael Carpenter, Joe Frimpong and Spencer Collins (Manager). Front row: Greg Ball, Grant Keywood, Danmien Ray, Craig Carley, Luke Dowling (capt), Scott Harris, Anthony Gale Ramzi Bedj-Bedj and Danny Ray.

WHYTELEAFE

Founded: 1946
Nickname: Leafe

CLUB PERSONNEL
Chairman: Markm Coole
President:
Secretary: Edward Lucas,
Braeside, Johns Road, Tatsfield,
Wetsreham,Kent.TN16 2AP Tel NO:
07710 859034 (M)
Commercial Manager:T.Douce
Press Secretary: Briabn Davis
Tel NO: 0208651 2999
Programme
Editor: Mark Cooper
36 pages £1.00
2005-2006
Captain: T.B.A.
Player of the Year: Lee Sidwell
Top Goalscorer: Lee Sidwell

Manager: Stuart Massey   **Asst.Manager:** Bernie Donnelly: **Physio**: John Knapton
Club Colours: Green& White Hoops/Green/Green
Change Colours: Yellow/Green/Green
Club Sponsor: Formark Scaffolding
Previous League: Athenian
Best Seasons: League: 9th Isthmian Division 1 2005-2006
F.A. Cup: 1st Round 1999-2000   **F.A.Trophy.:** 4th Round 1998-1999
F.A.Vase:5th Round 1980-1981 1985-1986
Ground address: 15 Church Road, Whyteleafe, Surrey CR3 0AR
Tel No: 02086605491(Ground 1208645 0422 (Boardroom)
Club Website:
Capacity: 5,000   **Seats**:400   **Covered**: 600   **Floodlights**: Yes
Simple Directions: Five minutes walk from Whyteleafe (BR) - turn right from station, and left into Church Road
Midweek Home Matchday: Tuesday
Clubhouse: Every evening & lunches at w/e. Hot & cold food, pool, darts, gaming machines
Club Shop: Yes
Local Radio: Mercury.
Local Press: Croydon Advertiser

CLUB STATISTICS

Record   **Attendance:** 2,210 v Chester City F.A. Cup 1999-2000

Career Goalscorer:

Career Appearances:

Record Transfer Fee   **Paid**: £1,000 to Carshalton Athletic for Gary Bowyer

                  Received: £25,000 for Steve Milton

Senior Honours: Isthmian Lge Div 2 South R-up 88-89; Surrey Sen. Cup 68-69 (R-up 87-88);

Previous Leagues: Leagues: Caterham & Edenbridge, Croydon, Thornton Heath & Dist.,

                  Surrey Intermediate (East) 54-58, Surrey Senior 58-75, Spartan 75-81,

                  Athenian 81-84

Back row, left to right: Back row, left to right: Stuart Massey, James Wastell, Lee Sidwell, Carlton Murray-Price, Bradley Drake, Tony Martin, Danny Oakins, Scot Simpson, Curtis Warmington and Bernie Donnelly. Front row: Leigh Douce, Lewis Taylor, Danny Edwards, Luke Basford, Dean Hamlin, Chris Head, Sarah Dunbar and Tim Strong.

FOOTBALL LEAGUE

STEP 1

FOOTBALL
CONFERENCE

STEP 2

| CONFERENCE NORTH | CONFERENCE SOUTH |

STEP 3

| SOUTHERN PREMIER | NORTHERN PREMIER | ISTHMIAN PREMIER |

STEP 4

| SOUTHERN DIVISION 1 SOUTH &WEST MIDLAND | NORTHERN PREMIER DIV.1 | ISTHMIAN DIVISION 1 NORTH SOUTH |

STEP 5/6

Combined Counties	Hellenic	Northern League	Spartan South Midlands	Wessex
Eastern Counties	Kent	Northern Counties East	Sussex County	Western
Essex Senior	Midland Alliance	North West Counties	United Counties	

STEP 7

Anglian Combination	Dorset County	Kent County	Midland Combination	Peterborough & District	West Cheshire
Bedford & District	Dorset Premier	Leicestershire Senior	Midland League	Reading League	West Lancashire
Brighton & Hove	East Sussex	Liverpool County	North Berkshire	Somerset County	West Midlands (reg)
Cambridgeshire County	Essex & Suffolk Border	Manchester Football	Northampton Town Lge	South Western	West Sussex
Central Midlands	Essex Intermediate	Mid Cheshire League	Northamptonshire Comb.	Suffolk & Ipswich	Wiltshire League
Crawley & Disrict	Gloucesterhisre Co.	Mid Sussex	Northern Alliance	Teeside League	Worthing & District
Devon County	Herts Senior County	Middlesex County	Oxfordshire Senior	Wearside League	

COMBINED COUNTIES

SPONSORED BY: CHERRY RED RECORDS

President: Ron Monkley   **Chairman:** John Bennett
Hon. Secretary: Les Pharo.
Tel: 020 8339 0716 (H&Fx) Mobile: 07720 431613
email: secretary@combinedcountiesleague.co.uk

PREMIER DIVISION	P	W	D	L	F	A	Pts
1. Godalming Town	40	30	7	3	99	33	97
2. Merstham	40	24	9	7	64	26	81
3. Ash United	40	21	8	11	73	43	71
4. Colliers Wood United	40	22	4	14	93	63	70
5. Horley Town	40	20	9	11	54	41	69
6. Bedfont	40	19	10	11	69	45	67
7. Sandhurst Town	40	18	12	10	77	50	66
8. Chessington & Hook (-4)	40	17	12	11	82	46	59
9. Raynes Park Vale	40	18	3	19	71	82	57
10. Reading Town	40	15	9	16	65	59	54
11. Westfield	40	15	9	16	60	58	54
12. Mole Valley Predators	40	16	5	19	65	90	53
13. North Greenford United	40	15	7	18	72	70	52
14. Chipstead	40	13	10	17	56	65	49
15. Cobham	40	12	8	20	55	60	44
16. Cove	40	11	11	18	55	83	44
17. Guildford United	40	11	9	20	53	83	42
18. Frimley Green	40	11	8	21	45	78	41
19. Bedfont Green (2nd Div.1 04-05)	40	12	5	23	60	95	41
20. Feltham	40	9	6	25	49	90	33
21. Farnham Town	40	5	11	24	38	95	26

PREMIER DIVISION	1	2	3	4	5	6	7	8	9	10	11	12	13	14	15	16	17	18	19	20	21
1 Ash-United		1-2	2-1	0-1	5-1	0-1	2-1	2-0	2-0	3-0	1-1	3-5	3-0	2-0	0-0	6-0	1-0	3-3	2-2	1-1	3-0
2 Bedfont	1-2		4-2	1-1	2-0	0-0	2-2	1-0	7-0	1-0	6-2	1-2	4-0	2-0	1-3	4-2	2-1	1-2	1-1	1-4	1-1
3 Bedfont Green	1-4	1-1		2-6	2-1	2-1	2-3	1-1	0-1	1-2	2-2	2-6	4-1	0-1	1-4	4-1	1-2	1-6	2-1	0-2	2-1
4 Chessington &-Hook	0-1	4-0	4-1		0-0	3-3	2-0	1-2	2-0	6-1	5-1	0-1	0-0	0-0	0-0	1-4	3-0	2-1	1-1	1-1	4-0
5 Chipstead	2-0	0-0	5-1	2-2		2-1	0-1	3-3	3-0	4-0	0-2	2-4	2-1	1-1	0-2	1-3	1-1	1-2	2-1	0-0	2-0
6 Cobham	0-1	1-0	1-2	1-0	1-4		2-3	1-0	3-1	1-2	1-1	0-2	2-3	2-2	0-2	4-0	0-2	3-0	1-1	1-2	0-1
7 Colliers Wood Utd	4-2	1-0	1-3	3-4	3-1	4-2		2-0	2-2	4-0	5-2	0-3	4-0	0-1	0-2	5-1	4-1	2-0	4-0	1-1	2-4
8 Cove	3-2	2-2	2-2	4-4	0-2	0-3	0-2		2-1	3-0	1-0	0-1	6-3	2-2	0-4	0-3	2-0	1-2	0-2	0-2	2-2
9 Farnham Town	0-1	0-3	1-1	0-8	1-1	3-3	1-6	0-0		0-3	3-1	1-5	1-5	3-4	0-1	3-0	1-1	1-1	2-2	0-0	2-2
10 Feltham	2-1	0-1	0-2	0-2	4-1	1-1	5-3	1-2	1-0		1-2	1-2	1-4	1-1	0-2	2-3	0-0	1-4	3-1	2-4	1-1
11 Frimley Green	0-4	0-3	3-2	1-0	3-1	0-1	2-1	1-1	2-0	2-2		1-1	1-2	2-1	0-1	1-2	0-1	4-0	1-1	1-0	0-4
12 Godalming Town	1-1	0-2	4-0	5-1	0-0	1-0	3-2	5-0	1-0	3-0	3-3		3-0	1-2	0-0	5-0	3-1	1-0	1-1	3-2	2-0
13 Guildford United	2-1	0-2	0-3	0-0	1-1	1-2	3-1	1-1	2-1	3-3	0-1	1-4		3-4	1-0	2-2	1-4	0-0	0-4	2-2	4-0
14 Horley Town	1-1	1-0	3-2	1-3	2-0	2-0	0-2	4-0	1-2	2-0	3-0	1-0	0-0		2-0	0-0	1-0	3-1	0-1	0-4	0-1
15 Merstham	0-1	4-0	3-0	1-0	2-0	1-0	1-1	2-2	2-1	0-2	4-0	1-1	2-0	1-0		3-1	2-4	5-2	0-0	1-0	3-1
16 Mole Valley Predators	2-1	1-1	0-1	0-5	1-2	3-2	2-1	3-4	4-0	3-2	3-1	1-7	0-1	2-0	0-1		2-2	2-0	4-2	0-3	0-4
17 North Greenford Utd	2-3	2-1	2-3	1-1	1-2	1-2	2-3	5-3	1-2	4-0	2-0	0-1	4-1	1-1	0-0	0-4		6-0	2-6	5-1	1-5
18 Raynes Park Vale	1-0	1-2	3-1	2-1	2-3	0-5	2-4	5-1	3-2	3-2	3-0	1-4	4-1	3-2	1-2	3-1	4-2	5-2		1-0	0-7	1-2
19 Reading Town	0-2	0-3	5-2	0-2	3-0	5-2	0-3	1-2	3-1	4-0	2-1	1-2	2-1	0-1	1-0	2-0	1-2	0-2		2-3	0-0
20 Sandhurst Town	1-2	1-1	3-0	3-1	3-2	1-1	2-1	5-2	1-1	3-1	3-0	1-2	3-0	0-2	0-2	2-2	0-2	1-0	2-4		2-2
21 Westfield	1-1	0-2	2-0	2-1	4-1	1-0	1-2	0-1	5-0	3-2	2-0	0-1	1-3	0-2	1-1	1-2	1-4	2-0	1-2	1-1	

DIVISION ONE	P	W	D	L	F	A	Pts
1. Warlingham	32	25	4	3	102	37	79
2. AFC Wallingford (Promoted)	32	24	2	6	90	38	74
3. Bookham (Promoted)	32	22	7	3	113	33	73
4. Worcester Park	32	19	6	7	86	43	63
5. Hartley Wintney (-3)	32	21	3	8	74	44	63
6. Tongham	32	19	3	10	118	58	60
7. Hanworth Villa	32	18	5	9	94	53	59
8. Coney Hall	32	15	7	10	95	56	52
9. Farleigh Rovers	32	13	5	14	55	57	44
10. Crescent Rovers	32	13	5	14	56	65	44
11. Staines Lammas	32	11	4	17	58	70	37
12. Sheerwater	32	9	4	19	44	90	31
13. Monotype	32	8	6	18	45	89	30
14. Merrow	32	6	2	24	47	114	20
15. Chobham & Ottershaw	32	5	4	23	34	108	19
16. Shottermill & Haslemere	32	5	3	24	36	98	18
17. Netherne	32	3	2	27	38	132	11

DIVISION ONE	1	2	3	4	5	6	7	8	9	10	11	12	13	14	15	16	17
1 AFC Wallingford		1-2	6-0	4-1	5-1	1-0	2-1	3-2	4-0	3-1	3-2	2-0	1-0	7-0	4-3	0-2	5-1
2 Bookham	2-3		1-1	3-2	5-0	4-2	2-5	2-0	8-0	6-0	3-2	4-1	3-0	0-0	5-1	2-2	1-1
3 Chobham & Ottershaw	1-4	0-8		0-3	3-3	0-2	1-4	0-2	0-1	0-2	4-1	0-2	4-4	0-3	1-4	1-4	4-1
4 Coney Hall	2-3	2-3	13-0		1-3	5-2	2-2	1-1	3-0	6-1	5-1	5-3	3-1	4-2	3-3	1-2	4-1
5 Crescent Rovers	1-1	3-5	2-3	0-1		1-1	4-3	6-0	2-0	0-3	4-1	2-0	1-0	2-0	0-4	1-0	1-4
6 Farleigh Rovers	1-2	0-2	3-1	2-1	1-0		2-6	2-4	3-2	2-3	4-1	1-1	2-0	2-1	2-3	3-4	0-1
7 Hanworth Villa	2-1	1-3	6-1	3-3	5-0	1-3		1-3	2-1	2-1	1-0	4-2	6-0	0-1	1-2	2-0	1-1
8 Hartley Wintney	2-0	1-1	1-0	1-0	3-0	2-0	2-2		4-0	1-2	6-0	4-0	6-0	2-1	1-4	3-1	3-0
9 Merrow	1-5	0-4	3-2	1-5	2-2	0-3	3-1	2-4		0-4	6-1	2-3	4-0	2-4	1-6	3-4	1-5
10 Monotype	1-1	0-9	0-0	1-3	0-2	1-1	1-7	0-2	3-0		2-2	5-1	3-5	1-3	0-7	0-2	1-2
11 Netherne	0-5	0-9	4-5	2-5	0-3	2-2	0-7	1-2	6-0	0-3		5-3	0-2	2-1	0-5	0-5	0-4
12 Sheerwater	1-0	1-1	3-0	0-0	1-0	1-2	1-5	0-2	3-3	3-1	2-1		3-1	1-4	1-5	0-3	2-3
13 Shottermill & Haslemere	0-2	0-8	0-1	0-6	0-4	1-3	1-2	2-1	2-4	1-1	4-1	4-2		3-4	2-4	1-8	0-0
14 Staines Lammas	0-4	0-3	2-0	0-0	3-2	2-2	1-2	3-4	2-1	3-3	7-1	1-2	3-1		1-2	4-5	0-1
15 Tongham	1-4	0-2	9-1	3-3	1-3	1-2	5-3	0-2	10-1	5-1	9-1	10-1	3-0	3-1		2-3	1-1
16 Warlingham	5-0	2-0	2-0	4-1	3-3	2-0	1-1	6-3	6-1	1-0	9-1	2-0	2-1	5-1	4-0		2-1
17 Worcester Park	2-4	2-2	5-0	4-1	6-0	1-0	3-5	4-0	3-2	9-0	2-0	8-0	3-0	3-0	3-2	1-1	

FIRST ROUND

Colliers Wood Utd	v	Warlingham	4-2
Sheerwater	v	Reading Town	0-4
Horley Town	v	Bookham	4-0
Netherne	v	Hartley Wintney	0-8
Staines Lammas	v	Tongham	1-2
Southall	v	Chobham	8-2
Merstham (H)	v	Farleigh Rovers	0-0*, 3-2p
Shottermill & Hasl'	v	Hanworth Villa	1-0

(Hanworth Villa re-instated)

SECOND ROUND

Hanworth Villa	v	Mole Valley Predators	3-2
Sandhurst Town	v	Monotype	2-0
AFC Wallingford	v	Coney Hall	4-1
Horley Town	v	Southall	1-2
Farnham Town	v	Worcester Park	3-4
Feltham	v	Merrow	2-1
Cobham	v	Guildford United	2-1
Tongham	v	Raynes Park Vale	4-0
Cove	v	Ash United	4-3
Frimley Green	v	Colliers Wood United	0-1
Reading Town	v	North Greenford United	1-2
Chipstead	v	Godalming Town	0-4
Crescent Rovers	v	Merstham (H)	1-4
Westfield	v	Bedfont	2-1
Hartley Wintney	v	Bedfont Green	4-0

THIRD ROUND

Westfield	v	Chessington & Hook	2-1
Colliers Wood	v	North Greenford United	1-2
Feltham	v	Hartley Wintney	3-0
Southall	v	Sandhurst Town	AW
Tongham	v	Godalming Town	1-2
Hanworth Villa	v	Worcester Park	2-5, HW
AFC Wallingford	v	Cove	2-1
Merstham (H)	v	Cobham	3-1

QUARTER-FINALS

Westfield	v	Godalming Town	0-2
Feltham	v	North Greenford United	4-5
Sandhurst Town	v	Merstham (H)	2-3
AFC Wallingford	v	Hanworth Villa	1-3

SEMI-FINALS

North Greenford Utd	v	Godalming Town	0-1
Merstham (H)	v	Hanworth Villa	4-0

THE FINAL

Godalming Town	v	Merstham (H)	4-0

LEAGUE CONSTITUTION 2006-07 - PREMIER DIVISION

ASH UNITED

Founded: 1911
Nickname:

Chairman: Robert Atkins   **Vice-Chairman:** Jerry Kerrigan   **Manager:** Terry Eames
Secretary: James Avenell, 82 Ewins Close, Ash, Aldershot, Hants. GU12 6SB. Tel/Fax: 01252 321528
Press Officer: Gareth Whatmore (07739 657994)
Programme: 36 pages Price: 1.00 **Editor:** Secretary
GROUND ADDRESS: Youngs Drive off Shawfield Road, Ash,Near Aldershot   **Tel:** 01252 745757
Capacity: 1,500   **Seats:** None   **Covered:** Yes   **Floodlights:** Yes
Simple Directions: A323 towards Ash, left into Shawfield Road, then left into Youngs Drive. One mile from BR stations
Midweek Home Matchday: Tuesday   **Clubhouse:** Yes   **Club Shop:** No
Previous League(s): Surrey Senior, Aldershot Senior   **Previous Ground:** Ash Common Recreation 70-71
Club Colours: Green with red trim/green/red   **Change Colours:** All blue
BEST PERFORMANCES
League: Champions 81-82 86-87 98-99   **F.A. Cup:** 2nd Qualifying Rd. 98-99   **F.A.Vase:** 4th Rd 98-99
RECORD Attendance: 914 v AFC Wimbledon 2002-03 **Goalscorer:** Shaun Mitchell 44   **Apps:** Tommy Burton 540
Senior Honours: Co.Co. Champions (3) and Aldershot Senior Cup 98-99 01-02

BANSTEAD ATHLETIC

Founded: 1944
Nickname: A's

Chairman: Terry Molloy   **Manager:** Graeme Banyard   **Coach:** Ian Green & Matt Lavallin
Secretary: Terry Parmenter. Tel: 07940 387041 (M). Email: terryparmenter@blueyonder.co.uk
Programme: Print Centre Tel: 01372 740113.
GROUND ADDRESS: Merland Rise, Tadworth, Surrey KT20 5JG   **Tel:** 01737 350 982
Capacity: 3,500   **Seats:** 250   **Covered:** 800   **Floodlights:** Yes
Simple Directions: From the M25: Leave the M25 at Junction 8, and head North towards London. After the 3rd roundabout, turn left at the next set of traffic lights into Reigate Road, there is a petrol station at this junction.Continue past Asda supermarket and turn at the next set of lights, turn left into Great Tattenhams. Take the 3rd left into Merland Rise and you will find Banstead Athletic FC approx 500m up on your left. A large sign is placed outside the shared entrance to Banstead Sports Centre. From the North: Aim for the A217 (Brighton Rd) or the A2022. Where these 2 roads meet, head South towards the M25. At the second set of lights, turn right into Tattenham Way. Continue across the next set of lights into Great Tattenhams and take the 3rd left into Merland Rise. The club is approx 500m ahead, on the left hand side.
Midweek Home Matchday: Tuesday   **Clubhouse:** Yes.   **Club Shop:** Yes.
Previous League(s): Surrey Int., Surrey Snr 49-65, Spartan 65-75, London Spartan 75-79, Athenian 79-84, Isthmian 84-06
Club Colours: Amber & black/amber/black   **Change Colours:** All red
BEST PERFORMANCES
F.A. Cup: 3rd Qual.Rd. 86-87, 00-01.   **F.A.Vase:** Semi-finals 96-97
RECORD Attendance: 1,400 v Leytonstone, FA Amateur Cup 1953 **Goalscorer:** Harry Clark   **Apps:** Dennis Wall
Senior Honours: Surrey Snr Lg(6) 50-54 56-57 64-65, Lg Cup 57-58. London Spartan Lg Cup (2) 65-67. Athenian Lg Cup(2) 80-82. Surrey Int. Lg(2) 47-49, Cup 46-47 54-55.

BEDFONT

Founded: 1968
Nickname:

Chairman: Mick Carroll. **President:** Roger Cooper

Manager: John Morris **Asst.Manager:** Mark Wilson **Coach:** Ron Griffin:

Secretary: Les KIng, 14 Harlequin Close,Isleworth, Middlesex. TW7 7LA

Tel No:0208 894 5525 (H) 0208 392 3021 (W)

Programme Editor: Les KIng (0208891 1985) **Programme:** 20pages 50p

GROUND ADDRESS: The Orchard, Hatton Road, Bedfont, Middlesex TW14 9QT **Tel. No:** 020 8890 7264

Directions: Turn down Faggs Road opposite Hatton Cross (Picadilly Line) station on Great South Western Road (A30) then sharp right into Hatton Road.

Capacity: 2,000 **Seats:** 100 **Covered:** 50 **Floodlights:** Yes

Midweek Home Matchday: Tuesday **Clubhouse:** Yes **Club Shop:** No

Club Colours: Yellow & blue/blue/blue **Change Colours:** All red or white/navy//navy

BEDFONT GREEN

Founded: 1965
Nickname:The Green

Chairman: Doug White **Vice-Chairman:** Des Vertannes **Manager:** Tom Fountain

Secretary: Stewart Cook, 22 Denman Drive, Ashford, Middlesex TW15 2AR **Asst.Manager**: Paul Butler

Tel No: 01784 246677 **email:** stewart.cook@bedfontgreenfc.co.uk

Sponsors: Connexion World Cargo,Axiom

Programme: 40 Pages Price £1.00

GROUND ADDRESS: Avenue Park, Western Avenue, Greenford, Middlesex UB6 8GA **Tel. No:** 0208 578 2706

Simple Directions: Off A40

Midweek Home Matchday: Wednesday **Clubhouse:** Yes **Club Shop:** No

Club Colours: Navy/red/white **Change Colours:** White/red/navy

BEST PERFORMANCES

League: Co.Co Div.1 R-up 2004-05

Senior Honours: Combined Counties Division 1 Runners-up 2004-2005. Promotion achieved in five consecutive seasons.

Bedfont. Back Row (L-R): Len Postins (Asst. Manager), Danny Buckle, Dave Green, Luke Willis, Ray Sherwood, Kevin Campello, James Wood, Mark Postins, Gary Jenkins, Lee Pearce.
Front Row: James Danaher, Jimmy Williams, Paul Cook, Ken During, Adam Willis, Richard Bryant (Manager).
Photo: Arthur Evans.

BOOKHAM

Founded: 1921
Nickname:

Chairman: Garry Billing **President:** Gary Billing **Manager:**Glyn Mandeville

Secretary: Paul Chapman, 22 Strathcona Avenue, Bookham, Surrey KT 23 4HP

Tel Nos: 01372 450 764 (H) 01372 378666(W) 01372 379667 (Fax) 07729626034 (M)

Programme Editor: Paul Chapman

GROUND ADDRESS: Groundsharing with Dorking F.C. at Mill Lane (off the High Street) with Reserves at Chrystie

Recreation, Dorking Rd, Bookham. **Dorking Tel.No:** 01306 884 112 and **Chrystie Rec Tel No:** 01372 459 482

Capacity: 3000 **Seats:** 200 **Covered:** 600 **Floodlights:**Yes

Previous Leagues: Surrey Senior League, Isthmian League.

Club Colours: Yellow/black/yellow **Change Colours:** All Red

CAMBERLEY TOWN

Founded: 1896
Nickname: Krooners

Chairman: Ian Waldren **Manager:** Ken Ballard
Secretary: Paul Montague, 22 Glassonby Walk, Camberley, Surrey GU15 1SD **Physio:** Mike Quinn
Tel No: 01276 20817 (H). 07711 257716 (M). **Website:** www.camberleytownfc.co.uk
Press Officer & Programme Editor: Andy Vaughan **Programme:** 24 Pages £1.00
GROUND ADDRESS: Krooner Park,Krooner Road, off Frimley Road, Canberley, Surrey GU15 2QP (01276 65392)
Capacity: 3,000 **Seats:** 195 **Covered:** 280 **Floodlights:**Yes
Simple Directions: M3 jct 4 to Frimley, then B3411 (Camberley) ground is on left opposite the Standard pub.
Midweek Home Matchday: Tuesday **Clubhouse:** Open matchdays and some evenings **Club Shop:** Yes
Previous Names: Camberley & Yorktown 1896-1946 Camberley FC 46-67 **Grounds:** London Rd, Southwell Park Rd 05-09 .
Martins Meadow 09-12 **Leagues**:Ascot & Dist,W. Surrey, Aldershot Sen, Surrey Sen, Spartan 73-75, Athenian 75-77 82-84.
Isthmian.
Club Colours: Red & white stripes/red/red **Change Colours:** Green & white hoops/black/black
BEST PERFORMANCES: League: Isthmian Div 2 R -Up **F.A. Cup:** 1st Rd Proper 98-99 **F.A.Vase:** 6th Rd 85-86 & 98-99
RECORD Attendance: 3,500 v Crystal Palace, friendly 14.10.74 and competitive 2,066 v Aldershot Town Isth Div 2 25.08.90
Appearances: Brian Ives **Victory:** 15-0 v Royal Engineers, friendly 14.10 74
Defeat: 0-11 v Abingdon Town (a) Isthmian Div 2 25.08.90
Senior Honours: Isthmian Div 2 R-up 78-79 Surrey Sen. Cup 78-79 R-up 35-36 Surrey Junior Cup (2) Aldershot Sen Cup(2)

CHERTSEY TOWN

Founded: 1890
Nickname:Curfews

Chairman: Steve Powers **Vice-President:** Sav Ramayon **President:** Cllr Chris Norman
Manager: Roy Butler **Asst. Manager:** Mark Turner **Physio**: Peter Chessman
Secretary: Chris Gay, 23 Richmond Close, Frimley, Camberley, Surrey GU16 8NR. Tel: 01276 20745 (H). 07713 4733313 (M).
Programme Editor: Chris Gay **Programme:** 36 Pages £1.50l) **email:** ctfc freeserve.co.uk
GROUND ADDRESS: Alwyns Lane, Chertsey, Surrey Kt 16 9DW **Ground Tel. No:** 01932 561774
Capacity: 3,000 **Seats:** 250 **Covered:** 1,000 **Floodlights:** Yes
Simple Directions: Alwyns Lane is off Windsor Street at north end of the town shopping centre.
Midweek Matchday: Tuesday **Clubhouse:** Weekday evenings and week-end lunchtimes **Club Shop:**Yes (Daniel Dullaway)
)Previous Leagues: West Surrey (pre 1899),Surrey Jnr 1899-1920, Surrey Intermediate 20-46, Surrey Senior 46-63,
Metropolitan 63-66, Gtr London 66-67,Spartan 67-75, Lon Spartan 75-76,Athenian 76-84, Isthmian 84-85 Co Counties 85-86
Previous Grounds: The Grange (pre World War1) and The Hollows (pre 1929)
Club Colours: Blue & white stripes/white/white **Change Colours:** Yellow & Black
BEST PERFORMANCES: League: Isthmian Premier **F.A. Cup:** 3rd Qualifying Round 92-93 **F.A.Vase:** 6th Rd 87-88 91-92
F.A.Amateur Cup: 3rd Qualifying Round **F.A.Trophy:** 2nd Qualifying Round:
RECORD Attendance: 2,150 v Aldershot Isthmian Div 2 04.12.93 **Goalscorer:** Alan Brown 54 62-63 **Appearances:**
Senior Honours: Isthmian Div 2 R-up 94-95 , Div 3 R-up, Surrey Senior Cup R-up 85-86

CHESSINGTON & HOOK

Founded: 1968
Nickname:

Chairman: Graham Ellis **President:** Ray Hall **Manager:** Paul Ellis

Secretary: Chris Blackie,17 Finlay Close, Chessington, Surrey KT9 1X

Tel Nos: 0208391 4376 (H) 07748 877704 (M) 032358 **Programme:** £1.00

GROUND ADDRESS: Chalky Lane,Chessington, Surrey KT 9 2PW **Tel:** 01372 745777

Capacity: 3,000 **Seats:**160 **Covered:** 600 **Floodlights:** Yes

Simple Directions: Turn off A243 into Chalky Lane opposite Chessington World of Adventure Theme Park.

Midweek Home Matchday: Tuesday **Clubhouse:** Yes **Club Shop:** No

Previous Leagues: Middlx 68-69 Surrey Co 69-72 Home Co 72-78 Comb.Co 78-81 Surrey Prem ,Surrey Comb, Surrey Prem.

Club Colours: All Blue **Change Colours:** All red

LAST SEASON

League: 7th **F.A. Cup:** 1st Qualifying Round Round **F.A. Vase:** 4th Round

CHIPSTEAD

Founded: 1906
Nickname: Chips

Chairman: Don Faircloth   **President:** Dave Argent   **Manager:** Tony Webb

Secretary: Geoff Corner, 20 Sunnymeade Avenue, Carshalton Beeches, Surrey SM5 4JF

Tel No: 0181 642 0827

Programme Editor: Terry Antell   **Programme:** 36 Pages - 50p

GROUND ADDRESS: High Road, Chipstead, Surrey **Tel No:** 01737 553250

Capacity: 2,000   **Seats:** 30   **Covered:** 100   **Floodlights:** Yes

Simple Directions: From the Brighton Road northbound, go left into Church Lane and left into Hogcross Lane. High Road is on the right.

Midweek Home Matchday: Tuesday   **Clubhouse:** Yes   **Club Shop:** No

Previous Leagues: Surrey Intermediate 62-82 Surrey Premier 82-86

Club Colours: Green & White/Black/Black   **Change Colours:** All Red

BEST PERFORMANCES

League: Champions Co.Co. 89-90   **F.A. Cup:** 98-99   **F.A.Vase:** 3rd replay 98-99

RECORD Attendance: 1,170   **Goalscorer:** Mick Nolan 124

Senior Honours: Co.Co Champions 89-90 R-Up (3)

COBHAM

Founded: 1892
Nickname: Hammers

Chairman: Chris Wolston   **President:** David Robinson   **Manager:** Matt Alexander

Secretary: Ken Reed, 29 Waterer Gardens ,Tadworth, Surrey KT 20 5PS   **Coach:** Ian Savage

Tel No: 01737 352641

GROUND ADDRESS: Leg O'Mutton Field, Anvil Lane, Downside Bridge Road, Cobham, Surrey KT11 3BD **Tel:** 07787 383407

Capacity: 2,000   **Seats:** None   **Covered:** Yes   **Floodlights:** Yes

Simple Directions: A3 turnoff at A245 and take A307 (Portsmouth) towards Leatherhead. Turn right into Between Street and right again into Downside Road and again opposite car park.

Previous Ground: Cobham Rec   **Previous Leagues:** Surrey Senior   **Sponsor:** Prestege Couriers

Club Colours: Red&Black hoops/black/black **Change Colours:** All White

BEST PERFORMANCES

League: Co.Co Runners Up 98-99 04-05   **F.A. Cup:** 1st Qualifying Round 02-03   **F.A.Vase:** 3rd Rd 1998-99

Midweek Home Matchday: Tuesday   **Clubhouse:** Yes   **Club Shop:** No

RECORD Attendance: 2,000 Charity Game 1975

Chessington & Hook United. Back Row (L-R): Paul Ellis (Manager), Matthew Bennett, Dan Moorhouse, Tom Duffell, Mark Russell, Stuart Lascelles, Andree Brown, Darren Smith, Paul Norris (Jt Manager), David Field (Coach). **Front Row:** John Martin (Coach), Ross Shoefield, Robbie Burns, Andy Heath, Danny Heath, Chris Barnes, Paul West, Dan Laverich, David Lynsey (Coach). Photo: Gordon Whittington.

Colliers Wood. Back Row (L-R): Steven Griffiths, Freddie Fleming, Lee Hogan, Tony Webb, Ramzi-Bedj Bedj.
Front Row: Phil Hughes, Samuel Mead, Marc Hudson, Jon Dale, Daniel Cormack, Anthony Finn.

Photo: Alan Coomes.

COLLIERS WOOD UNITED

Founded: 1874
Nickname: The Woods

Chairman: Tony Eldridge   **President:** Ron Palmer   **Manager:** Steve Griffiths

Secretary: Tony Hurrell, 1 Inglewood, Pixton Way, Forestdale, Croydon, Surrey

Tel NOs: 0208 651 3259 (H) 0208 942 8962 (W) 07956 983947 (M)

GROUND ADDRESS: Wibandune Sports Ground, Lincoln Green, Opposite 199-213 Robin Hood Way, Wimbledon SW20 0AA

Tel. No: 0208 942 8062

Capacity: 2,000   **Seats:** 108   **Covered:** 100   **Floodlights:** Yes

Simple Directions: On A3 Kingston on Thames by-pass, one mile from Robion Hood junction southbound.

Midweek Home Matchday: Tuesday   **Clubhouse:** Open every evening and lunchtime   **Club Shop:** Yes

Club Colours: Blue & Black/black/black   **Change Colours:** All Red

COVE

Founded: 1897
Nickname:

Chairman: P.Wentworth   **President:** Ron Brown   **Manager:**
Secretary: Graham Brown, 6 Longfield Close, Haley Estate, Farnborough GU14 8HQ   **Sponsors:** Sunnyside Removals
Tel No & Fax: 01252 519031
Programme Editor: Graham Brown (01252 650920)   **Programme:** 30 Pages 50p
GROUND ADDRESS: Oak Farm Fields, 7 Squirrels Lane, Farnborough, Hants GU14 8PB **Tel:** 01252 543615
Capacity: 3,500   **Seats:** 105   **Covered:** 200   **Floodlights:** Yes
Simple Directions: Farnborough BR(2miles) follow Union St., right at lights into Prospect Rd, left into West Heath Rd and right into Romayne Close. Follow signs to Cove FC.
Midweek Home Matchday: Tuesday   **Clubhouse:** Open all evenings and week-end lunchtimes **Club Shop:** No
Previous Leagues: Aldershot Jnr, Aldershot Intermediate 45-48, Surrey Intermediate 48-71, Surrey Senior 71-73, Hampshire 74-81, Combined.Counties 81-90 95-2001 and Isthmian 90-5
Club Colours: Yellow & black stripes/black/black   **Change Colours:** Red & white stripes/white/white
LAST SEASON: League: 16th   **F.A. Cup:** Preliminary Round.   **F.A. Vase:** 1st Preliminary Round
Top Scorer: Jon Finnieston   **Player of the Year:** Andy Newbury   **Captain:** Antony Ricketts
BEST PERFORMANCES
F.A. Cup: 2nd Qual.Rd 2000-01   **F.A.Vase:** 5th Rd 2000-01
RECORD Attendance: 1,798 v Aldershot Isthmian Div 3 01.05.93
Senior Honours: League & Cup Double Winners 2000-01 & Co-Co League Cup 81-82 and Aldershot Senior Cup (5)

DORKING
Founded:1880
Nickname: The Chicks

Chairman: Jack Collins   **Vice-Chairman:** Ray Collins   **Manager:** Steve Lunn
Secretary: Ray Collins, 11Richmond Way, Fetcham,Surrey KT22 9NP
Tel No: 01372 453867
Press Officer & Programme Editor: Bryan Bletso   **Programme:** 48 Pages 5391.00
GROUND ADDRESS: Meadowbank, Mill Lane, Dorking, Surrey RH4 1DX   **Ground Tel. No.:** 01306 884112
Capacity: 3,600   **Seats:** 200   **Cover:** 800   **Floodlights:** Yes
Midweek Home Matchday: Tuesday   **Clubhouse:** Open daily   **Club Shop:** Yes
Previous Leagues: Surrey Senior 22-56 77-78 Corinthian 56-63 Athenian 63-74 78-80 Southern 74-77
Previous Names: Dorking Town 77-82 Guidford & Dorking (when club merged with Guildford in 1974)
Club Colours: Green & white hoops/green/green   **Change Colours:** All Navy Blue
BEST PERFORMANCES
F.A. Cup: 1st Rd 92-93   **F.A.Trophy:** 2nd Rd 91-92   **F.A.Vase:** 5th Rd 2001-02
RECORD Attendance: 4,500 v Folkestone Town F.A.Cup 1955 & v Plymouth A F.A.Cup 92-93 **Goalscorer:** Andy Bushell
Appearances: Steve Lunn **Victory:** 7-0 v Barking Isthmian Div 1 92-93
Senior Honours: Isthmian Div 2 88-89 Surrey SEn.Cup R-up (2) Surrey Sen.Shield (2) R-up (3)

EGHAM TOWN
Founded: 1877
Nickname: Sarnies or Town

Chairman: Peter Atkins   **V-Chairmen:** Peter Barnes & Brian Askew   **President:** Peter Barnes
Manager: Peter Burdett   **Coach:** Alf Coulton   **Physio :** Ken Weaver
Secretary: Beverley Godzisz, 21 Huntingfield Way, Egham, Surrey TW20 8DU **Tel No:** 01784 463914 (H) 07917 570368 (M)
Programme Editor: David Tilley (01536 403667)   **Programme:** 32 Page £1.00
GROUND ADDRESS: Runnymead Stadium, Tempest Road, Egham, Surrey TW20 8HZ   **Tel:** 01784 43526
Capacity: 5,635   **Seats:** 335   **Covered:1,120**   **Floodlights:** Yes
Simple Directions: M25 jct 13 follow signs for Egham under M25 at roundabout, left to end, left to mini roundabout over railway crossing, left to end (Pooley Green Rd) right. Tempest Road second right.
Midweek Home Matchday: Tuesday   **Clubhouse:** Open daily evenings w/e lunches   **Club Shop:** No
Previous Names: Runnymead Rovers 1877-1905 and Egham F.C. 1905-63 **Previous Leagues:** Hounslow & District 1896-1914 Surrey Intermediate 19-22 Surrey SEnior 22-28 65-57 Sparatan 29-33 67-74 Parthenon 64-65 Athenian 74-77
Previous Grounds: Angklers Rest 1877-1914 Manorcroft Rd. 19-26 Vicarage Rd. 26-27 28-39 Green Lane 27-28
Club Colours: Yellow/green/yellow   **Change Colours:** All Blue
BEST PERFORMANCES: F.A. Cup: 4th Qual.Rd.
RECORD Attendance: 1,400 v Wycombe W F.A.Cup 1972 **Goalscorer:** Mark Butler   **Appearances:** Dave Jones 850+
Record Fees (in and out) for Mark Butler   **Senior Honours**: Surrey Sen.Cup R-Up 91-92

EPSOM& EWELL
Founded: 1917
Nickname: e's

Chairman: Peter Lumm   **President:** Stella Lamont   **Manager:** Ray Purvis
Secretary: D.Wilson, 3 Delaporte Close, Epsom, Surrey KT 127 4AF   **Coach:** Mark Freeborough
Tel No: 01372 729817   e-mail: davidwilson@moose.co.uk   **Physio:** John Carleton
Programme Editor: Stella Lamont   **Programme:** 28/32 pages £1.50   Club Website: www.eefc.net
GROUND ADDRESS: Groundshare with Banstead F.C. (Isthmian Divison One)   **Tel:**
Capacity: 3,500   **Seats:** 250   **Covered:** 800   **Floodlights:** Yes
Simple Directions: Follow signs to Tattenham Corner(Epsom Racetrack) then To Banstead Sports Centre
Midweek Home Matchday: Tuesday   **Clubhouse:** Normal licensing, food available.   **Club Shop:** No
Previous Names: Epsom Town (previously Epsom FC) merged with Ewell & Stoneleigh in 1960
        Leagues: Surrey Senior 24-27 73-75 London 27-49 Corinthian 49-93 Athenian 63-73 75-77
        Grounds: Horton Lane,Epsom 25-26 and West Street ,Ewell 1926-93
Club Colours: Royal & White   Change Colours: All Yellow
BEST PERFORMANCES
League: Isthmian League Div 1 **F.A. Cup:** 1st Rd 1933-34   **F.A.Trophy:** 2nd Rd 8-82   **F.A.Vase:** Runners-Up 74-75
RECORD Attendance: 5,000 v Kingstonian F.A.Cup 2nd Qual Rd 15.10 49 **Goalscorer:** Tommy Tuite **Appearances:**
Senior Honours: F.A.Vase Finalists 74-75 Isthman Lg Div 2 77-78 Surrey Senior Cup 80-81 R-up (3)

GUILDFORD CITY
Founded: 1996
Nickname: The City

Chairman: Aran Meadows   **President:** Jim Betts   **Manager:** Dave Vaughan

Secretary: Paul Milton. Tel: (M) 07803 169499

Programme Editor: Chris Pegman

GROUND ADDRESS: Spectrum Leisure Centre, Parkway, Guildford, Surrey GU1 1UP. Tel: (Spectrum) 01483 443322

Capacity:1,100   **Seats:** 135   **Covered:** Yes   **Floodlights:** Yes

Simple Directions: From Guildford main line station, take no.100 shuttle bus to Spectrum. From A3, exit at Guildford – follow signs to leisure centre.

Previous Leagues: Surrey Senior League

Club Colours: Red & white stripes/black/black   **Change Colours:** All red

MERSTHAM

Founded: 1892
Nickname:

Chairman: Ted Hickman   **President:** Bill Lawton   **Manager:** Mick Sullivan
Secretary: Richaed Baxter, 2 Wood Street, Merstham, Surrey. RH1 3PF   **Asst.Manager**: Mick Stratford
Tel Nos: 01737 645748 (H) 01293 450809 (W) **email**: richardbaxter01@hotmail.com
Press Officer: Roger Peerless   **Programme:** Yes
Ground Address: Moatside Ground, Weldon Way, Merstham, Redhill, SurreyRH1 3QB   **Tel No:** 01737 644046
Capacity: 2,500   **Seats:** 174   **Covered:** 100   **Floodlights:** Yes
Simple Directions: Leave Merstham village (A23) by School Hill take 5th right (Weldon Way) clubhouse and car park on right.Ten minutes walk from Merstham BR.
Midweek Home Matchday: Tuesday   **Clubhouse:** Open daily   **Club Shop:** No
Previous Leagues: Redhill & Dist., Surrey Co, S.E.Intermediate, Surrey Senior 64-78   **Club Sponsors:** The Tiling Company
Club Colours: Amber& Black stripes, black/amber   **Change Colours:** All Blue
Last Season: League: 2nd   **F.A. Cup:** 1st Qualifying Rd.   **F.A. Vase:** 2nd Qualifying Rd.
Top Scorer: Jemal Carr   **Player of the Year:** Chris Boulter   **Captain:** Chris Boulter
BEST PERFORMANCES
League: Runners-Up Co.Co. 87-88 89-90 05-06 League Cup R-Up: 87-88 89-90 05-06   **F.A. Cup:** 3rd Qualifying Round
F.A.Vase: 4th Round
RECORD Attendance: 1,587 v AFC Wimbledon 09.11.02   **Goalscorer:**   **Appearances:**
Senior Honours: Combined Counties Runners-Up 87-88 89-90

North Greenford F.C.   Photo: Arthur Evans.

NORTH GREENFORD UNITED

Founded: 1944
Nickname: Blues

Chairman: John Bivens   **President:** John Bignell   **Vice Cahirman:** Tony Foniss
Secretary: Mrs B Bivens, 1 THe Green, Sarrett, Hertfordshire WD3 6AY   **Manager:** Mick Harvey
Tel. No: 01923 270057 (H& Fax) e-mail: barbarabivens@onetel.net
Press Officer: John Bivens (0923 270057)   **Programme Editor:** Steve Goldfinch (01923 262121)
GROUND ADDRESS: Berkeley Fields, Berkeley Avenue, Greenford, Middlesex UB6   **Tel:** 0208 422 8923
Capacity: 1,500   **Seats:** 150   **Covered:** 100 standing   **Floodlights:** Yes
Simple Directions: Nearest Railway Station Greenford (Cenral Line) & Sudbury Hill (Piccadilly). Bus Metro Link 92
Midweek Home Matchday: Tuesday   **Clubhouse:**Yes   **Club Shop:** No
Club Colours: Blue & white/blue/blue   **Change Colours:** Red& white/Red/Red
LAST SEASON
League: 10th   **F.A. Cup:** Prelim. Rd.   **F.A. Vase:** 1st Rd
Player of the Year: Daniel Hughes   **Captain:** Daniel Murphy

RAYNES PARK VALE

Founded: 1995
Nickname: The Vale

Chairman: Syd Toulson   **Vice-Chairman:** Nigel Thorn   **Director of Football:** Steve Smith

Managers: Lee Dobinson & Brian Immes   **Coach**: Gary Clark

Secretary: Paull Armour, 9 Banstead Road, East Ewell Surrey KT17 3EP

Tel No: 07980 914211 **e-mail**: paul.armour2bt.com

Press Officer: Name (Tel)   **Programme:**

GROUND ADDRESS: Prince George's Playing Field, Raynes Park, SW20 9NB   **Tel:** 07714339747

Capacity: 2,000   **Seats:** 200   **Covered:**100   **Floodlights:** Yes

Simple Directions: Nearest Railway Station is Raynes Park. London Transport 163 &152

Midweek Home Matchday: Tuesday   **Clubhouse:**

Club Colours: Red& Blue/red/blue   **Change Colours:** Yellow/blue/yellow

RECORD Attendance:1,871 v AFC Wimbledon (at Carshalton Ath FC)

Senior Honours: CO.Co div 1 Champions 2002-03

READING TOWN

Founded: 1966
Nickname: Town

Chairman: Roland Ford   **Manager:** Colin Millard
Secretary: Richard Grey, 6 Milestone View Court, Lowfield Road, Caversham Park, Reading RG4 6ND
Tel No: 0118 948 4920 **email**: richardgrey@aol.com
Programme Editor: Richard Wickson   **Programme:** Pages 20 Price: 50p
GROUND ADDRESS: Reading Town Sports Ground, Scours Lane, Tilehurst, Reading, Berks. Tel No: 0118945 3555
Capacity: 2,000   **Seats:** Yes   **Covered:** Yes   **Floodlights:** Yes
Simple Directions: Leave Reading on Oxford Rd.(A329) past Battle Hospital. Scour Lane is first right after roundabout.
Midweek Home Matchday: Tuesday   **Clubhouse:** Yes   **Club Shop:**
Previous Names: Lower Burghfield, XL United, Vincents Utd., Reading Garage and ITS Reading Town.
Previous Leagues: Chiltonian 89-95, Reading & Dist. 66-89   **Ground:** Adwest Sports Ground and Kings Meadow
Club Colours: Red/black/black.   **Change Colours:** All Red
LAST SEASON: League: 10th   **F.A. Cup:** Preliminary Round.   **F.A. Vase:** 2nd Qualifying Round
Top Scorer: Graham Lewis 15   **Player of the Year:** Gary Clifford   **Captain:** Graham Jack
BEST PERFORMANCES
League: Co.Co. Runners -Up 97-98   **F.A. Cup:** 1st Qual.Rd.2000-01   **F.A.Vase:** 4th Rd 96-97
RECORD Attendance: 1,067 v AFC Wimbledon 2002-2003   **Defeat:** 0-10 v Feltham (A) 96-97
Victory: 7-0 v Cranleigh/Viking Sports and AFC Wimbledon.
Senior Honours: Co.Co .Lg R-up 97-98, Chiltonian Champions 94-95 and Berks & Bucks Sen.Trophy R-up 96-97

SANDHURST TOWN

Founded: 1910
Nickname: Fizzers

Chairman: Michael Morgan   **President :** Malcolm Watts: **Manager:** Peter Browning

Secretary: Mike Elsmore, 67 Avocet Crescet, Sandhurst, Brks. GU47 0XW

Tel. Nos: 01252 768217 (W) 01344 778145 (H)   **Programme:** Yes

GROUND ADDRESS: Bottom Meadow, Memorial Ground, Yorktown Road, Sandhurst   **Tel:** 07831 366140

Capacity: 2,500   **Seats:** Eight   **Covered:** Yes   **Floodlights:** Yes

Simple Directions: Reach A321 from either M3 Jct4 & A331 or M4 Jct 10 & A329. Park in main council offices' car park off

A321 and walk down tarmac path to ground. Nearest station Sandhurst

Midweek Home Matchday: Tuesday   **Clubhouse:** Yes   **Club Shop:** No

Previous Leagues: Reading & Dist., East Berks,Aldershot Senior 79-84 Chiltonian 84-90

Club Colours: Red/black/black   **Change Colours:** yellow/blue/yellow

F.A. Cup: 1st Qualifying Round   **F.A.Vase:** 2nd Rd. 0-02 02-03

RECORD Attendance: 1,067 v AFC Wimbledon 02-03   **Victory:** 9-1 v Cranleigh 2000   **Defeat** 0-8 v Cobham 1991

WEMBLEY

Founded: 1946
Nickname:The Lions

Chairman: Brian Gumm   **President:** Eric Stringer   **Manager:** Scott Cousins
Secretary: Mrs Jean Gumm, 14 Woodfield Avenue, North Wembley, Middlesex HA0 3NR **Asst.Manager:**Roger Linton
Tel No: 0208 908 3353   **Commercial Manager:** Nick Bennett
Press Officer: Richard Markiewicz   **Programme:** 28 Pages £1.00   **Prog.Ed:** Richard Markiewicz
GROUND ADDRESS: Vale Farm, Watford Road, Sudbury, Wembley HA0 4UP   **Tel:** 0181 904 8169
Capacity:2,000   **Seats:** 350   **Covered:** 350   **Floodlights:**Yes
Simple Directions: 400 yards from Sudbury Town station (underground) or 10 minutes walk from North Wembley BR
Midweek Home Matchday: Tuesday   **Clubhouse:** Evenings & lunchtime w/e   **Club Shop:** No
Previous Leagues: Middlesex 1946-49, Spartan 49-51, Delphian 51-56, Corinthian 56-63 Athenian 63-75
Club Colours: Red& white/red/red   **Change Colours:** All Gold
LAST SEASON: League: 13th   **F.A. Cup:** Extra Prelim.Rd.   **F.A. Vase:** 2nd Qualifying Round
Top Scorer: **Player of the Year:**   **Captain:**
BEST PERFORMANCES: League: **F.A. Cup:** 1st Rd.Proper 80-81
F.A.Trophy: 1st Rd. Proper 91-92   **F.A.Amateur Cup:** 2nd Rd 66-7 68-9
RECORD Attendance: 2,654 v Wealdstone F.A.Am. Cup 52-53 **Goalscorer** Bill Handrahan 105 (1946-52)
Appearances: Spud Murphy 505 (78-88) **Victory:**11-1 v Hermes, London Sen Cup 63 **Defeat:**0-16 v Chelsea London Chall.C
Fee received: £10,000 from Brentford for Gary Roberts **Fee Paid:** Nil.
Senior Honours: Middx. Sen.Cup 83-84 86-87 R-up (7) Athenian Lg R-up 74-75 London Senior Cup R-up 55-56

Sandhurst Town - winners of the Aldershot FA Cup.   Photo: Eric Marsh.

Colney Hall   Photo: Gordon Whittington.

LEAGUE CONSTITUTION 2006-07 - DIVISION ONE

CB HOUNSLOW UNITED

Secretary: Stephen Hosmer. **Tel:** (M) 07831 393559
Email: stephen.hosmer@btinternet.com
Ground: Osterley Sports Club, Tentelow Lane,
Norwood Green, Southall, Middlesex UB2 4LW
Tel: 0208 574 7055
Directions: From the A4 (Great West Road)
Turn left at Master Robert, Church Rd. Turn left at Heston
Road. Follow for 1 mile. Turn right at Norwood Green
(Tentelow Lane). Club is 1 mile on the Right.
Colours: All blue

CHOBHAM

Secretary: Deborah Bexon, 40 Newton Way, Tongham,
Farnham, Surrey GU10 1BY. Tel (h) 01252 318276
Ground: Chobham Recreation Ground, Station Road,
Chobham, Surrey GU24 8AZ. **Tel** 01276 857 876
Directions: Leave M3 At J3. Left At Lights, Follow Road
to Roundabout, First Left, Next Roundabout Turn Right.
Continue Through Village, Left at Next Roundabout.
Ground is on the Right.
Colours: All yellow & blue

CONEY HALL

Secretary: Chris Beaumont. **Tel:** 07764 250620
Email: chris@wotherspoon.net
Ground: Tiepigs Lane, West Wickham, Bromley,
Kent BR4 9BT. Tel 0208 462 9103
Colours: Red & black stripes/black/black

CRESCENT ROVERS

Secretary: Michael Bishop, 64 Wolsey Crescent,
New Addington, Croydon, Surrey CRO 0PF
Tel (h) 01689 842996 (b) 020 8667 8380
Email: michael@bishop842.freeserve.co.uk
Ground: Wallington Sports & Social Club,
34 Mollison Drive, Wallington, Surrey SM6 9BY
Tel 020 8647 2558
Colours: Green, white & black/black/black

FARLEIGH ROVERS

Secretary: Mrs Val Wilcocks, 238 The Glad,
Shirley, Croydon, Surrey CRO 7UJ
Tel (h) 0208 406 3493 (m) 07754 626364
Ground: Parsonage Field, Harrow Road,
Warlingham CR6 9EX. **Tel** 01883 626 483
Directions: From M25 junction 6 left at lights up Godstone
Hill (Caterham bypass) to roundabout. Take fourth turning
off of roundabout. Up Succombs Hill then right into Westhall
Rd. Right at the green then second left into Farleigh Rd.
Left at mini round about continue still on Farleigh Rd . Right
at the Harrow Pub. This is Harrow Road. Right at the end of
the houses and the ground is behind the houses.
Colours: Black & red/black/black

FARNHAM TOWN

Secretary: Sandra Charlton. **Tel:** (M) 07789 593157
Email: charltsand@aol.com
Ground: Memorial Ground, West Street, Farnham,
Surrey GU9 7DY. **Tel:** 01252 715305
Directions: Take A31 towards Farnham station. Cross over
lights. At Oxbridge roundabout take the third exit to the town
centre at the mini roundabout take the 2nd exit.
Colours: Claret & blue/white or blue or claret/sky blue

FELTHAM

Secretary: John Cronk. **Tel:** (M) 07985 736394
Email: (work) john.cronk@pel.co.uk
Ground: Hampton & Richmond Borough FC, Beveree,
Station Road, Hampton, Middlesex TW12 2BX
Tel: 0208 979 2456
Directions: On leaving hampton station (br) walk along sta-
tion road in the direction of hampton court, h & r boro fc 1/2
mile.
Colours: Blue & white/blue/blue

FRIMLEY GREEN

Secretary: Mark O'Grady. **Tel:** (M) 07812 026390
Email: mogradyuk@yahoo.co.uk
Ground: Frimley Green Recreation Ground, Frimley Green
Road, Frimley Green, Camberley, Surrey GU16 6SY
Tel: 01252 835089; (f) 01252 545656
Directions: By Road: Exit M3 at junction 4 and follow signs
to Frimley centre. In Frimley High street proceed to the mini
roundabout in front of the White Hart PH and take the exit
to the right of the PH. into Church Road. The road turns
right at the top of the hill and becomes Frimley Green Road.
Proceed approx 1/2 of a mile, straight over the mini roundabout at the entrance to Johnson Wax factory, and the turning into the ground is on the left, just past Henley Drive,
which is on your right.
Colours: All blue

HANWORTH VILLA

(Promoted from the Middlesex County League 2005)
Secretary: Dave Brown. **Tel:** (M) 07713 503149
Email: brown@park-road.fsnet.co.uk
GROUND ADDRESS: Rectory Meadows, Park Road, off
Hounslow Road, Hanworth, Middlesex TW13 6PN
Directions: From M3 take the A316 towards London, leave A314 sign posted
Hounslow, turn left at traffic lights then left at second mini roundabout this is park road.
Follow the road past the Hanworth Naval club on the right hand side and Procter's builders' yards
on the left. Follow the road round the 90 degree bend and drive to the end of Park road past the
Village hall. Turn right past the last house and you have entered Rectory Meadows.
From London going towards the M3 leave the A316 at the junction with the A312 Hampton Road
West. At the traffic light junction with the A314 Hounslow Road turn left. At the first mini roundabout
(jet garage on the corner) turn right into Park Road then as above.
From Heathrow area follow the A312 to the junction with the A314 Hounslow Road, turn right at the
traffic lights then as above.
Colours: Red & black stripes/black/red

HARTLEY WINTNEY

Secretary: Gerald Wykes. **Tel:** (M) 07720 474214.
Email: gerry.wykes@ntlworld.com
GROUND ADDRESS: Memorial Playing Fields, Green
Lane, Hartley Wintney, Hants, RG27
Tel: 01252 843 586
Directions: A30 west through Camberley, left at parade of
shops at beginning of village, then sharpe right and ground
is on the right.
Colours: Orange/black/black

HORLEY TOWN

Secretary: Mrs Joanna Freeman
Email: jfreeman261@hotmail.com
Ground: The New Defence, Court Lodge Road,
Horley, Surrey RH6 8RS.
Tel: 01293 822000; (f) 01293 773666
Directions: From centre of town go North up Victoria where
it meets the A23, straight across to Vicarage Lane, 2nd left
into Court Lodge Road follow it through estate and we are
behind adult education centre.
Colours: All claret

MERROW

Secretary: James Moseley, 27 Watersmeet Close,
Weybrook Park, Guildford, Surrey GU4 7NQ
Tel (h) 01483 301468 (m) 07736 518426
Ground: The Urnfield, Downside Road,
Guildford, Surrey GU4 8PH
Tel 01483 567 545
Directions: Downside Rd, feeds from Warren road which is
off the Epsom Road. It can also be reached from Tangier
Road which again is off the Epsom Road.
Colours: All Red

SALFORDS
(Formerly Netherne Village)
Secretary: Aidan Dempsey. Tel: (M) 07957 180137
Email: chairman@salfordsfc.co.uk
Ground: Netherne CASC, Woodplace Lane, Coulsdon,
Surrey CR5 1NE. Tel: 01737 557509
Directions: From M25 J7 travel North on the A23 towards
Croydon. Past Star Lane traffic lights then right at next
lights into Netherne Drive.
Colours: Sky blue & white/navy/sky blue

SHEERWATER
Secretary: Trevor Wenden.
14 Byrefield Road, Guildford, Surrey GU2 9UH
Tel (h) 01483 838578 (m) 07791 612008
Email: trevor.wendon2@ntlworld.com
Ground: Sheerwater Recreation Ground,
Blackmore Crescent, Sheerwater Estate,
Woking, Surrey GU21 5QJ. Tel 01932 348 192
Directions: From M25(J11) take the A320 towards Woking,
At Six Cross Roudabout take the exit to Monument Road.
At the lights turn left into Eve Road for Sheerwater Estate.
First left is Blackmore Crescent, Entrance is Quarter of a
mile on left.
Colours: All royal blue.

SOUTH PARK
Secretary: Kelvin Beckett. Tel: (M) 07933 027165
Email: secretary.spfc@hotmail.co.uk
Ground: Snoxhill Playing Fields, Knowle Lane, Cranleigh,
Surrey GU6 8JW
Directions: Passing through Cranleigh High Street, turn
into Knowle Lane. After 100 yards turn left into sports field
Colours: Green/red/red

STAINES LAMMAS
Secretary: Bob Parry. 18 Hurstdene Avenue,
Staines, Middlesex TW18 1JQ
Tel (h) 01784 453886 (b) 0208 344 0309
(f) 01784 469196 (m) 07771 947757
Ground: Laleham Recreation Ground, The Broadway,
Laleham, Staines, Middlesex TW18 1RZ
Tel 01784 465 204
Directions: From M25 Junction 13 to Staines. A30
through to A308; right at Fordbridge roundabout; left at mini
roundabout to B377 into Laleham; entrance opposite Turks
Head Pub.
Colours: All Blue

TONGHAM
Secretary: Roger Creed. Tel: (M) 07958 628156
Email: rogerp@rcreed.freeserve.co.uk
Ground: Poyle Road Recreation Ground, Poyle Road,
Tongham, Surrey GU10 1DU. Tel: 01252 782 893.
Directions: From A31, Hogs Back and heading towards
Farnham, take the A331 Blackwater Valley road towards
Aldershot and M3. At first roundabout take slip road off and
look for the 3rd exit, sign posted Tongham. Go past
Cricketers pub on right and continue on until mini round-
about (opposite White Hart Pub), take left turn and ground
can be found on right after 150 metres
Colours: Red/black/red

WARLINGHAM
Secretary: Les Badcock,
29 Verdayne Gardens, Warlingham,
Surrey CR6 9RP
Tel (h) 01883 626287 (b) 020 8409 8851
(m) 07890 589030
Email: lesbadcock@hotmail.com
Ground: Verdayne Playing Fields, Warlingham, Surrey
CR6 9RP. Tel: 01883 626 718
Directions: Verdayne Gardens is off LImpsfield Road
(B269) between Sanderstead and Warlingham
Colours: Black & White Stripes/black/black

WESTFIELD
Secretary: Michael Lawrence. Tel: (M) 07780 684416
Email: michaelgeorgelawrence@hotmail.com
Ground: First Team - Woking FC, Kingfield Stadium,
Kingfield Road, Woking, Surrey GU22 9AA
Reserves - Woking Park, off Elmbridge Lane, Kingfield,
Woking, Surrey GU22 7AA
Tel: First Team - 01483 729230 Reserves - 01483 771106
Directions: Follow signs to Woking Leisure Centre on the
A247
Colours: Yellow/black/black

WORCESTER PARK
Secretary: Tony McCarthy
25 Lutyens House, Churchill Road,
London SW10 3AB
Tel (h) 0207 834 7544 (m) 07961 829070
Ground: Skinners Field, Green Lane,
Worcester Park, Surrey KT4 8AJ.
Tel 020 8337 4995
Colours: All Blue

Hartley Wintney   Photo: Gordon Whittington.

544

EASTERN COUNTIES LEAGUE

SPONSORED BY: RIGEONS
Founded 1935
President: Malcolm Nunn
General Secretary: Nigel Spurling, 16 Thanet Road, Ipswich, Suffolk IP4 5LB
Tel: 01473 720893 secretary@ridgeonsleague.co.uk

PREMIER DIVISION		P	W	D	L	F	A	Pts
1.	Lowestoft Town	42	30	4	8	121	43	94
2.	Bury Town (Promoted)	42	29	5	8	100	32	92
3.	AFC Sudbury (Champ 04-05) Promoted	42	28	5	9	114	56	89
4.	Wisbech Town	42	25	7	10	98	55	82
5.	Mildenhall Town	42	23	9	10	100	68	78
6.	Needham Market (2nd Div.1 04-05)	42	22	9	11	79	41	75
7.	Ipswich Wanderers (1st Div.1 04-05)	42	23	6	13	69	38	75
8.	Wroxham	42	21	6	15	77	62	69
9.	Leiston	42	21	5	16	89	69	68
10.	Soham Town Rangers	42	18	11	13	75	51	65
11.	Diss Town	42	20	5	17	89	78	65
12.	Dereham Town	42	18	10	14	99	64	64
13.	Histon Reserves	42	15	11	16	71	84	56
14	Kirkley (3rd Div.1 04-05)	42	15	6	21	60	76	51
15.	Kings Lynn Reserves	42	12	13	17	68	78	49
16.	Woodbridge Town	42	14	6	22	64	83	48
17.	Newmarket Town	42	13	6	23	53	91	45
18.	Halstead Town	42	11	7	24	67	124	40
19.	Cambridge City Reserves	42	10	8	24	60	107	38
20.	Norwich United	42	10	6	26	47	82	36
21.	Harwich & Parkeston	42	10	2	30	41	100	32
22.	Clacton Town	42	0	1	41	20	179	1

PREMIER DIVISION	1	2	3	4	5	6	7	8	9	10	11	12	13	14	15	16	17	18	19	20	21	22
1 AFC Sudbury		1-0	6-0	6-1	2-2	4-2	5-2	1-0	3-1	0-4	4-3	3-1	4-1	1-0	5-0	2-0	5-0	2-0	0-1	1-3	3-1	0-4
2 Bury Town	2-1		2-0	5-0	2-1	4-0	5-0	5-1	2-0	2-0	1-1	5-0	1-0	1-0	1-2	3-0	2-1	3-1	1-3	0-1	7-2	5-0
3 Cambridge City Res.	2-1	2-5		6-1	1-5	0-5	2-2	3-1	1-2	2-1	1-1	3-1	0-5	0-4	0-2	1-6	0-2	0-3	3-2	3-4	3-2	1-1
4 Clacton Town	0-5	1-8	0-4		1-6	0-8	0-2	1-2	1-3	0-6	0-0	2-4	0-4	0-7	3-5	0-5	1-4	0-2	0-5	0-7	0-4	1-3
5 Dereham Town	1-4	1-0	4-2	8-0		3-0	2-1	4-1	1-2	1-2	3-0	3-2	3-0	4-2	2-3	1-1	0-2	0-1	2-2	1-1	1-2	2-0
6 Diss Town	1-5	0-1	4-0	4-1	0-5		1-1	2-1	3-1	0-1	5-1	3-2	1-2	2-1	7-3	1-3	1-2	3-1	1-3	1-0	2-1	0-0
7 Halstead Town	1-4	1-1	4-2	9-2	4-1	1-4		2-0	4-1	1-7	2-2	3-8	2-6	0-2	0-7	1-2	0-0	2-1	1-0	2-3	2-1	0-1
8 Harwich & Park.	1-1	1-4	1-0	3-0	0-7	2-1	0-4		1-2	1-2	2-3	1-2	1-5	0-4	0-6	0-2	1-2	1-1	2-0	2-0	3-0	0-3
9 Histon Reserves	2-3	2-0	2-1	2-0	2-4	2-2	2-4	3-2		0-1	2-1	2-5	3-3	0-7	1-3	0-3	1-1	1-0	0-0	1-5	3-2	2-2
10 Ipswich W'derers	0-2	0-0	3-0	4-0	2-2	2-1	1-0	0-1	0-1		1-0	1-1	3-1	1-1	0-1	1-1	2-0	2-0	3-1	1-3	0-0	3-0
11 Kings Lynn Res.	2-4	1-1	2-2	5-0	1-1	9-6	3-1	1-1	1-1	2-1		2-2	1-1	1-5	0-3	2-1	4-1	1-0	0-1	0-4	0-1	0-3
12 Kirkley	1-2	0-2	0-1	1-0	2-1	1-2	0-0	2-0	4-2	0-2	2-1		1-1	0-1	1-1	1-2	2-0	2-0	0-6	1-2	3-0	1-3
13 Leiston	4-2	0-1	4-1	3-0	1-5	4-2	3-0	2-1	0-4	1-0	2-3	0-1		4-2	2-1	1-0	1-1	3-1	0-1	2-2	3-0	1-2
14 Lowestoft Town	0-3	3-0	3-2	4-0	3-1	1-0	3-0	2-1	0-1	3-1	3-1	3-1	5-1		4-0	2-1	9-0	5-0	4-1	4-3	3-1	2-1
15 Mildenhall Town	1-6	1-1	1-1	3-0	2-2	0-1	5-3	2-2	5-3	3-2	3-1	2-0	1-1	1-1		0-0	2-0	5-1	1-1	2-1	0-0	4-3
16 Needham Market	2-2	0-1	2-0	5-0	5-1	2-1	6-0	1-0	1-1	1-2	3-1	0-1	2-1	3-2	2-3		1-1	0-0	0-0	3-1	2-1	0-1
17 Newmarket Town	2-4	0-4	2-2	4-0	2-1	2-2	2-1	0-2	2-1	0-1	1-3	2-0	1-5	0-4	4-2	0-3		2-3	1-5	0-2	1-2	0-2
18 Norwich United	2-1	1-5	1-1	1-0	1-1	2-3	3-0	3-1	3-3	0-2	0-2	0-1	2-6	1-3	1-5	0-2	0-1		2-1	1-1	2-3	0-1
19 Soham Town Rgs	2-1	0-2	0-2	1-0	3-1	1-2	2-2	8-1	2-2	0-1	0-0	1-1	4-2	1-2	2-2	3-0	1-0	2-1		1-0	3-2	2-2
20 Wisbech Town	1-1	0-1	4-2	4-2	1-1	2-3	7-1	3-1	1-0	1-0	2-1	4-0	3-1	0-3	2-1	0-0	1-4	3-2	1-1		3-1	4-2
21 Woodbridge Town	1-1	2-1	4-1	3-1	0-0	1-2	8-3	2-1	1-4	0-1	1-1	3-0	0-2	3-3	1-4	0-3	4-2	1-0	2-1	1-4		0-2
22 Wroxham	2-3	1-3	2-2	4-1	1-4	0-0	9-0	3-1	0-3	2-1	0-3	3-1	0-1	2-0	2-0	2-3	4-1	0-2	2-1	0-4	2-0	

DIVISION ONE		P	W	D	L	F	A	Pts
1.	Stanway Rovers	42	33	4	5	106	29	103
2.	Felixstowe & Walton	42	30	5	7	107	48	95
3.	Fulbourn Institute	42	30	4	8	109	60	94
4.	Tiptree United	42	29	3	10	125	56	90
5.	Walsham le Willows	42	23	10	9	91	46	79
6.	Whitton United	42	22	7	13	83	63	73
7.	Ely City	42	20	10	12	88	68	70
8.	Haverhill Rovers	42	21	7	14	77	60	70
9.	Swaffham Town	42	19	12	11	90	71	69
10.	Debenham LC	42	17	10	15	60	70	61
11.	Fakenham Town	42	15	11	16	64	69	56
12.	Saffron Walden Town	42	14	12	16	56	62	54
13.	Great Yarmouth Town	42	14	10	18	54	60	52
14.	Godmanchester Rovers	42	12	10	20	53	73	46
15.	Long Melford	42	9	11	22	59	84	38
16.	Stowmarket Town	42	10	8	24	63	95	38
17.	Cornard United	42	11	4	27	59	96	37
18.	Gorleston (-4)	42	9	12	21	50	74	35
19.	March Town United	42	9	6	27	46	91	33
20.	Downham Town	42	8	9	25	41	99	33
21.	Hadleigh United	42	6	13	23	38	78	31
22.	Thetford Town	42	7	10	25	47	114	31

DIVISION ONE	1	2	3	4	5	6	7	8	9	10	11	12	13	14	15	16	17	18	19	20	21	22
1 Cornard United		1-0	5-1	1-2	2-2	4-2	3-4	0-4	0-4	3-1	2-0	1-2	1-1	2-4	3-2	3-6	4-2	1-4	2-3	1-2	1-2	0-5
2 Debenham LC	1-0		4-2	1-0	3-1	0-4	0-1	1-1	0-0	1-0	2-1	2-3	3-2	2-2	3-2	1-1	3-3	0-2	1-1	2-3	1-2	0-2
3 Downham Town	0-2	1-0		1-0	0-1	0-3	1-4	1-2	2-1	0-5	0-1	1-1	0-0	3-0	0-7	5-2	1-1	0-1	1-3	0-2	2-1	
4 Ely City	2-0	3-0	7-1		1-1	2-0	4-0	3-1	2-1	3-0	1-1	1-3	1-1	1-1	1-2	1-2	1-1	3-0	2-0	3-6	4-0	1-4
5 Fakenham Town	2-4	2-0	1-1	1-1		0-1	2-2	2-0	2-1	1-0	1-2	2-2	2-4	2-1	0-1	1-2	3-0	1-1	3-2	0-2	0-1	
6 Felixstowe & Walton	2-0	6-1	6-1	0-0	3-0		2-3	3-1	2-0	3-0	4-2	1-0	5-2	6-0	1-0	2-1	3-1	1-1	4-1	2-1	2-3	2-0
7 Fulbourn Institute	1-0	5-0	4-0	3-0	5-1	2-3		1-0	3-1	1-1	1-0	1-2	7-2	7-0	3-1	1-0	3-0	3-3	4-0	1-6	2-1	2-0
8 Godmanchester R.	2-1	1-2	1-1	2-8	2-2	0-1	2-2		1-0	0-2	1-0	1-1	1-1	1-0	2-3	1-2	4-0	0-3	2-0	0-4	1-2	2-2
9 Gorleston	0-3	1-3	2-3	4-4	0-1	2-2	2-6	0-2		0-2	1-0	1-3	1-0	3-0	0-1	0-2	1-0	2-3	2-2	1-6	1-1	2-1
10 Great Yarmouth T.	0-0	3-0	1-1	1-2	1-4	0-2	1-3	1-2	1-1		0-0	1-0	2-0	3-0	0-2	0-5	2-1	2-1	2-2	1-4	1-1	1-3
11 Hadleigh United	1-1	3-4	1-1	2-2	0-0	1-4	0-3	2-1	1-3	1-1		3-1	1-1	1-0	1-1	0-3	1-1	1-3	3-1	0-4	2-2	1-2
12 Haverhill Rovers	4-2	1-2	3-1	3-1	3-1	3-2	0-1	3-4	0-0	3-1	1-0		3-1	2-0	2-2	1-4	3-0	1-0	3-2	5-2	2-2	0-2
13 Long Melford	3-0	0-1	1-3	0-1	3-3	1-4	1-2	0-3	3-0	2-5	1-1	0-3		1-0	2-2	1-2	5-2	2-2	1-1	2-0	0-1	2-0
14 March Town Utd	3-1	0-2	1-2	2-3	0-3	2-4	0-2	1-0	1-3	0-0	2-0	3-1	1-0		1-4	0-1	2-1	3-2	4-2	0-3	1-4	1-1
15 Saffron Walden T.	1-0	1-1	2-2	3-0	2-2	2-2	0-1	1-2	0-0	2-0	4-1	1-1	0-3	2-1		1-0	0-1	1-0	3-0	0-1	0-0	2-3
16 Stanway Rovers	4-1	0-1	4-0	2-3	1-0	4-1	3-2	6-0	0-0	2-0	1-0	2-0	2-1	3-1	5-0		5-1	3-0	2-0	1-1	1-0	5-0
17 Stowmarket T.	3-1	2-4	5-3	3-2	0-3	1-2	0-1	1-1	2-2	0-2	2-0	2-0	1-2	1-1	2-4	1-2		3-0	3-0	0-2	1-5	1-2
18 Swaffham Town	1-0	2-2	1-0	6-1	1-3	2-2	7-2	1-1	2-2	2-0	2-2	1-1	2-0	3-2	2-1	1-2	3-0		6-2	1-4	2-4	3-6
19 Thetford Town	1-2	2-1	3-0	2-3	1-3	0-6	2-6	2-1	1-1	1-4	3-0	0-6	2-2	2-0	1-1	0-3	2-2	1-1		1-5	0-4	0-0
20 Tiptree United	7-0	2-0	3-1	4-0	2-0	5-1	3-1	3-1	1-3	0-2	4-1	3-1	5-1	4-3	5-1	0-1	2-2	3-4	5-0		0-2	2-2
21 Walsham le Willows	2-0	1-1	4-0	0-2	7-1	0-0	5-0	2-0	3-0	1-1	4-0	2-0	4-1	3-1	0-0	0-1	3-6	0-3	8-1	1-2		1-3
22 Whitton United	3-1	2-1	1-1	3-4	3-2	1-2	0-2	3-1	2-1	0-3	2-0	2-0	3-2	3-1	4-0	2-2	1-3	3-4	4-0	1-3	0-0	

L E A G U E   C U P

PRELIMINARY ROUND

Conard United	v	Tiptree United	2-6
Debenham LC	v	Stowmarket Town	0-3
Dereham Town	v	Downham Town	1-0
Godmanchester R	v	Mildenhall Town	1-2
Kirkley	v	Great Yarmouth Town	1-2
March Town United	v	Soham Town Rangers	2-4
Needham Market	v	Ipswich Wanderers	4-4*, 6-5p
Norwich Town	v	Gorlseton	0-2
Stanway Rovers	v	Long Melford	2-1
Walsham-le-Willows	v	Woodbridge Town	2-3
Whitton United	v	Harwich & Parkeston	2-6

FIRST ROUND

Bury Town	v	Needham Market	1-0
Cambridge City R.	v	Ely City	2-1
Tiptree United	v	Clacton Town	5-0
Dereham Town	v	Swaffham town	1-3
Diss Town	v	Thetford Town	5-0
Felixstowe & Wal.U	v	Stowmarket Town	2-1
Halstead Town (H)	v	Haverhill Rovers	2-1
Histon Reserves	v	Soham Town Rangers	2-6
Hadleigh United	v	Harwich & Parkeston	2-4
King's Lynn Res.	v	Wroxham	7-4
Great Yarmouth T.	v	Fakenham Town	2-1
Leiston	v	Woodbridge Town	2-2*, 9-8p
Lowestoft Town	v	Gorleston	3-1
Mildenhall Town	v	Saffron Walden Town	3-0
Newmarket Town	v	Fulbourn Institute	4-6
Stanway Rovers	v	AFC Sudbury	2-3
Bury Town	v	Soham Town Rangers	4-3

SECOND ROUND

Diss Town	v	Swaffham Town	8-2
Felixstowe & Wal.U	v	Lowestoft Town	1-5
Halstead Town (H)	v	Tiptree United	0-3
Harwich & Parkeston	v	AFC Sudbury	1-2
King's Lynn Res.	v	Cambridge City Reserves	3-2
Leiston	v	Great Yarmouth Town	3-1
Mildenhall Town	v	Fulbourn Institute	2-0

QUARTER-FINALS

Bury Town	v	AFC Sudbury	4-5
Diss Town	v	King's Lynn Reserves	1-3
Lowestoft Town	v	Leiston	2-1
Tiptree United	v	Mildenhall Town	2-5

SEMI-FINALS

Lowestoft Town	v	King's Lynn Reserves	2-0
Mildenhall Town	v	AFC Sudbury	1-2

THE FINAL

Lowestoft Town	v	AFC Sudbury	1-2

CRC

Chairman: Terry Baker   **Manager:** Jez George

Secretary: James Smith. Email: jamessmith@cambridge-united.co.uk

Programme Editor: James Smith.

GROUND ADDRESS: Abbey Stadium, Newmarket Road, Cambridge CB5 8LN. **Tel:** 01223 566 500

Capacity: 9,217   **Seats:** 200   **Covered:** Yes   **Floodlights:** Yes   **Club Shop:** Yes

Simple Directions: See Cambridge United FC.

Midweek Home Matchday: Wednesday

Club Colours: Amber/black/amber   **Change Colours:** Navy blue/sky/sky

CLACTON TOWN
Founded:
Nickname:

Chairman: David Ballard   **Company Secretary:** Dawn Watson: **Owner:** John Shuttleworth   **Manager:** Ian Pridmore
Secretary: Stephen Andrews, 26 Clacton Road, St Osyth,Essex. CO16 8PA **Tel No:** 07771520157
Programme Editor: Karl Fuller (07930 104454)   **Programme:** 40 Pages Price £1.00
GROUND ADDRESS: The Rush Green Bowl, Rush Green Road, Clacton-on-Sea , essex CPO16 7BQ **Tel No:** 01255 432590
Capacity: 3,000   **Seats:** 200   **Covered:** Yes   **Floodlights:** Yes   **Club Shop:** Yes
Simple Directions: A133 to Clacton. Right into St Johns Rd at roundabout then 4th left into Cloes Lane. The third rifght is
Rushgreen Rd and ground is half a mile on right.
Midweek Home Matchday: Tuesday   **Clubhouse:** LIcensed club open daily with hot & cold food.
Previous Leagues: Easter Cos 35-37 38-58 Southern 58-64
Previous Grounds: Clacton Stadium, Old Road 06-87 Gainsford Avenue (temp)
Club Colours: All White & Royal Blue   **Change Colours:**Yellow/yellow/royal blue
BEST PERFORMANCES
League: Southern League Div 1 59-60   **F.A. Cup:** 1st Rd 60-61   **F.A.Vase:** 4th Rd. 74-75 99-00
RECORD Attendance: 3,505 v Romford F.A.Cup 1952 at Old Road.
Senior Honours: Southern Lg Div 1 1959-60 Eastern Co R-up 36-37 53-54 64-65 74-75 east Anglian Cup 53-54 99-00

DEREHAM TOWN
Founded: 1890
Nickname: Magpies

Chairman: George Hayes   **Vice-Chairman:** Terry Cator   **Manager:** Simon Barnes
Secretary: Ray Bayles, 62 Church View Close, Sprowston, Norwich NR7 8QA   Sponsors : TEL Concrete
Tel No: 01603 789905(H) 07903 246901(M) **Website:** www.derehamtownfc.com
Programme Editorial Team: Barnes Print   **Programme:** 20 Pages 50p
GROUND ADDRESS: Aldiss Park, Norwich Road, Dereham, Norfolk.   **Ground Tel.No:** 01362 6904
Capacity: 3,000   **Seats:** 50   **Covered:** 500   **Floodlights:** Yes
Simple Directions: From Dereham town centre folow A47 and ground is on left.
Midweek Home Matchday: Tuesday   **Clubhouse:** Yes   **Club Shop:** Yes (01362 690460)
Previous Names: Dereham and Dereham Hobbies   **Ground:** Recreation Ground 1890-1998
Previous Leagues: Dereham & district, E.Anglian Ang.Combination until 1998
Club Colours: Black & white/black/white   **Change Colours:** All red
Best Performances
League: 15th Eastern Premier Div 04-05   **F.A.Vase:** 4th Rd replay
RECORD Attendance: 2,800 v Norwich C. 2005   **Senior Honours:** Eastern Counties League Div 1 R-Up 2000-01

DISS TOWN
Founded: 1888
Nickname: Tangerines

Chairman: Des Tebble   **Managers:** Robert Fleck & Daryl Sutch   **President:** Peter Ewings
Secretary: Steve Flatman, 31 Aldrich Way, Roydon, Diss, Norfolk. IP22 4FJ   Spponsors:CAMICO
Tel No: 01379 641406 (H) 07855 531341 (M)
Programme Editor: Gary Enderby (01379 608767)   **Programme:** 16 Pages £1,00
GROUND ADDRESS: Brewers Green Lane, Diss, Norfolk   **Ground Tel. No:** 01379 651223
Capacity: 2,500   **Seats:** 280   **Covered:** Yes   **Floodlights:** Yes   **Shop:** Yes
Simple Directions: Off B1066 Diss -Thetford rosd near Roydon school. One and a half miles from Diss(BR)
Midweek Home Matchday: Tuesday   **Clubhouse:** Open weekday and matchday evenings & Sunday lunchtime
Previous Leagues: Norwich & Dist., Norfolk & Suffolk 35-64, Anglian Combination 64-82
Ground: Roydon Road 1886-1982
Club Colours: Tangerine/Navy/Tangerine   **Change Colours:** Sky blue/Navy/Navy
LAST SEASON
League: 12th   **F.A. Cup:** Preliminary Round.   **F.A. Vase:** 1st Round
Top Scorer: Matty Clements   **Player of the Year:** Dale Vince   **Captain:** Matthew Wright
Best Performances
League: 2nd Eastern Co. Prem   **F.A. Cup:**   **F.A.Vase:** Winners 1994-95
RECORD Attendance: 1,731 v Atherton LR .F.A.Vase SF 19.03.94 **Goalscorer:**   **Appearances:** DesTebble
Senior Honours: F.A. Vase Winners 94-95 R-Up Eastern Co.

FELIXSTOWE & WALTON UNITED
Founded: 1890
Nickname: Seasiders

Secretary: Chris & Jayne Ryan, 43 Brook Lane, Felixstowe, Suffolk IP11 7LG
Tel No: 01394 275873
Ground: Dellwood Avenue, Felixstowe IP11 9HT Tel: 01394 282917
Email:felixstowe@btinternet.com **Web:** http:/www.felixstowe,btinternet.co.uk
Directions: A14 to Felixstowe. Turn right at 3rd r'bout then 1st left - ground100 yds on left. 5 mins walk from Felixstowe (BR) and town centre
Capacity: 2,000 Seats: 200 Cover: 200 Floodlights: Yes
Clubhouse: Bar, snack bar, TV, **Club Shop:** Yes, including enamel badges
HONOURS Suffolk Senior Cup 66-67, 74-75 and 98-99 (as Walton United)
PREVIOUS Leagues: Essex & Suffolk Border; Ipswich & District
Names: Felixstowe Port & Town, Felixstowe Town, Felixstowe United
Merged with Walton United in 2000 **Grounds:** Tennis Club,Ferry Road.
RECORD Attendance: 1,500 v IpswichTown, floodlight inauguration 25/1/91
AWARD Wirral Eastern Counties Programme of the Year 2003-2004

Sponsors: M.C.P.
Colours: Red & white stripes/black/red
Change: Yelow & Blue/yellow/yellow
Midweek Matches: Tuesday
Programme: 48 pages, £1.00
Editor: Chris & Stuart Daynes
Tel: 01394 275747
Local Press: East Anglia Daily Times
CLUB PERSONNEL
Pres: Dave Ashford Chairman: Tony Barnes
Manager: Steve Potts
2005-2006
Top Scorer: Daniel Phillips & Gavin Crane 27
Ps.o.Y.:Dan Phillips,Paul Cudworth & Stuart
Simmons **Captain:** Jimmy Andrews

HALSTEAD TOWN
Founded: 1879
Nickname: The Town

Chairman: Jimmy Holder **President:** Michael Gage **Manager:** Tony Kinsella
Secretary: Stephen Webber, 12 Ravens Avenue, Halstead, Essex CO9 1NZ **Physio**: Brian Dunster
Tel No: 01787 486959 (H) 01284 767278 (W) 07906 111146(M)
Sponsor: RDM Ltd (Catering Equipment) **Club HIstorian/Statistician:** Dave Osborne (01787 475604)
Programme Editor: Andy Mzon (01376 340098) **Programme:** 24 Pages £1.00
GROUND ADDRESS: Rosemary Lane, Broton Industrial Estate, Halstead, Essex CO9 2HR **Tel:** 01787 472082
Capacity: 2,000 **Seats:** 400 **Covered:** 400 **Floodlights:** Yes
Simple Directions: from A1311 Chelmsford to Braintree road follow signs to Halsetead
Midweek Home Matchday: Tuesday **Clubhouse:** Open evenings and matchdays **Club Shop:** No
Previous Leagues: North Essex, Halstead & Dist., Haverhill, Essex & Suffolk Border , Essex Senior 80-88
Club Colours: Black & White quarters/red/red **Change Colours:** Red/white/red
LAST SEASON
League: 18th **F.A. Cup:** 2nd Qualifying Round **F.A. Vase:** 1st Round.
Top Scorer: Ben Cranfield 19 **Player of the Year:** Luke Passfield **Captain:** Stuart Fergus
Best Performances:
League: Champions Eastern Co. 94-5 95-6 **F.A. Cup:** 4th Qualifying Round 1998-99 **F.A.Vase:** 4th Rd 1994-95
RECORD Attendance: 4,000 v Walthamstowe Avenue Essex Senior Cup 1949
Senior Honours: Eastern Co.Champions 94-95 95-96 R-Up 93-94 Essex Senior Trophy: 94-95 96-97 & Essex Jnr.Cup (2)

Felixstowe & Walton United F.C. Back Row (L-R): Andy Crump, Stuart Simmons, Danny Phillips, Jimmy Andrews, Dwayne Edwards, Paul Cudworth, James Peachey, Shaun Pugh, Gavin Crane, Jamie Drury, Gavin Frost, Rob Juby (Trainer). **Front:** Danny Spencer, James Buckle, Daniel Glencastle, Steve Potts (Manager), Steve Buckle (Asst. Manager), Matt Buckle, Lewis Pemberton, Glenn Snell.

HARWICH & PARKESTON

Founded: 1875
Nickname: Shrimpers

Chairman: Tony Armstrong   **President:** Tony Harvey   **Manager:** Mick Formoy
Secretary: Andy Schooler, 21 The Vineway, Harwich, Essex CO12 4AX **Tel No:** 01255 504590 (H) 07974 692473 (M)
Press Officer: Carl Allan   **Programme:** 28 Pages - 50p   **Editor:** Carl Allan (01255 552510)
GROUND ADDRESS: Royal Oak, Main Road, Dovercourt, Harwich,CO12 4AA   **Tel No:** 01255 503649
Capacity: 5,000   **Seats:** 350   **Covered:**1,000   **Floodlights:** Yes
Simple Directions: On main road into Dovercourt. 600 yards from Dovercourt (BR)
Midweek Home Matchday: Tuesday   **Clubhouse:** Open every day with function rooms   **Club Shop:** No
Club Colours: White & black/black/black   **Change Colours:** All red   **Previous Ground:** Phoenix Field, Sea Front
LAST SEASON 21st
Top Scorer: Jimmy Chatters   **Player of the Year:** Lee Race   **Captain:** Martin Calver
BEST PERFORMANCES
League: Joint Champions 35-36   **F.A. Cup:** 1st Round (6)   **F.A.Amateur Cup:** Finalists 1898-9 52-3 **F.A.Vase:** Q-F 90-91
RECORD Attendance: 5,649 v Romford F.A.Amateur Cup 4th Rd 1938
Senior Honours: F.A.Amateur Cup Finalists (2) Eastern CoLg 35-36 Athenian Div 1 R-up Essex Senior Cup (2) Essex Senior Trophy 89-90 AFA Senior Cup 35-36 36-37

HISTON RESERVES

Secretary: Mrs Lisa Baldwin, 5 Caxton Lane, Foxton, Cambridge CB2 6SR   Tel No: 01223 872989 (H) 0845 3455472 (M)
Colours: Red & BLack stripes/black/black   **Change Colours:** Sky & navy blue/black/black
Ground: Bridge Road, Impington, Cambridge **Tel Nos:** 01223 237373 or Fax 01223 237373
Directions: Leave A14 northern Cambridge bypass on B1049 (signposted Histon and Cottenham) Ground half a mile on right.

Ipswich Wanderers   Photo: Peter Barnes.

IPSWICH WANDERERS

Founded: 1983
Nickname: Wanderers

Chairman: Ed Nicholls   **President:** Pat Emerson   **Manager:** John Clarkson
Secretary: Dennis Miller, Saracen's House, 25 St Margarets Green, Ipswich,IP4 2BN
E-mail: dennis@ipswichwanderers.co.uk;   Tel NO 07717 203957 (M)   **Sponsor:** Car Glass & Trim
GROUND ADDRESS: Humber Doucey Lane,Ipswich,Suffolk IP4 3NR   **Ground Tel. No.:** 01473 728581
Capacity: 2,000   **Seats:** 50   **Covered:** Yes   **Floodlights:** Yes
Simple Directions: Take Woodbridge out of Ipswich, then left fork into Playford Road. Take first left into Humberdoucy Lane. Ground is 300 yards on right.
Midweek Home Matchday: Tuesday   **Clubhouse:** Full facilities on matchdays.   **Club Shop:** Yes
Previous Name: Loadwell Ipswich   **Previous Leagues:** Litle David Sunday League
Club Colours: All Blue   **Change Colours:** Red& black/black/red& black
LAST SEASON
League: Champions Eastern Div 1   **F.A. Cup:** Preliminary Rd.   **F.A. Vase:** .1st Qualifying Rd
Top Scorer: Rene Swann   **Player of the Year:** Mark Goldfinch   **Captain:** Marc Lowe
BEST PERFORMANCES
League: **F.A. Cup:** 2nd Qual.Rd.   **F.A.Vase:** 1st Rd
RECORD Attendance: 335 v Woodbridge Eastern Co Lg 93-94
Senior Honours: Eastern Counties League Div 1 Champions 1997-98 and 2004-05

KING'S LYNN RESERVES

Founded:
Nickname:

Secretary: Nigel Link, 58 Hall Lane, West Winch, Kings Lynn PE33 0PP Tel Nos: 01553 841089 (H) 07768 615333(M)
Colours: All Blue & Gold   **Change Colours:** Orange & Black/ Black & Orange/Black
Ground: The Walks Stadium, Tennyson Road, Kings Lynn PE 30 5PB. **Tel Nos:** 01553 760060 and Fax : 01553 762159
Directions: At mini roundabout arriving from A10/A47 take Vancouver Avenue. Ground on left after half a mile .

KIRKLEY

Founded: 1886
Nickname:

Chairman: Bob Jenkerson   **Vice-Chairman:** Colin Smith/Jeremy Woodruff   **Manager:** Nick Shorten

Secretary & Press Officer: Alan Mower, 9 Smiths Walk, Quilton Broad, Lowestoft, Suffolk NR33 8QN

Tel No: 01502 508245 (H) 07909 694523 (M)

Programme Editor: David Armstrong   **Programme:** 20 Pages 50p

GROUND ADDRESS: Kirkley Recreation Ground, Walmer Road, Lowestoft, Suffolk   **Tel:** 01502 513549

Capacity: 1.000   **Seats:** 150   **Covered:** 150   **Floodlights:** Yes

Simple Directions: From A12 to Lowestoft town centre and go over roundabout at Teamways Garage and past Teamways Pub. Take next left into Walmar Road.

Midweek Home Matchday: Wednesday   **Clubhouse:** Yes   Club Shop: Yes

Previous League: Anglian Combination

Club Colours: Royal Blue   **Change Colours:** All Red

BEST PERFORMANCES

League: 3rd Div 1 2004-05   **F.A.Vase:** 2nd Rd 2004-05

RECORD Attendance: 341 v Diss Town   **Goalscorer:** Barry Dale 241   **Apps:** Barry Dale 495

Senior Honours: Suffolk Senior Cup (5)

LEISTON

Founded: 1880
Nickname:

Chairman: Andrew Crisp   **Manager:** Glenn Driver

Secretary: David Rees, P.O. Box 38, Leiston, Suffolk IP16 4LE

Tel No: 01728 635544

Press Officer: Secretary   **Programme:** Yes   **Editor:** James Mayhew

GROUND ADDRESS: LTAA, Victory Road, Leiston, Suffolk IP 16 4LD   Tel No: 01728 833030 (H)

Tel No. & Fax: 01728 830308

Capcity: 2,000   **Seats:** 53   **Covered:** 500   **Floodlights:** Yes

Midweek Home Matchday: Tuesday   **Clubhouse:**   **Club Shop:**

Club Colours: All Royal Blue   **Change Colours:** Yellow/blue/blue

RECORD Attendance: 271 v AFC Sudbury 13.11.04

LOWESTOFT TOWN

Founded: 18185
Nickname: Blues

Chairman: Peter Gamble   **President:** Roy Harper   **Managers:** Micky Chapman & Ady Gallagher

Secretary: Terry Lynes, 31 Avondale Road, Lowestoft, Suffolk NR32 2HU   **Sponsors:** Gary Bennett Driving School.

Tel No: 01502 564034 (H) 07930 872947 (M)

Programme Editor: Shaun Cole (07946 438298))   **Programme:** 44 Pages £1.00

GROUND ADDRESS: Crown Meadow, Love Road, Lowestoft,   **Ground Tel. No:** 01502 573818

Capacity: 3,000   **Seats:** 466   **Covered: 500**   **Floodlights:** Yes

Simple Directions: Just off A 12 Ten minutes from Lowestoft BR

Midweek Home Matchday: Tuesday   **Clubhouse:** Pub hours.   **Club Shop:** Yes

Previous League: Norfolk & Suffolk 1897-1935

Club Colours: Royalblue/white/white   **Change Colours:** White and Navy Blue

LAST SEASON: League: Champions   **F.A. Cup:** 2nd Qualifying   **F.A. Vase:** 4th Round

Top Scorer: Garry McGee   **Player of the Year:** Carl Poppy   **Captain:** Ian Smith

BEST PERFORMANCES

League: Eastern Counties Champions (9)   **F.A. Cup:** 1st Rd (5)   **F.A.Vase:** 5th Round

RECORD Attendance: 5,000 v Watford F.A.Cup 1st Rd 67 **Goalscorer:**   **Appearances:**

Senior Honours: Eastern Co (9) Suffolk Premier Cup (9) Suffolk Sen Cup (10) East Anglian Cup (10)

MILDENHALL TOWN

Founded: 1890
Nickname: The Hall

Chairman: Martin Tuck   **Vice-Chairman:** Bill Flynn   **Manager:** Trevor Munns

Secretary: Brian Hensby, 14 Sanderling Close, Mildenhall, Suffolk IP28 7LE Tel Nos: 01638 715772 (H) 07932 043261 (M)

Programme: £1.00   **Editor** : Frank Marshall **Tel No:** 01638 720616   **Fx.Sec:** Brian Hensby 01638715772

GROUND ADDRESS: Recreation Way, Mildenhall, Suffolk   **Ground Tel:** 01638 713449

Capcity: 2,000   **Seats:** 50   **Covered:** 200   **Floodlights:** Yes

Simple Directions: Next to swimming pool and car park a quarter of a mile from town centre.

Midweek Home Matchday: Tuesday   **Clubhouse:** Match days and functions. Light refreshments available.

Previous Leagues: Bury & District, Cambridge League 2B , 1B & premier

Club Colours: Amber/black/black   **Change Colours:** White & Red/Red/Red   **Sponsor:** Safepac International

Best Performances

League: 6th Eastren Co. 2004-05   **F.A. Cup:** 2nd Qualifying Rd.   **F.A.Vase:** 4th Rd.

RECORD Attendance: 450 v Derby County Friendly July 2001

Senior Honours: Suffolk Junior Cup 1899 -1900

Mildenhall Town: Stuart Baverstock (gk), Dean Milton, Steve Coyle, Paul McCormick, Adam Broomhead, Kevin Burgess, Kev Terry, Tommy Ellis, Craig Duffell, Lee Smith, Keiron Philpot. Photo: Arthur Evans.

Newmarket Town Back Row (L-R): Benny Murray, Darren Coe, Tommy Crawford, Dave Walton, Dave Werthman, Andy Mee. **Front:** Marcus Herin, Laurence Church, Tom Porter (Mascot), Lee Reed, Jamie Alsop, Sam Reed. Photo: Arthur Evans.

NEEDHAM MARKET

Founded: 1927
Nickname:

Chairman: David Bugg **Manager:** Danny Laws & Chris Tracey
Secretary: Derrick Bloomfield, 33 Quinton Road, Needham Market, Suffolk IP6 8DA. Tel No: 01449 720693(H)
Programme Editor: Paul Grainger
GROUND ADDRESS: Bloomfields, Quinton Road, Needham Market, Suffolk   Ground **Tel. No.: 01449 721000**
Capacity: 1,000   **Seats:** 250   **Covered:** 250   **Floodlights:** Yes
Simple Directions: Quinton Road is off Barretts Lane which in turn is off Needham Market High Street
Midweek Home Matchday: Tuesday   Clubhouse: Club Shop: No
Previous Leagues: Ipswich & District, Suffolk & Ipswich until 1996
Previous Grounds: Youngs Meadow, and Crowley Park until 1996
Club Colours: Red & Black   **Change Colours:** All Blue
LAST SEASON
League: 6th Eastern Counties Premier
Top Scorer: Stuart Jopling   **Player of the Year:** Nathan Munson   Captain: Stuart Jopling
Best Performances
League: **F.A. Cup:**   **F.A.Vase:** 4th Round
RECORD Attendance: 700 v Ipswich Town **Goalscorer:** Alvin King   **Apps:**
SENIOR HONOURS:

NEWMARKET TOWN

Founded: 1877
Nickname:The Jockeys

Chairman: Allen Collen   **President:** M.J.Nicholas   **Manager:** Dave Abbs
Secretary: Elaine Jeakins, 140 New Cheveley Road, Newmarket CB8 8BY
Tel Nos: 01638 602525 (H) 01638 750201 (W) 07801 815682 (M)
Press Officer: Peter Lea (01638 602927) **Programme:** 24 pages £1.00   **Editor:** Peter Lea (01638 602927)
GROUND ADDRESS: Cricket Field Road, off New Cheveley Road , Newmarket   **Tel No:** 01638 663637
Capacity: 1,750   **Seats:** 144   **Covered:** 150   **Floodlights:** Yes
Simple Directions: Four hundred yards from Newmarket BR.Turn right into Green Road and right at cross roads into new
Cheveley Rd. Ground is at top on left.
Midweek Home Matchday: Tuesday **Clubhouse:**Matchdays only. refreshments available.**Club Shop:** Yes
Previous Leagues: Bury Senior,Ipswich Senior, Essex & Suffolk Border, United Counties 1934-37 Eastern Counties
Club Colours: Yellow & navy/navy/blue   **Change Colours:** Red and Black
LAST SEASON League: 17th   **F.A. Cup:** Extra Prielim Rd.   **F.A. Vase:** Quarter Finals
Top Scorer: Paul Shaw   **Player of the Year:** Paul Shaw
Best Performances League: 3rd   **F.A. Cup:** 4th Qualifying Rd 1992-93   **F.A.Vase:** 6th Round 2005-062
RECORD Attendance: 2,701v Abbey United (Now Cambridge United) F.A.Cup 01.10.49
SENIOR HONOURS: Suffolk Senior Cup 34-35 93-94 Suffolk Premier Cup 93-94 94-95 96-97

NORWICH UNITED

Founded: 1903
Nickname: Planters

Chairman: John Hilditch   **President:** Vinnie Jones   **Manager:**Paul Franklin

Secretary: Keith Cutmore, 42 Desmond Drive, Old Catton, Norwich. MR6 7JN

Tel No: 01603 407 148 (H) 07946 033588 (M)

Programme Editorial Team: Simon Barnes Printing

Ground: Plantation Park, Blofield, Norwich, Norfolk.NR13 4PL (01603 716963)   **Programme:** 24 Pages 50p

Capacity: 3,000   **Seats:** 100   **Covered:** 1,000   **Floodlights:** Yes

Midweek Home Matchday: Tuesday   **Clubhouse:** Matchdays with hot & cold food.   **Club Shop:** Yes

Gothic Clubb, Heartseae Lane, Norwich (until 1990-91)

Club Colours: Yellow & Blue/Blue/Blue   **Change Colours:** All red

RECORD Attendance: 401 v Wroxham Eastern Co Lg 91-92 **Goalscorer:** M.Money   **Appearances:** Tim Sayer

Senior Honours: Eastern Co's 90-91 2001-02 R-Up 89-90

SOHAM TOWN RANGERS

Founded: 1947
Nickname:Town or Rangers

Chairman: Colin Murfitt   **Prsident:** Vinnie Jones
Secretary: Karen Prewett, 10 Blackthorne Court, Soham, Ely, Cambs.CB7 5DQ   **Sec's Tel No:** 07760 222487
Tel Nos: 01353 721788 (H) 07917 417516 (M) e-mail: ladycaroline@tesco.net
Manager: Ian Benjamin   **Physio:** M.Dury
Press Officer: Name (Tel)   **Programme**Editor: Fred Parker
GROUND ADDRESS: Julian Martin Lane, Soham, Ely, Cambs. CB7 5YT   **Tel:** 01353 720732
Capacity: 2,000   **Seats:** 250   **Covered:** 1,000   **Floodlights:**Yes   **Shop:** Yes
Simple Directions: A142 between Newmarket and Ely. At roundabout at northern end of by-pass turm left towards town centre
and then right at the corner shop into Julius Martina Lane. Ground is on the left.
Midweek Home Matchday: Tuesday   **Clubhouse:** Three barsand function room for hire. **Contact:** M.Howe
Previous Name(s): Soham Town and Sham Rangers merged in 1947   **Previous League(s):** Peterborough & District
Club Colours: Green/Black/Gree   **Change Colours:** Blue/black/blue
BEST PERFORMANCES
F.A. Cup: 3rd Qualifying Round 70-71   **F.A.Vase:** 5th Rd v Newbury T (h) 04-05
RECORD Attendance: 3,000 v Pegasus . F.A.Amateur Cup 1963

STANWAY ROVERS

Founded: 1956
Nickname: Rovers

Secretary: Alan Brierley, 19 Barley Way, Stanway, essex CO 3 0YD
Tel No: 01206 521606 (H) 07747 755516 (M)
Ground: `Hawthorns', New Farm Road, Stanway, Colchester, Essex CO3 0PG (01206 578187)
Directions: Leave A12 at Jct 26 to A1124. Turn right(from London)or left from Ipswich onto
Essex Yeomanry Way. A1124 towards Colchester 1st right into Villa Rd,then left into Chaple Rd,
and left into New Farm Rd. Ground 400 yds on left.Nearest BR station is Colchester North
Capacity: 1,500   **Seats:** 100   **Cover:** 250   **Floodlights:** Yes   **Shop:** No
Clubhouse: 6.45-11pm eves, 12-11pm Sats. Rolls, soup, tea, coffee etc available matchdays
Club Shop: Pennants & ties (Club website:lineone.net/ m alan brierley
HONOURS Essex Intermediate Cup R-up 89-90 90-91, Essex & Suffolk Border Lg R-up 91-2
(Div 1 86-87, Div 2 81-81 85-86), Essex Junior Cup R-up 74-75
PREVIOUS   Leagues: Colchester & E Essex; Essex & Suffolk. Border (pre-1992)
               Ground: Stanway Secondary School, Winstree Road (20 years)
RECORD **Gate:** 210 v Harwich & P ECL Div 1 04 **Win:** 10-0 v Thetford Town 3.11.01
and v March Town 9.12.00 ECL Div 1 **Defeat:** 0-10 v Sudbury Town (A), E.C.L. Cup

FACT FILE
Sponsors: R.J.Brett Contracts
Colours: Gold& black/black/black& gold
Change : Navy, red & white/navy/navy & red
Midweek matchday: Wednesday
Reserves' Lge: Essex & Suff. Border
Programme: 12 pages, 50p
Editor: Mick Norfolk
Local Press: Essex Co.Standard, Eve Gazette
CLUB PERSONNEL
Chairman: Roy Brett
President: Richard Deguille
Manager:James McIntyre
Physio: John Chandler

WISBECH TOWN

Founded: 1920
Nickname: Fenmen

Chairman: Barry Carter   **Vice-Chairman:** David Parsons   **Managers:** Dick Creasey
Secretary: Colin Gant, 5 Oxford Place, Terrington-St-Clement, Kings Lynn   **Assistant Manager:** Darren Edey
Tel Nos: 01553 828600 (H) 07803 021699 (M)
Programme Ediotor: Spencer Larham   **Programme:** 16 Pages 50p
GROUND ADDRESS: Fenland Park, Lerowe Road, Wisbech, Cambs.   **Ground Tel. No.:** 01945 584176
Capacity: 3,800   **Seats:** 284   **Covered:** 1,000   **Floodlights:** Yes
Simple Directions: Follow A47 bypass to the West Walton turn off roundabout where there is a Little Chef. Take left for
Wisbech, Lerowe Road is first left after 30 mph sign.
Midweek Home Matchday: Tuesday   **Clubhouse:** Open every evening   **Club Shop:** Open Matchdays
Previous Leagues: Peterborough 1920-35 United Co. 35-50 Eastern Counties 50-52 70-97 Midland 52-58 Southern 97-2002
Club Colours: Red/red/red   **Change Colours:** Yellow/green/yellow
Last Season: League: 4th   **F.A. Cup:** Preliminary Round. .   **F.A. Vase:** 3rd Round
Top Scorer: Liam Harrold 38   **Player of the Year:** Mark Jimson   **Captain:** Steve Appleby
BEST PERFORMANCES
League: Southern League   **F.A. Cup:** 2nd Rd 57-58 97-98   **F.A.Vase:** S-F 84-85 85--86
RECORD Attendance: 8,044 v Peterborough United, Midland League 25.08.57
       Goalscorer: Bert Titmarsh 246 (1931-37) **Appearances:** Jamie Brighty (731)
Senior Honours: Southern Lg Div 1 61-62 Utd Co Champions (3) East Anglian Cup 87-88 R-Up (2)

WOODBRIDGE TOWN

Founded: 1885
Nickname:The Woodpeckers

Chairman: Keith Dixon   **President:** Andrew Dalby   **Manager:** Mick Stockwell
Secretary: Eric Smy, 9 Bury Hill, Woodbridge, Suffolk IP12 1LF   **Sponsor** Brafe Engineering
Te.lNos: 01394 384213(H)
Programme Editor: Richard Scott   e-mail: richardhscott@btinternet.co.uk   **Programme:** 20-24 Pages 50p
GROUND ADDRESS: Notcutts Park, Seckford Hall Rioad, Woodbridge, Suffolk IP12 4DA **Tel:** 01394 385308
Capacity: 3,000   **Seats:** 50   **Covered:** 200   **Floodlights:** Yes
Simple Directions: From Lowestoft turn leftinto Woodbrisge at last roundabout (or first roundabout from Ipswich). Rake first
turning left and first left again. Drive to ground at end of road on left.
Midweek Home Matchday: Tuesday   **Clubhouse:** Full facilities plus hot & cold food on matchdays **Club Shop:** No.
Previous League: Suffolk & Ipswich   **Previous Ground:** Kingston PF
Club Colours: Black & white/black/black   **Change Colours:** Yellow/blue/yellow
BEST PERFORMANCES
League: Eastern Co Prem   **F.A. Cup:** 3rd Rd Qualifying 97-98 00-01   **F.A.Vase:** 6th Rd 98-99
RECORD Attendance: 3,000 v Arsenal (opening floodlights 02.10.90
Senior Honours: Suffolk Senior Cup (4)

WROXHAM

Founded: 1892
Nickname: Yaghtsmen

Chairman: Tom Jarrett   **Manager:** Damian Hilton   **Sponsor:** Dolphin Autos & Optic
Secretary: Matt Carpenter, 17 Hughes Court, Hethersett,Norfolk NR9 3PT
Tel.Nos: 01603 811956 (H) 07866 731081 (M) e-mail: secretary@wroxhamfc.com   **E-mail:** secretary @wroxhamfc.com
Press Officer: Secretary   **Programme:** 40 Pages £1.00   **Editor:** Barnes Print
GROUND ADDRESS: Trafford Park,Skinners Lane, Wroxham,Norfolk NTR12 8SJ**Tel No:**01603 783538
Capacity: 2,500   **Seats:** 50   **Covered:** 250   **Floodlights:** Yes
Simple Directions: From Norwich, turn left at former Castle Pub and keep left to ground. Under two miles from Wroxham &
Hoveton BR. Buses 722,724 and 717   **Website:** www.wroxhamfc.com
Midweek Home Matchday: Tuesday   **Clubhouse:** Bar, pool, darts, hot & cold food etc   **Club Shop:** Online
Previous Leagues: Norwich City, East Anglia, Norwich & Dist, Anglian Combination
Previous Grounds: Norwich Rd, The Avenue & Keys Hill
Club Colours: Blue & White stripes/blue/nlue   **Change Colours:** White/Red/Red
LAST SEASON League: 8th   **F.A. Cup:** 3rd Qualifying Round   **F.A. Vase:** 2nd Qualifying Round
Top Scorer: Adrian Coote 25   **Player of the Year:** Lee Gilmore   **Captain:** Justin Fox
BEST PERFORMANCES
League: Eastern Counties Champions (6)   **F.A. Cup:** 3rd Qualifying Round 01-02 05-06 **F.A.Vase:** Quarter-Final 2001-02
RECORD Attendance: 1,011 v Wisbech T Eastern Co.Lg. 16.03.93 **Goalscorer:** Matthew Metcalf **Appearances:** Stu Larter
Senior honours: Eastern.Counties Champions Lg (6) R-up (3), Norfolk Senior Cup (3)

LEAGUE CONSTITUTION 2006-07 - DIVISION ONE

CORNARD UNITED

Secretary: Chris Symes, 22 Greenacres, Mile End, Colchester, Essex CO4 (01206 851627)

Ground: Blackhouse Lane Sportsfield, Great Cornard, Suffolk (01787 376719)

Directions: Left off r'bout on A134 coming from Ipswich/Colchester intoSudbury, follow signs for Country Park - ground is immediately opposite along Blackhouse Lane

Capacity: 2,000   **Seats:** 250   **Cover:** 500   **Floodlights:** Yes   **Club Shop:** No

Clubhouse: Open matchdays & Sunday lunchtimes. Matchday Tea, coffee, colddrinks, & snacks

HONOURS   Eastern Co's Lg Div 1 89-90 (Lg Cup R-up 92-93), Essex & Suffolk BorderLg 88-89 (Lg Cup 88-89), Suffolk Snr Cup 89-90, Suffolk Jnr Cup R-up 84-85, Harwich Senior Charity Cup 2001-02, Eastern Floodlight League Cup 2001-02

PREVIOUS   **Leagues:** Sudbury S/day 64-65; Bury St Edmunds & Dist 65-72; Colchester71-78; Essex Suffolk Bord 78-89. **Grounds:** Cornard Rec 64-71; Great CornardUpper School 71-85

RECORDS: Appearances: Keith Featherstone   **Goalscorer :** Andy Smiles

Attendance: 400 v Colchester Utd 1997   **Win:** 18-2 v St Peters House, Colchester Lge 14/9/72

Defeat: 4-10 v Finningham, Bury Lge 7/2/68

FACT FILE
Founded: 1964   Nickname: Ards
Sponsors: Pizza Town
Colours: Blue & white
Change colours: White/Navy Blue/Navy
Midweek Matches: Tuesday
Reserve League: Essex & Suffolk Border
Prog:16 pages Ed:Neil Cheese(01787311368)
Local Press : Suffolk Free Press,
East Anglian Daily Times

CLUB PERSONNEL
Chairman: Michael Ford
Vice-Chair: Mike Ford
Manager: Chris Symes
Ass.t Manager:Jason Stalker Physio: Mike Ford

DEBENHAM LC FC

Chairman: Malcolm Roberts

Manager & Secretary: Mel Aldis, Managers Office, Debenham Leisure Centre, Gracechurch St, Debenham, Suffolk IP14 6BL

Tel Nos: 01728 860650 (H+W)   01728 861127 (**Fax**)   07810 293266 (M)   **e-mail:** martin@durie.net

Previous Name(s):   **Previous League (s):** Suffolk & Ipswich

Club Colours: Yellow/black/yellow   **ChangeColours:** Royal blue/navyblue/navy blue

LAST SEASON:

League: 10th Division One   **F.A. Cup:** N/A   **F.A. Vase:** N/A

Top Scorer: Ian Gedney   **Player of the Year:** Matt Norman   **Captain:** John Farrell

BEST PERFORMANCES

League: 2nd Suffolk & Ipswich Lg.   **F.A. Cup:** N/A   **F.A.Vase:** N/A

Programme Editor: Steve Thorley(01728 861101)

GROUND ADDRESS: Debenham Leisure Centre, Gracechurch Street, Debenham, Stowmarket, Suffolk. IP14 6BL

Tel. No: 01728 861560 (H) 07799 566507 (M) 01728 861556 (W)   e-mail: aldis@mel 861358.fsnet.co.uk

Capacity: 1,000   **Seats:** 114   **Covered:** 114   **Floodlights:** Yes

Midweek Home Matchday: Tuesday   **Clubhouse:** Yes   **Club Shop:** No

RECORD Attendance: 400   **Goalscorer:** Lee Briggs   **Appearances:** Steve Nelson

SENIOR HONOURS: Runners-Up Suffolk & Ipswich League 2004-2005

DOWNHAM TOWN

Secretary: F. Thorne, 6 Maple Rd., Downham Market, Norfolk, PE38 9PY. (01366 382563)

Ground: Memorial Field, Lynn Road, Downham Market, Norfolk (01366 388424)

Directions: One and a quarter miles from Downham Market (BR) - continue to townclock, turn left and ground is three quarters of a mile down Lynn Road

Capacity: 1,000   **Seats:** 60   **Cover:** No   **Floodlights:** Yes

Clubhouse: Bar open matchdays, refreshments & snacks available

HONOURS   Peterborough Lg (5) 62-63 73-74 78-79 86-88; Norfolk Senior Cup 63-64 65-66 (R-up(3) 66-69)

PREVIOUS   **League:** Peterborough

RECORD   **Attendance:** 325 v Wells Town Norfolk Senior Cup, 1998-99

FACT FILE
Founded: 1881
Nickname: Town
Sponsor: Lynwere Engineering
Colours: Red/red/red
Change colours: Sky/Navy/sky
Midweek Matches: Tuesday
Programme: Yes, with entry
Editor: Chairman

CLUB PERSONNEL
Chairman: John Fysh
President: David Green
Manager: Jerry Rose
Captain: Marcus Fendley

ELY CITY

Secretary: Derek Oakey, 11 Frederick Talbot Close, Soham, Nr. Ely Cambs, CB7 5EY

Tel: 01353 722141 (H) 01353 722179 (W) email: derk.oakey@tesco.net

Ground: Unwin Sports Ground, Downham Road (01353 662035)

Directions: A10 Ely by-pass turn off for Downham. 3 miles (approx) from Ely(BR)

Capacity: 1,500   **Seats:** 150   **Cover:** 350   **Floodlights:** Yes

Clubhouse: Open matchdays, refreshments available

Club Shop: Metal Badges: Yes

HONOURS   Cambs Snr Cup 47-48, Eastern Co's Lg R-up 69-70 (Lg Cup 79-80) Jewson Eastern Div 1 Winners 1996-97,R-up 1999-00,Cup Winners 99-00

PREVIOUS   **Leagues:** Peterborough; Central Alliance 58-60

               Grounds: Paradise Ground (1890 1986)

BEST SEASON   **FA Cup:** 1st Rd 56-56 (2 v Torquay)

RECORD   **Gate:** 260 v Soham, Eastern Co's Lg Div 1, 12/4/93

               At old ground: 4,260 v Torquay, FA Cup 56-57

FACT FILE
Founded: 1885Nickname: Robins
Colours: All red with white trim
Change colours: All Blue
Midweek Matches: Tuesday
Programme: 24 pages- 50p
Editor: Derek Oakley
Local Press: Ely Standard (01353 667831)
Club Website: elycityfc.com

CLUB PERSONNEL
Chairman: Robert Button
Manager: Dennis Lightning

FAKENHAM TOWN

FACT FILE
Founded: 1884
Nickname: Ghosts
Sponsors: Aldiss
Colours: Amber & black/black/amber
Change colours: Blue &white
Midweek Matchday: Tuesday
Reserves' League: Anglian Comb
Programme: 32 pages, 50p
Editor: Tony Miles
Tel: 01328 855489
Local Press : Dereham & Fakenham Times

Secretary: Ivor Darby, 16 Smith's Lane, Fakenham, Norfolk
Tel No: 013283 856618 (H)   07981 341810 (M)
Ground: Clipbush Lane, Fakenham NR21 8SW   Tel/Fax: 01328 856222
Directions: Corner of A148 & Clipbush Lane
Capacity: 3,000   Seats: 264   Cover: 500   Floodlights: Yes
Clubhouse: Bar, TV. Refreshments available Tel: 01328 855859 Club Shop: Yes
HONOURS Norfolk Snr Cup 70-71 72-73 73-74 91-92 93-94 94-95;,98-99 Eastern Co's Premier
Division R-up: 98-99, Lg Div1, R-up 91-92; Anglian Comb. Cup 78-79
PREVIOUS **Leagues:** N Norfolk 1884-1910; Norwich & Dist 10-35; Norfolk & Suffolk 35-
64; Anglian Comb 64-87
Grounds: Hempton Green 1884-89; Star Meadow 89-1907;
Barons Hall Lawn 1907-96
BEST SEASON **FA Vase:** 98-99 3rd Rd **FA Cup:**
RECORD **Gate:** 1100 v Watford-official opening of new ground

CLUB PERSONNEL
Chairman: Nigel Allen
President:Bill Clayton
Press Officer: J Cushion
Commercial Manager: Paul Wright
Manager: Paul Tong & Kevin Bush

GODMANCHESTER ROVERS

FACT FILE
Founded: 1911   Nickname: Goddy/Rovers
Sponsors: Ace Cabs,Notleys and Sears
Colours: All Sky blue
Change: Greenor Orange/white/black
Midweek Matches: Wednesday
Programme: 16 pages + entry £1.00
Editor: Nick Forshaw
CLUB PERSONNEL
President: Mick Gould
Chairman: Keith Gabb
Manager: Ian Jackson
Asst Man: Ian Baker
Coach: Errol McCammon
Captain: Stuart Wood
Physio: Sandra Holmes
General Manager: Daryl Potter

Secretary: Wally Carson, 16 Lakeway. Stukeley Meadows, Huntingdon, Cambs. PE29 6SU
Tel: 01480 434493   e-mail: goddysec@btinternet.com
Ground: Bearscroft Lane, Godmanchester, Cambs.PE29 2LQ (07950 367417)
Directions: From A14 turn off for Godmanchester. Take A1198 towards Wood Green
Animal Shelter,Bearscroft Lane is half mile from A14 on left down
Capacity: **Cover:** 150 **Floodlights:** Yes **Club Shop:** No
Clubhouse: Temporary portacabins. New clubhouse to be opened in Spring 2005
Previous League: Cambridgeshire League and Hunts County League.
Honours: Hunts Junior Cup 1938-39 and 1988-89
Kershaw Premier League Cup 1994-95
Club Records: **Attendance**: 138 v Cambridge City Reserves Dec.2003.

GORLESTON

Chairman: Jimmy Jones **Managers:** Gary Ingram & Lee Harvey
Secretary: Kevin Meale c/o club
Programme Editorial Team: Simon Barnes Printing **Programme:** 56-60 pages £1,00
GROUND ADDRESS: Emerald Park, Woodfarm Lane, Gorleston, Great Yarmouth **Tel:** 01493 602802
Capacity: 5,000 **Seats:** 2,000 **Covered:** 4,000 **Floodlights:** Yes
Simple Directions: On Magdalen Estate follow signs to Crematorium, turn left and follow road to ground.
Midweek Home Matchday: Tuesday **Clubhouse:** Full facilities and hot fod on matchdays **Club Shop:** No
Previous Leagues: Gt.Yarmouth & District, Norfolk & Suffolk and Anglian Combination.
Club Colours: All Green **Change Colours:** All White
BEST PERFORMANCES
League: Eastern Co.Champions (4) **F.A. Cup:** 1st Round 51-52 57-58 **F.A.Vase:** 5th Round 2002-2003
RECORD Attendance: 4,473 v Orient F.A.Cup 1st Rd. 29.11.51
Senior Honours: Eastern Co Champions 52-53 72-73 79-80 80-81 Norfolk Senior Cup (13) R-Up (25)

GREAT YARMOUTH TOWN

Chairwoman: Julia Banham **Manager**: Kevin Rowark
Secretary: Brian Smith, The Bungalow, Humberstone Farm, Cobholm, Great Yarmouth, Norfolk NR31 0AZ
Tel No & Fax: 01493 656099 and 07710 200838 (M)
Programme: 40 Pages - £1.00 **Edited** by Barnes Print, Dereham
GROUND ADDRESS: Wellesey Recreation Ground, Wellesey Road, Great Yarmouth **Tel:** 01493 843373
Capacity: 3,600 **Seats:** 500 **Covered:** 2,100 **Floodlights:** Yes
Simple Directions: Just off Marine Parade 200yards north of Britannia Pier. Half a mile from BR.
Midweek Home Matchday: Tuesday **Clubhouse:** Hot & Cold food,TV, **Club Shop:** yes
Previous League(s): Norfolk & Suffolk
Club Colours: Amber & black stripes/black/black **Change Colours:** All Blue
Top Scorer: Shane Ward **Player of the Year:** Ben Le Compte **Captain:** Nathan Peake
BEST PERFORMANCES
League: Eastern Co. Champions 68-69 **F.A. Cup:** 2nd Rd 52-53 **F.A.Vase:** S-Final 82-83
Record Attendance: 8,944 v C.Palace F.A.C.1st Rd 52-3 **Goals** Gordon South 298 (27-47) **Apps**:Mark Vincent 700 1984- 05
SENIOR HONOURS: Champions 68-9, R-up (4) East Anglian Cup (3) Norfolk Senior Cup(12)

HADLEIGH UNITED

FACT FILE
Founded: 1892 Nickname: Brettsiders
Colours: White & navy/navy/white
Change colours: All Yellow
Midweek Matches: Tuesday
Reserves' Lge: Essex & Suff. Border
Programme: 12 pages, 50p
Editor: Chairman

Secretary: Ken Ramsey, 11 Wilson Road, Hadleigh, Suffolk.IP7 5HT (01473 829065)
Ground: Millfield, Tinkers Lane, Duke Street, Hadleigh, Suffolk Tel: 01473 822165

Directions: Turn off A12 approx halfway between Ipswich & Colchester. Take B1070 & follow signs to Hadleigh. Duke Street is off the High Street - turn left by Library
Capacity: 3,000 Seats: 250 Cover: 500 Floodlights: Yes
Clubhouse: Open matchdays. **Website:** hadleigh-utd.co.uk

HONOURS Ipswich & Dist./Suffolk & Ipswich Lg 53-54 56-57 73-74 76-77 78-79
(Mick McNeil) Lg Cup 76-77 80-81 81-82 86-87;
Suffolk Senior Cup 68-69 71-72 82-83.03-04 Eastern Co.Lg Champions 93-94
PREVIOUS **Leagues:** Suffolk & Ipswich (prev. Ipswich & D.)(pre-1991)
Grounds: Grays Meadow, Ipswich Road
RECORD **S - Gate:** 518 v Halstead Town, FA Vase Replay 17.1.95
Win: 8-1 v Chatteris(A) 17/1/95
Defeat: 0-7 v Harwich & Parkston (H) 12/10/96, & Wisbech (H) 26/4/97

CLUB PERSONNEL
President: K.Grimsey
Chairman: John Chenery
01473 829065
Manager: Dean Skinner

HAVERHILL ROVERS

FACT FILE
Founded: 1886 Nickname: Rovers
Colours: All red Change: All Blue
Midweek Matches: Tuesday
Programme: 24 pages,50p
Editor: Ray Esdale (01440 704670)
Local Press : Haverhill Echo,
Cambridge Evening News

Secretary: Karen Smith, 14 Burton Close, Haverill Suffolk CB9 9AA
Tel: 01440 761004 (H) 07929 882648 (M)
Ground: Hamlet Croft, Haverhill, Suffolk Tel: 01440 702137

Directions: Centre of Haverhill

Capacity: 3,000 Seats: 200 Cover: 200 Floodlights: Yes
Clubhouse: Open matchdays and functions. Snacks available
HONOURS Eastern Co's Lg 78-79 Lg Cup 64-65; Essex & Suffolk Border Lg 62-63 63-64;
East Anglian Cup 90-91; Suffolk Sen Cup 96-97
PREVIOUS **League:** Essex & Suffolk Border
RECORD **Attendance:** 1,537 v Warrington Town, FA Vase QF 86-87

CLUB PERSONNEL
Chairman: John Stephens
President: N Haylock
Press Officer: Steven Esdale
(01440704670)
Manager:Richard Carter Physio: Nel Franklin
Captain: Marcis Hunt

LONG MELFORD

FACT FILE
Formed: 1868
Nickname : The Villagers
Colours:Black & White stripes /black/black
Change Colours: Sky Blue/ white
Midweek Matchday: Monday
Programme: Price: £1 Pages: 32 (all colour)
Editor: Richard Kemp (01787 378149)

Secretary: Richard Powell,14 North Rise,Great Cornard,Sudbury,
Suffolk CO10 0DE Tel No: 01787 377969 (H) 07831 177838 (W)
Ground: Stoneylands, New Road, Long Melford, Suffolk. Tel: 01787 312187
Directions: Turn down St Catherine Road off Hall St (Bury-Sudbury road) and then turn left into New Road.
Capacity: Covered Seating: 106 Covered Standing: 406 Floodlights: Yes/No
Clubhouse: Licensed bar with smart function facilities for parties of a hundred.
Contact: Michelle (01787 312187)
Club Shop:
Previous Leagues: Essex & Suffolk Border Lge. until 2002
Honours: Suffolk Senior Cup (8) , Essex & Border League Champions (5)
Runners-Up (3) Border League Cup Winners (3) Runners -Up (4)

CLUB PERSONNEL
Chairman: Colin Woodhouse
Vice Chairman: Simon
GardenPresident:Richard Kemp
Manager: John Taylor
Captain: Steve Arnold
Reserve Team managers; Jim Walker
Physio:Sue Hopkins

MARCH TOWN UNITED

FACT FILE
Founded: 1885
Nickname: Hares
Club colours: Yellow/blue/yellow
Change colours: Blue & white/black/black
Midweek Matches: Tuesday
Programme: Free
Editor: G.Wesley
Local Press : Cambs Times, Fenland
Advertiser, Peterborough Evening Telegraph

Secretary: Ray Bennett, 47 Ellingham Ave, March, Cambs PE15 9TE (01354 659901)

Ground: GER Sports Ground, Robin Goodfellows Lane, March (01354 653073)

Directions: 5 mins from town centre, 10 mins from BR station
Capacity: 4,000 Seats: 500 Cover: 2,000 Floodlights: Yes
Clubhouse: On ground, seating 150. Light refreshments available

HONOURS Eastern Co's Lg 87-88 (Lg Cup 60-61), Utd Co's Lg 53-64, Cambs
Invitation Cup 54-55, East Anglian Cup 53-54 (jt withBarking)
PREVIOUS **Leagues:** Peterborough; Isle of Ely; Utd Co's 48-54
Ground: The Avenue (prior to 1946)
BEST SEASON FA Cup 1st Rd53-54 77-78,
RECORD **Gate:** 7,500 v King's Lynn, FA Cup 1956

CLUB PERSONNEL
Chairman: Gary Wesley
Manager : Alan Russell
Top Goalscorer: Ashley Brand

SAFFRON WALDEN TOWN

Secretary: Peter Rule, 48 Church Street, Saffron Walden, Essex CB10 1JQ

Tel Nos: 01799 501462 (H) 01992 476614 (W) 07956 668578 (M)

Ground: The Meadow, Catons Lane, Saffron Walden,Essex CB10 2DX (01799 522789)

Directions: Into Castle St off Saffron-W High St. Then left at T jct and 1st left by Victory Pub.

Capacity: 3,500 **Seats:** 274 **Cover:** 120 **Floodlights:** Yes **Clubhouse** : Yes **Club Shop:** No

Previous Leagues: Haverhill & Dist, Stansted & Dist,Cambs Sen,Herts * Essex Border,North

Essex,Essex& Suffolk Border,Spartan, Parthenon, Herts Co, Essex Sen(71-74) (96-03) Eastern

Co(74-84) and Isthmian (84-96) **Ground:** Saffron Walden Common 1872-1890

CLUB RECORDS: Attendance: 6,000 v Rainham Ath. Essex Junior Cup Final at Braintree

Scorers: Alec Ramsey 192, William Barker 178 Appearances: Les Page 538 David Argent 483

Best Season F.A.Cup: 2nd Q Rd Replay 84-85 1-2 v Kings Lynn **F.A.Vase** 5th Rd 90-1

SeniorHonours: Since 1990: E.Anglian Cup R-Up 94-5,Essex Sen Lg 73-74 &1999-2000

STOWMARKET TOWN

Chairman: Andrew Horrex **Prersident:** John Bultitude **Manager:** Colin Macrow

Secretary: Sandra Gooding, 67 Kipling Way, Stowmarket, Suffolk(01449 775327) **Sponsors:** Barnards

Programme Editor: Brian Seaman (01449 775166) **Programme:** 20 pages £1.00

GROUND ADDRESS: Greens Meadows Stadium, Bury Road, Stowmarket, Suffolk **Tel:** 01449 612533

Capacity: 2,000 **Seats:** 200 **Covered:** 450 **Floodlights:** Yes

Simple Directions: About 800 yards from Stowmarket station (BR).Turn righta lights and haed outof town over roundabout into Bury Road, Groundis on the right

MIdweek Home Match:. Wednesday **Clubhouse:** Open evenings and week ends.**Club Shop** : No

Previous Names: Stowuplands Corinthians, Stowmarket Corinthians and Stowmarket F.C.

Previous Leagues: Ipswich & District, Essex & Suffolk Border League 1925-52

Club Colours: Gold & black/black/black **Change Colours:** All Red

Best Performances

League: Eastern Co.Premier R-Up 91-92 **F.A. Cup:** 2nd Qualifying Round **F.A.Vase:** 4th Round 1983-84

Record Attendance: 1,200 v Ipswich Town friendly July 1994

SENIOR HONOURS: Eastern Counties Runners-Up 91-92 Suffolk Premier Cup (4) Suffolk Senior Cup (10)

SWAFFHAM TOWN

Secretary: David.Ward, 14 Mount Close,Swaffham. PE37 7BX
Tel: 01760 722516 (H) 01760 720130 (Fax) 07771 960863 (M)
Email Address: pepward@aol,com

Ground: Shoemakers Lane, Swaffham, Norfolk (01760 722700)
Capacity: 2,000 Seats: 50 Cover: 250 Floodlights: Yes

Clubhouse: Open Tuesday, Thursday, Saturday plus functions

HONOURS Norfolk Snr Cup (2), Anglian Comb. 89-90 (Div 1 88-89)
Jewson Divison 1 Champions 00-01

PREVIOUS Leagues: Dereham, Anglian Combination

RECORD Attendance: 250 v Downham Town, Eastern Co's League Cup 3/9/91

THETFORD TOWN

Secretary: Bob Richards, 60 Nunnery Drive, Thetford, Norfolk IP243EN
Tel Nos: 01842 764282 (H) 01284 701121 (W)
Email Address: omwgh@lineone.net

Ground: Recreation Ground, Mundford Road, Thetford, Norfolk Tel: 01842 766120

Directions: Off bypass (A11) at A143 junction - ground 800yds next to sports ground

Capacity: 2,000 **Seats:** 400 **Cover:** 400 Floodlights: Yes

Clubhouse: Bar, teas, refreshments, light meals & snacks **Club Shop:** No

HONOURS Eastern Co's Lg R-up 89-90, Norfolk & Suffolk Lg 54-55;
Norfolk Senior Cup 47-48 90-91

PREVIOUS Leagues: Norfolk & Suffolk **Grounds:** None

RECORD Attendance: 394 v Diss Town, Norfolk Snr Cup 91

Players progressing: Dick Scott (Norwich C.), Kevin Seggie (Leeds U.),Simon Milton (Ipswich T.)

Local Press: Thetford & Watton Times, Bury Free Press

TIPTREE UNITED

Secretary:	John Wisbey, 103 Peace Road, Stanway, Colchester, Essex
	Tel Nos: 01206 564222 (H) 07703 585814 (M)
	Email: johnwisbey@tiptreeunited.com
Ground:	Chapel Road, Tiptree, Essex Tel: 01621 815213
Directions:	Enter town on B1023 - Chapel Road is left at second crossroads,
	ground 200yds on left. 3 miles from Kelverdon (BR).
	Served by Eastern NationalColchester to Maldon bus
Capacity:	2,500 Seats: 150 Cover: 300 Floodlights: Yes
Clubhouse:	Open daily 7-11pm (all day Fri & Sat) & 12-2.30, 7-10.30 Sun.
	Large bar, two snooker tables, pool, darts, netball, badminton, pigeon club,
	bingo. Dance hall seats 180, small hall seats 60. Club Shop: No
HONOURS	Essex Snr Tphy 80-81, Eastern Co's Lg 81-82 (Lg Cup 81-82 84-85),
	Essex Snr Lg R-up 75-76 77-78, Harwich Charity Cup (4),
	Jewson Eastern Div 1 Champions 99-00 and F.A.Vase Finalists 2001-2002
PREVIOUS	Leagues: Essex & Suffolk Border; Essex Senior 78-84
RECORD	Attendance: 1,920 for F.A.Vase Semi-Final v AFC Sudbury 2002

FACT FILE

Founded: 1933   Nickname:The Jam -Makers
Sponsors: Gralostar
Colours: Red& blackstripes/black/black
Change colours: Yellow/blue/white
Midweek Matchday: Tuesday
Reserves:Ridgeons Reserve League
Programme: 32 pages, £1 Editor: Secretary
Local Press : Colchester Evening Gazette,
Essex County Standard'
Essex Pitch of the Year & Southern R-up
Website: www.tiptreeunited.com
CLUB PERSONNEL
Chairman: Ed Garty   President: Peter Fidge
Manager:Jody Brown Captain: Mark Emerson
2004-2005
Top Goalscorer: Terry Warwick
P.O.Y. Gavin Armitage

WALSHAM-LE WILLOWS

Secretary:	Keith Crabbe,4 Staple Close, Walsham le Willows, Bury St Edmunds, Suffolk
	IP31 3DB Tel Nos: 01359 259490 (H) 07979 771303 (M)
Ground:	Walsham Sports Club, Summer Road, Walsham-le-Willows, Suffolk IP31 3AH
	Tel No: 01359 259298
Directions:	From Bury - Diss road (A143) turn off down Summer Lane in Walsham -le -
	Willows and ground is on the right
Clubhouse:	Yes

Previous Leagues: Bury & District (Founder Members), Suffolk & Ipswich (1989-05)

Honours: Suffolk Senior Cup Winners 2005-2006 R-Up 2004-05,
            Suffolk Junior Cup 1987-88 1988-89 1989-90 R-Up 1973-74

FACT FILE

Formed 1888

Colours: Blue & Yellow/blue/blue

Change colours:Red & black/red/red

Midweek Matches: Wednesdays

CLUB PERSONNEL

Chairman: Mike Powles (07971 613933)

Manager: Paul Smith

Programme Editor: Chairman

Website: www.walshamlewillowsfc.co.uk

WHITTON UNITED

Secretary: Phil Pemberton,10 Coleridge Road, Ipswich 1P8 4EX
Tel Nos: 01473462618 (H) 07931 735148 (M)
Ground: King George V Playing Field, Old Norwich Road, Ipswich, Suffolk. Tel: 01473 464030

Directions: Turn off A14, junction A1156 approx 3 miles west of A12/A14junction
Capacity: 600 Seats: No   Cover: 100   Floodlights: Yes
Club Shop: No
Clubhouse: Licensed Bar. Hot & Cold Food available

HONOURS	Suffolk Senior Cup 58-59 62-63 92-93; Suffolk & Ipswich Lge 46-47 47-48
	65-66 67-68 91-92 92-93, Jewson Fairplay Trophy 96-97, 97-98
PREVIOUS	Leagues: Suffolk & Ipswich Grounds: Old Norwich Rd, Ipswich
RECORD	Attendance: 528 v Ipswich Town 29/11/95
	League 244 v Ipswich Wanderers13/1/96

FACT FILE

Formed: 1926   Nickname: None
Sponsors: Speedyhire
Colours: Green/Green/whiten
Change colours:Yellow/Yellow/Black
Midweek Matches: Tuesday
Programme: 24pages- 50p
Editor: John Green 014736 742920 (H)
CLUB PERSONNEL
Chairman: Jeff Crane President: Russell
Woodward
Fixture Sec: Alan Elliott (01473 461931)
Manager: Ronnie Mauge

ESSEX SENIOR LEAGUE

Chairman & Press Officer: Robert Errington
Secretary: David Walls, 2 Hillsfield Cottage, Layer, Breton,
Essex CO2 0PS.   Tel & Fax: 01206 330146
Email: EssexSer@wallsd.freeserve.co.uk

		P	W	D	L	F	A	Pts
1.	AFC Hornchurch	30	25	3	2	71	21	78
2.	Waltham Abbey	30	18	6	6	64	28	60
3.	Tilbury	30	16	7	7	63	37	55
4.	Barkingside	30	15	10	5	44	30	55
5.	Burnham Ramblers	30	15	9	6	72	44	54
6.	Sawbridgeworth Town	30	12	11	7	47	28	47
7.	Concord Rangers	30	14	5	11	36	32	47
8.	Brentwood Town	30	11	7	12	46	41	40
9.	London APSA	30	7	11	12	36	52	32
10.	Southend Manor	30	9	5	16	37	57	32
11.	Basildon United (-1)	30	8	8	14	47	76	31
12	Romford	30	6	11	13	38	54	29
13.	Eton Manor	30	6	8	16	35	57	26
14.	Hullbridge Sports	30	6	7	17	38	60	25
15.	Bowers & Pitsea	30	7	4	19	36	65	25
16.	Stansted	30	5	8	17	31	59	23

		1	2	3	4	5	6	7	8	9	10	11	12	13	14	15	16
1	AFC Hornchurch		1-0	3-0	3-1	4-1	4-0	3-3	3-0	4-1	1-0	3-0	1-0	2-0	1-2	1-1	1-0
2	Barkingside	1-4		3-0	1-0	2-1	1-4	1-0	3-2	3-1	1-1	2-0	1-1	4-0	2-2	2-2	0-0
3	Basildon United	2-4	0-2		4-3	2-1	1-6	0-3	2-2	2-2	1-4	2-1	2-2	1-2	4-2	3-2	0-3
4	Bowers & Pitsea	0-1	1-3	0-2		0-3	1-0	1-2	2-4	3-2	1-1	2-0	1-4	1-4	2-1	1-1	0-1
5	Brentwood Town	0-3	2-0	0-2	2-2		1-3	1-0	3-0	2-2	4-1	4-1	0-3	3-0	4-0	1-2	3-0
6	Burnham Ramblers	2-3	3-0	5-2	5-3	1-1		2-0	1-2	3-2	4-1	1-1	0-0	7-1	2-3	3-1	2-1
7	Concord Rangers	0-1	0-1	0-2	2-0	2-0	1-3		0-0	2-1	0-2	0-0	1-0	2-0	0-0	0-1	4-3
8	Eton Manor	1-2	0-1	3-1	3-3	0-2	1-1	0-4		0-0	1-0	1-1	0-2	1-4	2-2	1-4	1-3
9	Hullbridge Sports	0-4	0-2	6-2	1-0	1-1	2-2	2-1	1-3		2-1	3-1	2-2	0-2	0-1	0-1	2-5
10	London APSA	2-2	0-0	4-4	3-1	2-0	1-1	0-1	2-2	2-1		1-1	0-1	1-2	2-2	0-1	0-4
11	Romford	0-2	2-3	2-2	0-2	2-2	2-2	1-3	3-2	3-0	0-0		1-1	1-1	4-1	1-3	1-1
12	Sawbridgeworth Town	1-3	0-0	1-1	4-1	0-0	3-1	0-1	1-0	3-0	1-1	3-2		5-0	1-0	0-1	4-1
13	Southend Manor	1-3	1-1	3-1	0-2	0-2	1-1	1-2	0-2	0-1	1-2	1-2	1-1		4-1	2-1	1-0
14	Stansted	0-2	1-3	2-2	0-1	1-1	0-2	0-1	1-0	2-2	0-1	0-1	2-1	1-1		2-3	0-3
15	Tilbury	1-2	1-1	5-0	3-1	3-0	3-4	1-1	2-0	2-1	8-1	1-2	2-2	2-0	4-2		1-3
16	Waltham Abbey	1-0	0-0	0-0	5-0	2-1	1-1	5-0	3-1	1-0	4-0	5-2	2-0	4-3	3-0	0-0	

L E A G U E   C U P

GROUP A	P	W	D	L	F	A	Pts
Brentwood Town	6	3	1	2	8	8	10
Burnham Ramblers	6	3	0	3	14	8	9
Southend Manor	6	2	2	2	6	9	8
Sawbridgeworth Town	6	2	1	3	7	10	7

GROUP C	P	W	D	L	F	A	Pts
AFC Hornchurch	6	6	0	0	23	6	18
Tilbury	6	3	0	3	12	9	9
Hullbridge Sports	6	2	1	3	10	17	7
London APSA	6	0	1	5	5	18	1

GROUP B	P	W	D	L	F	A	Pts
Eton Manor	6	3	1	2	9	5	10
Romford	6	2	2	2	6	4	8
Stansted	6	2	2	2	5	9	8
Bowers & Pitsea	6	2	1	3	5	7	7

GROUP D	P	W	D	L	F	A	Pts
Barkingside	6	3	2	1	9	6	11
Basildon United	6	2	2	2	7	6	8
Concord Rangers	6	2	2	2	7	7	8
Waltham Abbey (H)	6	1	2	3	5	9	5

QUARTER-FINALS - 1st leg

Romford	v	Barkingside	2-0
Tilbury	v	AFC Hornchurch	2-2
Basildon United	v	Burnham Ramblers	0-2
Brentwood Town	v	Eton Manor	1-0

QUARTER-FINALS - 2nd leg

Barkingside	v	Romford	2-1
AFC Hornchurch	v	Tilbury	1-0
Burnham Ramblers	v	Basildon United	1-0
Eton Manor	v	Brentwood Town	0-5

SEMI-FINALS - 2nd leg

BurnhamRamblers	v	Brentwood Town	1-2
Romford	v	AFC Hornchurch	AW

SEMI-FINALS - 1st leg

Brentwood Town	v	Burnham Ramblers	0-0
AFC Hornchurch	v	Romford	1-0

THE FINAL

AFC Hornchurch	v	Brentwood Town	2-0

LEAGUE CONSTITUTION 2006-07

BARKING

Formed: 1880
Nickname: THe Blues

Chairman: Dennis Elliott   **Manager:** Jay Devereaux   **Coach:** Ashley Marsh   **Physio:** Paul Baskin
Secretary: Anthony Mercer, 97a Ravensbourne Gardens, Ilford, Essex IG5 0XQ Tel No: 0208 551 3995
Press Officer & Programme Editor: Derek Pedder   **Programme:**   £1.00
GROUND ADDRESS: Mayesbrook Park, Lodge Avenue, Dagenham RM8 2JR **Tel:** 0208 595 6511
Capacity: 2,500   **Seats:** 200   **Covered:** 600   **Floodlights:** Yes
Simple Directions: Off A13 on A1153 (Lodge Avenue) and ground one mile on lft. Buses 5 or 87 to Lodge Avenue. Barking BR
or Upney (tube)   **Website:** www.barking-fc.co.uk
Midweek Home Matchday: Tuesday   **Club Shop:** Manager Brad Robinson   **Clubhouse:** Yes
Previous Names: Barking Rovers,Barking Woodville, Barking Institute, Barking Town, Barking & West Ham United,
Previous Leagues: Athenian, Isthmian and Southern
Previous Grounds: Eastbury Field, Kennedy Estate,Movers Lane, Barking Recreation, Merry Fiddlers and Vicarage Field (73)
Club Colours: Royal Blue and White   **Player of the Year:** Tony Tucker   **Captain:** Tony Tucker
Top Scorer: Wayne Vaughan
BEST PERFORMANCES
League: Isthmian League Champions 78-79 **F.A. Cup:** 2nd Round Replay 1981-1982   **F.A.Vase:** 5th Round 1996-1997
RECORD Attendance: 1,972 v Aldershot F.A.Cup 2nd Rd 1938 **Goalscorer:**Neville Fox 241 (65-73)**Apps:** Bob Makin 566
SENIOR HONOURS: F.A.Amateur Cup Finalists 1926-27, Isthmian League Champions 1978-79Athenian League 34-35
London Senior Cup (4) Runners-Up (3) Essex Senior Cup (7) R-Up (8)

BARKINGSIDE

Formed:1898
Nickname:

Chairman: John Taylor   **Manager:** Rod Stringer
Secretary: JohnTaylor, 2 Courage Close, Hornchurch,Essex RM11 2BJ Tel No: 01708 456373
Press Officer: Name (Tel)   **Programme:** Price   **Editor:** John Taylor
GROUND ADDRESS: Oakside, Station Road, Barkingside, Ilford, Essex   **Tel:** 020 8550 3611
Capacity: 3,000   **Seats:** 350   **Covered:** 850   **Floodlights:**Yes
Simple Directions: From London A12 Eastern Ave to Green Gate, left to Hurns Rd and into Barkingside. Right to Craven
Gardens. Right to Carlton Drive and into Station Rd. Ground on right next to Barkingside station.
Midweek Home Matchday: Monday   **Clubhouse:** Sun 1-12 pm.Match nights 6.30-11pm   **Club Shop:** No
RECORD Attendance: 957 v Arsenal Res, London Lg. 1957
SENIOR HONOURS: Spartan Lg 96-97, R-up 90-91, London Senior Cup 96-97, Gt London Lg 64-65, S.S.Mid Sp.Prem 98-99
Previous Leagues: Ilford & District 1898-1925, Ilford Minor 44-47 ,South Essex 47-48, Walthamstow 48-50, London 50-64
Greater London 64-71,Metropolitan-London 71-75 Spartan 76-96, Spartan South Midlands 1996-99 and Essex Senior 1999.
Club Colours: Sky Blue/Navy Blue/Navy   **Change Colours:** All Red

BASILDON UNITED

Founded: 1963
Nickname:

Chairman: Dennis Taylor   **President:**J.Oakes   **Manager:** John Doyle

Secretary: Marc Day, 1 Geary Drive,Brentwood, Essex CM14 4UH Tel No: 01277 229566 (H) 07958004858 (M)

Press Officer: Frank Ford (07789 534174)   **Programme:** 16 Pages Price £1.00 **Editor:** Secretary

GROUND ADDRESS: Gardiners Close, Gardiners Lane, Basildon, Essex SS14 3AW   **Tel:** 01268 520268

Capacity: 2,000   **Seats:**400   **Covered:1,000**   **Floodlights:Yes**

Simple Directions:A176 off A127, left at round't into Cranes Farm Rd.Left at lights then Gardiners Close is first left.

Midweek Home Matchday: Wednesday   **Clubhouse:** Open lunchtimes, evenings and week ends **Club Shop:** No

RECORD Attendance: 4,000 v West Ham. Ground opening 11.8.70   **Goalscorer:**   **Apps:**

SENIOR HONOURS: Isthmian Div 2 83-84 Essex Sen: (5)Lg Cup (3) Essex Senior Trophy 78-79

Previous Name: Armada Sports   **Previous League(s):** Grays & Thurrock, Greater London 68-70, Essex Senior 70-80, Athenian 80-81, Isthmian 81-91

Club Colours: Amber & Black stripes/Black/Black   **Change Colours:** Grey and silver

Brentwood Town   Photo: Alan Coomes.

BEAUMONT ATHLETIC

Founded: 1993
Nickname:

Chairman: M T Hussein   **Manager:** Mamun Chowdury   **Asst. Manager:** Astab Miah

Director of Football: Jim Reeves. Tel: 0207 791 1182. **Coach:** Gibran Chenia

GROUND ADDRESS: Mile End Stadium, Rhodeswell Road, London E14 7TW   **Tel:** 07779 245 922

Simple Directions: From M2/A2 continue onto A102 through Blackwell Tunnel. Left onto A13 towards centre of London and right into Burdett Road (A1205) then left at the second set of lights into St Pauls Way leading onto Rhodeswell Road. Ground is on right.

Previous Ground: **Previous League(s):** Surya Basmati League, Asian League.

BOWERS & PITSEA

Founded: 1946
Nickname:

Chairman: Barry Hubbard   **Vive Chairman:** Bert Warner   **Manager:** Marc Massey

Secretary: Lee Stevens, 59 Cross Green,Lee Chapel South, Basildon, Essex SS165Q (07910 626727)

Programme: 30 Pages - £1.00 Price   **Editor** Lee Stevens

Website: www.bowersandpitseafc.netfirms.com

GROUND ADDRESS: Len Salmon Stadium, Crown Avenue, Off Kenneth Rd., Pitsea, Basildon   **Tel:** 01268 452068

Capacity: 2,000   **Seats:** 200   **Covered:** 1,000   **Floodlights:**Yes

Simple Directions: At Pitsea Broadway (B1464) turn into Rectory Rd and then into Kenneth Rd.Crown Avenue is at top.

Midweek Home Matchday: Wenesday   **Clubhouse:** Open every night   **Club Shop:** Yes

RECORD Attendance: 1,800 v Billericay Town F.A.Vase

SENIOR HONOURS:

Previous Ground: Gun Meadow, Pitsea.   **Previous League(s):** Thurrock& Thameside Combination and Olympian League

Club Colours: All Claret   **Change Colours:** All Sky Blue

BRENTWOOD TOWN

Founded: 1955
Nickname:Blues

Chairman: John Edgeworth   **Manager:** Andy MacDonald

Secretary: Ray Stevens, Woodside, 7 Woodlands Aveue, Hornchurch, Essex RM11 2 QT (07768 006370)

E-Mail: info@brentwoodtownfc.co.uk   **Programme:** 50p **Editor:** Ken Hobbs Website:www.brentwoodtownfc.co.uk

GROUND ADDRESS: Brentwood Centre, Donninghurst Rd, Brentwood, Essex.Tel No:01277 215151 Ext 713

Capcity:1,000   **Seats:** 50   **Covered:** 100   **Floodlights:** Yes

Simple Directions: From High St. (Wilson's Corner) turn north into Ongar Rd then third mini roundabout right into Donninghurst Road.

Midweek Home Matchday: Tuesday   **Clubhouse:** Open Tues,Thurs evenings and matchdays. **Club Shop:** No

SENIOR HONOURS:

Previous Name(s): Manor Ath, Brentwood Ath.Brentwood F.C.   **Previous League(s):** Romford & Dist.,South Essex Comb.,

Club Colours: Sky Blue /Navy Blue   **Change Colours:** All Yellow   London & Essex Border,Olympian

BURNHAM RAMBLERS

Founded:
Nickname:

Chairman: William Hannan   **President:** Ron Hatcher   **Manager:** Derek Robinson

Secretary: Shaun Pugh, 6 The Chase, South Woodham Ferrers, Essex CM3 5PN   **Tel No:** 07770676727

Club Website: www.burnhamramblersfc.co.uk **Programme**: 32 pages £1.00   **Editor:** Martin Leno (Tel)

GROUND ADDRESS: Leslie Fields Stadium, Springfield Rd., Burnham on Cr. CM0 8TE   **Tel No:** 01621 784383

Capacity: 2.000   **Seats:**156   **Covered:** 300   **Floodlights:**Yes

Simple Directions: B1010 from South Woodham Ferrers Rt turn 1/2 mile before town

Midweek Home Matchday: Tuesday   **Clubhouse:** Mon-Fri 7-11pm Sat: 12-11 Sun: 12-5pm **Club Shop:** No

RECORD Attendance:1,500 vArsenal (Opening stand)

SENIOR HONOURS: Olympian Lg 65-66 Harry Fisher Memorial Trophy 96-97 Sportsmanship Award 96-97

Essex Senior League Runners-Up 2004-2005

Previous Leagues: N.Essex, Mid-Essex, Olympian, S.E.Essex   **Previous Grounds:** Wick Rd., Millfields and Saltcourts

Club Colours: Sky Blue/Black/Sky Blue   **Change Colours:** Red/White/Blue

CLAPTON

Founded: 1878
Nickname:Tons

Chairman: T.B.A.   **Chief Executive:** Vince McBean   **Manager:** Rod Clarke

Secretary: Colin Walton, 2 Mansfield Road, Ilford, Essex 1G1 3AZ   **Asst.Manager**: Colin Walton

Programme Editor: Barbara Walton   **Programme:** 12 Pages £1.00

GROUND ADDRESS: The Old Spotted Dog, Upton Lane, Forest Gate, Lonon E7 9NP   **Tel:** 0208 4720822

Capacity: 2,000   **Seats:** 100   **Covered:** 180   **Floodlights:** Yes

Simple Directions: BR to Forest Gate. Tube to Plaistow (District Line). Docklands Light Railway to Prince Regent then 325 bus to ground.

Midweek Home Matchday: Tuesday   **Clubhouse:** Match days and function rooms to hire.   **Club Shop:** No

Previous Leagues: Southern 1894-96 (founder members) London 1898-97

Club Colours: Red & white stripes/black/black   **Change Colours:** Yellow/black/black

LAST SEASON: League: 16th   **F.A. Cup:** Extra Prelim. Rd.   **F.A. Vase:** 2nd Qualifying Rd.

Top Scorer: Adrian Sterling   **Player of the Year:** Adam Sturdy   **Captain:** Adam Sturdy

BEST PERFORMANCES

League: Isthmian Champions (2) **F.A. Cup:** 3rd Rd Proper 25-26 **F.A.Vase:**   **F.A.Amateur Cup :** Winnners (5)

RECORD Attendance: 12,000 v Tottenham Hotspur F.A.Cup 1898-99   **Goalscorer:**   **Apps:**

Senior Honours: F.A.Amateur Cup 06-07 08-09 14-15 23-24 24-25 R-up 04-05 Isthmian League Champions: 10-11 22-23 Runners -up: 05-06 07-08 09-10 24-25 Div 2 82-83 London Senior Cup (2) Essex Senior Cup (4) London Charity Cup, Essex Senior Trophy. Clapton were the first English club to play on the continent, beating a Belgian Select XI at Easter 1890.

CONCORD RANGERS

Founded: 1967
Nickname:

Chairman: Antony Smith — **Manager:** Eddie Crace

Secretary: Chris Crerie, The Clubhouse, Thames Road, Canvey Island, Essex SS8 0HH (0790952 8818)

Website: www.concordrangersfc.co.uk — **Programme:** 20 Pages 50p — **Ed:** Secretary

GROUND ADDRESS: Thames Road, Canvey Island, Essex. — **Tel:** 01268 691780/515750

Capacity: 1,500 — **Seats:** Yes — **Covered:** Yes — **Floodlights:** Yes

Simple Directions: A 130 onto Canvey Island. Turn right into Thorney Bay Road. Then right again into Thames Road.

Midweek Home Matchday: Tuesday — **Clubhouse:** Yes — **Club Shop:** No

RECORD Attendance: 1,500 v Lee Chapel North F.A.Sunday Cup 89-90 **Goalscorer:** **Apps:**

SENIOR HONOURS: Essex Senior Lg.97-8 03-04, R-Up 02-03, Lg Cup: 96-7, Southend & District Lg & cup 84-85, Southend Alliance Lg& Cup 87-8 and Wirral Programme Award 93-94

Previous Leagues: Southend & Dist., Essex Intermediate(pre 1991) — **Previous Ground:** Waterside

Club Colours: Yellow& Blue/Blue/Yellow — **Change Colours:** Red/Black/red

ETON MANOR

Founded: 1901
Nickname: The Manor

Chairman: Reg Curtis — **Manager:** Kirk Whitelock

Secretary: Larry McDonald, 20 Heynes Rd., Dagenham, Essex. RM8 2SX Tel No: 0208 5902863

General Manager: Alex Lee — **Programme:** 12 pages with entry — **Editor** Secretary

GROUND ADDRESS: Groundsharing with Tilbury F.C. (01375 843093)

Capacity: 1.000 — **Seats:** 60 — **Covered:** 60 — **Floodlights:** Yes

Simple Directions: As for Tilbury F.C. (Ryman League)

Midweek Home Matchday: Tuesday — **Clubhouse:** Yes — **Club Shop:** No

RECORD Attendance: 600 v Leyton Orient. Opening floodlights **Goalscorer:** Dave Sams **Appearances:**

SENIOR HONOURS: Essex Sen.Cp R-Up 37-8, London Lg (4), Lg Cup 55-6, Gt London Lg 64-5,.Essex Lg Sportsmanship 76

Previous Leagues: London 33-59, Aetolean 59-64, Gt London 64-69 Metropolitan 69-75 **Previous Name(s):** Wildernes Leyton

Club Colours: Sky/Navy/Navy — **Change Colours:** Yellow /Navy/Sky

HULLBRIDGE SPORTS

Founded: 1945
Nickname:

Chairman: Robin Ogilvie — **Manager:** Steve Davidson

Secretary: Mrs Beryl Petre , 58 Grasmere Avenue, Hull bridge, Essex SS5 6LF Tel No: 01702 230630 **(H)** 01702 230420 (M)

Website: www.sportsworldwide.co.uk — **Programme:** Yes

GROUND ADDRESS: Lower Road, Hullbridge, Hockley, Essex ss5 6BJ Tel No: 01702 230420

Capacity: 1,500 — **Seats:** 60 — **Covered:** 60 — **Floodlights:** Yes

Simple Directions: From A130 turn into Rawreth Lane down to mini roundabout ,left across next mini-roundabout up hill. Ground signed on right just past garage.

Midweek Home Matchday: Tuesday — **Clubhouse:** Lounge bar,function hall with bar — **Club Shop:** No

RECORD Attendance: 800 v Blackburn R. F.A.Youth Cup 99-00 **Goalscorer:** **Apps:**

SENIOR HONOURS:

Previous Leagues: Southend & District, Southend Alliance — **Previous Ground:** Pooles Lane Recreation

Club Colours: Royal Blue & White/blue/white — **Change Colours:** Red & white/black/black

LONDON APSA

Founded:
Nickname:

Chairman: Zulfi Ali — **Manager:** John Higley

Secretary: Zabir Bashir,145 Caistor Park Road, Stratford, London E15 3PR

Tel No; 07956 660699 (M)

Programme Editor: Zabeer Khan (07958046181)

GROUND ADDRESS: Terrance McMillan Stadium, Newham Leisure Centre, 281 Prince Regent Lane, Plaistow, London E13 8SD tel Nos: 0207 511 4477 and Fax 0207 511 6463

Capacity: 4.000 — **Seats:** 400 — **Covered:** 400 — **Floodlights:** Yes

Simple Directions: Nearest Station: Plaistow (District Line) and Stage Coach No.147

Midweek Home Matchday: Tuesday — **Clubhouse:** — **Club Shop:**

Previous League: London Intermediate League>2003

Club Colours: All Blue — **Change Colours:** Yellow/blue/yellow

Concord Rangers.   Photo: Alan Coomes.

ROMFORD (2002)

Founded: 1992
Nickname:The Boro

Chairman: Steve Gardener   **Manager:** Mark Reed
Secretary: Colin Ewenson , 71 Riverside Rd., Romford RM5 2NR Tel No: 07973 717 075
Press Officer: Steve Gardner   **Programme:** 40 pages £1.20
GROUND ADDRESS: Ford Sports & Social; Club,Rush Green Rd., Romford, RM5 2NR   **Tel No:** 01708 745678
Capacity:2.500   **Seats:** 175   **Covered:** 300   **Floodlights:**
Simple Directions:
Midweek Home Matchday: Tuesday   **Clubhouse:** Yes   **Club Shop:** No
RECORD Attendance:820 v Leatherhead (Isth Lg 2)   **Goalscorer:** Danny Benstocks **Apps:** S.Horne 234
Senior Honours: Essex Sen. 95-96 Lg Cup 95-96 Isthmian Div 2 96-97 East Anglian Cup 97-8
Previous Grounds: Hornchurch 92-95 Ford Utd: 95-96 Sungate 96-01 **Previous Leagues:** Essex Sen 92-96 Isthmian 96-02
Club Colours: All blue with two gold hoops   **Change Colours:** All white with two white hoops.
BEST PERFORMANCES
League: Champions 95-96   **F.A. Cup:** 4th Qual Rd 97-8 99-00   **F.A.Vase:** 5th Rd 96-7

Eton Manor   Photo: Alan Coomes.

SAWBRIDGEWORTH TOWN

Founded: 1890
Nickname: Robins

Chairman: Steve Day   **President:** Ron Alder   **Manager:**Don Watters

Secretary: Mrs Leslie Atkins, 41 The Orchards, Sawbridgeworth CM 21 0DE Tel No: 07973 717075

Programme Editor: Ron Aider(01279 722360)

GROUND ADDRESS: Crofters End, West Road, Sawbridgeorth, Herts CM21 0DE   **Tel No: 01279 722039**

Capcity:2.500   **Seats:**175   **Covered:** 300   **Floodlights:**Yes

Simple Directions: Just under a mile from BR station. Up station road and into West Road.

Midweek Home Matchday: Tuesday   **Clubhouse:** Yes   **Club Shop:** No

RECORD Attendance: 610 v Bishops Stortford

SENIOR HONOURS: Essex Olympian 71-72, Essex Sen R-up 92-3 94-5 Spartan 36-53, Herts Sen Trophy 90-1 93

Previous Grounds: Hyde Hall, Pishobury, Hand & Crown. **Previous Leagues:** Essex Olympian, Spartan 36-53

Club Colours: Red & Black Stripes /Black/Black   **Change Colours:** Sky Blue & White

SOUTHEND MANOR

Founded: 1955
Nickname: The Manor

Chairman: Robert Westley   **Vice-Chairman:** Geoff Gorham   **Manager:** Steve Sinnett

Secretary: Steve Durrant, 11 Clayton Rd., Southend On Sea. Tel No: 01702 301572   **Sponsor**: Info-Line

Press Officer/Prog.Ed.: Chris Hunt Tel No: 01702 615897 **Programme:** 10 Pages -50p

GROUND ADDRESS: Southchurch Park Arena, Lifstan Way, Southend 0n Sea   **Tel No:** 01702 615577

Capcity: 2,000   **Seats:** 500   **Covered:** 700   **Floodlights:** Yes

Simple Directions: Take A1159 off A127 and turn right after a mile at 2nd roundabout by Invisible Man pub. Then due South for a mile and ground is on right near sea front.

Midweek Home Matchday: Tuesday   **Clubhouse:** Open every evening   **Club Shop:** No

RECORD Attendance: 1,521 v Southend United 22.7.91 opening floodlights.   **Goalscorer:**   **Apps:**

SENIOR HONOURS: Essex Senior Trophy 92-3, Essex Sen.Lg: 90-1, R-up: 99-00, League Cup 87-8 Essex Sen Cup 01-02

Previous Leagues: Southend Borough Combination and Southend Alliance **Previous Grounds:** Victoria Spts &Oakwood Rec

Club Colours: Yellow/Black/yellow   **Change Colours:** All white

STANSTED

Founded: 1902
Nickname: Blues

Chairman: Terry Shoebridge   **President:** Bob Marin   **Manager:** Alan Penfold

Secretary: Terry Shoebridge, 2 Dawson Close, Saffron Walden, Essex CB10 2AR   Tel No:01799 527937

General Manager: Tony Mercer   **Programme editor:** Dave Ryan   **Sponsor:**BBI Medical Locums

GROUND ADDRESS: Hargrave Park, Cambridge Road, Stanstead, Essex CB10 2AR   **Tel:** 01279 812897

Capcity:2,000   **Seats:** 200   **Covered:** 400   **Floodlights:** Yes

Simple Directions: Nearest Station: Stansted MountFitchet (ER) or Bus Route 301 from Bishops Stortford

Midweek Home Matchday: Tuesday   **Clubhouse:** Matchdays until 11pm   **Club Shop:** No

RECORD Attendance:828 v Whickham (F.A.Vase 83-84)

SENIOR HONOURS:

Previous Leagues: Spartan, London, Herts County   **Previous Grounds:** Greens Meadow and Chapel Hill

Club Colours: Blue/Blue/White   **Change Colours:** Yellow & Black/Black/ Yellow

arena
SEATING

AFFORDABLE SEATING FOR SALE

Take a Seat!

from our broad range of seating products

From 50 to 50,000... Arena Seating have the solution

Arena Seating has invested in the design and development of a comprehensive range of tiered seating products, which provide solutions for the smallest to the very largest of clubs, venues and clients.

From bespoke designed covered and uncovered stands for larger venues, to our LT Portastand that is aimed at smaller local clubs and is delivered on a truck fully assembled, we have a product range to suit every seating requirement.

Contact us to see how we can enhance your venue.

WWW.ARENASEATING.COM

Arena Seating
Arena House Membury Lambourn Woodlands Hungerford Berkshire RG17 7TQ
T. 01488 67 48 00 **W.** www.arenaseating.com **E.** info@arenaseating.com

PART OF THE ARENA GROUP

HELLENIC LEAGUE

SPONSORED BY: **SPORT ITALIA**
Founded: 1953
Patron: Sir Henry Cooper OBE, KSG. (2001)
Chairman: Michael Broadley
Secretary: Brian King, 83 Queens Road, Carterton, Oxon OX18 3YF
Tel: 01993 212738 **Fax:** 01993 212775 **E-mail:** office@hellenicleague.co.uk

PREMIER DIVISION		P	W	D	L	F	A	Pts
1.	Didcot Town	40	34	3	3	124	31	105
2.	Bishops Cleeve	40	29	5	6	108	45	92
3.	Abingdon United	40	27	3	10	88	40	84
4.	North Leigh	40	25	6	9	78	40	81
5.	Slimbridge	40	24	6	10	90	45	78
6.	Witney United	40	23	4	13	88	51	73
7.	Carterton	40	23	3	14	73	51	72
8.	Shrivenham (1st Div.1W. 04-05)	40	22	5	13	82	58	71
9.	Wantage Town	40	19	7	14	73	70	64
10.	Ardley United	40	18	6	16	70	63	60
11.	Milton United	40	14	9	17	62	69	51
12.	Highworth Town (Champions 04-05)	40	13	10	17	62	72	49
13	Pegasus Juniors	40	12	11	17	53	74	47
14.	Almondsbury Town	40	13	6	21	50	64	45
15.	Shortwood United	40	12	6	22	55	79	42
16.	Hungerford Town	40	11	8	21	31	65	41
17.	Fairford Town	40	11	6	23	42	73	39
18.	Abingdon Town	40	9	10	21	45	88	37
19.	Chipping Norton Town	40	6	7	27	43	99	25
20.	Kidlington (3rd Div.1 W. 04-05)	40	7	1	32	42	108	22
21.	Henley Town	40	5	4	31	28	102	19

PREMIER DIVISION	1	2	3	4	5	6	7	8	9	10	11	12	13	14	15	16	17	18	19	20	21
1 Abingdon Town		0-5	0-2	0-3	1-3	1-3	1-0	1-2	4-2	1-1	0-0	1-0	1-0	2-2	1-3	1-1	2-2	1-2	2-2	0-0	1-6
2 Abingdon United	1-0		0-1	2-3	1-2	1-0	0-2	1-3	3-1	4-0	5-1	0-0	3-0	0-2	1-1	3-1	2-0	4-1	2-1	3-1	1-0
3 Almondsbury Town	1-1	2-4		0-1	0-1	0-1	4-4	1-0	3-0	2-1	1-2	0-1	3-1	0-0	1-1	3-3	0-3	2-0	0-1	3-1	1-3
4 Ardley United	6-3	2-2	2-0		1-2	0-2	5-1	3-5	1-1	3-0	2-2	2-3	3-0	0-0	1-0	1-0	0-1	1-4	2-0	1-2	0-1
5 Bishops Cleeve	7-0	1-5	2-0	4-2		3-2	5-1	1-1	3-0	4-1	5-0	1-0	6-2	3-1	3-0	3-0	1-2	1-4	3-2	2-2	
6 Carterton	3-0	0-1	4-2	2-1	2-1		3-0	2-1	2-0	2-1	2-1	4-1	3-2	0-2	0-3	0-1	4-0	2-2	0-5	0-1	0-2
7 Chipping Norton Town	0-3	2-3	0-2	0-2	2-8	1-6		0-3	2-2	2-1	0-1	3-1	2-0	5-1	0-3	1-1	0-2	1-1	1-4	1-1	0-2
8 Didcot Town	4-0	3-1	4-0	4-1	1-1	3-1	3-0		5-0	4-0	0-0	3-0	3-2	6-1	1-0	7-0	5-3	3-0	2-0	5-1	4-0
9 Fairford Town	3-1	1-0	2-3	1-2	1-5	2-0	2-1	0-1		0-1	0-0	0-1	2-1	0-2	0-3	3-1	0-2	1-2	2-1	2-2	0-2
10 Henley Town	0-3	0-3	1-2	0-4	1-5	0-2	0-0	0-2	0-2		2-1	0-1	5-1	1-4	1-3	1-1	1-4	0-1	0-2	0-4	2-3
11 Highworth Town	4-2	1-3	1-1	1-1	1-2	1-4	1-1	1-3	2-1	4-0		2-1	6-0	2-1	1-0	0-4	7-0	1-4	2-2	0-4	1-2
12 Hungerford Town	0-0	0-1	2-1	1-3	1-1	1-2	3-1	1-2	0-0	2-2	1-0		1-0	0-0	0-1	1-1	2-0	0-2	2-0	3-1	0-4
13 Kidlington	0-1	0-3	0-1	1-3	3-1	0-1	3-0	2-4	3-1	2-0	2-3	0-0		0-4	0-4	2-1	0-4	1-5	0-6	1-3	2-1
14 Milton United	0-1	1-3	1-0	2-3	1-2	1-1	2-1	1-3	6-2	2-0	0-3	3-0	1-4		1-2	3-5	0-0	4-1	1-1	2-3	0-3
15 North Leigh	3-2	2-0	4-1	1-0	1-2	2-2	2-0	0-4	3-0	2-1	1-0	3-0	4-2	0-1		5-0	2-0	1-3	0-4	2-0	1-1
16 Pegasus Juniors	1-1	0-2	2-1	4-1	1-3	0-3	3-1	2-3	2-1	0-1	3-1	2-0	4-1	0-0	0-1		1-1	2-1	1-1	3-2	1-1
17 Shortwood United	1-0	0-2	3-1	1-1	0-4	1-5	2-4	0-4	2-2	0-1	1-0	4-0	1-2	1-3	5-0			0-0	0-2	1-2	3-5
18 Shrivenham	7-0	0-5	1-2	5-0	1-2	3-0	3-1	0-4	0-3	5-1	0-1	3-1	4-1	3-1	1-3	3-0	2-0		2-0	2-2	0-0
19 Slimbridge	4-1	0-2	3-1	3-1	1-0	1-0	6-2	1-3	1-0	6-1	1-0	3-0	8-3	1-1	1-1	3-0	2-1	1-0		3-4	3-1
20 Wantage Town	3-2	1-5	0-2	1-2	0-0	2-1	1-0	1-0	0-1	3-0	2-2	3-0	2-1	4-3	3-2	1-1	2-3	2-4	3-1		3-1
21 Witney United	1-3	4-1	2-1	1-0	0-2	1-2	3-0	2-6	0-1	7-1	7-1	5-0	2-1	0-1	0-3	2-0	3-1	4-1	0-1	4-0	

DIVISION ONE WEST		P	W	D	L	F	A	Pts
1.	Winterbourne United	34	24	5	5	98	36	77
2.	Harrow Hill	34	18	9	7	61	40	63
3.	Tytherington Rocks	34	19	5	10	79	54	62
4.	Headington Amateurs	34	18	8	8	59	39	62
5.	Wootton Bassett Town	34	17	10	7	58	30	61
6.	Trowbridge Town	34	17	9	8	65	44	60
7.	Old Woodstock Town	34	16	8	10	55	46	56
8.	Cheltenham Saracens	34	14	12	8	54	40	54
9.	Letcombe	34	14	6	14	51	45	48
10.	Pewsey Vale	34	13	7	14	54	51	46
11.	Hook Norton	34	13	7	14	57	58	46
12.	Cricklade Town	34	13	5	16	55	67	44
13.	Malmesbury Victoria	34	11	9	14	50	56	42
14.	Cirencester United	34	11	5	18	50	64	38
15.	Purton (-3)	34	7	9	18	33	64	27
16.	Easington Sports	34	6	9	19	37	71	27
17.	Clanfield	34	5	4	25	30	74	19
18.	Ross Town	34	5	3	26	36	103	18

DIVISION ONE WEST	1	2	3	4	5	6	7	8	9	10	11	12	13	14	15	16	17	18
1 Cheltenham Saracens		3-0	1-0	2-3	0-0	0-0	1-2	2-0	1-1	4-0	1-0	0-4	0-0	5-1	0-0	2-1	1-1	1-0
2 Cirencester United	1-1		1-0	2-1	3-0	0-1	2-3	6-3	0-2	1-2	1-2	0-3	4-0	2-2	2-2	0-1	2-2	2-2
3 Clanfield	1-1	3-0		1-0	0-3	1-2	1-3	4-1	0-3	1-2	0-4	1-2	1-0	1-0	2-3	0-2	1-4	1-3
4 Cricklade Town	2-2	0-3	3-0		3-2	1-1	1-1	2-1	1-3	0-3	3-5	2-1	4-1	2-4	2-1	1-3	1-4	1-1
5 Easington Sports	0-3	1-3	1-1	2-3		1-3	2-2	0-2	0-1	1-2	2-1	3-0	1-2	0-0	0-4	1-1	0-2	1-1
6 Harrow Hill	0-2	2-0	2-0	3-1	3-2		2-3	1-1	2-0	2-1	1-1	4-2	3-2	1-4	0-0	3-0	3-3	0-1
7 Headington Amateurs	1-1	0-1	3-0	0-1	1-2	2-1		2-0	0-0	3-1	2-0	1-0	1-1	2-0	4-0	2-4	1-2	1-0
8 Hook Norton	2-2	4-0	4-0	1-0	2-3	2-3	2-2		5-1	1-0	2-3	3-2	4-0	1-0	2-0	1-0	0-7	0-2
9 Letcombe	1-3	3-2	6-4	1-2	4-1	0-2	2-3	1-1		2-0	2-1	2-1	1-1	5-0	0-0	1-2	0-2	0-2
10 Malmesbury Victoria	1-1	0-1	2-1	2-4	1-1	0-2	0-0	3-3	1-0		1-3	1-1	3-1	3-0	1-2	5-3	1-1	0-2
11 Old Woodstock Town	3-2	4-2	0-0	2-0	2-0	0-1	2-2	2-1	0-1	1-0		3-1	1-1	3-1	1-1	1-8	0-3	1-0
12 Pewsey Vale	2-1	3-0	2-1	3-1	1-1	0-1	1-3	2-0	2-0	3-3	1-0		6-1	2-2	0-2	1-1	2-1	2-1
13 Purton	2-0	3-2	1-1	0-0	1-1	3-0	0-1	1-1	0-4	0-2	2-2	1-0		3-0	0-3	1-3	0-2	0-1
14 Ross Town	1-5	1-3	2-1	1-4	1-5	0-7	1-4	1-3	0-1	3-2	0-1	2-1	1-3		3-7	0-5	0-1	0-5
15 Trowbridge Town	1-2	3-2	5-0	4-0	3-0	1-1	1-3	1-0	2-1	1-1	2-0	0-0	2-1	4-2		7-2	1-2	1-0
16 Tytherington Rocks	1-2	1-0	3-2	3-2	4-0	1-1	2-0	1-2	0-0	2-5	0-4	3-2	4-1	6-1	4-0		4-2	0-0
17 Winterbourne United	5-1	6-1	4-0	3-2	5-0	3-1	2-0	3-1	2-1	4-0	1-1	5-0	2-0	3-1	5-0	2-3		1-3
18 Wootton Bassett Town	3-1	0-1	1-0	1-2	6-0	2-2	3-1	1-1	2-1	1-1	1-1	1-1	3-0	2-1	1-1	2-1	4-3	

DIVISION ONE EAST	P	W	D	L	F	A	Pts
1. Hounslow Borough	34	23	4	7	99	45	73
2. Bicester Town	34	21	8	5	78	36	71
3. Wokingham & Emmbrook	34	21	5	8	86	47	68
4. Chalfont Wasps	34	20	4	10	80	49	64
5. Englefield Green Rovers	34	20	4	10	73	46	64
6. Penn & Tylers Green	34	20	4	10	69	46	64
7. Bisley Sports	34	19	5	10	81	51	62
8. Binfield	34	19	2	13	70	44	59
9. Kintbury Rangers	34	18	4	12	81	48	58
10. Eton Wick (Champions 04-05)	34	17	5	12	73	64	56
11. Badshot Lea	34	13	6	15	81	74	45
12. Oxford Quarry Nomads (-3)	34	14	4	16	67	81	43
13. Finchampstead	34	10	7	17	58	60	37
14. Holyport	34	10	4	20	58	90	34
15. Rayners Lane	34	11	1	22	57	90	34
16. Chinnor	34	5	5	24	34	82	20
17. Banbury United Reserves	34	4	4	26	29	108	16
18. Prestwood	34	1	4	29	24	137	7

DIVISION ONE EAST	1	2	3	4	5	6	7	8	9	10	11	12	13	14	15	16	17	18
1 Badshot Lea		1-2	3-1	1-5	4-2	2-2	3-0	0-4	7-1	1-1	1-1	2-4	2-5	1-3	2-3	5-2	1-4	2-2
2 Banbury United Reserves	1-5		1-2	1-4	0-7	1-2	2-2	2-5	0-2	2-2	4-2	1-2	1-1	2-1	0-1	1-1	0-2	0-2
3 Bicester Town	0-0	4-1		0-3	1-2	2-2	3-2	0-0	3-3	1-1	6-1	1-0	1-0	2-0	5-2	6-0	3-2	3-3
4 Binfield	2-4	6-0	0-1		1-1	0-1	3-0	2-1	0-0	5-4	2-3	0-4	0-1	2-0	2-1	3-0	2-1	0-1
5 Bisley Sports	2-0	4-1	2-3	2-0		0-1	2-0	2-1	7-2	1-1	3-2	0-3	4-3	4-0	4-4	8-0	3-1	1-2
6 Chalfont Wasps	0-2	5-0	3-1	2-1	2-0		7-0	2-3	3-0	4-1	5-4	4-1	1-0	1-3	0-0	2-1	3-4	1-2
7 Chinnor	1-5	3-0	0-2	0-4	1-4	0-3		0-4	2-4	1-2	0-0	1-4	1-3	3-0	0-2	2-0	4-2	2-5
8 Englefield Green Rovers	3-1	5-1	1-1	1-2	1-2	2-1	1-0		3-0	1-0	2-0	1-1	1-2	4-1	2-1	4-2	7-1	0-1
9 Eton Wick	3-1	2-0	1-3	3-2	1-1	4-3	0-0	0-1		2-1	5-0	0-2	2-5	6-0	0-3	1-1	5-0	4-0
10 Finchampstead	0-0	5-1	1-3	0-1	3-0	1-2	1-0	0-1	2-3		3-2	0-0	0-2	3-4	0-4	6-0	3-2	0-2
11 Holyport	0-6	4-1	1-3	1-3	4-2	0-2	0-0	1-3	2-3	4-1		3-2	1-6	3-1	0-1	2-1	2-2	2-5
12 Hounslow Borough	9-3	6-0	0-0	3-2	1-2	3-1	3-3	7-1	2-0	6-4	2-1		2-1	3-1	3-2	5-0	2-1	4-2
13 Kintbury Rangers	1-2	2-0	0-1	0-2	0-0	2-7	4-1	4-0	4-1	1-0	5-2	1-0		1-2	2-1	9-0	7-0	3-3
14 Oxford Quarry Nomads	4-3	6-0	0-5	3-1	3-2	1-2	3-0	1-1	4-0	1-1	1-5	1-0	2-2		0-1	5-0	5-1	1-4
15 Penn & Tylers Green	4-3	4-0	0-4	0-3	3-0	3-1	1-0	3-1	0-3	2-1	2-1	1-5	3-0	4-0		7-1	2-0	0-1
16 Prestwood	0-5	1-2	0-6	0-3	1-4	0-2	2-5	0-6	1-4	0-5	0-2	1-3	1-2	3-3	0-0		1-6	0-5
17 Rayners Lane	1-0	2-0	0-1	1-3	1-2	3-1	1-0	5-0	1-5	1-2	0-2	1-6	2-1	3-6	1-3	2-3		2-0
18 Wokingham & Emmbrook	1-3	5-1	1-0	3-1	0-1	2-2	2-0	0-2	0-3	0-3	7-0	3-1	2-1	8-1	1-1	6-1	5-1	

THE GLS FOOTBALL CHALLENGE CUP

PRELIMINARY ROUND

Shortwood United	v	Cheltenham Saracens	4-2
Bindfield	v	Ardley United	0-4
Carterton	v	Bisley Sports	3-0
Chipping Norton	v	Almondsbury Town	0-4
Clanfield FC	v	Fairford Town	0-1
Finchampstead	v	Englefield Green Rovers	2-1
Henley Town	v	Badshot Lea	1-2
Highworth Town	v	Easington Sports	1-0
Holyport FC	v	Chalfont Wasps	1-4
Hounslow Borough	v	Abingdon United	1-3
Hungerford Town	v	Abingdon Town	2-1
Middle Barton	v	Harrow Hill	AW
Milton United	v	North Leigh FC	0-2
Old Woodstock T.	v	Bishops Cleeve	2-0
Oxford Quarry N.	v	Rayners Lane	3-1
Pegasus Juniors	v	Headington Amateurs	2-0
Penn & Tylers G.	v	Kintbury Rangers	2-3
Prestwood	v	Kidlington	0-3
Purton FC	v	Pewsey Vale	2-3
Ross Town	v	Shrivenham	0-7
Wantage Town	v	Bicester Town	2-1
Winterbourne Utd	v	Cricklade Town	3-0
Witney United	v	Chinnor FC	4-2
Wokingham & E.	v	Banbury United Reserves	6-0
Wotton Bassett T.	v	Cirencester United	2-2*, 5-4p
Trowbridge Town	v	Tytherington Rocks	1-3

FIRST ROUND

Letcombe FC	v	Malmesbury Victoria	2-1
Abingdon United	v	Witney United	3-1
Badshot Lea	v	Ardley United	2-2, 1-3r
Carterton	v	Didcot Town (H)	0-2
Eton Wick	v	Finchampstead	1-2
Highworth Town	v	Hook Norton	4-2
Kintbury Rangers	v	Oxford Quarry Nomads	5-2
Kidlington	v	Chalfont Wasps	2-8
North Leigh	v	Alondsbury Town	3-1
Pewsey Vale	v	Tytherington Rocks	1-2
Shrivenham	v	Harrow Hill	0-2
Shortwood United	v	Fairford Town	0-1
Slimbridge	v	Hungerford Town	1-0
Wantage Town	v	Wokingham & Emmbrook	5-1
Wootton Bassett T.	v	Winterbourne United	1-4

Old Woodstock T.	v	Pegasus Juniors	2-1

SECOND ROUND

Abingdon United	v	Tytherington Rocks	1-2
Fairford Town	v	North Leigh	1-6
Kintbury Rangers	v	Winterbourne United	3-1
Slimbridge	v	Highworth Town	3-0
Wantage Town	v	Finchampstead	2-3
Chalfont Wasps	v	Didcot Town (H)	1-2
Ardley United	v	Harrow Hill	2-0
Letcombe	v	Old Woodstock Town	4-1

QUARTER-FINALS

North Leigh	v	Didcot Town (H)	0-4
Slimbridge	v	Finchampstead	4-0
Ardley United	v	Kintbury Rangers	3-0
Tytherington Rocks	v	Letcombe	1-0

SEMI-FINALS (played over two legs - home & away)

			1st Leg	2nd Leg
Didcot Town (H)	v	Slimbridge	2-1	1-1
Ardley United	v	Tytherington Rocks	2-0	1-1

THE FINAL

Ardley United	v	Didcot Town (H)	0-5

Action from the Didcot Town versus Abingdon United match which the home side won 3-1. Photo: Peter Barnes.

ABINGDON TOWN
Founded: 1870
Nickname: The Abbots

Chairman: Tom Larman   **President:** Dr.Tim Reynolds   **Manager:** Keith Stopps
Secretary: Wendy Larman, 3 Belmont House, Wantage OX12 9AS   **Assistant Manager**: Craig Larman
Tel No: 01235 763985
Press Officer: Tony Stoyle (07771 816615)   **Programme Editor:** Tom Larman Jnr. (07810 445782
GROUND ADDRESS: Culham Rd., Abingdon OX14 3HP   **Ground Tel.No:** 01235 521684
Capacity: 3,000   **Seats:** 271   **Covered:** 1,771   **Floodlights:** Yes
Simple Directions: On A415 road to Dorchester-on-Thames half a mile south of town centre.
Midweek Home Matchday: Tuesday   **Clubhouse:** Open every evening   **Club Shop:** Fully stocked
Previous Leagues: Oxford & Dist.,West Berks, Reading Temperance, North Berks, Reading & Dist., Spartan, Hellenic and London Spartan.
Previous Name: Abingdon FC (merged with St Michaels in 1899)
Club Colours: Yellow & green/green/yellow   **ChangeColours:** Black & white
BEST PERFORMANCES: League: **F.A. Cup:** 4th Q.Rd. Replay 1992-93   **F.A.Vase:** 5th Rd Replay 1989-90
RECORD Attendance: 4,000 v Swindon Town. Maurice Owen Benefit1950s **Goalscorer:**   **Appearances:** Roger Charles
Senior Honours: Berks & Bucks Senior Cup 1958-59, R-Up 88-89 92-93, Isthmian Div 2 (Sth) 90-91, London Spartan 88-89 Hellenic Lg.(4) R-Up (3) Berks & Bucks Junior Cup 06-07

A.F.C.WALLINGFORD
Founded: 1995

Chairman: Gerry O'Garr   **Manager:** Andy Gordon
Secretary: Richard May, 43 St.Johns Road, Wallingford,Oxon.
Tel Nos: 01491 734804 (H) 07973 736386 (M)
Previous Name: Wallingford Town   **Previous Leagues:** Chiltonian, Co.Counties
Club Colours: Red & Black Hoops/Black/Black   **Change Colours:** Blue & White
GROUND ADDRESS: Wallingford Sports Park   **Tel:**
Capacity: 1,500   **Seats:** 40   **Covered:** 100   **Floodlights:** Yes
Simple Directions: Use Wallingford by-pass and leave at Hithercroft Round-about towards Wallingford. Ground 100 Yards on Left.
Midweek Home Matchday: Tuesday   **Clubhouse:**Open evenings and week-ends   Club Shop:
RECORD Attendance: 280 v Reading Town **Goalscorer:** Carl Henry 68 1997-98   **Apps:** Anthony Hill 240
SENIOR HONOURS: Chiltonian Premier Lg. 97-98,Co.Counties Premier R-up 2000-01 Berks & Bucks SenTrophy R-Up 00-01

ALMONDSBURY TOWN
Founded: 1897
Nickname: Almonds

Chairman: Bob Jenkins   **Vice-Chairman:** Andy Jefferies   **Manager:** Paul Weeks
Secretary: Roger Perry, 61 Brookridge House, Standfast Rd, Henbury, Bristol BS10 7HW
Tel Nos: 01179 590309 (H)07834 093437(M) **Press Officer:** Name (Tel)   **Programme Editor**: Bill Bundy
Programme: 20 Pages 25p
GROUND ADDRESS: Oakland Park, Gloucester Road, Almondsbury, Bristol   **Tel:** 01454 612220
Capacity: 2,000   **Seats:** None   **Covered:** None   **Floodlights:** Yes
Simple Directions: Adjacent to M5 jct 16. Follow A38 Thornbury and ground is first left.
Midweek Home Matchday: Tuesday   **Clubhouse** Open daily.   **Club Shop:** No
Previous League: Bristol Weslyan, Bristol Suburban, Bristol Premier Comb ,Glos. Co   **Ground**: Almondsburyu Rec.
Club Colours: Navy & Sky Blue/Navy/Navy   **Change Colours:** Red/black/black   **Sponsor:** South Gloucester Taxis
Best Performances
RECORD Attendance: 2,100 Hellenic Cup Final. Newport AFC v Abingdon U. 89-90
Senior Honours: Glos. F.A. CHallenge Trophy 1978-79 R-up 8081 Glos Sen Am.Cup 87-88 Hellenic Lg.83-84 R-Up 82-83

ARDLEY UNITED
Founded:
Nickname:

Chairman: Norman Stacey   **President:** Ben Gow
Manager: Peter Foley   **Coach**: Tony Blossom   **Physio**: Clive Wright
Secretary: Norman Stacey,Ardley House, Somerton Road, Ardley.Oxon. OX27 7NS
Tel Nos: 01869 345597 (H & F)
Press Officer: Peter Foley   **Programme Editor:** Mandy Reed
GROUND ADDRESS: The Playing Field, Oxford Road, Ardley OX27 7PA   **Ground Tel. No:** 01869 346429:
Capacity: 1,000   **Seats:** 100   **Covered:** 200   **Floodlights:**
Simple Directions: M40 jct 10 take B430 towards Middleton Stoney. Ground is on the right after half a mile.
Midweek Home Matchday: Tuesday   **Clubhouse:** Yes   **Club Shop:** No
Previous League: Oxford Senior until 1993
Club Colours: Sky blue/Navy blue/Sky blue   **Change Colours:** All Yellow
BEST PERFORMANCES
League: Hellenic Premier 8th
RECORD Attendance: 120 v Oxford City 1999
Senior Honours: Hellenic League Div 1 Champions 96-97 97-98

BICESTER TOWN

Founded: 1876
Nickname: Foxhunters

Chairman: David Simpson   **Manager:** Tim Fowler

Secretary: Phil Allen, 38 Bassett Avenue, Bicester, Oxon. OX26 4TZ **Tel:** 01869 252 125 (H). 01869 343 688 (B)

Press Officer: Chairman   **Programme Editor:** Phil Allen

GROUND ADDRESS: Sports Ground, Oxford Round, Bicester, Oxon.   **Gropund Tel.No:** 01869 241036

Capacity: 2,000   **Seats:** 150   **Covered:** 550   **Floodlights:** Yes

Simple Directions: from Oxford, past Tescos on outskirts of town-ground on right.

Midweek Home Matchday: Tuesday   **Clubhouse:** One Bar.   **Club Shop:** No

Previous Name: Slade Banbury Road (pre 1923)   **Previous League:** Oxford Senior

Club Colours: Red & white stripes/white/red

BEST PERFORMANCES

League: Hellenic Champions 1960-61   77-78

RECORD Attendance: 955 v Portsmouth Opening of floodlights 01.02.94

Senior Honours: Hellenic League (2)

CARTERTON TOWN

Founded: 1922
Re-Formed 1946 +1983

Chairman: Nick Truman   **Presidents:** K.Trethowan & R.Ferryman   **Sponsor:** Green King Brewery

Manager: Steve Hail   **Assistant Manager:** Gary Brown

Secretary: John McCarthy, 37 Cranwell Avenue, Carterton, Oxon. OX18 3SB

Tel No: 01993 213003 (H)   **Press Officer:** T.B.A.

Programme Editor: Gordon Maxwell(01993 212803) **Programme:** 20 Pages 50p   **Website:** ww.cartertontownfc.co.uk

GROUND ADDRESS: Kilkenny Lane, Carterton, Oxfordshire.   **Ground Tel. No:** 01993 842410

Capacity: 1,500   **Seats:** 75   **Covered:** 100   **Floodlights:** Yes

Simple Directions: From the Burton-Carterton road take Swinbrook Rd then turn into Kilkenny Lane (one track road)

Midweek Home Matchday: Tuesday   **Clubhouse:** Lounge and fully licensed bar open daily.   **Club Shop:** No

Previous League: Witney & District

Club Colours: Red with green trim/green/red **Change Colours:** Black & white/black/black

RECORD Attendance: 650 v Swindon Town July 2001   **Goalscorer:** Phil Rodney   **Apps:**

Senior Honours: Oxon. Senior Cup: R-up 90-91 96-97 98-99 Hellenic Div 1 89-90 933-94

CHIPPING NORTON TOWN

Re-Formed: 2001
Nickname: Magpies

Chairman: Nigel Harrison

Manager: Mark Johnson

Secretary: Nigel Harrison,Copstone House,Charlbury Road, Hailey, Oxon

Tel No: 01993 703319 (H ,W &Fax) **E-mail:** happyhaulier@btinternet.com

Press Officer & Programme Editor: Sean Robson (07879 635212)   Editor (Tel)

GROUND ADDRESS: Walterbush Road,Chipping Norton, Oxon. OX7 5DP   **Tel.No:** 01608 645311 or 01608 642562:

Capacity: 2,000   **Seats:** 50   **Covered:** 150   **Floodlights:** Yes

Simple Directions: From South: A361 to Chipping Norton past school on right, take first left into Waterbush Road.

Midweek Home Matchday: Tuesday   **Clubhouse:** Yes   **Club Shop:**No

Club Colours: Black&white stripes/black/black   **Change Colours:** Yellow/blue/yellow

Top Scorer: Mark Dennis 11   **Player of the Year:** Anthony Akers   **Captain:** Mark Johnson

RECORD Attendance: 1,000 v Wolverhampton Wanderers 1981   **Goalscorer:** Kevin Drinkwater **Appearances:**

Senior Honours: Hellenic League Div 1 West R-up 2002-03

FAIRFORD TOWN

Founded:1891
Nickname: Town

Chairman: Ken Locke   **President:** Michael Tanner   **Manager:** Kevin Maloney

Tel No: 01285 712136   **e-mail:** william@beach747.freeserve.co.uk   **Programme:** 20 Pages £1.00

Editor /Press Officer: Michael Tanner   **Sponsor:** Polypipe Shirts

GROUND ADDRESS: Cinder Lane, London Road,Fairford, Cirencester, Glos.   **Tel:** 01285 712071

Capacity: 2,000   **Seats:** 100   **Covered:** 250   **Floodlights:** Yes

Simple Directions: Cinder Lane is off A417 (Lechlade-Fairford). From Lechlade turning is on left.

Midweek Home Matchday: Tuesday   **Clubhouse:** Open every evening and match days   **Club Shop:** Yes

Previous Leagues: Cirencester & District (pre 1946), Swindon & District 1946-70

Club Colours: Red/white/red   **Change Colours:** All Blue

LAST SEASON League: 17th   **F.A. Cup:** 1st Qualifying Round.   **F.A. Vase:** 2nd Qualifying Round.

Top Scorer: Lee Stoddart   **Player of the Year:** Gary Hill   **Captain:** Lee Clark

Last Season: League:17th   **F.A.Cup:** 1st Qualifying   **F.A.Vase:** 2nd Qualifying Round

Best Performances

League: Hellenic Premier R-up (4)   **F.A. Cup:** 1st Qualifying Round   **F.A.Vase:** 1st Round

RECORD Attendance: 1,525 v Coventry City. Friendly in July 2000 **Goalscorer:** Pat Toomey

Victory: 9-0 v Moreton Town   **Defeat:** 0-9 v Sharpness.

Senior Honours: Glos Challenge Trophy (3) Hellenic Lg R-up (4) Glos Junior Cup 62-63

HARROW HILL

Secretary:	Mark Rawl;ings, 22 Mannings Road, Highmeade, Drybrook, Glos. GL17 9HS 01594 542799 (H)
Match Sec:	Robert Partridge, 20 Littledean Hill Road, Cinderford, Glos., GL14 2BE Tel: 01594 825360 (H) 01594 825225 (B) Club Email: harrowhillafc@aol.com
Ground:	Larksfield Road, Harrow Hill, Glos. GL17 9PB Tel: 01594 543873
Directions:	Take A40 west out of Gloucester, follow A40 for 8 miles then takeA4136 to Longhope, pass by on the outskirts of Michealdean, up steep hill(Plump Hill), then second turn on the right signed Harrow Hill. At phone box onthe left turn right into Larksfield Road, ground on right at top of hill.
RECORD	**Attendance:** 350 v Cinderford Town 1992

FACT FILE
Founded: 1932 Nickname: Harry Hill
Colours: claret & blue/bluet/blue
Change Colours:Blue & black/black/blue
Midweek Matchday: Wednesday
CLUB PERSONNEL
Chairman: Reg Taylor
Press Officer:Mark Rawlings
markrawlings@drybrook.freeserve.co.uk
Manager: Steve Boseley
Coach:Rob Whittington
Physio: Rob Partridge

HIGHWORTH TOWN
Founded: 1893
Nickname: Worthians

Chairman: Rodney Haines   **President:** Alan Vockins   **Manager:** John Fisher
Secretary: David Evans, 36 Lismore Road, Highworth, Swindon, Wiltshire. SN6 7HU
Tel Nos: 01793 764712 (H)07989 487363 (M)   **Sponsor**: BHG
Press Officer: Fraser Haines   **Programme Editor:** Mike Markham   **Programme:** 16 Pages 60p
GROUND ADDRESS: Elm Recreation Goround, Highworth SN6 7DD   **Tel:**
Capacity: 2,000   **Seats:** 150   **Covered:** 250   **Floodlights:**Yes
Simple Directions: Take A361 from Swindon past Simpsons garage over roundabout, then sharp left into The Green by Vet's surgery. Ground is 60 yards on left next to Sports Hall.
Midweek Home Matchday: Tuesday   **Clubhouse:** Yes. Hot food available.   **Club Shop:** No
Previous Leagues: Swindon & District and Wiltshire
Club Colours: Red/black/black   **Change Colours:** Sky Blue & white
BEST PERFORMANCES
League: Champions 2004-05   **F.A. Cup:** 3rd Qualifying Round   **F.A.Vase:** 2nd Round
RECORD Attendance: 2,000 v QPR for opening of floodlights. **Goalscorer:** Kevin Higgs **Appearances:** Rod Haines
Senior Honours: Wiltshire Senior Cup 63-64 72-73 95-96 97-98 R-Up 88-89 Hellenic Champions 04-05 R-Up 99-00

HOUNSLOW BOROUGH F.C.

Secretary:	Edward Mee, 78 Manor Lane, Feltham, Middlesex TW13 4JA
Tel Nos:	0208 230 2992 (H); 0208047 2251 (B); 07556 438670 (M))
E-mail	hounslowborough.f.c@lineone.net
Ground:	Grosvenor Vale, Ruislip, Middlesex, HA4 6JQ 0208 560 2892
Capacity:	Covered Seating: Covered Standing: Floodlights: Yes/No
Directions:	From M25 onto M4 at junction 3 then follow signs to Central London. At Gillett Corner turn left into Syon Lane. Ground 100 metres on the left.From A40 turn at Target Roundabout and follow A312 Hayes by pass to A4 then follow signs to Central London until Gillett Corner, turn left and ground on the left.
Record Gate	150 v Rayners Lane **Previous League:** Chiltonian League

FACT FILE
Colours: Blue & white/blue/blue
Change cols.: Red & blue/red/red
Midweek matchday: Tuesday
Press Officer: Fiona Price (0208 5802718)
Web site: www.hounslowboroughfc.co.uk
CLUB PERSONNEL
Chairman: Stefan Poulos
Manager:Denis Bainborough
Captain: Garry Hedges
Coach:Daniel Batler

HUNGERFORD TOWN
Founded: 1886
Nickname: Crusaders

Chairman: Andrew Fitton   **President:** Sir Seton Wills   **Manager:** Alan Clark
Secretary: Norman Matthews, 72 Chilton Way, Hungerford, Berks. RG170IF
Tel Nos: 01488 684117 (H) 08703 004041 (W) 07768761795 (M)
Press Officer: Ron Tarry   **Programme:** 24 Pages 50p   **Editor:**Martyn Leach
GROUND ADDRESS: Bulpit Lane, Hungerford, Berks. RG17 0AY0 **Tel No:** 1488 682939 (club) 01488 684597(boardroom)
Capacity: 2,500   **Seats:** 170   **Covered:** 400   **Floodlights:** Yes
Simple Directions: M4 jct 14 to A4. Turn right and then left before Bear Hotel. Through town centre on A338 and left into Priory Road then left again into Bulpit Lane. Over crossroads and ground is on the left.
Midweek Home Matchday: Tuesday   **Clubhouse:** Yes Contact: Kim James   **Club Shop:** Opens on request
Previous League(s): Newbury & District, Swindon & District, Hellenic 58-78 Isthmian 1978-2003
Club Colours: White/navy blue/navy blue   **Change Colours:** All Yellow
Last Season:League: 16th   **F.A. Cup:** Preliminary Round   **F.A. Vase:** 1st Round
Top Scorer: Ryan Lucas   **Player of the Year:** Luke Brewer   **Captain:** Dean Flockton
BEST PERFORMANCES
League: 3rd Isthmian DivisionTwo 1979-1980 **F.A. Cup:** 1st Round 1979-80   **F.A.Vase:** S-Finals 77-8 79-80 88-9
RECORD Attendance: 1,684 v Sudbury T. F.A.Vase S-F 88-89 **Goalscorer**: Ian Farr 268 **Appearances:** Dean Bailey 400+
Transfer Fee Paid: £4,000 to Yeovil Town for Joe Scott **Fee Received:** £3,800 from Barnstaple Town for Joe Scott
Senior Honours: Berks & Bucks Senior Cup 1981-82 R-up 75-6 76-7 Isthmian Representative in Anglo Italian Cup 1981

KIDLINGTON F.C.

Founded: 1909
Nickname:

Chairman: Geoff Talboys   **President:** Gordon Norridge   **Manager:** Paul Lee

Secretary: David Platt, 57 Cherryy Close, Kidlington, Oxon. OX5 1HJ   **Asst.Manaager:** Kelvin Alexis

Tel Nos: 01865 370266 (H) 07768 908002 (M)   **Physio:** Chris Perkins

Press Off : Simon Dickens (01865 371110) **Programme Ed:** Chairman   **Programme:** 32 pages £2.00

GROUND ADDRESS: Yarnton Rd., Kidlington,Oxford   **Ground Tel No.:** 01865 841526

Simple Directions: From Kidlington (roundabout) at junction of A4260 & A34 take A423north to Kidlington and after tfourthset of lights turn left into Yarnton Road. Ground is 200 yards on the left.

Midweek Home Matchday: Wednesday   **Clubhouse:** Two bars open after matches   **Club Shop:** No

Previous League: Oxford Senior

Club Colours: Green/white/green & white   **Change Colours:** All Blue

BEST PERFORMANCE   **F.A.Cup** N/A   **F.A.Vase** 5th Rd 1976-77

RECORD attendance: 2,500 Charity Game 1973

MILTON UNITED

Founded: 1909
Nickname: United

Chairman: Pat Horsman   **President:** John Cannon   **Manager:** Gary Ackling

Secretary: Jenny Hinckes,23 School Lane,Milton, Abingdon OX14 4EH   **Asst.Man:** Graham Brewerton

Tel No: 01235 820433 (H) 07786 854383 (M)   **Physio:** Richard Fox

Press Officer/ Programme Editor: Secretary

GROUND ADDRESS: The Sportsfield, Milton Hill, Potash Lane,Milton Heights, Oxon.   **Tel:** 01235 832999

Capacity: 2,000   **Seats:** 50   **Covered:** 100   **Floodlights:** Yes

Simple Directions: Leave A34 at Milton, 10 miles south of Oxford. Take A4130 towards Wantage then first left after 100metres and first right into MIlton Hill. Ground 200m on left.   **Club Shop:** No

Midweek Home Matchday: Tuesday   **Clubhouse:** Open Matchdays plus Mon-Sat evenings and Sunday lunchtime.

Previous League: North Berks.

Club Colours: Sky blue & claret/blue/sky & claret   **Change Colours:** All white

BEST PERFORMANCES

League: Hellenic Champins 1990-91   **F.A. Cup:** N/A   **F.A.Vase:** 2nd Rd 2004-05

RECORD Attendance: 605 League Cupp Final 2005(Carterton v Didcot Town)   **Goalscorer:** Nigel Mott

Senior Honours: Hellenic Premier 90-91 Div 1 89-90 Berks & Bucks intermediste Cup 90-91

Pegasus Juniors Back Row: (L-R): Lewis Jones, Mark Smith, Bryn Watkins, David Hart, Matthew Aubrey, Lee Mussell. **Front Row:** Paul Brown, Daniel Sobocinski (Capt), Ben Price, Jamie Cuss, Robert Laurie.

Photo: Arthur Evans.

NORTH LEIGH

Founded: 1908
Nickname:

Chairman: Peter King   **President:** Mrs Christine Smith   **Manager:** Mark Gee
Secretary: Les Reynolds, 37 Perrott Close, North Leigh, Oxford. OX 18 2EG
Tel No: 01993 845507(H) 01635 577018 (W) 07760 171762 (M)
Press Officer: Barry Norton (01933 88177)   **Programme:** 20 Pages £1.00
GROUND ADDRESS: Eynsham Hall Park Sports Ground, North Leigh, Nr. Witney Oxon OX8 6PW
Tel No: 01993 881427
Capacity: 2,000   **Seats:** 100   **Covered:** 200   **Floodlights:** Yes
Simple Directions: Ground is situated off A4095 Witney to Woodstock road, three miles east of Witney. Entrance 300 yards east of main park entrance.
Midweek Home Matchday: Tuesday   **Clubhouse:** Open matchdays   **Club Shop:** No
Previous League(s): Witney & District
Club Colours: Yellow/Black/Black   **Change Colours:** Claret & Blue
LAST SEASON: League: 7th   **F.A. Cup:** 3rd Qualifying Round   **F.A. Vase:** 2nd Round
RECORD Attendance: 326 v Andover F.A.Vase 17.01.04   **Goalscorer:** P.Coles   Appearances: P.King
Senior Honours: Hellenic Div 1 R-up 92-93 Oxon Charity Cup (2) Oxon Senior Cup R-up 94-95

PEGASUS JUNIORS

Founded: 1955
Nickname: The Redmen

Chairman: Roger Hesten   **President:** Mark Ellis   **Manager:** Steve Griffiths
Secretary: Trevor Jones, 219 Ledbury Rod, Hereford, HR1 1QE (01432 351459)
Press Officer: Chris Wells (01432 358345)) **Programme:** £1,00   **Editor:**Julie Nicholas (07771857027)
GROUND ADDRESS: Old School Lane, Hereford. (New Ground)HR 4 9LW   **Tel:**
Capacity: 1000   **Seats:** 110   **Covered:** Yes   **Floodlights:** Yes
Simple Directions: A49 Ross road over Greyfriars Bridge, Victoria Street to end of Edgar Street then left to next roundabout where you turn right.Take right at roundabout after Leisure Centre then next right and ground is on left.
Midweek Home Matchday: Tuesday   **Clubhouse:** On ground at Old SchoolLane
Previous League: Leisure Centre
Club Colours: All Red   **Change Colours:** White/blue/white
LAST SEASON League: 13th
Top Scorer: Chris Mortlock 10   **Player of the Year:** Mark Smith   **Captain:** Robert Laurie
BEST PERFORMANCES
F.A. Cup: First Entry this season   **F.A.Vase:** 2nd Round
Record Attendance: 1,400 v Newport AFC 1989-90
Senior Honours: Herefordshire Senior Amateur Cup 71-72, Worcs Senior Urn 85-86, HerefordshireCo.Challenge Cup (6)

Shrivenham. Back Row: (L-R): Michael MacInally, Paul Carson, Mark Peters, Jon Peters, Luke Alford, Mark Stevens, Steve Avenell, Steve Thomas. **Front Row:** Paul O'Connell, Alex Green, Tate Hulbert, Russell Byrne, Andy Brien, Nathan Hall. Photo: Arthur Evans.

SHORTWOOD UNITED

Founded: 1900
Nickname: the Wood

Chairman: Peter Webb   **Vice-Chairman:** W.Stratford & W.Lewis   **Manager:** John Evans
Secretary: Mark Webb, 7 Cotswold Cottage, Shortwood, Nailsworth, Stroud , Glos. GL6 0SE
Tel No: 01453 836233 (H) 0781 2842724 (M)
Press Officer: Secretary   **Programme Editer:** Kenton Postlethwaite   **Programme:** 18 Pages 50p
GROUND ADDRESS: Meadowbank, Shortwood, Nailsworth, Glos   Ground **Tel No.:** 01453 8333936
Capacity: 2,000   **Seats:** 50   **Covered:** 150   **Floodlights:** Yes
Simple Directions: From A345 take first right into co-op car park. Park top left hand side next to bowls & tennis club and walk through.
Midweek Home Matchday: Wednesday   **Clubhouse:** Open daily with hot food avialable   **Club Shop:** No:
Previous Leagues: Stroud, Glos Northern Senior and Glos.Co.
Club Colours: Red & white/white/white   **Change Colours:** Blue/blue/yellow
LAST SEASON
League: 15th
Top Scorer: Chris Davis   **Player of the Year:** James Price   **Captain:** Tim Haddock
BEST PERFORMANCES
League: Hellenic Champions 1984-85 91-92 **F.A. Cup:** 1st Qaulifying Round   **F.A.Vase:** 3rd Round
RECORD Attendance: 1,000 v Forest Green R F.A.Vase 5th Rd 81-2 **Goalscorer:** Peter Grant **Appearances:** Peter Grant
Senior Honours: Glos. Trophy (3) Glos Sen.Am. Cup (2) Hellenic Champions (2) R-up (3)

SHRIVENHAM

Founded:
Nickname:

Chairman: Ian Richardson   **Vice Chairman:** Robb Forty
Manager: Alan Dyton & Tony Garland   **Asst.Manager:** Peter Horwat   **Coach:** Neil Batton   **Physio:** Alan Jennings
Secretary: Matthew Hampson, 12 Grange Drive, Swindon, Wilts. SN3 4LD   **e-mail:** hampson.m@googlemail.com
Tel Nos: 01793 3300983 (H) 07748 804593 (M) **e-mail:** matthew.hampson@atlworld.com
Programme Editor & Press Officer: Matthew Hirst (07989 603948) e-mail: matt@h2creative.co.uk
GROUND ADDRESS: The Recreation Ground, Shrivenham SN6 8BJ   Ground **Tel. No.:** 017767 371414
Capacity: **Seats:**   **Covered:**   **Floodlights:**
Simple Directions: Off Highworth Road, Shrivenham village is signposted off A420, six miles east of Swindon and four miles west of Faringdon.
Midweek Home Matchday: Tuesday   **Clubhouse:**   **Club Shop:**
Previous Name(s):   **Previous Leagues:** North Berks Leagues
Club Colours: Blue & white hoops/blue/white **Change Colours:** Yellow/black/yellow
LAST SEASON
League: Champions Div 1 West   **F.A. Cup:** N/A   **F.A. Vase:** N/A
BEST PERFORMANCES--
League: 8th Hellenic Premier 2005-2006   **F.A. Cup:** N/A   **F.A.Vase:** N/A
RECORD Attendance: 800 v Aston Villa 2000

SLIMBRIDGE

Founded: 1902
Nickname: Swans

Chairman: John Mack   **Manager:** Doug Foxwell   **Coach:** John Hamilton
Secretary & Press Officer: David Phillips, 14 Woodcock Close, Abbeydale, Gloucester GL4 4WT
Tel Nos: 01452 414766 (H & Fax) and 07754 088063 (Matchdays only)
Programme Editor: Secretary   **Sponsors:** Ellis Transport Ltd.
Capacity: 1,500   **Seats:** 159   **Covered:** 100   **Floodlights:** Yes
Simple Directions: From A38 take A 4135 to Dursley and ground is 100yards on left.
Midweek Home Matchday: Tuesday   **Clubhouse:** Yes   **Shop:** No - badges at bar
Previous League: Gloucestershire County League
Club Colours: Blue/blue/white   **Change Colours:** Red or Black/black/red
LAST SEASON:League: 5th Premier.   **F.A. Cup:** Extra Preliminary Round   **F.A. Vase:** 3rd Rd
Top Scorer: ERobbie Carroll 38   **Player of the Year:** Ashley Thomas   **Captain:** Leon Sterling
Best Performances
League: 4th 2003-04 04-05   **F.A. Cup:** Extra Preliminary Round   **F.A.Vase:** 3rd Round
RECORD Attendance: 525 v Shortwood United 24.08.03 Hellenic League
Senior Honours: Hellenic Div West 2002-2003, Gloucestershire F.A.Trophy 2003-2004,2005-2006 Glos Co.Lg R-up 2001-02 Hellenic Floodlit Cup 2003-2004 , 2005-2006

THAME UNITED

Founded:1883
Nickname:United

Chairman: Jim Tite   **Vice-Chairman:** Bernard Wakelin   **Manager:** Mark West
Secretary: Fred Saulsbury, 86 Station Road, Chinnor, Osfordshire OX39 4HA
Tel Nos: 01844 351073 (H) 07721 026099 (M)
Press Officer: Name (Tel)   **Programme:** 24 Pages - £1.00 **Editor:** Wendy Garrad
GROUND ADDRESS: Windmill Road, Thame, Oxon. OX9 2DR   **Tel:** 01844 213017
Capacity: 3,600   **Seats:** 284   **Covered:** 850   **Floodlights:** Yes
Simple Directions: Into Nelson Street from Market Square. 3 miles from Haddenham &Thame Parkway (BR). Nearest bus stop at Town Hall (half mile away)
Midweek Home Matchday: Tuesday   **Clubhouse:** Open evenings and week end lunchtimes
Previous Leagues: Oxon Senior,Hellenic 1959-87, South Midlands 1987-91 & Isthmian 1991-2004
Previous Name: Thame F.C
Club Colours: Red & Black,Black,Red & Black   **Change Colours:** Green & White
BEST PERFORMANCES
F.A. Cup: 3rd Qualifying Round   **F.A.Vase:** S-Final 1998-99
RECORD Attendance: 1.035 v Aldershot, Isthmian, Div 2 4/4/94 **Goalscorer:** Not Known **Appearances:** Steve Mayhew
Senior honours: Isthmian Lg Div 2 94-95, Div 2 R-up 98-99 Div 3 R-up 92-93; Hellenic Lg 61-62 69-70, Premier Div Cup (4); Sth Mids Lg 90-91; Oxon Snr Cup (9)

WANTAGE TOWN

Founded: 1892
Nickname:Alfredians

Chairman: Tony Woodward   **President:** Fred Carroll   **Manager:** Richard Bourne
Secretary: John Culley, Lorien, Winter Lane, West Hanney, Wantage, Oxfordshire OX12 0LF
Tel No: 01235 868359 (H)   **Sponsor:** Asvogal
Programme Editor: David Broadis (01235 769300)   Press **Officer:** Ross Sheppard
GROUND ADDRESS: Alfredian Park, Manor Road,Wantage, Oxon.   **Ground Tel.No:** 01235 764781
Capacity: 1,500   **Seats:** 50   **Covered:** 300   **Floodlights:** Yes
Simple Directions: From Wantage town centre take Hungerford road (A338) Ground is on the right opposite the recreation
ground before you leave the town.
Midweek Home Matchday: Tuesday   **Clubhouse:** Yes Mon-Fri 7.30-11 Sat noon-2.30 4-7pm. **Club Shop:** No
Previous Leagues: Swindon & Dist., 1901-12 30-35 47-56 N.Berks: 12-22 38-40 46-47 Reading & Dist. 22-30 35-38
Club Colours: Green& white/white/black   **Change Colours:** Blue & white/black/white
Best Performances
League: 2nd Helenic Premier 81-82   **F.A. Cup:** 3rd Qualifying Round   **F.A.Vase:** 5th Ropund
RECORD Attendance: 550 v Oxford United July 2003
Senior Honours: Hellenic Runners Up 81-82 Oxon Senior Cup 82-83

WITNEY UNITED

Founded:
Nickname:

Chairman: Steve Lake   **Vice-Chairman:** John Bircher   **Manager:**Spencer Keye
Secretary: Adrian Bircher, 13 Colwell Drive ,Witney, Oxon. OX28 5NJ   **Asst.Manager**: Steve Paish
Tel Nos; 01993 200913(H) 01865 393361 (W) 07747 123411 (M)   **Press Officer**: Mark Reid
e-mail: adrian1.bircher@ntlworld.com   **Physio:** Wayne Probert
Programme Editor: Richard Wickson (0783 452543)
GROUND ADDRESS: Marriotts Stadium,Downs Road,Witney OX8 5LY   **Ground Tel No:** 01993 702549
Capcity: 3,500   **Seats:** 280   **Covered:** 2,000   **Floodlights:** Yes
Simple Directions: From A40 eastbound (towards Oxford). Take first exit at roundabout towards Minster Lovell. After two miles
turn right into Downs Road (signposted for Witney Lakes golf Club) and ground is half a mile on right.
Midweek Home Matchday: Tuesday   **Clubhouse:** Yes   **Club Shop:** Yes
Club Colours: Yellow & Black/Black/Black   **Change Colours:** All Green

Slimbridge F.C. Back-Row (L-R): H Brooke (Physio), M Foxwell, Mike Green, Matt Green, A Varnam, R Colwell.
Middle Row: J Hamilton (Coach), S Badham, Ashley Thomas, Adam Thomas, A Axton, N Haisley, W Morford.
Front Row: J Cole, L Sterling (Capt), P Miller, D Foxwell (Manager), E Ward, J Tustain, J Embling.

Wantage Town - Back Row (L-R): Marcus Brown (Physio), Bryn Ingram, Richard Bourne, Adam Giles, Sean Purcell, Gary Swann (Capt), Matt Shelton, Kevin Lloyd (Coach).
Front: Danny Allen, Gavin Jones, Paul Day, Ellis Langford, Andy Hallett. Photo: Arthyr Evans.

BANBURY UNITED RESERVES

Ground: The Stadium, off Station Approach, Banbury, Oxfordshire
Tel: 01295 263354 / 261899
Directions:Ground is very close to the BR station.
Secretary: Barry Worsley C/o SOL Systems,Unit 4 , Mallorie House,
Beaumont Road, Banbury, OX16 1RH Tel: 07870 782840 (M)
Colours: Red & Gold or White

CHELTENHAM SARACENS

Secretary & Bob Attwood, 179 Arle Road, Cheltenham GL51 8LJ

Press Officer: Tel: 01242 515855 (H) 01242 241819 (B) 01242 222994 (Fax)

Ground: Petersfield Park, Tewkesbury Road, Cheltenham GL51 9DX(01242 584134)

Directions: Follow signs to Cheltenham BR and take Gloucester Road for 2 miles north.

Left at lights past Tesco into Tewkesbury Road

Clubhouse: Two minute walks away at 16-20 Swindon Rd, Cheltenham

HONOURS Glos Snr Cup 91-92 Glos Primary Cup 71-72, Winners Hellenic Div 1 99-00

PREVIOUS League: Cheltenham 1964-86

RECORD Attendance: 327 v Harrow Hill 31.8.03

FACT FILE
Founded: 1964   Nickname: Saras
Colours: Blue&yellow/blue/yellow
Change colours: Green/black/black
Midweek Matchday: Wednesday
Reserves League: Hellenic Reserve section
Programme : 20 pages, 50p
Editor: Robert Attwood   01242 690405
CLUB PERSONNEL
Chairman: Chris Hawkins (01242 692332)
Man:Gerald Oldham Physio: Chris Hawkins

CIRENCESTER UNITED

Secretary/Press Officer: Gordon Varley, 95 Vaisey Rd, Cirencester, Glos GL7 2JW
Tel: 01285 657836 (H) 0973 631650 (M) 01367 718259 (B)
Ground: Grounnd sharing with Cirevncester Town
Directions: As for Corinium Stadium
Capacity: 4,500   Seats: 550   Cover: 550   Floodlights: Yes Club Shop: No
Clubhouse: Training nights & matchdays. Rolls & sundries available
HONOURS Glos Snr Amtr Cup R-up 86-87 89-90; Cirencester Lg 72-73 74-75 (Div 2(3)71-73
74-75, Lg Cup 74-75, Res. Cup 74-75); Cheltenham Lg 76-77 83-84 (Div 275-76, Lg Cup 83-84
(R-up 86-87), Snr Charity Cup 86-87); Stroud Charity Cup86-87 (Section A 82-83 83-84); Arthur
Shipway Cup 86-87 (R-up 87-88 92-93);Fairford Hospital Cup R-up(4) 83-85 90-91 92-93;
Hellenic Res Div 95-96, Cup 96-97
PREVIOUS Leagues: Cirencester & Dist.(4 yrs); Cheltenham (8 yrs)
RECORDS Scorer: M Day   Appearances: J.Stratford 310
2005-2006 Top Goalscorer Phil Hall   Players of the Year: Phil Hall & Ian McSherry

FACT FILE
Founded: 1970 Nickname: Herd
Colours: Red & black/black/red
Change colours: All Blue
Midweek Matchday: Wednesday
Programme: 40 pages, 50p
Editor: N Warriner (01285 656187)
CLUB PERSONNEL
President: RickTrinder
Chairman: Ivor Probert
Press Officer: Lee Clatworthy
Manager: Richard Smith
Assistant Manager: Jon Hathaway
Captain: Dave Reeves
Physio: Carly Montgomery

CLANFIELD

Secretary: Jenni Fisher, 62 Mill Lane, Clanfield, Oxon. Tel No: 01367 810471
Ground: Radcot Road, Clanfield, Oxon   Tel: 01367 810314

Directions: Situated on the A4095, 8 miles west of Witney & 4 miles east of Faringdon,
at the southern end of Clanfield. Buses from Witney - contact Thames
Transit for details
Capacity: 2,000   Seats: No   Cover: 300   Floodlights: No
Clubhouse: Every evening & Sat/Sun lunch   Club Shop: No

HONOURS Oxon Jnr Shield 32-33, Oxon I'mediate Cup 67-68, Witney & Dist. Lg 66-67 (Div 1
65-66, Div 2 64-65), Hellenic Lg Div 1 69-70 (Premier Div Cup 72-73, Div1 Cup 69-70 85-86),
Jim Newman Mem. Tphy 83-84 87-88, Faringdon Thursday Memorial Cup 69-70 71-72 96-97

PREVIOUS Leagues: North Berks; Witney & District
RECORD Attendance: 197v Kidlington August 2002

FACT FILE
Founded: 1890   Nickname: Robins
Sponsors: Olphert & Lamb
Colours: All red
Change colours: Yellow & Black/black/black
Reserves' League: Hellenic Lge Res. section
Prog: 8 pages, with admission Ed: Secretary
CLUB PERSONNEL
President: B Wallis Chairman: J Osborne
Manager: Jason Court
Press Officer & Physio: Trevor Cuss

CRICKLADE TOWN

FACT FILE

Colours: Green/black/green

Midweek Games: Tuesday (6.30 KO)

Secretary: Peter Johnson, 24 Home Ground, Cricklade, Wilts. SN6 6JG

(H) 01793 752 493 (H) 07710 091304 (W & M)

Ground: Cricklade Leisure Centre, Stone Lane, Cricklade SN6 6JW. Tel: 01793 750 011

Directions: Cricklade is eight miles North of Swindon signposted off the A419. Leisure

Centre is signposted off the B4040 Malmesbury Road.

PREVIOUS Leagues: Wiltshire League

CLUB PERSONNEL

Chairman: Alisdair Ross

Manager: Graham Jackson

Press Officer: Peter Johnson

Tel: 01793 752 493

peterjohnson29@hotmail.com

Programme Editor: Moz Fisher

Tel: 01793 751 415

moz99@aol.com

EASINGTON SPORTS

Secretary: Paul Dowers,136 Longfellow Road, Banbury, Oxon. OX16 9LB
Tel Nos: 01295 258816 (H) 07852 102217 (M)

Ground: Addison Road, Banbury, Oxon, OX16 9DH (01295 257006)

Club Email: matt@wiggins1.freeserve.co.uk

Directions: From Oxford A423. After passing under flyover on the outskirts of Banbury take first turning left into Grange Road then third right into AddisonRd. Ground at top on left. One and a half miles from Banbury (BR)

Capacity: 1,000 Seats:0 Cover: 30 Floodlights: No

Programme: Editor: Ron Bloxham(07970 871447)

Clubhouse: Changing rooms, showers, bar facilities and food

HONOURS Oxon Snr Cup R-up, Oxon Intermediate League & Cup, Oxon Snr Lg

PREVIOUS Leagues: Banbury Jnr; Oxon Snr; Warwick Combination
Ground: Bodicote

RECORD Attendance: 250 v Witney Town 68

FACT FILE

Founded: 1946

Colours: All Red

Change colours: Blue/ white

Midweek Matchday: Wednesday

Reserves' League: Hellenic Res. section

CLUB PERSONNEL

Chairman: T.B.A.

President: Bob Cogbill

Manager: Mark Fenemore

Physio: Bernie Jarvis

HOOK NORTON

Secretary: Geoff James, Speedwell, Brick Hill, Hook Norton, Oxon
Tel No: 01608 737476

Ground: The Bourne, Hook Norton OX15 5PB 01608 737132

Capacity: 500Covered Seating, dugouts and Floodlights will be installed in time for the 2007-2008 season

Directions: From Oxford – A44 to junction with A361 turn right, take 1st left to a 'T' junction, turn right & enter village, after 30 MPH turn left then 1st left into 'The Bourne', take 1st left into ground.

Clubhouse: On ground

Previous League: Oxfordshire Senior League

Record Gate: 244 v Banbury United 12th Dec 1998

Honours: Oxford Senior League Champions 1999-2000
Hellenic Lge Div.1 West Champions 01-02
Oxfordshire Senior Cup Runners-Up 2002-2003

Best Season FA Vase: 2nd Qualifying Round.

FACT FILE

Founded: 1898

Nickname: Hooky

Sponsors: Smiths of Bloxham.

Colours: Royal Blue & White

Change colours: Maroon and silver

Midweek fixtures: Wednesday

Program Editor: Mark Willis 01608 737640

email: enquiries@kmslitho.co.uk

CLUB PERSONNEL

Chairman: Mike Barlow

Sec.& Press Officer: Geoff James

Tel No: 01608 737476

e-mai;l: geoff@jams8390.fsnet.co.uk

Manager/Coach: Ben Spiro

AssistantManager: Adrian White

Physio: Julian Pakela

2005-2006

Top Scorer: Richard Northover

Captain: Mark Tyler

LETCOMBE

Secretary: Des Williams, 8 Larkdown, Wantage, Oxon OX12 8HE

Tel No: 01235 764130 **email:** deswilliams@larkdown.fslife.co.uk

Ground: Bassett Road, LetcombeRegis Oxon OX12 9JU

Capacity: 1,500 **Seats** 50 **Covered** 50 **Floodlights:** No

Directions: Take B4507 from Wantage (Signposted White Horse) and turn left to

Letcombe Regis after half a mile. Ground on far side of village on right.

Honours: North Berks Div 1 Champions 1989-90 Chiltonian Lg. Div 1 Champions 1990-1

Hellenic Div 1 East Runners -Up 2003-2004

Previous Leagues: North Berks 1961-90, Chiltonian 1990-93

FACT FILE

Colours: Purple/Navy/Purple

Change colours: Red/Red/Green

Midweek Matches:Tuesday

Programme: Yes

Editor: Russell Stock

CLUB PERSONNEL

Chairman: Dennis Stock

Manager: Kevin Bailey

Assistant Manager: Brian Monnery

LYDNEY TOWN

Secretary: Roger Sansom,17 Woodland Rise,,Lydney, Glos. GL15 5LH
Tel Nos: 01594 843210 (H) 01594 846423 (W) 01594 846404 (Fax)
Ground: Lydney Recreation Ground, Swan Road,Lydney GL15 5PH
Directions From Gloucester_ take Lydney Road off A48 down Highfield Hill and into town centre, Take first left into Swan Road after second set of pelican lights. From Chepstow: -atby-pass roubdabout take Lydney road. Go over railway crossing thentake seconed right turn.
Record Gate: 375 v Ellwood Nov 5th 2005
Previous League: Gloucestershire County

FACT FILE
Colours: Black & white stripes/Black/Black.
Change colours:All Blue
Midweek fixtures: Tuesday
website lydney@hellenicleague.co.uk:
CLUB PERSONNEL
Chairman: Peter L:iddington
Press Officer: Secrtary
Programme Editor:Mark allen
Tel No: 07771 626747
Manager:Stuart Liddington
Top Scorer: Matt Timmins 30

MALMESBURY VICTORIA

Secretary: Sue Neale, 30 Gastons Road, Malmesbury, Wilts. SN16 0BE
Tel: 01666 823560   E-Mail: paul.neale@btconnect.com

Ground: Flying Monk Ground, Gloucester Road, Malmesbury
Tel: 01666 822141
Website: www.malmesbury-victoria.com
Directions: From A429 (sign for Tetbury), pass Nurdens to roundabout and go past school then take next left B4014 signposted Sherston. Go down hill to mini roundabout, straight over roundabout. Go past Somerfield's super store, narrow right turning into ground behind super store.
Previous Leagues: Wiltshire Premier League
Honours: Wiltshire League Champions 99-00 Wiltshire Senior Cup 01-02
2005-2006 **Player of the Year**:Bob Hunt   **Top Goalscorer**: Neil Fisher

FACT FILE
Sponsor: Malmesbury Plumbing & Heating
Nickname: The Vic's
Colours: Black & white stripes/black/red
Change colours: Yellow/Blue/Yellow
Midweek fixtures: Tuesday or Wednesday
CLUB PERSONNEL
Chairman: Paul Neale 01666 823560
Press Officer: John Wilkins 01666 824112
Prog Ed: Sarah Neale 01666 823560
Manager: Tom Dryden
Captain: Jon Wilkins Coach: Phil Goulding

OLD WOODSTOCK TOWN

Secretary: Ian F. Lenegan
c/o Workplace Systems plc.,Precedent Drive, Rooksley, Milton Keynes MK13 8PP
Tel:08362 42300(H), 01908 251301or 251311 (W) 01908 201287 (Fax)
Ground: New Road, Woodstock
Directions: A44 from Oxford into centre of Woodstock, turn right opposite The Crown into Hensington Road. After half a mile the road bends to the right, take the first turning right into New Road, ground half-way along on the left.

HONOURS Oxfordshire Sen. Lge 98-99

PREVIOUS **Leagues:** Oxfordshire Senior League

FACT FILE
Founded:
Midweek Matchday: Tuesday
Colours: Blue & red/blue/ red
Change colours: White/green/blue
Programme : Yes Editor: Mike Harris
CLUB PERSONNEL
President: Ian F Lenagan
Chairman: Ted Saxton
Press Officer: Mick Harris (01865 376018)
Manager: Andrew Townsend
Coach:Trevor Stokes
Physio: Graham Bowerman

PEWSEY VALE

Chairman: Alan Ritchie   **Vice-Chairman:**   **Manager:** Dave Turner
Secretary: Shiela Britten, 13 The Ivies, Manninggord ~BruceSN 9 6HJH
Tel Nos: 01672 564382 (H)
Pohramme Editor: Chairman
GROUND ADDRESS: Reveation Ground,Kings Corner, Ball Park, Pewsey SN9 5HP   **Tel:** 01672 563664
Capacity: 1,000   **Seats:**   **Covered:** Yes   **Floodlights:** Yes
Simple Directions:
Midweek Home Matchday: Tuesday   **Clubhouse:**   **Club Shop:**
Previous Name(s): PewseyY.M.until late 40s **Previous League:** Wiltshire County (pre 1993) Western League 1993-2001
Club Colours: Black & white/black/black   **Change Colours:**
LAST SEASON
League: 22nd   **F.A. Cup:** N/A   **F.A. Vase:** 2nd Qualifying Round
RECORD Attendance:107 v Purton 27.08.2001

PURTON

FACT FILE
Founded: 1923   Nickname: The Reds
Sponsors: The Care Company

Secretary: Steve Hall, 15 Finetree Avenue, Swindon, Wilts. SN25 3BY
Tel: 01793 525194

Colours: All red   Change: Sky blue/white

Ground: The Red House, Purton, Tel: 01793 770262 (Saturday afternoons only)

Midweek Matchday: Wednesday

Directions: Purton is on B4041 Wootton Bassett to Cricklade Road. Ground nearvillage hall

Programme: 36--40 pages

Capacity: Unlimited   Seats: None   Cover: None   Floodlights: No

Editor: Alan Eastwood (01793 729844)

Clubhouse: Open after matches and before matches on Saturdays

CLUB PERSONNEL

HONOURS Wiltshire Lg Div One 48-49 85-86, Div 2 83-84, Div 3 86-87;   Wilts
Senior Cup (6) 38-39 48-49 50-51 54-55 87-88, 88-89,94-95 Wilts Yth Cup 77-78 85-86 88-89,
Fairford Hosp. Cup (3) 87-89 93-94 Hellenic Lg. Div One 95-96, Divison One West Champions
2003-04, Hellenic Supplement Cup 2001-02

President: Alan Eastwood
Chairman: Gary Norman
Press Officer: Alan Eastwood
Manager: Chris Pethick Captain: Darren King

2004-2005

RECORD   Attendance: 508 v Dorcan 5.5.85

P.o.Y.: Bryan Halestrap

PREVIOUS   Leagues: Wiltshire Premier, Hellenic Div.1 West

Top Goalscorer: Simon Pugh

ROSS TOWN

FACT FILE
Founded:1993

Secretary: Chris Parsons, 23 Alton street, Ross-on-Wye HR9 5JJ
Tel: 01989 564673 (H) 07818096156 (W)

Nickname: Riversiders

Ground: Ros Sports Centre, The Riverside, Wilton Road. HR9 5JA

Colours: Red /black/black
Change colours:Green/Green/White
Midweek Matchday: Tuesday/Wednesday

Directions: From Gloucester take A40 to Ross-on-Wye, after passing through Weston
under Penyard take secnd left off mini roundabout on edge of town and take
A449 off next roundabout.

CLUB PERSONNEL
Patron: Dave Sexton

HONOURS Hereford Lge 94-95, Charity Shield 95-96; Hereford FA Charity Bowl 94-95;
Worcester & Dist Lge 95-96, Baylis Cup 95-96; Hereford FA County Chall Cup
97-99 R-up 95-96; 98-99 Pershore Hospital Charity Cup R-up 95-96, Hellenic
Lg Cup R-up: 99-00

Chairman: Peter Gilmour
Director of Football and
Press Officer: Chris Parsons (01989 566712)
Manager: Martin Thomas
Coach: Chris Parsons
Physio: Sylvia Durham

PREVIOUS   Leagues: Hereford Lg, Worcester & District League.

RECORD   Attendance: 147 v Harrow Hill 26/3/97

TROWBRIDGE TOWN

FACT FILE

Secretary: Robin Sims, 5 Chirton Place, Trowbridge, Wilts. BA 14 0XT
Tel Nios: 01225 764591 (H) 07776 450686 (M)

Colours: Yellow with black stripe/black/black
Change colours: All white/black/bvlack

Ground: Woodmarsh, Bradley Road, Trowbridge, Wilts.

Midweek Matches: Tuesday

Capacity: 1,500 **Floodlights:** No (Floodlit cup matches at Westbury United)

Programme: Yes

Directions: From A350 Trowbridge by pass go towards Westbury and turn tight after a
mile at Yarnbrook roundabout towards Trowbridge. Under railway bridge and
take North Bradley exit at next roundabout. Continue to Marsh Turn and
ground is 50 yards on left.

Editor: Andrew Meaden
Tel No: 01373 827788

CLUB PERSONNEL
Chairman: John Fitchen

Record

Attendance: 369 v Tytheringtonb Rocks 28.08.05

Manager: Neil Kirkpatrick

TYTHERINGTON ROCKS

FACT FILE
Colours: Amber & Black/black/black
Change colours: Green & Black/white/green

Secretary: Graham Shipp, 21 Elmdale Crescent, Thornbury, Bristol BS35 2JQ
Tel Nos: 07811 318424 (M) 01179365377 (W)

Midweek Matches:Wednesday
Reserves' Lge: Bristol Surburban

Ground: Hardwicke Playing Field, Tytherington
Tel No: 07837555776

Programme:Yes
Editor: Ron Holpin
Tel No: 01454 614303

Capacity: 1,500   **Floodlights:** No

Directions: M5 Jct 14 take A38 for Bristol. Tytherington turn off is approx yhree miles. Enter
the village and ground is signposted.

CLUB PERSONNEL
Chairman& Press Officer: Ted Travell

Previous

League: Glos.County League

Manager: Jamie Burton
Captain: Mike Airs

WINTERBOURNE UNITED

FACT FILE
Formed:1911
Nickname: The Bourne
Colours: All Red
Change colours: Yellow/Black/Yellow
Midweek fixtures: Tuesday or Thursday

Secretary: Geoff Endicott, 27 Star Barn Road,Winterbourne , Bristol BS36 1NU
Tel:01454 778207 (H) 07778678823 (M)
e-mail: g.endicott@btopenworld.com

Ground Parkside Avenue, Winterbourne, Bristol BS36 1LX 01454 850059
Directions Leave Junction 1 of M32 turn left then left again at traffic lights, sign posted Yate. Keep on road for two miles into Winterbourne After Ridings High School turn right into Parkside Avenue, ground on right.
Clubhouse: Yes.
Previous League: Gloucester County League
Honours: Gloucester County League Champions 00-01
Hellenic League Div 1 West Champions 2005-2006

CLUB PERSONNEL
Chairman: Robyn Maggs
Tel: 01454 887338
Press Officer: Chairman
Program Editor: Chairman
Manager Stewart Jones
Coach: Terry Northam
Physio: Ken Purnell

WOOTTON BASSETT TOWN

Chairman: Mark Smedley   **President:** Keith Lodge
Manager: Paul Burke   **Asst, Manager:** Bryan Wood
Secretary: Rod Carter,14 Blackthorn Close, Wootton Bassett,Swindon SN14 7JE
Tel. Nos: 01793 851386 (H) 01793 494367 (W) 01793 494355 (Fax) 07957 996283 (M)
Press Officer: Secretary **Editor**: Fred Doherty (07771 860309) **Programme:** 12 Pages £1.00)
GROUND ADDRESS: Gerard Buxton Sports Ground, Rylands Way,Wootton Bassett, Swindon. **Tel**: 01793 853880
Capacity: 2,000   **Seats:** None **Covered:** 350 **Floodlights:** Yes
Simple Directions: M4 jct 16 to Wootton Bassett (A3102) left at second roundabout (Prince of Wales pub on right) and then second left into Longleaze. Rylands Way is third right by shops. Ground 100 yards on right.
Midweek Home Matchday: Tuesday   **Clubhouse:** Open matchdays   **Club Shop:** No
Previous League(s): Wiltshire League prior 1988
Club Colours: Blue &yellow /blue/yellow   **Change Colours:** Maroon & Yellow
RECORD Attendance: 2,103 v Swindon T July 1951 **Goalscorer:** Brian 'Tony' Ewing   **Appearances:** Steve Thomas
Senior Honours:Wilts Senior cup R-up 02-03 03-04 87-88 **F.A.Amateur Cup**: Quarter Final 1926-27

LEAGUE CONSTITUTION 2006-07 - DIVISION ONE EAST

BADSHOT LEA

FACT FILE
Nickname: The Baggys
Colours:Sky Blue/Claret/Sky Blue
Change colours:Sky Blue/claret/sky blue
Midweek Matches: Tuesday
Programme: Yes Editor: Secretary

Secretary: Mark Broad, 57 Lambourne Way, Tongham, Surrey GU10 1AB
Tel Nos: 01252 659990 (H) 07743 694930 (M)
email: badshotleafc@aol.com
Ground: Recreation Ground,The Green, Badshot Lea, Farnham,Surrey GU9 9LB
Tel No: 01252 316076
Capacity: 1,500   (Floodlit Cup matches played at Farnham Town FC.)
Directions: From M3 Jct 4 take A331 towards Farnham for 5 miles. Turn off towards Aldershot on A323 and then left after 400 yards at first junction. At Badshot Lea village crossroads, go over lights then left into The Green after 150 yards and drive round green to car park.

CLUB PERSONNEL
Chairman: Stuart Page
email: stpagw@02.co.uk
Manager: David Ford
Assistant Manager & Press Officer:
Nathan Fealey

BINFIELD

FACT FILE
Colours: All red.
Change colours:All Blue
Midweek fixtures: Tuesday
Nickname: Moles

Secretary: Rob Challis, 49 St Mary's Road, Sindlesham, Wokjingham, Berks. RG41 5DA Tel Nos 01189 782220 (H) 01628644215 (W) 07818 457808 (M)
Ground: Stubbs Lane Binfield   01344 860822
Directions From A329 Bracknell to Wokingham Road, turn by the Travel Lodge into St. Marks Rd, through the village into Terrace Road South & North,then at T junction by All Saints' Church turn right & then left into Stubbs Hill.

Record Gate: 268 v Englefield 2001-02
Previous League: Chiltonian

CLUB PERSONNEL
Chairman: Rob Jones
Press Officer: Rob Aston
Programme Editor: Rob Jones
Manager:Richard Witty
Asst. Maager: Rob Aston

BISLEY SPORTS

Secretary Michael Clement, 35 Slaidburn Green, Forest Park, Bracknell, Berkshire.
RG12 0GG **Tel No:** 01344 452937
Tel: 01483 475003 (H) 01483 736286 (B) E-mail: mclem0@aol.com

Ground: Lion Park, Church Lane, Bisley GU24 9EB
Tel: 07795 094941

Directions: Exit M3 at Junction 3. Head southbound on A322 towards West End & Bisley.
Go over two roundabouts then turn left opposite the Hen & Chicken P. House
into Church Lane, ground is about 400 yards on left hand side.

FACT FILE
Colours:Shirts – Blue /black/white
Change colours: Red/white/black
Midweek fixtures: Tuesday
CLUB PERSONNEL
Chairman:Simon Hollis
email:simon@bisleyfc.com
Press Officer: See Secretary
Programme Editor: Mike Clement
Tel: 01483 472432
Manager: Andy Clement Tel: 07767 605291
Coaches: John Cook & Bruce Henderson

CHALFONT WASPS

Secretary: Bob Cakebread, 8 Pheasant Walk, Chalfont St.Peter, Bucks. SL9 0PW
Tel Nos: 01494 873469 (H) 0208 3320044 (W)

Match Sec/Press Off. r: Bob Isherwood 01494 871445 (H)

Ground: Crossleys, Bowstridge Lane, Chalfont. HP8 4QN Tel: 01494 875050

Directions On entering Chalfont St. Giles Village from A413 (Aylesbury - Uxbridge
Road), turn left into Bolostridge Lane immediately after the shops. After a quarter of a mile
turn right into Crossleys by a small green. Ground is directly ahead through the gates
Record Attendance: 50 v Harrow Hill Rovers 00-01
Previous League: Chiltonian

FACT FILE
Colours: Yellow & black striped/black/black.
Change colours: All Green
Midweek fixtures: Tuesday
Nickname: The Stingers

CLUB PERSONNEL
Chairman: Steve Waddington
Manager: Martin Stone
Press Officer: Michael Levine
Programme Editor:Al Yeomans

CHINNOR

Secretary: Richard Carr, 1 Harrison Place, Thame, Oxon. OX9 3TB
Tel Nos: 01844 217501 (H) 07786 115089 (M) 01844 215110 (FAX)

Ground: Station Road, Chinnor, Oxon OX39 4PV
Tel No: 01844 352579

Capacity: 1,500   **Floodlights:** No

Directions: M40 Jct 6 and follow B34009 towards Princes Riisborough. Enter Chinnor
after 3 miles and turn left at The Crown Pub roundabout. Ground is 400
yards on right.

FACT FILE
Colours: All Royal Blue
Change colours:All Royal Blue
Midweek Matches: Tuesday
Programme: Yes
Editor: Ed Janes
james.matthews@waterstones.co.uk
CLUB PERSONNEL
Chairman: Richard Carr
Press Officer: Neil Pearson
Tel No: 07720 401077
Manager: Terry Cozens
Assistant Manager: John Hathaway

Badshot Lea F.C.   Photo: Eric Marsh.

ENGLEFIELD GREEN ROVERS

Secretary   Terry Chapman, 64 Warwixk Avenue, Egham, Surrey TW20 8LT
Tel NO: 01784 4333321(H)

Ground: Coopershill Lane Englefield Green   01784 43566

Directions: Leave M25 at junction 13, A30 by passing Egham, at top of Egham Hill
turn right at traffic lights. After passing Village Green on the left take 2nd
turning right at the north east of green. Ground on right after half a mile.

Record Gate: 100 v Eton Wick, 1999

FACT FILE
Colours: Green & White hoops /white/white
Change cols.: Red & white halves/white/white
Midweek fixtures: Tuesday
Nickname: The Rovers
CLUB PERSONNEL
Chairman: Paul Solari
ManagerKevin McDonagh
Physio, Press Off & Prog Ed: Peter Casey

ETON WICK

Secretary :   Barrie Shurville, 21 The Wheat Butts, Eton Wick, Berks., SL4 6JH.
& Press Officer   01753 862969 (H)   07860262614 (B)
& Prog Editor
Ground: Haywards Mead, Eton Wick SL4 6JN Tel No: 01753 852749
Directions: From M4 junction 7 follow A4 to Maidenhead. At first roundabout
(Sainsbury's) take B3026 towards Eton Wick. Ground is on the right after
the parade of shops. From Eton take B3026 and ground is on the left
after the Catholic church.
Record Gate   500 v Andover, 1993   FA Vase
Previous League: Chiltonian League

FACT FILE
Nickname: The Wick
Cols:Amber/black/black   Change:All white
Midweek matchday: Tuesday
CLUB PERSONNEL
Chairman: Micky Foulkes 01753 733629
Manager: Andrew Howard
Captain: Mick McManus
Physio: Olly Walsh

FINCHAMPSTEAD

Secretary: Ray Grant,13 Bluecoat Walk, Bracknell, Berks. RG 1 2 9NP
Tel : 01344 640653   **Web Site:** www.finchampsteadfc.co.uk
Press Officer: Tichard Whitchurch-Bennett, 22Mayflower Drive, Yateley: GU46 7RR
Tel No: 07740 283210 (H)
Ground: Finchhampstead Memorial Park, The Village, Finchampstead RG114JR
Tel: 01189732890
Directions: A321 from Wokingham, then fork right onto B3016. At the Greyhound
pub turn right onto the B3348. The ground is 200 yards on the right.
Record Gate: 425 v Sandhurst, 1958/ 9   **Previous League:** Chiltonian

FACT FILE
Nickname: Finch
Colours: Sky blue & white/black/black
Change colours: All red
Midweek fixtures: Wednesday
CLUB PERSONNEL
Chairman: Kieron Brown (01344 452007)
E-mail: aquaspec@globalnet.co.uk
Manager: Steven McClurg
Coach : Willie Graham

HEADINGTON AMATEURS

Secretary: Stephen Giles, 67 Lucerne Ave.,Bure Park,Bicester, Oxon.OX26 3EG
Tel No: 01869 246141   Email Address: steve.giles3@ btinternet.com
Ground: Barton Rec., Barton Village Road, Barton, Oxon Tel: 01865 760489
Directions: From Green Rd r'bout, Headington, (on A40) take Barton/Islip exit(1st exit coming
from Witney, last coming from London), turn left into NorthWay, follow road for half mile -
ground at bottom of hill on left Seats: None Cover: None Floodlights: No Club Shop: No
Clubhouse: Tues & Thurs 6-11, Sat matchdays 4.45-11. Rolls, chips,burgers, hot dogs, etc
HONOURS   Oxon Snr League(4) 72-74 75-77 (R-up 71-72 74-75 77-78 81-82 84-85, Div1 68-
69, Presidents Cup(2) 72-74 (R-up 71-72 77-78 84-85)), Oxon Charity Cup75-76 (Intermediate
Cup 88-89), Hellenic League Div 1 R-up 87-88
PREVIOUS Leagues: Oxford City Junr 49-66; Oxford Sen 67-88 **Grounds:**Romanway,Cowley
RECORDS **Attendance:** 250 v Newport AFC 91 **Scorer:** Tony Penge **Appearances:**Kent
Drackett   **Win:** 6-0 v Carterton (H) 91 **Defeat:** 0-9 Highworth Town (a) 2002 RPM Records Cup
Player Progressing: James Light (Oxford United) 1970s

FACT FILE
Founded : 1949   Nickname: A's
Sponsors: Shaun Bradford Decorating & Construction
Colours: All red   Change: Yellow/blue/white
Midweek matchday: Tuesday
Programme: 8 pages, £1 with entry
Editor: Donald Light (01865 454209)
CLUB PERSONNEL
President: Shaun.Bradford
Chairman: Donald Light
Press Officer: Donald Light
Manager: Dean Fitzgerald
Coach/Physio:Michael Maciak
2005-2006
P.o.Y.: Steve Bell Top Scorer: Chris Baker
Captain: Mark Evans

HENLEY TOWN

Chairman: Andrew Bryan   **Manager:** Bobby Wilkinson
Secretary & Press Officer: Tony KIngston, 50 Birchill Avenue, Reading, Berks RG2 7JU
Tel Nos: 01189 670196 (H) 07712139592 (M)
Prohramme Editor: Mike Trendall (01491 577075)
GROUND ADDRESS: The Triangle, Mill Lane, Henley on Thames,Oxon RG9 4XB   **Tel:** 01491411083
Capacity: 2,000   **Seats:** 60   **Covered:** 100   **Floodlights:** Yes
Simple Directions: A4155 from Henley Mill Lane is approx. one mile on the left past Newtown Industrial estate and before the Tesco roundabout.
Midweek Home Matchday: Tuesday   **Club Shop:** No   **Previous Ground**: Reading Road
Clubhouse: Open evenings and all day at week ends
Club Colours: White/black/black   **Change Colours:** Yellow & Green
Last Season: League:21st   **F.A.Cup**: Priliminary Round   **F.A.Vase**:2nd Qualifying Round
RECORD Attendance: 2,000 v Reading 1922 **Goalscorer:** M.Turner
Senior Honours: Oxon Senior Cup (5) Hellenic Lg Div 1 East 2000-01

Henley Town F.C. Back Row: (L-R): Danny Seaward, Bobby Wilkinson (Manager), Stuart White, Adam Brown, Michael Prattley, Michael Turner, Tristan Dennis, Michael Davis, Andy Bryan (Chairman), Tom Cook (Asst. Manager). **Front:** Shane Small-King, Justin Forde, Paul Freeman, Mark Bartley (Capt), Chris Jewell, David Tarpay. Photo: Arthur Evans.

HOLYPORT

		FACT FILE

Secretary: Grahm Broom,4 Rutland Place, Maidenhead, Berks SL6 4JA

Colours: Claret/green/yellow
Change: Blue/red/red
Midweek matchday: Wednesday

Tel: 01628 631741 (H) 07768 746594 (M&B)

Ground: Summerleaze Village, SL6 8SP

CLUB PERSONNEL
Programme Editor: Mark Burton
Tel: 01494 436331
Chairman: Jason Andrews
Manager: Mark Burton

Directions: From the A4 at Maidenhead take B4447 towards Cookham. Turn right into Ray Mill Road West and leftinto Blackwater laneat T junction. Entrance to ground on leftat sharp nbend.

Previous League: East Berks. Lge >2002

KINTBURY RANGERS

FACT FILE
Colours: Amber & Black/Black/Amberk
Change colours: Green & Black/Black/Green
Midweek Matches: Wednesday
Programme: Yes
Editor: Craig Angell
Tel No: 01488 658445

Secretary: Cheryl Angell,49 Glendale Avenue, Wash Common, Newbury, Berkshire RG14 6TC Tel NO: 01635 35612 (H) 07778 216999 (M)
Ground: Recreation Ground, Inkpen Road, Kintbury, Berks RG17 9TY
Tel No: 01488 657001
Capacity: 1,500   **Clubhouse:** Yes.   **Floodlights:** Yes

CLUB PERSONNEL
Chairman: Bert Newman
Manager & Press Officer: Jim Greenwood
Tel No: 01635 281293
Safety Officer: Mark Annetts (01488 658846)

Directions   **From East**: M4 Jct 13, take A34 South then exit A4 to Hungerford then left at Kentbury crossroads.**From West:** M4 exit Jct 14 to Hungerford. Turn left at A4 and then right at Kintbury cross roads. In village follow road to shops and turn left. Ground is 200 yards on right.
Honours: North Berks League Champions 2003-2004

MARLOW UNITED

Secretary: Alan Turner,14 Seymour,Court Road, Marlow, Bucks SL7 3AY
Tel Nos: 01628 487832 (H&F) 01795 417285 (W)
Ground: Wilks Park, Magpie Lane,Flackwell Heath,HP10 9EA
Directions Follow Marlow to Bourne End road and turn left just before Bourne End turn into Sheepridge Lane (signposted Flackwell Heath). At end of lane turn left and Wilks Road is behind The Magpie pub.on right
Previous League: Reading

FACT FILE
Colours: White/Sky Blue/Sky Blue
Change colours:Red or White
Midweek fixtures: Tuesday

CLUB PERSONNEL
Chairman & Match Sec.: Bernard
Press Officer: Secretary
Programme Editor: Neil Dickens
Manager:Kevin Carvell

OXFORD QUARRY NOMADS

Secretary: Amanda Blake, 43 Merton Way, Yarnton, Oxford. OX5 1NN (01865 841282)
Ground: Oxford City F.C., Court Place Farm Stadium, Marsh Lane, Marston , Oxford OX3 0NQ. Tel: 01865 744 493
Directions: Access the Oxford Ring Road - Follow directions to the Northern By-Pass (A40). Along this stretch of by-pass, a fly-over is visible - exit at the fly-over follow the directions to John Radcliffe Hospital, Court Place Farm is 200 metres from the fly-over.
Clubhouse: Open matchdays, most refreshments available.
RECORD **Attendance:** 334 v Headington Amateurs 25.08.03
PREVIOUS **Name:** Quarry Nomads until 2005. **League:** Chiltonian
HONOURS Hellenic League Div.1 (East) Champions 2002-03

FACT FILE
Formed: 1936
Colours: Blue & white hoops/blue/white
Change colours:
Midweek fixtures: Tuesday
Prog. Editor: Colin Taylor
E-mail: ctoxford@btinternet.com
Chairman: Keith Dalton
Press Officer:Keith Dalton 01865 450 256
Manager: Dereck Beesley

PENN & TYLERS GREEN

Secretary: John Ostinelli, 2 Wynn Grove, Hazlemere , Bucks.HP10 8DW
Tel.No.:01494 815290 (H)
Ground: Elm Road, Penn, Bucks HP10 8LF   Tel: 01494 815346

Directions: Entrance to ground is off the main Hazlemere to Beaconsfield road. From Beaconsfield follow the road through Penn towards Hazlemere, pass the pond on green & ground entrance is on the right before going downhill.
Record Attendance: 125 v Chalfont Wasps 00-01
Previous League: Chiltonian

FACT FILE
Colours: All Blue
Change colours: All yellow
Midweek fixtures: Tuesday
Program Editor: Neil Bellamy 01494 812492

CLUB PERSONNEL
ChairmanGavin Lance
Press Officer: Neil Bellamy
Manager: Chris Allen

PRESTWOOD

Secretary:: Stephen Walker, 22 Almond Road, Burnham, Bucks. SL1 8HA
Tel No:01628 6038819H)   07875 271309 (M)
Ground: Prestwood Sports Centre 01494 865946

Directions: From the Chequers Public House in the Centre of Prestwood, take the road signposted to Great Hampden. The ground is approximately half a mile on the left.
Previous Leagues: Chiltonian League

FACT FILE
Formed:
Colours: Claret / claret
Change colours: orange/ blck/orange
Midweek fixtures: Tuesday
CLUB PERSONNEL
Chairman: MIke Bickerton
Manager:Steven Simmons 01494 725217

RAYNERS LANE

Secretary: Tony Pratt, 4 Stirling Close Cowley Uxbridge Middx. UB8 2BA
Tel No: 01895 233853 (H)
Ground: The Farm Sports &Social Club,151 Rayners Lane, South Harrow HA2 0XH **Tel No:** 0208 868 8724
Directions: From A40 Polish War Memorial (First junction after Northolt Aerodrome) turn left into A4180 (West End Road), approx. 500m turn right into Station Approach, at lights turn right into Victoria Road Sainsbury's on the right). At next roundabout continue straight on to lights at junction with Alexandra Avenue (Matrix pub/restaurant on left). Continue straight on over lights and take 2nd turning left into Rayners Lane. Ground is approx. half a mile on   left.
Record Gate 550 v Wealdstone, 1983 Season 2000/2001: Member of the Hellenic Lg
2004-2005 Top Scorers: Darren Gardiner 16 each

FACT FILE
Nickname: The Lane
Colours: Yellow/green/yellow
Change colours: White/red/white
Midweek fixtures: Tuesday
CLUB PERSONNEL
Chairman & Press Officer: Richard Mitchell
Prog.Ed: Peter Randell(0208 8687940)
Manager: Mick Turtleflo (07970 816095)
Physio: Danny Butler Captain: Simon
Hordern P.O.Y.: Danny Butler

WOKINGHAM & EMMBROOK

Secretary: Paul Denman,46 Welbeck, Bracknell, Berks. RG12 8UH
Tel Nos: 01344 485398 (H) 07786 231491 (M)

Ground: Lowther Road, Wokingham RG141 1JB
Tel No: 0118 9780209

Capacity: 1,500

Directions: Turn off Reading Road in Wokingham into Forest Road and then turn right
into Lowther Road. Entrance is on the right.

PREVIOUS **Names**: WokinghamTown & Emmbrook Sports
Leagues: Isthmian League (Wokingham).
Reading League (Emmbrook Sports).

FACT FILE
Formed: 2004 Changed name after merger
Colours: Orange/black/black
Change colours: White/white/orange
Midweek Matches: Tuesday
Programme Editor: Mike Bounds

CLUB PERSONNEL
Chairman:Keiron Brownl
Manager: T.B.A..

KENT LEAGUE

President: P C Wager   **Chairman:** Denise Richmond
Vice Chairman: Steve Lewis
Hon. Secretary & Treasurer: A R Vinter, Bakery House, The Street, Chilham, Nr Canterbury, Kent CT4 8BX
Tel: 01227 730457   Fax: 01227 738880

PREMIER DIVISION		P	W	D	L	F	A	Pts
1.	Maidstone United	30	22	6	2	85	23	72
2.	Beckenham Town	30	22	4	4	96	24	70
3.	Thamesmead Town	30	18	6	6	73	41	60
4.	Erith & Belvedere	30	17	7	6	50	31	58
5.	Whitstable Town	30	16	7	7	64	38	55
6.	VCD Athletic	30	15	5	10	50	31	50
7.	Herne Bay	30	14	7	9	52	33	49
8.	Lordswood	30	12	9	9	49	45	45
9.	Deal Town	30	13	4	13	53	62	43
10.	Tunbridge Wells	30	10	7	13	39	41	37
11.	Slade Green	30	9	7	14	31	56	34
12.	Hythe Town	30	7	6	17	41	51	27
13.	Greenwich Borough	30	7	3	20	36	69	24
14.	Erith Town	30	5	5	20	22	64	20
15.	Sporting Bengal United	30	3	6	21	27	107	15
16.	Sevenoaks Town	30	3	5	22	18	70	14

PREMIER DIVISION		1	2	3	4	5	6	7	8	9	10	11	12	13	14	15	16
1	Beckenham Town		5-1	2-1	4-0	4-1	1-3	0-0	4-0	2-3	9-0	4-0	3-1	8-0	3-0	4-0	6-2
2	Deal Town	0-2		2-3	5-1	7-3	1-4	2-1	1-2	1-5	0-0	4-0	3-2	1-0	1-3	1-3	2-2
3	Erith & Belvedere	1-1	2-1		2-0	3-1	1-2	3-1	2-0	0-1	2-1	2-2	3-2	1-2	0-0	0-0	1-0
4	Erith Town	1-2	1-2	0-4		0-3	0-1	1-2	2-4	1-1	1-0	0-1	1-3	1-2	0-1	1-1	0-0
5	Greenwich Borough	0-7	2-0	0-1	1-1		1-2	2-1	0-0	0-2	1-0	0-2	1-2	4-3	0-2	0-1	3-5
6	Herne Bay	0-1	0-1	1-2	3-0	0-2		3-2	3-2	0-1	3-0	4-0	8-0	1-1	1-1	0-1	1-1
7	Hythe Town	1-2	1-1	1-1	3-3	3-1	0-3		1-0	2-2	1-0	1-2	4-0	1-3	2-3	0-1	0-2
8	Lordswood	0-5	2-0	2-2	6-0	3-2	1-1	2-2		0-5	4-0	0-0	7-0	0-3	1-0	1-2	3-2
9	Maidstone United	1-1	3-1	2-1	5-0	4-1	1-0	5-2	0-1		5-0	2-0	9-0	5-0	2-1	3-0	1-2
10	Sevenoaks Town	2-6	1-1	2-1	0-1	1-3	2-2	0-1	1-1	0-4		1-3	1-0	0-3	0-1	3-3	1-5
11	Slade Green	0-2	1-2	1-2	1-0	1-1	1-0	2-1	0-1	1-2	2-1		2-2	0-4	2-0	1-7	2-5
12	Sporting Bengal United	0-3	1-2	1-1	2-3	4-1	2-2	0-6	1-1	5-0	1-1	1-1		0-7	0-0	1-5	0-7
13	Thamesmead Town	2-1	6-1	2-3	2-1	3-2	6-0	3-0	1-1	1-1	2-0	1-1	5-0		2-0	1-0	0-0
14	Tunbridge Wells	2-2	3-4	1-2	0-1	3-0	0-2	2-1	1-1	2-3	2-0	1-1	5-1	2-3		0-1	2-1
15	VCD Athletic	0-2	1-2	0-1	0-1	2-0	0-1	1-0	1-2	1-1	1-0	3-0	7-0	2-2	3-0		1-3
16	Whitstable Town	2-0	2-3	0-2	3-0	2-0	1-1	1-0	3-1	1-1	2-0	2-1	3-0	4-3	1-1	0-2	

DIVISION ONE		P	W	D	L	F	A	Pts
1	Thamesmead T. Res.	22	15	5	2	50	23	50
2	Whitstable Town Res.	22	13	3	6	46	32	42
3	Cray Wanderers Res.	22	11	5	6	51	34	38
4	Bromley Reserves	22	12	2	8	42	34	38
5	Erith Town Reserves	22	10	4	8	50	42	34
6	Dartford Reserves	21	9	5	7	38	27	32
7	Ramsgate Reserves	22	8	6	8	38	45	30
8	Ashford Town Reserves	21	8	4	9	38	46	28
9	Erith & Belvedere Res.	22	7	6	9	43	47	27
10	Maidstone United Res.	22	6	4	12	31	53	22
11	Herne Bay Reserves	22	3	5	14	25	46	14
12	Deal Town Reserves	22	3	3	16	20	43	12

DIVISION TWO		P	W	D	L	F	A	Pts
1	Folkestone Invicta	20	14	4	2	53	16	46
2	Sevenoaks Town Res.	20	11	4	5	32	22	37
3	Chatham Town Res.	20	11	1	8	47	42	34
4	Slade Green Reserves	20	9	6	5	36	22	33
5	Tunbridge Wells Res.	20	8	7	5	42	34	31
6	Lordswood Reserves	20	8	4	8	42	39	28
7	VCD Athletic Res.	19	6	4	9	27	43	22
8	Tilbury Reserves	20	5	5	10	26	33	20
9	Greenwich Borough Res.	19	5	5	9	23	37	20
10	Sittingbourne Reserves	20	4	5	11	24	42	17
11	Hythe Town Reserves	20	3	5	12	24	46	14

LEAGUE CONSTITUTION 2006-07

BECKENHAM TOWN

Formed: 1971
Nickname:Reds

Chairman: JohnWeatherhead   **Vice-Chairman:** B.Holloway   **Manager:** Kevin Sugrue

Secretary: Peter Palmer, 36 Inglewood, Pixton Way, Selsdon, Surrey CR0 9LP   **Asst.Manager**: Jason Taylor

Tel No: 020 865 13363 (H) 07774 728758

Press Officer: Name (Tel)

GROUND ADDRESS: Eden Park Avenue, Beckenham, Kent   **Ground Tel.No.:** 07774 728758

Capacity: 4,000   **Seats:** 120   **Covered:** 120   **Floodlights:** Yes

Simple Directions: M25 to A21 and on to Bromley then follow signs to Beckenham. Ground one mile west of town on A214

Midweek Home Matchday: Tuesday   **Clubhouse:** All day at week ends.   **Club Shop:** Yes

Previous Leagues: S.E.London Amateur 71-73,Metropolitan 7-75 & London Spartan 75-82

Previous Ground: Stanhope Grove, Beckenham (60 years)

Club Colours: All red   **Change Colours:** Yellow/Blue/Blue

RECORD Attendance: 720 v Berkhamsted F.A.Cup 94-95 **Goalscorer:** Ricky Bennett   **Appearances:** Lee Fabian 985

Senior Honours: Kent Senior Trophy R-Up 81-82 93-94

Beckenham Town F.C.   Photo: Alan Coomes.

CROYDON

Founded: 1953
Nickname: The Trams

Chairman: Jim Moody   **Vice-Chairman:**   **Manager:** Mick Read

Secretary: Steve Hutson, **c/o club**   **Press Officer:** Simon Hawkins (07710 459858)

Programme: 20 Pages £1.00   **Editor:** Vince Mitchell (01892 542671)

GROUND ADDRESS: Croydon Sports Arena, Albert Rd.,South Norwood, SE25 4QL   **Tel:** 0208 654 3462/8555

Capacity: 6,000   **Seats:** 450   **Covered:** 1,000   **Floodlights:** Yes

Simple Directions: From Portland Rd, into either Belmont Rd or Grasmer Rd . The stadium is off Albert Rd in South Norwood.

Midweek Home Matchday: Wednesday   **Clubhouse:** Open daily at lunch time and evenings   Club Shop: Yes

Previous Leagues: Surrey Senior 53-63 Spartan 63-64 Athenian 64-74   **Previous Name:** Croydon Amateurs1953-74

Club Colours: Sky Navy   **Change Colours:** Red & white

LAST SEASON: League: 22nd Isth. Div 1   **F.A.Cup:** Extra Prelim.Rd.   **F.A.Trophy**: Prelim Rd.

Top Scorer: **Player of the Year:**   **Captain:**

BEST PERFORMANCES

League: Isthmian Premier   **F.A. Cup:** 2nd Rd Replay 1979-80   **F.A.Vase:** 4th Rd. 1994-95

F.A.Trophy: 2nd Rd 81-82 82-83   **F.A.Amateur Cup**: 3rd Rd 71-72

RECORD Attendance:1,450 v Wycombe F.A.Cup 4th Q 1975 **Goalscorer:** Alec Jackson 111   **Fee Paid: f**or Steve Brown **Received:** from Sutton U for Peter Evans **Appearances:** Alec Jackson (1977-88 452 and Tony Luckett (1962-73) 411

Senior Honours: Isthmian Div 1 99-00 Surrey Sen. Cup81-82 R-Up2) London Sen.Cup 2001-02

DEAL TOWN

Founded: 1908
Nickname: Town

Chairman: David Saunders   **Vice-Chairman:** Bob Chivington   **Manager:** Derek Hares

Secretary: Colin Adams, 156 Mill Hill, Deal, Kent CT14 9JA

Tel No: 01304 372784

Press Officer & Prog.Ed.: Secretary   **Programme:** 30/40 Pages £1.00

GROUND ADDRESS: Charles Sports Ground, St Leonards Road, Deal, Kent.**Tel:** 01304 375623

Directions: A258 through Walmer, left into Cornwall Road,continue into Hamilton Road, veer left into Mill Road and follow round to right into Manor Road, right into St Leonards Road and ground is 100 yards on right.

Capacity: 2,500   **Seats:** 180   **Covered:** 180   **Floodlights:** Yes

Simple Directions: A258 through Walmer, left into Cornwall Raod, rightinto St Leonards Road

Midweek Home Matchday: Tuesday   **Clubhouse:** Matchdays & Functions   **Shop:** Yes

Previous Leagues: Kent 09-59, Aetolian 59-63, Southern 63-66 and Greater London 66-71

Club Colours: Black & white hoops/black/black   **Change Colours:** Red7 blckstripes/black/red

BEST PERFORMANCES: League: Kent Champions 53-54 99-00   **F.A.Vase:** Winners 99-00

Attendance: 2,495 v Newcastle Town F.A.Vase S-F 26.03.2000

Senior Honours: F.A.Vase Winners 99-00, Kent League (2) R-Up (2) and Kent Senior Trophy (2) R-Up (2)

ERITH & BELVEDERE

Founded: 1922
Nickname: Deres

Chairman: John McFadden   **Vice-Chairman:** Peter Bird   **Manager:** Barry Lakin
Secretary: Kellie Discipline, 23 Stuart Evans Close, Welling, Kent DA16 1SH **TEL No:** 01322 526184(H) 07932 756837 (M)
GROUND ADDRESS: Sharing with Welling Utd.: Park View Road Ground, Welling, Kent DA16 1SY **Tel. No.:** 0181 3011196
Capacity 4,000   **Seats:** 1,070   **Covered:** 1,000   **Floodlights:**Yes
Simple Directions: As for Weling United (Conference South)
Midweek Home Matchday: Tuesday   **Clubhouse:** Yes   **Club Shop:** Yes
Previous Names: Belvedere & District FC9Formed 1018restructured 1922)
Previous Leagues: Kent 22-29 31-39 78-82 London 29-31 Corinthian 45-63 Athenian 63-78 Southern 83-04
Club Colours: Blue&white quarters /blue/blue**Change Colours:** All Red
BEST PERFORMANCES:LEAGUE: **F.A. Cup:** 4th Qual.Rd   **F.A. Trophy:** 3rd Qual.Rd.
F.A.Vase: 3rd Rd.   **F.A.Amteur Cup:** Runners Up 1923-24 37-38
RECORD Attendance: 5,573 v Crook C.W. F.A.Amteur Cup 1949 Goalscorer:Colin Johnson 284(61-71)
Apperances: Dennis Crawford 504 (1956-71) **Victory:** 14-2 v Royal Marines Kent Lg 1933 **Defeat:** 0-15 v Ashford Kent Lg 37
SENIOR HONOURS: F.A.Am.Cup Finalists (2) Athenian Lg R-up 70-71 Kent Lg 81-82 London Sen.Cup 44-45 R-Up 38-39

ErithTown F.C.
Back Row (L-R): Dominic Coward, Paul Springett, Mike Maunsell, Chris Connelly, Robert Browning, Sean Cooney.
Front Row: Danny Little, Wayne Barrett, Chris Arnold, Darren Pruce, Jamie Lovell.

Photo: Alan Coomes.

ERITH TOWN

Founded: 1959
Nickname:The Dockers

Chairman: Albert Putman   **Vice-Chairman:** Phil Legg   **Manager:** Willie O'Sullivan
Secretary: Jim Davie, 6 Dashwood Close, Broomfield Road, Bexleyheath, Kent. DA6 7NU
Tel No: 020 8306 7068
Press Officer: Matthew Panting   **Programme Editor:** Ian Birrell   **Programme:** 40-52 Pages £1,00
GROUND ADDRESS: Erith Sports Stadium,Avenue Road, Erith, Kent DA8 3AJ   **Tel:** 01322 350271
Capacity: 1,450   **Seats:** 1,006   **Covered:** 1,066   **Floodlights:** Yes
Simple Directions: Off the A206 at Erith, into Victoria Road then left at T junction into Avenue Road. First right along driveway which leads to leisure car park. Stadium is on left.
Midweek Home Matchday: Monday   **Clubhouse:** Use Leisure facilities   **Club Shop:** No
Previous Leagues: London Metropolitan Sunday 1959-91 & London-Spartan 1991-96
Previous Names: Woolwich Town 1959-89 and 1990-97
Club Colours: Red &Black stripes/black/black **Change Colours:** White/red/red
RECORD Attendance: 325 v Charlton Athletic (Friendly) **Goalscorer:** Ben Hackett 42 (in season) and Dean Bowey
Victory: 7-2 V Canterbury City Kent Sen. Trophy 2000 **Defeat** 0-8 v Deal Town
Senior Honours: London Senior Cup R-Up 2000

592

FAVERSHAM TOWN
Founded: 1884
Nickname: Lillywhites

Chairman: Bob Macy   **Manager:** Terry Cordice   **Coach:** Paul Copley

Physio: Natalie Norris.

Secretary: Alan Trent, 8 Chobham Chase, Faversham, Kent ME13 7QD

Tel No: 01795 537552 (H) 07709937518 (M)

GROUND ADDRESS: Salters Lane,Faversham,Kent ME13 8ND   **Ground Tel. No.:** 01795 5919000

Capacity: 2000   **Seats:** 200   **Covered:** 1800   **Floodlights:** Yes

Simple Directions: From junction 7 of M2 follow A2 ground on left after 2 miles.

Midweek Home Matchday: Tuesday

Previous League: Kent County League until 2003

Club Colours: White/Black/white   **Change Colours:** All old godl

GREENWICH BOROUGH
Founded: 1928
Nickname: Boro

Chairman: T.Hassan   **Manager:** L.Hussein
Secretary: Janet Hogg c/o GBFC
Tel Nos: 0207 3543509 or 07970 986537 (M)   **Asst.Manager**: K.Crowhurst
Programme Editor: Keith Harmer (07930 618911(M)   **Programme:** 16 Pages £1.00
GROUND ADDRESS: Harrow Meadow, Eltham Green Rd., Eltham, London SE9   **Tel:** 0208 8595788
Capacity: 2,500   **Seats:** 50   **Covered:** 50   **Floodlights:** Yes
Simple Directions: From South Circulaar (A205). Ground is opposite McDonalds in Greenwich.
Midweek Home Matchday: Tuesday   **Clubhouse:** Yes   **Club Shop:** No
Previous Leagues: S.London Alliance, Kent Amateur and London Spartan 77-84
Previous Names: London Borough of Greenwich   **Previous Ground:** Erith &n Belvedere F.C. 1992-93
Club Colours: All Red   **Change Colours:** All Blue
BEST PERFORMANCES
League: Kent Lg.Champ[ions 86-87 87-88   **F.A.Vase:** 5th Rd. 1989-90
RECORD Attendance: 2,000 vCharlton Athletic (Turning on Floodlights) 1978
Senior Honours: London Spartan 79-80 Kent Senior Trophy: 1984-85

HERNE BAY
Founded: 1886
Nickname:The Bay

Chairman: J.Bathurst   **Vice-Chairman:** W.Dordoy   **Manager:** Jason Lillis
Secretary: Simon Harris,18 Landon Rd, Herne Bay CT6 6UP (rolandhb@hernebayfc.co.uk)   **Asst.Manager:** Neil Brown
Programme Editor & Press Officer: Ray Kelly **Programme:** 36 pages £1.00   **Physio:** Dave Silman
GROUND ADDRESS: Winch's field, Stanley Gardens, Herne Bay, Kent.   **Ground Tel No:** 01227 374156
Capcity: 3,000 **Seats:** 200   **Covered:** 1,500 **Floodlights:** Yes   **Website:** ww.hernebayfc.co.uk
Simple Directions: Leave new Thanet Way at Herne Bay/Canterbury exit. Fllow signs to Herne Bay via Canterbury Road.Take first left after railway bridge into Spencer Raod then first left into Stanley Gardens. Ground on left.
Midweek Home Matchday: Tuesday   **Clubhouse:** Open Matchdays   **Club Shop:** Yes
Previous Leagues: East Kent, Faversham & District, Canterbury & District, Kent Amateur, Kent, Aetolian & Athenian.
Previous Ground: Memorial Park 1886-1953   **Sponsors:** Aimteq Group Holdings Ltd.
Club Colours: Blue & White   **Change Colours:** Red & Black
LAST SEASON League: 7th   **F.A. Cup:** 1st Qualifying Round   **F.A. Vase:** 2nd Round
Top Scorer: Stuart King   **Player of the Year:** Gary Cook   **Captain:**Jack Delo
BEST PERFORMANCES
League: Kent League Champions (4)   **F.A. Cup:** 4th Qualifying Round 70-71 86-87   **F.A.Vase:** 5th Rd 1996-7
RECORD Attendance: 2,303 v Margate F.A.Cup 4th Qual Rd 70-71
Victory 19-3 v Hythe 1900 **Defeat** v RAF Manston 0-11 Kent Am Lg 94 **Fee Received**: £3,000 Mark Munday (Gravesend) 94
Senior Honours: Kent Amateur Cup 5-8 Kent League 91-2 94-5 96-7 97-8 R-up (2)

HYTHE TOWN (2001)
Founded: 1992
Nickname: Town

Chairman: Paul Markland   **Manager:** Paul Fisk   **Physio**: Debbie Bishop
Secretary: Martin Giles, 21 Wych Elm Way, Hythe, Kent CT21 6QE
Tel Nos: 01303 265962 (H) 01303 267619 (W) **e-mail:** infohythetownfc.co.uk   **Website:** www.hythetownfc.co.uk
Press Officer: Richard Giles   **Programme:** 60p   **Editor:** Martin Whybrow
GROUND ADDRESS: Reachfields Stadium, Fort Rd., Hythe, Kent   **Ground Tel:** 01303 264932 or 238256
Simple Directions: On A 259 west out of Hythe, turn left after light railway lights (Fort Road) Entrance at end.
Midweek Home Matchday: Tuesday   **Clubhouse:** Open week-ends,matchdays and training nights **Club Shop:**No
Previous Names: Hythe Town and Hythe Town 1988 Ltd   **Previous League(s):** Kent County and Southern
Club Colours: All Red   **Change Colours:** All Blue
Last Season
League: 12th   **F.A. Cup:** Preliminary Rd.   **F.A. Vase:** 4th Round
Top Scorer: Richard Sinden   **Player of the Year**: Roy Godden   **Captain:** Ian Hayes
Best Performances:
F.A. Cup: 4th Qual.Rd 1989-90   **F.A.Vase:** Semi-FInal 1989-90
RECORD Attendance: 2,147 v Yeading F.A.Vase Semi-Final 1990
Senior Honours: None since 2001

Greenwich Borough F.C. Photo: Alan Coomes.

Lordswood F.C.
Back Row (L-R): Dave Forster, Andy Forster, Bob Chiverton, Gavin Hopper, Sam Colyer, Andy Doerr.
Front Row: Steve Sharp, Ray Broad, Sean Hetterley, Nick Smith, Lyndon Guscott.

Photo: Alan Coomes.

LORDSWOOD

Founded: 1968
Nickname:Lords

Chairman: R.Constantine **Manager:** P.Piggott

Secretary: Steve Lewis, Sunnybrook,Gorsewood Road, Hartley, Longfield, Kent DA3 7DF

Tel Nos: 01474 708233 (H) 01233 822300 (W) 07775 541573(M)

Press Officer: D.Harman **Programme:** Yes

GROUND ADDRESS: Lordswood Sports Social Club, North Dane Way, Walderslade, Chatham, Kent ME5 9XX

Tel No: 01634 69138

Capacity: 600 **Seats:** 125 **Covered:** 125 **Floodlights:**Yes

Simple Directions: Please phone for dircetions.

Midweek Home Matchday: Wednesday **Clubhouse:** Yes **Club Shop:** No

Previous League: Kent County League until 1968

Club Colours: Orange/Black/Black **Change Colours:** Maroon

RECORD Attendance: 650

SEVENOAKS TOWN

Founded: 1883
Nickname:

Chairman: **Vice-Chairman:** **Manager:**

Secretary: Edwin Diplock, 23 Holly Bush Lane, Sevenoaks, Kent. YTN13 3TH

Tel No: 01732 454280

Press Officer: Name (Tel) **Programme:**

GROUND ADDRESS: Greatness Park, Seal Road, Sevenoaks, Kent **Ground Tel. No.:** 01732 454280

Capacity: 2000 **Seats:** 110 **Covered:** 200 **Floodlights:** Yes

Midweek Home Matchday: Tuesday

Previous League: Kent County League until 2003

Club Colours: Azure & blackstripes/black/black **Change Colours:** Navy & scarlet quarters/navy/navy

SLADE GREEN

Founded: 1946
Nickname:The Green

Chairman: Brian Smith **President:** P.Johnson

Manager: Phil Miles **Coach:** Peter Little **Physio:** Graham Barber

Secretary: Bruce Smith, 15 Gumping Road, Orpington, Kent BR5 1RX

Tel No: 01689 858782

Press Officer & Programme Editor: Robert Smith (01322 287982) **Prog:** 44 pages free with admission

GROUND ADDRESS: The Small Glen, Moat Lane, Slade Green, Erith, Kent **Tel:** 0132222 351077

Capacity: 3,000 **Seats:** 150 **Covered:** 400 **Floodlights:** Yes

Simple Directions: Off A206 between Erith & Dartford. 400 yards from Slade Green BR station.

Midweek Home Matchday: Tuesday **Clubhouse:** Yes **Club Shop:** No

Previous Leagues: Dartford 46-52 Kent Amateur 52-62 Greater London 62-70 **Sponsors**: Threes & Fours

Previous Name: Slade Green Athletic 46-49

Club Colours: All Green **Change Colours:** All White

RECORD Attendance: 3,000 v Millwall (friendly) 25.07.92 **Goalscorer:** Colin Dwyer **Appearances:** Colin Dwyer

Senior Honours: Kent Senior Trophy: 91-92 R-Up 80-81

SPORTING BENGAL UNITED

Founded: 1996
Nickname:

Chairman: Suroth Miah **Vice-Chairman:** **Manager:** Micky Leslie

Secretary: Sana Miiah, 11 Shadwell Gardens, Cable Street, London E1 2QG

Programme Editor: Nasyar Miiah

GROUND ADDRESS: Mile End Stadium, Rhodeswell Rd., Off Burdett Rd., London E14 **Tel:** 0208 9801885

Simple Directions: From M2/A2 continue onto A102 through Blackwell Tunnel. Left onto A13 towards centre of London and right into Burdett Road (A1205) then left at the second set of lights into St Pauls Way leading onto Rhodeswell Road. Ground is on right.

Midweek Home Matchday: Wednesday

Previous Leagues: Asian League until 1999 and London Intermediate 1999-2000

Club Colours: All Royal Blue **Change Colours:** Gold/black/black

RECORD Attendance: 4,235 v Touring Phalco Mohammedan S.C. Goalscorer

Slade Green F.C. - Back Row (L-R): Tony Gallagher, Jason Elliott, Gary Arterton, Mark Penny, Robert Browning, Shaun Maylon. **Front Row:** Lee Jull, Scott Lewis, Glenn McTaggart, Tony Weir, Lee Barber. Photo: Alan Coomes.

V.C.D. Athletic F.C. - Back Row (L-R): Chris Whitehouse, Mark greatorex, Martin Driscoll, Paul Foley, Lee Coburn, Steve Porter, Grant Wallis, James Brown, Phil Turner, Martin Ford (Manager). **Front Row:** Danny Penny, Ashley Proberts, David Hunt, Kevin Winchcombe, Steve Hogg, Stuart Abbott, Clayton Proberts. Photo: Alan Coomes.

Whitstable Town F.C. Back Row (L-R): Marc Seager, Leon Ingram, Michael Adcock, Rob Thomas, Mark Hickson, Andy Constable. **Front Row:** Tom Parker, Andy Martin, Gary Ward, Shane Davies, Marcus Perona. Photo: AlanCoomes.

THAMESMEAD TOWN

Founded: 1970
Nickname: The Mead

Chairman: Nicky O'Keefe　　　**Vice-Chairman:** John Kelly　　　**Manager:** Paul Blade
Secretary: David Joy, The Cottage, Halcot Avenue, Bexleyheath, Kent DA6 7QB　　　**Physio:** Allen Martin
Tel No: 01322 5588429　　　**Press Officer:** Keith McMahon
Sponsors: Hawk Roofing　　　**Programme:** Price 1,00　　　**Editor:** Albert Panting
Ground: Bayliss Avenue, Thamesmead, London SE28 8NJ　(Tel No: 0181 311 4211)
Capacity: 400　　　**Seats:** 125　　　**Covered:** 125　　　**Floodlights:**Yes
Simple Directions: From Dartford Tunnel A2 to London, exit Danson interchange and follow signs for Thamesmead and Abbey Wood. From Abbey Wood BR go north east along Harrow Manor Way into Crossways at 3rd roundabout. Bayliss Avenue is third on right. Bexley bus 272 stops in Crossway near Bayliss Avenue.
Midweek Home Matchday: Tuesday　　　**Clubhouse:** Full facilities open daily　　　**Club Shop:**No
Previous League: London Spartan 1980-91　　　**Previous Ground:** Meridian Sports Ground, Charlton
Club Colours: Green & white/green/green　　　**Change Colours:** All Blue
RECORD Att:400 v Wimbledon ground opening 1988　**Goalscorer:** Delroy D'Oyley **Victory** 9-0 v Ket Police, Kent Lg.19.04.94
Senior Honours: Spartan Lg Div 3 Kent League Div 2 94-95 Kent Senior Trophy 2004-2005

TUNBRIDGE WELLS

Chairman: N.Sales　　　**President**: W.Wager　　　**Vice-Chairman:** J.Farnie　　　**Manager:** K.Metcalfe
Secretary: Barry Whitlock, 5 Squirrel Way, Tunbridge Wells. TN2 3LW　　　**Sec's Tel No**: 07774 893218
Programme Editor: Simon Harris　　　**Programme:** 40 Pages -£1.00　　**Website:** www.tunbridgewellsfc.co.uk
GROUND ADDRESS: CulverdenStadium, Culverden Down, Tunbridge Wells, Kent TN4 9SH　　**Tel:** 01892 520517
Capacity: 3,750　　　**Seats:** 250　　　**Covered:** 1,000　　　**Floodlights:** Yes
Simple Directions: Leave town on main Tonbridge road (A26) and turn left into Culverden Down
Midweek Home Matchday: Wednesday　　　**Clubhouse:** Open matchdays　　　**Club Shop:**No
Previous Grounds: Down Lane 1906, Combley Park 06-10, Swis Cottage 1014, Down Farm19-39, St Johns 47-50, Eridge Road 50-67　　**Previous Names:** None but predecessors include T.W. Rangers and T.W. United
Club Colours: All red　　　**Change Colours:** Yellow/blue/blue
BEST PERFORMANCES
League: 2nd 1984-85　　　**F.A. Cup:** 3rd Qualifying Round　　　**F.A.Vase:** 3rd Round
RECORD Attendance: 967 v Maidstone U. F.A.Cup 1969 **Goalscorer:** John Wingate 151 **Apps:** Tony Atkins 410
Victory: 10-0 v Deal (H) May 1986　**Defeat:** 1-11 v Deal Town　(H) 20.02.93
Senior Honours: Kent League Champions 84-85 Kent Senior Trophy　R-up 85-86 91-92

VICKERS CRAYFORD, DARTFORD ATHLETIC

Founded: 1916
Nickname: The Vickers

Chairman: Michael Bonello
Manager: Martin Ford　　　**Asst.Manager/Physio:** Peter Burke　　　**Coach:** Roy Passey
Secretary: Arthur Fox,Lyons Place, Upper St Helens Road, Hedge End Southampton SO30 0JB
Tel No: 02380 493346
Programme: 40 pages 50p
GROUND ADDRESS: Sharing with Thamesmead Town in the same league.　　　**Tel:** 01813114211
Midweek Matchday: Wednesday　　　**Clubhouse:** Yes　　　**Club Shop:** No
Previous Grounds: Flamingo Park, Sidcup (pre 1994),VCD Sports & Social Club,Old Road Crayford.
Previous League(s): Kent County
Club Colours: Green & white/green/green　　　**Change Colours:** Blue & white/blue/blue
RECORD Victory: 10-1 v Canterbury City 14.05.01 **Defeat** 0-5 v Deal Town 20.04 02
Senior Honours: West Kent Cup 87-88

WHITSTABLE TOWN

Founded: 1885
Nickname:Oystermen/Natives

Chairman:　Joe Brownett　　　**Vice-Chairman:**　Alan Gower　　　**President**: George Gifford
Manager: Matt Toms　　　**Assistant Managers:** Marc Seager & Mark Lane **Physio:** Graeme Brown
Secretary: Alan Gower,110 Queens Road, Whitstable, Kent CT5 2JJ
Tel No: 01227 277875(H) 01306 884488 (W)　07973 125638 (H)
Programme Editor: Jon Homer　　　**Programme:** 48 Pages　£1.00　　　**Website:** whitstabletownfc.co.uk
GROUND ADDRESS: Belmont Road, Belmont, Whitstable, Kent.　　　**Ground Tel.No.:** 01227 266012
Capacity: 2.000　　　**Seats:** 500　　　**Covered:**1,000　　　**Floodlights:** Yes
Simple Directions: From Thanet Way (A299) left at Tescos' roundabout and down Millstrood Road. Ground at bottom of road 400 yards from Whitstable BR station.
Midweek Home Matchday: Tuesday　　　**Clubhouse:** Open matchdays & functions　**Club Shop:** Yes
Previous League(s): E.Kent 1897-1909, Kent 09-59, Aetolian 59-60, Kent Amateur 60-62 63-64 S.E.Anglian 62-63, Gtr London 64-67 Kent Premier 67-68 (also in New Brompton, Thanet & Faversham & District leagues over the years
Club Colours: Red & white/white/red　　　**Change Colours:** Yellow/blue/yellow
RECORD Crowd: 2,500 v Gravesend F.A.Cup 19.10.87 **Goalscorer:** Barry Godfrey　**Appearances:** Frank Cox 429 (50-60)
Senior Honours: Kent Amateur Cup 28-29 Kent Senior Trophy R-Up (3)

MIDLAND FOOTBALL ALLIANCE

SPONSORED BY: POLYMAC SERVICES
President: Malcolm Lycett **Chairman:** Mick Joiner
Secretary: Peter Dagger, 32 Drysdale Close,
Wickhamford, Worcestershire WR11 7RZ
Tel: 01386 831763 Fax: 01386 833488
E-mail: PDagger@talk21.com

		P	W	D	L	F	A	Pts
1.	Chasetown	42	29	7	6	74	32	94
2.	Stourbridge	42	29	5	8	110	55	92
3.	Malvern Town	42	27	4	11	95	56	85
4.	Romulus	42	23	11	8	84	49	80
5.	Leamington	42	21	11	10	79	44	74
6.	Racing Club Warwick	42	22	7	13	72	55	73
7.	Quorn	42	21	6	15	71	51	69
8.	Coalville Town	42	21	6	15	63	60	69
9.	Barwell	42	20	8	14	83	66	68
10.	Boldmere St Michaels	42	17	12	13	60	48	63
11.	Tipton Town)	42	15	13	14	74	69	58
12.	Oldbury United	42	16	10	16	58	58	58
13.	Loughborough Dynamo	42	16	8	18	53	53	56
14.	Alvechurch	42	16	7	19	59	64	55
15.	Stratford Town	42	15	6	21	49	55	51
16.	Studley	42	14	7	21	54	81	49
17.	Biddulph Victoria	42	12	9	21	55	83	45
18.	Oadby Town	42	10	14	18	50	64	44
19.	Causeway United	42	9	7	26	49	89	34
20.	Westfields	42	8	9	25	48	88	33
21.	Cradley Town	42	5	9	28	38	94	24
22.	Rocester	42	4	8	30	36	100	20

		1	2	3	4	5	6	7	8	9	10	11	12	13	14	15	16	17	18	19	20	21	22
1	Alvechurch		3-3	2-1	1-0	5-0	1-2	3-2	2-1	1-4	0-1	0-1	3-1	2-0	0-2	0-2	3-0	1-3	2-2	1-1	3-0	1-0	2-1
2	Barwell	2-1		3-1	0-4	2-1	1-1	3-0	2-1	0-4	2-0	0-2	0-3	1-1	1-2	1-2	6-0	1-2	1-0	1-2	4-1	2-4	2-0
3	Biddulph Victoria	2-1	1-4		1-3	5-0	0-2	1-0	1-1	1-1	2-2	3-1	2-1	2-1	0-1	1-0	2-2	1-2	0-4	0-2	0-0	3-5	1-1
4	Boldmere St.M	2-0	3-3	3-1		0-0	1-2	1-2	1-1	2-3	1-1	0-1	1-1	1-1	0-0	3-1	1-1	0-1	2-0	2-3	1-1	2-1	1-1
5	Causeway Utd	0-3	1-3	0-1	1-1		0-1	1-3	4-0	0-3	1-4	1-2	3-0	0-0	0-2	2-0	3-3	1-2	3-3	0-2	2-2	1-2	1-0
6	Chasetown	3-2	2-1	2-0	3-0	2-1		1-1	5-0	0-2	1-0	3-1	0-0	1-2	1-2	2-1	1-0	2-0	1-0	1-0	1-1	1-1	2-0
7	Coalville Town	3-1	0-4	2-1	0-0	1-2	0-1		1-0	1-0	1-1	1-0	5-1	0-2	1-0	0-2	2-1	1-2	3-4	1-1	4-2	3-2	1-0
8	Cradley Town	1-3	0-2	1-2	2-0	1-3	1-4	1-3		0-4	1-3	1-3	1-1	0-0	0-2	1-2	3-3	1-1	0-2	1-0	3-5	0-0	1-1
9	Leamington	1-1	1-1	5-0	0-0	3-1	1-3	2-0	4-1		1-3	0-2	1-0	2-0	1-1	2-1	4-0	1-1	1-2	1-0	3-0	3-0	3-0
10	Loughborough	4-0	1-2	1-1	3-1	3-0	0-1	0-1	0-2	0-0		0-1	1-0	0-2	0-3	4-2	0-0	0-1	0-1	3-1	0-1	1-0	3-1
11	Malvern Town	5-0	5-3	5-0	3-2	1-3	3-1	2-3	6-2	4-1	2-1		2-0	1-0	2-1	2-3	2-0	2-2	6-3	1-1	2-1	0-2	3-1
12	Oadby Town	0-1	0-1	3-3	0-1	5-2	1-2	2-1	1-1	0-3	1-1	1-1		0-0	1-4	0-3	1-0	0-3	3-3	2-1	6-0	0-2	4-2
13	Oldbury United	1-0	2-1	2-3	1-2	2-0	0-3	2-4	2-1	4-1	2-3	2-1	2-3		1-2	0-2	4-1	1-0	0-3	2-4	4-0	3-1	3-3
14	Quorn	3-0	3-0	1-1	3-0	1-1	0-2	1-0	6-0	1-1	2-0	3-5	0-2	1-2		1-2	1-3	0-1	1-5	0-1	2-0	3-2	3-3
15	Racing Club W.	0-0	4-4	2-0	1-0	1-1	3-1	2-2	2-1	0-1	2-0	3-1	1-2	2-2	0-1		3-1	1-2	1-3	2-1	0-0	4-1	2-2
16	Rocester	1-1	4-5	1-3	0-2	0-1	0-2	0-2	1-0	0-0	0-2	1-2	2-2	2-1	1-3	0-2		4-2	0-5	1-4	0-1	0-0	1-3
17	Romulus	0-2	2-2	5-0	0-2	4-2	1-1	4-0	2-0	2-2	4-0	1-1	0-0	1-1	2-1	2-5	5-0		0-2	1-1	3-0	1-0	4-0
18	Stourbridge	2-0	1-0	3-1	0-2	4-1	0-2	4-2	3-2	2-1	4-1	2-1	1-1	3-0	2-4	6-1	4-1	0-4		1-2	5-1	3-2	4-1
19	Stratford Town	2-1	2-1	2-1	2-3	1-2	1-3	0-2	0-1	1-3	1-1	1-0	2-0	0-1	0-2	1-2	2-0	1-3	0-2		2-2	1-0	3-0
20	Studley	2-4	0-2	3-1	1-2	3-2	0-1	3-0	1-0	3-1	2-0	0-2	0-0	2-0	0-1	1-2	2-0	2-3	0-4	1-0		2-3	1-0
21	Tipton Town	2-2	1-4	2-2	2-5	3-0	2-0	0-0	6-1	2-2	0-2	1-4	1-1	2-2	2-2	3-0	4-1	2-2	2-1	4-2			2-1
22	Westfields	1-0	0-0	0-3	2-0	3-2	0-5	1-2	0-2	3-2	2-3	2-4	1-0	0-0	1-0	0-1	3-1	0-4	1-5	1-2	3-3	1-1	

L E A G U E   C U P

FIRST ROUND

Alvechurch	v	Boldmere St. Michaels	1-0
Barwell	v	Stratford Town	2-1
Cradley Town	v	Studley	2-4
Romulus	v	Tipton Town	1-2
Westfields	v	Oldbury United	2-1
Stourbridge	v	Loughborough Dynamo	1-0

SECOND ROUND

Barwell	v	Westfields	3-0
Chasetown	v	Oadby Town	3-0
Coalville Town	v	Causeway United	3-0
Leamington	v	Rocester	4-1
Malvern Town	v	Alvechurch	2-3
Quorn	v	Tipton Town	1-2
Racing Club W.(H)	v	Biddulph Victoria	1-0
Stourbridge	v	Studley	5-0

THIRD ROUND

Barwell	v	Alvechurch	2-0
Chasetown	v	Stourbridge	5-2
Leamington	v	Coalville Town	2-2
Tipton Town	v	Racing Club Warwick (H)	2-0

SEMI-FINALS (played over two legs, home and away)

			1st	2nd
Chasetown	v	Leamington	1-3	1-0
Tipton Town	v	Barwell	0-1	0-1

THE FINAL

Barwell	v	Leamington	3-1 Att: 820

LEAGUE CONSTITUTION 2006-07

ALVECHURCH

Formed: 1929 Re-Formed 1994
Nickname: The Church

Chairman: Peter Eacock   **Director of Football:** Colin Strong   **Patron:** Roy Yardley   **Manager:** Peter Frain

Secretary: Stephen Denny, 11 Shawhurst Croft, Hollywood, Birmingham B47 5PB

Tel. Nos : 01564 822302 (H) 07710012733 (M)   **Website:**www.alvechurchfc.com

GROUND ADDRESS: Lye Meadow, Redditch Road, Alvechurch, Worcs.   **Tel:** 0121 445 2929

Capacity: 3,000   **Seats:** 100   **Covered:** 300   **Floodlights:**Yes

Simple Directions: M42 Jct 2 follow signs to Redditch. At island turn right to Alvechurch.Ground one mile on right.

Midweek Home Matchday: Tuesday   **Clubhouse:** Open evenings +matchdays   **Club Shop:** No

Previous Name: None, but Predecessors Alvechurch FC (1929 -1992)   **Previous League:** Midland Combination

Club Colours: Gold/black/black   **Change Colours:** All Blue

Senior Honours: Midland Combination Premier Champions 2002-2003 and Worcs Senior Urn Winners 2003-04 2004-05

ATHERSTONE TOWN

Formed: 2004
Nickname: The Adders

Chairman: Graham Read

Secretary: Peter Lowe.

Tel. Nos : (H) 01827 735 640 (M) 07733 023 803

GROUND ADDRESS: Sheepy Road, Atherston, Warwickshire.   **Tel:** 01827 717 829

Simple Directions: From junction 10 M42 join the A5 towards Nuneaton/Atherstone (South). After 3.7 miles at roundabout sign posted B4116 SheepyMagna/Twycross turn left into Holly Lane. At next roundabout turn right into Rowland Way, in 300 yards past Gypsy Lane turn through red gates on the right into club carpark.

Club Colours: Red with white/white/red   **Change Colours:** Yellow with black/blue/yellow

Previous League(s): Midland Combination

Senior Honours: Midland Combination Premier Champions 2005-06

Barwell F.C. Back Row (L-R): Steve Greenhill (Assistant Manager), Vic Coleman (Physio), Carl Adams, Dean Sargeant, Steve White, Danny Spencer, Dave Sharpe, Danny Kitching, Stuart Burton, Dave Hart, Adam Cheater, Karl Noble, Ian Blyth (Coach).
Front: Reece Lester, Nick Pollard, Michael Skubala, Bob Steel (Manager), Scott Clamp (capt), Dave Laing (Chairman), Andy Tiday, Dale Turner, Craig Noble.

BARWELL

Founded: 1986
Nickname:The Kirkby Roaders

Chairman: David Laing   **Vice-Chairman:** Colin Burton   **Manager:** Bob Steel
Secretary: Mrs Shirley Brown, 101 Eskdale Rooad, Hinckley, LE10 0NW
Tel Nos: 01455 446048 **E-mail:** shirley.brown16@ntlworld.com
Press Officer: Merv Nash   **Editor** Lee Wright   **Programme:** 38 Pages £1.00
GROUND ADDRESS: Kirkby Road, Barwell, Leics.   **Ground Tel. No.:** 01455 843067
Capacity: 2,500   **Seats:** 256   **Covered:** 750   **Floodlights:**Yes
Simple Directions: From A47 from Earl Shilton go over lights and after a mile take Barwell sign at roundabout and then over mini roundabout in village and turn right into Kirkby Road. Ground is 400 yards on right.
Midweek Home Matchday: Tuesday   **Clubhouse:** Open daily.   **Club Shop:** No
Previous Names: Barwell Athletic FC and Hinckley FC amalgamated in 1992
Previous Leagues: Midland Comb 92-94, as BarwellAth. Leics Sen. and as Hinckley FC Central Midlands 86-88
Club Colours: Yellow/green/green   **Change Colours:** All Sky Blue
LAST SEASON: League: 9th
Top Scorer: Craig Noble 23   **Players of the Year:** Scott Clamp & Karl Noble   **Captain:** Scott Clamp
BEST PERFORMANCES
League: 3rd Midland Alliance   **F.A. Cup:** 1st Qualifying Round   **F.A.Vase:** 5th Rd 2000-01
RECORD Attendance: **Goalscorer:** Andy Lucas   **Apps:** Adrian Baker
SENIOR HONOURS: League Cup Winners 2005-2006

BIDDULPH VICTORIA

Founded: 1969
Nickname:The Vics

Chairman: Terry Greer   **Vice-Chairman:** John Shalcross
Manager: Stuart Heeps   **Asst.Manager:** Matt Grehan   **Physio:**Neville Kelter
Tel No: 01782 523259   **Sponsor:** Priory Property Services   **Web:** www.biddulphvictoriafc.co.uk
Press Officer & Programme Editor: Sec.   **Programme:** 40 Pages £1.00
Club Colours: Sky Blue & Maroon   **Change Colours:** Yellow & Navy Blue
GROUND ADDRESS: Tunstall Road, Biddulph, Stoke-on-Trent   **Ground Tel.No.:** 01782 522737
Capacity: 2,500   **Seats:** 224   **Covered:** 224   **Floodlights:** Yes
Simple Directions: Entering Biddulph from Congleton on A527. drive through town and over lights. to ground 250yds on left.
Midweek Home Matchday: Tuesday   **Clubhouse:** lpm Sats & 7pm week ends   **Club Shop:** No
Previous Names: Knypersley Victoria until 2002
Previous League(s): Leek & Moorlands 69-78 Staffs Co.(North) 78-83 Staffs Senior 83-90.West Mids (Reg) 90-94
LAST SEASON: 17th
Top Scorer: John Paul Jones   **Players of the Year:** Stephen Intihar & John Paul Jones **Captain:** Scott Burge
League: 6th MIdland Alliance   **F.A. Cup:** 4th Qualifying Rd.   **F.A.Vase:** 2nd Rd 97-98
RECORD Attendance: 1,100 v Port Vale (friendly) 1989 **Goalscorer:** John Burndred 128 **Appearances:**Terry Stanway 682
SENIOR HONOURS:

BOLDMERE ST.MICHAELS

Founded: 1883
Nickname: Mikes

Chairman: Keith Fielding   **Vice-Chairman: Dave Holvey**   **Manager:** Rob Mallaband

Secretary: Rob Paterson, 6 Salisbury House, Church Road, Erdington, Birmingham B422 DR

Tel No: 0121 382 4472 (H) 07779 805111 (M)

Programme: 32 Pages(£5.0 charge inc prog)**Programme Editor:** D.Holvey (0121 35363210)

Ground Address:Trevor Brown Memorial Ground, Church Road, Boldmere, Sutton Coldfield B37 7DN

TelNo: 0121 373 4435/384 7531   Website: www.clubwebsite.co.uk/boldmerstmichaelsfc/

Capacity: 2,500   **Seats:** 230   **Covered:**400   **Floodlights:** Yes

Simple Directions: A38 & A5127 fronm City towards Sutton Coldfield, left at Yenton lights onto A452 (Chester Rd). Church Road is sixth turning on the right.

Midweek Home Matchday: Tuesday   **Clubhouse:** Open every evening and some lunchtimes **Club Shop:**No

Previous Leagues: West Midlands

Club Colours: White/black/black   **Change Colours:** All Amber

Senior Honours: Birmingham Junior Cup AFA Senior Cup 47-48   **F.A.Amateur Cup:** Semi-Final 47-48

CAUSEWAY UNITED

Founded: 1957
Nickname:

Chairman: Steve Hulston   **Vice-Chairman:** John Truscott   **Manager:** Andy Mole

Secretary: Malcolm Powell,11 Birch Drive,Halesowen, West MidlandsB62 9HU   **Coaches** : Rob & Steve Shilvock

Tel Nos:0121 6024237 (H) 07977 057050 (M) 01575 434269 (M)   **Sponsor:** Hayley Green Commercials

Progtamme Editor: Kevin Boote   **Programme:** 24 Pages £1.00   Website:www.causewayunited.co.uk

GROUND ADDRESS: Groundshare with Tividale F.C.   **Tel:** 01384 211743

Capacity: 5,000   **Seats:**420   **Covered:** 1,420   **Floodlights:** Yes

Simple Directions: M5 jct 3, A456 (signed Kidderminster) right onto A 459 at first island.Left at next island (A458) then 3rd left at next islnd into Grammar School Lane, on to Old Hawne Lane and ground is 400 yards on left.

Midweek Home Matchday: Tuesday   **Clubhouse:** Open daily Tel No: 0121 602 2210

Club Colours: All Blue   **Change Colours**: All Red

BEST PERFORMANCES

League: 11th   **F.A. Cup:** 1st Qualifying Round   **F.A.Vase:** 3rd Rd

RECORD Attendance: 150   **Appearances:** Malcolm Power 300+

COALVILLE TOWN

Founded: 1994
Nickname: The Ravens

Chairman: Glyn Rennocks   **Vice-Chairman:** Steve Price   **President:** Mick Jordan

Manager: Lee Harriman

Secretary: Robert Brooks, 17 Ashland Drive, Coalville, Leics. LE67 3NH   **Sec's Tel: No:** 01530 833269 (H)

Press Officer: Dan Gallagher   **Programme:** 20 Pages £1.00 **Website:** www.coalvilletownfc.co.uk

GROUND ADDRESS: Owen Street Sports Ground,Owen Street, Coalville   **Ground Tel. No.:** 01530 833365

Capacity: 2,000   **Seats:** 240   **Covered:** 240   **Floodlights:** Yes

Simple Directions: From M21 take A511 towards Coalville. At third roundabout take third exit,then at fourth roundabout bear left to Coalville centre. At second lights left into Velvoir Road and second right into Owen St. Ground is at left at top of road.

Midweek Home Matchday: Tuesday   **Clubhouse:** Match days & training nights   **Club Shop:** No

Previous Names: Ravenstoke Miners Athletic 25-58, Ravenstoke F.C. 58-95 Colaville F.C. 95-98

Previous Leagues: Coalville & Dist. Amateur 1926-29 33-35 46-74 N.Leicester 74-91 & Leics Sen 1991 -2003

Club Colours: Black & white/White/Red   **Change Colours:** All Maroon

BEST PERFORMANCES

League: 3rd Mid land Alliance 2004-2005   **F.A. Cup:** 1st Round Proper   **F.A.Vase:** 1st Round

RECORD Attendance: 1,500   **Appearances:** Nigel Simms

Senior Honours: Leics Sen. Cup (as Coalville Town) 99-00 R-Up 01-02

CRADLEY TOWN

Founded: 1948
Nickname: Hammers

Chairman: Trevor Thomas   **President:** Roy Kirton

Manager: Trevor Thomas   **Asst.Manager**: David Connell   **Physio:** Steve Burrell.

Secretary: David Attwood, 4 Birch Coppice, Quarry Bank, Brierley Hill,   **Sponsor:** Stables Solicitors

W.Midlands. DY 5 1AP **Tel No:** 01384 637430 **Programme:** Yes   **Press Officer:** Trevor Thomas (01384 569658)

GROUND ADDRESS: Beeches View, Beeches View Avenue, Cradley,Halesowen B63 2HB   **Tel. No:** 01384 569658

Capacity:1,000   **Seats:** 200   **Covered:** 350   **Floodlights:** Yes   **Programme** : Yes   **Club Shop:** No

Simple Directions: M5 jct 3 A456 Rt at 2nd island into Hagley Road. 3rd left to Rosemary Rd. Straight into LansdowneRd /Dunstall Rd. then left at T jct into Hntingtree Rd/Lutley Mill Rd.Left at next T jct into Stourbridge Rd and left nto Beeches Rd East. First left into Abbey Rd. and right into Beeches View Avenue. Ground entrance between houses 48 and 50

Midweek Home Matchday: Tuesday   **Clubhouse:** Open matchdays only with food available

Previous Leagues: Metropolitan, Brierley Hill, Kidderminster,West Mids Amateur, Midland Comb 71-82 West Midlands 82-99

Previous Name: Albion Haden United   **Club Colours:** Red/black/red   **Change Colours:** All Sky Blue

LAST SEASON: League: 21st   **F.A. Cup:** 1st Qualifying Round   **F.A. Vase:** 2nd Round

Top Scorer: Stuart How   **Player of the Year:** Tim Beech   **Captain**:Richard Oakley

Best Performances: League: 12th Mid. Alliance **F.A.** Cup: 1st Qualifying Round   **F.A.**Vase: 2ndt Round 2005-06

RECORD Attendance: 1,000 v Aston Villa friendly   **Goalscorer:** Jim Nugent   **Appearances:** R.J.Haywood

Fee Paid: £1,000 to Oldswinford for Darren Marsh   **Received:** £20,000 from Swansea 1991 for John Williams

Victory: 9-1 v Wolverhampton U (H) W Mids 1990   **Defeat:** 0-9 v Paget Rangers (A) Inv.Cup 97

FRIAR LANE & EPWORTH
Formed: 2003

Chairman: Clive Gibbons
Secretary: Robert Beeson.
Tel. Nos : (H) 01664 424 086 (M) 07759 745 780
GROUND ADDRESS: Whittier Road, Off Knighton Lane, Aylestone Park, Leicester, LE2 6FT   **Tel:** 0116 283 3629
Simple Directions: Northbound M1......Leave M1 at junction 21A and follow B5380 to Braunstone Frith, Kirkby Muxloe. At the roundabout take the 3 rd exit and join M1 towards London and then follow directions as Southbound below.
Southbound M1.....Leave M1 at junction21 and at roundabout take 1 st exit onto A5460 to Leicester, go left and at roundabout take first exit onto A563 (signposted Outer Ring Leicest5er South and East). At traffic lights continue onto Soar Valley Way A563. At traffic lights continue until you reach Pork Pie roundabout, take 2 nd exit onto B5366 (signposted city centre) continue and then turn right into Copinger Road and then left into Whittier Road and the ground is on the right.
Club Colours: White/black/black   **Change Colours:** Orange/black or white/orange
Previous League(s): Leicestershire Senior
Senior Honours: Leicestershire Senior Premier Champions 2005-06

LEAMINGTON
Founded: 1891 Re-Formed 2000 Nickname: Brakes

Chairman: Mick Brady   **Vice-Chairman:** Vic Shepherd   **President**: David Hucker
Manager: Jasen Cadden   **Asst.Manager**: Darren Tank
Secretary: Brian Knibb, 61 Villiers St., Leamington Spa, Warwicks. CV32 5YA   **Sec's Tel No**: 01926 429066
Programme Editor: Roger Vincent   **Programme:** 24 Pages Price £1.00
GROUND: New Windmill Ground, Harbury Lane, Whitmarsh, Leamington Warwicks.CV33 9JR **Tel No**: 01926 430406
Capacity: 5,000   **Seats:** 120   **Covered:** 720   **Floodlights:** Yes
Simple Directions: Via M40 follow signs to Leamington Spa. On outskirts turn rt at roundabout towards Harbury. Over traffic lights towards Harbury.(With Leamington to the left and Bishops Tachbrook to the rihjt) Ground is about two miles on left.
Midweek Home Matchday: Tuesday   **Clubhouse:** New and fully equipped and operational   **Club Shop:** Yes
Previous Names: Leamington Town, Lockheed Leamington and AP Leamington
Previous League (as Leamington F.C.) Midland Combination
Club Colours: Gold/Black/Gold   **Change Colours:** All Royal Blue
LAST SEASON :League: 5th Midland Alliance   **F.A. Cup:** 1st Round   **F.A. Vase:** 4th Rd.
Top Scorer: Richard Adams   **Player of the Year:** Jon Adams   **Captain:** Steve Thompson
BEST PERFORMANCES: League: 5th Mid.Alliance 05-06   **F.A. Cup:** 1st Rd 05-06   **F.A.Vase:** 4th Rd 03-04 05-06
RECORD Attendance: 1,263 v Rugby Town 2001   **Goalscorer:** Josh Blake   **Appearances:** Josh Blake (250)
Senior Honours: Mid Alliance Cup R-Up 05-06 Midl Comb Champions 2004-05 R-Up 03-04 Div 1 R-up 2001-2 Div 2 Winners 2001-02

LOUGHBOROUGH DYNAMO
Founded: 1955 Nickname: The Moes

Chairman: Frank Fall   **Sponsor:** Harlequin Express
Joint Managers: Doug Keast & Adam Beasley   **Physio**: Dave Commons
Secretary: Brian Pugh, 15 Coe Avenue, Thorpe Acre, Loughborough. LE11 4SE
Tel No: 07775 825 321
Press Officer: Brian Pugh (0777 582 5321)   **Programme:** Yes
GROUND ADDRESS: Nanpanton Sport Ground, Loughborough, Leics..   **Ground Tel.** No: 01509 612144
Capacity: 1,500   **Seats:** 250   **Covered:** Yes   **Floodlights:** Yes
Simple Directions: From Junction 23 of M1 take A521 towards Loughborough, turn right at Snells Nook Lane then left at Napanatan Lane and right at Watermead Lane.
Midweek Home Matchday: Tuesday   **Clubhouse:** Open Matchdays   **Club Shop:** No
Club Colours: Gold/black/gold   **Change Colours:** All Blue
LAST SEASON
League: 13th   **F.A. Cup:** Extra Preliminary Round   **F.A. Vase:** 1st Qualifying Round
Top Scorer: Nathan Jones   **Player of the Year:** Ian Guant   **Captain**: Ian Guant
Best Performances
League: 13th Midland Alliance 2005-06   **F.A. Cup:** Extra Preliminary Round 2005-06 **F.A.Vase:** 2nd Round 2004-05
Senior Honours: Leics Sen Lg Champions 03-04, Div 1 01-02 and Leics. Senior Cup 02-03 03-04

MARKET DRAYTON TOWN   Formed: 1969

Chairman: Julian Parton
Secretary: Brian Garratt.
Tel. Nos : (H) 01630 654 618 (Fax) 01630 658 859
GROUND ADDRESS: Greenfields Sports Ground, Greenfield Lane, Market Drayton. **Tel:** 01630-655088
Simple Directions: Via Wolverhampton....Take A41 to Tern Hill Island, turn right towards Newcastle under Lyme. Go straight ahead at the first roundabout (by Muller Factory) and at next roundabout (by the Gingerbread Pub). After 200 yards, before going over bridge, turn right into Greenfields Lane. The ground is 150 yards on the right. Car parking is in the Rugby Club opposite the ground.
Via M6...Leave motorway at junction 15 at traffic island turn right onto the A519. In approx 200 yards at the first set of traffic lights turn right (signposted Market Drayton) then join A53 going left towards Market Drayton. When you reach Market Drayton stay on bypass to first traffic island by the Gingerbread Pub and follow directions as above.
Via A50... Travel into Stoke passing the Britannia Stadium and Incinerator on your left. At the traffic island turn left onto the A500 heading towards the M6. At the traffis island at the end of the A500 turn left and follow directions as above.
Club Colours: All Red   **Change Colours:** All blue
Previous League(s): West Midlands (Regional) League
Senior Honours: West Midlands Premier Champions 2005-06

OADBY TOWN   Founded: 1937
Nickname:

Chairman: Brian Fletcher-Warrington   **President:** David Bonner   **Manager:** Lee Adam
Directors: K.G.Farrant, M.V.Burton, L.C.Adam and I.Phillips,
Secretary: Jim Hubbard, 85 Trevino Drive,Leicester, LE4 7PH   **Programme Editor:** Kevin Zupp
Tel Nos: 0116 2214405(H) 0116 2715728 (W) 07939 393207 (M)   Website: www.oadbytoenfc.co.uk
Ground Address: Topps Park, Wigston Rd., Oadby, Leics. LE2 5QG.   **Contact:** Mr M.V.Burton   **Tel. No:** 0116 2718885
Capacity: 5,000   **Seats:** 224   **Covered:** 224   **Floodlights:** Yes
Simple Directions: M68 M1 Jct 21 Follow A46 to Leicester take 4th turning off roundabout to Narborough /Enderby. Left at outer ring road A563 towards Oadby. Rt at lights after 4.5 miles towards Wigston. One Mile to roundabout turn left first exit to Oadby and ground is another mile on right opposite Leicester Tigers Training Ground.
Midweek Home Matchday: Tuesday   **Clubhouse:** Open all day.   **Club Shop:** Yes
Previous League: Leicestershire Senior
Club Colours: All red   **Change Colours:** All Blue
BEST PERFORMANCES
League: Champions 99-00   **F.A. Cup:** 2nd Qual.Rd.   **F.A.Vase:** Semi-Final 2002-2003
Senior Honours: Mid. F. Alliance 99-00 Leics Sen Lg (8) Leics Senior Cup 68-69, 70-71, 2004-2005

OLDBURY UNITED   Founded: 1958
Nickname: The Blues

Chairman: Eddie Winkett   **Vice-Chairman:** Alan Griffin   **Sponsors:** GLS Football.Com
Manager: Morton Bartlett   **Asst.Manager:** Martin Thomas   **Physio:** Gavin Blackwell
Secretary: Paul Roberts, 2 Primrose Close, Cradley Heath,W Mids. B64 5BN**Tel Nos:** 01384 865581 9H0 07930516639 (M)
Press Officer & Programme Editor: Rob Shinfield   **Programme:** 28 Pages   Price £1.
GROUND ADDRESS: The Cricketts, York Road, Rowley Regis,Warley, West Midlands.   **Tel:** 0121 5595564
Capacity: 3,000   **Seats:** 300   **Covered:** 1,000   **Floodlights:** Yes
Simple Directions: M5 Jct 2 follow Blackheath and Halesowen signs. First left at lights and fourth right into York Road (turning before motorway flyover). Ground 200 yards on left.
Midweek Home Matchday: Tuesday   **Clubhouse:** Open daily.   **Club Shop:** No
Previous Leagues: Oldbury 58-62 Warwick & W.Mid All.62-65 (Worcs (MIdland) Comb 65-82 Southern 82-86
Previous Names: Queens Colts 58-62 Whiteheath United 62-65
Club Colours: Sky Blue/Navy Blue/Navy Blue   **Change Colours:** Yellow/Red/Red
LAST SEASON: League: 11th   **F.A. Cup:** First Qualifying Round.   **F.A. Vase:** 3rd Round.
Top Scorer: Lee Booth   **Player of the Year:** Ben Smith   **Captain:** Andy Dodd
RECORD Attendance: 2,200 v Walsall Wood Walsall Cup Final 1982 **Victory** 10-1 v Blakenall   **Defeat:** 1-9 v Moor Green
Senior Honours: Staffs Sen.Cup 87-88 West Mids Lg 92-93 Midland Comb R-up 78-79 Walsall Sen Cup: 82-83 Worcs Sen Urn 86-87 Birmingham Senior Amateur Cup

QUORN   Founded: 1924
Nickname:

Chairman: Stuart Turner   **President:** John Unwin
Manager: Marcus Law   **Coach:** Paul O'Brien   **Physio:** Alan Cook
Secretary: Reg Molloy, 96 Grange Drive, Melton Mowbray, Leics. LE13 1HA
Tel Nos: 01664 564665 and 07729 173333 (M) **email :** k.molloy@ntlworld.com
Press Officer: Stewart Warrington
Commercial Manager: Chairman   **Sponsors**: Unwins Electrical Loughborough
GROUND ADDRESS: Sutton Park, Farley Way, Quorn, Leics.   **Ground Tel No:** 01509 620232
Capacity: 1,550   **Seats:** 350   **Covered:** 350   **Floodlights:** Yes
Simple Directions: Jct 23 M1 follow signs to Loughborough and turn right at second roundabout following signs to Leicester A6. Right at fourth roundabout to Quorn then left at first lights and ground is on left.
Midweek Home Matchday: Tuesday   **Clubhouse:**   **Club Shop:**
Club Colours: All red   **Change Colours:** Black & white/black/black
LAST SEASON: League: 7th   **F.A. Cup:** Extra Prelim.Rd.   **F.A. Vase:** 3rd Round.
Top Scorer: Liam Turner   **Player of the Year:** Kris Nurse   **Captain:** Robert Betts
Senior Honours: Leics Sen Cup 1940,1952 1954 Leics Sen Lg 2000-01,2001-02 Div1 (3)

RACING CLUB WARWICK

Founded: 1919
Nickname: Racers

Chairman: Jim Wright **Vice-Chairman:** David Turnham **Manager:** Jose Ascensao
Secretary: Pat Murphy, 20 Dadglow Road, Bishops Itchington, Southam, Warwicks. SCV47 2TG. **Tel No:** 01926 612625
Programme Editor: Graham Toney **Programme:** 20 Pages £1.00
GROUND ADDRESS: Toiwnsend Meadow, Hampton Road, Warwick, Cv34 6JP Ground **Tel. No.:** 01926 495786
Capacity: 1,280 **Seats:** 200 **Covered:** 250 **Floodlights:** Yes
Simple Directions: On the B4189 Warwick to Redditch road (via Henley) by owners & trainers car park of Warwick Racetrack
Midweek Home Matchday: Tuesday **Clubhouse:** Every evening and w/e lunchtimes **Club Shop:** Fully stocked
Previous Leagues: B'ham & W.Mids., Warwicks Comb.,W.Mids Regional, 67-72 Midland Comb 72-89, Southern 89-2003
Previous Name: Saltisford Rovers 1919-68
Club Colours: Gold/Black/Black **Change Colours:** White/Gold/White
LAST SEASON: League: 6th **F.A. Cup:** Extra Preliminary Round **F.A.Vase:** 3rd Round
Top Scorer: James Wood 20 **Player of the Year:** Robert Betts **Captain:** Robert Betts
BEST PERFORMANCES: League: **F.A. Cup:** 3rd Qual.Rd. 1992-93 **F.A.Vase:** 4th Round 1977-78
RECORD Attendance: 1,280 v Leamington F.C. Mid Alliance 26.12.05 **Goalscorer:** Steve Edgington 200
Appearances: Steve Cooper 600+ **Victory** 9-1 v Knowle **Defeat:** 0-7 v Redditch United
Fee Paid: £1,000 to Bedworth United for Dave Whetton **Fee Received:** £40,000 from Stoke City for Ben Foster.
Senior Honours: Midland Combination 1987-88

ROMULUS

Founded: 1979
Nickname:

Chairman: John Wright **Vice-Chairman:** **Manager:**

Secretary: Roger Evans, 34 Leam Drive, Burntwood, Staffs.WS7 9TG

Tel No: 0121 354 8261 (H) 07877 27330 (M) **Website:** www.romulus-fc.co.uk

GROUND ADDRESS: Vale Stadium, Farnborough Road, Castle Vale, Birmingham B35 7BE

Tel: 01217476969 Fax 0121 7476868 E-mail: information@romulus-fc.co.uk

Capacity: 2,000 **Seats:** 500 **Covered:** 600 **Floodlights:** Yes

Simple Directions: Bus 67 from Birmingham city centre or phone secretary.

Midweek Home Matchday: Tuesday **Clubhouse:** **Club Shop:**

Club Colours: Red& white/red/red **Change Colours:** Blue /black/black

BEST PERFORMANCES

League: 4th Mid Alliance 2005-2006 **F.A. Cup:** Extra Preliminary Round 2005-06 **F.A.Vase:** 1st Round 2005-2006

ROCESTER

Founded: 1876
Nickname: Romans

Chairman: Alf Hawksworth **Vice-Chairman:** **Manager:** Damian Grocott
Secretary: Gilbert Edgerton, 23 Eaton Rd., Rocester, Uttoxeter. Staffs. ST14 5LL **Tel No:** 01889 590101
Commercial Manager: Vicky Burman, Tel No: 01889 590768/590804
Programme Editor: Barry Brosnan (01889 567795) **Programme:** 32 Pages £1.00
GROUND ADDRESS: Hillsfield, Mill Street, Ricester, Uttoxeter, Staffs. Ground **Tel. No.:** 01889 590463
Capacity: 4,000 **Seats:** 230 **Covered:** 500 **Floodlights:** Yes
Simple Directions: From A50 roundabout adjoining Little Chef at Uttoxeter take B5030 to Rocester & Alton Towers. Turn right into Rocester village after three miles over narrow bridge. In village centre bear right at sharp left hand bend into Miill St. Ground 500 yards on left just past cotton mill.
Midweek Home Matchday: Tuesday **Clubhouse:** Open on Matchdays **Club Shop:** Yes
Previous Leagues: Ashbourne, Leek & Moorland, Cheadle & District,. Uttoxeter Amateur, Sttafford 53-57 Staffs Co.North, 57-84, Staffs Senior 84-87, West Midlands 87-94 Midland Alliance 94-99 03-4 N.P.L. Div. 1 04-05
Club Colours: Amber & Black/Black/Black **Change Colours:** All Blue
LAST SEASON: League: 22nd **F.A. Cup:** Preliminary Round **F.A. Trophy:** 1st Rd.
Top Scorer: Adam Baum 10 **Player of the Year:** **Captain:** Carl Allen
BEST PERFORMANCES: League: NPL 22nd Div 1 **F.A. Cup:** 3rd Qual. Rd. 97-98 **F.A.Vase:** 5th Rd. 1986-87
RECORD Fee Received: £12,000 from Birmingham City for Mark Sale 1994 **Appearances:** Peter Swanwick 1962-1982
Senior Honours: Midland Alliance98-99 West Midlands R-Up 89-90 Staffs F.A.Vase 85-86 87-88

STRATFORD TOWN

Founded: 1944
Nickname:

Chairman: Craig Hughes **Vice-Chairman:** Phil Day **Manager:** Ian Britton
Secretary: Rod Abrahams, 68 Montague Road, Warwick, CV34 5LJ
Tel No: 07816 862969
Press Officer: Name (Tel) **Programme:** 24 Pages Price 1,00 **Editor:** Alan Hawkins
GROUND ADDRESS: Masons Rd., off Alcester Rd., Stratford-upon-Avon, Warks.
Tel No: 01789 297479
Capacity: 1,100 **Seats:** 300 **Covered:** 400 **Floodlights:** yes
Simple Directions: Follow A422 Alcester/Worcester from town centre. Masons road is first right after the railway bridge.
Midweek Home Matchday: Tuesday **Clubhouse:** Open every night **Club Shop:** Yes all accessories
Previous Leagues: W.Mids 57-70 Mid Comb 70-73 75-94 Hellenic 70-75
Club Colours: Blue & white **Change Colours:** Tangerine & Black
Top Scorer: Craig Pountney 32 **Player of the Year:** Craig Pountney/ Patrick Connelly **Captain:** Nigel Niblett
RECORD Attendance: 1,078 v Aston Villa , B'ham Sen Cup Oct 1996 **Goalscorer:** **Appearances:**
Senior Honours: Midland Comb: 56-7 86-7 Birmingham Senior Cup 62-63 Midland Alliance Cup 02-3 03-4

STUDLEY

Founded: 1971
Nickname: Bees

Chairman: Ian Ballinger **Vice-Chairman:** Alec James

Manager: K.Rowlands **Asst.Manager:** T.Whittington **Coach:** Steve Cooper **Physio:** Darren Oldrey

Secretary: Alec James, 14 Eldersfield Close, Church Hill North, Redditch, Worcs. B98 9 NG

Tel Nos: 01527 455796(H) 07840878923 (M)

Press Officer: Dave Chiswell **Programme Editor:** Alec James **Programme :** 50p

GROUND ADDRESS: The Neehive, Abbeyfields Drive, Studley, Warwicks. B80 7BE **Tel:** 01527 853817

Capacity: 1,500 **Seats:** 200 **Covered:** Yes **Floodlights:** Yes

Simple Directions: M42 Jct 3 onto A435 to Redditch. Over Island at Dog & Duck onleft continue

Midweek Home Matchday: Tuesday **Clubhouse:**Yes full facilities on ground open daily. **Club Shop:** No

Previous Leagues: Redditch & South Warwicks Sunday Comb.,71-87 and Midland Comb.**Previous Name:** BLKL Works

Club Colours: All sky blue with navy trim **Change Colours:** All white

RECORD Attendance: 810 v Leamington 03-04 **Goalscorer:** Brian Powell **Appearance:** Lee Adams 523

Senior Honours: Midland Comb. Rup 2000-01 Worcs F.A.Sen. Urn 00-01 01-02 02-03 B'ham Vase R-up 96-97

TIPTON TOWN

Founded: 1948
Nickname:

Chairman: Kevin Jennings **Manager:** John Hill

Secretary: Angela Boden, 6 Jackson Close, Burberry Grange, Tipton, W.Mids. DY4 0BH

Tel No: 0121 505 1200 (H) 07921 167173 (M)

Programme Editor: Dave Barnfield **Sponsor:**

GROUND ADDRESS: Tipton Sports Academy, Wednesdbury Oak Road, Tipton W Mids **Tel. No.:** 0121 5025534

Capacity: 1,000 **Seats:** 200 **Covered:** 400 **Floodlights:** Yes

Simple Directions: M6 Jct 9 through Wednesbury taking A461 until right at island signed to Tipton. At next island turn full right towards Bilston & Wolverhamptobn. After a third of a mile turn left at lights and ground is on the left.

Midweek Home Matchday: Wednesday **Clubhouse:** Open with excellent food at week ends **Club Shop:** No

Previous League: West Midlands

Club Colours: Black & white stripes/black/bllack **Change Colours:** All Royal Blue

BEST PERFORMANCES

League: W.Mid Champions 2004-2005 **F.A. Cup:** **F.A.Vase:** 4th Round

RECORD Attendance: 1,100 v Wolves in 01.08.88 **Goalscorer:** **Appearances:**

Senior Honours: West Midland s Champions 2004-05

WESTFIELDS

Founded: 1966
Nickname: The Fields

Chairman: John Morgan **Vice-Chairman:** Brian Jones **President:** Graham Preece

Management Team: Sean Edwards, Darren Lync and Chris Ferriday

Secretary & Chief Executive: Andrew Morris,17 Fayre Oaks Green, Kings Acre,Hereford HR4 0QT

Tel No: 01432 264711 **Programme Editor:** Andy Morris **Sponsors:** allpay.net

GROUND ADDRESS: allpay park, Widemarsh Common, Hereford HR4 9NA **Ground Tel. No:** 07860410548

Capacity: 2.000 **Seats:** 150 **Covered:** 150 **Floodlights:** Yes

Simple Directions: Just off A49 at Widemarsh Common north of city centre.

Midweek Home Matchday: Tuesday **Clubhouse:** On Ground **Club Shop:** Yes

Club Colours: Maroon & Sky Blue/ Sky/Sky **Change Colours:** Sky Blue/White/Maroon

LAST SEASON:League: 20th **F.A. Cup:** 2nd Qualifying Round **F.A. Vase:** 2nd Round

Top Scorer: Mark Davis **Players of the Year:** Jon Hill & Anthony Rivett **Captain:** Mark Hibbard

BEST PERFORMANCES : League: Midland Alliance 6th 2004-2005 **F.A. Cup:** 2nd Qual. Round 2005-2006

F.A.Vase: 4th Round 1986-1987

RECORD Attendance: 518 v Rushden & Diamonds F.A.Cup 96 **Goalscorer:** Paul Burton **Appearances:** Jon Pugh

Senior Honours: Hereford Senior Cup 85-6 88-9 91-2 95-6 01-02-02-03 04-05 05-06 Worcs. Junior Cup 79-80 West Midlands League Champions 2002-03

MOORE & CO CONSTRUCTION SOLICITORS LEAGUE

NORTH WEST COUNTIES

President: William King   **Chairman:** Dave Tomlinson
Secretary: Geoff Wilkinson, 46 Oaklands Drive, Penwortham, Preston PR1 0YY
Tel: 01772 746312 (H) Email: Geoffjwilkinson@aol.com

DIVISION ONE		P	W	D	L	F	A	Pts
1.	Cammell Laird (-6)(1st Div.2 04-05)	42	35	3	4	126	36	102
2.	Skelmersdale United	42	28	7	7	119	48	91
3.	Alsager Town	42	27	7	8	87	43	88
4.	Nantwich Town	42	26	6	10	91	37	84
5.	Salford City	42	23	10	9	79	46	79
6.	Newcastle Town	42	21	9	12	97	52	72
7.	Curzon Ashton	42	20	8	14	72	66	68
8.	St Helens Town	42	20	7	15	70	68	67
9.	Colne (-6)	42	22	3	17	84	70	63
10.	Maine Road	42	17	10	15	65	56	61
11.	Abbey Hey	42	14	12	16	61	70	54
12.	Congleton Town	42	15	8	19	50	63	53
13.	Squires Gate	42	12	15	15	43	62	51
14.	Silsden (-6) (2nd Div.2 04-05)	42	16	8	18	76	75	50
15.	Trafford (-3)	42	13	13	16	71	56	49
16.	Glossop North End	42	12	11	19	62	78	47
17.	Bacup Borough	42	13	8	21	44	62	47
18.	Ramsbottom United	42	9	18	15	45	60	45
19.	Atherton Collieries	42	7	9	26	43	93	30
20.	Atherton LR	42	7	8	27	40	115	29
21.	Stone Dominoes	42	5	5	32	39	146	20
22.	Formby	42	4	7	31	43	105	19

DIVISION ONE

	1	2	3	4	5	6	7	8	9	10	11	12	13	14	15	16	17	18	19	20	21	22
1 Abbey Hey		0-0	3-2	3-1	0-0	0-4	1-4	2-3	2-2	2-2	4-1	2-1	0-5	2-1	1-3	0-1	3-0	3-1	1-1	2-1	3-1	2-1
2 Alsager Town	3-0		3-1	4-1	1-0	0-1	0-1	4-0	2-1	2-1	4-2	3-1	2-0	0-4	2-2	5-1	3-1	1-1	1-0	0-1	4-2	1-1
3 Atherton Coll.	0-3	1-4		2-2	2-1	1-4	1-3	0-2	2-1	3-0	2-3	1-1	0-1	2-2	1-0	0-2	3-3	0-8	1-1	0-2	0-0	2-3
4 Atherton LR	0-4	1-2	1-5		0-5	0-9	0-1	1-4	2-4	3-3	0-0	0-2	0-3	0-8	1-0	0-0	0-1	1-0	1-2	0-2	3-0	0-2
5 Bacup Borough	2-1	0-2	2-1	0-0		1-3	1-3	0-0	2-2	3-1	2-1	0-2	1-4	0-3	2-0	0-2	0-4	0-1	0-2	3-2	0-0	
6 Cammell Laird	4-1	1-1	1-0	3-0	1-2		4-3	3-0	3-0	7-1	2-0	3-2	2-0	2-4	4-2	4-2	1-0	1-1	5-1	3-1	10-0	3-2
7 Colne	4-0	1-4	3-0	2-3	2-0	2-3		2-0	1-0	4-2	6-0	2-3	2-3	1-1	2-1	1-2	2-1	4-1	3-1	3-2	0-1	0-4
8 Congleton Town	2-0	2-1	2-0	1-1	2-1	0-2	3-2		0-1	6-4	0-2	0-1	0-0	0-1	1-2	1-2	1-2	1-1	0-1	1-3	0-1	2-1
9 Curzon Ashton	2-1	3-1	4-1	4-3	3-1	1-4	5-0	0-1		1-0	2-1	2-2	1-5	1-0	2-1	2-2	0-1	1-0	1-1	2-0	4-0	1-3
10 Formby	0-1	1-4	2-0	1-1	1-2	0-2	1-6	0-2	4-1		2-2	2-3	0-3	1-4	0-1	0-2	0-5	0-1	0-1	3-1	1-1	
11 Glossop N. End	1-1	0-2	2-0	1-2	1-1	1-4	0-1	1-2	1-2	2-0		2-2	0-5	0-3	1-1	2-4	3-1	2-1	2-0	3-3	5-2	1-1
12 Maine Road	1-1	1-0	1-1	3-1	1-0	1-3	2-0	1-2	1-2	1-0	2-2		0-4	0-1	3-0	0-4	1-3	0-1	4-0	1-2	3-0	2-0
13 Nantwich Town	3-1	0-2	4-1	7-0	2-0	0-2	1-0	1-1	5-0	1-0	2-1	1-1		3-1	3-0	1-0	2-0	1-2	1-2	2-1	5-0	3-0
14 Newcastle Town	0-0	0-1	4-1	4-2	2-1	1-2	2-0	5-2	3-1	3-0	1-2	0-1	2-0		1-1	2-2	3-2	1-2	1-1	4-4	6-1	1-1
15 Ramsbottom Utd	2-2	1-1	1-1	1-0	2-2	1-0	2-3	2-1	1-1	1-2	0-3	1-1	0-3	1-3		2-2	2-0	2-0	0-0	0-0	1-1	1-0
16 Salford City	3-1	0-1	2-0	4-0	2-1	0-1	1-1	2-0	2-4	4-0	2-0	1-1	1-1	0-1	1-1		3-2	2-2	0-1	1-2	6-0	3-2
17 Silsden	2-1	2-2	4-0	3-0	1-1	1-5	1-2	1-1	2-3	6-3	1-1	2-1	2-1	1-3	0-0	0-1		1-5	5-2	4-2	3-0	2-2
18 Skelmersdale U.	3-3	6-1	1-1	6-2	2-0	2-1	2-0	3-0	2-1	1-1	0-2	3-1	4-1	5-1	2-1	2-1	4-1		4-0	6-1	9-0	5-3
19 Squires Gate	2-1	0-2	5-0	1-2	3-1	0-3	0-0	0-0	0-0	1-1	1-0	0-0	2-2	2-5	1-1	1-3	1-1	0-1		1-1	3-0	2-1
20 St Helens Town	1-1	1-4	0-1	2-2	0-2	1-3	6-1	1-2	2-0	2-1	2-1	2-1	2-0	2-1	2-0	0-2	3-2	2-5	1-0		2-1	1-0
21 Stone Dominoes	0-2	0-6	0-2	4-0	0-1	0-3	1-3	2-1	0-3	3-2	3-5	2-7	1-2	0-6	3-3	0-1	1-7	2-4	1-1	3-3		0-3
22 Trafford	0-0	0-1	2-3	2-3	0-1	0-0	4-3	4-1	1-0	4-0	2-2	0-2	0-0	1-0	1-1	2-2	1-2	1-2	5-0	3-1	8-0	

DIVISION TWO		P	W	D	L	F	A	Pts
1.	FC United of Manchester	36	27	6	3	111	35	87
2.	Flixton	36	24	7	5	93	37	79
3.	Nelson	36	23	5	8	82	53	74
4.	Winsford United	36	19	8	9	65	41	65
5.	Padiham	36	19	5	12	76	52	62
6.	Great Harwood Town	36	18	8	10	51	33	62
7.	Ashton Town	36	17	7	12	59	57	58
8.	Norton United	36	13	12	11	45	47	51
9.	Blackpool Mechanics	36	13	10	13	48	51	49
10.	Oldham Town	36	14	6	16	46	49	48
11.	Eccleshall	36	13	7	16	50	64	46
12.	New Mills	36	13	7	16	46	62	46
13.	Chadderton (-3)	36	13	8	15	51	62	44
14.	Cheadle Town (-6)	36	14	6	16	55	53	42
15.	Holker Old Boys	36	11	8	17	58	74	41
16.	Darwen	36	11	2	23	47	61	35
17.	Leek CSOB	36	7	7	22	51	82	28
18.	Daisy Hill	36	7	6	23	38	75	27
19.	Castleton Gabriels (-8)	36	2	3	31	38	122	1

DIVISION TWO	1	2	3	4	5	6	7	8	9	10	11	12	13	14	15	16	17	18	19
1 Ashton Town		0-4	2-0	2-1	0-1	3-2	2-2	4-3	0-4	2-1	1-2	2-1	4-2	0-2	1-0	1-1	1-0	2-4	1-0
2 Blackpool Mechanics	1-3		4-3	2-1	0-1	0-0	3-2	1-2	2-4	0-2	1-0	2-2	1-0	1-2	2-0	0-0	0-0	3-1	2-0
3 Castleton Gabriels	1-1	3-2		1-4	1-2	1-2	4-3	0-1	0-3	2-6	0-6	1-4	1-2	3-7	0-5	1-4	0-1	0-1	1-3
4 Chadderton	1-3	2-2	4-2		0-3	1-0	2-0	1-0	2-3	0-0	2-2	1-1	1-0	2-2	1-2	4-3	3-1	1-4	0-1
5 Cheadle Town	0-0	2-0	6-0	1-2		0-2	1-2	2-0	3-3	0-4	2-3	3-4	4-1	1-2	1-0	0-0	0-2	3-3	0-1
6 Daisy Hill	0-3	0-0	1-1	1-2	1-2		1-0	1-4	0-3	2-5	0-2	3-2	2-0	1-2	2-3	2-1	0-3	1-2	1-1
7 Darwen	0-2	3-1	3-1	2-1	1-2	3-2		1-2	1-2	1-2	2-1	3-1	2-1	0-1	5-0	0-1	2-1	1-4	2-3
8 Eccleshall	3-1	1-2	5-1	2-0	0-3	2-0	1-0		0-0	1-1	1-2	3-1	1-2	1-1	1-2	2-0	1-1	1-3	2-2
9 FC United of Manchester	2-1	4-2	10-2	4-0	1-1	6-0	2-0	7-1		1-2	0-1	4-1	8-1	5-0	6-1	1-2	1-0	3-2	2-1
10 Flixton	3-2	2-0	4-2	1-1	4-1	2-2	2-0	6-0	1-1		1-2	5-0	5-1	2-3	2-0	1-1	6-1	2-1	3-0
11 Great Harwood Town	1-2	0-0	1-1	3-0	2-0	2-3	3-2	2-0	1-1	1-2		1-0	0-0	3-5	0-0	1-0	0-0	1-0	0-1
12 Holker Old Boys	2-2	2-1	6-0	1-2	3-1	2-1	2-0	1-0	0-2	0-0	2-1		3-2	3-3	3-1	2-0	2-2	0-1	0-4
13 Leek CSOB	1-1	5-0	2-0	1-3	2-4	2-2	0-0	0-0	2-5	1-4	0-1	5-1		0-2	2-0	1-2	0-2	1-1	3-2
14 Nelson	3-2	0-3	3-0	4-1	1-0	3-1	3-2	7-2	1-3	1-2	1-2	5-0	3-1		4-0	2-2	1-3	1-0	2-1
15 New Mills	0-3	1-1	3-1	1-0	1-1	3-0	1-0	0-1	0-2	0-5	1-0	1-1	5-4	1-2		1-1	3-1	2-2	2-1
16 Norton United	0-2	0-0	1-0	1-1	4-3	1-0	0-2	4-1	1-3	0-1	0-0	2-1	2-1	1-1	1-1		2-1	2-1	2-2
17 Oldham Town	4-1	1-1	3-2	0-2	0-1	3-1	3-0	1-0	0-1	0-1	0-2	2-1	3-2	2-0	1-4	2-1		1-1	0-1
18 Padiham	4-1	1-2	3-1	4-0	1-0	3-1	1-0	2-3	1-2	5-3	2-0	4-2	6-2	0-2	1-0	1-2	2-1		1-2
19 Winsford United	1-1	1-2	4-1	2-2	2-0	2-0	2-0	2-1	2-2	2-0	0-2	3-1	1-1	2-0	3-1	4-0	3-0	3-3	

SEASON	WINNERS	FINALISTS
1982-1983	Darwen	Skelmersdale United
1983-1984	Ellesmere Port & Neston	Stalybridge Celtic
1984-1985	Leek Town	Radcliffe Borough
1985-1986	Warrington Town	Clitheroe
1986-1987	Colne Dynamoes	Leyland Motors
1987-1988	Warrington Town	Colwyn Bay
1988-1989	Colwyn Bay	Warrington Town
1989-1990	Knowsley United	Warrington Town
1990-1991	Vauxhall GM	Darwen
1991-1992	Ashton United	Burscough
1992-1993	Burscough	Nantwich Town
1993-1994	Rossendale United	St Helens Town
1994-1995	Nantwich Town	Trafford
1995-1996	Burscough	Flixton
1996-1997	Newcastle Town	Trafford
1997-1998	Kidsgrove Athletic	Vauxhall GM
1998-1999	Vauxhall GM	Prescot Cables
1999-2000	Skelmersdale United	Newcastle Town
2000-2001	Formby	Curzon Ashton FC
2001-2002	Prescot Cables	Atherton Collieries
2002-2003	Mossley	Clitheroe
2003-2004	Bacup Borough	Newcastle Town
2004-2005	Cammell Laird	Skelmersdale United
2005-2006	Salford City	Cammell Laird

Maine Road's Steve Cheetham hooks the ball clear of Silden's Martin Packer, during Silden's 2-1 league win.

Photo: Darren Thomas.

LEAGUE CONSTITUTION 2006-07 - DIVISION ONE

ABBEY HEY
Formed: 1902
Nickname:

Chairman: James Whittaker **Manager:** Chris Bailey **Coach :** Lol McMahon
Secretary: Tony McAllister, 10 Walmer Street, Abbey Hey, Gorton, Manchester M18 8QP **Physio**: Pete Blundell
Tel Nos: 0161 230 7098 (H) 07786 222596 (M)
Programme Editor: Gordon Lester
GROUND ADDRESS: Abbey Stadium, Goredale Avenue, Gorton, Manchester 18
Tel No: 0161 231 7147 (Club)
Capacity: 1,000 **Seats:** 100 **Covered:** 300 **Floodlights:** Yes
Simple Directions: A57 towards Hyde, right into Woodland Avenue, approx one and a half miles past Belle Vue junction, right again into Ryder Brow Road. Then first left after bridge into Goredale Avenue
Midweek Home Matchday: Tuesday **Clubhouse:** Open matchdays and also sells club accessories.
Previous Leagues: Manchester Amateur, South East Lancs., Manchester League
Club Colours: Red & white/red/red&white **Change Colours:**
LAST SEASON: League: 14th **F.A. Cup:** Prelim.Rd. **F.A. Vase:** 1st Qual. Rd.
Top Scorer: Tim Bailey **Player of the Year:** Rick Watson **Captain:** David Brocklehurst
RECORD Attendance: 400 v Manchester City XI October 1999
Senior Honours: Manchester County Amateur Cup: (3) Manchester Challenge Trophy (3) Manchester Lg (5) Lancs Lg (2)

ATHERTON COLLIERIES
Founded: 1916
Nickname: The Colts

Chairman: Steve Payne **Vice-Chairman:** Paul Gregory
Manager: Alan Lord **Assistant Manager:**Michael Clegg **Physio**: Paul Chapman
Secretary: Emil Anderson, 109 Douglas St., Atherton M46 9EB
Tel No: 0161 288 6288 (W) 07968548056 (M)
Programme Editor: Secretary **Programme:** 40 pages £1.00
GROUND ADDRESS: Alder St.,Atherton, Greater Manchester. **Ground Tel. No:** 07929 374641
Capacity: 2,500 **Seats:** 300 **Covered:** 1,000 **Floodlights**: Yes
Simple Directions:M61 Jct 5 towards Westhoughton, left onto A6 and right onto A579 into Atherton. Left into High St.at first light and 2nd left into Alder St and ground. **Club Shop:** No, but badges & progs on sale
Midweek Home Matchday: Monday **Clubhouse:** Mon-Fri evenings and at week end from lunch time
RECORD Attendance: 3,300 on Lancs Comb 1920's
Previous Leagues: Bolton Combination 20-50 52-71, Lancs. Combination 50-52 71-78 Cheshire County 78-82
Club Colours: Black & red /black/blac **Change Colours:** All light blue
BEST PERFORMANCES: League:
RECORD Attendance: 3,300 in Lancashire Combination in 1920's
Senior Honours: Lancs Co F.A.Shield 19-20 22-23 41-42 45-46 56-57 64-65 **Goalscorer**: **Appearances**

ATHERTON L.R.
Founded: 1957
Nickname: The Panthers

Chairman: Alan Grundy **Financial Director:** Ray Price **Manager:** Mark Cox
Secretary: Christine Rowlands,25 Douglas Street, Atherton, Manchester M46 9FB
Tel No: 01942 894463(H) 07870 432655 (M)
Programme Editor: Tim Lees **Programme:** 80 Pages Price £1.00 (Best in League for 7th consecutive year)
GROUND ADDRESS: Crilly Park, Spa Road, Atherton, Gtr Manchester **Ground Tel No:** 01942 883950
Capacity: 3,000 **Seats:** 250 **Covered:** 3 sides **Floodlights:** Yes
Simple Directions: M61 Jct 5 follow signs to Westhoughton, left into A6, right onto A579 and right again into Upton Road passing Atherton Central station. Next left into Springfield Rd. left again into Hillside Road then Spa Road
Midweek Home Matchday: Tuesday **Clubhouse:** Normal licensing hours **Club Shop:** No
Previous Leagues: Bolton Comb.,Cheshire County 80-82, NWCL 82-94 and NPL 94-97 **Previous Name:** Laburnum Rovers
Club Colours: Yellow / Blue /Yellow **Change Colours:** All White or All Red
LAST SEASON
League: 15th
BEST PERFORMANCES
League: NWCL Champions 92-3 93-4 **F.A. Cup:** 3rd Qualifying Round 96-97 **F.A.Vase:** Semi-Final 1993-94
RECORD Attendance: 2,300 v Aldershot Town F.A.Vase Q-Final replay 93-94 **Goalscorer:** Shaun Parker **Apps:** Jim Evans
Senior Honours: NWCo Champions 92-93 93-94 Champs Trophy 92-93 93-94

BACUP BOROUGH
Founded: 1875
Nickname: The Boro

Chairman: Ken Peters **Manager:** Brent Peters
Secretary: Frank Manning, 38 Acre Avenue, Stacksteads, Bacup OL13 0HN **Asst.Manager:** Simon Holding
Tel No: 01706 877460(H) 07709 542254 (M) **Sponsor:** B & E Boys Ltd.
Programme Editor: Frank Hudson **Programme:** 22 Pages £1.00
GROUND ADDRESS: West View, Cowtoot Lane, Blackthorn, Bacup , Lancashire **Tel:** 01706 878655
Capacity: 3,000 **Seats:** 500 **Covered:** 1,000 **Floodlights:** Yes
Simple Directions: From M62 M66 onto A681 through Rawtenstall to Bacup town centre. Left onto A671 towards Burnley. Right after 300 yards begore Irwell Inn, climbing Cooper St, right into Blackhorn Lane then first into Cowtoot Lane to ground.
Midweek Home Matchday: Thursday **Clubhouse:** Open matchdays and private functions **Club Shop:** No
Previous Name: Bacup F.C. **Previous League:** Lancs Combination1903-82
Club Colours: Black & white stripes/black/black **Change Colours:** Yellow/blue/blue
League: **F.A. Cup:** 3rd Qualifying Rd **F.A.Vase:** 4th Rd 1997-98
RECORD Attendance: 4,980 v Nelson 1947 **Goalscorer:** Jimmy Clarke **Appearances:**
Senior Honours: Lancs Junior Cup 1910-11 R-Up 22-213 74-75

Action from Curzon Ashton's 1-0 away league win against Congleton Town.

Photo: Mark Wood.

COLNE F.C.

Founded: 1996
Nickname:

Chairman: James Webster   **Vice-Chairman:** Bill Slinger   **Manager:** Nigel Coates
Secretary: Dave Blacklock, 7 Linton Gardens, Barrowford,Nelson. BB9 8RG. **Tel No:** 01282 696340
Press Officer: James Webster (01282 774572)   **Programme Editor:** Brian Coates
GROUND ADDRESS: Holt House Stadium, Holt House, Colne   **Ground Tel. No:** 01282 862545
Capacity: 1,800   **Seats:** 160   **Covered:** 1,000   **Floodlights:** Yes
Simple Directions: Enter Colne from M65 to roundabout, follow signs left to Keighley. Left at next roundabout , continue on Harrison Drive over mini roundabout and follow road to ground.
Midweek Home Matchday: Wednesday   **Clubhouse:** Open matchdays   **Club Shop:** Yes
Previous League: East Lancashire League
Club Colours: All   **Change Colours:** Sky Blue/Royal Blue/Royal Blue
BEST PERFORMANCES
League: 10 th NW Co   **F.A. Cup:**   **F.A.Vase:** S-F 2002-2003
RECORD Attendance: 1,742 v AFC Sudbury F.A.Vase S-F 2004 **Goalscorer:** Geoff Payton **Appearances:** Richard Walton
Senior Honours: BEP Cup Winners 96-97 N.W.Co Div 2 Champions 03-04

CONGLETON TOWN

Founded: 1901
Nickname: Bears

Chairman: Peter Evans   **Vice-Chairman:** Steve Burgess   **Managers:** Paul Moore & Ian Street
Secretary: Ken Mead, 45 Bollin Drive,Congleton, Cheshire CW12 3RR
Tel No: 01260 278152 (H) 01260 295777 (W) 07710 405674 (W)
Press Officer: Ken Mead (07710405674)   **Programme:** 48 Pages £1,00
GROUND ADDRESS: Booth Street Ground., Crescent Road,Congleton, Cheshire   **Ground Tel. No:** 01260 74460:
Capacity: 5,000:   **Seats:** 250   **Covered:** 1,200   **Floodlights:** Yes
Simple Directions: Approaching Congleton via Clayton by pass take second right after fire station, into Booth St. Two miles from Congleton.
Midweek Home Matchday: Tuesday   **Clubhouse:** Match days only   **Club Shop:** Yes
Previous Leagues: Crewe & Dist., North Staffs., Macclesfield, Cheshire 20-39 46-65 78-82 Mid Cheshire 68-78 North West Co 82-87 NPL 87-01   **Previous Names:** Congleton Hornets >1901
Club Colours: White/black/black   **Change Colours:** Yellow & Blue
BEST PERFORMANCES: League: 10th N.P. L.   **F.A. Cup:** 1st Rd 89-90   **F.A.Vase:** 4th Rd 76-77 80-81
RECORD Attendance: 6,800 v Macclesfield, Cheshire Lg. 53-54 **Goalscorer:** Mick Biddle 150 +
Appearances: Ray Clack 600+ Graham Harrison 600+ **Fee received:** £5,000 from Leeds United for D.Frost **Paid:** Unknown
Senior Honours: N.W.Co Lg R-up 85-86 Cheshire Senior Cup: 20-21 37-38

CURZON ASHTON

Founded: 1963
Nickname:The Blues

Chairman: Harry Galloway   **Vice-Chairman:** Ronnie Capstick   **Manager:** Gary Lowe
Secretary: Robert Hurst, 36 Russell Road, Partington, Manchester M31 4DZ
Tel/Fax: 0161 775 3883 and 07713 252310 (M)
Press Officer: Graham Shuttleworth   **Prog.Ed:** Robert Hurst(0161 775 3883)   **Programme:** 64 £1.20
GROUND ADDRESS: Tameside Stadium, Richmond St., Ashton-under-Lyme, Lancs   **Tel:** 0161 330 6033
Capacity: 5,000   **Seats:** 504   **Covered:** Yes   **Floodlights:** Yes
Simple Directions:t.
Midweek Home Matchday: Tuesday   **Clubhouse:** Open every evening.
Club Shop: Contact Ron Howe (0161 220 8345)
Previous Leagues: Manchester Amateur, Manchester>1978, Cheshire Co., N.W.Co 82-86 NPL 87-97
Club Colours: All Blue   **Change Colours:** All Red
BEST PERFORMANCES: League: **F.A. Cup:** 3rd Qual.Rd replay 89-90
F.A.Trophy: 2nd Qual.Rd 82-83 84-85   **F.A.Vase:** S-F 79-80
RECORD Attendance: 1,826 v Stamford F.A.VASE S-F 1980 **Goalscorer:** Alan Sykes   **Appearances:** Alan Sykes
Victory: 7-0, v Ashton United **Defeat:** 0-8 v Bamber Bridge
Senior Honours: Manchester Premier Cup (5) N.W.Co Div 2 R-up 99-00

FC UNITED OF MANCHESTER

Secretary: Luc Zentar, 221 Ducie House, 37 Ducie Street, Manchester M1 2JW

Ground: Groundsharing with Bury F.C. at Gigg Lane,Bury,Bl9 9HR

Tel No: 0161 236 1070 Fax:0161 236 1070

Directions: Leave the M66 at Jct 3 and take the left hand exit and follow road until you come to

A56 Manchester road T junction. Turn towards Bury at these h lights and you will pass the Swan

and Cemetery Pub and playing filelds on the left. At the end of the playing fields turn right into

Gigg Lane for ground.

Capacity: 11,669   **Clubhouse:** Yes   **Club Shop:** No

Previous Leagues: N.W.Co. Div 2

Honours: Champions N.W.Co Div 1 2005-2006

FACT FILE
Formed: 2005   Nickname: FC
Colours: Red/white/black
Change Colours:White or Blue
Midweek home matchday: Wenesday
Programme - Pages: 32 Price: £2.00

CLUB PERSONNEL
Manager: Karl Marginson
Player Asst. Manager: Phil Power
Player Coach: Darren Lyons
Physio: Mark Cooney

FC United - Back row (L-R): Mark Cooney (Physio), Joshua Howard, Simon Carden, Michael Lomax, Stuart Rudd, Joz Mitten, Barrie George, Philip Melville, Samuel Ashton, Liam Coyne, Kevin Elvin, Robert Nugent, Steven Spencer, David Brown, Karl Marginson (Team Manager).
Front: George Hayden (Kit Manager), Adie Orr, Mathew Taylor, Rhodri Giggs, David Chadwick, Steven Smith, David Swarbrick, Alexander Mortimer, Rory Patterson, William Ahern, Gareth Ormes, Phil Power (Assistant Manager), Darren Lyons (Team Coach).

FLIXTON

Secretary: Paul Chadwick15 Coniston Road, Flixton,Manchester M41 6PS(01254 777800)
Ground: Valley Road, Flixton, Manchester M41 8RQ Tel: 0161 747 7757
Directions: Leave M60 take B5214 signed Urmston. At 2nd R'about take 3rd exit. Take right only lane on the exit into Davyhulme Rd. Follow road to Valley Rd, just after a left hand bend after 1.5 miles. Ground is at the other end of the road. Coaches as above and carry on to the next R'about take 4th exit (Woodbridge Rd). The ground is at the bottom of this road.
Capacity: 2,000   **Cover:** 650   **Seats:** 250
Clubhouse: Open daily 3.00pm-11pm. Sandwiches available most eves **Club Shop:** No
Previous Leagues: S. Manchester & Wythenshawe 60-63; Lancs & Cheshire 63-73; Manchester 73-86; NWC 86-96; NPL 97-00
Best season FA Vase: Semi-final 95-96
Record Attendance: 1,543 v Brigg Town FA Vase Semi-Final 95-96
HONOURS NWC Div I 95-96, Div 2 94-95 Lg.Cup 94-95 95-96 R-up 87-88, Div 3 R-up 86-87; Manc. Lg R-up x 3, Div 1 77-78, Open Tphy 80-81; Lancs Amtr Cup 79-80 (R-up 80-81); Manc. Chal. Tphy 83-84 R-up x 2; Manc. Prem. Cup R-up 86-87 91-92; Man.Am Cup R-up 88-89

FACT FILE
Formed: 1960   Nickname: Valiants
Colours: Blue & white stripes/blue/blue
Change Colours: Gold/black/black
Midweek home matchday: Tuesday
Reserves' League: NWCo FL Res Div
Programme - Pages: 36 Price: £1.00
Editor: Andrew Harney
CLUB PERSONNEL
Chairman: Len Heywood Pres: F H Eadie
Manager: Paul Wright
Matchday Contact: Paul Chadwick
Tel : 0161 747 6315 (H) or 07754 416889 (M)

FORMBY
Founded: 1919
Nickname: Squirrels

Chairman: Chris Wewh
Manager: Peter Hennerty   **Player-Coach:** W.Knowles
Secretary: G.Greenall, 103 Yewdale Road, Wigan, AN4 0EA
Tel. No: 01942 749939
GROUND ADDRESS: Altcar Road, Fornby, Merseyside, L37 4EL   **Ground Tel.No:** 01704 833505
Capacity: 2,000   **Seats:** 220   **Covered:** 500   **Floodlights:** Yes
Simple Directions: Turn right at lights opp. Tesco into Altcar Rd. Over mini roundabout and ground is on rt next to refuse tip.
Midweek Home Matchday: Tuesday   **Clubhouse:** No. Snack Bar on matchdays   **Club Shop:** Yes
Previous Leagues: Liverpool Co.Comb. 1919-68, Lancs Comb. 68-71,Cheshire Co. 71-82
Club Colours: Yellow/blue/yellow   **Change Colours:** Green/black/green
Programme: 36 Pages   £1.00
BEST PERFORMANCES
F.A. Cup: 1st Rd 73-74   **F.A.Trophy:** 1st Rd 1973-74   **F.A.Vase:** 2nd Rd 96-97
RECORD Attendance: 602 v Southport Liv. Sen.Cup 2003-04
Senior Honours: Liverpool Senior Cup 77-78 R-Up 84-85 Lancashire Co.Am.Cup 34-35

GLOSSOP NORTH END
Founded: 1886 Re-formed 1992
Nickname:Hillmen

Chairman: Peter Hammond   **President:** C.T.Boak   **Manager:** Micky Boyle   **Asst.Manager:** Ian Boyle   **Physio:** Mick Parr
Secretary: Peter Hammond, 15 Longmoor Rd., Simmondley, Glossop, Derbys. SK13 9NH 01457 863852 (H)
Press Officer: Secretary   **Prog Ed:** JohnHamilton (01457 866216)   **Programme:** 32 Pages 50p
GROUND ADDRESS: Surrey St., Glossop,Derbys.   **Ground Tel. No:** 01457 855469
Capacity: 2,374   **Seats:** 209   **Covered:** 509   **Floodlights:** Yes
Simple Directions: A57 to Glossop. Left at lights (near Tesco sign) into Glossopbrook Rd., then follow road to top of hill and ground is on right. Buses 236 &237 from Manchester. Blossop Central BR
Midweek Home Matchday: Tuesday   **Clubhouse:** Matchdays   **Club Shop:** Yes
Previous Leagues: Midland 1896-98, Football League.1898-1915, Manchester Lg 156-56. 66-78 Lancs Comb. 56-66 Cheshire County 78-82
Previous Names: Glossop North End 1886-1896 and Glossop FC 1898-1992
Club Colours: All Royal Blue   **Change Colours:** All Gold
BEST PERFORMANCES: League: F .A. Cup: Quarter Final 1909 **F.A.Amateur Cup** Q-final 08-09 **F.A.Vase:**
RECORD Attendance: 10,736 v P.N.E. F.A.Cup 1913-14
Fee received: £3,000 from Oldham Athletic for Andy Gorton **Paid:** £3,000 to Lincoln City for Andy Gorton
Senior Honours: Manchester Premier Cup 1997 & 1998 Derbyshire Senior Cup 2000-01

MAINE ROAD
Founded: 1955
Nickname: Blues

Chairman: Ron Meredith   **President:** F.G.Thompson   **Manager:** Chris Simms
Secretary: Derek Barber, Flat 4, Maple Courrt, 259 Wellington Rd., Heaton Moor,   **Physio**: Gordon Woods
Stockport, SK4 5BS **Tel No:** 0161 431 8243 (H) 07707 667821 (M)
Press Officer & Programme Editor: Secretary   **Programme:** 48 Pages ≈£1.00
GROUND ADDRESS: Manchester County F.A.Ground, Brantingham Road, Chorlton-cum-Hardy, Manchester M21
Tel.No: 0161 861 0344
Capacity: 2,000   **Seats:** 200   **Covered:** 700   **Floodlights:** Yes
Simple Directions: M60 Jct 7 A56 towards City Centre. Right onto A5145. Left at 2nd lights into Withington Rd. First left into Brantingham Rd and ground is 300 yards on left.
Midweek Home Matchday: Tuesday   **Clubhouse:** Matchdays   **Club Shop:** No
Previous Leagues: Rusholme Sunday 55-66, Manchester Amateur Sunday 66-72 and Manchester 72-87
Club Colours: Silver & Navy Blue/navy/Silver & Navy   **Change Colours:** All sky blue
BEST PERFORMANCES
F.A. Cup: 2nd Qualifying Round.   **F.A.Vase:** 4th Rd. 94-95
RECORD Attendance: 875 v Altrincham F.A.Cup 90-91
Senior Honours: Manchester County Premier Cup 1987-88 Challenge Cup (4)

NANTWICH TOWN

Founded: 1884
Nickname: Dabbers

Chairman: Clive Jackson **Vice-Chairman:** Jon Brydon **Pres:** Michael Chatwin **Head Coach:** Steve Davis **Physio:** Paul Kelly
Secretary: Bernard Lycett,'Rivington' Clay Lane, Haslington, Crewe CW11 5SE **Tel No:** 91270 564066 (H) 07876320280 (M)
Programme Editor: Michael Chatwin (e-mail: mdchat@hotnail.com) **Programme:** 24 Pages £1.00
GROUND ADDRESS: Jackson Avenue, off London Road, Nantwich, Cheshire. **Ground Tel. No.:** 01270 621771
Capacity: 1,500 **Seats:** 150 **Covered:** 555 **Floodlights:** Yes
Simple Directions: M6 jct 16 A500 for Nantwich (about 8 miles) continue on A52 over railway crossing, then second right into Jackson Avenue. From Chester use A51 . Three miles from Crewe BR
Midweek Home Matchday: Tuesday **Clubhouse:** Open matchdays **Club Shop:** No
Previous Leagues: Shropshire & Dist.,The Combination 1892-94, Lancs .Comb.12-15, The Combination 19-38, Manchester , Mid Cheshire, Cheshire County 68-82
Club Colours: All Green **Change Colours:** Yellow and Blue
LAST SEASON: League: 4th **F.A. Cup:** 2nd Qualifying Round **F.A. Vase:** Winners
Top Scorer: Andy Kinsey 24 **Player of the Year:** Andy Kinsey **Captain:** Phil Parkinson
BEST PERFORMANCES: Lg: 6th N.W.Co. **F.A. Cup:** 5th Qual. Rd. 1900-01 1903-04 **F.A.Vase:** Winners 2005-2006
RECORD Attendance: 5,121 v Winsford United Cheshire Senior Cup 2nd Rd Replay 19.02.21
Goalscorer: Bobby Jones 60 (Total) Gerry Duffy 42 (in season 61-62) **Fee Received:** £4,000 from Stafford R for D.Dawson
Victory: 15-0 v Ashton Utd Man. Lg. 66-7 **Defeat:** 0-12 v Chirk (A) F.A.Cup 2nd Qual. 1889-90
Senior Honours: Cheshire Senior Cup 75-76 & R-Up (5)

NELSON

Secretary: Alan Ridehalgh, Mere clough Barn,Long Causeway, Cliviger,Burnley BB10 4RL
Tel Nos: 01282 832089 H) 07764 290718 (M)
Ground: Victoria Park, Lomeshaye Way, Nelson, Lancs (01282 613820)
Directions: M65 jct 13, 1st left (A6068 Fence), 2nd left (B6249 for Nelson),2nd right sign Lomeshaye Village to grd
Capacity: 1500 **Seats:**150 **Cover:** 200 **Floodlights:** Yes
Clubhouse: Bar open matchdays **Club Shop:** Yes

HONOURS Lancs Lge 54-55; Lancs Comb. 1949-50 51-52; Lg Cup 49-50 50-51 59-60; Bridge Shield 75-76 81-82; Lancs Jnr Cup 54-55; N.W.C. Div 2 Cup 96-97.

BEST SEASON
FA Cup: 2nd Rd Proper 30-31(replay) **FA Vase:** 2nd Rd 2001-02

PREVIOUS Leagues: Lancashire 1889-98 1900-01; Football League 1898-1900; Lancashire Comb. 01-16 46-82; N.W.C. 82-88; West Lancashire 88-92.

FACT FILE
Founded: 1881 Nickname: Blues
Colours: Blue & white stripes/bluek/blue
Change colours: Gold and blue.
Midweek matchday: TuesdayReserve
League: N.W.C. Res. Div.
Website: www.nelsonfc.co.uk
CLUB PERSONNEL
Chairman: A.Pickering
Man Director: L.Treitl Treasurer: S.Smith
Manager: Dave Hall Asst. Man:Ian Lang
Captain: Andy Howarth

Nantwich Town F.C. - Back Row (L-R): Steve Davis (Player/Manager), Richard Smith, Adam Beasley, Andy Kinsey, Stuart Scheuber, Phil Parkinson (Capt), **Front Row:** Paul Taylor, Rob Hackney, Andy Taylor, Matt Blake, Danny Griggs. Mascots: Liam Wynn, Rosie Embley, Kyle Hart. Photo: Arthur Evans.

NEWCASTLE TOWN

Founded: 1964
Nickname: Castle`

Chairman: Carl Birchall   **General Manager:** John Cotton   **Sponsors:** Beswicks Solicitors & Red Industries
Secretary: Ray Tatton, 20 Glencastle Way,Trentham,Stoke on Trent Staffs. ST14 8QE   **Manager:** Nigel Gleghorn
Tel Nos: 01782 644916 (H)) 07974220689 (M)   **Website:** www.newcastletown.co.uk
Press Officer: Secretary   **Programme:** 44 Pages £1.00   **Editor:** Les Morris (07879466523)
GROUND ADDRESS: Lyme Valley Parkway Stadium, Lilleshall Road, Clayton, Newcastle -under-Lyne
Tel. Nos: 01782 662351 and club & fax 01782 662350 **Capacity**: 4,000   **Seats:** 300   **Covered:** 1,000   **Floodlights:** Yes
Simple Directions: M6 jct 15 then A 500 for Stoke, left at roundabout A 519 for Newcastle and then right at 2nd roundabout
into Stafford Avenue. First left into Tittensor Road to ground. Three miles from Stoke on Trent (BR)
Midweek Home Matchday: Tuesday   **Clubhouse:** Saturday Matchdays12-7.30 Midweek 5-11pm Club **Shop:** Yes
Previous Leagues: As a Sunday club Hanley & Dist., North Staffs, Potteries & Dist. as a Saturday club Newcastle & District,
Staffs Co. & Mid Cheshire. **Previous Names:** Parkway Hanley (1964), Clayton Park & Parkway Clayton).Merged as NTFC 86
Club Colours: Royal Blue/royal blue/white   **Change Colours:** Yellow/Black/Yellow
LAST SEASON: League: 6th   **F.A. Cup:** 1st Qualifying Round   **F.A. Vase:** 3rd Round
Top Scorer: Michael Lennon 33   **Player of the Year:** Mark Beeston   **Captain:** Dean Gillick
BEST PERFORMANCES: F.A. Cup: **League:** Runners Up Div 1 N.W.Co 04-05   **F.A.Vase:** S-F1999-00
RECORD Attendance: 3,948 v Notts Co F.A.Cup 96   **Goalscorer:** Andy Bott 149   **Appearances:** Dean Gillick 632
Victory: 8-0 v Skelmersdale 9-2 v Abbey Hey **Defeat:** 0-5 v Eastwood Hanley (A)
Senior Honours: N.W.Co Div 1 R-up 95-96 96-97 99-00 04-05 Staffs Senior Cup R-up 95-96

RAMSBOTTOM UNITED

Founded: 1966
Nickname:

Chairman: Harry Williams   **Vice-Chairman:** Geoff Lay   **Manager:** Lee Schulper
Secretary: Malcombe Holt, 23 Newcombe Road, Holcombe Brook,   **Asst.Manager:** Lee Cryer
Ramsbotham, Lancs Tel No: 01204 883085 (H) 0776 1828487 (M)
Press Officer: Chris Bootham   **Programme:** 46 Pages £1.00)
GROUND ADDRESS: Riverside Ground, Acre Bottom, Ramsbottom   **Tel:** 01706 822458(match details)
Simple Directions: M66 (North) to jct 1 take A56 towards Ramsbottom. One mile left into Bury New Road. Left after Mondi
Paper Mill along road parellel with East Lancs Railway.
Midweek Home Matchday: Tuesday   **Clubhouse:** Yes   **Club Shop:** No
Previous Leagues: Bury Amateur, Bolton Combination and Manchester League
Club Colours: Blue with white trim/blue/white   **Change Colours:** Red/black/black
BEST PERFORMANCES
F.A. Cup: 3rd Qual.98-99   **F.A.Vase:** 2nd Rd 98-99 99-00
RECORD Attendance: 829 v Southport F.A.Cup 3rd Q.98-99
Senior Honours: N.W.Co Div 2 Champions 96-97

SALFORD CITY

Founded: 1940
Nickname: Ammies

Chairman: Ged Carter   **Manager:** Gary Felows
Secretary: Bill Taylor, 23 Westwood Drive, Prendelebury , Salford, M27 4JT   **Secs'Tel No:** 0161 736 1840
Press Officer: Frank McCauley (01942 815600)
Editor: Scott White   **Programme:** 24 Pages £1.00   **Sponsors**: Avis Steel
GROUND ADDRESS: Moor Lane, Kersal, Salford, Manchester   **Ground Tel.** No: 0161 792 6287
Capacity: 8,000   **Seats:** 260   **Covered:** 600   **Floodlights:** Yes
Directions: M62 Jct 17 A56 Bury New Road to Manchester, through four sets of lights then righjt into Moor Lane. Ground is
500 yards on left. Four miles from Manchseter Victoria BR. Buses: 96, 139, 94, and 95 to Moor Lane.
Midweek Home Matchday: Tuesday   **Clubhouse:** Open matchdays only   **Club Shop:** No
Previous Leagues: Manchester 63-80 Cheshire County 1980-82
Previous Names: Salford Central, 40-63 Salford Amateurs 1963 until merger with Anson Villa, Salford F.C.
Club Colours: Dark Blue with silver trim/silver/silver   **Change Colours:** Yellow & sky blue
BEST PERFORMANCES
League: 2nd NW.Co   **F.A. Cup:** 3rd Qualifying Round 2005-2006   **F.A.Vase:** 2nd Rd
RECORD Attendance: 3,000 v Whickham F.A.Vase 1981   **Goalscorer:**   **Appearances:**
Senior Honours: Lancs Amateur Cup: 72-73 74-75 76-77 Manchester Senior Cup

SILSDEN

Founded: 1904
Nickname:

Chairman: Sean McNulty   **Manager:** Andy Geary   **Assistant Manager:** Paul Schofield
Secretary: John Barclay,Belton House, 51 Hainsworth Road, Silsden, West Yorkshire BD20 0LY
Tel Nos: 01535656213 (H& Fax) 07808 825132 (W)
Programme Editor: Peter Hanson
GROUND ADDRESS: Keighly Rugby League Club, Cougar Park, Roydings Park, Keighly
Tel.No: 01535 213111 **Fax:** 01535 213100:
Simple Directions: A629 to Keighly. Left at roundabout for Bradford and immediately left again into Roydings Avenue. Cougar
Park on right.
Midweek Home Matchday: Wednesday   **Clubhouse:** Yes
Previous Leagues: Craven & District & West Riding County Amateur
Club Colours: Red/black/red   **Change Colours:** White/red/white
BEST PERFORMANCES
League: 2nd   Div 2 N.W.Co   **F.A. Cup:** 1st Qualifying Round 04-05   **F.A.Vase:** 2nd Round 2004-05
RECORD Attendance: 2,000
Senior Honours: N.W.Co Div1 R-Up 2004-05

SQUIRES GATE

Founded: 1948
Nickname:

Chairman: Phil Days   **V-Chairman:** Steve Whitehouse   **Manager:** Stuart Parker

Secretary: John Maguire, 2 Squires Court, Cairn Grove, Blackpool, FY4 2RA

Tel. Nos:01253 348512(H) 01253 330466 (M)

Programme: 20 Pages £1.50   **Editor**: David Tebbitt

GROUND ADDRESS: School Road, Martom, Blackpool, Lancs.   **Ground Tel. No:** 01253 798584

Capacity: 1,000   **Seats:** 100   **Covered:** One side.   **Floodlights:** Yes

Simple Directions: M6 to M55 jct 4, left onto A583 then right at first lights (Whitehall Road) and follow signs for airport. Ground approx 1.5 miles on right.

Midweek Home Matchday: Tuesday   **Clubhouse:** Yes   **Club Shop:** No

Previous League: West Lancs. pre 1991

Club Colours: All royal Blue   **Change Colours:** Yangerine /Navy Blue/ Tangerine

RECORD Attendance: 600 v Everton friendly 1995

ST HELENS TOWN

Founded: 1946
Nickname: Town

Chairman: Jim Barrett   **Manager:** J.Gibiliru   **Assistant Manager:** Ian Street   **Coach:** Carl Measey

Secretary: Jim Barrett, 4 Grant Close, St.Helens, Merseyside WA10 2FHG   **Tel No:** 01744 735703

Press Officer: J. Barrett/J. Voller   **Programme Editor & Match Day Sec:** J.Voller: 01744 832633 (H & Fax)

GROUND ADDRESS: Groundshare with St Helens Rugby League Club at Knowsley Rd./ Dunriding Lane, St Helens, Merseyside. WA10 4AD **Ground Tel:** 08707 565252 **e-mail**: sthelenstownfc@hotmail.co.uk**Website**: www.sthelenstownafc.com

Capcity: 19,100   **Seats:** 2,362   **Covered:** 12,408   **Floodlights:** Yes

Simple Directions: From South M62 jct 7 take fifth exit A570 to St Helens, follow route to Liverpool and follow signs for ground.From North Jct 26 off M6 then on M58 to L'pool exit M58 at jct 3 to A570 to St Helens.7miles to A580. Sgns for ground.

Midweek Home Matchday: Tuesday   **Clubhouse:** Black Bull Pub on Knowsley Road   **Club Shop:** Yes

Previous Leagues: Lancs Comb. 1903 1921, Reformed 1946 Liverpool Co Comb. 46-49 Lancs Comb 49-75, Chesh Co.75-82

Previous Grounds: Park rd. 1903 21, Hoghton Rd. 46-52, City Rd. 52-53 Hoghton Rd, 53-2000 .

Club Colours: Red & white stripes/red/red   **Change Colours:** Royal Blue

BEST PERFORMANCES: League: Lancs Comb.Champions 1972 **F.A. Cup:** 4th Q Rd .85-86 **F.A.Vase:** Winners 1986-87

RECORD Attendance: 4,000 v Man City Bert Trautman transfer match April 1950 **Goalscorer:** S.Pennington

Appearances: Alan Wellens **Victory:** 12-0 v Abbey Hey NWCo Div 1 01 **Defeat** 1-8 v Liverpool Res. Liverpool Sen Cup 1960

Senior Honours: F.A.Vase Winners 86--87 Lancs Comb 71-72 Lancs Junior Cup R-up 66-67

Squires Gate F.C. - Back Row (L-R): Peter Taberner, Chris Days, Mark Ashall, Steve Palmer, Mark Beattie, Chris Taylor. **Front Row:** Chris Cairns, Steve Gibson, Ben Morris, Paul Ryan, Craig Blinkhorn. Photo: Alan Coomes

STONE DYNAMOES

Founded: 1987
Nickname: The Doms

Chairman: Chris Haines   **Physios:** Steve Killeen & Chris Blake   **Manager:** Kevin Sheldon
Secretary: Colin Heath,46 Walton Grange,Stafford Road, Stone, Staffs. ST15 0ET
Tel No: 01785 615143 (H)   **Sponsors:** Disco.Co
GROUND ADDRESS: Springback Stadium, Kings Park, Meir Heath, Stoke on Trent, Staffs. **Tel No:** 07866 098198
Capacity: 1,000   **Seats:** 250   **Covered:** Yes   **Floodlights:** Yes
Programme Editor: Colin Heath
Simple Directions: From Stone town centre take A520 (Leek/Meir). Bear right at Swynnerton Arms pub and follow A520
(Leek) to top of hill. Right at first mini roundabout into Hilderstone Rd, (signed B5066 Sandon). Ground 1mile on right
Midweek Home Matchday: Wednesday   **Clubhouse:** Yes
Previous League: Midland League
Club Colours: Red/white/black   **Change Colours:** White/black/white
LAST SEASON: League: 21st
Top Scorer: Adam Soane   **Player of the Year:** Adam Soane   **Captain:** Jordan White
BEST PERFORMANCES:
League: N.W.Coumties Div 1   **F.A. Cup:** 2nd Qual. Round 2004-05 05-06   **F.A.Vase:** 5th Rd Replay 2003-04
RECORD Attendance: 330 v Eastwood Town F.A.Vase 10.02.04   **Goalscorer:**   **Appearances:**
Senior Honours: Midland League Champions 99-00 R-up 96-97. N.W.Co Div 2 Winners 2002-03

TRAFFORD

Founded: 1990
Nickname: The North

Chairman: Tom Walmsley   **President:** David Brown   **Manager:** Danny Johnson
Secretary: Graham Foxall, 90 Grosvenor Rd, Urmston,M41 5AQ **Tel:** 0161 747 4502   **Asst.Manager:** Danny Jones
Programme Editor: David Murray   **Programme:** 44 Pages £1.00   **Website:** www.traffordfc.co.uk
GROUND ADDRESS: Shawe View, Pennybridge Lane, Flixton, Urmston, Manchester M41 5DL**Tel.No:** 0161 747 1727
Capacity: 2,500   **Seats:** 292   **Covered:** 740   **Floodlights:** Yes
Simple Directions: M60 Jct 9 B5158 towards Urmston. At first roundabout take first exit.Then right at first lights into Moorside
Rd. At next roundabout take second exit into Bowfell Rd. Next lights sharp left, then immediately right into Pennyridge Lane
next to Bird -in-Hand pub parking on left after 100 yards.
Midweek Home Matchday: Tuesday   **Clubhouse:** Yes   **Club Shop:** Yes
Previous Leagues: Mid Cheshire 90-92, N.W.Co., 92-97 and N.P.L.,97-03   **Prev.Name:** North Trafford 90-94
Club Colours: All white   **Change Colours:** All Yellow
LAST SEASON: League: 15th   **F.A. Cup:** 2nd Qualifying Rd.   **F.A. Vase:** 2nd Rd
Top Scorer: Glyn Barker 14   **Player of the Year:** Simon Woodford   **Captain:** Martyn Andrews
BEST PERFORMANCES
League: **F.A. Cup:** 2nd Qualifying Round   **F.A.Trophy:** 3rd Rd   **F.A.Vase:** 5th Rd
RECORD Attendance: 803 v Flixton (NPL 97-98)   **Goalscorer:** Garry Vaughan 88   **Appearances:** Garry Vaughan 293
Senior Honours: NWCL Div 1 96-97 Manchester Prem Cup R-Up 94-95 ,96-97 Manchester Am. Cup 96-7 01-02 03-04
Manchester Challenge Trophy 2004-05

LEAGUE CONSTITUTION 2006-07 - DIVISION TWO

ASHTON ATHLETIC

Secretary: Steve Halliwell, 20 Kings Road, Golborne, Warrington, Cheshire WA3 3PJ
Tel: (H) 01942 517 728. (M) 07944 296 340

Ground: Brocstedes Park, Brocstedes Road, Ashton in Makerfield, Wigan.
Tel: 01942 716 360

Directions: Take junction 25 off the northbound M6 (signed A49 Wigan) down the slip road to a roundabout. Turn right onto A49 towards Ashton (Wigan Rd). At the first traffic lights (shops on junction) turn right onto the B5207 (Downall Green Road) over the motorway bridge then second right into Booths Brow Road and second right again into Brocstedes Road. First right down single track road to ground.

PREVIOUS Leagues: Lancashire Combination, Manchester Amateur League.

FACT FILE
Founded: 1968
Colours: Yellow/navy/yellow
Change colours: Sky blue/navy/sky blue
Midweek matchday: Tuesday
Programme Editor: TBA

CLUB PERSONNEL
President: J Witherington
Chairman: Steve Halliwell

ASHTON TOWN

Secretary: Rhianne Williams,44 Tintern Avenue, Astley,Tyldesley,Manchester M29 7WL
Tel No: 0773145450 (M) E-mail: williams8529@aol.com

Ground: Edge Green Street, Ashton-in-Makerfield, Wigan WN4 8SY (01942 510677)
Directions: M6 Jct 23, A49 to Ashton-in-M. Right at lights onto A58 towards Bolton. After 3/4 mile turn right at `Rams Head' P.H. into Golbourne Rd. After 200 yds right into Edge Green Str. Ground at end.
Floodlights: No

HONOURS Warrington Lg Guardian Cup.
PREVIOUS Leagues: Warrington, Lancs Comb. 03-11 71-78, Ches. Co. 78-82.
BEST SEASON FA Vase: Prelim. Rd 84-85
RECORD Gate: 600 v Accrington Stanley 76-77

FACT FILE
Founded: 1962
Colours: Red with white trim/red/red
Change colours: All sky blue
Midweek Matches: Tuesday

CLUB PERSONNEL
President: W Pomfrett
Chairman: Ian Williams
Manager: Norman Hickson

BLACKPOOL MECHANICS

Secretary: William Singleton, 36 Colwyn Avenue, Blackpool FY4 4EU (01253 692863)
Ground: Jepson Way, Common Edge Rd, Blackpool, Lancs FY4 5DY (01253 761721).
Directions: M6 to M55,Exit Jct 4 follow Airport signs. Left at r'bout along A583 across round about to lights, right into Whitehill Rd along to roundabout.Take Lytham St Annes to T junction and traffic lights.Across main road into Jepson Way and ground..Rail to Blackpool North - then bus 11c from Talbot Rd bus station (next to rail station) to Shovels Hotel, Common Edge Rd.
Capacity: 2,000   **Seats:** 250   **Cover:** 1,700 **Floodlights:** Yes
Clubhouse: Match days, training nights. Dancehall. Matchday, hot food.
Club Shop: Manager Andrew Sneddon (01253 729962). Ties, sweaters, old programmes, badges.
HONOURS Lancs Comb Bridge Shield 72-73; NW Co's. Lg Div 3 85-86; W Lancs Lg 60-61 62-63; Lancs County FA Shield 57-58 60-61:
PREVIOUS Leagues: Blackpool & Fylde Comb., West Lancs, Lancs Comb. 62-68.
Grounds: Stanley Pk 47-49
RECORD Gate: 1,200 v Morecambe, Lancs Comb, August 1968

FACT FILE
Founded: 1947   Nickname: Mechs
Sponsors: Dutton Forshaw, Blackpool
Club colours: Tangerine/white/tangerine
Change colours: All blue
Midweek matchday: Tuesday
Programme: 10 pages, 50p
Editor: William Singleton
CLUB PERSONN
Chairman: Henry David Baldwin
President: Lawence Wright
Commercial Manager: John Sanderson
Manager: Stuart Parker
Asst Man.: Wayne Hughes
Coach: Terry Green
Captain: Mark Ashall

BOOTLE

Secretary: John Doran, 54 Amaury Road, Thornton, Liverpool L23 9UZ.
Tel: (H) 0151 281 0145. (B) 0151 934 2991. (M) 07866 912 625
Ground: New Bucks Park, Vestey Road, Off Bridle Road Bootle, L30 4UN.
Tel: 0786-691-2625.
Directions: At Liverpool end of M57and M58 follow signs for Liverpool (A59 (S)), for 1 1/2 miles. At Aintree racecourse on left and Aintree Train Station on right ,turn right at lights into Park Lane. Turn left at second set of lights into Bridle Road. After 200 yards turn left at lights into Vestey Estate , ground 200 yards.
HONOURS Liverpool County Comb. 1964-65, 65-66, 67-68, 68-69, 69-70, 70-71, 71-72, 72-73, 73-74. Cheshire League Div.2 78-79.
PREVIOUS **Leagues:** Liverpool Shipping Lge, Lancashire Combination, Cheshire League, Liverpool County Combination.
RECORDS **Gate:** 750 v Casrshalton, FA Trophy 2nd Round January 1981.

FACT FILE
Colours: All Royal blue with gold trim
Change colours: All yellow
Midweek matchday: Tuesday

CLUB PERSONNEL
Chairman: Frank Doran Jnr
Fixture Secretary: Joseph Doran

CASTLETON GABRIELS

Secretary: Jim Picken, 4 Vicarage View, Castleton, Rochdale OL11 2UA
Tel. Nos:01706 655061 (H) 07818 208692 (M)
Ground: Butterworth Park, Chadwick Lane, off Heywood Rd., Castleton, Rochdale.
Tel: 01706 527103)
Directions: M62 Jct 20, A6272M to r'bout. Left towards Castleton (A664Edinburgh Way) to next r'bout, keeping Tesco Superstore to the left, take 1st exit to next r'bout, take 2nd exit into Manchester Rd (A664), after just under mile turn right at `Top House' P.H. into Heywood Rd., to end & ground on right
Capacity: 1,500 **Seats**: 400 **Cover**: 650 **Floodlights**: Yes
Clubhouse: Open seven nights a night and all day Saturday. Pie & peas and sandwiches available matchdays (pie & peas only at Reserve matches) **Club Shop:** No
HONOURS Manchester Lge 86-87, Murray Shield 86-87; Res Div Cup 95-96.
PREVIOUS **Leagues:** Rochdale Alliance 24-84; Manchester 84-89.
Name: St Gabriels (pre-1960s) **Ground:** Park pitches; Springfield Pk 60-81.
RECORDS **Gate:** 640 v Rochdale, pre-season friendly 1991 **Win:** 8-0 v Squires Gate N.W.Co.Div 2 94 **Defeat:** 1-10 v Blackpool Mechanics N.W.Co.Div 2 95

FACT FILE
Founded: 1924 Nickname: Gabs
Club Sponsors: Kick Off
Colours: Sky & Navy/Sky & Navy/Navy
Change colours: All red
Midweek matchday: Tuesday
Reserves ' League: N.W.C. Res. Div.
Programme: 28 pages, 50p
Editor:David Jones (01942730220(W)

CLUB PERSONNEL
Chairman: Jim Picken
Vice Chairman: R Butterworth
Press Officer: Secretary
Manager/Coach:David Jones
Assistant Manager:Roy Grundy
Coach: Neil Mills

CHADDERTON

Secretary: Louise Kershaw, 186 Burnley Lane,Chadderton, Oldham. OL1 2QW
Ground: Andrew Street, Chadderton, Oldham, Lancs (0161 624 9733)
Directions: **From M62 Jct 20** take A627(M) to Manchester. Motorway becomes dual carriage way. Left at first major traffic lights A669 Middleton Rd, then first left into Butterworth Street. Andrew Street is second right. Oldham Werneth (BR) 1 mile or Mills Hill (BR) I mile.
From M60 Jct 21 onto A663 to A699. Right at lights. Second left(Burnley St) and second left again(Andrew St).Buses 24,181,182 to Middleton Rd from Lever Street of Piccadilly Gardens.
Capacity: 2,500 **Seats**: 200 **Cover**: 600 **Floodlights**: Yes
Clubhouse: Matchdays only. Hot & cold snack during & after games **Club Shop:** No
HONOURS M'chester Am Lg 62-63, North Div 55-56, M. Prem Cup R-up 82-83, Chall Tphy 71-72, R-up 72-73, M. Lg Div 1 66-67, Div 2 64-65, Gilgryst Cup 69-70, Murray Shield 55-56, Lancs Comb. Cup R-up 81-82, Alf Pettit & Hulme Celtic Cup 61-62, NWC F/lit Tphy R-up 92-93
RECORD **Gate:** 2,652 v FC United 2006 **Appearances:** Billy Elwell 750+ (64-90)

FACT FILE
Founded: 1947 Nickname: Chaddy
Colours: AllRed
Change colours:
Sky blue/navy blue/navy blue
Midweek Matches: Tuesday
Programme: 28-32 pages
Editor: David Greaves
Previous Leagues: Oldham Am, Manchester
Am, Manchester 64-80, Lancs Comb 80-82

CLUB PERSONNEL
Chairman: David Greaves
President: Harry Mayall
Manager: Paul Buckley & Derek Ogden
Captain: Mark Egerton

CHEADLE TOWN

Secretary: Terry Musgrave, 8 Fernwood Avenue, Gorton, Manchester M18 7PY
Tel Nos: 0161 231 5208 (H) 07865 085488 (M)
Ground: Park Road Stadium, Park Road, Cheadle, Cheshire SK8 2AN (0161 4282510).
Directions: M60 Jct 2, follow signs towards Cheadle (A560), first left after lights into Park Road, ground at end. 1 mile from Gatley (BR), buses from Stockport.11,170, 310,312 and 371
Capacity: 2,500 **Seats:** 150 **Cover:** 300 **Floodlights** Yes
Clubhouse: Open every night. Food available **Club Shop:** No
HONOURS Manchester Lg Div 1 79-80 (R-up 80-81 81-82); Manchester Amtr Cup 79-80;Lamot Pils Cup 90-91; NWCFL Div 2 Trophy R-up 95-96, Reserve's League Cup 99-00
PREVIOUS **Leagues:** Manchester (pre 1987)
RECORD **Attendance :** 1,700 v Stockport County, August 1994.
Scorer: Peter Tilley **Appearances:** John McArdle

FACT FILE
Founded: 1961
Colours: Yellow/blue/yellowChange
colours: Red/white/red
Midweek Matches: Wednesday 7.45
Reserves' Lge: N.W.Co Res Div.
Prog: 24 pages,£1.00 Ed: Stuart Crawford

CLUB PERSONNEL
President: Freddie Pye
Chairman: Chris Davies
Vice-Chairman: Peter Healey
Press Off:Chris Davies (0161 428 2510).
Manager:Trevor Howard
Asst.Manager: Steve Brockenbrau
Player Coach: Tony Coyle
Captain: Rob Kempton

DAISY HILL

Secretary: Bob Naylor, 8 Bailey Fold, Westhoughton, Bolton, Lancs BL5 3HH
Tel: 01942 813720
Ground: New Sirs, St James Street, Westhoughton, Bolton, Lancs. Tel: 01942 818544
Directions: M61 Jct 5, A58 (Snydale Way/Park Road) for 1.5 miles, left into Leigh Road
(B5235) for 1 mile, right into village then left between Church and School into St
James Street. Ground 250 yds on the left. Half mile from Daisy Hill (BR)
Capacity: 2,000   **Seats:** 200   **Cover:** 250   **Floodlights:** Yes   **Club Shop:** No
Clubhouse: Open normal licensing hours during any football activity. Snacks on matchdays
HONOURS Bolton Comb Prem Div 62-63 72-73 75-76 77-78, Lg Cup 59-60 61-62
71-72 72-73; Lancs Shield 61-62 71-72 86-87:
PREVIOUS **Leagues:** Westhoughton; Bolton Comb.; Lancs Combination. 78-82.
Name: Westhoughton Town **Record Goals & Apps:**Alan Roscoe 300-450
RECORD **Attendance:** 2,000 v Horwich RMI,Westhoughton Charity Cup Final 79-80

FACT FILE
Founded: 1894(first known records)
Reformed: 1952
Colours: All royal blue   Change: All red
Midweek Matches: Wednesday
Programme: 40 pages £1.00
Editor: Robert Naylor.

CLUB PERSONNEL
Chairman:T.B.A.
Manager: Tommy Mould
Captain: T.B.A.

DARWEN

Secretary: Fran Eccles,c/o Club Tel No: 01254 777800 (H) 07946 369069 (M)
Ground: Anchor Ground, Anchor Road, Darwen, Lancs BB3 0BB.
Clubhouse: Matchday only
Directions: A666 Blackburn / Bolton road, 1 mile north of Darwen town centre,turn right at
Anchor Hotel, ground 200 yds on left. One and a half miles from Darwen (BR),
bus 51 to Anchor Hotel.From M65 Jct 4 signs to Darwen.Left at A666,1/2 mile left
at anchor Hotel. ground 200 yds on left
Capacity: 4,000 **Seats:** 250 **Cover:** 2,000 **Floodlights:** Yes **Shop:**No
HONOURS Lancs Comb 31 32 73 75: Comb Cup 30 31 75; Lancs Jun Cup 73; Geo Watson
Trophy 73; LFA Yth Cup 75; NWC Cup 83; Lancs F/Lit Trophy 90; NWC Res Div
Cup 94; Blackburn & Dist Yth Lge 94 95 97, Cup 94 95 97; NW All Chall Cup 96.
PREVIOUS **Leagues:**Football Alliance 1889-91, Football Lg 1891-99, Lancs Lg 99-
03,Lancs Comb. 03-75, Ches. Co. 75-82. **Ground:** Barley Bank
RECORD **Gate:** (Anchor Ground) 10,000 v Fleetwood Lancs Jun Cup 1920
14,000 v Blackburn Rovers 1882
BEST SEASON **FA Cup:** Semi Finals 1881

FACT FILE
Founded: 1875
Sponsors:
Colours: Red & white/white/red
Change colours: All blue
Midweek Matches: Tuesday
Programme: 20 pages, £1.00
Editor:D.Narah
Local papers: Lancs Evening Telegraph
CLUB PERSONNEL
President: E Devlin
Chairwoman: Mrs Kath Marah
Manager: S Mullen
Asst Manager: M Atkinson
Physio: Mick Sharples

ECCLESHALL

Secretary: Richard Marsh, 58 Leawood Road,Trent Vale, Stoke- on -Trent Staffs. ST4 6LA
Ground Pershall Park, Chester Rd, Eccleshall, Staffordshire (All post to Secretary please)
Tel: 01785 851351(matchdays).
Directions: From M6 jcts 14 or 15 find way to Eccleshall High Street (B5026) drive towards
Loggerheads. Pass church, cricket and tennis clubs for a mile, to the sign for
Pershall. Ground is 100 yards past sign on right.
Previous Leagues: Stafford & District, Staffs Aliance,Staffs County Lg (N) & Midland League
Honours: Staffs Co. Lg (N) Champions 1982, 1984Co Lg (N) Cup Winners 1983,
Staffs F.A.Vase Winners 2003 Finalists 1984 1985 & 2006
Midland League Champions 1900 2002-2003 Runners -Up 2000

FACT FILE
Formed: 1971
Colours: Blue & black stripes/black/black
Change: Tangerine/navy blue/tangerine
Midwek Matchday: Wednesday

CLUB PERSONNEL
Chairman: Andy Mapperson
Manager: Mark Askey
Coach: Steve Bradbury
Programme Editor:Russell Demattoe
2005-2006
Player of the Year Steve Millington
Captain: Danny Stevens
Top Scorer: Russell Dematteo

HOLKER OLD BOYS

Secretary: John Adams, 20 Middlefield,Barrow in Furness, Cumbria. LA14 4AU
Tel: 01229 431121 (H) 07979 783710(M)
Ground: Rakesmoor Lane, Hawcoat, Barrow-in-Furness, Cumbria LA14 4QB
Tel No:01229 828176
Directions: M6 Jct 36, A590 to Barrow-in-Furness, on entering Barrow, continue on
A590 past Kimberley Clark Paper Mill. Take Bank Lane, first left into Hawcoat.At
top of hill turn left into Rakesmoor Lane. Ground 200yds on right.
Capacity: 1,750   Seats: 220Cover: 500   Floodlights: Yes
Clubhouse: Tue,Thur & Fri 8-1am, Sat noon-1am, Sun 8-12pm.
Pies & peas on matchdays   **Club Shop:** No
HONOURS W Lancs Lg 86-87, R-up 85-86; Lancs Junior Shield 88-89 90-91.
PREVIOUS **Leagues:** North Western; Furness Premier; West Lancs 70-91.
RECORDS **Attendance:** 2,303 v F.C.United F.A.Cup at Craven Park 2005-2006 **Win:** 12-0
Defeat: 1-8 v Newcastle T. (H) 91-92   **Top Scorer:** Dave Conlin
2005-06 **Top Goalscorer:** Paul Southward 20 **Player of the Year.:** Craig Salton

FACT FILE
Founded: 1936   Nickname: Cobs
Sponsors: Schofield Construction
&Specsavers
Colours:Green+white sleeves/white/green
Change: All red
Midweek Matches: Tuesday
Programme: 32pages, £1.00

CLUB PERSONNEL
President: David Ainsbury
Chairman:Stephen Livingstone
Vice-Chairman: Dick John
Press Officer: John Taylor
Manager: Derek Birrell
Coach: Colin Athersmith
Physio: Mark Hetherington
Captain: Gareth Brunton

LEEK C.S.O.B.

Secretary: Stan Lockett, 5 Fitzherbert Close, Swynnerton, Stone, Staffs ST150PQ,
Tel: 01782 796551 (H) 07944 493106 (M)
Fixture Sec: Patricia Lacey (01538 384705)
Ground: Harrison Park, Macclesfield Road, Leek, Staffs,   Tel: 01538 383734
Club Email: stan@slockett.freeserve.co.uk
Directions: M6 south Junc 17, A534 to Congleton - follow signs for Leek (A54), carry on to junction with A523, right onto A523, this road is direct to Leek, ground 8 miles on right just into Leek.
Capacity: 3,600   **Seating:** 625 **Covered Terracing:** 2,675   **Floodlights:** Yes
PREVIOUS Leagues: Leek & Moorland Lge, Staffs County North, Refuge Midland Lge.
RECORDS Attendance: 2,590 v FC United August 2005
BEST SEASON FA Cup: 3rd Q 98-99   FA Vase: 1st Round 2000-01
HONOURS Refuge Midland Lge 95-96. Lge Cup 94-95 95-96; Leek Cup 94-95 95-96;
Midland Ref Charity Shield 95-96; Sportsline Chall Cup 95-96.
NWCL Div. 2winners - Programme of the Year 2001/02

FACT FILE
Founded: 1945 Sponsors: Cafe 'Bhujon'
Colours: Blue & white stripes/Black
Change colours: All White
Midweek Matchday:Tuesday
Programme: Yes   Editor: Stan Lockett
CLUB PERSONNEL
Chairman: Chris McMullen
Managers: Chris McMullen &
Andrew Walters
Asst Mans: Lee Mycock & Paul Campion
Physios: Keith Tatton & Dennis Lowndes
Captain: Daniel Hyde
2005-206
Leading GoalscorerColin Fletcher 16
Player of the Year:Daniel Hyde

NEW MILLS A.F.C.

Secretary: Allan Jones.79 Laneside Road, New Mllls, High Peak. SK 22 4NP

Tel No: 07748626448 (M)

Ground: Church Lane, New Mills, High Peak, SK22 4NP Tel No: 01663 747435

Capacity: 1,650   **Seats:** 120   **Cover:** 400   **Floodlights:** Yes

Clubhouse: Open seven days a week.

Directions: From Stockport, A6 to Swan Hotel, turn left down hill through lights and then turn left at St George's church. Ground on right.

PREVIOUS **Leagues:** Manchester League

Name: New Mills St Geirges until 1919

CLUB RECORD

Attendance: 4,500 v Hyde United 1922

FACT FILE
Formed: 1900 Reformed 1919
Sponsor: Princes Cruises
Colours: All amber with black trim
Change colours: All white
Midweek Matches: Monday
Prog: 40 pages £1.00 Editor: Glyn Jones
CLUB PERSONNEL
Chairman: Ray Coverley
Press Officer: Allan Jones (01663 744649)
Manager: Tony Hancock
Assistant Manager: Paul Kirkham
Captain: Martin McDonald

NORTON UNITED

Secretary: Dennis Vickers, 86 Ford Green Road, Smallthorne, Stoke-on-Trent ST6 1NX
Tel: 01782 822727 (H) 01785 354200 (B)

Ground: Norton CC & MWI, Community Drive, Smallthorne, Stoke-on-Trent
Tel: 01782 838290
Directions: M6 J16, A500 to BUrslem/Tunstall, turn off on A527, bear right at traffic island to Burslem, through lights to Smallthorne, take 3rd exit on mini r'about, turn right by pedestrian crossing into Community Drive, ground 200 metres on left.
Nearest Station: Stoke-on-Trent (mainline) Longport (local)

PREVIOUS **League:** Midland League to 2001

RECORDS **Attendance:** 165 v Alsager Town 2002

HONOURS Midland League - Champions 00-01 98-99 96-97, League Cup 00-01 96-97 91-92;
Staffs FA Senior Vase 98-99

FACT FILE
Founded: 1989
Colours: Black & white stripes/black/black
Change Cols.: Red & black
stripes/white/white
Midweek Matchday: Wednesday
Programme: Pages: Price:
Editor:

CLUB PERSONNEL
Chairman: Stephen Beaumont
8 Maitland Grove, Trentham, Stoke-on-
Trent.
Tel: 01782 642321 (H)

OLDHAM TOWN

Secretary: David Shepherd, 24 Hilary Avenue, Bardsley, OLdham, Lancs. OL8 2TD
Tel No: 0161 665 1375 (H) 07803 122501(W) 07915 075506 (M)
Ground: Whitebank Stadium, Whitebank Rd, Hollins, Oldham, Lancs OL8 3JH
Tel: 0161 624 2689
Directions: M62 jct 18, M66 to Heaton Pk, right on to A576, left at 2nd lights on to A6104, fol low Victoria Ave. on to Hollinwood Ave. under bridge to roundabout take 2nd exit onto Hollins Road, follow Hollins Rd for one & a half miles to Fire Station, left on through gate leading onto Elm Rd and follow to next left, Whitebank Rd on left.
Capacity: 1,000   Seats: 101   Cover: Yes   Floodlights: Yes
Clubhouse: Open evenings and matchdays
HONOURS NWC: Div 2 97-98, R-up 94-95; Div 3 R-up 85--86; Lg.Champions 97-98
Res Div R-up 94-95, Cup 94/95;

PREVIOUS **Leagues:** Manchester Amateur; Lancashire Comb. 81-82.

RECORD **Attendance:** 495 v Halifax Town, 1996.

FACT FILE

Founded: 1964
Colours: Blue,white,blue
Midweek Matches: Tuesday
Programme: 16 pages, 50p
Editor: Secretary

CLUB PERSONNEL

Chairman: Ken Hughes
Manager: Len Cantello

PADIHAM

Secretary:	Alan Smith,242 Burnley Road, Padiham, Lancs. BB112 8SS (01282 771963)
Ground:	Arbories Memorial Sports Ground, Well Street, Padiham, Lancs. BB12 8LE Tel: 01282 773742
Directions:	M65, J8, then follow A6068 (signed Clitheroe & Padiham). At lights at bottom of hill, turn right into Dean Range/Blackburn Road towards Padiham. At the next junction turn into Holland street opposite church, then into Well Street at the side of the Hare & Hounds pub to the ground. Nearest rail station: Burnley Floodlights: Yes
Honours:	Lancs Amateur Cup R-up 66, Lancs Amateur Shield R-up 97, Burnley, Pendle & Rossendale Hosp. Cup 96,05 R-up 91 03 Lancs Comb.. George WatsonTrophy 81, R-up 82; NWC Div. 3 R-up 83-84; W. Lancs Div.1 99-00, Div.2 71-72 76-77 R-up 96-97, Pres. Cup R-up 79 94 97; E. Lancs Amat Lge R-up 06-07
Best Season:	FA Cup: Third Rd., 1883-84
Previous	**Leagues:** Lancashire Comb.; NW Counties; West Lancs.; N.E. Lancs; NE Lancs Combination; East Lancs Amateur Lge.

FACT FILE
Formed: 1878
Colours: Royal blue & white/white/red
Change: Alkl/White
Midweek Matchday: Wednesday
Programme: £1.00
Editor:Alan Smith
CLUB PERSONNEL
Chairman: Mick Muldoon
(0034 96574 7866)
Manager:Steve Wilkes
2005-2006
P.o.Y.:Paul Filds
Top Goalscorer: Paul Filds
Captain: Craig Chadwick

RUNCORN LINNETS

Secretary : Tony Waddington, 7 Moorland Drive, Abbotts Lodge, Runcorn, Cheshire WA7 6HL.

Tel: (H) 01228 822 615. (M) 07716 541800

Ground Address: Wincham Park Stadium, Chapel Street, Whincham, Northwich, Cheshire CW9 6DA. Tel/Fax: 01606 43008

Directions: From junction 19 of the M6, follow A556 towards Northwich for 3 miles, before turning right at the beginning of the dual carriageway, onto the A559. After 3/4 of a mile, turn right at the traffic lights at the "Slow & Easy" pub. After another 3/4 mile, turn left opposite the "Black Greyhound" Inn into Wincham Lane. The ground is 1/2 mile on the left immediately after crossing the canal.

FACT FILE
Founded: 2006
Colours: Yellow with green trim/green/ yellow with green trim
Change colours: Red with black trim/ black/red with black trim
Midweek matchday: Tuesday
Programme Editor: Derek Greenwood
linnetdg@tiscali.co.uk
CLUB PERSONNEL
Chairman: Stuart White

WINSFORD UNITED

Secretary :	Robert Astles, 40 Aldersey Road,Crewe,Cheshire CW2 8NR Tel: 01270 661623
Ground Address:	Barton Stadium, Wharton, Winsford, Cheshire CW7 3EU (01606 593021).
Directions:	From north; M6 J19, A556 towards Northwich to Davenham, then A5018 to Winsford. From south; M6 J18, A54 through Middlewich to Winsford. Ground quarter mile off main road in Wharton area of town. 1 mile from Winsford (BR).
Capacity:	6,000 Cover: 5,000 Seats: 250
Clubhouse:	Mon-Sat 12pm-11pm, Sun12.00-10.30pm **Club Shop:** Yes, contact Secretary
Previous Lges:	The Combination 02-04; Cheshire Co. 19-40, 47-82; N.W.C. 82-87, N.P.L 87-01.
CLUB RECORDS	**Attendance:** 7,000 v Witton Albion 1947.**Goalscorer:** Graham Smith 66.
Apps:	Edward Harrop 400.. **Fee Received:** £127,000 forAndy Oakes from Derby Countyf
BEST SEASON	FA Cup: 2nd Rd 1887-8 1st Rd 1975-6 91-2 FA Trophy: Qtr Finals 77-78.
HONOURS	N.P.L. R-up 92-93, Div 1 R-up 91-92, Lg Cup 92-93, Presidents Cup 92-93; Cheshire Co. Lg 20-21 76-77 (R-up 74-75 79-80),Lg Cup x 7 R-up x 3; Cheshire Snr Cup 58-59 79-80 92-93; Mid-Cheshire Snr Cup 90-91 92-93 (R-up 88-89); Cheshire Amateur Cup 00-01 02-03; Lancs Comb/Cheshire County Inter-Lg Cup 62-63.

FACT FILE
Founded: 1883   Nickname: Blues
Colours: All Royal Blue
Change colours: All Orange
Midweek matchday: Wednesday
Programme: Pages: 24 Price: £1.00
Editor: R. Astles
CLUB PERSONNEL
Chairman: Mark Loveless
President: David Lawson
Vice Chairman: David Taylor
Manager: Chris Willcock
2005-2006
Captain :Mark Quinn
Player of the Year: Neil Marsh
Top Goalscorer: Rob Hopley

NORTHERN COUNTIES EAST

SPONSORED BY:

President: Frank Catt   **Chairman:** Tom Dixon

Secretary/Treasurer:

Barry Wood, 6 Restmore Avenue, Guiseley, Leeds LS20 9DG

Tel & Fax: 01943 874 558

PREMIER DIVISION	P	W	D	L	F	A	Pts
1. Buxton	38	30	5	3	102	27	95
2. Liversedge	38	25	5	8	106	49	80
3. Harrogate Railway	38	22	7	9	92	49	73
4. Sheffield	38	20	10	8	63	43	70
5. Arnold Town (-3)	38	21	7	10	72	45	67
6. Pickering Town	38	19	9	10	63	42	66
7. Sutton Town (1st Div.1 04-05)	38	17	9	12	78	57	60
8. Selby Town	38	17	5	16	58	60	56
9. Thackley (-3)	38	18	3	17	59	62	54
10. Armthorpe Welfare	38	13	8	17	65	77	47
11. Glapwell	38	12	11	15	46	71	47
12. Garforth Town (2nd Div.1 04-05) (-1)	38	12	11	15	61	68	46
13. Mickleover Sports	38	12	8	18	51	73	44
14. Eccleshill United	38	12	7	19	66	70	43
15. Shirebrook Town	38	13	4	21	59	85	43
16. Glasshoughton Welfare	38	11	5	22	52	70	38
17. Hallam	38	10	8	20	44	73	38
18. Maltby Main (-1)	38	9	11	18	52	70	37
19. Long Eaton United (-3)	38	8	8	22	47	86	29
20. Brodsworth Miners Welfare	38	6	5	27	47	106	23

PREMIER DIVISION	1	2	3	4	5	6	7	8	9	10	11	12	13	14	15	16	17	18	19	20
1 Armthorpe Welfare		0-2	3-1	0-5	1-2	1-5	1-2	1-0	2-0	0-2	1-3	3-0	1-2	1-1	1-0	4-2	1-2	3-2	0-6	5-1
2 Arnold Town	1-1		2-0	0-2	7-2	3-3	0-2	4-0	2-1	1-2	3-1	2-2	0-1	2-1	0-1	2-1	1-0	3-1	1-2	3-1
3 Brodsworth Miners Welfare	0-2	0-1		0-3	1-5	1-2	4-2	2-3	0-6	2-3	3-0	4-3	2-3	1-2	2-2	0-4	0-5	0-1	0-1	
4 Buxton	2-1	2-1	3-3		3-1	2-1	9-0	2-0	4-0	3-0	1-0	4-0	2-1	2-1	2-3	4-0	5-0	2-1	1-6	4-2
5 Eccleshill United	1-1	0-2	1-1	0-0		3-1	2-2	2-1	2-1	2-3	2-3	1-1	7-1	0-1	0-1	1-0	2-3	6-0	2-1	1-2
6 Garforth Town	2-2	3-1	1-2	0-1	1-0		2-2	1-0	1-2	0-0	1-4	2-3	1-1	0-0	0-2	1-2	2-0	0-0	4-1	0-3
7 Glapwell	1-1	0-2	2-1	0-0	0-4	1-1		0-4	1-2	1-4	2-1	0-3	2-0	0-0	1-4	0-1	0-0	3-2	2-2	2-0
8 Glasshoughton Welfare	3-1	1-3	5-0	1-2	1-2	6-3	3-0		0-2	2-3	1-2	2-1	1-0	2-1	1-1	1-0	0-1	0-1	2-2	1-1
9 Hallam	1-4	0-1	3-2	1-1	1-0	1-5	2-2	2-2		1-2	0-3	2-1	1-1	0-0	3-1	2-2	1-4	0-1	1-1	0-1
10 Harrogate Railway	5-3	3-2	5-0	1-4	1-1	1-2	2-0	8-1	5-1		0-1	2-2	1-2	6-1	1-1	3-1	1-0	2-5	2-2	4-1
11 Liversedge	2-3	1-1	4-0	1-1	6-1	5-3	7-2	2-0	3-2	1-0		7-2	2-1	2-3	2-2	5-1	1-2	8-2	2-3	5-4
12 Long Eaton United	2-0	1-5	2-4	0-2	4-2	2-4	1-1	2-0	1-0	0-3	1-1		0-1	0-1	0-1	2-0	2-2	1-2	1-1	3-2
13 Maltby Main	2-2	2-2	2-2	0-3	1-1	2-2	2-1	0-0	1-2	4-2	0-2	2-1		2-3	1-1	1-3	2-2	5-2	1-2	0-1
14 Mickleover Sports	2-5	2-2	4-2	0-6	2-0	0-1	0-3	3-1	4-3	4-1	1-2	3-2	0-4		0-0	0-1	1-3	3-2	0-2	1-3
15 Pickering Town	3-3	1-2	2-0	0-1	3-2	2-1	0-0	2-1	4-1	0-0	0-1	4-2	2-0	2-0		1-0	1-1	6-1	0-1	5-1
16 Selby Town	5-2	3-1	4-1	0-3	2-0	0-0	2-1	0-4	2-0	1-3	0-0	3-0	3-1	2-0	4-1		1-2	1-4	3-2	0-2
17 Sheffield	0-0	0-3	4-0	1-0	3-2	4-1	1-0	3-1	0-1	0-4	0-4	8-0	1-1	1-1	1-0	1-1		2-0	2-1	1-0
18 Shirebrook Town	3-5	1-1	2-4	0-4	0-3	2-3	1-2	4-1	1-1	1-0	0-4	2-0	2-1	3-2	1-2	0-2	0-0		1-2	1-2
19 Sutton Town	3-0	0-1	5-0	1-3	6-2	5-0	1-2	4-0	0-2	0-0	0-5	2-2	2-1	1-1	4-2	3-2	1-1	0-1		1-2
20 Thackley	1-0	1-2	1-1	0-4	2-1	1-1	2-3	0-1	4-0	0-2	1-0	2-0	4-2	2-1	1-0	0-1	1-3	1-2	5-1	

STEP 1 — CONFERENCE
STEP 2 — CONFERENCE Nth & Sth
STEP 3 — NPL - SOUTHERN - ISTHMIAN PREM
STEP 4 — NPL - SOUTHERN - ISTHMIAN
STEP 5/6 — NORTHERN COUNTIES EAST
STEP 7

DIVISION ONE

		P	W	D	L	F	A	Pts
1.	Carlton Town	30	23	4	3	68	27	73
2.	Retford United	30	20	5	5	74	28	65
3.	Tadcaster Albion	30	21	1	8	55	35	64
4.	Gedling Town	30	19	5	6	75	34	62
5.	Winterton Rangers	30	18	7	5	71	27	61
6.	Parkgate	30	18	5	7	87	40	59
7.	Lincoln Moorlands	30	16	1	13	56	40	49
8.	Borrowash Victoria	30	15	4	11	50	45	49
9.	Worsborough Bridge	30	11	5	14	57	67	38
10.	Staveley MW	30	9	4	17	44	57	31
11.	Pontefract Collieries	30	6	7	17	43	64	25
12.	Rossington Main	30	7	4	19	38	67	25
13.	South Normanton Athletic	30	7	3	20	45	87	24
14.	Hall Road Rangers	30	6	5	19	38	82	23
15.	Teversal	30	5	6	19	28	78	21
16.	Yorkshire Amateur	30	4	4	22	29	80	16

DIVISION ONE

	1	2	3	4	5	6	7	8	9	10	11	12	13	14	15	16
1 Borrowash Victoria		1-3	1-1	0-1	3-0	0-2	3-2	2-4	0-2	3-2	0-5	3-2	2-0	1-3	0-0	4-0
2 Carlton Town	3-1		3-2	1-1	0-2	2-0	3-0	0-0	1-0	3-1	4-0	1-0	1-0	1-5	3-0	6-0
3 Gedling Town	1-0	0-3		3-1	3-1	2-0	1-0	1-3	3-1	3-0	4-1	2-1	1-1	3-2	5-1	6-0
4 Hall Road Rangers	1-4	0-3	0-6		1-0	2-2	0-1	0-2	2-3	1-3	1-2	2-3	5-1	0-0	0-2	3-3
5 Lincoln Moorlands	1-3	1-2	1-4	9-1		2-0	1-0	3-0	1-0	2-0	1-0	1-2	3-0	0-2	3-1	1-2
6 Parkgate	5-1	1-2	4-0	4-0	4-2		6-3	2-0	5-1	4-0	1-1	1-2	6-0	4-2	4-1	3-0
7 Pontefract Collieries	0-2	0-0	0-6	5-0	0-2	2-3		1-3	3-3	3-0	1-2	2-1	0-0	2-2	1-1	4-2
8 Retford United	0-0	2-0	1-1	2-1	2-0	2-2	5-1		4-1	1-2	2-0	1-2	7-1	1-0	6-2	3-0
9 Rossington Main	0-2	1-2	2-2	2-3	1-5	2-0	3-1	0-3		1-2	0-1	1-2	0-2	0-5	1-4	1-1
10 South Normanton Athletic	2-5	1-4	2-1	6-4	1-2	2-8	1-1	1-3	2-3		0-5	0-2	2-0	1-3	0-2	4-1
11 Staveley MW	0-1	0-2	1-2	2-3	1-3	2-2	1-3	1-3	0-4	4-2		0-2	2-1	0-3	1-1	1-2
12 Tadcaster Albion	0-3	0-3	1-1	3-0	2-1	0-3	3-1	1-0	4-0	4-0	2-1		2-0	2-1	3-1	2-0
13 Teversal	0-1	3-4	0-4	3-2	1-1	0-3	2-1	0-6	4-1	4-4	3-3	0-1		0-4	0-4	1-0
14 Winterton Rangers	0-0	4-5	2-0	1-1	2-1	1-1	2-0	1-1	0-0	5-1	2-1	3-1	3-0		2-0	5-0
15 Worsborough Bridge	4-2	1-1	1-4	5-0	0-3	4-3	4-3	1-4	2-4	2-2	1-3	2-3	4-0	0-4		3-1
16 Yorkshire Amateur	1-2	0-2	0-3	1-2	2-3	2-4	2-2	1-3	1-0	3-1	1-3	1-2	1-1	0-2	1-3	

FIRST ROUND

Hall Road Rangers v	Retford Town	5-3
Lincoln Moorlands v	Rossington Main	2-1
Parkgate v	South Normanton Athletic	7-1
Staveley MW v	Carlton Town	2-4

SECOND ROUND

Armthorpe Welfare v	Carlton Town	3-5
Arnold Town v	Gedling Town	0-1
Buxton v	Brodsworth MW	7-1
Glapwell v	Borrowash Victoria	2-0
Glasshoughton Welv	Long Eaton United	0-2
Harrogate Railway v	Hallam	3-1
Lincoln Moorlands v	Hall Road Rangers	2-1
Mickleover Sports v	Winterton Rangers	2-4
Parkgate v	Garforth Town	2-0
Pontefract Colls. v	Thackley	1-7
Selby Town v	Sutton Town	4-3
Sheffield (H) v	Eccleshill United	5-1
Tadcaster Albion v	Maltby Main	1-2
Teversal v	Liversedge	1-3
Worsbrough B.MW v	Shirebrook Town	2-1
Yorkshire Amateur v	Pickering Town	1-2

THIRD ROUND

Carlton Town v	Parkgate	4-4, 3-3r*, 1-4p
Gedling Town v	Harrogate R.	1-1, 3-3r* 5-3p
Lincoln Moorlands v	Buxton	3-1
Liversedge v	Mickleover Sports	2-0
Maltby Main v	Long Eaton United	3-2
Pickering Town v	Glapwell	1-0
Selby Town v	Thackley	1-1
Sheffield (H) v	Worsbrough Bridge MW	3-1

QUARTER-FINALS

Liversedge v	Parkgate	8-1
Maltby Main v	Buxton	0-2
Selby Town v	Pickering Town	1-1, 4-2r
Sheffield (H) v	Gedling Town	6-1

SEMI-FINALS

Buxton v	Liversedge	0-2
Sheffield (H) v	Selby Town	3-1

THE FINAL (2 legs home & away)   1st leg 2nd leg

Sheffield (H) v	Liversedge	0-2	1-3

Thackley's Kyle Shah controls the ball under pressure from a Hallam defender, during his sides 4-0 league win.

Photo: Darren Thomas.

LEAGUE CONSTITUTION 2006-07 - PREMIER DIVISION

ARMTHORPE WELFARE
Formed: 1926
Nickname: Wellie

Chairman: Stephen Taylor   **Vice-Chairman:** Roy Francis   **Manager:** Carl Leighton
Secretary: Maureen Cottam,15 Cranfield Close, Armthorpe, Doncaster DN3 3LN
Tel Nos: 01302 832514 (H) 07763 328177 (M)   **Press Officer:** Sharon Morgan
Programme Editor: Tony Ingram (01302 842795)   **Programme:** 24 pages 50p
GROUND ADDRESS: Church Street, Armthorpe, Doncaster DN3 3AG   **Ground Tel. No:** 07763 328177 (matchdays only)
Capacity: 2,500   **Seats:** 200   **Covered:** 40   **Floodlights:** Yes   **Club Shop:** No
Simple Directions: M18 jct 4 A630 left at first roundabout then right at second. Ground 400 yard on left.
Midweek Home Matchday: Tuesday   **Clubhouse:** No. Refreshments on ground. Wheatsheaf Hotel used after game.
PreviousLeague: Doncaster Senior
Club Colours: All White   **Change Colours:** Navy/white/navy
BEST PERFORMANCES
League: 2nd 1987-88   **F.A. Cup:** 3rd Qualifying Round 86-87   **F.A.Vase:** 3rd Rd 1984-85
RECORD Attendance: 2,000 v Doncaster R Charity Match 1985-86 **Goalscorer:** Martin Johnson **Appearances:** Gary
Leighton   **Victory:** 7-0 v Stocksbridge PS NCE 84-85 7 Brodsworth MW NCE 00-01 **Defeat:** 0-7 v Belper Town NCE 86-87
Senior Honours: Northern Counties East R-up 87-88 West Riding Challenge Cup: 81-82 82-83

ARNOLD TOWN
Founded: 1989
Nickname: Eagles

Chairman: Roy Francis   **Vice-Chairman:** Paul Stanley   **President:** Alan Croome
Joint Managers: Andy Muldoon & Calvin Plummer   **Physio:** Trevor Wells
Secretary: Roy Francis, 3 Arnot Hill Road, Arnold, Nottingham NG5 6LJ **Tel No:** 0115 9522634 (H) 07966 151496(M)
Press Officer & Programme Editor: Paul Stanley (0115 9566951)   **Programme:** 52 Pages Price 1.00
GROUND ADDRESS: King George V Recreation Ground, Gedling, Gedling Road, Arnold. Notts (0115 9263660)
Capacity: 2,450 **Seats:** 150 **Covered:** 950 **Floodlights:** Yes **Shop:** All club accessories. Martin Williams (0115 9598759)
Simple Directions: From A1M/A614/A60 to lights (Harvester on right) left through lights to St Albans Rd. then through lights
by Wilkinsons left into Hallams Lane. Ground on right opposite market.
Midweek Home Matchday: Tuesday   **Clubhouse:** matchdays & training nights.
Previous Name: Arnold F.C.(founded1928 as Arnold St.Marys) merged with Arnold Kingswell (founded 1962) in1989
Previous League: Central Midland 89-93. **As Arnold:** Bulwell & Dist., Notts Spartan,Notts Comb.,Central All. Midland 63-82,
NCE 82-6.Central Mids 86-9.**As Kingswell:** Notts Yth/Am.,Notts Spartan,E.Mids .,Midlan 76-82,,NCE82-86, C Midlands 86-89
Club Colours: Yellow with blue/blue/yellow **Change Colours:** All Red   **Res Lg.:** CML Res Premier Div
LAST SEASON: League: 5th   **F.A. Cup:** Prelim Rd.   **F.A. Vase:** 5th Rd. 2001-02 2005-6
Top Scorer: David Wilkins 28   **Player of the Year:** David Wilkins   **Captain:** Chris Peet
BEST PERFORMANCES: N.Co.East Champions 85-86 **F.A. Cup:** 1st Rd Replay 77-78 **F.A.Vase:** 5th Rd 01-02
RECORD Attendance: 2,200 v Hucknall T 16.04.90   **Goalscorer:** Pete Fletcher 100 **Appearances:** Peter Davey 346
Senior Honours: Notts Senior Cup (10) R-up (5) NCE 85-86 C.Midlands 92-93 Midland CoLg R-up 70-71

BRODSWORTH WELFARE
Founded: 1912
Nickname:Broddy

Chairman: Gordon Jennings   **Vice-Chairman:** Bob Laws   **Manager:** Alan Radford
Secretary & Prog.Ed: Nigel Hyde, 5 Stonegate, Thorne, Doncaster DN8 5NP   Sponsor: G.L S.com
Tel Nos: 01405 818330(H) 01405 818330 (Fax) 07952 812811(M)
Press Officer: Diane Hyde (07720832147)   **Programme:** 30 Pages
GROUND ADDRESS: Welfare Ground, Woodlands, Nr Doncaster DN6 7PP   **Tel:** 01302 728380
Capacity: 3,000   **Seats:** 228   **Covered:** 500   **Floodlights:** Yes   **Shop:**Yes
Simple Directions: From A1 take A638 to Doncaster. Left after Woodlands pub into Welfare Road. Ground 50 yards on left.
Midweek Home Matchday: Tuesday   **Clubhouse:** Yes, matchdays. Catering : Diane Hyde (07720832147)
Previous Leagues: Doncaster Senior, Sheffield and Yorkshire
Club Colours: All Blue   **Change Colours:** Green/white/green
BEST PERFORMANCES
League: 12th N.Co.East Premier   **F.A. Cup:** 4th Qualifyimg Rd 19 26-27   **F.A.Vase:** 3rd Rd 97-98
RECORD Victory: 9-0 v Blidworth MW NCE 97-98 **Fee Received:** £ 2,550 + for Danny Schofield from Huddersfield Town
Senior Honours: Sheffield Junior Cup: 83-84

CARLTON TOWN

Secretary: Paul Shelton, 28 Freda Close, Gedling, Nottingham NG4 4GP.   Founded: 1904
     Tel: 0115 987 7527 (H) 07886 017396 (M)   Colours: Yellow/Blue/Yellow
     email: paul.shelton1@btopenworld.com   Change colours: Navy/sky/sky
Ground: Stoke Lane Gedling, Nottingham. Tel: 0115 987 3583   Midweek Matchday: Tuesday
Directions: A612 Nottingham to Southwell Road. Stoke Lane is situated off A612 between   Programme Editor: Andrew King
     Gedling & Burton Joyce (signed Stoke Bardolph).   Club Website: carltontownfc.co.uk
     Ground 200 yards on left over level crossing.   **Nearest BR Station:** Carlton.   Chief Executive: Michael Garton
Capacity: 600   **Seats:** 164   **Cover:** 200   **Floodlights:** Yes   President: Roger Smith
Clubhouse: Yes Tel: 0115 940 2531   **Club Shop:** No   Press Officer: Pam Jephson
PREVIOUS Name: Sneinton F.C.   Head Coach: Tom Brookbanks
     Leagues: Central Midlands >2003   Assistants: Dave Nairn
HONOURS: Notts Alliance - Div 1 92-93, Div 2 84-85; Notts Intermediate Cup 91-92;   Physio: Martin Jephson
     Central Midlands Supreme Division Champions: 2002-2003

ECCLESHILL UNITED
Founded: 1948
Nickname: The Eagles

Chairman: Barry Philp **Manager:** Ray Price **Physio:** Gordon Raynor
Secretary: Pamel Waite, 27 Cotswold Avenue, Wrose, Shipley, WestYorks. BD 18 ILS **Tel No:** 01274 583008
Press & Programme Editor: Secretary **Programme:** 24-28 pges -50p
GROUND ADDRESS: Plumpton Park, Kingsway, Wrose, Bradford BD2 1PN **Ground Tel No:** 01274 615739
Capacity: 2,225 **Seats:** 225 **Covered:** 415 **Floodlights:** Yes
Simple Directions: From A 650 Bradford Inner Ring road onto Canal Road and branch right at Staples (Dixons Car show-rooms on right) fork left after 30mph sign to junction with Wrose Road (across junction) continuation of Kings Road. First left onto KIngsway and ground is 200 yards on right. Bradford BR - 2miles. Buses: 624 or 627
Midweek Home Matchday: Tuesday **Clubhouse:** Normal licensing hours **Club Shop:** Yes
Previous Name: Eccleshill F.C. **Previous Leagues:** Bradford Amateur and West Riding Amateur
Club Colours: Blue & white stripes/blue/blue **Change Colours:** All Yellow
BEST PERFORMANCES
League: 8th N.Co. E. 2003-04 **F.A. Cup:** 2nd Qual.Rd. **F.A.Vase:** 5th Rd 1999-2000
RECORD Attendance:715 v Bradford C 96-7 **Victory:** 10-1 v Blackpool Mech's FAC **Defeat:** 0-6 v Rossendale (a) Lg Cp
Goalscorer: Stuart Taylor
Senior Honours: NCE Div 1 96-7, Bradford F.A. Senior Cup 85-86 Wet Riding Cup R-Up 99-00

GARFORTH TOWN
Founded: 1964
Nickname:The MIners

Chairman: Tom Murray **President:** Norman Hebbron **Chief Executive:** Simon Clifford
Manager: Simon Clifford **Asst.Manager**: Vernon Blair **Coach:** Richard Caldwell **Physio:** Paul Cavell
Performance Director & Secretary: Steve Nichol,35 Lambton Drive, Hetton-le-Hole, Tyne & Wear DH5 0EW
Tel Nos: 07984 786782 (M) 0113 244 1980 (Fax) **e-mail:** s,nichol@icfds.com **Sponsors:** ICFDS/SOCATOTS
Programme Editor: Chris Mather Tel Nos: 0113 286 3453 (H) 07870 211482 (M) **Programme:** 32 Pages £1.00
GROUND ADDRESS: The Marston's Stadium, Cedar Ridge, Garforth, Leeds LS25 2PF **Tel** 0113 286 4083or0113 2877145
Email address: info@garforthtown.com **website**: www.garforthtown.com
Capacity: 3,000 **Seats:** None **Covered:** 200 **Floodlights:** Yes
Simple Directions: M1 Jct 47. Take Garforth turning (A642). After 200 yards turn left into housing estate opposite White House (Cedar Ridge) Stadium at end of lane. **Previous League(s):** Leeds Sun.Comb.64-72, West Yorks.,72-78 Yorks 78-83
Midweek Home Matchday: Tuesday **Clubhouse:** Full Licensing Hours **Club Shop:** Yes
Club Colours: Yellow/blue/blue **Change Colours:** Red & Black/Black/Black
LAST SEASON: League: 10th Divison One **F.A. Cup:** Prelim. Rd. **F.A. Vase:** 2nd Qualifying Rd
Top Scorer: Greg Kelly **Player of the Year:** Brett Renshaw **Captain:** Brett Renshaw
BEST PERFORMANCES: 9th N.Co.E. **F.A. Cup:** 2nd Qual.Rd. 91-92 97-98 **F.A.Vase:** 6th Rd 85-86
RECORD Attendance: 1,385l v Tadcaster Albion (Socrates debut) 20.11.04l (Record for League)
Goalscorer: Simeon Bambrook 67 **Appearances:** Philip Matthews 82-93
Senior Honours: NCE Div 1 97-98 R-up 96-97 04-05 West Riding County Cup 97-98 99-00

GLAPWELL
Founded: 1985
Nickname:

Chairman: Roger Caton **Manager:** Lee Wilson **Asst Mans:** Junior Glve & Tony Marsden
Secretary: Ellen Caton, High Ridge, 111 The Hill, Glapwell, Chesterfield S44 5LU **Website**
Tel Nos: 01246 854648 (H& Fax) 07976 838423 (M) email: ellen@decaton.fsnet.co.uk www.glapwellfc.freeserve.co.uk
Programme: 48 Pages Price 1.00 **Editor:**Paul Harrison(07890 580346) **Com. Man:**Andrew Saunders
Capacity: 1,500 **Seats: 300** **Covered:** Yes **Floodlights:** Yes
Simple Directions: M1 Jct 29 Take A617 towards Mansfield. Take filter lane left to Boilsover Road after pub Ground facing-use entrance next to garden centre.
Midweek Home Matchday: Tuesday
Clubhouse: Yes **Club Shop:** Yes
Previous Leagues: Sutton & Skeg. and Central Midlands
Club Colours: Black & white stripes/white/white. **Change Colours:** All yellow
BEST PERFORMANCES
League: N.Co.E.Champions 92-93 **F.A. Cup:** 1st Qual;ifying 2003-2004 **F.A.Vase:** 2nd Rd 96-97
Senior Honours: Central MidInds 93-94 Derbyshire Senior Cup 97-98 R-up 00-01 (on pens)

GLASSHOUGHTON WELFARE
Founded: 1964
Nickname:

Chairman: T.B.A. **President:** R.Rooker **Manager:** Wayne Day
Secretary: Eric Jones, Marrica, Westfield Avenue, Cutsyke, Castleford WF10 5JJ **Tel No:** 01977 556257 (H)
Programme Editor: Nigel Lea Tel No: 07739 475674 (M) **Programme:** 20 Pages 20p
GROUND ADDRESS: Glasshoughton Welfare, Leeds Road, Glasshoughton, Castleford **Tel:** 01977 511234
Capacity: 2,00 **Seats:** None **Covered:** 250 **Floodlights:** Yes
Simple Directions: Leave M62 at exit 31 or 32. Travel towards Castleford from exit 32 the road comes into Glasshoughton. From exit 31 turn right at roundabout at Whitwood Tech. College. Ground is on Leeds Road.
Midweek Home Matchday: Tuesday **Clubhouse:** Bar with refreshments **Club Shop:** No
Previous Name(s): Anson Sports 1964-76 **Previous League:** West Yorkshire
Club Colours: All Blue **Change Colours:** All Yellow
BEST PERFORMANCES
F.A. Cup: 2nd Qualifying Round 98-99 **F.A.Vase: 2nd Round 00-01**
RECORD Attendance: 300 v Bradford City1990 **Victory:** 8-1v Garforth T. Co Cup 00-01 **Defeat:**0-8 V Hucknall T NCE 97-8
Senior Honours: West Riding County Cup 93-94

HALLAM
Founded: 1860
Nickname: Countrymen

Chairman: Ernie Forrest **Vice Chairman:** P.Hogan **President:** B.Crowshaw **Manager:** Guy Glover
Secretary: Mark Radford, 34 Farview Road, Sheffield S5 7TB
Tel Nos: 0114 249 7287 (H) 0114 203 3073 (W)
Press Officer & Programme Editor: Secretary **Programme:** £1.00
GROUND ADDRESS: Sandygate Road, Crosspool, Sheffield S10 5SE **Ground Tel.No:** 0114 230 9484
Capacity: 1,000 **Seats:** 250 **Covered:** 400 **Floodlights:** Yes
Simple Directions: A57 Sheffield to Glossop Rd., left at Crosspool shopping centre signed Lodge Moor on to Sandygate Road. Ground half a mile on left opposite Plough Inn.
Midweek Home Matchday: Wednesday **Clubhouse:** Matchdays.with hot & cold snacks. **Club Shop:** Yes
Previous League: Yorkshire 52-82
Club Colours: White/Blue/Blue **Change Colours:** Red/black/black
LAST SEASON: League: 16th **F.A. Cup:** 2nd Qualifying Round **F.A. Vase:** 1st Round..
Top Scorer: Peter Smith 26 **Players of the Year:** Peter Smith & Danny Spooner **Captain:** Tom Franklin
BEST PERFORMANCES: League: **F.A. Cup:** 3rd Qualifying Rd.1957 **F.A.Vase:** 5th Rd 80-81
RECORD Attendance: 2,000 v Hendon F.A.Amateur Cup 1959 & 13,855 v Dulwich at Hillsborough F.A.Am. Cup 1955
Goalscorer: Anthony. Wilson 9 **Appearances:** P.Ellis 500+s:
   Victory: 7-0 v Hatfield Main (H) 92-3 & v Kiveton Park (H) 69-70 **Defeat** 0-7 v Hatfield M.88-89
SENIOR HONOURS: N.Co. East League Cup 03-04 Div 1 R-up 90-91 94-95 Sheffield & Hallamshire Senior Cup (4) R-up (1)

LIVERSEDGE
Founded: 1910
Nickname:Sedge

Chairman: Robert Gawthorpe **Manager:** Eugene Lacey **Coach:** Kym Farrand
Secretary: Michael Balmforth, 7 Reform Street, Gomersal, Cleckheaton BD19 3RJ
Tel Nos: 01274 862123 (H) 07792 039145 (M) **Sponsors:**Readymix (Huddersfield)
Press Officer & Prog Ed: Secretary **Programme:** 38 Pages £1.20 **Website:** www.liversedgefc.co.uk
GROUND ADDRESS: Clayborn Ground, Quaker Lane, Hightown Road,Cleckheaton BD19 3RJ **Tel. No:** 01274 862108
Capacity: 2,000 **Seats:** 250 **Covered:** 750 **Floodlights:** Yes
Simple Directions: M62 Jct 26 then A638 into Cleckheaton. Right at lights on corner of Memorial Park through next lights and under railway bridge. First left after bridge into Hightown Rd and Quaker Lane is a 1/4 mile on the left.
Midweek Home Matchday: Tuesday **Clubhouse:** Matchdays and traing nights **Club Shop:** Yes
Previous Leagues: Spen Valley, West Riding Co.Amateur,22-72 Yorkshire 72-82 **Previous Ground:** Primrose Lane, Hightown
Club Colours: All blue **Change Colours:** Yellow
LAST SEASON: League: 2nd **F.A. Cup:** 4th Qualifying Round **F.A. Vase:** 2nd Qualifying Rd.
Top Scorer: Paul Walker 22 **Player of the Year:** Kyle Sutcliffe **Captain:**John Borland
BEST PERFORMANCES
League: N.Counties Premier Div R-up 05-06**F.A. Cup:** 4th Qual Rd 2004-2005 **F.A.Vase:** 3rd Qualifying Rd. (5)
RECORD Attendance: 986 v Thackley **Goalscorer:** Denis Charlesworth **Appearances:** Barry Palmer
Senior Honours: West Riding Co Challenge Cup 48-9 51-2 69-70 89-90 N.Co E Div 1 R-up 89-90
N.Co.E. Lg Cup Winnners 05-06

LONG EATON UNITED
Founded: 1956
Nickname: Blues

Chairman: Jim Fairley **Vice-Chairman:** **Manager:** Adam Bamford
Secretary: Jim Fairley, 13 Redland Drive, Chilwell, Nottingham, NG9 5JZ **Physio:** John Burns
Tel. Nos: 0115 919 9447 (H) 07971 416444(M)
Programme Editor: Geoff Whitehead (01332 872849) **Programme:** 20 Pages 50p
GROUND ADDRESS: Grange Park, Station Road, Long Eaton, Derbys. NG10 2EG **Tel:** 01332 872849
e-mail address: long.eatonutd@virgin.net **Website address:** leufc.com
Capacity: 5,000 **Seats:** None **Covered:** 500 **Floodlights:** Yes
Simple Directions: M1 Jct 25 take A52 towards Nottingham. Left onto B6003 by Bardiilis Garden Centre, then right at lights (A453) and second left into Station Road. Ground opposite Speedway Stadium.
Midweek Home Matchday: Tuesday **Clubhouse:** Open matchdays with snacks available. **Club Shop:** No
Club Colours: All blue **Change Colours:** Red/black/black
RECORD Attendance: 2,000 F.A.Cup 1973
Senior Honours: Derbyshire Senior Cup: 64-65 75-76

MALTBY MAIN
Founded: 1916
Nickname: Miners

Chairman: Graham McCormick **President:** H.Henson **Manager:** Shaun Goodwin
Secretary: John Mills, 11 Norwood Avenue, Maltby, Rotherham S66 7EA **Asst.Manager:** Bryn Webster
Tel No: 01709 813609
Programme Editor: Nick Dunhill Tel No: 01709 815676 (H) **Programme:** 36 pages 70p
GROUND ADDRESS: Muglet Lane, Maltby, Rotherham S66 7JQ **Tel:** 07941 057883
Club email address: enquiries@maltbymainfc.f9.co.uk **website address:** www.maltbymainfc.f9.co.uk
Capacity: 2,000 **Seats:**150 **Covered:** 300 **Floodlights:** Yes
Simple Directions: Exit M18 at Jct 1 with A631. Two miles into Maltby, then turn right at crossroads at Queens Hotel corner on to B6427. Ground is 3/4 mile on left.
Midweek Home Matchday: Wednesday **Clubhouse:** No. Miners Welfare Club opposite **Club Shop:** No
Previous League(s): Sheffield County Senior and Yorkshire League 33-84
Previous Names: Maltby Main 1916-65 (disbanded), Maltby Miners Welfare 1970-96
Club Colours: Red/black/black **Change Colours:** All Yellow
BEST PERFORMANCES: League: 4th N.Co E Prem 92-93 **F.A. Cup:** 2nd Qualifying Rd **F.A.Vase:** 3rd Rd 87-88 93-94
RECORD Attendance:1,500 v Sheffield Wed. (Friendly) 91-92 **Goalscorer:** **Appearances:**
Senior Honours: Sheffield & Hallamshire Senior Cup 77-78

MICKLEOVER SPORTS

Founded: 1948
Nickname: Sports

Chairman: Michael Brain **Manager:** Martin Rowe
Secretary: Tony Shaw, 80 Onslow Road, Mickleover, Derby DE3 5JB **Sec's Tel & Fax:** 01332512826
Programme Editor: Stephen Pritchard Tel No: 01332 511359
GROUND ADDRESS: Micklever Sports Ground, Station Road, Mickleover,Derby
Capacity: 1,500 **Seats:** 280 **Covered:** 480 **Floodlights:** Yes **Club Shop:** No
Simple Directions: Derby ring road A38 to A52 turn off at Markeaton Park Island. Take turning to Ashbourne A52, then 2nd left into Radbourne Lane. Take 3rd left into Station Road.Ground on corner.
Midweek Home Matchday: Wednesday **Clubhouse:** Open Thursdays (7-11) to Sundays 11am-11pm)
Club Colours: Red /Black/Black **Change Colours:** All Blue
Top Scorers: Tommy Leighton and Karl Payne **Player of the Year:** Marc Strzyzewski & Paul Stevens **Captain:** Colin Holness
BEST PERFORMANCES
League: 7th Premier League 04-05 **F.A. Cup:** 2nd Qualifying Rd. 98-99 **F.A.Vase:** 3rd Rd Replay 2003-04
Senior Honours: Northern Co East Div. One 2002-2003, Wilkinson Sword Trophy Winners and Derby Senior Cup R-up 02-03

PICKERING TOWN

Founded: 1888
Nickname: Pikes

Chairman: Anthony Dunning **President:** J.P.Jennison **Manager:** Alex Mathie
Secretary: Geoiff Raw, 3 Pool court, Pickering, N.Yorks. **Asst.Manager:** Mark Wood
Sec"s Tel No: 01751 474528 (H) 0772 901 5654 (M) e-mail: geoffraw@hotmail.com
Programme Editor: 48 Pages - £1.00 **Editor** Gerry Gregory **Tel No:** 01751 473818 **Sponsor:** Flamingo Land
GROUND ADDRESS: Recreation Club, Mill Lane (off Malton Road), Pickering, N.Yorks. **Tel No:** 01751 473317
Capcity: 2,000 **Seats:** 200 **Covered:** 500 **Floodlights:** Yes **Club Shop:** No
Simple Directions: A169 from Malton. On entering Pickering, take first left past Police Station and B.P. garage into MIll Lane. Ground 200yards on right.
Midweek Home Matchday: Tuesday **Clubhouse:** Open match days with hot food available
Previous Leagues: Beckett, York & District, Scarborough & District, Yorkshire 1972-1982
Club Colours: All Blue **Change Colours:** All Yellow
LAST SEASON
League: 5th **F.A. Cup:** 1st Qualifying Rd. **F.A. Vase:** 6th Rd.
Top Scorer: Mark Swales **Player of the Year:** Dean MacAuley **Captain:** Dean MacAuley
League: N.Co. East Runners-Up **F.A. Cup:** 2nd Qual Rd 99-00 01-02 **F.A.Vase:** 6th Round 2005-06
RECORD Attendance: 1,412 v Notts County (friendly) in August 1991
Senior Honours: N.Co.E. R-up 92-93 North Riding Cup 90-91 Wilkinson Sword Trophy 2000-01

RETFORD UNITED

Secretary: John Shaw,14 Constable Close, Dronfield, N.E.Derbys. S18 1TE
Tel No:01246 416130 (H)07751 561488 (M)
E-mail: jamescrlewis@btinternet.com

FACT FILE
Founded: 1987
President: Dean Vivian
Chairman: T.B.A.
Manager: Mark Shaw
Assistant Manager: Peter Duffield
Physio: Dave Lester

Ground: Cannon Park, Leverton Rd., Retford, Notts.
Tel: 01777 710300 and (Tel & Fax) 01777 869468 Social Club 01777 710300
Club E-mail: secretary@ retfordunited.co.uk **Website:** www.retfordunited.co.uk

Directions: From A1 take A620 past Ranby Prison and into Retford. At large r'about take 3rd exit. Pass Morrisons superstore to lights. Right at lights, then left at next set. Follow Leverton Rd. out of town. Cannon Park on RHS after two bridges.
Capacity: 2,000 Covered Standing: 300 Floodlights: Yes

Colours: Black & White stripes/Black/Black
Change colours: Claret & Blue/Claret/Claret
Midweek Matchday: Tuesday
Programme Editor: John Knight
07919 372561(M)

Previous League: Central Midlands

SELBY TOWN

Founded: 1918
Nickname:The Robins

Chairman: Michael Dunne **President:** Andy Bodle **Manager:** B.Lyon
Secretary: Thomas Arkley, 176 Abbots Rd., Selby. N.Yorks Y08 8AZ **Asst.Manager/Coach:** G Cygan
Tel No: 01757 700356 (H) 07830218657 (M)
Programme: 34 Pages Price 1.00 **Editor:** Gary Taylor
Ground: Flaxly Road Ground, Richard St., Scott Rd. Selby N.Yorks YO 8 0BS
Capacity: 5,000 **Seats:** 220 **Covered:** 350 **Floodlights:**Yes
Simple Directions: From Leeds,left at main traffic lights down Scott Rd., then first left into Richard St.
Midweek Home Matchday: Wednesday **Clubhouse:** Bar at ground open on all matchdays **Club Shop:** Yes
Previous League: Yorkshire 1920-82 **Previous Ground:** Bowling Green, James Street 1920-51
Club Colours: All Red **Change Colours:** All Blue
LAST SEASON: League: 8th **F.A. Cup:** Preliminary Round. **F.A. Vase:** 3rdt Round.
Top Scorer: Ian Twitchen 18 **Player of the Year:** Andrew Dawson **Captain:**Andrew Cox
BEST PERFORMANCES
League: 2nd N.Co.E 2004-05 **F.A. Cup:** 2nd Rd Proper 54-55 **F.A.Vase:** 4th Rd 95-96
RECORD Attendance: 7,000 v Bradford PA F.A.Cup 1st Rd 53-54 **Goalscorer:** Graham Shepherd 158 (63-82)
Victory: 14-1 V Altoffs . W.Rid C. 35 **Defeat:** 0-14 v Bradford PA Res Yorks Lg.1928
Senior Honours: N.Co E Div 1 95-96 R-up 89-90 W.Riding Sen Cup 37-38 W.Riding Chall.Cup 34-5 35-6 Yorks Lg (5)

SHEFFIELD

Founded: 24.10.1857
Nickname: The Club

Chairman: Richard Tims **President:** Alan Methley: **Manager**: David McCarthy
Secretary: Stephen Hall, Flat 55, Regent Court, Bradfield Road, Hillsborough, Sheffield S6 2BU **Tel No:** 0114 2205026
Programme: 40Pages - £1.00 **Editor:** Craig Williamson **Tel No:** 0114 2581108
GROUND ADDRESS: The Bright Finance Stadium (Coach & Horses), Sheffield Road,Dronfield, Sheffield
Ground Tel.No.: 01246 291338
Capacity: 1,100 **Seats:** 250 **Covered:** 500 **Floodlights:**Yes
Simple Directions: M1 J29 to A617 into Chesterfield. Turn right into dual carriageway (A61) at traffic island.Over two islands and follow signs to Dronfield/Gosforth Valley. At entrance to Dronfield,The Coach & Horses ground is afoot of hill, on the right.
Midweek Home Matchday: Tuesday **Clubhouse:** Licensed Bar open matchdays. **Club Shop:** Yes
Previous League(s): Abbeydale Park, Dore(1956-1989,Sheffield Amateur Sports Club, Hillsborough Park 1989-91, Sheffield International Stadium (Don Valley) 1991-94,Sheffield Sports Stadium, Don Valley 94-97 **Previous League:** Yorkshire 49-82
Club Colours: Red& Black/Black/Red **Change Colours:** All Blue
LAST SEASON: League: 4th **F.A. Cup:** 1st Qualifying Round **F.A. Vase:** 1st Round
Top Scorer:James Tevendale 18 **Player of the Year:** Darren Holmes & Tom Jones **Captain:**Chris Hilton
BEST PERFORMANCES
F.A.Amateur Cup: Winners 02-03 **F.A. Cup:** 4th Qualifying Rd. 2000-01 **F.A.Vase:** Runners-Up 1976-77
RECORD Attendance: 2,000 v Barton Rovers F.A.Vase S-F 76-77
Senior Honours: F.A.Amateur Cup 1903-04 Vase Runners-Up 76-77 Sheffield Senior Cup Winners 2004-2005 2005-2006

SHIREBROOK TOWN

Founded: 1985
Nickname:

Chairman: Stephen Brown **Manager:** S.Greenwood **Asst.Manager:** G.Charlesworth
Secretary: Stephen Wall, 26 Carter Lane, Shirebrook, Mansfield, Notts. NG 20 8NA **Tel No:** 01623 747638
Programme: 12 Pages -50p **Editor:** G.Howarth **Tel No:** 01623 748375 **Sponsors:** Tony Perrin Solid Fuels
GROUND ADDRESS: Shirebrook Staff & Sports Social Club, Langwith Rd., Shirebrook, Mansfield , Notts. NG20 8OL
Tel No: 01623 742535 **Official Website:** www.shirebrooktown.co.uk
Capacity: 2,000 **Seats:** 300 **Covered:** 400 **Floodlights:** Yes
Simple Directions: M1 jct 29 A 617 to Mansfield. 2.5 miles B6407 to Shirebrook then through town to Langwith Road.
Midweek Home Matchday: Wednesday **Clubhouse:** with refreshments at ground **Club Shop:** No
Previous Names: Shire Colliery **Previous League:** Central Midlands
Club Colours: All red & black **Change Colours:** All Blue
LAST SEASON
League: 15th
Top Scorer: Rob Orton **Player of the Year:** Martin Rowbotham **Captain:**Craig Charlesworth
BEST PERFORMANCES
League: N.Co E Premier 10th **F.A. Cup:** 3rd Qual. 2002-03 **F.A.Vase:** 4th Rd. 2001-02
RECORD Appearances: Craig Charlesworth 345
Senior Honours: Central midlmnds Supreme Chmpions 00-01 01-02 N.Co.E Div 1 Champions 2003-2004

SUTTON TOWN

Re-Formed 2002:
Nickname: Town

Chairman: James Warren
Manager: Les McJannet **Asst.Manager**: Mark Place **Physio:** Kip Garton
Secretary: Stuart Marriott, 7 Willow Close, Broadmeadows, South Normanton, Alfreton, Derbyshire DE55 3AP
Tel No: 01773 862489 (H) 07745 648007 (M) **e-mail:** stuartmarriott124@hotmail.co.uk
Programme Editor: Secretary **Programme:** 22 Pages £1.00
Previous Name: North Notts. **Previous League:** Central Midlands until 2003
Club Colours: Claret & Sky/Claret/Claret **Change Colours:** All Royal Blue with yellow trim
BEST PERFORMANCES
League: Champions **F.A. Cup:** 1st Rd Proper 2004-05 **F.A.Vase:**
GROUND ADDRESS: The Fieldings, Huthwaite Rd, Sutton-in-Ashfield, Notts. NG17 2HB **Tel:** 01623 552376
Capacity: 1,500 **Covered:** Seats: 200 **Covered Standing:** None **Floodlights:** Yes
Simple Directions: M1 Jct 28.Then A38 towards Mansfield. Take the A38 at Kings Mill island then first left (Sutton sign) and first right into Hosiery Mill Island.
Midweek Home Matchday: Tuesday **Clubhouse:** Yes (01623 405660) **Club Shop:** Yes
RECORD Attendance: 4,004 v Notts Co
Senior Honours: Northern Counties East Div 1 Champions 2004-2005 Central Midlands Supreme Division R-Up 2002-2003

THACKLEY

Founded: 1930
Nickname:

Chairman: T.B.A.
Manager: John Boyle **Asst.Manager**: Paul Atkinson **Physio**: John Laidler
Secretary & Prog Ed: Stewart Willingham, 3 Kirklands Close, Baildon, Shipley, W.Yorks BD17 6HN
Tel.Nos: 01274 598589 (H) 01274 776686 (Fax) 01274472277 (W) **e-mail:** stuwillingham@hotmail.com
Programme Editor: Secretary **Programme:** 20 pages £1.00
GROUND ADDRESS: Dennyfield, Ainsbury Avenue, Thackley, Bradford BD 15 9AU **Ground Tel. No.:** 01274 615571
Capacity: 3,000 **Seats:** 300 **Covered:** 600 **Floodlights:** Yes
Simple Directions: On main Leeds/Keighley road (A657) turn off down Thackley Rd. at Thackley corner which is two miles from Shipley traffic lights and a mile from Greengates lights. Ground is 200 yards down Ainsbury Avenue.
Midweek Home Matchday: Tuesday **Clubhouse:** Tue-Sun evenings, matchdays and w/e lunchtimes.
Club Shop: Fully stocked. Contact: Geoff Scott (01274 611520)
Previous League(s): Bradford Am., W.Riding Co Am.,West Yorks,Yorks 67-82 **Prev. Name(s):** Thackley Wesleyians 1930-39
Club Colours: Red/white/red **Change Colours:** All white
BEST PERFORMANCES: League: N.Co.E. Runners-Up 94-95 **F.A. Cup:** 2nd Qualifying Rd. **F.A.Vase:** 5th Rd 80-81
RECORD Attendance: 1,500 v Leeds United 1983
Senior Honours: N.C.E. R-up 94-95 West Riding County Cup 63-64 66-6773-74-74-75

AFC EMLEY

Secretary: Richard Poulain, 14 Cheviot Avenue, Meltham, Holmfirth, HD9 4DW
Tel Nos: (H) 01484 859 975. (M) 07702 712 287 or 07866 511 921
Ground: The Welfare Ground, Off Upper Lane, Emley, nr Huddersfield,
West Yorkshire HD8 9RE
Directions: From M1 Junction 38: Travel on road signposted to Huddersfield through the village
of Bretton to the first roundabout. Take first exit off this roundabout signposted
Denby Dale. After approximately one mile turn right at road signposted Emley. After
2 miles enter the village of Emley. Entrance to ground is opposite a white bollard in
centre of road. (Narrow entrance). From M1 Junction 39: Travel on road signposted
toward Denby Dale. Travel for approximately 3 miles up hill to first roundabout. Take
2nd exit and follow directions as above.
Capacity: 2000   **Seats:** 330   **Cover:** 1000
Clubhouse: Yes
Previous **League:** West Yorkshire League 2005-06

FACT FILE
Founded: 2005
Colours:Sky & maroon/maroon/sky
Change colours: All white
Midweek Matchday: Wednesday
Programme Editor: Richard Poulain

CLUB PERSONNEL
Chairman: Graham Roys
Manager: Ray Dennis
Assistant Manager: Nicky Bramald
Physio: Danny Murphy

BORROWASH VICTORIA

Founded: 1911
Nickname: Vics

Chairman: IanAnderson   **Manager/Coach:** Bob Sykes   **Assistant Manager:** John Kinane
Secretary: Ian Collins, 30 Margreave Road, Chaddesden,Derby DE21 6JD   **Sponsors:** Robinson Construction
Tel. Nos: 01332 739437(H) 07733 055212 (M)   **Press Officer:** Secretary
Programme: 30 Pages - **Editor:** Secretary
GROUND ADDRESS: Robinson Construction Bowl, Borrowash Road, Spondon, Derby DE21 7PH
Ground Tel No: 01332 678312
Capacity: 5,000   **Seats:**Yes   **Covered:** 500   **Floodlights:**Yes
Simple Directions: M1 jct 25. A52 towards Derby., 3rd left off by-pass into Borrowash Road. Ground 400 yards on left.
Spondon BR 2 miles
Midweek Home Matchday: Tuesday   **Clubhouse:** Normal pub hours. Hot & Cold food. **Club Shop:** No
Previous League(s): Derby Sunday School & Welfare 1952-57 Derbgy Comb. Midland 79-82 N.C.E. , Central Midlands.
Club Colours: Red & White Stripes/Black/Black   **Change Colours:** Navy Blkue / Sky Blue/Sky Blue
LAST SEASON: League: 8th   **F.A.Cup:** 1st Qualifying Round   **F.A.Vase:** 2nd Round
Player of the Year: Paul Galloway & Aaron Johnson   **Captain:** James Parkinson   **Top Goalscorer:** Paul Galloway
BEST PERFORMANCES
League: **F.A. Cup:** 4th Qualifying Round 91-92   **F.A.Vase:** 5th Rd. 1990-01 2000-01
RECORD Victory: 11-1 **Defeat** 3-8 **Goalscorer:** Paul Acklam **Appearances:** Neil Kellogg
Senior Honours: N.C.R. Div 1 2000-01 Div 1 South 1983-84 R-up 84-85 Derbyshire Senior Cup R-up 1990-1991

DINNINGTON TOWN

Chairman: Mark O'Brien   **Manager:** Steve Toyne   **Assistant Manager:** Neville Burbeary
Secretary: Chris Deans, 14 Cockshutts Lane, Oughtibridge, Sheffield S35 0FX
Tel. Nos: 0114 286 4696 (H) 0113 227 4961(W) 07802 542335(M)
Programme Editor: Liam Cartledge
GROUND ADDRESS: 131 Laughton Road, Dinnington, Near Sheffield S25 2PP   **Tel:** 01909 518555
Capacity: 2000   **Seats:** 80   **Covered:** 200
Simple Directions: From M1 junction 31 follow A57 Worksop Road for one mile. Left at first lights onto B6463 -Todwick Road
and on to Monks Bridge Road for two miles. At petrol station roundabout take third exit towards Dinnington.Take first left at
Morrell Tyres and straight on past The Squirrel pub. Dinnington Resource Centre is on the left 300yards down Laughton Road.
Midweek Home Matchday: Wednesday   **Clubhouse:** Yes
Previous League(s): Central Midlands League 2000-06.
Club Colours: Yellow/Black/Yellow   **Change Colours:** All white
SENIOR HONOURS: Central Midlands League Cup 2002-03, 05-06

GEDLING TOWN

Secretary: Roland Ash, 80 Portland Road, Carlton, Nottingham NG4 3PXZ
Tel Nos: 0115 952 0846 (H) 0115967 0047 W) 07973 388654 (M)
Ground: Riverside Ground, (rear of Ferryboat Inn), Stoke Lane, Stoke Bardolph, Nott'm
NG14 5HX 01159402145(Matchdays only) e-mail: alan_davey@hotmail.com
Directions: A612 Nottingham-Lowdham-Southwell road. Just before Burton Joyce turn right
into Stoke Lane to Ferryboat P.H. Approx 1.5 miles. Ground at rear of pub.
Capacity: 2,000   Seats: 250   Cover: 500   Floodlights: Yes
Clubhouse: Matchdays only. Refreshments. Licensed bar.   **Club Shop:** No
Honours: Central Mids Lg Prem 97-98 R-up 91-92 Div 1 90-91, (Res Prem 96-97 97-98);
Wakefield Floodlit Trophy 92-93 R-up 95-96; Ken Marsland Cup (Res) 93-94;
Notts Amtr Lg 89-90 (Snr Cup R-up 89-90).Res Lg & Cp Winners 98-99, NCECup
01-02, Notts Cup 01-02
Best season FA Vase: 3rd Rd 96-97
RECORDS **Attendance:** 250 v Arnold Town.
Win: 11-0 v Radford 91-92 **Defeat:** 2-5 v Staveley MW 93-94.
Goalscorer: Rob Orton 98 in 124   **Appearances:** Gary Ball 300+

FACT FILE
Founded: 1986
Colours: Blue & yellow/blue/yellow
Midweek Matchday: Tuesday
Prog 32 pages 50p
Editor:Brendon Richardson(0115 845 8233)
Press Secretary: Tony White(07879654533

Chairman: Roland Ash (0115 9403361)
Manager: Dave King
Assistant Manager: Mark Hurst
Physio: Keith Waters

Lincoln Moorlands F.C.

Photo: Gordon Whittington.

HALL ROAD RANGERS

Secretary: Alan Chaplin, 33 Lee Street,Holderness Road,Hull HU8 8NH
Tel No: 01482 703775

Ground: Dene Park, Dene Close, Beverley Rd, Dunswell, Nr Hull (01482 850101).

Directions: M62 to A63, turn left before Humber Bridge onto A164 to Beverley,after approx 5 miles turn right onto A1079. In 2 miles turn left at large roundabout to ground 20 yards on right.

Capacity: 1,200   **Seats:** 250   **Cover:** 250   **Floodlights:** Yes

Clubhouse: Open all week for drinks and bar snacks, snooker, pool and darts.   **Shop:** Yes

HONOURS N.C.E. Lg Div 2 90-91, Yorks Lg Div 3 72-73 79-80, E. Riding Snr Cup 72-73 93-94. Wilkinson Sword Trophy2004

PREVIOUS Leagues: East Riding Co.; Yorks 68-82   **Ground:** Hull Co-Op (to 1968)

BEST SEASON   FA Cup: Prelim Rd. 2003-04 **FA Vase:** 3rd Round 99-00

RECORDS   Attendance: 1,200 v Manchester City Aug 93 **Goalscorer:** G James
Apps: G James **Players progressing:** Gerry Ingram (Blackpool),. Mark Greaves (Hull City)

FACT FILE

Founded: 1959   Nickname: Blues
Sponsor: Admiral Signs of Hull Ltd.
Colours: Blue & white hoops/ blue/ blue.
Change : Red & Black Stripes,black/black
Midweek Matches: Wednesday
Prog:24 pages, £1.00
Editor: Martin Layton (01482 863724)
Local Press: Hull Daily Mail

CLUB PERSONNEL

Chairman:
Robert Smailes (01482 821354 (H))
Director of Football: Nigel Dalee)
Press Off:Craig Ellyard (07952 109536)
Manager:Steve Richards
Assistant Manager/ Coach:Paul Smith

LINCOLN MOORLANDS

Secretary: Graham Peck, 128 Granson Way, Washingborough,Lincoln LN4 1HF
Tel Nos: 01522 792170 (H) 07815 458196 (M))

Ground: Moorland Sports Ground, Newark Rd, Lincoln LN5 9LY
Tel: 01522 520184   Office & Fax: 01522 874111

Directions: From north A1 to Markham Moor. Take A57 until Lincoln by-pass and then turn right onto A46. At 3rd r'about left into Doddington Rd. Continue until Newark Rd. - ground on left after 800 yards.
From Newark enter Lincoln on A46, go past Forum Shopping Centre for approx. 3/4 mile. Ground on left signposted 'Moorlands Club'.

Capacity: Seats: 200   Cover: 200   Floodlights: Yes

Clubhouse: Yes   **Club Shop:** No

HONOURS: Central Midlands Supreme 99-00, R-up 00-01, Lincolndshire Senior A 00-01 Wilkinson Sword trophy 2004-2005

FACT FILE

Founded: 1989 Nickname: The Moors

Colours:Sky Bue+Navy quarters/Navy/ Sky

Change colours: Orange/black/orange

Midweek Matchday: Tuesday

Prog: 40 pages Price £1.00 Ed:Secretary

CLUB PERSONNEL

Chairman: Graham Longhurst

Match Secretary: as Secretary

Manager:John Priestley

NOSTELL M.W.

Chairman: Granville Marshall **Manager:** Alan Colquhoun **Assistant Manager:** Gary Baker **Physio:** Laura Davis
Secretary: Granville Marshall, 82 Springhall Avenue, Crofton, Wakefield. WF4 1HD
Tel Nos: 01924 211065 (H) 0113 2976066 (W) 07769 714998 (M)
e-mail: granvillemarshall@hotmail.com   **Programme Editor:** Craig Stephens
GROUND ADDRESS: The Welfare Grounnd, Crofton Community Centre,Middle Lane, New Crofton, Wakefild. WF4 1LB
Tel. No: 01924 866010   **Club e-mail:** granvillemarshall@hotmail.com **Website**: www.nostell.wyfl.co.uk
Capacity: 750   **Seats:** 50   **Covered:** 100
Simple Directions: From M I jct 39 or M62 jct 31 head towards Wakefield. Then from Wakefield take A638 Doncaster Road past Wakefield Trinity RFC then after two miles go under bridge and turn right opposite Crofton Arms Pub . Through Crofton village then left at Slipper Pub and right into MIddle Lane.The ground is at Crofton Cmmiunity Centre which is signposted.
Midweek Home Matchday: Tuesday
Previous League(s): Wakefield League 1950-66. West Yorkshire 1966-68. Wakefield League 1969-82.
West Yorkshire 1982-2006
Club Colours: Yellow/Black/Yellow
SENIOR HONOURS: West Yorkshire League Premier Division 2004-05.

PARKGATE

Secretary: Bruce Bickerdike, 2 Cardew Close, Rawmarsh, Rotherham S62 6LB
Tel: 01709 522305 Fax: 01709 528583.
Ground: Roundwood Sports Complex, Green Lane, Rawmarsh, Rotherham S62 6LA
Tel: 01709 826600   Website: www.parkgatefc.co.uk   Email:
bruce@parkgatefc.co.uk
Directions: From Rotherham A633 to Rawmarsh. From Doncaster A630 to Conisbrough, then A6023 through Swinton to Rawmarsh. Grd at Green Lane - right from Rotherham, left from Conisbrough at the Crown Inn. Grd 800yds right
Capacity: 1,000   Seats: 300   Cover: 300   Floodlights: Yes   **Club Shop:** No.
Clubhouse: Licensed bar, 2 lounges. Meals available lunchtime Saturday & Sunday
HONOURS S&HSC Finalists 97-98 & 95-06, Wilkinson Sword Trophy R-up 98-99
PREVIOUS Leagues: Sheffield County Senior Lge; Yorkshire 74
Names: BSC Parkgate (82-86); RES Parkgate (pre-1994).
RECORD Attendance: v Worksop 1982
BEST SEASON FA Cup: 2nd Qual. Rd 97-98   **FA Vase:** 1st Round, 6 times
2005-2006: Top Scorers: Brian Cusworthy & Caine Cheetham

FACT FILE
Founded: 1969
Nickname: The Gate or The Steelmen
Sponsors:Pro-Fit (UK) Limited
Colours: Red & white
Change: Blue & yellow
Midweek matches: Tuesday
Programme: 20 pages, £1.00
Editor: Stuart Bisby (01709 545219)
CLUB PERSONNEL
President: Paul Cristinacce
Chairman: Albert Dudill
Press Officer: Secretary
Manager: Vince Brady
Assistant Manager/Coach: Russ Eagle
Coach: John Eagle
Physio: John eaglle

Parkgate F.C. - Back Row (L-R): Vinnie Brady (Manager), John Eagle (Physio), Bob Mourwood, Matt Plant, Matt Turner, Lee Manderson, Luke Dawson, Richard Haigh, Russ Eagle (Assistant Manager).
Front Row: Ryan Johnson, Gavin Gould, Chris Fawcus, Mark Cooper, Brian Cusworth (Capt), Richard Patterson, Caine Cheetham, Adam Fretwell, Matt Outram.

PONTEFRACT COLLIERIES

Secretary: Frank Maclachlan, 188 Watling Road, Ferry Fryston, Castleford WF102QY
Tel: 01977 512085 (H), 07710 586447 (M)
Email: webmaster@pontefractcollieries.co.uk
Ground: Skinner Lane, Pontefract, West Yorkshire (01977 600818)
Directions: M62 jct 32 towards Pontefract. Left at lights after roundabout for park entrance and retail park. Traffic thro town should follow racecouse signs thro lights to roundabout and back to lights. Monkhill (BR) 1/2 mile. Baghill (BR) 1 mile. Tanshelf (BR) 1/2 mile .All Leeds and Castleford buses pass ground.
Capacity: 1,200   **Seats:** 300   **Cover:** 400   **Floodlights:** Yes   **Club Shop:** Occasionally
Clubhouse: Fully licensed. Hot & cold snacks. Openmatch days
HONOURS N.C.E. Lg Div 1 83-84 95-96 (Div 2 R-up 82-83); Lg Cup, R-up: 96-97 Floodlit Comp 87-88 88-89; Yorks Lg Div 3 81-82; W. Riding Co. Cup R-up 87-88 90-91;Embleton Cup (4) Castleford FA Cup (5) Wilkinson Sword 95-96 R-Up: 99-00.02-03
PREVIOUS Leagues: West Yorkshire 58-79; Yorkshire 79-82
RECORD Attendance: 1,000 v Hull City, floodlight opening 1987.

FACT FILE
Founded: 1958   Nickname: Colls
Sponsors: Easy Hire
Colours: Blue & black halves/black/black
Change :All green
Midweek Matches: Tuesday
Programme: 40 pages £1.00
Editor:Rod Naylor(01977 602266
Local Press: Pontefract & Castleford Express
Website: www.pontefractcollieries.co.uk
CLUB PERSONNEL
Chairman:Michael Slater
Manager: Roly Lynes.
Assistant Manager: Graham Asquith
Physio: Mick Slater   Captain: Simon Cornell
Top Scorers: Jon Leigh 12

ROSSINGTON MAIN

Secretary: Gerald Parsons, School Bungalow, Hayfield Lane, Auckley, Doncaster DN8 3NB, Tel: 01302 770249(H) 07941 811217 (M)
Ground: Welfare Ground, Oxford Street, Rossington, Doncaster   Tel: 01302 865524
Directions: Enter Rossington and go over the railway crossings. Pass the Welfare Club on right, Oxford Street is next right - ground is at bottom.8miles from Doncaster (BR)
Capacity: 2,000   **Seats:** 200   **Cover:** 500   **Floodlights:** Yes
Clubhouse: Evenings & matchdays, Sandwiches, rolls, satellite TV, pool.   **Club Shop:** No

HONOURS Cen. Mids. Prem Div. 84-85, Lg. Cup 83-84 84-85; Doncaster Sen Lge 44-45, Lg. Cup 44-45; DDSALShield 90-91 R-up 89-90.
PREVIOUS Leagues: Doncaster Sen, Yorkshire Lge, Sheffield County Sen, Cent Mids.
RECORDS Attendance: 864 v Leeds United 8/91.
Goalscorer: Mark Illman   **Appearances:** Darren Phipps
BEST SEASON
FA Cup: 2nd Qual. Rd. 25-26   FA Vase: 2nd Round 88-89

FACT FILE
Founded: 1920   Nickname: The Colliery
Sponsor: RJB Mining
Colours: All blue
Change colours: Blue & black
Midweek matches: Tuesday
Reserves' League: Beefeater County Sen
Programme: 50p
Editor: Peter Murden

CLUB PERSONNEL
Chairman: Gerald Murden (01302 867542)
Joint Managers: D Ridley & L Ostle
Physio: J White

SOUTH NORMANTON ATHLETIC

Secretary: Andrew Meredith, 183 Sough Road,South Normanton,Alfreton, Derbys.DE22 2LE
Tel: 07766 077204 (M)

Ground: Exchem Sports Ground, Lees Lane, South Normanton, Derby
Tel: 01773 581491

Directions: M1 Junc 28, B6019 towards South Normanton. Turn right after 1mile (in South Normanton) at BP garage into Market Street, after 1/4 mile turn left, immediately after The Clock pub into Lees Lane, ground at bottom on right.
Capacity: 3000   **Seats:** 150   **Cover:** 300   **Floodlights:**Yes

Clubhouse Open on matchdays. Food available.
Club Shop: No

PREVIOUS Leagues: Central Midlands League

Chairman: Colin Price
Managers: Glyn Spacey & Mark Harvey
2005-2006
Player of the Year Grant Russell
Captain: John Peel
Top Goalscorer: Nick Thorpe
Programme: Yes - The Shiner
Editor: Kevin Adams (07903 936238)

Club Re-Formed: 1980
Colours : Yellow & blue hoops/blue/y&b
Change: Red/white/red
Midweek Matchday: Tuesday

STAVELEY MINERS WELFARE

Secretary: Mrs Jane Burnand, 119 Middlecroft Rd.,Staveley, Chesterfield S433XU
Tel. Nos: : 01246 474350 (H) 07714 086404 (M)
Ground: Inkersall Road, Staveley, Chesterfield, Derbyshire   Tel: 01246 471441
Directions: M1 jct 30, follow A619 Chesterfield - Staveley is 3 miles from jct30. Turn left at GK Garage in Staveley town centre into Inkersall Rd - ground 200yds on right at side of Speedwell Rooms. Frequent buses (47, 70, 72, 75, 77) from Chest'ld stop in Staveley centre 3 mins walk.
Capacity: 5,000   **Cover:** 400   **Seats:** 220   **Floodlights:** Yes
Clubhouse: The Staveley Miners Welfare, 500 yds from ground, open before and after games
Club Shop: Yes, contactRod Walker 01246 473655
HONOURS County Sen Lg Div 2 92-93, Div 3 91-92, Chesterfield & D. Amat Lg R-up89-90 90-91, Byron (Lge) Cup 89-90, R-up 90-91.NCE Div 1 R-up 97-98
PREVIOUS Leagues: Chesterfield & D. Amat 89-91; County Sen 91-93.
BEST SEASON   FA Cup: FA Vase: 98-99, 3rd Rd at least
RECORDS **Attendance:** 280 v Stocksbridge, Sheffield Senior Cup 22/1/94
Goalscorer: Mick Godber   **Appearances:** Shane Turner

FACT FILE
Founded: 1989   Nickname: The Welfare
Colours: All Royal Blue
Change colours: Yellow/Green/Green
Midweek matches: Tuesday
Programme: 32pages, £1.00
Editor: Steve Durcan (01246 474544)

CLUB PERSONNEL
Chairman: Dennis Burnand
Tel: 01246 474350 (H)

TADCASTER ALBION

Founded: 1892

Secretary: Howard Clarke,17 Springhill Court,Tadcaster,N.Yorks.LS24 8DN (01937 835017)

Ground: The Park, Ings Lane, Tadcaster, LS24 9AY. Tel: 01937 834119

Directions: From West Riding and South Yorks, turn right off A659 at John Smith's Brewery Clock. From East Riding turn left off A659 after passing over river bridge and pelican crossing (New Street). Bus station over Bridge. Services 740 & 743

Capacity: 1,500   **Seats:** 60   **Cover:** 400   **Floodlights:**Yes

Clubhouse: Yes   **Club Shop:** No

RECORD   **Attendance:**1,200 v Winterton F.A.Vase 4th Rd 1996-7

     Victory: 13-0 v Blidworth MW, NCE 97-98 (Lg Record)   **Defeat**: 2-10 v Thackley

PREVIOUS   **Leagues:** York, Harrogate, Yorkshire (73-82)

BEST

SEASONS   **FA Cup:** 2nd Qual. Rd. 98-99   **FA Vase:** 5th Round 77-78

FACT FILE
Colours: Yellow + Navy/navy /navy
Change colours: Red/black/Black
Sponsors: Wrtherby Whaler
& Tobin Scaffolding
Midweek Matchday:Tuesday Prog: 20 pages
Prog Ed: Andy Battersby (0776 9681060)
e-mail: batts9@hotmail.co.uk
CLUB PERSONNEL
Chairman: Kevin Derry
President: Lord Edward Stourton
Match Sec: 01937 835017 (H/B)
Manager: Jim Collis Captain: T.B.A.
2005-06
Leading Goalscorer: Steve Ward
Players o.t Year: Rob Youhill & Danny Pitts

TEVERSAL

Founded: 1923
Nickname:

Chairman: Peter Bradshaw   **Vice-Chairman:**   **Manager:**

Secretary: Kevin Newton, 8 Vere Avenue, Sutton-in-Ashfield, Notts.NG17 2DS. **Tel No**: 01623 461145(H)   07711 358060 (M)

e-mail: kevin.newton@teversalfc.co.uk **Programme Editor:** Secretary   **Website**: www.teversalfc.co.uk

GROUND ADDRESS: Teversal Grange Sports ans Social Centre, Carnarvon Sttreet, Teversal,

Sutton-in-Ashfield .Notts. NG17 3HJ   **Tel No**: 01623 555944   **e-mail**: enquiries@teversaltc.co.uk

Capacity: **Seats**:   **Covered**:   **Floodlights**:

Simple Directions: From A6075 Stanton Hill to Teversal road. At roundabout take B6014 and take second turning into Coppywood Close in Teversal and drive to the top, follow road round with ground at top.

Midweek Home Matchday: Tuesday   **Clubhouse:**   **Club Shop:**

Previous Name(s):   **Previous League(s):** Central Midlands League

Club Colours: White with red panels/black/red   **Change Colours:**

LAST SEASON

League: Champions Central Midlands Lge   **F.A. Cup:** Pelim Round   **F.A. Vase:**

TRECORD Attendance:

SENIOR HONOURS: Central Midlands League 2004/05.

WINTERTON RANGERS

Secretary: G Spencer, 2 Dale Park Ave.,Winterton,Scun'pe,N Lincs.DN15 9UY (01724 732039)

Ground: West Street, Winterton, Scunthorpe, South Humberside (01724 732628).

Directions: From Scunthorpe take A1077 Barton-on-Humber for 5 miles. On entering Winterton take 3rd right (Eastgate), 3rd left (Northlands Rd)and 1st right (West St.). Ground 200yds on left

Capacity: 3,000   Seats: 200   Covered: 200   Floodlights: Yes   **Club Shop:** No.

Clubhouse: Open matchdays & evenings Mon-Sat, hot & cold food available on matchdays

HONOURS   Lincs Jnr Cup 47-48 61-62; Lincs Snr `B' Cup 69-70; Yorks Lg 71-72 76-77 78-79 (Lg Cup 80-81); N.C.E. Div 2 89-90; S'thorpe Lg & Cup many times.

PREVIOUS   **Leagues:** Scunthorpe & Dist. 45-65; Lincs 65-70; Yorkshire 70-82.

BEST SEASON   FA Vase: QF 76-77 **FA Cup:** 4th Qual Rd replay 76-77, 2-3 after 3-3

RECORD   **Attendance:** 1,200 v Sheffield Utd, official floodlight opening, Oct. 78

      Fee received: £5,000 for Henry Smith (Leeds United, 1979)

FACT FILE
Founded: 1930   Nickname: Rangers
Colours: Royal Blue & White Trim.
Change colours: All red
Midweek matches: Wednesday
Programme: 28-36 pages, 50p
Editor: Brian Crowderr (01724 844322)
Local Press: Scunthorpe Evening Telegraph
CLUB PERSONNEL
Chairman:David Crowder
Vice- Chairman: Ken Edgehill
Press Officer: Brian Crowder
Manager: Peter Daniel

WORSBROUGH M.W. & ATHLETIC

Secretary: Charlie Wyatt, 4 Springfield Road, Hoyland Common, Barnsley,S.Yorks. S74 0BE Tel & FAX: 01226 747774 (H)   07977 947760 (M)

Ground: Park Road, Worsbrough Bridge, Barnsley Tel: 01226 284452

Directions: On the A61 Barnsley-Sheffield road two miles south of Barnsley, 2miles from M1 jnt 36 opposite Blackburns Bridge. Two and a half miles from Barnsley (BR). Yorkshire Traction run buses every 10 mins thru Worsbrough Bridge.

Capacity: 2,000   Seats: 175   Cover: 175   Floodlights: Yes

Clubhouse: Yes   **Club Shop:** No

HONOURS   Northern Co's East Div 1 R-up 90-91 (Div 3 R-up 85-86); Sheffield SnrCup R-up 72-73; County Snr Lg 65-66 69-70 (R-up 62-63, Lg Cup 65-66); Barnsley Lg 52-53 58-59 59-60, Lg Cup 56-57 58-59 (R-up 53-54), Beckett Cup 57-58.

PREVIOUS   **Leagues:** Barnsley 52-61; Sheffield County Snr 62-71; Yorkshire 71-82.

RECORD   **Attendance:** 1,603 v Blyth Spartans, FA Amateur Cup 1971

BEST SEASON FA Cup: 1st Qual. Rd 78-79 79-80 80-81   **FA Vase:** 3rd Round 90-91

FACT FILE
Founded: 1923
Reformed: 1947
Colours: Red & Black/Black/Black
Change colours: Yellow/black
Midweek Matchday: Tuesday
Programme:60 pages, £1.00
Editor: Secretary

Chairman: John Cooper

Record Holders
Appearances: Billy Pickering
Goals: Frank Briscoe

YORKSHIRE AMATEUR

Secretary: Karl Blackburn, 6 HIlton PLace, leeds LS8 4HE Tel Nos 0113 262 3629 (H)
07971 002126 (M)
Ground: The Bracken Edge, Sycamore Avenue, Leeds LS8 4DZ Tel: 0113 262 4093
Directions: From South M1 to Leeds, then A58 Wetherby Road to Fforde Green Hotel, left at
lights and proceed to Sycamore Ave. (on right). From East A1 to Boot & Shoe Inn
then to Shaftesbury Hotel, turn right into Harehills Lane, then to Sycamore
Avenue. 2.5miles from Leeds (BR). Buses 2, 3 & 20 from Briggate toHarehills Ave.
Capacity: 1,550   Seats: 200   Cover: 160   Floodlights: Yes   **Club Shop:** Yes
Clubhouse: Bar, tea bar, games, lounge. Every night 8.30-11, Sat matchdays 12-11, Sun 12-3.
HONOURS FA Amtr Cup SF 31-32; West Riding Co. Cup (3); Yorks Lg 31-32, Div 2 58-59 (R-up
52-53 71-72), Div 3 77-78, Lg Cup 32-33; Leeds & Dist. Snr Cup. **PREVIOUS League:** Yorks 20-
24 30-82. **Ground:** Elland Road 1919-20 **RECORD Attendance:** 4,000 v Wimbledon, FA Amateur
Cup QF 1932. **Players progressing:** Gary Strodder & Stuart Naylor (W.B.A.), Peter Swan (Leeds
U) Brian Deane (Doncaster R) **BEST SEASONS: FA Cup:** 1st Rd 31-32 45-46
FA Vase: 3rd Round 93-94   **FA Amateur Cup:** Semi-Finals 31-32

FACT FILE

Founded: 1918   Nickname: Ammers
Sponsors: Screeching Parrot
Colours: White/navy/red
Change colours: All red
Midweek Matches: Tuesday
Programme: 12 pages, 50p
Editor: Jamie Steel(07818 841125)
Local Press: Yorkshire Post, Yorkshire
Evening Post and North Leeds Advertiser

CLUB PERSONNEL

Chairman:Ken Blackburn
President: Rayner Barker
Manager: Denis Metcalfe
Coach:Jim McKay Physio: Terry Davies

NORTHERN LEAGUE

SPONSORED BY: ARNGROVE

Founded 1889 (Second oldest League in the World)
President: George Courtney MBE   **Chairman:** Mike Amos
Hon. Secretary & Treasurer: Tony Golightly, 85 Park Road North, Chester-le-Street,
Co Durham DH3 3SA Tel: 0191 388 2056 Fax: 0191 3891 1385
E-mail: tonygol@northernlge.fsnet.co.uk

DIVISION ONE		P	W	D	L	F	A	Pts
1.	Newcastle Blue Star(3rd Div.2 04-05)	40	28	6	6	87	34	90
2.	Bedlington Terriers	40	22	8	10	86	61	74
3.	Dunston Federation Brewery (Champions 04-05)	40	20	11	9	82	45	71
4.	Billingham Town	40	18	13	9	81	54	67
5.	West Auckland Town	40	20	7	13	76	53	67
6.	Morpeth Town	40	19	10	11	68	50	67
7.	Billingham Synthonia	40	17	12	11	65	58	63
8.	Chester Le Street Town	40	18	9	13	64	64	63
9.	Newcastle BBP	40	18	8	14	81	62	62
10.	Whitley Bay	40	17	9	14	68	51	60
11.	Durham City	40	15	13	12	58	44	58
12.	Tow Law Town	40	15	9	16	63	65	54
13.	West Allotment Celtic (1st Div.2 04-05)	40	14	8	18	77	83	50
14.	Sunderland Nissan (2nd Div.2 04-05)	40	14	8	18	64	73	50
15.	Jarrow Roofing Boldon CA	40	14	7	19	65	76	49
16.	Ashington	40	13	9	18	64	60	48
17.	Thornaby	40	14	6	20	72	85	48
18.	Horden CW	40	12	11	17	55	65	47
19.	Shildon	40	11	14	15	55	65	47
20.	Esh Winning	40	3	7	30	32	103	16
21.	Brandon United	40	4	3	33	35	147	15

DIVISION ONE	1	2	3	4	5	6	7	8	9	10	11	12	13	14	15	16	17	18	19	20	21
1 Ashington		1-3	0-1	0-1	6-1	1-2	3-3	1-1	4-0	1-1	3-1	0-3	1-2	0-2	1-1	1-2	6-1	0-1	3-1	1-0	0-2
2 Bedlington Terriers	0-3		1-0	2-1	5-0	1-1	0-1	1-0	3-2	1-0	3-2	0-1	3-2	1-0	5-3	4-3	3-0	3-3	3-2	0-1	0-0
3 Billingham Synthonia	1-0	4-3		1-1	3-0	4-1	1-1	1-0	4-0	1-1	3-2	1-4	4-2	1-1	0-1	1-0	0-3	3-0	1-0	2-1	3-3
4 Billingham Town	0-0	4-4	3-3		5-0	2-1	1-2	2-1	3-0	4-1	2-2	1-2	1-2	1-2	3-2	0-0	4-2	2-1	4-2	4-1	3-1
5 Brandon United	1-3	3-2	0-3	1-0		0-3	0-6	1-5	2-2	0-5	3-4	1-1	0-3	0-4	1-6	0-2	0-5	0-8	1-1	1-2	1-5
6 Chester Le Street T.	1-1	2-2	2-0	2-2	3-1		2-3	3-2	2-0	2-1	2-0	2-0	1-0	1-1	2-0	0-1	0-1	3-2	3-5	2-2	1-4
7 Dunston Fed. Brewery	1-1	2-3	3-3	1-1	3-2	3-0		0-2	6-0	4-1	2-1	1-0	2-0	0-0	3-2	1-1	0-0	3-1	4-0	0-1	5-2
8 Durham City	4-0	2-1	0-1	0-2	2-1	3-1	1-1		0-0	0-0	2-2	1-0	2-4	1-0	2-2	2-1	5-0	0-0	2-1	2-1	0-0
9 Esh Winning	1-4	0-5	4-0	0-0	0-2	1-3	0-2	0-0		1-1	1-1	0-3	0-2	1-2	0-2	1-2	1-4	0-1	1-4	1-3	2-1
10 Horden CW	1-4	0-1	2-2	0-2	3-0	0-1	2-1	1-0	2-0		1-2	3-3	2-1	1-1	0-0	1-2	2-1	2-2	1-0	0-0	1-2
11 Jarrow Roofing Boldon CA	2-1	2-3	2-1	2-2	4-2	4-0	0-3	1-0	2-1	0-3		3-0	0-3	1-2	2-2	3-4	1-1	5-1	2-0	1-1	0-3
12 Morpeth Town	2-0	2-1	0-1	1-4	3-2	1-1	2-0	0-0	2-3	5-1	4-1		0-3	2-3	2-0	3-3	4-1	0-2	1-0	2-0	2-1
13 Newcastle BBP	2-1	2-2	1-1	0-3	2-1	1-1	2-0	3-3	1-1	8-2	1-0	1-1		1-2	1-2	0-3	6-3	1-1	6-2	3-0	2-2
14 Newcastle Blue Star-	3-0	1-2	2-1	2-1	8-0	5-1	1-0	3-2	4-0	1-0	4-1	3-1	1-0		2-1	7-2	0-3	1-1	0-1	3-1	3-1
15 Shildon	0-0	0-2	1-0	1-1	3-2	1-3	2-0	1-4	2-1	1-4	1-2	0-0	2-1	0-0		1-1	2-4	3-1	3-3	1-1	2-2
16 Sunderland Nissan	1-2	0-4	3-3	4-0	3-1	0-2	2-2	2-2	6-2	0-1	3-0	0-2	1-6	0-1	0-0		0-4	2-4	0-1	2-1	1-2
17 Thornaby	1-3	1-5	4-2	1-1	8-1	1-1	0-2	0-1	4-2	3-1	1-0	2-3	0-2	0-2	1-3	4-3		0-4	2-1	1-6	0-1
18 Tow Law Town	0-3	0-0	3-0	1-2	1-2	1-2	1-7	2-1	3-2	3-0	1-0	0-2	2-1	3-2	0-0	3-1	2-2		0-3	1-2	0-0
19 West Allotment Celtic	5-1	3-3	1-1	1-4	4-1	4-1	1-1	1-1	5-1	1-5	2-6	1-1	4-0	1-4	3-1	1-2	2-2	3-1		1-2	1-5
20 West Auckland Town	2-2	5-1	1-2	2-2	7-0	3-2	3-1	3-1	3-1	3-1	4-0	2-2	3-0	0-2	1-0	1-0	1-0	1-2	2-3		1-2
21 Whitley Bay	3-2	2-0	1-1	3-2	4-0	0-1	0-2	0-1	3-0	1-1	0-1	1-1	2-3	0-2	4-0	0-1	2-1	1-0	1-2	1-2	

DIVISION TWO

		P	W	D	L	F	A	Pts
1.	Consett	38	33	3	2	134	31	102
2.	Northallerton Town	38	25	8	5	86	30	83
3.	Darlington RA	38	23	5	10	83	46	74
4.	Penrith	38	20	10	8	73	46	70
5.	Crook Town	38	19	11	8	95	43	68
6.	Washington	38	17	10	11	68	54	61
7.	Norton & Stockton Ancients	38	17	9	12	83	73	60
8.	Spennymoor Town	38	16	11	11	70	66	59
9.	Whickham	38	16	10	12	84	64	58
10.	Marske United	38	12	13	13	62	69	49
11.	Ryton	38	13	9	16	51	65	48
12.	North Shields	38	13	8	17	57	67	47
13.	Prudhoe Town	38	12	10	16	45	49	46
14.	Seaham Red Star	38	11	12	15	60	59	45
15.	Hebburn Town	38	12	9	17	46	67	45
16.	Alnwick Town (-3)	38	12	1	25	62	93	34
17.	Kennek Ryhope CA	38	5	13	20	41	76	28
18.	South Shields (-6)	38	10	4	24	51	95	28
19.	Guisborough Town	38	7	7	24	35	86	28
20.	Peterlee Newtown	38	5	1	32	48	155	16

DIVISION TWO	1	2	3	4	5	6	7	8	9	10	11	12	13	14	15	16	17	18	19	20
1 Alnwick Town		1-3	0-2	1-4	3-2	2-1	4-0	1-0	1-2	1-2	1-3	2-1	10-0	1-3	1-3	2-1	2-2	2-3	1-2	1-2
2 Consett	5-0		2-1	1-1	12-1	6-0	2-0	4-1	5-0	2-0	4-1	3-1	6-2	1-0	1-0	2-1	3-0	5-1	2-2	5-0
3 Crook Town	4-1	1-3		3-0	3-1	0-1	1-1	5-0	3-1	0-0	3-3	3-0	6-1	2-1	6-0	3-3	2-1	6-1	3-0	4-1
4 Darlington RA	2-1	1-2	1-1		1-0	2-0	1-2	3-1	0-0	4-3	1-4	5-2	2-1	0-1	3-0	1-2	0-0	2-0	3-0	
5 Guisborough Town	0-2	1-0	1-2	0-5		0-1	0-0	1-1	1-2	0-2	1-1	2-3	0-3	1-0	2-1	3-2	0-2	1-1	1-2	0-2
6 Hebburn Town	4-1	0-7	1-1	0-2	1-0		0-0	0-1	2-2	0-3	2-1	1-0	4-5	1-0	0-2	1-3	2-0	2-2	1-2	1-1
7 Kennek Ryhope CA	2-0	2-5	2-3	0-3	2-2	0-2		2-2	0-2	1-3	1-2	0-2	1-0	0-0	1-2	1-1	1-2	5-2	0-0	1-1
8 Marske United	1-2	2-2	0-5	2-3	2-0	1-1	1-1		2-3	2-2	3-2	1-1	8-2	0-1	0-3	1-1	1-0	0-0	2-3	1-1
9 North Shields	3-1	1-3	2-1	0-3	4-0	0-0	1-1	0-2		0-3	0-2	1-1	4-0	1-1	5-0	1-3	2-1	3-1	1-6	1-1
10 Northallerton Town	6-0	3-0	3-1	2-0	2-1	2-0	1-1	1-2	4-0		0-0	2-3	3-0	1-4	2-1	1-1	8-0	1-1	4-1	4-1
11 Norton & Stockton-Ancients	3-1	1-2	3-2	1-8	2-2	2-3	2-1	2-1	4-1	1-3		3-4	5-1	3-1	1-1	1-1	3-0	1-4	4-4	3-3
12 Penrith	4-1	1-3	1-0	4-1	1-0	0-0	1-0	2-2	2-1	0-1	1-2		4-0	2-2	0-0	2-2	1-0	5-1	2-1	1-1
13 Peterlee Newtown	1-4	0-5	0-7	1-3	0-2	1-2	0-5	2-4	0-4	3-4	2-6	2-3		0-0	3-5	1-3	3-1	0-5	0-3	2-5
14 Prudhoe Town	3-0	0-5	1-1	1-3	5-1	4-2	1-1	1-1	2-1	0-1	0-1	0-0	0-2		2-1	1-0	1-2	0-0	1-0	2-3
15 Ryton	1-4	0-6	2-1	0-4	5-1	0-0	2-1	1-2	2-1	1-1	1-2	0-2	4-1	0-0		3-3	2-2	2-0	1-2	1-4
16 Seaham Red Star	0-3	1-2	0-0	1-3	0-3	4-1	3-0	2-3	1-1	2-1	1-4	1-1	4-0	1-2	1-1		3-1	1-3	1-1	1-0
17 South Shields	4-1	1-8	0-4	1-2	7-1	1-6	3-4	1-3	1-3	0-3	1-1	2-1	2-4	3-1	2-1	0-3		2-2	1-0	2-3
18 Spennymoor Town	5-0	1-2	1-1	3-2	3-1	2-1	4-2	4-1	2-2	0-2	2-1	2-6	4-2	2-1	0-1	2-1	2-0		1-1	1-0
19 Washington	3-2	1-3	0-0	1-1	0-0	5-2	7-1	1-1	1-0	0-3	1-2	0-2	6-2	2-0	1-0	1-0	4-1	1-0		3-3
20 Whickham	6-1	1-2	4-4	4-1	1-2	2-0	7-0	5-3	1-0	0-2	2-1	2-4	8-0	1-2	0-0	0-3	3-0	2-2	3-0	

L E A G U E   C U P

FIRST ROUND

South Shields	v North Shields	2-0
Ryton	v Crook Town	1-3
West Auckland T.	v Durham City	3-1
Peterlee Newtown	v Sunderland Nissan	2-4
Whickham	v Chester-Le-Street	2-0
Alnwick Town	v Billingham Town	1-4
Whitley Bay	v Northallerton Town	2-4
Brandon United	v Morpeth Town	1-3
West Allotment Celtic	v Hebburn Town	4-0

SECOND ROUND

Ashington	v Shildon	2-1
Dunston Fed. (H)	v Washington	5-4*
West Auckland T.	v Spennymoor Town	3-1*
Whickham	v Guisborough Town	5-0
Kennek Ryhope C.A.	v Norton & Stockton A.	2-2*, 2-4p
Seaham Red Star	v Marske United	5-2
Bedlington Terriers	v Horden C.W.	3-2
Esh Winning	v Newcastle Blue Star	4-4*, 1-3p
Penrith	v Sunderland Nissan	3-2
Prudhoe Town	v Tow Law Town	0-3
Thornaby	v Northallerton Town	4-1
Crook Town	v Jarrow Roofing	2-4
Darlington Railway A.	v South Shields	3-2
Morpeth Town	v Billingham Synthonia	1-0
Consett	v Billingham Town	2-1
West Allotment Celtic	v Newcastle Benfield Bay Plastic	0-1

THIRD ROUND

Ashington	v Dunston Fed. (H)	0-1*
Jarrow Roofing	v Seaham Red Star	4-1
Morpeth Town	v Tow Law Town	4-1*
Bedlington Terriers	v Darlington Railway Athletic	0-2
Norton & Stockton A.	v Newcastle Blue Star	1-2
Thornaby	v Consett	1-5
Penrith	v Newcastle Benfield Bay Plastic	2-1
Whickham	v West Auckland Town	0-1

FOURTH ROUND

Jarrow Roofing	v Dunston Fed. (H)	1-2
Newcastle Blue Star	v Penrith	2-1
Morpeth Town	v West Auckland Town	1-2*
Darlington Railway A.	v Consett	2-2*, 3-5p

SEMI-FINAL

Dunston Fed. (H)	v West Auckland Town	4-0
Consett	v Newcastle Blue Star	0-1

THE FINAL

Dunston Fed. (H)	v Newcastle Blue Star	0-1*

LEAGUE CONSTITUTION 2005-06 - DIVISION ONE

ASHINGTON

Formed: 1883
Nickname: The Colliers

Chairman: Jim Lang   **Presidents:** Sir Bobby and Jack Charlton   **Manager:** Tony Harrison
Secretary: Brian Robinson, 80 Milburn Road, Ashington, Northumberland NE63 0PG   **Asst Manager:** Jimmy Harmison
Tel No: 01670 852832 (H) 01670 521212(W)   **Physio:** Ken Barton
Press Officer: Brian Bennett (01670 856606) **Prog Editor:** Ed Marchett (01670854585)   **Programme:** 50p
GROUND ADDRESS:
Capacity: 2,000   **Seats:** 350   **Covered:** 1,200   **Floodlights:** Yes   **Club Shop:** Yes
Simple Directions: 200 yards north at traffic lights at centre of town.
Midweek Home Matchday: Tuesday   **Clubhouse:** Open 6-11pm & 11 am on market day (Tues). Closed Wed & Sun
Previous Leagues: Northern Alliance 1892-93, 1902-14 69-70 Football League, North Eastern 14-21 29-58 62-64, Midland
58-60 Northern Counties 60-62, Wearside 64-65 N.P.L. 68-69
Club Colours: Black & white stripes/black/black   **Change Colours:** Blue & white/blue/blue
BEST PERFORMANCES
F.A. Cup: 3rd Rd 1926-27   **F.A.Amateur Cup:** S-Final 73-74   **F.A.Vase:** 3rd Round Replay 1990-91
RECORD Attendance: 13,199 v Rochdale F.A.Cup 2nd Rd 09.12.50
Senior Honours: Northumberland Senior Cup (9) Northumberland Challenge Bowl (6)

BEDLINGTON TERRIERS

Chairman: Graham Burnard **Manager:** Keith Perry & Tony Lowrey **Coaches:** Mel Harmison & Dean Gibb
Vice-Chairman: John Feary
Secretary: Bill Lowery,27 Mirlaw Road,Cramlington, Northumberland NE23 6UB
Tel Nos: 01670 713099 (H)
Press Officer: Secretary **Programme:** 24 Pages 1.00 Editor (Tel)
GROUND ADDRESS: Welfare Park, Park Rd., Bedlington, Northumberland **Tel:** 01670 825485
Capacity: 3,000 **Seats:** 300 **Covered:** 500 **Floodlights:** Yes
Simple Directions: Into Bedlington, turn left at Northumberland Arms on Front St, then 2nd rt. Ground 100 yrds on rt.
Midweek Home Matchday: Tuesday **Clubhouse:** Open every evening and Sat & Sun lunchtime.Club Shop:No
Previous Name(s): Bedlington Mechanics 49-53 Bedlington Utd. 61-65 **Previous League:** Northern Alliance
Club Colours: Red & white/red & white/white **Change Colours:** Blue 7 white/blue & white/blue
BEST PERFORMANCES
League: Champions Northern League **F.A. Cup:** 2nd Rd **F.A.Vase:** Finalists 1998-99
RECORD Attendance: 1,013 v Blyth Spartans Northern League 85-86 **Goalscorer:** John Milner
Senior Honours: Northern Lg Div 1 97-8 98-9 99-00 00-01 01-02 R-up (2) Div 2 94-95 Northumberland Sen. Cup (4)

BILLINGHAM SYNTHONIA
Founded: 1923
Nickname: Synners

Chairman: Stuart Coleby **President:** Frank Cook **Manager:**Stuart Coleby
Secretary: Graham Craggs, 10 Embleton Grove, Wynard, Stockton on Tees, TS22 5SY **Tel No:** 01740 645367
Press Officer: Secretary **Programme:** Pages - 20 + ads Price - 50p **Ed.:** David Lealman(01642 559540)
GROUND ADDRESS: The Stadium , Central Avenue, Billingham, Cleveland. Press Box **Tel No:** 01642 532348
Capacity: 1,970 **Seats:** 370 **Covered:** 370 **Floodlights:** Yes
Simple Directions: Take A1027 off A19 signposted Billingham continue along Central Avenue and ground is on left opposite office block. One mile from Billingham BR **Sponsors:** Jack Hatfield Sports
Midweek Home Matchday: Wednesday **Clubhouse:** On the ground.Open normal club hours. **Club Shop:** Yes
Previous Name(s): Billingham Synthonia Recreation **Previous League:** Teeside 1923-the war.
Club Colours: Green& whitequarters/white/white **Change Colours:** All Yellow
BEST PERFORMANCES
League: Champions 56-7 88-9 95-6 **F.A. Cup:** Ist Rd (6) **F.A.Vase:** 4th Rd 2003-04
Last Season: 7th **Top Scorer:** Colin Iley **Playerof the Year:** Neil Radigan **Captain:** Shaun Hope
RECORD Attendance: 4,200 v Bishop Auckland 6/9/58 **Goalscorer:** Tony Hetherington **Apps:** Andy Harbron
Senior Honours: Northern Lg (4) R-up (4) Lg Cup (3) Div 2 86-7 Teeside36-7 N.Riding Sen Cup(2) N.Riding Am Cup(4) Durham Challenge Cup (2)

BILLINGHAM TOWN
Founded: 1967
Nickname:The Social

Chairman: Tommy Donnelly **President:** G.A.Maxwell **Manager:**Michael Watson **Ass.Man.:** Lee Tucker **Coach:** Mark Scott
Secretary: Glenn Youngman, 13 Blackthorn Grove,Fairfield, Stockton,Cleveland, TS19 7DG
Tel Nos: 01642 862058 (H) 01642 655516 (W) 07984 258608 (M)
Press Officer: Chairman 01642 555332 (H) 01642 370101 (W) **Programme:** 28 Pages 50p **Editor:** Peter Martin c/o club
GROUND ADDRESS: Bedford Terrace, Billingham, Cleveland Tel No: 01642 560043
Capacity: 3,000 **Seats:** 176 **Covered:** 600 **Floodlights:** Yes
Simple Directions: Leave A19 on A1027 (to Billingham).Left at third roundabout. 1st left over bridge, left to ground.
Midweek Home Matchday: Tuesday **Clubhouse:** Open matchdays.Hot & Cold food. **Club Shop:** No
Previous Name(s): Billingham Social Club **Previous League(s):** Stockton & District 68-74 Teeside7-82
Club Colours: All Blue **Change Colours:** Yellow/green/green
BEST PERFORMANCES
League: 21st Northern Div 1 **RECORD** Attendance:1,500 v Man City F.A.Youth Cup 1985
Record Goalscorer: Paul Rowntree 396 (1990-2001) **Appearances:** Paul Rowntree 505
SENIOR HONOURS: Durham Cup 76-7 77-8 03-04 North Riding Senior Cup R-up 76-7 81-2

BISHOP AUCKLAND

Chairman: Terry Jackson **Manager:** Brian Healy
Secretary: Tony Duffy, 90 Escomb Road, Bishop Auckland, Co.Durham DL14 6TZ
Tel Nos: 01388 602 809 (H) 07974 286812 (M)
Press Officer: Secretary **Programme:** 28 Pages - £1.20 Editor: Kevin Illingworth
GROUND ADDRESS: ground sharing with Shildon F.C.Tel: 01388773877
Capacity: 4,000 **Seats:** 480 **Covered:** 1000 **Floodlights:** Yes
Simple Directions: In the town centre,one mile from the BT station and 300 yards from the Durham-Bishop Auckland bus stop
Midweek Home Matchday: Wednesday
Clubhouse: Open on match days **Club Shop:**Club items on sale on matchdays
Previous Leagues: Northern Alliance 1890-91 and Northern League 1893-1988
Club Colours: Sky and Navy Blue Quarters/ Blue/Blue **Change Colours:** White
BEST PERFORMANCES
League: Northern Premier League **F.A. Cup:** 4th Round 1954-55 **F.A.Trophy** 6thRound (4)
F.A.Amateur Cup: Winners (10)
RECORD Attendance:17,000 v Coventry City F.A.Cup 2nd Round 06.12.62
Appearances: Bob Hardisty Transfer Fee Received: £10,000 from Bolton Wanderers for Jeff Smith
SENIOR HONOURS: F.A.Amateur Cup Winners (10) R-up (7) Northern League (19) R-Up (17) Durham Challenge Cup (13))

CHESTER-LE-STREET TOWN

Founded: 1972
Nickname: Cestrians

Chairman: John Tomlinson   **Vice-Chairman:** Jack Thornback   **Manager:** Stuart Sherwood
Secretary: William Gardner, 15 Waverley Road, Low Fell, Gateshead, Tyne & Wear NE9 7TU
Tel Nos: 0191 4824325 (H) 07747 112861 (M)
Press Officer: Jack Thornback (0191 388 3554) **Programme Editor**: K.Greener   **Programme: 40** Pages 50p)
Ground Address: Moor Park, Chester Moor, Chester-le-Street, Co.Durham   **Tel:** 0191 388 3363
Capacity: 3,500   **Seats:** 150   **Covered:** 1,500   **Floodlights:** Yes
Simple Directions: Ground lies approx 2 miles south of town centre on A617 Durham road.
Midweek Home Matchday: Tuesday   **Clubhouse:** Open daily   **Shop:** No
Previous Leagues: Newcastle City Am72-75 Washington 75-77 Wearside 77-83   **Pre. Name:** Garden Farm 72-78
Club Colours: Blue & white hoops/white/white   **Change Colours:**
All Yellow
BEST PERFORMANCES: League: **F.A. Cup:** 4th Qual.Rd.   **F.A.Vase:** 5th Rd 3rd Replay 84-85
RECORD Attendance: 893 v Fleetwood F.A.Vase 18.02.85 **Appearances:** Colin Wake 361
Victory: 9-0 v Washington 28.02.98   **Defeat**: 0-7 v Consett 06.11.96
Senior Honours: Northern Lg Div 2 83-84 97-98

CONSETT

Secretary: Ian Hamilton, 29 Grange St. Delves Lane, Consett, Co. Durham DH87AG
Tel: 01207 509366 (H) 07947 130726 (M) email: thesecretarycafc@aol.com
Ground: Belle Vue Park, Ashdale Road, Consett, County Durham (01207 503788)
Directions: Quarter of mile north of town centre - along Medomsley Rd, left down Ashdale Rd, ground 100m yards on left. Follow signs for Sports Centre and Baths
Capacity: 4,000   Seats: 400   Cover: 1,000   Floodlights: Yes
Clubhouse: Matchdays, and evenings on request. Darts & pool   **Club Shop:** No
PREVIOUS Leagues: Northern Alliance 19-26 35-37; North Eastern 26-35 37-58 62-64; Midland 58-60; Northern Counties 60-62; Wearside 64-70
BEST SEASON: FA Cup: 1st Rd 58-59, 0-5 v Doncaster Rov. (A) **FA Trophy:** 2nd Rd 78-79
HONOURS North Eastern Lg 39-40 Div 2 26-27, Lg Cup 50-51(jt) 53-54, Durham Challenge x5 R-up x2, Northern Lg R-up 76-77 Div 2 88-89, Lg Cup 78-79 80-81, Northern Counties Lg 61-62, Sunderland Shipowners Cup 67-68, Monkwearmouth Charity Cup 67-68, Wearside Lg R-up 68-69 69-70.

FACT FILE
Founded: 1899   Nickname: Steelmen
Colours: Red with black & white trim/black/red
Change colours:Sky blue/dark blue/sky blue
Midweek Matches: Wednesday
Programme: 16 pages, 30p
Programme Editor: Andrew Pearson
CLUB PERSONNEL
Chairman: Derek .Nicholls
Vice Chairman: Stuart Moffat
President: John Hirst
Press Officer: Andrew Pearson
Manager: Colin Carr
Physios: Brian Nicholson & Jim Vipond

DARLINGTON RAILWAY ATHLETIC

Founded: 1996
Nickname:

Chairman: Doug Hawman   **Vice-Chairman:** Ken Bousfield   **Manager**: Dave Woodcock
Secretary: Martyn Jackson, 6 Westlands Road, Darlington, Co.Durham DL3 9JJ
Tel No: 01325 240498
GROUND ADDRESS: Railway Social Club, Brinkburn Road,Darlington, Co.Durham   **Tel:** 01325 468125
Capacity: 2,500   **Seats:** 175   **Covered:** 250   **Floodlights:** Yes
Simple Directions: Take A68 off A1 towards Darlington.Turn left opp.pub on right into Brinkburn Rd. Ground is 400 yds on left.
Midweek Home Matchday: Wednesday   **Clubhouse:**Yes it serves all sports at the complex.   Club Shop:
Club Colours: All red   **Change Colours:** Blue & White
Last Season: 3rd. Northern League Div 2
League: Champions Wearside.   **F.A. Cup:** N/A   **F.A. Vase:** 1st Round
BEST PERFORMANCES
League: 3rd Northern Div 2 2005-2006   **F.A. Cup:** N/A   **F.A.Vase:** 1st Round 2005-06

DUNSTON FEDERATION BREWERY

Founded: 1975
Nickname: 'The Fed'

Chairman: Malcolm James   **Vice-Chairman:** Fred Fowles   **Manager:** Bobby Scaife
Secretary: Bill Montague, 12 Dundee Close, Chapel House, Newcastle-upn-Tyne NE5 1JJ (0191 2672250)
Press Officer: Name (Tel)   **Programme:** 60 pages 50p Price   **Editor:** Ian McPherson (0191 420 5583)
GROUND ADDRESS: Federation Park,Wellington Road, Dunston, Gateshead   **Tel:** 0191 493 2935
Capacity: 2,000   **Seats:** 120   **Covered:** 400   **Floodlights:** Yes
Simple Directions: Dunston/Whickham exit off A1(M) .Ground is 400 yards north along Dunston Road on the left.
Midweek Home Matchday: Tuesday   **Clubhouse:** Matchdays only. Hot and cold snacks   **Club Shop:** No
Previous Name(s): Whickham Sports,Dunston Mechanics Sports.   **Previous Ground:** Dunston Public park 75-86
Previous leagues: Northern Amateur and Wearside League   **Sponsor`:** Newcastle Federation Brewery
Club Colours: All blue with white trim   **ChangeColours:** All red
LAST SEASON: League: 3rd   **F.A. Cup:** 2nd Qual.Rd   **F.A. Vase:** 3rd Rd
Top Scorer: Graeme Armstrong   **Player of the Year:** Michael Farrey   **Captain:** Billy Irwin
Best Performances League: Champions   **F.A. Cup:** 4th Qual .Rd 03-04   **F.A.Vase:**Quarter Finals 1992-93**CORD Attendance:** 1,550 v Sunderland -Shipowners Cup Final 01.04.88 **Goalscorer:** Paul King   **Apps:** Paul Dixon
Senior Honours: Northern Champions 03-04, Champion & Cup Winners 04-05 R-up 00-01 Div 2 92-93 Durham Co.Trophy 81-82 Sunderland Shipowners Cup 87-88 Durham County Chllenge Cup R-Up 2004-05

DURHAM CITY
Re-formed 1949:
Nickname: City

Chairman: Stewart Dawson   **President:** David. Asprey
Manager: Andy Gowans   **Assistant Manager:** Mark Cameron
Secretary & Press Officer: Kevin Hewitt,21Cherrytree Drive, Langley Park, Co.Durham DH7 9FX
Tel Nos: 0191 3733878 (H+ Fax) 0191383 3441 (W) 07930815389 (M)
Programme Editor: Gordon Wright   **Programme:** 50 pages
GROUND ADDRESS: Archibalds Stadium,Belmont Ind. Estate, Durham DH1 1GG   **Tel:** 0191 3869616
Capacity: 2,700   **Seats:** 270   **Covered:** 750   **Floodlights:** Yes
Simple Directions: At Jct 62 on A1M take A 690 towards Durham City. Follow signposts for Belmont Industrial estate.
Midweek Home Matchday: Tuesday   **Clubhouse:** Two bars and function rooms   **Club Shop:** No
Previous Leagues: Victory 1918-19, N.Eastern 19-21, 28-38, Football League 21-28 Warside 38-39 50-51
Previous Grounds:Holiday Park 21-38, Ferens Park 49-94 (club disbbanded in 1938
Club Colours: Yellow/Blue/White   **Change Colours:** All White
Best Performances:League: Northern League Champions 94-95   **F.A. Cup:** 2nd Rd 25-26 57-58
F.A.Vase: S-F 2001-02   **F.A.Amateur Cup:** 2nd Rd Replay 1957-58 **F.A.Trophy:** 1st Rd.83-84 94-95
RECORD Attendance: 2,750 v Whitley Bay F.A.Vase S-F 2001-02 **Goals (Season):** Lee Ludlow 45 **Apps:** Joe Raine 552
Senior Honours: Northern Lg. Champions 94-95 R-up 70-71 Durham Challenge Cup R-Up (3)

HORDEN COLLIERY WELFARE
Founded: 1980
Nickname: Colliers

Chairman: Norman Stephens   **Manager:**
Secretary: Rob Jones, 1 York Road, Peterlee, Co.Durham SR8 2DS **Tel Nos:** 0191 587 0949 (H) 07932 951842 (M)
Press Officer: Secretary   **Programme:** 26 Pages - £1.00
GROUND ADDRESS: Welfare Park, Park Road, Horden, Peterlee Co.Durham   **Tel:** 0191 587 3549
Capacity: 3.000   **Seats:** 200   **Covered:** 370   **Floodlights:**Yes
Simple Directions:A 19 to Peterlee. Signposted from there.
Midweek Home Matchday: Wednesday   **Clubhouse:** Open normal hours hot & cold food   **Club Shop:** Yes
Previous Name: Horden Athletic   **Previous League(s):** Wearside 07-35 63-75 North Eastern 35-58 62-64
Club Colours: Red/black/black   **Change Colours:** Yellow/nlue/yellow
LAST SEASON
League: 18th   **F.A. Cup:** 3rd Qual. Rd.   **F.A. Vase:** 2nd Rd
Top Scorer: L.Ure.   **Player of the Year:** Phil Naisbett   **Captain:** Phil Naisbett
BEST PERFORMANCES
League: Northern Div 1   **F.A. Cup:** 2nd Rd 1938-39   **F.A.Vase: 2nd Rd** 1991-1992 2002-03 2004-05 2005-06
Record Attendance: 8.000 F.A.Cup 1937
Senior honours: Durham Challenge Cup (5) Northern League Div 2 R-up 02-03

JARROW ROOFING BOLDON C.A.
Founded: 1987
Nickname: Roofing

Chairman: Richard McLoughlin   **Vice-Chairman:**   **Sponsors:** Jarrow Roofing
Manager: Richard McLoughlin   **Physio**: John Cullen
Secretary: Martyn Wood, 43 Harton House Road, South Shields, Tyne & wear NE34 6EE
Tel No: 0191 4560324
Press Officer & Prog.Ed.: Brian Marshall 0191 4217011 or 07816664961   **Programme:** 20 Pages -Free.
GROUND ADDRESS: Boldon CA Sports Ground, New Road, Boldon Colliery   **Ground Tel. No.:** 0191 519 1391
Capacity: 3,500   **Seats:**150   **Covered:** 800   **Floodlights:** Yes
Simple Directions: A 19 to junction with A184 (Sunderlamd/Newcastle). Follow signs for Boldon Asda then to North Road Social Club. Ground is behind club. East Boldon BR 800 yards.
Midweek Home Matchday: Tuesday   **Clubhouse:**Open evenings and w/e lunchtimes. Hot food.   **Club Shop:** Yes
Previous Leagues: Mid-Tyne, Tyneside Amateur and Vaux Wearside
Club Colours: Blue & Yello   **Change Colours:** Red & Black
BEST PERFORMANCE
F.A.Vase: Semi-Final 2004-2005
RECORD Attendance: 500 v South Shields **Goalscorer:** Mick Hales   **Appearances:** Paul Chow
Senior Honours: F.A.Vase S-F 2004-05

MORPETH TOWN
Founded:
Nickname:

Chairman: Keith Jewitt   **Vice-Chairman:**   **Manager:**Steve Walker
Secretary: Les Scott. 1 Bennetts Walk, Morpeth, Northumberland NE61 1TP
Tel No: 01670 517390(H) 0780 3483509 (M) **e-mail:** les@craikpark.fsnt.co.uk   **Press Officer:** Secretary
Programme: Yes
GROUND ADDRESS: Craik Park, Morpeth Common, Morpeth,Northumberland   **Tel:** 01670 513785
Capacity: 1,000   **Seats:** 150   **Covered:** 150   **Floodlights:**Yes
Simple Directions: Morpeth is signed off the A1 onto A197. Take the B6524 turn right at Mitford sign, then right to ground after about a mile next to Morpeth Common.   Website: www.clubwebsite.co.uk/morpethtownfc/
Midweek Home Matchday: Tuesday   **Clubhouse:** Yes   **Club Shop:** No
Previous Ground: Storey Park, Morpeth pre 1992   **Previous League:** Northern Alliance pre 1994
Club Colours: Yellow/ black/black   **Change Colours:** Blue/white/blue
LAST SEASON
League: 4th   **F.A. Cup:** Prelim. Rd.   **F.A. Vase:** 1st Rd.
Top Scorer: Kevin Henderson   **Player of the Year:** Chris Phillipson   **Captain:** Iain Nickalls
BEST PERFORMANCES
League: 4th Northern League 2005-06   **F.A. Cup:** 4th Qualifying Round. 1998-99   **F.A.Vase:** 4th Round 2003-2004
SENIOR HONOURS: Northern Alliance (2) Challenge Cup (3)

NEWCASTLE BENFIELD BAY PLASTICS
Founded: 1989
Nickname:

Chairman: Jimmy Rowe
Manager: Keith Sheardown   **Asst.Manager:** Lee Boyle   **Physio:** Mel Bolam
Secretary: Mark Hedley, 12 Co-Operative Terrace, West Allotment, Tyne & Wear, NE27 0DY
Tel No: 0191 2702178 (H) 07973 699506 (M)
Programme Editor: Stan Gate   **Programme:** 48 Pages £1.00
GROUND ADDRESS: address   **Tel:**
Capacity: 2,000   **Seats:** 150   **Covered:** 250   **Floodlights:** Yes
Simple Directions: From Newcastle towards coast take second exit right after lights at Corner House pub into Benfield Road. Ground on left opposite Walkergate Hospital and adjacent to school.
Midweek Home Matchday: Tuesday   **Clubhouse:** Yes   **Club Shop:** No
Previous Leagues: Northern Alliance
Club Colours: All white   **Change Colours:** Maroon & Blue
BEST PERFORMANCES
League: 4th Northern League Div 1   **F.A. Cup:**   **F.A.Vase:**
SeniorHonours: Northern Alliance Champions 2002-03 and Northumberland Senior Cup Runners-Up 2004-05

NEWCASTLE BLUE STAR
Founded: 1930
Nickname: Star

Chairman: Derek Sayers   **Manager:** Eric Tait   **Assistant Manager:** Dean Gibb
Secretary: Jim Anderson, 38 Western Avenue, West Denton, Newcastle, NE5 5BU   **Tel No:** 0191 243 1025
Press Officer: Bob Morton   **Programme Editor:** Dave Eastman   **Programme:** 44 Pages £1.00
GROUND ADDRESS: Wheatsheaf Sports Ground, Woolsington, Newvastle-on-Tyne NE13 8DF
Tel. No.: 0191 286 0425   **E-mail:** nbsfc@blueyonder.co.uk   **Website: www.nbsfc.co.uk**
Capacity: 2,000   **Seats:** 300   **Covered:** 500   **Floodlights:** Yes
Simple Directions: From central station follow airport signs for seven miles. Ground is by Wheatsheaf Hotel on left.
Midweek Home Matchday: Tuesday   **Clubhouse:** Open every day   **Club Shop:** No
Previous Leagues: Newcastle Business Houses 32-38, N. E. Amateur, Tyune side Amateur, , N.Comb.& Wearside 75-85
Club Colours: All Blue   **Change Colours:** All red
LAST SEASON
League: Champions
BEST PERFORMANCES
League: Champions 2005-2006   **F.A. Cup:** 1st Rd. 84-85   **F.A.Vase:** Winners 77-78
Senior Honours: F.A.Vase Winners 77-78   Northumberland Senior Cup (4) R-Up (3) Champions Northern League 2005-06

SHILDON
Founded: 1890
Nickname: Rilwaymen

Chairman: Gordon Hampton   **Vice-Chairman:** G.Elliott   **President:** John Atkinson
Manager: Ray Gowan   **Assistant Manager:** David Bayles   **Physio:** Neil Jennings
Secretary: Gareth Howe, Dean House, 32/34 Dean Street,Shildon, Co.Durham DL4 1HA
Tel Nos: 01388 772473 (H) 01325 382 323 (W) 07976 822453 (M)
Programme Editor: Secretary   **Programme:** 48 Pages 50p
GROUND ADDRESS: Dean Street, Shildon, Co.Durham   **Ground Tel. No:** 01388 773877
Capacity: 4,000   **Seats:** 480   **Covered:** 1000   **Floodlights:** Yes
Simple Directions: In the town centre one mile from BR station and 300 yds from Durham-Bishop Auckland bus stop.
Midweek Home Matchday: Wednesday   **Clubhouse:** Matchdays only   **Club Shop:** No
Previous Leagues: Auckland & District 1892-86 Wearside 1896-97, North Eastern 07-32
Club Colours: All purple with black trim   **Change Colours:** White/black/white
League: Northern Lg. Champions (5)   **F.A. Cup:** 2nd Rd 36-37   **F.A.Vase:** 1st Rd 86-87
RECORD Attendance: 2,350 v Northern Hillsborough Fund 1969 **Goalscorer:** Jack Downing 61(1936-7) **Apps:** Bryan.Dale
Senior Honours: Northern Lg Champions (5) R-up (2) Durham Challenge Cup (3) Drham Am Cup (2)

SUNDERLAND NISSAN
Founded: 1988
Nickname:

Chairman: Alan Hill
Manager: Wilf Constantine   **Assistant Manager:** Paul Pitman
Secretary: Harry English, 22 Rushcliffe, Fulwell, Sunderland SR6 9RG
Tel Nos: 0191 548 7194 (H) 0191 415 2340 (W) 07889 469961 (M)   I
Programme Editio: Ian Hopper
GROUND ADDRESS: Nissan Sorts Complex, Washington Road, Sunderland SR5 3NS   **Tel:** 0191 415 2354 0r 415 2773
Capacity: **Seats:**   **Covered:**   **Floodlights:**
Simple Directions: North along A1M use A690 (signed Sunderland) connect with A19 north, after passing the A1231 turn off with plant on your left. Past plant and follow signs for Nissan office.
Midweek Home Matchday: Tuesday   **Clubhouse:** Open daily   **Club Shop:** No
Previous Names: Washington Nissan   **Previous League(s):** Wearside to 2001
Club Colours: Blue & Black stripes/Blue/Blue   **Change Colours:** Red & white/white/white

TOW LAW TOWN

Founded: 1890
Nickname: Lawyers

Chairperson: Sandra Gordon   **Manager:** Graeme Forster
Secretary: Bernard Fairbairn, 3 Coppice Walk, Mowden Park, Darlington Co.Durham DL14 9JT
Press Officer: Secretary   **Programme:** Yes
GROUND ADDRESS: Ironworks Ground, Tow Law, Bishop'sAuckland   **Ground Tel.No.:** 01388 731443
Capacity:6,000   **Seats:** 200   **Covered:** 300   **Floodlights:** Yes
Simple Directions: Just off High Street in Tow Law town centre.
Midweek Home Matchday: Tuesday   **Clubhouse:** Every Evening   **Club Shop:** Yes
Previous League(s): None
Club Colours: Black& white stripes/black   **Change Colours:** Red & white
BEST PERFORMANCES
League: Northern League Champions (3)   **F.A. Cup:** 2nd Rd Replay 67-68   **F.A.Vase:** Runners-Up 1997-98
F.A.Amateur Cup: 3rd Round Replay 1970-71
RECORD Attendance: 5,500 v Mansfield Town F.A.Cup 1967
Senior Honours: F.A.Vase Runners-Up 97-98, Rothmans National Cup 77, Northern Lg.Champions 23-24 24-25 94-95, Durham Challenge Cup 1895-96 and Durham Amateur Cup 1892-93

WEST ALLOTMENT CELTIC

Founded: 1892
Nickname: West

Chairman: Roland Mather   **Manager:** Terry Mitchell

Secretary: Ted Ilderton, 3 Waterloo Rad, Wellfield, Whitley Bay, NE25 9JF

Tel Nos: 0191 251 8825 (H) and 07795 246245 (M) email: ted966@blueyonder.co.uk

Press Officer: Name (Tel)   **Programme:**

GROUND ADDRESS: Blue Flames Sports Ground, NE12 9FA   **Ground Tel. No:** 01912702178

Simple Directions: From Newcastle take A189 to junction with A191, Follow road east for one and a half miles. Turn right immediately after Station Road (B1317) junction and traffic lights, then turn right into ground.

Midweek Home Matchday: Tuesday   **Clubhouse:**   **Club Shop:**

Club Colours: Green & white hoops/green/green   **Change Colours:** All Blue

WEST AUCKLAND TOWN

Founded: 1892
Nickname: West

airman: Jim Polfreyman   **Manager:** David Bayles   **Asst. Manager:** Lee Ellison
Secretary: Allen Bayles, 11 Edith Terrce, West Auckland, Co.Durham DL14 9JT
Tel Nos: 01388 833783 (H& Fax) 01388 605221or 01388 661366
Press Officer: Stuart Alderson (01388 834211) **Sponsors:** EBAC Ltd F.Hudson Transport
GROUND ADDRESS: Darlington Road, West Aucklnd,Co.Durham   **Tel:** 01388 834403
Capacity: 3,000   **Seats:** 250   **Covered:** 250   **Floodlights:** Yes
Simple Directions: Take A68 out o West Auckland and ground is on right . Bus from Bishop Auckland, Newcastle or Durham
Midweek Home Matchday: Tuesday   **Clubhouse:** On Ground   **Club Shop:** No
Previous Name(s): St Helens United (1919 only)   **Previous League(s):** Auckland & District
Club Colours: All white   **Change Colours:** All blue
BEST PERFORMANCES
League: Northern League Champions 59-60 60-61 **F.A. Cup:** !st Rd 58-9 61-2 98-99   **F.A.Vase:** 4th Rd 01-02
Record Attendance: 6.000 v Dulwich Hamlet F.A.Amateur Cup 1958-59
SENIOR HONOURS:F.A.Amateur Cup Finalists 60-61 Northern Champions (2),Durham Ch.Cup 53-64
Sir Thomas Lipton Trophy (First 'World Cup' as featured in Captain's Tale) 1909 1911

WHITLEY BAY

Founded: 1897
Nickname: The Bay

Chairman: Paul Mcllduff **Vice-Chairman:** Peter Siddle **President :** Sid Cope   **Press Officer:** Peter Fox (0773 982 7237)
Manager: Ian Chandler   **Assistant Manager:** Steve Cuggy   **Coach:** David Styles   **Physio:** Glen Martin
Secretary: Derek Breakwell, 27 Kings Road, Whitley Bay, Tyne & wear, NE26 3Ed **Tel. Nos:** 0191 2527940 (H) 07889 888187
Previous League: Tyneside 09-10, Northern Alliance 50-55 N.Eastern 55-58 Northern 58-88 N.P.L. 88-2000
Club Colours: Blue & white stripes/blue/blue   **Change Colours:** All Red
LAST SEASON: League: 10th   **F.A. Cup:** 1st Qualifying Round   **F.A. Vase:** 2nd Round.
Top Scorer: Lee Kerr 15   **Player of the Year:** Brian Rowe   **Captain:** Brian Rowe
BEST PERFORMANCES: League: N.P.L.Premier   **F.A. Cup:** 3rd Rd 89-90   **F.A.Vase:** Winners 2001-02
F.A.Amateur Cup: S-Final 65-66 68-69   **F.A.Trophy:** 3rd Rd 1986-87 **Previous Name:** Whitley Bay AthAthletic 1950-58
Programme: 24 Pages £1.00
GROUND ADDRESS: Hillheads Park, Rink Way off HIllheads Road, Whitley Bay Tyne & wear NE25 8HR
Te. No: 0191 291 3637 (Club) or 0191 291 3636 (Fax & Matchday office)
Capacity: 4,500   **Seats:** 450   **Covered:** 650   **Floodlights:** Yes
Simple Directions: One mile walk from town centre. Leave St Pauls Church southwards turn right at roundabout and around third left at rear of Ice Rink. One mile from Whitley Vay or Monkseaton metro stations.Buses 308,317,344,810,811
Midweek Home Matchday: Tuesday   **Clubhouse:** Open daily   **Club Shop:** Fully Stocked
RECORD Attendance: 7,301 v Hendon F.A.Am. Cup 65 **Goalscorer:** Billy Wright 307   **Apps:** Bill Chater 640
Senior Honours:N.P.L.Div 1 Champs. 90-91, Northern Lg 64-65 65-66 R-Up (4) & Nortr umberland Sen.Cup (11) R-Up (8)

ALNWICK TOWN

Secretary: Darren Middleton, 1 Fire Station Houses, Alnwick, NE66 2PB(1665 603781)
Ground: St James' Park, Alnwick, Northumberland Tel: 01665 603162
Directions: 35 miles north of Newcastle on A1, take the slip road to Alnwick,then first left. At roundabout turn left, ground is then on your left.
Capacity: 2,500   **Seats:** 100   **Cover:** 200   **Floodlights:** Yes
HONOURS Northern Lg Div 2 R-up 88-89, Northern Alliance 37-38 62-63 63-64 65-66 67-68 68-69 69-70 70-71 71-72 (R-up 59-60 61-62 66-67 72-73, Lg Cup 61-62 65-6667-68 68-69 70-71, Subsidiary Cup 80-81), Durham Central Lg Cup 64-65, Northumberland Benevolent Bowl 86-87, Northumberland SNR Cup R-up 61-62,Northumberland Amtr Cup 71-72.
PREVIOUS   **League:** Northern Alliance 35-39 46-64 64-82
     Names: Alnwick United Services; Alnwick United.
BEST SEASON
     FA Cup: 3rd Qual. Rd 51-52 (3-4 at Blyth), 57-58 (4-6 at Easington Coll.).
     FA Trophy: 3rd Qual. Rd 90-91.
RECORD   **Attendance:** 600 v Bedlington Terriers, Northern Alliance 1971.

FACT FILE
Founded: 1879
Colours: Black & white stripes/black/black
Change colours: Green and yellow
Midweek Matches: Tuesday

Local Press: Northumberland Gazette

CLUB PERSONNEL
Chairman: Alan Wilcox
Manager: Malcolm Beusle
Press Officer: Secretary

BRANDON UNITED

Founded: 1968
Nickname:United

Chairman: Bill Fisher   **Vice-Chairman:** John Dickinson   **Manager:** B.J.Heijmans   **Physio:** Alan Clark
Secretary: Ian Flint,16 Maplewood Court, Langley Park, Durham.DH7 9FZ
Tel Nos: 0191 3730940 (H) 07881 716217 (M)
Press Officer:T.B.A.   **Programme:** Yes 50p
GROUND ADDRESS: Welfare Ground, rear of Commercial Street, Brandon, Durham Tel No: 0191 378 2957
Capacity: 3,000   **Seats:** 200   **Covered:** 300   **Floodlights:**Yes   **Shop:** No
Simple Directions: A690 - 3 miles west of Durham City   Bus 50 from Durham.
Midweek Home Matchday: Wednesday   **Clubhouse:** Open every day lunch and evening. Week end entertainment
Previous Leagues: Durham & District Sunday 68-77, Northern Alliance 1977-80, Northern Amateur 80-81 & Wearside 81-83
Club Colours: All Red   **Change Colours:** All Blue
LAST SEASON
League: 18th   **F.A. Cup:** 1st Qual.Rd.   **F.A. Vase:** 2nd Qual.Rd.
Top Scorer: Kevin Shoulder   **Player of the Year:** Marc Irwin   **Captain:** Marc Irwin
RECORD Att.: 2,500 F.A.Sunday Cup   **Goalscorer:** Tommy Holden   **Apps:** Derek Charlton 1977-86
Senior Honours: Northern League Champions 2002-03 Div 2 84-85 F.A.Sunday Cup 75-76

CROOK TOWN

Secretary/Press Officer: Kieron Bennett, 4 Cloverhill,Chester le Street, Co.Durham. DH2 2LZ
Tel No: 07838 387335
Ground: Millfield Ground, West Road, Crook, County Durham (01388 762959)
Directions: 400 yds west of town centre on Wolsingham Road (A689). Nearest BR station is Bishop Auckland (5 miles). Buses 1A & 1B from Bishop Auckland or X46& X47 from Durham
Capacity: 3,500   **Seats:** 400   **Cover:** 300   **Floodlights:** Yes
Clubhouse: Lic Bar open matchdays. Hot & Cold Food available from Shop **Club Shop:** Yes
PREVIOUS   **Leagues:** Auckland & Dist. 1894-96; Northern 1896-28 29-30; Durham Central 28-29; North Eastern 30-36; Wartime Durham & North'rland 40-41;Durham Cen.41-45.
BEST SEASON FA Trophy: 3rd Rd 76-77   **FA Cup:** 3rd Rd, v Leicester 31-32. 2nd Rd (4), 1st Rd.(10) **FA Vase:** 4th Rd 99-00 **FA Amateur Cup:** Winners x 5, plus S-F x 3
HONOURS   FA Amateur Cup Winners 00-01 53-54 58-59 61-62 63-64; Northern League (5) (R-up 4) League Cup (3), (R-up 4); Durham Challenge Cup (4); Durham Benefit Bowl (6); Ernest Armstrong Memorial Trophy 1997.

FACT FILE
Formed: 1889   Nickname: Black & Ambers
Sponsors: S.T.C.H.
Colours: Amber/black/black
Change colours: All White
Midweek Matches: Wednesday
Programme: Yes   Editor: Secretary

CLUB PERSONNEL
Chairman: Stephen Buddle
Vice-Chairman: Eddie Ryan
President: SirTom Cowie O.B.E.
Joint Managers: Alan Oliver & Graeme Oliver
Physio: Jimmy Vipond

ESH WINNING

Founded: 1967
Nickname: Stags

Chairman: Charles Ryan   **Vice-Chairman:** David Parkinson   **Manager:** Steve Corden

Secretary: Alan Morton, West Terrace, Waterhouses, Esh Winning, Durham DH7 9BQ

Tel No: 0191 3733611(H) 07929747885 (M)

Programme Editor: Nigel Quinn   **Programme:** 20 Pages 50p

GROUND ADDRESS: West Terrace, Waterhouse, Durham   **Ground Tel. No:** 0191 3733872

Capacity: 3,500   **Seats:** 160   **Covered:** 500   **Floodlights:** Yes

Simple Directions: Durham via Ushaw Moor to Esh Winning. Ground is one mile further on at Waterhouses.

Midweek Home Matchday: Tuesday   **Clubhouse:** Open daily   **Club Shop:** No

Previous Names: Esh Winning Pineap[ple until 1982   **Previous Leagues:** Durham &Dist. Sunday, N.Alliance 81-2

Club Colours: Yellow & Green/green/yellow   **Change Colours:** Green & Navy

BEST PERFORMANCES

F.A. Cup: 2nd Qual Rd.90-91 04-05   **F.A.Vase:** 2nd Rd 83-84.04-05

RECORD Attendance: 900 v Liverpool Fantal F.A.Sunday Cup **Goalscorer:** Mark Drake   **Appearances:** Paul Hewitson

Senior Honours:

GUISBOROUGH TOWN

FACT FILE
Founded: 1973   Nickname: Priorymen
Sponsors: Hensons Windows & Conservatories
Colours: Red & white stripes/Black/Red
Change colours:Yellow
Midweek matchday:Wednesday
Reserves ' League: Teesside Strongarm
Programme: 32pages, 50p
Editor: Stuart Burns
Local Press: Northern Echo,
Middlesbrough Evening Gazette
CLUB PERSONNEL
Chairman: Richard Corden
Vce Chairman: Keith Watson
Press Officer: Stuart Burns
Manager: Steve Corden
Asst Manager: Tiger Wyke
Physio: Gary Hinchley

Secretary: Lesley Clark, 15 Scarteen Close, Guisborough, Cleveland TS14 7PB
    Tel: (H) 01287 281 293 (M) 07891 595 267

Ground: King George V Ground, Howlbeck Rd, Guisborough, Cleveland (01287 636 925)

Directions: From west: bear left at 2nd set of lights, left into Howlbeck Rd after quarter mile, ground at end. Buses from Middlesbrough

Capacity: 3,500   **Seats:** 150   Cover: 400   Floodlights: Yes Club Shop: Yes

Clubhouse: Open evenings & weekends. Hot & cold snacks & drinks from kitchen on matchdays

HONOURS FA Vase R-up 79-80; Northern Lg Cup 87-88 (Div 2 R-up 86-87),
Northern Alliance 79-80 (R-up 78-79, Lg Cup 78-79);
N. Riding Sen. Cup 89-90 90-91 91-92 92-93 94-95.

PREVIOUS **Leagues:** Middlesbrough & District; South Bank; Northern Alliance 77-80;
Midland Counties 80-82; Northern Counties (East) 82-85.

BEST SEASON
FA Cup: 1st Round Proper 88-89, 0-1 v Bury   **F.A.Vase:** Finalists 79-80
FA Trophy: 1st Rd Proper 90-91 91-92 92-93
CLUB RECORDS   **Gate:** 3,112 v Hungerford, FA Vase SF, 1980
(at Middlesbrough FC - 5,990 v Bury, FA Cup 1st Rd 1988) **Goalscorer:** Mark Davis 341
Appearances: Mark Davis 587 **Win:** 6-0 v Ferryhill & v Easington **Defeat:** 0-4 v Billingham Syn.

HEBBURN TOWN

FACT FILE
Founded: 1912 Nickname: Hornets
Colours: Yellow& navy stripes /navy blue
& navy blue.
Change colours:All white
Midweek Matches: Wednesday
Prog: 24 pages, 30p Ed: Steve Newton
CLUB PERSONNEL
Chairman: Bill Laffey
Vice-Chair: Brian Errington
Press Officer: Alan Armstrong
0191 483 2046
Manager: Tony Robinson
Assistant Manager: Vin Pearson
Coach: Norman Dryden
2005-2006
Player of the Year: Garry McCartney
Top Scorer: Garry McCartney
Captain: Joe Donaghy

Secretary: Iom Derrick, 63 Staneway, Felling, Gateshead, NE10 8LS.Tel: 0191 442 1563
Tel No: 0191 4421563 (H & Fax) 0191 2251444 (W)

Ground: Hebburn Sports & Social Ground, Victoria Road West, Hebburn Tel: 0191 483 5101

Directions: On the main road through the town about 1 mile from railway station. Hebburn lies on the Metroline - excellent bus service from Heworth Metro **Clubhouse:** 7-11 mon,11am-1pm Sat and 12-2.0 p.m. Sun.Pool ,darts etc.**Ground Capacity:** 2,000 **Seats:**153 **Cover:**420 **Lights**:Yes

PREVIOUSLeagues: Jarrow & Dist. Jnr 12-14; S Shields Comb. 19-22; Tyneside Comb. 22-27;
Tyneside 27-39; Northern Comb. 41-44 45-59; North Eastern 44-45 59-60; Wearside 60-89.

Names: Reyrolles; Hebburn Reyrolles (pre-1988), Hebburn 88-00 **Club Shop:** No

HONOURS Shields Gazette Cup 91-92, Wearside Lg 66-67 (Monkwearmouth Charity Cup 68-69), Durham Challenge Cup 42-43 91-92, Tyneside Lg 38-39, Northern Comb. 43-44, Gateshead Charity Cup 35-36 37-38, Palmer Hospital Cup 27-28, Hebburn Aged Miners Cup 35-36, Heddon Homes Cup 42-43, Hebburn Infirmary Cup 35-36 36-37 37-38 38-39, Craven Cup 99-00.

BEST SEASON FA Vase: 2nd Rd 91-92 **FA Cup:** 2nd Qual. Rd rep. 89-90, 0-3 v South Bank (A)

RECORD Attendance: 503 v Darwen, FA Cup Prel. Rd replay 7/9/91 **Win:** 10-1 **Defeat** 3-10

MARSKE UNITED

FACT FILE
Founded: 1956   Nickname: The Seasiders
Colours: Yellow/royalblue/white
Change: Royal/sky/yellow
Midweek matchday: Wednesday
Programme: 60 pages 50p
Editor: Moss Holtby (01642 475612)
Local Press: Sunday Sun, Middlesbrough
Evening Gazette, Northern Echo
CLUB PERSONNEL
Chairman: John Hodgson
Vice Chairmperson: Janet Pippen
President: Raymond Jarvis
Commercial Manager: John nHodgson
Manager: Darren Trotter
Assistant Manager: Mark Williams
Physios: James Atkinson
Coaches: Darren Trotter &Mark Williams
Kit Manager: Colin Gilbert

Secretary: Ian Rowe, 19 High Row, Loftus, Saltburn By The Sea, Cleveland. TS134SA
& Press Officer Tel: 01287 643440 (H) 01642 230546 (B) 01642 241273 (Fax)

Ground: Mount Pleasant, Mount Pleasant Ave., Marske, Redcar, Cleveland. Tel: 01642 471091

Directions: From A19 take A174 exit marked Yarm, Teesport, Redcar, Whitby and head east towards Saltburn until Quarry Lane r/about. Take 1st left (A1085) into Marske, 1st right (Meadow Rd) then 1st left (Southfield Rd),then 1st left again Mount Pleasant Ave directly into car park. By train: Darlington to Saltburn, Marske station 300 yds from ground.

Capacity: 2,500   Seats: 169   Cover: 300   Floodlights: Yes

Clubhouse: Open every night and weekend lunchtimes. Food served after all games
Contact : Janet Pippen (01642 474985)

HONOURS N Riding Sen Cup 94-95; N Riding County Cup 80-81 85-86; Teesside Lg 80-81 84-85; Wearside Lg 95-96, R-up 93-94 94-95 96-97, Cup 92-93 94-95 95-96; M/mouth Charity Cup 93-94 95-96; Sunderland Ship. Cup 95-96 96-97.N.Lg Cup R-up: 00-01

PREVIOUS **Leagues:** Cleveland & South Bank 56-76, Teesside 76-85, Wearside 85-97.

BEST SEASON FA Cup: 2nd Qual Rd., 00-01   **FA Vase:** Qtr Final replay, 00-01

RECORDS **Attendance:** 1,359 v Bedlington Terriers (F.A.Vase) **Win:** 16-0 v North Shields
Defeat: 3-9 **Goalscorer:** Chris Morgan 169 **Appearances:** Mike Kinnair 583

NORTH SHIELDS

Secretary: Dave Thompson, 38 Barnstable Road, North Shields. Tel: 0191 259 0249

Ground: Ralph Gardner Park, West Percy Rd., N.Shields, Tyne & Wear, NE29 OES

Directions: South: Through Tyne Tunnel, follow signs to North Shields. Travel along Howden Rd (A187) past N.Shields sports centre on left. Continue to next r'about and take 2nd left onto Coach Lane (sign posted Tynemouth) then take 4th left into West Percy Rd. Ground on left, entrance next left. West: From Newcastle take A1058 Coast Rd. At Billy Mill r-about turn right, signed N.Shields, continue over min r-about towards Town Centre. At next r'about (Collingwood Arms) turn right, then second left, ground on left.

Clubhouse: Yes

HONOURS: FA Amateur Cup 68-69, Northern Lge 68-69, N.C.E. Prem. Div. 91-92, R-up 89-90, 90-91, Lge. Cup 90-91,Wearside Lge 98-99, 01-02 03-04. R-up 00-1. Sunderland Shipowners Cup 98-99.03-04 Presidents Cup 91-92. Monkwearmouth Charity Cup 00-01. Northumberland Senior Bowl 98-99, 00-01.

Founded: 1896
Nickname: Robins
Sponsors: Beacon Centre/E.D.S./Quadrant
Colours: All red
Change colours: Blue & black/black/black

Chairman: Alan Matthews.
Treasurer:Mike Taylor
Manager: Wilf Keilty

2005-06
Captain: David Little.
Players of the Year:
Anthony Robson & Mark Cass
Leading Scorer: Eddie Miller

NORTON & STOCKTON ANCIENTS

Secretary: June Teasdale, 8 Sheraton House, Norton Hall, Stockton TS 20 1GB

Tel No: 0774573 4430

Ground: Norton (Teesside) Sports Complex,Station Road, Norton, Stockton-on-Tees, Cleveland (01642 530203) Clubhouse (01642 5540310) Norton Trust (01642 361974)

Directions: Norton village is two miles from Stockton centre, turn into Station Road on outskirts of village to rail crossing and turn left.

Capacity: 2,000   **Seats:** 200   **Cover:** Yes   **Floodlights:** Yes

Clubhouse: Full bar facilities, 150 yds from ground

HONOURS Northern Lg Cup 81-82

PREVIOUS Leagues: Teesside (pre-1982) **Name:** Norton & Stockton Cricket Club Trust

BEST SEASON   **FA Cup:** 1st Qual Rd (4) 88-89 90-93   **FA Vase:**

RECORD   **Attendance:** 1,430 v Middlesbrough, Friendly 88

FACT FILE
Formed: 1959 Nickname: Ancients
Colours: Amber&black/black /black
Change: All Yellow
Midweek Matches: Wednesday
Programme: 12 pages with entry
Club Website:www nortonfootball .co.uk
CLUB PERSONNEL
Chairman: Peter Aldridge Pres: Barry Lee
Press Officer: Ken Steele (01642 898787)
Manager: Ray Morton Asst : Brian Maitland
Coach & Physio Alan Gauifant

PENRITH

Secretary: Walter Brogden, 47 Folly Lane, Penrith, Cumbria CA11 8BU (01768 862551)
Ground: Southend Road Ground, Penrith, Cumbria
Tel: 01768 895990
Directions: M6 Jct 40, onto dual carriageway to Appleby & Scotch Corner, first left at next r'bout, approx 1/2 mile into Penrith on A6 into town, take 1st left for ground. 3/4 mile from Penrith (BR)
Capacity: 4,000   **Seats:** 200   **Cover:** 1,000   **Floodlights:** Yes
Clubhouse: Yes   **Club Shop:** No

RECORD   **Attendance:** 2,100 v Chester 1981
Goalscorer: C Short   **Appearances:** Lee Armstrong
Win: 13-2 v Parton Utd   **Defeat:** 0-13 v Bishop Auckland
Fee paid: £750 for A Carruthers (Netherfield)
Fee received: £1,000 for B Brown (Queen of the South)

SENIOR HONOURS Northern League R-up 61-62, Div 2 Champions 02-03; NW Co's Lg R-up 83-84; Cumberland Snr Cup [14], Craven Cup 2000-01, 05-06

PREVIOUS Leagues: Carlisle & Dist., Northern 48-82, NWC. 82-87 90-97, NPL 87-90.

FACT FILE
Founded: 1894
Sponsors: Arngrove Nickname: Blues
Colours: Blue/white/blue
Change colours: All yellow
Midweek Matches: Tuesday
Reserve team: No
Programme: 24 pages, 70p
Press Officer: Secretary
Local Press: Cumberland & Westmorland Herald, Cumberland News
CLUB PERSONNEL
Chairman: David Noble
Vice Chairman:Walter Brogden
Manager: David Heslop
Captain: Philip Thornton
2005-2006
Top Scorer: Dan Broadley
Player of the Year:Mark Jones

PRUDHOE TOWN

Secretary: Chris Lowther, 10 Westhills,Tantobie, Stanley, Co.Durham DH9 9RZ
Tel: 01207 230108
Ground: Kimberley Park, Broomhouse Road, Prudhoe, Northumberland NE42 5EH
Tel/Fax: 01661 835900 **Clubhouse:**Open evenings plus Sat/Sun lunchtimes
Directions: To Prudhoe along A695, turn right at `Falcon' Inn, 200 yds down Eastwood Rd., left into Broomhouse Rd., ground on right
Capacity: 5,000   **Seats:** 150   **Cover:** Yes   **Floodlights:** Yes
HONOURS Hexham & Dist. Lg 68-69 (Lg Cup 68-69), Newcastle & Dist. Lg 69-70 70-71, Lg Cup 69-70, Charity Shield 69-70 70-71), Northern Comb. 79-80, Northern   AmtrLg 71-72, Clayton Charity Cup 68-69, Northumberland Minor Cup 78-79, Northumberland Benevolent Bowl 79-80, Heddon Homes Charity Cup 81-82
PREVIOUS Leagues: Hexham & Dist 59-69; Newcastle & Dist 69-71; N. Comb.; Northern Amateur Alliance. 84-88
RECORD   **Attendance:** 2,500 v Blyth, N'mberland Snr Cup 1981

FACT FILE
Founded: 1959 Nickname: Citizens
Sponsors: Swinton Insurance
Colours: Orange/blue/orange
Change: White & blue chevrons/navy/sky
Midweek Matches: Tuesday
Prog 8 pages, 50p Ed: Rachel Lowther
CLUB PERSONNEL
Chairman: Alex Waters
Press Officer:ErnieGoodfellow (01661 836941)
Man: Gavin Liddle Asst. Man: Steven Burns
Physio: Ernie Goodfellow
Captain: Warren Fisher

PRUDHOE TOWN

FACT FILE

Secretary:	Chris Lowther, 10 Westhills,Tantobie, Stanley, Co.Durham DH9 9RZ
	Tel: 01207 230108
Ground:	Kimberley Park, Broomhouse Road, Prudhoe, Northumberland NE42 5EH
	Tel/Fax: 01661 835900 **Clubhouse:**Open evenings plus Sat/Sun lunchtimes
Directions:	To Prudhoe along A695, turn right at `Falcon' Inn, 200 yds down Eastwood
	Rd., left into Broomhouse Rd., ground on right
Capacity:	5,000 Seats: 150 Cover: Yes Floodlights: Yes

HONOURS Hexham & Dist. Lg 68-69 (Lg Cup 68-69), Newcastle & Dist. Lg 69-70 70-71,
Lg Cup 69-70, Charity Shield 69-70 70-71), Northern Comb. 79-80, Northerm   AmtrLg
71-72, Clayton Charity Cup 68-69, Northumberland Minor Cup 78-79, Northumberland
Benevolent Bowl 79-80, Heddon Homes Charity Cup 81-82

PREVIOUS **Leagues:** Hexham & Dist 59-69; Newcastle & Dist 69-71; N. Comb.;
Northern Amateur Alliance. 84-88

RECORD **Attendance:** 2,500 v Blyth, N'mberland Snr Cup 1981

Founded: 1959 Nickname: Citizens
Sponsors: Swinton Insurance
Colours: Orange/blue/orange
Change: White & blue chevrons/navy/sky
Midweek Matches: Tuesday
Prog 8 pages, 50p Ed: Rachel Lowther

CLUB PERSONNEL
Chairman: Alex Waters
Press Officer:
ErnieGoodfellow (01661 836941)
Manager: Gavin Liddle
Asst. Man: Steven Burns
Physio: Ernie Goodfellow
Captain: Warren Fisher

RYTON

Founded: 1970
Nickname:

Chairman: Michael Williams   **Vice-Chairman:**

Manager: Alan Patterson   **Coach:** Martin Kinsopp   **Captain:** David Hagan

Secretary: Steve Murray, 21 ST Cuthberts Park, Marley Hill, Newcastle upon TyneNE16 5EO

Tel No: 0191 496 0690 (H) 07970 201 640 (M)

Press Officer: Name (Tel)   **Programme:** Pages - ?? Price - ?? Editor (Tel)

GROUND ADDRESS: Kingsley Park, Stannerford Road, Crawcrook, Tyne & Wear NE40 3SN   **Tel:** 0191 413 4448

Capacity: 2,000   **Seats:**   **Covered:**   **Floodlights:**

Simple Directions: Travel north on A1 turn off for Blaydon then third exit from rooundabout. tTavel through Ryton & Crawcrook and then right at crossroads towards Wylam. Ground is on the right.

Midweek Home Matchday: Tuesday   **Clubhouse:** Yes   **Club Shop:** No

Previous Leagues: Northern Combination and Northern Alliance

Club Colours: Blue& Black/Blac   **Change Colours:** Orange and Black

RECORD Attendance: 1,800 v Newxastle United 1998

SEAHAM RED STAR

FACT FILE

Secretary:	John Smith, 33 Frederick St.,Seaham, Co.Durham.SR7 7HX Tel: 0191 5810423 H& W
Ground:	Seaham Town Park, Stockton Road, Seaham, Co. Durham (0191 581 1347)
Directions:	From Tyne Tunnel: A19 Teeside approx 8 miles; B1404 Seaham slip road, left at top
	of slip road. Right at traffic lights & first left past school into ground
Capacity:	4,000 Seats: 60 Cover: 200 Floodlights: Yes
Club Shop:	No
Clubhouse:	Mon-Sat 11am-11pm, Sun 12-2, 7-10.30pm Bars & restaurant, snooke & pool

HONOURS Northern Lg Cup 92-93, Phillips F'lit Tphy 78-79, Durham Chal. Cup 79-80,
Wearside Lg 81-82 (Lg Cup 81-82, Div 2 R-up 87-88, Monkwearmouth Charity Cup
R-up 79-80).

PREVIOUS **Name:** Seaham Colliery Welfare Red Star 78-87
Leagues: Sunday f'tball; Houghton & Dist. 73-74; Northern Alliance74-79; Wearside 79-83.

BEST SEASON **FA Cup:**   **FA Vase:** 5th Rd 78-79
FA Trophy 2nd Rd 89-90

RECORDS Gate: 1,500 v Guisborough, Wearside Lg & v Sunderland, floodlight opener 1979
Scorer: Tom Henderson   **Appearances:** Michael Whitfield

Formed: 1973   Nickname: The Star
Colours: Red & white stripes/blacjk/black
Change colours: All blue
Midweek matchday: Wednesday
Reserves ' League: Banks Youth League
Programme: 20 pages
Editor: David Copeland (0191 581 8514)

CLUB PERSONNEL
Chairman: JohnSmith
President: Michael English
Press Officer: Secretary (079030 33014)
Manager: Chris Copeland
Asst Man.: Paul Walker
Physio: Allan Jackson

SOUTH SHIELDS F.C.

FACT FILE

Secretary:	Philip Reay, 114 Bsil Way, South Shields,Tyne & Wear NE34 8UF(0191 5369159)
Ground:	Mariners Club, Filtrona Pk, Shaftesbury Ave, Jarrow, T. & W.r
	NE349PH(.01914279839)
Directions:	From A1(M) take A194(M) to South Shields, A194 town centre road for 5
	miles,ignore A1300 (Sunderland & coast) & turn left at next lights beside Co-op
	store into Simonside Ind. Est. (Shaftesbury Ave.), ground at bottomon right.
Capacity:	2,500 Seats: 150 Cover: 400 Floodlights: Yes
Clubhouse:	Two function suites, club kitchen **Club Shop:** Yes

HONOURS Northern Lge Div 2 R-up 95-96, Northern Alliance 74-75 75-76, Wearside Lg 76-
77 92-93 94-95, Monkwearmouth Charity Cup 86-87 (R-up 94-95), Shipowners Cup
92-93 (R-up 83-84)), Durham Chal. Cup 76-77 R-up 94-95.

BEST SEASON   **FA Vase** QF 75-76
PREVIOUS **Leagues:** Northern Alliance 74-76   **Ground:** Jack Clarke Park 74-92
RECORD   **Attendance:** 1,500 v Spennymoor, Durham Challenge Cup Final 94-95
L ocal Press: Shields Gazette, Newcastle Journal, Chronicle

Founded: 1974   Nickname: Mariners
Colours: Claret & blue/white/white
Change: All white
Midweek matchday: Tuesday
Reserve team: None
Programme: 60p Editor: Phil Raey

CLUB PERSONNEL
Chairman: John Rundle
Vice Chairman:T.B.A.
Press Officer: Secretary
Manager: Ray Lish
Asst Manager:Paul Bryson
Physio: Jim Wilkinson

SPENNYMOOR TOWN

Founded: 1890
Re-formed 2005

Chairman: Alan Murray   **Vice-Chairman:** Alan Courtney
Manager: Ken Houlahan   **Asst.Manager**: Peter Carey   **Coach**: Rob Spink   **Physio:** Mark Gibbons
Secretary: Allison Houlahan, The Aitches, 4 Close House Village, Bishop Auckland, Co.Durham DL14 8RR
Tel No: 01388 776633 (H) 07776 243178 (M) **Programme:** 48 pages £1.00   **Editor:** T.B.A.
GROUND ADDRESS: Brewery Field, Durham Road, Spennymoor, Co.Durham DL16 6JN   **Tel. No:** 01388811934
Capacity: 7,500   **Seats:** 300   **Covered:** 2,000   **Floodlights:** Yes
Simple Directions: From A167 North -leave at Croxdale (N.E.S.S. Factory) turn right into Durham Road (with cemetery on left). Ground is half a mile on the right.
Midweek Home Matchday: Tuesday   **Clubhouse:** Yes   **Club Shop:** To open soon.
Previous Name: Evenwood Town
Previous League (as Evenwood Town): Barnard Castle & Dist., Auckland & Dist., Wear Valley, Gaunless Valley, South Durham 1927-28 Northern League 1927-2005
Club Colours: Black & white stripes /black/black   **Change Colours:** All Red
LAST SEASON League: 5th   **F.A. Cup:** Extra Preliminary Round   **F.A. Vase:** 1st Qualifying Round
Top Scorer: Steven Houlahan   **Player of the Year:** Martin Houlahan   **Captain:** Ian Lowe
BEST PERFORMANCES League: Northern Champions 48-49 69-70 70-71   **F.A. Cup:** 1st Rd 1936
RECORD Attendance (as Evenwood Town) 9.000 v Bishop Auckland F.A.Amateur Cup 1931
Senior Honours: Northern League (3) Durham Challenge Cup 1969-70

STOKESLEY SPORTS CLUB

Ground: Stokesley Sports Club, Broughton Road, Stokesley. TS9 5JQ
       Tel: 01642 710051

Colours: Red & black/black/black
Midweek Matches: Wednesday

PREVIOUS Leagues: Wearside League 1999-2006.

HONOURS: Stokesley & District League 1975-76.

SUNDERLAND RYHOPE (Kenneck Ryhope CA)

Secretary: Owen Hayley, 34 Charter Drive,EastHerrington,Sunderland,Tyne &WearSR6 9RG
Tel Nos: 01915200827(H) 0191 4152340 (W) 07960 198838 (M)
Ground: Meadow Park,Beachbrooke, Stockton Road, Ryhope, Sunderland
       Tel No: 0191 523 6555
Directions: Ground on Waterworks Road near Ryhope & Cherry Knowle Hospitals.
       From Sunderland follow signs for A19 South
Capacity: 2,000   Seats: 150   Cover: 200   Floodlights: Yes
HONOURS   Northern League Div 2 R-Up 1981 and Northern Alliance League Cup1981.
PREVIOUS   **Names:** Ryhope Community Association F.C. amalgamted with Kennek Roker
       from Wearside League in 1999
Leagues: S. C. Vaux: Tyne & Wear; NorthEastern Amateur as Ryhope CA N.Alliance > 82
BEST SEASON F. A Cup 4th Q Rd 88-89 **FA Vase** 2nd Rd 1985 **F.A.Trophy:** 3rd Rd 86

FACT FILE
Founded: 1988
Colours: Red & white stripes/black/red
Change Colours: Claret & Sky
BlueMidweek Matchday:Wednesday
Prog 80p Pages:24 Ed: Owen Haley

CLUB PERSONNEL
Chairman: W.Mathieson
Tel: 0191 534 5496
Presidents: Ray Baines & Norman Taylor
Press Officer: Secretary
Manager:Tony Metcalfe
Physio: Ian Palfreyman

TEAM NORTHUMBRIA

Ground: Coach Lane Sports Ground, Coach Lane, Benton, Newcastle Upon Tyne . Tel: (0191) 2156575

Colours: White/black/black

Midweek Matches: Tuesday

PREVIOUS Names: Northumbria University >2003.   **Leagues:** Northern Alliance 1999-2006.

THORNABY

Founded: 1980
Nickname:

Chairman: Lol Lyons   **Vice-Chairman:**
Manager: Michael Watson   **Assistant Manager:** Peter May   **Physio:** Paul Sharkey
Secretary: Peter Morris, 20 Wheatear Road, Ingleby Barwick, Stockton-on-Tees, Clevelend TS17 0TB
Tel. No.: 01642 760779
Press Officer: Paul Beards (01642 897861)   **Programme:**
GROUND ADDRESS:Teesdale Park, Acklam Road,Thornaby, Stockton-on-Tees TS17 0TB   **Tel:** 01642 606803
Capacity: 5,000   **Seats:** 150   **Covered:** 350   **Floodlights:** Yes
Simple Directions: A19 to Thornaby turn off, ground half mile on right. One mile from Thornaby BR
Midweek Home Matchday: Tuesday   **Clubhouse:** Open daily with full social facilities for hire.**Club Shop:** No
Previous Names: Stockuon Cricket Club 65-80 Stockton 80-99 and Thornaby- on-Tees99-2000
Previous League(s): Stockton & Dist.,80-1 Wearside 81-85
Club Colours: Blue & white /white/white   **Change Colours:** All Sky blue
BEST PERFORMANCES: League: Northern **F.A. Cup:** 4th Qualifying Round   **F.A.Vase:** 3rd Round
RECORD Attendance: 3,000 v Middlesbrough friendly August 1986 **Goalscorer:**   **Appearances:** Michael Watson
Victory: 11-0 v Horden C.W. (Buchanan Cup) 1994-95
Senior Honours: North Riding County Cup : 1985-86

WASHINGTON F.C.

FACT FILE
Founded: 1949
Nickname: Mechanics
Colours: Red/black/red
Change colours: Yellow'Blue
Midweek Matches: Wednesday
Programme: 8 pages, 50p
Editor: Rob Goodwin

Secretary: Barry Spendley, 16 Raglan Oxclose, Washington, Tyne & Wear NE38 0LE

Tel: (H) 0191 415 5980 (B) 0191 417 7779

Ground: Albany Park, Spout Lane, Concord, Washington, Tyne & Wear NE37 2AB

Tel: 0191 417 7779

Directions: Ground situated opposite bus station.

Capacity: 3,000   Seats: 25   Cover: Yes Floodlights: Yes Club Shop: No

Clubhouse: Open normal licensing hours, with live entertainment, pool etc

PREVIOUS Leagues: Washington Amateur; Northern Alliance 67-68; Wearside 68-88

Ground: Usworth Welfare Park

RECORD   Gate: 3,800 v Bradford Park Avenue, FA Cup 1970

CLUB PERSONNEL
Chairman: Derek Armstrong
Tel: 0191 416 3956 (H)
Press Officer:John Oliver
Tel: 0191 416 3527
Manager:John Oliver
Captain: Kevin Leighton
Physio:Craig Langley

WHICKHAM

FACT FILE
Founded: 1944
Colours: Black & White stripes/ Black/Black
Change colours: All white
Midweek Matches: Wednesday Prog20p
Local Press : Newcastle Journal, Sunday
Sun, Evening Chronicle

Secretary: John Farrey, 61 Cherrytree Drive, Whickham, Newcastle upon Tyne. NE 16 4TQ
Ground: Glebe Ground, Rectory Lane, Whickham (0191 420 0186)
Directions: A692 (Consett) from A69. Left at r'bout signed Consett/Whickham. Uphill and right at mini-r'bout. Turn left into Rectory Lane (by Lloyds Bank) for 500 yds, club house on right
Capacity: 4,000   Seats: 100   Cover: Yes Floodlights: Yes
Clubhouse: Mon-Fri. 12-3 & 7-11, Sat.11-11, Sun. 12-2, 7.30-11   Souvenir Shop: No
HONOURS   FA Vase 80-81, Wearside Lg 77-78 87-88 (R-up 80-81 84-85, Lg Cup 86-87, Monkwearmouth Charity Cup 76-77, Sunderland Shipowners Cup 77-78 80-81), Northern Comb. 69-70 72-73 73-74 (Lg Cup 60-61 73-74)
PREVIOUS   Leagues: Derwent Valley -55; Northern Comb. 55-57 59-74; Tyneside Amtr 57-59; Wearside 74-88   **Ground:** Rectory Rec. Field
BEST SEASON FA Cup: 1st Qual. Rd. 89-90   **FA Vase:** Winners 80-81
RECORD   Gate: 3,165 v Windsor & Eton, F.A. Vase SF 81

CLUB PERSONNEL
Chairman: Brian Smith Manager: Toiny Ainley
Press Officer: Tony Ainley
Captain: Kris Holmes
2005-2006
P.o.Y.:Michael Hedley
Top Goalscorer: Ian Robson

SPARTAN SOUTH MIDLANDS

President: B F Smith **Chairman:** Pat Burns

Hon. Gen. Secretary: M Mitchell, 26 Leighton Court, Dunstable, Beds. LU6 1EW Tel: 01582 667291

PREMIER DIVISION	P	W	D	L	F	A	Pts
1. Oxford City	38	27	7	4	91	41	88
2. Hillingdon Borough	38	28	4	6	80	41	88
3. Hanwell Town	38	24	6	8	95	45	78
4. Harefield United	38	23	9	6	81	38	78
5. Aylesbury Vale	38	23	5	10	79	52	74
6. Leverstock Green	38	18	9	11	64	51	63
7. Holmer Green	38	18	7	13	69	59	61
8. Welwyn Garden City	38	16	10	12	59	45	58
9. Biggleswade United (3rd Div.1 04-05)	38	16	7	15	60	54	55
10. Tring Athletic	38	12	12	14	40	39	48
11. Broxbourne Boro V&E	38	14	5	19	66	63	47
12. St Margaretsbury	38	13	7	18	61	57	46
13. Oxhey Jets (1st Div.1 04-05)	38	12	8	18	54	60	44
14. London Colney	38	11	8	19	49	68	41
15. Biggleswade Town	38	11	8	19	52	74	41
16. Ruislip Manor	38	10	8	20	44	56	38
17. Langford	38	11	3	24	51	102	36
18. Royston Town	38	10	5	23	39	86	35
19. Haringey Borough	38	8	4	26	34	86	28
20. Harpenden Town	38	6	6	26	33	84	24

PREMIER DIVISION	1	2	3	4	5	6	7	8	9	10	11	12	13	14	15	16	17	18	19	20
1 Aylesbury Vale		2-1	1-0	1-4	2-0	3-1	3-2	1-0	0-1	2-0	6-0	1-5	3-2	1-0	2-1	8-0	1-1	2-0	4-2	3-2
2 Biggleswade Town	0-0		2-1	0-3	1-2	0-7	2-2	2-1	1-3	2-1	1-2	3-3	2-1	1-3	2-1	2-1	2-1	0-4	0-1	1-0
3 Biggleswade United	1-2	3-1		2-0	1-6	1-1	3-2	2-2	0-0	1-2	0-1	0-3	3-0	1-2	1-3	2-0	1-0	3-1	0-0	1-1
4 Broxbourne Borough V&E	2-3	3-3	1-3		1-3	1-2	2-0	2-0	2-3	3-1	2-3	3-4	1-3	1-1	3-0	4-0	2-1	0-0	2-1	1-0
5 Hanwell Town	2-1	3-1	1-2	1-0		0-2	3-1	4-1	3-1	4-2	8-1	4-0	6-1	1-2	3-1	8-1	3-2	3-2	2-0	1-2
6 Harefield United	1-0	2-1	2-0	4-1	0-1		3-0	0-0	2-1	2-3	3-1	0-0	4-0	2-3	1-0	6-0	0-0	3-0	2-3	3-1
7 Haringey Borough	0-1	1-1	2-1	1-3	2-1	1-2		0-1	1-3	1-2	0-3	0-0	1-0	0-3	2-1	3-1	1-3	2-1	1-0	0-3
8 Harpenden Town	1-4	1-0	1-3	4-2	1-3	0-0	1-2		0-1	2-3	2-4	0-0	2-1	0-6	1-3	1-2	1-0	1-1	2-1	1-2
9 Hillingdon Borough	3-1	1-0	2-2	3-2	2-1	1-2	4-0	3-1		2-1	5-2	3-0	2-3	2-2	2-1	2-0	2-1	1-2	3-1	1-1
10 Holmer Green	0-0	3-5	1-4	1-1	1-1	1-1	7-1	4-0	1-2		2-0	1-4	3-1	0-1	2-1	1-1	3-1	0-3	2-1	1-2
11 Langford	3-4	0-4	0-3	1-6	0-3	0-3	1-0	3-0	0-2	1-4		1-2	0-2	1-3	3-4	3-1	1-2	1-1	0-1	2-0
12 Leverstock Green	1-4	1-4	1-2	3-0	0-3	2-2	5-0	2-0	2-1	1-1	3-1		4-1	0-3	3-2	1-0	2-2	1-0	2-2	1-1
13 London Colney	1-1	4-2	0-3	2-1	1-1	1-1	3-0	3-1	0-3	1-2	2-2	1-0		0-0	2-0	3-4	0-2	1-2	0-1	0-1
14 Oxford City	3-2	5-1	3-1	1-0	1-1	6-3	4-0	2-0	2-3	1-1	6-3	1-0	3-1		1-4	1-0	6-3	1-3	2-1	2-0
15 Oxhey Jets	2-2	1-0	1-1	3-1	3-0	3-4	2-1	0-0	0-3	1-2	1-2	2-1	1-1	0-2		5-2	0-0	2-1	0-0	0-3
16 Royston Town	1-0	3-2	2-1	1-1	0-2	1-2	3-0	3-1	0-1	1-4	3-0	0-1	1-1	2-2	2-1		1-2	0-1	0-4	0-0
17 Ruislip Manor	0-3	1-1	1-3	2-1	0-1	1-2	2-1	3-1	2-3	0-3	1-1	0-1	5-0	0-1	2-0	0-2		2-1	1-1	0-1
18 St Margaretsbury	2-4	2-0	1-3	1-2	2-2	0-1	4-1	7-1	1-2	1-2	9-0	0-3	0-4	0-3	2-2	1-0	0-0		0-1	1-1
19 Tring Athletic	2-0	0-0	3-0	0-2	1-1	1-1	2-2	2-1	0-1	0-1	0-2	1-0	0-0	0-1	0-0	2-0	2-0	1-2		1-1
20 Welwyn Garden City	5-1	1-1	2-1	1-0	3-3	0-4	2-0	3-0	1-2	3-0	3-2	1-2	0-2	2-2	0-2	7-0	1-0	1-2	1-1	

DIVISION ONE

	DIVISION ONE	P	W	D	L	F	A	Pts
1.	Colney Heath	32	26	3	3	106	27	81
2.	Brache Sparta	32	23	3	6	76	38	72
3.	Stony Stratford Town	32	20	6	6	90	42	66
4.	New Bradwell St Peter	32	16	4	12	60	54	52
5.	Brimsdown Rovers	32	15	6	11	52	50	51
6.	Arlesey Athletic	32	15	5	12	71	57	50
7.	Hoddesdon Town	32	14	6	12	64	50	48
8.	Cockfosters	32	14	6	12	63	61	48
9.	Sun Postal Sports	32	13	5	14	58	61	44
10.	Bedford Utd & Valerio (-3)	32	15	2	15	52	86	44
11.	Kentish Town	32	11	8	13	65	68	41
12.	Dunstable Town '98	32	12	5	15	58	62	41
13.	Buckingham Athletic	32	12	4	16	46	54	40
14.	Winslow United	32	9	6	17	48	73	33
15.	Cranfield United	32	7	4	21	36	68	25
16.	Ampthill Town	32	6	3	23	43	90	21
17.	Amersham Town	32	4	4	23	30	77	16

DIVISION ONE		1	2	3	4	5	6	7	8	9	10	11	12	13	14	15	16	17
1	Amersham Town		3-2	1-5	1-1	0-1	0-0	0-2	0-2	1-3	1-3	3-1	3-0	1-2	0-4	1-5	2-3	1-2
2	Ampthill Town	0-0		2-2	0-3	1-4	2-1	2-3	0-1	1-5	4-0	0-1	1-0	0-2	1-3	3-6	2-3	0-5
3	Arlesey Athletic	1-0	4-3		14-0	0-4	4-0	3-1	3-6	1-1	4-1	2-1	1-7	1-3	2-0	3-0	0-0	2-3
4	Bedford United & Valerio	4-1	1-4	1-0		1-0	4-1	1-3	1-2	0-6	1-0	4-2	2-1	4-1	1-0	0-2	1-0	2-5
5	Brache Sparta	1-0	6-1	2-1	2-1		5-3	3-0	1-1	1-0	2-0	4-2	2-1	4-1	5-2	1-3	2-0	2-0
6	Brimsdown Rovers	5-3	1-1	1-0	3-1	3-1		0-2	0-4	1-4	2-0	3-0	1-2	1-1	1-2	3-2	2-1	2-0
7	Buckingham Athletic	2-0	2-1	2-4	0-2	2-0	2-1		4-5	0-3	0-1	1-3	2-0	0-3	3-4	1-2	1-0	3-0
8	Cockfosters	4-1	5-2	0-2	2-3	1-3	2-3	2-1		1-3	1-1	0-3	0-0	3-2	0-2	1-1	2-2	3-1
9	Colney Heath	1-0	4-1	4-2	4-1	1-0	1-1	0-2	3-0		3-1	4-1	4-0	6-0	3-0	3-4	6-2	4-1
10	Cranfield United	2-0	2-3	0-2	0-3	3-2	1-2	1-1	2-4	0-2		2-1	0-1	2-4	0-1	0-3	3-0	3-3
11	Dunstable Town 98	4-1	4-0	0-2	2-1	2-2	1-3	3-3	2-2	2-4	2-0		1-2	1-1	2-3	3-2	3-2	3-2
12	Hoddesdon Town	2-1	6-1	2-0	8-1	1-1	0-1	2-1	3-1	0-3	1-1	3-1		3-3	3-2	1-1	6-1	2-1
13	Kentish Town	1-2	3-0	5-1	1-1	2-3	1-3	3-0	1-2	0-4	3-4	1-1	2-1		6-0	3-3	1-1	1-2
14	New Bradwell St Peter	7-2	3-2	1-1	2-1	1-2	0-0	2-1	4-2	2-5	3-0	0-2	3-0	1-2		3-1	0-1	1-1
15	Stony Stratford Town	4-0	4-0	4-0	9-2	3-5	2-2	2-0	3-0	0-0	2-0	2-0	3-2	4-0	2-2		3-1	4-1
16	Sun Postal Sports	1-1	2-1	0-2	9-0	0-3	0-2	1-1	2-3	1-4	4-1	2-1	3-2	6-3	2-1	1-0		3-2
17	Winslow United	2-0	1-2	2-2	1-3	1-2	1-0	0-0	2-1	0-8	3-2	1-3	2-2	3-3	0-1	0-4	0-4	

FIRST ROUND

Aylesbury Vale	v Amersham Town	6-0
Leverstock Green	v St Margaretsbury	3-4
Oxhey Jets	v Hanwell Town	
Tie Awarded to Oxhey Jets		
Haringey Borough	v Crawley Green	0-1
Aston Clinton	v AFC Dunstable	1-2
Dunstable Town '98	v Loughton Orient	6-0
New Bradwell St Peter	v Markyate	6-1
Kent Athletic	v The 61FC (Luton)	3-0
Biggleswade Town	v Welwyn Garden City	3-1
Royston Town	v Buckingham Athletic	1-2 aet
Totternhoe	v Mursley United	1-2
Harpenden Town	v Hillingdon Borough	0-4
Sun Postal Sports	v Cockfosters	1-5 aet
Brache Sparta	v Kentish Town	3-0
Brxbourne Boro V&E	v Ruislip Manor	1-3
Bedford Utd&Valerio	v Ampthill Town	1-4
Harefield United	v Colney Heath	3-1
Holmer Green	v Caddington	3-1
Biggleswade United	v MK Scot	2-1
Padbury United	v Oxford City	0-9
Stony Stratford T.	v Langford	0-2
Flamstead	v Brimsdown Rovers	0-2
Tring Corinthians	v Kings Langley	0-1
Arlesey Athletic	v Winslow United	0-3

SECOND ROUND

New Bradwell St Peter	v Kings Langley	3-1
St Margaretsbury	v Hillingdon Borough (H)	0-1
Hoddesdon Town	v Cranfield United	4-0
Winslow United	v Aylesbury Vale	0-1
Shillington	v Oxhey Jets	A w/o
Holmer Green	v Biggleswade Town	1-0
Old Bradwell United	v Brache Sparta	1-3
Cockfosters	v Brimsdown Rovers	5-4*
Tring Athletic	v Mursley United	2-1
Ampthill Town	v Buckingham Athletic	1-6
Biggleswade United	v AFC Dunstable	3-4*

Second Round continued...

Ruislip Manor	v Kent Athletic	5-1
Langford	v Dunstable Town '98	2-1
London Colney	v Risborough Rangers	4-0
Oxford City	v Harefield United	3-2
Crawley Green	v Pitstone & Ivinghoe	2-1*

THIRD ROUND

Crawley Green	v Hoddesdon Town	1-0
Oxford City	v Hillingdon Borough (H)	1-3
Aylesbury Vale	v Brache Sparta	2-0
Oxhey Jets	v Tring Athletic	1-2
Langford	v London Colney	0-4
Buckingham Athletic	v Ruislip Manor	1-4
AFC Dunstable	v Cockfosters	3-1
Holmer Green	v New Bradwell St Peter	5-2

FOURTH ROUND

Aylesbury Vale	v Ruislip Manor	1-2
AFC Dunstable	v London Colney	2-5
Crawley Green	v Tring Athletic	1-2
Holmer Green	v Hillingdon Borough (H)	1-4

SEMI FINAL

Hillingdon Boro'(H)	v London Colney	2-2*, 2-1p
Ruislip Manor	v Tring Athletic	1-0

FINAL

Hillingdon Boro'(H)	v Ruislip Manor	1-2

Broxbourne Borough F.C. - Back Row (L-R): Tony Cornwall (Asst Manager), Peter Theo (Manager), Nick Swakins, Lee Newman, Will Viner, Uzo Opara, Emil Aiken, Louis Kyriacou, Tony Faulkner (Coach). **Front Row:** Opkapo Blessing, Adam Norman, Gary Taylor, Danny Ward, Tony Neilson.

Photo: Alan Coomes.

LEAGUE CONSTITUTION 2006-07 - PREMIER DIVISION

AYLESBURY VALE
Formed:
Nickname: The Moles

Chairman: Jon Franklin **Vice-Chairman:** Bill Harrison **Manager:** Trevor Griffiths
Secretary: Lynne Nappin, 6 Evesham Green, Aylesbury, Bucks. HP19 9RX
Tel Nos: 01296 486924 (H)
Press Officer: John Drury **Programme Editor:** T.B.A. Website: www.aylesburyvalefc.co.uk
GROUND ADDRESS: Haywod Sports & Social Club, Haywards Way,Aylesbury, Bucks **Tel:** 01296 423324
Capacity: 1,000 **Seats:** 50 **Covered:** 50 **Floodlights:**Yes
Simple Directions: Follow signs to Bicester from Aylesbury ring road. At fifth road island with Aylesbury Duck pub on right, turn right into Jackson Road and then second left into Haywood Way. Club is at bottom of the road.
Midweek Home Matchday: Tuesday **Clubhouse:** Yes **Club Shop:** No
Previous Name: Haywood United **Previous League:** Chiltonian
Club Colours: Claret & sky blueclaret/blue **Change Colours:** Yellow/green/yellow
Last Season
League: 3rd
Top Scorer: Glen Hawkins **Players of the Year:** Jonny Burns & Glen Hawkins **Captain:** Trevor Hercules
BEST PERFORMANCES
League: 3rd Spartan S.Mids. 2004-05 **F.A. Cup:** Preliminary Round 2005-06 **F.A.Vase:** 2nd Rd.
RECORD Attendance: 250 v Aylesbury United **Goalscorer:** **Appearances:** Ben Stevens
SENIOR HONOURS: Buckingham Charity Cup 2005-06

BIGGLESWADE TOWN
Founded:1874
Nickname:Waders

Chairman: Maurice Dorrington **President:** Bob Dorrington
Manager: Jon Mills **Coach:** Keith Newby
Secretary: Graham Arkwright 18 Grosvenor Gardens, Biggleswade, Beds SG18 0NF
Tel No: 01767 318370 **Website:** www.biggleswadetownfc.co.uk
Programme Manager: Andy McDonnell **Tel No:** 07963 679243 (M)
GROUND ADDRESS: Temporary sharing at Bedford Utd, McMullen Park, Meadow Lane, Cardington, Bedford MK44 3LW
Ground Tel No: 01767 312374
Previous Leagues: Biggleswade & Dist.02-20 Bedford & Dist 09-12 Utd Co (ex-Northants Lg) 20-39 51-55 63-80 Spartan 46-51, Eastern Co 55-63
Colours: All Green **Change Colours:** Blue & white stripes/blue/blue
BEST PERFORMANCES
League: 3rd 1992-93 **F.A. Cup:** N/A **F.A.Vase:** 3rd Rd
Simple Directions:
Midweek Home Matchday: Wednesday **Clubhouse:** Open matchdays
RECORD Attendance: 2,000 **Appearances:** Ray Fitzgerald

BIGGLESWADE UNITED
Founded: 1929
Re-Formed 1959

Chairman: Keith Jackson   **Manager:** Steve Wright   **Physio:** Phil Lunceford

Secretary: Tracey James, 17 Havelock Road, Biggleswade, Beds.

Tel Nos: 01767 316270 (H) 01223 372611 (W) 0771 466 1827 (M)

Press Officer: Name (Tel)   **Programme Editor:** Secretary   Club Website: www.intheteam.com/biggleswadeunited

Club Colours: Red & Navy/Navy/Red   **Change Colours:** Yellow /Blue/Blue

GROUND ADDRESS: Second Meadow, Fairfield Road, Biggleswade, Beds.   **Ground Tel. No.:** 01767 600408

Capacity: 2,000   **Seats:** 30   **Covered:** 130   **Floodlights:** Yes

Simple Directions: From A1 Sainsbury's roundabout take bridge over river and second left into Sun Street (before Peugot Garage. The first left into Fairfield Road and ground is at bottom of road and downa lane.

Midweek Home Matchday: Wednesday   **Clubhouse:** Open on matchdays.   **Club Shop:** No

Previous Leagues: Beds & District and Midland.

RECORD Attendance: 250 v Biggleswade Town

Senior Honours: Hunts F.A.Premier Cup 98-99 and Beds Senior Trophy 03-04 Beds Senior Cup 2001-02

BROXBOURNE BOROUGH V & E
Founded: 1959
Nickname:

Chairman: Peter Harris   **Sponsors:** Lush & Leanne Paris

Manager: Peter Theo   **Coach:** John McLoughlin

Secretary: Mandy Moss, 48 Harkness, Rosedale,Cheshunt EN7 6JY Tel Nos: 01992 614225 (H) 07951 857264 (M)

Programme Editor: Peter Harris **Tel No:** 01992 429297 (H)

GROUND : V&E club, Goffs Lane, Cheshunt, Herts   **Ground Tel. No.:** 01992 624281

Capacity: 500   **Seats:** 300   **Covered:** Yes   **Floodlights:** Yes

Simple Directions: M25 jct 5 A10 towards Chehunt. First left at first roundabout onto B198 (Cuffley & Goffs Oak), at the end of road turn right off roundabout into Goffs Lane. Clubhouse on immediate right open daily.

Midweek Home Matchday: Tuesday   **Club Shop:** No

Previous Names: Somerset Ambury V& E   **Previous League:** Herts Senior

Club Colours: White/Royal Blue/Royal Bue   **Change Colours:** Red/black/black

BEST PERFORMANCES

League: 5th 2001-02   **F.A. Cup:** 1st Qualifying Round   **F.A.Vase:** 1st Rd

RECORD Attendance: 120   **Goalscorer:** Wayne Morris   **Appearances:** Brian Boehmer

CHALFONT ST PETER
Founded: 1926
Nickname:Saints

Chairman: Denis Mair   **Manager:** Danny Edwards

Secretary: Nigel Orr, Trio Nicol Rd., Chalfont St.Peter Bucks. SL9 9NF

Tel No: 01753 887209   **Press Officer:** Nick Simon (0776 5963184) **Programme:** 30 Pages £1.00

GROUND ADDRESS: Mill Meadow, Amersham Rd., Chalfont St Peter SL9 7BQ   **Tel:** 01753 885797

Capacity: 4,500   **Seats:** 220   **Covered:** 120   **Floodlights:** Yes

Simple Directions: A413 from Uxbridge (London) to Chalfont road. Turn left 100 yards after second major roundabout (between ambulance station and Community Centre).

Midweek Home Matchday: Tuesday   **Clubhouse:** Open every evening   **Club Shop:** yes

Previous Leagues: G.W.Comb 1948-58, Parthenon 58-59, London 60-62, Spartan 62-75 ,L. Spartan 75-76,Athenian 76-84 Isthmian 84-06

Club Colours: Red/green/red   **Change Colours:** White/red/white

BEST PERFORMANCES: F.A. Cup: 3rd Qual.Rd.   **F.A.Vase:** 4th Rd 87-88

RECORD Attendance: 2,550 v Watford benefit match 1985 **Goalscorer:** Unknown   **Appearances:** Colin Davies

Transfer Fee: Paid: £750 to Chertsey for Steve Church 1989

Senior Honours: Isthmian LG. Div 2 87-88, Athenian Lg R-up 83-84, Berks & Bucks Intermediate Cup 52-53

COLNEY HEATH

Secretary:	Daniel Burr, 151C Dellfield, St Albans, Herts AL1 5HA	Chairman:Martin Marlborough
	Tel No: 07776 375891 (M)	Other Club Officer(s):
		Manager:Craig Johnstone
Ground:	The Pavillion Recreaton Ground, High St., Colney Heath, St. Albans, Herts.	Craig Johnstone (07886 400217)
	Tel: 01727 819370	Programme Editor Martin Marlborough
Directions:	Turn off the A414 (was A405) into Colney Heath village and the ground is	Colours:
	behind the school on the left.	Black & White stripes/Black/Black & white
		Change Colours:
Honours:	Champions S.S.Midlands Div 1 2005-2006	Red/white/red

EDGWARE TOWN

Founded: 1939
Nickname: Wares

Chairman: Ken Batten   **Manager:** Steve Newing
Secretary: Paul Gregory, 2 North Dowe, Mill Hill, London NW7 3AT
Tel No: (H) 0208 959 2535. (B) 01694 476 602. (M) 07808 050 656.
Programme Editor: Paul Gregory
GROUND ADDRESS: White Llon Ground, High Street, Edgware HA8 5AQ   **Ground Tel.No:** 0181 9526799
Capacity: 5,000   **Seats:** 200   **Covered:** 1,500   **Floodlights:** Yes
Simple Directions: Left out of Edgware underground station (Northern Line), left again at crossroads and ground is 300 yards on right in Edgware High Street.
Midweek Home Matchday: Tuesday   **Clubhouse:** Evenings and w/e lunchtime.   **Club Shop:** No.
Previous Name: Edgware F.C.   **Previous Leagues:** Corinthian 46-53, Athenian 64-84 , LondonSpartan 84-90,Isthmian 90-06
Club Colours: All green   **Change Colours:** Yellow/blue/yellow
BEST PERFORMANCES
League: **F.A. Cup:**   **F.A.Vase:** 5th Rd. 91-92
RECORD Attendance: 8,500 v Wealdstone F.A.Cup 1948 **Goalscorer:** Steve Newing   **Appearances:** John Morgan
Senior Honours: Isthmian Div 3 91-92 London Spartan 87-88 89-90 London Senior Cup R-up 47-48

HAREFIELD UNITED

Founded: 1868
Nickname: Hares

Chairman: Keith Ronald   **President:** Dave West   **Manager:** Stuart Levy
Secretary: Ray Green, Hillside, Harefield, Middlesex   **Assistant Manager:** Jeff Fanner
Tel No: 01895 825521 (H) 07834 771212 (M)
Programme Editor: Keith Ronald (07867 791239) **Programme** 12-40 Pages Price £1.00
GROUND ADDRESS: Preston Park, Breakespeare Road North, Harefield, Middlesex UB9 6DG Tel No: 01895 823474
Capacity: 1,200   **Seats:** 150   **Covered:** Yes   **Floodlights:** Yes
Simple Directions: M25 jct 16 to M40 East, left at first roundabout, ground on right. Nearest station Denham (BR)
Midweek Home Matchday: Tuesday   **Clubhouse:** Open daily (01895 823474)   **Club Shop:** No
Previous Leagues: Uxbridge & Dist., Gt.Western Comb., Parthenon, Middlesex, Athenian and Isthmian, Spartan
Club Colours: Red/black/black   **Change Colours:** White/red/red
LAST SEASON
League: 4th   **F.A. Cup:** Extra Prelim.Rd.   **F.A. Vase:** 3rd Rd.
Top Scorer: Danny Jordan   **Player of the Year:** Craig Totton   **Captain:** Gary Williams
BEST PERFORMANCES
League: Athenian League R-up 83-84   **F.A. Cup:** 2nd Qualifying Round   **F.A.Vase:** 6th Rd. 89-90
RECORD Attendance: 430 v Bashley F.A.Vase   **Goalscorer:**   **Appearances:**
Senior Honours: Middx. Premier Cup 85-86 Athenian Lg R-up 83-84 S.S.M.Div 1 R-up 01-02 Cup Winners 2003 + 2004

Harefield United F.C.   Photo: Arthur Evans.

HARINGEY BOROUGH

Founded: 1907
Nickname: Borough

Chairman: Aki Achillea | **Manager:** Ged Searson
Secretary: John Bacon, 7 Everett Close, West Cheshunt, Herts. EN7 6XD
Tel No: 01707 873 187   **Website:** www.haringeyboroughfc.com
Programme Editor: Secretary
GROUND ADDRESS: Coles Park, White Hart Lane, Tottenham   **Ground Tel No:** 0208 8891415
Capacity: 2,500   **Seats:** 280   **Covered:** Yes   **Floodlights:** Yes
Simple Directions: From Jct 25 M25 turn south onto A10 for approx 6 miles going straight over jumction with N.Circular Rd (A406). After one mile turn right at traffic lights into White Hart Lane. Ground approx 500 yards. Wood Green (underground)
Midweek Home Matchday: Tuesday   **Clubhouse:** Yes   **Club Shop:** No
Previous Leagues: London 07-14, Isthmian 19-52 84-88 Spartan 52-54 Delphian 54-63 Athenian 63-84
Club Colours: Yellow/Green/Yellow   **Change Colours:** Green/Black/Green
LAST SEASON: 19th   **F.A.Cup:** Extra Preliminary Round   **F.A.Vase** 2nd Qualifying Round
Top Scorer: Uduma Kalu   **Player of the Year:** Tommy Lambourne   **Captains:** Varied
BEST PERFORMANCES
League: 7th   **F.A. Cup:** 3rd Qualifying Rd.   **F.A.Vase:** 6th Rd 77-78
RECORD Attendance: 400
Senior H onours: F.A.Amateur Cup R-up 1919-20 London Senior Cup: 12-13 90-91Athenian League 1913-14

HERTFORD TOWN

Founded: 1908
Nickname: The Blues

Chairman: Mark Bohm   **Manager:** Gary Connor
Secretary & Press Officer: Stephen Hedley, 29 Upper Field Road,
Welwyn Garden City, Herts AL7 3LP. **Tel No:** 01707 333712
Programme Editor: Elaine Waumsley Email: elainewaumsley@ntlworld.com
GROUND ADDRESS: Hertingfordbury Park, West Street ,Hertford.   **Tel. No:** 01992 583716
Capacity: 6,500   **Seats:** 200   **Covered:** 1,500   **Floodlights:** Yes
Simple Directions: Off town by-pass heading East. Turn off at Ford garage.
Midweek Home Matchday: Tuesday   **Clubhouse:** Yes   **Club Shop:** Yes
Previous Leagues: Herts Co, Spartan,21-47 48-59, Delphian 59-63, Athenian 63-72 and Eastern Co 72-73
Club Colours: All Blue   **Change Colours:** All red
Top Scorer: Kevin Cooper   **Player of the Year:** Danny Wackett   **Captain:** Dave Greenwood
BEST PERFORMANCES
League: Isthmian Div 1 **F.A. Cup:** 4th Qualifying Round 73-74 **F.A.Trophy:**   **F.A.Vase:**
RECORD Attendance: 5,000 v Kingstonian F.A.Amateur Cup 2nd Rd 55-56 **Goalscorer:**   **Appearances:** Robbie Burns
Senior Honours: Herts Senior Cup 66-67 East Anglian Cup 62-63 69-70

HOLMER GREEN

Founded: 1908
Nickname:

Chairmen: John Anderson   **Vice-Chairman:**   **Manager:** Richard Mikurenda
Secretary: Don Want,Whickham Lodge, 10 Sheepcote Dell Roiad, Holmer Green, High Wycombe HP 15 6TH
Tel No: 01494 718287 (H)   **Website:** www.hgfc1908.freeserve@hotmail.co.uk
Programme Editor: Bill Scholes   **Programme:** Included with admission
GROUND ADDRESS: Watchet Lane, Holmer Green, High Wycombe, Bucks   **Tel:** 01494 711 485
Capacity: 1,000   **Seats:** 25   **Covered:** Yes   **Floodlights:** Yes   **Club Shop:** Badges
Simple Directions: From Amersham on A404 High Wycombe Road. After approximately 2 miles turn right into Sheepcote Dell Road. Continue until end of road by Bat & Ball Public House. Turn right then immediately left. Continue approximately 1/2 mile until two mini-roundabouts, turn left in front of the Mandarin Duck into Watchet Lane. Ground 150 yards on right.**Midweek**
Home Matchday: Tuesday   **Clubhouse:** Sats 12pm-11pm Midweek 7-11pm
Previous Leagues: Chesham 1908-34 Chesham 34-38 Wycombe Comb. 84-95 Chiltonian 95-98
Club Colours: Green& white/green/green   **Change Colours:** All Blue
Senior Honours: Berks & Bucks Sen Trophy R-up 98-99 B7 B Junior Cup Winners 52-3 63-4 S.Mids Sen Div Champs (2

KINGSBURY LONDON TIGERS

Chairmen: Abdul Khalidut   **Manager:** Eddie Cardoso

Secretary: Mesba Ahmed, London Tigers, 1st Floor Office, Wech Community Centre, Athens Gardens, Elgin Ave, W9 3RS

Tel No: (B) 0207 289 3395. (M) 07956 353 615.

Programme Editor: Jawar Ali. **Tel:** (B) 0207 289 3395.

GROUND ADDRESS: From Edgware Road A5 NW9, turn into Kingsbury Road and up the hill. Townsend Lane is the third turning on the left (McNicholas building on the corner). Follow the road to the bottom of park and drive into the ground on the left.

Club Colours: Orange/black/black

Change Colours: Yellow/blue/yellow

LANGFORD
Founded: 1908
Nickname: Reds

Chairman: Mick Quinlan   **President:** Ted Rutt   **Manager:** Roy Boon
Secretary: Frank Woodward, 4 West View, Langford, Biggleswade, Beds. SG18 9RT
Tel No: 01462 701015 (H) 07837 849950 (M) **Website:** in theteam.com/langford   **Sponsor:**T.B.A.
Programme Editor: Bob Davies (01438 238066)   **Programme:** with admission
GROUND ADDRESS: Forde Park, Langford Road,Henlow, Beds. SG16 6AF   **Tel:** 01462 816106
Capcity: 2,000   **Seats:** 109   **Covered:** 100   **Floodlights:** Yes   **Shop:** Yes
Simple Directions: Halfway between Langford and Henlow on the A6001 Hitchin to Biggleswade road. Bus 177 on main Hitchin-Biggleswade route stops right outside ground.
Midweek Home Matchday: Tuesday   **Clubhouse:** Weekday evenings,matchdays and Sunday lunchtime
Previous Name(s):   **Previous League(s):**
Club Colours: Red & Yellow/Red./Red   **Change Colours:** Amber/Black/Amber
Last Season: 17th   **Top Scorer:** Rob Groves 15   **Player of the Year:** Rob Groves
BEST PERFORMANCES
League: S.Mids Champions 88-89   **F.A. Cup:** Preliminary Round 2005-2006   **F.A.Vase:** 2nd Round 1995-96
RECORD Attendance: 450 v Q.P.R. 75 th Anniversary 22.06.85
Senior Honours: S. Mids Champions 88-89 R-up 03-04 N.Beds Charity Cup ((9)

LEVERSTOCK GREEN
Founded: 1895
Nickname: The Green

Chairman: Bill Dawes   **Manager:** Mick Vipond   **Coach:** 'Biff' Huber
Secretary: Brian Barter, 11 Curlew Close, Berkhamsted, Herts HP4 2HZ   **Sponsors:** M.J.L.Prestige Cars
Tel No: 01442 862322   **Website:** www.levgreenfc.co.uk
Press Officer: Alan Lee   **Programme:** 40/44 Pages price: £1.00   **Editor:** Brian Barter
GROUND ADDRESS: Pancake Lane, Leverstock Green, Hemel Hempstead**.**   **Ground Tel.No:** 01442 246280
Capacity: 1,500   **Seats:** 50   **Covered:** 100   **Floodlights:** Yes
Simple Directions: From M1 leave at A4147 to 2nd roundabout. Take 1st exit to Leverstock Green. Pancake Lane is on the left after 300 yards past the Leather Bottle pub.
Midweek Home Matchday: Tuesday   **Clubhouse:** Opens one hour before kick off **Club Shop:** No
Previous Leagues: West Herts (pre 1950) and Herts County 50-91
Club Colours: White/Green/Green   **Change Colours:** Yellow& Blue/Blue/Blue
LAST SEASON
League: 6th   **F.A.Cup**: Preliminary Round   **F.A. Vase:** 2nd Round
Top Scorer: James Armstrong   **Players of the Year:** Mark Welling   **Captain:** Steve Boad
RECORD Attendance: 1,000   **Goalscorer:**   **Appearancess:**Johnnie Wallace
Senior Honours: S.Midlands Senior Div. 96-97 League Cup Runners-Up 2005-06

LONDON COLNEY
Founded: 1907
Nickname: Blueboys

Chairman: Ray Flanagan   **Vice-Chairman:** Steve Ypey   **President:** Keith Parsons
Manager: Lee Ward   **Physio:** J.Burt   **Sponsors**: Elder Plastics
Secretary: Dave Brock,50 Seymour Rd., St Albans, Herts AL3 5HW tel No: 01727 761644 (H)
Programme Editor: Clive Attwood 07951 270749 (M) **Programme** £4.00 with entry.
GROUND ADDRESS: Cotslandswick, London Colney (01727 822132)   **Tel:**
Capacity: 1,000   **Seats:** 180   **Covered:** 180   **Floodlights:** Yes
Simple Directions:
Midweek Home Matchday: Tuesday   **Clubhouse:** Open after games. Hot foor available.   **Club Shop**
Previous Ground: Whitehorse Lane 07-75   **Previous League(s):** Mid Herts 1907-54 Herts County 07-92
Club Colours: All Royal Blue   **Change Colours:** Red/black/black
Top Scorer: Steve Flain 23   **Player of the Year:** Dean Shuttleworth   **Captain:** Eamonn Rogers
BEST PERFORMANCES
League: SSM Premier Champions 2001-02 **F.A. Cup:** 1st Quallifying Dd.   **F.A.Vase:** 4th Rd
RECORD Attendance: 300,v St Albans City Herts Sen.Cup 98-99   **Goalscorer:**   **Appearances:**
Senior Honours: SSM Premier Div 01-02 S.Mids SEn Div 94-95 R-up 93-94

OXHEY JETS
Founded:
Nickname: Jets

Chairman: Phil Andrews   **Vice-Chairman:**   **Manager:** Benny Higham
Secretary: David Fuller, 4 Sage Close, Biggleswade, Beds. SG18 8WH   **Sponsor:** RW Transport
Tel No: 01767 227147 (H) 07786 627659 (M)   **Commercial Manager**: Jim Wagner
Programme Editor: David Fuller07799 413205 (M) Prog with admission   **Pres Officer:** John Elliott
GROUND ADDRESS: Althem Way, South Oxhey, Watford,   **Ground Tel.No.:** 0208 8421 6277
Capacity: 1,000   **Seats:** 100   **Covered:**100   **Floodlights:** Yes
Simple Directions: From Bushey station take Pinner road (A4008) and then along Oxhey Lane towards Harrow. Right at lights into Little Oxhey Lnae. Altham Way is on left after crossing raiiway bridge.
Midweek Home Matchday: Wednesday   **Clubhouse:** Yes   **Club Shop:** No
Previous League: Herst Senior County
Club Colours: All Royal Blue   **Change Colours:** All White
LAST SEASON
League: 13th SSM Premier Division   **F.A. Cup:** Preliminary Round   **F.A. Vase:** 2nd Qual.Rd.
Top Scorer: Jamie Arthur 36   **Player of the Year:** Marc Ayres   **Captain:** Chris Harding
BEST PERFORMANCES
League: 13th Premier Division SSM   **F.A. Cup:** Preliminaryu Round   **F.A.Vase:** 2nd Qual.Rd.
RECORD Attendance: 257 v Barnet Herts Senior Cup 05-06   **Goalscorer:**   **Appearances:** Ian Holdom
SENIOR HONOURS: SSML Division 1 Champions 2004-2005 Herts Senior Centenary Trophy 2004-2005

ROYSTON TOWN

Founded: 1875
Nickname: Crows

Chairman: Graham Phillips   **Vice-Chairman:** Bernard Brown   **President:** Alan Barlow
Secretary: Elaine Phillips, 14 Roan Walk, Royston, Herts. SG8 9HT
Tel No: 01763 241041 (H) 07792 612225(M)
Programme Editor: Secretary   **Programme:** 16 Pages 30p
GROUND ADDRESS: Garden Walk, Royston, Herts. SG8 7HP   **Ground Tel.No:** 01763 241204
Capacity: 4.000   **Seats:** 300   **Covered:** 300   **Floodlights:** Yes
Simple Directions: From Baldock take A505 to Royston by pass, then right at second island onto A10 towards London. Second left is Garden Walk and ground is 100 yards on left.
Midweek Home Matchday: Tuesday   **Clubhouse:** Open daily.   **Club Shop:** Yes
Previous Leagues: Buntingford & Dist.18-28, Cambs 28-50, Herts Co.,50-59 62-77 South Mids. 59-62 77-84 Isthmian 84-94
Club Colours: White /Black/White   **Change Colours:** Red & White/Red/Red
BEST PERFORMANCES
League: Isthmian League   **F.A. Cup:** 2nd Qualifying Round.   **F.A.Vase:** 4th Round 1978-79 1982-83
RECORD Attendance: 876 v Aldershot 13.02.93 **Goalscorer:**Trevor Glasscock 289 (68-82) **Appearances:** Fred Bradley 713
Senior Honours: S.Mids Lg R-Up 79-80

RUISLIP MANOR

Founded: 1938
Nickname: The Manor

Chairman: Ken Garrett   **Manager:** Shayne Chandler   **Physio:** Gary Strudwick
Secretary: Dave McCardle, 26 Longhale,Pitstone, LU7 9GF   **Sponsors:** Light Years
Tel No: 07963696009
Press Officer/Programme Editor: Chris Thomas (01895 636930)   **Programme:** 24 Pages Price: 50p
GROUND ADDRESS: Grosvenor Vale, off West End Rd.,Ruislip, Middlesex
Tel Nos: 01895 637487 (office) and 676168 (boardroom)
Capacity: 3,000   **Seats:** 250   **Covered:** 600   **Floodlights:** Yes
Simple Directions: A40 to Ruislip, turn off on A4180 ,right at roundabout into West End Rd.. Right in to Grosvenor Vale after 1.5 miles. Ground at end.
Midweek Home Matchday: Monday   **Clubhouse:** Yes   **Club Shop:** Yes
Previous Leagues: Uxbridge 38-39 Middx Sen 39-46 London 46-58 Spartan 58-65 Athenian 65-84 Isthmian 84-96
Club Colours: Black & White/Black/Black   **Change Colours:** Claret & Blue/Blue/Claret
LAST SEASON: League: 16th   **F.A. Cup:** 1st Qualifying Round   **F.A. Vase:** 1st Qual.Rd.
Top Scorer: Frankie Aitomare   **Player of the Year:** Steve Flower   **Captain:** Ray Walsh
BEST PERFORMANCES
League: Isthmian Lg.Div 2 R-Up 92-93   **F.A. Cup:** 4th Qualifying Round 90-91   **F.A.Vase:** 3rdRd.
RECORD Attendance: 2,000 v Tooting & Mitcham U F.A.Amateur Cup 1962 **Senior Honours:** Isthmian Lg Div 2 R-up 92-93 Athenian Lg Div 2 72-73 Middx Senior Cup S-F (6)

Ruislip Manor F.C.   Photo: Gordan Whittington

ST MARGARETSBURY

Founded: 1894
Nickname: Athetic

Chairman: Dave Stock   **President:** R.L.Groucott   **Gen Manager:** Martin Gutteridge
Manager: Ian Hart   **Asst. Manager:** Ray Greenall   **Coach**: Dave Steedman   **Physio**: John Ellliott
Secretary: Jeannette Stone,19 Roundcroft,Cheshunt,Herts. EN7 6DQ
Tel; No: 07930 815614 (M)l
Programme Editor: Gary Stock(07956 394554)   **Programme:** Incl.with £4 admission
GROUND ADDRESS: Station Road, Stanstead St. Margarets, Nr Ware. Herts.   **Tel:** 01920 870473
Capacity: 1,000   **Seats:** 60   **Covered:** 60   **Floodlights:** Yes
Simple Directions: Harlow/Chelmsford exit from A10 to A414 take B181 at Amwell roundabout after 300 yards towards Stanstead Abotts. Ground a quarter of a mile on the right.
Midweek Home Matchday: Tuesday   **Clubhouse:** Open daily   **Club Shop:** No
Previous Leagues: East Herts, Hertford & District, Waltham & District, 47-48 Herts Co., 48-92
Club Colours: Red & Black/Black/Black   **Change Colours:** All White
BEST PERFORMANCES
F.A.Cup: 3rd Qualifying Rd 01-02 03-04.   **F.A.Vase:** 3rd Rd 85-86
RECORD Attendance: 450 v Stafford Rangers F.A.Cup 2001-02
Senior Honours: Spartan Lg 95-96 Herts Senior Centenary Trophy 92-93 Herts Cghaity Shield 97-98

TRING ATHLETIC

Founded: 1958
Nickname: Athetic

Chairman: Alan Foskett   **Manager:** Mick Eldridge   **Asst Manager:** Ray Brimson
Secretary: Ralph Griffiths, 42 Bedgrove, Aylesbury, Bucks.HP21 7BD   **Coach**: Richard Vincent
Tel No: 01296 426425   07766 753059 (M)   **Club Website:** www.tafc.co.uk
Programme Editor: Barry Simmons   **Programme:** 64 Pages £1.50   **Sponsors:** The Grass Roots Group
GROUND ADDRESS: The Grass Roots Stadium, Pendley Sports Center, Cow Lane, Tring, Herts. HP23 5NT
Tel No: 01442 89114
Capacity: 1,233   **Seats:** 150   **Covered:** 100+   **Floodlights:** Yes
Simple Directions: From M25 Jct 20 take A41. After 11 miles take B4635 signposted to Tring. On leaving motorway turn right at roundabout and left into Cow Lane. Sports Centre is 300 yards on right.
Midweek Home Matchday: Tuesday   **Clubhouse:** Matchdays, training nights and Sunday lunch.   **Shop:** Yes
Previous League(s): West Herts 58-88
Club Colours: Red/Black/Black   **Change Colours:** Yellow/green/yellow
BEST PERFORMANCES
League: Senior Divison Champions   **F.A. Cup:** Preliminary Round 2005-2006 **F.A.Vase:** 2nd Qualifying 2004-052005
RECORD Goalscorer: Andy Humphreys 209 **Appearances:** Mark Boniface 642
Senior Honours: S.S.Mids Senior Div: 99-00

WELWYN GARDEN CITY

1921Founded:
Nickname: Citizens

Chairman: T.B.A.   **Vice-Chairman:**
Manager: Howard Cowley   **Physio:** Danny Milliken
Secretary: Malcolm Kiely,14 Oak Piece. Oaklands, Welwyn ,Herts AL6 0XE
Tel No: 01438 717430 (H) 07782 154908 (M)   **Website:** www.wgfc.com
Programme Editor: David Fallon (01438 235701)   **Programme:** 24 Pages 50p
GROUND ADDRESS: Herns Lane, Welwyn Garden City   **Ground Tel. No:** 01707 329358
Capacity: 1,500   **Seats:** 40   **Covered:** 120   **Floodlights:** Yes
Simple Directions: Follow signs for industrial areas. From A1 Take one way system opposite Avdel Ltd.(signed Hertford B195) take second exit off one way system and Ground is 400 yards on left.
Midweek Home Matchday: Tuesday   **Clubhouse:** Open every evening   **Club Shop:** Yes
Previous Ground: Springfields   **Previous League(s):** Spartan,Metropolitan and Greater London
Club Colours: Sky Blue/Claret/Sky Blue   **Change Colours:** Claret/Sky Blue/Claret
Last Season: League: 8th   **F.A. Cup:** did not enter   **F.A. Vase:**1st Qualifying Round
BEST PERFORMANCES
League: S. Mids. Champions 73-74 **F.A. Cup:** 2nd Qualifying Round 2005-06 **F.A.Vase:** 2nd Rd 2mnd Replay 1974-75

AMERSHAM TOWN

Secretary: Michichael Gahagan, 7 Ely Close, Lincoln Park, Amersham, Bucks.
HP7 9HS   Tel No: 01494 724798
Email: michaelgahagan@ukonline.co.uk

Ground: Hollways Park, Slough Road, Beaconsfield, Bucks, HP9 2SG
Tel: 01494 676868

Directions: From M40 junction 2 take exit marked A355 to Slough. After 50 yards turn right across the break in the dual carriageway and through the gateway marked Hall Barnes Estate. Follow the road for 200 yards and the ground is on the right.

Chairman: Arsin Begri
Manager: Ted Gromnicki
Programme Editor: Stephen Cogdell

Colours:
Black & white stripes/black/black & white
Change Colours:
Yellow/blue/yellow & blue

AMPTHILL TOWN

Secretary: Eric Turner, 34 Dunstable Street, Ampthill, Beds MK45 2JT.
Tel:01525 403128 (H & B)

Ground: Ampthill Park, Woburn Road, Ampthill, Beds. Tel: 01525 404440

Directions: From Ampthill Town Centre follow signs to Woburn then take the first right into Ampthill Park

Chairman: Steve Burton
Tel: 01525 719978
Manager: SteveGoodridge
Programme Editor: As Secretary

Colours: Yellow /Blue/Yellow
Change Colours: All Red

ARLESEY ATHLETIC

Secretary: Simon Allen, 30 Plum Tree Road,Lower Stondon, Beds. SG16 6NE
Tel Nos: 01462 816129 (H) 07771 578292 (M)
Email: ron.ward3@ntlworld.com

Ground: c/o Arlesey Town F.C.

Capacity: 2,9 20   **Seats:** 150   **Cover:** 600   **Floodlights:** Yes

Directions: As for Arlesey Town

Clubhouse: Yes

CLUB PERSONNEL
Chairman: Simon Allam
Manager: Darren Staniforth
Programme Editor: Matt Allam

Colours: All Dark Blue
Change colours: Al Red

BEDFORD VALERIO UNITED   Formed: 1957

Chairman: Alan Hurst   **Manager:** Dave Parker
Secretary: Paolo Riccio, c/o !st & 2nd Floor, 64A Sty Loyes Street,Bedford MK40 1EB
Tel Nos: 07724 907626 (M)
Programme Editor: Geoffrey Seagrave
GROUND ADDRESS: McMullen Park, Meadow Lane, Cardington, Bedford MK45 3SB **Tel:** 01234 831024
Capacity: 5.000   **Seats:** 25   **Covered:** 100   **Floodlights:** Yes
Simple Directions: M1 jct 13 A421 to Bedford by-pass. Third exit A603 ground 500 yards on left.
Midweek Home Matchday: Wednesday   **Clubhouse:** Open matchdays   **Club Shop:** No
Previous Names: Printers Diemer-Reynolds (pre 72)
Previous Leagues: Bedford & Dist, 57-70, 80-89 United Co 70-80
Previous Grounds: Allen Park 57-80, Fairhiill, Clapham Road 80-93, Hillgrounds Kempston 3-96
Club Colours: Blue & white/black/black   **Change Colours:** Blue & white/blue/blue
RECORD Attendance: (at Fairhill) 1,500 v Bedford TS.Mids Div 1.92 **Goalscorer:** Neil Tysoe 22**Apps:** Simon Fordham 418

BRACHE SPARTA

Secretary & Prog Ed: Chris Juraszek, 104-106 Park Street,Luton, Beds. LU1 3EY(07952371089)
GROUND: Foxdell Sports Ground, Dallow Rd, Luton LU1 1UP (01582 720751).
Directions: From M1 jct11, take A505 towards Luton. Right at Chaul End roundabout. Across A505 keep B&Q on left, into Dallow Rd. Ground 50 yds on right by Foxdell junior school.
Capacity: 400 Cover: 100 Seats: 25 Floodlights: Yes Club Shop: No
Clubhouse: Open daily 12-3 & 7.30-11. Light snacks & refreshments etc available
HONOURS: South Mids Lg R-up 92-93, 96-97 (Div 1 R-up 83-84 87-88), Lg Cup R-up 75-76 80-81 92-93 97-98, Premier Div Cup Winners 97-98 R-up 91-92, Res Div 2 R-up 75-76, Res Cup R-up 87-88; Luton & Dist. Lg 67-68 69-70 70-71 71-72; William Pease Trophy 66-67 67-68 70-71 71-72; Beds Interm Cup 71-72 (R-up 68-69 70-71), BedsJnr Cup 82-83; Leighton Challenge Cup R-up 69-70 South Mids Lg Prem Div 1 North Champions 97-98, Beds Premier Cup R-up. 97-98

FACT FILE
Founded: 1960 Nickname: The Foxes
Colours: White/Black/White & Black
Change Colours: Yellow/Blue/Yellow
Midweek matches: Tuesday
Career Record Goalscorer: Keith Denness

CLUB PERSONNEL
Chairman: Pear Armitage
Manager: Mark Smith
Programme Editor: Pear Armitage

BRIMSDOWN ROVERS

Secretary: Peter Wade, 5 Goldsdown Close, Enfield. EN3 7RR Tel No: 020 8804 7053
GROUND: Brimsdown Sports & Social Club, Goldsdown Road, Enfield, Middlesex EN3 7RP
Tel: 020 8804 5491 **Directions:** BR from Liverpool Street to Brimsdown or Southbury (half amile away). By road off Green Street, itself off Hertford Road (A1010). Buses 191 or307
Capacity: 2,300 Seats:150 Cover:300 Floodlights: Yes Club Shop: No
Clubhouse: Large lounge & clubroom, games room & stage 3 bars (300 capacity) Big TV screen
HONOURS: Spartan Champions 92-93. Spartan Lg Cup 95-96, SSML Div 1 Cup 2005-06
RECORD: Gate: 412 v Chesham Utd, FA Cup 3rd Qual. Rd 12/10/91
BEST SEASON: FA Vase: 3rd Rd 93-94 **FA Cup:** 3rd Qual. replay 91-92
PREVIOUS: Leagues: Northern Suburban **Names:** Durham Rovers; Brimsdown FC
2005-2006 Player of the Year &Top Goalscorer: Michael Pelley **Captain:** Michael Pelley

FACT FILE
Chairman: Gary Brooker
Manager: Gordon Boateng
Founded: 1947
Colours: Black & white stripes/black/black
Change: Red & white stripes/white/red
Midweek Matchday: Wednesday
Programme Editor: Peter Wade
Prog.with admission

BUCKINGHAM ATHLETIC

Secretary: Charles Bassano, 62 Moreton Road, Buckingham MK18 1PE
Tel No: (H) 01280 817 801. (B) 01280 823 288. (M) 07810 755 193.

Ground: Stratford Fields, Stratford Rd, Buckingham
Tel: 01280 816945

Directions: From Milton Keynes take the A422 Stony Stratford-Buckingham road -ground on left just before town centre. From Oxford, Aylesbury or Bletchley, take the ring road to the A422 Stony Stratford roundabout, turn left, the ground is situated at the bottom of the hill on the left

FACT FILE
Colours: Sky Blue/white/sky
Change Colours: All yellow

Chairman: John Webb
Manager: Simon Spooner
Programme Editor: John Webb

COCKFOSTERS

Secretary: Graham Bint, 15 Chigwell Park, Chigwell, Essex IG7 5BE (0208 500 7369)
GROUND: Cockfosters Sports Ground, Chalk Lane, Cockfosters, Barnet (0208 449 5833)
Directions: M25 Jct 24 (Potters Bar), take A111 signed Cockfosters - ground 2 miles on right. Adjacent to Cockfosters underground station (Picadilly Line). Bus 298 to Cockfosters station
Capacity: 1,000 Seats: 30 Cover: 80 Floodlights: Yes Club Shop: No
Clubhouse: 7-11pm Tues & Thurs, 4-11pm Sat, 12-3pm Sun. Hot & cold food onmatchdays
HONOURS: London Interm Cup 70-71 89-90, Herts Snr Co. Lg 78-79 80-81 83-84 R-up 82-83 84-85, Aubrey Cup 78-79 84-85 R-up 70-71 77-78, Herts Interm Cup 78-79 R-up x3
Previous Leagues: Wood Green & Dist. 21-46/ Northern Suburban 46-66/ Herts Snr Co.66-91
BEST SEASON: FA Vase: 2nd Round 91-92
RECORDS: Gate: 408 v Saffron Walden, Herts Senior County Lg 68-69

FACT FILE
Founded: 1921 Nickname: Fosters
Colours: All Red Change:White/Blue/Blue
Editor: A Simmons (0208 440 7998)
Chairman: Colin Bell(01727 823458)
Manager: David Craig

CRANFIELD UNITED

Secretary: Jim Brandom, 31 Lordsmead, Cranfield, Beds. MK43 0HP
Tel No: 01234 751501 (H) 07831 676557 (M)
Ground: Crawley Road, Cranfield Tel Nio: 01234 751444
Directions: Take North Crawley/Newport Pagnell road from village of Cranfield. Ground is on left before leaving speed limit signs.

CLUB PERSONNEL
Chairman: Brian Dosser
Manager: Chris Johnson
Programme Editor: Larr Corkey

Colours:All Red
Change colours: White/black/white

HARPENDEN TOWN

Founded: 1891
Nickname: Town

Chairman: Nick Archer　　　　**Vice-Chairman:**　　　　**Manager:** Steve Cornwell
Secretary: Les Crabtree, 11 Wensley Close, Harpenden, Herts AL5 1RZ
Tel Nos: 01582 622 669. (M) 07968 120 032
Programme Editor: Chairman
GROUND ADDRESS: Rothamsted Park, Amanbury Lane, Harpenden, Herts.　　　**Tel No:** 01582 715724
Capacity: 1,500　　　　**Seats:** 25　　　　**Covered:** 100　　　**Floodlights:** Yes
Simple Directions: A1081 to Harpenden. Turn into Leyton Road at Georgr Public House . Then left into Amanbury Road and left again into pay and display car park- entrance is signposted inopposite corner next to swimming pool.
Midweek Home Matchday: Tuesday　　　**Clubhouse:** Open Matchdays　　　**Club Shop:** No
Previous Name: Harpenden F.C. 1891-1908:　　　**Previous League(s):** Mid Herts and Herts County
Club Colours: Yellow/blue/blue　　　　**Change Colours:** White/red/red
BEST PERFORMANCES
League: Champions S.Mids 61-62 64-65　　　**F.A. Cup:** 1st Qualifying Rd　　　**F.A.Vase:** 2nd Round
RECORD Attendance:　　　**Goalscorer:**　　　**Apps:**
Senior Honours: S.Mids Champions (2) Herts Junior Cup (5)

HODDESDON TOWN

Founded: 1879
Nickname: Lilywhites

Chairman: Roger Merton　　　**President:** Peter Haynes
Manager: Geoff O'Vell　　　**Coach:** Mark Mezem　　　**General Manager:** Jim Briggs
Secretary: Jane Sinden, 22 Hatley Road, Wrestlingworth,Sandy, Beds. SG19 2EH　　　**Sec's Tel. No:** 07968 120032 (M)
Programme Editor: Mrs Jane Sinden (01767 631297)　　　**Website:** www.hoddesdontownfc.co.uk
GROUND ADDRESS:' Lowfield', Park View, Hoddesden, Herts EN11 8PX　　　Tel: 01992 463133
Capacity: 3,000　　　**Seats:** 100　　　**Covered:** 250　　　**Floodlights:** Yes
Simple Directions: A10 A1170 in to Hoddesdon. Over 1st roundabout, right at 2nd roundabout and follow signs tp Broxbourne keeping to the left. Turn right at 1st mini roundabout into Cock Lane and 2st right is Park View. Ground 200yards on left.
Midweek Home Matchday: Tuesday　　　**Clubhouse:** Open all hopme games　　　**Club Shop:** Yes
Previous League(s): East herts 1896-1908 11-21 herts Co. 08-25 N.Middx & Dist. 10-22 Spartan 25-75 London Spartan 75-77 Athenian 77-84 South Midlands 84-97
Club Colours: White/black/black　　　**Change Colours:** Navy Blue/yellow/navy
BEST PERFORMANCES: **League:** Spartan League 70-71 **F.A. Cup:**　　　**F.A.Vase:** First Winners 1974-75
RECORD Attendance: 3,500 v West Ham United opening floodlights. 1975
Senior Honours: F.A.Vase winners 1974-75 Spartan League 70-71 R-up (3)

KENTISH TOWN

Secretary:　　Cliff Rhodes,13 Linley Road, London N17 6RP
　　　　　　Tel Nos: 0208 808 6797 (H) 07707 944911 (M)
Ground:　　c/o Hendon F.C. , Claremont Road, Brent Cross, London NW2 1AE
　　　　　　Tel No: 0208 201 9494
Directions:　　From junction 1 off M1 take second exit on the roundabout into Illing Road. Then
　　　　　　at fourth mini roundabout tirn right into Claremont Road.

CLUB PERSONNEL
Chairman: Gregg Hazelgrove
Manager:Frank Zanre
Programme Editor: Kevin Young
Tel No: 07916 332701 (M)

Colours: All Navy Blue
Change colours: All Red

NEW BRADWELL St PETER

Secretary: Nicola Cox, 81a Stratford Road, Wolverton Milton Keynes MK13 8NQ(07870 483697)
Ground: Recreation Ground, Bradwell Rd, New Bradwell, Milton Keynes MK13 7AT
Tel.: 01908 313835　　**Capacity: 2,000** Seats: 30　Cover: 100　Floodlights: Yes
Directions: From M1 Jnt 14 go towards Newport Pagnell, left at 1st r-about into H3 (A422 Monks Way). Over 5 r-abouts, right at 6th island into V6 (GraftonSt.), At 1st roundabout go right the way round (back on yourself) then take 1st left at mini-r'about turn left into Bradwell Rd. Go straight over next mini r'about. Ground immediately on left.
Clubhouse: Members only (member can sign in 2 guests). Evenings & w/e mid day. No food.
HONOURS: Sth Mids Lg Div 1 76-77 83-84 Sen Div Champs 97-98, (Res Div 2 R-up 76-7), Berks& Bucks Senior Trophy 1999-2000

FACT FILE
Founded: 1902　　Nickname: Peters
Colours: All Maroon
Change Colours: All Sky Blue
Programme Editor:　Steve Orchard
01327 352014 (H)
CLUB PERSONNEL
Chairman John Haynes
Manager: Steve Orchard

STONY STRATFORD TOWN

Secretary: Maurice J Barber, 26 Boundary Cres., Stony Stratford, Milton Keynes MK11 1DF   Tel: 01908 567930 (H)
GROUND: Sports Ground, Ostlers Lane, Stony Stratford (01908 562267).
Directions: From Dunstable use old A5, Watling Street. Approaching Bletchley continue on A5 loop road (Hinkley) to end of dual c'way to A422/A508 r'bout. First exit, thru lights, 2nd right into Ostlers Lane.
Capacity: 600 Seats: 30   Cover: 120   Floodlights: Yes   Club Shop: No
Clubhouse: Open evenings & weekends
HONOURS: Sth Mids Lg R-up 70-71 71-72 (Div 1 93-94, Div 1 Cup 93-94)
PREVIOUS: Leagues: North Bucks & Dist.; Northampton Combination
RECORD: Attendance: 476 v Aston Villa U21, floodlight opening 12.11.96

Formed: 1898   Sponsor:Maritz
Colours:Sky blue/navy/navy
Change Colours:All yellow
Midweek matches: Tuesday
Reserves' League: SSM Res. Div. One
Chairman: Kevin Gallacher
Manager:Craig Connell
Capt:Stuart Milne
Programme Editor: Paul Grimsley
Tel No: 01908 569828
2005-06
Leading goalscorer: Marc Redsull
P.o.Y.:Marc Redsull

SUN POSTAL SPORTS

Secretary: Joe Tibbles, 4 Lambert Court,Bushey Grove Road,m Watford, Herts WS23 2HF,

Tel Nos: 01923 468069 (H) 07713 710617(M)

Ground: Bellmount Wood Avenue, Watford, Herts. Tel: 01923 227453

Directions: From Watford take A411 towards Hemel Hempstaed . Left into Langley Way at 2nd traffic lights. Take third exit at next roundabout into Ca`ssiobury Drive then take first left into Bellmount Wood Avenue. Turn right for Club entrance on left hand bend.

PREVIOUS Name: Sun Postal Sports >2003 Sun Sports >2005

Leagues: Herts Senior County Lge. >2003

Chairman: Jim Kempster
Manager: Gordon Wallis
Programme Editor: T.B.A.

Colours: Yellow & blue/blue & yellow/yellow
Change Colours: All Blue

WINSLOW UNITED

Secretary: David Ward, 28 Park Roafd, Winslow, Buckingham, MK 18 3DL
Tel Nos: 01296 713202 (H) 07944 258838 (M) W mail: davden@tesco.net
Ground: RecreationGround, Elmfields Gate, Winslow, Bucks. MK18 3JH
Tel No: 01296 713057
Directions: A413 from Aylesbury to Winslow. Right from High Street into Elmfield Gate. Ground 100yards on left. PLease park in Public Hall Car Park opposite ground.

CLUB PERSONNEL
Chairman: Colin O'Dell
Manager: TBA
Programme Editor: Secretary

FACT FILE

Colours: Yellow/Blue/Yellow
Change colours: Red & black/black/red

League action from the match between Old Bradwell United versus Aston Clinton. Photo: Steve Ayre.

DIVISION TWO

		P	W	D	L	F	A	Pts
1.	Aston Clinton	34	29	3	2	142	30	90
2.	AFC Dunstable	34	27	2	5	104	35	83
3.	Kent Athletic	34	25	4	5	79	31	79
4.	Tring Corinthians	34	20	7	7	106	47	67
5.	Crawley Green	34	20	5	9	77	47	65
6.	Kings Langley	34	19	5	10	70	45	62
7.	Old Bradwell United	34	18	2	14	71	63	56
8.	Totternhoe	34	15	7	12	70	63	52
9.	M.K. Scot	34	14	8	12	76	60	50
10.	Flamstead	34	13	7	14	65	69	46
11.	The 61FC (Luton)	34	13	6	15	58	54	45
12.	Risborough Rangers	34	11	8	15	70	72	41
13.	Caddington	34	12	5	17	62	64	41
14.	Pitstone & Ivinghoe	34	7	8	19	39	84	29
15.	Mursley United	34	7	6	21	41	72	27
16.	Markyate	34	3	4	27	29	117	13
17.	Padbury United	34	3	4	27	43	137	13
18.	Loughton Orient	34	4	1	29	33	145	13

DIVISION TWO		1	2	3	4	5	6	7	8	9	10	11	12	13	14	15	16	17	18
1	AFC Dunstable		0-3	3-0	3-1	1-0	3-1	0-1	8-0	4-1	2-0	2-0	3-1	6-0	5-0	5-1	3-1	2-2	0-2
2	Aston Clinton	1-2		4-2	3-0	7-0	4-0	2-4	7-0	6-2	4-0	3-1	8-1	10-1	8-0	2-2	1-0	5-0	5-2
3	Caddington	2-3	1-7		1-4	1-2	2-3	1-1	5-1	2-0	4-0	1-0	0-1	2-0	4-2	1-1	1-4	4-1	0-2
4	Crawley Green	1-2	3-3	2-0		4-0	0-0	1-1	7-0	3-0	4-1	2-0	1-2	6-3	3-1	2-1	1-0	2-0	2-5
5	Flamstead	2-4	2-3	1-2	1-0		1-3	4-0	6-2	3-1	0-3	1-0	3-0	1-0	0-0	2-2	0-1	2-4	0-3
6	Kent Athletic	3-0	0-2	0-0	1-1	4-0		2-1	5-1	1-0	3-0	1-0	2-0	3-0	2-0	2-1	2-1	0-0	3-1
7	Kings Langley	1-2	1-3	1-0	3-1	2-3	3-1		8-0	2-1	0-0	3-2	1-2	3-1	0-2	3-4	1-0	5-1	3-1
8	Loughton Orient	0-0	0-6	2-5	1-2	0-5	0-6	1-3		0-2	2-3	2-3	1-2	4-2	2-7	0-1	1-2	2-3	2-8
9	Markyate	0-5	1-4	1-6	1-5	2-2	0-7	1-2	0-1		0-5	1-3	0-2	4-2	0-2	0-2	0-3	0-4	0-4
10	MK Scot	2-2	0-3	2-2	3-1	4-1	0-1	3-5	3-0	8-2		1-1	4-2	5-0	3-0	1-1	2-3	1-2	2-6
11	Mursley United	1-2	1-7	1-2	3-1	3-3	0-1	1-3	4-0	0-0	1-1		0-4	2-3	1-1	3-2	1-6	1-4	1-3
12	Old Bradwell United	1-2	1-3	2-1	2-3	2-2	3-1	2-1	0-1	1-0	2-2	2-1		6-0	4-0	6-1	1-2	3-7	2-0
13	Padbury United BTFC	3-8	1-4	1-5	1-1	0-5	2-7	0-3	2-4	4-4	0-3	1-0	2-4		3-0	0-0	0-5	4-5	1-3
14	Pitstone & Ivinghoe	0-4	0-5	3-2	1-3	1-1	3-4	2-4	2-0	1-1	1-4	0-1	3-2	1-1		1-3	3-1	0-4	0-4
15	Risborough Rangers	0-7	0-4	2-0	0-1	1-4	0-2	0-1	7-0	6-0	2-2	3-4	3-2	9-2	4-1		4-2	1-2	2-2
16	The 61 FC	0-5	1-2	2-2	1-2	3-5	0-3	0-0	3-0	0-2	3-1	2-0	1-3	2-1	0-0	3-3		3-0	1-1
17	Totternhoe	1-4	1-3	2-0	1-4	1-1	1-2	0-0	2-2	4-1	0-4	3-0	1-2	9-1	1-1	1-0	1-0		1-1
18	Tring Corinthians	3-2	0-0	3-0	2-3	5-2	1-3	1-0	16-1	12-1	0-3	1-1	3-1	3-1	0-0	4-1	2-2	2-1	

LEAGUE CONSTITUTION 2006-07 - DIVISION TWO

AFC DUNSTABLE

Secretary: Craig Renfrew, 75B Princes Street. Dunstable. LU6 3AS. Tel: 01582471794 (H), 01234 265444 (B)

Ground: Lancot Park. Dunstable Road, Totternhoe (01582 663735)

Directions: From Dunstable Town Centre take the B489 Tring Road. At the 4th roundabout turn right, signposted Totternhoe. The pitch is located within Dunstable Town Cricket Club which is on the right just before entering the village of Totternhoe

Previous Name: Old Dunstablians

Honours: South Midlands Division 2 - 03/04.

ASTON CLINTON

Secretary: Mike Dedman, 49, Chiltern Street, Aylesbury, Bucks HP21 8BN. Tel: (H) 01296 420 482. (M) 07799 537 495.

Ground: London Road, Aston Clinton HP22 5HL Tel: 01296 631 818

Directions: The ground is situated in Aston Clinton village off the main road (old A41) The ground is opposite the Duck Inn pub. Aston Clinton can be approached on the B489 from Dunstable or via the A418 from Leighton Buzzard.

CADDINGTON

Secretary: Mick Gregory, Pipers Farm, Mancroft Road, Aley Green, Luton LU1 4DR.
Tel: (H) 01582 841 386. (M) 07778 010 066

Ground: Caddington Recreation Club, Manor Road, Caddington (01582 450151) **Directions:** On entering village turn into Manor Road (adjacent to shops and village green), proceed 500 metres: Clubhouse and ground on left side next to Catholic Church

CRAWLEY GREEN

Secretary: Robert Freeman, 44 Carteret Road, Luton LU2 9SZ
Tel: (H) 01582 616 640. (M) 07979 497 047.
Ground: Crawley Green Recreation Ground, Crawley Green
Road, Luton, Beds. 01582 451058 **Directions:** From M1 jct 10 ,
to r'about at end of motorway slip road into Airport Way. At 4th
r'about turn right into Crawley Green Rd. Ground is 1/2 mile on
left past Ashcroft High School.

FLAMSTEAD

Secretary: Samantha Devoti, 64 Trowley Road, Flamstead
AL3 8EA Tel (B) 01582 842 030. (M) 07900 895 811
Ground: Flamstead Sports Assoc., Friendless Lane, Flamstead,
St Albans, Herts (0582 841307)
Directions: From Dunstable Town Centre travel south on A5
Trunk Roadtowards the M1. Follow for approximately 3 miles
then turn right oppositeHertfordshire Moat House Hotel. Ground
and parking approximately half a mile onthe corner of the first
right turn

KENT ATHLETIC

Secretary: Steven Yeomans, 38 Denham Close, Luton LU3 3TS
Tel: (H) 01582 650 854. (M) 07961 077623
Ground: Kent Social Club, Tenby Drive, Leagrave, Luton Tel:
01582 582723 **Directions:** M1 J11 take A505 towards Luton.
Take the first turning on the left (Stoneygate Road), straight over
at r'about turn right at lights into Beechwood Road. Take the
first road on the left and then the first right into Tenby Drive.
Ground and car park 100 yards on left

KINGS LANGLEY

Secretary: Andy Mackness, 79 Weymouth Street, Apsley, Hemel
Hempstead, Herts HP3 9SJ
Tel: 01442 398186 (H) 020 7587 4153 (B) 07976 692801 (M)
Ground: Gaywood Park, Hempstead Road, Kings Langley. Tel:
01923 264489
Directions: From M25 leave at Junction 20. Take A4251 to Kings
Langley. The ground is approx. 1 mile on the right.

LOUGHTON ORIENT

Secretary: Neil Cardwell, 17 Swallowfield, Great Holm, Milton
Keynes MK8 9BH. Tel: (H) 01908 560929. (M) 07810 306398
Ground: Loughton Sports & Social Club, Lincesdale Grove,
Loughton, Milton Keynes. Tel: 01908 690668
Directions: From M1 Jct 14 follow H6, Childs Way for 5 miles
until V4 Watling Way (Knowlhill r-about), right to Loughton r-
about, right along H5 Portway 1st right Linceslade Grove.
Previous Name: Abbey National (Loughton)

MARKYATE

Secretary: Lisa Dumpleton, 48 Parkfield, Markyate, St Albans
AL3 8RD. Tel: (H) 01582 841654. (M) 07961 843 532
Ground: The Playing Fields, Cavendish, Markyate, Hertfordshire
(01582 841731)

MK SCOT

Secretary: Dennis Rogers. 21 Oliver Road, Bletchley, Milton
Keynes, Bucks MK2 2LP. (H) 01908 644 394. (M) 07904 091998.
Ground: Scot Sports & Social Club, Selbourne Avenue,
Bletchley, Milton Keynes MK3 5BX. Tel: 01908 368 881.

MURSLEY UNITED

Secretary: Bob Dixon, 40 Tweedale Close, Mursley, Bucks MK17
0SB. Tel: (H) 01296 720187. (M) 07852 229126
Ground: Station Road, Mursley, Milton Keynes MK17 0SU
Directions: A421 Bletchley to Buckingham Road, first right in village

OLD BRADWELL UNITED

Secretary: Mick Ennis, 6 Wolsey Gardens, Bradwell Village,
Milton Keynes MK13 9BH
Tel: (H) 01908 313 932. (B) 01908 270900
Ground: Abbey Road, Bradwell, Milton Keynes (01908 312355)
Directions: M1 junction 14 go towards Newport Pagnell. Turn
left at firstroundabout into H3 Honks Way. Go six r'abouts then
left onto V6 Grafton Street.Take 1st right at mini-r'about into
Rawlins Road and then 2nd left intoLoughton Road. Take 1st
right into Primrose Road and at the 'T' junction turnright into
Abbey Road.

PADBURY UNITED

Secretary: Odette O'Driscoll, 25 Leven Close, Bletchly, Milton
Keynes MK2 3DS. Tel: (H) 01908 379778. (M) 07706 411624
Ground: Springfields,Playing Fields, Padbury **Directions:**
From Buckingham follow ring road with signs,to Aylesbury
(A413), then towards Buckingham and Padbury is two miles
south of the town A413 and three miles north west of Winslow on
A413. Turn off opposite bus shelter on Springfields Estate and
follow road forward.

PITSTONE & IVONGHOE

Secretary: Jeni Deighton, 21 Old Farm, Pitstone, Leighton
Buzzard LU7 9RB. Tel: 01296 660544. (M) 07944 243460
Ground: Pitstone Recreation Ground, Vicarage Road, Pitstone,
Bucks Tel: 01296 661271
Directions: Tring Rd (B489) from Dunstable, turn right for
Ivinghoe, and continue through to Pitstone r-about; ground left
then right. From Aylesbury -left at `Rising Sun' in Aston Clinton,
keep on that road to Pitstone r'bout; ground right then right.
Bus 61 from Luton or Aylesbury. Nearest BR stations are Tring or
Cheddington.

RISBOROUGH RANGERS

Secretary: Nick Bishop, 28 Stratton Road, Princes Risborough,
Bucks HP27 9AX. Tel: 01844 342934. (B) 01844 276173
Ground: `Windsor', Horsenden Lane, Princes Risborough.
(01844 274176) **Directions:** Rear of Princes Risborough BR
Station (Chiltern Line). A4010 fromAylesbury thru Princes
Risborough, fork right onto A4009, left by thatched cottage, over
railway bridge, immediate right ground 150 yds on right

THE 61 FC (LUTON)

Secretary: Richard Everitt, 44 Somersby Close, Luton LU1 3XB.
Tel: 01582 485095 (H)
Ground: Kingsway, Beverley Road, Luton, Beds. 01582 495417
Directions: M1 jct 11, A505 to Luton centre, right at 1st island,
1st left, Beverley Rd is 3rd left, entrance in Beverley Rd, exactly
1 mile junction 11.All Luton to Dunstable buses pass ground -
alight at Beech Hill Bowling Club. 1mile from both Leagrave &
Luton BR stations

TOTTERNHOE

Secretary: Jim Basterfield, 41 Park Avenue, Totternhoe,
Dunstable, Beds LU6 1QF. Tel: 01582 667941 (H)
Ground: Totternhoe Recreation Ground, Dunstable (01582
606738)
Directions: Turn off the main Dunstable to Tring Road B489.
Ground on right as you enter Totternhoe. Five miles from
Leighton Buzzard (BR), 7 miles from Luton. Bus 61 Luton-
Aylesbury

TRING CORINTHIANS

Secretary: Gary Mendham. 72 Mill View Road, Tring, Herts
HP23 4EN. (H) 01442 823 589. (M) 07985 726 431.
Ground: Icknield Way, Tring HP23 5HJ. Tel: 07985 726 431.

SUSSEX COUNTY LEAGUE

SPONSORED BY: BADGER ALES
FOUNDED 1920

President: Peter Strange   **Chairman:** Peter Bentley
Secretary: Paul Beard, 2 Van Gogh Place, Bersted, Bognor Regis PO22 9BG
Tel: 01243 822063 (H)   07966 457908 (M)   Fax: 01243 822063   www.scfl.org.uk

DIVISION ONE		P	W	D	L	F	A	Pts
1.	Horsham YMCA (Champions 04-05)	38	27	7	4	83	31	88
2.	Ringmer	38	24	7	7	68	34	79
3.	Whitehawk	38	20	7	11	66	36	67
4.	Littlehampton Town	38	20	7	11	63	44	67
5.	Eastbourne Town	38	19	8	11	69	44	65
6.	Crowborough Athletic (1st Div.2 04-05)	38	19	8	11	68	45	65
7.	Arundel	38	16	15	7	61	43	63
8.	Chichester City United	38	17	9	12	61	55	60
9.	Hassocks	38	15	12	11	63	48	57
10.	Hailsham Town	38	13	13	12	43	46	52
11.	Sidley United	38	16	4	18	65	80	52
12.	Wick (2nd Div.2 04-05)	38	14	9	15	56	49	51
13.	Shoreham (3rd Div.2 04-05)	38	15	6	17	58	59	51
14.	Eastbourne United Assoc	38	12	8	18	48	62	44
15.	Three Bridges	38	10	12	16	46	50	42
16.	East Preston	38	8	15	15	41	60	39
17.	Worthing United	38	9	12	17	41	60	39
18.	Redhill	38	10	4	24	39	78	34
19.	Rye & Iden United	38	4	8	26	38	83	20
20.	Southwick	38	2	9	27	28	98	15

DIVISION ONE	1	2	3	4	5	6	7	8	9	10	11	12	13	14	15	16	17	18	19	20
1 Arundel		2-0	2-0	2-2	3-2	1-1	0-0	2-0	1-0	1-1	4-0	0-1	1-3	4-1	2-1	6-1	2-2	3-1	4-2	1-1
2 Chichester City United	1-1		2-1	1-0	0-4	1-2	2-2	2-3	0-1	2-1	3-1	2-1	2-1	3-2	4-0	2-2	1-4	1-2	1-0	2-2
3 Crowborough Athletic	1-1	2-3		1-2	0-0	5-2	2-0	2-1	0-2	0-1	4-0	2-3	3-0	1-0	7-0	4-1	3-0	1-0	2-1	1-0
4 East Preston	2-0	1-0	2-2		0-0	1-1	2-2	1-0	2-6	1-1	1-2	1-1	2-2	1-1	2-1	1-2	2-2	0-0	2-4	0-0
5 Eastbourne Town	0-1	0-1	1-1	3-3		1-1	3-2	0-1	0-1	0-0	3-1	1-0	2-1	3-2	5-2	6-0	1-0	1-3	3-1	2-1
6 Eastbourne United Assoc	0-1	1-2	1-2	1-0	2-1		1-1	1-1	1-4	0-4	2-1	0-1	2-1	2-3	0-1	2-2	1-2	2-1	0-1	1-2
7 Hailsham Town	0-3	1-1	2-0	0-0	1-1	1-2		0-0	0-1	2-0	2-0	0-0	3-2	1-3	2-1	1-0	0-0	0-2	1-3	0-2
8 Hassocks	1-1	0-1	3-2	2-1	5-2	2-2	2-2		1-2	2-4	2-0	0-0	6-1	0-1	6-2	2-0	3-0	2-1	2-0	0-1
9 Horsham YMCA	4-2	1-1	5-1	0-0	2-1	3-1	0-0	2-0		2-0	2-0	1-2	2-2	1-2	5-2	5-0	0-1	1-1	3-0	2-0
10 Littlehampton Town	1-1	2-0	3-1	2-0	2-1	0-3	2-1	2-2	1-2		2-1	1-2	3-1	4-0	2-0	2-2	2-1	0-0	1-0	
11 Redhill	2-1	1-3	0-0	1-2	0-3	0-2	1-3	0-5	1-2	2-1		1-3	3-0	1-4	4-1	2-0	2-1	0-4	0-0	1-2
12 Ringmer	1-1	2-0	3-4	3-0	0-2	3-1	0-1	4-0	1-1	2-1	4-1		2-1	2-1	3-0	3-0	1-0	0-0	1-1	2-0
13 Rye & Iden United	1-1	0-5	0-3	2-0	0-2	1-2	2-2	1-1	1-3	0-6	1-2	0-2		0-1	0-0	2-2	0-1	0-1	1-1	2-0
14 Shoreham	0-0	1-1	0-0	3-0	1-1	3-1	2-4	3-3	0-1	2-1	2-1	0-1	4-2		2-3	1-0	0-3	0-2	0-2	2-3
15 Sidley United	2-0	2-0	2-2	3-1	1-4	4-0	0-1	4-2	1-1	0-1	1-0	4-0	5-3	2-1		6-1	2-0	0-2	0-3	3-2
16 Southwick	0-1	2-2	0-2	2-0	0-4	0-5	1-2	1-1	0-4	2-3	2-2	1-3	1-1	0-1	1-3		0-0	0-2	0-1	2-2
17 Three Bridges	1-2	2-2	0-1	3-1	4-1	0-1	0-1	0-2	1-2	1-1	1-2	2-0	1-3	3-1	3-1			1-1	1-2	4-0
18 Whitehawk	5-1	3-2	1-2	1-0	0-1	2-0	1-2	0-1	2-3	3-0	4-1	3-1	2-0	2-1	1-1	2-0	1-1		2-0	5-0
19 Wick	1-1	0-2	1-1	1-2	1-3	2-0	3-0	0-0	2-3	1-2	0-1	1-2	3-0	3-1	3-2	4-1	1-1	4-1		1-2
20 Worthing United	1-1	2-3	0-2	2-3	0-1	1-1	1-0	0-0	1-3	2-0	1-2	0-6	1-3	0-3	2-2	5-0	1-1	1-1	0-0	

DIVISION TWO		P	W	D	L	F	A	Pts
1.	Oakwood	34	25	5	4	87	25	80
2.	Selsey	34	23	6	5	80	28	75
3.	St Francis Rangers (+3)	34	20	8	6	85	42	71
4.	Westfield	34	18	4	12	67	52	58
5.	Crawley Down	34	15	10	9	61	43	55
6.	Wealden	34	16	7	11	64	62	55
7.	East Grinstead Town	34	17	3	14	70	61	54
8.	Mile Oak (-3)	34	15	7	12	61	53	49
9.	Seaford	34	12	6	16	57	64	42
10.	Sidlesham	34	10	11	13	53	56	41
11.	Broadbridge Heath	34	12	5	17	53	69	41
12.	Lancing	34	11	7	16	42	53	40
13.	Pagham	34	9	12	13	65	63	39
14.	Storrington	34	11	6	17	47	63	39
15.	Steyning Town	34	10	8	16	50	69	38
16.	Saltdean United	34	11	3	20	45	75	36
17.	Midhurst & Easebourne	34	8	7	19	42	70	31
18.	Bexhill United	34	3	5	26	28	109	14

DIVISION TWO	1	2	3	4	5	6	7	8	9	10	11	12	13	14	15	16	17	18
1 Bexhill United		2-3	1-3	0-2	1-3	2-2	1-1	0-5	1-1	1-2	0-4	0-4	2-1	1-5	0-2	2-1	1-3	1-3
2 Broadbridge Heath	3-0		1-2	0-0	0-2	3-0	2-1	0-5	2-2	3-2	2-4	1-2	2-1	0-3	0-1	3-0	1-2	1-0
3 Crawley Down	4-1	4-0		3-0	2-1	2-0	1-2	0-1	0-0	4-1	3-1	2-0	1-1	1-2	5-1	3-2	2-0	2-3
4 East Grinstead Town	5-1	2-1	0-0		2-1	4-2	1-1	0-3	1-4	1-3	4-1	0-3	1-2	0-4	4-1	4-1	1-4	4-2
5 Lancing	2-0	3-1	0-1	1-3		2-2	1-0	1-2	2-1	2-0	1-2	1-0	2-2	0-0	0-1	4-0	1-3	0-5
6 Midhurst & Easebourne	5-0	0-1	1-1	0-5	2-0		2-0	0-0	0-1	2-1	3-2	3-3	1-1	1-5	2-1	3-2	1-2	0-3
7 Mile Oak	3-3	8-2	3-0	2-5	5-1	2-0		0-2	4-1	2-2	1-0	2-1	5-2	2-0	3-1	0-1	2-1	2-3
8 Oakwood	0-1	3-0	1-1	3-1	3-1	3-2	4-0		4-2	4-0	4-0	1-4	3-1	3-1	7-2	1-0	0-1	2-1
9 Pagham	9-0	1-1	3-2	0-5	1-1	1-1	1-1	1-1		0-1	2-0	1-1	1-1	1-4	6-1	2-2	1-3	1-2
10 Saltdean United	1-0	2-3	2-2	0-1	0-1	2-1	1-2	1-4	3-1		2-2	0-2	3-0	3-2	2-1	0-2	0-3	0-2
11 Seaford	3-0	1-1	1-1	5-0	2-1	1-0	0-1	0-4	4-1	1-6		2-3	3-1	1-3	2-2	0-1	4-0	1-3
12 Selsey	9-0	1-2	2-0	2-0	3-0	2-0	2-0	0-0	3-0	8-1	3-2		1-1	1-2	2-0	1-0	2-0	2-1
13 Sidlesham	4-2	4-3	5-0	1-0	2-0	3-0	1-1	0-1	1-2	0-2	0-0	1-5		2-4	2-1	3-2	1-1	0-1
14 St Francis Rangers	3-0	3-3	1-0	3-1	1-1	3-1	6-1	1-5	2-1	6-0	5-0	1-2	1-1		3-2	0-0	4-0	3-1
15 Steyning Town	1-1	2-1	1-4	2-4	1-1	1-2	2-3	1-0	1-4	1-0	3-1	1-1	1-1	3-3		3-0	0-1	3-1
16 Storrington	4-1	1-0	2-2	1-5	0-2	3-1	1-0	0-4	1-1	5-0	2-2	2-3	3-1	0-0	0-3		0-2	4-1
17 Wealden	3-1	2-6	2-2	1-2	2-2	3-2	1-1	1-1	3-9	4-1	1-2	1-1	0-5	3-0	3-3	4-0		4-2
18 Westfield	5-1	3-1	1-1	3-2	3-1	5-0	1-0	1-3	4-2	2-1	0-3	0-1	1-1	1-1	0-0	2-4	1-0	

JOHN O'HARA LEAGUE CUP
DIVISION ONE AND TWO CLUBS

FIRST ROUND

Hailsham Town	v Lancing	1-0
Saltdean United	v Crowborough Athletic	3-4
Three Bridges	v Bexhill United	2-0
Eastbourne Utd As.	v Storrington	2-0
Littlehampton Town	v Oakwood	2-3
Midhurst & Eastbo'	v Chichester City United	3-4

SECOND ROUND

Shoreham	v Broadbridge Heath	5-0
East Grinstead T.	v Ringmer	2-1
Hailsham Town	v Seaford Town	2-0
Mile Oak	v Worthing United	0-3
St. Francis Rangers	v Rye & Iden Untied	0-1
Westfield	v Horsham YMCA	1-5
East Preston	v Sidlesham	3-2
Eastbourne Utd As.	v Whitehawk (H)	1-4
Southwick	v Crowborough Athletic	3-4
Steyning Town	v Eastbourne Town	0-3
Arundel	v Selsey	1-2
Hassocks	v Crawley Down	6-0
Wealdon	v Wick	3-0
Pagham	v Chichester City United	0-3
Redhill	v Three Bridges	0-1
Oakwood	v Sidley United	1-2

THIRD ROUND

Hailsham Town	v East Preston	1-2
Selsey	v Chichester City United	3-1
East Grinstead T.	v Worthing United	1-3
Hassocks	v Eastbourne Town	1-1, 3-1r
Rye & Iden United	v Shoreham	0-3
Wealdon	v Horsham YMCA	2-1
Three Bridges	v Crowborough Athletic	3-4
Whitehawk (H)	v Sidley United	1-0

QUARTER-FINALS

Shoreham	v East Preston	6-2
Hassocks	v Crowborough Athletic	1-2
Selsey	v Whitehawk (H)	0-2
Worthing United	v Wealdon	1-6

SEMI-FINALS

Wealdon	v Whitehawk (H)	0-1
Shoreham	v Crowborough Athletic	2-1

THE FINAL

Whitehawk (H)	v Shoreham	1-2

Tommy Pattenden (right) beats Shoreham's keeper, Ronan Callaghan, to score Whitehawk's goal in the final of the John O'Hara Cup, however, it's Shoreham that can be seen celebrating the Cup win/ Photo: Roger Turner.

LEAGUE CONSTITUTION 2006-07 - DIVISION ONE

ARUNDEL
Founded: 1889
Nickname: Mulletts

Chairman: Bob Marchant **Manager:** Vic Short

Secretary: Kim Marchant, 6 Council Cottages, Warningcamp, Arundel, West Sussex BN **Tel :** 07795 054977 (M)

GROUND ADDRESS: Mill Road, Arundel, West Sussex **Ground Tel. No.:** 01903 882548

Capacity: 2,200 **Seats:** 100 **Covered:** 200 **Floodlights:** Yes

Simple Directions: A27 from Worthing to Arundel over Railway Bridge to roundabout . Second exit into Queen Street to town centre and turn right over bridge. Car park leading to ground 100 yards on right.

Midweek Home Matchday: Tuesday **Clubhouse:** Normal pub hours- two bars. **Club Shop:** No

Previous League: West Sussex 1896-1975 **Previous Grounds:** Castle Park and Station Rd. Ground

Club Colours: Red/white/red **Change Colours:** All blue

RECORD Attendance: 2,200 v Chichester League 67-68 Victory: 12-0 v Horsham YMCA (H) Sussex Co. Div 1 21.12.85

Goalscorer: Paul J. Bennett **Appearances:** 537 Paul Bennett (Goalkeeper)

Senior Honours: Sussex Co 57-58 58-59 86-87 Sussex Junior Cup 1907-08 Sussex RUR CharityCup (3)

CHICHESTER CITY UNITED
Founded: 2000

Chairman: John Hutter

Manager: Adrian Girdler. **Chief Coach:** Mick Catlin. **Physio:** Beccy Sigston.

Secretary: Peter Down, 14 Edith Cottages, Mill Road, West Ashling PO18 8DG. Tel: (H) 01243 574 597

GROUND ADDRESS: Church Road, Portfield, Chichester, West Sussex. PO19 4HN **Tel:** 01243 779875

Capacity: 2.000 **Seats:** None **Covered:** 200 **Floodlights:** Yes

Simple Directions: A27 from Arundel to Chichester, take road signposted to city centre then first left (Church Rd) after supermarket roundabout. One mile from Chichester (BR)

Midweek Home Matchday: Tuesday **Clubhouse:** Two bars and full facilities**.** **Club Shop:** Yes

Previous Names: Chichester FC (pre 1948) Chichester City 1948-2000 Amalgamated with Portfield in 2000

Club Colours: Yellow with blue trim/blue with yellow trim/blue. **Change Colours:** Yellow/Blue/Blue

2005-06: Top Scorer: Scott Tipper. **Player of the Year:** Neil Murfin. **Captain:** Alex Ward.

CROWBOROUGH ATHLETIC

Chairman: Malcolm Boyes **Manager:** Harry Smith & Simon Colbran

Secretary: Steve Singer, Craven Cottage, London Road, Crowborough, East Sussex

Tel Nos: 01892 662181 (H) 01892662 181 (W) 07795 422591(M)

GROUND ADDRESS: Alderbrook Recreation Ground, Fermor Road, Crowborough **Tel:** 01892 661893

Capacity: 2,000 **Seats: None** **Covered:** 150 **Floodlights:** Yes

Midweek Home Matchday: Tuesday **Clubhouse:** Yes **Club Shop:** No

Club Colours: Navy blue/white/navy blue **Change Colours:** White/red/red

BEST PERFORMANCE

League: Champions Sussex Div 2

EAST PRESTON
Founded: 1966
Nickname:

Chairman: Brian Harwood **President:** Greg Stanley **Manager:** Chris White
Secretary: Keith Freeman, 41 Ambersham Crescent, East Preston, West Sussex **Asst.Manager:** Sean Edwards
Tel No: 01903 771158
Programme Editor & Press Officer: Geoff Anscombe
GROUND ADDRESS: Roundstone Recreation Ground, Rast Preston,West Sussex **Tel:** 01903 776026
Capacity: 1,000 **Seats:** 50 **Covered:** 100 **Floodlights:** Yes
Simple Directions: Less than a mile from Angmering BR. A259 from Worthing to Roundstone Hotel(6miles) turn south over railway crossing left past Centyrion garage, right into Roundstone Drive.
Midweek Home Matchday: Tuesday **Clubhouse:** Open daily. **Club Shop:**
Previous Leagues: Worthing and West Sussex
Club Colours: White + black trim/black/white **Change Colours:** Yellow & Black Stripes
LAST SEASON
League: 17th **F.A. Cup:** Preliminary Round **F.A. Vase:** 2nd Qualifying Round
Top Scorer: Josh Biggs **Player of the Year:** Chris Yelling **Captain:** David Hall
BEST PERFORMANCES
League: **F.A. Cup:** 3rd Qualifying Round **F.A.Vase:** 2nd Rd.
RECORD Attendance: 604 v Worthing F.A.Cup **Appearances:** Terry Withers
Senior Honours: Sussex Co Lg Div 2 1997-98 Div 3 83-84

EASTBOURNE TOWN

Founded: 1882
Nickname: Bourne

Chairman: Roger Imich   **Manager:** Ady Colwell

Secretary: Mark Potter, FLat 2, Carillon House, 18 Eversfield Road, Eastbourne, East Sussex. BN21 2AS

Tel Nos: 01323 417336 (H) 07720 846857 (M)

GROUND ADDRESS: The Saffrons, Compton Place Road, Eastbourne, East Sussex.   **Tel:** 01323 723734

Capacity: 3,000   **Seats:** 200   Covered: Yes   Floodlights: Yes

Simple Directions: Turn south west off the A22 into Grove Rd (opp.BR station), the ground is a quarter of a mile on the right.

Midweek Home Matchday: Tuesday   **Clubhouse:** Fully licensed.   **Club Shop:** No

Previous Leagues: Southern Amateur 07-46, Corinthian 60-63 and Athenian 63-76

Club Colours: Yellow/blue/blue   **Change Colours:** Sky blue/black/white

RECORD Attendance: 7,378 v Hastings United 1953

Senior Honours: Sussex Co Lg Champions 76-77 Sussex Sen Cup (12) Sussex Rur Charity Cup (3) AFA Sen.Cup (2)

EASTBOURNE UNITED ASSOCIATION

Founded: 1894
Nickname: The U's

Chairman: Les Aisbitt
Manager: Brian Dennis
Secretary: Brian Dowling, 79 Harebeating Drive, Hailsham, East Sussex BN27 1JE
Programme Editor: Secretary
GROUND ADDRESS: The Oval, Channel View Ropad, Eastbourne, East Sussex   **Tel:** 011323 726989
Capacity: 3,000   **Seats:** 160   **Covered:** 160   **Floodlights:** Yes
Simple Directions: From A22 follow signs to Eastbourne East seafront. Turn left onto seafront and left again
into Channel View Road at Princess Park & ground is first right.
Midweek Home Matchday: Tuesday   **Clubhouse:** Yes, full facilities.**Club Shop:** Yes
Previous Names: Eastbourne OLd Comrades, Eastbourne UNited merged with Shine water Assoc. in 200
Previous Leagues: Sussex County 21-28 35-56 Metropolitan 56-64 Atthenian 64-77 and Isthmian 77-92
Club Colours: White/black/white   **Change Colours:** Green and White
BEST PERFORMANCES
League: Sussex Co Champions 1954-55   **F.A. Cup:** 3rd Qualifying Round   **F.A.Vase:** 3rd Round.
RECORD Attendance: 11,000 at Lynchmore
Senior Honours: Sussex Co Lg Champions 54-55 Sussex Sen.Cup (5) Sussex RUR Charity Cup 55-56

HAILSHAM TOWN

Founded: 1885
Nickname: The Stringers

Chairman: M.Francis   **President:** Graham Perry   **Manager:** Ken McCreadie
Secretary: Derek York, 59 Anglesey Avenue,Hailsham, East Sussex. BN27 3DN **Tel No:** 01323 848024 (H)
Programme Editor: G.Jones
GROUND ADDRESS: The Beaconsfield, Western Road, Hailsham, East Sussex   **Tel:** 01323 840446
Capacity: 2,000   **Seats:** None   **Covered:** 100   **Floodlights:** Yes
Simple Directions: A22 to Arlington Road, turn east, then left into South Road- left into Diplocks Way until Daltons. Four miles
from Polegate BR (Brighton- Eastbourne line).
Midweek Home Matchday: Tuesday   **Clubhouse:** Open every evening, matchdays and Sundays. **Club Shop:**
Previous Leagues: East Sussex, Southern Combination
Club Colours: Yellow & Green/ Green/Green **Change Colours:** All Blue
LAST SEASON:
League: 10th   **F.A. Cup:** Extra Preliminary Round   **F.A. Vase:** 2nd Qualifying Round
Top Scorer: Peter Cooper 16   **Player of the Year:** Paul Richardson   **Captain:** Paul Richardson
Best Performance:
League: 4th Sussex Premier League   **F.A. Cup:** 2nd Qualifying Round.   **F.A.Vase:** 5th Round 1988-89
RECORD Attendance: 1,350 v Hungerford T F.A.Vase Feb 89.**Goalscorer:** Howard Stevens 51 95-96 **Apps:** Phil Comber 713
Senior Honours: Sussex County Div 2 R-up 80-81 Sussex Junior Cup

HASSOCKS

Founded: 1902
Nickname: The Robins

Chairman: Jim Goodrum   **President:** Maurice Boxall   **Manager:** Dave John
Secretary: Dave Knight, 21 Farnham Avenue, Hassocks, West Sussex BN6 8NR
Programme Editor: Paul Elphick   **Programme:** 24 Pages 50p
GROUND ADDRESS: The Beacon, Brighton Rd., Hassocks   **Ground Tel. No.:** 01273 846040
Capacity: 1,800   **Seats:** 270   **Covered:** 100   Floodlights: Yes
Simple Directions: Off A273 Pyecombe Road to Burgess Hill. Ground is 300 yards south of Stonepound crossroads (B2116)
to Hurstpeirpoint or Hassocks.
Midweek Home Matchday: Tuesday   **Clubhouse:** Yes   **Club Shop:** No
Previous Leagues: Mid Sussex, Brighton & Hove & Dist. and Southern Counties Combination
Previous Grounds: Adastra Park, Hassocks (pre 1992)
Club Colours: All red   **Change Colours:** Mauve & Black
Last Season: League: 7th   **F.A. Cup:** 2nd Qualifying Round   **F.A. Vase:** 2nd Round
BEST PERFORMANCES
League: 7th 2005-06   **F.A. Cup:** 4th Qualifying Round   **F.A.Vase:** 2nd Rd 1998-99 2005-06
RECORD Attendance: 610 v Burgess Hill Town Sussex Co Lg. 96-97   **Goalscorer:** Pat Harding 43 in 2005-06

LITTLEHAMPTON TOWN

Founded: 1894
Nickname:Marigolds

Chairman: Neil Taylor   **President:** T.B.A.   **Manager:** Trevor Waller
Secretary: Alan Barnes, 10 Emmabrook Court, Sea Road, Littlehampton, W.Sussex BN16 2NG
Tel No: 01903 721219 and 07986 754098 (M) **email:** ltfcbarnes@aol.com   **Sponsor:** Enterprise Security
Programme: 52 Pages price £1.00 **Editor:** Alan Barnes
GROUND ADDRESS: The Sportsfield, St Flora's Road, Littlehampton   **Ground Tel No:** 01903 713944
Capacity: 4,000   **Seats:** 260   **Covered:** 260   **Floodlights:** Yes
Simple Directions: Ten minutes walk from BR station.Turn left along Terminus Road, through High St and Church Rd then left at junction with St Flora's Road..
Midweek Home Matchday: Monday   **Clubhouse:** Open on matchdays with   **Club Shop:** Yes
Club Colours: Gold.black/black   **Change Colours:** All white
LAST SEASON: League: 4th   **F.A. Cup:** Prelim.Rd.   **F.A. Vase:** 1st Rd.
Top Scorer: Mark Windsor   **Player of the Year:** Steve Davies   **Captain:** Steve Davies
BEST PERFORMANCES
League: Champions (5)   **F.A. Cup:** 1st Rd 90-91   **F.A.Vase:** Semi-final 90-91
RECORD Attendance: 4,000 v Northampton F.A.Cup 90-91   **Goalscorer:**   **Appearances::** Micky Phillips
SENIOR HONOURS: Champions 58-59(shared) 75-76 84-85 90-91 96-97 Sussex Senior Cup 1949 1970
Lost last season's F.A.Cup Preliminary Round v Tunbridge Wells 1516 on penalties after 40 kicks had been taken- a European record and only one short of the world record.

OAKWOOD

Secretary: Martin Brown. 89a Three Bridges Road, Three Bridges, West Sussex PO21 2SB
Ground: Tinsley Lane, Three Bridges, Crawley, West Sussex   Tel: 01293 515742

Directions: From A23 to Gatwick, take 1st set of lights into Manor Royal, pass next lights, over r'bout to warehouse marked Canon, turn right signposted Oakwood. Last clubhouse down lane. Two miles north of Three Bridges (BR)

Capacity: 3,000   Seats: 20   Cover: Yes   Floodlights: Yes

Club Shop: Yes, incl. metal badges
Clubhouse: Large bar area, pool tables, multidart boards. Board room & tea bar

HONOURS   Sussex Snr Cup R-up 92-93, Sussex Co. Lg Div 2 R-up 89-90 (Div 2 Cup 89-90, Div 3 84-85), Southern Comb. Cup 83-84, Sussex Co. Lge Div.2 05-06.
PREVIOUS   Leagues: Crawley & Dist., Southern Co's Comb
     Ground: Park pitches
RECORD   Attendance: 367   Appearances: Peter Brackpool

FACT FILE
Founded: 1966   Nickname: Oaks
Sponsors: Linden Plc
Colours: Red & black/black/black
Change colours: Blue& black/white/white
Midweek Matchday: Tuesday
Reserves' Lge: Sussex Co. Reserve section
Programme: 24 pages
Editor: Scott Packer Local Press: Crawley Observer, Crawley News

CLUB PERSONNEL
Chairman: Stuart Lovegrove
Manager:Bob Pyle

Oakwood F.C. Back Row (L-R): Lee Butcher, Joe ranson, Dean Stevens, Scott Kenward, Darren Cole, Steve Best.
Front Row: Ian Gander, Phil Butcher, Zak Newman, Gareth Neatley, Ben King.

Photo: Roger Turner.

REDHILL

Founded: 1894
Nickname: Reds/Lobsters

Chairman: Andy Wheeler | **Vice-Chairman:** Mark Lambert | **Manager:** Ian Dawes

Secretary: Dave Best, 36 Observatory Walk, Redhill, Surrey RH1 1HL

Tel No: 01737 217798 email: Dave_Dan Best@yahoo.co.uk_fc@hotmail.com

Programme Editor: Daniel Best | **Programme:** 50 Pages 50p

GROUND ADDRESS: Kiln Brow, Three Arch Road, Redhill, Surrey | Ground **Tel. No:** 01737 762129

Capacity: 2,000 | **Seats:** 150 | **Covered:** 150 | **Floodlights:** Yes

Simple Directions: On left hand side of A23 two and a half miles south of Redhill.

Midweek Home Matchday: Tuesday | **Clubhouse:** Yes Social Club | **Club Shop:** Yes

Previous Leagues: E&W Surrey, Spartan 09-10, Southern Sub, London21-23, Athenian 23-84 and Spartan 84-88

Club Colours: All Red | **Change Colours:** White & Black stripes/black/white

BEST PERFORMANCES

League: Athenian Champions 54-25 83-84 | **F.A. Cup:** 1st Rd 57-58 **F.A.Amateur Cup:** S-F 1925 | **F.A.Vase:** 2nd Rd.

RECORD Attendance: 8,000 v Hastings U. F.A.Cup 1956 **Goalscorer:** Steve Turner 119 **Appearances:** Brian Medlicott 766

Senior Honours: Athenian League (2) Surrey Senior Cup 28-29 65-66

RINGMER

Founded: 1906
Nickname: Blues

Chairman: Richard Soan | **President:** Sir George Christie | **Manager:** John Crumplin

Secretary: Mrs Dorothy Brook, 15 Chapel Road, Plumpton Green, East Sussex BN7 3DD

Tel No: 01273 890016 | **Sponsor:** Ecron

Press Officer & Programme Editor: David Ruffles (01273 813224)

GROUND ADDRESS: Caburn Ground, Anchor Field, Ringmer | Ground **Tel. No:** 01273 812738

Capacity: 1,000 | **Seats:** 100 | **Covered:** Yes | **Floodlights:** Yes

Simple Directions: From Lewes road turn right into Springett Avenue, opposite Ringmer village

Midweek Home Matchday: Tuesday | **Clubhouse:** Two bars, function room, boardroom tea bar **Club Shop:** Yes

Previous League: Brighton

Club Colours: Sky blue & navy blue/navy/navy | **Change Colours:** All white

LAST SEASON: League: Runners-Up | **F.A. Cup:** Preliminary Round | **F.A. Vase:** 2nd Qualifying Round.

Top Scorer: Dominic Shepherd | **Player of the Year:** Cl;ay Lamont | **Captain:**Julian Curnow

League: Sussex Champions 70-71 | **F.A. Cup:** 1st Rd 70-71 | **F.A.Vase:** 3rdRd 1977-78

RECORD Attendance: 1,200 in F.A.Cup 70-71 **Goalscorer:** | **Appearances:**

Senior Honours: Sussex Champions 70-71 R-up 01-02 Div 2 68-69 Sussex Senior Cup 72-73 R-Up 80-81 Sussex Junior Cup 25-26 and RUR Sussex Cup 2004-2005

RYE UNITED

Nickname: United

Chairman: Jim Sellman | **Manager:** Mike Robbins

Secretary: Michael Walton, 4 Staffords, Sea Road, Winchelsea Breach,REast Sussex TN36 4NA

Tel Nos: 01797 225838 (H) 07775 736412(M)

Programme Editor: Nick Walton

GROUND ADDRESS: Sydney Allnut Pavillion, Rye Football & Cricket Salts, Fish Market Rd., Rye (01797 223855)

Capacity: 1,500 | **Seats:** | **Covered:** 100 | **Floodlights:** Yes

Simple Directions: Outskirts of Rye on the A268 joins A259 opposite Skinners Rover garage

Midweek Home Matchday: Tuesday | **Clubhouse:** Yes | **Club Shop:** No

Club Colours: Red & black/black/black | **Change Colours:** Green & white/green/green

Best League Position: 2nd 2004-2005

RECORD Attendance: 120 | **Appearances:** Scott Price

Previous Leagues: Sussex County and Kent County until 2000

SELSEY

Founded: 1903
Nickname: Blues

Secretary: Richard Smith, 54 Grafton Road, Selsey PO20 0JE
Tel: (H) 01243 606 540. (M) 07879 410 321

Ground: High Street Ground, Selsey, Chichester, West Sussex Tel: 01243 603420
Capacity: 2,250 Seats: 50 Cover: Yes Floodlights: Yes

Directions: Through Selsey High Street to fire station. Take turning into car park alongside the station. Entrance is in the far corner. Regular buses from Chichester

Clubhouse: Bar, hospitality room, lounge, toilets, kitchen

HONOURS Sussex Co. Lg R-up 89-90 (Div 2 63-64 75-76 (R-up 86-87), Div 2 Cup 86-87 (R-up 84-85), Div 2 Invitation Cup 63-64, Sussex 5-aside 88-89), Sussex SnrCup R-up 63-64, Sussex I'mediate Cup 58-59, Sussex Jnr Cup(Reserves) 76-77,West Sussex Lg 54-55 55-56 57-58 58-59 60-61 (Malcolm Simmonds Cup 55-56 56-57 57-58 58-59)

PREVIOUS Leagues: Chichester & Dist.; West Sussex

RECORD Gate: 750-800 v Chichester or Portfield, 50's

FACT FILE
Colours: All blue
Change colours:All yellow

CLUB PERSONNEL
Chairman: David White
Manager:Danny Hinshelwood

Shoreham F.C.   Photo: Roger Turner.

SHOREHAM
Founded: 1892
Nickname: Musselmen

Chairman: Roger Brace   **President:** John Linfield
Managers: Jason Rutherford & Fred Proto
Secretary: Gary Mills, 21 Glover Avenue, Lancing, West Sussex Bn15 9RG
Tel No: 01903 761396 (H) 01273 794367 (W) 07801 477979 (M)
Press Officer: Ian Spottiswoode   **Programme:** 24 Pages 50p
GROUND ADDRESS: Middle Road, Shoreham-by-Sea, West Sussex   **Ground Tel. No.:** 01273 454261
Capacity:1,500   **Seats:** 150   **Covered:** 700   **Floodlights:** Yes
Simple Directions: From Shoreham (BR) go east over level crossing, up Dolphin Road. Ground is 150 yards on right.
Midweek Home Matchday: Tuesday   **Clubhouse:**Yes. Full facilities.   **Club Shop:**No
Previous Leagues: West Sussex   **Previous Ground:** Buckingham Park (pre-1970)
Club Colours: All Royal Blue   **Change Colours:** Red & Yellow
BEST PERFORMANCES
League: Sussex Co.Lg Champions (2)   **F.A. Cup:** 1st Qual.Rd. 1948-49 1987-88   **F.A.Vase:** 3rd Rd 1977-78 1994-95
RECORD Attendance:1,342 v Wimbledom (floodlights opening 86)
Senior Honours: Sussex Co Lg Champions 51-52 77-78 Sussex Sen.Cup

SIDLEY UNITED
Founded: 1906
Nickname:Blues

Chairman: Dickie Day   **Management Team:** Andy Laskey and Keith Miles
Secretary: Roy Maplesden, 222 Hillside Rd., Hastings TN34 2QT. Tel: (H) 01424 752039. (M) 07799 782186
Programme: Yes
GROUND ADDRESS: Gullivers Sports Ground, Glovrs Lane, Sidley, Bexhill on Sea   **Tel:** 01424 217078
Capcity: 1,500   **Seats:** None   **Covered:** 150   **Floodlights:** Yes   **Shop:** No but badges available
Simple Directions:
Midweek Home Matchday: Tuesday   **Clubhouse:** Large bar area with function room and tea bar
Previous Leagues: East Susex and Hastings & District
Club Colours: Navy blue & sky blue/navy/navy   **Change Colours:** Yellow & Black
BEST PERFORMANCES
League: Sussex Div 1 Champions 2000-01 **F.A. Cup:**   **F.A.Vase:** 1st Round
RECORD Attendance: 1,300 in 1959   **Goalscorer:**   **Appearances:** Jimmy Watson
Senior Honours: Sussex Div 1 2000-01 Sussex Intermediate Cup 47-48 Sussex Junior Cup 1924-25

THREE BRIDGES

Founded: 1901
Nickname: Bridges

Chairman: Alan Bell   **Vice-Chairman:** Paul Terry   **Manager:** Ali Rennie
Secretary: Martin Clarke,18 Mannnings Close, Pound Hill, Crawley RH10 3TX   **Press Officer:** Name (Tel)
Tel Nos: 01293 883726 (H) 07885 662940(M) **Programme Editor:** Andy West   Tel No: 01293 883163
Sponsors: Vines (Gatwick) BMW and Canadian Spar Airotron Aviation
GROUND ADDRESS: Jubile Field, Jubilee Walk, Three Bridges, Crawley, West Sussex   **Tel:** 01293 442000
Capacity: 3,500   **Seats:** 120   **Covered:** 600   **Floodlights:** Yes
Simple Directions: From Three Bridges station turn left towards Crawley. Turn right at second lights into Three Bridges road. Take first left (opposite Plough Inn) into Jubilee Walk.
Midweek Home Matchday: Tuesday   **Clubhouse:** Open every day 12noon-11pm   **Club Shop:**
Previous Leagues: Mid Sussex, East Grinstead, Redhill & Dist.,36-52
Previous Names: Three Bridges 01-18, Three Bridges Worth 36-52, Three Bridges United 54-64
Club Colours: Amber& Black/Black/Black   **Change Colours:** Blue & white/blue/white
LAST SEASON: League: 14th   **F.A. Cup:** Preliminary Round   **F.A. Vase:** 2nd Rd.
Top Scorer: Kevin Joyce   **Player of the Year:** Darren Pearce   **Captain:** Darren Pearce
BEST PERFORMANCES
League: Sussex League Runners Up (3)   **F.A. Cup:** 2nd Quaifying Rd   **F.A.Vase:** 5th Rd.
RECORD Attendance: 2,000 v Horsham 1948   **Goalscorer:**   **Appearances:** John Malthouse
Senior Honours: Sussex County League Runners-Up 85-6 87-8 88-9 Div 2 54-55 R-Up (4) Sussex R U R Cup 82-83

WHITEHAWK

Founded: 1945
Nickname: Hawks

Chairman: Wally Sweetman   **President:** Ron Wiltshire   **Manager:** Ian Chapman
Secretary: John Rosenblatt, 25 Arundel Street, Brighton, East Sussex BN2 5TH
Tel No: 07724 519370 (M)
GROUND ADDRESS: The Enclosed Ground, East Brighton Park Wilson Avenue, Brighton**Tel:** 01273 609736
Capacity: 3.000   **Seats:** None   **Covered:** 500   **Floodlights:** Yes
Simple Directions: Follow Brighton seafront towards Newhaven and turn inland (Arundel Road) opposite Marina. Take third right into Roedean Road then first left into Wilson Avenue
Midweek Home Matchday: Tuesday   **Clubhouse:** Yes fully licensed.   **Club Shop:** No
Names: Whitehawk & Manor Farm Old Boys until 1958   **Previous Leagues:** Brighton & Hove District
Club Colours: All Red   **Change Colours:** All Blue
BEST PERFORMANCES
League: Sussex League Champions (3)   **F.A. Cup:** 4th Qualifyimng Rd replay 88-89 **F.A.Vase:** 5th Rd 93-94
RECORD Attendance: 2.100 v Bognor Regis Town F.A.Cup 88-89 **Goalscorer:** Billy Ford **Appearances:** Ken Powell 1,103
Senior Honours: Sussex Co. Lg. Champions 61-62 63-64 83-84 Sussex Sen Cup 50-51 61-62 Sussex RUR Charity Cup (3)

WICK

Founded: 1892
Nickname: Wickers

Chairman: Barry Wadsworth   **Vice Chairman:** Keith Croft   **Manager:** Carl Stabler
Secretary: Allan Luckin,12 Lammas Close,Littlehampton,West Sussex BN17 6HU   **Asst.Manager:** Brett Torode
Tel No: 01903 714778 and 07816 954349 (M) **email:** allan@luckin.fsnet.co.uk
Ground: Crabtree Park, Coomes Way, Wick, Littlehampton, West Sussex   **Tel No:** 01903 713535
Capacity: 2,000   **Seats** 50   **Cover** 200   **Floodlights:** Yes
Directions: A27 to Crossbush.A284 towards Littlehampton. After one mile over level crossing left into Coomes Way next to Locomotive pub. Ground at end
Midweek Home Matchday: Tuesday   **Clubhouse:** Yes on first floor + Snacks   **Shop:** No
Previous League: West Sussex   **Previous Grounds:** Southfields Recreation
Club Colours: Red& black/black/black   **Change Colours:** All white
LAST SEASON
League: 12th Division One   **F.A. Cup:** First Qualifying Round   **F.A. Vase:** First Qualifying Round
Top Scorer: Danny Curd   **Player of the Year:** Peter Christodoulou   **Captain:** Tony Miles
BEST PERFORMANCES
League: Sussex Champions 89-90 93-94
RECORD Attendance: 900   **Goalscorer:**   **Appearances:**
Senior Honours: Sussex Div 1 (2), Sussex Senior Cup 92-93, Sussex RUR Charity Cup (3) and Sussex Junior Cup 59-60

WORTHING UNITED

Founded: 1988
Nickname: United

Chairman: Gary Downie   **Manager:** Paul Curtis
Secretary: Malcolm Gamlen, 1 Westbourne Avenue, Worthing, West Sussex BN14 8DE
Tel Nos: 01903 263655 (W) and 07743 322571 (M)
GROUND ADDRESS: The Robert Albion Memorial Ground, Lyons Way, Worthing   **Tel:** 01903 234466
Capacity: 1,000   **Seats:** 100   **Covered:** 500   **Floodlights:** Yes
Simple Directions: Via A27 from West past Hill Barn roundabout to second set of lights. Turn left into Lyons Way
Midweek Home Matchday: Tuesday   **Clubhouse:** Small Bar and Refreshments Outlet   **Club Shop:** No
Previous Names: Wigmore Athletic (1948 merged with Southdown (1988)   **Previous Ground:** Harrisons Road, Worthing
Club Colours: Blue & white/navy/navy   **Change Colours:** All red
RECORD Attendance: 180 v Northwood F.A.Vase 91-92

STEP 1
CONFERENCE

STEP 2
CONFERENCE Nth & Sth

STEP 3
NPL - SOUTHERN - ISTHMIAN PREM

STEP 4
NPL - SOUTHERN - ISTHMIAN

**STEP 5/6
SUSSEX COUNTY**

STEP 7

Three Bridges F.C. - Back Row (L-R): Allie Rennie (Assistant Manager), Lee Cox, Danny Wackett, Paul Curtis, Mark Burt, Kevin Townsend, Alan Mansfield, Steve Causon, Ryan Hackett, Sam Figg, Liam O'Brien, Derek Pyle.
Front Row: Leo Day, Darren Pearce (Capt), Pat Dunning, Liam Ahearn, Pat Massaro, Jose Goncalues.

Photo: Gordon Whittington.

Whitehawk F.C. - Back Row (L-R): Ian Chapman (Manager), Toby Phillips, Andy Beech, Ryan McBride, Michael Hunter, Wayne Chart, Keith Collingbourne, Russel Bromage (Assistant Manager).
Front Row: Peter Birch, Lee Newman, Stuart Garrod, Tommy Pattenden, BUss, Graham Martin.

Photo: Roger Turner.

BROADBRIDGE HEATH

Secretary: Ian Ford. 8 Bailey Close, Horsham, West Sussex RH12 5QR

Ground: Broadbridge Heath Sports Centre, Wickhurst Lane, Horsham   Tel: 01403 211311

Capacity: 1,300   Seats: 300   Cover: 300   Floodlights: Yes

Directions: Alongside A24, Horsham north/south bypass. From the A24 Horsham Bypass, at thelarge roundabout/underpass take the Broadbridge Heath Bypass towards Guildford and then at the first roundabout turn left into Wickhurst Lane.

Clubhouse: Bar. Kitchen serving meals,

HONOURS Sussex Yth Lg N. Div. 99-00, Southern Yth Lg S. Div. 00-01

PREVIOUS Leagues: Horsham, West Sussex, Southern Co's Comb

RECORD Attendance: 240

FACT FILE
Founded: 1919   Nickname: Bears

1st Team Sponsors: Master Tiles

Colours :Royal blue

Change: Red/black or white

Midweek matches: Tuesday

Programme Editor: Andy Crisp (01403 252273)

Admission: £2.50

CLUB PERSONNEL
Chairman: Keith Soane

President: G W Manketelow

Manager:Martin Gander

Captain: Warren Sweatman

CRAWLEY DOWN

Secretary: Colin MacCleater, 28 Beech Gardens, Crawley Down, West Sussex RH10 4JB
Tel No: 01342 713805 (H)

Ground: The Haven Sportsfield, Hophurst Lane, Crawley Down. Tel: 01342 717140
Website: www.crawleydownfc.com
Capacity: 1000   Seats: None   Cover: 50   Floodlights: Planned

Directions: From B 2028 South right into Vicarage Road ground 200 yarsd on left.
From B 2038 North left into Sandy Lane to War Memorial Hophurst Laneon left
From A22 Felbridge turnonto A264, fork left into Crawley Down. Two miles on right up hill.

Honours Sussex County Lge Div 3 R-Up 95-96
Sussex Intermediate Chall. Cup Runners-up 95-96

Previous League: Mid Sussex Football League

Record Attendance: 404 v East Grinstead Town 26.12 96

FACT FILE
Formed: 1993 Colours: All red

Change: White/black/black

Midweek Matchday: N/A

Programme:Yes

CLUB PERSONNEL
Chairman: Brian Suckling

Vice-Chairman: Michael Martin

President: Tony Clements

Match Secretary: Andy hale

Managers: Chris Sullivan

Physio: Michael Green

Captain: Paul Otway

EAST GRINSTEAD TOWN

Formed: 1890
Nickname: The Wasps

Chairman: Richard Tramontin   **President:** Colin Dixon   **Manager:** Bobby Smith

Secretary: Bruce Talbot, 16 Peverel Road, Ifield, Crawley, West Sussex (01293 543809)   **Sponsor:** Rydon Group

Press Officer: Secretary   **Programme:** 48 pages   Price £1.00   **Editor:** Bruce Talbot

GROUND ADDRESS: East Court, East Grinstead   **Ground Tel. No.:** 01342 325885

Capacity: 3,000   **Seats:** None   **Covered:** 400   **Floodlights:** Yes

Simple Directions: A264 Tunbridge Wells road (Moat Road) until mini roundabout at bottom of Blackwell Hollow ,turn immediately right by club sign then 1st left, ground 200 yards down lane past rifle club on right.

Midweek Home Matchday: Tuesday   **Clubhouse:** Open matchdays   **Club Shop:** No

Previous Leagues: Mid-Sussex 1900-15 Sussex County 20-32 Southern Amateur 32-35

Club Colours: Gold/Black/Black   **Change Colours:** All Blue

LAST SEASON:

League: 7th   **F.A. Cup: Extra** Preliminary Round   **F.A. Vase:** 1st Round

Top Scorer: Ben Burns 20   **Player of the Year:** Phiul Thompson   **Captain:** Drew Cooney

RECORD Attendance: 2,006 v Lancing F.A.Amateur Cup   **Appearances:** Guy Hill (19 seasons)

Senior Honours: Sussex Junior Cup 07-08 Mid Sussex Junior Cup 2001-02

LANCING

Secretary Brian Hill,17 Annweir Avenue, Lancing, West Sussex BN15 9NF
&Press Off :Tel: 01903 756165 (H&F)   email: brian@whill20.fsnet.co.uk

Ground: Culver Road, Lancing, West Sussex Tel: 01903 764398
Web-site: www.lancingfc.co.uk

Directions: From A27 turn south at Lancing Manor r'about into Grinstead Lane, 3rd turning on right North Farm Rd. Turn left then immed. right into Culver Rd. From railway station take 3rd turning on left heading north. Capacity: 2,400 Seats: 350   Cover: 350   Floodlights: Yes

Clubhouse: Open matchdays & training nights. Separate tea bar.   **Club Shop:** Yes

HONOURS Sussex Co. Lg R-up 49-50 64-65 (Div 2 57-58 69-70 (R-up 82-83), Div 2 Cup 81-82 92-93, Invitation Cup), Sussex RUR Charity Cup 65-66, Brighton Lg 46-47 47-48, Sussex Intermediate Cup 46-47, Brighton Charity Cup 83-84 84-85 86-87.

PREVIOUS League: Brighton Hove & District   **Name:** Lancing Athletic

RECORDS Attendance: 2,591 v Tooting, FA Amateur Cup 22/11/47 At Culver Road: 2,340v Worthing 25/10/52   **Career Appearances:** Dave Menzies 462 **Goals:** Paul Steele 113

FACT FILE
Founded: 1941   Nickname: Lancers

Sponsors: Bacon & Co. Estate Agents

Colours: Yellow/blue/yellow

Change colours: All red

Midweek Matches: Wed Programme: Yes

Reserves League: Sussex Co Res.West

Editor/Press Off.: Brian Nicholls

(01903 525468)

CLUB PERSONNEL
Chairman: John Brown   President: R G Steele

Match Sec: Don Stevens (01273 592653 (H)

Manager: Sammy Donnelly

LINGFIELD

Secretary: Pamela Tomsett, 61 Drivers Mead. Lingfield,Surrey RH7 6EX

Tel: 01342 832418 (H)

Ground: Sports Pavilion, Godstone Road, Lingfield, Surrey.

Tel: 01342 834269

Directions: A22, 4 miles north of East Grinstead, to Mormon Temple roundabout, take exit Lingfield (B2028) Newchapel Road for 1 1/2 miles. Left at T junction into Godstone Road (B2029) and ground is 1/2 mile on left.

CLUB PERSONNEL
Chairman: Bill Blenkin

Manager: Dennis Moore

FACT FILE
Colours:
Red & yellow stripes/black/yellow
Change colours:
Blue & white stripes/white/sky blue

MIDHURST & EASEBOURNE

Secretary: Ted Dummer, 14 Nine Acres, June Lane, Midhurst, W. Sussex GU29 9EP
Tel: 01730 813887 (H) email: acs@harrisonrenwick.com

Ground: Rotherfield, Dodsley Lane, Easebourne, Midhurst, W. Sussex GU29 9BE
Tel: 01730 816557

Directions: Ground one mile out of Midhurst on London Road (A286) opposite Texaco Garage. Ample car parking. Buses pass ground every hour

Capacity: 1,000   **Seats:** 60   **Covered** 60   **Clubhouse:** Yes **Shop** : No

Honours: Sussex County Division Two League Cup 1988-1989
Sussex County Division Three League Cup 2002-2003

CLUB PERSONNEL
Chairman: Alan Thompson

Manager: Dave Kelly
Coach: Robbie Pearce

FACT FILE
Colours: Royal blue/black/royal
Change colours: All red

MILE OAK

Secretary: Colin Brown, 19 The Crescent, Southwick, West Sussex BN42 4LB

Tel: 01273 591346

Ground: Chalky Road, Portslade, Brighton BN41 2YU .Tel: 01273423854

HONOURS Sussex Co.Lg.Div 2 Champions, Div 3 R-up 91-92 (Div 2 Cup R-up 92-93), Southern Counties Combination 86-87, Brighton Hove & District Lg 80-81, VernonWentworth Cup 85-86, Sussex Intermediate Cup R-up 88-89

PREVIOUS **Leagues:** Southern Counties Combination; Brighton Hove & District
Ground: Victoria Rec., Portslade   **RECORD Attendance:** 186

FACT FILE
Founded: 1960
Nickname: The Oak
Colours: Tangerine/black/tangerine
Change colours: All green
Midweek Matchday: Tuesday
Programme: Yes
Editor: C Tew (01273 416036)
Admission: £1.50
Local Press: Brighton Evening Argus,
Shoreham Herald

CLUB PERSONNEL
Chairman: Les Hamilton
Manager: Anthony Whittington

PAGHAM

Secretary: David Bolland, 23 Tennyson Road, Bognor `Regis PO21 2SB
Tel No: 01243 829973
Ground: Nyetimber Lane, Pagham, West Sussex   Tel: 01243 266112
Capacity: 2,000   Seats: 200   Cover: 200   Floodlights: Yes
Directions: Turn off A27 Chichester by-pass (signposted A259 Pagham). Ground invillage of Nyetimber. Three miles from Bognor (BR). Buses 260 & 240
Clubhouse: Bar open matchdays and some evenings. Hot food, pool, darts,satellite TV. Tea bar
Club Shop: No
HONOURS Sussex Co Lg Champions and R-up (4) Sussex RUR Charity Cup 88-89 R-up 93-4
PREVIOUS **Leagues:** Chichester 1903-50; West Sussex 50-69   **Grounds:** None

RECORDS **Gate:** 1,200 v Bognor, 1971 Susses Senior Cup
Win: 10-1 v Seaford Town (A), Sussex County League Division Two, 1970
Defeat: 0-7 v Newport IOW (H), FA Amateur Cup, mid-1970s
Most Appearances: Graham Peach   **Most Goals:** Dick De Luca
2005-2006 **Player of the Year:** Rob Wimble   **Top Scorer:** Rob Wimble

FACT FILE
Founded: 1903
Nickname: Lions
Sponsors: The Alex Public House
Colours: White/Black/Red
Change colours: Green/White/Green
Midweek Matchday: Tuesday
Reserves' League: Sussex Co. Res West
Programme: 20 pages, incl Admission
Editor: Jon Rose
Local Press: Bognor Observer
CLUB PERSONNEL
Chairman: Kevin Seal
Vice-Chairman: Edie Waghorn
President: A Peirce
Press Officer: Jon Rose(07766690114)
Commercial Manager: Michael Willis

PEACHAVEN & TELSCOMBE

Secretary: Mrs Margaret Edwards, 2,Tuscan Court, The Esplanade, Telscombe Cliffs, East Sussex BN10 7HF.
Tel: 01273 583022 (H) 07803 845329 (M)

Ground: The Sports Park, Piddinghoe Avenue, Peacehaven, E. Sussex
Tel: 01273 582471

Directions: From Brighton on A259, over r'bout & Piddinghoe Ave. is next left after 2nd set of lights - ground at end. From Newhaven, Piddinghoe Ave. is 1st right after 1st set of lights. 3 miles from Newhaven(BR). Peacehaven is served by Brighton to Newhaven & Eastbourne buses

CLUB PERSONNEL
Chairman: Jim Edwards

Manager: Darren Guirey

FACT FILE
Colours:
Black & white stripes/black/white
Change colours:
Yellow/blue/yellow

SALTDEAN UNITED

Secretary: Iain Fielding, 40 Rowan Way, Rottingdean, Brighton BN2 7FP
Tel: 01273 304995

Ground: Hill Park, Combe Vale, Saltdean, Brighton   Tel: 01273 309898
Capacity: 2,000   Seats: 50   Cover: Yes Floodlights: Yes   Club Shop: No

Directions: A259 coast road east from Brighton to Saltdean Lido, left into Arundel Drive West, and Saltdean Vale to bridle path at beginning of Combe Vale.
Club 200yds along track

Clubhouse: Licensed bar, lounge, darts, video games, board room, tea bar.Pool table

HONOURS Sussex Co. Lg Div 3 88-89, Div 2 95-96: John O'Hara Lg Cup Winners 2000
PREVIOUS **League:** Sussex County **Ground:** None
RECORD **Attendance:** 676

FACT FILE
Founded: 1966   Nickname: Tigers
Colours: Red & blackstripes/black/black
Change : Blue & white stripes/blue/blue
Programme: Yes   Editor:Mick Way
Local Press: Brighton Evening Argus &
Sussex Express

CLUB PERSONNEL
Chairman: Iain Fielding
Manager: Mark Smeaton

SEAFORD TOWN

Secretary: Ms Rosetta Sadler-King, Birling Lodge, Birling Gap Road, East Dean BN20 0AA Tel: (H) 01323 423589. (M) 07976 648580

Ground: The Crouch, Bramber Road, Seaford. Tel: 01323 892221

Directions: A259 to Seaford. At mini r'about by station,
turn LEFT (coming from Newhaven) or RIGHT (from Eastbourne).
At end of Church St., across junction, then left at end. After 500 m turn left up Ashurst Rd. Bramber Rd. is at the top.

Honours: Champions Sussex Division Two 2005-2006

FACT FILE

Colours: All red
Change: All white

CLUB PERSONNEL
Chairman: Dick Knight

Manager: Duncan Kneller

SIDLESHAM

Secretary: Michael Maiden,31 The Avenue,Hambrook, Nr Chichester, W. Sussex PO18 8TZ
Tel Nos: 01243 575628 (H) 07971 818761 (M)

Ground: Sidlesham Recreation Ground,Selsey Road Sidlesham.Chichester.E.Sussex PO20 7RD Tel No: 01243 603977
Capacity:1,500 **Covered Seating:** No **Covered Standing:** Yes **Floodlights:** Yes
Clubhouse: Open evenings 8-11 p.m.   **Club Shop:** No

Directions: From the Chichester bypass take the B2145, signposted Hunston/Selsey
Head towards Selsey. Upon entering Sidlesham the ground is on the right between houses.

Best Season: F.A.Vase: Second Round 2002-2003
HONOURS West Sussex League 1963-64 W.Sussex Lg Cup 1963-64,19787-79,1990-91
Sussex Intermediate Cup 1q9909-91. Sussex Co. Lg Cup Div 3 1991-92,1996-97.Div 3 Chamipons1996-97, Division 2 Champions 1999-2000 Div 2 CP 99-00
Div1 Cup r-uyp: 2000-01

FACT FILE
Founded: 1946
Colours: Yellow & Green/green/yellow
Change colours: Red /Black/Red
Midweek Matchday: Tuesdays
Prog: Yes 24 Pages 50P Ed: Sec.
CLUB PERSONNEL
Chairman: Brian Thomas
Tel: 01243 378930 (H)
077 30534516 (M)
Vice Chairman: Alan Parker
Manager: Lee Etherington
Assistant .Manager: Tom Evans

SOUTHWICK

Founded: 1882
Nickname: Wickers

Chairman: Barry Noonan   **Joint Managers:** Andy Aggutter & Domonic Shepherd
Secretary: Paul Symes. 55 Downsway, Southwick BN42 4WE
Programme Editor: Paul Symes (01273 594142)   **Club Email Address:** southwickfc@btconnect.com
GROUND ADDRESS: Old Barn Way, off Manor Hall Way, Southwick, Brighton BN43 4NT **Tel:** 01273 701010
Capacity: 3,500   **Seats:** 220   **Covered:** None   **Floodlights:** Yes
Simple Directions: A27 from Brighton take first left after Southwick sign to Leisure Centre. Ground adjacent. Five minutes walk from Fishergate or Southwick stations.
Midweek Home Matchday: Tuesday   **Clubhouse:** Open daily with matchday snacks   **Club Shop:** Ties & Badges
Previous Leagues: West Sussex 1896-1920, Sussex Co., 20-52 54-84, Metropolitan 52-54 Comb Co., 84-85 , Isthmian 85-92
Club Colours: Red& blackstripes/black/red   **Change Colours:** All White
Last Season
League: 20th   **F.A. Cup:** Preliminary Round   **F.A. Vase:** 1st Round
Top Scorer: Wayne Joseph & Marcus Strevens 6   **Player of the Year:** Tony Timms   **Captain:** Neil Harris
BEST PERFORMANCES
League: Isthmian Div 1 86-87   **F.A. Cup:** 1st Rd 74-75   **F.A.Vase:** 3rd Rd 1980 & 1986 **F.A.Amateur Cup:** 3rd Rd 28-29
RECORD Attendance: 3,200 V showbiz Charity Game
SENIOR HONOURS: Sussex County League Champions (6) Sussex Senior Cup Winners (10)

ST. FRANCIS RANGERS

FACT FILE

Previous Names: Ansty Rangers & St. Francis

Colours:Black & white/black/black

Change colours: All Green with white trim

Secretary: Patrick Bucknell, 79 Priory Way, Haywards Heath,West Sussex RH16 3NS
Tel Nos:01444 457726 (H) 07887615752 (M)
e-mail: twgoulds@hotmail.com

Ground: The Princess Royal Hospital, Lewes Road, Haywards Heath, RH16 4EX
Tel No: 01444 474021 and social club 01444441881

Directions: Enter through the main hospital entranceon the Lewes road and follow
signs to Sports Complex.

CLUB PERSONNEL

Chairman: John Goss

01444 232210(H) 07748 785240 (M)

Manager: Dan Bryan

STEYNING TOWN

Secretary: Mrs. Gina Barnes, 36 Shooting Field, Steyning W. Sussex BN44 3RQ
Tel: 01903 815387 (H)
Ground: The Shooting Field, Steyning, W. Sussex   Tel: 01903 812228)
Directions: Entering Steyning from the west. Take 1st left in the High St (Tanyard
Lane)

Follow into Shooting Field estate, ground is 4th turn on the left.
Entering Steyning from the east. From the High St., turn right into Church
St.. Turn left by Church into Shooting Field estate.
NB Coaches MUST park in Church Street Car Park.
HONOURS   Sussex Co Lg Champions 84-5,85-6 Lg Cup Winners: 78-9,83-4 85-6
Div 2, 77-78 Div 2 Cup 65-6 Merit Table winners 84-5 Div 3 R-Up 01-02 Cup R-up 00-01
CLUB RECORDS Attendance: 1,100 v Halesowen Town F.A.Vase Quarter Final 84-85
Biggest Win: 15-0 v Portslade Sussex Co Lg.1965-6
Biggest Defeat:1-11 v Littlehampton Town Sussex Sen. Cup 90-91

FACT FILE

Colours: All Red/white
Change: All blue
Programme: 36 pages
Website: www.steyningtownfc.org.uk
E-mail: ian@ikennett.freeserve.co.uk

CLUB PERSONNEL
Chairman: TBA
Manager: TBA

STORRINGTON

Founded: 1925
Nickname: Swans

Chairman: Malcolm McMichael

Manager: Russell Pentecost   **Assistant Manager & Physio**: Trevor Paish

Secretary: Keith Dalmon, 4 End Cottages, Storrington Road, Amberley, Arundel, BN18 9LX

Tel No: 01798 831887 (H) 07889 367956(M)

Programme Editor: Chairman   **Programme:** 8 Pages with admission

GROUND ADDRESS: Recreation Ground, Pulborough Road, Storrington   **Tel:**

Capacity: 1,000   **Seats:** None   **Covered:** 100   **Floodlights: Soon**

Simple Directions: A24 right at roundabout at Washington. Four miles to Storrington through village. Third exit at roundabout and second right into Spearbridge Road.

Midweek Home Matchday: Tuesday   **Clubhouse:** Yes   **Club Shop:** No

Club Colours: All Royal Blue   **Change Colours:** All White

Top Scorer: Neil Richardson   **Player of the Year:**   **Captain:** Rob Norris

BEST PERFORMANCES

League: Winning promotion as champs form Div 3 04-05   **F.A. Cup:** N/A   **F.A.Vase:** N/A

WEALDEN

Secretary: Kate Gilbert, MIckleton Cottage, Wilderness Lane, Hadlow Down, E.Sussex
TN22 4HX   **Tel Nos:** 01825 890764 (H)   07851410220 (M)
Email: Kate.wealden@hotmail.com

Ground: The Oaks,Wealden Football Club, Old Eastbourne Road, Uckfield, East Sussex.
Tel: 01825 890905

Capacity: 600   **Seats**: No   **Cover** :Yes   **Floodlights** : Yes

Clubhouse: Yes   **Shop**: No

Directions: Next to the Rajdutt Restaurant on the Old Eastbourne Road,
south of Uckfield town centre.

HONOURS Sussex County Lge Div. 3 R-up 99-00 Div 2 League Cup Winners 2004-05

FACT FILE

Colours: Light blue & Navy blue
Change colours: Navy & white hoops

Sponsor
Parker Building Supplies Ltd.

CLUB PERSONNEL
Chairman: Tom Parker
Manager: Andy Gander
Asst. Man. Mark Cox
Coach: Stuart Murdock

WESTFIELD

Secretary: George Chapman, Roker, 15 Heathlands, Westfield TN35 4QZ
Tel No: (H) 01424 751 825.

Ground: The Parish Field, Main Road, Westfield TN35 4SB
Tel No: 01483 751 011

Directions: From Hastings take the A21, turning right onto the A28 towards Ashford.
Travel through Westfield, and the ground is located off Westfield Lane on the
left

FACT FILE

Nickname: Parishioners

Colours: Yellow & Green/green/yellow
Change Colours: All dark blue

CLUB PERSONNEL
Chairman: G.A.Drinkwater

Manager: Steve Johnson

DIVISION THREE

		P	W	D	L	F	A	Pts
1.	Peacehaven & Telscombe	26	20	2	4	81	31	62
2.	Lingfield	26	19	3	4	73	29	60
3.	Rustington	26	17	4	5	65	31	55
4.	Newhaven	26	15	5	6	61	31	50
5.	Forest	26	13	7	6	51	37	46
6.	Ifield Edwards	26	13	1	12	68	52	40
7.	Hurstpierpoint	26	11	5	10	47	49	38
8.	Haywards Heath Town	26	10	7	9	57	41	37
9.	Little Common	26	10	3	13	43	50	33
10.	Bosham (-3)	26	9	5	12	44	58	29
11.	Uckfield Town	26	8	3	15	30	46	27
12.	Pease Pottage Village	26	7	5	14	39	51	26
13.	Wadhurst United	26	3	3	20	33	78	12
14.	Upper Beeding (+3)	26	0	1	25	14	122	4

DIVISION THREE

		1	2	3	4	5	6	7	8	9	10	11	12	13	14
1	Bosham		1-0	3-2	2-2	3-2	1-2	1-2	1-3	0-4	2-2	0-4	0-0	6-0	4-1
2	Forest	4-0		3-1	2-1	2-0	2-1	1-1	3-1	0-5	4-1	0-2	1-1	4-0	1-1
3	Haywards Heath Town	4-2	3-4		2-0	0-1	0-2	3-0	1-1	1-2	2-2	1-1	3-0	3-0	8-2
4	Hurstpierpoint	4-3	0-3	1-1		2-5	2-2	0-1	2-1	0-7	3-4	3-2	2-0	5-0	5-1
5	Ifield Edwards	7-0	2-2	5-2	1-2		1-3	6-3	4-3	3-5	5-1	1-2	0-2	3-1	2-1
6	Lingfield	0-0	3-1	3-3	1-2	2-0		3-1	3-1	1-0	2-1	4-1	5-0	2-0	7-1
7	Little Common	0-1	1-1	2-5	2-1	3-1	0-1		2-3	1-5	3-1	0-4	2-3	6-1	4-1
8	Newhaven	4-1	1-1	1-1	3-2	2-1	4-0	2-0		2-1	5-1	1-1	2-0	5-0	2-1
9	Peacehaven & Telscombe	1-0	3-3	4-2	1-0	3-1	4-2	3-0	2-2		2-0	4-2	3-2	5-1	3-2
10	Pease Pottage Village	3-2	4-1	1-1	0-1	2-3	0-1	1-2	1-0	2-1		1-2	1-2	3-1	1-1
11	Rustington	1-1	2-1	1-0	1-1	5-0	2-6	0-2	1-0	2-0	2-0		3-2	6-1	5-1
12	Uckfield Town	3-4	1-3	0-2	1-2	0-2	1-2	1-0	1-3	1-2	0-0	0-2		2-0	1-0
13	Upper Beeding	2-3	0-2	0-2	2-2	0-9	0-11	0-4	0-7	0-6	1-5	1-7	2-3		1-2
14	Wadhurst United	1-3	1-2	0-4	1-2	1-3	1-4	1-1	0-2	1-5	2-1	0-4	0-3	9-0	

LEAGUE CONSTITUTION 2006-07 - DIVISION THREE

BEXHILL UNITED

Secretary: Bill Trivett, 134 London Road, Bexhill On Sea TN39 4AA   Tel: (H) 01424 733004 (M) 07940 255222
Ground: The Polegrove, Brockley Road, Bexhill on Sea TN39 3EX Tel: 01424 220732
Directions: A 27 to L. Common then fourth exit off roundabout to Cooden Beach. Left and follow to end, turn right into Brockby Road. Ground at bottom of hill on right.
Colours: White/black/black Change Colours: Yellow/blue/yellow

BOSHAM

Secretary: Robin Baldwin, 44 Edgell Road, Westbourne Emsworth PO10 8UR Tel: (H) 01243 374593
Ground: Bosham Recreation Ground, Walton Lane, Bosham, W. Sussex Tel: 01243 574011
Directions: From Chichester take the A259 towards Portsmouth. On reaching Bosham turn left at the Swan P.H. roundabout. 1/2 mile to T junction, turn left & car park 50 yds on left.
Honours: Sussex County Lge Div. 3 99-00
Colours: All red. Change Colours: Gold/blue/blue

FOREST

Secretary: Peter Farley, 9 Owlbeech Way, Horsham, W.Sussex RH13 6AW. Tel: 01403 25256
Ground: Roffey Sports & Social Club, Spooners Rd., Roffey. Tel: 01403 210221
Directions: Spooners Rd. is off the main Crawley road, 100 yds from the `Star'PH, towards Crawley
Colours: White/green/white. Change: Green/white/green

HAYWARDS HEATH TOWN

Secretary: John Rea. 73 Lynchmere Avenue, North Lancing, West Sussex BN15 0PB
Ground: Hanbury Park Stadium, Haywards Heath Tel: 01444 412837
Directions: A272 to Haywards Heath town centre. At Sussex roundabout, north on B2708 (Hazelgrove Road) take first right into New England Road, then the 4th right (Allen Road) leads to ground.
Colours: Blue & white stripes/blue/blue

HURSTPIERPOINT

Secretary: Gill Stafford. 12 Ockley Lane, Keymer, Hassocks, West Sussex BN6 8BA.
Ground: Fairfield Rec. Ground, Cuckfield Road. (Tel: 01273 834783)
Directions: At Hurstpoint crossroads, go north into Cuckfield Road (B2117) for 1km. Ground entrance between houses nos.158 & 160
Colours: Blue & white quarters/blue/blue

IFIELD EDWARDS

Secretary: Rob Anderson, 1 Old Orchards, Church Rd, Worth, Crawley. RH107QA. Tel: 01293 886215)
Ground: Edwards Sports& Social Club, Ifield Green, Rusper Road, Crawley. Tel: 01293 536569)
Directions: From A23 Crawley by-pass going north, left at r'about signedCharlwood. Third left into Ifield Green, first right past Royal Oak (PH) into Rusper Rd
Colours: Red/black/black

LITTLE COMMON

(Promoted from East Sussex League)
Secretary: Margaret Cherry. 11 Bidwell Avenue, Bexhill-on-Sea, East Sussex TN39 4DB
Ground: Peartree Lane, Little Common, Bexhill TN39 4PH
Tel: 01424 845861
Colours: All claret

LOXWOOD

Secretary: George Read, 2 Grove Road   Petworth   GU28 0BT. Tel: (H) 01798-343839 (M) 07791-766857
Ground: Plaistow Road, Loxwood RH14 0SX
Colours: White/black/white

NEWHAVEN

Secretary: Peter Foote, 32 Valley Dene, Newhaven BN9 9NF
Tel: 01273 513232
Ground: Fort Road Recreation Ground Tel: 01273 513940
Directions: A259, follow one-way system around town, left at Police Station into South Road, which becomes Fort Road.
Colours: Red & whiter/red/red

PEASE POTTAGE VILLAGE

Secretary: Julian Smith, 17 Dickens Road, Tilgate, Crawley RH10 5AS   Tel: (H) 01293 413511 (M): 07906 021227
Ground: Finches Field, Pease Pottage, Crawley, W. Sussex
Tel: 01293 538651
Directions: Off M23/A23 towards Brighton, turn off at Pease Pottage (turn off just past Crawley). Past service station to roundabout, take 3rd exit over bridge sharp left, follow signs to Finches Field. Approx. 300 yards past "Grapes" P.H., on the right.
Colours: Royal blue & white/royal/white

ROTTINGDEAN VILLAGE

Secretary: David Carruthers
115 Sutton Avenue No Peacehaven BN10 7QJ
Tel: (H) 01273 584525   (M): 07831 582072
Ground: Rottingdean Sports Centre, Falmer Road
Rottingdean BN2 7DA
Tel: 01273 306436
Colours: Red/black/red

RUSTINGTON

Secretary: Paul Cox. 28 The Gilberts, Sea Road, Rustington BN16 2LY
Tel: (H) 01903 773253   (M): 07771 623224
Ground: Recreation Ground, Jubilee Avenue, Rustington, West Sussex
Tel: 01903 770 495
Colours: Royal blue/royal blue/white

UCKFIELD TOWN

Secretary: Peter Walsh
1 Claremont Rise, Uckfield, TN22 2AH
Tel (H): 01825 763201 (M): 07970 123331
Ground: Victoria Pleasure Ground, Uckfield. Tel: 01825 769400
Directions: Take Eastbourne road (old A22) south of Uckfield town centre. Entrance to ground is 1/2 mile on the right (just after the Police station)
Colours: Red/black/black

Action from a Sussex County Division 2 game between Pagham and Wealdon. Photo: Graham Cotterill.

UNITED COUNTIES LEAGUE

SPONSORED BY: EAGLE BITTER

Chairman: John R Weeks

Secretary: Allan Crick. Daisy Cottage, Shore Road, Frieston, Boston, Lincs PE22 0LN. Tel: 01205 760 162

Press Officer: Jeremy Biggs   Tel: 01780 763 048

PREMIER DIVISION	P	W	D	L	F	A	Pts
1. Woodford United	42	28	8	6	102	32	92
2. Potton United	42	28	8	6	92	51	92
3. Northampton Spencer	42	28	5	9	92	36	89
4. St Neots Town	42	25	5	12	81	52	80
5. Cogenhoe United (Champions 04-05)	42	23	8	11	86	64	77
6. Boston Town	42	22	9	11	88	60	75
7. Yaxley (-3)	42	21	6	15	71	49	66
8. Raunds Town	42	18	11	13	66	54	65
9. St Ives Town	42	18	4	20	64	76	58
10. Blackstones	42	15	12	15	79	68	57
11. Stotfold	42	15	10	17	84	74	55
12. Wootton Blue Cross	42	15	9	18	65	59	54
13. Bourne Town	42	15	9	18	68	73	54
14. Buckingham Town (-1)	42	15	7	20	77	84	51
15. Newport Pagnell Town	42	14	8	20	48	66	50
16. Stewarts & Lloyds	42	14	8	20	55	77	50
17. Holbeach United	42	12	10	20	63	70	46
18. Desborough Town (-1)	42	13	8	21	64	83	46
19. Ford Sports Daventry	42	13	6	23	59	84	45
20. Deeping Rangers	42	11	9	22	56	73	42
21. Long Buckby	42	11	7	24	65	87	40
22. Harrowby United	42	2	5	35	37	190	11

PREMIER DIVISION	1	2	3	4	5	6	7	8	9	10	11	12	13	14	15	16	17	18	19	20	21	22
1 Blackstones		2-3	1-3	1-2	4-1	3-0	1-1	5-2	7-0	2-0	3-3	2-1	0-5	1-1	5-1	3-4	3-2	2-2	3-2	0-0	3-0	2-2
2 Boston Town	1-0		1-0	1-0	2-2	1-0	5-5	1-0	4-0	2-0	2-1	4-1	5-1	1-3	1-1	4-0	4-1	1-2	2-1	1-1	3-0	1-0
3 Bourne Town	0-1	1-4		0-0	1-4	0-3	3-2	3-2	6-0	2-1	1-1	3-1	1-2	1-2	2-0	3-1	2-4	1-1	1-1			2-4
4 Buckingham T.	1-1	3-2	2-2		1-3	1-0	3-0	3-2	8-1	0-2	0-0	3-4	1-4	1-1	0-0	1-4	0-1	2-3	3-2	0-5	0-2	1-3
5 Cogenhoe U.	2-3	4-4	3-2	4-1		3-2	2-1	2-0	3-0	2-2	2-0	1-1	3-0	2-3	4-1	2-1	1-0	2-1	1-1	1-4	1-1	0-2
6 Deeping Rgers	3-2	4-3	1-4	0-2	2-6		4-1	3-3	2-3	3-1	3-0	1-0	0-5	1-2	2-2	0-1	0-3	1-1	1-1	0-2	3-1	0-0
7 Desborough T.	1-1	4-2	1-2	3-5	1-3	2-1		1-4	4-0	1-0	2-1	4-0	1-3	3-3	1-0	1-2	0-1	2-0	2-0	1-6	2-0	1-3
8 Ford Sports D.	1-1	0-1	0-1	5-2	0-1	1-0	3-0		2-3	1-2	4-1	3-1	0-4	2-1	1-3	2-0	2-2	0-1	1-1	0-4	2-1	0-1
9 Harrowby Utd	2-3	0-7	0-2	0-8	0-3	1-4	1-1	0-4		2-2	0-6	3-3	0-2	1-2	1-9	0-4	1-7	2-2	1-5	3-5	1-3	2-6
10 Holbeach Utd	2-2	6-0	0-0	1-3	3-3	2-4	0-0	5-1	5-0		0-1	1-0	1-1	3-1	1-2	0-3	5-0	2-3	0-1	0-4	1-3	
11 Long Buckby	1-1	4-3	1-3	1-5	0-3	1-2	2-0	1-2	6-1	2-3		4-1	0-6	1-3	4-2	0-1	1-2	1-1	1-2	2-3	2-4	3-1
12 Newport P.T.	1-0	0-3	0-0	0-0	0-1	1-0	2-1	2-2	3-0	2-1	1-1		0-3	2-5	1-0	1-2	0-2	1-0	1-1	0-1	2-0	3-0
13 Northampton S.	1-0	1-0	0-1	0-2	3-2	0-0	4-2	2-0	7-1	1-0	3-1	1-0		1-1	1-2	2-1	1-2	2-1	5-0	1-0	1-1	1-1
14 Potton United	2-1	1-1	5-2	4-2	2-1	2-1	3-0	4-1	4-1	2-1	2-1	1-0	2-1		0-0	1-2	3-1	4-2	1-0	4-0	2-2	4-1
15 Raunds Town	1-1	1-1	3-0	3-1	0-1	2-0	3-1	2-3	2-1	0-1	1-0	1-1	1-3	0-2		3-1	1-0	4-1	1-1	0-2	1-0	1-1
16 St Ives Town	2-1	1-3	0-5	2-4	2-2	1-1	1-1	3-0	2-0	1-3	0-2	4-0	0-2	3-1	0-0		1-2	1-4	1-2	1-0	4-1	1-3
17 St Neots Town	2-1	4-1	2-0	2-1	0-1	1-1	3-1	4-1	3-0	1-1	2-2	2-1	1-0	4-1	0-2	2-1		3-1	2-5	2-1	3-1	1-2
18 Stewarts & L.	0-2	0-1	2-0	2-2	2-0	2-1	1-1	3-0	3-1	1-2	1-3	0-4	0-5	1-4	0-2	2-1	3-2		2-0	2-0	1-0	1-3
19 Stotfold	3-1	1-1	2-3	1-2	4-2	1-1	1-3	5-0	9-0	2-2	5-0	2-3	0-3	0-1	3-1	3-1	2-4	3-2		0-4	2-2	0-2
20 Woodford Utd	3-2	3-1	3-0	5-2	3-0	2-0	3-0	0-0	10-0	4-0	4-1	3-1	2-0	1-0	2-2	6-0	1-2	0-0	0-0		1-0	2-0
21 Wootton B.C.	1-2	1-0	1-1	3-0	4-1	2-1	4-1	3-0	5-1	0-0	0-0	0-1	2-1	4-2	4-1	0-0	3-0	1-2	2-4	1-3		1-3
22 Yaxley	3-0	2-0	4-2	1-0	0-1	1-0	0-1	1-2	7-1	5-1	0-2	0-1	0-0	0-1	1-2	1-0	1-0	1-1	3-2	0-2	0-1	

DIVISION ONE	P	W	D	L	F	A	Pts
1. Sleaford Town	34	26	3	5	106	36	81
2. Wellingborough Town (Promoted)	34	22	11	1	74	19	77
3. Wellingborough Whitworths	34	21	5	8	77	38	68
4. AFC Kempston Rovers	34	19	7	8	61	38	64
5. Northampton ON Cheneks	34	19	5	10	66	43	62
6. Daventry Town	34	14	9	11	67	58	51
7. Eynesbury Rovers	34	15	5	14	63	68	50
8. Olney Town	34	14	6	14	69	59	48
9. Peterborough Northern Star	34	13	9	12	71	63	48
10. Rothwell Corinthians	34	13	7	14	59	57	46
11. Bugbrooke St Michaels	34	12	7	15	45	65	43
12. Huntingdon Town	34	12	5	17	45	53	41
13. Northampton Sileby Rangers	34	12	4	18	59	81	40
14. Blisworth (-1)	34	10	10	14	63	71	39
15. Irchester United	34	11	4	19	48	65	37
16. Thrapston Town	34	7	7	20	52	79	28
17. Higham Town	34	6	4	24	35	105	22
18. Burton Park Wanderers	34	3	6	25	26	88	15

DIVISION ONE	1	2	3	4	5	6	7	8	9	10	11	12	13	14	15	16	17	18
1 AFC Kempston Rovers		4-1	4-1	1-1	3-1	2-3	4-0	0-0	1-1	1-2	2-0	2-2	1-1	5-1	1-0	2-1	0-0	0-5
2 Blisworth	2-0		5-0	3-1	2-2	2-3	1-2	5-3	1-2	3-3	3-4	1-4	2-0	0-3	1-2	0-3	0-3	1-1
3 Bugbrooke St Michaels	0-1	0-1		3-2	3-1	1-2	1-0	1-1	2-1	1-1	1-1	1-0	4-3	0-3	1-4	2-1	1-1	1-2
4 Burton Park Wanderers	0-2	0-4	1-1		1-1	2-1	0-2	2-3	0-4	0-1	1-1	0-8	0-5	0-5	1-2	0-1	1-2	1-3
5 Daventry Town	1-0	3-3	3-0	0-1		4-1	1-0	1-1	1-0	1-1	4-3	3-1	2-2	3-2	2-0	2-1	1-1	1-4
6 Eynesbury Rovers	1-3	3-1	0-3	2-0	1-1		2-3	3-0	2-0	1-0	1-5	3-3	3-1	1-1	2-4	3-1	0-3	4-2
7 Higham Town	1-5	1-1	1-1	3-2	1-6	2-7		3-1	1-4	0-4	0-4	3-0	0-2	1-1	1-6	3-5	1-2	1-2
8 Huntingdon Town	0-1	3-2	1-3	2-0	0-0	3-1	0-0		1-0	0-1	2-3	0-1	3-1	0-1	1-2	3-0	1-3	1-0
9 Irchester United	2-4	0-0	2-3	1-0	2-1	1-1	3-1	3-1		0-2	0-3	1-2	2-3	3-0	3-1	2-5	0-5	0-3
10 Northampton ON Cheneks	1-0	2-3	4-1	4-0	1-3	3-4	3-1	0-2	2-1		4-0	3-1	5-2	3-1	0-1	4-4	1-2	2-0
11 Olney Town	0-1	1-1	5-1	1-0	4-1	2-1	4-0	1-2	4-1	1-2		4-2	1-2	7-1	1-3	2-0	1-3	0-2
12 Peterborough Northern Star	2-0	2-5	3-2	2-2	2-1	1-0	7-1	2-1	2-2	2-3	1-1		1-2	4-0	1-2	2-1	0-0	2-2
13 Rothwell Corinthians	0-3	3-3	1-2	4-1	4-1	0-1	4-1	1-0	2-0	2-2	1-1	2-2		1-0	0-1	3-0	0-3	0-3
14 Northampton Sileby Rangers	2-5	1-1	1-2	1-2	1-7	1-2	3-1	2-3	5-3	2-0	4-0	3-1	2-1		1-4	3-1	0-2	1-4
15 Sleaford Town	0-1	4-2	4-1	8-0	2-1	3-0	8-0	2-0	3-1	2-0	6-2	7-1	2-2	8-2		6-2	1-2	3-2
16 Thrapston Town	1-1	1-2	2-0	1-1	1-5	3-3	2-0	1-2	1-2	0-1	2-1	2-5	0-4	3-4	0-4		1-1	2-3
17 Wellingborough Town	5-0	0-0	1-1	3-1	5-1	3-1	7-0	4-2	2-0	0-1	1-1	1-0	4-0	0-0	0-0	1-1		2-0
18 Wellingborough Whitworths	0-1	7-1	2-0	3-2	4-1	4-0	2-0	3-2	0-1	1-0	3-0	2-2	1-0	3-1	1-2	2-2	1-2	

Christmas Eve saw a league record crowd of 1,150 at the local derby at Whitworths. Here Nick Mason gives Wellingborough Town a second minute lead, in a match the visitors went on to win 2-1. Photo: Gordon Whittington.

Action from the return league match between Wellingborough Town and Whitworths.
Photo: Peter Barnes.

LEAGUE CUP

PRELIMINARY ROUND

Raunds Town	v	Eynesbury Rovers	2-1
Deeping Rangers	v	Yaxley	1-3
Irchester United	v	Peterborough Northern Star	0-2
Long Buckby	v	Ford Sports Daventry	1-5
Blisworth	v	Stotfold	0-3
Potton United (H)	v	Huntingdon Town	2-1
St. Ives Town	v	Wellingborough Town	0-1
Blackstones	v	Rothwell Corinthians	5-3

FIRST ROUND

Buckingham Town	v	Ford Sports Daventry		AW
Yaxley	v	Wellingborough Town		4-0
Potton United (H)	v	Burton Park Wanderers		10-0
Higham Town	v	St. Neots Town		0-4
Woodford United	v	Olney Town		4-0
Peterborough N.S.	v	Northampton On Chenecks		2-0
Raunds Town	v	Stewart & Lloyds Corby		0-2
Newport Pagnell T.	v	Bugbrooke St. Michaels		1-0
Cogenhoe United	v	Blackstones		3-2
Daventry Town	v	AFC Kempston Rovers		1-0
Boston Town	v	Holbeach United	2-2*,	5-4p
Harrowby United	v	Northampton S.R.	2-2*,	2-4p
Northampton Sp.	v	Whitworths		3-0
Wootton B.C.	v	Sleaford Town		1-2
Bourne Town	v	Stotfold	1-1*,	2-4p

SECOND ROUND

Desborough Town	v	Stewarts & Lloyds Corby		3-1
Boston Town	v	St. Neots Town		2-3
Woodford United	v	Potton United (H)		1-0
Sleaford Town	v	Ford Sports Daventry	2-2*,	4-5p
Northampton S.R.	v	Northampton Sp.		1-5
Peterborough N.S.	v	Newport Pagnell Town		2-1
Stotfold	v	Yaxley		2-4
Cogenhoe United	v	Daventry Town		10-0

QUARTER-FINALS

Yaxley	v	Ford Sports Daventry		5-3
St Neots Town	v	Woodford United	2-2*,	3-2p
Cogenhoe United	v	Desborough Town		5-2
Peterborough N.S.	v	Northampton Spencer		1-2

SEMI-FINALS

Northampton Sp.	v	Yaxley	1-3
St. Neots Town	v	Cogenhoe United	4-1

THE FINAL

Yaxley	v	St. Neots Town	2-1

BLACKSTONES F.C.
Formed: 1920
Nickname: Stones

Chairman: Kevin Boor   **President:** Bill Sewell   **Manager:** Tony Lowther
Secretary: Ian MacGillivray, 20 New Road, Ryhall,Stamford, Lincs. PE9 4HL   **Assistant Manager**:Trevor Smith
Tel No: 01780 762263 (H) E-mail: imacgilli@aol.com
Press Officer: Secretary   **Programme:** 32 pages with entry   Prog Ed: Chairman (01780 754584)
GROUND ADDRESS: Lincoln Road, Stamford, Lincs.   **Ground Tel. No:** 01780 757835
Capacity: 1,000   **Seats:** 100   **Covered:** Yes   **Floodlights:** Yes
Simple Directions: A6121 Stamford to Bourne road. Second turning left after MacDonalds and Currys
Midweek Home Matchday: Wednesday   **Clubhouse:** Evenings, match day lunchtimes and w/e   **Club Shop:** No
Previous Names: Rutland Ironworks and Blackstone (until 1975)
Previous Leagues: PeterboroughWorks, Peterborough, Stamford & District
Club Colours: White/black/black   **Change Colours:** Orange/black/orange
LAST SEASON: League: 10th   **Top Scorer:** Ashley Stevens 23
BEST PERFORMANCES
League: **F.A. Cup:** 1st Qualifying Round   **F.A.Vase:** 2nd Round 97-98 01-02
RECORD Attendance: 700 v Glinton   **Goalscorer (in one game):** A.Dunn 6 v Brackley T 94
Victory: 11-0 v Brackley 22.01.94
Senior Honours: Lincs. Senior Cup 'A' 92-93 03-04

BOSTON TOWN
Founded: 1963
Nickname: Poachers

Chairman: Mick Vines   **Vice-Chairman:** J.Rose   **Manager:** Bob Don-Duncan
Secretary: Ron Bennett,172 Woodville Road, Boston, Lincs.PE21 8BU   **Physio:** Steve Greetham
Tell No: 01205 354252(H) 07985 471691 (M)
Press Officer: J.Rose (01205351501)   **Prog Ed:** John Knight (07881 848588)   **Programme:** 40 Pages 50p
GROUND ADDRESS: Tattershall Road, Boston, Lincs.   **Ground Tel. No:** 01205365470
Capacity: 6,000   **Seats:** 450   **Covered:** 950   **Floodlights:** Yes   **Club Shop:** Yes
Simple Directions:A 52 Grantham -Sleafiord, second left into Brotherton Road. Then Argyle St and over bridge ,and immediately left into Tattershall Road. Ground under a mile on left.
Midweek Home Matchday: Tuesday   **Clubhouse:** Open week day evenings, natchdays & functions.
Previous Leagues: Lincs 63-65, Central Alliance 65-66, Eastern Co. 66-68, Midland 68-82 N.Co E 82-87 C.Mids 87-91
Previous Ground: Mayflower Ground
Club Colours: All Blue   **Change Colours:** Yellow/Black/Black
LAST SEASON: League: 6 th
Top Scorer: Danny Matson 24
BEST PERFORMANCES
League: UCL Champions 94-95 2000-01   **F.A. Cup:** 1st Round 1976-77   **F.A.Vase:** Semi-Final 1994-95
RECORD Attendance: 2,700 v Boston United F.A.Cup 1970   **Goalscorer (in season):** Carl Smaller 48 94-95
Senior Honours: U.C.L. (2) Midland Co (3) C.Mids 88-89 Lincs Senior A Cup (5) Lincs Sen B Cup 65-66

BOURNE TOWN
Founded: 1883
Nickname: Wakes

Chairman: Terry Bates   **Vice-Chairman:**   **Manager:** Glen Notley
Secretary: Andy Anderson, 28a Abbey Road, Bourne, Lincs.   **Assistant Manager**: Steve Blades
Tel No: 01778 423892
Press Officer & Programme Editor: John Sinfield (01778 420844)   **Programme:** 30 Pages 75p
GROUND ADDRESS: Abbey Lawn, Abbey Road, Bourne, Lincs.   **Ground Tel. No:** 01778 4222992
Capacity: 3,000   **Seats:** 300   **Covered:** 750   **Floodlights:** Yes
Simple Directions: From Market Place take A151 Spalding Road. Ground is 500 yards on right.
Midweek Home Matchday: Tuesday   **Clubhouse:** Open matchdays.   **Club Shop:** Contact is Secretary.
Previous Leagues: Peterborough, UCL 47-56, Central Alliance 58-61 & Midland Co 61-63Club Colours:
Colours:Claret & Blue/Claret/Light Blue
LAST SEASON:League: 13th
Top Scorer: Miles Mason 11
BEST PERFORMANCES
League: U.C.L. Champions (4)   **F.A. Cup:**   **F.A.Vase:** 4th Rd. 89-90
RECORD Attendance: F.A.Trophy 1970   **Goalscorer: David Scotney**   **Appearances:**
Senior Honours: U.C.L Champions 68-69 69 7- 71-72 90-91 Lincs Senior 'A' Cup 1971-72 2005-2006

BUCKINGHAM TOWN
Founded: 1883
Nickname: Robins

Chairman: Tony Rosenburgh   **Vice-Chairman:** Derek Carpenter   **Manager:** Tony Joyce
Secretary: Brian Maycock, 31 Westfield, Buckingham,Bucks. MK18 1DZ   **Asst. Manager**: Stuart Black
Tel No: 01280 815529 (H) 07881970453 320318 (M)
Press Officer: Sue Horton   **Programme Editor:** Carl Wain: (01280 917194)
GROUND ADDRESS: Ford Meadow, Ford Street, Buckingham,   **Ground Tel. No:** 01280 816257
Capacity: 2,500   **Seats:** 200   **Covered:** 200   **Floodlights:** Yes
Simple Directions: From Town Centre take A413 (Aylesbury) and turn right at Phillips Ford Garage after 400 yard**s**.
Midweek Home Matchday: Tuesday   **Clubhouse:** Open evenings   **Club Shop:** Yes
Previous Leagues: Aylesbury & Dist., North Bucks, Hellenic 53-57, S.Mids 57-74, U.Co. L. 74-86 and Southern 86-97
Club Colours: All Red   **Change Colours:** All White
LAST SEASON: League: 13th   **F.A. Cup:** Prelim .Rd.   **F.A. Vase:** 1st Round
Top Scorer: Reuben Max-Grant 16
BEST PERFORMANCES
F.A. Cup: 1st Rd. 84-85   **F.A.Vase:** 6th Rd 90-91 92-93
RECORD Attendance: 2,451 v Orient F.A.Cup 84-85
Fee Paid: £7,000 to Wealdstone for Steve Jenkins 1992 **Received:** £1,000 from Kettering Town for Terry Shrieves.
Senior Honours: Southern Lg. Southern Div. 90-91 U.C.L. 83-84 85-86 Berks & Bucks Sen. Cup 83-84

Boston Town F.C.   Photo: Peter Barnes.

Buckingham Town F.C. Back Row (L-R): Tom Willshere, Lance Gentleking, Ruben Max Grant, James Lansdown, Morell Maison (Manager), Paul Stanley, Marcus Sawyer, Ian Trott, Bilal Hassan.
Front Row: Geoff Sharpe (Goalkeeping coach), Andy Prescott, Moses Ulaleye, Tony Joyce (Capt), Lewis Reid, Lee Grant, Andy Waight (Physio).

Photo: Arthur Evans.

COGENHOE UNITED

Founded: 1967
Nickname: Cooks

Chairman: Phil Roach   **Vice-Chairman:** Maurice Jaynot   **Manager:** Adam Sandy
Secretary: Maurice Jaynor, 47a Station Road,Cogenhoe , Northampton, NN7 1LU
Tel. No: 01604 890828 (H) 07703 357610
Press Officer: Name (Tel)   **Programme Editor:** Phil Wright **(01604 890737)**
GROUND ADDRESS: Compton Park, Brafield Road, Cogenhoe   **Tel:01604 890521**
Capacity: 5,000   **Seats:** 100   **Covered:** 200   **Floodlights:** Yes
Simple Directions: Turn off A428 at Brafield-on-the-Green, first turn right to Cogenhoe or A45 to Billing Aquadrome. Take second Cogenhoe turning on left.
Midweek Home Matchday: Tuesday   **Clubhouse:** Not open Mondays or Thursdays.   **Club Shop:** No
Previous Ground: Cogenhoe Village Playing Field 1967-84   **Previous Leagues:** Central Northants Comb. Prem 67-84
Club Colours: All Royal Blue   **Change Colours:** All Red
LAST SEASON
League: 5th
Top Scorer: Richard Turner 25
Record Attendance:1,000 Charity Game 90   **Goalscorer & Appearances**: Tony Smith
Senior Honours: UCL Champins 2004-2005

DEEPING RANGERS

Founded: 1964
Nickname: Rangers

Chairman: Graham Mason   **President:** Norman Fowler
Manager: Tuncay Korkmaz   **Asst Manager:** Dave Simpson
Secretary: Haydon Whitham, 3 Everingham, Orton Brimbles, Peterborough PE2 5XP
Tel Nos: 01733 238539 (H) 07736 548500 (M)   **Sponsor:** Acrabuild (Anglia) Ltd.
Programme Editor: Robin Crowson (01778 348287)
GROUND ADDRESS: Deeping Sports Club,Outgang Road, Market Deeping, Lincs.   **Tel:** 01778 344701
Capacity: 1,000   **Seats:** 180   **Covered:** 250   **Floodlights:** Yes
Simple Directions: From Deeping Town centre take A15 towards Bourne. Turn right at Towngate Tavern and club is quarter of a mile on left.
Midweek Home Matchday: Tuesday   **Clubhouse:** Bar and Lounge open daily   **Club Shop:**
Previous League: Peterborough & District
Club Colours: Claret & Blue   **Change Colours:** White/Claret/Sky Blue
LAST SEASON: League: 20th
Top Scorer: Mark Lovelace 10   **Player of the Year:** Tuncay Korkmaz   **Captain:** Dave Robertson
BEST PERFORMANCES
League: 4th Premier Division UCL   **F.A. Cup:** 1st Qualifying Round 2004-2005   **F.A.Vase:** 1st Round
Senior Honours: Lincs Junr Cup 83-4 87-8 88-9 Lincs SEnior B Cup 2000-01 UCL Div 1 R-up 2000-01 Peterboro FACup (3)

DESBOROUGH TOWN

Founded: 1896
Nickname: Ar Tam

Chairman: Andy Coe
Manager: Steve Noble   **Assistant Manager:** Graham Leech
Secretary: John Lee, 85 Breakleys Road, Desborough, Northants NN14 2PT
Tel No: 01536 760002   **Email:** johnlee@froggerycottage85.fsnet.co.uk
Press Officer & Programme Editor: John Lee   **Programme:** 32 Pages Price: 50p
GROUND ADDRESS: Waterworks Field, Braybrooke Rd., Desborough   **Ground Tel No:** 01536 761350
Capacity: 8,000   **Seats:** 250   **Covered:** 500   **Floodlights:** Yes
Simple Directions: Leave A14 at junction 3 and turn right at first roundabout.
Midweek Home Matchday: Tuesday   **Clubhouse:** Excellent facilities open every evening and week ends   **Shop:** No
Club Colours: All Blue   **Change Colours:** White & Black
LAST SEASON: League: 18th   **F.A. Cup:** Extra Prelim.Rd.   **F.A. Vase:** 2nd Round
Top Scorer: Tom Mills & Michael Byrne   **Players of the Year:** Paul Beresford/ Glyn Davies   **Captain:** Scott Munton
BEST PERFORMANCES: League: Co.Champions (9) **F.A. Cup:** 1st Rd 1926-27   **F.A.Vase:** 5th Rd 78-79
RECORD Attendance: 8,000 v Kettering Town **Victory:** 10-1 v Huntingdon Utd. (A) 1957 & v Stewarts & lloyds (A) 65
Fee Received: £8,000 from Northampton Town for Wakeley Gage.
Senior Honours: UCL Champions (9) R-up (6) Northants Senior Cup ((4)

FORD SPORTS DAVENTRY

Founded: 1968
Nickname:Motormen

Chairman: Dave Hutton   **Vice-Chairman:**
Manager: Darren Foster   **Asst.Man:** Andy Calvey   **Physio**: Ron Dawes
Secretary: Mick Fryatt, 2 Mayfield Drive, Davemtry, Northants NN11 5BQ
Tel Nos: 01327 876789 (H) 01327 305407 (W) 07958 172414 (M)
Programme Editor: John Hinton (01327 871768   **Programme:** 12 Pages
GROUND ADDRESS: Royal Oak Way Southg,Daventry, Northants.   **Ground Tel. No:** 01327 704914
Capacity: 1,000   **Seats:** Yes   **Covered:** Yes   **Floodlights:** Yes
Simple Directions: Enter Daventry on A45 or A361 and follow signs for Royal Oak Way
Midweek Home Matchday: Tuesday   **Clubhouse:** Yes   **Club Shop:** No
Previous League: Central Northants
Club Colours: Blue & White/Blue/Blue   **Change Colours:** Red & white/Red/Red
LAST SEASON
League: 19th   **Top Scorer:** Ian Pearce 13
BEST PERFORMANCES
League: U.C.L. Premier Champions 2001-02   **F.A. Cup:** 3rd Qualifying Round 1994-95 **F.A.Vase:** 2nd Rd.
Senior Honours: UCL Premier Champions 2001-02

HOLBEACH UNITED
Founded: 1929
Nickname: Tigers

Chairman: Roger Baker **President:** Francis Bissadike **Manager:** Shaun Keeble
Secretary: Dennis Sparrow, 112 Langwith Gardens, Holbeach, Lincs. PE12 7JN **Assistant Manager**: Paul Langford
Tel Nos: 01406 424336 (H) **e-mail**: dennis@trumpet.fsworld.co.uk
Programme Editor: Alan Wright (01406425743) **Programme:** 44 Pages 50p
GROUND ADDRESS: Carters Park, Park Road, Holbeach, Lincs. **Ground Tel. No:** 01406 424761
Capacity: 4.000 **Seats:** 200 **Covered:** 450 **Floodlights:** Yes
Simple Directions: From Kings Lynn right at traffic lights in town centre. Ground 200 yards on left
Midweek Home Matchday: Tuesday **Clubhouse:** Open every evening **Club Shop:** No
Previous Leagues: Peterborough, UCo.L 46-55, Eastern, 55-62 Midland Co 62-63
Club Colours: Old Gold/Black/Gold **Change Colours:** Sky & Navy Blue
LAST SEASON
League: 17th
BEST PERFORMANCES
League: UCL Champions 89-90 02-03 **F.A. Cup:** 1st Rd 82-83 **F.A.Vase:** 5th Rd 88-89
F.A.Trophy: 2nd Qualifying Rd.
RECORD Attendance: 4,094 v Wisbech 1954 Goalscorer **Appearances:**
Senior Honours: UCL Champions (2) Lincs Senior 'A' Cup (4) seniopr CUp 'B' 57-58

LONG BUCKBY AFC
Founded:
Nickname: Bucks

Chairman: Chris Healey **President:** Colin St.John **Manager:**Aidy Mann
Secretary: Dave Austin, 8 Pytchley Drive, Long Buckby, Northants. NN6 7PL **Assistant Manager:** Glen Botterill
Tel No: 01327 842788 (H) 07710723477 (M) **Programme Editor:** Eric Turvey (07989 903684)
GROUND ADDRESS: Station Road, Long Buckby **Ground Tel. No.:** 01327 842682
Capacity: 1,000 **Seats:** 200 **Covered:** 200 **Floodlights:** Yes
Simple Directions: On the Daventry -Long Buckby road 400 yards from station.
Midweek Home Matchday: Tuesday **Clubhouse:** Matchdays or functions **Club Shop:** No
Previous League(s): Rugby & Dist., Cen. Northanys Comb.pre 68 **Previous Name:** Long Buckby
Nomads
Club Colours: Blue/white/blue **Change Colours:** Red & Yellow/Red/Red
LAST SEASON
League: 21st **Top Scorer:** Dave Drinkwater 12
BEST PERFORMANCES
F.A. Cup: 1st Qual. Rd.92-93 **F.A.Vase:** 2nd Rd 85-86
RECORD Attendance: 750 v Kettering Town Northants Cup Final 1984
Senior Honours: Northants Senior Cup R-Up

NEWPORT PAGNELL TOWN
Founded: 1963
Nickname: Swans

Chairman: Richard Egan **Manager:** Terry Shrieves
Secretary: Stephen Handley, 31 Maulden Gardens, Giffard Park, Milton Keynes MK14 5JJ**Assistant Manager:** Tony Court
Tel No: 01908 614745 (H) 07867 528475
Programme Eitor: Danny Goodwin (01908 511400) **Programme:** 56 pages
GROUND ADDRESS: Willen Road, Newport Pagnell **Ground Tel. No.:** 01908 611993
Capacity: 2,000 **Seats:** 100 **Covered:** 100 **Floodlights:** Yes
Simple Directions: Adjacent to A422 Newport Pagnell by-pass
Midweek Home Matchday: Tuesday **Clubhouse:** Open every evening **Club Shop:** No
Previous Leagues: North Bucks 63-71 South Midlands 71-73
Club Colours: White & Green/Black/Black **Change Colours:** All Navy Blue
LAST SEASON
League: 15th **Top Scorer:** Gary Flinn 7
BEST PERFORMANCES
League: UCL Premier R-Up 2002-03 **F.A. Cup:** Preliminary Round **F.A.Vase:** 2nd Rd 84-85
Senior Honours:UCL R-up 02-03 Berks & Bucks Intermediate Cup 2001-02

NORTHAMPTON SPENCER
Founded: 1936
Nickname: Millers

Chairmen: Graham Wrighting **Manager:** Steve Jelley
Secretary: Nick Hillery,18 Countess Road, Northampton NN57DY **Assistant Manager:** Micky Heath
Tel Nos: 01604 756580(H) 07932 612198(M)
Press Officer & Prog.Ed: Andy Goldsmith (01604 412382) **Programme:** 20 pages 50p
GROUND ADDRESS: Kingsthorpe Mill, Studand Road, Northampton NN3 1NF **Ground Tel. No.:** 01604 718898
Capacity: 2,000 **Seats:** 350 **Covered:** 350 **Floodlights:** Yes
Simple Directions: Turn off Kingsthorpe Rd at traffic lights into Thornton Rd, first right into Studland Rd. Ground is at the end.
Midweek Home Matchday: Tuesday **Clubhouse:** Normal licensing hours **Club Shop:** No
Previous Name: Spencer School Old Boys **Previous Grounds:** Darlington Park 36-70 Duston High School 70-72
Club Colours: White and Green **Change Colours:** Claret/white/white
LAST SEASON
League: 3rd **Top Scorer:** Darren Frost 27
BEST PERFORMANCES
League: UCL Champions 91-92 **F.A. Cup:** 1st Qual.Rd. **F.A.Vase:** 4th Rd. 87-88
RECORD Attendance:800 v Nottm Forest 1993 to open new dressing rooms **Appearances:** P.Jelley 622 1984-2002
Senior Honours: UCL R-Up 91-92 R-up 92-93 97-98 Northants Senior Cup Winners 2005-06 R-up 90-91 93-94

Northampton Spencer F.C.   Photo: Arthur Evans

POTTON UNITED
Founded: 1943
Nickname: Royals

Chairman: John Shipp   **President:** Peter Hutchinson   **Manager:** Roy Bloxham
Secretary: Bev Strong,20 Berwick Way, Sandy, Beds. SG19 1TR   **Assistant Manager:** Dick Newman
Tel No: 01767 692251 (H) 07703 442565 (M)
Programme Editor: Mrs Bev Strong (01767 692251)   **Programme:** 28 Pages 50p Price
GROUND ADDRESS: The Hollow, Biggleswade Road, Potton   **Ground Tel. No:** 01767 261100
Capacity: 2,000   **Seats:** 200   **Covered:** 250   **Floodlights:** Yes
Simple Directions: Outskirts of Potton on Biggleswade Road (B1040) Sandy BR 3.5 miles. Buses from Biggleswade
Midweek Home Matchday: Tuesday   **Clubhouse:** Yes   **Club Shop:**
Previous Leagues: South Midlands 46-55 Centarl Alliance 56-61   **Previous Ground:** Recreation Ground pre 1947
Club Colours: All Blue   **Change Colours:** White/black/white
LAST SEASON
League: Runners Up   **F.A. Cup:** 1st Qualifying Round   **F.A. Vase:** 4th Round
Top Scorer: Brett Donnelly 41   **Player of the Year:** Garry Watts   **Captain:** Nathan Buckland
BEST PERFORMANCES
League: Utd Co Champions 86-87 88-89   **F.A. Cup:** 3rd Qualifying Rd. 74-75
F.A.Trophy: 3rd Qualifying Rd 71-72 72-73   **F.A.Vase:** 5th Rd 89-90
RECORD Attendance: 470 v Hastings Town F.A.Vase 1989   **Goalscorer:**   **Appearances:**
Senior Honours: Utd Co Champions 86-7 88-9, Div1 03-04, Beds Senior Cup(5), Hunts Prem Cup (4) & E.Anglian Cup 96-7

RAUNDS TOWN
Founded: 1946
Nickname: Shopmates

Chairman: Pete Scanlon,   **President:** Mahen Perera   **Manager:** Colin Ridgway
Secretary: David Jones, 21 The Shortlands, Irthlingborough, Northants. NN9 5XE   **Asst. Man:** Wayne Simmonds
Tel No: 01933 651874 (H) 07763492184 (M)
Programme Editor: Secretary   **Programme:** 50p
GROUND ADDRESS: Kiln Park, London Rd., Raunds, Northants NN9 6EQ **Tel Nos:**01933 623351or Matchdays: 460941
Capacity: 3,000   **Seats:** 250   **Covered:** 600   **Floodlights:** Yes
Simple Directions: Take Raunds turning at roundabout on A45 and ground is first left. Nearest station is Wellingborough
Midweek Home Matchday: Tuesday   **Clubhouse:** Open daily.   **Club Shop:** Open Matchdays
Previous Leagues: Rushden & Dist., Cen.Northants Comb., U.C.L., Southern 96-00
Previous Grounds: Greenhouse Field (until 1948) and The Berristers (1948-91)
Club Colours: Red & black/Black/Black   **Change Colours:** All Yellow
LAST SEASON: League: 8th   **Top Scorer:** Michael McKenzie 7
BEST SEASONS:League: UCL Champions 95-96 **F.A. Cup:** 4th Qualifying Rd.98-99   **F.A.Vase:** S-Final 94-95
RECORD Attendance: 1,500 v Crystal Palace ground opening 23.07.91   **Goalscorer:** Shaun Keeble 208
Appearances: Martin Lewis 355 (+29 subs) **Victory:** 11-2v Brackley 93   **Defeat:** 0-6 Baldock 83 v Buckingham 84-85
Senior Honours: UCL Champions 95-96 Northants Sen Cup 90-91 Hunts Prem Cup R-Up 92-93

ST. IVES TOWN

Founded: 1887
Nickname:Saints

Chairman: Neville Nania   **Joint Managers:** Warren Everdell & Jez Hall

Secretary: Chris George,16 Canberra Drive, Sy Ives, Cambs. PE17 3UR

Tel Nos: 01480 382257 (H) 07779 304758 (M)

Previous Leagues: Cambs.,Central Amateur, Hunts, Peterborough & District (pre -1985)

Club Colours: White & black   **Change Colours:** Red & Blue

LAST SEASON League: 9   **Top Scorer:** Chris Ewles 21

GROUND ADDRESS: WEstwood Road, St Ives **Ground Tel. No:** 01480 463207

Simple Directions: From A1123 Houghton Road, turn eight at lights into Ramsey Road. After Fire Station turn right into Westwood Road. Ground is at end of the road on the right.

Midweek Home Matchday: Tuesday   **Clubhouse:** Yes   **Club Shop:**No

ST NEOTS TOWN

Founded: 1879
Nickname: Saints

Chairman: Bob Page   **Directors:** John Carroll, Kenneth Harris and Neil Holmes   **Manager:** Steve Kuhne
Secretary: Peter Naylor, 6 Philip Gardens, Eynesbury, St Neots, Cambs. PE19 2QH
Tel. Nos: 01480 471256 (H) 07801 021516 (M)   **Website:** www.stneotsfc.com
Programme Editor: Dave Brown   **Commercial Manager:** Peter Hicks (01733 263656)
GROUND ADDRESS: Rowley Park, Cambridge Road, St Neots, Cambs.   **Ground Tel. No.:** 01480 470012
Capacity: 3,000   **Seats:** 250   **Covered:** 850   **Floodlights:** Yes
Simple Directions: Through town centre, under railway bridge and ground is first on the left.
Midweek Home Matchday: Tuesday   **Clubhouse:** Yes with many function rooms for hire.   **Club Shop:** No
Previous Leagues: S.Midlands 27-36 46-49 UCL 36-39 51-56 66-69 73-88 Cen.Alliance 56-60 Eastern Co. 69-73 Hunts 90-94
Previous Ground: Shortlands   **Previous Name:** St Neots & District. 1879-1957
Club Colours: Sky & Navy blue quarters/Navy/Navy   **Change Colours:** Amber& Black/Black/Black
LAST SEASON
League: 14th   **F.A. Cup:** Extra Prelimin.Rd   **F.A. Vase:** 3rd Rd.
Top Scorer: Liam Harrold 11
F.A. Cup: 1st Rd. 66-67   **F.A.Vase:** 5th Rd. 2001-02
RECORD Attendance: 2,000 v Wisbech 1966
Senior Honours: UCl Champions 67-68, Hunts.Sen. Cup (34) & Hunts Prem Cup 2001-02

STEWARTS & LLOYDS

Formed: 1935
Nickname: The Foundrymen

Chairman: Keith Julian   **Vice-Chairman:** Paul Mullen   **Manager:** Paul Ross
Secretary: Dave Foster, 29 Tettenhall Close, Corby, Northants.   **Coach: rob Clark**
Tel NOs: 01536 746004 (H) 07818 264220 (M)
Programme Editor: Vinny Keefe   **Programme:** 12 pages with admission
GROUND ADDRESS: Recreation Ground,Occupation Road, Corby.   Ground Tel. No.: 01536 401497
Capacity: 1,500   **Seats:** 100   **Covered:** 200   **Floodlights:** Yes
Simple Directions: Occupation Road is at the rear of Stewarts & Lloyds Leisure Club, next to Corby Town F.C.ground.
Midweek Home Matchday: Tuesday   **Clubhouse:** Licensed Bar   **Club Shop:** No
Previous League: Kettering Amateur
Club Colours: Red & White/Black/Black   **Change Colours:** Sky Blue & white stripes/black/sky
LAST SEASON:
League: 16th
Top Scorer: Derek Simmonds - 7   **Player of the Year:** John McKay   **Captain:** John McKay
BEST PERFORMANCES
League: UCL Premier R-Up 85-86   **F.A. Cup:**1st Qualifying Round (7)   **F.A.Vase:** 3rd Rd 96-97 01-02
Goalscorer: Joey Martiinn 46 (92-93)

STOTFOLD

Founded: 1945
Nickname: The Eagles

Chairman: Phil Pateman   **Vice-Chairman:** Alan Syme
Manager: Glen Clark   **AssistantManager:** Ian Croft   **Coach:** Ian Williscroft
Secretary: Julie Longhurst, 49 Astwick Road, Stotfold, Hitchin, Herts. SG5 4AV   **Sec's Tel No:** 01462 731167
Press Officer: Andy Trulock   **Programme** 22 pages with entry)   **Prog Editor:** Phil Pateman
GROUND ADDRESS: Roker Park, The Green, Stotfold, Hitchin, Herts   **GroundTel.No:** 01462 730765
Capacity: 5,000   **Seats:** 300   **Covered:**300   **Floodlights:** Yes   **Club Shop:**
Simple Directions: A507 from A1 right at lights, right at T jct. or A507 from Bedford via Shefford, left at lights right at T jct
Midweek Home Matchday: Tuesday   **Clubhouse:** Clubroom,bar,refreshments,dressing rooms and physio room.
Previous Leagus: Biggleswade & District, North Herts and South Midlands 51-84
Club Colours: Amber/black/black   **Change Colours:** All White
LAST SEASON
League: 11th
Top Scorer: Callum Donnelly   **Player of the Year:** Nigel Blower   **Captain:** Dave Cook
Best Performances
League: Utd Co. R-up 93-94   **F.A. Cup:** 2000-01   **F.A.Vase:** 4th Rd 94-5 97-8 00-01
RECORD Attendance: 1,000   **Goalscorer:** Roy Boon   **Apps:** Roy Boon & Dave Chellew
Senior Honours: Utd Co R-up 93-94 South Midlands Lg 80-81 Beds Senior Cup 64-5 93-94 Beds Prem Cup 81-2 98-9

Stotfold F.C. Back Row (L-R): Richard Beckett, Richard Petrisor, Jim Benton (Manager), Darren Dykes, Nigel Blower, Dean Chaman (capt), Ryan Frater, Liam George, Richard Pringle.
Front Row: James Potter, Jeff Brown, Jermaine Daley, Paul Harrington, Ade Bascombe, Stephen Blower.

Photo: Arthur Evans.

WELLINGBOROUGH TOWN (2004)

Founded: 2004
Nickname: Doughboys

Chairman: Dave Clingo	**Vice-Chairman:**	**Manager:** Nick Ashby

Secretary: Mick Walden, 3 Woodstock Close, Wellingborough, Northants. NN8 5YQ **Assistant Manager**: Les Hornby

Tel Nos: 01933 400063 (H) 07725 791350 (M) (M)

Programme Editor: Gary Ward (01933 675476 (H) **Programme:**

Previous Name(s): **Previous League(s):**

Club Colours: Yellow/Royal Blue/Royal Blue **Change Colours:** Navy Blue/Navy Blue/White

LAST SEASON: League: UCL Div 1 Runners Up **F.A. Cup:** N/A **F.A. Vase:** N/A

Club Website: www.wellingboroughtownfc.co.uk

GROUND ADDRESS: The Dog & Duck ,London Road, Wellingborough NN8 5BE **Tel: 01933 441388**

Simple Directions: Leave A45 at Wellingborough turn off, pass Tescos on left up to roundabout. Take first exit to town centre. Ground is 300 yards on the right.

Midweek Home Matchday: Tuesday

Senior Honours: UCL Division One Runners Up 2005-2006 Northants Junior Cup 2005-2006

WOOTTON BLUE CROSS

Founded: 187
Nickname: Blue Cross

Chairman: Tony Latham	**President:** John Clarke	**Manager:** Phil Silvestri

Secretary: Peter Bone, 18 Summerfield Drive, Wootton, Beds MK43 9FE

Tel No: 01234 313880 (H)

Press Officer: Secretary **Prog Ed**: Phil Kerrins (07771830269) **Programme:** 24 Pages

GROUND ADDRESS: Weston Park, Bedford Rd., Wootton **Ground Tel. No.:** 01234 767662

Capacity: 2,000 **Seats:** 50 **Covered:** 250 **Floodlights:** Yes

Simple Directions: Four miles south of Bedford on main road through village at rear od Post Office.

Midweek Home Matchday: Tuesday **Clubhouse:** Open every evening and w.e lunchtimes. **Club Shop:**No

Previous Grounds: Rec. Ground ,Fishers Field, Rose & Crown & Cockfield.

Previous League(s): Bedford & Dist. S.Midlands 46-55

Club Colours: Blue & white/blue/blue **Change Colours:** Yellow/red/yellow

LAST SEASON

League: 17th **F.A. Cup:** 1st qualifying Ropund **F.A. Vase:** 3rd Rd.

Top Scorer: Darek Jozwiak 19

BEST PERFORMANCES

F.A. Cup: 2nd Qual.Rd. **F.A.Vase:** 4th Rd. 2002-03

RECORD Attendance: 838 v Luton Beds Prem Cup 1988 **Senior Honours**: Beds Senior Cup 70-71 2001-02

YAXLEY

Founded:
Nickname:

Chairman: GRaeme Clark   **Vice Chairman:** Malcolm Whaley   **Sponsor:** Reads Removals

Manager: Jimmy Watson   **Asst.Manager:** Gary Cupston

Secretary: Mrs Anne Hall,67 Ringwood, South Bretton, Peterborough PE3 9SR

Tel Nos: 01733 2074 (H) 07762 778441 (M)

Press Officer: Name (Tel)   **Programme Editor:** Carole Green (01733 240905)

GROUND ADDRESS: Leading Drove,off The Holme Road, Yaxley.   Ground **Tel. No.:** 01733 244928

Capacity: 1,000   **Seats:** 150   **Covered:** Yes   **Floodlights:** Yes

Simple Directions: A1 then A15 at Norman Cross up to traffic lights. Right then right again and follow road for about a mile. Then right into Holme Road. Ground is about 200 yards on left.

Midweek Home Matchday: Tuesday   **Clubhouse:** Yes   **Club Shop:** No

Previous Leagues: Peterborough & Disr., Hunts, & West Anglia.

Club Colours: All Blue   **Change Colours:** All Red

LAST SEASON: League: 7th

Top Scorer: Ricky Hailstone 16   **Senior Honours:** Hunts. Senior Cup (7) UCL Cup 2005-2006

Yaxley F.C. celebrate winning the UCl KO cup.   Photo: Gordon Whittington.

LEAGUE CONSTITUTION 2006-07 - DIVISION ONE

A.F.C.KEMPSTON ROVERS

Secretary: Kevin Howlett,53 Silverdale Street, Kempston, Bedford MK42 8BE
Tel: 01234 852056(H)

Ground: Hillgrounds Leisure, Hillgrounds Rd, Kempston, Bedford Tel: 01234 852346.

Capacity: 2,000   Seats: 100   Cover: 250   Floodlights: Yes

Directions: M1 jct 13, A421 to Kempston, Hillgrounds Rd is off the B531 main Kempston-Bedford road. Entrance to Hillgrounds Road is opposite Sainsburys onthe B531 - ground can be found just over twi miles from Sainsburys entrance.British Rail to Bedford Thameslink/Midland then bus No.103 from Bedford town centre stops outside ground

Club Shop: No, but old programmes available from clubhouse

Clubhouse: Open 7-11pm Tues.- Sun. & w/e lunch 12-3pm. Sky TV, pool, hot pies & pasties.

PREVIOUS: League: South Midlands 27-53

BEST SEASON FA Vase: 5th Round 88-89

HONOURS U.C.L. Prem. 73-74 R-up 56-57 59-60, Div 1 57-58 85-86, Div 2 55-56 R-up 67-68, KO Cup 55-56 57-58 59-60 74-75 76-77; Beds Senior Cup 08-09 37-38 76-77 91-92 R-up 92-93

FACT FILE
Founded: 1884   Nickname: Walnut Boys
Club Sponsors: Bar Soviet
Colours: Red & white stripes/black/black
Change Colours: Blue & black stripes/white/black
Midweek matchday: Tuesday
Reserve League: Beds FA County Res. Lge
Programme: 24 pages, 40p
Editor: Mark Kennett (01234 400835)
CLUB PERSONNEL
President: Mr Doug Jack
Chairman: Russell Shreeves.
Vice Chairman: Kevin Howlett
Press Officer: Secretary
Managers: Clive Black
Asst. Manager: John Leeson

BUGBROOKE ST MICHAELS

Secretary: Roger Geary, 31 Kislingbury Rd, Bugbrooke, Northampton NN7 3QG
Tel: 01604 831678

Ground: Birds Close, Gayton Road, Bugbrooke Tel: 01604 830707
Capacity: 2,500 Seats: 120 Cover: Yes Floodlights: Yes

Clubhouse: Yes - normal licensing

Directions: M1.Jct 16 Take A45 to Northampton. At 1st roundabout follow signs to Bugrooke. Through village and club is immediately past last house on left.

CHONOURS Northants Junior Cup 89-90, Central Northants Comb. (6)
UCL Res Div 2 R-up 94-95 U.C.L. Div One Champions 98-99

PREVIOUS **League** : Central Northants Combination 1952-87 **Ground:** School Close

RECORD **Attendance:** 1,156 **Scorer:** Vince Thomas **Appearances:** Jimmy Nord

Players progressing: Kevin Slinn (Watford), Craig Adams (Northampton)

FACT FILE
Founded: 1929
Nickname: Badgers
Sponsors: Unusual Industries
Club colours: Black & white stripes/black/black
Change colours: All Navy Blue
Reserves' Lge: UCL Res. Div. 1
Programme: Eight pages
Editor: Debbie Preston
CLUB PERSONNEL
Chairman: A.Dyson
President: John Curtis
Manager: Nick Verity
Assistant Manager:Peter Robinson
Press Officer: Donna Clancy

BURTON PARK WANDERERS

Secretary: Mrs Sam Gordon, 186 Station Road, Burton Latimer,Noorthants. NN15 5NU
Tel: 01536 725977 (H), 07980 013506 (M)

Ground: Latimer Park, Polwell Lane, Burton Latimer Tel: 01536 725841
Capacity: 1,000 Seats: 100 Cover: 150 Floodlights: No

Directions: Entering Burton Latimer, turn off A6 Station Rd and right into Powell Lane; ground on the right

HONOURS UCL Div 1 R-up, Benevolent Cup R-up

PREVIOUS **League**: Kettering Amateur

RECORD **Attendance**: 253 v Rothwell, May 1989

Players progressing : Shaun Wills (Peterborough), Laurie Dudfield (Leicester City)

FACT FILE
Founded: 1961 Nickname: The Wanderers
Sponsor: Prescott Motors
Colours: Black & Azure
Change Colours: Orange & Navy Blue
Midweek matchday: Tuesday
Prog: 16 pages with entry Ed: Secretary
Local Press : Northants Evening Telegraph, Northants Post
CLUB PERSONNEL
Chairman: Geoff Chester
Vice Chairman: Stuart Coles
Managers: Andy & Carl Lambert
Physio: Stuart Coles

DAVENTRY

Founded: 1886
Nickname:

Chairman: Jo Berry **Manager:** Tony Perry

Secretary: Dave Hirons, 53 Airiil Crescent, Daventry , Northants NN11 9AZ

Tel Nos: 01536 725977 (H) 07980 013506 (M)

Programme Editor: Tony Perry **Programme:** 36 Pages

GROUND ADDRESS: Elderstubbs Farm, Browns Road, Daventry, Northants. Ground **Tel. No.:** 01327 706286

Capacity: 2,000 **Seats:** 250 **Covered:** 250 **Floodlights:** Yes

Simple Directions: Adjacent to A45 by-pass at top of Sraverton Road Sports Comp[lex

Midweek Home Matchday: Tuesday **Clubhouse:** Large Bar and Kitchin.

Previous Leagues: Northampton Town (pre-1987) and Central Northanys Combination 87-89

Club Colours: Purple & Yellow **Change Colours:**Yellow & Blue

LAST SEASON

League: 6th

BEST PERFORMANCES

F.A. Cup: Preliminary Round 94-95 03-04 **F.A.Vase:** 2nd Round 03-04

RECORD Attendance: 850 v Utrecht (Holland) 1989

EYNESBURY ROVERS

Secretary: Deryck Irons, 12 Hadleigh Close, Bedford MK41 8JW. Tel: 01234 268111
Email Address: deryckirons@aol.com **Website:** www.eynesburyrovers.org.uk

Ground: Hall Road, Eynesbury, St Neots Tel: 01480 477449
Capacity:2,000 Seats: 200 Cover: 500 Floodlights: Yes Club Shop: No

Directions: Two miles from A1, on South side of St Neots urban area, nearSt Neots Community College

Clubhouse: Large bar, committee room.Available for private hire

HONOURS UCL Div 1 76-77; Hunts Snr Cup (11), Hunts Premier Cup 50-51 90-91 95-96; Hinchingbrooke Cup (7) 46-4748-52 57-58 66-67; Cambs Invitation Cup 61-62; E Anglian Cup R-up 90-91 91-92;Hunts Scott Gatty Cup(4) (R-up 93-94 res); Hunts Jnr Cup 21-22 26-27 UCL

PREVIOUS **Leagues:** Sth Mids 34-39; UCL 46-52; Eastern Co's 52-63

BEST SEASON **FA Vase:** 3rd Rd 94-95 **FA Cup:** 4th Qual. Rd 54-55, 1-3 v Camb. Utd (A)

RECORD **Gate:** 5,000 v Fulham 1953 (Stanley Matthews guested for Eynesbury)

Players progressing: Chris Turner (Peterborough), Denis Emery (Peterborough)

FACT FILE
Founded: 1897 Nickname: Rovers
Sponsors: T.B.A.
Colours: Royal & white/royal/royal
Change Colours:Yellow /Navy/Yellow
Midweek matchday: Tuesday
Prog: 32 pages
Ed: Graham Mills (01480 385425)
CLUB PERSONNEL
Chair: Brian Abraham, V-Chair:Graham Mills
Manager: Dean Shipp
Asst Manager: Mark Garwood
2005-2006
Top Scorer: Peter Collins
Player of the Year: Ben Houseago

AFC Kempston Rovers F.C. After an indifferent start to the season they had an excellent New Year to finish Fourth in Division One.

Photo: Gordon Whittington.

Burton Park Wanderers　　　　　　　　　　　　　　　　Photo: Gordon Whittington.

HIGHAM TOWN

Secretary: Chris Ruff, 23 Queensway, Higham Ferrers, Northants. NN10 8BU Tel: 01933 358862
Ground: Recreation Ground, Vine Hill Drive, Higham Ferrers Tel: 01933 353751
Capacity: 1,000   Seats: Nil   Cover: 100   Floodlights: No
Directions: From Kettering 1st right on A6 after junction to St Neots. From Bedford, 3rd left after entering town on A6 from Rushden. Higham is served by London-Bedford-Corby United Counties Coachlines, and their local services Northampton-Raunds and Bedford-Kettering
Clubhouse: During season 8.30-11pm Tues, Thurs, Fri, Sat after games & 12-1.30pm Sun. Light refreshments available after Saturday games
HONOURS UCL Div 1 97-98, R-up 70-71 71-72 89-90 92-93 93-94 94-95 95-96 98-99; Northants Lg 21-22 22-23 R-up 23-24 26-27; Northants Snr Cup 21-22 R-up 30-31 32-33; Maunsell Premier Cup 22-23 33-34
PREVIOUS Leagues: Wellingborough 20-21; Northants (now UCL) 21-36; Rushden 46-50
RECORD Attendance: 5,700 v Chesterfield, FAC 4th qual. rd replay 22-23
Scorer: Jon Ogden 187 (Lge) **Appearances:** Brian Harbour 485
Best Win: 15-0 v Towcester T (H), UCL Div. 92/93

FACT FILE
Founded: 1895   Reformed: 1920 & 1946
Nickname: Lankies
Sponsors: Higham News
Colours: Sky & navy/navy/sky
Change colours:Green/black/black
Midweek matchday:: Tuesday
Reserves' Lge: UCL Reserve Div
Programme: 12 pages with admission
Editor: Secretary
CLUB PERSONNEL
Chairman: Howard Downs
Pres: Vijay Patel Vice Chairman: Brian Kirk
Match Sec:Robin James (01234 475563)
Manager: Jim Le Masurier.
Asst. Manager: Simon Stewart
Physio: John Nicholls

HUNTINGDON TOWN

Secretary: Russell Yezek,39 Thongsley,Huntingdon, Cambs. PE29 1NU.
               Tel Nos: 01480 394903 (H) 07974 664818 (M) e-mail:
               russell.jezek@ntlworld.com
Ground: Jubilee Park, Kings Ripton Road,, Huntingdon, Cambridgeshire
               Tel: 07929 651226
Capacity: 1,000   Seats: None   Cover 100   Floodights : Yes
Directions   From A1/A14 junction follow A14 towards Huntingdon. Go across first round
               about onto A141 and then over three further roundabouts before turning left
               towards Kings Ripton. Ground is situated half a mile on left.
Clubhouse: Yes   **Club Shop:**   No
PREVIOUS League: Cambridgeshire League 'A' 2003
HONOURS: Cambridge League Div.1B Champions 1999-00 Hunts. Jumior Cup: 1999-00'
               2000-021 01-02 Hunts Scott Gatty Cup: 2001-02

FACT FILE
Colours: Red & Black /Red/Red
Change: Sky & Navy Blue
Sponsors: Qubic Recruitment
Programme Editor: Tony Bowkis
(07979 710715 (H)
CLUB PERSONNEL
Chairman: Hans Reif
Manager: Paul Swannell
Assistant Manager: Paul Turner

IRCHESTER UNITED

Secretary: Glynn Cotter, 3 Bank Hill View, Littlree HarrowdenWellingborough, Northants
               NN8 5UB   Tel Nos: :01933 402514 (H) 07802 728736 (M)

Ground: Alfred Street, Irchester Tel: 01933 312877
               Capacity: 1,000   Seats: None   Cover:Yes   Floodlights: Yes

Directions: Off Rushden Road to Wollaston Road, next to recreation ground

Clubhouse: Yes

HONOURS   Northants League Div 2 30-31 31-32, Rushden & District League (9)
               Northants Jnr.Cup 29-30,33-34,48-49 75-6,
BEST SEASON   **FA Cup:** Prel. Rd 34-35
               FA Vase: Preliminary Round 77-78
PREVIOUS   **Leagues:** Rushden & District 1936-69

FACT FILE
Colours: White & Red
Change: All Blue
Programme Editor: Glynn Cotter
CLUB PERSONNEL
Chairman: Geoff Cotter
Manager:Glynn Cotter
Assistant Manager: Martin Howarth
Physio: Mick Howarth

NORTHAMPTON O.N. CHENECKS

Secretary: Trevor Cadden, 26 Greenfield Road, Spinney Hill, NNorthampton NN3 2LW
             Tel Nos: 01604 407070 (H) 078887 652910 (M)
Ground: Old Northamptonians Sports Ground,Billing Road,Northampton
             Tel. No.: 01604 34045
             Capacity: 1,350   Seats: Yes   Cover: Yes   Floodlights: No
Directions: South ring road, exit A43 Kettering. Turn left at the lights, to the top of hill and
             the ground is 200 yds on right **Clubhouse:** Yes
HONOURS   UCL Div 1 77-78 79-80, Northants Jnr Cup R-up 93-94
PREVIOUS   **Leagues:** Northampton Town League (pre-1969)

FACT FILE
Founded: 1946
Colours:White & Navy Blue
Change colours: All red
Reserves' League: UCL Res Div 1
Midweek Matchday:
Prog.: 16 pages with entry
Editor: Des McGrath (07748 593423)
CLUB PERSONNEL
Chairman: Eddie Slinn
President: Claude Hasdell
Manager: Scott Carlin
Physio: John Goodger

Northampton O.N. Chenecks F.C.   Photo: Gordon Whittington.

OLNEY TOWN

		FACT FILE
Secretary:	Andrew Baldwin, 49 Midland Road, Olney, Bucks MK46 4BP	Founded: 1903
	Tel: 01234 711071 (H) 07932 141623 (M) email: a.baldwin@cranfield.ac.uk	Sponsors: Paulo's
	Club Website: www.olneytownfc.com	Colours: Green&white/green/green &white
Ground:	East Street, Olney , Bucks. Tel: 01234 712227	Change colours: Black&white/white/white
	Capacity: 2,000 Seats: None Cover: Yes Floodlights: No	Programme: 8 pages
Clubhouse:	Yes	Editor: Paul Tough (01908 617685)

FACT FILE
Founded: 1903
Sponsors: Paulo's
Colours: Green&white/green/green &white
Change colours: Black&white/white/white
Programme: 8 pages
Editor: Paul Tough (01908 617685)

Directions: Enter Olney on A509 from Wellingborough, 100yds on left enter East St, the ground is 200 yds on left

HONOURS UCL Div 1 72-73, Berks & Bucks I'mediate Cup 92-93

PREVIOUS **Leagues:** Nth Bucks, Rushden & District

CLUB PERSONNEL
Chairman: Paul Tough
President: Trevor Church
Manager: Andy Griffin Coach: Neil Bunker
Asst Manager: Pete Munting
Captain: Guy Stewart
Physio: Peter Munting

PETERBOROUGH NORTHERN STAR

FACT FILE
Founded : Early 1900
Sponsors: J/s Cars
Colours: Red/White/Black
Change:Blue & Black
Midweek Matchday: Wednesday
Prog: £2.00 Pages 28.
Editor: Rodney Payne (01733 703170)

Secretary:	Jim Canty, 25 Sherborne Road, Peterborough.Cambs.PE1 4RG
	Tel No : 01733 54883 Fax: 01733 554883
Match	Roger Pope,4 Meadow Walk, Yaxley, Peterborough PE7 3EX
Secretary	Tel Nos: 01733 705169 (H) 01733 582072 (W)
Ground:	Chestnut Avenue, Dogsthorpe, Eye, Peterborough, Cambs. 01733 564 894
	Capacity: 1,500 Seats: None Cover: Yes Floodlights: No
Directions	From A1 turn onto A1139 Fleton Parkway Jct 7 (near Perkins Engines) at
	Traffic Lights left into Eastfield Rd. Turn right at Barclays Bank then right
	again into Eastern Avenue. Second left is Chestnut Avenue.
	Capacity: 100 **Seats** Yes
	Floodlights Yes
PREVIOUS	**League** Peterborough League >2003
	Name: Eye United >2005
HONOURS	Peterborough League 2002-03

CLUB PERSONNEL
Chairman: Vince Elliott
Manager: Darren Young
Assistant Manager: Jim McBurnie

ROTHWELL CORINTHIANS

Secretary: Mark Budworth, 5 Jackson way, Kettering, Northants. NN15 7DL
01536 521973 (H) 07730 416960(M) email:mbudworth@budworthbrown.com

Ground: Seargents Lawn, Desborough Road, Rothwell, Northants.
Tel: 01536 418688
Capacity: Unknown   Seats: 50   Cover: 200

Floodlights: Yes
Directions A6 towards Desborough, on right opposite Greening Road
Club House: Yes   -
Club Shop: No
HONOURS East Midlands Alliance (2)
PREVIOUS **League** East Midlands Alliance

FACT FILE
Founded: 1930's
Nickname: Corinthians
Sponsor: Springfir Estates
Colours: Red & Black
Change colours: All Blue.
Programme: Yes Editor: Nick Garley
Tel No: 01536711694
CLUB PERSONNEL
Chairman: Mark Budworth
Vice Chairmperson: May Clelland
President: Terry Smith
Manager: Frank Iglapi
Physio: John Dickson

SILEBY RANGERS

(formerly Northampton Sileby Rangers)
Secretary: David Battams, 12 Geldock Road, Little Billing, Northampton NN3 9PH
Tel Nos: 01604 412654 (H) 07970 910463 (M)
Ground: Fernie Fields Sports Ground, Moulton, Northampton Tel: 01604 670366
Capacity: 700 Seats: 100   Cover: Yes   Floodlights: No
Directions: Approach from A43 Kettering - follow signs to Northampton as far as the large
roundabout with traffic lights (Round Spinney roundabout). Take the 5th exit signposted to
Moulton Park and after a quarter of a mile turn left in the ground. Approach from A45 - leave
A45 at the exit signposted to A43 Ring Road/Kettering/Corby and take the dual carriageway for
around 2 miles to the second roundabout. Take the 2nd exit signposted to Moulton Park and
after a quarter of a mile turn left into the ground.
Clubhouse: Large bar with food
HONOURS UCL Div 1 93-94,02-03 Benevolent Cup R-up 93-94; Northants Jnr Cup 93-94
96-97 97-98; 02-03 Northampton Town Lg 88-89 89-90
PREVIOUS **League:** Northampton Town (pre-1993)
Name: Northampton Vanaid >00 Northampton Sileby Rangers 2000-2004
RECORD Attendance: 78

FACT FILE
Founded: 1968 Nickname: Sileby
Sponsors: Travis Perkins
Colours: Red/Black/Black
Change colours:Yellow/Navy Blue/ Yellow
Midweek games: Tuesday
Programme Editor: Terry Whenham
Tel No: 07764 158569 (M)
CLUB PERSONNEL
Chairman: Rob Clarke Vice Chairman: G,Law
President: N.Gibbs
Manager: Gary Petts
Asst Man: Pete Robinson

SLEAFORD TOWN

Secretary: Ian Hughes, 9 The Innings, Sleafiord, Lincs. NG34 7GA
Tel Nos: 01529 415687 (H) 07748 434445 (M & W)
e-mail: secretary@sleafordtownfc.co.uk
Ground: The Stadium, Royal Air Force Cranwell Tel No: 07748 434445

PREVIOUS **Leagues:** Lincolnshire **Previous Ground:** Recreation Ground, Boston Road
HONOURS Lincolnshire League Premier Division Champions: 80-81,03-04, Div 2 68-69
Lincolnshire League Cup: Winners 80-01 89-90 90-91
League Charity Cup Winners 73-74
Lincolnshire Senior Cup 'B' Winners 85-86 99-00 01-02 02-03 03-04 05-06
UCL Division One 2005-2006

FACT FILE
Sponsors: Horne Bros Ltd.
Colours: Green with black band/Black/Black
Change colours: All Red
Midweek Matches:
Programme Editor:
Web site: www.sleafordtownfc.co.uk
CLUB PERSONNEL
Chairman: Kevin Scrupps
President: Dave Kelby
Vice Chairman: Paul Ellis
Commercial Manager: Gordon Marshall
Manager: Brian Rowland
Captain: StevenRowland
Physio: Eddie Elliott

THRAPSTON TOWN

Secretary: Mark Brown, 3 Drayton Place, Irthlingborough, Northants. NN9 5TD
01933 388671 (H) 07885 640947 (M) email: mark @datsprint.co.uk

Ground: Chancery Lane, Thrapston, Northants Tel: 01832 732470
Capacity: 1,000   Seats: Yes   Cover: Yes   Floodlights: Aug.06

Directions: Chancery Lane off A605 in town centre

Clubhouse: Yes

HONOURS Northants Junior Cup 87-88, 98-99, 03-04
Kettering Am Lg 70-71 72-73 73-74 77-78
UCL Div1 Runners -Up 99-00

PREVIOUS **League:** Kettering Amateur (pre-1978)

FACT FILE
Founded: 1960 Nickname: Venturas
Sponsor: IKEA
Colours: Yellow & Blue
Change colours: White & Black
Programme: Yes   Editor: Mark Brown
CLUB PERSONNEL
Pres:Dave Morson Chairman: Dave Harris
Vice Chairman: Barry Carter
Manager: Paul Smith
Assistant Manager: Mike Battams
Physio: Dave Timlin
Captain: Keith Morson

WELLINGBOROUGH WHITWORTHS

FACT FILE

Sponsor: Whitworth Brothers

Secretary: John Betts, 2 St Mary's Road, Bozeat, Wellingborough, Northants. NN29 7JU
07808 824 616 (M)

Colours: Red & Black

Change colours: Yellow & Blue

Programme Editor: John Betts

Ground: London Road, Wellingborough, Northants. Tel: 01933 227 324
Capacity: 1000   Seats: None   Cover: Yes   Floodlights: Soon

CLUB PERSONNEL

Chairman: Chris Beevor

Directions: Off London Road at Dog & Duck public house

President: Terry Faulkner

Clubhouse: Yes

Manager: Joe Smythe

Club Shop: No

Assistant Manager: Steve Medlin

PREVIOUS **Leagues:** Rushden & District; East Midlands Aliance (pre-1985)

Physio: Steve Herring

HONOURS Rushden & District Lg 76-77; Northants Jun Cup 96

Back Row (L-R): Steve Herring (Coach), Graham Clelland (Trainer), Ross Howes, Steve Mayhew, Danny Jackson, Phil Turner, Tom Francis (Captain), Anthony Sharp, david Coales, Steve Medlin (Assistant Manager), Sean Lonergan.
Front Row: Kris Line, James Daldy, Scott Atkinson, Stuart Goosey, Joe Smyth (Manager), Matthew Freeman, Daniel Spaughton, Neil Chance, Mitch Pengelly.

Photo: Gordon Whittington.

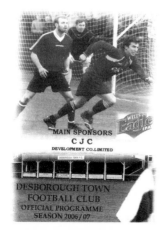

WESSEX LEAGUE

SPONSORED BY: **SYDENHAMS**
FOUNDED: 1986
President: Cyril Hurlock
Chairman: Alf Peckham   Vice Chairman: Ray Barnes
Hon. Secretary: Ian Craig, 7 Old River, Denmead, Hampshire PO7 6UX
Tel: 02392 230973   Fax: 02392 250980

PREMIER DIVISION		P	W	D	L	F	A	Pts
1.	Winchester City	42	34	5	3	112	31	107
2.	Thatcham Town	42	29	7	6	92	37	94
3.	Andover	42	27	5	10	120	64	86
4.	AFC Totton	42	25	9	8	101	40	84
5.	Gosport Borough	42	23	10	9	85	44	79
6.	Hamworthy United	42	21	12	9	65	40	75
7.	Bournemouth	42	21	10	11	72	45	73
8.	Poole Town (2nd Div.2 04-05)	42	21	8	13	79	60	71
9.	Fareham Town	42	19	10	13	74	61	67
10.	Christchurch	42	17	9	16	72	62	60
11.	Moneyfields	42	14	16	12	48	49	58
12.	Wimborne Town	42	15	10	17	60	61	55
13.	VT FC	42	13	15	14	65	66	54
14.	Bemerton Heath H	42	14	8	20	70	86	50
15.	Hamble ASSC	42	14	7	21	50	56	49
16.	Cowes Sports	42	12	10	20	48	67	46
17.	Lymington Town (1st Div.2 04-05)	42	10	14	18	42	71	44
18.	BAT Sports (Relegated to Div.3)	42	10	6	26	61	109	36
19.	AFC Newbury (Relegated to Div.3)	42	9	8	25	35	96	35
20.	Alton Town	42	8	9	25	51	99	33
21.	Brockenhurst	42	4	6	32	42	93	18
22.	Portland United	42	2	6	34	32	139	12

DIVISION ONE	1	2	3	4	5	6	7	8	9	10	11	12	13	14	15	16	17	18	19	20	21	22
1 AFC Newbury		0-5	2-1	2-1	0-4	0-1	2-1	1-0	0-5	3-0	0-4	0-7	1-1	0-1	4-1	2-4	0-1	2-0	1-2	1-4	1-3	1-2
2 AFC Totton	1-1		4-1	5-1	3-0	4-1	2-0	1-0	3-0	5-0	1-1	2-2	2-1	2-1	0-0	1-1	1-1	8-1	1-2	1-2	0-1	0-4
3 Alton Town	1-1	0-4		1-3	1-2	2-0	1-4	4-0	1-4	5-0	1-3	0-4	1-1	2-0	2-2	2-1	1-3	2-2	1-2	1-4	3-1	1-5
4 Andover	6-0	4-2	2-0		4-1	3-1	1-0	4-1	1-3	2-1	3-1	6-3	1-0	3-1	4-1	4-1	3-3	8-0	1-2	4-0	2-1	0-2
5 BAT Sports	1-3	1-8	2-2	1-4		3-3	3-6	3-2	2-3	1-0	1-3	0-3	0-2	1-2	2-1	0-2	2-4	0-2	0-3	0-1	5-4	0-4
6 Bemerton H.H.	5-0	3-3	1-1	2-2	3-1		3-1	3-2	1-2	1-0	0-3	1-2	2-1	1-6	1-3	1-1	1-2	7-0	3-3	2-1	1-3	1-6
7 Bournemouth	3-0	1-2	4-0	1-3	2-2	3-2		1-0	3-1	4-0	3-1	1-2	0-1	1-0	1-1	0-2	3-1	4-0	0-2	1-1	1-1	0-1
8 Brockenhurst	1-1	0-3	3-1	0-4	2-3	0-2	2-3		2-3	1-1	0-1	0-0	1-1	1-1	0-1	0-1	1-3	3-0	0-3	1-4	1-2	0-3
9 Christchurch	3-0	2-2	2-2	4-0	2-0	2-2	0-3	3-1		1-0	3-1	1-1	2-0	0-2	1-2	0-0	0-1	6-0	1-4	2-2	1-1	0-1
10 Cowes Sports	2-0	1-3	1-1	3-0	2-3	2-1	2-2	1-0	3-1		1-2	1-2	3-2	2-0	0-0	0-2	2-1	2-0	1-2	2-2	0-1	0-1
11 Fareham Town	2-0	1-2	1-1	2-1	1-3	1-0	3-2	4-2	0-3		0-0	1-0	1-0	2-2	1-1	0-1	1-1	1-3	3-3	3-1	3-3
12 Gosport Boro'	5-0	0-1	4-1	1-3	4-1	1-0	0-0	3-1	1-0	2-0	2-0		3-1	4-1	1-1	0-1	2-2	6-0	0-1	1-0	1-1	1-2
13 Hamble ASSC	4-0	0-3	2-1	2-2	2-0	2-0	0-2	3-0	2-0	0-1	1-5	4-1		1-0	1-1	2-1	3-1	0-1	0-1	1-0	0-3
14 Hamworthy U.	1-0	1-0	2-0	2-2	2-1	4-0	0-0	2-1	5-2	4-1	1-2	0-0	1-1		0-0	1-0	2-1	4-0	0-0	0-2	2-0	0-1
15 Lymington T.	0-0	0-2	1-2	0-6	1-1	2-1	1-2	1-3	1-4	1-1	0-3	0-1	2-1	0-2		1-1	4-2	1-0	0-4	0-0	3-1	2-3
16 Moneyfields	1-1	0-3	3-0	4-4	2-2	1-3	0-1	1-0	1-0	1-1	0-2	0-1	1-0	1-0	0-0		0-4	3-2	0-1	3-2	1-1	2-1
17 Poole Town	3-1	1-1	3-0	2-3	4-1	3-0	0-1	3-3	1-1	0-3	3-5	3-1	2-1	0-1	1-2	0-0		2-1	1-0	3-1	1-0	1-1
18 Portland United	1-1	1-3	0-2	1-4	3-3	3-4	0-1	1-5	0-1	1-1	0-2	1-5	2-1	0-1	0-1	1-3	1-5		0-4	1-1	3-4	0-8
19 Thatcham Town	1-1	1-0	4-0	3-1	2-0	2-3	0-2	3-2	2-1	1-1	0-0	2-4	1-1	1-2	4-1	2-0	4-1	6-1		2-0	5-0	0-1
20 VT FC	6-1	0-3	3-1	1-7	1-3	1-1	1-1	1-0	0-0	0-1	2-2	1-3	2-1	2-2	5-1	0-0	0-4	3-0	2-2		1-1	0-1
21 Wimborne Town	1-0	0-3	5-0	1-2	4-1	1-2	0-0	5-0	1-2	4-1	2-0	0-0	2-1	2-2	0-0	1-1	0-1	2-1	0-2	2-1		0-1
22 Winchester City	0-1	2-1	4-1	2-1	2-1	3-0	2-2	5-0	3-1	2-1	4-1	4-1	3-1	2-1	2-1	1-0	4-0	6-0	2-3	1-1	4-0	

700

DIVISION ONE

		P	W	D	L	F	A	Pts
1.	Locks Heath	42	31	5	6	96	28	98
2.	Hayling United	42	27	8	7	99	39	89
3.	Brading Town (Promoted)	42	27	7	8	96	50	88
4.	Downton (Promoted)	42	27	6	9	108	64	87
5.	Liss Athletic	42	26	5	11	99	57	83
6.	Horndean (Promoted)	42	22	6	14	95	67	72
7.	Fawley	42	20	9	13	76	53	69
8.	Stockbridge	42	18	13	11	82	52	67
9.	Ringwood Town (Promoted)	42	20	6	16	81	71	66
10.	United Services Portsmouth	42	18	11	13	86	72	65
11.	Farnborough North End	42	19	6	17	93	76	63
12.	East Cowes Vics	42	16	10	16	76	70	58
13.	Romsey Town	42	15	11	16	59	61	56
14.	Blackfield & Langley	42	14	13	15	81	69	55
15.	Petersfield Town	42	12	8	22	58	91	44
16.	Shaftesbury	42	10	10	22	53	96	40
17.	Hythe & Dibden	42	11	7	24	50	98	40
18.	Andover New Street	42	10	9	23	61	96	39
19.	Amesbury Town	42	10	4	28	55	109	34
20.	Alresford Town	42	8	9	25	49	86	33
21.	Bishops Waltham Town	42	7	7	28	57	112	28
22.	Whitchurch United	42	5	8	29	44	137	23

DIVISION TWO

	1	2	3	4	5	6	7	8	9	10	11	12	13	14	15	16	17	18	19	20	21	22
1 Alresford Town		1-2	2-1	3-0	0-5	0-1	1-2	3-0	0-1	2-2	1-1	0-0	1-4	0-3	1-2	2-5	0-2	0-1	1-1	4-0	1-1	0-6
2 Amesbury Town	3-0		2-4	1-1	0-3	1-2	1-2	2-3	2-1	1-4	0-2	1-6	2-1	1-4	0-3	2-1	1-5	0-2	1-1	2-1	2-2	3-2
3 Andover New S.	0-2	1-0		3-2	1-1	1-2	2-3	2-2	2-1	2-5	0-2	2-2	7-1	3-1	0-7	4-5	0-1	0-1	1-2	0-2	1-1	4-0
4 Bishops Waltham T.	0-0	3-1	0-2		3-0	0-3	2-8	2-4	1-6	3-1	0-5	1-4	1-4	0-1	0-1	0-3	0-1	1-0	5-2	0-3	2-2	1-1
5 Blackfield & Langley	1-1	5-1	4-0	4-2		2-3	4-4	1-2	3-3	0-1	0-3	1-1	1-1	0-1	0-0	3-2	0-2	2-3	5-3	2-1	3-1	6-1
6 Brading Town	1-0	3-2	3-0	6-1	3-0		2-3	5-1	1-0	0-1	3-3	2-3	2-1	2-1	1-2	3-1	2-4	2-1	3-1	1-1	2-2	4-3
7 Downton	2-1	0-1	1-1	2-0	2-1	0-1		1-0	2-1	2-0	2-4	2-1	8-1	2-1	2-0	1-3	0-0	3-2	3-2	1-1	2-0	2-0
8 East Cowes Vics	1-2	3-1	5-0	1-1	4-1	1-1	1-3		4-3	2-2	1-0	3-3	1-2	4-0	1-3	5-3	0-2	4-3	3-0	0-2	1-1	4-0
9 Farnborough N.E.	4-1	2-1	3-3	6-2	2-1	2-4	4-3	2-2		1-2	0-2	2-1	1-2	0-3	0-2	5-0	5-0	3-2	4-1	2-2	1-3	2-0
10 Fawley	1-0	2-0	5-0	3-2	1-1	0-1	1-1	0-1	1-0		1-3	1-2	3-0	3-2	0-1	0-0	2-1	2-2	6-0	2-4	3-1	4-1
11 Hayling United	6-0	3-0	2-1	4-1	0-0	1-2	2-1	0-0	4-1	3-0		3-2	3-0	2-2	0-3	3-0	0-0	3-0	1-0	1-0	1-1	5-2
12 Horndean	4-2	4-1	3-0	3-2	3-3	0-1	5-9	4-0	3-2	0-1	1-0		6-0	0-1	0-4	4-2	3-0	1-2	4-1	1-2	1-0	5-3
13 Hythe & Dibden	1-1	1-3	0-0	0-5	0-2	1-3	1-4	4-2	0-4	1-1	3-1	0-3		0-0	1-3	2-2	1-2	1-2	0-2	2-1	0-4	2-0
14 Liss Athletic	3-1	5-1	4-1	3-0	0-2	3-2	5-1	3-1	6-2	4-3	1-3	0-1	3-1		4-1	1-0	2-4	3-2	2-1	3-2	2-2	1-1
15 Locks Heath	3-0	3-0	2-1	3-1	5-1	1-0	0-1	3-1	0-1	2-1	1-1	4-2	3-0	2-0		0-1	2-2	2-0	0-0	0-1	4-1	3-0
16 Petersfield Town	2-1	5-4	1-2	3-2	3-3	0-3	0-4	0-4	1-4	0-0	1-1	0-2	1-1	0-2	0-3		0-3	1-0	0-2	2-5	1-4	1-1
17 Ringwood Town	5-3	0-4	4-0	2-1	1-3	1-1	3-1	2-1	0-1	2-2	1-2	3-1	1-2	4-2	0-3	0-1		3-2	3-5	0-0	2-4	3-4
18 Romsey Town	2-3	6-1	3-2	1-1	2-0	0-0	2-2	1-1	1-1	1-2	2-1	1-2	0-3	0-4	0-3	2-0	1-0		1-0	1-1	1-2	1-0
19 Shaftesbury	4-3	2-1	3-3	1-2	0-0	0-4	1-5	1-0	1-1	2-1	2-3	2-1	1-0	0-2	0-4	0-0	1-3	1-1		0-3	3-3	0-1
20 Stockbridge	1-1	2-0	1-1	4-1	1-1	2-2	0-4	0-0	4-1	2-1	0-2	1-1	1-1	1-2	2-2	2-0	2-0	1-2	5-2		4-1	10-0
21 United Services P.	2-1	5-0	5-1	3-1	2-1	3-2	5-1	1-0	2-3	0-2	0-5	0-1	5-3	0-3	1-2	2-1	2-2	2-2	4-1	3-1		2-0
22 Whitchurch United	0-3	3-3	0-2	4-4	0-5	0-7	1-6	0-2	1-5	0-3	0-6	0-3	3-0	0-7	0-5	3-1	1-7	0-0	1-1	0-3	1-1	

LEAGUE CUP

FIRST ROUND

AFC Newbury	v	AFC Aldermaston	2-1
AFC Totton	v	East Cowes Victoria	1-0
Alresford Town	v	Colden Common	3-6
Alton Town	v	Paulsgrove	2-1
Andover	v	Fleet Spurs	3-0
Bemerton Heath H.	v	Shaftesbury	3-2
Bishops Waltham T.	v	Fleetlands	0-2
Brockenhurst	v	BAT	6-0
Cowes Sports	v	Brading Town	0-0, HW
Downton	v	Hythe & Dibden	3-1
Hamble ASSC	v	Stoneham	1-0
Laverstock & Ford	v	Christchurch	0-1
Liss Athletic	v	Otterbourne	1-0
Locks Heath	v	AFC Portchester	2-0
Moneyfields	v	Clanfield	6-1
Petersfield Town	v	Overton United	6-4
Portland United	v	Ringwood Town	5-2
Thatcham Town	v	Tadley Calleva	2-3
United Services P.	v	Hamble Club	3-1
VT FC	v	Fareham Town	3-1
Wimborne Town	v	Lymington Town	1-0
Andover N.S.	v	Amesbury Town	4-2
Fawley AFC	v	Verwood Town	4-3
Hamworthy Utd (H)	v	Bournemouth	2-1
Netley Central S.	v	Horndean	2-1
Romsey Town	v	QK Southampton	7-1
Stockbridge	v	Farnborough North End	2-1
Whitchurch United	v	Winchester City	1-3
Gosport Borough	v	Hayling United	6-1

SECOND ROUND

Andover N.S.	v	United Services Portsmouth	1-0
Downton	v	Micheldever	H w/o
Petersfield Town	v	Tadley Calleva	3-3*. 7-6p
Winchester City	v	Locks Heath	2-0
Netley Central S.	v	VT FC	0-3
Alton Town	v	AFC Newbury	1-2
Andover	v	Colden Common	7-3
Brockenhurst	v	Portland United	4-4*, 9-10p
Gosport Borough	v	Liss Athletic	8-0

Hamble ASSC	v	Moneyfields	0-1
Wimborne Town	v	Stocksbridge	7-0
Poole Town	v	Fawley AFC	5-0
Romsey Town	v	Cowes Sports	2-1
Hamworthy Utd (H)	v	Bemerton Heath Harlequins	3-1
AFC Totton	v	Fleetlands	4-1
Blackfield & L.	v	Christchurch	0-5

THIRD ROUND

AFC Newbury	v	Poole Town	0-1
AFC Totton	v	Portland United	5-0
Andover	v	Moneyfields	1-0
Wimborne Town	v	Gosport Borough	2-0
Winchester City	v	Downton	3-0
Andover N.S.	v	VT FC	1-3
Hamworthy Utd (H)	v	Christchurch	1-0
Petersfield Town	v	Romsey Town	3-2

FOURTH ROUND

Poole Town	v	VT FC	2-0
AFC Totton	v	Petersfield Town	6-0
Winchester City	v	Wimborne Town	4-2
Andover	v	Hamworthy United (H)	3-3*, 4-1p

SEMI-FINALS

Andover	v	Poole Town	5-3
Winchester City	v	AFC Totton	2-3

THE FINAL

AFC Totton	v	Andover	1-0

LEAGUE CONSTITUTION 2006-07 - PREMIER DIVISION

A.F.C.TOTTON
Founded: 1886
Nickname: Stags

Chairman: Richard Maton **Vice-Chairman:** Ray Thurston **Manager:** Stuart Ritchie
Secretary: Richard Maton, 11 Wryneck,Lordswood,Southampton Hampshire SO16 8FJ
Tel.Nos: 02380 731114
Press Officer: Peter Chilcott (02380 860453) **Programme:** 30 Pages 50p **Website**: www.afctotton.co.uk
GROUND ADDRESS: Testwood Park, Testwood Place, Totton, Southampton, Hampshire SO80 3BE **Tel:** 02380 868981
Capacity: 2,500 **Seats:** 200 **Covered:** 250 **Floodlights:** Yes
Simple Directions: Five minutes walk from Totton BR.Turn off at roundabout in Totton centre into LIbrary Road. Then first right and second left into Testwood Place. Ground entrance is on the left.
Midweek Home Matchday: Tues (1st) Wed (2nd) **C lubhouse:** Open for matches and training evenings. **Club Shop:** No
Previous League: Hants: 1886-1986 **Previous Grounds:** Downs Park and Mayfield Park
Previous Name: Totton FC until merger with Totton Athletic 1979
Club Colours: All Blue **Change Colours:** Pink/Black/Black
LAST SEASON: League: 4th **F.A. Cup:** 3rd Qualifying Round **F.A. Vase:** 2nd Qualifying Round
Best Performances: League: 8th **F.A. Cup:** 4th Qualifying Round 82-83 **F.A.Vase:** 5th Rd.
RECORD Attendance: 600 v Windsor & Eton F.A.Cup 4th Q Rd. 82-83 **Goalscorer:** **Appearances:** James Sherlington
Senior Honours: Hampshire League Champions 81-82 84-85

ALTON TOWN

Founded: 1901
Nickname:

Chairman: Jim McKeil

Manager: Mick Doyle   **Assistant Manager:** Clive Ventham   **Physio:** Kim Andrews

Secretary: Andy Sharatt, 4 Goodwins Green, Alton, Hants. GU34 2NS   **Website**: www.altontownfc.com

Tel No: 01420 89527 (H) 07808 812713 (M) **e-mail:** manager.basingstoke@carsons.co.uk

Press Officer: Name (Tel)   **Programme:**

GROUND ADDRESS: Alton (Bass) Sports Ground, Anstey Road, Alton, Hants. GU34 2LS **Tel:** 01420 82465

Capacity: 2,000   **Seats:** 200   **Covered:** 250   **Floodlights:** Yes

Simple Directions: A31 from Winchesterto Alton road, proceed through town and ground is opposite Anstey Lane.

Midweek Home Matchday: Tuesday   **Clubhouse:** Sports Club   **Club Shop:** No

Previous League: Hampshire League> 2002

Club Colours: White/black/black   **Change Colours:** All Blue

LAST SEASON: 20th

Best F.A. Cup Season: 1st Round 1972-1973 v Newport County (a) 1-5

Senior Honours: Hampshire Champions 2001-02 Hants Senior Cup 1958, 1969, 1972 & 1978

BEMERTON HEATH HARLEQUINS

Founded: 1989
Nickname: Quins

Chairman: Eddie Boswell   **President:** Peter Say   **Managers** :Steve Slade

Secretary: Andy Hardwick, 20 Herbert Road, Salisbury, Wilts. SP2 9LF   & John Sainty

Tel No: 01722 333015 (H) 0 07810 128292 (M)

Press Officer: Name (Tel)   **Programme:** Pages - 30 Price - 50p Editor (Tel)

GROUND ADDRESS: The Clubhouse, Western Way, Bemerton Heath, Salisbury, Wilts.   **Tel No:** 01722 331218

Capacity: 2,100   **Seats:** 200   **Covered:** 350   **Floodlights:** Yes

Simple Directions: Out of Salisbury turn right of A36 to Bristol road at Skew Bridge. First left into Pembroke Road for half a mile then second left along Western Way. Ground is a quarter mile at the end.

Midweek Home Matchday: Tuesday   **Clubhouse:** Week day evenings plus lunchtimes at w/e **Club Shop:** No

Previous Names: Bemerton Ath., Moon F.C.& Bemerton Boys merged in 1989

Previous Leagues: As Bem Athletic: Salisbury & Wilts Comb. As Moon: Salisbury & Andover Sunday

Club Colours: Black & white diamond s/black/black   **Change Colours:** Amber/white/amber

BEST PERFORMANCES

League: 3rd in Wessex Premier   **F.A. Cup:** 3rd Qualifying Round   **F.A.Vase:** 5th Rd.

RECORD Attendance:1,118 v Aldershot Town F.A.Cup 1st Q 94 **Goalscorer:**   **Appearances:** Keith Richardson

Senior Honours: Wiltshire Senior Cup 1992-93

BOURNEMOUTH

Founded: 1875
Nickname: Poppies

Chairman: Robert Corbin **Vice-Chairman:** John Field   **Manager:** James Wood   **Assistant Manager:** Gary Fletcher

Secretary: Mike Robins, 7 Wesley Road, Poole, Dorset. BH12 3BE

Tel Nos: 01202 268503 (H) 01202 688746 (W) 07956 892435 (M) **e-mail**: maam.robins@ntlworld.com

Press Officer: Steve Jones   **Programme:** £1,00   **Editor**: Mike Robins

GROUND ADDRESS: Victoria Park, Namu Road, Winton, Bournemouth, Dorset, BH9 2RA**Tel:**01202 515123 or 07956 892435

Capacity: 3,000   **Seats:** 250   **Covered:** 250   **Floodlights:** Yes

Simple Directions: From A347 pass Redhill Common on right, round one way system and filter left at Ensbury Park Hotel. Left at next lights into Victoria Avenue

Midweek Home Matchday: Tuesday   **Clubhouse:** Open Daily   **Club Shop:** Badges, Ties & Progs

Previous Names: Bournemouth Rovers 1875-88 Bournemouth Dean Park 1888-90

Previous Leagues: Hampshire   **Previous Ground:** Dean Park:1888-90

Club Colours: All Red   **Change Colours:** All Blue

LAST SEASON:League: 7th   **F.A. Cup:** Qualifying round   **F.A. Vase:** 3rd Rd.

Top Scorer: Scott Joyce 38 (25 league 13 cup) **Player of the Year:** Lamin Dibba   **Captain:** John White

BEST PERFORMANCES: League: 3rd   **F.A. Cup:** 2nd Qualifying Rd. 90-91   **F.A.Vase:** 3rd Rd 94-95,2005-06

RECORD Attendance: **Goalscorer:** Brian Chike   **Appearances:**

Transfer Fee Received: £1,500 from Wimborne for Chick Onoura

Senior Honours: Hampshire Intermediate Cup 49-50 69-70 Hampshire League 12-13 & 21-22

BRADING TOWN

Chairman: Roy Penny

Secretary: Mrs Laurie Abrahart. Morton Manor, Morton Manor Road, Brading, Isle of Wight PO36 0EP.

Tel: (H) 01983 400 327. (B) 01983 539 008. (M) 07702 715 400. e-mail: laurie.abrahart@shgroup.org.uk

Ground: Vicarage Lane, Brading, I. o. W. Tel: 01983 405 217

Directions: Off the A3055 Ryde to Sandown road. On entering Brading from Ryde take the first left off the mini roundabout – Vicarage Lane is adjacent to the main Brading car park.

Colours: White with red trim/red/red.   Club Website: www.bradingtown.com

Change colours: Blue & White/Black/Blue

Midweek Matchday: Wednesday

BROCKENHURST

Founded: 1898
Nickname: The Badgers

Chairman: Dave Stansbridge
Manager: Graham Kemp
Secretary: Paul Christopher, 2 Veralls Court, Earlswood Park, New Milton, Hants.
Asst.Man: Steve Hillyer
Tel No: 01425 617322
Physio: Paul Gaden
Press Officer & **Programme Editor:** Dave Stansbridge
Programme: 32 Pages price £1,00
GROUND ADDRESS: Grigg Lane, Brockenhurst, Hants
Ground Tel No: 01590 623544
Capacity: 2,000　　　**Seats:** 200　　　　**Covered:** 300　　　**Floodlights:** Yes
Simple Directions: M27 Jct 1 A 337 to Lyndhurst and on to Brockenhurst. Turn right at Carey's Manor Hotel into Grigg Lane. Ground is 200 yards on the right.
Midweek Home Matchday: Tuesday　　　**Clubhouse:** Open every evening
Previous League: Hampshire
Club Colours: Blue & White/Blue/Blue　　　**Change Colours:** Green/Black/Green
LAST SEASON: League: 21st
Top Scorer: Darren Crock　　　**Player of the Year:** Danny Marks　　　**Captain:** Ross Drew
BEST PERFORMANCES: League:　　**F.A. Cup:** 3rd Qual Round 2001-2, 04-05 **F.A.Vase:** 4th Rd 2000-2001
RECORD Attendance: 1,104 v St Albans City F.A.Am. Cup 1974 **Victory:** 10-1 v Knowle Hospital, Hants Cup 13.02.61
Defeat: 0-11 v Portsmouth Gas Co. Hants Div 2 10.10.36
Senior Honours: Hants Intermediate Cup 61-62 Bournemouth Senior Cup 60-61 Hampshire Lg 75-76 R-up (2)

CHRISTCHURCH

Founded: 1885
Nickname: Priory

Chairman: Ray Jones　　　**Manager:** Andy Leader　　　　**Coach:** Brian Le Breu
Secretary: Martin Wootten, Grove Copse, 17 Stour Way,Christchurch, Dorset BH23 2 PF
Tel No: 01202 474358(H0 07880 885636 (M)
Press Officer: Phil Old　　　**Programme:** 20 Pages Price £1.00　　　**Editor:** Dennis Miller
GROUND ADDRESS: Hurn Bridge Sports Club, Hurn Bridge, Avon Causeway, Christchurch BH23 6DY
Tel No: 01202 473792　　　**Website:** www.christchurchfc.co.uk
Capacity: 1,200　　　**Seats:** 215　　　　**Covered:** 265　　　**Floodlights:** Yes
Simple Directions: On A338 from Ringwood turn off left towards Hurn Airport. Take exit marked Sopley at mini roundabout before airport and ground is immediatelly on the right. Three miles from Christchurch BR.
Midweek Home Matchday: Tuesday　　　**Clubhouse:** Normal pub hours, food cooked at lunchtimes　　　**Club Shop:**
Previous League: Hampshire　　　**Previous Ground:** Barrack Rd Recreation Ground until 1984
Club Colours: All Royal Blue with white trim Blue/ blue　　　**Change Colours:** All red
BEST PERFORMANCES:　　　**F.A. Cup:** 2001-2002　　　**F.A.Vase:** 2nd Qualifying Round
RECORD Appearances: John Haynes
Senior Honours: Hants Junior Cup (3) Hants Intermediate Cup 86-87 Bournemoutth Sen.Cup (5)

COWES SPORTS

Founded: 1881
Nickname:

Chairman: Ian Lee　　　**Vice-Chairman:** Ron Bowler　　　**Manager:** Derek Ohren
Secretary: Lee Bray, 12 The Ridge, Medham Village, Cowes. I.O.W. PO31 8QN
Tel No: 01983 281889 (H) 07919 233674 (M)
Press Officer: Pete Jefferies　　　**Club Website:** www.cowessportsfc.com　　　**Programme Editor:** Andrew Cooper
GROUND ADDRESS: Westwood Park, Reynolds Close, off Park Road, Cowes, Isle of Wight PO13 7NT
Tel No: 01983 293793
Capcity: 1,850　　　**Seats:** 450　　　　**Covered:** 450　　　**Floodlights:** Yes
Simple Directions: Take Park road out of Cowes. Reynolds Close is half a mile up hill
Midweek Home Matchday: Tuesday　　　**Clubhouse:** Yes.open matchdays　　　**Shop:** No
Previous League: Hampshire (pre 1994)
Club Colours: Blue & white stripes/black/blue　　　**Change Colours:** All yellow
LAST SEASON
League: 13th　　　**F.A. Cup:** Prelim Round　　　**F.A. Vase:** 2nd Round
Top Scorer: Brendon Arnold　　　**Player of the Year:** Matthew Bowler　　　**Captain:** Adam Barsdell
BEST PERFORMANCES
League: Southern League S.W.Div 2 1899　　**F.A. Cup:** 4th Qual replay 57-58　　　**F.A.Vase:** 5th rd 99-00
Senior Honours: Southern Lg Div 2 SW 1899 Hampshire Lg (7) Hampshire Senior Cup (9) Isle of Wight Gold Cup (17)

DOWNTON

Founded: 1905
Nickname: The Robins

Chairman: Ian Drinkwater　　　**President:** R.Tanner　　　**Manager:** Jeff Softley
Secretary: Jim Blake, 35 Orchard Rd., Morgans Vale, Redlynch, Salisbury, Wilts. SP5 2JA
Tel No: (H) 01725 512 347. (M) 07712 180 548.
Programme Editor:　　　　　　　　　　　　　　　　　　　　　　**Sponsor:** 3663
GROUND ADDRESS: Brian Whitehead Sports Ground, Wick Lane, Downton
Tel No: 01725 512162
Capcity: 1,600　　　**Seats:** 250 **Cover:** 400 (incl 4 for wheelchairs)　　　**Floodlights:** Yes
Simple Directions: Travel south from Salisbury on A338 for about 7 miles. Turn richt into Wick Lane and ground is a quarter of a mile on left.
Midweek Home Matchday: Tuesday　　　**Clubhouse:** Bar with kitchen facilities　　　**Club Shop:** No
Previous Leagues: Bournemouth, hants (pre 1993)
Club Colours: Red/white/red　　　**Change Colours:** White/black/white
LAST SEASON
League: 22nd　　　**F.A. Cup:** Extra Preliminary Round　　　**F.A. Vase:**
Top Scorer: Kevin Thick　　　**Player of the Year:** Kevin Thick　　　**Captain:** Ben Smith
BEST PERFORMANCES:League:　　　**F.A. Cup:** 3rd Qualifying Rd　　　**F.A.Vase:**
RECORD Attendance: 55 v AFC Bournemouth (Friendly)
Senior Honours: Wilts Senior Cup: 79-80 80-81 R-up (3) Wilts Junior Cup 49-50Wessex Lg Cup 95-96

FAREHAM TOWN

Chairman: Bob Ralls **President:** Ken Atkins **Manager:** Louis Savage **Coach:** Louis Bell **Physio:** Lim Mackay
Secretary: Ian Tewson, 16 Martin Avenue, Stubbington, Fareham, Hants. PO14 2RT Tel No: 01329 662624(H) & 07930853235
Website: http://creeksiders.mysite.wanadoo-members.co.uk
GROUND ADDRESS: Cams Alders, Palmerston Drive, Fareham   **Ground Tel No:** 01329231151
Capcity: 2,000   **Seats:** 450   **Covered:** 500   **Floodlights:** Yes
Simple Directions: From M27 Jct 11Follow signs A32 Fareham to Gosport. Fork right onto B3385 signposted Lee on Solent
(Newgate Lane) Over bridge and immediate right into Palmerstone Drive.   **Clubcall:** 09066 555874
Press Officer: Name (Tel)   **Programme:** Price £1.00   **Prog.Editor:** Martin Ralls
Midweek Home Matchday: Tuesday **Clubhouse:** Open matchdays and available for functions   **Club Shop:** Yes
Previous League(s): Portsmouth, Hampshire and Southern   **Sponsor:** Ralls Group
Club Colours: Red/black/red   **Change Colours:** White/white/black
BEST PERFORMANCES League: Southern Lg   **F.A. Cup:** 1st Rd (4)   **F.A.Vase:** 3rd Rd 03-4 04--05
RECORD Transfer Fee Received: £45,0000 from Spurs for David Leworthy **Attendances:** at Cams Alders: 2,015 v Spurs in a
friendly 1985 and 6,035 at the Dell for the F.A.Trophy Semi-Final v Kidderminster Harriers 1987
Senior Honours: Hampshire Senior Cup 1957, 1963, 1968 1993 Hampshire League Champions

GOSPORT BOROUGH
Founded: 1944
Nickname: The Boro

Chairman: John Stimpson   **President:** H.Mizen   **Manager:** Mick Marsh
Secretary: Brian Cosgrave, 2 Cavanna Close, Gosport, Hampshire PO13 0PE   **Coach** Hugh Doyle
Tel No: 02392 592863 (H) 07764 848250 (M)   **Physio:** Zoe Huggins
Programme Editor: Roy Newman   **Programme:** 40 Pages £1.00   **Website:**www.gosportboroughfc.co.uk
Ground Address: Privett Park, Privett Rd,Gosport, Hants. Po12 3SX **Tel. Nos:** 02392 583986 (Club) 02392 501042(Office)
Capacity: 4,500   **Seats:** 450   **Covered:** 500   **Floodlights:**Yes
Simple Directions: Exit M27 at jct 11 then A32 Fareham to Gosport. At Brockhurst roundabout(after 3 miles) right into Military
Road past HMS Sulton, left into Privett Road at next roundabout. Ground is 300 yards on left.
Midweek Home Matchday: Tuesday   **Clubhouse:** Matchdays only   **Club Shop:**
Previous Names: Gosport Borough Athletic
Previous Leagues: Portsmouth1944-45, Hants 45-78 & Southern 78-92
Club Colours: Yellow/Blue/Yellow   **Change Colours:** Whit/Navy Blue/Navy Blue
BEST PERFORMANCES: League: **F.A. Cup:** 4th Qual.Rd.80-81   **F.A.Vase:** 6th Rd replay 77-78
F.A.Trophy: 1st Rd. 1988-89   **F.A.Amateur Cup:** 3rd Rd 47-48 66-67
RECORD Attendance: **Goalscorer:**   **Apps:**
Senior Honours: Southern Lg. Div 1 South R-Up 84-85, Hants Senior Cup 87-88 & S.W.Counties Pratten Cup 77- 78

HAMBLE AEROSTRUCTURES S & SC
Founded:
Nickname:

Chairman: Peter Mence   **President:** Ron Garner   **Manager:** Danny Bowers   **Res Team Man:** Paul Cotton
Secretary: Matthew Newbold, Flat 6, 70-72 Portsmouth Rd., Woolsten, Southeampton Hants SO19 9AN
Tel Nos: 023 80342421 (H) 07917 451823 (M) **email:** mattnewbold@fsmail.net
Programme: 32 Pages Price £1,00 **Editor:** Matt Newbold **Website:** www.clubwebsite.co.uk/hamblesscfc
GROUND ADDRESS: Folland Park, Kings Avenue, Hamble, Southampton SO31 4NF   **Tel:** 0238 0452173
Capcity: 1,000   **Seats:** 450   **Covered:** 150   **Floodlights:** Yes
Simple Directions: M27 jct 8 then B3397 to Hamble. From Hamble BR turn right proceed for one mile then turn right before
shops into Kings Road. Ground 200 yards on right in works sports ground.
Midweek Home Matchday: Tuesday   **Clubhouse:** Big social club   **Club Shop:** No
Previous Name(s): Folland Sports (pre 1990) Aerostructures SSC90-97
Club Colours: Maroon & Sky Blue   **Change Colours:** Sky & white stripes/black/sky
BEST PERFORMANCES: League: **F.A. Cup:**   **F.A.Vase:** 1st Rd.
Senior Honours: Southampton Senior Cup 84-5 86-7 91-2

HAMWORTHY UNITED
Founded: 1926
Nickname:

Chairman: Bruce Scammell   **Vice-Chairman:** John Masters   **Manager:** Alex Pike
Secretary: Peter Gallop, 51a Symes Road, Hamworthy , Poole, Dorset BH15 4PR   **Coach**: Paul Curtis
Tel No: 01202 670972 (H) 07859 933848 (M)
Press Officer: Name (Tel)   **Programme:** Yes
GROUND ADDRESS: The County Ground, Blandford Close, Hamworthy, Poole BH15 4BF**Tel:** 01202 674974
Capacity: 2,000   **Seats:**   **Covered:**   **Floodlights:** No
Simple Directions: From A35 follow signs for Poole & Hamworthy. in Upton take second exit at roundabout, stay on Blandford
Road. Past two sets of lights and take left into Blandford Close.
Midweek Home Matchday: Wednesday   **Clubhouse:** Yes   **Club Shop:** No
Previous Name: Hamworthy St.Michael merged with Trinidad Old Boys 1926 **Previous League(s):** Doreset Premier.
Club Colours: All Sky Blue   **Change Colours:** Maroon/Sky Blue/Blue
Senior Honours: Dorset Senior Cup R-Up 97-98

Poole Town F.C.

HORNDEAN

Secretary: Michael Austin
22 Abbas Green Havant Hampshire PO9 4EP
Tel: 02392 645335 (H) 07946 071966 (M)
Chairman: Robert Berry
Ground: Five Heads Park, Five Heads Road, Horndean, Hants. PO8 9NZ (01705 591363)
Directions: From north: J3 A3M, turn off aerial flyover, past Safeways on right, over r'about. Turn right at next r'about into A3 London Road, ground on left just past Good Intent PH. From south: J2 A3M, off at Horndean sign at end of slip road, turn left - then from Safeways above.
Floodlights: Yes
Colours: Red/black/red.
Change colours: Blue & white stripes/blue/blue

LYMINGTON TOWN

Chairman: Brian Perrett   **Vice-Chairman:**   **Manager:**
Secretary: Audrey Hodder, 6 Froman Close, Lymington, Hants. SO41 9 LQ
GROUND ADDRESS: The Sports Ground, Southampton Road, Lymington, Hampshire SO41 9HP   **Tel:** 01590 671305
Capacity: 3,000   **Seats:** 200   **Covered:** 300   **Floodlights:Yes**
Simple Directions: Follow the A337 to Lymington. Go over the lights after the Police Station (on right) and ground is approx 150 yards on the left.
Midweek Home Matchday: Tuesday
Club Colours: Red/white/black   **Change Colours:** Blue/blue/white
Best Performances
League: Champions Wessex Div 2   **F.A.Vase:** 2nd Rd

Moneyfields F.C.

MONEYFIELDS

Founded: 1987
Nickname: Moneys

Chairman: Gary Foster   **Manager:** Craig Stafford & Bobby De Soix   **Coach:** Alan Smith **Physio:** Kevin Evans

Secretary: David Jupe, 46 Kingscote Road, Waterlooville, Hants. PO6 4EN **Sponsors:** FINEST Windows & Conservatories

Tel No: 023 92 359571   **Reserves' League:** Sydenhams Wessex Combination

Press Officer: Name (Tel)   **Programme** 36 Pages Price £1.00   **Editors** : David Hayter

GROUND ADDRESS: Moneyfields Sports Centre, Moneyfields Ave, Copnor, Portsmouth,. PO3 6LA **Tel. No:** 0239 2665260

Capacity: 1,500   **Seats:** 150   **Covered:** 150   **Floodlights:** Yes

Simple Directions: From M27 on to A27. Exit Southsea A2030. & head south along A2030 exit. Rt. into Tangier Rd (4th rt turn). Follow Tangier Road until the Tangiers Pub. Take next right into Folkestone Road then Martin Road and club.

Midweek Home Matchday: Tuesday   **Clubhouse:** Open evenings daily.   **Club Shop:**Yes

Name: Portsmouth Civil Service

Club Colours: Yellow & navy blue/navy blue/yellow   **Change Colours:** Green & white/green/green

BEST PERFORMANCES: League: **F.A. Cup:** 1st Qualifying Round 2001-02   **F.A.Vase:** 2001-02

Senior Honours: Portsmouth Premier Champions (2) Portsmouth Sen Cup Winners 90-91 R-Up 91-92 Hants Div 1 96-97

RECORD Attendance: 250 v Fareham, Wessex Div1 01-02 **Goalscorer:** Lee Mould 86 **Apps:** Matt Lafferty 229

Victory: 9-0 v Blackfield & L 2001-02 Wessex Div 1 **Defeat:** 0-8 v Andover 1999-2000 Wessex Div 1:

POOLE TOWN

Founded: 1880
Nickname: The Dolphins

Chairman: Clive Robbins   **Managers:** Tom Killick   **Assistant Manager:**Gavin Reeves **Coach:** Steve Richardson

Secretary: Bill Reid, 15 Addison Close, Romsey, Hampshire SO51 7TL

Tel No: 01794 517991

Website: www.poole-town.fsnet.co.uk   **Sponsors:** Holton Homes Ltd.

Press Officer: Chris Reeves (01202 674425) **Programme:** 60-70 pages £1.00

GROUND ADDRESS: Tatnam Ground, Oakdale School, School Lane, off Palmer Rd, Flleets Lane, Poole, Dorset

Matchdays Tel. No: 07771 604289

Capacity: 2,000   **Seats:** 154 +6 for disabled   **Covered Standing:** 120   **Floodlights:** Yes

Simple Directions: From M27 take A31 towards Poole/Dorchester. Follow A31, Wimborne by-pass, follow Ferryport signs, left at Merley roundabout then right at next sign for Poole. Follow A3049 to major roundabout (Fleets Bridge) over into Fleets Lane then left into Palmer Road.. First right into School lane.

Midweek Home Matchday: Wednesday   **Clubhouse:** At Ground open on matchdays only   **Club Shop**

Previous Leagues: Western 22-26, Southern 26-30, Western 30-57, Southern 57-96 :Hampshire 1996-2004

Club Colours: Red & white halves/red/red & white   **Change Colours:** Sky blue with navy trim/shorts/socks

LAST SEASON: League: 8th Wessex Div 1   **F.A. Cup:** N/A   **F.A. Vase:** 1st Round

BEST PERFORMANCES: League: **F.A. Cup:** 3rd Rd 1926-27   **F.A.Vase:** 1st Round 2005-2006

Senior Honours: Dorset Senior Cup (12), Anglo-Italian Cup R-up 80-81 & Southern League R-Up 88-89

RINGWOOD TOWN

Chairman: David Atley

Secretary: Paul Reed, Sunkist Lumby Drive, Ringwood, Hants. BH24 3JJ

Tel. No: 07786 437070 (M)

Ground: The Clubhouse, Long Lane, Ringwood, Hampshire BH24 3BX.

Tel.No.: 01425 473448

Directions: To Ringwood on A31 (M27). From town centretravel one mile. Right into Moorhouse Lane at petrol station and turn into Long Lane after 200 yards. Ground 250 yards on left

Midweek Matches: Tuesday

Colours: Red & black/ black/red & black

Change colours: All blue

VT F.C.

Chairman: Trevor Lewis   **Manager:**

Secretary: Arthur Fox, 91 Thornleigh Road, Woolston, Southampton, Hampshire. SO19 9 DH

Tel Nos: 02380 493346 (H) 07733 392623 (M)

Club Website: www.vt-fc.com

GROUND ADDRESS: Vosper Thorneycroftt Sports Ground, Portsmouth Road, Sholing, Southampton, Hampshire. SO19 9RR

Tel. No: 02380 403829

Simple Directions: Exit jct 8 M27 follow signs for Hamble. Second exit to Ham at Windover roundabout. Take right hand lane andsecond exit at mini roundabout. After150 yards turn right to Portsmouth Road and after half a mile look out for large lay by on left. The entrance to ground is opposite next bus stop.

Midweek Home Matchday: Tuesday   **Clubhouse:**Yes   **Club Shop:** No

Club Colours: Yellow with blue trim/blue/yellow& blue.   **Change Colours:** Red with navy trim /navy/navy

RECORD Attendance: 150   **Goalscorer:** George Diaper 100+

VT F.C. Back Row (L-R): Mick Brown (Assistant Manager), Adam Gray, Ben Tyrell, Stephen Hall, Marc Diaper, Scott O'Rourke, Michael Spinney, Matthew Headnington, Marvin McLean, Dave Diaper (Manager), Kevin Harnett (Coach).
Front Row: Jason Bunce, Stephen Wheatland, Kevin Gibbens, John MacFarland, Gary Male, Neil Ward, Terry Speight.

Photo: Alan Coomes.

WIMBORNE TOWN

Founded: 1878
Nickname: Magpies

Chairman: Nick O'Hara **President:** Brian Maidment **Manager:** Paul Arnold
Secretary & Press Officer: Peter Barham, Chelmer, 17 Margards Lane, Verwood, Dorset, BH31 6LP
Tel Nos: 01202 826705 (H) 07956 833346 (M) **Programme Editor:** Ken Fergus **Prog:** 28 Pages £1,00
GROUND ADDRESS: The Cuthbury, Cowgrove Road, Wimborne, Dorset BH21 4EL **Tel:** 01202 884821
Capacity: 3,250 **Seats:** 275 **Covered:** 425 **Floodlights:** Yes
Simple Directions: Wimborne on Blandford Road behind Victoria Hospital **Website:** www.wimbornefc.co.uk
Midweek Home Matchday: Tuesday **Clubhouse:** Evenings and mid day at week ends. **Club Shop:** Yes
Previous Leagues: Dorset League, Dorset Combination and Western League 81-86
Club Colours: White with black trim/black/white **Change Colours:** Yellow/Green/Yellow
LAST SEASON: League: 7th **F.A. Cup:** Prelim.Rd. **F.A. Vase:** 2nd Rd
Top Scorer: Paul Rideout **Player of the Year:** Ollie Phillipson-Masters **Captain:** Stewart Kearn
BEST PERFORMANCES: League: Wessex Champions (3) **F.A. Cup:** 1st Rd Proper 82-83 **F.A.Vase:** Winners 1991-92
RECORD: Attendance: 3,250 V Bamber Bridge F.A.Vase Semi-Final 28.03.92 **Victory:** 9-0 v East Cowes Victoria 98-99 and Brockenhurst 99-00 **Defeat:** 2-6 v Thatcham Town 91-92 **Goalscorer:** Jason Lovell **Appearances:** James Sturgess
Fee Paid: £5,500 to Bashley for Jason Lovell 1992 **Fee Received:** £6,000 from Bashley for Jason Lovell 1989 and from Dorchester Town for Tommy Killick 1993.
Senior Honours: F.A.Vase Winners 1991-92, Wessex League: 91-92 93-94 99-00 R-up 92-93 96-97, Dorset Senior Cup Runners-Up 80-81 85-86 98-99 99-00 & Dorset Senior Amateur Cup 36-37 63-64

LEAGUE CONSTITUTION 2005-06 - DIVISION ONE

ALRESFORD TOWN

Chairman: Alan Binfield

Secretary: Trevor Ingram, 18 Corfe Close, Alresford, Hants. SO24 9PH

Tel: 01252 544 002 (B) 07770 387 462 (M)

email: trevor@ingramtribe.freeserve.co.uk

Ground: Alresbury Park, The Avenue, Alresford, Hants.

Tel: 01962 735100

Midweek Matchday: Tuesday

Colours: Black & white stripes/black/black with white trim

Change Colours: All blue

AMESBURY TOWN

Secretary: Tony Hinchliffe, 12 Lanes Close, Amesbury, Wiltshire SP4 7RW

Tel Nos: 01980 624 425 (H) 01985 220 914 (W)

Ground: Recreation Ground, Recreation Road, Amesbury, Wiltshire.

Capacity: 2,000 **Seats:** 120 **Cover:** Yes **Floodlights:** Yes **Clubhouse:** Yes

Directions: From A303 Countess Road Roundabout, towards town centre through lights and turn right by bus station. Left at end of road at T junction bt Lloyds Bank go over bridge and left into 'Recreation Road on sharp right bend.

PREVIOUS Leagues: Salisbury & District, Wiltshire County, Western , Hampshire

Name: Amesbury F.C.

RECORD Attendance: 625 v Taunton Town 1997

Colours: All Blue

Change Colours: All Red

FACT FILE

Formed: 1904

Sponsor: Wiltshire Glass & Windows

Colours: All Blue

Change colours: All Red

Midweek Matches: Yuesday

Programme Editor: Graham Ashman

CLUB PERSONNEL

Chairman: Michael Saunders

Manager: John Scott

Assistant Managert: Peter Taylor

Captain: Neil Sole

ANDOVER NEW STREET

Chairman: Graham Waters

Secretary: Jim Dunn, c/o Club e-mail: jim_dunn@talk21.com **Tel No:** 07986 471085 (M)

Ground: Foxcotte Park, Charlton, Andover SP11 0HS Tel No: 01264 358358

Clubhouse: Open all day Saturdays and Sundays and from 1900 hours on week days.

Directions: Follow ring road to Charlton.Turn rightat the Royal Oak Pub. Carry on for about 3/4 mile then take last exit from roundabout signposted to Sports Centre.

PREVIOUS Leagues: Andover & District, North Hants, Hampshire Premier

Name: New Street

HONOURS Hampshire Premier Runners-Up 2003-004. Trophyman Cup Winners 2003-4

RECORD Attendance: 240

FACT FILE

Formed: 1895

Colours: Green & black stripes/Black/Green

Change colours: All Yellow

Midweek Matches: Wednesday 7.45

Website: www.andovernewstreet.co.uk

Programme Editor: Dougie McCracken

Chairman: Graham Waters

BLACKFIELD & LANGLEY

Secretary: Clifford Burnell, 47 Wilverley Place, Blackfield, Southampton, Hants.S)45 1XX

Tel No; 02380 893325 (H) 07811644949 (M)

Ground: Gang Warily Rec., Newlands Rd, Blackfield, Southampton, Hants SO45 1GA

Tel: 02380 893 603

Capacity: 2,500 **Covered Seats:**180 **Covered Standing:** Nil **Floodlights:** Yes

Directions: A326 from Totton. At Holbury mini roundabout take the right fork signposted to Lepe and Fawley. After the 1st set of lights (170m) turn left into ground.

Nearest Railway station:

Clubhouse Opening hours and availability of food & snacks.

Previous Leagues: Southampton Senr Lg, Hampshire League, R-U Russell Cotes Cup

Honours: Hants Div97-98, Div 2 84-85, Southampton Senior Cup (4)

Club Records Attendance: 240

FACT FILE

Founded: 1935

Colours: Green/black/green

Change colours: Yellow/blue/blue

Midweek home matchday: Tuesday

Programme Price:£1.00 Pages:32

Editor:Steve Nockeridge (023 8089 3065)

website: www.blackfieldandlangleyfc.co.uk

CLUB PERSONNEL

Chairman: Ian Hoare

Tel: 023 8089 3325 (H) 023 8084 7659 (B)

Vice Chairman: Owen Lightfoot

President:Geoff Mercer

Manager:Tony Feeney

Asst. Man. / Coach: FChris HomerPhysio:

Captain: Kevin Love

EAST COWES VICTORIA ATHLETIC

Chairman: Dennis Cooper

Secretary: Darren Dyer, 5 Acorn Gardens, East Cowes, Isle of Wight PO30 2AP
Tel: 01983 298773 (H) 07725 293451 (M)

Ground: Beatrice Avenue Ground, East Cowes, I.O.W. Tel: 01938 297165

Directions: From the ferry: 1 mile from town centre on lower main road to Newport or Ryde near Whippingham Church adjacent to Osborne Middle School

Colours: Red & white stripes/black & red/black & red. **Midweek Matchday**: Tuesday 7.45 K.O.
Change colours: Light Blue with dark blue trim

FARNBOROUGH NORTH END
Chairman: Tim Copp   **Manager:** Paul Xiberras
Secretary: John Marchment. 4 Linstead Road, Farnborough, Hampshire GU14 9HH **Tel No:** 01276 34254
GROUND ADDRESS: Cody Sports & Social Club, Old Ively Road, Pyestock, Farnborough, Hampshire
Tel. No.: 01252 543009 (matchdays only)   **Website:** www.fnefc.co.uk
Capacity: 1,000   **Seats:**   **Covered:**   **Floodlights:** Yes
Simple Directions: Off M3 Jct 4 take A327 towards Farnborough, into Kennels Lane opposite Nokia building and turn right at roundabout. then left at next roundabout into old Aveley Road. Ground in front of clubhouse.
Midweek Home Matchday: Tuesday   **Clubhouse:** Yes   **Club Shop:** No
Previous Name: Covies   **Previous Leagues:** Hampshire and Surrey Intermediate
Club Colours: Red/Black/Red   **Change Colours:** Yellow/Green/Yellow
LAST SEASON: League: 11th **Top Goalscorer:** Paul Griffiths 18 **Player of the Year:** Rob Harkness **Captain** Rory Todd
BEST PERFORMANCE
League: 11th Wessex Div 1 2005-2006   **Programme:** Yes
Record Goalscorer: Paul Griffitrhs 320   **Appearances:** Andy Dermott 516

FAWLEY

		FACT FILE
Secretary:	Mrs Lin Gascoine. 28 Heatherstone Avenue, Dibden Purlieu, Southampton,	Formed: 1923
	Hampshire SO45 4LH. Tel: (H) 02380 844 365. (M) 07947 455 628.	Colours: All Blue
Ground:	Waterside Sports & Social Club, 179 Long Lane, Holbury, Southampton, Hants	Change colours: Yellow/navy/yellow
		Midweek Matches: Wednesday
	Tel No: 02380 893750	Programme: Editor: D.Walsh
Directions:	M27 Jct 2 westbound take A326 signposted Beaulieu & Fawley.-(8miles) Ground	**CLUB PERSONNEL**
	is 800 yards on right after Hardley roundabout.	Chairman: Colin Stewart
		Manager: Kevin Dawtry
PREVIOUS	**Leagues:** Hants Premier	Coach: Chris Tonar
	Names: Esso F.C.	Captain: DannyWalsh

HAYLING UNITED
Chairman: MIchael Thornton

Secretary: Shirley Westfield, 14 Harold Road, Hayling Island, PO11 9LT

Tel.No.: 02392 463305 (H) 07724 540916 (M

Previous Name(s):   **Previous League(s):**

Club Colours: Black & White Strip[es/ Black/Black   **Change Colours:** All Blue

GROUND ADDRESS: Hayling College, Church Road, Hayling Island Hampshire   **Tel:** 02392 637758

Simple Directions: A27 Hayling Island turn off over Langstone Bridge. After passing Yew Tree Pub turn left into Church Road at small roundabout after a mile. Continue through village to the end and at the sea front turn left. Take fourth left into St Andrews Road. Follow road round to the right and ground is on the right. All parking in front car park.

Midweek Home Matchday: Tuesday   **Clubhouse:** Yes   **Club Shop:** No

HYTHE & DIBDEN

Secretary: Tony Moyst, 105 Hobart Drive, Hythe, Southampton SO40 6FD Tel: (H) 02380 847 335.

Chairman: Robert Parsons

Ground: Ewart Rec Ground, Jones Lane, Hythe, Southampton (02380 845264 -matchdays only)
At Dibden r'about on A326, take 1st left into Southampton Rd. Continue to Waterside PH, turn left into Jones Lane. Ground 200 yards on left.

Colours: Green & white/white/white.
Change colours: Sky blue/navy/sky

Midweek Matchday: Tuesday

LAVERSTOCK & FORD

Chairman: Peter Sanger
Secretary: Brian Ford
11 Chantry Road Wilton Salisbury Wiltshire SP2 0LT
Tel: 01722 743314 (H/F) Email: laverstock-fc@purbeck99.fsnet.co.uk
Ground: The Dell Church Road Laverstock Salisbury Wiltshire SP1 1TQ Tel: 01722 327401
Directions From Southampton – At the end of the carriageway from Southampton (A36) turn right at Petersfinger. Turn left at the traffic lights over the narrow bridge then take the next turning into Manor Farm Road. Take the next turning right into Laverstock Road, (do not turn left under the railway bridge). Keep left into Laverstock village, past the Church and the Club is situated on the left hand side directly opposite the Chinese takeaway and shop. From Bournemouth – Follow the A36 to Southampton past Salisbury College and straight across the Tesco roundabout take the first left into Petersfinger Road (take the corner slowly, the road goes back on itself) then follow directions as above.
Colours: Green and White hooped shirts/green/green
Change Colours: Blue and Black striped shirts/black/black
Midweek matchday: 1st team Tuesday

LISS ATHLETIC

Chairman: Mick Alder

Secretary: Mrs Pam Collins, 8 Mill Road Terrace, Liss , Hampshire GU33 7AX

Tel Nos: 01730 893505 (H) 07779 490268 (M)

Ground: Newman Collard Playing Field, Hill Brow Rd, Liss, Hants (01730 894 022)

Midweek matchday: Tuesday

Colours: Maroon/Navy/Navy

Change Colours: All Blue

LOCKS HEATH

Secretary: Sheila Mundy. 40 Holly Hill Lane, Sarisbury Green, Southampton, Hampshire SO31 7AD. Tel: (H) 01489 602 634. Email: mundy.house@btopenworld.com

Chairman: David Mundy

Ground: Locks Heath Rec, Warsash Rd, Titchfield Common, Hampshire PO14 4TX (01489 600 932)

Directions: M27 J9, follow A27 for Fareham. Past GEC factory then 4th exit at next r'about into Warmarsh Rd. Left at next r'about. Ground .75 mile on right.

Colours: Red & black/black/red.   **Midweek Matchday**: Tuesday
Change colours: Yellow/Blue/Yellow   **Website**: www.locksheathsports.co.uk

PETERSFIELD TOWN

Secretary: Mark Nicholl, 49 Durford Rd, Petersfield, Hants GU31 4ER Tel: 01730 300518 (H) 07949 328240 (M) email: mnicoll@cwctv.net

Chairman: David Ayre

Ground: Love Lane, Petersfield, Hants GU31 4BW Tel: 01730 233416

Directions: Off A3 circulatory system in Petersfield town centre (well signposted) or 10 min. walk from Petersfield railway station.

Colours: Red & black stripes/black/black.   **Club Website**: www.petersfieldfc.co.uk
Change colours: All Green

Midweek Matches: Tuesday

ROMSEY TOWN

Chairman: Ken Jacobs

Secrtary: Melvyn Finch. 1 PArk View, Sowden Close, Hedge End, Southampton, Hampshire SO30 4EP. Tel: 01489 690 025.

Ground: The By-Pass Ground, South Front, Romsey, Hampshire SO51 8GJ.
Tel: (Clubhouse) 01794 512 003.
Midweek Matches: Wednesday

Colours: White with black trim/black/black
Change colours: All Blue.

SHAFTESBURY

Chairman: Peter Stacey

Secretary: Chris Woods. 16 Crookhays, Shaftesbury, Dorest SP7 8DX.
Tel: (H) 01747 853 602. (B) 01258 482 839.

Ground: Cockrams, Coppice Street, Shaftesbury (01747 853 990)

Cover: Yes   **Floodlights:** Yes   **Clubhouse**: Yes

Midweek Matches: Wednesday 7.45 K.O.

Colours: Red & White stripes/Black/Red

Change colours: Green & White stripes/Green/Green

STOCKSBRIDGE

Chairman: Trevor Dance

Secretary: Robin Smith, Curlews Farm, Quarley, Andover, Hants. SP11 8PT
Tel: (H) 01980 629 781. (B) 01264 773 545. Email: andrewsallsorts@aol.com

Ground: Stockbridge Recreation Ground, High Street, Stockbridge, Hants.

Directions: Off Stockbridge High Street. 1st right at the BT sub-station into the Recreation Ground

Midweek Matches: Wednesday 7.45 K.O.

Colours: All red.
Change colours: All blue

UNITED SERVICES PORTSMOUTH

Chairmen: Lt. Richard Stephenson RN (07717 457551)
Secretary: Bob Brady, 3 Brook Close, DSarisbury Green, Southampton, Hants. SO31 7DW
Tel Nos: 01489 612648 and 07887 541782 (M) **E-mail**: bob brady@nats.co.uk
Programme Secretary: Tim Gilks c/o Club **Tel No**: 02392 820667

Ground: Victory Stadium, HMS Temeraire, Burnaby Road, Portsmouth PO1 2EJ
Tel: (Office) 02392 724 235. (Clubhouse) 02392 725 315
Directions: From Portsmouth Harbour (BR), turn right onto The Hard, pass under the rail bridge and turn left into Park Road, after approx 200 yards take 1st right into Burnaby Road. Ground 100 metres on the right.
Midweek Matches: Tuesdays
Colours: Navy Blue/White/Red
Change colours: All red   **Previous Name:** Portsmouth Royal Navy

VERWOOD TOWN

FACT FILE

Chairman: Michael Fry

Colours: Red/black/black

Secretary: Judith Fry,19a Noon Hill Road, Verwood, Dorset. BH 31 7DB
Tel Nos: 01202 822826 (H&F) 07969 213770(M)

Change colours:

Ground: Potterne Park, Potterne Way, Verwood, Dorset BH21 6RS
Tel N0: 01202 814007 (No floodlights)

Yellow & Black stripes/Yellow/Yellow .

Directions Leave the A31 at Ringwood and take the B3081 towards Verwood (approx 5 miles) Pass through Ebblake Industrial Estate traffic lights and proceed to Woodlinken Drive and turn left. Continue down Woodlinken Drive into Lake Road. At 'T' junction turn left into Newtown Road. At next 'T' junction, Manor Road, turn left and then continue for approx 100 yards then turn let into Potterne Way and the ground is at the end of the road.

Midweek Matches: Tuesday

Club Website: judith@VTFC.co.uk

WARMINSTER TOWN

FACT FILE

Chairman: Peter Russell

Secretary: Glen Shuttlewood.11 Portway,Warminster, Wiltshire BA12 8QG

Colours: Red&blackstripes/black/red&white

Tel Nos: 01985 212033 (H) 07801 555094 (M)

Ground: 73 Weymouth Street, Warminster, Wiltshire BA12 9NS

Change colours:

Tel No: 01985 217828

Directions A36 from Salisbury, head for town centre, turn left at traffic lights in

Blue & White Stripes/Blue/Red&White

town centre signposted A350 Shaftesbury. Club is situated approx.

400 yards on left hand side at top of Weymouth Street.

Midweek Matches: Wednesday

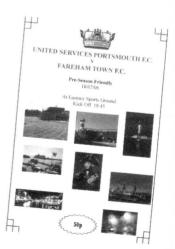

DIVISION THREE

		P	W	D	L	F	A	Pts
1.	Paulsgrove	30	20	6	4	91	34	66
2.	Laverstock & Ford (Promoted)	30	19	6	5	62	37	63
3.	Verwood Town (Promoted)	30	19	3	8	73	42	60
4.	Colden Common	30	17	5	8	86	45	56
5.	Netley Central Sports	30	16	5	9	62	41	53
6.	Fleetlands	30	15	7	8	59	36	52
7.	Tadley Calleva	30	16	4	10	52	40	52
8.	Otterbourne	30	14	6	10	56	45	48
9.	AFC Aldermaston	30	12	5	13	64	68	41
10.	Overton United	30	11	7	12	54	53	40
11.	AFC Portchester	30	11	4	15	57	61	37
12.	Ordnance Survey	30	10	6	14	69	68	36
13.	Clanfield	30	11	3	16	56	62	36
14.	Fleet Spurs	30	8	3	19	60	75	27
15.	QK Southampton	30	2	3	25	24	123	9
16.	Hamble Club	30	1	3	26	17	112	6

DIVISION THREE	1	2	3	4	5	6	7	8	9	10	11	12	13	14	15	16
1 AFC-Aldermaston		4-2	5-2	3-2	3-3	2-0	5-3	2-3	0-1	1-1	0-5	2-2	3-1	4-1	0-2	0-3
2 AFC Portchester	4-1		6-1	3-1	1-3	1-4	2-1	1-2	0-0	1-4	2-2	0-2	0-2	7-1	2-1	3-2
3 Clanfield	1-2	4-1		1-5	2-1	1-2	4-0	2-0	0-1	2-0	0-3	2-0	2-5	7-1	4-2	2-3
4 Colden Common	2-2	5-0	2-1		6-0	3-1	2-0	1-2	2-0	4-2	3-0	1-1	3-1	2-2	0-2	1-4
5 Fleet Spurs	5-2	1-3	2-0	3-2		0-1	8-0	0-2	1-3	3-5	2-3	2-3	2-2	3-0	1-2	0-2
6 Fleetlands	4-3	3-3	0-2	1-3	2-1		7-0	2-3	2-2	2-1	2-0	3-0	1-1	2-0	3-0	1-0
7 Hamble Club	0-5	0-3	0-1	1-8	1-4	0-4		2-5	2-1	0-2	1-3	1-1	0-7	1-3	1-1	1-5
8 Laverstock & Ford	1-4	0-0	0-0	1-3	2-1	2-0	2-1		2-2	5-4	1-1	2-1	1-0	5-0	4-0	3-1
9 Netley Central Sports	3-1	3-2	4-1	1-1	3-0	0-2	4-0	2-1		4-2	1-0	2-1	0-1	9-0	1-2	1-3
10 Ordnance Survey	5-1	2-3	1-1	3-3	5-4	1-1	3-0	1-4	2-4		2-5	1-1	4-0	5-0	0-1	2-2
11 Otterbourne	1-3	3-1	1-1	1-4	3-2	0-0	3-0	0-0	2-3	6-2		4-1	1-1	3-1	0-2	1-2
12 Overton United	2-1	2-1	4-2	2-4	2-2	3-1	4-0	0-2	4-0	1-4	0-1		0-2	2-2	3-1	6-1
13 Paulsgrove	4-0	1-0	3-2	3-1	5-0	3-3	10-1	2-2	3-0	2-0	4-0	7-0		7-2	1-0	2-1
14 QK Southampton	3-1	0-4	1-6	0-7	0-2	0-5	0-0	1-2	0-7	1-3	2-3	0-5	1-5		1-5	1-5
15 Tadley Calleva	1-3	3-0	2-1	3-2	4-2	1-0	3-0	1-3	0-0	4-1	2-0	0-0	2-2	2-0		1-2
16 Verwood Town	1-1	3-1	5-1	1-3	6-2	0-0	2-0	2-0	4-0	2-1	0-1	2-1	2-4	4-0	3-2	

LEAGUE CONSTITUTION 2006-07 - DIVISION THREE

AFC ALDERMASTON
Secretary: Christine Collier,16 River Gardens, Purley on Thames, Berkshire RG8 8BX. Tel: (H) 0189 422 951. (M) 07884 254 706.
Chairman: Martin Desay
Ground: Aldermaston Rec. Society, Aldermaston, Reading, Berks.
Tel: 01189 824 544
Colours: All Blue. Change Colours: Yellow/white/red

AFC NEWBURY
Secretary: Ron Renton, 105 The Oaks Newbury Berkshire RG14 7UY Tel: 01635 842588 (H) 07811 462291(M)
football_newbury@yahoo.com
Chairman:Steve Hartley
Ground:
Colours:Red/black/red
Change Colours: Green/black/red

AFC PORTCHESTER
Secretary: Colin Brans. 2 Eden Rise, Fareham, Hampshire PO16 0UL. Tel: (H) 01329 311 560.
Chairman: Steve Woods
Ground: Wicor recreation Ground, Cranleigh Road, Portchester, Hampshire PO16 9BD. Tel: (Clubhouse) 07798 734 678. (Office) 01329 311 560.
Colours: Tangerine with black trim/black/black
Change Colours: Black & white stripes/white/white

BAT SPORTS
Secretary: Bob Walsh, 30 Hammonds Lane Totton Southampton Hampshire SO40 3LG
Tel: 02380 486470 (H) 07977 514090 (M)
rwalsh9014@aol.com
Chairman:Michael Clark
Ground: BAT ports Ground Southern Gardens Southampton SO40 8RW Tel: 02380 862143
Colours:Blue & yellow trim/blue & yellow trim/blue
Change Colours: All red

BISHOPS WALTHAM TOWN
Secretary: Charles Bailey, 46 Claylands Road Bishops Waltham Southampton SO32 1BH
Tel: 01489 894888 (H/B)
chjbailey@aol.com
Chairman:Clive Dugmore
Ground: Priory Park Elizabeth Way Bishops Waltham Southampton SO32 1BQ Tel: 01489 894269
Colours:Red & black stripes/black/red
Change Colours: Blue & white/blue/blue

CLANFIELD
Secretary:Stuart Wallis. 6 Anvill Close, Waterlooville, Hampshire PO7 8RN.
Tel: (H) 02392 268 151. (B) 02392 230 023.
(M) 07765 238 231. (F) 02392 230 093.
Chairman: Graham Reeve
Ground: Peel Park, Charlton Lane, Clanfield, Waterlooville, Hants. Tel: 07765 238 231
Colours: Blue & Black stripes/ Black/Black
Change colours: White/sky blue/white

COLDEN COMMON
Secretary: Malcolm Vaughan, 18 Grays Close Colden Common Winchester SO21 1UG
Tel: 07765 407406 (M)
mvaughan2209@btinternet.com
Chairman: Cliff Banford
Ground: Colden Common Recreation Ground, Main Road, Colden Common (01962 712 365)
Colours: Red & white stripes/black/red
Change Colours: Yellow & royal blue/royal blue/royal blue

FLEET SPURS
Secretary: David Baverstock, 46 Lysons Road Aldershot Hampshire GU11 1NF
Tel: 01252 338572 (H) 07766 334551 (M)
david.baverstock@bmwfin.com
Chairman: Chris Stokes
Ground: Kennels Lane, Sherwood, Farnborough, Hampshire
Colours: Red & blue/blue/blue
Change Colours: Yellow/black/black

FLEETLANDS
Secretary: George Mason, 8 Spring Garden Lane Gosport Hampshire PO12 1HY
Tel: 01329 589333 (H) 07962 139312 (M)
gcmason8@freenet.uk.com
Chairman: Craig Ancell
Ground: Lederle Lane, Gosport, Hants PO13 0AA
Tel: 02392 239 723
Colours: Red & black stripes/black/black
Change colours: Sky blue

HAMBLE CLUB
Secretary: Colin Williams. 16 Coach Road, Hamble, Southampton, Hants SO31 4JW. Tel: (M) 07977 324 923
Chairman: John Foster
Ground: Shell Mex Ground, Hamble Lane, Hamble-le-Rice, Southampton, Hampshire
Colours: Blue with red trim/blue/blue
Change Colours: Green/black/black

OTTERBOURNE
Secretary: Robin Broom. 249 Passfield Avenue, Eastleigh, Hampshire SO50 9NB. tel: (H) 02380 328 992.
Chairman: Jack Goodchild
Ground: Oakwood Park, off Oakwood Avenue, Otterbourne, Hampshire SO21 2ED. Tel: 01962 714 681
Colours: Red & black stripes/black/red
Change Colours: Light & dark blue/dark blue/dark blue

OVERTON UNITED
Secretary: Mrs Anita Wheeler, 3 Lordsfield Gardens, Overton, Hants RG25 2EW. Tel: (H) 01256 771 241. (B) 01256 608 432
Chairman: Philip Wheeler
Ground: Recreation Centre, Bridge Street, Overton
Tel: 01256 770 561
Colours: Blue & white stripes/white/blue
Change: Yellow & blue/blue/blue

PAULSGROVE
Secretary: Paul Lipscombe. 5 Braunston Close, Paulsgrove, Portsmouth PO6 4EN. Tel: (H) 02392 711 744.
(B) 02392 250 052. (M) 07861 102 436
Chairman: Jim Garcia
Ground: The Grove Club, Marsden Road, Paulsgrove, Portsmouth. Tel 01705 324 102
Colours: All navy blue
Change Colours: Red/black/black

QK SOUTHAMPTON
Secretary: Don Campbell. 81 Lumsden Avenue, Shirley, Southampton SO15 5EJ. Tel: (M) 07801 550 337
Chairman: Steve Rice
Ground: Lordshill Recreation Centre, Southampton, Hampshire SO16 9BP. Tel: 023 8073 2531
Colours: All yellow & navy
Change Colours: Green/green/yellow

TADLEY CALLEVA
Secretary: Steve Blackburn, 7 Bramdean Close, Tadley, Hanrts. RG26 3RD Tel: (M) 07787 501028
Chairman: Andy Shoulder
Ground: AWE Recreational Society Aldermaston Near Tadley RG7 4PR
Colours: Gold & black/black/black
Change Colours: White/royal blue/royal blue

WELLOW
Secretary: Matt Taylor, 1 The Hollies Gurneys Mead Wellow Romsey Hampshire SO51 6GH
Tel: 01794 324131 (H) 07789 900963 (M) 01794 322281 (F)
matthew.taylor35@btinternet.com
Chairman: John Traies
Ground: Hatches Farm Romsey Road West Wellow Hampshire
Tel: 07985 283471
Colours: White/black/black
Change Colours: Orange/white/white

WHITCHURCH UNITED
Secretary: Diane Lovett, 14 Martin Close Oakridge Basingstoke Hampshire RG21 5JY
Tel:01256 417654 (H) 07801 440497 (M)
diane@wls.co.uk
Chairman: Gary Lovett
Ground: Longmeadow Winchester Road Whitchurch Hampshire RG28 7RB
Tel: 01256 892493
Colours: Red & white stripes/black/black
Change Colours: Blue & white hoops/blue/blue

WESTERN LEAGUE

SPONSORED BY: TOOLSTATION

President: Rod Webber   **Chairman:** Cliff Ashton
Secretary: Ken Clarke, 32 Westmead Lane, Chippenham, Wiltshire SN15 3HZ
Tel: 07790 002279 (8am - 9pm)   **Fax:** 01249 652952
Email: ken.clarke@toolstationleague.com

PREMIER DIVISION		P	W	D	L	F	A	Pts
1.	Bideford	38	29	7	2	93	25	94
2.	Corsham Town	38	24	10	4	78	30	82
3.	Bristol Manor Farm	38	24	4	10	86	43	76
4.	Welton Rovers	38	19	12	7	61	39	69
5.	Calne Town (2nd Div.1 04-05)	38	19	10	9	70	41	67
6.	Willand Rovers (1st Div.1 04-05)	38	18	11	9	63	42	65
7.	Frome Town	38	18	10	10	61	45	64
8.	Bitton	38	18	9	11	63	41	63
9.	Hallen	38	15	12	11	71	54	57
10.	Brislington	38	15	8	15	55	53	53
11.	Bridgwater Town	38	15	7	16	66	54	52
12.	Radstock Town (3rd Div.1 04-05)	38	14	5	19	62	73	47
13.	Barnstaple Town	38	12	9	17	54	62	45
14.	Melksham Town	38	12	8	18	43	68	44
15.	Odd Down	38	11	10	17	34	44	43
16.	Bishop Sutton	38	7	13	18	36	52	34
17.	Keynsham Town	38	5	11	22	34	78	26
18.	Devizes Town	38	7	5	26	27	94	26
19.	Torrington	38	6	7	25	33	89	25
20.	Backwell United	38	3	10	25	30	93	19

PREMIER DIVISION	1	2	3	4	5	6	7	8	9	10	11	12	13	14	15	16	17	18	19	20
1 Backwell United		2-2	1-1	1-3	1-3	0-9	0-5	0-0	1-4	1-4	0-2	0-0	0-2	1-0	3-1	0-4	3-6	0-4	1-1	2-4
2 Barnstaple Town	1-1		1-3	0-0	3-1	0-2	3-1	1-2	0-2	0-2	1-1	1-2	2-4	3-0	4-1	1-0	5-2	5-1	0-1	2-2
3 Bideford	2-0	7-0		2-0	2-0	5-1	0-0	3-0	2-1	1-0	8-1	4-2	0-0	5-2	5-0	5-1	3-1	3-0	1-1	0-0
4 Bishop Sutton	1-1	2-0	0-1		1-1	2-2	3-1	1-3	0-3	1-4	5-1	0-0	0-0	2-2	1-0	0-0	0-1	1-1	0-2	2-2
5 Bitton	1-0	1-1	0-1	2-0		2-1	3-1	0-1	0-1	0-0	7-1	1-1	3-1	1-1	2-0	0-1	1-1	3-1	4-1	0-1
6 Bridgwater Town	0-1	0-3	1-2	4-0	1-1		2-1	0-2	2-2	0-1	2-1	1-2	4-2	2-1	1-3	1-1	2-2	5-0	0-2	0-0
7 Brislington	4-1	2-1	0-0	2-1	2-1	0-1		0-2	1-3	1-1	2-1	1-3	1-2	1-1	1-1	0-3	1-1	1-3	1-3	1-0
8 Bristol Manor Farm	1-1	1-1	2-3	2-1	6-0	2-1	1-2		1-1	2-4	4-0	0-2	1-2	6-1	0-1	5-0	3-0	5-1	4-2	2-1
9 Calne Town	2-1	6-0	1-1	1-0	0-1	1-1	0-5	1-2		1-1	4-0	2-0	3-2	1-0	4-3	0-1	5-2	4-0	0-0	2-0
10 Corsham Town	2-1	3-0	4-0	2-1	2-0	1-0	4-1	3-0	1-1		5-3	1-1	5-0	4-1	2-0	2-0	2-1	3-0	0-1	1-1
11 Devizes Town	1-0	1-0	0-3	1-0	0-2	0-2	0-2	1-5	0-3	0-0		2-0	0-2	0-1	1-0	1-0	0-1	0-0	1-1	1-4
12 Frome Town	1-0	3-2	2-3	2-0	1-2	1-0	1-2	2-5	2-1	2-1	2-1		3-4	0-0	0-0	0-1	1-1	0-0	2-2	4-1
13 Hallen	2-1	1-1	0-2	0-0	1-1	3-1	1-1	2-1	2-2	2-2	8-1	1-3		2-0	1-2	0-0	3-2	6-0	0-1	0-2
14 Keynsham Town	1-1	0-2	0-5	1-3	0-4	1-2	0-1	1-2	0-0	2-2	4-1	0-4	1-1		1-1	1-4	0-1	1-1	0-2	1-2
15 Melksham Town	4-1	1-0	0-3	1-0	1-3	2-6	1-1	1-0	1-1	1-2	0-0	0-1	0-6	1-1		2-0	0-5	2-3	0-2	3-1
16 Odd Down	3-0	1-2	0-1	1-2	0-2	0-2	0-0	0-2	3-2	1-1	2-0	0-3	1-1	1-1	0-1		1-0	2-0	0-1	0-1
17 Radstock Town	4-1	1-3	1-3	1-0	0-4	1-2	3-2	1-3	2-1	0-2	3-2	1-1	2-1	1-2	4-2	0-2		0-1	3-1	2-2
18 Torrington	1-1	2-0	0-1	1-1	2-4	0-2	2-3	0-3	0-2	0-1	4-0	0-3	1-4	1-3	0-3	1-1	1-4		0-1	0-1
19 Welton Rovers	5-1	0-3	0-1	2-1	1-1	2-0	1-1	2-4	3-0	3-1	4-0	1-2	1-1	2-1	1-1	1-1	2-1	4-1		1-1
20 Willand Rovers	2-0	0-0	2-1	1-1	2-1	4-3	1-0	0-1	0-2	0-2	3-1	3-2	3-1	5-0	1-2	1-1	3-0	6-0	0-0	

DIVISION ONE

		P	W	D	L	F	A	Pts
1.	Dawlish Town	42	33	6	3	115	33	105
2.	Chard Town	42	29	10	3	87	27	97
3.	Street	42	24	11	7	80	39	83
4.	Ilfracombe Town	42	23	9	10	82	50	78
5.	Westbury United	42	22	10	10	95	50	76
6.	Bridport	42	22	6	14	81	60	72
7.	Larkhall Athletic	42	19	11	12	93	56	68
8.	Portishead	42	18	12	12	59	49	66
9.	Shrewton United	42	18	7	17	88	79	61
10.	Bradford Town	42	15	13	14	71	81	58
11.	Clevedon United	42	15	12	15	62	67	57
12.	Longwell Green Sports	42	15	9	18	49	52	54
13.	Weston St Johns (-3)	42	18	3	21	63	81	54
14.	Cadbury Heath	42	15	8	19	70	62	53
15.	Saltash United	42	15	7	20	71	84	52
16.	Biddestone	42	13	11	18	54	59	50
17.	Wellington	42	14	8	20	69	81	50
18.	Almondsbury	42	10	11	21	46	70	41
19.	Minehead	42	9	9	24	47	100	36
20.	Shepton Mallet	42	10	4	28	34	85	34
21.	Clyst Rovers	42	7	7	28	47	92	28
22.	Elmore	42	4	4	34	42	148	16

DIVISION ONE

	1	2	3	4	5	6	7	8	9	10	11	12	13	14	15	16	17	18	19	20	21	22
1 Almondsbury		3-0	2-2	1-2	2-2	1-2	1-2	0-0	0-7	3-2	1-4	1-2	0-2	1-1	0-1	3-0	0-2	0-0	1-1	1-2	1-0	0-2
2 Biddestone	0-0		1-1	1-0	1-0	1-1	1-2	6-0	2-4	2-0	1-2	0-0	2-1	1-2	1-3	1-2	3-1	0-2	1-2	3-0	0-0	4-2
3 Bradford Town	1-3	1-1		2-6	1-0	1-1	1-1	3-1	2-4	3-3	2-2	2-2	1-1	2-2	0-0	1-0	2-0	2-8	3-1	6-1	1-2	1-0
4 Bridport	2-1	2-0	0-1		0-2	1-3	2-2	4-1	0-2	0-0	2-1	2-1	1-0	3-1	4-3	5-2	2-1	1-0	1-2	4-2	3-2	8-0
5 Cadbury Heath	2-1	1-2	4-0	4-1		0-1	3-1	2-1	1-4	5-0	0-2	1-1	4-0	3-0	0-1	2-2	2-0	4-4	2-2	1-2	1-1	0-0
6 Chard Town	3-0	1-0	3-0	1-0	3-0		5-0	3-0	4-1	5-2	2-1	1-3	0-0	6-0	0-0	2-0	5-0	1-0	0-0	3-2	2-1	1-0
7 Clevedon Utd	2-2	4-1	1-2	0-2	1-0	0-2		1-4	1-0	4-0	0-0	2-2	1-1	3-0	1-0	2-0	2-0	2-2	2-3	4-1	4-2	3-0
8 Clyst Rovers	2-3	3-1	2-3	1-2	2-0	0-2	0-2		0-4	3-0	3-3	1-1	0-1	4-0	2-2	4-0	0-1	0-2	0-5	1-4	1-2	0-1
9 Dawlish Town	4-0	0-0	4-0	2-2	3-2	2-1	2-1	0-0		6-1	3-1	2-0	2-0	3-0	1-1	4-1	5-0	5-1	2-1	1-0	0-0	7-0
10 Elmore	0-2	2-1	1-1	0-2	0-4	2-4	1-1	0-1	1-4		1-5	1-4	1-2	1-3	1-2	1-6	3-2	0-3	2-5	4-2	0-3	1-3
11 Ilfracombe T.	0-1	2-1	0-4	2-2	2-1	1-2	3-1	3-2	0-1	3-2		1-0	2-1	2-0	1-0	3-0	1-0	2-0	1-0	3-3	1-1	3-1
12 Larkhall Ath.	0-0	1-1	2-1	1-0	1-0	1-3	1-1	5-0	1-1	11-0	0-2		0-0	9-1	3-1	8-0	3-1	1-2	4-2	1-0	1-3	1-1
13 Longwell G.S.	2-1	2-2	0-4	2-1	3-0	1-2	0-0	1-1	0-1	3-1	0-0	1-2		5-0	0-3	1-2	1-0	2-0	1-0	1-2	3-2	1-1
14 Minehead	1-0	0-1	6-1	1-1	0-5	1-1	1-1	3-1	0-2	4-0	1-1	2-3	3-1		0-4	1-2	3-1	1-3	0-2	1-1	1-2	3-1
15 Portishead	2-1	0-0	2-0	4-2	2-1	1-3	1-1	2-2	0-1	3-2	1-1	1-3	0-1	1-0		1-1	1-0	1-0	1-1	1-2	2-0	1-1
16 Saltash United	4-2	2-2	1-2	0-1	1-2	2-1	3-1	3-0	1-2	1-2	4-3	3-1	0-0	2-3			3-2	2-1	1-1	4-2	1-2	3-4
17 Shepton Mallet	0-0	0-2	3-1	1-1	1-3	0-3	1-0	2-1	0-3	2-1	0-6	1-4	1-4	3-2	1-0	0-5		1-0	0-1	0-0	0-0	2-1
18 Shrewton Utd	2-4	2-3	3-1	1-5	1-0	1-1	5-0	3-2	3-7	7-1	4-5	4-1	1-0	3-1	2-3	2-2	3-1		2-2	3-1	2-0	4-2
19 Street	1-0	1-0	4-2	1-0	1-1	0-0	2-1	3-0	1-3	4-0	1-0	2-0	1-0	8-1	1-0	1-1	2-0	1-1		4-1	2-0	1-2
20 Wellington	1-2	3-2	2-3	1-2	1-3	1-1	0-1	6-0	1-0	6-1	0-6	0-3	0-1	0-0	1-1	2-0	2-1	4-0	1-1		1-2	4-2
21 Westbury Utd	0-0	4-0	1-1	4-2	6-0	0-0	7-3	1-0	3-4	6-0	3-2	3-1	1-1	5-0	5-0	3-1	3-2	5-0	1-3	3-3		2-0
22 Weston St.J.	5-1	0-2	0-3	3-0	4-2	0-2	3-0	2-1	0-2	7-1	1-0	4-2	2-1	3-0	0-3	1-2	1-0	2-1	0-3	0-1	0-4	

Independent

From Bristol to Wiltshire and Weymouth, and all the way down to Land's End

FIRST. BEST. EVERY SUNDAY.... for Non-League and League Football coverage
– PLUS much, much more sport, news and features

Barnstaple Town F.C. Back Row (L-R): John Clarke (vice-President), Richard Hevingham, Darren Parish, Antony Cassinelli, Nick Quinn, Ricky Mannaio, Jeff Parish, Robert Guppy, John Vaughan, Desmond Edwards, Aaron Harper-Penman, Dominic Rivans, Tom Hunnibell, Sam Nark, Dave Griffiths (Physio). **Front Row:** Jake crush, Shane Tolley, Jake Barwick, David Cooke (Secretary), Jeff Evans (Manager), Jon Brend (President), Roy Lucas (Chairman), Doug Green (Business Manager), Lee Barrow (Coach), Mark Thomas, Chris Wood.

BARNSTAPLE TOWN

Founded: 1906
Nickname: Barum

Chairman: Steve James **President:** John Brend **Manager:** Jeff Evans **Physio:** Dave Griffiths
Secretary: David Cooke, 51 Walnut Way, Barnstaple, Devon, EX32 7RF **Tel No:** 01271 326088
Programme Editor: David Cooke **Programme:** £1.00 **Sponsor:** Brend Hotels
GROUND ADDRESS: Mill Road, Barnstaple, North Devon **Ground Tel. No:** 01271 343469
Capacity: 5,000 **Seats:** 250 **Covered:** 1,000 **Floodlights:** Yes
Simple Directions: A361 towards Ilfracombe (from M5 Jct 26) in Barnstaple follow A36 (Ilfracombe signs). Mill Road is second left after crossing small bridge
Midweek Home Matchday: Wednesday **Clubhouse:** Full license with canteen on match days **Shop:** Yes
Previous League(s): North Devon, Devon & Exeter, S.Western
Previous Name: Pilton Yeo Vale
Club Colours: All Red **Change Colours:** All Blue
LAST SEASON: League: 13th **F.A. Cup:** 1st Qualifying Round **F.A. Vase:** 1st Qualifying Round
Top Scorer: Kevin Squire **Player of the Year:** Jeff Parish **Captain:** Mark Thomas
BEST PERFORMANCES
League: Western Champions 52-53 & 79-80 **F.A. Cup:** 1st Rd replay 51-52 **F.A.Vase:** 4th Rd 94-95
RECORD Attendance: 6,200 v Bournemouth F.A.Cup 1st Rd 51-52 **Goalscorer:** **Apps:** Ian Pope
Transfer Fee Paid: £4,000 to Hungerford Town for Joe Scott **Fee Received:** £6,000 from Bristol City for Ian Doyle**Senior Honours:** Western Champions (2) R-Up (2) Div 1 (2) Devon Pro Cup (12) Devon Sen Cup 92-93

BIDEFORD

Founded: 1949
Nickname: The Robins

Chairman: Roy Porchl **President:** Albert Keegan **Manager:** Sean Joyce
Secretary: Kevin Tyrrell, 69 Laurel Avenue, Bideford, Devon EX39 3AZ **Tel No:** 01237 4707747
Marketing & Promotions: Rachael Shortridge **Programme:** 32 Pages 50p **Prog. Editor:** Ian Knight & Ron Ackland
GROUND ADDRESS: The Sports Ground, Kingsley Road, Bideford **Ground Tel No:** 01237 474975
Capacity: 6,000 **Seats:** 375 **Covered:** 1,000 **Floodlights:** Yes
Simple Directions: A 361 for Bideford - ground on right as you enter town.
Midweek Home Matchday: Tuesday **Clubhouse:** Open lunchtimes and evenings. Contact: Sue Tyrrell **Club Shop:**
Previous Leagues: Devon & Exeter 47-49, Western 49-72, Southern 72-75 **Previous Name:** Bideford Town
Colours: All red **Change Colours:** All Blue
BEST PERFORMANCES
League: Southern League **F.A. Cup:** 1st Rd replay 64-65 **F.A.Vase:** Semi-Final 2003-2004
RECORD Attendance: 6,000 v Gloucester C F.A.Cup 4th Qual. Rd 1960 **Goalscorer:** Tommy Robinson 259
Appearances: Derek May 527 **Victory:** 16-0 v Soundwell 50-51 **Defeat:** 0-12 v Paulton Rovers 96-97
Senior Honours: Western League Champions (8) Div 1 51-2 Div 3 49-50 Devon Senior Cup 79-80

BISHOP SUTTON

Founded: 1977
Nickname: Bishops

Chairman: George Williams
President: Roy Penney
Managers: Keith Brown
Secretary: Steve Hillier, 9 Greyfield Commmon, High Littleton, Bristool BS39 6YL
Tel No: 01761 479083 (H) 07713 681235 (M)
Programme Editor: Secretary
GROUND ADDRESS: Lake View Football Field, Bishops Sutton, Bristol   **Ground Tel No:** 0127533097
Capacity: 1,500   **Seats:** 100   **Covered:** 200   **Floodlights:** Yes   **Club Shop:** No
Simple Directions: On A368 at rear of Butchers Arms pub. Ground is signposted when entering village.
Midweek Home Matchday: Tuesday   **Clubhouse:** Open Matchdays
Previous Leagues: Weston & District (Youth), Bristol & Avon, Somerset Senior >1991
Previous Ground: Adjacent cricket field.
Club Colours: All Blue   **Change Colours:** All Yellow
LAST SEASON Top Scorer: Liam Fussell   **Player of the Year:** Sam Payne   **Captain:** James Caradine
BEST PERFORMANCES: **F.A. Cup:** 1st Qualifying Rd.   **F.A.Vase:** 3rd Round 1998
Record Attendance: 400 v Bristol City   **Victory:** 15-0 v Glastonbury Reserves
Senior Honours: Somerset Junior Cup 1980-81

BITTON

Founded: 1922
Nickname:

Chairman: John Langdon   **President:** Roy Ewans
Manager: Andy Black   **Sponsors**: John Dean Builders
Secretary: Dean Shephard, 16 Stephens Drive, Barrs Court, Warmley, Bristol. BS30 7AA
Tel No: 0117 960 7364 (H) 07710 187547 (M)
Press Officer: Name (Tel)   **Programme:** 36 Pages £1.00
GROUND ADDRESS: The Recreation Ground, Bath Road, Bitton BS30 6HX   **Ground Tel. No:** 0117 932 3222
Capacity: 1,000   **Seats:** 48   **Covered:** 200   **Floodlights:** Yes
Simple Directions: M4 Jct 18. Take A46 towards Bath.Then A420 at first roundabout for Wick/Bridgeyate. On approach to
Bridgeyate turn left at mini roundabout onto A4175. Go 2.2. miles then left for Bath on the A431. Ground is 100 yards on right.
Midweek Home Matchday: Wednesday   **Clubhouse:** Weekdays 7.30-11.0 Sat & Sunday all day. **Club Shop:** No
Previous Leagues: Avon Premier Combination,Glos County.
Club Colours: Red & white stripes/black/black   **Change Colours:** Yellow/Green/Yellow
LAST SEASON: League: 8th
BEST PERFORMANCES
League: **F.A. Cup:**   **F.A.Vase:** 4th Round 2004-05
RECORD Attendance: **Goalscorer:** A.Cole   **Appearances:**
Senior Honours: Glos Junior Cup R-up 1990 Glos Senior Amateur Cup 1995 Glos Challenge Trophy R-up 1997

BRIDGWATER TOWN 1984

Founded: 1984
Nickname: The Robins

Chairman: Alan Hurford   **Patron:** A.J.'Tom' Pearce   **President**: Keith Setter
Manager: Craig Laird & Paul Rich   **Sports Injury Therapist:** Dave Callow L.C.S.P.(Assoc) F.A.Dip.
Secretary: Alan Slade, 16 High Street, Cannington, Bridgwater, Somerset   **Press Officer:** Gordon Nelson (01823 271167)
Programme: Voted best in the Western League 2004-2005   **Editor:** Roger Palmer   07734 842282 or Fax 01278 422456
GROUND ADDRESS: Fairfax Park, College Way, Bath Road, Bridgwater   **Ground Tel No:** 01278 446899
Capacity: 2,500   **Seats:** 128   **Covered:** 200   **Floodlights:** Yes
Simple Directions: M5 jct 23 follow signs to Glastonbury (A39), turn right for Bridgwater (A39) . Follow signs for Bridgwater
College via College Way Ground on right after Rugby Club. One mile from Bridgwater (BR)
Midweek Home Matchday: Tuesday   **Clubhouse:** Open on matchdays   **Club Shop:** Refreshments
Previous Name: Bridgwater Town: **Previous League:** As BTFC Southern
Club Colours: Red / White /Red   **Change Colours:** Blue/white/white
LAST SEASON: League: 11th   **F.A. Cup:** Preliminary Round   **F.A. Vase:** 2nd Round
Top Scorer: Ryan King   **Player of the Year:** Ryan king   **Captain:** Rob Snook
BEST PERFORMANCES
League: Southern League   **F.A. Cup:** 2nd Qual Rd   **F.A.Vase:**   5th Rd. 2004-2005
RECORD Attendance: 1,112 v Taunton Town 26.02.97
Senior Honours: Somerset Senior Cup 93-94 95-96 Western Lg Div 1 Champions 95-96 Somerset Senior League: (3)

BRISLINGTON

Founded: 1956
Nickname: Bris

Secretary: Kevin Jacobs, 179 Bishopsworth Road, Bedminster Down, Bristol BS13 7LG

Programme: Yes

GROUND ADDRESS: Ironmould Lane, Brislington, Bristol.   **Tel No:** 0117 977 4030 **Capacity**:

2,000   **Seats:** 144   **Covered:** 1,500   **Floodlights:** Yes

Simple Directions: On A4 Bristol to Bath road, about 500 yards on Bath side of Park & ride opposite Wyevale Garden Centre.

Midweek Home Matchday: Tuesday   **Clubhouse:** Open Matchdays   **Club Shop:** No

Previous Leagues: Somerset Senior until 1981

Club Colours: Red & black/black/red   **Change Colours:** Yellow & black/yellow/yellow

BEST PERFORMANCES

League: Western Premier R-up 2002-03   **F.A. Cup:** 2nd Qualifying 2003-2004   **F.A.Vase:** 3rd Rd 1989-90

Senior Honours: Somerset Senior Cup 92-93 R-up 93-94 Western Premier R-up 2002-03

BRISTOL MANOR FARM

Founded: 1964
Nickname: The Farm

Chairman: TBA   **Manager:** Steve Fey
Secretary: Jeff Wilson, 26 Raymond Road, Bedminster,Bristol B53 4QP
Tel Nos: 01179497610(H) 07886 955941 (M) **email:** bristolmanorfarmfc@hotmail,com
Programme: Yes
GROUND ADDRESS: The Creek, Portway, Sea Mills, Bristol BS9 2HS   **Ground Tel No:** 017968 3571
Capacity: 2,000   **Seats:** 98   **Covered:** 350   Floodlights: Yes
Simple Directions: M5 Jct 18 (Avonmouth Bridge) follow A4 for Bristol. U turn on dual carriage way by Bristol & West sports ground and return for half a mile on A4. Ground entrance is down narrow lane on left hidden entrance)
Midweek Home Matchday: Tuesday   **Clubhouse:** Open every evening   **Club Shop:** No
Previous League(s): Bristol Suburban 64-69 Somerset Senior 69-77   **Previous Name:** Manor Farm O.B. 1964-68
Club Colours: Red/Black/Black   **Change Colours:** All yellow
Top Scorer: David Anyinsah   **Player of the Year:** James Hughes   **Captain:** Matthew Baird
BEST PERFORMANCES
League: 3rd Western Premier   **F.A. Cup:** 3rd Qualifying Round   **F.A.Vase:** 6th Rd
RECORD Attendance: 500 v Portway, Western League 1974 **Goalscorer:**   **Appearances:** M.Baird
Senior Honours: Glos Trophy 87-88 Glos Amateur Cup 89-90

CALNE TOWN

Founded: 1887
Nickname: Lilywhites

Secretary: Laurie Drake, 22 Falcon Road, Calne, Wiltshire SN11 8PL
Tel Nos: 01249 819186 (H) 01249 897310 (H) 07768 742524(M)   **Sponsor:** Creft Nicholson Homes
Programme: Yes
GROUND ADDRESS: Bremhill View, Calne, DSN11 9EE   **Ground Tel.No:** 01249 653323
Capcity: 2,500   **Seats:** 78   **Covered:** 250   **Floodlights:** Yes
Simple Directions: Take A4 from Chippenham near Calne, turn left at first roundabout onto A3102,the Calne by pass. At next roundabout turn right, next left then right and right again.
Midweek Home Matchday: Tuesday   **Clubhouse:** Open every day.   **Club Shop:** No
Previous Names: Calne Town(1886) & Harris Utd merged as Harris Utd. 1921-67   **Previous Lgs:** Wilts Co. pre 1986
Club Colours: Whiite/Black/Black   **Change Colours:** All Blue
RECORD Attendance:1,100 v Swindon Friendly 25.07.87 **Goalscorer:** Robbie Lardner   **Appearances:** Gary Swallow 259
Victory: 11-1 v Heavitree (H)   **Defeat:** 2-7 v Odd Down (A)
Senior Honours: Western League Div 1 Runners Up 1992-93 2004-05 Wiltshire Semior Cup (3) R-up (4)

CHARD TOWN

Founded: 1920
Nickname: Robins

Secretary: Michael Hawes, 18 Norrington Way, Chard, Somerset TA20 2JP
    Tel Nos: 01460 67730 (H) 07906 904138 (M)
Ground: Dening Sports Field, Zembard Lane, Chard TA20 1JL Tel: 01460 61402
Capacity: 1,500   Seats: 60   Cover: 200   Floodlights: Yes

Directions: Follow sports centre signs off main A30 High Street along Helliers Road. Right into Upper Combe Street and left into Zembard Lane . BR 7miles Axminster or 8 miles Crewkerne
Clubhouse: Matchdays & most evenings. Snacks served

HONOURS   Som. Snr Lg 49-50 53-54 59-60 67-68 69-70 (Lg Cup 61-62 71-72 76-77); Western Lg Div 1 R-up 83-84 87-88 95-96 05-06, (Merit Cup 82-83, Comb. Cup(Res) 91-92 (R-up 92-93)); Som. Snr Cup 52-53 66-67; S W Co's Cup 88-89; Western Com Lge 96-97, Cup 96-97.

BEST SEASON   FA Cup: 2nd Qual Rd. 77-78 82-83   **FA Vase:** 4th Rd 1989-90

PREVIOUS   **Leagues:** Somerset Snr 20-24 48-75; Perry Street 25-48 **Grounds:** None
2005-06   **Top Scorer:**Foster **Captain:**Paul Nicholls   **Player of the Year:** Steve Devlin

FACT FILE
Colours: All red
Change: All Blue
Midweek matches: Tuesday
Prog: 24 pages with entry. Ed: Ian Hallett

CLUB PERSONNEL
Chairman: Brian Beer
President: Roy Lock

Manager: Stuart Parris
Assistant Manager: Craig Rice

CORSHAM TOWN

Founded: 1884

Chairman: John Gingell   **Vice-Chairman:** Joy Brown
Manager: Colin Bush   **Assistant Manager:** John Woods   **Physio:** Jon Lock
Secretary: Richard Taylor, 7 Cresswells, Corsham, Wilts. SN13 9NJ
Tel No: 01249 714406   **e-mail:** info@corshamtownfc.co.uk
Programme: Yes
GROUND ADDRESS: Southbank Ground, Lacock Road, Corsham, Wilts. SN13 9HS   **Tel:** 01249 715609
Capacity: 1,500   **Seats:** No   **Covered:** Yes   **Floodlights:** Yes
Simple Directions: From A4 turn into Corsham at the Hare & Hounds pub roundabout, taking the Melksham road (B3353) past The Methuen Arms pub then straight across the next mini roundabout into Lacock road. Ground is 1/2 mile on right
Midweek Home Matchday: Tuesday   **Clubhouse:** Yes   **Club Shop:** Yes
Previous League: Wiltshire County
Club Colours: Red&white/white/red   **Change Colours:** Yellow/blue/blue
BEST PERFORMANCES
League: 2nd Western Premier 2004-2005, 05-06   **F.A. Cup:** 2nd Qualifying Rd.   **F.A.Vase:** 2nd Rd.
RECORD Attendance: 550 v Newport Co. F.A.Cup 94-05   **Goalscorer:**   **Appearances:** Craig Chaplin
Senior Honours: Wiltshire Senior Cup 1975-76 1996-97 2004-05

Dawlish Town F.C. - Division One Champions 2005-06 - Back Row (L-R): A Kerswell (Assistant Manager), M Parker, L Fenner, C Cliff-Brown, M Rock, C Fenner, C Slough, D Vicary, A Lynch, C Myers (Player Manager). **Front Row:** R Veale, J Wheeldon, A Raybould, G Head, D Worthington, E Edwards (Kit Man).

DAWLISH TOWN
Founded: 1889

Secretary:	JohnWathen c/o Dawlish Town F.C.
Ground:	Playing Fields, Sandy Lane, Exeter Road, Dawlish Tel: 01626 863110
	Website: www.dawlishtownafc.co.uk
Directions:	Approx 1 mile from centre of town, off main Exeter road (A379)
	Capacity: 2,000 Seats: 200 Cover: 200 Floodlights: Yes
Clubhouse:	Open nightly, all day Saturday and Sunday situated in car park opposite ground

HONOURS   Western Lg Div 1Champions 05-06 R-up 98-99, Lg Cup 80-81 83-84, Devon Premier Cup 69-70 72-73 80-81, Devon Snr Cup 57-58 67-68, Devon St Lukes Cup 82-83 (R-up 81-82), Carlsberg Cup 96

BEST SEASON   **FA Vase:** Quarter Finals 86-87

PREVIOUS   **League:** Devon & Exeter   **Ground:** Barley Bank 1875-1900

RECORD   **Gate:** 1,500 v Heavitree Utd, Devon Prem. Cup Q-Final
Defeat: 0-18 v Clevedon (A), Western Lge Prem. Div. 92-93

FACT FILE
Colours: Yellow/green/green
Change Colours:Green/blac/black
Midweek matchday: Tuesday
Programme: Yes
CLUB PERSONNEL
Chairman: Dave Fenner
Manager: Chris Myers
Coach:Richard Hancox
Captain: Craig Fenner
Physio:Derek Gibson
2005-2006
Player of the Year: Mark Rock
Top Goalscorer: Carl Cliff-Brown

DEVIZES TOWN
Founded: 1883
Nickname: Town

Chairman: Ross Rossiter	**President:** Chris Dodd	**Manager:** Paul Thompson
Secretary: Rolfe Wallen, 2 Cromwell Road, Devizes, Wilts SN10 3EJ		**Asst Man:** Brian Newlands
Tel Nos: 01380 721217 or 01380 720648 **Email**: phil@avontrophies.co.uk		**Physio:** Gaye Timbrell

Press Officer: Paul Humphries   **Programme:** Price £1.00   **Editor:** Andy Muckle   **Sponsors:** The Rising Sun & Four Seasons
GROUND ADDRESS: Nursteed Road, Devizes (01380 722817)
Capcity: 2,500   **Seats:** 130   **Covered:** 400   **Floodlights:** Yes
Simple Directions: Off Nursteed Road (A 342 signposted Andover) town ground on right opposite Eastleigh Road.
Midweek Home Matchday: Tuesday   **Clubhouse:** Open daily with function room and Sky TV Club **Shop:** In club
Previous Name: Southbroom (until early 1900s)   **Previous League(s):** Wilts Combination and Wilts Premier
Club Colours: Red & white/black/red   **Change Colours:** Blue & white/black/blue
LAST SEASON: League: 17th   **F.A.Cup:**Preliminary Round   **F.A.Vase:** 3rd Round
Top Scorer: Jamie Mullings   **Player of the Year:** Gary Campbell   **Captain:** Rob Hannah
BEST PERFORMANCES
League: 5th Western Premier 20002-01   **F.A. Cup:** Extra Prelim.Rd.   **F.A.Vase:** Quarter Finals 1982 & 2001
Senior Honours: Western Div 1 99-00 Wiltshire Senior Cup (14)

FROME TOWN

Founded: 1904
Nickname: The Robins

Chairman: Gavin Hares **Manager:** Andy Crabtree **Asst.Man.** Derek Graham
Secretary: Ian Pearce, 52 Woodhayes Road, Frome, Somerset BA11 2DQ
Tel No: 01373 462787(H) 07811 511222(M) **Club Website:** www.frometownfc.co.uk
Programme: 48 Pages Price £1.00 **Editor:** Ian Pearce **Sponsors:** Mirage Signs
GROUND ADDRESS: Badgers Hill, Berkley Road, Frome Tel No: 01373 464087
Capacity: 2,000 **Seats:** 150 **Covered:** 200 **Floodlights:** Yes
Simple Directions: Ground is on the Westbury Road one mile from town centre and from Frome BR
Midweek Home Matchday: Wednesday **Clubhouse:** Open evenings and week-ends **Club Shop:** No
Previous Leagues: Somerset Senior, Wilts League and Wilts Premier
Club Colours: All Red with white trim **Change Colours:** All Yellow with blue trim
LAST SEASON: League: 7th **F.A.Cup:** Preliminary Round **F.A.Vase:** Second Round
Top Scorer: Mark Salter **Player of the Year:** Jon Crowley **Captain:** Dean Ranger
League: Western Champions 78-79 **F. A. Cup:** 1st Rd Proper v Leyton Orient 1954-55 **F.A.Vase:** Quarter-Final 2004-2005
RECORD Attendance: 8,000 v Leyton Orient F.A.Cup 1st Rd 1958
Victory: 15-0 v Glastonbury, Somerset Senior Lg. (h) 1906-07 **Defeat:** 1-11 v Dorchester Town , Western Lg. 58-59
Senior Honours: Western Lg. 78-79 Div1 1919-20 01-02 Div 2 R-up 54-55 Somerset Sen Cup (3) Somerset Prem Cup (3)

HALLEN

Founded: 1949

Chairman: Barrie Phillips **Manager:** Dave Mogg
Secretary: Charmaine Phillips. Email: phillipsb@hallenfc.fsnet.co.uk
email: Graham Brunsdon@Blueyonder.co.uk **Tel No:** 07780 994771 (M)
GROUND ADDRESS: Hallen Centre, Moorhouse Lane, Hallen, Bristol BS10 7RT **Tel:** 01179 505559
Capacity: 2.000 **Seats:** 200 **Covered:** 200 **Floodlights:** Yes
Simple Directions: From Jct 17 M5 follow A4018 signed Bristol. At 3rd roundabout turn right into Crow Lane. On to T junction, right and right again by Henbury Lodge Hotel. Left at next mini roundabout into Avonmouth Way. Proceed to Hallen village and turn left at crossroads into Moorhouse Lane.
Midweek Home Matchday: Wednesday **Clubhouse:** Yes **Club Shop:**
Previous Name(s): Lawrence Weston Ath.s(80s) Lawrence Weston Hallen (pre 1991) **Ground:** King's Weston -early1980s
Previous League(s): Gloucestershire Co.Lg. (pre 1993) Hellenic 93-2000
Club Colours: Royal Blue/black/royal blue **Change Colours:** All yellow
RECORD Attendance: 803 V Bristol Rpovers 1997
Senior Honours: GFA Challenge Trophy 1992-93 R-Up 1989-90 2004-2005 GFA Jun Cup: 1969-70 Hellenic Div1 R-up 96-97

KEYNSHAM TOWN

Founded: 1895
Nickname: K's

Chairman: Steve Nicholls **Manager:** Gary Silverthorne
Secretary: John Peake, 27 Orwell Drive, Keynsham, Bristol.
GROUND ADDRESS: Ground Field, Bristol Road, Keynsham, Bristol. **Ground Tel.No:** 0117986876
Capacity: 2,000 **Seats:** 72 **Covered:** 170 **Floodlights:** Yes **Club Shop:** No
Simple Directions: Ground is on A4175 off Bristol to Bath A4. On left immediately after 30mph sign
Midweek Home Matchday: Wednesday **Clubhouse:** Matchdays and some evenings
Previous Leagues: Bristol & District, Bristol Comb., Bristol Premier and Somerset Senior.
Club Colours: Gold/black/gold **Change Colours:** Green and white
Top Scorer: Dean Maggs **Player of the Year:** Steve Jones **Captain:** Lee Zabeck
Senior Honours: Somerset Senior Cup 51-52 57-58 02-03

MELKSHAM TOWN

Founded: 1876
Nickname:

Chairman: Michael Perrin **Vice-Chairman:** Jackie Ferrett **Manager:** Kelvin Highmore
Secretary: David Phillips, 37 Duxford Close, Bowerhill, Melksham, Wilts. SN12 6XN
Tel No: 01225 706 904 07870 746107 (M)
Programme Editor: Graham Carruthers
GROUND ADDRESS: The Conigre, Melksham.Tel No: 01225 702843
Capacity: 1,500 **Seats:** 150 **Covered:** 600 **Floodlights:** Yes
Simple Directions: Just off main square in grounds of Melksham House.
Midweek Home Matchday: Monday **Clubhouse:** Every evening and w/e lunchtimes **Club Shop:**
Previous Leagues: Wiltshire 1894-1974 93-94 Western 74-93 **Previous Grounds:** Challymead and Old Broughton Rd Field
Club Colours: Yellow & Black stripes/Black/Yellow **Change Colours:** White/Navy Blue
LAST SEASON
League: 14th **F.A. Cup:** 1st Qualifying Round **F.A. Vase:** 2nd Qualifying Round
Top Scorer: Simon Price & Gavin Eyre **Player of the Year:** Josh Brigham **Captain:** Simon Price
BEST PERFORMANCES
League: 3rd **F.A. Cup:** 2nd Qualifying Rd. 54-55 57-58 **F.A.Vase:** 3rd Rd (3) F.A.Amateur Cup: 1st Rd 68-69
RECORD Attendance: 2,821 v Trowbridge Town F.A.Cup 57-58
Senior Honours: Wiltshire Shield (6) Western League Div 1 79-80 96-97 Wiltshire Senior Cup (4)

722

ODD DOWN
Founded: 1901

Secretary: M Keen.

Email: odddownafc@hotmail.com

Programme Editor: Secretary **Programme:** Yes

GROUND ADDRESS: Lew Hill Memorial Ground, Combe Hay Lane, Odd Down   **Ground Tel.No:** 01225 832491

Capacity: 1.000   **Seats:** 160   **Covered:** 250   **Floodlights:** Yes

Simple Directions: Ground is behind the Park & Ride car park on main A367 in Odd Down

Midweek Home Matchday: Wednesday   **Clubhouse:** Open Matchdays.   **Club Shop:** No

Previous Leagues: Wilts Premier. Bath & District and Somerset Senior

Club Colours: Yellow& Blue/Blue/yellow   **Change Colours:** Black& White

RECORD Appearances: Steve Fuller 475   **Goalscorer:** Joe Matano 104

Victory: 1-1 v Minehead (H) Western Prem 19.03.94

RADSTOCK TOWN
Founded: 1895
Nickname:

Secretary: Graham Seymour, 12 Weskey Avenue, Westfield, Radstock, Somerset BA3 3XB

Tel Nos: 01761 437889 (H) 01761 437889 (W) 07792 965017 (M)   **Press Officer:** Name (Tel)

GROUND ADDRESS: Southfields Recreation Ground, Southfields, Radstock.   **Ground Tel. No:** 01761 435004

Capacity: 1,500   **Seats:** 80   **Covered:** Yes   **Floodlights:** Yes

Simple Directions: At the double roundabout in Radstock town centre take the A362 towards Frome. The ground is on the right hand bend , third turning. Turn right into Southfield, the ground is 200 yards ahead.

Midweek Home Matchday: Tuesday   **Clubhouse:** Yes   **Club Shop:** No

Club Colours: Red & black/black/black   **Change Colours:** All Yellow

Top Scorer: Craig Bryant   **Player of the Year:** Lee Bryant   **Captain:** Lee Bryant

STREET
Founded: 1880
Nickname: The Cobblers

Secretary:	Darren Stone, 65 Brooks Road, Street, Somerset BA16 0TA	**FACT FILE**
	Tel Nos: 01458 448932 (H) 07719 317629 (M)	Colours: White/Green/White
Ground:	The Tannery Field, Middlebrooks, Street, Somerset	Change colours: Red & white/red/red
	Tel: 01458 445987 Matchdays 01458 448227	Midweek home matchday: Tuesday
Directions:	Sign posted from both ends of A39 & B3151, Station Castle Cary	Programme: Yes
Capacity:	2,000 Seating: 120 Cover: 25 Floodlights: Yes Club Shop: No	
Clubhouse:	Substancial s ocial facilities	**CLUB PERSONNEL**
HONOURS:	Western Lge R-up 52-53	Chairman: Mark Clark
RECORDS:	**Attendance:** 4,300 v Yeovil Town FA Cup 17/11/47	Manager: Alan Hooker
PREVIOUS:	**Leagues:**	Assistant Manager: Simon Culliford
	Grounds: Victoria Field, Tunpike Ground	Physios: Dick Pickersgill, Andrew Lee

TORRINGTON
Founded: 1908
Nickname: Torrie Or Supergreens

Chairman: Winston Martin   **Manager:** Robbie Herrera   **Asst.Manager:** Paul Feasby

Secretary: David Priscott, 6 Highfield Terrace, Bishops Tawton, Barnstaple EX 32 0AN   **Coach:** Mark Kersey

Tel Nos: 01271 328316 (H) 07757 149900 (M) email: afctorrington@msn.com   **Captain:** Chris Slough

Programme Editor: Secretary   **Programme:** Yes

GROUND ADDRESS: Vicarage Field, School Lane, Great Torrington   Ground **Tel.No:** 01805 622853

Capacity: 4,000   **Seats:** 100   **Covered:** 1,000   **Floodlights:** Yes   **Club Shop:** No

PreviousLeagues: N.Devon, Devon & Exeter,S.Western77-84

Club Colours: Green & White   **Change Colours:** Yellow & Blue

BEST PERFORMANCES

League: Runners-Up Western Prem 90-91   **F.A. Cup:** 2nd Qual.Rd.   **F.A.Vase:** 5th Rd 84-85

Simple Directions: Left at parish church in town centre then right at swimming pool. Ground with good parking behind pool.

Midweek Home Matchday: Tuesday   **Clubhouse:** Week day evenings and weekends from lunchtime.

RECORD Goalscorer: Trevor Watkins 254   **Appsearances:** Mike Gilbert 533

SENIOR HONOURS: Runners Up 90-91 Div 1 Champions 02-03

WELTON ROVERS

Founded: 1887
Nickname: Rovers

Chairman: Rae James
Manager: Chris Mountford

Secretary: Malcolm Price, 18 Hayes Park Road, Midsomer Norton, Bath Somerset BA3 2EW

Tel No: 07970 791644 (M)

Prpramme Editor: S.Rogers
Programme: 36 Pages £1.00

GROUND ADDRESS: West Clewes, North Road, Midsomer Norton BA3 2QD
Ground Tel. No: 01761 412097

Capacity: 2,400
Seats: 300
Covered: 300
Floodlights: Yes

Simple Directions: A367 Bath to Radstock road. turn right at foot of hill onto A362. Ground is on right after two miles.

Midweek Home Matchday: Tuesday
Clubhouse: Open every evening
Club Shop: No

Club Colours: Yellow/Blue/Yellow
Change Colours: All Red

BEST PERFORMANCES

League: Western Premier Champions (5)
F.A. Cup: 2nd Rd Proper.
F.A.Vase: 5th Rd.

RECORD Attendance: 2,000 v Bromley F.A.Amateur Cup 1963 **Goalscorer:** Ian Henderson 51

Senior Honours: Western Premier Champions 1911-12 64-65 65-66 66-67 73-74 Somerset Senior Cup (10)

WILLAND ROVERS

Founded: 1946
Nickname: Rovers

Chairman: Mike Mitchell
General Secretary: Richard Woodward
Sponsor: Stan Robinson

Manager: Clive Jones
Asst.Manager/Coach: Neil Greening
Physio: Keith Sutton

Secretary: David Campion, 7 Lime Crescent, Meadow Park, Willand, Devon EX15 2SL

Tel No: 01844 34591 (H) 01844 250550 (W) 07966544698 (M)
Website: www.willandrovers.co.uk

Programme Editor: Tony Baker (01884 820520)
Programme: Pages 50p

GROUND ADDRESS: Silver Street, Willand, Devon
Ground Tel. No: 01884 33885

Capacity: 2,000
Seats: 75
Covered: 150
Floodlights: Yes

Simple Directions: From M5 jct 27 follow signs to Willand. Ground is on left about a quarter of a mile after Willand village sign.

Midweek Home Matchday: Tuesday
Clubhouse: Yes matchdays

Club Colours: All white
Change Colours: Yellow/blue/yellow

LAST SEASON

League: 6th Premier Division

Top Scorer: David Steele
Player of the Year: Jak Martin
Captain: Danny Jee

BEST PERFORMANCES

League: Champion Western Div 1
F.A. Cup: Extra Preliminary Round 2005-2006
F.A.Vase: 3rd Rd Proper.

RECORD Attendance: 650 v Newton Abbot 1992-93 **Goalscorer:** Paul Foreman

Senior Honours: Devon County League 98-99 00-01

LEAGUE CONSTITUTION 2006-07 - DIVISION ONE

ALMONDSBURY

Secretary: Douglas Coles.

Email: doug2004.coles@blueyonder.co.uk

Ground: The Field, Almondsbury Sports & Social Club, Bradley Stoke , North Bristol BS34 4AA

Directions: M4 Jct 16. From South take first left exit lane at roundabout and then left at lights.Ground is 150 metres on right.. If arriving form East, third exit from round about after Exit 17

Clubhouse: Yes.

FACT FILE

Colours: Green & White/Green/White

Change colours: Yellow/Blue/ yellow & Blue

Midweek Matches: Tuesday

CLUB PERSONNEL

Chairman: Philip Church

BACKWELL UNITED

Formed: 1911
Nickname:Stags

Chairman: Andy Thorne
Manager: Andy Mathias

Secretary: Richard Hendricks. Email: wolfie21@blueyonder.co.uk

Programme: 42 pages Price 50p
Editor: Jonathon Rogers (01179 856138)
Press Officer: Secretary

GROUND ADDRESS: Backwell Recreation Ground, West Town Rd., Backwell, Avon
Tel: 1275 462612

Capacity: 1.000
Seats: 60
Covered: 150
Floodlights: Yes

Simple Directions: Near centre of Backwell on A370, Bristol to Weston-s-Mare Rd. 20mins walk from Nailsea & Backwell (BR)

Midweek Home Matchday: Tuesday
Clubhouse: Open daily 6.00 pm on week days.
Club Shop: No

Previous Leagues: Clevedon & Dist., Bristol C of E, Bristol Suburban (pre 1970) and Somerset Senior 70-83

Club Colours: Red/black/black
Change Colours: White/navy/navy

BEST PERFORMANCES: League: Western Premier **F.A. Cup:** 2nd Qualifying 1988-1989 **F.A.Vase:** 5th Round 200405

RECORD Attendance: 487 v Brislington League 02. 05.94 **Goalscorer:** Steve Spalding **Appearances:** Wayne Buxton

Victory: 10-1 v Downton F.A.Cup 1st Qual Rd 98-99 **Defeat:** 2-6 v Tiverton Town League Cup 1.2.94

Senior Honours: Somerset Senior Cup 81-82 Western Lg. Div. 1 Champions 89-90 and Promoted in 3rd place 94-95

BIDDESTONE

FACT FILE

Secretary: Keith Pound, 10 Frogwell Park, Chippenham, Wilts. SN14 0RB

Tel; Nos: 01249 657367 (H) 07740 156075 (M)

Ground: The Sports Ground, Yatton Road, Biddestomne, Chippenham SN14 7BZ

Tel No: 01249 716622

Directions: From Chippenham. Take A420 (towards Bristol) Left to Biddestone after 3 miles, The sports ground is on left as you enter the village. From Bath take A4 (towards Chippenham). Left at Cross Keys Pub at lights.and drive through village. Ground on right.

Colours:All bluee

Change colours: Yellow/black/yellow

Midweek Matches: Wednesday 6.30pm

CLUB PERSONNEL

Chairman: Andrew Short

BRADFORD TOWN

Chairman: Les Stevens

Manager: Mark Hodkinson   **Website:** www.webteams.co.uk and home.aspteam=bradfordtownfootballclub

Secretary: Colin Lewis, 69 Holbrook Lane, Trowbridge, Wiltshire BA14 0PS

Tel No: 01225 767425 (H) 07950276606 (M) **e-mail:** bradfordtownfc@yahoo .com

GROUND ADDRESS: Bradford Sports Club, Trowbridge Road, Bradford on Avon Wiltshire BA15 1EW

Ground Tel. No: 01225 866649

Simple Directions: On entering Bradford on Avon follow signs for A363 to Trowbridge. The ground is after a mini roundabout and behind a stone wall on the right.

Midweek Home Matchday: Tuesday

Previous League: Wiltshire Senior

Club Colours: Sky/navy/sky   **Change Colours:** Graphite & Red

BEST PERFORMANCES: League: Runners-Up Wiltshire League 04-5

BRIDPORT

Chairman: Adrian Scadding   **Founded: 1885**

Secretary: Keith Morgan   **Nickname:** Bees

Tel Nos: 01308 425 113

Programme Editor: Ian Hallett (01308 969795)   **Programme:** 40 Pages £1.00

GROUND ADDRESS: The Beehive, St Mary's Field, Bridport, Dorset   **Ground Tel No:** 01308 423834

Capacity: 2,000   **Seats:** 200   **Covered:** 400   **Floodlights:**Yes

Simple Directions: Take West Bay road from town centre and turn right judt before Palmers Brewery

Midweek Home Matchday: Tuesday   **Clubhouse:** Matchdays and functions   **Club Shop:** No

Previous League: Perry Street, Western 61-84 Dorset Combination 84-89

Club Colours: Red/Black/Red   **Change Colours:** All Blue

Best Performances

League: 7th Western Premier   **F.A. Cup:** 2nd Qualifying Rd.   **F.A.Vase:** 2nd Rd.

RECORD Attendance: 1,150 v Exeter City 1981 **Goalscorer: (in season)** Ellis Hoole 36

Fee Paid: £1,000 for Steve Crabb   **Fee Received:** £2,000 for Tommy Henderson.

Senior Honours: Dorset Senior Cup (8) Dorset Senior Amateur Cup (6)

CADBURY HEATH

FACT FILE

Secretary: Martin Painter, 44 Chesterfield Road, Downend, Bristol BS16 5RQ

Tel No: 0117 949 2844

Ground: Springfield, Cadbury Hearg Road, Bristol BS30 8BX

Tel No: 0117 967 5731

Directions: M5 & M4 to M32 Exit 1 to Ring Road. Left to Cadbury Heath at roudabout. Then right into Tower Road North and left at mini roundabout. Turn right into Cadbury Heath Road after 150 metres. Ground is on right via Cadbury Heath Sicil Club Car park.

Clubhouse: Yes

PREVIOUS **League:** Gloucestershire County Lge.

HONOURS Glos. County Lge 98-99, R-up 99-00

Colours: All Red

Change colours: White/black/black

Midweek Matches: Wednesday 6.30

CLUB PERSONNEL

Chairman: Steve Plenty

Manager: Lee Knighton

CLEVEDON UNITED

Secretary: Pat O'Brien
GROUND c/o Clevedon Town FC, Hand Stadium, Davis Lane, Clevedon, N. Somerset
Tel: 01275 871600 (ground)
Fax: 01275 871601 email: info@handstadium.co.uk
Directions: M5 Jct 20 - follow signs for Hand Stadium; first left into Central Way (at island just after motorway), 1st left at mini-r'bout into Kenn Rd, 2nd left Davis Lane; ground half mile on right. Or from Bristol(B3130) left into Court Lane (opposite Clevedon Court), turnright after 1mile, ground on left. Nearest BR station: Nailsea & Backwell. Buses from Bristol
Capacity: 3,650 Seats: 300 Cover: 1,600 Floodlights: Yes
Clubhouse: Yes in which clubs mementoes are also sold.
PREVIOUS League: Somerset County League >2003
RECORD Attendance: 420
HONOURS Somerset County Lge Prem. Div 98-99

CLUB PERSONNEL
Chairman:Alan Rides
President:Chris Brown
Vice-President: M.J.Williams
Manager: Andy LLewellyn
Captain: Andy Woodlands
Physio: Terry Banks
FACTFILE
Founded: 1970
Sponsor: Sea Palace Restaurant
(Weston super Mare)
Colours: All Red Change: All Blue
Midweek Matchday: Wednesday
Programme:£1.00 20 Pages
Editor: Paul Tiplar

CLYST ROVERS

Formed 1926 **Reformed:** 1951
Nickname: Rovers

Secretary: Maxine Perry
Email:maxcperry@btinternet.com
Programme: Yes
GROUND ADDRESS: Waterslade Park, Clyst Honiton, Devon. **Ground Tel. No.:** 01392 366424
Capacity: 3,000 **Seats:** 130 **Covered:** 350 **Floodlights:** Yes
Simple Directions: Exit M5 Jct 29 (S) head for Sowton Industrial Estate. At roundabout exit for A30 Honiton. Pass under motorway bridge, branch left onto Rockbeare Road, through Clyst Honiton and take first right after Hoiniton turning (200 metres) . Three miles from motorway.
Clubhouse: Excellent Food available open 90 minutes before kick off **Club Shop:** Yes
Previous Leagues: Exeter & Dist. 26-44 51-66 Exeter & Dist Sunday 67-82 South Western 81-92
Club Colours: All Yellow **Change Colours:** Green/black/black
Midweek Home Matchday: Tuesday

ELMORE

Secretary: Neville Crocker, Rivercroft,4 Little Silver, Tiverton, Devon EX16 4PH
Tel: 01884 2456634 (H) 07967 827126 (M)
Ground: Horsdon Park, Tiverton, Devon EX16 4DE Tel: 01884 252341
Directions: M5 Jct 27, A373 towards Tiverton, leave at first sign for Tiverton & Business Park. Ground is 500yds on right
Capacity: 2,000 **Seats:** 200 **Cover:** 200 **Floodlights:** Yes
Clubhouse: 11am-11pm Mon-Sat. Full canteen service - hot & cold meals & snacks
Club Shop: Yes
HONOURS East Devon Snr Cup 72-73 75-76, Western Lge R-up 94-95. Lge Cup 90-91 94-95, Div 1 R-up 90-91, Prem Div Merit Cup R-up 91-92, Div 1 Merit Cup 86-87 89-90 90-91, Devon St Lukes Cup R-up 90-91, Devon Snr Cup 87-88, Devon Intermediate Cup 60-61, Football Express Cup 60-61, Devon & Exeter g Div 2A 73-74 86-87(res)(Div 1A 76-77(res)), Devon Yth Cup 77-78.
PREVIOUS Leagues: Devon & Exeter 47-74; South Western 74-78 Grounds: None
RECORD Attendance: 1,713 v Tiverton Town Fri.April 14th 95
Appearances: P Webber **Win:** 17-0 **Defeat:** 2-7

FACT FILE
Founded: 1947
Nickname: Eagles
Club Sponsors: Ken White Signs
Colours: All Green
Change colours: Sky/navy/sky
Midweek matches: Tuesday
Programme: Yes
CLUB PERSONNEL
Chairman: Alan J Cockram

HENGROVE ATHLETIC

Secretary: Susan Gray
Ground: Norton Lane, Whitchurch, Bristol BS14 0BT
Tel: 01275 832 894
Directions: Take A37 from Bristol through Whitchurch village past Maes Knoll pub, over hump bridge taking next turning on right, which is Norton Lane. Ground is immediately after Garden Centre.
HONOURS Somerset County Premier Division 2005-06.
Somserset Senior Cup 1979-80.
PREVIOUS Leagues: Bristol Suburban League 1948-74, Somerset County League 74-06.

FACT FILE
Founded: 1948
Colours: Green & white/green/green
Change colours: Sky blue/navy/sky
Midweek matches: Tuesday

ILFRACOMBE TOWN

Secretary: Tony Alcock, 2 Worth Road, Ilfracombe, North Devon EX34 9JA Tel: 01271 862686.
Mobile: 07977 589199

Ground: Marlborough Park, Ilfracombe, Devon Tel: 01271 865939
Directions: A361 to Ilfracombe. Turn1st right in town after lights and follow Marlborough Rd to
the top, ground on left.**Capacity:** 2,000 **Seats:** 60 **Cover:** 450**Floodlights:** Yes
Club Shop: No
Clubhouse: Every night 7-11pm and weekend lunchtimes. Hot & cold meals on matchdays
HONOURS E Devon Prem Lg 25-26 28-29 29-30, N Devon Senior Lg, N Devon PremLg
66-67 70-71 81-82 82-83, Western Lg Div 2 R-up 52-53, Les Phillips Cup R-up 91
PREVIOUS Leagues: North Devon 04-14 20-22 60-84; EDevon Premier 22-31;Exeter & District
t 32-39 46-49; Western 49-59 **Grounds:** Shaftesbury Field; Brimlands; Killacleave (all pre-1924)
Names: Ilfracombe FC 02-09; Ilfracombe Utd 09-14; Ilfracombe Comrades 14-20
RECORDS **Attendance:** 3,000 v Bristol City, Ground opening, 2/10/24
Goalscorer: Kevin Squire 91 **Appearances:** Bob Hancock 459
Players progressing: Jason Smith (Coventry City and Swansea City via Tiverton Town)

FACT FILE
Founded: 1902   Nickname: Bluebirds
Sponsors: D.J.Sports Bar &
John Fowler Holiday Pacs
Colours: All Blue
Change: Yellow/Black/Yellow
Midweek matchday: Tuesday
Reserves ' League: North Devon
Prog: 8 pages, 40p Editor: Bill Creswell
CLUB PERSONNEL
Chairman: Bob Martin
Vice-Chairman: Alan Day
President: John Fowler
Manager:Kevin Pickard
Captain: Barry Yeo

LARKHALL ATHLETIC

Secretary: Garry Davy,84 London Road West, Bath, Somerset BA1 7DA
Tel Nos: 01225 852729 (H) 01225 468942 (W) 07879 603632 (M)

Ground: "Plain Ham", Charlcombe Lane, Larkhall, Bath. 01225 334952
Directions A4 from Bath, 1 mile from city centre turn left into St Saviours Rd. In Larkhall
Square fork left, and right at junction, road bears into Charlcombe Lane.
Ground on right as lane narrows

Capacity: 1,000   **Seats:** None **Cover:** 50 **Floodlights:** No

HONOURS Somerset Senior Cup 75-76, Somerset Senior Lg,; Western Lg Div 1 88-89 93-94
94-95(Div 1 Merit Cup (4) 83-86 87-88 (jt with Yeovil Res)
PREVIOUS **Leagues:** Somerset Senior

FACT FILE
Founded: 1914 Nickname: Larks
Colours: All Blue
Change colours: All Red
Midweek Matches: Wednesday
Programme: Yes

CLUB PERSONNEL
President: Tony Codd
Chairman:Jim McClay (01373 834050)

LONGWELL GREEN SPORTS

Founded: 1966
Nickname: Sports

Chairman: Chris Wyrill   **Vice-Chairman:** Simon Briton
Secretary: David Heal,4 Harptree Court, Longwell Green, Bristol BS30 7AG
Tel Nos: 0117 9478558 (H) 07771900413 (M) **Sponsor:** Optimum Drywall Systems
Programme Editor: Chairman   **Programme:** Yes
GROUND ADDRESS: Longwell Green Community Centre, Shellards Road,
Tel:
Capacity: 1,000   **Seats:** None   **Covered:** 100   **Floodlights:** Soon
Simple Directions: Leave Junction 1 M32 follow signs for Ring road (A4174).At Kingsfield roundabout turn into Marsham Way.
At first set of traffic lights turn left into Woodward Drive. Continue to mini roundabout and turn right into Parkway Road and
continue to Shellards Road. Ground is situated to the rear of the Community Centre
Midweek Home Matchday: Tuesday   **Clubhouse:** Yes   **Club Shop:** Yes
Previous League:
Club Colours: Blue & white/black/black   **Change Colours:** All green
Best Performance
League: 2nd Sussex Div 3 2004-05   **RECORD Attendance:** 500 v Mangotsfield 2005

MINEHEAD

Secretary: Trish Hill, 10 Warden Road, Minehead, Somerset TA24 5DS
Tel No: 01643 705604
Ground: The Recreation Ground, Irnham Road, Minehead, Somerset (01643 704989)
Directions: Entering town from east on A39 turn right into King Edward Road at Police station,
first left into Alexandra Rd and follow signs to car park;ground entrance within. Regular buses to
Minehead from Taunton, the nearesttrailhead. (Steam train 'holiday route' Taunton to Minehead)
Capacity: 3,500   **Seats:** 350   **Cover:** 400   **Floodlights:** Yes
Clubhouse: Yes   **Club Shop:** No
HONOURS Southern Lg R-up 76-77, Div 1 Sth 75-76, Merit Cup 75-76;
Western Lg R-up 66-67 71-72, Div 1 90-91 98-99, Alan Young Cup 67-68 (jt with
Glastonbury),Somerset Premier Cup 60-61 73-74 76-77
PREVIOUS **Leagues:** Somerset Senior; Southern 72-83
RECORD **Attendance:** 3,600 v Exeter City, FA Cup 2nd Rd, 77
BEST SEASON FA Cup: 2nd Rd 76-77, 1-2 v Portsmouth (A); 77-78, 0-3 v Exeter City (H)

FACT FILE
Founded: 1889
Colours: All Blue
Change colours: Yellow/black/black
Midweek Matches: Tuesday
Programme: Yes Editor: T.B.A.

CLUB PERSONNEL
Chairman: Adrian Giblett
Tel: 01643 821035
Managers:Stephen Perkins
Captain: Lee Nunn

PORTISHEAD

Founded: 1910
Nickname: Posset

Chairman: Bob Parsons   **Vice-Chairman:** Aide Phillips
Manager: Dave Willis   **Asst.Manager:** Mark Williams
Secretary: Brian Hobbs, 13 St Peters Road, Portsihead, Bristol BS20 6QY
Tel Nos: 01275 847612 (H) 07791 412724 (M)
Programme Editor: John Harris   **Programme:** Yes
GROUND ADDRESS: Bristol road, Portishead, Bristol Bs20 6QG
Capacity: 1,000   **Seats:** None   **Covered:** 150   **Ground Tel.No.:** 01275 817 600   **Floodlights:** No
Simple Directions: Follow A369 to Portishead and at outskirts of town take first exit left at roundabout. Ground is about 150 yards on left.
Midweek Home Matchday: Wednesday   **Clubhouse:** Social Chairperson: Maureen Howarth
Previous Name(s):   **Previous Leagues:** Somerset County
Club Colours: White/black/black   **Change Colours:** All Blue
BEST PERFORMANCE
League: Champions Somerset Co 04-05

SHEPTON MALLET

Secretary: John Bell, 43 Victoria Grove, Shepton Mallet, Somerset BA4 5NJ
Tel Nos: 01749 344687 (H) 01749 831878 (W) 07866 762372 (M)
Ground: The Playing Fields, Old Wells Rd., West Shepton, Shepton Mallett, Somerset BA4 5XN Tel: 01749 344609
Capacity: 2500   Covered Seating: 120   Floodlights: Yes
Directions: Take the Glastonbury road from Shepton Mallett town centre then turn right at the junction with Old Wells Rd (approx. 1/2 mile, near the "King William" P.H.) - the ground is 300 yards on the left.
Clubhouse: Yes, open match days
Previous League: Somerset Senior
HONOURS Somerset Senior League 2000-01
CLUB RECORDS Attendance: 274 v Chippenham Town F.A.Cup 2000-01

FACT FILE
Founded: 1986
Colours: Black&white/black/black
Change colours: Yellow/blue/yellow
Midweek matchday: Tuesday
Programme : Yes

CLUB PERSONNEL
Chairman: Brian Blinman

SHERBORNE TOWN

Secretary: Colin Goodland
Ground: Raleigh Grove, The Terrace Playing Field, Sherborne, Dorset
Tel: 01935 816 110
Directions: From Yeovil take A30 - marked Sherborne. On entering town turn right at traffic lights, over next traffic lights and at the next junction turn right. Go over bridge, take second left marked 'Terrace Pling Fields'. Turn into car park, football club car park is situated in the far right-hand corner.

HONOURS Dorset Premier League 1981-82.
Dorset Senior Cup 2003-04.

PREVIOUS Leagues: Dorset Premier League.

FACT FILE

Founded: 1894

Colours: Black & white/white/white

Change colours: Lime green/black/black

Midweek matches: Wednesday

SHREWTON UNITED

Secretary: Jayne Foot, 3 North Croft, Tilshead, Salisbury, Wiltshire SP3 4SE
Tel: 01980 621 284 (H) 01722 439516 (B) email: peterwithers@lineone.net

Ground: Recreation Ground, Mill Lane, Shrewton, Wiltshire. Tel: 07796 098 122
Directions: From A303 left at Winterbourne Stoke and left at The Royal Oak. Then turn right at mini roundabout on outskirts of village, and then turn left at the George Inn and follow Football Club signs. From Devizes A360 turn leftt at mini roundabout on outskirts of village, and then turn left at the George Inn and follow Football Club signs.

PREVIOUS League: Wiltshire League >2003

HONOURS Wiltshire Lge Prem Div. 2001-02 02-03, R-up 00-01,
Lge Senior Cup 01-02 02-03

FACT FILE
Colours: Maroon & Navy/navy/navy
Change Colours: All White & jade
Midweek Matchday: Tuesday

CLUB PERSONNEL
Chairman:Derek Harnett
Manager: Stuart Withers
Assistant Managers: T Tedd & P Jenks
Programme Editors:
P Withers, M Lock & D Logan

TRURO CITY

Secretary: Ian Anear. Email: ian.anear@gmail.com

Ground: Treyew Road, Truro, Cornwall TR1 2TH
Tel: 01872 225 400

Directions: Leave M5 at Junction 30 and join A30. Travel via Okehampton, Launceston, & Bodmin. At end of dua carriageway (windmills on right hand side) take left hand turning signposted Truro. After approximately 7 miles turn right at traffic lights, cross over three roundabouts following signs for Redruth. Approximately 500 metres after roundabout marked 'Arch Hill' ground is situated on left hand side.

PREVIOUS League: Cornwall County League, Plymouth & District League, Cornwall Senior League, South Western, Cornwall Combination

HONOURS Cornwall County League (West) 1929-30, 30-31, 31-32
Plymouth & District League 1936-37
Cornwall Senior League 1932-33, 33-34
Cornwall Combination League 1994-95, 98-99, 05-06
South Western League 1960-61, 69-70, 92-93, 95-96, 97-98
Cornwall Senior Cup x 15

FACT FILE

Founded: 1889

Colours: All white

Change Colours: Gold/black/black

Midweek Matchday: Tuesday

WELLINGTON TOWN

Secretary: Dave Grabham, 12 Drakes Park, Wellington, SomersetTA21 8TB
Tel. No: 01823 664946 (H), 01823 355687 (B) 07817 274585 (M)
email:digrabham@somerset.gov.uk
Ground: Wellington Playing Field, North Street, Wellington, Somerset Tel: 01823 664810
Directions: At town centre traffic lights turn into North St., then first left by Fire Station into the public car park that adjoins the ground
Capacity: 3,000 **Seats:** None **Cover:** 200 **Floodlights:** Yes **Clubhouse:** Yes **Club Shop:** No
HONOURS Western Lg Div 1 R-up 80-81, Merit Cup 91-92, Comb Lge 95-96;Comb Lge KO Cup 95-96 98-99; Somerset Snr Lg Div 1 R-up; Rowbarton & Seward Cup, Bill Slee Trophy
PREVIOUS Leagues: Taunton Saturday, Somerset Senior
RECORD Goalscorer: Ken Jones
BEST SEASON FA Cup: 1st Qual Rd. 81-82, 84-85 **FA Vase:** 2nd rd Prop 98-99

FACT FILE
Founded: 1892
Sponsors: A J Shire & Wadham Fencing
Colours: Blue/Black/Blue
Change cols: Blue & claret stripes/blue/blue
Midweek Matches: Wednesday
Reserve Lge: Devon & Exeter Sen Div 1
Programme: Yes   Editor: Chairman
CLUB PERSONNEL
Chairman: Ken Bird V-Chair:Graham Aspin
President: Alan Shire
Manager: Kevin Evans
Captain: Nick Woon
Reserves Manager:John Norman
Physio: Ken Pearson

WESTBURY UNITED

Secretary: Roger Arnold, 33 Downsview Road, Westbury , Wiltshire BA13 3AQ
Tel No:01483 722184 (H)
Ground: Meadow Lane, Westbury Tel: 01373 823409
Directions: In town centre, A350, follow signs for BR station, Meadow Lane on right (club signposted). Ten mins walk from railway station (on main London-South West and South Coast-Bristol lines)
Capacity: 3,500   **Seats:** 150   **Cover:** 150   **Floodlights:** Yes
Clubhouse: Evenings 7-11pm, Fri, Sat & Sun lunchtimes 12-3pm   **Club Shop:** No
HONOURS Western Lg Div 1 91-92, Wilts Senior Cup 31-32 32-33 47-48 51-52, Wilts Combination, Wilts Lg 34-35 37-38 38-39 49-50 50-51 55-56, Wilts Premier Shield R-up 92-93
PREVIOUS Leagues: Wilts Comb.; Wilts Co. (pre-1984)
    Ground: Redland Lane (pre-1935)
RECORD Gate: 4,000 - v Llanelli, FA Cup 1st Rd 37 & v Walthamstow Ave. FA Cup 37
Players progressing: John Atyeo (Bristol City)

FACT FILE
Formed: 1921
Nickname: White Horsemen
Colours: Green& White/Green/Green
Change Colours: Yellow/Blue/Yellow
Midweek Matches: Tuesday
Programme: 1Yes

CLUB PERSONNEL
Chairman: George Dowd
Vice Chairman: Bert Back
President: Ernie Barber

WESTON ST. JOHNS

Secretary: Cheryl Wilcox
Email: cherwilcox@aol.com
Ground: Coleridge Road, Bournville Estate, Weston-s-Mare, Somerset
Tel: 01934 612862
Directions: Leave M5 at J21and take main road into Weston-s-Mare.
Turn left at the 4th r'about into Winterstoke Road, then take the 2nd right into Byron Road and then 1st left into Coleridge Road.

PREVIOUS League: Somerset Senior Lge.
Names: Worle & Weston St. Johns amalgamated 2000
HONOURS R-up Somerset Sen. Lge. 99-00 (Worle)

FACT FILE
Colours: Blue & white/blue/blue
Change Colours: Red/white/red
Midweek Matchday: Tuesday

CLUB PERSONNEL
Chairman: Bob Flaskett
Manager: Jamie Crandon

Sports Lighting

Specialists in the Lighting of all Sports Applications

Tel; 01803 844 833   Fax; 01803 844 835

www.sportslighting.co.uk

Sports Lighting has been a family run business for the last 15yrs.

We do nationwide installations.

All our work comes with a 12months parts and labour guarantee.

We make on site surveys and advise for installation to suit your needs.

We make life easy for you, by supplying all the lux and spillage charts for your planning application FREE OF CHARGE.

Our light fittings are all asymmetric which cut out any possibility of light pollution and spillage.

All out work comes with the backing of the NICEIC as we are an approved contractor.

We are the main floodlighting contractor for Torquay Utd.

Sports lighting is always prepared to put money back into local sports by means of sponsorships tailored to meet the requirements of both parties.

FOOTBALL LEAGUE

STEP 1

FOOTBALL
CONFERENCE

STEP 2

CONFERENCE NORTH

CONFERENCE SOUTH

STEP 3

SOUTHERN PREMIER

NORTHERN PREMIER

ISTHMIAN PREMIER

STEP 4

SOUTHERN DIVISION 1
SOUTH &WEST   MIDLAND

NORTHERN PREMIER DIV.1

ISTHMIAN DIVISION 1
NORTH   SOUTH

STEP 5/6

Combined Counties	Hellenic	Northern League	Spartan South Midlands	Wessex
Eastern Counties	Kent	Northern Counties East	Sussex County	Western
Essex Senior	Midland Alliance	North West Counties	United Counties	

STEP 7

Anglian Combination	Dorset County	Kent County	Midland Combination	Peterborough & District	West Cheshire
Bedford & District	Dorset Premier	Leicestershire Senior	Midland League	Reading League	West Lancashire
Brighton & Hove	East Sussex	Liverpool County	North Berkshire	Somerset County	West Midlands (reg)
Cambridgeshire County	Essex & Suffolk Border	Manchester Football	Northampton Town Lge	South Western	West Sussex
Central Midlands	Essex Intermediate	Mid Cheshire League	Northamptonshire Comb.	Suffolk & Ipswich	Wiltshire League
Crawley & District	Gloucesterhisre Co.	Mid Sussex	Northern Alliance	Teeside League	Worthing & District
Devon County	Herts Senior County	Middlesex County	Oxfordshire Senior	Wearside League	

ANGLIAN COMBINATION

FORMED: 1964

SPONSORED BY:

DOLPHIN AUTOS

President: Tony Dickerson **Chairman:** Graham Jubb
Hon Secretary: Keith Johnson

PREMIER DIVISION		P	W	D	L	F	A	Pts
1.	Cromer Town	30	22	7	1	107	39	73
2.	Blofield United (04/05 Champions)	30	22	5	3	102	35	71
3.	Acle United	30	20	2	8	80	52	62
4.	Brandon Town	30	16	8	6	65	43	56
5.	Halvergate United (2nd Div.1 04/05)	30	15	6	9	57	42	51
6.	Sheringham (1st Div.1 04/05)	30	14	7	9	78	53	49
7.	Beccles Town	30	14	4	12	64	51	46
8.	Lowestoft Town Reserves	30	13	6	11	64	48	45
9.	Sprowston Athletic	30	10	7	13	72	81	37
10.	Norwich Union	30	11	3	16	35	71	36
11.	Wroxham Reserves	30	9	2	19	52	74	29
12.	North Walsham Town	30	8	4	18	55	78	28
13.	Attleborough Town	30	7	5	18	53	77	26
14.	St Andrews	30	6	7	17	31	71	25
15.	Watton United	30	6	5	19	45	93	23
16.	Gorleston Reserves(-3pts)	30	7	2	21	45	97	20

PREMIER DIVISION		1	2	3	4	5	6	7	8	9	10	11	12	13	14	15	16
1	Acle United		4-1	3-1	3-0	2-1	3-6	5-3	2-0	3-2	5-2	6-0	2-1	5-1	2-1	3-2	2-3
2	Attleborough Town	0-1		1-3	0-3	2-2	2-4	2-2	2-4	1-3	5-3	1-1	5-2	3-2	8-2	2-3	4-2
3	Beccles Town	3-2	2-1		0-1	1-2	1-1	2-3	0-1	0-2	6-1	5-0	3-2	8-1	6-0	3-1	6-1
4	Blofield United	2-1	3-0	4-1		3-1	1-1	5-0	4-1	2-0	3-3	6-0	2-1	0-1	6-2	4-1	5-1
5	Brandon Town	4-0	2-0	1-1	2-5		4-2	3-0	0-0	1-0	3-1	4-2	1-3	3-2	3-0	3-0	3-2
6	Cromer Town	2-0	5-0	6-0	3-2	2-2		3-2	1-1	3-2	3-0	4-0	1-1	4-2	7-0	8-1	2-1
7	Gorleston Reserves	1-3	2-0	0-2	1-6	0-2	0-8		1-5	1-4	2-2	4-2	1-5	1-2	4-3	0-3	2-0
8	Halvergate United	2-4	3-1	3-2	3-3	0-1	2-4	6-0		2-0	2-1	2-1	0-1	4-0	2-0	1-1	2-0
9	Lowestoft Town Reserves	3-3	2-2	1-2	0-2	1-1	1-2	6-3	2-0		4-1	1-3	3-1	2-2	2-1	9-0	4-2
10	North Walsham Town	1-1	1-4	1-1	0-5	4-3	0-2	5-0	0-3	0-2		1-0	1-2	3-5	2-1	0-2	2-1
11	Norwich Union	0-1	3-1	2-0	0-10	1-4	1-1	1-0	1-2	3-0	3-2		0-2	0-2	3-0	2-0	2-1
12	Sheringham	3-1	6-1	6-0	3-4	1-1	2-2	2-1	1-1	1-3	5-1	5-0		2-2	1-2	3-5	5-3
13	Sprowston Athletic	4-3	3-0	2-2	2-5	2-2	2-4	4-5	5-2	3-1	3-6	1-2	5-5		3-0	2-4	3-3
14	St Andrews	0-3	1-1	1-0	1-1	2-2	2-6	2-0	0-1	0-0	1-0	1-1	1-1	0-0		3-0	2-1
15	Watton United	2-3	1-2	0-1	2-2	1-2	1-5	1-5	2-2	1-1	1-9	0-1	1-4	1-6	3-1		1-1
16	Wroxham Reserves	1-4	2-1	1-2	1-3	3-2	3-5	3-1	2-0	2-3	0-2	4-0	0-1	1-0	2-1	5-4	

S E N I O R   C U P   (M U M M E R Y)

FIRST ROUND

Beccles Town	v	Gorleston Reserves	3-0
Brandon Town	v	Mattishall	6-4
Cromer Town	v	Halvergate United	5-3
Dereham Town R.	v	Dersingham Rovers	3-0*
Hempnall	v	North Walsham Town	1-3
Hindringham	v	Blofield United	1-2
Holt United	v	Wroxham Reserves	2-1
Horsfield United	v	Scole United	1-2
Lowestoft Town R.	v	Watton United	6-1
Mulbarton United	v	Attleborough Town	2-1
Sheringham	v	Sprowston Wanderers	3-2
Sprowston Athletic	v	Loddon United	3-1
St. Andrews	v	Aylesham Wanderers	2-1
Stalham Town	v	Acle United (H)	1-1* 4-2p
Wells Town	v	Norwich Union	Postponed AW
Wymondham Town	v	Southwold Town	1-3

SECOND ROUND

Brandon Town	v	Stalham Town	7-1
Cromer Town	v	Holt United	4-1
Dereham Town R.	v	Southwold Town	3-2
Lowestoft Town R.	v	North Walsham Town	1-2
Mulbarton United	v	Beccles Town	2-5
Scole United	v	Blofield United	0-2
Sheringham	v	Norwich Union	0-1
Sprowston Athletic	v	St. Andrews	3-3* 4-5p

QUARTER-FINALS

Beccles Town	v	St. Andrews	3-0
Blofield United	v	Dereham Town Res.	2-2* 3-4p
Brandon United	v	North Walsham Town	5-1
Norwich Union	v	Cromer Town	0-4

SEMI-FINALS

Brandon Town	v	Dereham Town Reserves	2-1
Cromer Town	v	Beccles Town	2-1

THE FINAL (at Wroxham FC)

Brandon United	v	Cromer Town	1-1* 3-4p

DIVISION ONE

		P	W	D	L	F	A	Pts
1	Dersingham Rovers	30	19	4	7	93	44	61
2	Mattishall	30	17	9	4	53	23	60
3	Southwold Town	30	18	3	9	63	38	57
4	Sprowston Wanderers	30	16	7	7	59	33	55
5	Wells Town	30	13	10	7	45	33	49
6	Hindringham	30	13	6	11	56	39	45
7	Loddon United	30	9	12	9	42	46	39
8	Wymondham Town	30	8	14	8	37	38	38
9	Hempnall	30	10	8	12	34	38	38
10	Stalham Town	30	10	8	12	49	55	38
11	Aylsham Wanderers	30	10	6	14	48	72	36
12	Holt United	30	9	4	17	42	65	31
13	Dereham Town Res.	30	8	6	16	31	42	30
14	Scole United	30	9	3	18	34	59	30
15	Horsfield United	30	8	6	16	30	64	30
16	Mulbarton United	30	6	8	16	34	61	26

DIVISION TWO

		P	W	D	L	F	A	Pts
1	Mundford	30	21	2	7	65	36	65
2	Long Stratton	30	19	2	9	60	38	59
3	Gayton United	30	17	6	7	79	51	57
4	Corton	30	13	6	11	55	52	45
5	Wortwell	30	12	8	10	49	51	44
6	Poringland Wanderers	30	13	4	13	62	53	43
7	Anglian Windows	30	12	7	11	61	56	43
8	Norwich St Johns	30	13	4	13	59	65	43
9	Caister United	30	13	3	14	69	69	42
10	Thorpe Rovers	30	12	6	12	54	58	42
11	Gt Yarmouth Town Res	30	12	5	13	64	64	41
12	Fakenham Town Res	30	12	3	15	60	74	39
13	Bungay Town	30	10	5	15	50	48	35
14	Reepham Town	30	7	8	15	48	65	29
15	Swaffham T. Res (-3pts)	30	8	5	17	55	79	26
16	Hellesdon	30	7	4	19	43	74	25

DIVISION THREE

		P	W	D	L	F	A	Pts
1	Kirkley Reserves	30	27	2	1	145	19	83
2	Norwich CEYMS	30	18	7	5	95	36	61
3	Norwich United Res	30	19	3	8	75	37	60
4	Downham Town Res	30	17	7	6	74	44	58
5	Acle United Res	30	17	4	9	91	45	55
6	Foster Athletic	30	14	3	13	61	55	45
7	Hempnall Res (-3)	30	14	4	12	87	70	43
8	CNSOBU	30	12	6	12	65	78	42
9	Thetford Town Res	30	10	8	12	51	64	38
10	Thorpe Village	30	9	9	12	39	61	36
11	Morley Village	30	10	5	15	67	94	35
12	South Walsham (-3)	30	10	5	15	56	82	32
13	Sprowston Athletic Res	30	9	4	17	64	94	31
14	Oulton Broad & Notleys	30	8	3	19	41	83	27
15	Necton	30	7	0	23	50	127	21
16	Harleston Town (-3)	30	2	4	24	37	109	7

DIVISION FOUR

		P	W	D	L	F	A	Pts
1	Beccles Caxton	30	23	4	3	93	29	73
2	Martham	30	22	4	4	84	37	70
3	Mattishall Reserves	30	18	5	7	86	45	59
4	Brandon Town Res	30	17	4	9	69	46	55
5	Beccles Town Res	30	16	5	9	65	52	53
6	Hindringham Res	30	13	6	11	70	61	45
7	Norwich Union Res	30	11	7	12	57	44	40
8	St Andrews Res	30	12	2	16	43	62	38
9	Blofield United Res	30	10	7	13	62	63	37
10	Loddon United Res	30	11	4	15	57	66	37
11	Bradenham Wanderers	30	10	5	15	51	74	35
12	Halvergate Utd R.(-3)	30	11	3	16	52	72	33
13	Bungay Town Res	30	10	3	17	62	90	33
14	Cromer T. Res (-3)	30	10	5	15	64	69	32
15	Attleborough Town Res	30	7	4	19	49	84	25
16	Newton Flotman	30	3	4	23	39	109	13

DIVISION FIVE

		P	W	D	L	F	A	Pts
1	Thetford Rovers	28	19	4	5	102	43	61
2	Caister United Res	28	17	3	8	78	54	54
3	Wymondham Town Res	28	15	7	6	58	45	52
4	Wells Town Res (-3)	28	16	6	6	72	33	51
5	Norwich St Johns Res	28	11	8	9	55	44	41
6	Sprowston W. Res (-6)	28	13	6	9	63	58	39
7	Watton Utd Res (-6)	28	14	3	11	53	49	39
8	North Walsham Tn Res	28	11	3	14	63	70	36
9	Stalham Town Res	28	11	1	16	58	74	34
10	Sheringham Res (-6)	28	12	1	15	74	69	31
11	Aylsham W. Res (-3)	28	8	8	12	58	77	29
12	Scole United Res (-6)	28	8	7	13	51	58	25
13	Mundford Res	28	6	6	16	49	72	24
14	Thorpe Village Res	28	6	4	18	30	88	22
15	Gayton Utd Res (-18)	28	6	7	15	42	72	7

DIVISION SIX

		P	W	D	L	F	A	Pts
1	Foulsham	26	21	3	2	97	28	66
2	Easton	26	21	2	3	87	29	65
3	East Harling	26	20	2	4	132	30	62
4	Dersingham Rovers Res	26	17	1	8	78	47	52
5	Mulbarton Utd Res(-3pts)	26	15	3	8	48	42	45
6	Norwich CEYMS Res	26	11	3	12	50	76	36
7	Wortwell Res	26	9	6	11	53	59	33
8	Long Stratton Res	26	9	6	11	45	64	33
9	CNSOBU Res	26	9	3	14	40	58	30
10	Thorpe Rov. R. (-6)	26	8	2	16	47	82	20
11	Reepham Town Res	26	5	4	17	35	77	19
12	Holt United Res (-6)	26	6	5	15	44	71	17
13	Horsford Utd Res (-3)	26	5	3	18	32	75	15
14	Poringland W'. Res (-3)	26	3	3	20	33	83	9

AVAILABLE END OF JULY 2006

EXPANDED TO 304 PAGES

In its seventh year, featuring over 9,500 teams with an extensive round-up of last season plus club movements/league constitutions for 2006/7, this is a *MUST* for followers of the non-League scene

Guarantee your copy by ordering from the publishers:-
Non-League Newsdesk Annual
6 Harp Chase
Taunton TA1 3RY
(cheques payable to **Non-League Newsdesk Annual**)
www.nlnewsdesk.co.uk

LEAGUE CONSTITUTION 2006-07 - PREMIER DIVISION

ACLE UNITED
Secretary: John Goward.
Ground:Bridewell Lane, Acle, Norfolk. Tel: 01493 751 372

ATTLEBOROUGH TOWN
Secretary: Gary Jeckell.
Ground:Recreation Ground, Station Road, Attleborough, Norfolk. Tel: 01953 455 365

BECCLES TOWN
Secretary: Gary Knights.
Ground: College Meadow, Common Lane, Bccles. Tel: 07729 782 817

BLOFIELD UNITED
Secretary: Matthew Eastaugh.
Ground: Old Yarmouth Road, Blofield, Norwich, Norfolk. Tel: 01603 712 576

BRANDON TOWN
Secretary: Paul Wright.
Ground: Remembrance Playing Field, Church Road, Brandon, Suffolk. Tel: 01842 813 177

CROMER TOWN
Secretary: Richard Cox.
Ground: Cabbell Park, Mill Road, Cromer, Norfolk. Tel: 01263 512 185

DERSINGHAM ROVERS
Secretary: Paul Richmond.
Ground: Manor Road, Dersingham.

HALVERGATE UNITED
Secretary: Colin Foreman.
Ground: Wickhampton Road, Halvergate. Tel: 01493 700 349

LOWESTOFT TOWN RESERVES
Secretary: Terry Lynes.
Ground: Crown Meadow, Love Road, Lowestoft, Suffolk. Tel: 01502 573 818

MATTISHALL
Secretary: Bob Burrell.
Ground: Playing Field, South Green, Mattishall. Tel: 01362 850 246

NORTH WALSHAM TOWN
Secretary: Steve Amies.
Ground: Sports Centre, Greens Road, North Walsham, Norfolk. Tel: 01692 406 888

NORWICH UNION
Secretary: Emma Ryder.
Ground: Pinebanks, White Farm Lane, Harvey Lane, Thorpe, Norfolk. Tel: 01603 824 125

SHERINGHAM
Secretary: Peter Bacon.
Ground: Recreation Ground, Weybourne Road, Sheringham NR26 8WD. Tel: 01263 824 804

SPROWSTON ATHLETIC
Secretary: Keith Tilney.
Ground: Sprowston Cricket Ground, Bakers Lane. Tel: 01603 404 042

ST ANDREWS
Secretary: Stuart Simms.
Thorpe Recreation Ground, Laundry Lane, Thorpe, Norfolk. Tel: 01603 300 316

WROXHAM RESERVES
Secretary: Matt Carpenter.
Ground: Trafford Park, Skinners Lane, Wroxham, Norfolk. Tel: 01603 783 538

BEDFORDFORDSHIRE LEAGUE

SPONSORED BY (PREMIER DIVISION ONLY):
McGIRLS MONEY MANAGMENT
President: Terry Sadler **Chairman:** Peter Onion
Secretary: Barry Snelson
Tel: 01234 344 417 Email: barry.snelson@ntlworld.com

PREMIER DIVISION	P	W	D	L	F	A	Pts
1. Caldecote (04/05 Champions)	26	18	6	2	67	33	42
2. Blunham (2nd Div.1 04/05)	26	19	1	6	79	38	39
3. Ickwell & Old Warden	26	15	7	4	66	37	37
4. AFC Kempston Town	26	16	4	5	65	32	36
5. Campton	26	15	4	7	68	49	34
6. Wilshamstead (3rd Div.1 04/05)	26	13	2	11	45	47	28
7. Dunton	26	9	3	14	44	48	21
8. Riseley Sports	26	8	5	13	46	56	21
9. Three Horseshoes Renhold (1st Div.1 04/05)	26	8	5	13	42	55	21
10. Bedford S.A.	26	8	4	14	43	77	20
11. Oakley Sports	26	8	3	15	50	61	19
12. Turvey	26	7	3	16	47	65	17
13. Sandy	26	7	1	18	37	63	15
14. Westoning Recreation Club (-2pts)	26	6	2	18	41	79	12

PREMIER DIVISION	1	2	3	4	5	6	7	8	9	10	11	12	13	14
1 AFC Kempston Town		5-0	1-2	0-1	0-3	3-0	2-1	4-1	0-1	4-0	0-0	4-1	2-4	3-2
2 Bedford S.A.	0-4		0-6	1-2	2-4	2-5	1-4	0-0	2-2	2-1	3-2	4-4	2-3	0-1
3 Blunham	2-3	6-4		1-2	5-1	5-1	2-1	3-2	1-0	3-2	4-0	1-0	4-0	7-1
4 Caldecote	1-2	7-1	5-3		3-3	2-0	2-2	4-0	0-0	4-1	5-4	1-4	2-1	2-1
5 Campton	3-5	3-3	3-0	0-2		3-1	2-5	5-3	4-0	4-0	2-1	4-2	2-1	4-3
6 Dunton	1-1	1-2	1-2	0-3	1-2		3-3	1-2	2-2	0-1	2-0	3-1	3-0	1-2
7 Ickwell & Old Warden	2-2	6-1	0-0	1-1	1-1	0-1		3-0	4-3	3-2	HW	5-2	3-0	2-2
8 Oakley Sports	0-4	2-3	2-4	2-3	0-2	4-2	5-3		2-3	4-2	1-1	1-1	5-1	0-2
9 Riseley Sports	2-2	1-4	2-4	1-2	4-1	2-1	1-4	3-2		4-1	2-3	1-2	3-0	1-3
10 Sandy	1-3	0-2	1-4	0-1	1-6	2-0	0-1	4-3	3-1		2-3	1-3	1-2	4-0
11 Three Horseshoes Renhold	0-2	3-0	HW	2-2	2-1	1-4	2-6	2-1	1-3	1-1		1-0	4-2	3-4
12 Turvey	0-4	1-2	4-2	1-7	0-3	1-3	1-2	1-3	1-1	3-0	4-2		3-4	1-2
13 Westoning Recreation Club	1-4	0-1	1-6	2-2	2-0	1-5	1-2	0-4	4-2	2-4	4-4	2-5		2-4
14 Wilshamstead	3-1	4-1	1-2	0-1	2-2	1-2	0-2	0-1	3-1	0-2	HW	2-1	2-1	

B R I T A N N I A   C U P

PREMIER CLUBS ONLY

FIRST ROUND

Turvey	v	Bedford S.A.	5-1
Westoning R.C.	v	AFC Kempston Town	3-2
Sandy	v	Caldecote	0-5
Three Horseshoes R.	v	Riseley Sports	1-2
Ickwell & Old Warden	v	Dunton	3-2
Oakley Sports	v	Wilshamstead	1-2

SEMI-FINALS

Westoning R.C.	v	Caldecote	1-7
Campton (H)	v	Wilshamstead	2-1

QUARTER-FINALS

Turvey	v	Westoning Recreation Club	1-3
Caldecote	v	Riseley Sports	3-1
Ickwell & Old Warden	v	Campton (H)	0-2
Wilshamstead	v	Blunham	5-1

THE FINAL (1st May)

Caldecote	v	Campton (H)	3-0

DIVISION ONE	P	W	D	L	F	A	Pts
1 Henlow	22	20	2	0	95	15	42
2 Sharnbrook	22	15	3	4	55	29	33
3 Luton Borough	22	11	8	3	57	35	30
4 Corinthians	22	11	5	6	62	50	27
5 Flitwick Town	22	7	7	8	53	55	21
6 Woburn	22	8	4	10	51	51	20
7 Stevington	22	6	5	11	40	49	17
8 Reddings Wood	22	5	6	11	40	56	16
9 Kempston	22	6	4	12	44	74	16
10 Meppershall Jurassic	22	5	4	13	51	78	14
11 Denbigh Hall S&S Bletchley (-2pts) (R)	22	6	3	13	32	60	13
12 Campton Reserves	22	3	7	12	29	57	13

A DIVISION ONE	P	W	D	L	F	A	Pts
1 Caldecote Reserves	20	14	4	2	70	31	32
2 Westoning R.C. Reserves	20	12	4	4	56	33	28
3 AFC Kempston T. Res	20	11	2	7	58	45	24
4 Blunham Reserves	20	10	4	6	48	45	24
5 Sandy Reservers	20	9	3	8	41	39	21
6 Woburn Reservers	20	7	6	7	54	46	20
7 Ickwell & Old Warden Res.	20	7	3	10	42	52	17
8 Bedford S.A. Reservers	20	6	5	9	45	62	17
9 Dunton Reservers	20	6	4	10	45	62	16
10 Wilshamstead Res.	20	5	4	11	60	65	14
11 Riseley Sports Res.	20	2	3	15	40	79	7

DIVISION TWO	P	W	D	L	F	A	Pts
1 Marston Social	26	19	5	2	95	26	43
2 Blunham Village	26	19	3	4	89	35	41
3 Royal Oak Kempston	26	17	5	4	68	32	39
4 Biggleswade Athletic	26	15	2	9	82	43	32
5 Marston Shelton Rovers	26	15	1	10	71	49	31
6 Great Barford	26	14	1	11	57	43	29
7 Mulberry Bush (-2)	25	14	2	9	79	49	28
8 Lidlington United	26	11	1	14	49	65	23
9 Sugar Loaf Meppershall (-2)	25	9	6	10	56	48	22
10 Bedford Albion	26	8	3	15	54	84	19
11 Twinwoods Thistle	26	7	2	17	52	87	16
12 Russell Park United	26	5	3	18	46	99	13
13 Potton Wanderers	26	5	2	19	33	84	12
14 Newnham Athletic	26	4	2	20	39	126	10

A DIVISION TWO	P	W	D	L	F	A	Pts
1 Exel United	18	13	3	2	79	29	29
2 Caldecote 'A'	18	13	1	4	88	29	27
3 Meppershall Jurassic Reserves	18	11	1	6	67	37	23
4 Stewartby Village	18	10	3	5	50	38	23
5 Oakley Sports Reserves	18	8	4	6	52	44	20
6 Blue Chip	18	7	5	6	60	50	19
7 Sandy 'A'	18	5	2	11	48	58	12
8 Flitwick Town Res. (-2)	18	5	2	11	32	70	10
9 Marsh Leys	18	5	0	13	27	78	10
10 Lidlington United Res.	18	1	3	14	22	92	5

LEAGUE CONSTITUTION 2006-07 - PREMIER DIVISION

AFC KEMPSTON TOWN	**LUTON BOROUGH**
BEDFORD S.A.	**OAKLEY SPORTS**
BLUNHAM	**RISELEY SPORTS**
CALDECOTE	**SANDY**
CAMPTON	**SHARNBROOK**
GOLDINGTON LIONS	**TURVEY**
HENLOW	**WESTONING RECREATION CLUB**
ICKWELL & OLD WARDEN	**WILSHAMSTEAD**

BRIGHTON HOVE & DISTRICT LEAGUE

SPONSORED BY : JUICE 107.2
President: Mr I Caplin **Chairman:** Mr D Jackson
Secretary: Mike Brown
Tel: 01273 708 587
Fixture Secretary: Ernie Coleman

PREMIER DIVISION		P	W	D	L	F	A	Pts
1.	Rottingdean Village	20	17	3	0	65	17	54
2.	Montpelier Villa	20	16	1	3	75	24	49
3.	Hanover (04/05 Champions)	20	12	5	3	37	24	41
4.	Master Tiles (1st Div.1 04/05)	20	10	5	5	39	31	35
5.	Alpha Sports	20	10	3	7	49	44	33
6.	American Express	20	6	8	6	31	31	26
7.	O & G United	20	4	8	8	27	45	20
8.	AFC St. Georges	20	6	1	13	34	56	19
9.	Rottingdean Utd 92 (2nd Div.1 04/05)	20	3	7	10	30	36	16
10.	Brighton Electricity	20	2	4	14	33	66	10
11.	Portslade Athletic	20	1	1	18	20	66	4

	PREMIER DIVISION	1	2	3	4	5	6	7	8	9	10	11
1	AFC St. George		1-4	3-3	3-2	1-3	0-2	1-4	4-5	3-1	4-2	0-5
2	Alpha Sports	2-1		1-2	4-1	2-2	0-4	1-2	4-1	2-1	2-0	2-5
3	American Express	2-1	3-3		1-1	1-3	1-1	1-2	1-1	3-0	2-1	1-2
4	Brighton Electricity	1-4	4-5	0-5		2-3	2-3	1-4	1-2	3-2	3-3	1-3
5	Hanover	3-1	1-0	0-0	2-1		2-1	2-3	HW	3-2	HW	1-1
6	Master Tiles	2-1	2-2	2-1	3-1	2-1		0-5	2-2	5-2	3-1	2-4
7	Montpelier Villa	6-1	5-2	4-0		2-1	2-1		8-0	3-0	1-4	1-3
8	O & G United	1-2	2-5	1-1	2-2	2-2	1-1	0-3		2-1	0-0	1-3
9	Portslade Athletic	1-2	2-4	0-1	1-3	1-5	2-1	0-5	1-2		2-2	1-7
10	Rottingdean United 92	4-0	1-4	2-2	2-2	0-1	1-2	3-3	2-2	1-0		1-2
11	Rottingdean Village	2-1	4-0	3-0	3-2	2-2	0-0	3-1	2-0	9-0	1-0	

DIVISION ONE		P	W	D	L	F	A	Pts
1	Blue House	18	14	2	2	68	28	44
2	Montpelier Villa II	18	11	3	4	50	24	36
3	Brighton Rangers	18	10	3	5	53	42	33
4	Legal & General	18	9	3	6	49	38	30
5	Southern Rangers O.B.	18	7	4	7	47	46	25
6	Coversure Athletic	18	6	5	7	31	43	23
7	FC Midlothians	18	6	1	11	38	70	19
8	Rottingdean Village II (P)	18	4	6	8	32	29	18
9	Midway (1948)	18	4	3	11	29	53	15
10	Harbour View	18	3	2	13	30	54	11

DIVISION TWO		P	W	D	L	F	A	Pts
1	Ovingdean	20	15	0	5	73	41	45
2	Real Conqeror	20	13	2	5	76	53	41
3	AFC Stadium	20	13	1	6	69	52	40
4	Brighton BBOB	20	10	4	6	68	57	34
5	Portsalde Rangers	20	10	2	8	58	53	32
6	Four Corners	20	9	3	8	56	49	30
7	Whitehawk III	20	7	6	7	43	56	27
8	Midway (1948) II	20	7	0	13	41	71	21
9	Lectern Sports	20	6	1	13	51	62	19
10	Portslade Athletic II	20	4	3	13	37	57	15
11	AFC Cosmos	20	4	2	14	39	60	14

DIVISION THREE.	P	W	D	L	F	A	Pts
1 Brighton Rangers II	18	12	3	3	56	23	39
2 C.C.K.	18	11	2	5	47	27	35
3 PJ Panthers	18	8	5	5	60	45	29
4 Autopaints (BTN)	18	9	2	7	48	43	29
5 AFC Stanley	18	8	4	6	39	45	28
6 Grand Parade	18	6	5	7	44	42	23
7 Portslade Sports	18	7	2	9	36	48	23
8 Ricardo	18	6	4	8	35	45	22
9 Rottingdean Dynamos	18	6	2	10	29	33	20
10 Montpelier Villa III	18	2	1	15	25	68	7

DIVISION FOUR.	P	W	D	L	F	A	Pts
1 American Express II	20	15	2	3	74	19	47
2 Rottingdean Village III	20	14	3	3	76	24	45
3 APS Wanderers	20	13	3	4	65	31	42
4 The Windmill	20	11	3	6	103	48	36
5 Adur Athletic III	20	10	2	8	68	56	32
6 Brighton A & E	20	9	3	8	58	47	30
7 Brighton BBOB II	20	9	2	9	46	57	29
8 Stoneham Park	20	8	3	9	84	61	27
9 Buckingham Arms	20	8	1	11	58	67	25
10 Southwick Dynamos	20	2	0	18	26	102	6
11 Marsfield Village V	20	0	0	20	19	165	0

LEAGUE CONSTITUTION 2006-07 - PREMIER DIVISION

AFC ST. GEORGE
Secretary: L. Saunders. 66 Moyne Close, Hove, East Sussex BN3 7JY. Tel: 01273 728 854.
Ground: Victoria Recreation Ground.

ALPHA SPORTS
Secretary: M.Mansell. 10 Hillside Way, Brighton, East Sussex BN2 4TR. Tel: 01273 275 093.
Ground: Aldrington Recreation Ground.

AMERICAN EXPRESS
Secretary: M.Harrington. 34 Wilmot Road, Shoreham By Sea, West Sussex BN43 6BN. Tel: 01273 462 350.
Ground: East Brighton Park.

BRIGHTON ELECTRICITY
Secretary: T.Carney. 69 Graham Avenue, Brighton, East Sussex BN1 8HB. Tel: 01273 550 715.
Ground: Braypool.

BRIGHTON RANGERS
Secretary: E.Riley. 6 Pett Close, Brighton, East Sussex BN2 5HS. Tel: 01273 676 458.
Ground: East Brighton Park.

HANOVER
Secretary: J.Pryer. 73 Stanford Avenue, Brighton, East Sussex BN1 6FB. Tel: 01273 888 137.
Ground: Stanher Park.

LEGAL & GENERAL (HOVE)
Secretary: A.Walter. 87 Old Shoreham Road, Southwick, West Sussex BN42 4RD. Tel: 01273 276 388.
Ground: Dyke Road Park.

MASTER TILES
Secretary: S.Walker. 35 Lustrells Vale, Saltdean, Brighton, East Sussex BN2 8FD. tel: 01273 302 702.
Ground: Happy Valley.

MONTPELIER VILLA
Secretary: M.Baxter. Ground Floor Flat, 29 Norton Road, Hove, BN3 3BF. Tel: 01273 276 859.
Ground: Sussex University.

O. & G UNITED
Secretary: D.Templeman. 40 Windlesham Close, Portslade, Brighton BN41 2LJ. Tel: 01273 882 011.
Ground: Aldrington Recreation Ground.

OVINGDEAN
Secretary: S.East. 93 Horton Road, Brighton, East Sussex BN1 7EG. Tel: 01273 243 902.
Ground: Happy Valley.

ROTTINGDEAN VILLAGE II
Secretary: D.Carruthers. 115 Sutton Avenue North, Peacehaven, East Sussex BN10 7QJ. Tel: 01273 584 525.
Ground: Rottingdean.

CAMBRIDGESHIRE COUNTY LEAGUE

SPONSORED BY:
KERSHAW MECHANICAL SERVICES LTD

PREMIER DIVISION		P	W	D	L	F	A	Pts
1.	Sawston United	28	22	3	3	80	20	69
2.	Great Shelford	28	19	2	7	67	27	59
3.	Cottenham United	28	16	5	7	69	43	53
4.	Cambridge University Press (2nd Sen.A 04/05)	28	16	4	8	77	47	52
5.	Over Sports	28	16	4	8	60	38	52
6.	Littleport Town	28	15	4	9	49	38	49
7.	Waterbeach	28	11	7	10	40	40	40
8.	Fordham	28	10	7	11	46	52	37
9.	Histon A	28	11	4	13	47	55	37
10.	Newmarket Town Reserves	28	9	7	12	42	46	34
11.	Great Paxton	28	9	6	13	51	66	33
12.	Eaton Socon (1st Senior.A 04/05)	28	9	2	17	44	73	29
13.	Somersham Town	28	6	3	19	35	72	21
14.	Linton Granta	28	6	1	21	36	71	19
15.	Hemingfords United	28	4	3	21	34	89	15

PREMIER DIVISION	1	2	3	4	5	6	7	8	9	10	11	12	13	14	15
1 Cambridge University Press		3-0	4-1	1-3	8-1	2-5	3-2	1-2	5-3	1-1	3-0	0-3	0-1	4-0	3-1
2 Cottenham United	3-0		4-0	3-2	2-2	2-0	1-0	3-3	2-0	1-3	4-1	3-5	1-1	4-1	1-4
3 Eaton Socon	2-3	3-2		3-1	1-2	2-1	6-1	0-2	5-3	1-3	0-7	1-2	0-8	2-0	1-1
4 Fordham	2-2	0-3	2-4		3-1	2-4	4-0	2-0	3-1	0-0	3-1	0-1	0-4	2-2	0-0
5 Great Paxton	2-4	1-4	1-1	2-3		3-1	2-2	1-0	6-3	2-4	1-3	0-4	0-2	5-1	2-4
6 Great Shelford	4-1	1-4	4-1	4-1	0-0		2-0	2-0	1-0	4-0	1-1	4-0	0-1	4-0	2-0
7 Hemingfords United	1-7	2-8	3-1	2-4	2-5	0-4		1-6	0-1	1-1	1-1	3-1	0-3	2-0	1-2
8 Histon A	1-2	2-3	2-1	2-2	0-3	1-4	5-1		1-0	0-1	3-2	1-3	0-5	2-0	1-1
9 Linton Granta	0-7	2-5	1-3	0-1	3-1	2-3	1-2	2-1		1-3	1-0	0-2	2-0	4-5	1-2
10 Littleport Town	1-2	1-0	3-0	3-0	1-3	1-2	6-2	1-0	3-1		0-1	2-0	1-2	2-0	1-0
11 Newmarket Town Reserves	2-2	1-3	2-3	1-1	2-2	1-0	3-0	1-3	2-1	4-1		0-2	0-1	3-1	0-0
12 Over Sports	2-4	1-1	3-0	0-3	1-2	0-1	4-1	2-2	1-1	2-1	4-1		3-3	5-0	2-1
13 Sawston United	1-1	3-1	5-2	4-0	3-0	1-4	3-1	8-1	2-0	4-0	5-0	0-3		3-0	2-0
14 Somersham Town	1-4	0-2	2-0	2-2	1-1	2-0	3-2	1-2	5-1	2-3	0-2	1-3	0-2		3-0
15 Waterbeach	2-0	1-1	1-0	2-0	3-0	1-5	2-1	2-4	0-1	2-2	0-0	2-1	0-3	6-2	

P R E M I E R   C U P

FIRST ROUND

Cottenham United	v Fordham	0-2
Eaton Socon	v Somersham town	5-0
Histon A	v Great Paxton	4-7
Newmarket Town R.	v Linton Granta	0-2
Over Sports	v Hemingfords United	6-1
Sawston United	v Great Shelford	2-1
Tuddenham Rovers	v Cambridge University Press	w/o
Waterbeach	v Littleport Town	1-3

SECOND ROUND

Fordham	v Great Paxton	2-2 4-5p
Over Sports	v Linton Granta	5-1
Cambridge Uni. P.	v Sawston United	0-3
Littleport Town	v Eaton Socon	5-0

SEMI-FINALS

Over Sports	v Great Paxton	6-0
Littleport Town	v Sawston United	2-1

THE FINAL (16th May at Histon FC)

Over Sports	v Littleport Town	2-1*

SENIOR A	P	W	D	L	F	A	Pts
1 Wickhambrook	28	17	8	3	63	37	59
2 Needingworth United	28	18	3	7	80	29	57
3 Wisbech Town Res	28	17	5	6	69	31	56
4 Mildenhall Town Res	28	12	10	6	45	29	46
5 West Wratting	28	13	6	9	51	43	45
6 Soham T. Rangers Res	28	13	5	10	58	46	44
7 Hardwick	28	13	4	11	45	44	43
8 Hundon	28	13	2	13	45	52	41
9 Lakenheath	28	11	3	14	63	71	36
10 Foxton	28	10	2	16	50	64	32
11 Bluntisham Rangers	28	8	7	13	36	56	31
12 Girton United (-3pts)	28	9	6	13	36	37	30
13 Gamlingay United	28	7	3	18	39	58	24
14 Brampton	28	5	8	15	39	70	23
15 Grampian (-6)	28	7	2	19	39	91	17

SENIOR B	P	W	D	L	F	A	Pts
1 Ely City Res	30	22	6	2	83	23	72
2 Fulbourn Institute Res	30	22	4	4	77	23	70
3 Ely Crusaders	30	18	5	7	85	58	59
4 Comberton United	30	15	4	11	62	49	49
5 Cherry Hinton	30	14	4	12	58	68	46
6 West Row Gunners	30	11	10	9	48	41	43
7 Willingham	30	13	4	13	70	68	43
8 Debden	30	11	8	11	56	59	41
9 Haddenham Rovers	30	11	7	12	54	47	40
10 Milton	30	11	7	12	54	55	40
11 Castle Camps	30	11	6	13	55	54	39
12 JM Sports	30	9	5	16	57	70	32
13 Swavesey Institute	30	8	7	15	46	74	31
14 Soham United	30	8	3	19	49	84	27
15 Sawston United Res	30	6	7	17	46	71	25
16 Great Chesterford	30	5	3	22	43	99	18

BIS 1A	P	W	D	L	F	A	Pts
1 Whittlesford United	26	22	2	2	83	26	68
2 West Wratting Res	26	16	5	5	64	36	53
3 Barrington	26	15	3	8	54	43	48
4 Tuddenham Rovers	26	15	2	9	69	38	47
5 Saffron Crocus	26	14	4	8	74	45	46
6 Fowlmere	26	11	5	10	51	45	38
7 Litlington Athletic	26	10	8	8	51	45	38
8 Sawston Rovers	26	11	3	12	56	47	36
9 Great Shelford Res	26	10	4	12	53	64	34
10 Steeple Bumpstead	26	9	4	13	41	43	31
11 Fulbourn Institute "A"	26	8	5	13	37	51	29
12 Camden United	26	7	5	14	46	68	26
13 Linton Granta Res	26	6	3	17	30	71	21
14 Melbourn	26	0	3	23	24	111	3

BIS 1B	P	W	D	L	F	A	Pts
1 Outwell Swifts	26	17	5	4	77	43	56
2 Barton Mills	26	16	2	8	54	49	50
3 Cottenham United Res	26	14	3	9	52	42	45
4 St Ives Rangers	26	14	3	9	57	52	45
5 Godmanchester Rovers Res	26	11	7	8	44	32	40
6 Waterbeach Res	26	11	6	9	51	34	39
7 March Town United Res	26	9	7	10	68	70	34
8 Great Paxton Res	26	9	5	12	52	53	32
9 Eaton Socon Res	26	9	5	12	62	64	32
10 Buckden	26	9	5	12	48	53	32
11 Bottisham Sports	26	8	5	13	32	49	29
12 Gransden Chequers	26	7	7	12	38	53	28
13 Littleport Town Res	26	8	4	14	30	49	28
14 Hemingfords Utd Res	26	7	2	17	30	52	23

BIS 2A	P	W	D	L	F	A	Pts
1 Helions Bumpstead	24	19	3	2	85	18	60
2 Girton United Res	24	19	3	2	85	30	60
3 Camb. Uni. Press Res	24	14	3	7	52	31	45
4 Comberton United Res	24	13	5	6	73	39	44
5 Thaxted	24	13	2	9	63	48	41
6 Duxford United	24	10	4	10	48	46	34
7 Balsham	24	7	7	10	54	59	28
8 Cambourne Rovers	24	8	4	12	32	40	28
9 Grampian Res (-3)	24	8	1	15	39	68	22
10 Papworth	24	5	6	13	29	71	21
11 Foxton Res (-3)	24	6	5	13	34	52	20
12 Mott MacDonald	24	5	3	16	26	76	18
13 Great Chesterford Res	24	5	2	17	36	78	17
14 Cherry Hinton Res (-3)	0	0	0	0	0	0	-3

BIS 2B	P	W	D	L	F	A	Pts
1 Fenstanton	26	19	5	2	73	25	62
2 Huntingdon Utd RGE	26	20	1	5	86	28	61
3 Needingworth Utd Res	26	17	3	6	61	28	54
4 Longstanton	26	15	2	9	78	60	47
5 Sutton United	26	13	5	8	80	64	44
6 St Ives Town Res	26	10	9	7	69	52	39
7 Stretham Hotspurs	26	10	4	12	52	51	34
8 Over Sports Res	26	11	1	14	42	50	34
9 Lode	26	10	4	12	54	67	34
10 Ely City "A"	26	8	5	13	44	58	29
11 Bluntisham R'gers Res	26	8	2	16	31	74	26
12 Milton Res	26	6	5	15	42	65	23
13 Isleham United	26	7	1	18	46	74	22
14 Somersham Town Res	26	3	3	20	29	91	12

BIS 3A	P	W	D	L	F	A	Pts
1 Hardwick Res	26	20	5	1	70	24	65
2 Camden United Res	26	17	3	6	76	48	54
3 Gamlingay United Res	26	17	0	9	73	50	51
4 Wilbraham	26	14	5	7	84	40	47
5 Withersfield	26	13	8	5	69	50	47
6 Bassingbourn	26	13	5	8	59	50	44
7 Whittlesford United Res	26	10	5	11	51	54	35
8 Ashdon Villa	26	10	3	13	43	59	33
9 Castle Camps Res	26	9	4	13	42	57	31
10 Great Chishill	26	9	3	14	58	60	30
11 Abington United	26	8	4	14	51	80	28
12 Hempstead United	26	7	3	16	68	86	24
13 Orwell (-3)	26	6	0	20	28	60	15
14 Sawston United "A"	26	4	2	20	39	93	14

BIS 3B	P	W	D	L	F	A	Pts
1 Newmarket White Lion	26	18	6	2	110	35	60
2 Witchford 96	26	18	2	6	92	40	56
3 Wisbech St Mary	26	16	8	2	72	32	56
4 Brampton Res	26	14	2	10	64	44	44
5 Huntingdon Utd RGE Res	26	12	7	7	79	59	43
6 The Vine	26	12	7	7	65	55	43
7 Fordham Res	26	13	2	11	70	59	41
8 Lakenheath Res	26	11	3	12	64	60	36
9 Dullingham	26	9	6	11	52	78	33
10 Hemingfords United A	26	7	8	11	47	71	29
11 Cottenham United "A"	26	8	4	14	59	76	28
12 Soham United Res	26	6	5	15	47	74	21
13 Little Downham Swifts	26	5	1	20	37	114	16
14 West Row Gunners Res	26	2	2	22	36	97	8

BIS 4A	P	W	D	L	F	A	Pts
1 Steeple Morden	26	19	3	4	81	39	60
2 Harston 1987	26	18	1	7	51	32	55
3 Elsworth Sports	26	17	3	6	73	38	54
4 Eaton Socon A	26	16	1	9	79	51	49
5 JM Sports Reserves	26	14	5	7	74	62	47
6 Sawston Rovers Res.	26	11	6	9	57	50	39
7 Cambridge Uni.Press A	26	11	2	13	55	57	35
8 Hundon Reserves	26	9	7	10	44	45	34
9 Saffron Crocus Res.	26	10	4	12	38	45	34
10 Fowlmere Reserves	26	10	4	12	44	63	34
11 Steeple Bumpstead Res.	26	7	3	16	47	66	24
12 Linton Granta A	26	7	2	17	31	71	23
13 Hardwick A (-6)	26	7	4	15	45	56	19
14 Comberton United A	26	2	3	21	36	80	9

BIS 4B	P	W	D	L	F	A	Pts
1 Wisbech St Mary Res	26	22	1	3	149	36	67
2 St Ives Town A	26	14	6	6	81	40	48
3 Pymore	26	14	6	6	76	58	48
4 Sutton United Res	26	10	11	5	73	63	41
5 Mepal Sports	26	11	5	10	70	56	38
6 Burwell Swifts	26	11	5	10	58	60	38
7 Willingham Res	26	10	7	9	69	56	37
8 Swavesey Institute Res	26	10	6	10	56	49	36
9 Barton Mills Res	26	10	6	10	49	56	36
10 Ely Crusaders Res	26	8	7	11	41	66	31
11 Exning Athletic	26	8	3	15	59	92	27
12 Milton A	26	7	5	14	48	82	26
13 Haddenham Rov. R. (-3)	26	6	4	16	39	74	19
14 Wicken Amateurs	26	3	4	19	44	124	13

BIS 5A	P	W	D	L	F	A	Pts
1 Figleaves	28	21	3	4	96	42	66
2 Fulbourn Sports & S.C.	28	21	0	7	84	40	63
3 Hundon A	28	19	4	5	78	51	61
4 Litlington Athletic Res	28	16	6	6	73	42	54
5 Saffron Rangers	28	17	2	9	88	62	53
6 Bottisham Sports Res	28	14	2	12	70	56	44
7 Lode Res	28	14	1	13	88	59	43
8 Steeple Morden Res	28	13	4	11	63	58	43
9 Dalehead Foods	28	13	3	12	73	68	42
10 Barrington Res	28	12	1	15	63	71	37
11 Barton	28	9	3	16	55	86	30
12 Papworth Res	28	7	3	18	51	98	24
13 Duxford United Res	28	6	4	18	48	69	22
14 Newport Veterans	28	4	2	22	32	98	14
15 Gransden Chequers R.	28	2	6	20	40	102	12

BIS 5B	P	W	D	L	F	A	Pts
1 Newmarket Town A	26	21	4	1	121	35	67
2 March Rangers	26	19	3	4	105	49	60
3 Wisbech St Mary A	26	19	3	4	71	31	60
4 Earith United	26	14	5	7	85	55	47
5 Fenstanton Res	26	14	3	9	70	46	45
6 Burwell Swifts Res	26	13	2	11	66	46	41
7 Outwell Swifts Res	26	11	3	12	41	58	36
8 Isleham United Res	26	9	7	10	67	58	34
9 Walsoken United	26	9	2	15	52	78	29
10 Littleport Town A	26	8	2	16	41	71	26
11 Cottenham United B	26	5	8	13	44	78	23
12 The Vine Res	26	5	3	18	47	95	18
13 Little Downham Swifts Res (-3)	26	5	5	16	43	78	17
14 Coldham United	26	4	2	20	32	107	14

LEAGUE CONSTITUTION 2006-07 - PREMIER DIVISION

CAMBRIDGE UNIVERSITY PRESS
CUP Sports Ground,Shaftesbury Road, Cambridge CB2 2BS

COTTENHAM UNITED
King George V Playing Field, Lambs Lane, Cottenham, Cambridge CB4 4TB
Tel: 01954 250 873

EATON SOCON
River Road, Eaton Ford, St Neots, Cambridgeshire PE19 3AU

FORDHAM
Recreation Ground, Carter Street, Fordham, Cambridgeshire CB7 5NJ

GREAT PAXTON
Recreation Ground, High Street, Great Paxton, Cambridgeshire PE19 6RP

GREAT SHELFORD
Recreation Ground, Woollards Lane, Great Shelford, Cambridgeshire CB2 5LZ
Tel: 01223 842 590

HISTON 'A'
Histon & Impington Recreation Ground.

LINTON GRANTA
Recreation Ground, Meadow Lane, Linton Granta, Cambridgeshire

LITTLEPORT TOWN
Sports Centre, Camel Road, Littleport, Cambridgeshire CB6 1PU

NEEDINGWORTH UNITED
Millfield

NEWMARKET TOWN RESERVES
Cricket Field Road, off New Cheveley Road, Newmarket, Suffolk CB8 8BG
Tel: 01638 663 637

OVER SPORTS
Over Recreation Ground, The Dole, Over, Cambridge, Cambridgeshire CB4 5NZ

SAWSTON UNITED
Spicers Sports Ground, New Road, Sawston, Cambridgeshire

SOMERSHAM TOWN
West End Ground, St Ives Road, Somersham, Huntingdon, Cambridgeshire PE27 3EN
Tel: 01487 843 384

WATERBEACH
Recreation Ground, Waterbeach, Cambridgeshire CB5 9NJ

WICKHAMBROOK
Recreation Ground, Wickhambrook.

CENTRAL MIDLANDS LEAGUE

SPONSORED BY: ABACUS LIGHTING

President: Mr R Holmes **Chairman:** Frank Harwood
General Secretary: Jeff Worrall
36 Spilsby Close, Cantley, Doncaster DN4 6TJ
Tel: 01302 370188 email: gensec@cmfl.wanadoo.co.uk

SUPREME DIVISION		P	W	D	L	F	A	Pts
1.	Barton Town Old Boys	40	30	4	6	112	41	94
2.	Dinnington Town	40	27	6	7	82	34	87
3.	Holbrook Miners Welfare	40	22	10	8	70	42	76
4.	Southwell City	40	22	9	9	64	36	75
5.	Gedling Miners Welfare	40	19	10	11	77	54	67
6.	Heanor Town	40	18	13	9	61	38	67
7.	Radford	40	19	10	11	68	49	67
8.	Dunkirk (Champions 04/05)	40	19	7	14	66	44	64
9.	Rainworth Miners Welfare	40	19	7	14	68	48	64
10.	Radcliffe Olympic	40	14	11	15	64	58	53
11.	Blackwell Miners Welfare	40	16	4	20	63	93	52
12.	Sandiacre Town (R)	40	13	10	17	61	77	49
13.	Clipstone Welfare	40	14	6	20	58	62	48
14.	Appleby Frodingham	40	12	7	21	44	60	43
15.	Pinxton (4th Prem 04/05) (-1pt) (R)	40	12	7	21	43	76	42
16.	Rolls Royce Leisure (-3)	40	11	9	20	48	72	39
17.	Graham St.Prims	40	11	5	24	62	90	38
18.	Greenwood Meadows (-3)	40	11	8	21	55	89	38
19.	Bolsover Town (3rd Prem 04/05) (R)	40	9	9	22	42	79	36
20.	Kimberley Town (5th Prem 04/05)	40	8	11	21	60	87	35
21.	Nettleham	40	9	7	24	43	82	34

SUPREME DIVISION	1	2	3	4	5	6	7	8	9	10	11	12	13	14	15	16	17	18	19	20	21
1 Appleby Frodingham		1-6	1-2	1-0	0-2	1-0	0-0	2-1	1-2	4-1	1-1	1-0	2-2	1-1	0-2	1-1	1-1	1-2	1-0	0-1	2-0
2 Barton Town Old Boys	4-0		6-0	3-1	2-1	2-3	1-0	2-1	3-2	5-0	0-2	1-0	2-0	3-0	5-0	1-2	4-0	0-0	5-2	3-3	4-2
3 Blackwell Miners Welfare	2-1	1-5		5-2	1-1	3-2	2-1	1-0	2-1	2-1	1-3	1-4	3-8	1-3	2-0	1-3	1-3	3-1	2-1	3-1	1-1
4 Bolsover Town	0-2	2-3	1-1		0-2	0-5	0-2	0-1	5-2	1-2	1-2	2-1	1-1	3-0	0-2	1-1	0-2	0-0	2-1	2-3	0-0
5 Clipstone Welfare	3-1	1-2	2-2	3-1		1-2	0-1	1-1	0-1	2-3	0-1	0-3	2-0	1-1	0-1	1-0	2-0	3-0	2-2	1-2	4-0
6 Dinnington-Town	0-1	2-1	2-1	0-0	4-1		4-0	2-0	4-1	4-3	0-0	1-1	2-2	4-2	1-0	2-0	1-0	2-1	2-0	3-1	0-1
7 Dunkirk	3-2	1-4	2-1	2-1	6-2	0-3		2-2	3-1	3-0	2-0	1-1	2-1	0-1	3-1	0-1	2-0	1-0	1-3	0-1	0-0
8 Gedling Miners Welfare	3-1	1-0	2-1	3-1	1-3	0-2	0-0		3-1	2-0	1-1	3-1	4-1	4-0	3-3	4-0	3-3	3-1	2-0	4-2	1-2
9 Graham Street Prims	0-3	2-4	6-1	1-1	2-3	0-3	1-5	2-2		0-2	0-4	1-2	0-1	0-1	2-2	2-1	1-3	2-0	3-1	2-0	1-0
10 Greenwood Meadows	0-1	0-3	1-4	1-2	1-1	0-3	1-2	1-5	4-3		2-2	0-1	3-1	3-2	1-0	1-3	1-2	2-4	3-1	1-1	1-1
11 Heanor Town	3-0	2-3	6-0	0-0	1-0	0-1	0-0	3-0	2-2	4-1		0-1	2-0	1-0	2-1	1-0	3-1	2-2	1-1	2-0	0-1
12 Holbrook Miners Welfare	1-0	1-1	2-1	4-1	2-0	3-2	1-2	1-1	2-2	2-1	3-0		1-0	7-1	4-2	2-0	0-2	2-2	2-1	2-1	1-1
13 Kimberley Town	2-0	0-5	0-1	2-3	4-0	0-2	0-0	1-5	5-4	2-2	3-0	1-3		3-3	1-2	2-4	2-2	0-2	1-3	3-2	1-1
14 Nettleham	4-3	0-2	2-3	0-1	1-4	0-1	1-0	2-3	1-2	2-1	1-1	0-2	1-2		2-3	2-1	0-3	1-3	0-0	1-2	0-2
15 Pinxton	0-3	0-3	3-2	0-2	2-0	0-2	1-0	1-3	1-0	1-0	0-4	0-0	1-1	1-3		0-4	1-5	1-3	1-2	3-0	1-3
16 Radcliffe Olympic	1-0	1-1	5-0	1-2	2-0	1-3	0-4	0-0	1-4	7-0	0-0	6-2	3-1	2-1	2-2		1-1	0-1	0-2	1-1	2-1
17 Radford	1-0	1-2	3-0	8-1	4-1	3-2	3-2	2-1	1-0	0-0	0-0	1-0	0-0	0-0	3-2		0-3	1-1	3-1	0-2
18 Rainworth Miners Welfare	2-0	2-4	1-0	4-0	0-2	0-1	2-1	0-1	5-1	4-0	1-3	1-1	4-1	0-0	3-1	1-1	4-2		4-0	1-1	2-1
19 Rolls Royce Leisure	3-2	0-4	2-1	0-0	2-1	1-3	1-8	2-0	0-1	0-1	4-2	0-1	3-3	1-2	0-0	1-1	4-1	2-1		0-2	0-3
20 Sandiacre Town	2-2	2-3	1-2	6-2	0-4	2-1	0-5	3-3	4-3	2-3	1-1	0-3	2-1	6-1	0-1	2-1	0-0	0-2	0-0		0-5
21 Southwell City	1-0	2-0	3-2	2-0	3-1	0-1	3-0	4-1	3-0	2-0	1-1	2-0	5-2	0-2	0-2	2-0	1-0	0-2		

743

FIRST ROUND

Bottesford Town	v	Blidworth Welfare	0-1
Clipstone Welfare	v	Thorne Colliery	8-4
Dunkirk	v	Forest Town	1-1, 0-3r
Kimberley Town	v	LSS Lucarlys	4-3
Kiveton Park	v	Holbrook Miners Welfare	1-0
Nettleham	v	Southwell City	0-1
Newark Town	v	Newark Flowserve	2-1
Pinxton	v	Harworth Colliery Institute	2-0
Santos	v	Barton Town Old Boys	1-3
Yorkshire Main	v	AFC Barnsley	0-4

SECOND ROUND

Bilborough Pelican	v	Blackwell Miners Welfare	4-0
Bolsover Town	v	Radford	1-0
Clipstone Welfare	v	Pinxton	2-0
Gedling Miners W.	v	Dinnington Town	1-3
Hatfield Main	v	Graham St. Prims	4-1
Heanor Town	v	Greenwood Meadows	2-1
Kimberley Town	v	Forest Town	2-0
Kiveton Park	v	Rolls Royce Leisure	2-1
Matlock United	v	Askern Welfare	1-2
Southwell City	v	Rainworth Miners Wel.	0-0, 4-1r
Newark Town	v	Bentley Colliery	0-2
Ollerton Town	v	AFC Barnsley	2-4
Radcliffe Olympic	v	Welbeck Welfare	1-2
Sandiacre Town (H)	v	Appleby Frodingham	3-0
Barton Town O.B.	v	Grimsby Borough	0-0, 0-1r
Thoresby Coll. Wel.	v	Blidworth Welfare	2-1

THIRD ROUND

Askern Welfare	v	Sandiacre Town (H)	2-1
Grimsby Borough	v	Southwell City	0-0, 2-0r
Bentley Colliery	v	Dinnington Town	0-3
Bilborough Pelican	v	Kimberley Town	2-1
Bolsover Town	v	Welbeck Welfare	3-3, 4-5r
Heanor Town	v	Clipstone Welfare	0-1
Kiveton Park	v	AFC Barnsley	1-0
Thoresby Coll. Wel.	v	Hatfield Main	2-0

QUARTER-FINALS

Askern Welfare	v	Grimsby Borough	2-2, 4-2r
Bilborough Pelican	v	Welbeck Welfare	5-2
Clipstone Welfare	v	Kiveton Park	3-0
Thoresby Coll. Wel.	v	Dinnington Town	0-0, 0-0r, 4-5p

SEMI-FINALS

Dinnington Town	v	Bilborough Pelican	2-1
Clipstone Welfare	v	Askern Welfare	0-1

THE FINAL (7th May)

Askern Welfare	v	Dinnington Town	1-2*

PREMIER DIVISION

		P	W	D	L	F	A	Pts
1	Bilborough Pelican	38	27	5	6	116	46	86
2	Askern Welfare	38	26	3	9	99	33	81
3	Bottesford Town	38	24	8	6	101	38	80
4	LSS Lucarlys	38	22	6	10	102	54	72
5	Grimsby Borough	38	21	8	9	93	55	71
6	Bentley Colliery	38	22	4	12	84	64	69
7	Thorne Colliery	38	21	3	14	96	95	66
8	Santos	38	18	9	11	88	60	65
9	Newark Town	38	17	9	12	62	52	60
10	Ollerton Town	38	17	6	15	71	57	57
11	Newark Flowserve	38	16	7	15	61	67	55
12	Kiveton Park	38	12	10	16	58	59	42
13	Forest Town (-1)	38	11	9	18	57	72	41
14	Matlock United (-6)	38	12	10	16	52	61	40
15	Yorkshire Main	38	10	6	22	55	103	36
16	Hatfield Main (+2)	38	7	8	23	45	100	31
17	Thoresby Colliery Wel (+2)	38	8	5	25	39	114	31
18	Welbeck Welfare	38	9	3	26	63	118	30
19	Blidworth Welfare	38	8	5	25	44	84	29
20	Harworth Colliery Institute	38	4	12	22	29	83	24

PREMIER RESERVES

		P	W	D	L	F	A	Pts
1	Arnold Town Reserves	34	25	5	4	123	48	80
2	Southwell City Reserves	34	21	6	7	84	57	69
3	Retford Utd Reserves	34	17	10	7	84	43	61
4	Holbrook M.W.R. (+2)	34	17	8	9	76	60	61
5	Nettleham Reserves	34	16	5	13	62	45	53
6	Rainworth Miners Wel.R.	34	15	8	11	69	59	53
7	Radford Reserves	34	14	11	9	68	58	53
8	Dunkirk Reserves	34	15	6	13	60	48	51
9	Heanor Town Res. (-1)	34	13	8	13	82	70	46
10	Sandiacre Town Res.	34	13	6	15	59	62	45
11	Bilborough Pelican Res.	34	13	6	15	83	88	45
12	Clipstone Welfare Res.	34	13	5	16	64	79	44
13	Teversal Reserves	34	12	5	17	56	66	41
14	Carlton Town 'A'	34	12	3	19	57	101	39
15	Forest Town Reserves	34	10	6	18	39	65	36
16	Radcliffe Olympic Res.	34	9	8	17	49	63	35
17	Thoresby C. Wel. Res.	34	6	7	21	34	78	25
18	Graham St.Prims Res.	34	6	5	23	49	108	23

DIVISON ONE RESERVES

		P	W	D	L	F	A	Pts
1	Santos Reserves (+3)	26	21	2	3	64	25	68
2	Appleby Frodingham R.	26	18	2	6	80	40	56
3	Welbeck Welfare Res.	26	15	3	8	91	55	50
4	Newark Flowserve Res.	26	15	4	7	75	36	49
5	Bottesford Town Res.	26	15	3	8	71	33	48
6	Bolsover TownReserves	26	13	5	8	70	50	44
7	Bilborough Pelican 'A'	26	13	5	8	47	36	41
8	Blidworth Reserves	26	11	2	13	42	62	35
9	Blackwell M. W. Res.(-1)	26	9	4	13	52	60	30
10	Ollerton Town Reserves	26	9	3	14	29	72	30
11	Matlock United Res.	26	9	1	16	47	71	28
12	Newark Town Reserves	26	5	4	17	54	79	19
13	Sandiacre Town 'A'	26	4	2	20	29	92	14
14	Kimberley Town Res.	26	3	4	19	42	82	13

LEAGUE CONSTITUTION 2006-07 - SUPREME DIVISION

APPLEBY FRODINGHAM ATHLETIC

Secretary: Steve Lumley-Holmes. Kingswood, Church Street, Swawby, Brigg DN20 9AE. Tel: 01652 654 044. (M) 07904 196 430.

Ground: Brumby Hall Sports Ground, Ashby Road, Scunthorpe, Lincs. Tel No: 01724 843 024 / 402 134. Clubhouse at Ground

Directions: From the M18 take J5 onto the M180. From M180 take J3 onto the M181 which is Scunthorpe (West), at the roundabout turn right onto A18, straight on at the mini roundabout (McDonalds). At the next large roundabout take the 3rd exit (A18) up the hill to the next roundabout. Turn left and the entrance to the ground is 500 yards on the left.

Colours: Red/Black/Black **Change:** Sky blue/navy/sky blue

ASKERN WELFARE

Formed: 1924

Secretary: Ian Tallentire. 4 Gargrave Close, Askern, Doncaster DN6 0NN. Tel No: 01302 702 872. (M) 07717 284 673.

Ground: Askern Welfare Sports Ground, Doncaster Road, Askern, Doncaster. Tel No: 07717 284 673.

Directions: Leave the A1 at Junction A639. Follow signs Askern/Campsall at T-Junction turn right. Take 2nd right at "Anne Arms". Ground 2nd on right (Manor Way). Car park available at the rear of Miners Welfare Club .

Colours: White/black/black.

Change: Black & white stripes/white/red or white

BARTON TOWN OLD BOYS

Formed: 1995 after amalgamation of Barton Town and Barton Old Boys.

Secretary: Peter Mitchell, 56 Brigg Road, Barton-on-Humber, North Lincs.DN18 5DR Tel No: 01682 632 382 (H) 07900 105 204 (M)

Ground: Marsh Lane Football Ground, Barton-on-Humber, North Lincs Tel No: Please use Secretary's mobile number.

Directions: Approaching from the South on A15, Barton is the last exit before the Humber Bridge. Follow the A1077 into the town. Turn right at the mini roundabout at the bottom of the hill into "Holydyke". Take second left onto George Street and then into King Street. Marsh Lane is opposite the junction of King Street and High Street. The ground is at the end of Marsh Lane, on the right, immediately after the cricket ground.

Colours: Sky blue/White/Sky blue **Change:** All navy blue

BILBOROUGH PELICAN

Formed: 1994

Secretary: Duncan Costin. 12 Calstock Road, Woodthorpe, Nottingham NG5 4FH. Tel No: 01159 199 371. (M) 07736 211 400.

Ground: Brian Wakefield Sports Ground, Lenton Lane Nottingham Tel No: 0115 986 8255

Directions: M1 J26 follow Ring Road A610, go under Clifton Bridge. Down Lenton Lane and the ground is the last on lane after Dunkirk .

Colours: All blue.

Change: All red.

BLACKWELL MINERS WELFARE

Secretary: Steve Harris, 6 Pennine Close, Newton, Alfrteon, Derbys. DE55 5UD. Tel Nos: 01773 779 172(H) 01246 501 561(W) 07890 198 776 (M)

Ground: Wefare Ground, Primrose Hill, Blackwell, Derbys. DE55 5JE Tel No: 07890 198 776 / 01773 811 295 . Clubhouse at ground.

Directions: Leave the M1 at J28 take A38 towards Mansfield, at McArthurGlen take B6406 to Hilcote. At Hilcote Arms Pub turn left. Ground is on the left after 1 mile.

Colours: Red/black/red.

Change: Yellow & blue stripes/blue/yellow.

BOTTESFORD TOWN

Formed: 1974

Secretary: Tony Reeve. 61 Skelton Road, Scunthorpe DN17 1RB. Tel No: 01724 352 939.

Ground: Birch Park, Ontario Road, Bottesford, Scunthorpe Tel: 01724 871883.

Directions: Exit M180 via M181-Scunthorpe. At circle (Berkeley Hotel), turn right into Scotter Road. At circle (Asda) straight ahead, 2nd left into South Park road then on to Sunningdale Road, turn right into Goodwood Road, Birch Park at end (right turn).

Colours: Royal blue with yellow trim/royal blue/royal blue.

Change: Red with black trim/red/red.

CLIPSTONE WELFARE

Formed: 1928

Secretary: John Tait, 51 Goldsmith Road, Mansfield, Notts. NG18 5PF Tel No: 01623 478 655

Ground: Clipstone Lido Ground, Clipstone Road, East Clipstone, Nr Mansfield , Notts.

Directions: On B6030 from Mansfield, ground is on left between Forest Town & Clipstone.

Colours: White with red trim/red/red

Change: Green with white & black trim/white/green

DUNKIRK

Formed: 1946

Secretary: Steve Throsell, 24 Kingfisher Wharf, Castle Marina, Nottingham NG7 1GA Tel No: 0115 947 3903. (M) 07903 322 446.

Ground: The Ron Steel Sports Ground, Lenton Lane, Clifton Bridge, Nottingham Tel No: 0115 985 0803

Directions: M1 J25 Take A52 to Nottingham, at Ring Road (QMC Island) turn right towards M1 South A52 Grantham, over flyover, get into the left hand lane (City Centre) at island turn right (Ind.Est. West) then left onto Lenton Lane, follow road past hotel and the ground is 200yds on the right.

Colours: Red/black/black **Change:** All blue

GEDLING MINERS WELFARE

Foremd: 1919

Secretary: Norman Hay, 182 Gedling Rd., Arnold, Notts.NG5 6NY Tel No: 0115 926 5598. (M) 07748 138 732.

Ground: Plains Sports & Social, Plains Road, Mapperly, Nottingham NG3 5RH. Tel No: 0115 926 6300

Directions: Ground situated on B684 in Mapperley. Approached from Nottingham via Woodborough Road. From the North of the Country via A614 by Lime Lane Junction to Plains Road.

Colours: Yellow/blue/yellow **Change:** White/white/blue

GRAHAM STREET PRIMS

Formed: 1904

Secretary: David Lillie, 6 Sidmouth Close, Church View, Alvaston, Derby DE24 0QY. Tel No: 01332 725 107. (M) 07812 809 954.

Ground: Asterdale Sports Centre, Borrowash Road, Spondon, Nr Derby. Tel No: 01332 668 656.

Directions: M1 J25 towards Derby on the A52, take the 3rd turning on the left (directly under the pedestrian bridge) Borrowash Road-golf driving range on the left, approximately 400 yards further on turn left into the Asterdale Sports Ground. Ground situated at the rear of the Sports Centre.

Colours: Red & white stripes/black/black

Change: All white

GREENWOOD MEADOWS.

Formed: 1987
Secretary: Brian Hall, 34 Sullivan Close, Marmion Estate,Nottingham NG3 2HX Tel No: 0115 958 2459
Ground: Greenwood Meadows, Lenton Lane, Nr Clifton Bridge, Nottingham. Tel. No: 0115 986 5913.
Directions: Nottingham Ring Road (A52 Clifton Bridge) From M1 J24 take A453 Nottingham to Clifton Bridge, Lenton Ind. Est. West. Turn left into Old Lenton Lane, ground 2nd right on the lane.
Colours: Green/navy/green **Change:** Yellow/green/yellow

HEANOR TOWN

Formed: 1883
Secretary: Michael Knibbs,16 Kensington Avenue, Heanor, Derbyshire DE75 7SE. Tel No: 01773 715 328. (M) 07870 618 340.
Ground: The Town Ground, Mayfield Avenue, Heanor, Derbys DE75 7EN. Tel No: 01773 713 742 / 715 815. Clubhouse on ground. Capacity 4,500 Cover 2,000 Two stands and Floodlights
Directions: From Nottingham and J26 M1, take A610 Ripley then A608 Heanor. From Derby take A608 Mansfield to Heanor. Ground 200 yards from the Market Square.
Colours: White/black/black **Colours:** Red/white/white

HOLBROOK MINERS WELFARE

Formed: 1996
Secretary: David Allsopp, 50 Jubilee Rd., Shelton Lock, Derby DE 24 9FE Tel No: 01332 704 090. (M) 07803 043 147.
Ground: The Welfare Ground, Shaw Lane, Holbrook, Derbys. DE56 0TF. Tel No: 01322 880 259.
Directions: From A38 take B6179 for Kilburn. Turn left at the traffic lightsfor Belper. One mile on turn left at 'Bulls Head' for Holbrook. Two miles on turn right at 'Venture' garage into Shaw Lane. Ground 100 yards on the right.
Colours: Blue & black halves/black/black **Change:** Red/black/red

KIMBERLEY TOWN

Formed: 1947
Secretary: Mrs P L Critchley. 21 Rowborn Drive, Sheffield, S35 0JR. Tel: 0114 251 7742.
Ground: The Stag Ground, Nottingham Road, Kimberley NG16 2ND. Tel: 01159 382 788.
Directions: M1 J26 take road to Nottingham at first roundabout take road signed Kimberley Town, travel 11/2 miles, 'Stag Pub' on the right-hand side, go 400yds, entrance to car park.
Colours: Maize/black/maize **Change:** All navy

NETTLEHAM

Re-formed: 1938
Secretary: Charles H Shaw. 4 Willowfield Avenue, Nettleham,Lincoln LN2 2TH. Tel: 01522 823 912. (M) 07837 016 482.
Ground: Mulsanne Park, Field Close, Greenfields, Nettleham. Tel: 01522 750 007.
Directions: Leave the Lincoln ByPass at the roundabout taking A46 Grimsby, after half a mile turn right into Nettleham, follow road for 1 mile past Village Centre up small hill take 2nd right into Greenfields then 1st left into Field Close.
Colours: All royal blue **Change:** Yellow/green/yellow

RADCLIFFE OLYMPIC

Formed: 1876
Secretary: Maurice Baxter. 104 Main Road, Barnstone, Nottingham NG13 9JP. Tel: 01949 869 541. (M) 07817 150 513.
Ground: Recreation Gd. Wharf Lane, Radcliffe-on-Trent, Nottingham. Tel: 07947 593 546 / 07717 663 873.
Directions: A52 from Nottingham turn left at RSPCA at signs marked Radcliffe on Trent into village, turn left at the Church into Wharfe Lane, ground is 300 yards on the left.
Colours: All navy **Change :** All white

Nettleham F.C.

Photo: Gordon Whittington.

RADFORD

Formed: 1964 as Manlove & Alliots FC.

Secretary: Arthur Lowe, 1 Gayhurst Green, Old Basford, Nottingham NG6 0CL. Tel: 0115 977 0020.

Ground: Berridge Road West, off Radford Road, Radford, Nottingham NG7 5EH. Tel No: 0115 9423 250

Directions: M1 J26 take A610 to Nottingham at dual carrigeway turn left. Move to right hand lane and go immediately right into Wilkinson Street. At top of street turn right and at second pelican crossing turn right into the ground.

Colours: Claret & Sky Blue /claret/claret **Change:** Gold/black/black

RAINWORTH MINERS WELFARE

Formed: 1922 as Rufford Colliery FC

Secretary: Les Lee. 18 The Hollies, Rainworth, Mansfield NG21 0FZ. Tel No: 01623 490 053. (M) 07855 490 404.

Ground: Welfare Ground,Kirklington Road, Rainworth, Mansfield, Notts NG21 0JY. Tel: 07740 576 958. Clubhouse: 01623 792 495.

Directions: Via A614 to A617 to Rainworth onto Kirklington Road. From M1 J27, A608 through Annesley at 4 way crossing turn right onto B6020 follow road to Rainworth. At T-Junction in Rainworth turn left and right at traffic lights onto Kirklington Rd, ground is on left.

Colours: All white **Change:** All royal blue

F.A.Vase Finalists 1981-82.Record Attendance 5,071 S-Final.

ROLLS ROYCE LEISURE

Formed: Football clubs using the name Rolls Royce have played at the Hucknall site since 1935.

Secretary: Nicola Burton. 103 Annesley Road, Hucknall, Nottingham NG15 7DR. Tel: 0115 963 3593. (M) 07967 512 201.

Ground: Rolls Royce Leisure Sports Ground, Watnall Road, Hucknall NG15 6EU. Tel: 0115 964 2380.

Directions: M1 J27, follow sign A611 to Hucknall. Turn right onto bypass at 2nd roundabout turn right onto Watnall Road. Take 2nd left after Fire Station.

Colours: All royal blue **Change:** Yellow/blue/yellow

SOUTHWELL CITY

Secretary: Pat Johnson, 63 The Ropewalk, Southwell, Notts. NG25 0AL Tel No: 01636 812 594

Ground: War Memorial Recreation Ground, Bishops Drive, Southwell, Notts. Tel No: 01636 814 386

Directions: The War Memorial Recreation Ground know as 'The Park' is at the end of Bishop's Drive which is the turning near Southwell Minister off Westgate A612.

Colours: Black & white stripes/black/black **Change:** Sky blue/blue/sky

LEAGUE CONSTITUTION 2006-07 - PREMIER DIVISION

BENTLEY COLLIERY	**LOUTH UNITED**
BLIDWORTH WELFARE	**NEWARK FLOWSERVE**
BOLSOVER TOWN	**NEWARK TOWN**
CALVERTON M W	**OLLERTON TOWN**
FOREST TOWN	**PINXTON**
GRIMSBY BOROUGH	**SANDIACRE TOWN**
HARWORTH COLLIERY	**THORESBY CW**
INSTITUTE	**THORNE COLLIERY**
HATFIELD MAIN	**WELBECK WELFARE**
KIVETON PARK	**YORKSHIRE MAIN**

CRAWLEY & DISTRICT LEAGUE

Chairman: Ken Watts
General Secretary: Elaine Sangster
email: elaine_cdfl@blueyonder.co.uk

PREMIER DIVISION		P	W	D	L	F	A	Pts
1.	Merstham Newton (Champions 04/05)	24	18	2	4	87	32	56
2.	Boca Elite FC (1st Div.1 04/05)	24	16	1	7	55	35	49
3.	South Park FC (-1pt)	24	14	6	4	66	32	47
4.	Ifield Edwards II	24	14	4	6	58	46	46
5.	Phoenix	24	11	9	4	48	31	42
6.	Three Bridges A	24	11	3	10	55	56	36
7.	Horley Albion	24	9	5	10	44	64	32
8.	Oakwood III	24	9	4	11	54	57	31
9.	Trumpton Town	24	9	2	13	53	56	29
10.	Holland Sports	24	6	6	12	42	60	24
11.	Central Sussex College	24	7	2	15	51	71	23
12.	St Francis Flyers	24	4	3	17	32	53	15
13.	Trident	24	4	1	19	21	73	13

PREMIER DIVISION		1	2	3	4	5	6	7	8	9	10	11	12	13
1	Boca Elite		2-0	2-2	2-3	5-2	1-0	3-0	1-0	0-3	0-4	6-3	6-1	0-1
2	Central Sussex College	0-1		2-3	2-2	1-2	0-5	2-0	1-3	3-7	5-4	3-5	6-0	4-0
3	Holland Sports	2-0	1-5		1-1	1-1	1-4	4-3	0-4	0-3	0-4	3-0	6-0	3-7
4	Horley Albion	2-7	3-2	3-2		0-3	1-5	2-0	1-1	1-6	3-1	2-3	2-2	3-2
5	Ilfield Edwards II	1-3	5-0	1-0	1-3		0-4	3-2	1-1	4-3	1-0	2-3	3-0	3-2
6	Merstham Newton	1-0	6-1	8-0	4-0	3-4		4-3	3-3	2-2	2-1	2-1	5-1	6-2
7	Oakwood III	1-3	5-0	2-2	5-3	6-3	2-4		2-2	1-3	2-1	1-1	4-3	4-2
8	Phoenix	2-3	2-2	2-1	0-0	1-1	2-3	4-2		3-3	3-1	3-0	3-0	2-1
9	South Park	3-1	2-0	2-2	6-1	2-2	1-2	2-3	1-1		4-0	HW	5-1	1-1
10	St Francis Flyers	0-3	4-2	2-2	0-2	1-3	0-7	1-2	0-1	1-3		2-3	2-1	1-1
11	Three Bridges A	3-4	6-4	1-0	6-1	2-4	1-0	1-1	1-2	3-2	1-1		2-0	2-5
12	Trident	AW	0-2	0-5	0-3	0-3	1-4	1-3	2-0	AW	2-1	2-6		HW
13	Trumpton Town	1-2	3-4	3-1	3-2	3-5	4-3	3-0	1-3	0-2	HW	6-1	2-4	

S E N I O R   C U P

FIRST ROUND

Greets Inn	v	Worth Park Rangers	5-2
Virgin Holidays	v	South Park	2-20

SECOND ROUND

County Oak	v	Wingspan	4-1
Merstham Newton	v	St Francis Flyers	0-1
Phoenix	v	Worth Park Rangers	15-0
Three Bridges A	v	Windmill	4-7
Trident	v	Boca Elite	2-1
Broadfield	v	Stones	4-0
Horley Albion	v	GSK Sports & Social	3-4
Maidenbower Vill.	v	Central Sussex College	3-2
Pelham Wanderers	v	FC Spartak	1-4
Southside Rovers	v	Sussex Elite	4-3
Black Dog	v	Seebrook Rovers	8-4
Holland Sports	v	Real Hydraquip	3-0
Oakwood III	v	Greets Inn	5-0
South Park	v	Sporting Crawley	4-0
Border Wanderers	v	Trumpton Town (H)	1-3
Ifield Edwards II	v	Rowfant Village	4-2

THIRD ROUND

Broadfield	v	Trumpton Town (H)	3-1
Soutside Rovers	v	FC Spartak	3-1
Holland Sports	v	GSK Sports & Social	5-2
Oakwood III	v	Maidenbower Village	7-1
South Park	v	Trident	6-1
Windmill	v	St Francis Flyers	2-1
Black Dog	v	Phoenix	1-4
Ifield Edwards II	v	County Oak	2-3

QUARTER-FINALS

County Oak	v	Windmill	3-2
Oakwood III	v	South Park	1-2
Pheonix	v	Holland Sports	2-3
Broadfield	v	Southside Rovers	4-3

SEMI-FINALS

Broadfield	v	County Oak	1-2
Holland Sports	v	South Park	2-3

THE FINAL (4th April - Broadfield Stadium)

County Oak	v	South Park	0-6

LEAGUE CONSTITUTION 2006-07 - PREMIER DIVISION

BLETCHINGLEY	**MERSTHAM NEWTON**
CENTRAL SUSSEX COLLEGE	**OAKWOOD III**
GSK PHOENIX	**THREE BRIDGES A**
HOLLAND SPORTS	**TRUMPTON TOWN**
HORLEY ALBION	**WINDMILL FC**
IFIELD EDWARDS II	

DIVISION ONE		P	W	D	L	F	A	Pts
1	Windmill FC	16	13	1	2	81	17	40
2	FC Spartak	16	12	1	3	64	31	37
3	Sporting Crawley	16	12	0	4	53	24	36
4	St Francis Flyers II	16	10	1	5	61	33	31
5	South Park II FC	16	7	1	8	36	43	22
6	Real Hydraquip	16	6	1	9	37	39	19
7	Worth Park Rangers	16	4	2	10	34	66	14
8	Horley Albion II	16	2	2	12	25	62	8
9	Virgin Holidays	16	1	1	14	24	100	4

DIVISION TWO		P	W	D	L	F	A	Pts
1	County Oak FC	18	15	0	3	90	21	45
2	Broadfield	18	13	3	2	74	26	42
3	Greets Inn	18	11	3	4	80	28	36
4	Maidenbower Village	18	11	3	4	65	25	36
5	Black Dog	18	11	1	6	68	51	34
6	Ifield Edwards III	18	8	3	7	65	50	27
7	Phoenix II	18	6	1	11	44	53	19
8	Wingspan	18	4	0	14	25	99	12
9	Seebrook Rovers	18	1	3	14	19	106	6
10	Stones	18	1	1	16	21	92	4

DIVISION THREE		P	W	D	L	F	A	Pts
1	Sussex Elite (+2)	20	17	2	1	69	14	55
2	GSK Sports & Social FC	20	14	2	4	70	35	44
3	Ifield Edwards IV (P)	20	9	4	7	43	36	31
4	Southside Rovers (-1)	20	9	4	7	47	30	30
5	Boca Elite II FC	20	9	1	10	32	39	28
6	Virgin Holidays II FC	20	8	2	10	46	58	26
7	Rowfant Village	20	7	4	9	43	40	25
8	Pelham Wanderers	20	7	4	9	36	39	25
9	Real Hydraquip II	20	6	4	10	48	50	22
10	Sporting Crawley II	20	4	3	13	32	58	15
11	Border Wanderers	20	4	2	14	20	87	14

DEVON COUNTY LEAGUE

SPONSORED BY: AXEWORTHYS' OFFICE SUPPLIES
President: Carl Throgmorton
Chairman: David Moore **Vice Chairman:** Mark Hayman
Hon. Secretary: Philip Hiscox, 19 Ivy Close, Wonford, Exeter EX2 5LX
Tel/Fax: 01392 493995 Email: pahiscox@hotmail.com

		P	W	D	L	F	A	Pts
1.	IVYBRIDGE TOWN	38	31	4	3	122	38	97
2.	PLYMSTOCK UNITED	38	23	8	7	93	41	77
3.	HOLSWORTHY	38	23	5	10	90	67	74
4.	OTTERY ST MARY	38	21	7	10	85	60	70
5.	DARTMOUTH	38	21	7	10	79	56	70
6.	NEWTON ABBOT	38	20	6	12	83	49	66
7.	BUDLEIGH SALTERTON	38	20	5	13	78	59	65
8.	NEWTON ABBOT SPURS	38	19	7	12	75	58	64
9.	TEIGNMOUTH	38	18	9	11	90	66	63
10.	TOTNES & DARTINGTON	38	17	8	13	78	62	59
11.	ELBURTON VILLA *	38	15	6	17	59	59	54
12.	CREDITON UNITED	38	16	4	18	53	65	52
13.	BUCKLAND ATHLETIC	38	14	6	18	63	82	48
14.	ALPHINGTON	38	13	7	18	56	79	46
15.	VOSPERS OAK VILLA	38	12	7	19	68	75	43
16.	UNIVERSITY OF EXETER *	38	14	2	22	66	71	40
17.	CULLOMPTON RANGERS	38	10	4	24	56	95	34
18.	APPLEDORE	38	10	2	26	45	95	32
19.	STOKE GABRIEL	38	4	6	28	42	117	18
20.	ST. LOYES	38	2	4	32	31	118	10

	1	2	3	4	5	6	7	8	9	10	11	12	13	14	15	16	17	18	19	20
1 Alphington		2-0	4-1	3-2	1-5	3-3	1-3	1-3	2-1	3-1	2-1	3-0	1-2	0-5	3-0	1-2	3-2	2-2	2-1	1-5
2 Appledore	0-2		2-1	0-4	1-0	6-1	0-3	2-1	1-3	0-2	2-1	1-1	1-3	0-1	2-1	2-2	4-2	1-3	2-1	4-0
3 Buckland Athletic	3-3	1-0		3-2	3-1	1-0	1-2	1-1	4-5	0-2	2-1	3-1	0-1	0-3	0-0	4-0	1-1	1-1	1-4	3-2
4 Budleigh Salterton	3-1	5-0	3-1		2-1	2-1	5-2	3-0	1-3	0-2	0-4	1-1	1-0	2-1	3-1	3-1	1-3	3-3	1-2	5-1
5 Crediton United	4-0	2-1	4-2	0-2		1-2	0-1	1-0	3-2	0-3	3-2	2-1	0-0	0-1	1-0	2-1	1-2	2-1	3-7	3-1
6 Cullompton Rangers	0-1	2-1	1-3	0-1	1-0		0-7	1-3	6-1	1-4	1-4	0-2	1-2	0-1	5-0	3-0	1-4	0-7	1-2	1-1
7 Dartmouth	1-0	6-0	4-3	3-0	0-0	0-0		3-2	3-5	2-3	1-0	2-1	2-2	2-4	2-0	3-2	3-2	0-3	2-0	0-0
8 Elburton Villa	2-0	5-0	3-0	1-1	0-0	1-6	1-3		0-2	0-2	0-1	2-2	1-4	2-0	4-1	6-0	0-3	1-0	1-0	
9 Holsworthy	3-0	1-0	6-1	3-2	5-3	1-1	0-1	3-3		0-1	2-1	2-1	5-2	2-0	6-1	3-0	4-2	0-2	1-1	2-1
10 Ivybridge Town	4-1	2-1	1-3	2-0	2-1	8-1	2-1	4-2	6-1		1-1	2-0	3-0	3-1	10-1	6-1	1-1	3-1	2-1	2-2
11 Newton Abbot	1-0	5-1	5-1	4-2	1-0	5-3	0-2	0-2	2-2	1-3		0-3	1-1	1-2	4-0	2-0	2-1	2-1	4-1	3-0
12 Newton Abbot Spurs	2-2	5-0	2-1	1-2	8-0	3-2	3-1	2-1	2-1	1-1	4-2		0-3	0-3	3-1	2-0	1-1	2-1	2-1	2-1
13 Ottery St Mary	1-0	2-0	1-3	5-4	1-2	2-1	2-0	4-3	1-4	3-1	1-2	1-4		0-0	0-0	8-1	2-2	3-4	2-1	3-1
14 Plymstock United	5-0	8-0	5-0	0-2	1-0	4-0	1-1	2-0	1-1	1-7	1-1	3-0	1-1		5-2	6-3	9-3	1-1	3-0	1-2
15 St Loyes	0-3	3-1	1-4	1-4	1-1	2-1	2-7	0-1	2-3	1-3	2-6	1-2	0-2	0-2		0-4	0-1	1-4	0-1	2-3
16 Stoke Gabriel	2-2	2-5	3-1	1-2	1-3	1-2	1-1	0-1	1-2	1-8	0-6	2-2	0-4	1-1	3-1		1-3	1-3	1-3	1-2
17 Teignmouth	5-0	2-0	1-1	1-1	5-0	4-1	4-0	1-2	2-3	3-4	1-1	4-2	2-4	0-0	4-1	4-0		2-2	2-0	4-0
18 Totnes & Dartington	0-0	1-0	0-2	2-2	1-0	2-3	5-3	0-0	0-1	0-1	0-4	3-2	2-6	0-2	5-0	5-1	0-1		3-1	4-1
19 University of Exeter	4-3	3-1	5-1	0-1	1-2	2-3	0-1	2-1	3-1	0-6	0-1	1-3	2-5	1-4	3-0	1-1	4-1	7-0		0-2
20 Vospers Oak Villa	0-0	6-3	1-2	1-0	1-2	3-0	1-1	2-3	4-0	1-4	1-1	1-2	4-1	3-4	2-2	4-0	4-5	1-3	1-0	

THROGMORTON LEAGUE CUP

FIRST ROUND

Ivybridge Town	v	Appledore	6-0
Newton Abbot	v	Stoke Gabriel	5-1
Teignmouth	v	Alphington	2-0
Totnes & Dartington	v	Cullompton Rangers	3-1

SECOND ROUND

Buckland Athletic	v	Vosper Oak Villa	1-0
Crediton United	v	Newton Abbot	0-2
Dartmouth	v	University of Exeter	2-1
Holsworthy	v	Budleigh Salterton	3-2
Newton A. Spurs	v	Elburton Villa	1-2
Ottery St. Mary	v	Totnes & Dartington SC	1-0
St. Loyes	v	Plymstock United	1-5
Teignmouth	v	Ivybridge Town	1-2

QUARTER-FINALS

Holsworthy	v	Newton Abbot	3-2
Ivybridge Town	v	Buckland Athletic	4-0
Ottery St. Mary	v	Elburton Villa	5-1
Plymstock United	v	Dartmouth	3-0

SEMI-FINALS

Holsworthy	v	Ottery St. Mary	2-5
Ivybridge Town	v	Plymstock United	1-2

THE FINAL

Ottery St. Mary	v	Plymstock United	1-2

LEAGUE CONSTITUTION 2006-07

ALPHINGTON
Secretary: Norman Lyne-Lye 01392 661 008. **Ground:**The Chronicles, Alphington, Exeter, Devon. **Tel:** 01392 279 556

APPLEDORE
Secretary: Michelle Copp 01805 624 774. **Ground:**Marshford, Appledore, Devon. **Tel:** 01237 477 099

BUCKLAND ATHLETIC
Secretary: Christine Holmes 01626 369 345. **Ground:** Homers Heath, Kingsteignton, Devon.

BUDLEIGH SALTERTON
Secretary: Nick Pannell 01395 445 877. **Ground:**Greenway Lane, Budleigh Salterton, Devon EX9 6SC. **Tel:** 01395 443 850

CREDITON UNITED
Secretary: Mary Avery 01363 773 912. **Ground:**Lords Meadow, Commercial Road, Crediton, Devon. **Tel:** 01363 774 671

CULLOMPTON RANGERS
Secretary: Marcus Scott 01884 32662. **Ground:** Speeds Meadow, Duke Street, Cullompton, Devon EX15 1DW. **Tel:** 01884 33090

DARTMOUTH
Secretary: Keith Greeno 01803 832 720. **Ground:** Longcross, Dartmouth, Devon. **Tel:** 01803 832 902

ELBURTON VILLA
Secretary: Dean Baker 01752 518 113. **Ground:** Haye Road, Elburton, Devon. **Tel:** 01752 480 025

HOLSWORTHY
Secretary: Ivor Phillips 01409 253 907. **Ground:** Upcott Field, North Road, Holsworthy, Devon. **Tel:** 01409 254 295

IVYBRIDGE TOWN
Secretary: Paul Cocks 01752 346 150. **Ground:** Erme Valley, Ivybridge, Devon. **Tel:** 01752 896 686

NEWTON ABBOT
Secretary: Kevin Besford 01626 351 892. **Ground:** Coach Road Stadium, Coach Road, Newton Abbot, Devon TQ12 5DS. **Tel:** 01626 335 011

NEWTON ABBOT SPURS
Secretary: Ashley Dawes 01626 833 828. **Ground:** Recreation Ground, Newton Abbot, Devon. **Tel:** 01626 365 343

OTTERY ST MARY
Secretary: Clare Walker 01404 815 358. **Ground:** Washbrook Meadows, Butts Road, Ottery St Mary, Devon EX11 1EL **Tel:** 01404 813 539

PLYMSTOCK UNITED
Secretary: Dave Baskwill 01752 706 284. **Ground:** Dean Cross, Plymstock, Devon. **Tel:** 01752 406 776

STOKE GABRIEL
Secretary: Andy Horn 01803 323 428. **Ground:**Churchward Memorial Ground, Broadley Lane, Stoke Gabriel, Totnes, Devon. **Tel:** 01803 782 223

TEIGNMOUTH
Secretary: Nick Pearce 01626 770 431. **Ground:** Coombe Valley, Teignmouth, Devon. **Tel:** 01626 776 688

TOTNES AND DARTINGTON (Formed 2005 from a merger of Totnes Town and Dartington S.C.)
Secretary: Ken Phillips 01803 864 430. **Ground:** Foxhole Sports Ground, Dartington, Devon. **Tel:** 01803 868 032

UNIVERSITY OF EXETER
Secretary: Charlotte Edwards 01392 263 505. **Ground:** University Sports Ground, Topsham, Devon. **Tel:** 01392 264 452

VOSPERS OAK VILLA
Secretary: John Davey 01752 216 901. **Ground:** The Mill, Plymouth, Devon. **Tel:** 01752 363 352

WITHERIDGE
Secretary: Chris Cole 01884 860 351. **Ground:** The Playing Fields, Witheridge, Nr Tiverton.

2005-06 Cullompton Rangers F.C.
Gary Hayes, Luke Robinson, Jamie Cottrell, Lee Riggs, Mike Taylor, Ray Pratt (Manager), James Ingham-Hill, Andy Bassett, Ross Waring and Matthew Scott. Front row: John Cheffings, Tom Bedows, Bradley Cox, Paul Robinson, Duncan Floyd (Asst.Manager) and Ryan Gibbs.

FEEDER LEAGUES

SOUTH DEVON LEAGUE

PREMIER DIVISION	P	W	D	L	F	A	Pts	DIVISION ONE	P	W	D	L	F	A	Pts
Upton Athletic	26	33	1	2	73	22	70	Liverton United	26	19	4	3	67	30	61
Brixham Villa	26	22	1	3	68	19	67	Bovey Tracey	26	19	0	7	106	31	57
Buckfastleigh Rangers	26	17	4	6	44	28	52	Waldon Athletic	26	17	3	6	65	39	54
East Allington United	26	14	5	7	68	46	47	Chagford	26	15	3	8	74	43	48
Hele Rovers	26	12	5	9	58	34	41	Ipplepen Athletic (-3)	26	14	6	6	73	50	45
Galmpton United	26	12	2	12	49	42	38	Loddiswell Athletic	26	12	5	9	75	57	41
Bishopsteignton Utd (-3)	26	12	4	10	54	37	37	Upton Athletic Reserves	26	12	4	10	70	58	40
Kingsteignton Athletic	26	8	3	15	28	50	27	Newton 66	26	12	4	10	50	48	40
Totnes & Dartington R(-3)	26	8	3	15	30	53	24	Ashburton	26	11	3	12	51	61	36
Newton Abbot Spurs R.	26	7	5	14	33	42	23	Abbotskerswell	26	6	5	15	48	74	23
Newton Abbot Res. (-10)	26	8	4	14	33	53	19	Kingsteignton Res. (-3)	26	8	0	18	31	89	21
Brixham United	26	5	4	17	28	65	19	Chudleigh Athletic (-3)	26	7	1	18	41	84	19
Chelston	26	6	1	19	23	73	19	Dartmouth Reserves (-6)	26	7	2	17	45	82	17
Victoria Rangers (-3)	26	5	6	15	35	59	18	Paignton Villa	26	3	2	21	33	84	11

DEVON & EXETER LEAGUE

PREMIER DIVISION	P	W	D	L	F	A	Pts
Heavitree Social United	30	19	10	1	65	34	67
Witheridge (Promoted)	30	18	7	5	66	32	57
St Martins	30	15	7	8	71	50	52
Feniton	30	15	7	8	72	53	52
Thorverton	30	15	7	8	58	42	52
Exeter Civil Service	30	16	3	11	69	43	47
Sidmouth Town	30	14	3	13	61	58	45
Pinhoe	30	13	4	13	56	71	43
Axminster Town	30	12	6	12	47	46	42
University of Exeter	30	11	4	15	50	55	37
Exmouth Town	30	8	9	13	48	57	33
Buckland Athletic	30	8	8	14	38	57	32
Hatherleigh Town	30	8	5	17	43	62	29
Cullompton Rangers	30	7	6	17	42	74	27
Seaton Town	30	6	8	16	33	59	26
Topsham Town	30	6	4	20	46	72	20

NORTH DEVON LEAGUE

PREMIER DIVISION	P	W	D	L	F	A	Pts
Boca Seniors	30	27	0	3	124	28	81
Morwenstow	30	23	3	4	96	33	72
Georgeham	30	19	3	8	80	45	60
Dolton	30	18	6	6	85	53	60
Braunton	30	18	4	8	94	46	58
Shamwickshire	30	16	6	8	73	39	54
Appledore Reserves	30	10	7	13	46	48	37
Barnstaple AAC	30	10	7	13	51	60	37
Bradworthy	30	10	5	15	62	79	35
Northam Lions	30	10	5	15	51	81	35
Holsworthy	30	8	8	14	37	53	32
Hartland	30	9	5	16	43	79	32
Putford	30	8	6	16	53	59	30
Kilkhampton	30	8	3	19	47	84	27
Clovelly	30	7	4	19	36	78	25
Ilfracombe Town	30	2	2	26	25	138	8

PLYMOUTH & WEST DEVON LEAGUE

PREMIER DIVISION	P	W	D	L	F	A	Pts
Wessex Lopes Arms R	24	17	5	2	61	33	56
University of Plymouth(A)	24	17	4	3	70	21	55
Friary Vaults Mount G.	24	16	6	2	68	21	54
Tamarside (A)	24	14	2	8	55	32	44
Plymstock United Res.	24	12	3	9	52	40	39
Horrabridge Rangers (A)	24	10	3	11	47	54	33
Elburton Villa Reserves	24	9	3	12	45	50	30
Lee Motor	24	8	3	13	38	69	27
The Falcon FC (A)	24	7	4	13	28	42	25
Plymouth Parkway Res.	24	6	6	12	43	50	24
Oddfellows Arms	24	7	3	14	44	71	24
Vospers Oak Villa Res.	24	3	8	13	29	54	17
Breakwater Breakers (A)	24	4	2	18	35	78	14

DORSET PREMIER LEAGUE

Founded: 1957
President: Alan Burt   **Chairman:** Mike Mock
Secretary: Geoff Theobald, 41 South Road, Corfe Mullen
Wimborne, Dorset BH21 3HZ   Tel: 01202 445 503

		P	W	D	L	F	A	Pts
1.	Holt United	34	26	4	4	79	22	82
2.	Sherborne Town (Promoted)	34	22	5	7	100	43	71
3.	Dorchester Town Reserves	34	22	5	7	71	35	71
4.	Gillingham Town	34	18	10	6	71	37	64
5.	Hamworthy Utd Reserves (-3)	34	17	6	11	70	53	54
6.	Hamworthy Rec. (04-05 Champions)	34	15	7	12	60	49	52
7.	Dorchester United	34	15	6	13	72	56	51
8.	Westland Sports	34	14	9	11	61	55	51
9.	Poole Borough (-3)	34	16	5	13	75	62	50
10.	Bournemouth Sports	34	13	6	15	53	60	45
11.	Stourpaine	34	12	6	16	56	92	42
12.	Bridport Reserves	34	11	6	17	39	58	39
13.	Sturminster Newton (-3)	34	12	5	17	45	65	38
14.	Swanage Town (-3)	34	10	8	16	50	73	35
15.	Cobham Sports (-3)	34	9	7	18	58	74	31
16.	Blandford United	34	8	5	21	42	74	29
17.	Cranborne FC	34	5	7	22	28	71	22
18.	Wareham Rangers	34	3	9	22	39	90	18

		1	2	3	4	5	6	7	8	9	10	11	12	13	14	15	16	17	18
1	Blandford United		1-3	0-1	3-4	2-1	1-2	1-3	2-4	1-1	2-1	3-1	1-5	1-3	2-0	0-3	1-1	3-1	2-1
2	Bournemouth Sports	4-0		8-1	0-0	2-0	0-3	2-1	1-3	0-2	1-1	1-2	3-1	0-4	1-0	1-2	0-3	2-1	1-3
3	Bridport Reserves	2-0	1-1		0-2	2-0	0-2	0-1	2-0	2-4	0-3	2-2	3-0	0-2	1-2	1-2	2-0	1-1	2-1
4	Cobham Sports	1-2	5-0	3-0		0-3	1-3	6-5	1-1	1-3	1-3	0-4	3-1	1-3	2-3	1-2	6-2	1-1	1-1
5	Cranborne	3-1	2-1	1-1	3-0		0-1	1-6	0-1	0-1	0-0	1-4	0-1	0-4	2-4	0-2	2-1	2-2	0-0
6	Dorchester Town Reserves	2-1	1-0	2-1	1-1	2-0		4-0	3-1	3-0	2-1	0-2	1-1	1-6	6-2	0-1	0-1	3-0	5-0
7	Dorchester United	2-1	6-0	4-2	2-1	3-0	0-2		2-0	2-0	1-1	0-1	0-1	3-1	6-2	1-2	1-2	8-0	3-1
8	Gillingham Town	3-1	0-0	1-1	1-3	4-0	2-0	2-2		4-2	2-0	0-2	6-0	3-0	1-1	1-0	2-2	1-1	1-2
9	Hamworthy Recreation	1-0	1-1	3-0	3-1	2-2	0-2	2-2	0-3		0-3	3-1	1-2	4-2	0-0	3-4	5-1	4-1	0-1
10	Hamworthy United Reserves	4-3	2-1	2-0	2-0	4-1	0-4	5-1	2-3	4-1		0-4	4-5	1-4	3-2	3-0	2-1	2-1	0-0
11	Holt United	1-0	2-3	0-1	3-0	2-0	3-1	2-0	1-1	1-0	3-0		1-1	3-0	1-0	2-0	5-0	3-1	4-1
12	Poole Borough	6-0	1-4	2-3	2-1	3-0	1-1	3-1	3-3	2-1	0-4	0-2		2-3	0-2	4-1	2-2	5-0	3-0
13	Sherborne Town	3-0	1-2	2-1	4-0	6-0	3-3	1-1	2-2	0-2	1-1	1-2	4-2		10-0	4-0	4-1	3-2	3-0
14	Stourpaine	1-1	4-2	0-0	3-1	3-2	1-3	1-1	1-6	1-4	3-1	0-6	2-8	0-2		2-2	0-4	4-2	3-1
15	Sturminster Newton United	1-1	0-2	2-1	2-3	1-1	1-1	1-1	0-2	0-1	2-4	1-2	0-3	2-5	1-3		3-2	3-1	1-3
16	Swanage Town & Herston	3-1	0-5	2-3	2-2	2-0	0-2	1-0	0-2	1-1	1-1	0-3	0-3	2-5	3-2	0-1		4-2	4-4
17	Wareham Rangers	2-2	1-1	1-2	2-2	1-1	1-4	6-0	0-1	0-4	0-4	0-3	3-2	0-3	1-4	2-1	0-1		1-5
18	Westland Sports	0-2	5-0	2-0	4-3	0-4	3-1	1-3	0-4	1-1	3-2	1-1	2-0	1-1	6-0	4-1	1-1		1-1

LEAGUE CUP

FIRST ROUND

Dorchester United	v	Cobham Sports	2-1
Cranborne	v	Gillingham Town	2-3

SECOND ROUND

Bridport Reserves	v	Sturminster Newton United	1-0
Dorchester T. Res.	v	Blandford United	2-0
Dorchester United	v	Swanage Town & Herston	2-1
Hamworthy Rec.	v	Gillingham Town	1-0
Hamworthy U. Res.	v	Westland Sports	0-0, 2-1r
Poole Borough (H)	v	Holt United (tie awarded to Holt Utd)	
Stourpaine	v	Bournemouth Sports	1-2
Wareham Rangers	v	Sherborne Town	1-4

QUARTER-FINALS

Dorchester T. Res.	v	Bournemouth Sports	1-1, 4-2r
Dorchester United	v	Bridport Reserves	3-0
Sherborne Town	v	Holt United	0-2
Hamworthy Rec.	v	Hamworthy United Reserves	3-1

SEMI-FINALS

Hamworthy Rec.	v	Dorchester United	1-2
Holt United	v	Dorchester Town Reserves	2-1

THE FINAL

Dorchester United	v	Holt United	1-2

LEAGUE CONSTITUTION 2006-07

BLANDFORD UNITED
Chairman: M.Westwood
Secretary: Mrs Debbie Royal.
16 Medbourne Close, Blandford Forum DT11 7UA. Tel: 01258 456 752.
Email: theroyals@tesco.net.
Ground: Recreation Ground, Park Road, Blandford Forum, Dorset.
Colours: All royal blue.
Change colours: Green & Yellow/Green/Green.

BOURNEMOUTH SPORTS CLUB
Chairman: Steve Harvey.
Secretary: Mrs Kim Harvey.
80 Canford Cliffs Rd, Poole, Dorset BH13 7AB. Tel: 01202 734 380
Ground: Chapel Gate, East Parley, Christchurch, Dorset BH23 6BD
Tel: 01202 581933.
Colours: Gold & Black/black/gold. **Change colours:** All red.

BRIDPORT Reserves
Chairman: Adrian Scadding
Secretary: Keith Morgan.
95 Orchard Cres., Bridport DT6 5HA. Tel: 01308 425 115.
Ground: St Mary's Field, Skilling Hill Rd, Bridport. Tel: 01308 423 834.
Colours: Red/black/red. **Change colours:** Blue/blue/white.

COBHAM SPORTS (formerly Flight Refuelling)
Chairman: David Williams.
Secretary: David Williams.
48-50 Parkstone Rd, Poole, Dorset BH15 2PG. Tel: 07989 333 504.
Ground: Merley Park, Merley, Wimborne, Dorset Tel: 01202 885 7773.
Colours: All blue. **Change colours:** All white.

CRANBORNE
Chairman: Mrs Delia Haggarty.
Secretary: Mrs Teresa Cluett.
1 Firday's Heron, Cranborne, Wimborne BH21 5QJ. Tel: 01725 551 130.
Ground: Cranborne Recreation Ground, Penny's Lane, Cranborne.
Tel: 01725 517 440.
Colours: Black & white stripes/black or white/black.
Change colours: Yellow/black/yellow.

DORCHESTER TOWN Reserves
Chairman: Eddie Belt.
Secretary: David Martin
21 Diggory Crescent, Dorchester DT1 2SP. Tel: 01305 262 345 (H)
07971 172 795 (M).
Ground: The Avenue Stadium, Weymouth Ave. Tel: 01305 262 451.
Colours: Black & white stripes/black/black **Change colours**: All yellow.

DORCHESTER UNITED
Chairman: Mrs Nicky Hillier
Secretary: Mark Richards.
52 Meadow View, Charminster, Dorchester DT2 9RE. Tel: 01305 251 413.
Ground: Sandringham Sports Centre, Armada Way, Dorchester.
Colours: Sky & navy blue/navy/navy.
Change colours: Yellow & red/red/red.

GILLINGHAM TOWN
Chairman: John Radford.
Secretary: Roger Monksummers.
29 Cloverfields, Gillingham SP8 4UP. Tel: 01747 822 202.
Email: gillinghamtownfc@ntlworld.com.
Ground: Hardings Lane, Gillingham. Tel: 01747 823673.
Colours: Tangerine/black/black.
Change colours: Sky blue & navy/navy/sky blue.

HAMWORTHY RECREATION
Chairman: Robert Harris.
Secretary: Ray Willis.
52 Heckford Road, Poole BH15 2LY Tel: 01202 773 290. (H).
07712 913 067 (M). Email: raydot2@hotmail.com.
Ground: Hamworthy Club, Magna Rd, Canford Magna, Wimborne,
Dorset BH21 3AE Tel: 01202 881 922.
Colours: All green. **Change colours:** Lime green/navy/lime green.

HAMWORTHY UNITED RESERVES
Chairman: Bruce Scammell.
Secretary: Peter Gallop.
51a Symes Road, Hamworthy, Poole BH15 4PR. Tel: 01202 670 792.
Email: plrg54@hotmail.com.
Ground: The County Ground, Blandford Close. Tel: 01202 674 974.
Colours: Marron & sky blue/marron/maroon.
Change colours: Black & yellow/black/yellow.

HOLT UNITED
Chairman: Terry Bradford.
Secretary: Keith Habgood.
55 Middlehill Road, Colehill, Wimborne BH21 2SB. Tel: 07703 066987.
Ground: Petersham Lane, Gaunts Common, Holt. Tel: 01258 840 379.
Colours: Red/black/black. **Change colours:** All white.

POOLE BOROUGH
Chairman: Sid Murrell.
Secretary: Giles Kilshawe-Fall.
167 Longfleet Road, Poole BH15 2HS. Tel: 01202 669 304 (H).
07956 622 359 (M). Email: giles@kilshawe.freeserve.co.uk
Ground: Turlin Moor Recretaion Ground, Blandford Moor, Hamworthy, Poole.
Colours: Yellow & black/black/yellow.
Change colours: Red & grey/red/grey.

PORTLAND UNITED (resigned from Wessex League)
Chairman: Peter Turrell.
Secretary: Alan Atkinson.
73 Reforne, Portland, Dorset DT5 2AN. Tel: 01305 821 298.
Ground: New Grove Corner, Grove Road, Portland. Tel: 01305 861489
Colours: All Royal blue. Change colours: Red/black/black.

STOURPAINE
Chairman: Martin Oliver.
Secretary: Tim Lillywhite.
28 Hopegood Close, Charlton Marshall, Blandford Dorset DT11 9QA.
Tel: 01258 459 467.
Ground: Dick Draper Memorial Fields, Stourpaine, Blandford Forum.
Colours: Royal blue & yellow/royal blue/royal blue & yellow.
Change Colours: Orange/navy/orange.

STURMINSTER MARSHALL (prmoted from Dorset Senior)
Chairman: Merrick Smith.
Secretary: David Miller.
The Dell, 91 High Street, Sturminster Marshall, Dorset BH21 4AT.
Tel: 01258 857 314.
Ground: Churchill Close, Sturminster Marshall.
Colours: Green & black/black/black.
Change colours: Red & white/red/red.

STURMINSTER NEWTON UNITED
Chairman: S.Stockley.
Secretary: Richard Frear.
44 Green Close, Sturminster Newton DT10 1BL Tel: 01258 473 036.
Email: snufc@fsmail.net.
Ground: Barnetts Field, Honeymead Lane, Sturminster Newton,
Dorset. Tel: 01258 471 406.
Colours: Red/black/red. Change colours: White/blue/blue.

SWANAGE TOWN & HESTON
Chairman: Len Marsh.
Secretary: Anthony King.
2 Begbie Cottages, Worth Matravers, Swanage, Dorset BH19 3LQ
Tel: 01929 429 192.
Ground: Day's Park, De Moulham Road, Swanage. Tel: 01929 424673
Colours: White/black/white.
Change colours: Yellow/blue/yellow.

WESTLAND SPORTS
Chairman: Brian Rousell.
Secretary: Philip Wells.
24 Broadmeade, Yeovil, Somerset BA21 3RN.
07919 915 144 (M). Email: philswells@hotmail.com.
Ground: Alvington Lane, Yeovil.
Colours: All blue. C hange colours: All White.

EAST SUSSEX LEAGUE

SPONSORED BY: K & P MOTORING WORLD

Founded: 1896
President: J Cornford   **Chairman:** R Milton
Hon. Secretary: P Hammond
Baytrees, Maple Close, Bexhill-on-Sea TN39 4SU
Tel: 01424 843 006

PREMIER DIVISION	P	W	D	L	F	A	Pts
1. Hawkhurst United	22	18	2	2	84	24	56
2. Hollington United (-3)	22	15	3	4	80	29	45
3. St Leonards Social	22	13	2	7	70	39	41
4. Bodiam	22	12	3	7	49	50	39
5. A.F.C. Peasmarsh	22	11	3	8	45	43	36
6. Eastbourne W.M.C. (1st Div.1 04-05)	22	8	5	9	53	55	29
7. Peche Hill Select	22	9	1	12	44	48	28
8. Mountfield United	22	8	2	12	52	59	26
9. Rock A Nore	22	7	3	12	59	60	24
10. Ticehurst (2nd Div.1 04-05)	22	5	8	9	35	51	23
11. Punnetts Town	22	6	4	12	43	77	22
12. Rye & Iden United	22	1	2	19	19	99	5

PREMIER DIVISION	1	2	3	4	5	6	7	8	9	10	11	12
1 A.F.C. Peasmarsh		3-3	3-1	0-3		4-2	2-1	3-1	2-1	2-0	4-2	1-1
2 Bodiam	3-2		3-0	1-4	0-4	3-2	2-2	4-0	1-5	6-1	1-2	2-1
3 Eastbourne W.M.C.	2-4	6-2		1-1	0-3	1-2	2-3	2-3	3-0	2-2	4-3	1-1
4 Hawkhurst United	3-0	2-1	9-2		3-3	4-3	2-1	9-0	4-3	8-0	1-0	4-0
5 Hollington United	2-3	7-0	0-5	2-3		10-0	6-1	6-0	2-5	10-0	1-1	3-3
6 Mountfield United	1-2	1-2	3-0	0-1	1-2		4-1	1-1	4-1	9-1	5-2	1-1
7 Peche Hill Select	1-0	3-4	1-2	1-6	2-3	3-4		3-1	3-0	3-1	1-4	0-1
8 Punnetts Town	2-5	1-2	3-3	1-5		5-2	0-2		1-5	4-0	2-6	2-1
9 Rock A Nore	8-2	3-5	4-7	0-3	1-2	6-1	1-3	3-3		3-1	1-5	1-1
10 Rye & Iden United	2-3	0-0	1-4	2-1	1-5	1-2	0-4	1-7	2-7		0-3	1-2
11 St Leonards Social	3-1	1-2	4-4	2-0	0-2	4-3	2-1	9-1	5-1	6-1		4-0
12 Ticehurst	0-0	0-2	0-1	1-8	1-6	4-1	1-4	5-5	0-0	8-1	3-2	

CONSTITUTION 2006-07 - PREMIER DIVISION

BODIAM	**PECHE HILL SELECT**
EASTBOURNE W.M.C.	**RIDGE WEST GARAGE**
HAWKHURST UNITED	**ROCK A NORE**
HEATHFIELD HOTSPURS	**PEASMARSH & IDEN**
HOLLINGTON UNITED	**ST. LEONARDS SOCIAL**
MOUNTFIELD UNITED	**TICEHURST**

DIVISION ONE

		P	W	D	L	F	A	Pts
1	Hollington United	20	16	3	1	60	26	51
2	Heathfield Hotspurs	20	15	2	3	76	18	47
3	Ridge West Garage	20	14	4	2	69	20	46
4	Sedlescombe	20	13	4	3	49	24	43
5	J.C. Tackleway	20	11	0	9	40	33	33
6	Sandhurst	20	10	2	8	43	44	32
7	Hooe Sports	20	8	2	10	36	44	26
8	Ninfield United	20	6	3	11	36	45	21
9	Firehills Seniors	20	3	1	16	36	69	10
10	Wadhurst United	20	2	1	17	26	86	7
11	Rye & Iden United	20	1	0	19	13	75	3

DIVISION FOUR

		P	W	D	L	F	A	Pts
1	Hastings Rangers (-3)	22	18	1	3	108	49	52
2	Battle Baptists	22	12	7	3	64	32	43
3	Red Lion	22	11	5	6	71	54	38
4	Hawkhurst United	22	9	8	5	46	40	35
5	Victoria Baptists	22	9	5	8	48	57	32
6	Battle Rangers (-3)	22	8	6	8	56	63	27
7	St Helens	22	6	7	9	55	48	25
8	Bodiam	22	7	3	12	36	58	24
9	Punnetts Town	22	5	6	11	49	64	21
10	Northiam 75	22	6	3	13	35	65	21
11	Old Centmodians (-6)	22	7	3	12	41	53	18
12	Travaux (-4)	22	5	5	12	46	72	16

DIVISION TWO

		P	W	D	L	F	A	Pts
1	Icklesham Casuals	20	15	2	3	67	17	47
2	Bexhill A.A.C.	20	14	2	4	60	20	44
3	Northiam 75	20	13	2	5	41	34	41
4	Crowhurst	20	13	1	6	56	27	40
5	White Knight	20	11	1	7	59	42	34
6	Little Common	20	9	3	8	49	36	30
7	Old Hastonians	20	8	1	11	41	40	25
8	Hastings Rangers	20	8	0	12	46	49	24
9	Burfield Tyres	20	7	1	12	38	39	22
10	Mayfield	20	2	1	17	21	122	7
11	Cranbrook Town	20	2	0	18	25	77	6
12	Hillcrest	0	0	0	0	0	0	0

DIVISION FIVE

		P	W	D	L	F	A	Pts
1	Eastbourne Fishermen	20	18	1	1	64	18	55
2	Robertsbridge United	20	15	1	4	72	22	46
3	Benbow (-3)	20	16	1	3	69	19	46
4	Bexhill A.A.C.	20	10	2	8	50	44	32
5	Heathfield Hotspurs	20	9	1	10	42	44	28
6	Icklesham Casuals	20	7	5	8	42	57	26
7	Mountfield United	20	6	5	9	39	57	23
8	Sedlescombe	20	5	3	12	27	51	18
9	J.C. Tackleway	20	4	3	13	30	53	15
10	Sandhurst (-3)	20	4	4	12	16	54	13
11	Wadhurst United	20	2	2	16	23	55	8
12	Oceans	0	0	0	0	0	0	0

DIVISION THREE

		P	W	D	L	F	A	Pts
1	Athletico	20	14	2	4	62	28	44
2	J.C. Tackleway	20	11	6	3	62	36	39
3	Herstmonceux (-5)	20	11	5	4	51	34	33
4	Little Common	20	9	4	7	58	48	31
5	Burwash	20	9	4	7	41	35	31
6	Magham Down	20	8	4	8	54	42	28
7	Catsfield	20	8	3	9	38	41	27
8	Beulah Baptists	20	5	8	7	37	39	23
9	Wittersham	20	6	4	10	42	51	22
10	Pebsham Sibex	20	6	2	12	27	45	20
11	Westfield	20	2	0	18	23	96	6

DIVISION SIX

		P	W	D	L	F	A	Pts
1	Panako	20	13	6	1	69	37	45
2	Cinque Ports	20	12	5	3	64	42	41
3	Beulah Baptists	20	12	2	6	50	33	38
4	Orington	20	10	2	8	72	58	32
5	Herstmonceux (-3)	20	10	4	6	46	47	31
6	White Knight	20	8	2	10	53	57	26
7	Peche Hill Select	20	6	6	8	38	40	24
8	Hastings Rangers	20	6	4	10	48	54	22
9	Pelham (-9)	20	8	4	8	58	52	19
10	Hastings A.P.F. (-1)	20	3	3	14	36	69	11
11	Magham Down	20	3	0	17	24	69	9

ESSEX & SUFFOLK BORDER LEAGUE

SPONSORED BY: KENT BLAXHILL BUILDING PRODUCTS

President: Brian Tatum   **Deputy President:** John Compnay
General Secretary: Richard Degville
Bordersecretary@borderleague1.freeserve.co.uk

PREMIER DIVISION		P	W	D	L	F	A	Pts
1.	Gas Recreation (04-05 Champions)	30	19	7	4	74	43	64
2.	West Bergholt	30	19	4	7	79	45	61
3.	Bury Town Reserves	30	18	6	6	62	37	60
4.	Lawford Lads	30	18	3	9	60	43	57
5.	Weeley Athletic	30	16	4	10	54	35	52
6.	Mistley United	30	13	11	6	56	25	50
7.	Earls Colne (2nd Div.1 04-05)	30	12	8	10	64	59	44
8.	Hatfield Peverel (1st Div.1 04-05)	30	12	3	15	43	47	39
9.	Little Oakley	30	11	5	14	48	57	38
10.	Dedham Old Boys	30	11	5	14	35	46	38
11.	St Osyth	30	11	4	15	61	53	37
12.	Essex University	30	10	6	14	53	55	36
13.	Walton Town	30	10	6	14	48	54	36
14.	Coggeshall Town (3rd Div.1 04-05)	30	9	5	16	45	76	32
15.	Alresford Colne Rangers	30	8	6	16	41	60	30
16.	Kelvedon Social	30	1	1	28	25	113	4

DIVISION ONE	P	W	D	L	F	A	Pts
1 Witham Town Res.	28	23	3	2	92	24	72
2 Tiptree Heath (P)	28	21	1	6	78	37	64
3 Great Bentley (P)	28	18	5	5	88	40	59
4 Mersea Island	28	15	5	8	68	53	50
5 Gas Recreation Res.	28	14	3	11	49	54	45
6 Gosfield United	28	12	7	9	80	47	43
7 Bures United	28	11	7	10	61	64	40
8 Coggeshall Town Res.	28	10	9	9	53	48	39
9 West Bergholt Res.	28	11	6	11	55	70	39
10 Boxted Lodgers	28	10	7	11	41	56	37
11 Bradfield Rovers	28	9	7	12	50	55	34
12 Dedham Old Boys Res.	28	8	5	15	42	64	29
13 Weeley Athletic Res.	28	5	5	18	30	65	20
14 Alresford Reserves	28	3	4	21	26	83	13
15 Glemsford & Cavendish U.	28	2	2	24	28	81	8

DIVISION TWO	P	W	D	L	F	A	Pts
1 Brightlingsea Regent	30	25	2	3	101	35	77
2 West Suffolk College	30	22	3	5	83	30	69
3 Mistley United Res.	30	19	3	8	68	50	60
4 Earls Colne Reserves	30	18	4	8	60	36	58
5 Foxash Social	30	16	5	9	58	44	53
6 Little Oakley Reserves	30	14	6	10	60	38	48
7 Sudbury Athletic	30	14	4	12	53	44	46
8 Great Bentley Res.	30	14	4	12	41	41	46
9 Hedinghams United	30	12	5	13	70	72	41
10 Lawford Lads Res.	30	10	3	17	50	55	33
11 Boxted Lodgers Res.	30	9	4	17	53	85	31
12 Kelvedon Social Res.	30	9	2	19	49	96	29
13 St Osyth Reserves	30	8	4	18	59	54	28
14 Bures United Reserves	30	7	4	19	41	73	25
15 Hatfield Peverel Res.	30	7	3	20	37	76	24
16 Mersea Island Res.	30	6	4	20	35	89	22

LEAGUE CUP

FIRST ROUND

Gas Recreation	v	West Suffolk College	3-2
Alresford Colne R.	v	Little Oakley	2-2*, 3-4p
Walton Town	Bye		
West Bergholt (H)	v	Bradfield Rovers	3-0
Coggeshall Town	v	Earls Colne	2-3
Gosfield United	v	St Johns	2-0
Hatfield Peverel	v	Dedham Old Boys	0-3
Hedinghams Utd	v	Tiptree Heath	1-1*, 1-2p
Brightlingsea Reg.	v	Glmsford & Cavendish	3-4*
Mistley United	v	Great Bentley	4-2*
Essex University	v	Witham Town Reserves	1-3
Foxash Social	v	Mersea Island	1-5
Lawford Lads	v	Bury Town Reserves	1-0
Weeley Athletic	v	St Osyth	2-3
Boxted Lodgers	v	Bures United	0-1
Sudbury Athletic	v	Kelvedon Social	3-1

SECOND ROUND

Gas Recreation	v	Little Oakley	4-2
Walton Town	v	West Bergholt (H)	5-4
Earls Colne	v	Gosfield United	2-2* 3-1p
Dedham Old Boys	v	Tiptree Heath	3-1
Glemsford & Cav.	v	Mistley United	0-4
Witham Town Res.	v	Mersea Island	2-2*, 5-4p
Lawford Lads	v	St Osyth	4-0
Bures United	v	Sudbury Athletic	1-2

THIRD ROUND

Gas Recreation	v	Walton town	3-0
Earls Colne	v	Dedham Old Boys	0-0*, 5-4p
Mistley United	v	Witham Town Reserves	2-3
Lawford Lads	v	Sudbury Athletic	7-0

SEMI-FINALS

Gas Recreation	v	Earls Colne	4-0
Witham Town Res.	v	Lawford Lads	0-1

THE FINAL

Gas Recreation	v	Lawford Lads	3-2

LEAGUE CONSTITUTION 2006-07 - PREMIER DIVISION

ALRESFORD COLNE RANGERS	**LAWFORD LADS**
COGGESHALL TOWN	**LITTLE OAKLEY**
DEDHAM OLD BOYS	**MISTLEY UNITED**
EARLS COLNE	**ST. OSYTH**
ESSEX UNIVERSITY	**TIPTREE HEATH**
GAS RECREATION	**WALTON TOWN**
GREAT BENTLEYHATFIELD	**WEELEY ATHLETIC**
PEVEREL	**WEST BERGHOLT**

ESSEX OLYMPIAN LEAGUE
(Formerly The Essex Intermediate League)

SPONSORED BY: BALISTON SPORTS & LEISURE WEAR

President: Eddie Rhymes   **Chairman:** Brian Stubbings
Secretary: Peter Godfrey
petergodfrey@nospameofl.co.uk

SENIOR DIVISION ONE		P	W	D	L	F	A	Pts
1.	Harold Wood Athletic	22	17	4	1	41	14	55
2.	Frenford Senior	22	13	6	3	42	24	45
3.	White Notley (1st Div.2 04-05)	22	14	2	6	49	27	44
4.	White Ensign (04-05 Champions)	22	12	3	7	48	29	39
5.	Bishops Stortford Swifts	22	10	4	8	34	23	34
6.	Kelvedon Hatch	22	9	4	9	26	29	31
7.	Manford Way	22	9	3	10	37	26	30
8.	Roydon (2nd Div.2 04-05)	22	7	3	12	21	39	24
9.	Takeley	22	5	6	11	26	43	21
10.	Epping	22	4	8	10	22	36	20
11.	Old Chelmsfordians	22	4	5	13	24	41	17
12.	Debden Sports	22	3	2	17	13	52	11

SENIOR DIVISION ONE		1	2	3	4	5	6	7	8	9	10	11	12
1	Bishops Stortford Swifts		0-1	1-0	1-3	1-1	2-1	1-1	4-0	2-0	2-1	2-1	2-3
2	Debden Sports	0-2		1-1	1-2	0-3	0-3	0-0	1-2	1-4	2-0	2-8	0-3
3	Epping	1-1	1-2		0-2	0-0	0-1	2-0	3-3	1-3	1-2	0-0	2-1
4	Frenford Senior	0-4	3-0	3-0		1-1	2-1	2-0	5-4	5-1	3-1	1-2	2-2
5	Harold Wood Athletic	1-0	2-1	2-0	1-1		1-0	2-0	2-1	4-0	2-1	3-2	3-2
6	Kelvedon Hatch	2-2	1-0	2-2	0-1	1-0		0-4	1-1	3-1	1-2	0-3	2-3
7	Manford Way	2-1	3-0	6-1	0-1	0-1	0-1		4-1	4-0	3-2	0-1	2-3
8	Old Chelmsfordians	1-0	3-0	1-1	1-1	0-1	0-1	1-3		2-0	1-3	1-4	0-4
9	Roydon	1-0	2-0	0-3	1-1	0-2	0-1	1-1	1-0		2-2	2-1	1-0
10	Takeley	0-4	2-0	1-1	2-2	1-4	1-1	0-3	0-0	1-0		1-1	0-3
11	White Ensign	1-2	4-1	3-0	1-0	2-4	1-3	3-0	HW	2-0	4-1		1-3
12	White Notley	2-0	3-0	1-2	0-1	0-1	3-0	2-1	2-1	3-1	3-2	3-3	

DIVISION TWO		P	W	D	L	F	A	Pts
1	Canning Town (+2)	28	20	4	4	71	29	66
2	Mountnessing	28	19	2	7	70	33	59
3	Galleywood	28	17	5	6	54	31	56
4	Faces (-1)	28	16	7	5	59	37	53
5	Springfield (+2)	28	10	9	9	40	36	41
6	Ryan	28	11	8	9	57	55	41
7	Stambridge United	28	11	7	10	34	39	40
8	Rayleigh Town	28	11	6	11	51	49	39
9	Shell Club (Corringham)	28	10	8	10	47	51	38
10	Sandon Royals	28	9	8	11	31	29	35
11	Benfleet	28	9	4	15	47	56	31
12	Shenfield A.F.C.	28	8	7	13	37	49	31
13	Herongate Athletic	28	6	8	14	21	42	26
14	Broomfield	28	4	4	20	26	53	16
15	Linford Wanderers	28	2	7	19	31	87	13

DIVISION THREE		P	W	D	L	F	A	Pts
1	Ongar Town	26	20	5	1	83	36	65
2	Upminster	26	17	3	6	60	40	54
3	Leigh Ramblers	26	12	7	7	44	38	43
4	Leytonstone United	26	10	10	6	49	37	40
5	Metpol Chigwell	26	11	7	8	51	44	40
6	Hannakins Farm	26	10	8	8	63	54	38
7	Hutton	26	9	7	10	44	50	34
8	Basildon Town	26	9	6	11	48	55	33
9	Writtle	26	7	8	11	42	45	29
10	Westhamians	26	7	7	12	42	58	28
11	Great Baddow	26	6	8	12	32	33	26
12	Ramsden	26	6	6	14	51	65	24
13	Barnston A.F.C.	26	6	5	15	40	81	23
14	Runwell Hospital	26	5	7	14	42	55	22

FIRST ROUND

Debden Sports	v	Barnston	1-2
Ongar Town	v	Manford Way	0-3
Herongate Athletic	v	Writtle	3-3*, 3-4p
Old Chelmsfordians	v	Galleywood	0-3
Roydon	v	Epping	2-1
Hutton	v	Basildon Town	5-2
Metpol Chigwell	v	Upminster	2-1
Canning Town	v	Great Baddow	2-0
Bishops Stortford S	v	White Ensign	2-4
Ryan	v	Leigh Ramblers	1-3

SECOND ROUND

Leigh Ramblers	v	White Notley	0-3
Manford Way	v	Ramsden	6-1
Barnston AFC	v	Runwell Hospital	2-4
Sandon Royals	v	Mountnessing	1-0
Leytonstone Utd	v	Hutton	1-1*, 2-4p
White Ensign	v	Linford Wanderers	5-0
Shenfield AFC (H)	v	Harold Wood Athletic	0-1
Takeley	v	Metpol Chigwell	4-1
Rayleigh Town	v	Galleywood	0-1
Benfleet	v	Writtle	4-0
Kelvedon Hatch	v	Hannakins Farm	5-0

Broomfield	v	Faces	0-1
Roydon	v	Canning Town	1-2
Springfield	v	Sheel Club (Corringham)	2-4
Frenford Senior	v	Westhamians	7-2

THIRD ROUND

Hutton	v	White Notely	1-3
Harold Wood Ath.	v	Kelvedon Hatch	2-1
Faces	v	Runwell Hospital	10-0
Takeley	v	Sandon Royals	4-1
Frenford Senior	v	Manford Way	1-0
Galleywood	v	Shell Club (Corringham)	3-2
Canning Town	v	Stambridge United	1-0
White Ensign	v	Benfleet	2-1

QUARTER-FINALS

Galleywood	v	Canning Town	0-1
Takeley	v	White Ensign	1-3
Harold Wood Ath.	v	Frenford Senior	3-1
White Notley	v	Faces	4-0

SEMI-FINALS

Harold Wood Ath.	v	White Notley	1-0
White Ensign	v	Canning Town	2-1

THE FINAL (16th May)

White Ensign	v	Harold Wood Athletic	0-2

LEAGUE CONSTITUTION 2006-07 - SENIOR DIVISION

BISHOP'S STORTFORD SWIFTS (Joined League 1966 - FOUNDER MEMBER)
Ground: Silver Leys, Hadham Road (A1250), Bishop's Stortford, Herts.
Tel: 01279 658941

CANNING TOWN (2000)
Ground: Goosley Playing Field, St. Albans Avenue, East Ham E6.

EPPING (1976 as Coopersale, Changed Name to Eppingsale 1992 and Epping in 1999)
Ground: Stonards Hill Rec Ground, Tidy's Lane, Epping, Essex.

FRENFORD SENIOR (1995)
Ground: Oakfields Sports Ground, Forest Road, Barkingside, Essex.

GALLEYWOOD (1990)
Ground: Clarkes Field, Slades Lane, Galleywood, Chelmsford.

HAROLD WOOD ATHLETIC (1977)
Ground: Harold Wood Recreation Park, Harold View, Harold Wood, Essex.
Tel: 01708 348827

KELVEDON HATCH (1985)
Ground: New Hall, School Road, Kelvedon Hatch, Brentwood, Essex.
Tel: 01277 372153

MANFORD WAY (1999)
Ground: London Marathon Sports Ground, Forest Road, Hainault, Essex.
Tel: 020 8500 3486

MOUNTNESSING (1984)
Ground: Henderson Sports & Social Club, Kenilworth Road, Harold Park, Romford.

ROYDON (2001)
Ground: Roydon Playing Fields, Harlow Road, Roydon, Essex.

TAKELEY (1978)
Ground: Station Road, Takeley, near Bishop's Stortford, Hertfordshire.
Tel: 01279 870404

WHITE ENSIGN (2002)
Ground: Borough Football Combination Headquarters, Eastwoodbury Lane, Southend-on-Sea, Essex.

WHITE NOTLEY (1988)
Ground: Oak Farm, Faulkbourne, Witham.

GLOUCESTERSHIRE COUNTY LEAGUE

Chairman: Robert Stewart
Hon. Secretary: Ron Holpin
27, Brockley Close, Little Stoke, Bristol BS34 6HA

		P	W	D	L	F	A	Pts
1.	Lydney Town	32	23	7	2	87	28	76
2.	Highridge United (Champions 04-05)	32	20	6	6	73	31	66
3.	Yate Town Res	32	17	8	7	61	36	59
4.	Totterdown P.O.B.	32	16	8	8	70	46	56
5.	Patchway Town	32	17	5	10	55	39	56
6.	Ellwood	32	15	9	7	60	35	54
7.	Taverners	32	15	6	11	56	46	51
8.	Henbury Old Boys (-7pts)	32	17	6	9	56	45	50
9.	Roman Glass St George	32	15	4	13	49	47	49
10.	Thornbury Town	32	13	5	14	56	56	44
11.	Hardwicke	32	12	6	14	60	61	42
12.	Axa F.C.	32	10	8	14	56	59	38
13.	Kings Stanley	32	10	7	15	56	62	37
14.	D.R.G. Stapleton	32	7	6	19	44	79	27
15.	Sea Mills Park	32	6	4	22	36	92	22
16.	Wotton Rovers	32	4	4	24	31	103	16
17.	Pucklechurch Sports	32	3	5	24	31	72	14

		1	2	3	4	5	6	7	8	9	10	11	12	13	14	15	16	17
1	AXA		4-2	1-1	4-4	1-4	0-2	3-1	1-2	2-4	4-1	1-2	3-1	2-4	3-2	1-1	6-1	1-1
2	DRG Stapleton	2-2		3-2	1-0	2-3	1-2	1-0	2-3	2-2	3-2	1-2	1-2	1-2	0-1	3-3	4-2	1-2
3	Ellwood	3-2	3-1		1-0	3-0	0-0	1-1	1-1	0-0	4-0	6-1	3-2	1-1	2-5	1-2	8-0	0-1
4	Hardwicke	2-4	2-2	1-2		0-1	2-2	1-2	2-1	0-3	1-1	3-0	2-1	2-4	1-2	3-1	3-1	1-0
5	Henbury Old Boys	2-1	2-0	1-2	0-5		0-4	1-1	1-1	1-1	5-3	2-0	3-1	1-1	3-1	2-0	1-2	1-2
6	Highridge United	2-1	5-0	0-0	3-2	1-0		0-2	1-1	0-1	1-0	1-2	6-2	0-1	2-1	2-1	4-0	2-0
7	Kings Stanley	0-2	2-0	2-2	2-5	0-1	2-3		1-4	1-4	0-0	0-4	3-0	1-1	1-5	0-1	7-1	3-0
8	Lydney Town	3-0	3-0	4-2	6-0	1-1	4-2	2-0		3-1	2-1	1-1	5-0	1-0	1-2	4-0	5-1	2-0
9	Patchway Town	0-1	2-0	2-0	3-1	1-2	0-3	0-2	1-4		1-0	0-2	5-0	1-0	0-0	1-1	2-0	2-1
10	Pucklechurch Sports	0-2	1-1	0-2	1-3	3-4	0-4	4-3	0-1	0-1		1-1	3-0	2-3	1-2	0-4	2-2	0-3
11	Roman Glass St George	2-0	4-2	0-0	0-3	0-2	1-2	4-2	1-3	0-3	1-0		2-0	3-1	3-0	1-1	4-0	0-2
12	Sea Mills Park	1-1	5-0	2-1	2-2	0-5	0-5	2-6	1-6	1-2	2-0	2-1		1-2	0-3	1-5	0-2	2-6
13	Taverners	2-0	7-3	2-0	4-1	1-1	1-5	4-1	1-1	3-1	3-2	2-1	1-2		1-2	0-2	0-1	1-1
14	Thornbury Town	0-0	1-3	0-2	2-3	1-2	2-1	1-3	1-3	2-1	3-1	1-2	2-2	1-0		1-2	6-2	2-2
15	Totterdown POB	2-0	7-0	0-3	2-2	3-1	3-3	2-2	1-3	1-2	2-1	2-1	2-0	4-0	5-1		3-1	2-2
16	Wotton Rovers	3-1	1-1	0-3	1-2	1-2	0-4	2-4	0-4	1-5	0-1	1-3	0-0	0-3	2-2	2-5		0-3
17	Yate Town Reserves	2-2	0-1	0-1	2-1	2-1	1-1	1-1	2-2	5-3	4-0	2-0	4-1	1-0	2-1	2-0	5-1	

Lydney Town League Champions 2005-06
BackRow (L-R): S.Liddington (Manager), A.Lee (Physio), R.Scott, R.Thomas, D.Bishop, D.Clarke, N.Hook, P.Macklin, M.Timmins, A.Neale, K.Averis, P.Elliott(Asst.Manager), S.Bennetto (Groundsman), Liddington(Chairman).
Front Row: M.Crabbe, R. Elliott, M.Saunders, J.Macklin(Capt.), M.Reddan, J.Kear, S.Warren, R. Sansom (Secretary).

Highridge United Les James League Cup winners 2005-06
Back Row (L-R): Steve Phillips,Tom Windows, Craig Liddell, Tyrone McNeeley ,Nicky Snow , Mike Jenkins ,Andy White ,Grant Farrell, Lee Rendle. **Middle row:** Goal keeper Richard Jenkins.
Front row: Tom Clark , Jon Berry , Steve Miles (manager) , Mike Berry ,Steve Dowling.

L E S   J A M E S   L E A G U E   C U P

PRELIMINARY ROUND

Highridge United	v	Taverners	1-0

FIRST ROUND

Roman Glass St. G.	v	Hardwicke	0-1
Patchway Town (H)	v	Lydney Town	0-1
Puckleworth Sports	v	Totterdown P.O.B.	0-2
Highridge United	v	Sea Mills Park	7-1
Henbury Old Boys	v	Kings Stanley	3-1
Wotton Rovers	v	Thornbury Town	1-2
Yate Town Res.	v	Ellwood	0-1
AXA	v	D.R.G. Stapleton	2-0

QUARTER FINALS

Highridge United	v	Totterdown P.O.B.	5-1
Hardwicke	v	Henbury Old Boys	1-2
Lydney Town	v	Ellwood	4-0
AXA	v	Thornbury Town	2-1

SEMI-FINALS

AXA	v	Highridge United	1-3
Lydney Town	v	Henbury Old Boys	1-1*, 4-3p

THE FINAL

Highridge United	v	Lydney Town	1-0

LEAGUE CONSTITUTION 2006-07

AXA
Axa Sports Ground, Station Road, Henbury, Bristol.
Tel: 0117 950 2303

BERKLEY TOWN
Station Road, Berkeley, Gloucester.

D.R.G. STAPLETON 237
Frenchay Park Road, Frenchay, Bristol, Gloucestershire.
Tel: 0177 956 0390.

ELLWOOD
Bromley Road, Ellwood, Coleford, Gloucestershire
Tel: 01594 832927

HANHAM ATHLETIC
The Playing Fields Pavillion, 16 Vicarage Road, Hanham, Bristol.
Tel: 07976 540387

HARDWICKE
Hardqicke Playing Fields, Green Lane, Hardwicke, Gloucestershire.
Tel: 01452 720587

HENBURY
Arnall Drive Playing Fields, Lorain Walk, Henbury, Bristol, Gloucestershire.
Tel: 0117 959 0475

HIGHRIDGE UNITED
Lakemead Grove, Highridge, Bristol, Gloucestershire.
Tel: 0117 978 4878

KINGS STANLEY
Marling Close, Broad Street, Kings Stanley, Gloucestershire.
Tel: 01453 828975

PATCHWAY TOWN
Scott Park, Coniston Road, Patchway, Bristol, Gloucestershire.
Tel: 0117 949 3952

PUCKLECHURCH SPORTS
Pucklechurch Recreation Ground, Abson Road, Pucklechurch, Bristol, Gloucestershire.
Tel: 0117 937 2102

ROMAN GLASS ST GEORGE
Bell Hill, Whiteway Road, St George, Bristol, Gloucestershire.
Tel: 0117 983 7707

SEA MILLS PARK
Kings Weston Sports Ground, Napier Miles Road, Kingsweston, Bristol.
Tel: 0117 982 8307

TAVERNERS
Nailsworth Primary School, Forest Green, Nailsworth, Gloucester.
Tel: 01453 834 860

THORNBURY TOWN
Mundy Playing Fields, Kington Lane, Thornbury, Bristol.
Tel: 01454 413 645

TOTTERDOWN PORT OF BRISTOL
City & Port of Bristol Sports Ground, Nibley Road, Shirehampton, Bristol.
Tel: 0117 982 3927

WOTTON ROVERS
Synwell Stadium, Synwell Lane, Wotton-under-Edge, Gloucestershire.
Tel: 01453 842 929

YATE TOWN RESERVES
Lodge Road, Yate, Bristol, Gloucestershire.
Tel: 01454 228 103

HERTS SENIOR COUNTY LEAGUE

Chairman: Cecil T Husdon
General Secretary: Brian Smith
1 Malthouse Place, Newlands Avenue, Radlett Herts WD7 8EX
Tel: 01923 856 183   Email: Brian.Smith@SOPHCO.com

PREMIER DIVISION		P	W	D	L	F	A	Pts
1.	Whitewebbs	30	23	3	4	76	22	72
2.	Hatfield Town	30	20	3	7	86	44	63
3.	Hadley (Champions 04-05)	30	14	10	6	57	34	52
4.	Buntingford Town (1st Div.1 04-05)	30	15	6	9	51	43	51
5.	Bedmond Sports & Social (+3)	30	12	6	12	54	49	45
6.	Metropolitan Police Bushey	30	13	5	12	68	62	44
7.	Codicote	30	13	5	12	58	52	44
8.	Hinton	30	11	9	10	57	58	42
9.	Sandridge Rovers (-3)	30	12	7	11	49	44	40
10.	Bushey Rangers	30	12	4	14	46	48	40
11.	London Lions	30	10	7	13	48	52	37
12.	Little Munden (2nd Div.1 04-05) (+3)	30	8	10	12	51	71	37
13.	Wormley Rovers	30	8	8	14	46	62	32
14.	Elliott Star	30	9	4	17	55	72	31
15.	Chipperfield Corinthians	30	6	6	18	43	75	24
16.	Evergreen (-3)	30	6	3	21	44	101	18

PREMIER DIVISION		1	2	3	4	5	6	7	8	9	10	11	12	13	14	15	16
1	Bedmond Sports & Social		2-1	3-1	2-0	HW	4-2	1-2	0-4	1-0	2-2	1-2	0-0	1-2	2-0	0-3	1-1
2	Buntingford Town	4-2		HW	1-2	1-1	1-1	2-0	2-2	0-3	3-2	4-2	5-1	4-2	1-1	1-0	1-2
3	Bushey Rangers	1-0	0-0		2-1	3-0	1-0	2-0	0-3	4-1	0-1	3-2	0-3	1-4	2-2	1-2	1-0
4	Chipperfield Corinthians	2-1	2-3	1-4		1-1	4-2	4-2	2-1	0-3	0-2	3-3	1-1	0-2	1-2	0-2	1-2
5	Codicote	4-2	6-0	1-3	2-1		2-4	3-1	3-3	2-3	5-3	4-2	0-3	2-1	0-1	2-0	2-2
6	Elliott Star	0-3	1-4	0-6	4-0	1-2		4-3	3-1	2-2	2-3	2-3	0-2	0-4	4-1	0-1	2-1
7	Evergreen	0-5	0-2	2-1	2-2	0-1	1-4		1-6	0-4	0-1	4-4	3-2	2-3	2-1	0-4	8-4
8	Hadley	2-2	1-0	2-0	4-0	1-5	3-2	4-1		1-2	1-1	4-1	0-0	1-2	0-0	1-1	0-0
9	Hatfield Town	1-3	1-0	6-0	7-1	1-2	3-1	8-1	0-1		4-3	4-1	3-2	2-1	3-2	3-2	1-1
10	Hinton	0-3	1-1	2-2	3-3	2-0	3-0	2-2	3-1	1-3		5-0	1-0	3-1	0-2	1-3	0-4
11	Little Munden	3-3	0-2	2-1	3-3	1-0	3-1	2-1	1-1	0-4	1-1		1-0	1-1	0-5	1-3	2-2
12	London Lions	3-2	1-2	0-2	2-0	2-2	2-6	8-0	0-2	1-8	7-2	2-2		1-1	0-0	0-3	2-0
13	Metropolitan Police Bushey	5-3	4-1	3-2	4-3	0-3	2-3	4-2	2-4	2-3	3-3	3-3	3-0		0-2	2-3	1-1
14	Sandridge Rovers	0-2	1-2	2-1	5-3	2-0	2-2	3-1	0-1	1-1	1-1	2-1	0-1	3-4		0-3	4-1
15	Whitewebbs	2-1	0-2	2-2	2-0	3-0	3-0	9-1	0-0	5-0	3-1	2-1	3-1	3-1	2-0		4-0
16	Wormley Rovers	2-2	2-1	3-0	1-2	5-3	2-2	1-2	0-2	3-2	1-4	0-3	0-1	2-1	3-4	0-3	

DIVISION ONE		P	W	D	L	F	A	Pts
1	Standon & Puckeridge	26	19	4	3	85	44	61
2	Hertford Heath (-3)	26	18	4	4	75	39	55
3	Knebworth	26	15	5	6	73	42	50
4	Bovingdon	26	16	1	9	85	46	49
5	Lemsford (-3)	26	12	5	9	61	55	38
6	St Peters	26	10	7	9	41	45	37
7	Sarratt	26	11	3	12	58	52	36
8	Buckhurst Hill	26	10	6	10	54	54	36
9	Loughton	26	9	6	11	49	54	33
10	Cuffley (+6)	26	6	3	17	31	67	27
11	Allenburys Sports	26	8	2	16	45	68	26
12	Old Parmiterians	26	7	4	15	39	64	25
13	Croxley Guild	26	7	2	17	39	75	23
14	North Mymms	26	6	4	16	32	62	22

A U B R E Y   C U P

FIRST ROUND

Stanton & Puck.	v	Knebworth	3-0
North Mymms	v	Hadley	1-4
Hertford Heath	v	St Peters	AW
Buckhust Hill	v	Sandridge Rovers	0-4
Codicote	v	Cuffley	5-1
Wormley Rovers	v	Hatfield Town	0-5
Elliott Star	v	Bushey Rangers	1-0
Sarratt	v	Old Parmiterians	3-2
Lemsford	v	Loughton	4-0
Buntingford Town	v	Met. Police Bushey	7-1
Allenburys Sports	v	London Lions	4-2
Little Menden	v	Hinton	0-3
Croxley Guild	v	Bovingdon	3-2
Evergreen	v	Chipperfield Corinthians	3-2

SECOND ROUND

Lemsford	v	Hatfield Town	3-4
Elliott Star	v	Hadley	0-4
Evergreen	v	Sarratt	0-1
Codicote	v	Croxley Guild	6-1

Standon & Puck.	v	Bedmond Sports & Social (H)	2-4
Hinton	v	Allenburys Sports	2-3
Buntingford Town	v	St Peters	3-0
Whitewebbs	v	Sandridge Rovers	2-0

QUARTER FINALS

Hadley	v	Allenburys Sports	1-0
Codicote	v	Sarratt	3-0
Hatfield Town	v	Buntingford Town	2-2, AW on pens
Bedmond S & S (H)	v	Whitewebbs	1-0

SEMI-FINALS

Buntingford Town	v	Codicote	2-1
Bedmond S & S (H)	v	Haldey	0-1

THE FINAL (1st May)

Hadley	v	Buntingford Town	1-0

LEAGUE CONSTITUTION 2006-07

BEDMOND SPORTS & SOCIAL
Ground: Toms Lane Recreation Ground, Toms Lane, Bedmond, Hertfordshire
Tel: 01923 267 991

BUNTINGFORD TOWN
Ground: Sainsbury Distribution Depot, London Road, Buntingford.

BUSHEY RANGERS
Ground: Moatfield, Bournehall Lane, Bushey, Hertfordshire
Tel: 020 8386 1875

CODICOTE
Ground: John Clements Memorial Ground, Bury Lane, Codicote, Hertfordshire
Tel: 01438 821 072

ELLIOTT STAR
Ground: Pursley Football Ground, London Road, Shenley, Hertfordshire

HADLEY
Ground: Hadley Sports Ground, Brickfield Lane, Arkley, Barnet, Hertfordshire
Tel: 020 8449 1144

HATFIELD TOWN
Ground: Birchwood Leisure Centre, Longmead, Birchwood, Hatfield, Hertfordshire
Tel: 01707 270 772

HERTFORD HEATH

HINTON
Ground: Holtwhites Sports & Social, Kirkland Drive, Enfield, Middlesex
Tel: 020 8363 4449

KNEBWORTH

LONDON LIONS
Ground: Laing Sports, Rowley Lane, Barnet, Hertfordshire
Tel: 020 8441 6051

METROPOLITAN POLICE BUSHEY
Ground: Met. Police Sports Club, Aldenham Road, Bushey, Watford
Tel: 01923 243947

SANDRIDGE ROVERS
Ground: Spencer Recreation Ground, Sandridge, St Albans, Hertfordshire
Tel: 01727 835 506

STANDON & PUCKERIDGE

WHITEWEBBS
Ground: The Whitewebbs Centre, Whitewebbs Lane, Enfield, Middlesex
Tel: 01992 760 716

WORMLEY ROVERS
Ground: Wormley Sports Club, Church Lane, Wormley, Hertfordshire
Tel: 01992 460 650

KENT COUNTY LEAGUE

SPONSORED BY: **BRITISH ENERGY**

Founded: 1922

President: E Diplock   Chairman: C T C Windiate

Secretary: G Jenkins

Kings View, Shottenden Lane, Molash, Canterbury, Kent CT4 8EZ

Tel: 01233 740143   Email: geoff@kcfl2000.freeserve.co.uk

PREMIER DIVISION		P	W	D	L	F	A	Pts
1.	Lewisham Borough	28	18	4	6	57	30	58
2.	Faversham Town (-1) (Promoted)	28	17	4	7	47	32	54
3.	Sheerness East	28	16	3	9	56	44	51
4.	Bromley Green	28	14	4	10	67	54	46
5.	Stansfeld O & B Club	28	12	10	6	43	33	46
6.	Milton Athletic	28	14	3	11	60	48	45
7.	Cray Valley (PM) (Champions 04-05)	28	11	9	8	54	36	42
8.	Norton Sports (1st Div.1 East 04-05)	28	12	5	11	43	43	41
9.	Snodland	28	10	4	14	37	50	34
10.	Rusthall (1st Div.1 West 04-05)	28	9	6	13	45	46	33
11.	Bearsted	28	9	5	14	34	48	32
12.	Fleet Leisure	28	7	7	14	47	57	28
13.	Old Roan	28	7	7	14	41	53	28
14.	Crockenhill	28	6	8	14	31	64	26
15.	Lydd Town	28	6	5	17	18	42	23

PREMIER DIVISION		1	2	3	4	5	6	7	8	9	10	11	12	13	14	15
1	Bearsted		1-3	3-1	1-2	3-2	2-5	4-1	1-0	1-0	0-1	1-4	1-2	0-3	4-1	0-0
2	Bromley Green	1-1		2-3	3-3	0-1	3-0	1-4	1-1	4-3	4-1	1-6	1-1	3-2	5-2	6-0
3	Cray Valley (PM)	5-0	3-0		5-0	3-4	1-2	0-1	2-0	0-0	3-1	2-4	2-1	2-2	1-0	2-2
4	Crockenhill	0-0	1-7	2-1		2-1	2-2	3-4	0-1	0-4	1-0	3-3	1-1	1-4	0-1	1-0
5	Faversham Town	1-0	2-1	2-2	0-0		0-0	0-2	3-1	2-3	4-2	3-0	1-0	2-0	2-1	1-1
6	Fleet Leisure	0-2	3-4	3-3	4-0	0-2		0-3	0-1	2-4	0-2	1-1	3-4	1-2	1-1	0-1
7	Lewisham Borough (Community)	2-1	4-1	1-0	3-0	1-2	1-1		3-0	1-0	1-2	1-0	2-1	1-2	3-0	4-2
8	Lydd Town	0-1	0-1	0-3	1-1	0-1	0-3	2-0		1-2	0-0	1-0	1-3	1-2	1-2	1-3
9	Milton Athletic	3-1	2-1	1-4	4-2	3-2	6-3	2-2	3-0		3-0	1-1	5-2	1-0	0-1	0-2
10	Norton Sports	2-2	2-1	0-0	1-2	1-2	4-2	1-5	0-1	2-1		2-1	1-0	5-1	2-1	2-2
11	Old Roan	1-1	2-4	2-2	0-0	2-0	0-2	0-2	2-1	0-4	1-4		1-1	3-2	3-4	1-4
12	Rusthall	1-3	0-2	1-0	5-1	1-3	1-2	0-2	1-2	3-0	1-1	3-0		5-3	2-0	1-1
13	Sheerness East	2-0	1-3	2-2	4-2	1-2	3-3	2-0	3-0	3-2	1-0	1-0	4-2		3-1	1-0
14	Snodland	1-0	4-1	0-2	2-1	1-2	2-3	2-2	0-0	3-2	1-3	1-3	1-0	2-1		2-2
15	Stansfeld O&B Club	4-0	1-3	0-0	2-0	1-0	2-1	1-1	1-1	5-1	2-1	1-0	2-2	0-1	1-0	

DIVISION ONE WEST		P	W	D	L	F	A	Pts
1	Holmesdale	24	20	2	2	78	15	62
2	Orpington	24	19	2	3	72	25	59
3	Phoenix Sports	24	16	2	6	43	23	50
4	Metrogas	24	13	2	9	40	31	41
5	Greenways	24	9	6	9	45	46	33
6	Fleetdown Utd	24	10	3	11	29	39	33
7	Larkfield & NH Wands.	24	9	4	11	37	40	31
8	Belvedere	24	8	6	10	37	40	30
9	Bromleians Sports	24	9	1	14	30	50	28
10	Bly Spartans	24	7	5	12	33	48	26
11	Samuel Montagu YC	24	6	5	13	30	47	23
12	Eynsford (-1)	24	4	6	14	29	62	17
13	Halls	24	3	2	19	31	68	11

DIVISION ONE EAST		P	W	D	L	F	A	Pts
1	Hollands & Blair	24	17	5	2	67	25	56
2	New Romney	24	15	4	5	68	41	49
3	Tyler Hill	24	13	5	6	70	52	44
4	Oakwood	24	11	8	5	54	28	41
5	Sheppey Utd	24	10	8	6	57	52	38
6	Betteshanger Welfare	24	11	4	9	41	43	37
7	Kennington (-3)	24	11	4	9	50	50	34
8	University of Kent	24	8	5	11	46	43	29
9	St. Margarets	24	8	5	11	57	57	29
10	Borden Village	24	7	4	13	56	67	25
11	Uniflo	24	6	5	13	48	59	23
12	APM Mears	24	5	3	16	31	69	18
13	Tenterden Town	24	1	6	17	31	90	9

DIVISION TWO WEST		P	W	D	L	F	A	Pts
1	Westerham	24	19	3	2	69	14	60
2	Bridon Ropes	24	19	3	2	75	25	60
3	Tonbridge Invicta	24	13	6	5	62	36	45
4	New Bromleians	24	13	6	5	46	37	45
5	Chipstead	24	12	2	10	50	37	38
6	Farnborough OBG	24	12	2	10	42	38	38
7	Borough Utd	24	11	4	9	71	63	37
8	Wickham Park	24	10	4	10	68	60	34
9	Old Bexleians	24	8	0	16	34	65	24
10	Meridian	24	6	2	16	38	67	20
11	Old Addeyans (-3)	24	6	3	15	40	63	18
12	Chislehurst	24	4	3	17	27	67	15
13	Eltham Palace	24	2	4	18	30	80	10

DIVISION TWO EAST		P	W	D	L	F	A	Pts
1	Staplehurst	22	14	4	4	49	20	46
2	Ashford Borough (-3)	22	15	3	4	74	40	45
3	Lanes End	22	12	5	5	59	36	41
4	Sutton Athletic	22	11	6	5	52	30	39
5	Putlands Athletic	22	10	3	9	40	38	33
6	Otford Utd	22	8	7	7	40	25	31
7	UK Paper	22	9	2	11	40	37	29
8	Woodstock Park	22	8	5	9	37	41	29
9	Atcost	22	7	4	11	43	43	25
10	Pembury	22	7	3	12	31	45	24
11	Guru Nanak	22	6	5	11	38	51	23
12	Platt Utd	22	1	1	20	14	111	4

INTER-REGIONAL CHALLENGE CUP

FIRST ROUND

Holland & Blair	v	Bromley Green	1-2
University of Kent	v	Kennington	4-3
Sheerness East	v	Bearsted	3-2
St. Margarets	v	Betteshanger Welfare	2-1
Lewisham Boro' (C)	v	Fleet Leisure	6-3
Bromlians Sports	v	Fleetdown United	2-0
Halls	v	Larkfield & New Hythe W.	1-4
Eynsford	v	Bly Spartans	2-8
Holmesdale	v	Snodland	1-0

THIRD ROUND WEST

Sheerness East	v	Tenterten Town	10-0
Tyler Hill	v	Sheppey United	1-2
Borden Village	v	Norton Sports	0-2
St. Margarets	v	Faversham Town	3-1
Old Roan	v	Samuel Montagu Y.C.	3-4
Metrogas	v	Holmesdale	1-2
Phoenix Sports	v	Belvedere	1-2
Stansfeld O & B C.	v	Orpington (H)	1-0

SECOND ROUND

APM Mears	v	Norton Sports	0-5
Borden Village	v	New Romney	2-1
Bromley Green	v	Tyler Hill	1-2
Sheerness East	v	Milton Athletic	2-0
Faversham Town	v	Uniflo	5-2
Sheppey United	v	Lydd Town	3-3*, 5-4p
St. Margarets	v	Oakwood	1-0
Samuel Montagu	v	Rusthall	2-0
Cray Valley (PM)	v	Orpington (H)	1-6
Metrogas	v	Lewisham Borough (Com.)	2-1
Greenways	v	Stansfield O&B Club	1-3
Bly Spartans	v	Phoenix Sports	1-2
Holmesdale	v	Crockenhill	3-1
Belvedere	v	Larkfield & New Hythe W.	5-2
Old Roan	v	Bromlians Sports	3-1

QUARTER-FINALS

Stansfeld O & B C.	v	Holmesdale	2-3
Belvedere	v	Sheerness East	1-4
Sheppey United	v	Norton Sports	5-6
St. Margarets	v	Samuel Montagu Y.C.	5-1

SEMI-FINALS

| St. Margarets | v | Holmesdale | 0-4 |
| Norton Sports | v | Sheerness East | 4-3 |

THE FINAL

| Holmesdale | v | Norton Sports | 2-3 |

Lewisham Borough (Community) with the Premier Division trophy following their victory over Faversham Town.
Photo: Jason Dodd.

Sid Medley receiving a certificate from league Chairman Cyril Windiate commemorating Faversham Town's promotion to the Kent League.
Photo: Philip Smith.

PREMIER DIVISION CONSTITUTION 2006-07

BEARSTED
Founded: 1895
Secretary: Mrs Liz Owen, 21 Copsewood Way, Bearsted,
Maidstone, Kent ME15 8PL Tel: 01622 630647.
Ground: Honey Lane, Otham, Maidstone. Tel: 07793 170 599.
Colours: White/blue/blue
Change Colours: All yellow

BROMLEY GREEN
Founded: 1930
Secretary: Stanley Donald,12 Oast Meadow ,Willesborough,
Ashford,Kent TN24 0AS Tel: 01233 627 916 (H) 01580 753 322 (B)
Ground: The Swan Centre, Newtown Road, South Willesborough,
Ashford, Kent Tel: 01233 645 982
Colours: Green & white stripes/green/white
Change Colours: All Green & yellow

CRAY VALLEY PAPERMILLS
Founded: 1981
Secretary: Steve Chapman, 97 Yorkland Ave., Welling DA16 2LG
Tel: 07775 685 438 (H) 07795 644953 (B)
Email: steve.chapman4@homeoffice.gsi.gov.uk
Ground: Badgers Sports Ground, Middle Park Ave., Eltham,
London SE9 5HT. Tel: 020 8850 4273
Colours: Green/black/black
Change Colours: Sky blue/white/white

CROCKENHILL
Founded: 1946
Secretary: Miss Lucy Smith, 4 Jacob Court, Spencer Road,
Bromley, Kent BR1 3SU. Tel: 0208 402 7496
Email: lucy@lsg-ca.co.uk
Ground: The Wested Meadow, Wested, Eynsford Road,
Crockenhill, Kent. Tel: 01322 666 067
Colours: Red & white stripes/ black/ black
Change Colours: Maroon & blue/blue/blue

FLEET LEISURE
Secretary: Robert Taylor, 24 Sun Lane, Gravesend, Kent DA12
5HG. Tel: 01474 332 208 (H) 01375 852 729
Email: robert.taylor@rwenpower.com
Ground: Fleet Leisure & Sports Club, Nelson Road, Northfleet,
Kent DA11 7EE. Tel: 01474 359 222
Colours: All red.
Change Colours: Gold/black/black.

HOLLANDS & BALIR
Laurance Plummer, 15 Romany Road, Gillingham, Kent ME8 6UT
Tel: 01634 360 255 (H) 01634 233 425 (B) 07850 693 694 (M)
Email: laurance.plummer@bt.com
Ground: Star Meadow Sports Club, Darland Avenue, Gillingham,
Kent ME7 3AN. Tel: 01634 573 839
Colours: All red
Change Colours: All blue

HOLMESDALE
Founded 1956
Secretary: Mark Hayes, 563 Mierscourt Road, Rainham Kent ME8
8RB Tel: 01634 327 954 (H) 01342 837 202 (B)
Email: markhayes@blueyonder.co.uk
Ground: Holmesdale Sports & Social Club, Oakley Road, Bromley
Kent BR2 8HG Tel: 020 8462 4440
Colours: Yellow & Green/ Green/ Green.
Change Colours: All blue.

LEWISHAM BOROUGH (COMMUNITY)
Founded: 2003
Secretary: Joseph Collymore, 37 Vaughan Williams Close,
Deptford SE8 4AW Tel: 0208 691 2543 (H) 07956 865 316 (B).
Email: tenembee@hotmail.com
Ground: LadywellAreana, Doggett Road, Catford, London SE6
4QX. Tel: 0208 314 1986
Colours: Blue/white/blue.
Change Colours: Gold & navy stripes/navy & white stripes/white.

MILTON ATHLETIC
Founded: 1926
Secretary: Paul Duffin, 18 Hales Road, Tunstall, Sittingbourne,
Kent ME10 1SR Tel: 01795 422 882 (H) 07971 098 037 (B)
Email: paul.duffin@creo.com
Ground: UK Paper Sports Ground, Gore Court Road,
Sittingbourne, Kent ME10 1QN Tel: 01795 564 213 or 477 047
Colours: Royal blue/royal blue/white
Change Colours: Yellow/royal blue/white

NORTON SPORTS
Founded: 1927
Secretary: Colin Page, 22 Haysel, Sittingbourne, Kent ME10 4QE
Tel: 01795 426 675 (H) 0207 577 1873 (B).
Email: c_page@blueyonder.co.uk.
Ground: Norton Park, Provender Lane, Norton, Faversham,
Kent ME9 9JU Tel: 07970 549 355
Colours: Sky Blue & white/ black /white
Change Colours: Red & green/green/red

OLD ROAN
Founded: 1905
Secretary: Brian Riley, 33 Buckler Gardens, Mottingham, London
SE9 3BD Tel: 0208 857 0401. Email: riley@oldroanfc.fsnet.co.uk
Groud: John Roan Playing Fields, Kidbrooke Park Road,
Kldbrooke, London SE3 9NF Tel: 0208 856 1012
Colours: Blue & black stripes/ black/ black
Change Colours: Red & white/white/blue

RUSTHALL
Secretary: Michael Mace, 'The Roos', 28 Allan Close, Rusthall,
Tunbridge Wells, Kent TN4 8PL. Tel: 01892 540 634 (H).
01892 518578 (B). Email: smsmace@msn.com
Ground: Jockey Farm, Nellington Road, Rusthall, Tunbridge
Wells, Kent TN4 8SH. Tel: 07803 476 814
Colours: Green/green/green
Change Colours: Blue & yellow trim/blue/blue

SHEERNESS EAST
Founded: 1932
Secretary: Jonathan Longhurst, 34 Sunnyside Avenue, Minster
Sheerness, Kent ME12 2EN Tel: 01795 870 093 (H)
01795 668 515 (B). Email: jonl@bond-group.co.uk
Ground: Sheerness East Working Mens Club, Queenborough Rd.,
Halfway, Sheerness, Kent ME12 3BZ Tel: 01795 662 049
Colours: Yellow/blue/blue
Change colours: Red & black stripes/black/black

SNODLAND
Founded: 1940
Secretary: Terry Reeves, 136 Townsend Road, Snodland, Kent
ME6 5RN Tel: 01634 240 076. Email: trallballs@aol.com
Ground: Potyn's Field, Paddlesworth Road, Snodland, Kent ME6
5DL Tel: 01634 243 961
Colours: All Sky blue
Change colours:Yellow/red/black

STANSFELD OXFORD & BERMONDSEY CLUB
Founded: 1897
Secretary: Colin Lush, 126a, Glenhurst Ave, Bexley, Kent DA5
3QN. Tel: 01322 553 062 (H)07762 528 955 (M)
Email: colin.lush1@tiscali.com
Ground: Greenwich University Sports ground, Kidbrooke Lane,
Kidbrooke, London SE9 6TA. Tel: 0208 850 0210
Colours: Yellow/blue/blue
Change Colours: All white

Steve Pettitt (British Gas) - middle - presenting Hollands & Blair with the Division One East trophy at the league dinner. Photo: Philip Smith.

Mark Hayes receiving FA Groundsman of the Year award from league Vice-President Philip Smith.
Photo: Lorraine Smith.

DIVISION ONE EAST CONSTITUTION 2006-07

ASHFORD BOROUGH
Secretary: Andrew Found, 11 Chichester Close, Ashford, Kent TN23 4QB. Tel: (H) 01233 620160.
Email: andyfound@btinternet.com
Ground: Sandyacres Sports & Social Club, Sandyhurst Lane, Ashford, Kent TN25 4PD. Tel: 01233 627 373.
Colours: All green.
Change Colours: All yellow.

BETTESHANGER WELFARE
Founded: 1939
Secretary: Mrs Wendy Guy, 38 Charles Road, Deal, Kent CT14 9AT. Tel: (H) 01304 367 020.
Ground: Betteshanger Welfare Ground, Cavell Square, Mill Hill, Deal, Kent CT14 9HR. Tel: 01304 372 080
Colours: Red & white hoops/blue/red & white
Change colours: Sky blue/blue/blue

BORDEN VILLAGE
Secretary: Stuart Lancashire, 38 Ferry Road, Iwade, Sittingbourne, Kent ME9 8RH. Tel: 0207 219 5347 (B).
Email: stuartlanky@yahoo.co.uk
Ground: Borden Playstool, Wises Lane, Borden, Sittingbourne, Kent ME9 8LP. Tel: 07921 912 209
Colours: Claret & blue/claret/sky blue
Change Colours: Yellow, emerald & black/black/yellow & green hoops

KENNINGTON
Founded: 1888
Secretary: Kevin Hayden, 36 Alec Pemble Close, Kennington, Ashford, Kent. TN24 9PF Tel: 01233 627 826 (H)
01233 642 677 (B) Email: k.j.hayden@talk21.com
Ground: Kennington Cricket Club Club, Ulley Road, Kennington, Ashford, Kent TN24 9HY. Tel: 07887 995 219
Colours: Sky blue/navy/navy
Change Colours: Red/navy/navy

LYDD TOWN
Founded: 1885
Secretary: Bruce Marchant, 14 Quested Road, Folkestone, Kent.CT19 4BY Tel: 01303 275 403 (H) 01303 297 122 (B)
Email: brucemarchant@hotmail.com
Ground: The Lindsey Field, Dengemarsh Road, Lydd, Kent TN29 9JH Tel: 01797 321 904.
Colours: Red & green/green/green
ChangeColours:All Blue

NEW ROMNEY
Founded: 1895
Secretary: Alan Chandler, 124 Jefferstone Lane, St Marys Bay, Kent TN29 0SG Tel: 01303 873 872 (H) 07879 481 028 (B)
Ground: The Maud Pavilion, Station Road, New Romney, Kent TN28 8LQ Tel: 01797 364 858
Colours: Navy & yellow/blue/yellow
Change Colours: Orange/blue/orange

OAKWOOD
Founded: 1924
Secretary: William Cossey, 12 Mallard Way, Downswood, Maidstone, Kent ME15 8XH. Tel: (H) 01622 862585.
(B) 0207 9573109. Email: wcossey@cbi.com
Ground: Otham Sports Club, Honey Lane, Otham, Maidstone, Kent ME15 8RG. Tel: 07963 303 831
Colours: Red/black/red
Change colours: White/black/red

SHEPPEY UNITED
Secretary: Phil Lumsden, 119 Coronation Road, Sheerness, Kent ME12 2QR. Tel: 01795 660 742 (H). Email: phillumsden@hotmail.om
Ground: Medway Ports, Holm Place, Halfway, Sheerness, Kent ME12 3AT. Tel: 01795 668 054
Colours: Red & white stripes/red/red
Change Colours: Blue & white stripes/blue/blue

STAPLEHURST & MONARCHS UNITED
Secretary: Mrs Anita Holness, 2 Dane Mead Villas, George Street, Staplehurst, Tonbridge, Kent TN12 0RB. Tel: (H) 01580 891782
Ground: The Old County Ground, Norman Road, West Malling, Kent ME19 6RL. Tel: 07703 288 622.
Colours: Red/white/white
Change Colours: Sky blue/navy/navy

St MARGARETS
Founded: 1970 Re-formed:1993
Secretary: John Barlow, 4 Almonry Cottage, The Street, Northbourne, Deal Kent CT14 0LG. Tel: 01304 363 529 (H)
07852 188194 (B). Email: stmargaretsfc@stmargaretsfc.fsworld.co.uk
Ground: The Alexandra Field, Off Kingsdown Road, St Margarets at Cliffe, Nr Dover, Kent CT15 6BD. Tel: 07852 188 194.
Colours: Red & blue stripes/blue/blue.
Change Colours: Red/blue/blue

TYLER HILL
Founded: 1950
Secretary: Bill Clark, 23 Hanscombe House, Forty Acres Road, Canterbury Kent CT2 7TL. Tel: 01227 768 358 (H).
07930 100 034 (B). Email: billclark.10@btinternet.com
Ground: Hersden Recreation Ground, Hersden, Nr. Canterbury, Kent CT3 4HY Tel: 07930 100 034
Colours: Red, black & white/red/red.
Change Colours: Red/white/white

UNIFLO
Secretary: David Pullen, 13 Listmas Road, Chatham, Kent ME4 5LJ Tel: 01634 811 992 (H) 07786 548 061 (B)
Ground: The Old County Ground, Norman Road, West Malling, Kent ME19 6RL. Tel: 07786 548 061
Colours: All Blue
Change Colours: All white

UNIVERSITY OF KENT
Founded: 1967
Secretary: Richard Baines, 1 Stour Close, Chartham, Canterbury, Kent CT4 7JF. Tel: (H) 01227 738090. (B) 07801 037150.
Email: info@cityawards.co.uk
Ground: Oast House, Parkwood Road, Off Giles Lane, Canterbury, Kent CT2 7SY. Tel: 01227 827 430
Colours: Black & white stripes/black/black & white
Change Colours: Yellow/black/black

British Energy's Steve Pettitt (left)
receiving Pennant from league Chairman Cyril Windiate
with General Secretary Geoff Jenkins in the background.
Photo: British Energy.

Steve Pettitt presenting Holmesdale with
the Division One West trophy at the
league dinner. Photo: Philip Smith.

DIVISION ONE WEST CONSTITUTION 2006-07

BELVEDERE
Founded: 1923
Secretary: Ray Sampson-Chambers, 90 Glenview, Abbey Wood,
London SE2 0SH. Tel: 0208 312 0426 (H).
Email: sam.cham@btinternet.com
Ground: Belvedere Sports & Social Club, 101a Woolwich Road,
Abbey Wood, London SE2 0DY. Tel: 01322 436 724
Colours: Red & white/red/red
Change: Blue & yellow stripes/blue/blue

BLY SPARTANS
Founded: 1982
Secretary: Tony Wheeler, 14 Lynnette Ave., Rochester, Kent ME2
3NH Tel: 01634 713 404 (H) 07775 735543 (M)
Email: blyspartans@yahoo.co.uk
Ground: Bly Spartans Sports Ground, Rede Court Road, Strood.
Kent ME2 3TU. Tel: 01634 710 577
Colours: Maroon/white/maroon
Change: Grey/black/black

BRIDON ROPES
Secretary: Richard Clements, 3 Fenwick Close, Woolwich,
London SE18 4DD. Tel: (H) 0208 244 1167. (B) 01322 442 323.
Ground: Meridian Sports & Social Club, Charlton Park Lane,
Charlton, London SE7 8QS. Tel: 0208 856 1923.
Colours: Blue& white/blue/blue.
Change Colours: Red/navy/navy.

BROMLEIANS SPORTS
Founded 1922
Secretary: Stephen Millward, 24 Palace Road, Bromley Kent BR1
3JT. Tel: 020 8466 1911 (H) 01252 387 992 (B)
Email: stephen.millward@uk.zurich.com
Ground: Scrubs Farm Sports Ground, Lower Gravel Road,
Bromley, Kent BR2 8LL Tel: 020 8462 5068
Colours: Light blue/dark blue/light blue
Change Colours: All red

FLEETDOWN UNITED
Founded: 1971
Secretary: Brian Wakeman, 670 Princes Road, Dartford, Kent
DA2 6JG Tel: 01322 228 680. Email: brian_wakeman@hotmail.com
Ground: Lower Heath Lane, Dartford, Kent DA1 2QE
Tel: 01322 273 848
Colours: Tangerine/black/tangerine
Change colours: Blue &white stripes/ blue/blue

GREENWAYS
Founded: 1965
Secretary: William Miller, 14 Cygnet Gardens, Northfleet, Kent
DA11 7DN Tel: 01474 560 913 (H) 07930 481 606 (B)
Ground: Fleet Leisure & Sports Club, Nelson Road, Northfleet,
Kent DA11 7EE. Tel: 01474 359 222.
Colours: Green & black/black & green/green & black
Change Colours: Sky & navy/navy/sky & navy

HALLS
Founded: 1919
Secretary: Stephen Challis, 45 Kingsley Avenue, Dartford, Kent
DA1 5DH. Tel: 01322 228 244 (H) 07956 990 148 (B)
Email: hallsfc@hotmail.com
Ground: Bexley Park Sports & Social Club, Calvert Drive, Bexley,
DA2 7GU. tel: 01322 527 973.
Colours: Yellow & blue stripes/blue/yellow
Change Colours: All navy

LARKFIELD & NEW HYTHE WANDERERS
Secretary: Darren Hamer, 13 Briar Close, Larkfield, Maidstone,
Kent ME20 6NA. Tel: (H) 01732 872260. (B) 07960 588 151.
Email: dh.mic@btinternet.com
Larkfield & New Hythe Sports Ground, New Hythe Lane, Larkfield,
Maidstone, Kent ME20 6PU. Tel: 07724 050971
Colours: Maroon & royal blue stripes/royal blue/royal blue
Change Colours: Black & white stripes/black/black

METROGAS
Secretary: John Williams, 44 Sidewood Road, New Eltham,
London SE9 2HA. Tel: 07802 194 043 (M)
Email: john.L3.williams@bt.com
Ground: Metrogas Sports Ground, Marathon Playing Fields, Forty
Foot Way, Avery Hill Road, New Eltham SE9 2EX.
Tel: 0208 859 1579
Colours: Black & white stripes/blue/blue
Change Colours: Red/black/black

ORPINGTON
Secretary: Les Hill, 8 Cudham Lane North, Orpington, Kent BR6
6BZ. Tel: 01689 600 932 (H) 07702 889540 (B)
Email: leshill44@hotmail.co.uk
Ground: Green Court Sports Club, Green Court Road,
Crockenhill, Kent BR8 8HE. Tel: 01322 666 442
Colours: Amber/black/black
Change Colours: White & sky blue/sky blue/sky blue

PHOENIX SPORTS
Secretary: Alf Levy, 5 Guild Road, Erith, Kent DA8 2PS
Tel: 01322 330 399 (H) 07795 182 927 (B)
Email: alf@alfllevy.freeserve.co.uk
Ground: Phoenix Sports Club, Mayplace Road East, Barnehurst,
Kent DA7 6JT. Tel: 01322 526 159
Colours: Green/black/black
Change Colours: White & red/black/white

SAMUEL MONTAGU YOUTH CLUB
Founded: 1934
Secretary: Ian Wareing, 231 Bedonwell Road, Bexleyheath, Kent
DA7 5QA. Tel: (H) 07799 661 157.
Email: iwareing@hotmail.com
Ground: 122 Broadwalk, Kidbrooke, London SE3 8ND
Tel: 0208 856 1126
Colours: Red & black stripes/black/black
Change Colours: Blue & black stripes/black/blue

WESTERHAM
Secretary: Doug Sayers, 15 Quebec Avenue, Westerham, Kent
TN16 1BJ. (H) 01959 565 520. (B) 07802 732 105.
Email: dougsayers@gmail.com
Ground: King George Playing Fields, Costells Mewadow,
Westerham, Kent TN16 1BL. Tel: 01959 561 106.
Colours: Red/black/black.
Change Colours: Sky blue/navy/sky.

LEICESTERSHIRE SENIOR LEAGUE

SPONSORED BY: EVERARDS BREWERY

Founded 1903

President: A.Wheeler   **Chairman:** David Jamieson
Hon Secretary: Robert Holmes, 9 Copse Close, Hugglescote,Coialville, Leics
LE67 2GL
Tel/Fax: 01530831818   Email: robertholmes@leicssenior1.freeserve.co.uk
Press Officer: Dave Lumley, 8 Pinewood Close, Countesthorpe, Leicester LE8 5TS
TelFax: 0116 277 8455   Email: davelumley@leicssenior.freeserve.co.uk

PREMIER DIVISION		P	W	D	L	F	A	Pts
1.	Friar Lane & Epworth	34	24	4	6	88	42	76
2.	Barrow Town	34	24	2	8	84	50	74
3.	St Andrews	34	20	4	10	86	53	64
4.	Thurnby Rangers (Champions 04-05)	34	19	7	8	67	37	64
5.	Highfield Rangers	34	19	6	9	64	44	63
6.	Stapenhill	34	18	7	9	76	41	61
7.	Ibstock United	34	19	2	13	76	57	59
8.	Kirby Muxloe	34	15	9	10	65	39	54
9.	Rothley Imperial	34	15	7	12	56	49	52
10.	Downes Sports	34	14	9	11	51	40	51
11.	Holwell Sports	34	13	6	15	51	40	45
12.	Birstall United	34	12	6	16	45	53	42
13.	Blaby & Whetstone Athletic	34	11	7	16	43	72	40
14.	Thurmaston Town	34	11	4	19	53	70	37
15.	Ratby Sports	34	9	5	20	43	76	32
16.	Ellistown	34	6	4	24	43	101	22
17.	Aylestone Park	34	6	2	26	49	89	20
18.	Anstey Nomads	34	4	3	27	28	115	15

PREMIER DIVISION	1	2	3	4	5	6	7	8	9	10	11	12	13	14	15	16	17	18
1 Anstey Nomads		1-0	1-5	0-5	0-2	2-2	0-2	1-6	0-1	0-3	0-6	1-1	3-1	0-1	0-3	0-0	3-2	2-5
2 Aylestone Park	6-0		1-2	1-2	2-3	0-0	2-0	0-2	3-1	1-1	0-1	1-3	1-2	0-3	2-6	1-3	2-3	1-5
3 Barrow Town	2-1	1-6		1-0	3-1	2-0	5-0	2-1	4-0	2-0	3-0	2-1	4-2	3-1	2-1	4-1	5-1	0-6
4 Birstall United	3-1	4-2	1-3		3-3	0-1	2-1	0-1	1-1	2-1	2-3	0-0	1-0	1-0	0-3	3-2	1-1	0-2
5 Blaby & Whetstone Athletic	4-2	1-1	2-6	1-0		0-0	2-0	0-4	2-1	0-0	1-0	0-2	1-2	0-4	3-1	1-4	1-1	1-1
6 Downes Sports	4-1	2-1	2-0	1-0	2-3		5-2	0-2	0-0	4-1	5-2	0-2	1-0	1-1	1-2	0-2	0-1	1-2
7 Ellistown	5-1	4-0	0-6	1-3	1-1	1-6		1-2	2-3	0-7	0-3	0-0	2-3	3-1	2-3	2-3	3-4	0-1
8 Friar Lane & Epworth	5-1	5-1	7-0	3-0	1-0	3-0	1-1		2-1	3-2	4-1	2-6	6-3	1-0	3-1	3-3	3-2	2-0
9 Highfield Rangers	5-1	5-1	0-0	2-1	2-1	1-2	4-1	1-1		1-0	5-2	1-2	3-4	4-0	1-1	3-1	2-0	1-0
10 Holwell Sports	6-0	4-0	0-4	3-1	4-1	0-1	0-1	0-2	0-2		0-2	1-0	1-1	0-1	1-0	4-1	3-1	
11 Ibstock United	11-1	3-4	2-1	2-0	3-2	2-1	2-1	5-2	0-2	0-0		0-1	5-0	2-2	0-1	0-4	1-0	2-1
12 Kirby Muxloe	4-1	2-1	1-2	6-2	0-0	2-1	7-0	2-2	2-4	1-1	1-2		0-1	2-1	5-2	1-1	2-3	0-1
13 Ratby Sports	1-2	3-2	0-5	1-2	0-1	0-2	1-3	0-2	0-2	1-1	2-4	0-2		1-5	5-3	1-1	1-1	1-1
14 Rothley Imperial	2-0	4-3	1-1	2-2	4-0	0-0	4-1	0-3	1-2	4-0	1-6	0-0	1-2		0-0	2-1	2-0	1-0
15 St Andrews	5-1	4-0	3-2	2-1	9-2	1-1	4-0	3-0	1-2	0-2	3-0	2-2	3-2	1-2		3-4	5-4	2-0
16 Stapenhill	2-0	4-0	1-0	2-0	4-0	1-1	8-0	2-0	5-0	0-1	4-0	1-4	0-1	3-0	2-1		0-3	0-0
17 Thurmaston Town	2-0	2-1	5-0	0-2	1-2	2-3	3-3	0-3	2-0	0-3	1-3	1-0	2-0	2-3	1-3	2-4		0-3
18 Thurnby Rangers	3-1	3-1	1-2	0-0	3-1	1-1	4-0	3-1	1-1	2-1	2-1	2-1	3-1	4-2	1-3	3-3	2-0	

DIVISION ONE		P	W	D	L	F	A	Pts
1	Anstey Town	30	22	4	4	71	31	70
2	Bardon Hill Sports (P)	30	21	4	5	85	44	67
3	Ashby Ivanhoe	30	18	9	3	80	49	63
4	Sileby Town	30	19	5	6	72	36	62
5	Lutterworth Athletic	30	17	7	6	69	34	58
6	Asfordby Amateurs	30	16	6	8	51	32	54
7	Lutterworth Town	30	13	8	9	66	58	47
8	Saffron Dynamo	30	14	5	11	56	49	47
9	Narborough & Littlethorpe	30	13	5	12	42	50	44
10	Cottesmore Amateurs	30	13	3	14	62	52	42
11	Ravenstone	30	10	5	15	55	61	35
12	Earl Shilton Albion	30	7	6	17	50	76	27
13	Huncote Sports & Social	30	6	5	19	35	61	23
14	HM Desford Sports	30	6	6	19	30	63	21
15	Leicestershire Constabulary	30	5	3	22	30	66	18
16	North Kilworth	30	0	1	29	27	119	1

776

LEAGUE CUP

FIRST ROUND

Thurmaston Town	v	Blaby & Whet' Ath.	1-1*, 4-5p
Rothley Imperial	v	Ibstock United	0-1

SECOND ROUND

Asfordby Amateurs	v	Ravenstone	5-0
Lutterworth Town	v	North Kilworth	5-2
Bardon Hill Sports	v	Lutterworth Athletic	2-1
Narborough & L.	v	Anstey Town	0-2
Saffron Dynamo	v	Ashby Ivanhoe	6-0
Leicestershire Con.	v	HM Desford Sports	4-0
Cottesmore Am.	v	Sileby Town	2-1
Earl Shilton Albion	v	Huncote Sports & Social	1-3
Anstey Nomads	v	Ratby Sports	1-0
Ibstock United	v	Aylestone Park	2-1
Birstall United	v	Holwell Sports	1-4
Stapenhill	v	St. Andrews	1-1*, 4-5p
Downes Sports	v	Highfield Rangers	1-1*, 12-13p
Blaby & Whet' Ath.	v	Barrow Town	1-4
Thurnby Rgers (H)	v	Friar Lane & Epworth	3-2
Ellistown	v	Kirby Muxloe	0-1

THIRD ROUND

Bardon Hill Sports	v	Saffron Dynamo	1-3
Anstey Town	v	Leicestershire Constabulary	0-1

Cottesmore Am.	v	Huncote Sports & Social	3-1
Lutterworth Town	v	Asfordby Amateurs	2-1
Holwell Sports	v	Anstey Nomads	5-0
Kirby Muxloe	v	Barrow Town	2-1
Thurnby Rgers (H)	v	Highfield Rangers	4-1
Ibstock Welfare	v	St. Andrews	5-2

QUARTER-FINALS

Ibstock Welfare	v	Saffron Dynamo	3-1
Thurnby Rgers (H)	v	Lutterworth Town	2-0
Cottesmore Am.	v	Holwell Sports	2-5
Kirby Muxloe	v	Leicestershire Constabulary	4-1

SEMI-FINALS

Holwell Sports	v	Kirby Muxloe	4-0
Ibstock United	v	Thurnby Rangers (H)	2-1

THE FINAL

Ibstock United	v	Holwell Sports	0-2

LEAGUE CONSTITUTION 2006-07 - PREMIER DIVISION

ANSTEY NOMADS (V)

Secretary: Chris Hillebrandt, 31 Peartree Close, Anstey, Leicester LE7 7TD Tel NO: 0116 2122458

Ground: Cropston Road, Anstey, Leicester Tel No: 0116 236 4868

Directions: Take Jct 21A off M1 to Newark on A46. Turn to Anstey after 2 miles then 3rd exit at village roundabout. Ground is half mile on right.

Colours: Red & white/black/red   **Change:** All Green

AYLESTONE PARK

Secretary: Pete Burrows, 27 Cartwright Drive, Oadby, Leics LE2 5HN Tel: 0116 271 2682

Ground: Dorset Avenue, Fairfield Estate, Leicester Leic. Tel No: 0116 277 5307

Colours: Red & white/red/red   **Change:** AllBlue

BARDON HILL

Secretary: Adrian Bishop, 138 Bradgate Drive, Coalville, Leics. LE67 4HG Tel No: 07922 289 319

Ground: Bardon Close, Coalville, Leics. (off A511). LE67 4BS Tel. No: 01530 815569

Colours: Blue & White/Blue/ Blue

Change: All Purple

BARROW TOWN

Secretary: Alan Dawkins,72 Beaumont Road, Barrow-on-Soar, Loughborough, Leics. LE12 8PJ Tel No: 01509 413288

Ground: Riverside Park, Meynell Road, Quorn, Leics. Tel No: 01509 620650

Directions: Access via Quorn Lodge Road and Barrow Road.

Colours: Red/black/black   **Change:** Yellow/blue/blue

BIRSTALL UNITED

Secretary: Gary Fox, 138 Duncan Road, Aylestone, Leicester. LE2 8EDTel: 0116 283 3526 Bus: 0116 283 7212 Mobile: 07730 676 719

Ground: Meadow Lane, Birstall, Leics.Tel No: 0116 267 1230

Directions: Ground situated on A6 between Leicester & Loughborough. (Club will supply maps). Tel: 0116 267 1230

Colours: All navy   **Change:** All red

BLABY & WHETSTONE ATHLETIC

Secretary: Roger Morris,2 Chantry Close,Huncote, Leics. LE8 3AE Tel No: 0116 286 3819

Ground: Blaby &Whetstone Boys Club, Warwick Road, Whetstone Tel No: 0116 286 4852

Colours: All navy.   **Change:**All white

DOWNES SPORTS

Secretary: Chris Rowley,25 Granby Road, Hinckley, Leics. LE10 0PW Tel Nos: 01455 449848

Ground: Leicester Road, Hinckley.Tel No: 07725 824 200

Directions: Off the northern Leicester perimeter road.

Colours: Tangerine/black/black   **Change:**Red & white/blue/red

ELLISTOWN

Secretary: Sue Matthews, 21 Federation Street, Enderby, Leics. LE19 4NP Tel No: 0116 286 5328

Ground: 1Terrace Road, Ellistown. Tel: 01530 230 159

Colours: Yellow/blue/blue   **Change:**White/black/white

HIGHFIELD RANGERS

Secretary: Maurice Christian,18 Blankly Avenue,Leicester LE5 5FA Tel NO: 0116 273 4002

Ground: 443 Gleneagles Avenue, Rushey Mead, Leicester . Tel No: 0116 266 0009

Colours: Yellow/Black/Yellow

Change Colours: All Red

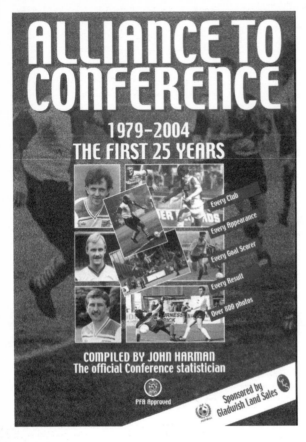

HOLWELL SPORTS

Secretary: Colin Moulds, 12 Needham Close, Melton Mowbray, Leics.
LE13 1TW. Tel No: 01664 862391(H) 07790 876119 (M)
Ground: Welby Road, Asfordby Hill, Melton Mowbray, Leics.
Tel No: 01664 812715
Colours: Yellow & green/green/green
Change: White/Black/Black

IBSTOCK UNITED

Formed: 2005 when Ibstock Welfare and Ibstock Youth merged.
Secretary: Ralph Wilkinson, 6 Valley Rd., Ibstock, Leics. LE67 6NY
Tel No: 01530 450243
Ground: The Welfare, Leicester Rd., Ibstock. Leics.
Tel: 01530 264 982. Clubhouse: 01530 260 656.
Directions: A511 towards Coalville and follow signs to Ibstock.
Colours: Red & black/white/white **Change:** Blue & white/black/black

KIRBY MUXLOE S.C.

Secretary: Kirsty Moloney, 16 Church Lane, Ratby, Leics. LE6 0JE
Tel: 0116 239 2916
Ground: Ratby Lane, Kirby Muxloe. Tel No: 0116 239 3201
Colours: All blue
Change Colours: Black & white/black/black

RATBY SPORTS

Secretary: Trevor Burdett, 10 Oaktree Close, Groby, Leicester
LE6 0GY Tel No: 0116 287 6001
Ground: Ratby Sports club,Desford Lane, Ratby.
Tel NO: 0116 239 3474
Colours: All red **Change:** All Blue

ROTHLEY IMPERIAL

Secretary: Lynne Simmons, 43 Telford Way, Thurnby, Leicester. LE5
TLX. Tel: 0116 241 6601
Ground: Loughborough Road, Mountsorrell, Leicester, Leics.
Tel No: 0116 237 4003
Colours: Gold/dark blue/dark blue
Change Colours: White/black/black

ST ANDREWS

Secretary: Les Botting, 2 Neston Road, Saffron Lane, Leicester.
LE 2 6RD Tel No: 0116 224 3961 (H) 0779 350 0937(M)
Ground: Canal Street, off Aylestone Rd, Old Aylestone, Leicester.
Tel No: 0116 283 9298
Directions: Aylestone Road to Granby Road, to Canal St.
Colours: Black & White/Black/Red **Change:** Orange/Navy/Orange

STAPENHILL

Secretary: Graham Pullinger, 1 Stable Mews Station Road, Woodville,
Swadlincote, Derbys. DE11 7DD Tel No: 07866 647504 (M)
Ground: Maple Grove, Stapenhill, Burton-on-Trent, Staffs.
Tel No: 01283 562471
Colours: All red
Change Colours: Black & White stripes/Black/Black

THURMASTON TOWN

Secretary: Reg Malloy, 96 Grange Drive, Melton Mowbray, Leics
Tel No: 01664 564665 (H) 0116 222 3636 (W)
Ground: Elizabeth Park, Checklands Rd., Thurmaston
Tel No: 0116 2602519
Colours: Black & White Stripes,Black/Black **Change:** All Red

THURNBY RANGERS

Secretary: Neil Heggs, 32 The Halfcroft, Syston, Leicester. LE7 1LD
Tel: Mobile: 07801 860 815 Bus: 0116 269 8959
Ground: Dakyn Road, Thurnby Lodge, Leicester.
Tel NO: 0116 243 3698
Colours: Green/red/green **Change:** Red/green/red

Lutterworth Town. Back Row: (L-R) Ben Wilkes, Russ Douglas, Adam Southin, Craig Heald, Lee Jacques, David Haycock, Sean O'Callaghan, Anthony Walker, Nathaniel Ryder.
Front: Chris Jacques, Mark Jackson, Carl Heald, Christopher Brylka, Rob Wynne, Antonio Maisto, Craig Sutton.
Photo: Gordon Whittington.

LIVERPOOL COUNTY PREMIER

President: T McFarlane   **Chairman:** George Parry
Secretary: John Deal, 24 The Pastures, Crossens, Southport PR9 8RH
Tel: 01704 211955

		P	W	D	L	F	A	Pts
1.	Speke	28	19	4	5	59	21	61
2.	Waterloo Dock (Champions 04-05)	28	16	5	7	64	38	53
3.	Bootle	28	16	2	10	65	43	50
4.	Lucas Sports	28	15	5	8	66	50	50
5.	Birchfield	28	15	4	9	47	33	49
6.	South Sefton Borough	28	14	5	9	55	39	47
7.	St. Dominics	28	12	7	9	43	32	43
8.	Penlake	28	12	5	11	67	60	41
9.	St. Aloysius (-3)	28	13	5	10	43	42	41
10	Ford Motors	28	12	5	11	47	46	41
11	South Liverpool	28	11	7	10	47	36	40
12	Mossley Hill Athletic	28	6	6	16	41	55	24
13	Aigburth Peoples Hall	28	5	6	17	36	63	21
14	Cheshire Lines	28	5	5	18	32	67	20
15	Kingsley United	28	2	3	23	24	111	9

		1	2	3	4	5	6	7	8	9	10	11	12	13	14	15
1	Aigburth Peoples Hall		2-1	0-1	2-3	0-2	2-2	4-2	0-0	2-2	1-3	2-2	4-4	1-2	0-5	1-2
2	Birchfield	4-3		1-3	2-0	0-1	5-1	2-1	3-1	3-2	0-0	1-0	0-1	2-2	1-1	1-0
3	Bootle	4-0	2-4		5-1	2-1	8-1	2-2	1-1	3-2	3-2	3-0	3-1	0-1	0-2	3-2
4	Cheshire Lines	1-1	0-2	1-2		1-3	3-0	3-3	2-2	1-4	0-2	0-3	0-1	0-0	0-2	2-3
5	Ford Motors	3-0	2-3	3-4	3-1		4-0	3-5	0-5	1-1	0-1	1-1	0-3	1-3	0-2	2-2
6	Kingsley United	1-2	1-0	1-6	1-2	1-3		1-5	0-4	1-3	2-2	0-7	0-4	1-5	1-2	2-5
7	Lucas Sports	0-3	1-0	5-3	5-2	1-0	2-0		2-3	3-2	4-2	3-4	0-2	0-0	2-1	5-2
8	Mossley Hill Athletic	2-1	0-2	2-3	2-2	0-2	1-2	1-5		4-0	1-3	0-2	2-1	1-2	3-3	0-1
9	Penlake	6-3	3-1	2-1	4-0	1-2	6-2	1-3	5-1		2-2	1-0	1-4	5-1	2-2	3-2
10	South Liverpool	2-0	0-1	2-0	1-4	1-2	6-0	0-0	4-3	3-3		1-2	0-0	2-0	4-1	1-2
11	South Sefton Borough	2-0	1-3	2-1	5-1	1-3	2-2	3-2	2-0	1-3	2-0		1-0	3-4	2-0	1-1
12	Speke	3-0	1-1	1-0	3-0	3-0	6-0	0-1	1-0	2-1	2-1	3-0		2-1	2-2	2-1
13	St. Aloysius	3-0	0-3	1-0	2-1	2-3	4-0	1-1	2-1	2-0	0-2	0-3	0-5		0-1	1-2
14	St. Dominics	0-2	2-0	1-2	0-1	1-1	5-0	1-2	0-0	3-1	1-0	2-1	2-1	0-0		0-1
15	Waterloo Dock	1-0	2-1	1-0	4-0	1-1	7-1	4-1	4-1	7-1	0-0	2-2	0-1	2-4	3-1	

P E T E R   C O Y N E   (G E O R G E   M A H O N)   C U P

FIRST ROUND

Aigburth Peoples H.v	South Liverpool	1-2
Kingsley United	v St. Dominics	0-4
Lucas Sports	v Halewood Village	HW
Mossley Hill Ath.	v St. Aloysius	5-1
Penlake	v Cheshire Lines	3-2
South Sefton Boro' v	Ford Motors	4-2
Speke	v Birchfield	3-0
Waterloo Dock (H)	v Bootle	3-0

QUARTER-FINALS

Penlake	v Mossley Hill Athletic	2-3
South Liverpool	v Lucas Sports	1-6
Speke	v St. Dominics	1-4
Waterloo Dock (H)	v South Sefton Borough	1-0

SEMI-FINALS

Lucas Sports	v St. Dominics	2-5
Mossley Hill Ath.	v Waterloo Dock (H)	2-3

THE FINAL (5th May)

St. Dominics   v   Waterloo Dock (H) 2-2*, HW on pens

LEAGUE CONSTITUTION 2006-07 - PREMIER DIVISION

BIRCHFIELD
Edge Hill College, St Helens Road, Ormskirk, Merseyside L39 4QP. Tel: 01695 584 745

COLLEGIATE OLD BOYS

CROXTETH RED RUM

EAST VILLA

FORD MOTORS
Ford Sports & Social Club, Cronton Lane, Widnes. Tel: 0151 424 7078

LUCAS SPORTS
IM Marsh Campus, Barkhill Road, Aigburth, Liverpool L17 6BD. Tel: 0151 231 5230

MACKETS

N. E. LIVERPOOL TECHNICAL COLLEGE

OLD XAVERIANS

PENLAKE
Edge Hill College, St Helens Road, Ormskirk, Merseyside. Tel: 01695 584 745

ROMA

SOUTH SEFTON BOROUGH
Mill Dam Field, Bridges Lane, Sefton.

SPEKE
Dunlops Sports Ground, Speke Hall Avenue, Speke, Liverpool 24. Tel: 0151 486 1588

ST ALOYSIUS
King George V Sports Ground, Longview Lane, Liverpool 36. Tel: 0151 443 5712

ST DOMINICS
St Dominics School, Lordens Road, Huyton, Liverpool 14. Tel: 0151 489 8279

WATERLOO DOCK
Edinburgh Park, Townsend Lane, Liverpool L6 0BB. Tel: 0151 263 5267

MANCHESTER FOOTBALL LEAGUE

Honorary President: Norman Noden **President:** Phil Morris
League Secretary: Phil Platt.
26a Stalybridge Road, Mottram, Hyde, Cheshire SK14 6NE
Tel: 01457 763 821 Email: phil@platt8603.fsnet.co.uk

PREMIER DIVISION		P	W	D	L	F	A	Pts
1.	Prestwich Heys (Champions 04-05)	32	20	6	6	71	35	66
2.	Wythenshawe Amateurs	32	19	5	8	61	36	62
3.	Avro	32	18	8	6	61	39	62
4.	East Manchester	32	17	7	8	73	53	58
5.	Leigh Athletic (-3)	32	18	6	8	59	40	57
6.	Rochdale Sacred Heart (2nd Div.1 04-05)	32	16	3	13	64	57	51
7.	Stockport Georgians (-3)	32	16	6	10	53	40	51
8.	Dukinfield Town	32	15	5	12	67	54	50
9.	Springhead	32	11	14	7	66	50	47
10.	Breightmet United	32	11	4	17	61	75	37
11.	Hindsford AFC (3rd Div.1 04-05)	32	10	7	15	46	62	37
12.	AFC Blackley (1st Div.1 04-05)	32	9	6	17	55	68	33
13.	Monton Amateurs	32	8	8	16	64	70	32
14.	Royton Town	32	9	5	18	41	69	32
15.	Irlam MS	32	9	4	19	67	81	31
16.	Atherton Town	32	8	7	17	45	83	31
17.	Wilmslow Albion	32	6	3	23	38	80	21

DIVISION ONE		P	W	D	L	F	A	Pts
1	Whitworth Valley	34	23	8	3	101	34	77
2	Hollinwood	34	24	1	9	106	62	73
3	Gregorians	34	20	7	7	89	37	67
4	Ashton Athletic	34	19	6	9	65	38	63
5	Wythenshawe Town	34	18	5	11	80	50	59
6	Walshaw SC	34	16	10	8	75	44	58
7	Elton Vale	34	17	4	13	71	53	55
8	Wigan Robin Park	34	17	4	13	65	46	55
9	Chapel Town (-3)	34	16	8	10	78	61	53
10	Manchester Juniors	34	15	6	13	54	56	51
11	Heywood St James	34	14	5	15	79	72	47
12	Salford AFC (-3)	34	16	1	17	60	74	46
13	Fives Athletic (-1)	34	12	4	18	54	91	39
14	Tintwistle Villa (-3)	34	10	6	18	41	70	33
15	Stand Athletic	34	9	4	21	57	84	31
16	Pennington	34	5	9	20	39	91	24
17	Manchester Titans	34	4	5	25	52	121	17
18	Milton	34	3	3	28	36	118	12

G I L G R Y S T   C U P

PRELIMINARY ROUND

Stockport Georgians (H) v Prestwich Heys	5-3
Wythenshawe Am. v East Manchester	1-3

FIRST ROUND

AFC Blackley	v Breightmet United	4-3
Atherton Town	v Wilmslow Albion	5-4
Hindsford AFC	v Leigh Athletic	2-3
Irlam MS	v Monton Amateurs	5-1
Springhead	v Royton Town	5-2
Dukinfield Town	v Stockport Georgians (H)	0-1
East Manchester	v Avro	2-2* 4-2p

QUARTER-FINALS

Leigh Athletic	v Atherton Town	3-0
Stockport Georgians (H) v Irlam MS	2-3*
AFC Blackley	v East Manchester	1-2
Springhead	v Rochdale Sacred Heart	0-2

SEMI-FINALS

Leigh Athletic	v Irlam MS	5-1
Rochdale S. H.	v East Manchester	2-4

THE FINAL

East Manchester	v Leigh Athletic	1-2

LEAGUE CONSTITUTION 2006-07 - PREMIER DIVISION

AFC BLACKLEY
Formed: 1967
Previous Names: Belden>03; B.I.C.C. 1995-2000. BTCL 1967-95
Secretary: John Hall. Tel: 0161 437 3527
Ground: PLant Hill Park, PLant Hill Rd, Blackley.
Directions: from Junction 20 of the M60, turn right towards Manchester. At next crossroads, turn right onto Victoria Avenue and follow for approximately one and a half miles. Turn left into Plant Hill Road, and the ground is approximately half a mile along road on your left. .
Colours: Black & white/black/black

ATHERTON TOWN
Formed: 1964
Secretary: Gerald Butler, 43 Hope Fold Ave., Atherton, Lancs M29 0BW Tel: 01942 870 326 or 07906 587958
Ground: Howe Bridge Sports Centre, Howe Bridge, Atherton Tel: 01942 884 882
Directions: Via A580 to Lowton By-Pass (A579) signposted Leigh, follow to Lovers Lane (B5235) and turn right, turn right at lights onto Leigh Road (B5215) and entrance to Howe Bridge Sports Centre is immediately on your left.
Via M61 to junction 4 and turn right onto A6 (Salford Road), turn left at first lights onto Newbrook Road (A579) and follow into Atherton. From Atherton, follow B5215 towards Leigh for approx 800 yards and entrance to Howe Bridge Sports Centre is immediately on your left.
Colours: Yellow/green/yellow

AVRO
Formed: 1998 (reformed)
Secretary: Karen Birch, 27 Brooks Drive, Failsworth, Manchester M35 0L5 Tel: 0161 682 6731
Ground: Lancaster Club, Broadway, Failsworth 0161 681 7985
Directions: From the City Centre, follow Oldham Road (A62) to junction with Broadway (A663) signposted Chadderton. Turn left and entrance to Lancaster Club is approximately a quarter of mile on left hand side.
From the M60, exit at 22 towards the City Centre on Oldham Road (A62). At junction with Broadway (A663), signposted Chadderton, turn right and entrance to Lancaster Club is approximately a quarter of mile on left hand side.
Colours: Red and black

BREIGHTMET UNITED
Formed: 1889
Secretary: Roy Haslam, Tel: 01204 535 933 or 07796 134093
Ground: Moss Park, Bury Road, Breightmet, Manchester Tel: 01204 533 930
Directions: From Bolton Town Centre, follow A58 (Bury Road) into Breightmet. Entrance is on right, just behind Hy-Speed Tyres.
Colours: Black & white/black/red

DUKINFIELD TOWN
Formed: 1948
Secretary: Jason Walker. Tel: 0161 343 1722 or 07748 634862
Ground: Blocksages Playing Fields, Birch Lane, Dukinfield. Tel: 0161 303 2690
Directions: From south, exit M67 at junction 3 (Hyde) and follow signposts for Dukinfield (B6170 - Newton Street), The ground is approximately one and a half miles up B6170 on   your left.
From the M60, exit at junction 23 and head towards Ashton Town Centre. From Town Centre, follow A627 (King Street) to junction with Chapel Street (adjacent Town Hall). Turn left and follow to junction and then turn right into Foundry Street (B6170). Ground is approx 880 yards on right.
Colours: Yellow/blue/blue

EAST MANCHESTER
Formed: 1960 (called ICL until 1985)
Secretary: Dave Wilkinson. Tel: 0161 303 9182
Ground: GMT Ground, Mount Road, Gorton.
Directions: Take A57 from Manchester or Hyde to Belle Vue junction. Turn into Mount Road (B6178) and the ground is approximately one mile on the left after Mellands Playing Fields.
Colours: All royal blue

GREGORIANS
Formed: 1959
Secretary: Terry O'Neil. Tel: 0161 442 6839 & 07740 585459
Ground: Woodbank Park Athletics Stadium, Little Moor, Stockport.
Directions: From Manchester, follow the A6 into Stockport. Turn left onto Longshut Lane (B5465) and continue onto Hempshaw Lane and then St. Mary's Way. Turn right onto Hall Street, and take the 9th left turn into Turncroft Lane. Turn first right into community centre car park. Access to Woodbank Park is at the rear of the car park. Follow the path into the park to reach the football ground.
From M60 (Clockwise), exit M60 at Junction 26 for Stockport. Continue to roundabout and take 2nd left onto St. Mary's Way. Turn left onto Hall Street and take the 9th left turn into Turncroft Lane. Turn first right into community centre car park. Access to Woodbank Park is at the rear of the car park. Follow the path into the park to reach the football ground.
From M60 (Anti-Clockwise), exit M60 at Junction 27 for Stockport. Continue under motorway and take 3rd left onto St. Mary's Way. Turn left onto Hall Street. Continue along Hall Street and take the 9th left turn into Turncroft Lane. Turn first right into community centre car park. Access to Woodbank Park is at the rear of the car park. Follow the path into the park to reach the football ground.
Colours: All maroon.

HINDSFORD AFC
Formed: 1926
Secretary: Ken Cunliffe. Tel: 0161 790 8555 or 07771 552 619
Ground: Squires Lane, Tyldesley
Directions: Exit M61 at junction 4 and turn right onto A6 (Salford Road), turn left at first lights onto Newbrook Road (A579) and follow into Atherton. Follow signposts for Tyldesley onto Tyldesley Road (A577). At junction of Castle Street and Elliot Street in Tyldesley town centre, turn right into Elliot Street and follow onto Squires Lane. Ground is at the end of Squires Lane. Or exit A580 at junction with A577 signposted Wigan. Follow road through Mosley Common into Tyldesley and onto Elliot Street. Follow onto Squires Lane and ground is at the end of road.
Colours: Red/navy/navy

HOLLINWOOD
Formed: 1962
Secretary: Ken Evans. Tel: 01706 840987 or 07740 442818
Ground: Lime Lane, Hollinwood, Oldham. Tel: 0161 681 3385
Directions: From the City Centre, follow Oldham Road (A62) through Failsworth. Before junction with M60, turn right into Mersey Road North. At junction with Roman Road, turn left. Cross over motorway and take first right into Lime Lane and ground is at the end of the road.
Exit M60 at junction 22 and turn left onto A62 (Oldham Road). Take first left and at roundabout, take second exit onto Victor Street. At junction with Roman Road, turn left. Cross over motorway and take first right into Lime Lane and ground is at the end of the road.
Colours: Sjy blue/navy/navy

IRLAM MITCHELL SHACKLETON
Formed: 1970 (called Mitchell Shackleton until 2001)
Secretary: Ian Street, 11 Senior Road, Peel Green, Eccles, M30 7PZ Tel: 0161 789 7061 or 07718 756402.
Ground: Silver Street, Irlam
Directions: From Junction 11 of the M60, follow the signs for Irlam onto Liverpool Road (A57). Follow road to first traffic island, and bear right onto Liverpool Road (B5320). Take the seventh road on the right onto Silver Street, and follow for approximately a quarter of a mile, where ground is on the right.
Colours: Blue & white hoops/blue/blue

LEIGH ATHLETIC
Formed: 1959
Secretary: Brendan Smith. Tel: 01942 824406 or 07879 475899
Ground: Madley Park, Charles St., Leigh Tel: 01942 673500
Directions: Exit A580 at junction with A574 onto Warrington Road and follow into Leigh town centre. Turn right into King Street and turn right into Church Street ('Boars Head' Pub). Take 6th left into Charles Street and ground straight ahead.
Colours: Yellow/ blue/ yellow

MONTON AMATEURS
Formed: 1916
Secretary: Tony Lee, 28 Wheatley Rd, Swinton, Manchester M27 3RW Tel: 0161 793 8033 or 07836 321 193
Ground: Granary Lane, Worsley, Manchester
Directions: Exit M60 at junction 13 and follow signposts for Eccles onto Barton Road (B5211). Take second right into Granary Lane and ground at end of road.
Colours: All navy blue

PRESTWICH HEYS
Formed: 1938
Secretary: Norman Deardon Tel: 0161 959 1305
Ground: Sandgate Rd, Whitefield   Tel: 0161 773 8888
Directions: Exit M60 at junction 17 and follow signposts for Whitefield (A56). After leaving roundabout,take first right into Clyde Road and go straight across at traffic lights onto Thatch Leach Lane. Follow to mini-roundabout opposite The Frigate Public House and turn right into Sandgate Road. Ground is over motorway on left hand side.
Colours: Red & white strips/black/red

ROCHDALE SACRED HEART
Formed: 1955
(called Robinson's >1985; RSH>87 & Sacred Heart>2001)
Secretary: Robert Taylor. Tel: 01706 869 640 or 07787 832 051
Ground: Fox Park, Belfield Mill Lane, Rochdale
Directions: Exit M62 onto A627(M) signposted Rochdale. Take second exit at roundabout onto Edinburgh Way (A664) and first exit onto Queensway (A664). Follow over junction with Oldham Road onto Kingsway (A664) and across junction with Milnrow Road (A640) onto Albert Royds Street. Take first left after railway onto Belfield Mill Lane to ground.
Colours: Red & white/white/white

ROYTON TOWN
Formed: 1988
Secretary: Phil Dean. Tel: 01706 882 310
Ground: Crompton Cricket Club, Glebe Road, Shaw, Oldham.Tel: 01706 847421
Directions: From M62, exit at junction 20 onto A627(M) signposted Oldham. At first exit, follow A663 (Broadway) onto A66 (Shaw Road). At roundabout, take second exit (Crompton Way), and then first left onto Rochdale Road. Glebe Road is fourth turning on your right and ground is at the end of the road.
Colours: Yellow & green/green/yellow

SPRINGHEAD
Formed: 1926
Secretary: Vicky Cunningham.
Tel: 0161 633 8938 or 077960 776 746
Ground: St John Street, Lees, Oldham Tel: 0161 627 3760
Directions: From Oldham, take Lees Road (A669) for approximately one mile and then turn left into Elliot Street, leading into St John Street. The entrance to the ground is on your right.
Colours: Red/white/white

STOCKPORT GEORGIANS
Formed: 1908
(Amalgamated with Adswood Amateurs in 1987)
Secretary: Sean Bennett.
Tel: 0161 792 9579 or 07780 914 887
Ground: Cromley Road, Woodsmoor, Stockport.
Tel: 0161 483 6581
Directions: From Stockport, follow A6 (Wellington Road South) and turn right into Bramhall Lane (A5102). Turn left at first roundabout into Woodsmoor Lane and first right into Flowery Field. Bear right into Cromley Road and ground is at bottom of road on right.
Colours: Red/black/black

WHITWORTH VALLEY
Formed: 1964
Secretary: John Taylor. Tel: 01706 853535 or 07957 846436
Ground: Rawstron Street. Whitworth
Directions: Exit M62 onto A627(M) signposted Rochdale. Take first exit at roundabout onto Edinburgh Way (A664) and third exit at next roundabout onto Manchester Road (A58). Take second exit from roundabout onto St Mary's Gate (A58) and first exit at next roundabout onto Whitworth Road (A671). Follow into Whitworth centre and turn left at Tong Lane. Take second right into Rawston Street to ground.
Colours: All navy blue

WYTHENSHAWE AMATEURS
Formed: 1959
Secretary: Geoff Sullivan. Tel: 0161 437 6232.
Ground: Longley Lane, Wythenshawe, Manchester.
Directions: From North and West, exit M60 at junction 5 onto Princess Parkway (A5103) (southbound). Turn off at first exit signposted Northenden, and turn left on Palatine Road. Take third right into Moor End, and then turn left onto Longley Lane. The entrance to ground is third right, opposite Overwood Road. From East, From M60/M56 exit at junction 2. Go right at roundabout towards Northenden onto Sharston Road (B5168). Turn left at junction with Longley Lane, and entrance to ground is second left opposite Overwood Road.
Colours: Blue & white stripes/blue/blue

MID CHESHIRE LEAGUE

SPONSORED BY: CHESHIRE BUILDING SOCIETY
Founded 1948
President: R Atherton　　**Chairman:** J Walton
Hon. Secretary: Rob Goodwin-Davey
rob.goodwindavey@bt.com

DIVISION ONE		P	W	D	L	F	A	Pts
1.	Middlewich Town	30	21	6	3	83	20	69
2.	Witton Albion Res. (2nd Div.2 04-05)	30	17	8	5	66	37	59
3.	Knutsford	30	15	7	8	65	46	52
4.	Greenalls Padgate St Oswalds	30	13	8	9	55	47	47
5.	Styal	30	12	10	8	53	42	46
6.	Garswood United	30	12	8	10	55	38	44
7.	Crosfields (-3)	30	11	11	8	49	42	41
8.	Linotype/Cheadle HN	30	10	9	11	46	52	39
9.	Poynton	30	10	7	13	45	54	37
10.	Trafford Reserves	30	10	7	13	45	54	37
11.	Bollington Athletic	30	9	9	12	50	74	36
12	Pilkington	30	7	11	12	46	62	32
13.	Barnton (Champions 04-05)	30	7	9	14	42	77	30
14.	Daten	30	7	7	16	42	51	28
15.	Rylands	30	7	7	16	29	55	28
16.	Eagle Sports	30	6	8	16	38	58	26

DIVISION ONE		1	2	3	4	5	6	7	8	9	10	11	12	13	14	15	16
1	Barnton		2-2	0-2	4-1	1-1	0-8	3-1	0-1	1-2	0-3	2-2	0-1	2-1	2-1	3-3	0-2
2	Bollington Athletic	3-1		3-0	1-2	2-2	3-2	0-2	2-1	2-2	0-7	3-1	3-2	1-1	1-1	3-4	0-1
3	Crosfields	5-0	2-2		1-1	2-1	2-2	1-2	2-5	3-1	0-4	2-2	3-1	1-2	2-1	4-0	4-2
4	Daten	0-1	8-0	0-3		2-2	0-1	2-3	2-2	1-1	0-3	4-1	6-1	1-2	0-2	1-2	0-2
5	Eagle Sports	2-1	1-1	1-1	1-2		2-1	0-2	1-2	3-1	0-4	0-1	0-2	1-2	3-3	3-2	3-3
6	Garswood United	7-0	2-3	0-0	0-0	3-0		1-1	2-1	0-2	0-3	0-2	1-3	1-1	3-3	1-1	2-0
7	Greenalls Padgate St Oswalds	1-1	2-5	2-2	1-1	2-0	1-2		1-3	1-1	1-1	4-1	2-0	2-1	2-1	5-3	2-3
8	Knutsford	1-1	4-1	1-0	0-2	6-3	4-3	1-2		2-0	1-3	7-2	0-1	3-0	2-2	3-0	2-5
9	Linotype/Cheadle HN	2-2	1-0	3-0	2-1	0-3	1-3	3-2	2-4		0-0	3-1	3-3	1-1	1-0	2-1	0-0
10	Middlewich Town	7-0	9-0	1-1	4-1	2-1	1-0	2-1	2-3	5-2		2-1	3-0	3-1	0-0	4-0	1-1
11	Pilkington	5-5	1-1	1-2	2-1	0-0	0-2	1-1	1-1	3-2	1-2		5-2	3-2	0-1	2-1	1-4
12	Poynton	1-2	5-2	1-1	2-0	3-2	0-1	3-3	1-2	2-2	0-0	0-0		0-2	0-1	0-1	4-4
13	Rylands	0-3	1-0	0-2	0-1	2-0	0-2	2-1	1-1	0-3	0-3	2-2	1-2		0-3	0-0	2-2
14	Styal	4-4	2-2	0-0	4-0	1-0	2-2	1-3	3-1	2-0	2-1	2-2	2-0	5-1		1-0	0-4
15	Trafford Reserves	4-1	0-2	3-1	0-0	1-2	1-0	1-2	0-0	3-2	2-1	2-2	2-4	3-0	3-2		1-2
16	Witton Albion Reserves	4-0	5-2	0-0	3-2	3-0	1-3	1-0	1-1	3-1	1-2	2-0	0-1	3-1	3-1	1-1	

DIVISION TWO		P	W	D	L	F	A	Pts
1	Gamesley	30	19	5	6	96	37	62
2	Woodley Sports Res.	30	16	9	5	81	44	57
3	Crewe FC	30	17	5	8	65	38	56
4	Golborne Sports	30	15	9	6	69	45	54
5	Warrington Town Res.	30	15	7	8	40	25	52
6	Broadheath Central	30	14	8	8	67	52	50
7	Club AZ	30	14	5	11	68	60	47
8	Maine Road Reserves	30	14	4	12	61	63	46
9	Curzon Ashton Res.	30	13	6	11	74	51	45
10	Whitchurch Alport	30	11	7	12	55	51	40
11	Monk FC	30	9	6	15	53	76	33
12	Glossop NE Reserves	30	8	7	15	42	65	31
13	Lostock Gralam	30	8	6	16	48	83	30
14	Billinge FC	30	8	5	17	42	68	29
15	Malpas	30	7	7	16	44	69	28
16	Fearnhead FC	30	3	2	25	28	106	11

RESERVES DIVISION		P	W	D	L	F	A	Pts
1	Linotype/Cheadle HN R.	30	22	5	3	69	35	71
2	Broadheath Central R.	30	21	4	5	68	31	67
3	Styal Reserves	30	17	7	6	86	42	58
4	Pilkington Reserves	30	14	9	7	58	36	51
5	Witton Albion Youth FC	30	13	5	12	50	38	44
6	Poynton Reserves	30	10	11	9	63	49	41
7	Garswood United Res.	30	10	11	9	52	39	41
8	Middlewich Town Res.	30	11	7	12	49	45	40
9	Daten Reserves	30	11	7	12	45	52	40
10	Golborne Sports Res.	30	10	7	13	50	60	37
11	Rylands Reserves	30	10	4	16	60	63	34
12	Greenalls Padgate ST O Res.	30	9	6	15	49	66	33
13	Billinge Reserves	30	7	9	14	39	56	30
14	Eagle Sports Reserves	30	8	6	16	42	97	30
15	Crosfields Reserves	30	7	4	19	36	78	25
16	Gamesley Reserves	30	6	6	18	42	71	24

JB BARKER CUP

FIRST ROUND

Pynton	v	Daten	1-2
Witton Albion Res.	v	Knutsford	1-2
Middlewich Town(H)	v	Greenalls Padgate St.Os.	3-1
Barnton	v	Styal	0-6
Rylands	v	Crosfields	3-2
Pilkington	v	Garswood United	2-4
Trafford Reserves	v	Bollington Athletic	0-2
Linotype/Cheadle	v	Eagle Sports	1-2

QUARTER-FINALS

Garswood United	v	Knutsford	4-1
Eagle Sports	v	Styal	2-3
Bollington Athletic	v	Rylands	3-0
Daten	v	Middlewich Town (H)	0-4

SEMI-FINALS

Bollington Athletic	v	Middlewich Town (H)	0-2
Garswood United	v	Styal	1-0

THE FINAL

Middlewich Town(H)	v	Garswood United	1-3

LEAGUE CONSTITUTION 2006-07 - DIVISION ONE

BARNTON AFC

Formed: 1946

Chairman: Mrs Barbara Leicester.

Manager: Mark Came

Secretary: Mike Allen, 12 Chepstow Close, Winsford, Cheshire

Tel: 01606 554553 (H), 07845 375175 (M)

E-mail: mikesuepaul@supanet.com

Ground: Townfield, Townfield Lane, Barnton, Northwich

Directions: Turn off the A533 (Northwich to Runcorn) at the Beech Tree Inn (Barnton Village) into Beech Lane. Turn right at the 'T' junction with Townfield Lane - the ground is 200 yards on the left.

Colours: Black & White Stripes/black/black

Change Colours: Blue/blue/red

CROSFIELDS FC

Formed: 1904

Chairman: Michael Hickey

Manager: Steve Saunders

Secretary: Geoff Bell. 61 Windmill Lane, Penketh, Warrington WA5 2AT. Tel: 01925 790 713 (H). 07841 175 268 (M)

Ground: Hood Lane Rec., Gt. Sankey, Warrington

Tel: 01925 411 730

Directions: From centre of Warrington leave travelling West on the A57 along Sankey Way. Keep straight on at large roundabout after 1 mile. After a further mile turn right at the traffic lights into Cromwell Avenue. Take 1st left at next island into Cannons Road then 3rd left into Hood Lane North. Ground at end on the left.

Colours: All navy. **Change Colours:** Red & black/black/black

DATEN FC

Formed: 1948

Chairman: Trevor Farrington

Manager: Sean Bate

Secretary: Michael Henshall, 21 Upwood Rd., Lowton, Warrington WA3 2RL Tel: 01925 724 471 (H).

Ground: Culcheth Sports Club, Charnock Road., Culcheth WA3 5SH. Tel: 01925 763 096

Directions: From M6 Jct 21 take the B road heading northwards and parallel to the M6 until the roundabout junction with A574. Turn right onto A574 towards Culcheth/Leigh and cross the M6. Turn left at the 1st roundabout and travel through Birchwood, over M62, past HM Remand Centre, Risley and into Culcheth. Pass Harrow Inn on the right, library on the left and at the end of the row of shops on the right, turn right into Charnock Road.

Colours: Blue & white stripes/black/black

Change Colours: Maroon & yellow/red/red

GAMESLEY

Formed: 1991

Chairman: Michael Dewhust

Manager: Graham Smith

Secretary: Gary Weatherhead, 36 Winster Mews, Gamesley, Glossop SK13 0LU. Tel: 01457 866393 (H), 07980 158490 (M)

Ground: Melandra Park, Gamesley, Glossop.

Directions: From M60 ring road, pick up the M67 at Denton roundabout signposted Sheffield. At the end of the motorway, take first exit A57. Forward to the traffic lights and go straight ahead (A57). At bottom of hill take the right lane and at the traffic lights turn right (A57). Bottom of the road at mini roundabout, take the second exit (A57). Go straight through first set of main traffic lights and at second set of lights take the right hand lane and turn right up the hill. Take the first right hand turn at the park (Cottage Lane). Follow the ring road round, becomes Melandra Castle Road, keep going round and the first building on the right is Gamesley Centre.

Colours: Green & white hoops/white/white. **Change Colours:** Black & white stripes.

GARSWOOD UNITED FC

Formed: 1967

Chairman: Barry Mavers

Manager: Gary Bickerstaffe

Secretary: Tony McKeown,44 Dunsdale Drive, Ashton, Wigan WN4 8PT Tel No: 01942 724 259 (H). 07785 384 990 (M).

Ground: The Wooders, Simms Lane End, Garswood, Wigan. Tel: 01744 892 258

Directions: A580 towards Liverpool, turn right into Liverpool Road (A58), left into Garswood Road (signposted Garswood 3/4 mile). Follow round, left at triangle, up to crossroads. Straight ahead. Entrance 100 yards on left.

Colours: All sky blue. **Change Colours:** Orange & grey/grey/orange

GREENALLS PADGATE ST OSWALDS

Formed: 1935

Chairman: Graham Millins

Manager: Ian Lomax

Secretary: George Jones. 125 Vulcan Close, Padgate, Warrington WA2 0HN. Tel: 01925 820 239 (H). 07713 350 036(M)

Ground: Carlsberg Tetley Social Club, Long Lane, Warrington, Cheshire. Tel: 01925 634 971.

Directions: From Junction 9 M62, take A49 towards Warrington. Proceed to 2nd roundabout and take first left into Long Lane. Proceed along Long Lane, turn into Fisher Avenue and first right into car park.

Colours: Green & black/black/green. **Change Colours:** All yellow.

Previous Name: Padgate St Oswalds

KNUTSFORD FC

Formed: 1948

Chairman: Lees Ingles

Manager: Stewart Dow

Secretary: Kevin Deeley, 28 East Street, Guide Bridge, Manchester, M34 5DX. Tel: 0161 320 9650 (H). 0161 945 8885 (B). 07968 112 664 (M).

Ground: Manchester Road, Knutsford

Directions: Situated on A50 Knutsford/Warrington road 1/2 mile West of Knutsford Town Centre, before Cottons Hotel.

Colours: Red /black/black. **Change Colours:** White/navy/navy

LINOTYPE & CHEADLE HEATH

Formed: 1919
Chairman: George Gibbons
Manager: Alan Pannett
Secretary: Brian McGuiness, 36 Barrington Road, Altrincham, Cheshire WA14 1HJ. Tel: 0161 929 0021. 07834 977 356 (M).
Ground: The Heath, Norbreck Avenue, Norbreck Avenue, Cheadle, Stockport, Cheshire SK8 2ET.
Tel: 0161 282 6574
Directions: M60 J2. Follow signs for Stockport County FC, turn right at Farmers Arms, turn right at roundabout into Bird Hall Lane, take 4th right Shaftesbury Ave, follow to bottom, turn left, ground on right immediately after bridge.
Colours: Claret & blue/blue/maroon. **Change:** White/black/black
Previous Names: Linotype FC. Cheadle Heath FC.
Merged 2004.

MIDDLEWICH TOWN FC

Formed: 1998
Chairman: Steven Morris
Manager: Terry Murphy
Secretary: Lisa Duckett, 9 Rosewood Drive, Winsford, Cheshire CW7 2UZ. Tel: 01606 551 435 (H).
Ground: Seddon Street, Middlewich Tel: 01606 835 842
Directions: Exit M6 J18 towards Middlewich, through traffic lights, turn first right then left, follow road to Seddon Street 200 yards on left. Parking on ground.
Colours: Red/black/red
Change Colours: All blue

PILKINGTON

Formed: 1938
Chairman: David Burrows
Manager: Alex Wright
Secretary: Thomas Walsh, 63 Chapel Street, St Helens WA10 2BJ.
Tel: 01744 613 681 (H). 0870 420 4804 (B). 07771 766348 (M)
Ground: Ruskin Drive, St Helens. Tel: 01744 28866.
Directions: From M6 junction 23 to A580. Approx 400 metres after 4th set of traffic lights, turn left and continue to Hope & Anchor pub. Turn right into Bishop Road and continue to halt sign. Continue across halt following road around to Ruskin Road (second road on left). Ground in Ruskin Road on right.
Colours: Sky & navy blue/navy/navy
Change Colours: Yellow /green/yellow

POYNTON

Formed: 1883
Chairman: Mark Warburton
Manager: Mark Warburton
Secretary: James Williams. 9 Dawlish Close, Bramhall, Cheshire SK7 2JD. Tel: 0161 440 7838 (H).
0161 931 4114 (B). 07970 410 320 (M).
Ground: London Road North, Poynton SK12 1AG.
Tel: 01625 875 765.
Directions: On main A523 between Macclesfield and Hazel Grove, approx 300 yards from centre of Poynton village traffic lights.
Colours: Red & black/black/red
Change Colours: All white

RYLANDS

Formed: 1911
Chairman: Alan Jackson
Manager: Terry Selby
Secretary: Stephen Eagland. 85 Gorsey Lane, Warrington WA2 7SQ. Tel: 01925 414 258 (H)
Ground: Rylands Recreation Club, Gorsey Lane, Warrington. Tel: 01925 635 700.
Directions: From Junction 21 on M6, follow A57 towards Warrington. At third set of traffic lights, turn right and through the next lights. Under railway bridge and entrance to the ground 100 yards on right.
Colours: Blue/black/blue
Change Colours: Claret & amber/claret/claret

STYAL

Formed: 1912
Chairman: Barry Green
Manager: Martin Scholes
Secretary: Alan Jones. 1 Oak Brow Cottages, Altrincham Road, Styal SK9 4JE. Tel: 01625 530 270 (H)
Ground: Altrincham Road, Styal. Tel: 01625 529 303.
Directions: From M56 Junction 5 Manchester Airport, follow Wilmslow signs at roundabouts. Turn right at traffic lights at end of Ringway Road onto B5166, Styal Road, which becomes Hollin Lane. Altrincham Road is 3rd right. Ground 300 yards on right.
Colours: Yellow/blue/blue **Change Colours:** White/navy/white

TRAFFORD RESERVES

Formed: 1990
Chairman: Tom Walmsley
Manager: Anthony Jackson
Secretary: Graham Foxall. 90 Grosvenor Road, Urmston, Manchester M41 5AQ. Tel: 0161 747 4502 (H).
07796 864 151 (M)
Ground: Shawe View, Pennybridge Lane, Flixton M41 5DL.
Tel: 0161 747 1727.
Directions: Leave M60 at J8, take A6144M towards Carrington/Lymm. At 2nd set of traffic lights, turn right onto B5158 signposted Flixton. Stay on this road, passing the railway station at Flixton. At next set of traffic lights turn right, then immediately right after the Bird in Hand Pub into Pennybridge Lane. Car Park on left adjacent to the ground.
Colours: All white
Change Colours: All yellow

WITTON ALBION RESERVES

Formed: 2001
Chairman: Mike Worthington
Manager: Neil Gill
Secretary: Phil Hassall, 8 Diploma Drive, Middlewich, Cheshire CW10 9RA
Tel: 01606 832185 (H), 01606 832734 (B), 07761 486531 (M)
Ground: Moss Farm Leisure Complex, Moss Road.
Tel: 01606 783835.
Directions: From Northwich Town Centre, head for Winnington and turn into Moss Road, complex is signposted.
Colours: Red & white/red/white
Change Colours: All sky blue

WOODLEY

Formed: 2005
Chairman: Jim Rushe
Manager: Jim Rushe
Secretary: Phyl Rushe, 367 Warrington Road, Wigan WN2 5XB. Tel: 01947 865948 (H), 07904 070240 (M)
E-mail phyl.rushe@btinternet.com
Ground: Ridgeway Road, Timperley, Altrincham, Cheshire Tel: 0161 283 1376.
Directions: Off Shaftsbury Avenue, turn onto Thorley Lane, then left into Ridgeway Road, ground 300 yards on right .
Colours: Blue/navy/navy. **Change Colours:** Yellow/black/black

MID SUSSEX LEAGUE

SPONSORED BY: GARY HOOPER HOLT LLP
General Secretary: Lawrence Parsons
Tel: 01444 242 023. 07715 491 414 (M)
lawrie.parsons9@btinternet.com

PREMIER DIVISION		P	W	D	L	F	A	Pts
1.	East Grinstead United	26	20	2	4	76	23	62
2.	Maresfield Village	26	18	5	3	72	27	59
3.	Old Varndeanians	26	19	1	6	83	28	58
4.	Willingdon Athletic (1st Div.1 04-05)	26	14	7	5	48	31	49
5.	Wisdom Sports (Champions 04-05)	26	13	5	8	57	40	44
6.	Jarvis Brook	26	13	2	11	45	39	41
7.	Balcombe	26	12	3	11	44	34	39
8.	Hassocks III	26	9	7	10	56	52	34
9.	Lewes Bridgeview	26	9	3	14	42	41	30
10.	Lindfield	26	8	2	16	34	67	26
11.	Cuckfield Town	26	7	2	17	24	66	23
12.	Newick	26	6	4	16	37	72	22
13.	Nutley	26	5	4	17	36	96	19
14.	Buxted	26	3	5	18	31	69	14

PREMIER DIVISION		1	2	3	4	5	6	7	8	9	10	11	12	13	14
1	Balcombe		2-2	5-0	1-2	2-1	1-0	1-0	1-0	0-2	3-1	4-0	1-3	0-1	1-3
2	Buxted	0-5		1-2	0-1	1-7	7-4	0-3	2-2	0-2	2-5	2-2	1-4	0-2	0-4
3	Cuckfield Town	0-4	2-1		1-4	1-8	3-0	2-0	1-2	0-1	1-0	1-2	0-4	0-3	1-5
4	East Grinstead United	1-1	2-1	4-1		4-0	2-1	3-1	3-0	2-1	9-0	11-0	2-0	2-1	3-2
5	Hassocks III	1-2	1-0	1-1	1-0		0-2	3-2	1-3	2-2	5-3	1-1	0-3	3-3	4-2
6	Jarvis Brook	1-0	4-0	3-0	1-2	1-1		0-1	2-0	1-2	3-1	HW	1-0	1-0	2-2
7	Lewes Bridgeview	0-1	1-0	3-0	1-5	1-3	0-1		6-0	0-1	0-0	8-0	0-2	1-1	0-0
8	Lindfield	2-3	2-2	1-3	0-1	2-1	0-6	2-0		0-1	2-0	6-3	0-7	1-2	1-5
9	Maresfield Village	4-1	3-0	5-1	1-1	2-2	6-0	1-2	7-1		2-0	7-1	2-1	5-0	5-1
10	Newick	2-2	2-0	5-1	0-6	2-2	1-5	1-2	1-3	1-3		4-2	1-5	0-2	3-2
11	Nutley	3-1	1-7	0-1	1-0	1-6	2-3	1-7	4-1	2-2	1-2		2-5	2-2	2-1
12	Old Varndeanians	2-1	5-0	HW	4-1	3-2	5-3	6-1	0-1	5-0	6-0	7-0		1-4	3-2
13	Willingdon Athletic	2-1	1-1	1-1	1-0	3-0	2-0	4-1	2-0	1-3	3-2	4-2	1-1		2-2
14	Wisdom Sports	1-0	0-1	3-0	2-5	5-0	1-0	3-1	3-2	2-2	0-0	3-1	2-1	1-0	

DIVISION ONE		P	W	D	L	F	A	Pts
1	Felbridge (-1)	24	16	3	5	76	39	50
2	Plumpton Athletic (+2)	24	13	7	4	56	42	48
3	Forest Row	24	14	5	5	58	36	47
4	Barcombe (+2)	24	10	7	7	68	55	39
5	Heath Pilgrims	24	9	5	10	42	46	32
6	Old Varndeanians II	24	8	7	9	56	48	31
7	Sporting Lindfield	24	8	6	10	56	64	30
8	Wisdom Sports II	24	7	7	10	48	55	28
9	Wivelsfield Green	24	6	9	9	50	57	27
10	Turners Hill	24	7	6	11	52	72	27
11	Village of Ditchling	24	7	5	12	47	69	26
12	Ardingly	24	6	5	13	42	59	23
13	Uckfield Town II (-1)	24	5	8	11	50	59	22

DIVISION TWO		P	W	D	L	F	A	Pts
1	Hartfield	24	15	6	3	55	27	51
2	Rotherfield	24	12	4	8	50	37	40
3	Hurstpierpoint II	24	12	4	8	57	44	40
4	Franklands Village	24	11	3	10	64	52	36
5	Burgess Hill Albion	24	11	2	11	56	44	35
6	Crawley Down III (+2)	24	9	6	9	44	45	35
7	Peacehaven United (+3)	24	10	2	12	40	62	35
8	Handcross Village	24	10	4	10	67	52	34
9	Pease Pottage Village II (-3)	24	11	4	9	58	61	34
10	East Grinstead United II	24	6	7	11	46	70	25
11	East Grinstead Town III (-1)	24	5	2	17	42	114	16
12	Maresfield Village II	24	0	3	21	20	73	3

DIVISION THREE

		P	W	D	L	F	A	Pts
1	Willingdon Athletic II	22	21	0	1	103	10	63
2	Ashurst Wood	22	14	2	6	74	35	44
3	Cuckfield Wheatsheaf	22	13	4	5	65	42	43
4	Horley Athletico	22	12	5	5	51	35	41
5	Roffey	22	11	3	8	59	35	36
6	Scaynes Hill	22	11	2	9	68	43	35
7	East Grinstead Mariners	22	9	3	10	44	54	30
8	Cuckfield Town II	22	8	2	12	44	64	26
9	Lindfield II (+2)	22	5	4	13	33	52	21
10	West Hoathly (-1)	22	6	4	12	31	65	21
11	Burgess Hill Athletic	22	4	1	17	32	109	13
12	Plumpton Athletic II	22	2	2	18	26	86	8

DIVISION FOUR

		P	W	D	L	F	A	Pts
1	AFC Ringmer	20	17	2	1	81	21	53
2	East Court	20	14	2	4	93	35	44
3	Fletching	20	14	1	5	49	29	43
4	Dormansland Rockets	20	10	3	7	45	33	33
5	Lewes Bridgeview II	20	10	1	9	37	48	31
6	Wealden III	20	8	1	11	36	58	25
7	Old Varndeanians III(+3)	20	5	4	11	35	54	22
8	Crowborough Athletic III	20	6	3	11	47	58	21
9	Uckfield Town III	20	6	2	12	42	64	20
10	Ardingly II	20	5	0	15	44	68	15
11	Nutley II (-3)	20	4	3	13	24	65	12

DIVISION FIVE

		P	W	D	L	F	A	Pts
1	Keymer & Hassocks	22	17	0	5	70	29	51
2	Roffey II	22	14	3	5	50	24	45
3	Danehill	22	11	4	7	68	52	37
4	Lingfield III	22	11	4	7	54	43	37
5	Scaynes Hill II	22	12	1	9	55	47	37
6	Turners Hill II	22	11	3	8	61	38	36
7	Fairwarp	22	10	2	10	54	54	32
8	Newick II	22	9	1	12	42	43	28
9	Fairfield	22	6	6	10	38	45	24
10	Handcross Village II	22	7	3	12	30	68	24
11	Buxted II	22	4	5	13	29	57	17
12	Village of Ditchling II	22	3	2	17	25	76	11

DIVISION SIX

		P	W	D	L	F	A	Pts
1	Wisdom Sports III	22	14	3	5	74	43	45
2	Burgess Hill Albion II	22	14	2	6	51	34	44
3	Barcombe II	22	11	6	5	51	24	39
4	Willingdon Athletic III	22	11	5	6	53	43	38
5	Jarvis Brook II	22	11	3	8	50	39	36
6	Rotherfield II	22	10	4	8	52	47	34
7	East Grinstead United III	22	10	3	9	53	67	33
8	East Grinstead Mariners II	22	8	3	11	46	57	27
9	Wivelsfield Green II	22	7	3	12	47	57	24
10	Ansty Sports & Social	22	6	3	13	37	51	21
11	Heath Pilgrims II	22	6	1	15	40	71	19
12	Cuckfield Town III	22	3	6	13	32	53	15

DIVISION SEVEN

		P	W	D	L	F	A	Pts
1	St Francis Rangers III	22	20	1	1	82	13	61
2	Copthorne Rovers (P)	22	17	2	3	99	25	53
3	Horsted Keynes II (P)	22	15	3	4	72	33	48
4	Ashurst Wood II (P)	22	10	8	4	45	29	38
5	Bolney Rovers (P)	22	9	4	9	43	44	31
6	Burgess Hill Athletic II(-1)	22	9	4	9	55	50	30
7	Maresfield Village III	22	8	4	10	35	59	28
8	Hartfield II	22	8	3	11	58	65	27
9	Dormansland Rockets II	22	6	2	14	34	49	20
10	Lindfield III (+2)	22	5	2	15	32	83	19
11	Cuckfield Wheatsheaf II	22	4	6	12	37	63	18
12	Danehill II	22	1	1	20	16	95	4

DIVISION EIGHT

		P	W	D	L	F	A	Pts
1	Copthorne Rovers II	22	19	0	3	104	23	57
2	Felbridge II	22	14	2	6	62	34	44
3	Uckfield Town IV (-3)	22	13	2	7	60	42	44
4	Balcombe II	22	12	5	5	77	41	41
5	Fletching II	22	12	3	7	45	34	39
6	Scaynes Hill III	22	11	6	5	43	34	39
7	Forest Row II	22	11	3	8	42	34	36
8	Chailey II	22	9	1	12	44	36	28
9	Village of Ditchling III	22	5	2	15	28	85	17
10	Handcross Village III	22	4	4	14	33	87	16
11	Wealden IV (R)	22	4	0	18	35	73	12
12	Lindfield IV (-3)	22	3	2	17	25	75	8

DIVISION NINE

		P	W	D	L	F	A	Pts
1	Crowborough Athletic IV	22	17	2	3	82	31	53
2	Fairwarp II	22	12	1	9	57	47	37
3	Maresfield Village IV	22	11	3	8	47	34	36
4	Burgess Hill Albion III	22	11	2	9	56	61	35
5	Lindfield V	22	10	2	10	54	61	32
6	Ardingly III (+3)	22	8	2	12	53	49	29
7	Plumpton Athletic III (+3)	22	8	2	12	50	47	29
8	West Hoathly II (-3)	22	9	3	10	52	55	27
9	Cuckfield Town IV (-6)	22	8	4	10	65	53	22
10	Scaynes Hill IV (+3)	22	4	1	17	22	91	16
11	Buxted III	22	3	0	19	31	100	9

MONTGOMERY CHALLENGE CUP

FIRST ROUND

Heath Pilgrims	v	Wisdom Sports	1-0
Jarvis Brook	v	Village of Ditchling	2-0
Handcross Village	v	Uckfield Town II	3-2
East Grinstead Utd	v	Horsted Keynes	9-3
Lewes Bridgeview	v	Felbridge	3-3*, 4-3p
Buxted	v	Forest Row	3-2
Maresfield Village	v	Barcombe	4-1
Balcombe	v	Turners Hill	4-0
Newick	v	Ardingly	2-1
Old Varndeanians (H)	v	Lindfield	2-1

SECOND ROUND

Sporting Linfield	v	Nutley	4-2
Heath Pilgrims	v	Jarvis Brook	1-5
Handcross Village	v	Plumpton Athletic	5-2
East Grinstead Utd	v	Lewes Bridgeview	7-3
Buxted	v	Cuckfield Town	2-2*, 3-4p
Maresfield Village	v	Balcombe	3-0
Willingdon Athletic	v	Newick	3-0
Hassocks III	v	Old Varndeanians (H)	1-2

QUARTER-FINALS

Sporting Lindfield	v	Jarvis Brook	0-10
Handcross Village	v	East Grinstead United	1-8
Cuckfield Town	v	Maresfield Village	0-5
Willingdon Athletic	v	Old Varndeanians (H)	3-1

SEMI-FINALS

Jarvis Brook	v	East Grinstead United	3-7
Maresfield Village	v	Willingdon Athletic	AW

THE FINAL (22nd April)

East Grinstead Utd	v	Willingdon Athletic	2-3

LEAGUE CONSTITUTION 2006-07 - PREMIER DIVISION

BALCOMBE

CUCKFIELD TOWN

EAST GRINSTEAD UNITED

FELBRIDGE

HASSOCKS III

JARVIS BROOK

LEWES BRIDGEVIEW

LINDFIELD

MARESFIELD VILLAGE

NEWICK

OLD VARNDEANIANS

PLUMPTON ATHLETIC

WILLINGDON ATHLETIC

WISDOM SPORTS

MIDDLESEX COUNTY LEAGUE

SPONSORED BY: CHERRY RED RECORDS

Founded 1984
President: Peter Rogers   **Chairman:** Reg Johnson
Secretary: Stephen C. Hosmer, 27 St Georges Road, Hanworth, Middx.
TW13 6RD Tel: (H) 020 8894 1244 (Fax) 020 8894 0499
(M) 07831 393559 Email: stephen@hosmer.freeserve.co.uk

PREMIER DIVISION		P	W	D	L	F	A	Pts
1.	Battersea Ironsides	30	21	6	3	55	22	69
2.	C.B. Hounslow United (Promoted)	30	18	9	3	71	35	63
3.	Neasden Foundation (1st Div.1 04-05)	30	17	4	9	60	37	55
4.	London Tigers	30	16	6	8	80	40	54
5.	Wraysbury	30	15	8	7	76	49	53
6.	Walthamstow Avenue & Pennant	30	14	9	7	44	36	51
7.	Crown & Manor	30	15	3	12	60	46	48
8.	Spelthorne Sports	30	14	6	10	38	36	48
9.	FC Deportivo Galicia	30	13	2	15	47	54	41
10.	Brazilian	30	12	4	14	61	55	40
11.	Bedfont Sports (2nd Div.1 04-05)	30	11	7	12	53	51	40
12.	Willesden Constantine	30	11	6	13	59	59	39
13	Ealing	30	8	3	19	48	72	27
14	Marsh Rangers	30	6	3	21	27	69	21
15	Mauritius Sports	30	6	3	21	35	82	21
16	Stonewall	30	3	1	26	22	93	10

PREMIER DIVISION		1	2	3	4	5	6	7	8	9	10	11	12	13	14	15	16
1	Battersea Ironsides		1-0	0-5	1-0	1-0	3-0	4-2	2-1	5-2	HW	3-0	2-3	7-1	HW	3-0	1-1
2	Bedfont Sports 0-1	0-1		1-1	2-2	1-2	2-1	0-1	1-5	7-0	3-1	1-4	1-0	5-1	3-2	2-3	1-4
3	Brazilian	0-1	4-4		1-2	6-0	1-0	1-0	3-1	3-0	1-1	1-3	0-1	1-2	2-3	0-2	2-4
4	C.B. Hounslow United	1-1	1-1	4-0		2-0	4-3	3-2	2-2	5-0	HW	1-3	1-0	3-0	1-1	2-1	4-3
5	Crown & Manor	0-2	3-2	4-1	0-3		3-0	1-2	1-2	4-0	1-1	1-0	2-2	6-0	2-0	2-2	0-3
6	Ealing	1-3	2-3	1-3	1-1	1-4		4-2	1-4	4-2	4-1	2-1	0-1	1-2	2-3	0-2	2-2
7	FC Deportivo Galicia	0-3	2-2	3-2	0-3	1-2	3-1		1-3	2-1	2-3	0-2	0-1	2-0	0-2	3-2	0-3
8	London Tigers	1-1	2-0	4-0	2-2	2-0	5-0	1-3		HW	5-0	1-1	3-3	6-0	0-1	4-3	8-1
9	Marsh Rangers	0-0	1-2	0-3	2-6	0-2	1-1	0-1	0-5		HW	0-2	0-1	4-0	2-3	0-4	2-1
10	Mauritius SportsAW	4-0	3-6	0-4	2-4	0-4	1-4	2-1	1-3			1-8	D	0-4	1-4	0-6	2-5
11	Neasden Foundation	1-0	0-1	1-2	2-2	2-0	0-1	5-0	3-2	HW	2-1		1-0	4-1	AW	3-2	5-3
12	Spelthorne Sports	1-2	1-1	3-5	1-6	HW	2-0	3-2	3-1	HW	3-0	0-0		2-0	0-1	2-1	1-1
13	Stonewall	0-3	1-5	0-4	1-2	1-4	2-4	0-2	1-4	0-2	1-2	1-2	0-3		0-2	0-2	1-2
14	Walthamstow Avenue & Pennant	1-1	0-0	3-1	2-0	1-4	HW	0-3	0-0	2-2	0-2	1-1	2-0	5-1		1-1	0-3
15	Willesden Constantine	0-3	1-0	2-2	2-3	2-6	3-4	1-1	3-2	0-3	1-4	6-4	2-1	4-1	1-1		0-0
16	Wraysbury	1-1	0-2	2-0	1-1	4-2	9-3	0-3	2-3	5-0	6-2	3-0	2-0	0-0	3-3	2-0	

DIVISION ONE	P	W	D	L	F	A	Pts
1 Sport London E Benfica	22	15	5	2	46	19	50
2 Bison	22	14	4	4	60	27	46
3 Parkfield Youth Old Boys	22	14	4	4	58	25	46
4 Fenerbahce	22	11	5	6	50	34	38
5 The Wilberforce Wanderers	22	10	4	8	48	44	34
6 St John's Athletic	22	9	2	11	32	45	29
7 North Greenford Utd S.	21	7	6	8	39	40	27
8 Harefield Ex-Servicemens	22	7	6	9	31	49	27
9 Hounslow Wanderers (-3)	22	6	5	11	34	43	20
10 Islington Shooting Stars	22	5	5	12	41	62	20
11 South Kilburn	21	5	4	12	28	39	19
12 FC Ealing Assyrians	22	3	0	19	24	64	9

DIVISION TWO	P	W	D	L	F	A	Pts
1 Signcraft	20	12	6	2	70	25	42
2 North Hayes Academicals	20	11	5	4	45	35	38
3 Bridge Rovers (-3)	20	12	2	6	39	27	35
4 Puma 2000	20	9	6	5	54	39	33
5 LPOSSA	20	8	6	6	52	48	30
6 Brentham	20	8	6	6	39	40	30
7 Harefield Wednesday	20	8	5	7	43	37	29
8 Haringey Town	20	3	10	7	38	45	19
9 South Acton	20	5	4	11	27	47	19
10 Brunel University	20	3	5	12	36	65	14
11 Barn Elms	20	2	3	15	30	65	9

Soccer Speaker
a new brand of sports speaker

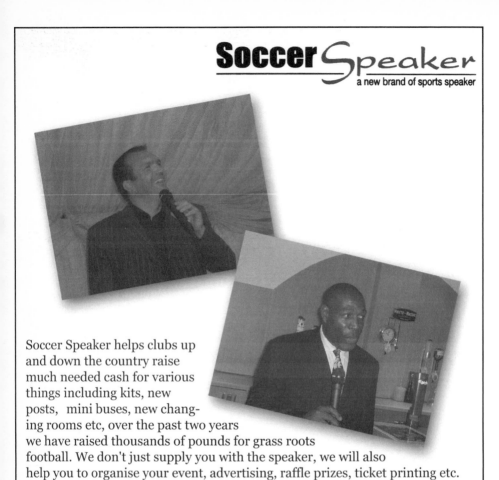

Soccer Speaker helps clubs up and down the country raise much needed cash for various things including kits, new posts, mini buses, new changing rooms etc, over the past two years we have raised thousands of pounds for grass roots football. We don't just supply you with the speaker, we will also help you to organise your event, advertising, raffle prizes, ticket printing etc.

No job is too small, we organise things for small clubs, pie & a pint with 50 guests and a speaker right up to your bigger events with a 5 course meal, speaker, comedian & compare. Auction items are also available, all come with a photo of the piece being signed along with a double your money back certificate of authenticity.

Soccer Speaker are Neil Razor Ruddock's official agents for all his sportsman's dinners, Neil is one of the best speakers on the circuit, his stories from the jungle and his footballing career are hilarious, other names available include Ronnie Whelan, Mike Summerbee, John Aldridge, Ron Chopper Harris, Frank Bruno, Jeff Winter, Peter Osgood, John McGovern, Duncan McKenzie, Tommy Docherty, Henry Cooper and many more (see website for details)
See **www.soccerspeaker.com**

DIVISION THREE

		P	W	D	L	F	A	Pts
1	Harrow St Mary's Yth O.B.	26	18	5	3	79	32	59
2	Imperial College O.B.	26	17	5	4	93	41	56
3	Camden & Ampthill Football Acad.	26	17	4	5	92	45	55
4	Amis-BK/London United	26	17	2	7	46	27	53
5	Blue Marlin	26	15	5	6	81	48	50
6	FC Tilburg Regents	26	12	3	11	55	57	39
7	Harlington	26	12	1	13	54	56	37
8	Stedfast United	26	10	5	11	66	72	35
9	Renegades	26	8	6	12	53	44	30
10	Greens United (-3)	26	7	6	13	52	63	24
11	Samba Soccer School (-3)	26	8	2	16	50	63	23
12	Warren	26	5	6	15	41	89	21
13	Hayes Town	26	5	5	16	30	62	20
14	ACA	26	2	3	21	22	115	9

LEAGUE CONSTITUTION 2006-07

BEDFONT SPORTS
BISON
BRAZILIAN
EALING
FC DEPORTIVO GALICIA
KINGS MEADOW
MARSH RANGERS
MAURITIUS SPORTS (CMB)
NEASDEN FOUNDATIONS
PARKFIELD YOUTH OLD BOYS
SOUTHALL
SPELTHORNE SPORTS
SPORT LONDON E BENFICA
WALTHAMSTOW AVENUE & PENNANT
WILLESDEN CONSTANTINE
WRAYSBURY

MIDDLESEX FEDERATION LEAGUE CUP

PRELIMINARY ROUND
Bridge Rovers	v	Harefield Ex-Servicemens R.	4-1
Brunel Uni. Res.	v	Signcraft	1-3
Battersea Ironsides	v	North Greenford Utd S. Res.	4-0
Turkish Comm.	v	Samba Soccer School	3-2

FIRST ROUND
Brentham	v	Ealing	2-4
Chingford Town	v	Bedfont Sports	1-9
Harlington	v	Haringey Town	1-2
Fenerbahce	v	Mauritius Sports	2-1
Marsh Rangers	v	South Kilburn	1-2
North Hayes Acade'	v	Spelthorne Sports	4-2
Greens United	v	Eastcote-Richings Park	3-3*, 5-4p
Stonewall Reserves	v	Harrow St Mary's Youth O.B.	0-3
St John's Athletic	v	Walthamstow Ave & Penn.	1-2
St Georges	v	FC Tilburg Regents Res.	7-1
Sport Lond E Benf.	v	Enfield Reserves	4-1
Young Stars	v	Stedfast United	AW
Samba Soccer S.R.v		Islington Shooting Stars	1-11
FC Tilburg Regents	v	Hounslow W'derers R.	3-3*, 6-7p
ACA	v	LPOSSA	1-19
Brentham Reserves	v	C.B. Hounslow Utd Res.	2-5
Brazilian (H)	v	Neasden Foundation	1-3

SECOND ROUND
FC Deportivo Gal.	v	Battersea Ironsides	0-1
Bridge Rovers	v	FC Ealing Assyrians	3-0
Harefield Wed.	v	Fenerbahce	3-3*, 3-4p
Turkish Community	v	Blue Marlin	AW
North Hayes Ac. R.	v	Ealing	1-0
Brunel University	v	Bethnal Green Utd	5-4
Crown & Manor	v	Imperial College O.B.	5-0
Renegades	v	Amis-BK/London Utd	2-2*, 3-2p
Bedfont Sports	v	South Acton	3-2
Haringey Town	v	Bison	0-2
Puma 2000	v	Sport London E Benfica	2-3
C.B. Hounslow U 3.	v	North Hayes Academicals	2-3
Spelthorne Sp. R.	v	Parkfield Youth Old Boys	0-3
South Kilburn	v	Greens United	5-1
Hayes Town	v	Walthamstow Ave. & Penn.	1-2
Stonewall	v	North Greenford Utd S.	2-4
Hounslow W'derers	v	Islington Shooting Stars	3-1
Stedfast United	v	Warren	2-1
Signcraft	v	St Georges	7-2
Harrow St Marys YOB	v	Barn Elms	4-1
Hendon A	v	Southall Reserves	HW

THIRD ROUND (cont.)
London Tigers	v	Camden & Ampthill F. A.	2-1
Hounslow Boro A	v	Puma 2000 Reserves	10-0
Hanworth Villa Res.	v	Willesden Constantine	1-4
Wraysbury	v	Bedfont Sports Reserves	6-4
The Wilberforce W.	v	Hounslow Wanderers Res.	12-1
London Tigers Res.	v	Barnhill	HW
Harefield Wed. Res.	v	Harefield Ex-Servicemens	HW
CB hounslow Utd	v	London Soccer Academy	1-3

THIRD ROUND
Willesden Constan.	v	North Hayes Academicals	4-1
Harrow St Marys YOB	v	Hounslow Wanderers	2-2*, 4-5p
London Tigers Res.	v	Crown & Manor	2-2*, 3-4p
Bridge Rovers	v	Parkfield Youth Old Boys	0-6
Bedfont Sports	v	London Soccer Academy	2-4
Brunel University	v	LPOSSA	0-4
Sport London E.B.	v	North Hayes Academicals R	3-0
Blue Marlin	v	Neasden Foundation	0-1
Signcraft	v	CB Hounslow Utd Res.	3-2
Wraysbury	v	South Kilburn	3-1
The Wilberforce W.	v	Stedfast United	4-0
Renegades	v	London Tigers	2-6
Hounslow Boro' A	v	Harefield Wednesday	0-3
Battersea Ironside	v	Fenerbahce	3-2
Walthamstow Av. P.	v	Bison	3-1
North Greenford US	v	Hendon A	3-1

FOURTH ROUND
Wraysbury	v	North Greenford Utd S.	0-0*, 4-2p
Harefield Wed. Res	v	Parkfield Youth Old Boys	1-8
Signcraft	v	Sport London E Benfica	1-3
London Tigers Res	v	Battersea Ironsides	0-2
Walthamstow A.P.	v	LPOSSA	HW
Willesden Cons.	v	Neasden Foundation	1-0
London Soccer Ac	v	London Tigers	2-1
The Wilberforce W.	v	Hounslow Wanderers	5-2

QUARTER-FINALS
Walthamstow A.P.	v	Sport London E Ben.	2-2*, 4-2p
Willesden Cons.	v	Battersea Ironsides	1-0
London Soccer Ac	v	Parkfield Youth Old Boys	3-4
The Wilberforce W.	v	Wraysbury	1-2

SEMI-FINALS
| Walthamstow A.P. | v | Wraysbury | 5-3 |
| Parkfield Youth OB | v | Willesden Constantine | 1-3 |

THE FINAL (29th April)
| Walthamstow A.P. | v | Willesden Constantine | 1-0 |

MIDLAND COMBINATION

President: Les James **Chairman:** Roy Craddock
Secretary: Nigel Wood
30 Glaisdale Road, Birmingham B28 8PX
Tel: (h) 0121 244 6412 (m) 07967 440007 (f) 0121 249 0974
e-mail: nigel.r.wood@blueyonder.co.uk

PREMIER DIVISION		P	W	D	L	F	A	Pts
1.	Atherstone Town (1st Div.1 04-05)	42	32	7	3	131	27	103
2.	Coventry Sphinx	42	33	4	5	150	61	103
3.	Barnt Green Spartak	42	28	3	11	82	51	87
4.	Feckenham	42	25	6	11	107	64	81
5.	Bridgnorth Town	42	24	7	11	75	48	79
6.	Bolehall Swifts	42	24	6	12	90	59	78
7.	Shifnal Town	42	23	8	11	86	44	77
8.	Nuneaton Griff	42	19	6	17	73	72	63
9.	Castle Vale	42	18	8	16	73	76	62
10.	Alveston	42	18	4	20	65	61	58
11.	Coleshill Town	42	14	9	19	79	93	51
12.	Brocton	42	13	10	19	56	70	49
13.	Southam United	42	13	9	20	56	65	48
14.	Highgate United	42	13	8	21	51	86	47
15.	Coventry Copsewood (-3)	42	14	7	21	56	79	46
16.	Pershore Town	42	14	3	25	63	88	45
17.	Meir K.A.	42	12	9	21	55	92	45
18.	Dudley Sports	42	11	11	20	51	71	44
19.	Pilkington X.X.X	42	11	8	23	62	108	41
20.	Massey Ferguson	42	11	5	26	46	91	38
21.	Cadbury Athletic (-4) (2nd Div.1 04-05)	42	11	8	23	68	92	37
22.	Continental Star	42	5	6	31	51	128	21

PREMIER DIVISION	1	2	3	4	5	6	7	8	9	10	11	12	13	14	15	16	17	18	19	20	21	22
1 Alveston		0-3	0-3	0-1	1-1	1-0	3-1	1-2	3-4	3-0	1-2	3-2	1-2	1-3	5-2	1-0	1-2	3-1	5-2	1-0	1-2	0-2
2 Atherstone T.	3-1		6-0	2-2	0-0	2-0	0-2	3-0	4-1	9-0	1-0	2-2	2-0	2-2	3-0	1-0	5-0	1-1	7-0	0-1	3-1	0-0
3 Barnt Green S.	0-1	1-2		1-0	4-1	1-0	1-0	3-0	3-3	2-1	2-0	0-2	3-0	1-2	2-0	3-1	4-2	4-2	3-0	3-1	1-0	2-1
4 Bolehall Swifts	4-3	0-6	4-1		3-1	2-0	5-1	2-1	3-1	2-0	3-0	2-4	4-1	4-1	3-0	2-0	7-0	0-3	2-1	2-2	0-4	2-1
5 Bridgnorth T	1-0	0-2	1-1	3-0		0-1	2-1	6-1	4-2	3-2	2-0	0-2	3-2	1-0	1-0	0-1	3-0	1-1	2-1	4-1	0-2	5-2
6 Brocton	2-0	0-1	2-0	1-1	0-1		3-3	3-3	0-3	3-0	2-2	1-0	0-2	3-0	1-1	5-3	3-0	1-4	0-1	1-2	1-1	2-1
7 Cadbury Ath.	1-2	0-3	1-3	3-1	0-1	3-3		2-5	2-4	2-0	1-2	4-7	3-2	1-3	1-2	1-1	1-1	4-3	0-1	3-2	2-0	1-2
8 Castle Vale	0-3	3-3	2-3	0-0	2-0	2-1	1-1		1-1	1-0	2-1	1-2	2-1	1-3	4-2	3-2	0-1	1-4	5-0	0-2	2-1	1-1
9 Coleshill Town	1-0	1-4	0-5	2-2	1-2	4-3	0-1	2-3		1-1	3-0	1-3	4-2	0-4	1-2	5-2	1-3	0-1	1-1	0-0	3-1	2-1
10 Continental Star	1-3	0-7	0-3	1-6	1-6	1-1	1-2	2-3	2-5		1-5	0-4	1-1	3-7	0-1	1-0	1-2	2-0	2-3	1-1	0-2	1-4
11 Coventry C.	0-3	0-1	2-1	2-1	0-3	0-1	2-2	2-1	3-1	4-1		0-1	1-4	0-4	2-1	1-1	2-2	2-2	2-1	1-3	1-2	1-1
12 Coventry S.	5-1	2-3	6-1	3-4	1-1	3-0	6-4	1-4	4-1	7-3	4-1		5-0	2-1	5-0	11-0	5-3	4-1	4-3	6-1	1-1	2-0
13 Dudley Sports	0-4	0-5	1-1	0-2	0-1	2-2	1-3	0-1	0-2	2-2	1-1	1-2		0-0	3-4	5-0	1-0	2-1	1-2	0-0	2-2	
14 Feckenham	1-1	1-3	3-2	3-1	1-2	3-0	3-1	5-2	5-5	3-2	2-0	2-5	3-0		4-1	0-1	2-0	3-0	1-1	5-1	1-0	5-1
15 Highgate Utd	1-0	1-7	1-2	2-1	2-2	1-3	0-4	0-1	0-0	2-0	4-0	1-1	0-0	2-0		0-4	1-2	2-0	2-1	3-3	2-5	1-7
16 Massey Ferg.	0-0	0-4	0-1	0-1	3-1	3-2	1-1	2-1	0-5	2-2	3-2	1-3	0-1	0-4	3-1		0-4	4-0	0-2	0-4	1-2	
17 Meir KA	1-4	0-4	1-2	0-4	2-1	1-1	0-0	3-3	1-0	0-3	0-2	1-2	1-1	7-3	1-0	1-0		4-5	0-0	2-2	0-0	3-2
18 Nuneaton Griff	1-2	2-1	1-0	1-3	0-1	1-0	1-0	5-2	5-3	3-1	2-5	0-3	0-4	1-1	2-0	3-0		2-1	3-1	1-1	3-1	
19 Pershore Town	2-0	2-3	1-0	0-3	3-1	0-1	3-0	0-3	3-0	3-6	3-4	0-1	0-1	1-3	4-0	1-2	5-3	0-3		3-1	3-5	2-0
20 Pilkington XXX	0-1	0-8	0-5	3-3	0-3	6-2	3-2	1-3	3-3	2-3	1-3	3-4	1-3	2-6	1-0	0-4	2-3	1-0	0-4		1-6	2-1
21 Shifnal Town	2-1	0-2	0-1	0-1	1-1	5-0	4-1	5-2	5-1	5-0	2-0	1-3	0-1	4-1	1-1	2-1	1-0	0-0	3-1	3-1		3-2
22 Southam Utd	0-0	1-3	1-2	1-0	0-1	1-0	4-2	0-0	1-2	1-0	1-2	1-6	1-1	0-0	0-2	1-0	2-1	4-1	2-0	0-0	0-1	

DIVISION ONE

		P	W	D	L	F	A	Pts
1	Knowle	34	21	8	5	62	22	71
2	Northfield Town	34	20	9	5	84	30	69
3	Ettington	34	19	4	11	62	50	61
4	Fairfield Villa	34	18	5	11	59	43	59
5	Burntwood Town	34	15	6	13	57	58	51
6	Thimblemill R.E.C.	34	15	6	13	59	66	51
7	Stockingford A.A.	34	14	8	12	75	54	50
8	Polesworth North Warwick	34	14	8	12	64	49	50
9	Mile Oak Rovers	34	14	6	14	49	43	48
10	Archdale '73	34	13	7	14	48	60	46
11	Handsworth United (-3)	34	14	5	15	81	77	44
12	Heather Athletic	34	12	8	14	45	49	44
13	Littleton	34	12	3	19	61	70	39
14	Loughborough	34	11	6	17	42	70	39
15	West Midlands Police	34	11	4	19	49	59	37
16	Leamington Hibernian	34	10	5	19	42	61	35
17	Newhall United (-3)	34	8	11	15	46	74	32
18	Kenilworth Town K.H.	34	8	5	21	38	88	29

DIVISION TWO

		P	W	D	L	F	A	Pts
1	Bartley Green	26	17	7	2	67	26	58
2	University of Birmingham	25	16	5	4	69	24	53
3	Earlswood Town	26	14	7	5	47	27	49
4	Coton Green	26	11	9	6	47	42	42
5	Enville Athletic	26	11	5	10	58	54	38
6	Feckenham Reserves	26	12	2	12	41	43	38
7	Droitwich Spa	25	10	5	10	31	30	35
8	Cadbury Athletic Res.	25	10	3	12	39	42	33
9	West Hagley (-3)	26	9	6	11	51	50	30
10	Continental Star Res.	25	7	6	12	42	58	27
11	Castle Vale Res.	25	7	5	13	34	60	26
12	Chelmsley Town	25	6	5	14	45	64	23
13	Warwick Town	25	5	7	13	35	45	22

Kenilworth Town K.H. Reserves resigned from the competition without playing a match.
Nunnery Wood resigned - records expunged.
Himley Athletic resigned on 9th March, rule 12c applies, league table determined by points average per game.

DIVISION THREE

		P	W	D	L	F	A	Pts
1	Halesowen Town Res.	28	18	6	4	84	25	60
2	Coventry Sphinx R. (P)	28	18	6	4	79	22	60
3	Perrywood (P)	28	18	5	5	66	36	59
4	Barnt Green Spartak R.	28	17	4	7	58	41	55
5	Worcester City 'A' (P)	28	16	5	7	54	36	53
6	Greenhill	28	16	2	10	49	42	50
7	Coleshill Town Res.	28	14	7	7	53	34	49
8	Droitwich Spa Res.	28	11	6	11	52	62	39
9	Knowle Reserves	28	11	5	12	50	57	38
10	Shipston Excelsior	28	10	5	13	47	65	35
11	Heather Athletic Res.	28	7	8	13	25	43	29
12	Northfield Town Res.	28	7	4	17	43	64	25
13	Wellesbourne	28	3	3	22	35	88	12
14	Chelmsley Town Res.	28	2	5	21	27	71	11
15	Ettington Reserves (-6)	28	2	9	17	38	74	9

Bolehall Swifts Reserves resigned, records expunged.

RESERVE DIVISION

		P	W	D	L	F	A	Pts
1	Rushall Olympic	28	19	4	5	72	25	61
2	Mickleover Sports	28	17	4	7	56	43	55
3	Hinckley United	28	16	5	7	71	42	53
4	Oadby Town	28	16	3	9	61	45	51
5	Boldmere St. Michaels	28	15	4	9	54	36	49
6	Quorn	28	15	3	10	61	52	48
7	Tipton Town	28	12	9	7	55	39	45
8	Bromsgrove Rovers	28	13	5	10	75	75	44
9	Gresley Rovers	28	13	4	11	47	51	43
10	Shepshed Dynamo	28	11	4	13	53	59	37
11	Barwell	28	10	4	14	36	48	34
12	Chasetown	28	8	3	17	40	58	27
13	Loughborough Dynamo (-3)	28	9	3	16	51	74	27
14	Atherstone Town	28	2	1	25	30	94	7
15	Rugby Town (-12)	28	4	4	20	51	72	4

CHALLENGE CUP
PREMIER AND DIVISION ONE CLUBS

FIRST ROUND

Alveston	v	Feckenham	1-2
Atherstone Town	v	Bridgnorth Town	4-1
Castle Vale	v	Pilkington XXX	1-0
Archdale '73	v	Meir K.A.	2-3
Highgate United	v	Northfield Town	0-1
Newhall United	v	Southam United (H)	0-1
Shifnal Town	v	Stockingford A.A.	2-0, 3-0r
Kenilworth Town KH	v	Massey Ferguson	0-2
Bolehall Swifts	v	Cadbury Athletic	2-1

SECOND ROUND

Brocton	v	Feckenham	1-2
Fairfield Villa	v	Polesworth North Warwick	6-5
Knowle	v	Mile Oak Rovers	1-2
Heather Athletic	v	Massey Ferguson	1-4
Burntwood Town	v	Meir K.A.	3-1
Castle Vale	v	Ettington	1-2
Loughborough	v	Littleton	3-2
Pershore Town	v	Bolehall Swifts	3-2
West Midlands Police	v	Coventry Sphinx	0-1
Coleshill Town	v	Nuneaton Griff	1-3
Shifnal Town	v	Thimblemill R.E.C.	4-3
Coventry Copsewood	v	Dudley Sports	2-1*
Barnt Green Spartak	v	Leamington Hibernian	2-1
Atherstone Town	v	Continental Star	3-1
Handsworth United	v	Southam United (H)	6-1

THIRD ROUND

Massey Ferguson	v	Ettington	1-1*, 3-2p
Fairfield Villa	v	Burntwood Town	5-1
Nuneaton Griff	v	Coventry Sphinx	0-4
Shifnal Town	v	Loughbrough	10-0
Pershore Town	v	Mile Oak Rovers	4-0
Northfield Town	v	Atherstone Town	0-3
Handsworth United	v	Feckenham	1-3
Coventry Copsewood	v	Barnet Green Spartak	1-2

QUARTER-FINALS

Massey Ferguson	v	Pershore Town	0-4
Shifnal Town	v	Fairfield Villa	5-1
Coventry Sphinx	v	Feckenham	3-4
Barnt Green Spartak	v	Atherstone Town	1-5

SEMI-FINALS (played over two legs home and away)

Pershore Town	v	Feckenham	1-1	3-3*, 3-5p
Atherstone Town	v	Shifnal Town	3-0	0-0

THE FINAL

Atherstone Town	v	Feckenham	2-1

ALVESTON

Formed: 1927

Chairman: Martin Beese

Secretary: Peter Boyle,2 Kettlewell Close, Woodloes Park, Warwick CV34 5XE Tel NOs: 01926 774843 (H) 07818 466436 (M)

Ground: Home Guard Club, Main Street, Tiddington, Stratford-upon-Avon. Tel: 01789 297718

Social Club Telephone : 01789 297718

Club Email martin.beese@fleet.gecapital.com

Directions: Leave the M42 J2 - follow signs to Redditch, taking the dual carriageway bypass. At island turn right (signposted Alvechurch). Ground is approximately 1/2 mile on the right hand side. The ground is actually located on the Redditch Road just south of Alvechurch village.

Colours: Maroon & sky blue/sky blue/ maroon & sky blue

Change: Yellow/black/yellow& black

BARNT GREEN SPARTAK (V)

Formed: 1992

Chairman: Avtar Singh

Secretary: G.J.Singh, 9 Showell Green Lane, Sparkhill, Birmingham B11 4NP Tel: 07968 587 648

Ground: Lye Meadow, Redditch Road, Alvechurch, B48 7RS Tel: 0121 445 2929.

Directions: From M42 Jct 2 follow signs to Redditchalong the dual carriageway by pass. At traffic island turn right and ground is approximately 1km on right.

Colours: Tangerine/black/tangerine

Change colours: Royal Blue & white/Blue/Blue

BOLEHALL SWIFTS (V)

Formed: 1953

Chairman: Mick Ross

Secretary: Philip Hill, 64 Rene Road, Bolehall,Tamworth,Staffs. B77 3NN Tel: 07812 449054 (M)

Ground: Rene Road, Bolehall, Tamworth Tel: 01827 62637

Directions: Take M42 north, leaving at J10. Turn left onto the A5 heading for Tamworth. Leave the A5 at the second exit, marked Glascote and Amington Industrial Estate. Turn right onto Marlborough Way until next island. Turn left at the island down the B5000 then take a right into Argyle Street (opposite the chip shop). At the T-junction, turn left into Amington Road. Drive over the canal bridge, take the second right into Leedham Avenue, then the right fork into Rene Road. The club is situated 150 yards on the right immediately after the school.

Colours: Yellow/green/yellow

Change: Blue

BRERETON SOCIAL

Formed: 1899

Chairman: Jon Moore

Secretary: Paul Fisher, 55 Birch Lane, Brereton, Rugeley, Staffs. WS15 1EJ. Tel: Home 01889 577983 Mobile 07811 360391

Ground: Red Lion Ground, Armitage Lane, Brereton, Rugeley, Staffs. WS15 1ED

Tel: 01889 585526

Directions: From M6 Junction 11 follow A460 to Rugeley, on reaching large roundabout at Rugeley take A51 (signposted Lichfield). At end of dual carriageway in Brereton turn left at traffic lights into Armitage Lane. Entrance is 100 yards on right.

Colours: Red & White Striped Shirts, Red Shorts, White Socks.

BROCTON

Formed: 1937

Chairman: Brian Townsend

Secretary Homer.124 John Street,Chadsmoor,Cannock WS11 5HR. Tel No: 01543 571964

Ground:C/o Heath Hayes F.C.Coppice Colliery, Heath Hayes, Cannock Staffs (07976 26928ons: From M6 , J11 take A460 signposted Cannock. At 1st island turn right on to A460 signposted Rugeley / Cannock Business Parks. Straight on at the next island.

*Upon reaching A5 straight on at island signposted Rugeley / Hednesford still on A460. Straight on at next two islands then at 3rd Island turn right on to A5190 (not A5790 as in handbook) signposted Lichfield. Straight on at next island then, in 1.5 miles, you will pass a Texaco garage on right hand side. Take next right after the garage into Newlands Lane. The entrance to the ground is 50 yards down on the left under a green barrier.

NB Ensure that you go down the Newlands Lane after the garage as it says above; there is another Newlands Road entrance before, which used to be the same road in a horseshoe. But has now been divided by the toll road, and if you go down the first one you'll have to turn round and come back.

Colours: Green & White/White/Green

Change colours:

CADBURY ATHLETIC

Formed: 1994

Chairman: Andy Clarke

Secretary: Ron Thorn, 3 Kingshurst Road, Northfield, Birmingham B31 2LN Tel Nos: 0121 624 8288 (H) 07751 838715(M)

Ground: Cadbury Recreation Ground, Bournville Lane, Birmingham. B14 6DL. Tel No: 0121 458 2000 x 3316 or 0121 454 4264

Directions: From M5 jct 4 take A38 to Birmingham, turn eight at Selly Oak lights (A4040) travel one mile down Oak Tree Lane/ Lindem Road to Bourbille Lane, turn left and ground is on the left.

Colours: All Purple.

Change Colours: Royal Blue & black/blue/blue.

CASTLE VALE

Formed: 1964

Chairman: Ray Kite

Secretary: William Mort, 178 Plantsbrook, Road, Sutton Coldfield, Birmingham, W./Mids.Tel Nos: 0121 3512931 (H)

Ground: Vale Stadium, Farnborough Road, Castle Vale, Warwick B35 7BE. Tel: 0121 747 6969.

Directions: Leave M6 J5 and turn right at island onto A452. At the island with the Spitfire sculpture turn right into Tangmere Drive, then right onto Farnborough Road. The ground is on the right hand side after approximately 1/2 mile.

Colours: Old Gold/black/gold

Change Colours: All white

COLESHILL TOWN

Formed: 1894
Chairman: Mark Bishop
Secretary: Allan Blackwell, 35 Wardour Drive, Chelmsley Wood,
W.Mids. B37 7UA Tel Nos: 0121 6053614(H) 07749 913196 (M)
Ground: Pack Meadow, Packington Lane, Coleshill, Birmingham B46
3JQ Tel: 01675-463259
Directions: Travelling from north or south of the city. M6 to junction 4.
Take A446 (signposted Lichfield) for 1/2 mile then turn right across the
dual carriageway (B4117) signposted Coleshill. After approximately 1/2
mile turn right into Packington Lane. The ground is on the left hand
side a further 1/2 mile down the road.
Colours: Green/black/green
Change Colours: Blue/white/blue

CONTINENTAL STAR

Formed: 1973
Chairman: Keith John
Secretary: Ashley Lewis, 25 Cemetry Road, Smethwick, W.Midlands.
B67 6BB Tel No: 0121 532 9497 (H)
Ground: Red Lion Ground, Somerfield Road, Walsall WS32EJ
Tel: 019222 405 835
Directions: From the M5 J2 - Turn right at the large island towards
Wolverhampton. Turn left at the first set of traffic lights into Newbury
Lane and the ground is 50yrds on the right.
Colours: All white
Change Colours: Yellow & blue

COVENTRY COPSEWOOD

Formed: 2005 (Formerley Coventry Marconi)
Chairman: D Abercrombe
Secretary: Peter Scanlon, 61 Norton Hill Drive, Wyken, Coventry
W.Mids. CV6 3DB Tel Nos: 02476 616576 (H) 02476 332382 (W)
Ground: Allard Way, Copswood, Coventry. Tel: 02476 635992
Directions: From the M40, follow A46 signs to Coventry and Leicester.
Stay on this road until very end. You reach a roundabout with a flyover.
Go round the roundabout following M69 signs. This road takes you
past Asda and you reach a set of traffic lights with a roundabout. Take
second left turn off the roundabout, again following M69 signs onto
Allard Way. Stay on Allard Way, go under the railway bridge and the
ground is 400 yards on right.
Colours: White with blue trim/bluewhite
Change colours: All red

COVENTRY SPHINX

Formed: 1946
Chairman: Vic Jones
Secretary: Neil Long, 9 Villa Road, Coventry.VCV6 3DB.
Tel Nos: 02476 260877 (H) 07973 371942 (M)
Ground: Sphinx Drive, off Siddeley Avenue, Stoke Aldermoor,
Coventry Tel: 01203 451361
Social Club Tel.: 02476 451361
Directions: From the M40, follow A46 signs to Coventry and Leicester.
Stay on this road until very end. You reach a roundabout with a flyover.
Go round the roundabout following M69 signs. This road takes you
past Safeway's and you reach a set of traffic lights with a roundabout.
Take second left turn off the roundabout, again following M69 signs
onto Allard Way. Stay on Allard Way for 1 1/2 miles until you reach the
major crossroads with traffic lights. Get in the left hand lane and turn
onto the Binley Road for three-quarters of a mile. At the Bull's Head
public house turn left into Bull's Head Lane. Follow the road round for
1/4 mile and then merge right into Siddeley Avenue. Sphinx Drive is
approximately 50 yards on the left hand side on the bend.
Colours: Sky blue & white/black/white
Change Colours: All red

FECKENHAM

Formed: 1881
Chairman: Malcolm Hawkes
Secretary: Glynn Carr, 37 Tennyson Rd, Redditch, Worcs. B97 5BL.
Tel No: 01527 454 800 (messsages only please)
Ground: Groundshare with Redditch United F.C. Valley Stadium,
Bromsgrove Road, Redditch B97 4RN Tel: 01527 67450
Directions: Take the M42 to Junction 1, and take the A38, following the
signs for Bromsgrove. Stay on the A38 to Bromsgrove Golf Course. Turn
left at roundabout onto the A448 to Redditch. Take first exit after approxi-
mately five miles, take third exit off roundabout, cross over the dual car-
riageway, then take the first right into Birchfield Road, past the Foxlydale
Public House. Then turn left into Red Lane, leading into Bromsgrove Road.
The Valley Stadium is approximately 1/2 mile on the left.
Colours: Green & White Hoops/Green/Green
Change Colours: All Yellow

HEATH HAYES

Formed: 1964
Chairman: Paul Mallen
Secretary: Mrs. Kathlyn Davies, 4 Prince Street, West Chadsmoor,
Cannock, Staffs. WS11 5RT
Tel: 01543 426054 Email: kathlyndavies@aol.com
Ground: Coppice Colliery Ground, Newlands Lane, Heath Hayes,
Cannock, Staffs. WS12 3HH
Tel: 01543 279022
Directions: From M6 Junction 11 take A4601 to Cannock, at 1st island
turn right onto A460 to Rugeley/Cannock Business Parks. At double
island (A5) straight on, still on A460, over next 2 islands, at 3rd island
turn right onto A5190, signposted Lichfield, carry on past Texaco
garage on the right, take next turn right into Newlands Lane, entrance
to ground is 50 yards down lane on the left under green barrier. If
using the M6 Toll motorway, leave at exit immediately after pay plaza,
signposted A34 Walsall, Cannock & Rugeley, then follow the above
directions from A5.
Colours: Blue & White Striped Shirts, Blue Shorts, White Socks.

HIGHGATE UNITED

Formed: 1947
Chairman: James Sims
Secretary: Philip Inman, 39 Goldthorn Avenue, Sheldon, Birmingham
B26 3LA Tel NOs: 0121 694 9250 (H) 07958 433199 (M)
Ground: The Coppice, Tythe Barn Lane, Shirley, Solihull B90 1PH
Tel: 0121 7444 194
Directions: Leave the M42 J4 onto the A34 towards Birmingham. After
1 1/2 miles and second island take first exit signposted Lucas & Dog
Kennel Lane for 3 1/2 miles. Take the first exit off the next island sign-
posted Tidbury Green & Tanworth Lane. After 150 yards turn right into
Dickens Heath Road for 1/2 mile. Then turn right into Tythe Barn Lane.
Go straight over at the traffic lights over a hump back bridge (unsuit-
able for coaches). The ground is a further 1/2 mile on the left.
Colours: Red/Black/Red & Black
Change Colours: All white

MASSEY FERGUSON

Formed: 1956
Chairman: Joe Swords
Secretary: Terry Borras, Massey Ferguson FC, c/o Massey Ferguson
Social Club, Broad Lane, Coventry CV5 9LA. Tel: 02476 675745 (H)
07909 685137 (M)
Ground: Massey-Ferguson Sports Ground, Banner Lane, Tile Hill,
Coventry (01203 694400)
Directions: From M42 or M6 take the A45 to Coventry. At the first set
of lights bear left onto Broad Lane. Travel down Broad Lane until you
reach Vauxhall dealers on your right. Turn left opposite the Vauxhall
Dealers into Banner Lane. Then take the third gate on your right sign-
posted Sports Ground. Follow this road until you see the car park
behind the main stand.
Colours: Red & Black stripes, Black, Black
Change Colours: Yellow/ Blue / White

MEIR K.A.

Formed: 1972
Chairman: Des Reaney
Secretary: Chris Robinson, 12 The Broadway, Meir, Stoke-on-Trent
ST3 5PE Tel: 07759 302 537.
e-mail: chris.meirka@tiscali.co.uk
Ground: Kings Park, Hilderstone Road, Meir Heath, Stoke-on-Trent
Tel: 01782 388 465.
Directions: At M6 J14 take the A34 to Stone, then the A520 to Meir
Heath, and B5066 into Hilderstone. The ground is on the right after
approximately 1/2 mile.
Colours: Yellow/navy/navy
Change colours: All Red

NUNEATON GRIFF

Formed: 1972
Chairman: John Gore
Secretary: Pete Kemp,205 Haunchwood Road,Nuneaton, Warwicks.
CV10 8DS
Tel: 02476 737459 (H) 07761611338 (M)
Ground: The Pingles Stadium, Avenue Road, Nuneaton. Tel: 024 76
37 0688
Directions: At M6 J3 turn left onto A444 (Nuneaton). Stay on the A444
over the Bermuda Park, McDonalds and George Eliot Hospital round-
abouts, until reaching the large roundabout with the footbridge over the
road. Carry straight on and downhill, taking the right hand lane. At bot-
tom you reach Coton Arches Island. Take the second exit (Avenue
Road) and travel 1/2 mile to the Cedar Tree Pub traffic lights, turning
left into the stadium car park service road.
Colours: Blue & white/white/ blue
Change colours: All yellow

PERSHORE TOWN

Formed: 1988
Chairman: Graham Merchant
Secretary: Barbara Hodgkiss Tel Nos: 01905 452 885
or 0787 9845539
Ground: King George V Playing Fields, King Georges Way, Pershore,
Worcs (01386556902).
Directions: Leave the M5 J7 (Worcester South), taking the first left
A44 to Pershore. On entering the town, at the second set of traffic
lights turn left. The ground is 200 yards on the left hand side.
Colours: Blue & White/blue/blue
Change: AllRed

PILKINGTON XXX

Formed: 2002
Chairman: M Beeney
Secretary: John McVey, 84 Clee Road,West Heath,Birmingham B31
3RU Tel: 07715 011043
Ground: Triplex Sports,Eckersall Road,Kings Norton, Birmingham B38
8SR
Directions: Leave the M42 J2. At the roundabout take the third exit
onto the A441 (Redditch Road). Stay on the A441 over two round-
abouts and after about 4 1/2 miles turn left into Camp Lane. After 300
yards, the road changes to Eckersall Road. The ground is on the right.
Colours: Green/green/white
Change colours:

SOUTHAM UNITED

Formed: 1905
Chairman: Charles Hill
Secretary: Alan Freeman, 3 Old Road, Southam, Warwickshire Cv47
1GF. Tel: 01926 817 711
Ground: Banbury Road Ground, Southam, Leamington Spa.Warwicks
CV 47 0BJ. Tel: 01926 812091
Directions: Leave the M40 J12 (Gaydon). Turn right onto the B4451 at
top of slip road. Southam is signposted. It is approximately 6 1/2 miles
from motorway to the ground. As you approach Southam ignore sign-
posts for town centre and go straight over at the first island, and right at
the second island past the 24 hour garage (Banbury Road). The
ground is 100 yards on the right.
Colours: Yellow & Royal Blue/blue/blue
Change colours: White & Black/black/black

WALSALL WOOD

Formed: 1919
Chairman: David Collins
Secretary: David Cartwright, 299 Walsall Road, Stone Cross, West
Bromwich. B71 3LN
Tel: Home 0121 588 6021 Business 07877 641075
Mobile 07932 390381
Ground: Oak Park, Lichfield Road, Walsall Wood, Walsall. WS9 9NP
Tel: 01543 361084
Colours: Red Shirts, Red Shorts, Red Socks.
Directions:From North using M6 south to junction 12, take A5 until
large island just outside Brownhills (next island after the Turn pub on
left), take A452 Chester Road North through Brownhills High Street to
traffic lights at Shire Oak pub on right. Turn right onto A461 for Walsall,
go to next traffic lights. Immediately after lights turn right onto Oak
Park Leisure Centre car park (rear of Kentucky Fried Chicken).
Proceed diagonally over car park and follow road round to ground
entrance.
From North using M5/M6. Go onto M6 North and leave at junction 9.
Take A4148 for Walsall. Proceed for about 2 miles over several islands
until going down a hill alongside the Arboretum on the right. At large
island at bottom of hill turn right onto A461 for Lichfield. Proceed for
about 4 miles and go through Walsall Wood villagr (after Barons Court
Hotel on right), up the hill after village, Oak Park is on the left opposite
Fitness First, turn left and go diagonally across Oak Park Leisure
Centre car park and follow road roubd to the ground entrance.

LEAGUE CONSTITUTION
2006-07 - DIVISION ONE

ARCHDALE '73
BARTLEY GREEN
BURNTWOOD TOWN
ETTINGTON
FAIRFIELD VILLA
HEATHER ATHLETIC
KENILWORTH TOWN KH
KNOWLE
LEAMINGTON HIBERNIAN
LITTLETON
MILE OAK ROVERS
NEWHALL UNITED
NORTHFIELD TOWN
STOCKINGFORD
THIMBLEMILL R.E.C.
UNIVERSITY OF BIRMINGHAM
WEST MIDLANDS POLICE

STAFFORDSHIRE COUNTY SENIOR

WAS THE MIDLAND LEAGUE

LEAGUE CONSTITUTION 2006-07

ABBEY HULTON UNITED
Birches Head Road, Abbey Hulton, Stoke-on-Trent, Staffordshire
Tel: 01782 544 232

ALSAGER TOWN RESERVES
The Town Ground, Woodland Court, Alsager, Cheshire
Tel: 01270 882 336

BALL HAYE GREEN
Rear off Ball Haye Green WMC, Ball Haye Green, Leek, Staffordshire
Tel: 01538 371 926

ECCLESHALL AFC
Pershall Park, Chester Road, Eccleshall ST21 6NE
Tel: 01785 851 351

FEGG HAYES
Northwood Stadium,Keelings Road, Hanley,
Tel: 01782 - 234400

FLORENCE
Florence Miners Welfare, Lightwood Road, Stoke-on-Trent, Staffordshire
Tel: 01782 312 881

FOLEY
Whitcombe Road, Meir, Stoke-on-Trent, Staffordshire
Tel: 01782 595 274

GOLDENHILL WANDERERS
Sandyford Cricket Club, Shelford Road, Sandyford, Stoke-on-Trent, Staffordshire

HANFORD
Biddulph Victoria FC, Tunstall Road, Biddulph.

HANLEY TOWN
Abbey Lane, Abbey Hulton, Stoke-on-Trent, Staffordshire
Tel: 01782 267 234

NEWCASTLE TOWN RESERVES
Lyme Valley Parkway Stadium, Lilleshall Road, Clayton, Newcastle-under-Lyne
Tel: 01782 662 351

NORTON
Norton CC & MW Institute, Community Drive, Smallthorne, Stoke-on-Trent, Staffordshire
Tel: 01782 838 290

REDGATE CLAYTON
Northwood Lane, Clayton, Newcastle-under-Lyme, Staffordshire
Tel: 01782 717 409

ROCESTER RESERVES
Hillsfield, Mill Street, Rocester, Uttoxeter
Tel: 01889 590 463

STALLINGTON
Stallington Hospital, Fulford Lane, Stallington Road, Blythe Bridge, Staffordshire
Tel: 07785 338 804

STONE DOMINOES RESERVES
Springbank Stadium, Kings Park, Hilderstone Road, Meir Heath, Stoke
Tel: 01782 761 891

WOLSTANTON UNITED
Bradwell Community Centre, Riceyman Road, Bradwell, Stoke-on-Trent, Staffs
Tel: 01782 660 818

NORTH BERKSHIRE LEAGUE

President: Bill Gosling   **Chairman:** Les Addison
Hon. GeneralSecretary: Dave Rich
14 Sandy Lane, Shrivenham, Swindon, Wilts SN6 8DZ
Tel: 01793 782 270 07779 860 255
Email: dave.rich@nbfl.co.uk

DIVISION ONE		P	W	D	L	F	A	Pts
1.	Lambourn Sports	22	17	1	4	64	31	52
2.	Drayton (Champions 04-05)	22	15	3	4	54	31	48
3.	Ardington & Lockinge	22	14	5	3	46	26	47
4.	Coleshill United (2nd Div.2 04-05)	22	13	6	5	63	41	43
5.	Faringdon Town	22	13	2	7	40	26	41
6.	Saxton Rovers	22	8	3	11	30	36	27
7.	Marcham	22	6	5	11	30	47	23
8.	Blewbury	22	6	4	12	37	63	22
9.	Steventon (1st Div.2 04-05)	22	5	5	12	41	56	20
10.	East Hendred	22	6	2	14	29	44	20
11.	Grove Rangers	22	5	4	13	29	44	19
12.	Harwell International	22	4	2	16	27	45	14

DIVISION ONE		1	2	3	4	5	6	7	8	9	10	11	12
1	Ardington & Lockinge		4-2	3-2	5-2	2-1	2-0	2-2	1-0	0-2	4-1	2-2	1-1
2	Blewbury	2-2		2-5	2-0	0-3	2-2	2-2	4-2	2-6	5-1	2-1	3-2
3	Coleshill United	2-3	7-0		3-4	2-1	5-1	0-0	4-2	6-5	4-4	2-1	2-2
4	Drayton	3-1	6-1	0-1		2-0	2-0	2-2	1-0	1-1	5-2	2-1	4-2
5	East Hendred	0-3	4-2	0-1	0-2		1-0	2-3	2-1	0-1	0-0	4-1	1-2
6	Faringdon Town	0-0	1-0	3-1	1-2	4-0		3-1	2-1	1-0	2-1	3-1	2-1
7	Grove Rangers	1-2	1-2	1-2	0-1	3-2	0-4		3-2	2-3	2-0	0-1	2-3
8	Harwell International	0-1	1-0	1-3	1-4	3-3	2-5	2-1		0-1	0-1	1-1	4-1
9	Lambourn Sports	1-0	4-0	3-0	6-3	4-1	3-2	4-0	4-1		0-0	1-3	4-2
10	Marcham	1-2	2-2	1-4	0-5	5-2	1-0	1-0	1-0	1-4		0-2	5-2
11	Saxton Rovers	0-3	3-1	0-3	1-2	2-0	0-2	1-3	2-1	1-0	1-1		2-3
12	Steventon	1-3	4-1	4-4	1-1	1-2	0-2	0-2	5-7	1-1	0-3		

DIVISION TWO	P	W	D	L	F	A	Pts
1 A.F.C. Wallingford 'A'	22	19	0	3	79	20	57
2 Shrivenham 'A'	22	16	1	5	70	32	49
3 Appleton (Abingdon)	22	14	2	6	58	34	44
4 Kintbury Rangers Res.	22	13	2	7	59	32	41
5 Sutton Courtenay	22	12	1	9	44	37	37
6 Harwell Village	22	11	2	9	55	49	35
7 Bampton & Buckland	22	10	1	11	47	55	31
8 Saxton Rovers Res.	22	7	1	14	32	64	22
9 A.F.C.Benson	22	6	3	13	43	65	21
10 Northcroft	22	6	2	14	42	64	20
11 Long Wittenham	22	6	1	15	42	87	19
12 Lambourn Sports Res.	22	3	2	17	25	57	11

DIVISION THREE	P	W	D	L	F	A	Pts
1 Wootton & Dry Sandford	24	21	2	1	82	9	65
2 Blewbury Res.	24	14	7	3	54	32	49
3 Stanford in the Vale	24	13	3	8	51	34	42
4 Faringdon Reserves	24	11	5	8	46	33	38
5 Didcot Casuals	24	11	5	8	59	47	38
6 Benson Lions	24	12	1	11	55	42	37
7 Ardington & Lockinge R.	24	9	5	10	46	41	32
8 Kingsclere	24	9	4	11	39	43	31
9 Marcham Reserves	24	8	2	14	25	46	26
10 Drayton Reserves	24	8	1	15	32	72	25
11 Warborough &Shillingford	24	6	6	12	35	57	24
12 East Hendred Reserves	24	6	5	13	34	51	23
13 Hagbourne United	24	4	2	18	20	71	14

DIVISION FOUR	P	W	D	L	F	A	Pts
1 Coleshill United Res.	22	19	1	2	81	19	58
2 Crowmarsh Gifford	22	17	2	3	59	19	53
3 Challow United	22	15	2	5	76	41	47
4 Botley United	22	14	3	5	64	34	45
5 Uffington United	22	11	5	6	66	46	38
6 Hanney United	22	6	6	10	44	52	'24
7 Grove Rangers Res.	22	7	3	12	40	62	24
8 Harwell Int. Reserves	22	5	6	11	40	51	21
9 Bampton & Buckland R.	22	6	3	13	29	59	21
10 Stanford in the Vale R.	22	5	4	13	40	58	19
11 Long WittenhamRes.	22	4	4	14	22	61	16
12 Sutton Courtenay Res.	22	2	3	17	34	93	9

DIVISION FIVE	P	W	D	L	F	A	Pts
1 Wooton Reserves	20	16	3	1	68	18	51
2 Steventon Reserves	20	13	1	6	58	44	40
3 Uffington Reserves	20	11	4	5	53	34	37
4 Benson Reserves	20	10	5	5	52	25	35
5 Coleshill United 'A'	20	9	5	6	40	40	32
6 Didcot Casuals Res.	20	8	4	7	53	39	31
7 Faringdon Town 'A'	19*	7	2	10	25	27	23
8 Hanney United Res.	19*	6	2	11	30	38	20
9 Harwell Village Res.	20	6	0	14	44	73	18
10 Challow Reserves	20	4	3	13	30	64	15
11 Hagbourne Reserves	20	3	1	16	23	74	10
*Match declared void.							

L E A G U E   C U P

FIRST ROUND

Grove Rangers	v	Benson Lions	5-1
Lambourn Sports	v	Marcham	2-1*
Crowmarsh Gifford	v	Steventon	1-2
Botley United	v	Didcot Casuals	2-1
Bampton & Buckland	v	Blewbury	0-10
Uffington United	v	Northcroft	1-3
Drayton	v	Long Wittenham Athletic	4-1
Kingsclere	v	Challow United	0-6
Wotton & Dry Sand'v	East Hendred		3-0
Hagbourne United	v	Benson	1-3
Saxton Rovers	v	Harwell Village	4-0
Coleshill United			Bye
Ardington & Lock' (H)	v	Faringdon Town	1-3
Stanford in the Vale	v	Hanney United	4-3
Sutton Courtney	v	Harwell International	1-4
Appleton	v	Warborough & Shillinford	7-1

SECOND ROUND

Appleton	v	Blewbury	5-2
Stanford in the Vale	v	Botley United	2-1
Lambourn Sports	v	Faringdon Town	4-3
Benson	v	Harwell International	1-5
Saxton Rovers	v	Wootton & Dry Sandford	1-0
Drayton	v	Coleshill United	4-2
Northcroft	v	Steventon	2-3
Challow United	v	Grove Rangers	0-7

QUARTER-FINALS

Appleton	v	Drayton	0-1
Lambourn Sports	v	Stanford in the Vale	5-1
Saxton Rovers	v	Steventon	2-1
Harwell International	v	Grove Rangers	2-0

SEMI-FINALS

Drayton	v	Harwell International	2-1
Saxton Rovers	v	Lambourn Sports	0-2

THE FINAL (129th April at Abingdon Town FC)

Drayton	v	Lambourn Sports	2-2*, 3-4p

LEAGUE CONSTITUTION 2006-07

ARDINGTON & LOCKHINGE
Secretary: Steve Bolton, 53 Westfield Road, Long Wittenham OX14 4RF. Tel: 01865 407156(H) 07736 390308 (M)
Ground: White Road, Ardington, Wantage.
Colours: All royal blue.

BLEWBURY
Secretary: Mark Mills, 28 Saxon Heath, Long Wittenham OX14 4PX. Tel: 01865 407071 (H) 07810 298972 (M)
Ground: Bohams Road, Blewbury, Didcot.
Colours: All dark blue.

COLESHILL UNITED
Secretary: Ian Stonham, 1 Cedar Road, Faringdon SN7 8AY. Tel: 01367 241 673 (H).
Ground: Bottom of the Hill, Coleshill, Oxfordshire.
Colours: Orange shirts, black shorts.

DRAYTON
Secretary: Alan Alston, 3 Marcham Road, Drayton OX14 4JH. Tel: 01235 531425 (H), 01865 381 110 (B).
Ground: Recreation Ground, Lockway, Drayton, Abingdon.
Colours: Amber & black shirts, black shorts.

EAST HENDRED
Secretary: Mark Smith, 12 Mayfield Avenue, Grove, Wantage OX12 7LZ. tel: 01235 766766(H), 07771 645625(M).
Ground: Mill Lane, East Hendred.
Colours: Black & azure shirts, black shorts.

FARRINGDON TOWN
Secretary: Simon Harrington, 36 Fernham Road, Faringdon SN7 7LB. Tel: 01367 241406 (H), 07789 437 227 (M).
Ground: Tucker Park, Park Road, Faringdon.
Colours: Red & black shirts, black shorts.

GROVE RANGERS
Secretary: David Heggie, 11 West Hill, Wantage, Oxon OX12 9EF. Tel: 01235 762464 (H). 01235 772255 (B).
Ground: Recreation Ground, Cane Lane.
Colours: Sky blue shirts, claret shorts.

LAMBOURN SPORTS
Secretary: M Towell, 1 Child Street, Lambourn, Hungerford, Berks RG17 8NZ. Tel: 01488 72053 (H). 07816 822635 (M)
Ground: Bockhampton Road, Lambourn.
Colours: Light blue shirts, white shorts.

MARCHAM
Secretary: John Hill, 22 Parkside, Marcham OX13 6NN. Tel: 01865 391 651 (H).
Ground: Moreland Road, Marcham, Abingdon.
Colours: White & black shirts, black shorts.

SAXTON ROVERS
Secretary: Robert Bremner, 29 Overmead, Abingdon OX14 5NB. Tel: 07752 390039 (M).
Ground: Recreation Ground, Caldecott Road, Abingdon.
Colours: Red & black shirts, black shorts.

STEVENTON
Secretary: Steve Miles, 19 High Street, Steventon, OX14 4AX. Tel: 01235 847 158 (H), 07778 128 960 (M).
Ground: Steventon Green, Milton Lane, Steventon, Abingdon.
Colours: Light blue & white shirts, white shorts.

WALLINGFORD ATHLETIC
Secretary: Richard May, 43 St John's Road, Wallingford, Oxon OX10 9AW. Tel: 01491 834804 (H). 07973 736386 (M).
Ground: Bullcroft, St George's Road, Wallingford.
Colours: Red & black hooped shirt, black shorts.

NORTHAMPTON TOWN LEAGUE

SPONSORED BY: PETER SMITH RECRUITMENT

President: Brian Bennett **Chairman:** Roy Ainge
Hon. General Secretary: Sue Ainge
139 Euston Road, Far Cotton, Northampton NN4 8DX
Tel: 01604 764 865
Email: sueainge@lycos.co.uk

PREMIER DIVISION		P	W	D	L	F	A	Pts
1.	University College Northampton	18	14	2	2	102	19	44
2.	Broadmead Saints	18	12	3	3	82	32	39
3.	Duston United	18	12	3	3	67	33	39
4.	Thorpland United (+1)	18	10	2	6	61	51	33
5.	Airflow (Champions 04-05) (-1)	18	10	2	6	49	40	31
6.	Parklands	18	8	2	8	54	49	26
7.	T.W.S. (1st Div.1 04-05)	18	6	1	11	30	48	19
8.	Northampton Harlequins	18	4	3	11	26	64	15
9.	Ashley Rovers	18	2	2	14	19	64	8
10.	Delapre Old Boys	18	2	0	16	18	108	6

PREMIER DIVISION		1	2	3	4	5	6	7	8	9	10
1	Airflow		3-1	2-4	4-0	5-0	3-3	3-0	4-3	3-3	0-9
2	Ashley Rovers	1-5		1-5	1-0	2-6	0-0	1-5	0-1	2-3	1-8
3	Broadmead Saints	2-4	9-1		4-0	1-4	9-0	8-3	2-0	3-4	2-2
4	Delapre Old Boys	0-4	1-0	1-1		1-8	0-5	0-7	3-1	2-6	0-13
5	Duston United	6-2	0-0	3-3	7-2		3-1	4-2	2-1	5-2	0-1
6	Northampton Harlequins	2-1	4-1	3-4	2-1	0-5		1-1	0-1	0-11	0-9
7	Parklands	AW	2-4	1-3	5-2	2-6	5-3		5-1	3-2	2-1
8	T.W.S.	1-6	2-0	0-4	8-2	3-3	HW	2-5		0-3	1-3
9	Thorpland United	HW	5-2	2-2	7-2	1-4	4-2	5-3	1-3		0-5
10	University College Northampton	5-0	5-1	1-3	12-1	4-1	6-0	3-3	5-2	10-2	

DIVISION ONE		P	W	D	L	F	A	Pts
1	Airflow Reserves	24	20	2	2	106	36	62
2	Birchfield Rovers (P)	24	19	2	3	108	27	59
3	University College Northampton R.	24	18	2	4	81	27	56
4	Double Four	24	18	2	4	86	33	56
5	Asda George	24	10	4	10	85	59	34
6	FC Crispin	24	9	4	11	63	75	31
7	Prince Of Wales	24	8	2	14	46	74	26
8	Ashley Rovers Reserves	24	8	2	14	50	87	26
9	Denton	24	6	6	12	49	76	24
10	Hartwell	24	7	2	15	36	87	23
11	Kingsthorpe Wanderers	24	6	2	16	41	79	20
12	Northampton Diamonds	24	4	6	14	44	86	18
13	Northants Police	24	3	4	17	30	79	13

LEAGUE CONSTITUTION 2006-07

AIRFLOW
ASHLEY ROVERS
BIRCHFIELD ROVERS
BROADMEAD SAINTS
DUSTON UNITED
NORTHAMPTON HARLEQUINS
PARKLANDS
TACT
THORPLANDS UNITED
UNI. COLLEGE NORTHAMPTON

LEAGUE CUP - KNOCK-OUT STAGE

FIRST ROUND

Airflow Reserves	v	Prince of Wales	6-1
Asda George	v	Ashley Rovers Reserves	6-3
Delapre Old Boys	v	Northampton Diamonds	1-0
Denton	v	T.W.S.	0-3
Hartwell	v	Double Four	2-4
Kingsthorpe W.	v	FC Crispin	0-4
Northants Police	v	Birchfield Rovers	2-4

SECOND ROUND

Airflow Reserves	v	Airflow	4-6
Asda George	v	Ashley Rovers	1-3
Broadmead Saints	v	Uni College Northants Res.	2-1
Double Four	v	FC Crispin	6-3
Parklands	v	Duston United	AW
T.W.S.	v	Birchfield Rovers	1-3
Thorpland United	v	Northampton Harlequins	4-1
Uni College N'hants(H)	v	Delapre Old Boys	12-0

QUARTER-FINALS

Ashley Rovers	v	Thorpland United	0-9
Birchfield Rovers	v	Airflow	1-0
Double Four	v	Broadmead Saints	2-3
Duston United	v	Uni College Northants (H)	2-1

SEMI-FINALS

Broadmead Saints	v	Duston United	0-1
Thorpland United	v	Birchfield Rovers	4-1

THE FINAL

Duston United	v	Thorpland United	2-2*, 6-7p
			Att: 110

NORTHAMPTONSHIRE COMBINATION

SPONSORED BY: **TRAVIS PERKINS**

Founded:
Chairman: Keith Philpot
Secretary: David Jarrett
secretary@northantscombination.co.uk

PREMIER DIVISION

		P	W	D	L	F	A	Pts
1.	Corby Hellenic Fisher	28	18	6	4	90	34	60
2.	Moulton	28	17	6	5	56	30	57
3.	Kislingbury	28	15	9	4	67	40	54
4.	Milton	28	17	3	8	62	46	54
5..	Harpole	28	17	2	9	61	26	53
6.	Heyford Athletic	28	14	4	10	52	44	46
7.	Caledonian Strip Mills (Champions 04-05) (-4)	28	14	4	10	70	50	42
8.	Roade	28	10	5	13	54	57	35
9.	Priors Marston (1st Div.1 04-05) (+2)	28	8	8	12	40	60	34
10.	Rushden Rangers	28	8	8	12	62	67	32
11.	Stanion United (2nd Div.1 04-05)	28	9	4	15	52	72	31
12.	Kettering Nomads	28	8	6	14	34	44	30
13.	Corby St Brendans (-3)	28	9	4	15	58	91	28
14.	Weldon United	28	4	5	19	34	81	17
15.	Crick Athletic	28	2	6	20	32	82	12

PREMIER DIVISION

		1	2	3	4	5	6	7	8	9	10	11	12	13	14	15
1	Caledonian Strip Mills		1-5	12-0	2-2	1-0	0-2	2-1	5-2	5-1	2-2	2-0	1-3	4-0	0-5	3-0
2	Corby Hellenic Fisher	5-1		6-2	6-0	0-3	2-1	2-2	3-4	1-2	1-2	1-1	4-1	4-1	3-0	5-0
3	Corby St Brendans	3-1	0-5		3-2	1-5	1-0	3-2	4-4	2-4	0-5	3-1	4-1	4-0	5-2	3-0
4	Crick Athletic	3-4	0-1	4-1		0-1	0-5	0-4	1-1	1-5	0-4	2-4	1-6	4-3	4-4	1-2
5	Harpole	1-3	1-1	3-1	1-0		0-0	4-0	3-1	3-1	2-0	4-0	2-0	1-3	2-1	5-1
6	Heyford Athletic	1-7	1-4	8-1	2-0	2-1		1-1	1-0	0-4	2-3	0-3	1-1	2-1	5-3	5-1
7	Kettering Nomads	2-1	1-1	2-1	0-0	0-3	1-0		0-1	2-4	0-1	0-0	2-5	1-2	3-1	
8	Kislingbury	3-1	3-3	4-4	2-0	2-1	3-0	3-2		2-3	0-0	1-1	1-1	5-4	8-0	3-0
9	Milton	2-1	0-3	4-3	3-0	1-0	1-2	0-2	1-1		1-1	3-0	2-4	3-1	2-0	3-3
10	Moulton	0-1	0-3	4-3	1-0	1-0	2-0	2-0	1-1	0-1		3-0	4-0	3-3	3-2	2-1
11	Priors Marston	0-0	1-4	2-1	2-2	2-1	0-3	2-1	1-4	1-2	1-7		2-2	5-1	4-2	0-1
12	Roade	2-4	2-4	3-2	4-1	1-3	0-1	1-3	0-1	1-0	2-3	2-2		0-1	7-1	3-1
13	Rushden Rangers	3-1	3-3	6-2	6-0	3-2	2-2	0-0	0-1	0-2	1-1	5-1	2-2		1-4	2-2
14	Stanion United	1-1	0-4	0-0	2-1	0-4	1-3	1-2	0-2	5-3	3-0	1-1	4-0	4-2		3-2
15	Weldon United	1-4	1-6	1-1	3-3	0-5	1-2	1-0	0-4	2-4	0-1	2-3	2-3	3-3	2-1	

DIVISION ONE

		P	W	D	L	F	A	Pts
1	Corby Grampian (+2)	28	21	6	1	113	35	71
2	Brixworth All Saints	28	18	2	8	80	49	56
3	Bective Wanderers	28	17	3	8	86	53	54
4	Whitefield Norpol	28	16	4	8	82	50	52
5	Ravensthorpe Athletic	28	16	4	8	83	59	52
6	Spratton	28	12	5	11	58	63	41
7	Corby Pegasus	28	12	4	12	65	63	40
8	Harborough Spencer Utd	28	12	4	12	53	53	40
9	Stanwick Rovers	28	11	6	11	71	71	39
10	Queen Eleanor Gt.Houghton	28	10	6	12	69	74	36
11	Earls Barton United	28	10	5	13	54	56	35
12	Ringstead Rangers	28	8	5	15	39	55	29
13	Weedon	28	6	3	19	51	92	21
14	Corby Locomotives	28	5	2	21	32	91	17
15	Gretton (-10)	28	5	3	20	38	110	8

DIVISION TWO

		P	W	D	L	F	A	Pts
1	Welford Victoria	24	16	6	2	63	23	54
2	Medbourne	24	15	4	5	74	41	49
3	Clipston	24	14	6	4	51	33	48
4	A.F.C.Corby Town (-9)	24	18	1	5	92	37	46
5	Wootton St George	24	13	2	9	63	47	41
6	Burton United	24	13	1	10	69	61	40
7	Islip United	24	8	7	9	46	64	31
8	Wellingborough Railway Staff (-3)	24	9	6	9	64	57	30
9	Wilbarston	24	9	2	13	56	58	29
10	Finedon Volta	24	5	7	12	45	61	22
11	Wollaston Victoria	24	5	4	15	39	75	19
12	Wilby	24	5	2	17	39	82	17
13	Ristee Towers	24	0	4	20	23	85	4
14	Geddington W.M.C.	0	0	0	0	0	0	0

DIVISION THREE

		P	W	D	L	F	A	Pts
1	Corby Kingfisher Athletic	22	17	4	1	83	31	55
2	Rushden Corner Flag (-6)	22	16	2	4	80	30	44
3	Kettering Orchard Park	22	14	1	7	68	31	43
4	Wellingborough Old Grammarians	22	12	2	8	50	38	38
5	Corby Flamingo	22	9	5	8	50	53	32
6	Great Doddington	22	9	3	10	43	51	30
7	Dainite Sports	22	10	0	12	46	60	30
8	Weavers Old Boys	22	7	5	10	36	41	26
9	Corby Danesholme Vikings (-3)	22	9	1	12	55	67	25
10	Kettering Park Rovers	22	4	4	14	46	72	16
11	Yardley United	22	4	2	16	38	65	14
12	Wellingborough Wincanton S.A.S. (-6)	22	5	3	14	42	98	12

DIVISION FOUR

		P	W	D	L	F	A	Pts
1	Cold Ashby Rovers	20	18	2	0	72	14	56
2	West Haddon	20	11	1	8	49	33	34
3	Harlestone Park W.	20	9	5	6	50	36	32
4	Northampton Sapphires (-3)	20	11	2	7	57	47	32
5	Weekley Vale United	20	9	2	9	32	39	29
6	Wellingborough Raffertys (-6)	20	11	1	8	73	49	28
7	Wellingborough Oak Rangers	20	8	1	11	51	53	25
8	Brafield United	20	8	1	11	48	61	25
9	A.F.C. Sovereigns	20	6	3	11	35	52	21
10	Raunds Academy (-3)	20	7	1	12	41	55	19
11	Wellingborough Rising Sun	20	2	1	17	15	84	7

P R E M I E R   D I V I S I O N   C U P

FIRST ROUND

Corby Hellenic F.(H)	v	Stanion United	6-4
Crick Athletic	v	Caledonian Strip Mills	1-3
Harpole	v	Weldon United	4-1
Heyford Athletic	v	Milton	2-1
Moulton	v	Rushden Rangers	5-1
Priors Marston	v	Corby St Brendans	1-2
Roade	v	Kettering Nomads	3-0

QUARTER-FINALS

Caledonian Strip M	v	Corby Hellenic Fisher (H)	2-3
Harpole	v	Roade	1-0
Heyford Athletic	v	Corby St Brendans	2-0
Kislingbury	v	Moulton	2-1

SEMI-FINALS

Corby Hellenic F (H)	v	Harpole	2-5
Kislingbury	v	Heyford Athletic	1-2

THE FINAL

Harpole	v	Heyford Athletic	3-4

PREMIER LEAGUE CONSTITUTION 2006-07

BRIXWORTH ALL SAINTS
St Davids Close (entrance via Froxhill Crescent), Brixworth, Northants NN6 9EA

CALEDONIAN STRIP MILLS
West Glebe South Pavillion, Cottingham Road, Corby, Northants. NN17 1EL

CORBY GRAMPIAN
West Glebe South, Cottingham Road, Corby, Northants. NN17 1EL

CORBY HELLENIC FISHER
Burghley Drive, Corby, Northants. NN18 8DY

CORBY ST BRENDANS
Corby Rugby Club, Rockingham Road, Corby, Northants NN17 1AE

HARPOLE
Harpole Playing Field, Larkhall Lane, Harpole, Northampton. NN7 4DP

HEYFORD ATHLETIC
Nether Heyford Playing Field, Nether Heyford, Northants NN7 3LL

KETTERING NOMADS
Orlingbury Road, Isham, Nr Kettering, Northants. NN14 1HY

KISLINGBURY
Playing Fields, Beech Lane, Kislingbury, Northampton. NN7 4AL

MILTON
Collingtree Road, Milton Malsor, Northampton. NN7 3AF

MOULTON
Brunting Road, Moulton, Northampton. NN3 7QX

PRIORS MARSTON
Priors Sports Ground, Priors Marston, Warks CV47 7RR

ROADE
Connolly Way, off Hyde Road, Roade, Northants. NN7 2LU

RUSHDEN RANGERS
Hayden Road, Rushden, Northants. NN10 0HX

STANION UNITED
Village Hall, Brigstock Road, Stanion, Northants NN14 1BX

NORTHERN ALLIANCE

SPONSORED BY: WADE ASSOCIATES
Chairman: George Dobbins
Secretary: John McLackland, 92 Appletree Gardens
Walkerville, Newcastle upon Tyne NE6 4SX   Tel: 0191 262 1636

PREMIER DIVISION		P	W	D	L	F	A	Pts
1.	Team Northumbria	30	23	3	4	99	34	72
2.	Shankhouse (Champions 04-05)	30	18	8	4	57	21	62
3.	Carlisle City	30	18	5	7	68	31	59
4.	Heaton Stannington (-3)	30	18	4	8	53	36	55
5.	Northbank Carlisle	30	15	4	11	67	48	49
6.	Walker Central	30	15	4	11	60	43	49
7.	Blyth Town (-3)	30	14	8	8	65	42	47
8.	Seaton Delaval Amateurs	30	11	6	13	56	62	39
9.	Ponteland United	30	12	3	15	52	63	39
10.	Heddon	30	11	2	17	45	59	35
11.	Harraby Catholic Club	30	8	9	13	47	59	33
12.	Alnmouth	30	9	6	15	52	83	33
13.	Newcastle University (-6)	30	9	11	10	45	44	32
14.	Easington Colliery	30	7	3	20	41	76	24
15.	Murton	30	6	4	20	42	83	22
16.	Percy Main Amateurs	30	4	4	22	29	94	16

PREMIER DIVISION	1	2	3	4	5	6	7	8	9	10	11	12	13	14	15	16
1 Alnmouth		0-6	1-4	0-0	1-3	0-1	4-1	2-1	1-4	1-5	1-2	4-2	3-2	0-3	1-5	0-1
2 Blyth Town	1-1		1-3	2-2	3-3	3-2	1-0	3-4	2-2	1-2	7-0	1-3	4-1	1-1	0-0	2-1
3 Carlisle City	10-0	1-2		3-0	1-0	1-1	1-3	1-0	1-1	3-3	3-1	2-1	0-3	0-0	0-2	0-1
4 Easington Colliery	2-1	0-2	0-1		6-1	1-2	4-3	0-3	0-2	1-2	2-2	1-0	3-2	0-3	1-5	2-4
5 Harraby Catholic Club	3-4	1-3	2-2	3-2		1-2	1-3	2-1	2-2	2-1	2-0	1-1	1-1	0-3	0-2	1-1
6 Heaton Stannington	4-1	2-0	0-3	5-2	3-2		2-1	4-1	0-1	4-1	0-0	0-5	4-1	1-2	3-2	3-1
7 Heddon	5-6	1-3	1-0	0-2	1-2	1-1		1-2	2-0	2-0	1-1	2-1	1-0	2-0	2-3	1-6
8 Murton	1-2	0-1	1-6	4-3	1-1	2-2	3-1		1-1	1-1	0-3	2-4	0-1	0-2	3-5	1-6
9 Newcastle University	5-1	2-3	0-3	1-2	1-1	0-1	0-1	4-2		2-0	1-1	0-3	2-2	0-1	1-4	2-2
10 Northbank Carlisle	1-1	3-2	2-3	6-2	4-6	0-1	2-3	2-0	1-2		2-0	3-0	2-0	2-1	3-2	1-0
11 Percy Main Amateurs	1-4	2-7	0-4	2-1	1-3	0-2	1-3	5-0	0-2	0-7		2-3	2-3	0-3	0-7	1-2
12 Ponteland United	2-7	0-0	0-3	3-0	3-0	1-0	1-0	4-2	1-2	0-5	3-0		4-3	1-1	0-3	0-4
13 Seaton Delaval Amateurs	2-2	1-1	0-3	2-0	2-1	1-2	2-1	5-1	2-2	4-2	2-1	5-2		0-5	3-6	3-4
14 Shankhouse	1-1	1-0	1-2	4-2	1-0	1-0	4-0	3-2	1-1	1-1	6-0	3-2	0-0		0-1	3-1
15 Team Northumbria	4-1	2-0	2-4	4-0	2-2	0-1	4-1	7-1	2-1	3-1	7-0	4-1	3-1	1-1		5-2
16 Walker Central	1-1	1-3	2-1	4-0	1-0	2-0	2-1	1-2	1-1	0-2	6-1	3-1	0-2	0-1	0-2	

DIVISION ONE	P	W	D	L	F	A	Pts
1 Wallsend (-3)	24	17	4	3	64	26	52
2 Ashington Colliers	24	14	3	7	46	26	45
3 Penrith United	24	13	3	8	55	37	42
4 Rutherford	24	12	6	6	51	34	42
5 Chopwell Top Club	24	13	3	8	52	43	42
6 Gosforth Bohemians Garnet	24	12	5	7	45	42	41
7 Wark	24	11	3	10	60	51	36
8 Wallington (-3)	24	9	9	6	50	44	33
9 Cramlington Town	24	7	6	11	32	39	27
10 Hebburn Reyrolle (-3)	24	7	5	12	34	57	23
11 Newcastle East End Railway	24	5	6	13	36	58	21
12 Spittal Rovers	24	4	2	18	24	55	14
13 Haydon Bridge United	24	3	3	18	29	66	12

DIVISION TWO	P	W	D	L	F	A	Pts
1 Whitley Bay A	28	20	4	4	66	29	64
2 Gillford Park Spartans (-3)	28	19	3	6	99	53	57
3 Seaton Burn	28	16	6	6	53	47	54
4 Stocksfield	28	14	8	6	64	30	50
5 Lowick (-3)	28	12	8	8	51	44	41
6 Westerhope	28	11	7	10	61	51	40
7 Benfield Sports	28	11	7	10	65	73	40
8 Red Row Welfare	28	9	8	11	54	53	35
9 Adderstone Jesmond(-6)	28	11	7	10	45	45	34
10 Swarland	28	10	2	16	55	74	32
11 Newcastle Chemfica	28	8	7	13	52	59	31
12 Felling Fox	28	9	4	15	42	62	31
13 Newcastle British Telecom	28	7	4	17	43	72	25
14 Wallsend Town	28	7	3	18	46	71	24
15 Highfields United	28	4	6	18	46	79	18

LEAGUE CUP

FIRST ROUND

Wallsend	v	Northbnak Carlisle	1-2
Ashington Colliers	v	Walker Central	1-0
Haydon Bridge Utd	v	Wallington	3-6
Team Northumbria	v	Shankhouse (H)	1-0
Newcastle East E.R.	v	Gosforth Bohemians Garnet	4-3
Rutherford	v	Seaton Delaval Amateurs	2-1
Walker Fosse	v	Hebburn Reyrolle	4-1
Carlisle City	v	Harraby Catholic Club	6-0
Spittal Rovers	v	Chopwell Top Club	1-7
Heaton Stannington	v	Blyth Town	2-1
Ponteland United	v	Percy Main Amateurs	1-0
Cramlington Town	v	Alnmouth	2-4

SECOND ROUND

Ashington Colliers	v	Wark	4-0
Carlisle City	v	Ponteland United	3-0
Chopwell Top Club	v	Highfields United	4-0
Easington Colliery	v	Heddon	0-1
Heaton Stannington	v	Newcastle British Telecom	1-0
Gillford Park Spar.	v	Adderstone Jesmond	4-0
Lowick	v	Wallsend Town	5-1
Newcastle East E.R.	v	Walker Fosse	0-5
Newcastle Chemfica	v	Stocksfield	2-7
Newcastle Uni.	v	Murton	6-3
Northbank Carlisle	v	Swarland	4-0
Penrith United	v	Whitley Bay A	2-1
Red Row Welfare	v	Alnmouth	0-1
Seaton Burn	v	Benfield Sports	2-0
Wallington	v	Rutherford	1-3
Westerhope	v	Felling Fox	3-0

THIRD ROUND

Newcastle Uni.	v	Team Northumbria	2-3
Penrith United	v	Gillford Park Spartans	0-1
Chopwell Top Club	v	Team Northumbria	1-5
Heaton Stannington	v	Westerhope	1-2
Alnmouth	v	Heddon	0-4
Northbank Carlisle	v	Lowick	4-0
Ashington Colliers	v	Seaton Burn	4-2
Rutherford	v	Carlisle City	2-5

QUARTER-FINALS

Ashington Colliers	v	Gillford Park Spartans	3-2
Carlisle City	v	Westerhope	3-0
Team Northumbria	v	Heddon	2-1
Northbank Carlisle	v	Stocksfield	3-0

SEMI-FINALS

Northbank Carlisle	v	Carlisle City	1-5
Team Northumbria	v	Ashington Colliers	2-0

THE FINAL

Carlisle City	v	Team Northumbria	2-1

LEAGUE CONSTITUTION 2006-07 - PREMIER DIVISION

ALNMOUTH

Secretary: Neil Robson,63 Hunters Rd.,Spital Tongues,Newcastle Upon Tyne NE2 4ND Tel No: 07974 767637 (M)

Ground: Morpeth Town FC, Craik Park, Morpeth Common, Mprpeth NE61 2YX. Tel: 01670 513 785

Directions: Morpeth is signed off the A1 onto A197. Take the B6524, right at Mitford sign, then right after about a mile into the ground, next to Morpeth Common

ASHINGTON COLLIERS

Secretary: Mrs Vicky Brown, 32 Highfield Drive, Ashington, Northumberland NE63 9SR. Tel. No: 01670 856852.

Ground: Hirst Welfare, Ashington, Northumberland.

BLYTH TOWN

Secretary: Margaret Nicholls. 01670 360 181.

Ground: South Newsham Sports Ground, Blyth

Directions: Take sliproad off A189 (north) Spine Road signposted Blyth Beach and follow A1061 to roundabout. Go straight over and after small housing estate, take second left onto Sandringham Drive and first left into ground car park

CARLISLE CITY

Secretary: Jackie Williamson, 14 Etterby Street, Stanwix, Carlisle Tel No: 01228 523798

Ground: The Sheepmount Sports Complex, Carlisle Tel No: 01228 265599

Directions: Follow Workington signs on B6264 Brampton-Carlisle road. Take dual carriage way down hill (Carlisle Castle on right) and where road intersects doouble back on yourself an turn left just before castle .Ground is down hill on left.

EASINGTON COLLIERY

Secretary: Alan Purvis,12 Wark Crescent,Jarrow,Tyne & Wear NE32 4SH Tel No: 0191 4896930 (H)

Ground: Welfare Park Ground, Easington Colliery, Peterlee NE32 4SH Tel No: 0191 489 6930

Directions: South on A19 turn off after Hawthorn Services and turm left at roudabout for Easington Village. Right into Seaside Lane and continue to Zebra crossing after the Derby pub turn right and park OUTSIDE the Welfare Park. Walk three minutes through park

HARRABY CATHOLIC CLUB 1999

Secretary: Mike Little, 34 Springfiield Road, Harraby, Carlisle CA1 3QR Tel No: 01228 512887

Ground: Harrowby Community Centre, Edghill Road, Harraby **Directions:** A 69 over Rosehill roundabout. Second left on Eastern Way then first left into Arnside Road after 3/4 mile. Turn left at end of road, school and ground are 200 metres on left.

Sports Lighting

Specialists in the Lighting of all Sports Applications

Tel; 01803 844 833   Fax; 01803 844 835

www.sportslighting.co.uk

Sports Lighting has been a family run business for the last 15yrs.

We do nationwide installations.

All our work comes with a 12months parts and labour guarantee.

We make on site surveys and advise for installation to suit your needs.

We make life easy for you, by supplying all the lux and spillage charts for your planning application FREE OF CHARGE.

Our light fittings are all asymmetric which cut out any possibility of light pollution and spillage.

All out work comes with the backing of the NICEIC as we are an approved contractor.

We are the main floodlighting contractor for Torquay Utd.

Sports lighting is always prepared to put money back into local sports by means of sponsorships tailored to meet the requirements of both parties.

LEAGUE CONSTITUTION 2005-06 - PREMIER DIVISION

HEATON STANNINGTON

Secretary: John Lewis, 91 Bosworth Gardens, heaton,Newcastle upon Tyne. NE6 5UN Tel No: 0191 265 2618 (H) 07795 207985(M)

Ground: Grounsell Park, Heaton, Newcastle upon Tyne, Tyne & Wear. Tel No: 0191 2819230

Directions: From Newcastle left at Corner House Hotel traffic lights into Newton Road. On to roundabout and bear left for 30 yards. Ground is on right behind the shops.

HEDDON

Secretary: John Shaxon, 34 Broomridge Ave, Condercum Park, Newcastle-upon-Tyne NE15 6QP. Tel No: 0191 226 0278.

Ground: Bullocksteads Sports Ground, Newcastle-upon-Tyne.

NEWCASTLE UNIVERSITY

Secretary: Daniel Hall, 30 Cavendish Place, West Jesmond, Newcastle-upon-Tyne. Tel No: 07731 855357.

Ground: Cochrane Park, Etherstone Avenue, Newcastle-upon-Tyne NE7 7JE.

Directions: From Newcastle centre travel via Jesmond onto Coast Road. After Jesmond Dene immediately after lights at the Corner House take first sliproad and turn left onto A188. Right at roundabout at garage into Etherstone Avenue. Ground entrance is 200 yards on left.

NORTHBANK CARLISLE

Secretary: John Twentyman, 464 Warwick Road, Carlisle, Cumbria CA1 2SB. Tel No: 01228 532680.

Ground: Sheepmount Sports Complex, Carlisle CA3 8XL Tel: 01228 625 599

Directions: Same directions as Carlisle City F.C.

PETERLEE TOWN

Secretary: Billy Banks. Tel No: 07814 797 197.

Ground: Eden Lane, Peterlee, Co.Durham.

PONTELAND UNITED

Secretary: Alan E Birkinshaw, 21 Pinegarth, Darras Hall, Ponteland, Newcastle-upon-Tyne. NE20 9LF. Tel No: 01661 82540.

Ground: Ponteland Leisure Centre, Callerton Lane, Ponteland Tel No: 01661 825441

Directions: Left at lights entering Newcastle. Ground is 100yds on left adjacent to Leisure Centre.

SEATON DELAVAL AMATEURS

Secretary: Bill Fellows, 11 Ridley Street, Klondyke, Cramington NE23 6RH Tel No: 01670 731833

Ground: Wheatridge Park, Seaton Delaval

Directions: Take A190 to Seaton Delaval at Annitsford roundabout on A189 from Newcastle. Left at roundabout entering village. Ground is 450 yards on right next to Deal Garage and behind Market Garden

SHANKHOUSE

Secretary: Syd Ramsay, 6 Brinkburn Avenue, Cramlington, Northumberland NE23 6TB Tel No: 01670 715943

Ground: Sporting Club of Cramlington, Highburn, Cramlington NE23 6BN. Tel: 01670 591 970

Directions: From Tyne Tunnel, take A189 Spine Road from Moor Farm roundabout signposted Ashington & Blyth. Take A19 sliproad signposted Trading Estates & Morpeth then at the first roundabout tun left into Crawhall Lane (A1171).

WALKER CENTRAL

Secretary: Bob Mulroy, 44 Parsons Avenue, Walker, Newcastle-upon-Tyne NE6 2PP. Tel No: 0191 287 3189.

Ground: Monkchester Recreation Ground, Walker, Newcastle-upon-Tyne NE6 2LJ. Tel: 0191 265 7230.

Directions: From City: Shields Rd to Union Rd to Welbeck Rd and right into Monkchester Rd, left into ground between houses opposite Norbury Grove.

WALLSEND

Secretary: Andrew Robinson, 22 Cambridge Place, Barley Mow, Birtley, Tyne and Wear DH3 2DF. Tel No: 0191 4920556.

Ground: Shibdon Park, Shibdon Road, Blaydon-on-Tyne.

Carlisle City F.C. winners of the 2005-06 League Cup.

OXFORDSHIRE SENIOR LEAGUE

Secretary: Elaine Devonport
Tel: 07930 529894
Email: oxsele@yahoo.co.uk

PREMIER DIVISION	P	W	D	L	F	A	Pts
1. OUP	26	16	4	6	70	35	52
2. Eynsham	26	13	9	4	50	29	48
3. Berinsfield (Champions 04-05)	26	15	3	8	56	37	48
4. BCS Bardwell	26	14	4	8	59	44	46
5. Haddenham	26	13	7	6	56	43	46
6. Launton Sports	26	12	6	8	59	46	42
7. Garsington	26	10	8	8	52	46	38
8. Rover Cowley	26	11	3	12	62	54	36
9. Watlington	26	11	3	12	45	55	36
10. Charlton	26	9	3	14	39	54	30
11. Chadlington	26	7	7	12	41	48	28
12. Adderbury Park	26	5	7	14	36	73	22
13. Kidlington OB	26	5	5	16	30	65	20
14. Long Crendon	26	5	3	18	32	58	18

PREMIER DIVISION	1	2	3	4	5	6	7	8	9	10	11	12	13	14
1 Adderbury Park		0-2	0-2	3-4	0-5	1-4	1-1	2-2	2-1	0-3	1-0	0-7	0-5	4-1
2 BCS Bardwell	5-1		1-2	4-1	4-2	3-4	2-1	4-5	3-0	5-2	6-0	2-0	3-0	1-0
3 Berinsfield	2-2	0-0		3-1	0-0	3-4	1-3	4-1	3-2	1-3	3-0	0-2	5-1	2-1
4 Chadlington	1-1	0-0	0-1		0-2	0-2	5-1	1-2	1-1	2-3	4-0	1-1	4-3	1-0
5 Charlton	1-3	3-0	1-5	1-0		2-3	2-4	0-3	0-1	2-4	3-2	0-3	3-4	2-1
6 Eynsham	1-1	5-0	0-1	2-0	1-1		1-1	1-2	1-0	1-1	3-0	2-1	3-2	2-3
7 Garsington	2-1	2-2	3-1	5-1	4-0	1-1		0-0	1-1	1-0	2-1	1-1	0-1	5-2
8 Haddenham	1-2	1-1	0-1	1-1	1-3	0-0	3-2		5-2	3-3	1-0	1-3	2-1	4-3
9 Kidlington OB	5-2	1-2	1-5	2-2	2-2	0-2	3-1	1-2		0-3	2-1	0-5	0-2	1-1
10 Launton Sports	2-2	1-3	HW	2-5	1-2	2-2	4-2	3-2	9-0		5-1	1-2	3-2	0-1
11 Long Crendon	3-2	1-2	3-4	2-2	3-0	0-0	0-2	0-3	1-2	0-1		1-2	4-1	5-2
12 OUP	5-1	2-1	3-4	5-1	1-2	1-1	5-3	2-4	1-0	2-2	3-1		5-2	1-0
13 Rover Cowley	5-1	5-0	3-2	1-3	1-0	1-3	2-2	2-2	6-1	1-1	2-3	4-1		4-1
14 Watlington	3-3	5-3	2-1	HW	3-0	2-1	5-2	1-5	2-1	4-0	0-0	0-6	2-1	

DIVISION ONE	P	W	D	L	F	A	Pts
1 Kennington	24	18	5	1	85	31	59
2 Horspath	24	18	2	4	77	26	56
3 Stonesfield	24	15	3	6	82	35	48
4 Fritwell	24	13	5	6	79	40	44
5 Middleton Cheney	24	13	4	7	56	41	43
6 Marston	24	12	5	7	46	33	41
7 Enstone	24	8	7	9	40	32	31
8 WCOB & Bletch	24	7	8	9	58	59	29
9 King Sutton	24	8	3	13	47	58	27
10 Yarnton FC	24	5	5	14	32	64	20
11 Oakley	24	5	3	16	38	71	18
12 Garden City	24	4	1	19	21	81	13
13 Old Salesians	24	4	1	19	25	115	13

LEAGUE CONSTITUTION 2006-07
PREMIER DIVISION

ADDERBURY PARK
BCS BARDWELL
BERINSFIELD
CHADLINGTON
CHARLTON
EYNSHAM
GARSINGTON
HADDENHAM
HORSPATH
KENNINGTON
LAUNTON SPORTS
LONG CRENDON
OUP
ROVER COWLEY
WATLINGTON

P R E S I D E N T ' S   C U P

FIRST ROUND

BCS Bardwell	v	Rover Cowley	HW
Enstone	v	Middleton Cheney	1-0
Eynsham	v	Charlton	0-0*, 3-4p
Horspath	v	Adderbury Park	2-3
King Sutton	v	Garden City	4-0
Launton Sports	v	Watlington	1-0
Long Crendon	v	Garsington	0-2
Marston	v	Fritwell	1-1*,HW after pens.
Oakley	v	Yarnton FC	AW
Old Salesians	v	Kennington	1-8
OUP	v	Chadlington	3-0

SECOND ROUND

BCS Bardwell	v	Adderbury Park	3-2
Enstone	v	Garsington	3-0
Kennington	v	Stonesfield	3-3*, 4-3p
Kidlington OB (H)	v	OUP	0-5
King Sutton	v	Yarnton FC	2-3
Launton Sports	v	Charlton	3-0
Marston	v	Haddenham	3-0
WCOB & Bletch	v	Berinsfield	2-4

QUARTER-FINALS

BCS Bardwell	v	Launton Sports	1-0

(Match abbandoned after injury to player)

Launton Sports	v	BCS Bardwell	2-1
Berinsfield	v	Kennington	2-1
Enstone	v	Marston	2-1
Yarnton FC	v	OUP	0-6

SEMI-FINALS

Berinsfield	v	OUP	1-0
Launton Sports	v	Enstone	1-2

THE FINAL

Berinsfield	v	Enstone	1-0

PETERBOROUGH & DISTRICT LEAGUE

SPONSORED BY: MARSHALL

AFC FLETTON
ALCONBURY
CROWLAND TOWN
HAMPTON ATHLETIC
LEVERINGTON SPORTS
LONG SUTTON ATHLETIC
MOULTON HARROX
OUNDLE TOWN
PARSON DROVE
PERKINS SPORTS
PETERBOROUGH SPORTS
PINCHBECK UNITED
STAMFORD BELVEDERE
UPPINGHAM TOWN
WHITTLESEY UNITED
WIMBLINGTON OLD BOYS

READING LEAGUE

Formed: 1988
Chairman: John Dell
General Secretary: Mark Rozzier - Tel: 0118 969 3235

SENIOR DIVISION		P	W	D	L	F	A	Pts
1.	Cookham Dean	26	22	3	1	80	12	69
2.	Marlow United (Champions 04-05)	26	23	0	3	69	23	69
3.	Highmoor Ibis	26	20	2	4	64	18	62
4.	Ascot Utd	26	17	1	8	80	33	52
5.	Royal Mail	26	14	5	7	53	35	47
6.	Berks County Sports	26	11	4	11	50	34	37
7.	Woodley Town	26	9	8	9	40	46	35
8.	Mortimer	26	9	4	13	35	53	31
9.	Westwood United	26	8	4	14	36	55	28
10.	Reading YMCA	26	7	3	16	43	57	24
11.	Hurst	26	6	5	15	31	53	23
12.	Forest Old Boys	26	6	3	17	34	78	21
13.	Reading Old Blues (2nd Prem 04-05)	26	4	2	20	34	91	14
14.	West Reading	26	4	0	22	37	98	12

SENIOR DIVISION		1	2	3	4	5	6	7	8	9	10	11	12	13	14
1	Ascot Utd		1-0	0-1	6-0	1-0	1-2	1-3	5-0	7-1	7-2	1-2	9-0	3-1	1-1
2	Berks County Sports	1-3		0-1	7-0	0-2	2-0	1-2	4-1	5-0	0-2	1-1	5-1	4-0	2-1
3	Cookham Dean	2-1	4-0		1-0	1-0	4-0	2-0	0-0	10-0	4-0	2-0	7-0	2-0	0-1
4	Forest Old Boys	0-2	1-5	1-8		0-5	2-0	0-4	1-4	2-0	2-2	0-2	5-4	AW	2-3
5	Highmoor Ibis	3-2	4-0	1-1	3-1		5-1	1-0	2-1	3-0	1-0	0-1	1-0	4-1	7-1
6	Hurst	0-5	0-1	1-3	2-2	0-2		0-3	2-4	1-1	3-1	0-2	3-1	0-2	0-0
7	Marlow United	4-1	2-1	2-3	7-2	1-0	2-1		2-1	HW	5-2	4-0	4-1	1-0	3-2
8	Mortimer	1-3	1-1	0-2	3-1	0-4	0-3	0-5		2-0	0-5	4-2	4-2	1-0	1-3
9	Reading Old Blues	1-7	0-2	1-5	4-1	1-7	3-2	0-2	0-3		1-0	1-6	3-4	2-3	0-1
10	Reading YMCA	1-3	1-1	0-1	0-1	0-1	2-2	0-3	3-1	4-3		0-3	5-0	3-1	2-3
11	Royal Mail	2-3	3-0	4-4	0-2	1-1	2-0	0-2	1-0	3-2	4-1		6-0	2-2	1-2
12	West Reading	1-3	0-5	0-6	1-5	AW	1-2	1-2	1-2	7-2	3-2	2-3		1-6	0-5
13	Westwood United	1-2	2-1	0-3	4-2	3-4	1-5	2-4	1-1	1-5	1-3	0-0	2-1		2-1
14	Woodley Town	3-2	1-1	0-3	1-1	1-3	1-1	1-2	0-0	3-3	3-2	1-2	1-5	0-0	

PREMIER DIVISION		P	W	D	L	F	A	Pts
1	Reading Town Reserves	20	16	3	1	54	17	51
2	Rabson Rovers (P)	20	14	3	3	95	29	45
3	Shinfield	20	13	3	4	48	37	42
4	Woodcote S/R	20	11	4	5	44	28	37
5	Rides Dynamos	20	10	1	9	48	30	31
6	Spencers Wood	20	10	1	9	45	43	31
7	Newtown Henley	20	6	4	10	38	54	22
8	Sonning Common	20	6	2	12	22	41	20
9	Finchampstead	20	3	5	12	23	52	14
10	Goring United	20	3	3	14	19	65	12
11	Hurst Reserves	20	2	3	15	20	60	9

DIVISION ONE		P	W	D	L	F	A	Pts
1	Cookham Dean Res	22	15	4	3	53	21	49
2	Marlow United Res	22	14	2	6	50	40	44
3	AFC Corinthians	22	12	5	5	45	24	41
4	OLA Newbury	22	10	4	8	60	51	34
5	Radstock	22	10	4	8	41	42	34
6	Tadley Calleva Res	22	9	3	10	40	38	30
7	Taplow United	22	9	3	10	45	44	30
8	Wokingham & Emmbrook "A"	22	8	4	10	32	40	28
9	Frilsham & Yattendon	22	8	2	12	38	45	26
10	Highmoor Ibis Res	22	7	1	14	42	59	22
11	Unity	22	5	4	13	35	46	19
12	R.E.M.E Arborfield	22	5	4	13	31	62	19

DIVISION TWO

		P	W	D	L	F	A	Pts
1	Whitley Wood	20	15	3	2	68	29	48
2	Ascot Utd Reserves	20	13	3	4	42	20	42
3	Prospect United	20	12	2	6	58	32	38
4	Twyford & Ruscombe	20	10	5	5	39	21	35
5	S.R.C.C.	20	10	0	10	60	40	30
6	Whitley Rovers	20	8	3	9	34	44	27
7	Westwood United Res	20	7	2	11	39	49	23
8	Newtown Henley Res	20	5	5	10	26	42	20
9	Crowthorne Sports	20	5	3	12	27	61	18
10	Woodcote Stoke Row Res	20	4	5	11	22	51	17
11	Woodley Town Res	20	2	7	11	19	45	13

DIVISION THREE

		P	W	D	L	F	A	Pts
1	Marlow United "A"	22	18	2	2	80	29	56
2	Ashridge Park	22	18	1	3	107	25	55
3	Park United	22	17	3	2	72	16	54
4	Theale	22	13	3	6	63	36	42
5	Taplow United Reserves	22	11	1	10	48	42	34
6	Mortimer Reserves	22	10	3	9	47	46	33
7	Wokingham Wanderers	22	10	1	11	51	55	31
8	Englefield	22	7	2	13	48	91	23
9	Sonning	22	6	4	12	37	50	22
10	Highmoor Ibis "A"	22	6	2	14	56	86	20
11	Goring Reserves	22	1	4	17	28	93	7
12	Sonning Sports	22	1	2	19	31	99	5

DIVISION FOUR

		P	W	D	L	F	A	Pts
1	South Reading	26	24	0	2	144	18	72
2	Royal Mail Reserves (P)	26	20	3	3	114	40	63
3	Berks County Sports Rs (P)	26	17	2	7	82	24	53
4	Wokingham & Emmbrook "B" (P)	26	16	3	7	81	55	51
5	Theale Reserves (P)	26	14	3	9	60	58	45
6	Wargrave (P)	26	12	7	7	70	52	43
7	Compton	26	12	1	13	78	69	37
8	Rides Utd Reserves	26	10	4	12	82	58	34
9	Woodley Town "A"	26	10	4	12	33	59	34
10	Taplow United "A"	26	8	4	14	36	66	28
11	The Hop Leaf	26	7	1	18	45	109	22
12	Hurst "A"	26	6	3	17	38	78	21
13	Sonning Reserves	26	3	3	20	17	128	12
14	Linear United	26	3	2	21	30	96	11

SENIOR LEAGUE CONSTITUTION 2006-07

ASCOT UNITED

Ascot Race Course Car Park 10, Winkfield Road, Ascot SL5 7LJ

BERKS COUNTY SPORTS

Berks County Sports & Social Club, Sonning Lane, Sonning, Reading RG4 6ST

COOKHAM DEAN

Alfred Major Recereation Ground, Hillcrest Avenue, Cookham Rise, Miadenhead SL6 9NB

FOREST OLD BOYS

Holme Park (Adwest), Sonning Lane, Sonning, Reading RG4 6ST

HIGHMOOR IBIS

Prudential IBIS Sports Club, Scours Lane, Reading RG3 6AY

HURST

Cantley Park, Twyford Road, Wokingham RG40 5QT

MORTIMER

Alfred Palmer Memorial Playing Fields, West End Road, Mortimer, Reading RG7 3TJ

RABSON ROVERS

Lower Whitley Recreation

READING YMCA

Coley Park, St Saviours Road, Coley, reading Rg1 6EJ

ROYAL MAIL

Victoria Recreation Ground, Kentwood Hill, Tilehurst, Reading RG31 6DE

WESTWOOD UNITED

Cotsworld Sports Centre, Downsway, Tilehurst, reading RG31 6LX

WOODLEY TOWN

Woodford Park, Haddon Drive, Woodley, Reading RG5 4LL

SOMERSET F.A.

Tel: 01761 410 280 Fax: 01761 410 477 Email: secretary@somersetfa.com

30 North Road, Midsomer Norton, Radstock, Somerset BA3 2QD

PREMIER DIVISION

		P	W	D	L	F	A	Pts
1.	Hengrove Athletic	34	28	6	0	88	20	90
2.	Oldland Abbotonians (1st Div.1 04-05)	34	20	6	8	51	27	66
3.	Burnham United	34	18	11	5	63	37	65
4.	Bridgwater Town (-1)	34	17	11	6	70	35	61
5.	Mangotsfield United Res. (Champions 04-05) (-4)	33	18	8	7	76	32	58
6.	Nailsea United	34	17	7	10	72	39	58
7.	Wells City	33	16	8	9	68	58	56
8.	Paulton Rovers	34	15	7	12	51	34	52
9.	Welton Rovers	34	13	9	12	54	50	48
10.	Timsbury Athletic (3rd Div.1 04-05)	34	12	7	15	48	54	43
11.	Winscombe (2nd Div.1 04-05)	34	12	6	16	55	61	42
12.	Castle Cary	34	11	8	15	48	63	41
13.	Cleeve West Town	34	10	4	20	45	61	34
14.	Ilminster Town	34	9	7	18	31	74	34
15.	Fry Club (-1)	34	9	3	22	45	74	29
16.	Cheddar	34	7	7	20	53	78	28
17.	Stockwood Green	34	6	10	18	35	66	28
18.	Backwell United (-6)	34	3	3	28	27	117	6

PREMIER DIVISION

		1	2	3	4	5	6	7	8	9	10	11	12	13	14	15	16	17	18
1	Backwell United Reserves		0-3	1-5	1-3	3-3	0-5	3-4	0-3	0-1	1-3	0-5	0-3	0-5	0-0	4-0	1-6	1-1	2-1
2	Bridgwater Town Reserves	9-0		1-1	4-1	1-0	4-0	1-1	2-2	2-0	3-1	0-1	1-1	0-2	2-2	1-0	3-0	1-1	1-1
3	Burnham United	2-1	2-0		1-2	3-2	2-1	2-0	1-1	1-1	0-0	1-1	0-0	1-1	5-2	2-1	3-2	1-0	1-1
4	Castle Cary	2-0	0-2	2-3		1-1	2-1	2-3	0-5	0-1	1-2	1-3	0-3	0-4	3-1	2-1	2-2	1-1	1-1
5	Cheddar	7-0	0-2	0-2	1-3		5-1	1-2	0-1	4-1	1-1	1-3	2-1	1-1	1-2	2-2	0-5	2-3	1-1
6	Cleeve West Town	5-1	1-2	1-1	1-1	3-2		2-1	0-2	3-0	0-4	0-2	0-1	0-3	3-1	1-0	2-0	2-3	2-3
7	Fry Club	2-0	1-2	2-2	2-1	3-1	1-3		0-2	0-1	0-3	0-5	1-4	0-1	0-2	2-2	2-1	2-3	1-2
8	Hengrove Athletic	3-2	2-2	5-0	6-0	4-0	4-1	3-2		4-0	3-1	2-1	3-0	1-0	2-2	2-1	2-1	2-0	4-0
9	Ilminster Town	4-2	1-5	0-2	0-5	1-3	1-0	2-4	0-4		1-1	1-1	0-3	0-2	3-3	0-0	2-2	1-4	0-2
10	Mangotsfield United	11-0	1-0	3-1	0-0	8-1	0-0	6-2	0-1	1-2		2-2	1-0	5-0	2-0	3-0	1-0	1-0	3-2
11	Nailsea United	4-0	3-0	0-3	1-2	1-1	3-0	3-1	0-1	5-0	1-1		0-1	2-1	3-0	0-1	2-3	2-2	2-2
12	Oldland Abbotonians	2-0	1-1	1-0	0-1	6-0	2-1	2-0	1-1	0-1	1-1	1-5		1-0	1-0	3-0	0-2	2-1	2-1
13	Paulton Rovers	5-0	1-4	0-3	2-3	1-0	1-0	2-1	0-1	0-1	2-1	1-2	3-0		1-1	3-1	1-1	2-3	1-1
14	Stockwood Green	3-0	0-5	0-0	0-0	3-2	0-0	0-1	1-4	0-1	0-2	0-1	2-1	0-2		1-2	3-3	1-4	3-1
15	Timsbury Athletic	2-0	1-1	0-1	3-2	2-3	0-3	3-2	1-2	4-0	4-2	2-3	0-2	1-1	2-0		2-2	1-1	2-1
16	Wells City	2-1	5-2	2-8	3-2	3-2	2-1	3-2	0-0	2-1	Cancelled	2-1	0-0	0-0	2-1	1-3		5-2	2-0
17	Welton Rovers	2-0	1-1	1-0	1-1	3-0	3-1	1-0	1-2	1-1	1-3	2-1	0-1	1-2	1-1	2-3	2-1		0-2
18	Winscombe	1-3	1-2	2-3	3-1	1-3	4-1	3-0	0-4	4-2	0-3	4-3	0-2	2-0	3-0	0-1	2-3	3-2	

DIVISION ONE

		P	W	D	L	F	A	Pts
1	Shirehampton	34	24	5	5	102	38	77
2	Frome Town	34	24	5	5	66	27	77
3	Glastonbury Town	34	19	10	5	76	40	67
4	Brislington	34	19	6	9	69	42	63
5	St George Easton in Gordano	34	15	10	9	61	40	55
6	Westland United	34	14	10	10	63	50	52
7	Watchet Town	34	14	8	12	57	53	50
8	Keynsham Town (-2)	34	14	9	11	62	60	49
9	Taunton Blackbrook	34	14	6	14	60	57	48
10	Odd Down	34	14	5	15	54	60	47
11	Churchill Club 70	34	12	9	13	53	64	45
12	Worle	34	10	9	15	55	80	39
13	Nailsea Town	34	9	7	18	43	55	34
14	Tunley Athletic (-2)	34	9	8	17	44	66	33
15	Shepton Mallet (-2)	34	7	11	16	41	67	30
16	Bishop Sutton	34	7	8	19	41	66	29
17	Crewkerne (R)	34	6	9	19	40	70	27
18	Robinsons	34	5	5	24	24	78	20

DIVISION TWO

		P	W	D	L	F	A	Pts
1	Cutters Friday	32	23	5	4	92	32	74
2	Bishops Lydeard	32	19	6	7	81	25	63
3	Dundry Athletic	32	16	10	6	62	35	58
4	Larkhall Athletic	32	17	7	8	70	45	58
5	Portishead	32	17	6	9	64	41	57
6	Wells City Res. (-1)	31	14	7	10	55	41	48
7	Nailsea United Res.	32	13	8	11	51	45	47
8	Combe St Nicholas (-2)	32	14	6	12	51	38	46
9	Congresbury	32	13	7	12	60	52	46
10	Clevedon United (-1)	32	12	5	15	41	56	40
11	Wincanton	32	11	5	16	57	73	38
12	Street (-3)	31	10	7	14	62	52	34
13	Burnham United Res.	32	9	7	16	49	77	34
14	Saltford	32	9	5	18	46	61	32
15	Frome Collegians	32	8	8	16	31	57	32
16	Weston St Johns (-3)	32	8	6	18	48	97	27
17	Peasedown Athletic(-8)	32	2	7	23	39	13	5

DIVISION THREE

		P	W	D	L	F	A	Pts
1	Taunton Blackbrook Res.	26	20	4	2	85	23	64
2	Wrington Redhill	26	15	4	7	52	36	49
3	Berrow	26	14	5	7	67	35	47
4	Long Ashton	26	14	5	7	64	39	47
5	Timsbury Athletic Res.	26	15	2	9	59	48	47
6	Langford Rovers 2000	26	14	2	10	59	45	44
7	Imperial FC (-1)	26	14	2	10	52	47	43
8	Clutton	26	13	1	12	50	44	40
9	Hengrove Athletic Res.	26	9	7	10	47	43	34
10	Yatton Athletic	26	8	4	14	47	64	28
11	Fry Club Reserves	26	7	3	16	49	69	24
12	Cheddar Reserves	26	6	4	16	37	61	22
13	Banwell	26	5	3	18	34	86	18
14	Robinsons Res. (-2)	26	4	2	20	25	87	11

L E A G U E   C U P   -   P R E M I E R   &   D I V . 1

FIRST ROUND

Brislington	v	Winscombe	1-2
Backwell United R.	v	Castle Cary	0-3
Hengrove Athletic	v	Glastonbury Town	2-1
Tunley Athletic	v	Westland United	2-4

SECOND ROUND

Castle Cary	v	Stockwood Green	1-0
Bridgwater Town R.	v	Bishop Sutton	4-0
Churchill Club 70	v	Frome Town	3-2
Cleeve West Town	v	Taunton Blackbrook	2-4
Crewkerne	v	Hengrove Athletic	0-4
Ilminster Town	v	Keynsham Town	3-4
Nailsea Town	v	Odd Down	1-3
Nailsea United	v	Westland United	1-5
Oldland Abbotonians	v	Cheddar	3-0
Paulton Rovers R.	v	Shirehampton	1-0
Shepton Mallet	v	Burnham United	1-4
St George E.in G.	v	Welton Rovers Reserves	0-3
Timsbury Athletic	v	Robinsons	8-0
Watchet Town	v	Mangotsfield United R. (H)	0-2
Wells City	v	Winscombe	3-4
Worle	v	Fry Club	3-4

THIRD ROUND

Churchill Club 70	v	Taunton Blackbrook	6-0
Fry Club	v	Odd Down	0-1
Keynsham Town	v	Timsbury Athletic	1-3
Oldland Abbotonians	v	Bridgwater Town Reserves	0-2
Paulton Rovers R.	v	Hengrove Athletic	0-2
Welton Rovers R.	v	Mangotsfield United R. (H)	0-2
Westland United	v	Castle Cary	5-1
Wimscombe	v	Burnham United	0-4

QUARTER-FINALS

Churchill Club 70	v	Westland United	3-2
Hengrove Athletic	v	Bridgwater Town R.	2-2*, 1-4p
Mangotsfield U.R(H)	v	Timsbury Athletic	1-2
Odd Down	v	Burnham United	1-3

SEMI-FINALS

Churchill Club 70	v	Timsbury Athletic	0-2
Burnham United	v	Bridgwater Town Reserves	0-4

THE FINAL

Bridgwater Town R.	v	Timsbury Athletic	1-0

PREMIER LEAGUE CONSTITUTION 2006-07

BRIDGWATER TOWN RESERVES
Fairfax Park, College Way, Bath Road, Bridgwater, Somerset — Tel: 01278 446 899

BURNHAM UNITED
Burnham Road Playing Fields, Cassis Close, Burnham-on-Sea, Somerset — Tel: 01278 794 615

CASTLE CARY
Donald Pither Memorial Playing Fields, Castle Cary, Somerset — Tel: 01963 351 538

CHEDDAR
Bowdens Park, Draycott Road, Cheddar, Somerset — Tel: 01934 743 736

CLEEVE WEST TOWN
King George V Playing Fields, Meeting House Lane, Cleeve, North Somerset — Tel: 01934 832 173

FROME TOWN RESERVES
Badgers Hill, Berkley Road, Frome Somerset, BA11 2EH — Tel: 01373 464087

FRY CLUB
Fry Club, Somerdale, Keynsham, Bristol, North Somerset — Tel: 0117 937 6500

GLASTONBURY TOWN
Abbey Moor Stadium, Godney Road, Glastonbury BA6 9AF — Tel: 01458 831 671

HENGROVE ATHLETIC
Norton Lane, Whitchurch, Bristol, North Somerset — Tel: 01275 832 894

ILMINSTER TOWN
Recreation Ground, Ilminster, Somerset — Tel: 01460 54756

MANGOTSFIELD UNITED RESERVES
Cossham Street, Mangotsfield, Bristol, Gloucestershire — Tel: 0117 956 0119

NAILSEA UNITED
Grove Sports Ground, Old Church, Nailsea, North Somerset — Tel: 01275 856 892

OLDLAND ABBOTONIANS
Aitchinson Playing Fields, Castle Road, Oldland Common BS30 9SZ — Tel: 0117 932 8263

PAULTON ROVERS RESERVES
Athletic Ground, Winterfield Road, Paulton, Somerset — Tel: 01761 412 907

SHIREHAMPTON
The Recreation Ground, Penpole Lane, Shirehampton, Bristol BS11 0EA — Tel: 0117 923 5461

TIMSBURY ATHLETIC
Recreation Ground, North Road, Timsbur, Bath BA2 0JH — Tel: 01761 472 523

WELLS CITY
The Athletic Ground, Rowdens Road, Wells, Somerset — Tel: 01749 679 971

WELTON ROVERS RESERVES
West Clewes, North Road, Midsomer Norton, Somerset — Tel: 01761 412 097

WINSCOMBE
RecreatioN ground, The Lynch, Winscombe BS25 1AP — Tel: 01934 842 720

SOUTH WESTERN LEAGUE

SPONSORED BY: CARLSBERG

President: Tristan H Scott   **Chairman:** Bob Bell
Hon. Secretary: Philip Lowe
Tel/Mob: 01822 613715 / 07766 688 987   **Email:** phillowe442@hotmail.com
Press Officer: Mike Sampson, 23 Eliot Street, Weston Mill, Plymouth, Devon PL5 1AX
Tel/Mob: 01752 514326 / 07831 730 510   **Email:** mikewrite@blueyonder.co.uk

		P	W	D	L	F	A	Pts
1.	Bodmin Town	34	25	6	3	89	31	81
2.	Truro City (Promoted)	34	22	7	5	78	29	73
3.	Falmouth Town	34	22	5	7	88	42	71
4.	Liskeard Athletic	34	20	9	5	93	34	69
5.	St Blazey (Champions 04-05)	34	19	12	3	92	44	69
6.	Penryn Athletic	34	21	3	10	98	47	66
7.	Plymouth Parkway	34	19	8	7	78	54	65
8.	Wadebridge Town	34	17	5	12	47	46	56
9.	Tavistock	34	15	6	13	67	59	51
10.	Porthleven	34	12	5	17	50	62	41
11.	Launceston	34	11	7	16	51	66	40
12.	Millbrook	34	10	9	15	37	54	39
13.	Penzance	34	10	4	20	52	74	34
14.	Newquay	34	7	9	18	44	76	30
15.	Goonhavern	34	6	6	22	31	80	24
16.	Callington Town	34	5	3	26	31	88	18
17.	Torpoint Athletic	34	4	6	24	23	85	18
18.	St Austell	34	5	2	27	39	117	17

	1	2	3	4	5	6	7	8	9	10	11	12	13	14	15	16	17	18
1 Bodmin Town		7-3	2-2	3-1	4-0	4-3	2-0	5-0	0-1	4-2	5-1	1-0	5-1	1-1	4-1	5-1	0-0	2-0
2 Callington Town	2-5		0-1	0-1	0-2	0-7	1-1	1-2	1-3	4-1	1-2	0-1	2-1	1-4	1-1	2-0	0-0	0-2
3 Falmouth Town	1-0	5-0		2-1	0-0	3-4	1-1	2-2	5-2	0-3	2-1	5-2	3-2	5-1	6-1	1-0	2-3	7-0
4 Goonheavern	0-2	0-1	2-1		2-0	0-4	0-2	1-1	1-5	1-3	2-2	1-2	0-2	1-1	0-5	1-2	1-3	2-1
5 Launceston	0-1	1-0	1-3	2-1		1-2	1-1	2-2	3-1	3-0	0-2	0-0	1-1	0-1	1-3	1-1	1-1	2-4
6 Liskeard Athletic	2-2	3-1	2-1	3-1	3-2		4-0	2-2	1-0	2-0	0-2	6-0	8-1	2-3	2-2	1-1	1-2	0-0
7 Millbrook	0-1	2-1	0-3	2-1	6-2	1-1		2-0	1-4	0-2	2-2	0-2	2-0	2-2	0-0	1-0	0-4	1-2
8 Newquay	1-2	1-2	1-4	1-0	0-1	0-2	0-0		1-2	2-2	1-1	0-2	3-1	2-2	2-3	1-1	1-2	2-4
9 Penryn Athletic	0-2	2-0	0-1	6-0	4-2	2-4	2-2	8-1		3-4	2-2	3-1	4-0	2-3	2-1	5-0	0-4	6-0
10 Penzance	0-1	6-1	0-2	0-0	1-2	0-3	3-0	1-4	1-1		2-4	2-0	5-0	1-6	1-3	2-0	0-3	0-1
11 Plymouth Parkway	1-2	3-0	3-2	6-1	4-1	2-1	0-2	7-0	2-3	3-1		1-0	4-3	3-3	2-1	2-1	3-2	1-1
12 Porthleven	2-4	4-0	2-2	3-1	4-2	0-0	2-0	1-0	1-7	2-2	1-2		8-1	1-4	0-1	0-6	1-4	0-1
13 St Austell	1-3	4-2	3-4	1-3	0-4	0-10	3-1	0-3	1-7	0-2	0-2	4-0		0-3	0-6	2-1	1-3	1-2
14 St Blazey	0-0	6-1	1-4	7-0	5-1	2-2	3-1	1-0	0-2	4-1	3-3	4-1	3-1		4-2	4-1	1-1	1-1
15 Tavistock	1-4	2-1	1-3	1-1	1-2	0-2	0-2	2-4	3-1	5-3	3-1	0-2	2-1	1-1		4-2	1-2	2-0
16 Torpoint Athletic	1-5	2-1	0-4	1-4	1-3	0-6	0-1	1-1	0-3	0-2	0-1	0-0	2-2	0-5	1-5		0-3	1-0
17 Truro City	1-0	4-0	1-0	5-0	3-2	0-1	3-0	4-2	2-3	3-0	2-2	4-0	6-0	1-1	0-0	0-1		1-0
18 Wadebridge Town	1-1	2-1	0-1	2-1	1-1	1-2	1-0	0-1	2-0	5-1	1-0	2-1	1-0	2-3	0-3	3-0	4-1	

BODMIN TOWN
Formed: 1889
Chairman: Colin Hooper
Secretary: Nick Giles, 4 Sandra Way, Bodmin, Cornwall PL31 2PP.
Tel Nos: 01208 75794 (H) 07796 95370 (M)
Ground: Priory Park, Bodmin. Tel: 01208 269033 (office)
or 01208 78165 (clubhouse)
Directions: Just off town centre in Priory Park complex, at rear of town car park
Colours:
Amber/black/black
Change colours:
All white

CALLINGTON TOWN
Formed:
Chairman: Andrew Long
Secretary: Philip Brown, Mount Pleasant Cottage, Harrowbarrow, Callington PL17 8JL
Tel: 01822 833 851 (H) 01752 307 102 (B)
Ground: Ginsters, Marshfield Park, Callington Comm. College, Launceston Rd., Callington, Cornwall Tel: 01579 382 647
Directions: Turn into Callington Community College from the A388, Callington to Launceston road. Go to the top of the drive and bear left - the ground is 100m ahead
Colours: Red & black/black/black
Change colours: All light and dark blue

FALMOUTH TOWN
Formed: 1949
Chairman: John Garwood
Secretary: Colin Spargo,2 Grenville Crescent, Falmouth, Cornwall TR11 2NR
FAX: 0871 242 8221 Tel: 07941 591 764 (M) 01326 315 093(H)
e-mail: secfaltown@tiscali.co.uk
Ground: Bickland Park, Bickland Water Rd. Falmouth, Cornwall Tel: 01326 375156
Directions: Follow A39 to Tregoniggie Industrial Estate - will pass ground on left. 1 1/2 miles from Penmere Halt (BR) on Falmouth-Truro branch line.
Colours: Amber & black/black/amber
Change colours: Red/blue/blue

GOODHAVEN
Formed:
Chairman:
Secretary: Sue Rogers. Tel: 01209 715 111.
Ground: Reen Manor Park, Goonhavern, Newquay TR6 0AJ.
Tel: 01872 572 493
Directions:
Colours: White/black/white
Change Colours: Yellow/black/yellow

LAUNCESTON
Formed: 1891
Chairman: Keith Ellacott
Secretary: Chris Martin, 3 Tavistock Road, Launceston, PL15 9HA
Tel: 01566 776 175 (H)
Ground: Pennygillam, Pennygillam Industrial Estate, Launceston PL15 7ED. Tel: 01566 773 279
Directions: Follow signs to Pennygillam Ind. Est, just off main A30 - ground 400yds on left
Colours: All Claret
Change colours: Sky/Sky/Navy

LISKEARD ATHLETIC
Formed: 1889
Chairman: Ian Pook
Football Secretary: Brian Oliver, Windrush, Tremeddan Lane, Liskeard, Cornwall PL14 3DS
Tel Nos: 01579 342 869 (H) 01752 207 653 (W)   07974 636 964 (M)
Ground: Lux Park, Liskeard, Cornwall Tel: 01579 42665
Directions: Take Tavistock Rd (A390) from town centre, after 1/2 mile turn left on St Cleer Road (follow signs to Lux Park Sports Complex) & ground is 200 yards on left.
Colours: Blue/blue/blue or white
Change colours: Yellow & navy/navy/yellow & navy

MILLBROOK
Formed: 1973
Chairman: Martin Bettridge
Secretary: Nick Hill.
Tel Nos: 01752 364751(H) 07956 810516(M) Tel No: 01752 364751(H)
Ground: Mill Park, Millbrook, Cornwall (01752 822113)
Directions: From Torpoint Ferry - 3 miles to Antony on A374, fork left, after 1 mile turn left again and follow B3247 to Millbrook (3 miles), take road marked `Town Centre Southdown', right at mini-r'bout after 1/4 mile, ground clearly visible. From Tamar Bridge - follow signs for Torpoint, 2 miles after Polbathic right turning marked Millbrook, 5 miles to Millbrook then proceed as above
Colours: Black & white/black/black
Change colours: Red & blue/blue/blue

NEWQUAY
Formed: 1890
Chairman: Roy Swift
Secretary: Graham Drew, 28 Parc Godfrey, Pentire, Newquay TR7 1TY. Tel: 01637 851 610
Ground: Mount Wise, Newquay 01637 872935
Directions: .5 mile from Newquay BR, follow 2way system for 0.5 mile grd sign on Left at Clevedon Road   Website: www.newquayafc.com
Email: grdrew@tiscali.co.uk
Colours: Red & white stripes/white/white
Change colours: Blue & white stripes/white/white

arena
SEATING

AFFORDABLE SEATING FOR SALE

Take a Seat!
with The Arena Tiered Seating System

royal windsor

From 50 to 50,000... Arena Seating have the solution

The classic Arena demountable tiered seating system upon which we have built our reputation is available for sale. The system can be supplied for sale in 254mm or 152mm rise format as standard, providing a cost effective permanent or demountable grandstand solution for sports clubs and venues.

It can be permanently in position, moved around the venue or even added to on a sale or hire basis as requirements change.

Contact us to see how we can enhance your venue.

WWW.ARENASEATING.COM

Arena Seating
Arena House Membury Lambourn Woodlands Hungerford Berkshire RG17 7TQ
T. 01488 67 48 00   **W.** www.arenaseating.com   **E.** info@arenaseating.com

PART OF THE ARENA GROUP

PENRYN ATHLETIC
Formed:
Chairman: Peter Young
Secretary: Mike Young, 1 Dunvegan Road, Penryn, TR10 8HJ
Tel: 01326 374 098 (H) 01326 212 974 (B)
Ground: "Kernick", Kernick Road, Penryn, Cornwall.
Tel: 01736 75182 (Clubhouse)
Directions: From Truro take the NEW Falmouth road at Treluswell and at the Treleiver roundabout follow signs for Kernick Industrial Estate. Turn left at the new Asda store.
Colours: Red & black/black/red
Change colours: Yellow/blue/blue

PENZANCE
Formed: 1888
Chairman: Peter George
Secretary: John Mead, 8 Chyanclare, St Clare Street, Penzance TR18 2PG
Tel./Fax: 01736 369 066 (H)
Ground: Penlee Park, Alexandra Place, Penzance Tel: 01736 361964
Directions: Seafront road past harbour, after amusement arcade turn right at r'bout (Alexander Rd), ground second right. Fifteen minutes walk from Penzance(BR); directions as above.
Colours: Black & white/white/white
Change colours: Sky blue & white/sky blue/sky blue

PLYMOUTH ARGYLE
Chairman: Paul Stapleton
Secretary: Carole Rowntree. c/o P.A.F.C., Home Park, Plymouth PL2 3DQ Tel: 01752 302208 (W)
Ground: Bolitho Park, St Peters Rd, Manadon Plymouth PL2 3DQ
Directions: From Tamer Bridge take third exit (Manadon) and then sharp left into St.Peters Road. Ground is one mile on the right.
Colours: Green/white/green
Change colours: White/geen/white

PLYMOUTH PARKWAY
Formed: 1988
Chairman: Mark Rowles
Secretary: Duncan Hedges. 184 Clittaford Road, Southway, Plymouth PL6 6DJ. Tel: 01752 785 693 (H) 07980 450 295 (M)
Ground: Bolitho Park, St Peters Rd, Manadon Plymouth
Directions: From Tamer Bridge take third exit (Manadon) and then sharp left into St.Peters Road. Ground is one mile on the right.
Colours: Yellow/royal blue/yellow
Change colours: All claret

PORTHLEVEN
Formed: 1896
Chairman: Neil Clark
Secretary: Vidal James. Tel: 01209 313 768 (H)
Ground: Gala Parc, Mill Lane, Porthleven Tel: 01208 574181
Directions From Penzance on A394, B3304 into Porthleven, ground on left immediately before town. From Helston on B3304 ground on right as you exit town.
Colours: Yellow/black/yellow
Change colours: Blue/white/white

SALTASH UNITED
Formed: 1945
Chairman: Kevin Doddridge
Secretary: Luke Ranford. 8 Rogate Walk, Thornbury, Plymouth PL6. Tel: 01752 241 719 (H) 07880 299555 (M)
Ground: Kimberley Stadium, Callington Road, Saltash PL12 6DX
Directions: First left after crossing Tamar Bridge, through town centre, at top of town fork right at mini - roundabout, ground 400 yds ahead on left.
Colours: Red & white/black/black
Change colours: Blue/white/red

ST. AUSTELL
Formed: 1890
Chairman:
Secretary: Steve Bullen, 27 Poltair Park, Trevarthian Road, St Austell. PL25 4LY. Tel Nos: 01726 70138 (H) 07976 629 547 (M)
e-mail: browns@mtpleasantcott.fsnet.co.uk
Ground: Poltair Park, Poltair Road, St. Austell   Tel: 01726 66099
Directions: 5 mins walk north of St Austell (BR). Near Poltair school and St Austall Brewery
Colours: All White
Change colours: Red/black/red

ST. BLAZEY
Formed: 1896
Chairman: Harry Cooke
Secretary: Simon Tonkin, 17 Ropehaven Road, St Austell PL25 4DU
Tel: 01726 69148 (H). 07989 432 467 (M)
Ground: Blaise Park, Station Road, St Blazey, Cornwall PL24 2ND
Tel: 01726 814 110
Directions: From the A390, Liskeard-St Austell road, turn into Station Road at the taffic lights inSt Blazey village and the ground is 100 yards down on the left.
Colours: Green/Black/green
Change colours: All blue

TAVISTOCK AFC
Formed: 1888
Chairman: Derek Pethick
Secretary: Eric Pinch, 33 Oak Rd., Bishopsmead, Tavistock, Devon. PL19 9LJ. Tel No: 01822 611 339 and 07977 392 110 (M)
Ground: Langsford Park, Crowndale Rd, Tavistock (01822 614447)
Directions: A386 from Okehampton, through town taking signs for Plymouth bear left past Sir Frances Drake's statue on Plymouth Rd. First right into Crowndale Rd,ground is 150yards on left
Colours: Red & black/red & black
Change : All purple

TORPOINT ATHLETIC
Formed:
Chairman: Ian McCullum
Secretary: Vic Grimwood, 43 Hemerdon Heights, Plympton PL7 3EY
Tel: 01752 344 263 (H)
Ground: The Mill, Mill Lane, Torpoint, Cornwall Tel: 01752 812889
Directions: Bear left from Torpoint ferry, ground down hill on left after half a mile
Colours: Gold & black stripes/gold & black/black
Change colours: Red & white hoops/white/red & white

WADEBRIDGE TOWN
Formed: 1894
Chairman: Steve Cudmore
Secretary: Bob Steggles. Tel: 01637 872 677 (H). 01637 872 080 (W)
Ground: Bodieve Park, Bodieve, Wadebridge PL27 7AJ.
Tel: 01208 812 537
Directions: Top of Gonvena Hill, 400 yards from roundabout on Wadebridge by-pass.
Colours: All red. **Change:** Blue & white/blue/blue

SUFFOLK & IPSWICH LEAGUE

SPONSORED BY: **METALEC**
Founded 1896
President: Alan Gorham   **Chairman:** Peter Cocker
General Secretary: Mary Ablett
Email: maryablett@btinternet.com

SENIOR DIVISION		P	W	D	L	F	A	Pts
1.	East Bergholt United (Champions 04-05)	30	17	5	8	51	33	56
2.	Achilles	30	14	11	5	73	45	53
3.	Crane Sports	30	14	9	7	50	34	51
4.	Ransomes Sports	30	14	8	8	51	40	50
5.	Grundisburgh	30	14	6	10	52	36	48
6.	Westerfield United	30	14	6	10	64	57	48
7.	Haughley United (-4)	30	14	9	7	57	42	47
8.	Leiston St Margarets (3rd Div.1 04-05)	30	11	5	14	47	62	38
9.	Capel Plough	30	9	10	11	48	47	37
10.	Cockfield United	30	8	13	9	48	48	37
11.	Ipswich Athletic	30	9	9	12	51	48	36
12.	Melton St Audrys (-6)	30	12	5	13	45	57	35
13.	Felixstowe United	30	10	5	15	43	63	35
14.	Brantham Athletic (2nd Div.1 04-05)	30	8	8	14	47	66	32
15.	Framlingham Town	30	4	12	14	42	54	24
16.	Stonham Aspal (1st Div.1 04-05)	30	4	7	19	44	81	19

SENIOR DIVISION	1	2	3	4	5	6	7	8	9	10	11	12	13	14	15	16
1 Achilles		2-1	1-1	1-1	2-2	0-1	3-3	2-2	2-2	4-2	2-0	5-0	7-0	2-0	4-2	2-3
2 Brantham Athletic	2-3		0-0	1-4	1-5	2-6	0-2	1-1	0-6	0-0	2-1	1-3	1-1	1-1	1-0	1-5
3 Capel Plough	3-5	1-0		1-1	0-1	0-2	5-2	3-1	1-0	1-1	3-1	2-0	1-3	1-2	2-1	2-1
4 Cockfield United	0-0	1-3	1-1		1-1	0-3	2-0	1-1	4-1	1-1	3-2	2-2	5-1	0-0	0-0	1-3
5 Crane Sports	2-3	2-1	4-1	1-1		1-2	3-1	3-1	2-0	1-3	2-1	0-0	1-0	0-0	1-0	2-2
6 East Bergholt United	1-3	3-3	0-0	2-0	0-1		2-0	2-2	0-1	0-3	1-0	1-0	3-0	3-0	4-1	1-0
7 Felixstowe United	1-0	1-3	3-2	3-1	1-1	0-3		1-3	0-2	1-3	0-2	1-0	2-2	1-4	3-2	0-0
8 Framlingham Town	2-2	2-2	1-1	1-3	1-1	2-0	1-4		2-3	1-2	1-1	2-3	1-0	2-4	1-2	2-3
9 Grundisburgh	3-3	3-0	3-3	2-0	1-0	2-0	0-1	0-0		0-1	1-0	2-3	1-0	2-3	2-0	1-1
10 Haughley United	2-2	2-4	2-0	2-2	0-0	0-1	4-2	1-0	3-5		0-0	2-1	2-0	5-1	2-2	4-1
11 Ipswich Athletic	3-3	5-4	0-3	3-0	3-0	0-3	0-0	3-1	2-2	1-0		2-0	3-0	4-1	1-3	3-5
12 Leiston St Margarets	1-5	2-1	3-2	3-0	2-1	0-4	2-3	3-2	1-4	2-2	2-1		1-0	1-2	5-2	2-4
13 Melton St Audrys	1-0	0-2	3-1	1-1	3-1	3-2	3-0	1-0	3-2	2-0	1-1	2-1		3-1	2-2	2-3
14 Ransomes Sports	0-1	2-2	1-1	3-0	1-2	2-2	1-3	1-1	1-0	2-0	2-1	3-1	6-0		1-0	1-2
15 Stonham Aspal	3-2	2-4	3-1	4-7	1-5	0-1	4-1	0-3	1-1	1-4	1-4	2-2	2-5	1-3		0-2
16 Westerfield United	1-2	0-3	0-5	1-5	2-1	7-1	2-2	2-1	0-2	3-4	1-1	1-1	3-2	1-2	5-1	

DIVISION ONE		P	W	D	L	F	A	Pts
1	Coplestonians	26	17	5	4	65	30	56
2	Stowupland	26	15	8	3	60	35	53
3	BT Trimley	26	16	3	7	54	27	51
4	Old Newton United	26	13	8	5	58	35	47
5	Thurston	26	14	2	10	84	48	44
6	Stanton	26	11	7	8	48	44	40
7	St Edmunds 65	26	11	6	9	56	54	39
8	Needham Market 'A' (-6)	26	13	6	7	38	38	39
9	Woodbridge Athletic (-3)	26	8	7	11	34	47	28
10	Willis	26	6	7	13	36	64	25
11	Wickham Market	26	7	3	16	35	54	24
12	Bramford United	26	6	6	14	31	51	24
13	Ipswich Exiles	26	4	5	17	36	72	17
14	Wenhaston United (-3)	26	3	3	20	24	60	9

DIVISION TWO		P	W	D	L	F	A	Pts
1	St Johns	26	22	0	4	92	21	66
2	Mendlesham Kings Head	26	18	2	6	79	47	56
3	Halesworth Town	26	13	1	12	52	65	40
4	AFC Hoxne (-3)	26	11	9	6	56	53	39
5	Bacton United 89	26	10	7	9	74	72	37
6	Dennington United	26	10	7	9	53	55	37
7	Bramford Road Old Boys	26	10	6	10	52	45	36
8	Claydon	26	10	6	10	51	46	36
9	Stradbroke United	26	10	3	13	64	62	33
10	John Bull United	26	10	3	13	58	69	33
11	Coddenham	26	8	7	11	44	48	31
12	Salvation Army	26	9	4	13	47	58	31
13	Somersham	26	9	2	15	41	50	29
14	Murray Rangers (-3)	26	3	1	22	33	105	7

DIVISION THREE

		P	W	D	L	F	A	Pts
1	Bildeston Rangers	26	21	0	5	101	46	63
2	Peasenhall United	26	19	3	4	90	38	60
3	Sporting 87	26	15	4	7	63	35	49
4	Parkside United	26	15	2	9	82	57	47
5	Albion Mills	26	11	4	11	56	56	37
6	Elmswell	26	12	1	13	46	57	37
7	Sproughton Sports	26	9	4	13	53	64	31
8	Martlesham Athletic 98	26	9	4	13	49	78	31
9	Coplestonians 'A' (-6)	26	11	3	12	57	56	30
10	Ipswich United (-3)	26	10	3	13	71	75	30
11	Ufford Sports	26	9	3	14	35	70	30
12	St Clements Hospital(-6)	26	10	4	12	31	44	28
13	Walsham Le Willows 'A'	26	6	2	18	26	65	20
14	Henley Athletic	26	3	7	16	32	51	16

DIVISION FOUR

		P	W	D	L	F	A	Pts
1	Saxmundham Sports	26	22	3	1	113	27	69
2	Alstons	26	20	0	6	99	51	60
3	Tacket Street BBOB	26	13	6	7	70	40	45
4	Sizewell & Aldeburgh	26	13	5	8	80	66	44
5	Great Blakenham	26	14	1	11	55	48	43
6	Benhall St Mary	26	12	5	9	53	56	41
7	Ipswich Postals	26	11	3	12	73	68	36
8	Henley Athletic Res.	26	10	6	10	45	50	36
9	Tattingstone United	26	9	5	12	60	67	32
10	Waterside	26	8	6	12	52	65	30
11	East Bergholt Utd 'A' (-3)	26	9	2	15	67	91	26
12	Claydon Reserves (-3)	26	8	4	14	51	63	25
13	Bramford Road O.B. Res.	26	5	3	18	39	80	18
14	Haughley United 'A'	26	2	3	21	23	108	9

DIVISION FIVE

		P	W	D	L	F	A	Pts
1	Meadlands	26	21	3	2	118	29	66
2	Stowmarket Stag	26	20	4	2	82	31	64
3	Somersham Reserves	26	17	6	3	77	34	57
4	Trimley Red Devils (-6)	26	19	3	4	109	24	54
5	St Clements Hospital R.	26	11	7	8	67	50	40
6	Stonham Aspal 'A'	26	12	4	10	54	46	40
7	Bacton Utd 89 Res.	26	11	2	13	62	87	35
8	Stowupland 'A'	26	9	3	14	61	86	30
9	Needham Market Youth	26	7	4	15	40	62	25
10	Stradbroke United Res.	26	6	4	16	40	76	22
11	Salvation Army Res.	26	5	4	17	43	86	19
12	Mendlesham Kings Head Res.	26	4	7	15	43	87	19
13	Old Newton United 'A'	26	6	1	19	36	91	19
14	AFC Hoxne Res. (-6)	26	7	2	17	42	85	17

DIVISION SIX

		P	W	D	L	F	A	Pts
1	Woolverstone United	24	19	0	5	74	31	57
2	Claydon 'A'	24	16	2	6	81	35	50
3	Coddenham Reserves	24	14	6	4	68	32	48
4	Sproughton Sports Res.	24	14	1	9	50	38	43
5	Elmswell Reserves	24	11	5	8	50	54	38
6	Needham Market Vets	24	11	2	11	61	55	35
7	Peasenhall United Res.	24	9	4	11	41	58	31
8	St Johns Reserves	24	9	2	13	64	80	29
9	Albion Mills Reserves	24	8	4	12	50	62	28
10	Tacket Street BBOB Res.	24	7	5	12	40	54	26
11	BT Trimley 'A' (-4)	24	9	2	13	48	67	25
12	Halesworth Town Res.	24	6	6	12	42	57	24
13	Dennington United Res.	24	3	1	20	33	79	10

LEAGUE CUP

FIRST ROUND

Albion Mills	v Henley Athletic	2-1
Alstons	v St. Johns	3-6
Bildeston Rovers	v Meadlands	8-4
BT Trimley	v Thurston	4-0
Coddenham	v Trimley Red Devils	1-3
Great Blakenham	v Coplestonians	2-6
Ipswich Exiles	v Sporting 87	3-1
Martlesham Ath'98	v St. Clements Hospital	1-6
Murray Rangers	v Stowupland	0-1
Peasenhall United	v Waterside	5-0
St. Edmunds 65	v Benhall St. Mary	9-1
Sizewell & Aldeburgh	v Bramford United	2-4
Stanton	v Needham Market 'A'	1-0
Stowmarket Stag	v Walsham Le Willows 'A'	3-1
Ufford Sports	v Sproughton Sports 2-2*, AWpen	
Wenhaston United	v Woodbridge Athletic	2-0
Wickham Market	v Saxmundham Sports	2-3
Willis	v Elmswell	1-0
Woolverstone Utd	v Tacket Street BBOB	0-2
Dennington United	v Bacton United '89	2-1
JohnBull United	v Old Newton United	0-2
Parkside United	v AFC Hoxne	9-5

SECOND ROUND

Albion Mills	v Mendlesham Kings Head	1-0
Bramford United	v Somersham	3-2
Claydon	v Parkside United	9-3
Halesworth Town	v Bildeston Rangers	0-2
Ipswich Exiles	v Peasenhall United	4-2
Ipswich United	v Ipswich Postals	3-3*, 2-4p
Salvation Army	v Willis	3-4
Saxmundham Sports	v Dennington United	4-0
Sproughton Sports	v Bramford Road Old Boys	0-4
Stanton	v Coplestonians	0-1
St. Edmunds 65	v Tattingstone United	HW
St. Johns	v Wenhaston United	5-3
Stowmarket Stag	v St. Clements Hospital	3-0
Stowupland	v Old Newton United	3-5
Tacket Street BBOB	v Stradbroke United	2-3
Trimley Red Devils	v BT Trimley	5-4

THIRD ROUND

Albion Mills	v Trimley Red Devils	3-0
Bildeston Rangers	v Framlingham Town	1-2
Bramford Road OB	v Ransomes Sports	1-4
Bramford United	v Stonham Aspal	0-2
Capel Plough	v Achilles	1-3
Cockfield United	v Stowmarket Stag	11-0
Coplestonians	v Claydon	4-0
Felixstowe United	v Crane Sports (H)	2-3
Grundisburgh	v Stradbroke United	3-0
Haughley United	v St. Johns	2-5
Ipswich Athletic	v Ipswich Exiles	2-1
Ipswich Postal	v Willis	1-3
Old Newton United	v Brantham Athletic	4-0
Saxmundham Sports	v St. Edmunds 65	3-5
Westerfield United	v Melton St. Audrys	3-0
East Bergholt Utd	v Leiston St. Margaret's	1-0

FOURTH ROUND

Achilles	v Grundisburgh	4-0
Cockfield United	v Old Newton United	0-2
Crane Sports (H)	v Stonham Aspal	4-0
Ipswich Athletic	v Framlingham Town	4-2
Ransomes Sports	v Albion Mills	10-0
St. Edmunds 65	v Coplestonians	2-3
St. Johns	v Westerfield United	1-1*, 6-5p
East Bergholt Utd	v Willis	0-0*, 4-3p

QUARTER-FINALS

Achilles	v East Bergholt United	3-2
Coplestonians	v St. Johns	5-1
Crane Sports (H)	v Old Newton United	2-4
Ransomes Sports	v Ipswich Athletic	2-0

SEMI-FINALS

Coplestonians	v Achilles	2-4
Old Newton United	v Ransomes Sports	0-3

THE FINAL

Achilles	v Ransomes Sports	1-2

ACHILLES
Formed: 1937
Secretary : Sue Cook, 47 Fairfield Road, Ipswich IP3 9LB
Tel (home): 01473 720748. Mobile: 07815 513428
Ground: Pauls Social Club, Selmet Close, Ipswich IP2 9BA
Tel: 01473 604874
Colours: Red/black shirts, black shorts and stockings
Change Colours: Sky blue shirts, white shorts and stockings

BRANTHAM ATHLETIC
Secretary : Graham Mower, 1 Broughton Villa, Cattawade Street,
Brantham, Nr Manningtree, Essex   CO11 1SA
Tel (home): 01206 393296
Mobile: 07968 484182
Email (work): graham@maysfarmhaulage.co.uk
Ground: Brantham Athletic & Social Club, New Village, Brantham
Nr Manningtree CO11 1RZ. **Tel:** 01206 392506
Colours: Blue shirts, blue shorts, blue/white stockings
Change: Red shirts, black shorts, black stockings

CAPEL PLOUGH
Secretary : Samantha Powel, 200 Foxhall Road, Ipswich IP3 8HR
Tel (home): 01473 413820
Email (home): john@powell942.fslife.co.uk
Ground: Friars, Capel St Mary, Ipswich IP9 2XS
Colours: All blue
Change: All red

COCKFIELD UNITED
Secretary: Adrian Bullett, 4 Crowbrook Cottages, Cockfield,
Bury St Edmunds IP30 0HX
Tel (home): 01284 828032. Mobile: 07941 033462
Email (home): adrianbullett@aol.com
Ground: Great Green, Cockfield, Bury St Edmunds IP30 0HJ
Colours: All navy   **Change:** All red

COPLESTONIANS
Formed: 1975
Secretary: Peter Whittaker, 20 Deben Avenue, Martlesham Avenue,
Ipswich IP5 3QP
Tel (home): 01473 622863
Ground: Copleston High School, Copleston Road, Ipswich IP4 5HD
Tel: 01473 622 863
Colours: All maroon.
Change : White shirts, blue shorts and red stockings

CRANE SPORTS
Secretary: Andy Pearce, 43 Foden Avenue, Ipswich IP1 5PL
Tel (home): 01473 744266. Mobile: 07860 376363
Email (home): andy.g.pearce@bt.com
Ground: King George V Playing Field, Old Norwich Rd, IP1 6LE
Tel: 01473 464030
Colours: White, navy shorts and socks
Change: Orange shirts, navy shorts and orange socks

EAST BERGHOLT UNITED
Secretary: Carol Williams, 1 Kingfisher Drive, Great Blakenham
Ipswich IP6 0NG. Tel (home): 01473 830256 Mobile: 07999 542393
Email: carol_messenger@yahoo.co.uk
Ground: The Sports Pavilion, Gandish Road, East Bergholt
Colchester, Essex CO7 6TP
Colours: Green shirts, black shorts, green stockings
Change: All navy

FELIXSTOWE UNITED
Secretary: Danny Baines, 21 Fen Meadow, Trimley St Mary
Felixstowe IP11 0YZ
Tel (home): 01394 276076. Mobile: 07730 313390
Email (home): danny.baines@dhl.com
Ground: Kirton Recreation Ground, Back Road, Kirton, IP10 0PW
Colours: Black & White shirts, black shorts and socks
Change: Black & white stripes, black shorts and socks

GRUNDISBURGH
Secretary: Elaine Smith, Northbridge, 33 Colchester Road, Ipswich
IP4 3BT. Tel (home): 01473 414256 . Mobile: 07808 430412
Email: smitheln4@aol.com
Ground: The Playing Field, Ipswich Road, Grundisburgh,
Woodbridge IP13 6TJ
Tel: 01473 738234
Colours: All blue **Change:** All red

HAUGHLEY UNITED
Secretary: Adrian Hall, 83 Melford Road, Stowmarket, IP14 2PT
Tel (home): 01449 777945
Email (home): adrian.hall123@ntlworld.com
Ground: King George V Playing Field, Green Rd, Haughley, IP14 3RA
Tel: 01449 673460
Colours: Black/white striped shirts, black shorts and stockings
Change: Blue/white hooped shirts, white shorts, blue stockings

IPSWICH ATHLETIC
Secretary: Emma Ford, 7 Brockley Crescent, Ipswich IP1 5HT
Tel (home): 01473 748277
Email: emma.ford957@ntlworld.com
Ground: Bourne Vale Social Club, Halifax Road, Ipswich IP2 8RE
Colours: Red/white striped shirts, black shorts, white socks
Change: Navy shirts, dark blue shorts, navy socks

LEISTON ST. MARGARETS
Secretary: John Barker, Garden Cottage, Mill Hill Estate
Aldringham, Leiston IP16 4QB
Tel (home): 01728 831575. Mobile: 07775 663322
Ground: Junction Meadow, Abbey Road, Leiston IP16 4RD
Tel: 01728 831239
Colours: Red shirts, navy shorts, red socks. **Change:** All blue

MELTON ST. AUDRY'S
Secretary: Allan Kitchen, 213 Rose Hill Road, Ipswich IP3 8HF
Tel (home): 01473 720358
Mobile: 07903 088747
Email: allan.kitchen@btinternet.com
Ground: St Audrys Sports & Social Club, Lodge Farm Lane
Melton, Woodbridge IP12 1LX
Colours: Red shirts, black shorts and stockings
Change: All navy

RANSOMES SPORTS
Secretary: Sarah Howard, 195 Clapgate Lane, Ipswich IP3 0RF
Tel (home): 01473 713856. Mobile: 07808 077684
Email (home): sarah.end@ntlworld.com
Ground: Ransomes Sports and Social Club, Sidegate Avenue
Ipswich IP4 4JJ
Tel: 01473 726134
Colours: Red shirts, black shorts and stockings
Change: Blue shirts, blue shorts, white stockings

STOWUPLAND FALCONS
Secretary: Alan Muskett, 7 Reeds Way, Stowupland,
Stowmarket IP14 4BP
Tel (home): 01449 676365. Mobile: 07884 077043
Ground: The Village Hall, Church Road, Stowupland IP14 4BQ
Tel: 01449 771010
Colours: Tangerine shirts, black shorts, tangerine stockings
Change: Blue/white shirts, blue shorts and stockings

WESTERFIELD UNITED
Formed: 1947
Secretary: Roy Garwood, 13 Bixley Road, Ipswich IP3 8PJ
Tel (home): 01473 727271
Ground: Rushmere Sports Club, The Street, Rushmere St Andrew
Ipswich IP5 1DE . Tel: 01473 272 525
Colours: Blue shirts, white shorts, blue stockings
Change: All white

WEARSIDE LEAGUE

President: W Robson   **Chairman:** Peter J Maguire
Secretary: Tom Clark, 55 Vicarage Close, New Silksworth, Sunderland SR3 1UF
Tel: 0191 5211 242   Email: tclark2@virgin.net

		P	W	D	L	F	A	Pts
1.	Whitehaven Amateurs	34	26	4	4	118	27	82
2.	Stokesley SC	34	23	7	4	70	30	76
3.	Birtley Town	34	20	9	5	67	32	69
4.	South Shields Cleadon FC	34	21	4	9	64	48	67
5.	Teeside Athletic	34	21	3	10	64	34	66
6.	Cleator Moor Celtic	34	20	5	9	71	25	65
7.	Windscale	34	19	4	11	69	36	61
8.	Boldon CA (-3)	34	18	3	13	50	47	54
9.	Annfield Plain	34	17	2	15	63	67	53
10.	Jarrow FC	34	12	6	16	52	58	42
11.	Willington FC	34	12	2	20	48	68	38
12.	Sunderland Ryhope CW	34	11	4	19	48	73	37
13.	Wolviston FC	34	9	5	20	47	69	32
14.	South Shields Harton and Westoe CW	34	7	11	16	40	90	32
15.	New Marske Sports Club (-3)	34	9	6	19	53	74	30
16.	Gateshead Low Fell	34	7	8	19	41	69	29
17.	Coxhoe Athletic	34	7	3	24	36	81	24
18.	Nissan SSC Sunderland	34	2	4	28	28	101	10

		1	2	3	4	5	6	7	8	9	10	11	12	13	14	15	16	17	18
1	Annfield Plain		1-2	2-1	2-0	5-0	3-2	4-1	2-4	2-2	0-1	2-5	1-5	1-3	2-1	2-3	3-1	3-1	0-1
2	Birtley Town	3-0		2-0	1-0	1-1	3-2	3-2	1-0	1-1	1-1	6-1	0-0	0-2	2-2	1-0	4-1	1-4	4-3
3	Boldon CA	0-2	1-0		1-5	2-1	2-0	1-1	0-3	1-1	0-2	3-0	2-1	0-1	3-0	3-0	2-0	3-1	2-1
4	Cleator Moor Celtic	8-0	1-1	0-1		2-0	4-1	1-0	3-0	6-0	1-3	1-1	1-3	1-0	1-1	3-0	2-0	2-1	8-0
5	Coxhoe Athletic	0-1	0-4	2-3	0-3		2-5	2-4	2-1	0-2	0-0	3-1	0-4	1-2	4-0	0-2	4-0	0-2	1-2
6	Jarrow FC	1-3	1-0	0-0	0-1	6-0		5-2	1-2	2-0	0-1	6-0	1-0	0-3	1-0	1-1	2-1	1-0	3-4
7	New Marske Sports Club	1-4	0-1	2-3	0-1	2-1	0-1		2-3	2-1	1-5	1-1	0-2	1-1	2-0	2-0	6-0	0-2	1-4
8	South Sheilds Cleadon	0-3	1-1	1-2	2-2	4-1	1-0	2-1		4-0	0-2	2-0	1-4	2-0	3-0	1-0	3-2	0-4	1-0
9	Harton and Westoe CW	2-1	0-5	0-3	1-1	0-1	1-1	3-2	2-3		2-4	4-2	0-10	2-1	1-4	2-2	2-2	0-5	2-2
10	Stokesley SC	0-1	1-0	2-1	1-0	3-1	2-1	2-2	1-2	1-1		2-1	0-1	4-2	1-0	3-0	6-1	3-2	1-0
11	Sunderland Ryhope CW	0-1	1-3	2-0	0-1	5-1	3-0	2-2	0-3	0-0	2-3		2-5	0-2	2-1	2-3	2-1	1-2	0-5
12	Whitehaven Amateurs	7-1	2-2	6-1	0-2	4-1	8-0	7-0	3-1	5-0	3-1	2-1		2-2	6-0	6-0	3-1	0-1	6-0
13	Windscale	2-1	0-1	3-1	2-1	2-0	0-0	5-1	1-2	5-0	2-2	4-1	0-1		2-3	4-1	4-0	1-2	3-1
14	Wolviston FC	3-1	1-4	3-0	0-3	1-2	1-1	1-1	2-3	6-2	0-2	0-1	1-4	1-4		5-1	2-0	0-1	0-2
15	Gateshead Low Fell	1-1	1-3	0-1	1-3	1-1	3-1	6-2	3-3	1-3	2-2	0-1	1-2	1-0	2-2		1-2	1-4	2-0
16	Nissan SSC Sunderland	1-4	0-2	0-5	0-3	0-3	2-2	0-6	2-2	0-1	0-4	1-3	1-3	0-4	1-3	0-0		1-5	4-0
17	Teeside Athletic	3-0	1-1	1-2	1-0	3-1	3-1	0-2	0-1	3-0	0-0	1-2	2-2	2-1	1-2	2-1	2-1		1-0
18	Willington FC	2-4	0-3	2-0	1-0	4-0	2-3	0-1	1-3	2-2	0-4	2-3	0-1	0-1	3-1	1-0	3-2	0-1	

LEAGUE CUP

FIRST ROUND

New Marske S.C.	v	Wolviston FC	0-0*, 4-5p
Gateshead Low F.	v	Sunderland Ryhope CW	2-1

SECOND ROUND

Jarrow FC	v	South Shields Harton & W.	3-2
Willington FC	v	Teeside Athletic	3-2
Annfield Plain	v	Nissan SSC Sunderland	6-0
South Shields C.	v	Coxhoe Athletic	4-1
Whitehaven Am.	v	Boldon CA	2-3
Wolviston FC	v	Windscale	0-1
Stokesley S.C. (H)	v	Cleator Moor Celtic	5-1
Birtley Town	v	Gateshead Low Fell	3-2

QUARTER-FINALS

Annfield Plain	v	Jarrow FC	1-2
Birtley Town	v	Boldon CA	1-0
South Shields C.	v	Stokesley S.C. (H)	2-0
Willington	v	Windscale	0-4

SEMI-FINALS

South Shields C.	v	Jarrow FC	2-1
Windscale	v	Birtley Town	2-2*, AW on pens

THE FINAL

Birtley Town	v	South Shields Cleadon	1-0

LEAGUE CONSTITUTION 2006/07

ANNFIELD PLAIN
Secretary: M.Lawson, 24 Northgate,Anfield Plain,Stanley, Co.Durham DH9 7UY. Tel No: 01207 235 879. (M) 0783 336 6056
Ground: Derwent Park, West Road,Annfield Plain.
Directions: On A 693 road to Consett, 200 yards west of junction with A6067.The ground is behind new housing estate.

BIRTLEY TOWN
Secretary: Trevor Armstrong. 40 Dunvegan, Vigo, Birtley Co Durham DH3 2JH. Tel No: 0191 410 9219. (M) 07958 540 389
Ground: Birtley Sports Complex Tel No:
Directions: (From Durham) Off A1 (M) for Chester le Street, take 2nd turning off roundabout and then last turn off next roundabout(both signed to Birtley). Take first left after AEI cables and ground is at rear of sports complex.

BOLDON COMMUNITY ASSOCIATION
Secretary: Kevin Oliver. 14 Tracey Avenue, West Boldon NE36 0HT Tel No: 0191 519 4124. (M) 0777 078 1476.
Ground: Boldon Community Association, New Road, Boldon Colliery NE35 9DS. Tel No: 0191 536 4180
Directions: A19 to jct A184 Sunderland/Newxastle. Follow signs to Boldon Asda stores, then ground is behind North Road Social club

CLEATOR MOOR CELTIC
Secretary: Barry Close. 17 Crowgarth Close, Cleator Moor, Cumbria CA25 5AZ. Tel No: 01946 814 404. (M) 07859 884 930
Ground: Birks Road, Cleator Moor, Cumbria Tel No: 01946 812476
Directions: From the first Cockermouth roundabout on the A66 take the first left for Fitzington. Drive through to B5294. Follow road for half a mile take left on to narrow B9295 for a mile to Birks Rd. Club entrance is on right.

COXHOE ATHLETIC
Secretary: Paul Charlton. 16 Browning Hill, Coxhoe, Co Durham DH6 4HB. Tel No: 0191 377 3764. (M) 07939 418 067.
Ground: Beechfield Park, Coxhoe, County Durham.
Directions: From Jct 61 on A1M (Durham services) take the B6291 'to Coxhoe. Left turning after about a mile just after 'Trevors Barber'. Ground is situated behind Paving Factory which is opposite The Tarka Centre.

GUISBOROUGH BLACK SWAN
Secretary: Lesley Clark, 15 Scarteen Close, Guisborough TS14 7PB. Tel: 01287 281 293.
Ground: King George V

HARTLEPOOL
Secretary: Barry Murray, 110 Spalding Road, Fens Estate, Hartlepool TZ 5 2JP. Tel: 01429 299 428
Ground: Grayfields Enclosure

JARROW
Secretary: Susan Scott, 38 Hylton Road, Jarrow, Tyne & Wear. TelNo: 0191 489 4333. (M) 07917 416 214.
Ground: Perth Green Community Centre, Ass Inverness Road, Jarrow NE32 4AQ.
Directions: From A19 or A1M head for South Shields and turn rt into John Reid Rd. First slip rd into Brockley Whinns Estate, past Red Hackle pub, then 3rd left into Inverness and Rt to Perth Green Community Centre.

NEW MARSKE SPORTS CLUB
Secretary: David Taylor. 9 St Georges Crescent, New Marske, redcar TS11 8BT. Tel No: 01642 473 153. (M) 07765 363 909.
Ground: Gurney Street , New Marske, Redcar TS11 8EG.
Directions: A19 south onto A174 Redcar-Teesport. Follow A174 towards Saltburn turn right at roundabout with footbridge over road. Ground is 500 yards on left.

NISSAN SSC SUNDERLAND
Secretary: Colin McVay. 16 Longden Close, Hebburn, Tyne & Wear NE31 1NZ. Tel No: 0191 430 0221. (M) 07747 118 312.
Ground: Nissan Sports Complex, Washington Road, Sunderland SR5 3NS Tel No: 0191 415 2354 or 0191 415 2773
Directions: North along A1(M) to A690 (Sunderland) and connect with A19 north. Pass A1231 and plant on left. Follow signs for Nissan offices.

SOUTH SHIELDS CLEADON
Secretary: Doug Keys, 3 Tarragon Way, South Shields, Tyne & Wear NE34 8TA. Tel: 0191 536 7434
Ground: Jack Clark Park, Horsley Hill Road, South Shields, Tyne & Wear Tel No: 0191 454 2023

SOUTH SHIELDS HARTOE & WESTOE

Secretary: Bill Wells, 11 Lowery Gardens, Whiteleas, South Shields
NE34 8EP. Tel: 0191 5373 759
Ground: Harton Colliery Welfare, Boldon Lane NE34 0NA.
Directions: Take A194 to South Shields from A1M at Whitemoor Pool.
After about 2.5 miles rt to A1300 at 3rd roundabout.and then left at 2nd
roundabout onto Boldon Lane. Ground is 50 yards on right.

SUNDERLAND RYHOPE C.W.

Secretary: Dougie Benison. 14 Calthwaite Close,
Sunderland SR5 3QR. Tel No: 0191 516 5160 (B).
Ground: Ryhope Recreation Park, Ryhope Street, Ryhope,
Sunderland SR2 0AB. Tel No: 0191 521 2843
Directions: Take A19 (3miles south of Sunderland centre) to Ryhope
village. At village Green turn into Evelyn Terrace/Ryhope Street and on
to bank past Presto's for 600 yds. Ground on left.

TEESIDE ATHLETIC

Secretary: Kevin Fryett, 53 Fernwood, Redcar, Cleveland TS10 4NF
Tel No: 01642 470 963. (M) 07709 982 114.
Ground: Green Lane, Redcar TS10 3RW
Directions: From A1058 (tow Marske) Greeen Lane is sixth turning on
the left and car park is at the bottom of the road on the left.

WHITEHAVEN AMATEURS

SEcretary: Eric McGill. 23 Todholes Road, Cleator Moor, Cumbria
CA25 5PN. Tel No: 01946 814 950. (M) 07746 950 093.
Ground: Whitehaven County Ground, Coach Road, Whitehaven
CA28 2DD.
Directions: From A595 ignore town centre sign and turn right at lights
onto A5094. Turn left into Coach Road after half a mile then ground is
down narrow lane behind Rugby League Club.

WILLINGTON

Secretary: Alan Stewart. 8 East Bridge Street, Crook, Co-Durham
DL15 9BJ. Tel No: 01388 764 216. (M) 07791 870 635.
Ground: Hall Lane Ground, Hall Lane Estate, Willington DL15 0QF.
Tel No: 01388 746 221
Directions: Willington is on A690 7 miles west of Durham City & 2
miles east of Crook. Northern Bus Co. operates a service through
Willington from Crook or Durham City.

WINDSCALE

Secretary: Joe Shepherd. 15 Parklands Drive, Egremont, Cumbria
CA22 2JH. Tel No: 01946 821 548. (M) 0773 998 503.
Ground: Falcon Ground, Egremont CA22 2QN.
Directions: A66 to Bridgefoot. A595 Barrow road to bottom of hill
approaching Egrement and take 3rd exit off island to Smithfield/Gillfoot.
Ground in housing estate.

WOLVISTON

Secretary: Andy Anderson. 72 Clifton Avenue, Wolviston Court,
Billingham TS22 5BT. Tel No: 01642 863 180. (M) 07796 456 722.
Ground: Metcalfe Way, Wynyard Road, Wolivistion, Billingham,
Cleveland. TS22 5NE.
Directions: On Wynard road betwwen Thorpe Thewles & Wolviston
village take Wynard Road towards Thorpe Thewles. Ground on left
before St John Hall's Estate

Birtley Town F.C.
www.birtleytownfc.co.uk
Match Sponsor
Kingsley Coaches
Vs Whitehaven
Saturday 7th January 14.00 Kick Off

WEST CHESHIRE LEAGUE

SPONSORED BY: CARLSBERG-TETLEY
Founded 1892
President: Ken Halsall **Chairman & Hon. Treasurer:** Ray Prescott
Hon. General Secretary: Arthur Green, 46 Bertram Drive, Meols,
Wirral CH47 0LH Tel: 0151 6324946
Email: arthurlgreen@hotmail.com

DIVISION ONE

		P	W	D	L	F	A	Pts
1.	Poulton Victoria	30	20	6	4	66	31	66
2.	Aintree Villa (-3)	30	20	6	4	69	30	63
3.	Vauxhall Motors Reserves	30	16	5	9	66	46	53
4.	West Kirby	30	14	11	5	54	35	53
5.	Heswall (Champions 04-05)	30	15	7	8	45	35	52
6.	Mersyside Police	30	12	8	10	47	44	44
7.	Christleton	30	10	10	10	57	47	40
8.	Maghull	30	10	10	10	49	39	40
9.	New Brighton (1st Div.2 04-05)	30	10	7	13	48	53	37
10.	Ashville	30	10	5	15	38	47	35
11.	Ellesmere Port	30	8	11	11	28	47	35
12.	Cammell Laird Reserves	30	9	5	16	42	47	32
13.	Newton	30	8	8	14	41	51	32
14.	Castrol Social	30	8	6	16	31	65	30
15.	Runcorn Town (Mond Rgers) (2nd Div.2 04-05)	30	8	5	17	49	66	29
16.	Mallaby	30	4	6	20	28	75	18

DIVISION TWO

		P	W	D	L	F	A	Pts
1	Upton Athletic Assoc.	28	22	2	4	75	34	68
2	Blacon Youth Club	28	21	3	4	93	38	66
3	Maghull Reserves	28	20	4	4	67	32	64
4	Capenhurst Villa	28	16	5	7	55	31	53
5	Poulton Vics Reserves	28	15	5	8	61	39	50
6	Runcorn Town Res. (R)	28	12	8	8	61	65	44
7	Willaston (-3)	28	11	8	9	53	40	38
8	Chester Nomads	28	9	7	12	71	69	34
9	Manweb	28	9	4	15	45	63	31
10	Helsby	28	7	6	15	61	76	27
11	F.C. Pensby	28	7	5	16	43	63	26
12	Heswell Reserves	28	5	10	13	45	74	25
13	Halton (General Chems)	28	5	8	15	32	60	23
14	Ashville Reserves	28	5	7	16	48	61	22
15	Christleton Reserves	28	4	2	22	29	94	14

DIVISION THREE

		P	W	D	L	F	A	Pts
1	West Kirby Reserves	30	24	4	2	92	27	76
2	New Brighton Reserves	30	22	5	3	92	32	71
3	AFC Bebington Athletic	30	17	5	8	78	48	56
4	Mersey Police Reserves	30	15	7	8	77	47	52
5	Focus	30	15	6	9	55	46	51
6	St. Werburghs	30	14	7	9	75	59	49
7	Grange Athletic	30	13	6	11	60	83	45
8	Upton Athletic Assoc. R.	30	12	6	12	66	64	42
9	Ellesmere Port Reserves	30	12	5	13	57	61	41
10	Bronze Social	30	9	9	12	66	75	36
11	Manweb Reserves	30	10	4	16	70	85	34
12	Capenhurst Villa Res.	30	8	6	16	34	59	30
13	Mersey Royal	30	8	5	17	47	68	29
14	MBNA (-3)	30	8	7	15	54	71	28
15	Manor Athletic	30	3	7	20	31	86	16
16	Shaftesbury	30	3	5	22	48	91	14

PYKE CHALLENGE CUP

FIRST ROUND

Mallaby	v	Cammell Laird Reserves	1-4
Ashville	v	West Kirby	1-3
Ellesmere Port	v	Castrol Social	0-0*, 2-2*r, 3-4p
Heswall	v	Poulton Victoria	3-4
Maghull	v	New Brighton	5-2
Newton	v	Christleton	4-2
Merseyside Police	v	Vauxhall Motors Res. (H)	1-2
Runcorn Town (MR)	v	Aintree Villa	0-0*, 3-4r

QUARTER-FINALS

Cammell Laird Res.	v	Maghull	1-2
Newton	v	Poulton Victoria	0-5
Aintree Villa	v	Vauxhall Motors Res. (H)	0-5
West Kirby	v	Castrol Social	5-1

SEMI-FINALS

Poulton Victoria	v	Maghull	1-0
Vauxhall M. R. (H)	v	West Kirby	2-3*

THE FINAL

Poulton Victoria	v	West Kirby	2-3

DIVISION ONE CONSTITUTION 2006/07

AINTREE VILLA

Formed: 1954
Chairman: J. Hodson
Secretary: Alf Shepherd, 154 Altway, Aintree, Liverpool L10 6LG
Tel: 0151 526 9287 (H)
Ground: Aintree racecourse.
Directions: From Birkenhead or Wallasey Tunnel, take the A59 bearing left at the Black Bull Public House, continue through one set of traffic lights under railway bridge. Take 2nd turn on right into Melling Road, continue on this road until signpost for Golf Centre, turn right into Racecourse, follow road round to dressing rooms.
From Runcorn - M57 Motorway to Junction 6 [A506], turn left towards Liverpool. At 2nd set of traffic lights turn right into Aintree Lane. Over Canal Bridge to 'T' Junction, turn left and go past Blue Anchor Public House, next left into Melling Road and left into Racecourse at the signpost for the Golf Centre.
Colours: Tangerine/black/black
Change: Blue & white/blue/blue

ASHVILLE

Formed: 1949
Chairman: Ken Baker
Secretary: John Lawrenson.
Ground: Villa Park, Cross Lane, Wallasey Village, Wallasey,
Tel: 0151 638 2127
Directions: Via M53 to Junction 1, A551to Wallasey, turn right at first set of traffic lights on dual carriageway into Cross Lane. Ground approx. 100 yards on left.
Colours: White & black/black/black
Change: Blue & black stripes/blue/blue

BLACON YOUTH CLUB

Formed: 1964
Chairman: Peter Barnes.
Secretary: Colin Lawson.
Ground: Cairns Crescent Playing Fields, Cairns Crescent, Blacon, Chester.
Directions: Parkgate Road to the Ben Whitehouse Garage, approach new roundabout, take fourth exit into Blacon. Along Blacon Avenue to Parade Shops (R.H.S), take left turning opposite Parade Shops, first right, Western Avenue second right, Melbourne Road, first right, Cairns Crescent.
Colours: Black & white stripes/black/black
Change: All sky blues

CAMMELL LAIRD RESERVES

Formed: 1900
Chairman: John D Lynch
Secretary: Ray Steele. raysteele1@cammelllairdfc.co.uk
Ground: Kirklands, St Peters Road, Rock Ferry, Birkenhead
Tel: 0151 645 5991(Evenings). 0151 645 3121 (Daytime)
Directions: From Chester/M53, A41 towards Birkenhead; at New Ferry signpost take B5136 towards New Ferry. Approximately 1 mile you see a pedestrian crossing – turn right, down Proctor Road club is at the bottom of the road on left. From Liverpool – take the Birkenhead Tunnel then A41 for approximately 1 mile, take B5136 at big roundabout signposted New Ferry, Rock Ferry. Follow until 2nd set of traffic lights, Abbotsford Pub, turn left, then right into St Peter's Road. Club at bottom of road on the left.
Colours: All blue.
Change: All white.

CASTROL SOCIAL

Formed: formally Rivacre Rossfield, 1954
Chairman: Margaret Hughes
Secretary: Dave Bebbington
Ground: Castrol Sports & Social Club, Chester Road, Whitby, Ellesmere Port. **Tel:** 0151 355 1712.
Directions: (1) Exit Junction 14 on M56, travel along A5117, turn right at the 4th roundabout, Castrol Club is on the right hand side of the road.
(2) Exit junction 10 on M53 (from Birkenhead), turn right on to the A5117, turn right at the 3rd roundabout, Castrol Club is on the right hand side of the road.
(3) A41 to A5117 roundabout, (from Birkenhead), turn left (from Chester), turn right on to the A5117, turn left at next roundabout (Strawberry Hotel), Castrol Club is on the right hand side of the road.
Colours: Green & white stripes/green/green
Change: Navy/white/navy

CHRISTLETON

Formed 1896 **Re-Formed:** 1946
Chairman: Dave Kilfoyle
Secretary: Ken Price, 35 Canadian Ave, Hoole, Chester CH2 3HQ . **Tel:** 01244 313 513
Ground: Little Heath, Christleton **Tel:** 01244 332 153
Directions: M53 until exit signposted Nantwhich (A51), leave Motorway turn left on to A51, continue for 100 yards, turn right signposted (Littleton and Christleton), follow road to pond turn left, ground straight ahead.
Colours: Red/navy/navy.
Change: White/royal blue/royal blue

ELLESMERE PORT

Formed: formally Shell, 1924
Chairman: Andy Hayes
Secretary: Mrs Chrissie Hayes
Ground: Chester Road, Whitby, Ellesmere Port, South Wirral **Tel:** 0151 200 7080 / 7050.
Directions: (1) Exit M56 motorway junction 14, travel along A5117, turn right at 4th roundabout, Shell Club is on right hand side of road.
(2) Exit M53 motorway junction 10 [from Birkenhead], turn right on to the A5117, turn right at 3rd roundabout, Shell Club is on the right hand side of the road.
(3) A41 to A5117 roundabout,(from Birkenhead), turn left (from Chester) turn right on to A5117, turn left at next roundabout [Strawberry Hotel], Shell Club is on the right hand side of the road.
Colours: All royal blue.
Change: Sky blue & white/sky blue/sky blue.

HESWALL

Formed: 1891
Chairman: John Colligan
Secretary: Graham Sutherland
Ground: Gayton Pk,Brimstage Rd, Heswall, Wirral **Tel:**0151 342 8172.
Directions: From Birkenhead via Barnston Road to junction of Brimstage Road, turn left then first right. From Chester via Chester High Road to Gayton roundabout, take Brimstage Road then first right.
From West Kirby via Telegraph Road turn left at Gayton Roundabout, take Brimstage Road then first right.
Colours: Yellow/blue/yellow
Change: All white.

SOCCER BOOKS LIMITED
72 ST. PETERS AVENUE (Dept. NLD)
CLEETHORPES
N.E. LINCOLNSHIRE
DN35 8HU
ENGLAND
Tel. 01472 696226   Fax 01472 698546
Web site   www.soccer-books.co.uk
e-mail   info@soccer-books.co.uk

Established in 1982, Soccer Books Limited has one of the largest ranges of English-Language soccer books available. We continue to expand our stocks even further to include many new titles including German, French, Spanish, Italian and other foreign-language books.

With well over 100,000 satisfied customers already, we supply books to virtually every country in the world but have maintained the friendliness and accessibility associated with a small family-run business. The range of titles we sell includes:

YEARBOOKS – All major yearbooks including many editions of the Sky Sports Football Yearbook (previously Rothmans), Supporters' Guides, Playfair Annuals, North & Latin American Guides, Non-League Directories and European Football Yearbooks.

CLUB HISTORIES – Complete Statistical Records, Official Histories, Definitive Histories plus many more.

WORLD FOOTBALL – World Cup books, International Line-up & Statistics Series, European Championships History, International and European Club Cup competition Statistical Histories and much more.

BIOGRAPHIES & WHO'S WHOS – of managers and players plus Who's Whos etc.

ENCYCLOPEDIAS & GENERAL TITLES – Books on stadia, hooligan and sociological studies, histories and hundreds of others, including the weird and wonderful!

DVDs – Season's highlights, histories, big games, World Cup, player profiles, a selection of over 40 F.A. Cup Finals with many more titles becoming available all the time.

For a current printed listing containing a selection of our titles, please contact us using the details at the top of this page. Alternatively, our web site offers a secure ordering system for credit and debit card holders and lists our full range of over 1,300 books and 250 DVDs.

MAGHULL

Formed: 1921

Chairman: Les Jacques

Secretary: Danny Sherlock, 14 Alexander Drive, Lydiate, Merseyside L31 2NJ Tel: 0151 526 2306

Ground: Old Hall Field, Hall Lane, Maghull, Merseyside Tel: 0151 526 7320

Directions: M57, M58 or A59 to Switch Island, take A59 signposted Preston, turn right second set traffic lights, (overhead foot bridge) turn right into Hall Lane. Ground approx 80 yards on left hand side.

Colours: Royal blue & white hoops/royal blue/royal blue

Change: Yellow/black/black

MARINE RESERVES

Formed: 1894

Chairman: Paul Leary

Secretary: Geoff Kewley. geoffkewley@blueyonder.co.uk

Ground: Rossett Park, College Road, Crosby

Directions: ollege Road access from Liverpool/Southport Road (A565) at Merchant Taylor's school.

Colours: White/black/black

Change: Yellow/green/green

MERSEYSIDE POLICE

Formed: 1885

Chairman: James Evans.

Secretary: Colin White.

Ground: Police Club, Fairfield, Prescot Road, Liverpool L7 0JD Tel: 0151 228 2352

Directions: On leaving either Mersey tunnels towards Islington, Heading out of the city. Bear right on Islington to traffic light junction at Low Hill, turn left on to Prescot Road, ground ison the right hand side after 1 mile.

Colours: All royal blue

Change: Yellow/green/yellow or all white

NEW BRIGHTON

Formed: 1895

Chairman: Ray Mathias.

Secretary: Mick Lawton.

Ground: Harrison Drive, Wallasey Village, Wallasey

Directions: From M53 motorway leave at junction 1, at roundabout follow signs for A554, New Brighton. Follow road past Wallasey Golf Club, take 2nd right after Church on right hand side into Harrison Drive. Ground is first left turning after passing over the railway bridge.

Colours: Red & white/white/red

Change: Yellow/blue/white

NEWTON

Formed: 1933

Chairman: John Murray

Secretary: Alan Dabner, 79A Eleanor Road, Bidston, Wirral CH43 7RW. Tel NOs: 0151 653 2151 (H) 0151 993 2151 (B)

Ground: Millcroft, Frankby Road, Greasby, Wirral Tel: 0151 677 8382

Directions: From M53 motorway leave at junction 2, follow signs for West Kirby. ground on left at rear of houses about 3 miles along main (Frankby) road.

Colours: All graphite.

Change: White/sky blue/sky blue.

POULTON VICTORIA

Formed: 1935

Chairman: Steven McGlasson.

Secretary: Peter Leay. poulton.vicsfc@ntlworld.com

Ground: Victoria Park, Rankin Street, Wallasey Tel: 0151 638 3559

Directions: Exit M53 motorway, follow Wallasey Docks signs. Turn left at the roundabout past Poulton Victoria Club on the left, opposite the club turn right in to Limekiln Lane until you reach the Eagle Arms Public House, turn left in to Rankin Street, ground is at the top of the road on the right hand side.

Colours: All royal blue

Change: Yellow/black/black

UPTON ATHLETIC ASSOCIATION

Formed: 1964

Chairman: John Butcher.

Secretary: Barry Gaulton.

Ground: Cheshire County Sports Club, Plas Newton Lane, Chester CH2 1PR.

Tel: 01244 318 167

Directions: Exit M53 motorway at junction 12, turn right to Hoole roundabout, turn right at roundabout on to A41, signposted Chester Zoo, Upton. Take 1st turn right into Manning Lane, ground is 100 yards on the left.

Colours: All blue.

Change: All white.

VAUXHALL MOTORS RESERVES

Formed: 1963

Chairman: Alan Bartlam.

Secretary: Carole Paisey, 26 South Road, West Kirby, Wirral L48 3HQ Tel: 0151 6256 936.

Ground: Vauxhall Sports Ground, Rivacre Road, Hooton, Ellesmere Port. Tel: 0151 327 2115 (clubhouse). 0151 328 1114 (Ground & Office).

Directions: From M53 Motorway leave at A41 towards Hooton. At 1st set of traffic lights turn left in to Hooton Green, turn left at next 'T' junction. At end turn right ground is 100 yards on the right.

Colours: White/navy/white

Change: All sky blue

WEST KIRBY

Formed: 1895

Chairman: Alan Price.

Secretary: Margaret Hopkins. marghopkins@yahoo.co.uk.

Ground: Marine Park, Greenbank Road, West Kirby, Wirral. Tel: 0151 625 7734.

Directions: From West Kirby Concourse along Orryside Road, Anglesey Road into Greenbank Road, ground approximately 500 yards on the left hand side.

Colours: Black & white stripes/black/black

Change: All red or all blue

WEST LANCASHIRE LEAGUE

SPONSORED BY: AEGON

Chairman: Mr S M Ashworth
Hon. General Secretary: Mr H J Brown
10 Hazelwood Close, Thornton Cleveleys FY5 2SX

PREMIER DIVISION		P	W	D	L	F	A	Pts
1.	Kirkham & Wesham	30	25	5	0	96	19	80
2.	Charnock Richard	30	18	8	4	86	34	62
3.	Dalton United	30	14	9	7	61	40	51
4.	Eagley	30	14	4	12	59	53	46
5.	Fulwood Amateurs	30	12	8	10	50	52	44
6.	Euxton Villa	30	10	12	8	47	45	42
7.	Burnley United	30	12	6	12	53	56	42
8.	Coppull United	30	11	9	10	35	40	42
9.	Blackpool Wren Rovers	30	10	6	14	36	55	36
10.	Fleetwood Hesketh	30	8	11	11	35	36	35
11.	Freckleton	30	10	5	15	37	47	35
12.	Wyre Villa (-3)	30	10	5	15	45	62	32
13.	Turton	30	8	8	14	42	65	32
14.	Blackrod Town	30	7	10	13	38	52	31
15.	Barnoldswick Town	30	6	10	14	37	67	28
16.	Hesketh Bank	30	4	6	20	32	66	18

PREMIER DIVISION		1	2	3	4	5	6	7	8	9	10	11	12	13	14	15	16
1	Barnoldswick Town		2-2	1-4	2-1	1-1	2-2	1-0	1-1	2-1	0-0	0-0	1-4	5-0	2-6	1-1	1-3
2	Blackpool Wren Rovers	3-0		3-0	2-4	0-5	0-1	0-3	3-4	0-1	2-0	3-1	2-2	1-0	0-1	1-0	0-2
3	Blackrod Town	5-1	3-3		3-0	0-2	1-1	0-0	1-4	3-0	0-0	1-0	0-0	1-2	0-1	1-2	1-1
4	Burnley United	4-0	0-1	2-2		1-1	4-2	1-1	5-1	2-2	0-0	2-1	1-3	5-2	0-6	2-1	0-3
5	Charnock Richard	6-1	4-1	6-0	4-1		3-1	0-0	0-3	6-2	4-1	3-1	2-2	8-1	0-0	5-2	4-1
6	Coppull United	1-1	2-0	1-2	2-1	1-4		0-4	1-2	2-0	0-1	0-0	0-2	1-0	0-2	3-0	2-0
7	Dalton United	2-2	7-0	3-2	3-1	2-0	1-1		2-1	1-1	0-6	1-0	2-2	3-0	2-3	7-1	0-0
8	Eagley	1-4	1-0	0-4	1-2	1-2	0-1	3-2		3-0	1-2	1-4	5-3	1-0	2-4	1-1	5-2
9	Euxton Villa	3-0	0-0	3-0	3-2	1-1	0-0	4-2	0-2		3-3	1-1	2-1	3-0	1-1	0-0	3-1
10	Fleetwood Hesketh	1-2	1-2	1-1	1-0	2-1	1-1	0-0	0-1	2-4		0-1	0-0	3-1	1-2	0-1	3-1
11	Freckleton	2-1	1-1	1-2	1-4	1-2	0-1	1-2	1-7	3-2	0-0		1-2	2-1	0-2	1-0	4-1
12	Fulwood Amateurs	4-1	2-0	2-2	0-2	3-1	1-2	2-3	1-1	0-2	1-0	2-1		0-6	2-5	1-1	0-4
13	Hesketh Bank	0-0	1-2	3-0	0-0	0-0	1-1	1-4	0-2	2-2	3-3	0-1	0-3		1-5	1-2	4-0
14	Kirkham & Wesham	4-0	6-0	4-0	5-0	3-3	6-1	2-0	2-0	1-1	2-0	2-0	3-1	2-0		5-0	8-1
15	Turton	2-1	1-4	1-1	2-3	1-4	1-1	4-2	4-3	1-1	2-2	1-4	1-2	3-2	0-2		3-4
16	Wyre Villa	3-1	0-0	3-0	1-3	0-4	0-3	1-2	1-1	3-1	0-1	4-2	1-2	3-0	1-1	0-3	

DIVISION ONE		P	W	D	L	F	A	Pts
1	Haslingden St.Mary`S	26	20	2	4	82	40	62
2	Springfields	26	16	6	4	69	28	54
3	Stoneclough	26	15	6	5	72	47	51
4	Bae Barrow Sports C.	26	16	3	7	65	49	51
5	Poulton Town	26	14	2	10	62	49	44
6	Tempest United	26	12	6	8	54	49	42
7	Norcross & Warbreck	26	12	3	11	60	49	39
8	Whinney Hill	26	10	3	13	41	53	33
9	Garstang	26	7	8	11	44	57	29
10	Crosshills	26	7	5	14	44	63	26
11	Millom	26	8	2	16	57	81	26
12	Furness Rovers	26	6	6	14	41	54	24
13	Crooklands Casuals	26	6	4	16	33	49	22
14	Milnthorpe Corinthians	26	3	4	19	23	79	13

DIVISION TWO		P	W	D	L	F	A	Pts
1	Trimpell	26	19	4	3	83	35	61
2	Croston Sports	26	14	8	4	60	50	50
3	Thornton Cleveleys	26	15	5	6	67	46	50
4	Bolton County	26	12	4	10	51	44	40
5	Todmorden Borough	26	10	9	7	36	30	39
6	Bae Canberra	26	9	10	7	49	40	37
7	Mill Hill St. Peters	26	8	10	8	42	42	34
8	Glaxo Ulverston Rgers	26	9	9	8	40	42	33
9	Burnley Belvedere	26	9	6	11	50	57	33
10	Lancashire Constabulary	26	8	7	11	42	46	31
11	Furness Cavaliers	26	8	7	11	40	45	31
12	Askam United	26	8	5	13	38	45	29
13	Lostock St. Gerards	26	7	6	13	40	55	27
14	Bac/Ee Preston	26	1	2	23	20	101	5

RICHARDSON CUP

FIRST ROUND

Blackpool Wren R.	v	Blackrod Town	4-1
Eagley	v	Freckleton	1-5
Euxton Villa	v	Burnley United	1-3
Fleetwood Hesketh	v	Barnoldswick Town	1-0
Fulwood Amateurs	v	Wyre Villa	2-5
Hesketh Bank	v	Dalton United	0-3
Kirkham & W. (H)	v	Coppull United	2-1
Turton	v	Charnock Richard	1-3

QUARTER-FINALS

Charnock Richard	v	Blackpool Wren Rovers	4-2
Dalton United	v	Kirkham & Wesham (H)	0-4
Freckleton	v	Fleetwood Hesketh	2-3
Wyre Villa	v	Burnley United	3-5

SEMI-FINALS

Burnley United	v	Kirkham & Wesham (H)	1-4
Charnock Richard	v	Fleetwood Hesketh	1-1, AW on pens

THE FINAL

Kirkham & W. (H)	v	Fleetwood Hesketh	3-1

PREMIER LEAGUE CONSTITUTION 2006-07

BARNOLDSWICK TOWN
Mrs. L. James 01282 815361
37 Longing Lane
Barnoldswick
Colne
BB18 6BJ

BLACKPOOL WREN ROVERS
Mr. P. Kimberley 01253 349853
34 Priory Gate
Blackpool
FY4 2QE

BLACKROD TOWN
Mr. D. Almond 01942 793122
40 Landedmans
Westhoughton
Bolton
BL5 2QJ

BURNLEY UNITED
Mr. K. Blackburn 01282 415711
13 Salus Street
Burnley
Lancashire

CHARNOCK RICHARD
Mr. G. Randle 01772 496782
63 Broad Oak Lane
Penwortham
Preston
PR1 0UY

COPPULL UNITED
Mrs. K. Illingworth 01257 26627
3 Bankside
Clayton Le Woods
Chorley
PR6 7PZ

DALTON UNITED
Mr. D. Jones 01229 463619
25 Barnes Avenue
Dalton In Furness
LA15 8NE

EAGLEY
Mr. M. Hackin 01204 595863
260 Darwen Road
Bromley Cross
Bolton
BL7 9JG

EUXTON VILLA
Mr. B Morris 01257 268640
8 Yew Tree Avenue
Euxton
Chorley
PR7 6BH

FLEETWOOD HESKETH
Ms. S. Regan 01704 233243
105 Lytham Road
Southport
Merseyside
PR4 9UW

FRECKLETON
Mr. G. Dyson 01772 633851
77 Clitheroes Lane
Freckleton
Preston
Lancs
PR4 1SE

FULWOOD AMATEURS
Mr. T. Wilson 01772 464601
30 Wyresdale Crescent
Ribbleton
Preston
PR2 6UN

HASLINGDEN ST.MARY`S
Mr. J. Harrison 01706 214546
3 Broadway
Helmshoren
Rossendale
Lancs
BB4 4HB

KIRKHAM & WESHAM
Mr R. Davey 01772 685049
18 Carrwood Drive
Kirkham
Preston
PR4 2YQ

TURTON
Mr. E.P Charnock 01204 852608
15 Crown Point
Edgeworth
Turton
Bolton
BL7 0BD

WYRE VILLA
Mr. G. Bradley 01253 810637
Park Farm
Burned House Lane
Preesall
Poulton Le Fylde
FY6 0PQ

WEST MIDLANDS (REGIONAL) LEAGUE

SPONSORED BY: EXPRESS & STAR

Hon Secretary: Neil Juggins
14 Badgers Lane, Blackwell, Bromsgrove

PREMIER DIVISION		P	W	D	L	F	A	Pts
1	Market Drayton Town	42	32	8	2	102	33	104
2	Gornal Athletic	42	25	11	6	74	32	86
3	Great Wyrley (-1)	42	24	14	4	94	36	85
4	Bewdley Town	42	23	8	11	100	52	77
5	Wyrley Rangers	42	22	10	10	81	40	76
6	Lye Town	42	20	11	11	64	44	71
7	Goodrich	42	18	16	8	86	66	70
8	Tividale	42	20	8	14	73	50	68
9	Wellington	42	19	8	15	64	62	65
10	Dudley Town	42	18	8	16	74	71	62
11	Wednesfield	42	18	5	19	56	66	59
12	Bustleholme	42	15	9	18	66	73	54
13	Heath Hayes	42	14	12	16	53	64	54
14	Pelsall Villa	42	16	5	21	61	69	53
15	Shawbury United	42	15	6	21	74	87	51
16	Ludlow Town (-2)	42	12	11	19	62	90	45
17	Brierley & Hagley	42	11	6	25	50	83	39
18	Bromyard Town	42	10	8	24	53	79	38
19	Wolverhampton Cas	42	11	5	26	60	99	38
20	Smethwick Rangers (-1)	42	11	3	28	57	98	35
21	Kington Town	42	8	7	27	41	102	31
22	Ledbury Town	42	7	7	28	52	101	28

PREMIER DIVISION	1	2	3	4	5	6	7	8	9	10	11	12	13	14	15	16	17	18	19	20	21	22
1 Bewdley Town		2-2	1-1	5-0	4-0	3-1	3-0	2-1	2-1	3-1	3-1	2-2	2-2	1-0	4-1	5-1	1-1	1-0	4-1	2-3	1-0	0-2
2 Brierley & Hagley	2-0		1-4	1-0	1-2	1-1	0-1	0-5	0-0	1-0	6-0	3-7	0-1	1-5	0-2	4-0	1-0	0-1	2-0	1-2	1-2	2-2
3 Bromyard Town	1-1	2-1		0-1	1-3	2-6	0-2	1-3	1-2	3-0	1-3	0-0	2-3	1-1	2-0	1-2	2-0	1-2	0-3	1-0	1-4	0-5
4 Bustleholme	1-4	2-0	1-0		1-1	2-2	1-1	1-5	3-1	7-1	3-2	2-2	3-0	0-1	0-1	3-1	1-3	2-3	1-2	0-0	2-1	0-2
5 Dudley Town	4-3	1-2	2-1	4-0		2-2	0-0	3-5	1-0	1-3	4-0	5-1	0-6	1-4	2-0	3-1	2-1	3-1	1-1	3-0	3-1	0-2
6 Goodrich	0-0	2-0	0-3	3-2	3-2		1-0	0-3	1-1	2-1	6-0	1-1	0-0	2-6	2-1	5-2	4-1	3-1	0-4	2-2	4-1	2-2
7 Gornal Athletic	2-0	3-0	2-0	1-0	2-0	1-3		1-1	2-1	1-1	1-1	4-0	1-0	2-2	0-0	1-0	5-2	2-1	0-1	4-0	4-0	2-0
8 Great Wyrley	1-1	3-1	2-0	0-0	4-1	3-3	0-0		4-1	5-0	4-0	4-1	1-0	1-1	2-1	2-0	4-0	4-1	0-1	1-2	1-1	1-1
9 Heath Hayes	2-1	0-1	3-2	0-3	1-3	1-1	2-1	0-0		3-2	3-0	3-1	2-1	0-3	0-1	2-0	1-0	1-1	1-0	2-1	0-0	2-2
10 Kington Town	0-7	0-0	0-0	2-2	2-1	0-1	2-1	0-2	3-2		2-2	1-2	0-2	0-1	1-4	0-4	0-2	0-4	1-0	0-3	4-2	3-5
11 Ledbury Town	2-4	1-0	3-3	0-2	0-1	1-1	0-2	1-1	5-0	1-3		0-0	1-2	1-2	4-2	1-2	5-1	1-2	0-1	0-1	3-0	1-0
12 Ludlow Town	1-2	2-1	1-2	1-4	1-1	2-2	1-4	0-3	0-1	3-1	3-3		2-0	0-2	2-0	0-0	4-2	0-3	5-0	2-4	3-2	0-1
13 Lye Town	2-1	4-1	1-1	4-2	3-2	2-1	2-2	2-1	0-0	0-0	2-0	3-0		0-1	1-0	0-0	1-0	1-1	0-1	1-1	4-1	0-2
14 Market Drayton T	3-2	1-1	2-1	6-1	1-0	2-1	0-1	2-2	4-2	1-1	4-2	3-0	2-1		1-0	3-1	2-1	0-0	3-0	3-0	4-0	0-0
15 Pelsall Villa	1-3	1-0	3-2	2-3	1-1	0-3	1-2	2-2	1-1	4-2	6-0	4-2	1-1	1-2		2-1	4-1	1-0	0-3	2-0	0-1	0-1
16 Shawbury Utd	1-2	5-1	0-1	0-0	1-1	2-5	2-4	0-3	2-4	6-1	8-1	1-2	1-1	0-5	4-1		2-1	1-2	2-1	3-2	7-0	0-4
17 Smethwick R.	0-7	0-3	5-2	3-1	3-2	2-2	1-2	1-1	3-1	1-2	2-1	5-0	1-3	1-4	1-2	1-2		0-2	0-1	0-1	2-1	2-1
18 Tividale	2-1	5-2	3-0	2-1	0-2	2-2	1-2	2-1	1-1	2-1	4-1	1-2	1-2	1-3	1-2	1-1	4-0		4-0	3-0	5-0	1-1
19 Wednesfield	0-4	1-4	1-1	2-2	2-1	2-1	0-3	0-2	1-1	4-0	3-1	6-0	0-2	0-4	1-3	1-2	0-4	3-0		2-2	2-0	2-0
20 Wellington	2-1	3-1	4-3	0-2	2-2	1-1	1-1	0-1	2-1	1-0	1-0	1-3	3-1	1-4	4-1	2-3	4-1	0-1	2-0		3-1	0-0
21 Wolverhampton C.	1-3	3-1	1-3	3-2	3-1	2-3	0-3	2-2	2-2	2-0	3-2	1-1	1-2	1-2	5-2	1-2	8-2	0-2	2-1	0-2		1-2
22 Wyrley Rangers	3-2	7-0	1-0	1-2	1-2	0-1	1-1	2-1	4-0	2-1	2-2	2-1	1-2	1-0	7-1	2-0	0-0	1-2	2-1	5-0		

DIVISION ONE		P	W	D	L	F	A	Pts
1	Ellesmere Rangers	36	26	6	4	78	25	84
2	Brereton Social	36	27	2	7	112	40	83
3	Parkfield Leisure	36	26	3	7	102	45	81
4	Walsall Wood FC	36	24	5	7	92	40	77
5	Blackheath Town	36	23	4	9	75	44	73
6	Bilston Town	36	23	1	12	103	63	70
7	Bridgnorth Town Res.	36	16	4	16	71	69	52
8	Riverway	36	14	6	16	71	68	48
9	Stafford Town	36	14	6	16	78	80	48
10	Hinton	36	14	6	16	76	88	48
11	Malvern Town Reserves	36	14	3	19	71	77	45
12	Wolverhampton Utd	36	12	9	15	52	65	45
13	Cresswell Wanderers	36	13	5	18	64	81	44
14	Ludlow Town Res	36	9	10	17	60	89	37
15	Ashbourne United	36	10	6	20	43	70	36
16	Sporting Khalsa (-3)	36	11	3	22	64	98	33
17	Tenbury United	35	9	4	22	51	87	31
18	Malvern Rangers	36	8	2	26	51	99	26
19	Darlaston Town	35	5	1	29	41	127	16

DIVISION TWO		P	W	D	L	F	A	Pts
1	AFC Wulfrunians	26	22	4	0	83	7	70
2	Bilbrook	26	16	2	8	75	44	50
3	Shenstone P	26	15	5	6	60	37	50
4	Penkridge Town	26	14	3	9	43	39	45
5	Wednesbury Town	26	11	9	6	75	46	42
6	Bustleholme Res	26	11	7	8	53	44	40
7	Chaddesley Corbett	26	11	5	10	52	43	38
8	Bewdley Town Res	26	11	5	10	44	54	38
9	Wyrley	26	9	4	13	41	53	31
10	Brereton Town	26	7	6	13	46	60	27
11	Wolverhampton D	26	6	8	12	34	43	26
12	Dudley United	26	8	1	17	43	53	25
13	Mahal	26	3	9	14	36	68	18
14	Bromyard Town Res	26	3	2	21	23	117	11

PREMIER DIVISION CUP

FIRST ROUND

Bromyard Town	v	Wednesfield	4-2
Brierley & Hagley	v	Pelsall Villa	1-2
Heath Hayes	v	Tividale	3-1
Market Drayton	v	Ledbury Town	3-1
Wyrley Rangers	v	Ludlow Town	1-0
Kington Town	v	Gornal Athletic	2-0

SECOND ROUND

Kington Town	v	Goodrich	0-8
Bromyard Town	v	Smethwick Rangers	3-2
Great Wyrley	v	Wolverhampton Casuals	3-0
Dudley Town	v	Bewdley Town	3-2
Wyrley Rangers	v	Heath Hayes	3-0
Bustleholme	v	Pelsall Villa	1-2
Market Drayton T.	v	Wellington	2-0
Shawbury United	v	Lye Town	2-0

QUARTER-FINALS

Dudley Town	v	Wyrley Rangers	1-1*, 2-3p
Goodrich	v	Market Drayton Town	1-5
Shawbury Town	v	Bromyard Town	0-1
Pelsall Villa	v	Great Wyrley	0-3

SEMI-FINALS (played over two legs - home & away)

Wyrley Rangers	v	Bromyard Town	3-1 3-0
Market Drayton	v	Great Wyrley	0-2 1-1

THE FINAL (15th May at Goodrich FC)

Great Wyrley	v	Wyrley Rangers	0-2

PREMIER DIVISION CONSTITUTION 2006/07

BEWDLEY TOWN
Formed:1978
Chairman: Geoff Edwards.
Secretary: As for Chairman
187 Birmingham Road, Kidderminster, Worcs. DY10 2SJ
(H) 01562-755957 (M) 07733-264893 (F) 01562-755957
E-Mail: geoff.gedwards@tiscali.co.uk.
Ground: Ribbesford Meadows, Ribbesford, Bewdley, Worcs.
Directions: From Kidderminster follow signs to Bewdley on A456 past West Midlands Safari Park and follow signs to Town Centre at next Island. Go over River Bridge into Town and turn left at side of Church (High Street). Stay on this road for 1 mile. Entrance to ground on left, just before Woodman Public House.
Colours: All blue **Change:** All maroon

BRIDGNORTH TOWN
Formed: 1949
Chairman: Eric James Eagles
Secretary: Zoe Griffiths
3 Orchard Road, Erdington, Bridgnorth, Shrops. WV16 5JU
(H) 01746-763857(M) 07793-281582
E-Mail: zoebtfc@ad.com
Ground: Crown Meadow, Innage Lane, Bridgnorth.
Tel: 01746-762747
Directions: Follow signs for Shrewsbury A458 over River Bridge on bypass. At next island turn right (Town Centre). At "T" Junction turn right, first left into Victoria Road. Turn right at crossroads by Woodberry Down. Follow road round to right. Club is on the right 300 yards from crossroads.
Colours: All blue
Change: White/blue/white

BRIERLEY & HAGLEY
Formed: 1955
Chairman: Stephen Lea
Secretary: Amanda Webster. Tel: 01384 351 698.
Ground: Sports Ground, Stourbridge Road, Lye, W Mids DY9 7DD
Tel: 01384 896 748.
Directions: Situated on A458 Birmingham to Stourbridge Road. From M5 Junction 3, take road marked Kidderminster, as far as lights at the bottom of Hagley Hill. Turn right, then take the third turning off the first island. Carry straight on at the next island. Turn left at Lights/Crossroads, onto the A458. Ground approximately 400 yards on the left hand side.
Colours: All blue
Change: Yellow/white/white

BROMYARD TOWN
Formed: 1893
Chairman: Tony Watkins
Secretary: Tony Haverfield, 16 Highwell Avenue, Bromyard, Hereford HR7 4EL Tel & Fax: 01885 483655 (H) 07885 849948 (M)
Ground: Delahay Meadow, Stourport Road, Bromyard, Herfordshire HR7 4NT. Tel: 01885 483 974.
Directions: 1/4 mile outside Bromyard on the Stourport/Kidderminster road (B4203).The ground is on the right through iron gates,by O'Malleys Irish restaurant
Colours: Blue & black/black/blue.
Change: Yellow & green/green/yellow.

BUSTLEHOLME

Formed: 1975
Chairman: Brendan Appleyard
Secretary: Peter John Lewis, 19 Bernard Street, West Bromwich B71 1DJ. Tel: 0121 580 0573
Ground: c/o Bilston FC, Queen Street, Bilston, W. Mids WV13 7EX Tel: 01902 491 498
Directions: From M6 Jct 10, take A454 to Wolverhampton, then pick up A563 to Bilston. Turn left at second roundabout (you can see orange perimeter fence of the ground at the roundabout if you look to your right) Left at mini roundabout by the Ambulance Station, under the by-pass bridge. First left into Queen Street, ground is 500 yards on the left.
Colours: Yellow/green/green **Change:** All white

DUDLEY SPORTS

Formed: 1974
Chairman: Ashley Forrest
Secretary: John Lewis
Hillcrest Lodge, Hillcrest Avenue, Brierley Hill, West Mids. DY5 3QJ
(H) 01384-349413 (M) 07737-099385
E-Mail: kath-john.lewis@blueyonder.co.uk
Ground: Hillcrest Avenue, Brierley Hill, West Mids. DY5 3QH
Tel: 01384-826420
Directions: The Ground is situated in Brierley Hill, just off A461. It can be approached from Stourbridge off the Ring Road to Amblecote, turning right at third set of traffic lights or from Dudley passing through Brierley Hill Town centre.
Colours: Green & black stripes/black/green
Change: Yellow & navy/navy/navy

DUDLEY TOWN

Formed: 1893
Chairman: Nevil Jeynes
Secretary: Margaret Turner, 3,Straits Road, Lower Gornal, Dudley, DY3 2UY Tel: 01384 214 741
Ground: c/o Stourbridge F.C. War Memorial Ground, Amblecote, Stourbridge WV10 6NE. Tel: 01384 394 040.
Directions: From M5 Junction 4 follow signs for Stourbridge. From the Ring Road, take A491 sign posted Wolverhampton. The Ground is 300 yards on left, immediately after Traffic Lights and opposite Royal Oak Public House.
Colours: Red/black/black **Change:** Yellow/yellow/black

ELLESMERE RANGERS

Formed: 1969
Chairman: David Coles
Secretary: John Edge
21 Hillcrest, Ellesmere, Shrops. SY12 0LJ
(H) 01691-623587 (M) 07947-864357
Ground: Beech Grove Playing Fields, Ellesmere, Shrops.
Directions: Follow A5 to Whittington and then take A495 to Ellesmere. On approaching Ellesmere, turn left into Housing Estate opposite Lakelands School. At crossroads, turn left and after 100 yards turn right down Lane to Beech Grove Playing Fields.
Colours: Sky blue/navy/navy **Change:** Yellow/navy/yellow

GOODRICH

Formed: 1995
Chairman: Graham turvey
Secretary: Mick Fullard.
3 Limes Court, Upper Green, Tettenhall, Wolverhampton.
WV6 8RZ Tel: (M) 07866-681022
E-Mail: mick.fullard@goodrich.com
Ground: Goodrich Sports Ground, Stafford Road, Fordhouse, W. Mids WV11 1ND.
Directions: Turn onto M54 off M6 northbound and leave at junction 2. Turn left onto A449 to Wolverhampton. Go to 2nd set of traffic lights and turn right into slip road. Entrance to Sports Ground is 50 yards on the left.
Colours: All red **Change:** All blue

GORNAL ATHLETIC

Formed: 1945
Chairman: John Sheppard
Secretary: Kevin Williams
3 Wheatstone Close, Sedgley, West Mids. DY3 1SW
(H) 01384 830674 (M) 07762 585149 (F) 01902 662956
Ground: Garden Walk Stadium, Garden Walk, Lower Gornal DY3 2NR. Tel: 01384 358398
Directions: From Dudley Town centre follow A459 towards Sedgley. Left at Green Dragon Pub into Jews Lane.Take second exit at roundabout and down hill to Old Bulls Head Pub. Turn left into Redhall Rd and second left into Garden Walk.
Colours: Blue & white/white/blue & white
Change: All yellow & blue

GREAT WYRLEY

Formed: 1960
Chairman: Anthony Brough
Secretary: Dennis Holford.
483 Bloxwich Road, Leamore, Walsall. WS3 1XA
(H) 01922-442001 (M) 07763-705726
Ground: Hazelbrook, Hazel Lane, Great Wyrley, Cannock, Staffordshire WS6 6AA. Tel: 01922 410 366.
Directions: Take A34 through Great Wyrley, until you get to the Star Pubic House. Turn left into Hazel Lane. Ground is on the left hand side.
Colours: Red with black trim/black/red
Change: White with black trim/black/white

LEDBURY TOWN

Formed: 1893
Chairman: Chris Stephens
Secretary: Mike Clueit, 55 Lawnside Road, Ledbury, Herefordshire, HR8 2AE. Tel: 01531 633 182
Ground: New Street, Ledbury, Herefordshire Tel: 01531 631 463
Directions: Leave M50 at junction 2. Take A417 to Ledbury. At first island take first exit and at second island take fourth exit. ground is 100 yards on right.
Colours: Black & white/black/black & white **Change:** All Red

LUDLOW TOWN

Formed: 1876
Chairman: Robin Waters
Secretary: Shaun Bradley
32 Maple Close, Ludlow, Shrops. SY8 2PT
(M) 07775-664416
Ground: Bromfield Road, Ludlow. SY8 2BN
Tel: 01584-876000
Directions: Situated on the northern outskirts of Ludlow, just off A49 Shrewsbury/Hereford Road. From West Midlands and South follow signs A49 Shrewsbury until you reach the northern end of Ludlow bypass. Exit A49 onto B4361 sign posted Ludlow. Continue on for approx. 500 yards. Entrance to ground is on right hand side approx. 100 yards after entering 30 mph speed limit..
Colours: All red **Change:** Blue/white/blue

LYE TOWN

Formed: 1930
Chairman: Tony Archer
Secretary: John Woodhouse, 46 Surfeit Hill, Cradley Heath, Warley, West Midlands. B64 7EB
Tel Nos: 01384 633976 (H) 0121 627 6600 (W)
Ground: Sports Ground, Stourbridge Road, Lye (01384 422672)
Directions: On a A458 Birmingham-Stourbridge road about 400yds afterlights/crossroads at Lye. From M5 jct 3 take road marked Kidderminster to lights at bottom of Hagley Hill.Turn right to Merry Hill,at island 3rd exit towards Merry Hill. Straight over next island and turn off left at crossroads/lights.Ground is about 400yds on left. Quarter mile from Lye (BR).
Colours: Blue & white stripes/blue/blue
Change: Yellow/green/green

PELSALL VILLA

Formed: 1898
Chairman: Shaun Mason
Secretary: As for Chairman.
17 Pool Hayes Lane, Pool Hayes, Willenhall, West Mids. WV12 4PL (M) 07779-111023
Ground: The Bush Ground, walsall Road, Heath End, Pelsall, W. Mids WS3 4BP. Tel: 01922 692 748.
Directions: Take the Walsall Ring Road to the Arboreteum round-about. Follow signs for Lichfield (A34). At top of hill bear left. At second set of traffic lights turn left onto the B4154 signposted Pelsall. Go over railway bridge to Old Bush Public House. Ground is on right signposted Pelsall Cricket Club.
Colours: Red & black stripes/white or black/black or white
Change: Blue & white stripes/white or blue/white or blue

SHAWBURY UNITED

Formed: 1992
Chairman: Steven Leslie Skitt
Secretary: Cindy Wakenshaw
177 Mount Pleasant Road, Shrewsbury. SY1 3EY
(H) 01743-355762 (M) 07840-183491
E-Mail: cindywakenshaw@hotmail.com
Ground: Butlers Sports Centre, Bowens Field, Wem.
Tel: 01939-233287
Directions: Go into Wem town centre and at the Church junction turn right. Take the first left after pedestrian crossing, then first left with Hawkestone pub on corner. 2nd left into car park and ground.
Colours: All Royal blue **Change:** Red & white/white/white

SHIFNAL TOWN (NEW)

Formed: 1964
Chairman: Derek Groucott
Secretary: 4 Idsall Crescent, Shifnal, Shrops. TF11 8ES
(H) 01952-402255 (F) 01952-402255
Ground: Phoenix Park, Coppice Green Lane, Shifnal, Shrops.
Tel: 01952-463667
Directions: From M54 Junction 3, take A41 towards Newport and
Whitchurch. Take first left, signposted Shifnal. As you enter
Shifnal, take first turning on right signposted Football Stadium.
Ground is approximately 500 yards on left, just past Idsall School.
If Travelling along A464 Wolverhampton to Shifnal Road, then on
entering Shifnal just under Railway Bridge and before Traffic
Lights, turn right and sharp right again along Aston Street (Barclays
Bank on your right) Continue along this road until sharp right hand
bend with junction on your left, take this left and then sharp right
along Coppice Green Lane. Ground is approximately 500 yards on
left just past Idsall School.
Colours: Red & white stripes/black/red
Change: Sky blue & white stripes/sky blue/sky blue

TIVIDALE

Formed: 1954
Chairman: Donald Ashton
Secretary: Ruth Archer. Tel: 01384 242 912. (M) 07876 197758
Ground: The Beeches, Packwood Road, Tividale, Warley, W.
Midlands B69 1UL Tel: 01384 211 743
Directions: Dudley Port Station to Burnt tree, left towards
Birmingham, ground1 mile on right. Or, M5 jct 2, follow Dudley
signs A4123, after approx 2 miles turn left into Regent Rd & left
again into Elm Terraces, 1st left into Birch Crescent. Packwood Rd
is second left - ground at end of cul-de-sac
Colours: All Yellow
Change: All Blue

WEDNESFIELD

Formed: 1961
Chairman: Brian Saville.
Secretary: Brian Saville. Tel: 07890 501 331.
Ground: Cottage Ground, Amos Lane, Wednesfield,
Wolverhampton WV11 1ND Tel: 01902 735 506.
Directions: From Wolverhampton on the A4124 Wednesfield Rd.
Stay on road right through Wednesfield until island. Leave island at
1st exit (Wood End Rd), left after 200yds into Amos Lane. Ground
on right, approx. 400yds along. 3 miles Wolverhampton BR station.
Bus 559 to Wood End or 560 to Red Lion.
Colours: Red/black/black
Change: Black & White Stripes/white/white

WELLINGTON (WM)

Formed: 1968
Chairman: Philip Smith
Secretary: Michael Perkins, Haworth, Wellington, Hereford HR4
8AZ. Tel: 01432 830 523 (H)
Ground: Wellington Playing Fields, Wellington, Hereford,
Herefordshire HR4 8AZ. Tel: 01432 830 620.
Directions: The ground is situated off the A49, 8 miles south of
Leominster & 5 miles north of Hereford. At the end of the dual car-
riageway turn for Wellington. The ground is 1/4 mile from A49, on
the left , behind Wellington School and opposite the Church.
Colours: Tangerine & blue/blue/tangerine
Change: Blue/blue/tangerine

WOLVERHAMPTON CASUALS

Founded: 1899
Chairman: Barry Austin
Secretary: Michael Green, 63 St Phillips Avenue, Pennfields
Wolverhampton WV67ED. Tel: 01902 333677
Ground: Brinsford Stadium, Brinsford Lane, Coven Heath,
Wolverhampton WV10 7PR. Tel: 01902 783 214.
Directions: Onto M54 from M6 North, at Junc 2 turn right (A449 to
Stafford).Ground half a mile, turn right into Brinsford Lane. Billbrooke
(BR) 2 miles
Colours: All Green & white
Change: Gold/black/gold

WYRLEY RANGERS

Formed: 1988
Chairman: Roger Bird
Secretary: Alan Ryder. Tel: 01902 659 853.
Ground: Long Lane Park, Long Lane, Essington, Wolverhampton
WV1 2AA. Tel: 01922 406 604.
Directions: From M6 junction 11, take A462 and pick up third
turning on left A4210 (Broad Lane). Then first left into Long Lane.
Follow road for 0.5 mile and ground is on the left.
Colours: Red/red/red & white
Change: All grey

Wryley Rangers - winners of the Premier League Cup.   Photo: Mark Wood

WEST SUSSEX LEAGUE

PREMIER DIVISION	P	W	D	L	F	A	Pts
1. South Bersted	20	15	3	2	42	16	48
2. Loxwood (Promoted)	20	14	4	2	54	13	46
3. T D Shipley	20	12	3	5	50	27	39
4. Rogate	20	10	2	8	51	29	32
5. Dorking Wanderers	20	9	4	7	42	43	31
6. East Dean	20	7	3	10	32	37	24
7. University College Chichester	20	5	6	9	23	33	21
8. Clymping	20	5	5	10	23	50	20
9. Eastergate United	20	5	4	11	38	51	19
10. Henfield	20	5	3	12	36	48	18
11. Yapton	20	4	1	15	25	69	13

PREMIER DIVISION	1	2	3	4	5	6	7	8	9	10	11
1 Clymping		3-0	1-1	1-3	0-8	0-1	1-0	0-4	1-3	1-1	2-1
2 Dorking Wanderers	2-3		2-1	3-3	3-2	2-0	4-2	0-2	1-3	1-1	4-1
3 East Dean	3-1	1-5		5-2	0-0	0-3	1-0	1-0	3-2	0-2	8-3
4 Eastergate United	3-3	3-3	1-0		0-1	1-2	1-3	3-5	0-5	1-2	3-2
5 Henfield	1-2	2-3	2-2	3-2		1-6	2-2	2-5	2-5	2-3	4-1
6 Loxwood	4-0	4-0	1-0	3-0	5-0		4-2	1-1	3-1	0-0	4-0
7 Rogate	5-0	7-0	2-1	5-1	2-3	1-1		3-1	0-2	2-1	4-0
8 South Bersted	2-0	2-2	3-0	2-1	1-0	1-0	2-0		1-0	2-0	4-1
9 T D Shipley	5-1	0-1	3-0	2-2	3-1	3-3	HW	0-1		2-2	5-2
10 University College Chichester	2-2	3-1	0-2	0-3	1-0	0-2	3-7	1-1	1-2		0-2
11 Yapton	1-1	0-5	4-3	1-5	2-0	0-7	1-4	1-2	2-4	HW	

LEAGUE CONSTITUTION 2006-07

BARNHAM	**PREDATORS**
CLYMPING	**ROGATE**
DORKING WANDERERS	**SOUTH BERSTED**
EAST DEAN	**T D SHIPLEY**
EASTERGATE UNITED	**UNIVERSITY OF CHICHESTER**
HENFIELD	**UPPER BEEDING**

DIVISION ONE	P	W	D	L	F	A	Pts
1 Predators	20	16	4	0	58	14	52
2 Barnham	20	14	3	3	76	22	45
3 West Chiltington	20	14	2	4	48	22	44
4 Partridge Green	20	8	3	9	39	56	27
5 Angmering	20	9	2	9	48	49	26
6 Wittering United	20	6	6	8	29	30	24
7 Holbrook FC	20	6	2	12	27	48	20
8 Lower Beeding	20	6	2	12	28	57	20
9 Southwater	20	6	1	13	24	49	19
10 Cowfold	20	4	5	11	20	40	17
11 Faygate Utd	20	4	4	12	28	38	16

DIVISION TWO NORTH	P	W	D	L	F	A	Pts
1 T D Shipley Reserves	20	14	6	0	52	21	48
2 Fittleworth	20	11	8	1	45	21	41
3 Dorking Wanderers Res	20	12	2	6	58	26	38
4 Billingshurst	20	8	6	6	48	37	30
5 Ockley	20	8	6	6	50	53	30
6 Ashington Rovers	20	7	4	9	44	47	25
7 Pulborough	20	3	11	6	27	27	20
8 Alfold	20	4	8	8	32	37	20
9 Slinfold	20	5	2	13	32	74	16
10 Horsham Olympic	20	3	6	11	27	54	15
11 Watersfield	20	4	3	13	30	48	12

DIVISION THREE NORTH

		P	W	D	L	F	A	Pts
1	Rudgwick	22	17	2	3	77	31	53
2	Wisborough Green	22	16	2	4	64	27	50
3	Friends Provident	22	13	1	8	68	58	40
4	Holbrook FC Reserves	22	12	2	8	57	48	38
5	Capel	22	16	2	4	73	37	35
6	Horsham Baptists	22	10	2	10	59	63	32
7	Barns Green	22	8	6	8	50	41	28
8	Newdigate	22	8	0	14	45	59	24
9	Faygate Utd Reserves	22	6	3	13	40	65	21
10	Southwater Reserves	22	5	3	14	47	74	15
11	Loxwood Reserves	22	3	4	15	36	64	13
12	Henfield Reserves	22	4	1	17	43	92	13

DIVISION FOUR NORTH

		P	W	D	L	F	A	Pts
1	Billingshurst Reserves	22	15	4	3	65	31	49
2	Horsham Trinity	22	14	2	6	73	45	44
3	Ockley Reserves	22	10	6	6	54	38	36
4	Cowfold Reserves	22	10	5	7	55	52	35
5	Storrington III	22	10	3	9	79	58	33
6	Alfold Reserves	22	10	3	9	44	51	33
7	T D Shipley III	22	8	6	8	49	39	30
8	Wisborough Green Res	22	6	7	9	37	51	25
9	Fittleworth Reserves	22	8	1	13	54	75	25
10	Horsham Olympic Res	22	7	3	12	45	63	24
11	Henfield III	22	5	4	13	60	88	19
12	Rudgwick Reserves	22	4	6	12	43	67	18

DIVISION FIVE NORTH

		P	W	D	L	F	A	Pts
1	Warnham	22	20	0	2	97	23	60
2	Holbrook FC III	22	17	1	4	79	31	52
3	Horsham Trinity Res.	22	16	2	4	65	34	50
4	Ashington Rovers Res.	22	14	3	5	50	32	45
5	Partridge Green Res.	22	11	4	7	48	30	37
6	Norfolk Arms	22	9	2	11	39	49	29
7	Billingshurst II	22	7	3	12	35	46	24
8	Horsham Baptists Res	22	7	3	12	44	69	24
9	Newdigate Reserves	22	7	2	13	44	62	23
10	Barns Green Reserves	22	4	1	17	39	65	13
11	Slinfold Reserves	22	3	4	15	27	79	13
12	Southwater III	22	3	3	16	40	87	12

DIVISION TWO SOUTH

		P	W	D	L	F	A	Pts
1	Newtown Villa	22	16	4	2	65	23	52
2	Lancing United	22	15	1	6	53	33	46
3	Petworth	22	13	4	5	50	30	43
4	Rustington Reserves	22	12	4	6	46	28	40
5	Lavant	22	9	4	9	42	40	31
6	Chichester Hosp Res	22	9	4	9	33	38	31
7	Stedham United	22	8	6	8	37	31	30
8	Clymping Reserves	22	7	6	9	39	36	27
9	Worthing BCOB	22	7	6	9	37	41	27
10	Lodsworth	22	7	2	13	35	46	23
11	Hunston CC	22	6	2	14	34	46	20
12	Yapton Reserves	22	1	1	20	14	93	4

DIVISION THREE SOUTH

		P	W	D	L	F	A	Pts
1	Predators Reserves	16	11	2	3	70	24	35
2	Eastergate Utd Res.	16	10	4	2	39	21	34
3	Wittering Utd Reserves	16	9	4	3	39	18	31
4	Lancing United Res.	16	9	4	3	44	27	31
5	Angmering Reserves	16	9	3	4	44	31	30
6	Rogate Reserves	16	5	2	9	31	37	17
7	Ambassadors	16	5	1	10	20	43	16
8	Graffham	16	3	2	11	33	57	11
9	Fernhurst	16	0	0	16	16	78	0

DIVISION FOUR SOUTH

		P	W	D	L	F	A	Pts
1	Square Deal FC	20	15	4	1	86	20	49
2	Middleton On Sea	20	15	3	2	89	29	48
3	Newtown Villa Res.	20	13	2	5	61	30	41
4	Boxgrove	20	12	2	6	82	41	38
5	West Chiltington Res.	20	10	2	8	58	42	32
6	Milland	20	8	1	11	67	53	25
7	Coal Exchange	20	7	3	10	55	30	24
8	Petworth Reserves	20	7	1	12	37	49	22
9	Pulborough Reserves	20	7	0	13	50	46	21
10	Amberley	20	5	2	13	29	68	17
11	Graffham Reserves	20	1	0	19	11	217	3

DIVISION FIVE SOUTH

		P	W	D	L	F	A	Pts
1	Barnham Reserves	20	15	3	2	92	22	48
2	Selsey Town	20	14	4	2	87	19	46
3	The Wheatsheaf	20	15	1	4	81	29	46
4	Predators III	20	13	2	5	58	32	41
5	General Henry	20	9	3	8	50	60	30
6	Bosham Reserves	20	6	3	11	41	53	21
7	Angmering III	20	6	3	11	41	67	21
8	Regis Veterans	20	6	3	11	41	69	21
9	AFC Westmead	20	5	2	13	32	67	17
10	Tangmere	20	4	3	13	36	74	15
11	Rose Green Utd	20	3	1	16	41	108	10

DIVISION FIVE CENTRAL

		P	W	D	L	F	A	Pts
1	Littlehampton Rail Res.	16	15	0	1	58	19	45
2	Barnham III	16	12	2	2	70	22	38
3	Plaistow	16	9	2	5	42	30	29
4	Chapel	16	9	2	5	40	44	29
5	Watersfield Reserves	16	7	1	8	40	29	22
6	Lodsworth Reserves	16	5	1	10	23	44	16
7	Fernhurst Reserves	16	4	2	10	21	28	14
8	Holbrook FC IV	16	3	1	12	23	67	10
9	Harting	16	2	1	13	22	56	7

LEAGUE CUP

FIRST ROUND

Alfold	v	Angmering	0-5
Ashington Rovers	v	T D Shipley	2-1
Faygate United	v	Cowfold	1-2
Lancing United	v	Milland	6-1
Lodsworth	v	Wisborough Green	1-2
Newtown Villa	v	Holbrook FC	1-0
Ockley	v	Pulborough	3-2
Predators	v	Fittleworth	2-0
Rogate	v	Rustlington Reserves	4-0
Rose Green United	v	Lower Beeding	2-8
Storrington III	v	Square Deal FC	3-5
The Wheatsheaf	v	Hunston CC	4-5
Wittering United	v	Henfield	6-0
Littlehampton Rw	v	Watersfield	AW
Newdigate	v	Warnham	4-2
Harting	v	Loxwood	AW

SECOND ROUND

Ockley	v	Dorking Wanderers	1-4
East Dean	v	Newdigate	3-0
Hunston CC	v	West Chiltington	1-4
Lancing United	v	Worthing BCOB	2-1
Loxwood	v	Lower Beeding	4-3
Predators	v	Wisborough Green	7-0
Rogate	v	Horsham Athletic	HW
Slinfold	v	Southwater	1-3
Watersfield	v	Wittering United	4-6

Square Deal FC	v	Ashington Rovers	1-2
Angmering	v	Barns Green	3-0
Eastergate United	v	AFC Westmead	5-0
Barnham	v	Billingshurst	5-1
Newtown Villa	v	Cowfold	3-2
South Bersted	v	Clymping	7-8

THIRD ROUND

Barnham	v	Eastergate United	1-4
West Chiltingdon	v	Clymping	2-1
Lancing United	v	Rogate	4-3
Loxwood	v	Lavant	7-0
Southwater	v	Newtown Villa	7-6
Dorking Wanderers	v	Wittering United	2-3
East Dean	v	Ashington Rovers	2-1
Predators	v	Angmering	3-4

QUARTER-FINALS

Angmering	v	Southwater	4-0
West Chiltington	v	Lancing United	2-1
Wittering United	v	Loxwood	0-2
Eastergate United	v	East Dean	3-1

SEMI-FINALS

Loxwood	v	Eastergate United	2-4
West Chiltington	v	Angmering	1-3

THE FINAL

Angmering	v	Eastergate United	4-2

WILTSHIRE LEAGUE

SPONSORED BY: PLAISTER AUTO SERVICES

Formed: 1976
President: D C Kilford
Chairman: W B Shail
Hon General Secretary: J T Thorn
jim.thorn@wiltshirefootballleague.com

PREMIER DIVISION	P	W	D	L	F	A	Pts
1. Corsham Town (Champions 04-05)	32	22	7	3	79	23	73
2. Westside	32	21	4	7	90	58	67
3. Warminster Town	32	19	7	6	72	27	64
4. AFC Trowbridge Town Youth	32	18	6	8	75	44	60
5. Westbury United	32	17	8	7	60	38	59
6. Down Ampney (-2)	32	19	1	12	81	61	56
7. Melksham Town	32	16	5	11	63	52	53
8. Aldbourne	32	16	4	12	57	39	52
9. Devizes Town (-1)	32	14	3	15	64	70	44
10. Marlborough Town	32	11	9	12	55	57	40
11. New College Swindon	32	10	10	12	55	57	40
12. Calne Town (-1)	32	10	8	14	60	61	37
13. Shrewton United	32	10	4	18	64	80	34
14. Pewsey Vale (-2)	32	7	6	19	36	71	25
15. Bromham	32	7	4	21	48	88	25
16. Malmesbury Victoria	32	4	5	23	28	90	17
17. Purton (-1)	32	5	1	26	38	121	15

PREMIER DIVISION	1	2	3	4	5	6	7	8	9	10	11	12	13	14	15	16	17
1 AFC Trowbridge Town Youth		0-2	3-2	6-0	0-1	0-1	4-1	7-1	5-4	3-3	3-0	1-0	7-1	5-0	1-1	0-1	2-3
2 Aldbourne	1-2		5-2	1-2	1-0	1-1	2-0	2-0	0-1	1-5	4-2	4-3	3-0	7-0	0-1	0-1	7-0
3 Bromham	0-4	0-2		1-0	2-3	0-4	0-1	1-1	2-1	1-6	2-5	4-3	2-4	4-0	0-3	1-1	4-1
4 Calne Town	0-2	5-1	1-1		2-2	4-0	0-3	3-1	1-2	1-1	2-2	4-2	5-0	0-0	2-1	2-2	1-3
5 Corsham Town	6-0	2-1	3-0	3-1		5-2	2-2	4-0	2-0	3-0	1-0	3-0	3-1	6-0	1-1	2-1	1-2
6 Devizes Town	2-4	1-3	2-3	2-0	1-4		0-7	2-0	1-0	0-1	1-2	1-0	9-1	1-1	1-3	0-3	3-3
7 Down Ampney	6-0	2-0	5-1	3-2	1-4	4-1		1-0	2-0	2-0	3-0	4-0	7-0	4-1	2-5	5-0	0-8
8 Malmesbury Victoria	0-1	1-0	4-2	2-2	0-3	1-6	1-2		0-2	0-1	1-2	0-4	3-5	0-4	1-3	1-3	1-3
9 Marlborough Town	1-2	0-0	1-0	3-2	0-4	2-3	1-3	0-0		1-1	0-0	1-1	9-0	7-0	2-1	1-1	0-4
10 Melksham Town	0-3	0-1	2-1	3-0	1-1	1-3	2-5	4-1	1-1		2-1	2-1	1-0	1-2	1-2	5-1	2-3
11 New College	1-1	0-0	2-2	2-1	1-1	0-3	0-1	2-3	1-1	3-4		0-0	4-2	4-0	0-2	2-0	2-2
12 Pewsey Vale	1-1	0-1	2-3	1-8	0-0	4-3	3-2	1-1	1-0	1-2	0-5		2-0	0-2	0-5	0-1	0-2
13 Purton	1-0	2-3	5-3	0-4	1-5	1-5	2-1	1-1	0-4	1-3	1-4	1-2		0-5	1-2	1-5	2-3
14 Shrewton United	2-3	1-3	4-1	2-3	0-1	5-0	11-1	1-3	0-3	4-3	3-4	4-1	6-1		2-3	1-1	2-4
15 Warminster Town	0-0	1-0	2-0	1-1	0-0	1-2	3-1	7-0	2-0	4-0	5-0	1-2	2-0	1-1		1-1	6-1
16 Westbury United	1-1	3-0	2-1	4-1	2-0	0-2	2-0	9-0	2-0	1-3	1-1	0-0	6-3	2-0	2-1		1-0
17 Westside	1-4	1-1	7-2	4-0	0-4	6-1	4-2	3-0	2-2	0-2	5-3	5-1	2-0	3-1	2-1	3-0	

DIVISION ONE	P	W	D	L	F	A	Pts
1 Wroughton	28	27	0	1	132	20	81
2 Pinehurst OB	28	19	3	6	87	52	60
3 Stratton Rovers	28	17	3	8	81	48	54
4 Barron Heating	28	17	3	8	79	57	54
5 AFC Abbey Rod. (-3)	28	17	0	11	76	70	48
6 AFC Stratton	28	14	5	9	57	55	47
7 Westlecot United	28	13	3	12	65	66	42
8 Swindon Asians (-3)	28	14	1	13	77	65	40
9 Castle Combe	28	11	5	12	51	67	38
10 Blunsdon United (-1)	28	10	5	13	59	55	34
11 SKS Blyskawica (-2)	28	10	2	16	62	85	30
12 Biddestone (-2)	28	7	4	17	57	80	23
13 Minety (-3)	28	6	6	16	68	96	21
14 Marlborough Town R(-1)	28	5	3	20	34	94	17
15 Lower Stratton	28	1	1	26	43	118	4

DIVISION TWO	P	W	D	L	F	A	Pts
1 Chiseldon Castrol	24	21	3	0	77	12	66
2 AFC Rodbourne	24	16	3	5	71	41	51
3 Aldbourne Res (-3)	24	14	4	6	71	32	45
4 CHQ United	24	13	2	9	53	39	41
5 Blunsdon Utd Res	24	10	6	8	58	48	36
6 Stratton Rovers Res	24	10	3	11	40	52	33
7 Westlecot Utd Res (-1)	24	9	5	10	45	54	31
8 QT Swindon (-1)	24	9	4	11	44	65	30
9 Bromham Res (-1)	24	7	6	11	42	57	26
10 Wroughton Reserves	24	6	7	11	49	70	25
11 Blueprint (-4)	24	6	7	11	44	54	21
12 Purton "A" (-3)	24	6	5	13	41	60	20
13 Westside Reserves	24	0	3	21	23	74	3

S E N I O R   C U P

FIRST ROUND

Cricklade Town	v	Westside	A w/o
Melksham Town	v	Devizes Town	4-3

SECOND ROUND

Westside	v	Malmesbury Victoria	1-0
AFC Trowbridge TY	v	New College Swindon	H w/o
Aldbourne	v	Pewsey Vale	6-1
Shrewton United	v	Melksham Town	2-3
Westbury United	v	Down Ampney	1-1*, AW pens
Bromham	v	Warminster Town	0-3
Purton	v	Corsham Town	1-4
Calne Town	v	Marlborough Town	A w/o

QUARTER-FINALS

Westside	v	AFC Trowbridge Tn Youth	1-2
Aldbourne	v	Melksham Town	0-1
Down Ampney	v	Warminster Town	0-0*, AW pens
Corsham Town	v	Marlborough Town	2-0

SEMI-FINALS

AFC Trowbridge TY	v	Melksham Town	0-2
Warminster Town	v	Corsham Town	1-2

THE FINAL

Melksham Town	v	Corsham Town	0-2

LEAGUE CONSTITUTION 2006-07

AFC TROWBRIDGE TOWN YOUTH
Woodmarsh, North Bradley, Torwbridge BA14 0SA.

ALDBOURNE
Farm Lane, Aldbourne, Marlborough, Wiltshire SN8 2DS

BLUEPRINT - CHISELDON
Secretary: Andrew Derrick Tel: 07748 337 445 Email: andrew.derrick@reckittbenckiser.com

BRADFORD TOWN
Bradford on Avon Sports and Social Club, Trowbridge Road, Bradford on Avon, Wiltshire, BA14 0PS
Telephone 01225 866649

BROMHAM
Jubilee Field, Bromham, Chippenham, Wiltshire. Tel: 01380 850671

CALNE TOWN RESERVES
Bremhill View, Calne, Wiltshire. Tel: 01249 816716

CORSHAM TOWN RESERVES
Southbank, Lacock Road, Corsham, Wiltshire. Tel: 01249 715609

DEVIZES TOWN RESERVES
Nursteed Road, Devizes, Wiltshire. Tel: 01380 722817

MALMESBURY VICTORIA RESERVES
Flying Monk Ground, Gloucester Rd, Malmesbury. Tel: 01666 822141

MARLBOROUGH TOWN
Elcot Lane, Marlborough, Wiltshire. Tel: 01672 514033

MELKSHAM TOWN RESERVES
The Conigre, Melksham, Wiltshire. Tel: 01225 702843

NEW COLLEGE
Swindon Supermarine FC, Highworth Road, South Marston, Swindon. Tel: 01793 828778

PEWSEY VALE RESERVES
Recreation Ground, Ball Road, Pewsey, Wiltshire. Tel: 01672 562990

PURTON RESERVES
The Red House, Purton, Wiltshire. Tel: 01793 770262

SHREWTON UNITED RESERVES
Recreation Ground, Shrewton, Wiltshire

WESTBURY UNITED RESERVES
Meadow Lane, Westbury BA13 3AF. Tel: 01373 823 409

WESTSIDE
King Edward Place, Foxhill, Wanborough, Swindon. Tel: 01793 791 282

WROUGHTON

WORTHING & DISTRICT LEAGUE

SPONSORED BY: TAULKE FINANCE
Chairman: Peter Tomley
Secretary: Roy Terrington
Tel: 01903 721 494 Email: roy@terrington.freeserve.co.uk

PREMIER DIVISION		P	W	D	L	F	A	Pts
1.	Worthing Wanderers	20	17	2	1	81	27	53
2.	L & S Athletic	20	15	2	3	57	21	47
3.	Revenue	20	13	3	4	66	26	42
4.	Warren Sports	20	11	2	7	46	42	35
5.	Tabernacle	20	10	4	6	48	31	34
6.	GSK Sports (Champions 04-05)	20	8	3	9	39	58	27
7.	Adur Athletic	20	8	1	11	38	48	25
8.	Sompting	20	7	1	12	53	75	22
9.	Worthing Athletic	20	6	2	12	52	59	20
10.	East Worthing	20	2	1	17	18	59	7
11.	Ye Old Manor House	20	1	3	16	21	73	6

LEAGUE CONSTITUTION 2006-07 - PREMIER

ADUR ATHLETIC	**SOMPTING**
AFC BROADWATER	**TABERNACLE**
GSK SPORTS	**WARREN SPORTS**
L & S ATHLETIC	
NORTHBROOK	**WORTHING ATHLETIC**
REVENUE	**WORTHING WANDERERS**

DIVISION ONE		P	W	D	L	F	A	Pts
1	Northbrook	20	14	2	4	62	32	44
2	AFC Broadwater	20	12	6	2	45	22	42
3	Durrington RAFA	20	11	5	4	62	28	38
4	Worthing Mitsubishi	20	9	7	4	34	22	34
5	Goring St Theresa's	20	9	4	7	41	29	31
6	Worthing Albion	20	9	2	9	37	37	29
7	St Mary's	20	8	5	7	38	45	29
8	Revenue Reserves	20	8	1	11	33	38	25
9	Sompting Reserves	20	5	2	13	33	67	17
10	GSK Sports Reserves	20	4	2	14	35	61	14
11	West Worthing WMC	20	2	2	16	22	61	8

DIVISION TWO		P	W	D	L	F	A	Pts
1	L & S Athletic Reserves	16	13	3	0	63	16	42
2	Adur Athletic Reserves	16	11	1	4	48	13	34
3	Montague United	16	10	2	4	47	28	32
4	TMG	16	9	3	4	53	27	30
5	Woodside	16	6	2	8	31	40	20
6	Athletico Wenban Smith	16	5	4	7	31	33	19
7	Lancing United B	16	5	3	8	22	44	18
8	The Globe	16	2	3	11	19	44	9
9	Worthing Bcob Reserves	16	0	1	15	6	75	1

DIVISION THREE

		P	W	D	L	F	A	Pts
1	Shoreham RBL	22	21	0	1	110	14	63
2	Edge	22	16	1	5	64	33	49
3	Highdown Rovers	22	15	3	4	71	27	48
4	Worthing Wanderers R.	22	15	0	7	73	26	45
5	L & L	22	13	2	7	74	31	41
6	West Tarring WMC	22	10	4	8	44	51	34
7	Upper Beeding Res.	22	7	6	9	30	50	27
8	AFC Phoenix	22	6	3	13	38	70	21
9	GSK Sports B	22	5	3	14	30	85	18
10	Lancing United B B	22	4	4	14	19	73	16
11	RJ Cleaning	22	3	2	17	28	61	11
12	Northbrook Reserves	22	1	4	17	23	83	7

M I K E   S M I T H   T R O P H Y

FIRST ROUND

Durrington RAFA	v	Goring St. Theresa's	3-2

SECOND ROUND

GSK Sports	v	East Worthing	1-3
The Globe	v	Worthing Athletic	0-3
TMG	v	BTR Brakes	7-0
West Tarring WMC	v	Worthing Wanderers	0-12
Worthing Albion	v	Warren Sports	0-2
Highdown Rovers	v	Woodside	7-2
L & S Athletic	v	Tabernacle	1-0
Ye Old Manor H.	v	L & L	5-3
Athletico Wenban S	v	West Worthing WMC	4-0
Edge	v	Shoreham RBL	3-4
RJ Cleaning	v	AFC Phoenix	2-1
Sompting	v	Revenue	2-4
Worthing Rebels	v	St Mary's	AW
Northbrook	v	AFC Broadwater	5-1
Worthing Mitsubishi	v	Adur Athletic	3-6
Durrington RAFA	v	Montague United	4-2

THIRD ROUND

Warren Sports	v	St Mary's	7-3
Shoreham RBL	v	Athletico Wenbam Smith	3-0
Worthing Wanderers	v	TMG	HW
Revenue	v	RJ Cleaning	2-0
Adur Athletic	v	Ye Old Manor House	HW
East Worthing	v	Worthing Athletic	2-3
Highdown Rovers	v	Durrington RAFA	0-3
Northbrook	v	L & S Athletic	1-5

QUARTER-FINALS

L & S Athletic	v	Durrington RAFA	2-1
Revenue	v	Warren Sports	0-3
Worthing Athletic	v	Adur Athletic	5-1
Worthing Wanderers	v	Shoreham RBL	4-3

SEMI-FINALS

Worthing Athletic	v	L & S Athletic	1-5
Worthing Wanderers	v	Warren Sports	6-3

THE FINAL

Worthing Wanderers	v	L & S Athletic	5-2

YORKSHIRE LEAGUES SUPPLIED BY ROB GRILLO

WEST RIDING COUNTY AMATEUR LEAGUE

PREMIER DIVISION	P	W	D	L	F	A	Pts
Bay Athletic	26	20	3	3	66	19	63
Campion	26	20	2	4	100	34	62
Brighouse Town	26	16	4	6	66	37	52
Wibsey	26	13	6	7	60	42	45
Golcar United	26	14	3	9	51	47	45
Ovenden West Riding	26	14	2	10	49	43	44
Storthes Hall	26	11	5	10	41	49	38
Tyersal	26	10	5	11	41	49	35
Ardsley Celtic	26	9	3	14	34	52	30
Halifax Irish	26	8	2	16	44	63	26
Hemsworth MW	26	7	4	15	38	62	25
Eastmoor	26	6	5	15	28	46	23
Otley Town	26	3	8	15	35	52	17
Heckmondwike Town	26	4	2	20	29	87	14

DIVISION ONE	P	W	D	L	F	A	Pts
Hall Green United	26	19	3	4	66	34	60
Lower Hopton	26	16	7	3	77	28	55
Kirkburton	26	14	4	8	64	43	46
Wakefield City	26	14	4	8	50	32	46
Steeton	26	14	1	11	66	55	43
Farnley	26	12	6	8	52	44	42
Littletown	26	10	8	8	42	34	38
Altofts	26	9	9	8	53	62	36
Westwood	26	10	5	11	46	44	35
South Bradford	26	10	2	14	51	55	32
Dudley Hill Rangers	26	8	4	14	37	58	28
Marsden	26	6	4	16	34	84	22
Keighley Shamrocks	26	6	2	18	49	70	20
Salts	26	2	5	19	23	67	11

DIVISION TWO	P	W	D	L	F	A	Pts
Meltham	20	17	3	0	113	24	54
Westbrook YMCA	20	13	2	5	56	33	41
Ventus/Yeadon Celtic	20	12	2	6	75	48	38
Overthorpe Sports	20	10	3	7	54	38	37
Morley Town	20	10	0	10	56	55	30
Crag Road United	20	7	8	5	54	49	29
Hunsworth	20	8	1	11	45	56	25
Barclays	20	6	5	9	36	54	23
Dynamoes	20	5	2	13	29	60	17
Dudley Hill Athletic	20	5	1	14	34	75	16
Keighley Lifts	20	2	3	15	23	83	9
Roberttown w/d							

WEST YORKSHIRE LEAGUE

PREMIER DIVISION	P	W	D	L	F	A	Pts
Leeds Met Carnegie	30	20	7	3	96	28	67
Beeston St.Anthonys	30	21	3	6	72	25	66
Nostell Miners Welfare	30	21	3	6	72	31	66
Howden Clough	30	14	7	9	60	49	49
Carlton Athletic	30	15	4	11	51	43	49
Pontefract Sports	30	14	5	11	52	56	47
Bardsey	30	12	8	10	55	49	44
Whitkirk Wanderers	30	13	4	13	54	59	43
Boroughbridge	30	10	6	14	47	43	36
Aberford Albion	30	9	7	14	38	50	34
Ossett Common Rov	30	8	9	13	34	58	33
Wetherby Athletic	30	9	6	15	42	68	33
Knaresborough Town	30	8	5	17	27	48	29
Horsforth St.Margarets	30	8	4	18	43	74	28
Rothwell Athletic	30	8	3	19	36	69	27
Tadcaster Magnets	30	6	7	17	33	62	25

DIVISION ONE	P	W	D	L	F	A	Pts
Sherburn WR	28	22	4	2	80	15	70
Streetwork Soccer	28	20	6	2	67	34	66
AFC Emley	28	18	3	7	86	44	57
Churwell Lions	28	14	7	7	64	50	49
Robin Hood Athletic	28	14	6	8	64	56	48
Ilkley	28	12	6	10	57	48	42
Hartshead	28	11	4	13	53	55	37
Ripon City Magnets	28	9	7	12	61	49	34
Pool	28	9	7	12	65	64	34
Woodhouse Hill WMC	28	9	6	13	58	74	33
Barwick	28	8	7	13	48	61	31
Sandy Lane	28	9	1	18	40	79	28
Kellingley Welfare	28	8	2	18	39	59	26
Baildon Trinity Athletic	28	6	6	16	45	61	24
Mount St.Marys	28	4	2	22	26	104	14
Ryhill & Havercroft Sports w/d							

WEST YORKSHIRE continued

DIVISION TWO	P	W	D	L	F	A	Pts
Field S&S (Bradford)	28	23	2	3	101	26	71
Old Headingley	28	21	3	4	75	32	66
Kippax Athletic	28	19	1	8	98	59	58
Horbury Town	28	15	8	5	67	44	53
Hunslet	28	15	5	8	98	60	50
East End Park	28	15	5	8	72	51	50
Kippax Welfare	28	15	4	9	62	47	49
Stanley United	28	13	4	11	57	49	43
Rothwell Town	28	10	5	13	53	61	35
Featherstone Colliery	28	10	3	15	60	76	33
Boston Spartans	28	7	5	16	49	86	26
Great Preston	28	5	8	15	36	84	23
Upper Armley OB	28	5	5	18	45	84	20
Swillington Saints	28	4	3	21	44	92	15
Dewsbury Moor Ath	28	2	1	25	35	101	7
Victoria BC (Rothwell) w/d							

YORKSHIRE OLD BOYS LEAGUE

SENIOR A	P	W	D	L	F	A	Pts
Yorkshire Bank	22	14	5	3	52	28	47
Old Rovers	22	11	6	5	66	52	39
Western Juniors	22	12	3	7	43	35	39
Leeds University	22	9	9	4	48	32	36
Trinity & All Saints	22	10	5	7	67	43	35
Leeds Medics	22	9	6	7	47	33	33
Stanningley	22	10	3	9	49	47	33
St.Nicholas	22	8	5	9	54	45	29
Roundhegians	22	7	4	11	44	70	25
Collegians	22	5	3	14	41	69	18
Abbey Grange	22	5	2	15	37	71	17
Modernians	22	2	9	11	29	52	15

SENIOR B	P	W	D	L	F	A	Pts
Huddersfield Ams	22	17	2	3	71	28	53
Heckmondwike GSOB	22	17	1	4	77	25	52
Leeds Medics res	22	14	2	6	60	43	44
Centralians	22	10	6	6	37	26	36
FC Headingley	22	10	4	8	45	38	34
Ealandians	22	9	6	7	55	47	33
Yorkshire Amateurs res	22	10	1	11	43	42	31
Griffordians	22	9	2	11	52	59	29
Calverley	22	6	6	10	46	62	24
East Ardsley Wanderers	22	4	4	14	33	80	16
Batelians	22	3	4	15	46	70	13
Adel	22	3	2	17	27	72	11

DIVISION ONE	P	W	D	L	F	A	Pts
Wortley OB	22	18	3	1	66	24	67
Bramley Juniors	22	17	1	4	88	31	52
Sandal Wanderers	22	14	3	5	61	45	45
Colton Academicals	22	11	2	9	59	51	35
St.Bedes	22	10	5	7	44	42	35
Woodhouse Moor	22	9	5	8	52	59	32
Roundhegians res	22	9	1	12	52	56	28
Thornesians	22	8	2	12	40	56	26
Leeds Medics 3rds	22	6	4	12	45	49	22
Agnes Stewart	22	5	4	13	60	65	19
Modernians res	22	4	4	14	36	59	16
Modernians 3rds	22	2	4	16	22	88	10

DIVISION TWO	P	W	D	L	F	A	Pts
Alwoodley	22	17	3	2	79	36	54
Adel res	22	14	5	3	60	28	47
Wheelright	22	12	6	4	65	37	42
Almondburians	21	11	3	7	56	41	36
Leeds Independent	22	9	2	11	44	44	29
Griffordians	22	9	2	11	47	52	29
Centralians res	22	9	2	11	46	58	29
Commonside	22	7	4	11	55	58	25
Huddersfield Amateurs	22	7	4	11	49	59	24
Grangefield OB	21	7	2	12	40	56	23
Abbey Grange res	22	4	4	14	33	79	16
St.Bedes OB res	22	4	5	13	36	62	14

YORKSHIRE OLD BOYS LEAGUE continued

DIVISION THREE

	P	W	D	L	F	A	Pts
Wortley OB res	22	19	1	2	88	26	58
Trinity OB res	22	17	3	2	64	19	54
Batelians res	22	11	2	9	54	47	35
Heckmondwike res	22	11	2	9	63	61	35
Horbury Town OB	22	10	3	9	47	50	33
Colton Acads res	22	8	5	9	55	52	29
Thornesians res	22	8	3	11	36	58	27
Moortown OB	22	6	7	9	51	59	25
Modernians 4ths	22	6	5	11	46	60	23
Roundhegians 3rds	22	7	2	13	36	61	23
Leeds Medics 4ths	22	6	2	14	41	68	20
Centralians 3rds	22	2	7	13	20	40	13

DIVISION FOUR

	P	W	D	L	F	A	Pts
Shire Academics	22	22	0	2	108	30	60
Griffordians3rds	22	15	3	4	73	44	48
Woodhouse Moor res	22	13	6	3	57	33	45
Wheelright res	22	13	2	7	62	44	41
Batelians 3rds	22	9	4	9	62	58	31
Ealandians res	22	8	5	9	51	54	29
Sandal Wdrs res	22	8	4	10	44	52	28
Huddersfield Ams 3rds	22	8	1	13	47	79	25
East Ardsley Wdrs res	22	6	4	12	42	57	22
Collegians res	22	5	5	12	32	54	20
Abbey Grange 3rds	22	5	2	15	32	58	17
Modernians 5ths	22	3	2	17	30	77	11

DIVISION FIVE

	P	W	D	L	F	A	Pts
East Leeds Trinity	22	18	2	2	93	19	56
Colton Acads 3rds	22	14	4	4	91	58	46
Alwoodley res	22	14	3	5	89	35	45
Heckmondwike 3rds	22	14	3	5	74	47	45
St.Bedes OB 3rds	22	11	7	4	48	29	40
Abbey Grange 4ths	22	10	3	9	40	47	33
Thornesians 3rds	22	9	3	10	59	52	30
Collegians 3rds	22	7	4	11	51	59	25
Huddersfield Ams 4ths	22	6	1	15	38	86	19
Modernians 6ths	22	5	3	14	46	74	18
Centralians 4ths	22	3	4	15	37	89	13
Roundhegians 4ths	22	2	1	19	27	98	7

LEEDS RED TRIANGLE

PREMIER DIVISION

	P	W	D	L	F	A	Pts
Rawdon Old Boys	22	17	1	4	81	27	52
Wykebeck Arms Utd	22	14	5	3	58	30	47
Swinnow Athletic	22	14	3	5	69	40	45
Churwell New Inn	22	12	3	7	64	46	39
Arla Foods	22	12	2	8	52	45	38
Yew Tree	22	9	6	7	75	61	33
Farnley Nags Head	22	8	6	8	73	66	30
East Leeds	22	8	2	12	60	65	26
Garforth	22	6	3	13	56	80	21
Amaranth	22	5	2	15	39	65	17
Middleton Park	22	4	3	15	37	110	15
Elhaya African S&CC	22	4	2	16	44	73	14
Park FC w/d							

DIVISION ONE

	P	W	D	L	F	A	Pts
Queen FC	26	19	3	4	91	46	60
Halton Moor	26	17	3	6	96	70	54
Seacroft WMC	26	15	5	6	76	48	50
Skinners Arms	26	15	5	6	85	60	50
Drighlington Adwalton	26	12	6	8	54	51	42
New Farnley CC	26	12	5	9	57	51	41
Farsley Bay Horse	26	11	7	8	61	54	40
Bainbridge United	26	11	2	13	51	59	35
Farnley Sports	26	9	5	12	54	58	32
Leodis	26	8	6	12	49	66	30
Red Lion	26	8	4	14	73	82	28
Dynamo Turbot	26	8	2	16	47	60	26
Golden Fleece	26	3	5	18	26	63	14
Leeds Deaf	26	4	2	20	28	80	14
South Leeds w/d							

EAST LANCASHIRE LEAGUE (LANCS FA)

DIVISION ONE

	P	W	D	L	F	A	Pts
Rimington	26	19	1	6	70	30	58
Hurst Green	26	14	8	4	67	35	50
Stacksteads St.J	26	14	8	4	61	35	50
Colne United	26	13	6	7	73	50	45
Goodshaw United	26	11	7	8	65	53	40
Settle United	26	11	5	10	61	53	38
Rock Rovers	26	10	7	9	49	44	37
Worsthorne	26	10	6	10	62	57	36
Silsden 2004	26	8	8	10	45	47	32
Langho	26	8	8	10	49	56	32
Kelbrook	26	7	5	14	38	59	26
Enfield	26	7	4	15	35	59	25
Padiham res	26	7	2	17	38	79	23
Oswaldtwistle St.M	26	2	7	17	34	91	13

CRAVEN & DISTRICT LEAGUE

PREMIER DIVISION

	P	W	D	L	F	A	PTS
Oxenhope Recreation	22	18	3	1	91	33	57
Bronte Wanderers	22	16	4	2	84	35	52
Skipton LMS	22	16	2	4	86	44	50
Embsay	22	11	2	9	53	45	35
Gargrave	22	10	3	9	42	38	33
Waddington	22	9	7	6	60	48	31
WFC Clitheroe	22	9	3	10	64	73	30
Cononley Sports	22	7	4	11	54	55	25
Grassington United	22	5	6	11	36	52	21
Carleton	22	5	1	16	47	80	16
Grindleton	22	3	6	13	38	72	15
Crosshills 'A'	22	1	3	18	32	112	6
Skipton Bulldogs w/d							

DIVISION ONE

	P	W	D	L	F	A	Pts
Bradley	22	14	6	2	52	23	48
Hellifield Sports	22	13	5	4	61	39	44
Clitheroe Lions	22	12	7	3	55	27	41
Skipton Town	22	11	3	8	56	49	36
Oxenhope Rec res	22	10	5	7	41	42	32
Craven College OB	22	9	4	9	45	56	28
Embsay res	22	7	5	10	42	44	26
Intake	22	6	7	9	38	41	25
Rolls Royce	22	6	6	10	36	42	24
Silsden 2004 res	22	7	6	9	39	38	23
Skipton LMS res	22	6	2	14	37	57	20
Barrowford United	22	2	2	18	29	73	8

DIVISION TWO

	P	W	D	L	F	A	Pts
Pendle Athletic	22	18	0	4	92	36	54
Long Lee Juniors	22	13	4	5	68	31	43
Cowling	22	11	5	6	52	42	38
Keighley	22	10	7	5	65	54	37
Intake res	22	10	2	10	62	74	32
Gargrave res	22	8	6	8	63	58	30
Rolls Royce res	22	8	3	11	47	62	27
Horton	22	8	2	12	47	57	26
Waddington res	22	8	2	12	42	71	26
Cononley Sports	22	7	3	12	44	59	24
Grindleton res	22	7	3	12	51	71	24
Earby Town	22	4	3	15	63	81	15
McBrides w/d							

DIVISION THREE

	P	W	D	L	F	A	Pts
Grassington Utd res	22	16	4	2	68	24	52
Oakworth	22	16	2	4	93	27	50
Earby	22	15	2	5	72	44	47
Silsden White Star	22	13	4	5	61	40	40
Pendle Renegades	22	9	5	8	52	59	31
Barnoldswick Barons	22	8	5	9	59	47	29
Long Lee Juniors res	22	8	4	10	45	54	28
Carleton res	22	8	4	10	45	73	28
Bradley res	22	8	2	12	38	62	26
Ingleton 'A'	22	5	4	13	48	56	19
Hellifield Sports res	22	5	3	14	40	68	18
Cowling reserves	22	0	3	19	32	91	3
Skipton Bulldogs res w/d							

SPEN VALLEY LEAGUE

PREMIER DIVISION	P	W	D	L	F	A	Pts
Salfa Rangers	17	16	1	0	63	15	46
Wellington Wanderers	18	10	5	3	46	32	35
Kalon	17	10	3	4	68	34	33
Hare & Hounds	18	8	4	6	64	38	28
Soothill	18	6	7	5	37	37	25
Windmill (Wibsey)	18	6	7	5	37	38	22
Dewsbury WS	18	6	4	8	43	45	19
Howden Clough res	18	4	6	8	24	45	18
Commonside	18	1	3	14	31	82	6
Bosnia	18	1	2	15	34	81	5

DIVISION ONE	P	W	D	L	F	A	Pts
Wyke Wanderers	20	17	0	3	77	20	51
Old Bank WMC	20	15	2	3	98	35	47
Old Magnet	20	14	4	2	67	27	46
Barfield	20	10	4	6	73	49	34
Youth 2000	20	9	3	8	52	49	30
Norfolk	20	5	5	10	44	65	20
Inter Batley	20	6	2	12	30	69	20
Marsh	20	6	1	13	39	57	19
Windmill res	20	5	2	13	50	92	17
Wellington Wdrs res	20	5	0	14	34	78	15
Shooters	20	5	1	14	56	79	13

HALIFAX & DISTRICT LEAGUE

PREMIER DIVISION	P	W	D	L	F	A	Pts
Hebden Royd RedStar	22	17	5	0	81	17	56
Stainland United	22	15	3	4	69	40	48
Wheatsheaf	22	13	5	4	54	31	44
Elland United	22	11	5	6	71	42	38
Brighouse OB	22	10	3	9	44	40	33
Halifax Irish Centre	22	9	6	7	45	47	33
Shelf United	22	7	7	8	55	47	28
Ryburn United	22	8	4	10	41	54	28
Midgley United	22	7	5	10	48	47	26
Denholme United	22	6	1	15	49	65	19
St.Andrews	22	4	4	14	43	83	16
Greetland CC	22	0	2	20	20	107	2
Wadsworth Utd w/d							

DIVISION ONE	P	W	D	L	F	A	Pts
Holmfield	20	17	2	1	92	32	53
Sowerby United	20	12	2	6	52	34	38
Warley Rangers	20	11	4	5	63	36	37
Brighouse OB res	20	11	2	7	58	49	37
Mixenden United	20	9	9	2	46	26	36
Salem	20	8	2	10	55	44	26
Calder 76	20	7	4	9	44	31	25
Northowram	20	6	8	6	64	46	24
Sowerby Bridge	20	5	2	13	38	65	19
Friendly	20	4	2	14	27	69	14
Stump Cross	20	1	1	18	21	128	4
AFC Lords w/d							
Boothtown w/d							

DIVISION TWO	P	W	D	L	F	A	Pts
Martins Nest	24	20	2	2	97	28	62
Sowerby Bridge res	24	16	3	5	77	44	54
FC Fold	24	16	4	4	96	53	52
Volunteer Arms	24	14	2	8	107	67	44
Junction	24	11	6	7	68	59	39
Shelf United res	24	12	2	10	68	61	38
Ryburn United res	24	11	4	9	71	63	34
Halifax Irish res	24	11	1	12	56	62	34
Warley Rangers res	24	7	4	13	53	60	25
Copley United	24	7	3	14	55	103	23
Denholme United res	24	5	3	16	60	99	18
Stainland United res	24	2	6	16	55	108	14
Midgley United res	24	3	2	19	41	97	11

DIVISION THREE	P	W	D	L	F	A	Pts
Golden Lion	20	17	0	3	107	26	51
Pellon United	20	12	4	4	57	36	40
Hebden Royd RS res	20	11	4	5	53	28	37
Hipperholme Athetic	20	11	4	5	56	42	37
Bowling Green	20	10	2	8	66	52	35
Wheatsheaf res	20	7	7	6	41	39	28
Stafford	20	8	4	8	46	46	28
Calder 76 res	20	4	8	8	32	51	17
Wadsworth Utd res	20	4	4	12	28	57	16
Salem reserves	20	3	2	15	19	73	11
Sowerby United res	20	3	1	16	26	81	10
Friendly res w/d							
Ovenden Friendly Ath w/d							

HUDDERSFIELD & DISTRICT LEAGUE

DIVISION ONE	P	W	D	L	F	A	Pts
Heywood Sports	22	12	6	4	62	39	42
Sovereign Sports	22	12	6	4	52	36	42
Honley	22	11	5	6	58	39	38
Diggle	22	9	6	7	57	44	33
New Mill 94	22	8	8	6	44	35	32
Uppermill	22	8	7	7	36	35	31
Lepton Highlanders	22	8	6	8	51	44	30
Shepley	22	7	7	8	46	48	28
Britannia Sports	22	7	5	10	47	50	26
Meltham Athletic res	22	7	5	10	42	44	26
Wooldale Wanderers	22	6	8	8	43	40	26
Grange Moor	22	1	3	18	32	116	6

DIVISION TWO	P	W	D	L	F	A	Pts
Newsome WMC	24	16	5	3	77	36	53
Aimbry	24	14	3	7	65	37	45
Lindley Liberals	24	12	5	7	66	42	41
Netherton	24	12	5	7	46	36	41
Hepworth United	24	12	4	8	60	51	40
Slaithwaite United	24	10	7	7	60	48	37
KKS Ashbrow	24	10	6	8	55	56	36
Kirkheaton Rovers	24	9	5	10	47	51	32
Holmbridge	24	10	1	13	56	55	31
Moldgreen	24	10	0	14	48	65	30
Mount	24	8	6	10	46	41	30
Heyside	24	8	3	13	49	49	27
Skelmanthorpe United	24	0	0	24	12	120	0

DIVISION THREE	P	W	D	L	F	A	Pts
Scholes	26	19	4	3	85	39	61
Berry Brow Liberals	26	18	4	4	89	36	58
Linthwaite Athletic	26	18	4	4	87	46	58
Space	26	18	3	5	92	36	57
Cumberworth	26	15	8	3	61	30	53
Sikh Leisure Centre	26	13	5	8	73	43	44
Cravens	26	13	4	9	80	54	43
HV Academicals	26	11	4	11	61	65	37
Lindley	26	11	3	12	72	66	36
Scissett	26	7	1	18	50	70	22
Shelley	26	6	2	18	52	84	20
Hade Edge	26	6	0	20	36	101	18
Cartworth Moor	26	2	2	22	17	103	8
Fenay Bridge	26	2	2	22	41	123	8

DIVISION FOUR	P	W	D	L	F	A	Pts
Westend	22	20	1	1	103	16	61
Paddock Rangers	22	16	4	2	73	34	52
The Stag	22	13	0	9	54	42	39
Upperthong	22	10	4	8	65	45	34
Farnley Terriers	21	9	5	7	67	44	32
Flockton	22	9	4	9	58	50	31
Brook Motors	22	8	8	8	56	46	30
Elland	22	9	3	10	64	63	30
YMCA	22	9	3	10	54	66	30
Coach & Horses	22	6	3	13	41	68	21
Marsden res	21	5	1	15	40	75	16
Ireti Athletic	22	0	0	22	32	158	0
York CF w/d							
Holmfirth Town w/d							

WAKEFIELD & DISTRICT LEAGUE

PREMIER DIVISION	P	W	D	L	F	A	Pts
Airedale Celtic	22	17	2	3	90	25	53
Sandal Athletic	22	17	2	3	74	34	53
Snydale Athletic	22	13	3	6	73	53	42
Mitres Well	22	9	3	10	69	76	30
Walton	22	7	6	9	65	65	27
Slipper	22	7	4	11	53	59	25
Altofts res	22	8	4	10	45	61	25
Eastmoor res	22	7	4	11	51	68	25
Silcoates	22	7	3	12	66	87	24
St.Michaels	22	9	0	13	57	59	21
Fieldhead Hospital	22	8	3	11	47	66	21
Snydale Sports	22	4	4	14	53	90	16

DIVISION ONE	P	W	D	L	F	A	Pts
White Bear Kexboro	26	21	1	4	101	32	65
Fleece Horbury	26	19	4	3	99	41	61
AFC Thornhill	26	15	5	6	88	63	50
Wrenthorpe	26	14	6	6	80	47	48
Kingstone United WMC	26	14	1	11	73	59	43
Shepherds Arms	26	12	7	7	79	50	40
Knottingley Waterside	26	15	1	10	53	39	40
Thornhill	26	11	5	10	70	65	35
Nostell MW 'A	26	8	5	13	47	63	29
Wakefield City 'A'	26	8	3	15	42	66	27
AFC Foresters	26	8	1	17	63	107	25
Pinderfields Unison	26	6	3	17	66	92	21
Waterloo	26	5	1	20	31	97	16
Morley C&SC	26	3	2	21	45	116	5

WAKEFIELD & DISTRICT continued

DIVISION TWO

	P	W	D	L	F	A	Pts
Ryecroft Sports	22	18	1	3	69	29	55
Ferrybridge Amateurs	22	17	2	3	79	41	53
Crofton	22	11	2	9	55	57	35
Stanley Arms	22	12	1	9	54	42	34
Gawthorpe Shoulder	22	8	5	9	66	63	29
Jolly Miller	22	9	1	12	58	59	28
Cross Keys	22	9	3	10	57	54	27
Snydale Athletic res	22	6	7	9	47	56	25
Fleece Horbury res	22	8	6	8	54	54	24
Sandal Athletic res	22	6	3	13	49	63	21
Westgate Common	22	4	5	13	39	74	17
Ossett Panthers	22	5	2	15	51	86	11
Tingley Bulls w/d							

DIVISION THREE

	P	W	D	L	F	A	Pts
Stanley United res	26	21	4	1	101	28	61
White Rose	26	18	3	5	101	29	57
Wakefield United	26	16	2	8	56	40	50
Smawthorne Hotel	26	19	3	4	92	36	48
Slipper res	26	12	7	7	62	46	43
Park Tavern Rovers	26	13	3	10	63	50	42
Excel Knights	26	11	6	9	74	66	39
St.Michaels res	26	12	2	12	60	52	38
Little Bull	26	11	3	12	45	53	36
Cliffe Tree	26	6	6	14	66	84	20
Altofts 'A'	26	6	5	15	37	75	16
Mitres Well Vets	26	6	3	17	40	88	15
East Ardsley General	26	3	4	19	46	115	13
Snydale Sports res	26	1	3	22	36	117	3

BRADFORD T&A LEAGUE

	P	W	D	L	F	A	Pts
West Horton	26	20	5	1	94	20	65
IMS Celtic	26	17	3	6	103	51	54
Smiling Mule	26	15	4	7	74	51	49
Tyersal 'A'	26	15	3	8	81	47	48
Manningham West Bk	26	15	8	3	93	38	47
U Save DIY	26	13	6	7	76	41	45
East Bowling	26	14	2	10	99	54	44
Dynamoes All Stars	26	13	4	9	55	51	40
Dudley Hill Rgrs 'A'	26	7	5	14	54	72	26
West Bowling United	26	6	7	13	44	54	25
Ravenscliffe	26	7	3	16	66	125	24
Second West	26	7	1	18	61	86	22
Ventnor Youth	26	2	4	20	31	126	10
Bradford Arms	26	3	1	22	31	127	10
Kings Head w/d							

League Cup final: W.Bowling Utd 1 Manningham W. Bank 0

SELBY & DISTRICT LEAGUE

DIVISION ONE

	P	W	D	L	F	A	Pts
Pollington	18	13	3	2	76	35	42
South Milford	18	13	1	4	61	38	40
Bird In Hand	18	10	6	2	55	39	36
Garforth WMC	18	8	4	6	62	52	28
Knottingley	18	8	4	6	52	43	28
Airedale A	18	6	5	7	50	55	23
Riccall	18	5	5	8	54	55	20
Kellington	18	5	2	11	52	72	17
Airedale B	18	3	5	10	38	44	14
Black Dog	18	1	1	16	29	96	4

DIVISION TWO

	P	W	D	L	F	A	Pts
Yorkshire Penny	20	15	4	1	81	19	49
Pontefract Town	20	15	2	3	59	26	47
Rileys A	20	15	1	4	90	28	46
Hensall	20	14	3	3	69	22	45
Fairburn	20	10	0	10	55	58	30
Rileys B	20	8	1	11	44	50	25
Players Sports Bar	20	6	2	12	47	67	20
Bradley Arms	20	5	5	10	38	56	20
Wistow	20	6	0	14	46	83	18
Snaith	20	6	0	14	41	80	18
Drax	20	1	0	19	20	101	3
Townville Terr w/d							

EAST RIDING AMATEUR LEAGUE

PREMIER DIVISION

	P	W	D	L	F	A	Pts
AFC Wold	20	16	1	3	62	27	49
Kinnersley	20	13	2	5	51	29	41
Kingburn Athletic	20	12	3	5	44	28	39
Kinloss	20	10	2	8	49	38	32
Pinefleet Wolf res	20	10	2	8	47	40	32
AFC Preston	20	9	3	8	41	35	30
Sydney Smith	20	8	4	8	46	37	28
Orchard Park Tigers	20	9	1	10	64	61	28
AFC Charleston res	20	6	2	12	32	47	20
Hessle Sporting	20	3	2	15	24	55	11
Inglemire Rangers	20	2	2	26	22	85	4

DIVISION ONE

	P	W	D	L	F	A	Pts
Eddie Beadle	18	13	2	3	73	38	41
Spring Bank Tigers	18	12	4	2	62	33	40
Anlaby Park	18	9	5	4	39	32	32
Kingburn Athletic res	18	8	7	3	46	38	31
Cross Keys Cott'ham	18	8	2	8	46	46	26
Admiral Signs	18	7	3	8	44	41	24
Blackburn Leisure	18	6	4	8	55	53	22
Cavalier Wanderers	18	5	3	10	34	45	18
Dales	18	3	3	12	30	66	12
Harrison Solway	18	2	1	15	27	64	7

DIVISION TWO

	P	W	D	L	F	A	Pts
Crown	22	17	3	2	89	26	54
Orchard Pk Tigers res	22	16	3	3	110	45	51
Paull Wanderers	22	14	4	4	65	40	46
Cross Keys Tigers	22	10	5	7	68	53	35
Savoy	22	10	4	8	57	58	34
Hessle Sporting res	22	10	3	9	58	65	33
Jenko Sporting	22	9	3	10	60	64	30
Tenyas	22	10	0	12	49	58	30
Hull Wanderers	22	7	1	14	53	74	22
AFC Malt Shovel	22	6	3	13	32	55	21
Greatfield OB	22	4	3	15	41	79	15
XKeys Cottingham res	22	2	2	18	49	114	8

DRIFFIELD & DISTRICT LEAGUE

PREMIER DIVISION

	P	W	D	L	F	A	Pts
Yorkies	16	12	4	0	50	18	40
Bridlington Sports res	16	10	5	1	54	18	35
Driffield Rangers	16	10	2	4	40	26	32
Driffield El	16	10	1	5	41	36	31
Nafferton	16	5	3	8	34	37	18
Bridlington Excel	16	4	3	9	35	52	15
HuttonCranswick SRA	16	4	1	11	22	32	13
Burton Agnes	16	3	2	11	25	48	11
Bridlington Rovers	16	2	3	11	21	55	9
Cricketers w/d							

DIVISION ONE

	P	W	D	L	F	A	Pts
Driffield Rec	15	13	2	0	65	18	41
Bull & Sun Rangers	16	10	4	2	49	25	34
Poachers 4ths	16	10	3	3	58	38	33
Forester Athletic	16	9	1	6	48	37	28
Flamborough	16	8	2	6	43	36	26
Sterling Castle	16	4	4	8	25	43	10
Bridlington Seabirds	16	2	4	10	32	53	10
Hutton Cranswick 3rds	16	2	2	12	35	67	8
Driffield Wanderers	15	1	2	12	25	63	5

DIVISION TWO

	P	W	D	L	F	A	Pts
Rose & Crown Driff	18	13	3	2	58	27	42
Globe AFC	18	11	3	4	46	37	36
Bridge Cafe United	18	13	1	4	68	33	34
Bridlington Excel res	18	9	2	7	42	40	29
Bridlington Spts 3rds	18	7	3	8	46	42	24
Flamborough res	18	5	6	7	42	32	21
North Burton	18	6	1	11	37	48	19
North Frodingham res	18	5	1	12	51	72	16
Burton Agnes res	18	5	1	12	48	73	16
Middleton Rovers	18	5	1	12	38	72	16

DIVISION THREE

	P	W	D	L	F	A	Pts
Hutton Cran SRA OB	16	14	1	1	55	14	43
Nafferton CK	16	12	2	2	88	37	38
Nafferton SRA	16	12	2	2	60	20	38
Little Driffield	16	9	1	6	69	40	28
Pocklington 4ths	16	8	0	8	63	47	24
Forester Athletic res	16	7	0	9	36	43	21
Spiders	16	3	1	12	31	69	10
Langtoft	16	3	1	14	26	71	6
Driffield Star	16	1	1	14	12	99	4

EAST RIDING COUNTY LEAGUE

PREMIER DIVISION

	P	W	D	L	F	A	Pts
North Cave	18	10	4	4	45	33	34
Sculcoates Ams res	18	9	4	5	40	39	31
Rawcliffe Bridge Utd	18	9	3	6	49	32	30
Northfield Athletic	18	9	1	8	41	33	28
Long Riston	18	8	2	8	31	33	26
Howden Amateurs	18	7	4	7	34	45	25
Old George	18	6	5	7	31	25	23
Reckitts reserves	18	5	6	7	27	31	21
Poachers	18	6	3	9	25	33	21
FC Ridings	18	3	4	11	24	43	13

DIVISION ONE

	P	W	D	L	F	A	Pts
Boothferry Rangers	20	12	4	4	60	35	43
Holme Rovers	20	10	7	3	47	25	37
Skidby Millers	20	11	3	6	52	42	36
Easington United res	20	8	7	5	46	40	31
Warter	20	9	3	8	44	50	30
Westella & Willerby res	20	8	5	7	43	42	29
North Ferriby Athletic	20	9	4	7	61	51	28
Beverley Town res	20	6	6	8	35	35	24
Hornsea Town res	20	6	5	9	45	53	23
Hutton Crans. Utd res	20	3	5	12	27	52	14
Hall Road Rangers res	20	2	3	15	26	61	9

DIVISION TWO

	P	W	D	L	F	A	Pts
Dales Tigers YC	22	16	4	2	71	24	52
Anlaby United res	22	15	1	6	47	33	46
Alborough United	21	13	4	4	55	36	43
Lord Nelson Beverley	22	12	4	6	66	41	40
FC Swallow	22	11	4	7	63	44	37
South Cave United	22	10	3	9	67	54	33
Patrington United	22	8	8	6	40	40	29
Gilberdyke	22	9	2	11	38	44	29
Hedon United res	22	6	2	14	32	65	23
Leven Members Club	22	6	3	13	40	58	21
North Frodingham	21	3	2	16	36	68	11
North Newbald	22	2	3	17	19	67	9

DIVISION THREE

	P	W	D	L	F	A	Pts
Brandesburton res	18	13	2	3	53	31	41
Beaver	18	12	4	2	49	25	40
Hodgsons	18	13	1	4	51	40	40
Howden Ams res	18	8	4	6	44	34	28
Boothferry Rgrs res	18	7	3	8	38	35	24
Market Weighton Utd	18	7	1	10	42	48	22
Haltemprice OB	18	6	1	11	30	45	19
Withernsea res	18	5	3	10	43	60	18
Plexus Networking	18	4	2	12	34	48	14
Molescroft Rangers	18	3	3	12	33	51	12

DIVISION FOUR

	P	W	D	L	F	A	Pts
FC Peacock	22	19	1	2	87	29	58
West Hull Amateurs	22	18	3	1	77	25	57
North Cave res	22	15	3	4	72	39	48
Keysign Solutions	22	14	0	8	54	49	42
Roos	22	12	3	7	46	40	39
Long Riston res	22	12	1	9	45	64	37
Skidby Millers res	22	9	2	11	45	56	29
Cross Keys Howden	22	7	2	13	40	73	23
Holme Rovers res	22	4	5	13	23	39	17
Leven MC res	22	4	4	14	39	66	16
Westella/Willerby Jn	22	4	0	18	21	33	12
Shiptonthorpe Utd	22	2	0	20	12	48	4
(bottom 2 teams w/d)							

DIVISION FIVE

	P	W	D	L	F	A	Pts
Dads FC	26	17	6	3	86	38	57
Withernsea 3rds	26	15	7	4	58	33	52
Easington Utd Casuals	26	12	6	8	50	44	42
Molescroft Rgrs res	26	13	3	10	62	65	42
FC Peacock res	26	12	5	9	78	68	41
Howden Town	26	12	4	10	75	61	40
Patrington Stanley	25	11	7	8	54	43	40
Mkt Weighton Utd res	26	10	7	9	52	49	37
Hornsea Town 3rds	26	10	5	11	53	68	35
Skirlaugh	26	10	2	14	61	64	32
Brandesburton 3rds	26	9	3	14	69	78	30
Easington Village	26	7	4	15	50	66	25
Shiptonthorpe Utd res	26	7	4	15	51	79	25
Haltemprice Rangers	26	4	3	19	32	75	15

SHEFFIELD COUNTY SENIOR LEAGUE

PREMIER DIVISION

	P	W	D	L	F	A	Pts
Mexborough Main St.	26	19	4	3	76	28	61
Athersley Recreation	26	16	7	3	53	16	55
Stocksbridge PS res	26	12	10	4	58	34	46
Roy Hancock OCrown	26	11	8	7	55	42	41
HSBC	26	11	6	9	47	38	39
Hollinsend Amateurs	26	10	8	8	36	30	38
Houghton Main	26	10	7	9	33	36	37
Wombwell Main	26	9	8	9	42	35	35
Penistone Church	26	8	7	11	37	55	31
Edlington WMC	26	7	9	10	34	52	30
Thorpe Hesley	26	7	8	11	38	45	29
Oughtibridge WMSC	26	9	2	5	35	52	29
South Kirkby Colliery	26	5	5	16	24	54	20
Silkstone United	26	1	5	20	28	78	8

DIVISION ONE

	P	W	D	L	F	A	Pts
Sheffield Lane Top	24	15	4	5	78	36	49
Outo Kumpu S&SC	24	14	4	6	71	45	46
Dinnington Town res	24	12	6	6	41	30	42
Handsworth	24	10	8	6	61	50	38
Wickersley Old Boys	24	9	7	8	33	27	34
Parramore Sports	24	9	7	8	44	46	34
Georgia pacific	24	9	6	9	42	48	33
Dearne/Swinton	24	8	7	9	66	52	31
Elm Tree	24	9	4	11	46	57	31
Ecclesfield Red Rose	24	9	4	11	45	62	31
Frecheville CA	24	7	5	12	40	49	26
Dodworth MW	24	7	4	13	45	59	25
High Green Villa	24	1	8	15	21	72	11

DIVISION TWO

	P	W	D	L	F	A	Pts
Parkgate res	26	22	2	2	110	26	68
Half Moon	26	18	6	2	62	18	59
Worsbrough Common	26	14	7	5	58	24	49
Sheffield Bankers	26	14	5	7	56	31	47
Caribbean Sports	26	13	7	6	64	42	46
AFC Cutlers	26	12	6	8	62	53	42
Worsboro Bridge res	26	11	7	8	52	42	37
Phoenix	26	9	4	13	47	63	31
Sheffield Centralians	26	9	4	13	45	63	31
Everest	26	7	5	14	51	71	26
De La Salle OB	26	6	7	13	44	66	25
Armthorpe MW	26	5	5	16	41	64	20
Penistone Church res	26	4	7	15	45	87	19
Harworth CI res	26	1	2	23	13	100	5

DONCASTER SENIOR LEAGUE

PREMIER DIVISION

	P	W	D	L	F	A	Pts
Hemsworth St.Patrick	26	22	3	1	107	27	69
Kinsley Boys	26	20	2	4	101	28	62
Moorland	26	18	2	6	107	69	56
Pontefract Colls res	26	16	3	7	68	48	51
Swinton Station	26	14	7	5	69	35	49
Thorne Town	26	12	4	10	72	63	40
Mexborough Athletic	26	12	2	12	60	57	38
Rossington Main res	26	9	6	11	56	82	33
South Kirkby Coll res	26	9	4	13	43	57	31
Askern Welfare	26	7	6	13	41	70	27
Upton & Harewood Soc	26	7	3	16	57	73	24
Ackworth United	26	7	3	16	49	82	24
Eden Grove	26	2	3	21	29	84	9
Bawtry Town	26	2	1	23	31	117	7

DIVISION ONE

	P	W	D	L	F	A	Pts
Tickhill Athletic	18	15	1	2	75	27	46
Maltby Sheppey	18	10	3	5	43	23	33
AFC Beeches	18	10	1	7	44	38	31
Edlington Rangers	18	9	2	7	44	31	29
Sutton Rovers	18	9	2	7	47	48	29
The Star	18	8	4	6	36	35	28
Doncaster Coll Deaf	18	7	4	7	33	28	25
Hemsworth S.P res	18	4	6	8	30	42	18
Wickersley	18	5	1	12	27	48	16
Cooplands United	18	0	2	16	23	82	2
Cantley Hawthorn w/d							
Balby Rangers w/d							
Grimethorpe MW w/d							

SOUTH YORKSHIRE AMATEUR LEAGUE

PREMIER DIVISION	P	W	D	L	F	A	Pts
Jubilee Sports	20	19	1	0	95	18	55
Thorncliffe	20	17	0	3	83	27	51
G&Ts	20	16	0	4	85	38	48
Yew Tree	20	10	4	6	48	28	34
Cross Scythes	20	10	2	8	72	34	29
Phoenix res	20	8	5	7	35	42	29
Bradway	20	8	2	10	50	64	26
Oxspring United	20	4	1	15	51	91	10
Civil Service	20	3	1	16	30	84	10
Norwich Union	20	2	3	15	20	72	9
De La Salle OB res	20	2	3	15	16	87	9
Killamarsh Dyn w/d							

DIVISION ONE	P	W	D	L	F	A	Pts
Grimethorpe Athletic	20	16	3	1	85	15	51
Grove Central	20	14	4	2	78	32	46
Athersley Rec res	20	14	1	5	65	19	43
Dodworth MW res	20	13	1	6	71	44	40
Dale Tavern	20	10	4	6	72	35	34
Bagshawe Arms	20	10	4	6	64	37	34
Kiveton Park res	20	7	1	12	60	51	22
Jeld Wen	20	7	0	13	56	69	21
Sheffield Bankers res	20	4	4	12	30	62	16
Thurgoland Welfare	20	4	0	16	40	85	12
Bolsterstone Pagans	20	0	0	20	17	189	0
Thrybergh S&S w/d							

YORK & DISTRICT LEAGUE

PREMIER DIVISION	P	W	D	L	F	A	Pts
Dringhouses	28	22	1	5	86	37	67
Huntingdon Rovers	28	17	5	6	93	44	56
Thorpe United	28	17	5	6	72	50	56
York St.Johns College	28	14	6	8	69	57	48
Kartiers (Selby)	28	14	5	9	53	40	47
Old Malton St.Marys	28	15	2	11	52	49	47
Tate & Lyle Selby	28	12	3	13	54	49	39
Wigginton G'hoppers	28	12	3	13	56	61	39
Nestle Rowntrees	28	11	5	12	57	50	38
Copmanthorpe	28	10	4	14	55	60	34
Dunnington	28	9	5	14	45	67	32
Pocklington Town res	28	9	4	15	31	62	31
Malton Bacon Factory	28	7	7	14	33	45	28
Bishopthorpe United	28	7	6	15	44	61	27
Haxby United	28	3	1	24	20	88	10

DIVISION ONE	P	W	D	L	F	A	Pts
Heslington	24	17	4	3	64	25	55
Tockwith	24	18	1	5	56	28	55
Norwich Union	24	13	6	5	64	44	45
Ouseburn United	24	12	6	6	66	52	42
Rufforth United	24	10	5	9	45	38	35
Hamilton Panthers	24	10	2	12	53	64	32
Stamford Bridge	24	10	1	13	46	57	31
Easingwold Town	24	8	5	11	46	56	29
Amotherby & Swinton	24	8	3	13	43	47	27
Wilberfoss	24	8	3	13	39	45	27
Elvington Harriers	24	7	5	12	51	53	26
New Earswick	24	6	8	10	39	45	26
Post Office	24	2	5	17	23	81	11

DIVISION TWO	P	W	D	L	F	A	Pts
Poppleton United	22	15	5	2	53	21	50
Riccall United	22	14	6	2	69	17	48
Tadcaster Albion res	22	14	4	4	63	30	46
Sheriff Hutton	22	12	3	7	81	57	39
York Railway Institute	22	11	5	6	55	42	38
White Horse (C. Fent)	22	9	5	8	37	41	32
Fulford United	22	7	4	11	36	50	25
Selby RSSC	22	7	3	12	42	46	24
Civil Service	22	7	3	12	44	73	24
Moor Lane	22	6	4	12	41	60	22
Hemingbrough United	22	6	3	13	39	41	21
Barmby Moor	22	1	1	20	17	99	4

YORK & DISTRICT LEAGUE continued

DIVISION THREE	P	W	D	L	F	A	Pts
Huby United	24	20	3	1	93	19	63
Osbaldwick	24	18	3	3	84	35	57
Cawood	24	16	3	5	70	40	51
Norton United	24	13	2	9	51	51	41
St.Clements	24	11	5	8	55	52	38
LNER Builders	24	10	5	9	51	42	35
Stillington	24	10	3	11	44	37	33
Rawcliffe Rangers	24	9	3	12	81	72	30
Heworth	24	8	3	13	49	54	27
Strensall	24	8	2	14	61	58	26
Melbourne	24	8	1	15	37	70	25
Bishop Wilton	24	4	4	16	37	85	16
Wheldrake	24	2	1	21	32	130	7

STOKESLEY LEAGUE

	P	W	D	L	F	A	Pts
Rudds Arms	24	22	2	0	143	19	68
South Bank St.Peters	24	17	2	5	115	32	50
Corus Sports Club	24	14	4	6	82	59	46
Grangetown YCC	24	12	8	4	81	45	44
Ennis Square	24	13	3	7	106	63	42
Thornaby Village	24	13	2	9	74	74	41
Coulby Newham	24	12	2	10	55	59	35
Acklam Steelworks	24	9	6	9	50	75	33
St.Marys College OB	24	7	3	14	48	50	24
Stokesley SC	24	6	3	15	66	81	21
South Park Rangers	24	5	0	19	33	130	15
The Smithy	24	6	1	17	41	69	13
NS Bulls Head	24	1	0	23	24	162	0
Kings Head w/d							

WENSLEYDALE LEAGUE

	P	W	D	L	F	A	Pts
Leyburn United	26	24	0	2	140	31	72
Bowes	26	22	2	2	128	28	68
Middleham Town	26	22	1	3	99	40	67
Richmond Mavs 'A'	26	18	2	6	95	43	56
Carperby Rovers	26	18	2	6	76	37	56
Hawes United	26	14	1	11	55	54	43
Colburn Town	26	10	2	14	50	56	32
Reeth & District AC	26	9	5	12	56	84	32
Buck Inn United	26	8	2	16	42	60	26
Buck Inn Broncos	26	8	2	16	47	83	26
Hawes 'B';	26	6	4	16	31	84	22
Redmire United	26	6	0	20	35	80	18
Askrigg United	26	2	2	22	27	122	8
Spennithorne&Harmby	26	2	1	23	31	110	7

TEESSIDE LEAGUE

DIVISION ONE	P	W	D	L	F	A	Pts
Carlin How WMC	28	23	2	3	95	26	71
Thornaby YC	28	17	5	6	75	34	56
BEADS	28	16	3	9	83	53	51
Thornaby Athletic	28	15	4	9	59	36	49
Fishburn Park	28	13	7	8	54	33	46
Grangetown BC	28	14	3	11	78	55	45
Richmond Mavericks	28	14	3	11	71	56	45
Nunthorpe Athletic	28	14	5	9	50	50	44
Hartlepool Chester	28	12	7	9	59	47	40
Thornaby res	28	10	6	12	40	61	36
Hartlepool	28	10	5	13	53	58	35
Whinney Banks	28	3	10	15	46	85	19
Richmond Town	28	5	4	19	27	82	19
Dormans Athletic	28	7	3	18	55	91	15
Billingham Wanderers	28	2	3	23	47	125	9

DIVISION TWO	P	W	D	L	F	A	Pts
Mackinlay Park	26	20	1	5	96	36	61
Darlington Rugby Club	26	17	5	4	80	29	56
Guisborough Black Swan	26	17	3	6	89	44	54
Bedale Athletic	26	15	6	5	90	60	51
North Ormesby Spts	26	11	7	8	97	85	40
Stokesley SC res	26	11	6	9	45	43	39
Darlington RA res	26	12	0	14	71	60	36
Yorkshire Coble	26	13	3	10	68	66	36
Hartlepool res	26	10	4	12	65	55	34
Darlington SRM	26	10	0	16	48	59	30
Pickering Town res	26	7	5	14	57	70	26
Spraire Lads	26	6	3	17	43	97	18
Teesside Athletic	26	5	4	17	40	107	16
New Marske SC	26	4	1	21	34	112	10

Welcome to the start of four years of The FA Cup sponsored by E.ON.

As the proud new sponsor of this competition, I'd like to take this opportunity to introduce E.ON to you.

E.ON UK is the UK's largest integrated power and gas company with around 13,000 employees at over 40 different sites. We have 11 power stations producing enough electricity for around nine million homes and have one of the largest green generation portfolios in the UK. As Central Networks, we operate the power distribution network for 4.9m customers in central England. Our retail business (branded Powergen) is a leading energy supplier in the UK, with around six million electricity and gas customers, both residential and small business. E.ON UK forms part of the E.ON group, the world's largest investor-owned power and gas company.

Our partnership with The FA isn't solely about The FA Cup sponsored by E.ON. We are also sponsor of The FA Women's Cup, The FA Youth Cup and are The FA Schools Football Development Partner. The sponsorship of The FA Cup provides a fantastic opportunity for the business to raise awareness of who we are and what we do.

We recognise and respect that The FA Cup is the best domestic knockout cup competition in the world and take immense pride in the fact that, for the next four years, the competition will be The FA Cup sponsored by E.ON.

Operating as a good and responsible neighbour wherever E.ON works is at the heart of our business. The FA Cup sponsored by E.ON will allow us to connect with people who are involved in football at all levels, and build on our existing commitment to the communities where we operate and beyond.

We believe the success of our four-year partnership with The FA lies in our relationship with you and with all of the clubs who have helped to make The FA Cup such a truly fantastic competition.

I would like to wish you all the very best of luck in this season's FA Cup sponsored by E.ON.

Yours sincerely,

Mike Thompson
Head of Sponsorship

the
FOOTBALL
ASSOCIATION
COMPETITIONS

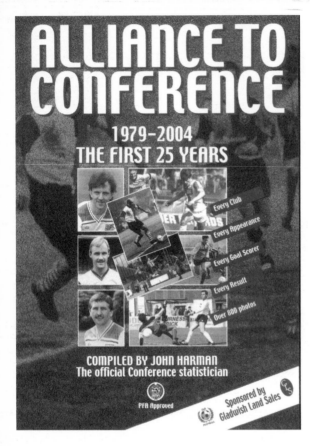

ENGLAND'S
NATIONAL GAME XI
England unbeaten
but Wales are Four Nations Champions

One of the best seasons in the history of the England team selected from Non-League Clubs resulted in three victories and a draw but no trophy.

Paul Fairclough has proved to be the most successful of managers at this level and has built a tremendous spirit and work ethic within an England squad, which can be compared with the atmosphere at the best club sides.

The team is now called The National Game XI and they are half way through the European Challenge Trophy, which is contested over two seasons.

Last season a 2-0 victory in Belgium was followed by a 3-1 success against Italy at Cambridge's Abbey Stadium and the squad moved confidently on to act as hosts and hopefully retain the championship in the Four Nations Tournament, which was successfully held in Sussex at Eastbourne Borough, Worthing and Bognor Regis.

A solid 2-0 victory was achieved over The Republic of Ireland, whose home football season runs through the Summer, before dominating their second match against Wales. Holding a 1-0 lead while squandering chance after chance appeared to be enough for another three point haul, but with eleven minutes to go a rare Welsh sortie into the England area was rewarded by a penalty for a crude tackle and Wales salvaged a point through never giving up and doggedly keeping England to their single goal.

This brought a thrilling last day as the Welsh beat Ireland 3-0 in a game which strangely kicked off before the England fixture, so the hosts knew they had to win by three goals to retain the championship. The Scottish side is, for some reason, only selected from East of Scotland League and Highland League players, but, wherever they come from the boys in blue from over the border take great pleasure in depriving England of success and this they did by keeping the score down to a 0-2 defeat. Once again England created plenty of chances and played well but full marks to the battling Welsh side who scored six goals in their three games, were undefeated and won the tournament for the third time in five years.

Full marks go to manager Andy Beattie and his colleagues and how sad it was that he resigned after criticism from the Welsh F.A. for not picking more players from the Welsh leagues.

The competition rounds the season off very well and gives a chance to the four national associations to honour their star players at their respective levels. In England's case the spirit and tactics were topped up successfully as the manager's exciting squad look forward to a season when they could win the European Challenge Trophy for the first time. Good luck to them in their home tie against Belgium at Burton Albion's impressive new Pirelli Stadium on 29th November.   T.W.

The England squad before their Four Nations Tournament decider against Wales. Photo: Keith Clayton.

ENGLAND'S MATCHES

DATE	OPP.	COMP	VENUE	RESULT		GOALSCORERS	ATT.
15.11.05	Belgium	ECT	A	W	2-0	Bishop 18, Carey 66	
15.02.06	Italy	ECT	H	W	3-1	Bishop 4, Blackburn 78, Mackail-Smith 85	
23.05.06	Rep. Ireland	FNT	H	W	2-0	Carr 74, Oli 82	824
25.05.06	Wales	FNT	H	D	1-1	Richards 29	1,024
27.05.06	Scotland	FNT	H	W	2-0	Richards 75, Mackail-Smith 90	2,036

ECT - European Challenge Trophy. FNT - Four Nations Tournament.

THE PLAYERS OF 2005-06

NAME		CLUB	PREVIOUS CAPS
Austin	Ryan	Burton Albion	
Baker	Carl	Southport	
Bishop	Andrew	York City	2
Blackburn	Chris	Morecambe	3
Blackett	Shane	Dagenham & Redbridge	
Boyd	George	Stevenage Borough	
Bridges	David	Cambridge United	
Brown	Aaron	Tamworth	
Carey-Bertram	Daniel	Hereford United	
Carr	Michael	Northwich Victoria	
Charnock	Kieron	Northwich Victoria	2
Craney	Ian	Accrington Stanley	3
Henry	Ronnie	Stevenage Borough	
Jalal	Shwan	Woking FC	1
Jones	Billy	Exeter City	
Jones	Paul	Exeter City	
Kempson	Darran	Morecambe	
Mackail-Smith	Craig	Dagenham & Redbridge	2
McLean	Aaron	Grays Athletic	
Mkandawire	Tamika	Hereford United	
Nutter	John	Grays Athletic	
Oli	Dennis	Grays Athletic	
Perkins	David	Morecambe	7
Richards	Justin	Woking	
Roberts	Gary	Accrington Stanley	
Robinson	Ryan	Morecambe	
Shaw	Jon	Burton Albion	
Slabber	Jamie	Grays Athletic	
Southam	Glen	Dagenham & Redbridge	7
Thurgood	Stuart	Grays Athletic	2
Travis	Simon	Hereford United	3
Wales	Steve	Yeading	

2005-06

ROBINSON	MKANDAWIRE	CHARNOCK	PERKINS	OLI	CRANEY	WALES	CARR	BOYD	BISHOP	SLABBER	JONES (B)	BROWN	CAREY-BERTRAM	MACKAIL-SMITH	JONES (P)	JALAL	BLACKBURN	BAKER	BRIDGES	SHAW	ROBERTS	AUSTIN	TRAVIS	KEMPSON	NUTTER	BLACKETT	THURGOOD	MCLEAN	RICHARDS	HENRY	SOUTHAM
x	x	x	x	x	x	x	x	x	x	x	x1	s	s	s1	s	s															
	x	x	x		x		x3	x	x5						s1	s4	x4	x	x1	s3	x2	s2	s5								
		x		x	x1		s1	x							s3	s	x				s2		x	x	x4	s4	x	x3	x2	s	s
		x		x	x3		s3	x							s1	s	x				s2		x	x	x	s	x	x2	x1	s	s
		x		x	s		x	x							s3	s	x				s4		x	s	x	s2	x	x	s1	x	x

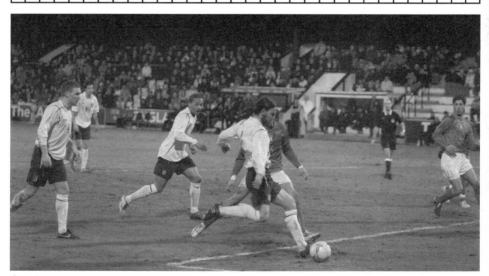

Chris Blackburn scores England's second goal against Italy in the European Challenge Cup tie played at Cambridge United. Photo: Keith Clayton.

FOUR NATIONS TOURNAMENT

FINAL TABLE	P	W	D	L	F	A	Pts	GD
WALES	3	2	1	0	6	2	7	4
ENGLAND	3	2	1	0	5	1	7	4
SCOTLAND	3	1	0	2	3	5	3	-2
REPUBLIC OF IRELAND	3	0	0	3	1	7	0	-6

OTHER RESULTS

Scotland	1	-	2	Wales
Republic of Ireland	1	-	2	scotland
Republic of Ireland	0	-	3	wales

FOUR NATIONS ACTION

Michael Carr takes on the Scottish defence (left), whilst below Aaron McClean sets himself to cross the ball in the same tie.

Above, Darren Jones (Wales) keeps his eye on the ball as England's George Boyd attacks down the wing. Right, England's Darran Kempson keeps close to Wales number 18, Moore, as he shapes up to cross the ball.

Photos: Keith Clayton.

ENGLAND'S RESULTS 1979 - 2006

BELGIUM
11.02.03	KV Ostend	1 - 3
04.11.03	Darlington	2 - 2
15.11.05	FC Racing Jets	2 - 0

FINLAND UNDER-21
14.04.93	Woking	1 - 3
30.05.94	Aanekoski	0 - 2

GIBRALTAR
27.04.82	Gibraltar	3 - 2
31.05.95	Gibraltar	3 - 2

HOLLAND
03.06.79	Stafford	1 - 0
07.06.80	Zeist	2 - 1
09.06.81	Lucca	2 - 0
03.06.82	Aberdeen	1 - 0
02.06.83	Scarborough	6 - 0
05.06.84	Palma	3 - 3
13.06.85	Vleuten	3 - 0
20.05.87	Kircaldy	4 - 0
11.04.95	Aalsmeer	0 - 0
02.04.96	Irthlingborough	3 - 1
18.04.97	Appingedam	0 - 0
03.03.98	Crawley	2 - 1
30.03.99	Genemuiden	1 - 1
21.03.00	Northwich	1 - 0
22.03.01	Wihemina FC	3 - 0
24.04.02	Yeovil Town	1 - 0
25.03.03	BV Sparta 25	0 - 0
16.02.05	Woking	3 - 0

IRAQ
27.05.04	Macclesfield	1 - 5

ITALY
03.06.80	Zeist	2 - 0
13.06.81	Montecatini	1 - 1
01.06.82	Aberdeen	0 - 0
31.05.83	Scarborough	2 - 0
09.06.84	Reggio Emilia	0 - 1
11.06.85	Houten	2 - 2
18.05.87	Dunfermline	1 - 2
29.01.89	La Spezia	1 - 1
25.02.90	Solerno	0 - 2
05.03.91	Kettering	0 - 0
01.03.99	Hayes	4 - 1
01.03.00	Padova	1 - 1
20.11.02	AC Cremonese	3 - 2
11.02.04	Shrewsbury	1 - 4
10.11.04	US Ivrea FC	1 - 0
15.02.06	Cambridge United	3 - 1

NORWAY UNDER-21
01.06.94	Slemmestad	1 - 2

REPUBLIC OF IRELAND
24.05.86	Kidderminster	2 - 1
26.05.86	Nuneaton	2 - 1
25.05.90	Dublin	2 - 1
27.05.90	Cork	3 - 0
27.02.96	Kidderminster	4 - 0
25.02.97	Dublin	0 - 2
16.05.02	Boston	1 - 2
20.05.03	Merthyr Tydfil	4 - 0
18.05.004	Deverondale	2 - 3
24.05.05	Cork	1 - 0
23.05.06	Eastbourne Boro'	2 - 0

SCOTLAND
31.05.79	Stafford	5 - 1
05.06.80	Zeist	2 - 4
11.06.81	Empoli	0 - 0
05.06.82	Aberdeen	1 - 1
04.06.83	Scarborough	2 - 1
07.06.84	Modena	2 - 0
15.06.85	Harderwijk	1 - 3
23.05.87	Dunfermline	2 - 1
18.05.02	Kettering	2 - 0
24.05.03	Carmarthen Town	0 - 0
23.05.04	Deverondale	3 - 1
28.05.05	Cork	3 - 2
27.05.06	Eastbourne Boro'	2 - 0

USA
20.03.02	Stevenage Boro.	2 - 1
09.06.04	Charleston USA	0 - 0

WALES
27.03.84	Newtown	1 - 2
26.03.85	Telford	1 - 0
18.03.86	Merthyr Tydfil	1 - 3
17.03.87	Gloucester	2 - 2
15.03.88	Rhyl	2 - 0
21.03.89	Kidderminster	2 - 0
06.03.90	Merthyr Tydfil	0 - 0
17.05.91	Stafford	1 - 2
03.03.92	Aberystwyth	1 - 0
02.03.93	Cheltenham	2 - 1
22.02.94	Bangor	2 - 1
28.02.95	Yeovil Town	1 - 0
23.05.99	St Albans	2 - 1
16.05.00	Llanelli	1 - 1
13.02.01	Rushden & Dia.	0 - 0
14.05.02	Boston	1 - 1
22.05.03	Merthyr Tydfil	2 - 0
20.05.04	Keith FC	0 - 2
26.05.05	Cork	1 - 0
25.05.06	Eastbourne Boro'	1 - 1

RESULTS SUMMARY 1979 - 2006	P	W	D	L	F	A
Belgium	3	1	1	1	5	5
Finland Under-21	2	0	0	2	1	5
Gibraltar	2	2	0	0	6	4
Holland	18	13	5	0	36	7
Iraq	1	0	0	1	1	5
Italy	16	5	6	4	21	19
Norway Under-21	1	0	0	1	1	2
Republic of Ireland	11	8	0	3	23	10
Scotland	13	8	3	2	26	15
USA	2	1	1	0	2	1
Wales	20	10	6	4	24	17
TOTAL RECORD	**89**	**48**	**22**	**19**	**146**	**90**

MANAGERS 1979 - 2006

		P	W	D	L	F	A
1979	Howard Wilkinson	2	2	0	0	6	1
1980 - 1984	Keith Wright	17	9	5	3	30	16
1985 - 1988	Kevin Verity	12	7	2	3	23	15
1989 - 1996	Tony Jennings	19	10	4	5	27	18
1997	Ron Reid	2	0	1	1	0	2
1998 - 2002	John Owens	14	8	5	1	22	10
2002 -	Paul Fairclough	23	12	5	6	38	28

GOALSCORERS 1979 - 2006

13 GOALS...
Carter

6 GOALS...
Ashford

5 GOALS...
Davison
C. Williams

4 GOALS...
Culpin
D'Sane, Roscoe
Johnson

3 GOALS...
Adamson
Guinan, Steve
Grayson
Hatch, Liam
Kirk Jackson
Mackhail-Smith, Craig
Opponents
Watkins

2 GOALS...
Alford, Carl
Barrett
Bishop, Andrew
Casey
Cordice
Elding, Anthony

2 goals continued....
Hayles
Hill
Howell
Mutrie
Patmore, Warren
Richards, Justin
Watson, J
Weatherstone, Simon
Whitbread

1 GOAL...
Agana
Anderson, Dale
Blackburn, Chris
Boardman, Jon
Bolton
Bradshaw
Browne
Carey-Bertram, Daniel
Carr, Michael
Cavell
Charles
Charley, Ken
Crittenden, Nick
Davies
Drummond, Stewart
Furlong, Paul
Hines
Humphreys
Kennedy, John
Kerr, Scott

Kimmins
King, Simon
Leworthy
McDougald
Mayes
Moore, Neil
O'Keefe
Oli, Dennis
Pitcher
Ricketts, Sam
Robbins
Robinson
Roddis
Rodgers, Luke
Rogers
Ryan, Tim
Sellars
Sheldon, Gareth
Sinclair, Dean
Smith, I.
Smith, O.
Southam, Glen
Stansfield, Adam
Stephens
Stott
S. Taylor
Thurgood, Stuart
Venables
Way, Darren
Webb
Wilcox

MOST CAPPED PLAYER

	Club	Caps	Seasons
John Davison	Altrincham	24	1979 - 1986

FULL INTERNATIONAL HONOURS

To date three players have played for England at both Full International and Semi-Professional levels.

Peter Taylor	Full: 1976	SPro: 1984	whilst at Maidstone United
Alan Smith	Full: 1988	SPro: 1982	whilst at Alvechurch
Steve Guppy	Full: 1999	SPro: 1993	whilst at Wycombe Wanderers

ENGLAND SEMI-PRO CAPS 1979 - 2006

KEY TO COUNTRY CODES:
B - Belgium E - Eire F - Finland G - Gibraltar
H - Holland I - Italy IQ - Iraq N - Norway
S - Scotland W - Wales US - U.S.A.

Players capped for the first time
during season 2005-06 are shown in bold.

Gary Abbott (Welling) **87** v I(s), S(s), **92** W(s)	3
David Adamson (Boston Utd) **79 v** S, H **80** v I,S, H	5
Tony Agana (Weymouth) **86** v E	1
Junior Agogo (Barnet) **03** v H, i (s), S	3
Carl Alford (Kettering T. & Rushden & Ds) **96** v E,H	2
Dale Anderson (Burton Albion) **02** v H **03** v I	2
Mark Angel (Boston United) **02** v W(s), E, S	3
Ian Arnold (Kettering Town) **95** v W(s), H	2
Jim Arnold (Stafford Rangers) **79** v S, H	2
Nick Ashby (Kettering & Rushden & Diamonds)	
94 v F, N, **95** v G **96** v E, H	5
Noel Ashford (Enfield & Redbridge Forest.)	
82 **v** G,H,S. **83 v** I,H,S, **84** W,H,S,I, **85** W,I(s), **86** E,E,	
87 W(s), I,H,S. **90** v W,E **91** I(s)	21
John Askey (Macclesfield) **90** v W	1
Ryan Austin (Burton Albion) **06** v I	1
Danny Bacon **04** v IQ	1
Carl Baker (Southport) **06** v I	1
Matt Baker (Hereford United) **03** v I, S, **04** E,S,IQ,US	6
Nicky Bailey (Barnet) **05** v H, E, S, W.	4
Paul Bancroft (Kidderminster H.) **89** v I,W **90** I,W.E, **91** v W	6
Chris Banks (Cheltenham T.) **98** v H, 99 W	2
Keith Barrett (Enfield) **81** v H,S,I **82** v G,I,H,S **83** v I,H,S	
84 v W(s), H, S **85** I,H,S	16
Laurence Batty (Woking) **93** v F(s), **95** v W,H,G	4
Mark Beeney (Maidstone) **89** v I(s)	1
Paul Beesley (Chester C.) **01** v H(s)	1
Dean Bennett (Kidderminster H) **00** v W(s)	1
Graham Benstead (Kettering) **94** v W,F,N(s)	3
Kevin Betsy (Woking) **98** v H(s)	1
Marcus Bignot (Kidderminster H) **97** v H	1
Andy Bishop (York City) **05** v I,H. **06** v B,I.	4
James Bittner (Exeter City) **04** v B,I	2
Chris Blackburn (Chester C. & Morecambe) **03** v I. **05** v I,H. **06** v I.	4
Shane Blackett (Dagenham & Red). **06** v E,S.	2
Greg Blundell (Northwich Victoria) **03** v H	1
Jon Boardman (Woking) **03** v I, S. **04** I,W,US	5
Jimmy Bolton (Kingstonian) **95** v G	1
Steve Book (Cheltenham Town) 99 **v** I,H,W	3
George Boyd (Stevenage Boro') **06** v B,I,E,W,S.	5
Lee Boylan (Canvey Island) **04** v US	1
Gary Brabin (Runcorn) **94 v** W,F,N	3

Mark Bradshaw (Halifax T.) **98** v H	1
Leon Braithwaite (Margate) **02 v** US	1
Colin Brazier (Kidderminster) **87** v W	1
David Bridges (Cambridge Utd) **06** v I	1
Stewart Brighton (Bromsgrove) **94** v W	1
Steve Brooks (Cheltenham) **88** v W(s) **90** v W,E	3
Derek Brown (Woking) **94 v** F(s,N	2
Kevan Brown (Woking) **95** v W,H,G **96** v H **97** v E	5
Wayne Brown (Chester C.) **01** v W, H(s), **02** v US, H(s),W,S.	
03 v H	7
Corey Browne (Dover) **94** v F(s),N(s), **95** v H(s)	3
David Buchanan (Blyth) **86** v E(s,E	2
Nicki Bull (Aldershot Town) **03** v B. **04** v I, H, E.	4
Brian Butler (Northwich) **93** v F	1
Steve Butler (Maidstone) **88** v W, **89 v** I,W	3
Gary Butterworth (Rushden & Diamonds)	
97 v E,H **98** v H 99 v I,H,W 00 v I	7
Chris Byrne (Macclesfield T.) **97** v H	1
DJ Campbell (Yeading) **05** v E, S.	2
Daniel Carey-Bertram (Hereford Utd) **06** v B	1
Danny Carlton (Morecambe) **04** v IQ	1
Michael Carr (Northwich) **06** v B,I,E,W,S.	5
Mark Carter (Runcorn & Barnet) v	
87 v W,I,H,S **88** v W, **89 v** I,W, **90** v I,E, **91** v I,W(s)	11
Kim Casey (Kidderminster) **86** v W,E,E(s), **87 v** W,I	5
Paul Cavell (Redbridge) **92** v W **93** v F	2
Peter Cavanagh (Accrington) **04** v B,I,E	3
Jon Challinor (Aldershot Town) **04** v B,I	2
Lee Charles (Hayes) 99 v I(s), H(s), W(s)	3
Anthony Charles (Aldershot/Farnborough) **04** v B,I	2
Kevin Charlton (Telford) **85** v W,I	2
Ken Charlery (Boston U) **01** vH(s)	1
Kieran Charnock (Northwich) **05** v E,W. **06** v B,I,E,W,S.	7
Andrew Clarke (Barnet) **90** v E,E	2
David Clarke (Blyth Spartans) **80** v I,S(s),H, **81** v H,S,I	
82 v I,H,S **83** v H,S **84** v H,S,I	14
Gary Clayton (Burton) **86** v E	1
Robert Codner (Barnet) **88** v W	1
John Coleman (Morecambe) **93** v F(s)	1
Darren Collins (Enfield) **93** v F(s), **94** v W,F,N	4
Matt Collins (Nuneaton Borough) **04** v I	1
Andy Comyn (Hednesford T.) **98** **v** H(s), 99 v I(s),H(s),W(s)	4
Steve Conner (Dartford, Redbridge & Dagenham & R)	
90 v I **91** v I,W **92** v W **93** v F	5
David Constantine (Altrincham) **85** v I,H,S **86 v** W	4
Robbie Cooke (Kettering) **89** v W(s), **90** v I	2
Scott Cooksey (Hednesford T.) **97** v E, **98** vH(s), **01 v** W(s),H	4
Alan Cordice(Wealdstone)**83** v I,H,S **84** vW,S(s), I(s),**85** I,H,S	9

Rob Cousins (Yeovil Town) **00 I v** I(s),H,W — 3

Gavin Cowan (Canvey Island) **04** v B,IQ — 2

Ken Cramman (Gateshead & Rushden & Diamonds)
96 v E **97** v E,H — 3

Ian Craney (Altrincham & Accrington) **03** v B. **04** US. **05** I.
06 v B,I,E,W. — 7

Nick Crittendon (Yeovil Town) **02** v US (s) — 1

Paul Cuddy (Altrincham) **87** v I,H,S — 3

Paul Culpin (Nuneaton B) **84** v W, **85** v W(s) ,I,H,S — 5

Michael Danzey (Woking) **99** v I,H — 2

Paul Davies (Kidderminster H.)
86 v W, **87** v W,I,S, **88** v W **89** v W — 6

John Davison (Altrincham)
79 v S,H **80** v I,S, **81** v H,S ,I **82** v G,I,H,S **83** I,H,S
84 W,H,I,S **85** v I,H,S **86** v W,E,E — 24

John Denham (Northwich Victoria) **80** v H — 1

Peter Densmore (Runcorn) **88** v W **89** v I — 2

Phil Derbyshire (Mossley) **83** v H(s) S(s) — 2

Mick Doherty (Weymouth) **86** v W(s) — 1

Neil Doherty (Kidderminster H.) **97** v E — 1

Stuart Drummond (Morecambe) **00** v I(s),H ,W **01 v** W ,H
02 v US, W,E(s), S **03** v H, I, W, S (s) — 13

Roscoe D'Sane (Aldershot Town) **03** v B(s),H(s),E,W.S. **04** B,I 7

Chris Duffy (Canvey Island) **03** v B — 1
Neil Durkin (Leigh RMI) **02** v H(s) — 1

Lee Elam (Morecambe) **03** v H,E,W,S)s) — 4

Anthony Elding (Stevenage Borough) **04** v B. **05** v I,H,E,W,S. 6

Paul Ellender (Scarborough) **01** v W(s) — 1

Lee Endersby (Harrow Bor.) **96 v** H — 1

Mick Farrelly (Altrincham) **87** v I,H,S — 3

Steve Farrelly (Macclesfield & Kingstonian)
95 v H(s),G(s), **00** v I,H,W(s) — 5

Trevor Finnegan (Weymouth) **81** v H,S — 2

Murray Fishlock (Yeovil Town) **99** v H(s) — 1

Amos Foyewa (Woking) **04** v E,W,S — 3

Richard Forsyth (Kidderminster) **95** v W,H,G — 3

Ian Foster (Kidderminster H) **00** v W(s) — 1

Paul Furlong (Enfield) **90 v** I,E,E **91** v I,W — 5

Mark Gardiner (Macclesfield T.) **97** v E — 1

Jerry Gill (Yeovil T.) **97** v E — 1

Matt Glennon (Carlisle Utd) **05** v W,S. — 2

John Glover (Maidstone Utd) **85** v W,I,H,S — 4

Mark Golley (Sutton Utd.)
87 v H(s),S, **88** v W, **89** v I,W, **92** v W — 6

Jason Goodliffe (Hayes) **00** v I, H,W, **01** W **02** US, W,E,S. 8

Paul Gothard (Dagenham & Redb.)
97 v E(s), **99** v I(s),W(s) — 3

Mark Gower (Barnet) **02** v H, W, E, S(s) — 4

Simon Grand (Carlisle) **05** v H. — 1

Neil Grayson (Cheltenham T.) **98** v H **99** v I,H,W — 4

Phil Gridelet (Hendon & Barnet) **89** v I,W, **90** v W,E,E — 5

Steve Guinan (Hereford) **04** v E,W,S,US — 4

Steve Guppy (Wycombe W.) **93** v W — 1

Scott Guyett (Southport) **01** v H, **03** v H,I,W,S. — 5

Tim Hambley (Havant & Waterlooville) **02** v H — 1

Steve Hanlon (Macclesfield) **90** v W — 1

David Harlow (Farnborough T.) **97** v E(s),H — 2

Stephen Haslam (Halifax) **05** v E,W,S. — 3

Liam Hatch (Barnet) **04** v E,W,S,IQ,US. **05** H. — 6

Wayne Hatswell (Chester City) **03** v E(s),W(s), —

Karl Hawley (Carlisle Utd) **05** v I,H. — 2

Barry Hayles (Stevenage Bor.) **96** v E,H — 2

Greg Heald (Barnet) **02** v H — 1

Brian Healy (Morecambe) **98** v H — 1

Ronnie Henry (Stevenage Boro) **06** v S. — 1

Tony Hemmings (Northwich) **93** v F — 1

Andy Hessenthaler (Dartford) **90** v I — 1

Kenny Hill (Maidstone Utd) **80** v I,S,H — 3

Mark Hine (Gateshead) **95** v W(s),H — 2

Simeon Hodson (Kidderminster) **94** v W,F,N — 3

Lewis Hogg (Barnet) **04** v B — 1

Colin Hogarth (Guiseley) **95 v** W,H — 2

Steven Holden (Kettering) **94** v W,F,N(s) **95** v H,G — 5

Mark Hone (Welling United) **90** v I **93** v F, **94** vW(s),F(s),N 5

Gary Hooley (Frickley) **85** v W — 1

Dean Hooper (Kingstonian) **98** v H — 1

Keith Houghton (Blyth Spartans) **79** v S — 1

Barry Howard (Altrincham) **81** v H,S,I **82** v G,I,H,S — 7

Neil Howarth (Macclesfield) **95** v H(s) **97** v E — 2

David Howell (Enfield) **85** v H(s),S(s) **86** v W,E **87** v W,I,H,S
88 v W, **89** v I,W **90** v I,E,E — 14

Lee Howells (Cheltenham T.) **98** v H **99 v** W — 2
Lee Hughes (Kidderminster Harriers) **96** v E,H **97** v E,H — 4

Delwyn Humphreys (Kidderminster H.)
91 v W(s) **92** v W **94** v W,F,N **95** v W,H — 7

Steve Humphries (Barnet) **87** v H(s) — 1

Nicky Ironton (Enfield) **83** H(s) **84** v W — 2

Jimmy Jackson (Gravesend & Northfleet) 03 v H(s) — 1

Simon Jackson (Woking) **05** v I. — 1

Justin Jackson (Morecambe & Rushden & Diamonds)
00 v W **01** v W — 2

Kirk Jackson (Stevenage Borough) **02** v US, E,S,(Yeovil Town)
03 v E,W,S(s) — 6

Shwan Jalal (Woking) **05** v H. **06** v I,E,W,S. — 5

Mark Janney (Dagenham & Redbridge) **03** v H — 1

Tony Jennings (Enfield)
79 v S,H **80** v I,S,H **81 v** H,S,I **82** v G,I,H,S — 12

Jeff Johnson (Altrincham) **81** v S,I **82** v G,I,H,S **83** v I,H,S
84 v H,S,I **84 v** I,H,S **86** v W(s),E,E — 18

Lee Johnson (Yeovil Town) **03** v I, H(s), E, W, S — 5

Paul Jones (Exeter City) **06** v I — 1

Steve Jones (Leigh RMI) **01** v H — 1

Tom Jones (Weymouth) **87** v W — 1

Tom Jordan (Tamworth) **04** v B — 1

Antone Joseph(Telford U. & Kidderm'terH.)**84** v S(s), **85** v W,I,
H,S **86** v W(s), **87** W,I(s),H, **88** v W **89** v I,W **90 v** I,E,E — 15

John Keeling (Purfleet) **03** v B(s) — 1

Darran Kempson (Morecambe) **06** v E,W. — 2

John Kennedy (Canvey Island) **03** v I, B, H, E, W. S. **04** IQ,US 8

Jon Kennedy (Accrington) **04** v I,IQ,US — 3

Andy Kerr (Wycombe) **93** v W — 1

Scott Kerr (Scarborough) **04** v E,W,S,IQ. **05** v I,H,E,W,S — 9

Lance Key (Kingstonian) 03 v B — 1

Ged Kimmins (Hyde Utd.) **96** v E(s),H(s) **97 v** E(s) — 3

Simon King (Barnet) **05** v I,H,S. — 3

Mike Lake (Macclesfield) **89** v I — 1

Martin Lancaster (Chester City) **03** vI (s)

Andy Lee (Telford U. & Witton A.) **89** I(s), **91** v I,W — 3

David Leworthy (Farnborough & Rushden & Diamonds)
93 v W, **94** v W **97** v E,H — 4

Adam Lockwood (Yeovil Town) **02** v E **03** v I — 2

,Kenny Lowe (Barnet) **91 v** I,W — 2

Craig McAllister (Basingstoke Town) **03** v B — 1

Martin McDonald (Macclesfield) **95** v G(s) — 1

Danny McDonnell (Worcester City) **04** v W — 1

Junior MacDougald (Dagenham & Redbridge) 01 v H(s) — 1
02 W, E(s), S(s) — 4

Mark McGregor (Forest Green Rovers & Nuneaton Borough)
00 v I(s),H(s) **01** v W(s) — 3

Kevin McIntyre (Doncaster Rovers) **00 v** H(s)W, **01 v** W(s)H — 4

John McKenna (Boston Utd)
88 v W(s), **90** v I,E,E **91 v** I,W, **92** vW — 7

Aaron McLean (Aldershot & Grays) **04** v B,I. **06** v E,W,S. — 5

David McNiven (Leigh RMI) **04** v W,S,IQ,US — 4

Craig Mackhail-Smith (Dag. & Red.) **05** v W,S. **06** v I,E,W,S. — 6

Tamika Mkandawire (Hereford Utd) **06** v B,I. — 2

Fiston Manuella (Aylesbury United) 03 v B — 1

John Margerrison (Barnet) **87 v** W — 1

Simon Marples (Doncaster Rovers) **00 v** I,H — 2

Leroy May (Stafford R.) **95 v** G(s) — 1

Bobby Mayes (Redbridge) **92 v** W — 1

Paul Mayman (Northwich Vic) **80 v** I,S — 2

Stewart Mell (Burton) **85v** W — 1

Neil Merrick (Weymouth) **80** v I(s),S — 2

Adam Miller (Aldershot Town) **04** v I — 1

Russell Milton (Dover) 94 v F,N — 2

Trevor Morley (Nuneaton) **84 v** W,H,S,I **85 v** W,S(s) — 6

Neil Moore (Telford United) **02** v US (s),H, W, E,S — 5

Dean Moxey (Exeter City) **05** v H. — 1

Chris Murphy (Telford United) **04** v B — 1

Karl Murrphy (Woking) **04** v B,I — 2

Tarkan Mustafa (Rushden & Diamonds) **01** v W,H — 2

Les Mutrie (Blyth Spartans) **79 v** S,H, **80** v I,S,H — 3

Mark Newson (Maidstone U) **84 v** W,H,S,I, **85** v W — 5

Doug Newton (Burton) **85** v W,H,S — 3

Paul Nicol (Kettering T) **91 v** I,W, **92** v W — 3

Richard Norris (Northwich Victoria) **03** v H, S, — 2

Steve Norris (Telford) **88** v W(s) — 1

John Nutter (Grays) **06** v E,W,S. — 3

Joe O'Connor (Hednesford T.) **97 v** E,H(s) — 2

Eamon O'Keefe (Mossley) **79 v** S,H — 2

Dennis Oli (Grays) **06** v B,E,W,S. — 4

Luke Oliver (Woking) **05** v H. — 1

Frank Ovard (Maidstone) **81** v H(s),S(s),I(s) — 3

Andy Pape (Harrow Bor. & Enfield) **85** v W(s,)H,S,
86 v W(s),E, **87** v W,I,H,S **88** v W, **89** IW, **90** I,W,E — 15

Brian Parker (Yeovil Town) **80 v** S — 1

Warren Patmore (Yeovil Town) **99** v I,H,W, **00 v** I,H, **01** W,H — 7

Gary Patterson (Kingstonian) **99** v I,H, **00** v H,W, **01 v** W,H — 7

Steve Payne (Macclesfield T.) **97 v** H — 1

Trevor Peake (Nuneaton Bor) **79** v S,H — 2

David Pearce (Harrow Bor) **84 v** I(s) — 1

David Perkins (Morecambe) **04** v B,I,E,S,IQ,US. **05** v I. **06** v B,I.9

Warren Peyton (Nuneaton Borough) **02** v H(s) **03** v I — 2

Brendan Phillips (Nuneaton Bor. & Kettering T.),
79 v S,H, **80 v** S(s),H — 4

Gary Philips (Barnet) **82 v** G — 1

Owen Pickard (Yeovil T.) **98** v H(s) — 1

Geoff Pitcher (Kingstonian) **99** v W, **00 v** I,H,W, **01** v W,H — 6

Phil Power (Macclesfield T.) **96** v E(s),H(s) — 2

Ryan Price (Stafford R. & Macclesfield)
92 v W(s) **93** v W,F **96** v E,H **97 v** H — 6

Steve Prindiville **98** v H(s) — 1

Andy Proctor (Accrington Stanley) **04** v IQ — 1

Marc Pullan (Crawley Town) **03** v B — 1

Robert Purdie (Hereford United) **04** v I. **05** v I. — 2

Wayne Purser (Barnet) **03** v I — 1

Mark Quayle (Telford United) **02** v H — 1

Simon Read (Farnborough) **92** v W(s) — 1

Matt Redmile (Barnet) **04** v E,W,S — 3

Andy Reid (Altrincham) **95 v** W — 1

Carl Richards (Enfield) **86 v** E — 1

Justin Richards (Woking) **06** v E,W,S. — 3

Derek Richardson (Maidstone U) **83 v** I, **84 v** W, **86** v E — 4

Ian Richardson (Dagenham & Red) **95** v G — 1

Kevin Richardson (Bromsgrove) **94** v W,F,N — 3

Paul Richardson (Redbridge) **92** v W, **93 v** W, F — 3

Scott Rickards (Tamworth) **03** v B. **04** B — 2

Sam Ricketts (Telford) **04** v B,E,W,S — 4

Adriano Rigoglioso (Morecambe) **03** v H(s) — 1

Anthony Rivierre (Welling United) **03** v B — 1

Terry Robbins (Welling) **92** v W, **93** v W,F, **94** v W,F,N — 6

Gary Roberts (Accrington) **06** v I,E,W,S. — 4

Mark Robinson (Hereford) **05** v E,W,S. — 3

Peter Robinson (Blyth S) **83** v I,H,S **84** W,I **85** v W — 6

Ryan Robinson (Morecambe) **06** v B. — 1

Nick Roddis (Woking) **01** v H **02** US,H,W,E(s),S — 6

Luke Rodgers (Shrewsbury) **04** v B,I. — 2

John Rogers (Altrincham) **81 v** H,S,I **82 v** I(s),S — 5

Paul Rogers (Sutton) **89** v W, **90** v I, E(2), **91** I,W — 6

Colin Rose (Witton Alb.) **96 v** E(s), H — 2

Kevin Rose (Kidderminster) **94 v** F(s),N — 2

Michael Rose (Hereford United) **03** v I, H, E, S — 4

Brian Ross (Marine) **93** v W(s),F(s), **94** v W(s) **95 v** W,H — 5

Carl Ruffer (Chester City) **01** v H(s) — 1

Tim Ryan (Southport & Doncaster Rovers)
98 v H, **99** v I,H,W, **00** v I,H,W **01** v W,H **02** v US,H,W,I,S — 14

Jake Sedgemore (Shrewsbury) **04** v E,W,S,IQ,US. — 5

Neil Sellars (Scarboro) **81** v H,S,I **82** v G,H(s),S, **83 v** I,H,S 9

Mark Shail (Yeovil T.) **93** v W 1

Jon Shaw (Burton Albion) **06** v I. 1

Simon Shaw (Doncaster Rovers) **99** v I,H 2

Peter Shearer (Cheltenham) **89 v** I(s) 1

Gareth Sheldon (Exeter) **04** v I,E,W,S,IQ,US. 6

Paul Shirtliff (Frickley A. & Boston U.) **86** vE,E **87** v W,I,H **88** v W **89 v** I, W, **90** v I,W,E,E, **92 v** W **93** v W,F 15

Paul Showler (Altrincham) **91** v I(s),W 2

Tim Sills (Kingstonian) **03** v B 1

Gordon Simmonite (Boston United) **79** v S(s,)H(s), **80** v I,S,H 5

Gary Simpson(Stafford R.) **86** v E,E, **87** v I,H,S,**90** v I,W,E,E 9

Wayne Simpson (Stafford) **94** v F,N(s) 2

Dean Sinclair (Barnet) **05** v I,H,E,W,S. 5

Terry Skiverton (Yeovil Town) **01 v** W **02** v US **03** v !,W, 4

Glenn Skivington (Barrow) **90** v I,W,E **91** v I,W 5

Jamie Slabber (Grays) **06** v B. 1

Adrian Smith (Kidderminster H) **00** v I(s),H(s),W 3

Alan Smith (Alvechurch) **82** v G,I,S 3

Ian Smith (Mossley) **80** v I,S,H(s) 3

Mark Smith (Stevenage Bor.)
96 v E,H **98** v H **99** v I,H,W **00** v I,H,W(s) 9

Ossie Smith (Runcorn) **84** v W 1

Phil Smith (Margate) **04** v B 1

Tim Smithers (Nuneaton) **85** v W(s),I **86** v W 3

Adam Sollitt (Kettering Town) **00** v I(s),H(s),W 3

Glen Southam (Bishop's Stort' & Dag & R.) **04** v E,W,S,IQ,US.
05 v W.S. **06** v S. 8

Craig Stanley (Hereford) **05** v E,W. 2

Adam Stansfield (Yeovil Town & Hereford) **02** v W (s), I, S 5
05 v E.S.

Simon Stapleton (Wycombe) **93** v W 1

Mickey Stephens (Sutton), **82** v G,S(s) **86 v** W,E,E(s) 5

Billy Stewart (Southport) **98** v H 1

Mark Stimson (Canvey Islland) **02** v US 1

Bob Stockley (Nuneaton Borough) **80** v H 1

David Stockdale (York) **05** v I. 1

Darren Stride (Burton Albion) **02** v H 1

Steve Stott (Kettering T., Rushden & Ds & Yeovil T.)
95 v W,H(s),G **96** v E,H **99** v H,W(s) 7

Ryan Sugden (Chester City) **03** v I 1

Ben Surey (Gravesend & Nflt.) **05** v I. 1

Andy Taylor (Exeter City) **05** v E,W.S. 3

James Taylor (Havant & Waterlooville) **02** v H,W, E(s),S(s) 4

Peter Taylor (Maidstone) **84** v HSI 3

Steve Taylor (Bromsgrove R.) **95** v G 1

Shaun Teale (Weymouth) **88** v W 1

Paul Terry (Dagenham & Redbridge) **03** vE (s), W(s), S 3

Stuart Terry (Altrincham) **95** v W 1

Brian Thompson(Yeovil & Maidstone) **79** v S,H **81** v H,S,I
82 v I,H,S **83** v I,H,S **84** v W,H,S,I 15,

Neil Thompson (Scarborough) **87** v W,I,H,S 4

Garry Thompson (Morecambe) **03** v I. **04** v E,W,IQ,US 5

Steve Thompson (Wycombe) **93** v W 1

Stuart Thurgood (Grays Ath.) **05** v I,H. **06** v E,W,S. 5

Kevin Todd (Berwick Rangers) **91** v W 1

Mike Tomlinson (Runcorn F.C.Halton) **03** v B (s) 1

Anthony Tonkin (Yeovil Town) **02** v US 1

Simon Travis (Forest Green R & Hereford) **02** v US, H. **05** v E.
06 v E,W,S. 6

Andy Tretton (Hereford) **04** v E,W,S,US 4

Mark Tucker (Woking) **96** v E 1

Tony Turner (Telford) **85 v** W 1

Paul Underwood (Rushden & D) **99** v I,H **00** v I**01** v W 4

David Venables(Stevenage B)**94 v** W(s)**95 v** H,G**96 v** E,H(s) 5

Jamie Victory (Cheltenham T.) **98** vH(s) 1

Ashley Vickers (Dagenham & Redbridge) **04** v IQ 1

David Waite (Enfield) **82** v G 1

Steve Wales (Yeading) **06** v B. 1

Paul Walker (Blyth) **86 v** W,E,E(s), **87 v** S(s) 4

Steve Walters (Northwich Victoria) **97** v H 1

Mark Ward (Northwich Victoria) **83** v S(s) 1

Steve Ward (Canvey Island) **03** v B 1

Dale Watkins (Cheltenham T.) **98** v H **99** v I(s), **00** v I,H,W 5

John Watson (Wealdstone, Scarborough & Maidstone)
79 v S(s),H **80** v I,S,H **81** v H,S,I **82** v I,H,S **83** v I,H,S
84 v W(s),H,S,I 18

Steve Watson (Farnborough Town) **02** v US(s), W(s), S 3,

Liam Watson (Marine) **95** v W,H(s) 2

Paul Watts (Redbridge Forest) **89** v W **90** v I,E,E **91** v I
92 v W **93** v W,F 8

Darren Way (Yeovil Town) **03** vI (s), E, W 3

Chris Weale (Yeovil Town) **03** v I (s), H (s), E, W. 4

Simon Weatherstone (Boston United) **02** v W(s),E,S(s) 3

Paul Webb (Bromsgrove R & Kidderminster H)
93 v F **94** v W,F,N(s) **95** v W,H,G **96** v E,H **97** v E,H 11

Aaron Webster (Burton Albion) **02 v** H(s),W,S(s) **03** v I 3

Mark West (Wycombe W) **91** v W 1

Steve West (Woking) **01** v W(s) 1

Barry Whitbread (Runcorn & Altrincham) **79 v** S,H
80 v I,S,H, **81 v** I 6

Tristram Whitman (Doncaster Rovers) **03** v W(s), S 2

Russ Wilcox (Frickley) **86** v W,E 2

Adam Wilde (Worcester City) **03** v B 1

Barry Williams (Nuneaton Borough) **99** v H(s),W 2

Colin Williams (Scarborough & Telford Utd.)
81 v H, S **82** v I,H,S 5

Roger Willis (Barnet) **91** v I(s) 1

Paul Wilson (Frickley Athletic) **86** v W 1

Andy Woods (Scarborough) **02** v US,H(s),W,S. 4

Simon Wormull (Dover Athletic) **99** v I(s),W **02 v** W,E,S. 5

Mark Yates (Cheltenham Town) **99** v I, W 2

Ismail Yakubu (Barnet) **04** v I,US. **05** v I,E,W,S. 6

The FA CUP

e·on

2005/06

CLUB BY CLUB RECORDS

ABBEY HEY

North West Counties Division One (Step 5)

Ex. Prelim.	(A)	v Cheadle Town	L	2-3	61
			McKenzie, Watson		

Best Performance: Preliminary Round 2004-2005

ABINGDON TOWN

Hellenic League Premier Division (Step 5)

Ex. Prelim.	(A)	v Moneyfields FC	L	1-6	67
			Langford		

Best Performance: 4th Qualifying Round Replay 1992-93.

ABINGDON UNITED

Hellenic League Premier Division (Step 5)

Ex. Prelim.	(A)	v Thamesmead Town	W	4-2	38
			Curtin (3), Hooper		
Preliminary	(A)	v BAT Sports	W	3-0	54
			Curtin (2), Odihambo		
1st Qual.	(H)	v Dulwich Hamlet	D	1-1	102
			Odihambo		
1Q Replay	(A)	v Dulwich Hamlet	L	2-3	115
			Hamp, McCalmon		

Best Performance: 2nd Qualifying Round 2000-01.

ACCRINGTON STANLEY

Conference National (Step 1)

4th Qual.	(H)	v Worcester City	D	1-1	940
			Roberts		
4Q Replay	(A)	v Worcester City	L	2-3	1331
			Roberts, Welch		

Best Performance: 3rd Round Proper Replay 2003-04.

AFC HORNCHURCH

Essex (Step 5)

Prelim	(H)	v Chalfont St Peter	D	0-0	87
Replay	(A)	v Chalfont St Peter	W	2-1	
			Bull, Drake		
1st Qual	(H)	v Stansted	W	2-0	415
			Holland (2)		
2nd Qual	(H)	v Worthing	L	1-4	544
			Heale		

Best Performance: 2nd Qualifying Round 2005-2006

AFC NEWBURY

Wessex League Division One (Step 5)

Ex. Prelim.	(H)	v Farnham Town	D	2-2	95
			Bessey, Prior		
E.P. Replay	(A)	v Farnham Town	W	3-2	90
			Bessey, Huntley, Prior		
Preliminary	(A)	v Epsom & Ewell	L	1-6	81
			Taylor		

Best Performance: 3rd Qualifying Round.2004-2005.

AFC SUDBURY

Eastern Counties Premier Division (Step 5)

Preliminary	(A)	v Long Melford	W	1-0	448
			Owen		
1st Qual.	(A)	v Bedford Town	D	2-2	460
			Head, Noble		
1Q Replay	(H)	v Bedford Town	W	2-1	441
			Abrahams, Noble		
2nd Qual.	(A)	v Welwyn Garden City	L	2-4	304
			English, Hyde		

Best Performance: 1st Round Proper 2000-01.

AFC TELFORD UNITED

Northern Premier Premier Division (Step 3)

1st Qual.	(H)	v Rugby United	D	1-1	1065
			Reynolds		
1Q Replay	(A)	v Rugby United	W	3-2	265
			Charie, Reynolds (2)		
2nd Qual.	(A)	v Nuneaton Borough	L	1-3	1174

Best Performance: 2nd Qualifying Round 2005-06.
As Telford United: 5th Round 1984-1985

AFC TOTTON

Wessex League Division One (Step 5)

Ex. Prelim.	(H)	v Milton United	W	5-0	80
			Gosney (2), Hamodu,		
			Potter, West		
Preliminary	(A)	v Whitehawk	W	2-0	80
			Byers, Osman		
1st Qual.	(A)	v Lordswood	W	2-1	71
			Whitcher (2)		
2nd Qual.	(H)	v Paulton Rovers	W	2-1	107
			Gosney		

Ian Brown, the Bedford 'keeper, punches clear from another AFC Sudbury attack in the 1st Qualifying Round.
Photo: Peter Barnes.

AFC Totton continued...

3rd Qual.	(A)	v Bishop's Cleeve	D	1-1	187
			West		
3Q Replay	(H)	v Bishop's Cleeve	L	0-4	322

Best Performance: 4th Qualifying Round 1982-83.

AFC WIMBLEDON
Isthmian League Premier Division (Step 3)

1st Qual.	(H)	v Ashford Town (Mx)	D	2-2	1868
			Butler, Daly		
1Q Replay	(A)	v Ashford Town (Mx)	W	2-0	720
			Butler, Moore		
2nd Qual.	(H)	v Walton & Hersham	L	0-3	1930

Best Performance: 3rd Qualifying Round 2004-05.

ALDERSHOT TOWN
Conference National (Step 1)

4th Qual.	(A)	v Bromley	W	1-0	1454
			Sills		
1st Rnd P.	(A)	v Burnham	W	3-1	1623
			Been, Brough, Heald		
2nd Rnd P.	(H)	v Scunthorpe Utd	L	0-1	3584

Best Performance: 2nd Round Proper 1999-2000 & 2004-05.

ALFRETON TOWN
Conference North (Step 2)

2nd Qual.	(A)	v St Helens Town	W	2-0	142
			Stevenson (2)		
3rd Qual.	(H)	v Whitby Town	W	2-1	230
			Blunt, Stevenson		
4th Qual.	(A)	v Hereford United	D	0-0	1768
4Q Replay	(H)	v Hereford United	D	1-1*	740
Hereford won 3-4 on penalties.			Turner		

Best Performance: 1st Round Proper 3rd Replay 1969-70

ALMONDSBURY TOWN
Hellenic League Premier Division (Step 5)

Ex. Prelim.	(A)	v Minehead	W	2-1	49
			Daridge, Hobbs		
Preliminary	(H)	v Cinderford Town	L	3-5	64
			Berry, Daridge, Lott		

Best Performance: Preliminary Round.

ALNWICK TOWN
Northern League Division Two (Step 6)

Preliminary	(A)	v Cammell Laird	L	0-6	115

Best Performance: 3rd Qualifying Round 1951-52, 1957-58.

ALSAGER TOWN
North West Counties Division One (Step 5)

Ex. Prelim.	(A)	v Winsford United	D	1-1	99
			Mitchell		
Ex.P. Replay	(?)	v Winsford United	L	0-1	120

Best Performance: 1st Qualifying Round 2004-2005

ALTON TOWN
Wessex League Division One (Step 5)

Preliminary	(A)	v Banstead Athletic	L	0-1	37

Best Performance: 1st Round Proper 1972 -1973

ALTRINCHAM
Conference National (Step 1)

4th Qual.	(A)	v Tamworth	L	1-3	801

Best Performance: 4th Round Proper 1985-86.

ALVECHURCH
Midland Alliance (Step 5)

Ex. Prelim.	(A)	v Norton United	L	0-1	60

Best Performance: 3rd Round Proper 1973-1974

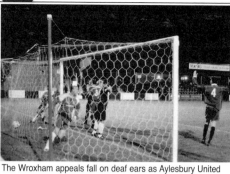

The Wroxham appeals fall on deaf ears as Aylesbury United score during their 3rd Qualifying Round tie.
Photo: Steve Ayre.

ANDOVER
Wessex League Division One (Step 5)

Ex. Prelim.	(H)	v Didcot Town	D	4-4	190
			Andrews (2), Asker, Bennett		
Ex.P. Replay	(A)	v Didcot Town	L	0-2	292

Best Performance: 1st Round Proper 1962-63.

ARLESEY TOWN
Southern League Division One East (Step 4)

Preliminary	(A)	v Marlow	W	3-2	88
			Finch, Gregson		
1st Qual.	(A)	v Heybridge Swifts	L	0-1	169

Best Performance: 4th Qualifying Round 2002-03.

ARMTHORPE WELFARE
Northern Counties East Premier Division (Step 5)

Preliminary	(A)	v Maine Road	W	2-0	40
			Soames (2)		
1st Qual.	(H)	v Mossley	W	3-1	94
			Buckthorp, Carchedi (2)		
2nd Qual.	(H)	v Rossendale United	L	0-2	110

Best Performance: 3rd Qualifying Round 1986-87.

ARNOLD TOWN
Northern Counties East Premier Division (Step 5)

Preliminary	(A)	v South Normanton Ath.	L	0-1	84

Best Performance: 1st Round 1977-78.

ARUNDEL
Sussex County League Division One (Step 5)

Prelim. Rd.	(A)	v Wick	D	1-1	155
Replay	(H)	v Wick	L	1-2	204
			Boxall		

Best Performance: 2nd Qualifying Round (5)

ASH UNITED
Combined Counties Premier Division (Step 5)

Ex. Prelim.	(A)	v Eastbourne United	W	2-1	68
			Bartley (2)		
Preliminary	(H)	v Leatherhead	D	1-1	111
			Smith		
Replay	(A)	v Leatherhead	L	2-3	235
			Bartley, Morris		

Best Performance: 2nd Qualifying Round 1998-99.

ASHFORD TOWN
Isthmian League Division One (Step 4)

Preliminary	(H)	v Slade Green	W	3-1	169
			Borman, Bradshaw, Thorogood		
1st Qual.	(H)	v Windsor & Eton	L	0-3	163

Best Performance: 2nd Round Proper 1961-62, 1966-67.

ASHFORD TOWN (MIDDX)

Southern League Divisio One West (Step 4)

Preliminary	(H)	v Whyteleafe	W 3-1	102
			Canning (2), Lake	
1st Qual.	(A)	v AFC Wimbledon	D 2-2	1868
			Breslin, Todd	
Replay	(H)	v AFC Wimbledon	L 0-2	720

Best Performance: 4th Qualifying Round 2004-05.

ASHINGTON

Northern League Division One (Step 5)

Ex. Prelim.	(A)	v Esh Winning	D 4-4	59
			Atkinson, Hogg (2), Lawrenson	
Replay	(H)	v Esh Winning	W 1-0	165
			Hogg	
Preliminary	(A)	v Pickering Town	D 2-2	228
			Rigg (2)	
Replay	(H)	v Pickering Town	L 1-2	282
			Rigg	

Best Performance: 3rd Round Proper 1926-27.

ASHTON UNITED

Northern Premier League Premier Division (Step 3)

1st Qual.	(A)	v Burscough	L 2-3	187
			Cornelly, Denham	

Best Performance: 1st Round Proper 1952-53.

ATHERTON COLLIERIES

North West Counties Division One (Step 5)

Preliminary	(A)	v Seaham Red Star	L 0-2	62

Best Performance: 3rd Qualifying Round 1994-1995

ATHERTON LR

North West Counties Division One (Step 5)

Preliminary	(H)	v Goole	D 1-1	86
			Bennett	
Replay	(A)	v Goole	L 0-2	193

Best Performance: 3rd Qualifying Round 1996-97.

AVELEY

Southern League Division One East (Step 4)

Preliminary	(H)	v Kingsbury Town	W 5-1	53
			Awuah, Brown, Paul (2)	
1st Qual.	(H)	v Burnham Ramblers	L 1-2	76
			Thomas	

Best Performance: 1st Round Proper 1970-71.

AYLESBURY UNITED

Southern League Premier Division (Step 3)

1st Qual.	(A)	v Northampton Spencer	W 2-1	208
			Edgeworth, McCafferty	
2nd Qual.	(A)	v Northwood	D 0-0	249
Replay	(H)	v Northwood	W 2-0	262
			Jaggard (2)	
3rd Qual.	(A)	v Wroxham	D 1-1	257
			Roberts	
Replay	(H)	v Wroxham	W 4-2	381
			Jaggard, Kearns, Roberts (2)	
4th Qual.	(H)	v Folkstone Invicta	L 0-2	646

Best Performance: 3rd Round Proper 1995.

AYLESBURY VALE

Spartan South Midlands Premier Division (Step 5)

Extra Prelim.Rd	(H)	v Kirkley	D 2-2	109
			Hawkins, Iannone	
Replay	(A)	v Kirkley	W 3-0	191
			Corbould, Hawkins, Talbot	
Prelim Round	(A)	v Welwyn Garden C	L 0-2	76

Best Performance: Preliminary Round 2005-2006

BACKWELL UNITED

Western League Premier Division (Step 5)

Preliminary	(A)	v Hamworthy United	L 0-4	122

Best Performance: 2nd Qualifying Round 1998-1999

BACUP BOROUGH

North West Counties Division One (Step 5)

Ex. Prelim.	(H)	v Pickering Town	L 0-5	60

Best Performance: 3rd Qualifying Round.

BAMBER BRIDGE

Northern Premier League Division One (Step 4)

Preliminary	(A)	v Cheadle Town	L 1-2	71
			Porter	

Best Performance: 2nd Round Proper Replay 1999-2000.

BANBURY UNITED

Southern League Premier Division (Step 3)

1st Qual.	(H)	v Kings Lynn	W 2-1	549
			Baird, Lamb	
2nd Qual.	(A)	v Brackley Town	D 1-1	680
			Gardner	
Replay	(H)	v Brackley Town	W 5-2	960
			Fuller (2), Gardner (2),	
			Gooderick	
3rd Qual.	(H)	v Hednesford Town	L 3-4	1005
			Baird (2), Gardner	

Best Performance: 1st Round Proper 1973-74.

BANSTEAD ATHLETIC

Isthmian League Division One (Step 4)

Preliminary	(H)	v Alton Town	W 1-0	37
			Fowler	
1st Qual.	(H)	v Moneyfields	W 3-0	72
			Savage (3)	
2nd Qual.	(H)	v Wealdstone	L 1-4	164
			Fowler	

Best Performance: 3rd Qualifying Round 1986-87, 2000-01.

BARKING & EAST HAM UNITED

Southern League Division One East (Step 4)

Preliminary	(H)	v St Margaretsbury	D 1-1	85
			Murat	
Replay	(A)	v St Margaretsbury	L 0-2	94

Best Performance: 2nd Rd Proper 1978-9, 79-80 replay, 81-82, 83-84.

BARKINGSIDE

Essex Senior League (Step 5)

Preliminary	(H)	v Leverstock Green	D 2-2	119
			Darbo, Hines	
Replay	(A)	v Leverstock Green	W 4-3	74
			Darbo (2), Thompson,	
			Williams	
1st Qual.	(H)	v Maldon Town	L 1-6	61
			Darbo	

Best Performance: 2nd Qualifying Round Replay 1998-1999

BARNSTAPLE TOWN

Western League Premier Division (Step 5)

Preliminary	(H)	v Clevedon United	W 4-1	130
			Hevingham, Squire (3)	
1st Qual.	(A)	v Paulton Rovers	L 2-3	102
			Barwick, Squire	

Best Performance: 1st Round Proper Replay 1951-52.

BARROW as a Non-Leagie-Club 1972-2006

Conference North (Step 2)

2nd Qual.	(H)	v Hebburn Town	W 5-1	911
			Flitcroft, Knight, Rushton,	
			Smith, Tarrant	
3rd Qual.	(A)	v Hyde United	W 3-2	469
			Anthony (2), Knight	
4th Qual.	(A)	v Northwich Victoria	L 1-4	1116
			Rankine	

Best Performance: 3rd Round Proper.

Crawley's Stuart Douglas sees his effort deflected over the bar by Braintree's Billy Burgess, during their 4th Qualifing Round match. Photo: Alan Coomes.

BARTON ROVERS

Southern League Division One East (Step 4)

Preliminary	(A)	v Wootton Blue Cross	D	1-1	79
		Barnes			
Replay	(H)	v WoottonBlue Cross	W	4-1	144
		Barnes, Case, Lincoln (2)			
1st Qual.	(A)	v Berkhamsted Town	L	0-3	144

Best Performance: 1st Round Proper 1980-81.

BARWELL

Midland Alliance (Step 5)

Preliminary	(A)	v Glapwell	L	1-3	46
		Noble			

Best Performance: 1st Qualifying Round 2004-05.

BASHLEY

Isthmian League Division One (Step 4)

Preliminary	(H)	v Hythe Town	W	4-0	106
1st Qual.	(H)	v Dover Athletic	L	0-1	141

Best Performance: 2nd Round Proper 1994-95.

BASINGSTOKE TOWN

Conference South (Step 2)

2nd Qual.	(A)	v Bognor Regis Town	D	1-1	552
		McKay			
Replay	(H)	v Bognor Regis Town	W	2-1	315
		Cook, Ray			
3rd Qual.	(A)	v Worthing	W	4-2	571
		Cook, Peters (2), Whiddett			
4th Qual.	(H)	v Chippenham Town	L	0-1	1072

Best Performance: 2nd Round Proper Replay 1997-98.

BAT SPORTS

Wessex LEague Division One (Step 5)

Preliminary	(H)	v Abingdon United	L	0-3	54

Best Performance: 1st Qualifying Round1998-1999 2005-2006

BATH CITY

Southern League Premier Division (Step 3)

1st Qual.	(H)	v Cinderford Town	W	1-0	404
		Bird			
2nd Qual.	(A)	v Gosport Borough	W	4-3	440
		Bird (2), Holland, Holloway			
3rd Qual.	(A)	v Weymouth	L	0-1	1232

Best Performance: 3rd Round Replay 1963-64.

BEACONSFIELD SYCOB

Southern League Division One West (Step 4)

Preliminary	(A)	v Raunds Town	W	2-0	65
		Chakaodza, Yee			
1st Qual.	(A)	v Welwyn Garden City	L	2-3	71
		Gumbs (2)			

Best Performance: 3rd Qualifying Round 1998-99.

BEDFONT

Combined Counties Premier Division (Step 5)

Preliminary	(A)	v Sidlesham	W	2-1	83
		Bryant, Postins			
1st Qual.	(H)	v Bromley	L	1-4	128
		Postins			

Best Performance: 2nd Qualifying Round 2003-2004

BEDFORD TOWN

Southern League Premier Division (Step 3)

1st Qual.	(H)	v AFC Sudbury	D	2-2	460
		Howarth, Rydeheard			
Replay	(A)	v AFC Sudbury	L	1-2	441
		Miller			

Best Performance: 4th Round Proper 1963-64, 1965-66.

BEDLINGTON TERRIERS

Northern League Division One (Step 5)

Ex. Prelim.	(A)	v Newcastle Benfield S.	W	4-2	153
		Robinson, Shandran (3)			
Preliminary	(A)	v Yorkshire Amateurs	L	1-2	75
		Cockburn			

Best Performance: 2nd Round Proper 1998-1999

BEDWORTH UNITED

Southern League Division One West (Step 4)

Preliminary	(H)	v Rocester	W	3-1	107

Doughty (2), Douglas

| 1st Qual. | (H) | v Solihull Borough | D | 1-1 | 141 |

Douglas

| Replay | (A) | v Solihull Borough | L | 2-3 | 173 |

Moore, Swan

Best Performance: 4th Qualifying Round 1983, 1989, 1990.

BELPER TOWN

Northern Premier League Division One (Step 4)

| Preliminary | (H) | v Leek CSOB | W | 1-0 | 148 |

Norbury

| 1st Qual. | (A) | v Westfields | W | 2-1 | 122 |

Gummer, Rushbury

| 2nd Qual. | (A) | v Chasetown | D | 3-3 | 167 |

| Replay | (H) | v Chasetown | L | 1-4 | 154 |

Lyons

Best Performance: 1st Round Proper 1887-88.

BEMERTON HEATH HARLEQUINS

Wessex League Division One (Step 5)

| Preliminary | (H) | v Ilfracombe Town | W | 1-0 | 64 |

Sanger

| 1st Qual. | (A) | v Penzance | W | 1-0 | 178 |

Findlay

| 2nd Qual. | (A) | v Worcester City | L | 0-7 | 579 |

Best Performance: 3rd Qualifying Round 1992 1993

BERKHAMSTED TOWN

Southern League Division One East (Step 4)

| Preliminary | (H) | v Newmarket Town | W | 2-0 | 131 |

Grace (2)

| 1st Qual. | (H) | v Barton Rovers | W | 3-0 | 144 |

Franklin, Mullins, Rowley

| 2nd Qual. | (A) | v Farnborough Town | L | 0-3 | 456 |

Best Performance: 3rd Qualifying Round 1987-88, 91-92, 92-93, 01-02.

BIDDULPH VICTORIA

Midland Alliance (Step 5)

| Preliminary | (A) | v Cradley Town | L | 1-2 | 41 |

Pope

Best Performance: 4th Qualifying Round

BIDEFORD

Western League Premier Division (Step 5)

| Preliminary | (A) | v Bishop's Cleeve | L | 1-3 | 114 |

Herrera

Best Performance: 1st Round Proper 1964-65.

BIGGLESWADE UNITED

Spartan South Midland League Premier Division (Step 5)

| Ex. Prelim. | (H) | v Haverhill Rovers | W | 6-0 | 86 |

Bull, O'Dell (2), Weeden(3)

| Preliminary | (A) | v Tring Athletic | W | 2-1 | 140 |

Buchanan, Russell

| 1st Qual. | (A) | v Hendon | L | 0-6 | 116 |

Best Performance: 1st Qualifying Round 2005-2006

BILLERICAY TOWN

Isthmian League Premier Division (Step 3)

| 1st Qual. | (A) | v St Margaretsbury | D | 0-0 | 228 |
| Replay | (H) | v St Margaretsbury | L | 2-3 | 302 |

Hockton

Best Performance: 1st Round Proper 1997-98, 2004-05.

BILLINGHAM SYNTHONIA

Northern League Division One (Step 5)

| Ex. Prelim. | (A) | v Brandon United | W | 5-0 | 71 |

Dunwell (3), Iley (2)

| Preliminary | (H) | v Fleetwood Town | W | 2-0 | 128 |

Dunwell, Iley

| 1st Qual. | (H) | v Retford United | W | 4-2 | 106 |

Dunwell (2), Flanagan, Hope

| 2nd Qual. | (H) | v North Ferriby United | L | 0-3 | 183 |

Best Performance: 1st Round Proper (6 occasions)

BILLINGHAM TOWN

Northern League Division One (Step 5)

| Preliminary | (A) | v Selby Town | W | 3-1 | 150 |

Clarke, Emms, Yale

| 1st Qual. | (A) | v Rossendale United | D | 2-2 | 107 |

Smith, Yale

| Replay | (H) | v Rossendale United | L | 2-3 | 166 |

Abel, Clarke

Best Performance: 1st Round 1955-56.

BISHOP AUCKLAND

Northern Premier League Division One (Step 4)

| Preliminary | (A) | v Pontefract Collieries | W | 3-2 | 62 |

I'Anson (3)

| 1st Qual. | (A) | v Chorley | D | 0-0 | 237 |
| Replay | (H) | v Chorley | W | 2-1 | 140 |

Hall, Irvine

| 2nd Qual. | (A) | v Skelmersdale United | D | 0-0 | 509 |
| Replay | (H) | v Skelmersdale United | L | 1-2 | 125 |

Sheeran

Best Performance: 4th Round Proper 1954-55.

BISHOP SUTTON

Western League Premier Division (Step 5)

| Preliminary | (A) | v Christchurch | L | 0-5 | 55 |

Best Performance: 1st Qualifying Round 2003-2004

BISHOP'S CLEEVE

Hellenic League Premier Division (Step 5)

| Ex. Prelim. | (H) | v Corsham Town | W | 1-0 | 94 |

Lee

| Preliminary | (H) | v Bideford | W | 3-1 | 114 |

Cox, Johnstone, Newell

| 1st Qual. | (A) | v Fairford Town | W | 1-0 | 75 |

Davis

| 2nd Qual. | (H) | v Bitton | W | 3-0 | 211 |

Johnstone (2), Slack

| 3rd Qual. | (H) | v AFC Totton | D | 1-1 | |

Tucker

| Replay | (A) | v AFC Totton | W | 4-0 | 332 |

Davis, Johnstone (3)

| 4th Qual. | (H) | v Eastbourne Borough | L | 0-1 | 625 |

Best Performance: 3rd Qualifying Round 2005-2006

BISHOP'S STORTFORD

Conference South (Step 2)

| 2nd Qual. | (A) | v Bishop's Stortford | W | 2-0 | 201 |

Edwards, Rainford

| 3rd Qual. | (A) | v Hayes | L | 0-2 | 231 |

Best Performance: 3rd Round Proper 1982-83.

BITTON

Western League Premier Division (Step 5)

| Preliminary | (H) | v Dawlish Town | W | 2-1 | 127 |

Jones, Rosslee

| 1st Qual. | (A) | v Liskeard Athletic | D | 1-1 | 102 |

Jones

| Replay | (H) | v Liskeard Athletic | W | 1-0 | 140 |

Mehew

| 2nd Qual. | (A) | v Bishop's Cleeve | L | 0-3 | 211 |

Best Performance: 2nd Qualifying Round 2005-2006

BLACKPOOL MECHANICS

North West Counties League Division Two (Step 6)

Ex. Prelim.	(H) v Newcastle Blue Star	L	1-2		80
	Chorlton				

Best Performance: 1st Qualifying Round 2004-2005

BLACKSTONES

United Counties League Premier Division (Step 5)

Preliminary	(A) v Willenhall Town	L	0-1		104

Best Performance: 1st Qualifying Round 1998-1999

BLYTH SPARTANS

Northern Premier League Premier Division (Step 3)

1st Qual.	(A) v Wakefield-Emley	W	2-1		162
	Gildea, Leeson				
2nd Qual.	(H) v Prescot Cables	W	1-0		484
	Dale				
3rd Qual.	(A) v Rossendale United	W	1-0		209
	Williams				
4th Qual.	(H) v Chase Town	D	2-2		926
	Snowden, Dale				
Replay	(A) v Chase Town	L	0-1		2134

Best Performance: 5th Round Proper Replay 1977-78.

BODMIN TOWN

South Western (Step 7)

Preliminary	(A) v Shortwood United	W	3-2		93
	O'Hagan, Swiggs (2)				
1st Qual.	(A) v Yate Town	L	0-2		170

Best Performance: 1st Qualifying Round 2004-05, 05-06.

BOGNOR REGIS TOWN

Conference South (Step 2)

2nd Qual.	(H) v Basingstoke Town	D	1-1		552
	Watson				
Replay	(A) v Basingstoke Town	L	1-2		315
	Watson				

Best Performance: 2nd Round Proper (On 4 occasions).

BOLDMERE ST MICHAELS

Midland Alliance (Step 5)

Preliminary	(A) v Holbeach United	W	2-0		56
	Charley, Thomas				
1st Qual.	(H) v Nantwich Town	L	0-3		94

Best Performance: 2nd Qualifying Round 1987-1988

BOREHAM WOOD

Southern League Division One East (Step 4)

Preliminary	(H) v Dereham Town	W	3-0		115
	Balic, Bangura (2)				
1st Qual.	(A) v Bury Town	D	2-2		166
	Bangura, Cooper				
Replay	(H) v Bury Town	W	4-2		128
	Black, Cooper (3)				
2nd Qual.	(H) v Welling United	L	0-2		267

Best Performance: 2nd Round Proper 1996-97.

BORROWASH VICTORIA

Northern Counties East Division One (Step 6)

Ex. Prelim.	(H) v Ford Sports Daventry	D	1-1		79
	Smith				
Replay	(A) v Ford Sports Daventry	W	2-1		50
	Burton (2)				
Preliminary	(A) v Coalville Town	L	0-3		117

Best Performance: 4th Qualifying Round 1926-27.

BOSTON TOWN

United Counties League Premier Division (Step 5)

Preliminary	(A) v Long Eaton United	L	2-4		63
	Collins, Nuttell				

Best Performance: 1st Round Proper 1976-77.

BOURNE TOWN

United Counties League Premier Division (Step 5)

Preliminary	(A) v Bromsgrove Rovers	L	1-4		274
	Haughton				

Best Performance: 3rd Qualifying Round 1961-62 65-66 71-72

BOURNEMOUTH

Wessex League Division One (Step 5)

Preliminary	(A) v Shepton Mallet	W	2-0		
	Benssaouda, Saadi				
1st Qual.	(H) v Mangotsfield United	D	1-1		130
	Joyce				
Replay	(A) v Mangotsfield United	L	0-7		197

Best Performance: 2nd Qualifying Round 1990-91.

BOWERS & PITSEA

Essex Senior League (Step 5)

Ex. Prelim.	(H) v Stotfold	D	2-2		68
	Fergus, Marron				
Replay	(A) v Stotfold	D	3-3*		65
Stotfold won 2-4 on penalties.					

Best Performance: Extra Preliminary Round Replay 2004-2005

BRACKLEY TOWN

Southern League Division One West (Step 4)

Preliminary	(A) v Ilford	W	2-0		68
	Murphy (2)				
1st Qual.	(A) v Chesham United	W	1-0		224
	Murphy				
2nd Qual.	(H) v Banbury United	D	1-1		680
	Beard				
Replay	(A) v Banbury United	L	2-5		960
	Beard, Murphy				

Best Performance: 2nd Qualifying Round 1997-98, 2005-06.

BRACKNELL TOWN

Southern League Division One West (Step 4)

Preliminary	(A) v Metropolitan Police	D	0-0		81
Replay	(H) v Metropolitan Police	L	0-2		131

Best Performance: 1st Round Proper 2000-01.

BRADFORD (PARK AVENUE)

Northern Premier League Premier Division (Step 3)

1st Qual.	(H) v Padiham	D	1-1		198
	Challender				
Replay	(A) v Padiham	W	4-1		305
	Calcutt, Challender, Flynn(2)				
2nd Qual.	(A) v Farsley Celtic	L	0-2		403

Best Performance: 6th Round Proper (3 occasions)

BRAINTREE TOWN

Isthmian League Premier Division (Step 3)

1st Qual.	(A) v Cheshunt	W	2-1		132
	Lorraine, Revell				
2nd Qual.	(H) v Didcot Town	W	2-0		306
	Lorraine, Revell				
3rd Qual.	(A) v Heybridge Swifts	D	1-1		360
	Griffiths				
Replay	(H) v Heybridge Swifts	W	3-1		479
	Griffiths (2), Riddle				
4th Qual.	(A) v Crawley Town	W	1-0		970
	Ofori				
1st Round	(A) v Shrewsbury Town (L2)	L	1-4		2969
	Quinton				

Best Performance: 1st Round 2005-2006

BRANDON UNITED

Northern League Division One (Step 5)

Ex. Prelim	(H) v Billingham Synthonia	L	0-5		71

Best Performance: 1st Round Replay 1988-1989

BRENTWOOD TOWN

Essex Senior League (Step 5)

Preliminary	(A)	v Thame United	W	1-0	49
1st Qual.	(H)	v Great Wakering Rovers	W	3-1	131
		Doyle, McDowell (2)			
2nd Qual.	(H)	v Windsor & Eton	L	1-2	144

Best Performance: 3rd Round 1969-1970

BRIDGWATER TOWN

Western League Premier Division (Step 5)

Preliminary	(H)	v Paulton Rovers	L	0-1	168

Best Performance: 2nd Round.1960-1961 1961-1962

BRIDLINGTON TOWN

Northern Premier League Division One (Step 4)

Preliminary	(H)	v Whitley Bay	D	2-2	180
		Heath, Palmer			
Replay	(A)	v Whitley Bay	L	0-4	189

Best Performance: 1st Round 1960-1961 1991-1992

BRIDPORT

Western League Division One (Step 6)

Preliminary	(H)	v Falmouth	L	0-3	139

Last Season: 1st Qualifying Round.

Best Performance: 3rd Qualifying Round. 1957-1958

BRIGG TOWN

Northern Premier League Division One (Step 4)

Preliminary	(H)	v Holker Old Boys	W	4-0	123
		Doyle, Drayton, Spall, Thompson			
1st Qual.	(A)	v North Ferriby United	L	1-3	213
		Nilsen			

Best Performance: 1st Round Proper 2001-02.

BRISLINGTON

Western League Premier Division (Step 5)

Preliminary	(A)	v Liskeard Athletic	L	0-2	73

Best Performance: 2nd Qualifying Round 2003-2004

BRISTOL MANOR FARM

Western League Premier Division (Step 5)

Preliminary	(A)	v Taunton Town	L	0-1	268

Best Performance: 3rd Qualifying Round.

BROCKENHURST

Wessex League Division One (Step 5)

Preliminary	(A)	v Chipstead	L	2-4	72
		Grale, Manning			

Best Performance: 3rd Qualifying Round 2001-02, 04-05.

BRODSWORTH MW

Northern Counties East Premier Division (Step 5)

Preliminary	(A)	v Durham City	L	0-5	127

Best Performance: 4th Qualifying Round 1926-27.

BROMLEY

Isthmian League Premier Division (Step 3)

1st Qual.	(A)	v Bedfont	W	4-1	128
		Amoako, Boateng, Logan, McDonnell			
2nd Qual.	(H)	v Chipstead	W	2-1	407
		McDonnell, Vines			
3rd Qual.	(H)	v Mangotsfield United	D	0-0	488
Replay	(A)	v Mangotsfield United	W	1-0	403
		Stone			
4th Qual.	(H)	v Aldershot Town	L	0-1	1454

Best Performance: 2nd Round Proper 1945-1946

BROMSGROVE ROVERS

Southern League Division One West (Step 4)

Preliminary	(H)	v Bourne Town	W	4-1	274
		Curtis (2), Johnson, Smith			
1st Qual.	(H)	v Newcastle Town	W	2-0	242
		Banner, Ramsey			
2nd Qual.	(H)	v Hinckley United	W	3-1	425
		Danks (2), Dyer			
3rd Qual.	(A)	v Halesowen Town	W	2-0	757
		Maguire, Ramsay			
4th Qual.	(H)	v Morecambe	L	0-2	919

Best Performance: 3rd Round 1993-1994

BROOK HOUSE

Isthmian League Division Two (Step 5)

Ex. Prelim.	(H)	v Leiston	D	1-1	77
		Dennison			
Replay	(A)	v Leiston	W	3-1	122
		Booth, Dennison, Papali			
Preliminary	(A)	v North Greenford Utd	W	6-1	65
		Augustine (3), Dennison, Owens, Papali			
1st Qual.	(H)	v Clacton Town	W	9-1	91
		Brydson, Dennison (2), Jones (2), Murphy, Papli(2)			
2nd Qual.	(A)	v Hayes	D	1-1	406
		Homer			
Replay	(H)	v Hayes	L	0-4	342

Best Performance: 2nd Qualifying Rreplay 2005-06.

BROXBOURNE BOROUGH V&E

Spartan South Midland League Premier Division (Step 5)

Ex. Prelim.	(H)	v Holmer Green	L	1-4	28

Best Performance: 1st Qualifying Round.

BUCKINGHAM TOWN

United Counties League Premier Division (Step 5)

Ex. Prelim.	(A)	v Chalfont St Peter	L	0-1	67

Best Performance: 1st Round Proper 1984-85.

BURGESS HILL TOWN

Isthmian League Division One (Step 4)

Preliminary	(A)	v Molesey	W	4-2	121
		Gedling, Greenfield (2), Price			
1st Qual.	(H)	v Walton & Hersham	L	0-4	169

Best Performance: 4th Qualifying Round 1999-2000.

BURNHAM

Southern League Division One West (Step 4)

Preliminary	(H)	v Selsey	W	2-0	49
		Deaner, Romeo			
1st Qual.	(A)	v Maidstone United	W	2-1	347
		Jones, Romeo			
2nd Qual.	(H)	v Lowestoft Town	D	1-1	110
		Miller			
Replay	(A)	v Lowestoft Town	D	1-1	249
Burnham won 4-2 on penalties.		Miller			
3rd Qual.	(A)	v Wealdstone	W	4-2	247
		Logie, Romeo, Horsted, OG.			
4th Qual.	(A)	v Canvey Island	D	1-1	363
		Miller			
Replay	(H)	v Canvey Island	W	2-1	607
		Romeo, Logie			
1st Round	(H)	v Aldershot Town	L	1-3	1623
		Miller			

Best Performance: 1st Round.2005-2006

BURNHAM RAMBLERS

Essex Senior League (Step 5)

Preliminary	(H) v Flackwell Heath	W	4-3	56
	Jones (4)			
1st Qual.	(A) v Aveley	W	2-1	76
	Jones, O'Reilly			
2nd Qual.	(A) v Harrow Borough	L	1-2	140
	Trenkle			

Best Performance: 2nd Qualifying Round 2003-2004

BURSCOUGH

Northern Premier League Premier Division (Step 3)

1st Qual.	(H) v Ashton United	W	3-2	187
	Byrne, Parry, Tong			
2nd Qual.	(A) v Droylsden	W	2-1	316
	Blakeman, Eaton			
3rd Qual.	(H) v Workington	W	2-0	303
	Parry, Gray			
4th Qual.	(A) v Hucknall Town	D	0-0	690
Replay	(H) v Hucknall Town	W	6-2	415
	Hussey, Gray (3), Eaton, Gedman			
1st Round	(H) v Gillingham (D1)	W	3-2	1927
	Bell (2) Rowan			
2nd Round	(A) v Burton Albion	L	1-4	4499
	Eaton			

Best Performance: 2nd Round Proper 2005-06.

BURTON ALBION

Conference National (Step 1)

4th Qual.	(H) v Leek Town	W	2-0	1467
	Shaw (2)			
1st Round	(A) v Peterborough Utd (D2)	D	0-0	3856
Replay	(H) v Peterborough United	W	1-0	2511
	Harrad			
2nd Round	(H) v Burscough	W	4-1	4499
	Gilroy (2), Stride, Harrad			
3rd Round	(H) v Manchester United (P)	D	0-0	6191
Replay	(A) v Manchester United	L	0-5	53564

Best Performance: 3rd Round Proper 1955-56, 1984-85, 2005-06.

BURY TOWN

Eastern Counties League Premier Division (Step 5)

Preliminary	(H) v Ely City	D	1-1	155
	McGavin			
Replay	(A) v Ely City	W	8-0	218
	McGavin, Miller (2), Parker Thrower (2), Wood (2)			
1st Qual.	(H) v Boreham Wood	D	2-2	166
	McGavin, Steward			
Replay	(A) v Boreham Wood	L	2-4	128
	Murkin, Tatham			

Best Performance: 1st Round Proper 1968-69.

BUXTON

Northern Counties East Premier Division (Step 5)

Preliminary	(A) v Newcastle Town	D	1-1	211
	Read			
Replay	(H) v Newcastle Town	L	1-2	376
	Copnell			

Best Performance: 3rd Round Proper 1951-52.

CALNE TOWN

Western Premier. (Step 5)

Ex. Prelim.	(H) v Shortwood United	L	0-2	56

Best Performance: 2nd Qualifying Round 1992--1993

CAMBERLEY TOWN

Ryman 2 (Step 5)

Prelim.	(A) v Mile Oak	D	1-1	61
Tie awarded to Camberley.		Cobett		
1st Qual.	(H) v Epsom & Ewell	W	1-0	73
	Reeves			
2nd Qual.	(A) v Cray Wanderers	L	1-4	139
	Walker.			

Best Performance: 1st Round 1998-1999

Chasetown defend at Cogenhoe.

Photo: Peter Barnes.

CAMBRIDGE CITY

Conference South (Step 2)

2nd Qual.	(A) v Evenwood Town	D	1-1	225
	Booth			
Replay	(H) v Evenwood Town	W	3-1	
	Simpson, Dobson, Gash.			
3rd Qual.	(H) v Hitchin Town	W	4-1	461
	Booth (3), J Simpson.			
4th Qual.	(H) v Lewes	W	2-1	588
	Booth (2)			
1st Round	(H) v Hereford United	L	0-1	1116

Best Performance: 2nd Round 2005-2006

CAMBRIDGE UNITED as a Non-League Club

Conference National (Step 1)

4th Qual.	(A) v Weymouth	L	1-2	1652
	Peters			

Best Performance: 2nd Round 1953-1954

CAMMELL LAIRD

N.Co.East 1 (Step 5)

Ex. Prelim.	(H) v West Allotment Celtic	W	4-1	130
	Collins, Hargreaves, McGuire, Morgan			
Prelim.	(H) v Alnwick Town	W	6-0	115
	Clampitt, Jebb, McQuire, Morgan (3)			
1st Qual.	(H) v Radcliffe Borough	W	2-1	175
	Cooke, Lynch			
2nd Qual.	(A) v Marine	D	1-1	358
	McGuire			
Replay	(H) v Marine	W	3-1	205
	McGuire, Clampitt, Wright.			
3rd Qual.	(A) v Hucknall Town	D	2-2	292
	McGuire (2)			
Replay	(H) v Hucknall Town	L	0-1	380

Best Performance: 3rd Qualifying Round Replay 2005-2006

CANVEY ISLAND

Conference National (Step 1)

4th Qual.	(H) v Burnham	D	1-1	363
	Ibe.			
Replay	(A) v Burnham	L	1-2	607
	Ibe.			

Best Performance: 3rd Round 2001-2002

CARLTON TOWN

N.Co. East 1 (Step 5

Prelim.	(A)	v Shepshed Dynamo	L	1-4	96
		Jefferies			

Best Performance: 2nd Qualifying Round 2004-2005

CARSHALTON ATHLETIC

Conference South (Step 2)

2nd Qual.	(A)	v Margate	L	0-1	773

Best Performance: 2nd Round 1982-1983

CARTERTON

Hellenic Premier (Step 5)

Prelim	(H)	v Didcot Town	L	0-3	109

Best Performance: 1st Qualifying Round 2004-2005

CAUSEWAY UNITED

Mid. Alliance (Step 5)

Prelim.	(A)	v Chasetown	L	0-2	111

Best Performance: 1st Qualifying Round 2004-2005 2005-2006

CHADDERTON

N.W.Co 2 (Step 6)

Prelim.	(A)	v Colne	W	2-1	111
		Baker, Clifton			
1st Qual.	(A)	v Frickley Athletic	L	0-2	214

Best Performance: 2nd Qualifying Round 1992-1993

CHALFONT ST PETER

Ryman 2 (Step 5)

Ex. Prelim.	(H)	v Buckingham Town	W	1-0	67
		Goddard			
Prelim.	(A)	v AFC Hornchurch	D	0-0	320
Replay	(H)	v AFC Hornchurch	L	1-2	104
		Cockrane			

Best Performance: 3rd Qualifying Round 1985-1986

CHARD TOWN

Western League Division One (Step 6)

Prelim.	(H)	v Wimborne Town	D	0-0	93
Replay	(A)	v Wimborne Town	L	0-2	200

Best Performance: 2nd Qualifying Round 1977-1978 1989-1990

Chipstead's Steve Eggleton puts Bromley's Adolf Amoaka under pressure in the 2nd Qualifying Round. Photo: Alan Coomes.

CHASETOWN

Midland Alliance (Step 5)

Prelim.	(H)	v Causeway United	W	2-0	111
		Bullimore, Edwards			
1st Qual.	(H)	v Gedling Town	W	2-1	76
		Edwards, Smith			
2nd Qual.	(H)	v Belper Town	D	3-3	167
		Bullimore (2), Edwards			
Replay	(A)	v Belper Town	W	4-1	154
		Whitcombe, Edwards,			
		Bullimore (2).			
3rd Qual.	(A)	v Cogenhoe United	D	1-1	184
		Whitcombe			
Replay	(H)	v Cogenhoe United	W	4-3*	374
		Bullimore, Edwards (2)			
4th Qual.	(A)	v Blyth Spartans	D	2-2	926
		Bullimore, Edwards.			
Replay	(H)	v Blyth Spartans	W	1-0	2134
		Edwards.			
1st Round	(H)	v Oldham Athletic (L1)	D	1-1	1997
		Harrison			
Replay	(A)	v Oldham Athletic	L	0-4	7235

Best Performance: 1st Round Replay 2005-2006

CHATHAM TOWN

Southern 1S (Step 4)

Prelim.	(H)	v North Leigh	W	2-0	154
		Cass, Denness			
1st Qual.	(H)	v Leatherhead	L	3-4	251
		Cass, Denness, Walker			

Best Performance: Quarter Final in 1888-1889

CHEADLE TOWN

N.W.Co. 2 (Step 6)

Ex. Prelim.	(H)	v Abbey Hey	W	3-2	61
		Lindon, Martin, Riley			
Prelim.	(H)	v Bamber Bridge	W	2-1	71
		Wakefield (2)			
1st Qual.	(A)	v Marine	L	0-4	191

Best Performance: 1st Qualifying Round 2005-2006

CHELMSFORD CITY

Ryman Premier (Step 3)

1st Qual.	(H)	v Harlow Town	D	1-1	301
		Halle			
Replay	(A)	v Harlow Town	W	1-0	206
		Lincoln			
2nd Qual.	(H)	v Dover Athletic	W	1-0	404
		Valdez			
3rd Qual.	(A)	v Nuneaton Borough	D	1-1	915
		R Edwards.			
Replay	(H)	v Nuneaton Borough	L	1-2*	379
		Allen			

Best Performance: 4th Round 1938-1939

CHERTSEY TOWN

Ryman 2 (Step 5)

Ex. Prelim.	(A)	v Sevenoaks Town	L	2-4	133
		Harper, Pomroy			

Best Performance: 3rd Qualifying Round 1992-1993

CHESHAM UNITED

Southern Premier (Step 3)

1st Qual.	(H)	v Brackley Town	L	0-1	224

Best Performance: 3rd Round 1979-1980

CHESHUNT

Southern Premier (Step 3)

1st Qual.	(H)	v Braintree Town	L	1-2	132
		Opara			

Best Performance: 4th Qual Rd.1958-9 1966-7 1970-71 1977-78

CHESSINGTON & HOOK UNITED

Co.Co. (Step 5)

Prelim.	(A)	v Sittingbourne	W	4-2	138
		Goddard, Moorhouse, Smith			
1st Qual.	(H)	v Hassocks	L	0-3	129

Best Performance: 1st Qualifying Round 2005-2006

CHESTER-LE-STREET TOWN

Northern 1 (Step 5)

Prelim.	(A) v Eccleshill United	W	2-1	52
		Cuthbertson, Shields		
1st Qual.	(A) v Curzon Ashton	W	2-0	110
		Bell, Cuthbertson		
2nd Qual.	(H) v Leigh RMI	L	1-3	193
		Wightman		

Best Performance: 4th Qualifying Round 1986-1987

CHICHESTER CITY UNITED

Sussex 1 (Step 5)

Ex. Prelim.	(H) v East Preston	L	1-2	48
		Tipper		

Best Performance: Preliminary Round 2003-2004 2004-2005

CHIPPENHAM TOWN

Southern Premier (Step 3)

1st Qual.	(H) v Falmouth Town	W	4-0	443
		Constable (2), Gilroy (2)		
2nd Qual.	(H) v Newport County	W	4-0	949
		Adams, Constable(2), Gilroy		
3rd Qual.	(H) v Sutton United	W	1-0	727
		Allison		
4th Qual.	(A) v Basingstoke Town	W	1-0	1072
		Harvey		
1st Round	(H) v Worcester City	D	1-1	2815
		Harvey		
Replay	(A) v Worcester City	L	0-1	4006

Best Performance: 1st Round Replay 2005-2006

CHIPSTEAD

C.C. (Step 5)

Prelim.	(H) v Brockenhurst	W	4-2	72
		Ageyi (2), Hatton (2)		
1st Qual.	(A) v Three Bridges	W	3-1	59
		Agyei (2), Young		
2nd Qual.	(A) v Bromley	L	1-2	407
		Agyei		

Best Performance: 2nd Qualifying Round 20052006

CHORLEY

N.P.L Div 1 (Step 4)

Prelim.	(A) v Tadcaster	D	2-2	110
		Barry, Bluck		
Replay	(H) v Tadcaster	W	2-0	176
		Martindale (2)		
1st Qual.	(H) v Bishop Auckland	D	0-0	237
Replay	(A) v Bishop Auckland	L	1-2	140
		Thompson		

Best Performance: 2nd Round 1986-1987 1990-1991

CHRISTCHURCH

Wessex (Step 5)

Prelim	(H) v Bishop's Sutton	W	5-0	55
		Chastka (2), Puckett,		
		Roberts, Woolner		
1st Qual.	(A) v Gloucester City	D	0-0	280
Replay	(H) v Gloucester City	W	3-0	103
		Roberts, Sotoudeh, Till		
2nd Qual.	(H) v Cirencester Town	L	0-2	165

Best Performance: 2nd Qualifying Round 2001-2002

CINDERFORD TOWN

Southern 1W (Step 4)

Prelim.	(A) v Alondsbury Town	W	5-3	81
		Bevan, Hoskins (2), Mayo,		
		Steadman		
1st Qual.	(A) v Bath City	L	0-1	404

Best Performance: 2nd Round 1995-1996

CIRENCESTER TOWN

Southern Premier(Step 3)

1st Qual.	(H) v Wimborne Town	W	5-3	147
		Hopkins (2), Horgan,		
		Richards (2)		
2nd Qual.	(A) v Christchurch	W	2-0	165
		Cowe (2)		
3rd Qual.	(H) v Havant & Waterloov'	W	2-1	278
		Halliday, Richards.		
4th Qual.	(A) v Ramsgate	L	0-3	697

Best Performance: 4th Qualifying Round 2001-2002

Darren Collins, Cogenhoe United, in midfield possession against Staveley MW.

Photo: Peter Barnes.

CLACTON TOWN

Eastern Prem. (Step 5)

Prelim	(A) v Royston Town	W	2-1	83
		Coyle		
1st Qual.	(A) v Brrok House	L	1-9	91
		Hillier		

Best Performance: 1st Round 1960-1961

CLAPTON

Ryman 2 (Step 5)

Prelim.	(A) v Stotfold	W	2-1	70
1st Qual.	(A) v Cogenhoe United	L	2-4	68
		Gray, Haastrup		

Best Performance:1st Round 1951-1952

CLEVEDON TOWN

Souther Div 1 W (Step6)

Prelim	(A) v Witney United	D	0-0	155
Replay	(H) v Witney United	W	3-2	162
		Haines, Holly (2)		
1st Qual.	(H) v Salisbury City	D	1-1	264
		Pitcher		
Replay	(A) v Salisbury City	L	2-4	506
		Holly, Jacobs		

Best Performance: 3rd Qualifying Round 1992-1993

CLEVEDON UNITED

Western Div 1 (Step 6)

Prelim.	(A) v Barnstaple Town	L	1-4	130
		Greenslade		

Best Performance: Preliminary Round 2005-2006

CLITHEROE

N.W.Co. 1 (Step 5)

Prelim	(A) v Harrogate Railway	W	2-1	138
		Jackson (2)		
1st Qual.	(A) v Goole	L	3-5	207

Best Performance: 1st Round 1882--85 +86

COALVILLE TOWN

Mid. Alliance Step (5)

Prelim.	(H) v Borrowash Victoria	W	3-0	117
		Knight, Tiday (2)		
1st Qual.	(A) v Ilkeston Town	L	0-1	336

Best Performance: 1st Round 2004-2005

COBHAM

Co.Co. (Step 5)

Prelim.	(H) v Egham Town	L	0-2		45

Best Performance: 1st Qualifying Round 2002-2003

COGENHOE UNITED

Utd.Co. Prem. (Step5)

Prelim.	(H) v Hanwell Town	W	4-1		78
			Page, Sandy, Thomson		
1st Qual.	(H) v Clapton	W	4-2		68
			Collins, Koriya (2), Sandy		
2nd Qual.	(H) v Staveley MW	W	3-2		91
			Koriya, Underwood (2)		
3rd Qual.	(H) v Chasetown	D	1-1		184
			MacGuire		
Replay	(A) v Chasetown	L	3-4*		374
			Le Masurier, Sandy, Smeathers		

Best Performance: 3rd Qualifying Round 2005-2006

COLNE

N.W.Co. 1 (Step 5)

Prelim.	(H) v Chadderton	L	1-2		111
			Simpson		

Best Performance: 2nd Qualifying Round 2004-2005

COLWYN BAY

N.P.L. Div 1 (Step 4)

Prelim.	(A) v Skelmersdale United	L	0-2		219

Best Performance: 2nd Round 1995-1996

CONCORD RANGERS

Essex (Step 5)

Ex. Prelim.	(H) v Kingsbury Town	L	0-1		53

Best Performance: EPR

CONGLETON TOWN

N.W.Co. 1 (Step5)

Ex. Prelim	(H) v Romulus	W	2-0		148
			Horrocks, Howard		
Prelim.	(H) v Corby Town	L	1-2		164
			Allen		

Best Performance: 1st Round 1989-1990

CONSETT

Northern 2 (Step 6)

Ex. Prelim.	(A) v Formby	D	1-1		57
			Tate		
Replay	(H) v Formby	W	5-1		97
			Brown, Forbes, Robson, Wilkinson (2)		
Prelim.	(A) v Spennymoor United	W	2-0		284
			Maw, Robson		
1st Qual.	(A) v Seaham Red Star	W	4-0		87
			Douglass, MacDonald, Maw, Wilkinson		
2nd Qual.	(H) v Ossett Town	L	1-5		166
			Douglass		

Best Performance: 1st Round 1988-19989

CORBY TOWN

Southern 1 E (Step 4)

Prelim.	(A) v Congleton Town	W	2-1		164
			Burrows, Marshall		
1st Qual.	(H) v Shepshed Dynamo	W	2-0		184
			Goodman, White		
2nd Qual.	(A) v Matlock Town	L	0-2		333

Best Performance: 3rd Round 1965-1966

CORINTHIAN CASUALS

Ryman 1 (Step 4)

Prelim.	(A) v Horsham YMCA	L	0-2		99

Best Performance: 1st Round 1965-1966 1983-1984

CORNARD UNITED

Eastern 1 (Step 6)

Prelim.	(A) v Halstead Town	L	0-7		114

Best Performance: 1st qualifying Round 2004-2005

CORSHAM TOWN

Western Prem. (Step 5)

Ex. Prelim.	(A) v Bishop's Cleeve	L	0-1		94

Best Performance: 2nd Qualifying Round 2004-2005

COVE

Co.Co. (Step 5)

Prelim.	(A) v Thatcham Town	L	0-3		80

Best Performance: 2nd Qualifying Round 2000-2001

COWES SPORTS

Wessex 1 (Step 5)

Prelim.	(A) v East Preston	W	1-0		51
			McDonald		
1st Qual.	(A) v Margate	L	0-4		672

Best Performance: 4th Qualifying Round 1957-1958

CRADLEY TOWN

Mid. Alliance (Step 5)

Prelim.	(H) v Biddulph Victoria	W	2-1		41
			How (2)		
1st Qual.	(H) v Eastwood Town	L	0-6		55

Best Performance: 1st Qualifying Round 2005-2006

CRAWLEY TOWN

Conference National (Step 1)

4th Qual.	(H) v Braintree Town	L	0-1		970

Best Performance: 3rd Round 1991-1992

CRAY WANDERERS

Ryman 1 (Step 4)

Prelim.	(A) v Steyning Town	W	6-0		80
			Jenkins, Main (2), Power, Taylor, Wood		
1st Qual.	(H) v Kingstonian	W	4-1		225
			Morris, Power (3)		
2nd Qual.	(H) v Camberley Town	W	4-1		139
			Main (2), Wood (2)		
3rd Qual.	(A) v Margate	W	3-0		807
			Love, Power (2).		
4th Qual.	(A) v Grays Athletic	L	0-2		1316

Best Performance: 1st Round 1954-1955

CROOK TOWN

Northern 2 (Step 6)

Prelim.	(H) v St Helens Town	L	0-3		103

Best Performance: 3rd Round 1931-1932

CROYDON

Ryman 2 (Step 5)

Prelim.	(H) v Frimley Green	D	1-1		56
			Henry		
Replay	(A) v Frimley Green	W	2-0		68
			Freeman, Murdoch		
1st Qual.	(A) v Horsham YMCA	W	2-1		72
			Freeman, Henry		
2nd Qual.	(A) v Staines Town	D	1-1		251
			Messi		
Replay	(H) v Staines Town	L	1-2		82
			Messi		

Best Performance: 2nd Round Replay 1979-1980

CROYDON ATHLETIC

Ryman 1 (Step 4)

Prelim.	(H) v Redhill	W	4-2		76
			Allen (3), Sheerin		
1st Qual.	(H) v Ramsgate	L	1-3		101
			Allen		

Best Performance: 2nd Qualifying Round 1994-1995

CURZON ASHTON

N.W.Co. 1 (Step 5)

Ex. Prelim.	(H) v Darwen	W	1-0		145
			Hardy, Wearden		
Prelim.	(H) v Garforth Town	W	1-0		141
			Edghill		
1st Qual.	(H) v Chester-Le-Street	L	0-2		110

Best Performance: 3rd Qualifying Round 1981-1982 1991-1992

DAGENHAM & REDBRIDGE

Conference National (Step 1)

4th Qual.	(A) v Forest Green Rovers	W	3-2		751
	Moore (2), Kandol.				
1st Round	(A) v Hartlepool United (L1)	L	1-2		3655
	Kandol.				

Best Performance: 4th Round 2002-2003

DARTFORD

Southern 1 E (Step4)

Prelim.	(H) v Dorking	L	1-2		281
	McClements				

Best Performance: 3rd Round 1935-1936 1936-1937

DARWEN

N.W.Co. 2 (Step 6)

Ex. Prelim.	(A) v Curzon Ashton	L	0-1		145

Best Performance: Semi-Final 1880 -1881

DAWLISH TOWN

Western 1 (Step 6)

Prelim.	(A) v Bitton	L	1-2		127
	Veale				

Best Performance: 1st Qualifying Round

DEAL TOWN

Kent (Step 5)

Prelim.	(A) v Sidley United	D	1-1		104
	Utterson				
Replay	(H) v Sidley United	W	2-1		143
	Athgate, Pollard				
1st Qual.	(A) v Dorking	W	3-1		91
	Bathgate, Pollard, Utterson				
2nd Qual.	(H) v Hitchin Town	L	1-3		211
	Pollard				

Best Performance: 3rd Qualifying Round 1982-1983 1992-1993

DEEPING RANGERS

Utd.Co. Prem. (Step 5)

Prelim.	(H) v Norton United	D	0-0		77
Replay	(A) v Norton United	L	0-1		42

Best Performance: 1st Qualifying Round 2004-2005

DEREHAM TOWN

Eastern Prem. (Step 5)

Prelim.	(A) v Boreham Wood	L	0-3		115

Best Performance: 1st Qualifying Round 2003-2004

DESBOROUGH TOWN

Utd.Co. Prem. (Step 5)

Ex. Prelim.	(A) v Wootton Blue Cross	L	0-2		67

Best Performance: 1st Round 1926-1927

DEVIZES TOWN

Western Prem. (Step 5)

Prelim.	(A) v Fairford	D	0-0		55
Replay	(H) v Fairford	L	0-3		85

Best Performance: 4th Qualifying Round1972-1973

DIDCOT TOWN

Hellenic Prem (Step 5)

Ex. Prelim.	(A) v Andover	D	4-4		190
	Concanon, Deavon (2), Parrott				
Replay	(H) v Andover	W	2-0		292
	Concanon (2)				
Prelim.	(A) v Carterton	W	3-0		109
	Beauon, Concanon				
1st Qual.	(H) v Herne Bay	D	0-0		239
Replay	(A) v Herne Bay	W	6-2		211
	Beauon (2), Bedwell, Concanon (3)				
2nd Qual.	(A) v Braintree Town	L	0-2		306

Best Performance: 2ndQualifying Round 2003-2004 2005-2006

DISS TOWN

Eastern Prem. (Step 5)

Prelim.	(A) v Needham Market	W	5-2		191
	Hardy (2), Ingram, Key (2)				
1st Qual.	(H) v Wroxham	L	0-2		228

Best Performance: 2nd Qualifying Round 1956-1957

DORCHESTER TOWN

Southern Premier (Step 3)

2nd Qual.	(H) v Team Bath	W	4-2		317
	Brown (2), Groves, Keeler				
3rd Qual.	(A) v Yeading	D	1-1		151
	Howes.				
Replay	(H) v Yeading	W	3-2		500
	Groves (2), Keeler				
4th Qual.	(H) v Welling United	L	1-2		533
	Browne.				

Best Performance: 2nd Round Replay 1981-1982

DORKING

Ryman 2 (Step 5)

Prelim.	(A) v Dartford	W	2-1		281
	Duffell, Smith				
1st Qual.	(H) v Deal Town	L	1-3		91
	Smith				

Best Performance: 1st Round 1992-1993

DOVER ATHLETIC

Ryman 1 (Step 4)

Prelim.	(A) v Lymington & New M.	W	2-0		172
	Matata, Wilkens				
1st Qual.	(A) v Bashley	W	1-0		141
	Wilkens				
2nd Qual.	(A) v Chelmsford City	L	0-1		404

Best Performance: 2nd Round 1975-1976

DROYLSDEN

Conference North (Step 3)

2nd Qual.	(H) v Burscough	L	1-2		316
	Halford				

Best Performance: 2nd Ropund 1978-1979

DULWICH HAMLET

Ryman 1 (Step 4)

Prelim.	(A) v Godalming Town	W	2-1		121
	Brady (2)				
1st Qual.	(A) v Abingdon Town	D	1-1		102
	Brady				
Replay	(H) v Abingdon Town	W	3-2		115
	Cort (2), Williams				
2nd Qual.	(A) v Hassocks	W	1-0		320
	Side				
3rd Qual.	(A) v Lewes	L	0-1		539

Best Performance: 1st Round Replay 1933-1934

Matt Simpson, Hassocks, attemps to go through the packed Dulwich Hamlet defence. Photo: Roger Turner.

Eastbourne Borough's No.11, Ollie Rowlands, pulls away from Oxford United's Lee Mansell. Photo: Roger Turner.

DUNSTABLE TOWN

S.S.M. (Step 5)

Prelim.	(A)	v Felixstowe & Walton U.	W	2-1	123
		Arthur, Covington			
1st Qual.	(A)	v Staines Town	D	1-1	174
		Strange			
Replay	(H)	v Staines Town	L	0-1*	118

Best Performance: 1st Round 1956-1957

DUNSTON FEDERATION BREWERY

Northern 1 (Step 5)

Prelim.	(A)	v Ossett Albion	W	3-0	103
		Armstrong, Graydon, Robson			
1st Qual.	(H)	v Thackley	W	4-1	140
		Armstrong, Robson, Thompson			
2nd Qual.	(H)	v Thornby	D	1-1	124
		Pickering			
Replay	(A)	v Thornby	L	1-2	126
		Benjamin			

Best Performance: 4th Qualifying Round 2003-2004

DURHAM CITY

Northern 1 (Step 5)

Prelim.	(H)	v Brodsworth MW	W	5-0	127
		Barnes, Brunskill (2),			
		Mackay, Ryan			
1st Qual.	(H)	v Hebburn Town	L	0-2	151

Best Performance: 2nd Round 1925-1926 1957-1958

EAST GRINSTEAD TOWN

Sussex 2 (Step 6)

Ex. Prelim.	(H)	v VCD Athletic	L	0-7	73

Best Performance: 2nd Qualifying Round 1947-194852-3 71-72

EAST PRESTON

Sussex 1 (Step 5)

Ex. Prelim.	(A)	v Chichester City Utd	W	2-1	48
		Biggs, Churchill			
Prelim.	(H)	v Cowes Sports	L	0-1	51

Best Performance: 3rd Qualifying Round 2004-2005

EAST THURROCK UNITED

Ryman Prem. (Step 4)

1st Qual.	(H)	v Harrow Borough	L	1-2	96
		Harris			

Best Performance: 4th Qualifying Round 2003-2004

EASTBOURNE BOROUGH

Conference South (Step 2)

2nd Qual.	(A)	v Redbridge	D	2-2	113
		Rowland, Tuck			
Replay	(H)	v Redbridge	W	5-1	359
		Rmasey, Rowland (2),			
		Smart, Tuck.			
3rd Qual.	(A)	v Met. Police	D	3-3	201
		Ramsay, Storey, Odubade.			
Replay	(H)	v Met Police	W	3-2	601
		Odubade (2), Rowland			
4th Qual.	(A)	v Bishop's Cleeve	W	1-0	625
		Ramsay.			
1st Round	(H)	v Oxford United (L2)	D	1-1	3770
		Rowland			
Replay	(A)	v Oxford United	L	0-3	4396

Best Performance: 1st Round Replay 2005-2006

EASTBOURNE TOWN

Sussex 1,(Step 5)

Prelim.	(A)	v Reading Town	W	3-1	44
		Dallaway (3)			
1st Qual.	(H)	v Gosport Borough	L	1-2	160
		Brockwell			

Best Performance: 4th Qual. Rd. 1946-47 50-51 67-68 68-69

EASTBOURNE UNITED

Sussex 1 (Step 5)

Ex. Prelim.	(H)	v Ash United	L	1-2	68
		Cham			

Best Performance: 4th QualifyingRound 1966-1967 1978-1979

EASTLEIGH

Conference South (Step 2)

2nd Qual.	(H)	v Havant & W'looville	D	0-0	470
Replay	(A)	v Havant & W'looville	L	1-4	329
		Forbes.			

Best Performance:3rdQualifying Round 1981-1982 2004-2005

EASTWOOD TOWN

N.P.L. 1 (Step 4)

Prelim.	(A)	v Lincoln Moorlands	D	0-0	74
Replay	(H)	v Lincoln Moorlands	W	3-2*	116
1st Qual.	(A)	v Cradley Town	W	6-0	55
		Garner, Knox (2),			
		Mitchell (2), Sucharewycz			
2nd Qual.	(H)	v Cambridge City	D	1-1	225
		Knox			
Replay	(A)	v Cambridge City	L	1-3	263
		OG.			

Best Performance: 1st Round 1999-2000

ECCLESHALL

N.W.Co. 2 (Step 6)

Prelim.	(A)	v Solihull Borough	L	0-2	115

Best Performance: Preliminary Round 2005-2006

ECCLESHILL UNITED

N..Co.E. Prem. (Step 5)

Prelim.	(H)	v Chester-Le-Street	L	1-2	52
		Wood			

Best Performance: 1st Qualifying Round 1992-1993

EGHAM TOWN

Ryman 2 (Step 5)

Prelim.	(A)	v Cobham	W	2-0	45
		Lusengo, Simms			
1st Qual.	(A)	v Folkestone Invicta	L	1-3	212
		Martin			

Best Performance: 4th Qualifying Round 1990-1991

ELMORE

Western Div 1 (Step 6)

Ex. Prelim.	(A) v Tuffley Rovers	D	0-0	45
Replay	(H) v Tuffley Rovers	W	1-0	85
	Rowland			
Prelim.	(H) v Torrington	W	2-0	43
	Blake, Carpenter			
1st Qual.	(A) v Highworth Town	L	1-2	135
	Tapp			

Best Performance: 2ndQualifying Round 1994-1995

ELY CITY

Eastern 1 (Step 6)

Prelim.	(A) v Bury Town	D	1-1	155
	Dewsbury			
Replay	(H) v Bury Town	L	0-8	218

Best Performance: 1st Round 1956-1957s

ENFIELD

Southern1E (Step 4)

Prelim.	(A) v Southall	L	0-5	48

Best Performance: 4th Round1980-1981

ENFIELD TOWN

Southern 1E (Step 4)

Prelim.	(A) v Soham Town Rangers	W	2-1	254
	Green, Howard			
1st Qual.	(H) v Waltham Abbey	W	3-0	314
	Negus (2)			
2nd Qual.	(H) v St Albans City	D	1-1	525
	Ofori			
Replay	(A) v St Albans City	L	0-3	436

Best Performance: 4th Round 1980-1981 (as Enfield F.C.)

EPSOM & EWELL

Ryman 2 (Step 5)

Prelim.	(H) v AFC Newbury	W	6-1	81
	Goodwin (2), Ingham, Jones, Read, Stones			
1st Qual.	(A) v Camberley Town	L	0-1	73

Best Performance: 1st Round 1933-34

ERITH & BELVEDERE

League (Step 5)

Ex. Prelim.	(H) v Hamble ASSC	W	4-2	99
	Adams (2), Dickson (2)			
Prelim.	(H) v Tooting & Mitcham	L	1-2	215
	Dakin			

Best Performance: 4th Qualifying Round

ERITH TOWN

Kent (Step 5)

Ex. Prelim.	(H) v Hassocks	L	0-3	46

Best Performance: 2nd Qualifying Round 2004-2005

ESH WINNING

Northern 1 (Step 5)

Ex. Prelim.	(H) v Ashington	D	4-4	59
	Coates, Hamilton, Soppitt, Wicling			
Replay	(A) v Ashington	L	0-1	165

Best Performance: 2nd Qualifying Round 1990-1991 2004-2005

ETON MANOR

Essex (Step 5)

Ex. Prelim.	(H) v Leverstock Green	L	0-1	35

Best Performance: 4th Qualifying Round 1956-1957

EVESHAM UNITED

Southern Prem. (Step 3)

1st Qual.	(A) v Tiverton Town	D	1-1	392
	Clarke			
Replay	(H) v Tiverton Town	L	0-1	130

Best Performance: 2nd Qualifying Roumd 1996-1997

EXETER CITY as a non-league club

Conference National (Step 1)

4th Qual.	(H) v Stevenage Borough	L	0-1	3421

Best Performance: 3rd Round Replay 2004-2005

EXMOUTH TOWN

Western Prem. (Step 5)

Prelim.	(A) v Odd Down	L	2-3	25
	Bingham, Gardner			

Best Performance: 4th Qualifying Round 1988-89 1989-1990

FAIRFORD TOWN

Hellenic Prem. (Step 5)

Prelim.	(H) v Devizes Town	D	0-0	55
Replay	(A) v Devizes Town	W	3-0	85
	Bowen, Chessell, Coles			
1st Qual.	(H) v Bishop's Cleeve	L	0-1	75

Best Performance: 1st Qualifying Round 2004-05 05-06

FAKENHAM TOWN

Eastern 1 (Step 6)

Ex. Prelim.	(H) v Long Buckby	W	2-0	52
	Pask (2)			
Prelim.	(H) v Waltham Forest	L	1-4	65
	Pask			

Best Performance:

FALMOUTH TOWN

South Western League (Step 7)

Prelim.	(A) v Bridport	W	3-0	139
	Body (2), Ralph			
1st Qual.	(A) v Chippenham Town	L	0-4	443

Best Performance: 1st Round 1962-1963 1967-1968

FAREHAM TOWN

Wessex 1 (Step 5)

Ex. Prelim.	(H) v Selsey	D	0-0	90
Replay	(A) v Selsey	L	2-3	250
	White, Wood			

Best Performance: 1st Round 1979-1980 1985-1986 1986-97

FARNBOROUGH TOWN

Conference South (Step 2)

2nd Qual.	(H) v Berkhamsted Town	W	3-0	456
	Gibbs (2), McBean			
3rd Qual.	(A) v Leatherhead	W	2-0	600
	Harkness 15, McBean 41.			
4th Qual.	(A) v Merthyr Tydfil	L	0-2	1019

Best Performance: 4th Round 2002-2003

FARNHAM TOWN

Co.Co.(Step 5)

Ex. Prelim.	(A) v AFC Newbury	D	2-2	95
Replay	(H) v AFC Newbury	L	2-3	90

Best Performance:

FARSLEY CELTIC

N.P.L. Prem. (Step 3)

1st Qual.	(A) v Pickering Town	W	2-1	146
	Bernard, Duxbury			
2nd Qual.	(H) v Bradford Park Ave.	W	2-0	403
3rd Qual.	(A) v Salford City	W	1-0	195
	Iqbal			
4th Qual.	(A) v Halifax Town	L	0-2	1469

Best Performance: 1st Round 1974-1975

FELIXSTOWE & WALTON UNITED

Eastern 1 (Step 6)

Ex. Prelim.	(A) v Haringey Borough	W	3-0	73
	Buckle (2), Morgan			
Prelim.	(H) v Dunstable Town	L	1-2	123
	Spurling			

Best Performance: Preliminary Round 2005-2006

FISHER ATHLETIC

Ryman Premier (Step 3)

1st Qual.	(H) v Tooting & Mitcham	W	6-2	159
	Barr, Griffiths (2), Riviere, Watts (2)			
2nd Qual.	(H) v Tonbridge Wells	L	2-3	257
	Barr, Watts			

Best Performance: 1st Round 1984-1985 1988-1989

FLACKWELL HEATH

Ryman 2 (Step 5)

Ex. Prelim.	(A) v Saffron Waldon Town	D	1-1	102
	Rolfe			
Replay	(H) v Saffron Waldon Town	W	3-1	82
	Hanson, Hill, Suarez			
Prelim.	(A) v Burnham Ramblers	L	3-4	56
	Cox (2), Jack			

Best Performance: 4th Qualifying Round 2002-2003

FLEET TOWN

Ryman 1 (Step 4)

Prelim.	(A) v Whitstable Town	D	3-3	162
	Noakes, Rose, Smart			
Replay	(H) v Whitstable Town	W	2-1	104
	Davies			
1st Qual.	(H) v Thatcham Town	W	3-2	138
	Davies, Girling, Rose			
2nd Qual.	(H) v Bishop's Stortford	L	0-2	201

Best Performance: 2nd Qualifying Round 1997-98 2005-2006

FLEETWOOD TOWN

N.P.L. 1 (Step 4)

Prelim.	(A) v Billingham Synthonia	L	0-2	128

Best Performance: 1st Round 1949-50 1965-66

FLIXTON

N.W.Co. 2 (Step 6)

Ex. Prelim.	(H) v Hebburn Town	L	1-2	64
	Gradwell			

Best Performance: 1st Qualifying Round 1991-92 2004-2005

FOLKESTONE INVICTA

Ryman Prem. (Step 3)

1st Qual.	(H) v Egham Town	W	3-1	212
	Dryden, Glover, Guest			
2nd Qual.	(A) v St Margaretsbury	W	1-0	212
	Everitt			
3rd Qual.	(H) v Staines Town	W	2-0	337
	Flanagan, Jones			
4th Qual.	(A) v Aylesbury United	W	2-0	646
	Dryden (2)			
1st Round	(A) v Chester City (L2)	L	1-2	2503
	Flanagan			

Best Performance: 1st Round 2005-2006

FORD SPORTS DAVENTRY

Utd Co. P. (Step 5)

Ex. Prelim.	(A) v Borrowash Victoria	D	1-1	79
	Pearce			
Replay	(H) v Borrowash Victoria	L	1-2	50
	Trill			

Best Performance: 3rd Qualifying Round Replay 1998-99

FOREST GREEN ROVERS

Conference National (Step 1)

4th Qual.	(H) v Dagenham & Red.	L	2-3	751
	Beswetherick, Meechan			

Best Performance: 2nd Round 1999-2000

FORMBY

N.W.Co 1(Step 5)

Ex. Prelim.	(H) v Consett	D	1-1	57
	Felton			
Replay	(A) v Consett	L	1-5	97
	Young			

Best Performance: 1st Round 1973-74

FRICKLEY ATHLETIC

N.P.L. Prem. (Step 3)

1st Qual.	(H) v Chadderton	W	2-0	214
	Evans, Scothern			
2nd Qual.	(H) v Northwich Victoria	L	1-4	392
	Callery			

Best Performance: 3rd Round 1985-1986

FRIMLEY GREEN

Co.Co. (Step 5)

Prelim.	(A) v Croydon	D	1-1	56
	Brightly			
Replay	(H) v Croydon	L	0-2	68

Best Performance: Preliminary Round Replay 2005-2006

FROME TOWN

Western Prem. (Step 5)

Prelim.	(H) v St Blazey	D	0-0	211
Replay	(A) v St Blazey			

Tie awarded to St Blazey, Frome unable to fulfil the tie.

Best Performance: 1st Round 1954-1955

GAINSBOROUGH TRINITY

Conference North (Step 2)

2nd Qual.	(H) v Goole	D	2-2	423
	Reeves, Rowen			
Replay	(A) v Goole	W	2-1	298
	Caudwell, Rowan			
3rd Qual.	(A) v Leigh RMI	D	1-1	165
	Higgins			
Replay	(H) v Leigh RMI	W	2-1	385
	Trout, Udenkwor			
4th Qual.	(H) v York City	L	0-4	1680

Best Performance: 3rd Round 1986-1987

GARFORTH TOWN

N.Co.E. Prem. (Step 5)

Ex. Prelim.	(A) v Rossington Main	D	1-1	79
	McCargo			
Replay	(H) v Rossington Main	W	3-0	88
	Blair, McCargo, Renshaw			
Prelim.	(A) v Curzon Ashton	L	0-1	141

Best Performance: 2nd Qualifying Round 1991-92 1997-98

GATESHEAD

N.P.L. Premier (Step 3)

1st Qual.	(H) v Warrington Town	W	4-0	235
	Feasey, Henderson (2),			
	Huntley			
2nd Qual.	(A) v Salford City	L	0-1	213

Best Performance: 1st Round 1980-81 1992-93

GEDLING TOWN

C.Mids. (Step 7)

Prelim.	(A) v Rushall Olympic	W	2-0	78
	Hatton, Richardson			
1st Qual.	(A) v Chasetown	L	1-2	76
	Clark			

Best Performance: 3rd Qualifying Round 2003-2004

GLAPWELL

N.Co.E Prem. (Step 5)

Prelim.	(H) v Barwell	W	3-1	46
	Clarke, Dooley, Hardwick			
1st Qual.	(A) v Stratford Town	W	3-1	112
	Grocutt, Roberts, Wilson			
2nd Qual.	(H) v Halesowen Town	L	0-1	171

Best Performance: 1st Qualifying Round 2003 -2004

GLASSHOUGHTON WELFARE

N.Co.E. (Step 5)

Prelim.	(H) v Woodley Sports	L	0-2	35

Best Performance: 3rd Qyualifying Round 2004-2005

GLOSSOP NORTH END

N..W.Co. 1e (Step 5)

Ex. Prelim.	(A) v Stourbridge	L	0-3	211

Best Performance: Quarter Final 1908-1909

GLOUCESTER CITY

Southern Premier (Step 3)

1st Qual.	(H) v Christchurch	D	0-0	280
Replay	(A) v Christchurch	L	0-3	103

Best Performance: 2nd Round 1989-1990

GODALMING TOWN

Co.Co. (Step5)

Ex. Prelim.	(A) v Westfield	W	2-1	61
		Blason, Douglas		
Prelim.	(H) v Dulwich Hamlet	L	1-2	121
		Blason		

Best Performance: 2nd Qualifying Round

GOOLE

N.P.L. 1 (Step 4)

Prelim.	(A) v Atherton LR	D	1-1	86
		Dickinson		
Replay	(H) v Atherton LR	W	2-0	193
		Shaw (2)		
1st Qual.	(H) v Clitheroe	W	5-3	207
		Davey (4), Shaw		
2nd Qual.	(A) v Gainsborough Trinity	D	2-2	423
		Constable, Shaw		
Replay	(H) v Gainsborough Trinty	L	1-2	298
		Shaw		

Best Performance: 3rd Round as Goole Town 1956-1957

GORLESTON

Eastern 1 (Step 6)

Ex. Prelim.	(H) v North Greenford Utd	L	2-4	84
		Bowles, Coe		

Best Performance: 1st Round 1951-52 1957-58

GOSPORT BOROUGH

Essex (Step 5)

Ex. Prelim.	(H) v Sandhurst Town	W	6-1	138
		Batten, Laidlaw (3), Scammell (2)		
Prelim.	(A) v Mole Valley (Predators)	W	8-0	58
		Heather, Laidlaw (5), Murphy, Scammell		
1st Qual.	(A) v Eastbourne Town	W	2-1	160
		Laidlaw (2)		
2nd Qual.	(H) v Bath City	L	3-4	440
		Dyer, Laidlaw, Scammell		

Best Performance: 4th Qualifying Round 1980-1981

GRANTHAM TOWN

Southern Premier (Step 3)

1st Qual.	(H) v Lincoln United	W	4-0	413
		Carruthers, Pell, Smith, Sturgess		
2nd Qual.	(A) v Leek Town	L	0-1	371

Best Performance: 3rd Round 1973-1974

GRAVESEND & NORTHFLEET

Conference National (Step 1)

4th Qual.	(A) v Kettering Town	L	0-3	1647

Best Performance: 4th Round 1962-1963

GRAYS ATHLETIC

Conference National (Step 1)

4th Qual.	(H) v Cray Wanderers	W	2-0	1316
		McLean, Kightly		
1st Round	(A) v York City	W	3-0	3586
		OG, Slabber, Poole		
2nd Round	(A) v Mansfield Town (L2)	L	0-3	2992

Best Performance: 2nd Round 2005-2006

GREAT HARWOOD TOWN

N.W.Co. 2 (Step 6)

Ex. Prelim.	(A) v Guisborough Town	D	1-1	77
		Anwar		
Replay	(H) v Guisborough Town	D	3-3*	95

Great Harwood Town won 4-2 on pens. Dean, O'Neill

Prelim.	(A) v Norton & Stockton A.	W	4-0	67
		Beard, Fisher, Pope, Rogers		
1st Qual.	(A) v Oldham Town	W	2-1	65
		Eastham, Watson		
2nd Qual.	(A) v Harrogate Town	L	0-3	346

Best Performance: 1st Round 1970-1971

Guiseley's Sam Denton holds off the challenge of Salford City's Nick Robinson. Photo: Darren Thomas.

GREAT WAKERING ROVERS

Southern 1E (Step 4)

Prelim.	(A) v Uxbridge	W	3-2	93
		O'Connell, Pitts (2)		
1st Qual.	(A) v Brentwood Town	L	1-3	131
		Richmond		

Best Performance: 2nd Qualifying Round 1998-1999

GREAT YARMOUTH TOWN

Eastern 1 (Step 6

Prelim.	(H) v Stanway Rovers	L	2-3	80
		Bussell, Fitchen		

Best Performance: 2nd Round 1952-53 1953-54

GRESLEY ROVERS

Southern Premier (Step 3)

Prelim.	(A) v Nantwich Town	L	1-3	131
		Holmes		

Best Performance: 1st Round 1991-2 1994-5 1999-2000

GUISBOROUGH TOWN

Northern 2 (Step 6)

Ex. Prelim.	(H) v Great Harwood Town	D	1-1	77
Replay	(A) v Great Harwood Town	D	3-3*	95

Great Harwood Town won 4-2 on pens.

Best Performance: 1st Round 1988-1989

GUISELEY

N.P.L. Premier (Step 3)

1st Qual.	(H) v Salford City	L	0-1	192

Best Performance: 1st Round 1991-92 1994-95 1999-2000

HADLEIGH UNITED

Eastern 1 (Step 6)

Ex. Prelim.	(A) v Witham Town	L	0-1	51

Best Performance:

HAILSHAM TOWN

Sussex 1 (Step 5)

Ex. Prelim.	(A) v Horsham YMCA	L	0-1	80

Best Performance: 3rd Qualifying Round 1989-1990

HALESOWEN TOWN

Southern Premier (Step 3)

1st Qual.	(H) v South Normanton Ath.	W	5-3	279
		Forinton (4), Lamey		
2nd Qual.	(A) v Glapwell	W	1-0	171
		Forsdick		
3rd Qual.	(H) v Bromsgrove Rovers	L	0-2	757

Best Performance: 1st Round 1955-56 1985-86 1986-87

HALIFAX TOWN

Conference National (Step 1)

4th Qual.	(H) v Farsley Celtic	W	2-0	1469
		Senior (2)		
1st Round	(H) v Rushden & D. (L2)	D	1-1	2303
		Senior		
Replay	(A) v Rushden & D.	D	0-0*	2133

Rushden & Diamonds won 5-4 on pens.

Best Performance: 2nd Round Replay 1994-95 (as Non-Lg Club)

HALL ROAD RANGERS

N.Co.E 1 (Step 6)

Prelim.	(A) v Oldham Town	L	0-2	55

Best Performance: Prelim Round 2003-4 2005-06

HALLAM

N.Co.E. Prem. (Step 5)

Prelim.	(A) v Newcastle Blue Star	L	0-2	62

Best Performance: 3rd Qualifying Round 1957-1958

HALLEN

Western Premier (Step 5)

Ex. Prelim.	(H) v Porthleven	W	3-0	78
		Pritchard, Scutt, Tricker		
Prelim.	(H) v Swindon Supermarine	L	1-3	83
		Collett		

Best Performance: 4th Qualifying Round 2004-2005

HALSTEAD TOWN

Eastern Premier (Step 5)

Ex. Prelim.	(A) v London APSA	W	2-0	94
		Heath (2)		
Prelim.	(H) v Cornard United	W	7-0	114
		Betts, Carmichael (2),		
		Cranfield (2), Defeo, Norfolk		
1st Qual.	(H) v Lowestoft Town	L	1-3	142
		Edwards		

Best Performance: 4th Qualifying Round 1998-1999

HAMBLE ASSC

Wessex 1 (Step 5)

Ex. Prelim.	(A) v Erith & Belvedere	L	2-4	99
		Cox, Lewis		

Best Performance: Extra Preliminary 2005-2006

HAMPTON & RICHMOND BOROUGH

Rymnman Premier (Step 3)

1st Qual.	(H) v Witham Town	W	3-0	226
		Paris, Yaku (2)		
2nd Qual.	(H) v Leatherhead	D	1-1	357
		Fontana		
Replay	(A) v Leatherhead	L	1-2	273
		Harper		

Best Performance: 1st Round 2000-2001

HAMWORTHY UNITED

Wessex 1 (Step 5)

Ex. Prelim.	(A) v Willand Rovers	W	1-0	167
		Legg		
Prelim.	(H) v Backwell United	W	4-0	122
		Lucas, Moores, Waldock,		
		Williams		
1st Qual.	(H) v Team Bath	L	0-2	132

Best Performance: 1st Qualifying Round 2004-2005

HANWELL TOWN

S.S.M. (Step 5)

Prelim.	(A) v Cogenhoe United	L	1-4	78
		Sheekey		

Best Performance: 3rd Qualifying Round 1997-1998

HAREFIELD UNITED

S.S.M. (Step 5)

Ex. Prelim.	(H) v Langford	L	2-3	33
		Jordan (2)		

Best Performance: 2nd Qualifying Round 80-1 86-7 87-88

HARINGEY BOROUGH

S.S.M. (Step 5)

Ex. Prelim.	(H) v Felixstowe & Walton	L	0-3	73

Best Performance: 3rd Qualifying Round 1986-1987

HARLOW TOWN

Southern 1E (Step 4)

Prelim.	(H) v Newport Pagnell Tn	W	4-2	119
		Lalite, Winston (2), Wraigt		
1st Qual.	(A) v Chelmsford Town	D	1-1	301
		Salmon		
Replay	(H) v Chelmsford Town	L	0-1	206

Best Performance: 4th Round 1991-1992

HARPENDEN TOWN

S.S.M. (Step 5)

Ex. Prelim.	(H) v Sawbridgeworth Town	W	2-1	61
		Gregory (2)		
Prelim.	(A) v March Town United	L	1-4	108
		Smith		

Best Performance: Preliminary Round 2003-2004, 04-05, 05-06

HARROGATE RAILWAY

N.Co.E Premier (Step 5)

Prelim.	(H) v Clitheroe	L	1-2	138
		Howarth		

Best Performance: 2nd Round 2002-2003

HARROGATE TOWN

Conference North (Step 2)

2nd Qual.	(H) v Great Harwood Town	W	3-0	346
		Grant (2), Smith		
3rd Qual.	(H) v Witton Albion	W	2-0	402
		Smith (2)		
4th Qual.	(H) v Scarborough	W	1-0	1591
		Smith		
1st Round	(A) v Torquay United (L2)	D	1-1	2079
		Holland		
Replay	(H) v Torquay United	D	0-0	3317

Torquay United won 6-5 on pens.

Best Performance: 1st Round Replay 2005-2006

HARROW BOROUGH

Isthmian Premier (Step 3)

1st Qual.	(A) v East Thurrock United	W	2-1	96
		Asombang, Onochie		
2nd Qual.	(H) v Burnham Ramblers	W	2-1	140
		Onochie (2)		
3rd Qual.	(H) v Welling United	L	0-1	258

Best Performance: 2nd Round 1983-1984

HARWICH & PARKESTON

Eastern Premier (Step 5)

Prelim.	(H) v Holmer Green	D	2-2	110
		Chatters, Lyness		
Replay	(A) v Holmer Green	W	5-2	104
		Calver, Meadows (2),		
		Morley, Springett		
1st Qual.	(A) v Woodford United	L	0-5	76

Best Performance: 1st Round 1934-5 36-7 53-4 61-2 63-4 76-7

HASSOCKS

Sussex 1 (Step 5)

Ex. Prelim.	(A) v Erith Town	W	3-0	46
		Harding (2), Hibbert		
Prelim.	(A) v Hillingdon Borough	D	0-0	64
Replay	(H) v Hillingdon Borough	W	2-1*	164
		Hibbert		
1st Qual.	(A) v Chessington & Hook	W	3-0	129
		Harding (2), Turner		
2nd Qual.	(H) v Dulwich Hamlet	L	0-1	320

Best Performance:

HASTINGS UNITED

Ryman 1 (Step 4)

Prelim.	(A) v VCD Athletic	W	2-0	122
		Olorunda, Ray		
1st Qual.	(H) v Tonbridge Angels	D	3-3	555
		Adams, Lopez, White		
Replay	(A) v Tonbridge Angels	L	1-2	454
		Ray		

Best Performance: 3rd Round 1953-54 1954-55

HAVANT & WATERLOOVILLE

Conference South (Step 2)

2nd Qual.	(A) v Eastleigh	D	0-0	470
Replay	(H) v Eastleigh	W	4-1	329
	Baptiste (2), Town, Davis			
3rd Qual.	(A) v Cirencester Town	L	1-2	278
	Harrison			

Best Performance: 1st Round 2000-2001 2002-2003

HAVERHILL ROVERS

Eastern 1 (Step 6)

Ex. Prelim.	(A) v Biggleswade United	L	0-6	86

Best Performance: 3rd Qualifying Road 1966-1967

HAYES

COnference South (Step 2)

2nd Qual.	(H) v Brook House	D	1-1	406
	Warner			
Replay	(A) v Brook House	W	4-0	342
	Knight , Warner, Scott, McAuley.			
3rd Qual.	(H) v Bishop's Stortford	W	2-0	231
	Goulding, McAuley			
4th Qual.	(A) v Histon	L	1-3	588
	Scott			

Best Performance: 2nd Round 1972-73 1991-92 199-2000

HEBBURN TOWN

Northern 2 (Step 6)

Ex. Prelim.	(A) v Flixton	W	2-1	64
	McCartney, Peterson			
Prelim.	(H) v Winterton Rangers	D	1-1	143
	Oliver			
Replay	(A) v Winterton Rangers	W	2-0	102
	Fulcher, McCartney			
1st Qual.	(A) v Durham City	W	2-0	151
	Fulcher, Marsden			
2nd Qual.	(A) v Barrow	L	1-5	911
	Fulcher			

Best Performance: 2nd Qualifying Round 1989-90

HEDNESFORD TOWN

Conference South (Step 2)

2nd Qual.	(H) v Moor Green	W	2-0	491
	Anthrobus, Bell			
3rd Qual.	(A) v Banbury United	W	4-3	1005
	Bell (2), Heath, Hunter			
4th Qual.	(H) v Vauxhall Motors	W	3-0	628
	Heath, Bell, McMahon			
1st Round	(A) v Histon	L	0-4	1080

Best Performance: 4th Round 1996-1997

HEMEL HEMPSTEAD TOWN

Southern 1W (Step 4)

Prelim	(A) v St Neots Town	W	4-1	145
	Carney, Findlay, Glynn, Hale			
1st Qual.	(A) v Ipswich Wanderers	D	1-1	126
	Heywood			
Replay	(H) v Ipswich Wanderers	W	4-1	155
	Carney, Glynn, Yoki (2)			
2nd Qual.	(A) v Thurrock	L	2-3	93
	Thomas (2)			

Best Performance: 3rd Qualifying Round 1962-1963

HENDON

Ryman Premier (Step 3)

1st Qual.	(H) v Biggleswade United	W	6-0	116
	Burgess, Fendo (3), Nabil, Pickett			
2nd Qual.	(H) v Met. Police	D	0-0	155
Replay	(A) v Met. Police	L	0-1	104

Best Performance: 3rd Round Replay 1973-1974

HENLEY TOWN

Hellenic Premier (Step 5)

Prelim.	(H) v Witham Town	L	2-4	78
	Farrelly, Masserella			

Best Performance: Preliminary Round 1949-50 2005-2006

HEREFORD UNITED

Nationwide Conference (Step 1)

4th Qual.	(H) v Alfreton Town	D	0-0	1769
Replay	(A) v Alfreton Town	D	1-1*	740
	Hereford won 4-3 on pens.	Stanley		
1st Round	(A) v Cambridge City	W	1-0	1116
	Brady			
2nd Round	(H) v Stockport County (L2)	L	0-2	3620

Best Performance: 4th Round Replay 1971-1972

HERNE BAY

Kent (Step 5)

Prelim.	(H) v Sevenoaks Town	W	3-2	117
	Brown, King, O'Connor			
1st Qual.	(A) v Didcot Town	D	0-0	239
Replay	(H) v Didcot Town	L	2-6	211
	King, Mitchell			

Best Performance: 4th Qualifying Round 1970-1971 1986-1987

HERTFORD TOWN

Ryman 2 (Step 5)

Prelim.	(H) v Ruislip Manor	L	1-2	85
	Scriven			

Best Performance: 4th Qualifying Round 1973-1974

HEYBRIDGE SWIFTS

Ryman Premier (Step 3)

1st Qual.	(H) v Arlesey Town	W	1-0	169
	Artun			
2nd Qual.	(A) v Wivenhoe Town	W	4-1	241
	Gillespie, Janney, Lee, Shin			
3rd Qual.	(H) v Braintree Town	D	1-1	360
	Lee			
Replay	(A) v Braintree Town	L	1-3	479
	Lee			

Best Performance: 1st Round 1994-95 1997-98 2002-03

HIGHWORTH TOWN

Hellenic Premier (Step 5)

Prelim.	(H) v Welton Rovers	W	1-0	122
	Saye			
1st Qual.	(H) v Elmore	W	2-1	135
	Bellinger, Corcoran			
2nd Qual.	(H) v Tiverton Town	L	1-7	284
	Saye			

Best Performance: 3rd Qualifying Round 2003-2004

HILLINGDON BOROUGH

S.S.M. (Step 5)

Prelim.	(H) v Hassocks	D	0-0	64
Replay	(A) v Hassocks	L	1-2*	164
	Lawrence			

Best Performance: 3rd Round 1969-1970

HINCKLEY UNITED

Southern Premier (Step 3)

2nd Qual.	(A) v Bromsgrove Rovers	L	1-3	425
	McGregor			

Best Performance: 2nd Round 2001-2002

HISTON

Conference South (Step 2)

2nd Qual.	(A) v Malvern Town	W	4-1	196
	Andrews, Barker, Haniver, Kennedy			
3rd Qual.	(H) v Welwyn Garden City	W	2-1	373
	Nightingale (2)			
4th Qual.	(H) v Hayes	W	3-1	588
	Gutzmore, Barker (2)			
1st Round	(H) v Hednesford Town	W	4-0	1080
	Jackman (2), I Cambridge, Nightingale			
2nd Round	(A) v Nuneaton Borough	D	2-2	3366
	Barker, Knight-Percival			
Replay	(H) v Nuneaton Borough	L	1-2	3000
	Vowden			

Best Performance: 2nd Round 2004-2005

HITCHIN TOWN

Southern Premier (Step 3)

1st Qual.	(H)	v Waltham Forest	W	4-1	168
		Ayres, Bridge, Cavill, Sozzo			
2nd Qual.	(A)	v Deal Town	W	3-1	211
		Hayes (2)			
3rd Qual.	(A)	v Cambridge City	L	1-4	461
		French			

Best Performance: 2nd Round 1973-74 1976-77

HOLBEACH UNITED

Utd.Co. Prem. (Step 5)

Prelim.	(H)	v Boldmere St Michaels	L	0-2	56

Best Performance: 1st Round 1982-1983

HOLKER OLD BOYS

N.W.Co. 2 (Step 6)

Prelim.	(A)	v Brigg Town	L	0-4	123

Best Performance: 2nd Qualifying Round 2004-2005

HOLMER GREEN

S.S.M. (Step 5)

Ex. Prelim.	(A)	v Broxbourne Borough	W	4-1	28
		Henney (3), Wildman			
Prelim.	(A)	v Harwich & Parkeston	D	2-2	110
		Henney, Shed			
Replay	(H)	v Harwich & Parkeston	L	2-5	104
		Shed, Tullett			

Best Performance: 1st Qualifying 2004-2005

HORDEN CW

Northern 1 (Step 5)

Ex. Prelim.	(A)	v Prudhoe Town	W	3-1	32
		Noodhouse, O'Riordan, Ure			
Prelim.	(H)	v Kendal Town	L	1-2	79
		Ure			

Best Performance: 2nd Round 1938-1939

HORSHAM

Sussex 1 (Step 5)

Prelim.	(A)	v Tonbridge Angels	L	1-3	457
		Carney			

Best Performance: 1st Round 1947-1948 1966-1967

HORSHAM YMCA

Sussex 1 (Step 5)

Ex. Prelim.	(H)	v Hailsham Town	W	1-0	80
		Trevor			
Prelim.	(H)	v Corinthian Casuals	W	2-0	99
		Grant (2)			
1st Qual.	(H)	v Croydon	L	1-2	72
		Duffield			

Best Performance: 4th Qualifying Round 1999-2000

HUCKNALL TOWN

Conference North (Step 2)

2nd Qual.	(A)	v Nantwich Town	W	1-0	190
		Gill			
3rd Qual.	(H)	v Cammell Laird	D	2-2	292
		Ward, Gill			
Replay	(A)	v Cammell Laird	W	1-0	395
		Nangle			
4th Qual.	(H)	v Burscough	D	0-0	690
Replay	(A)	v Burscough	L	2-6	415
		Gill, Timons			

Best Performance: 4th Qualifying Round Replay 2005-2006

HULLBRIDGE SPORTS

Essex (Step 5)

Ex. Prelim.	(H)	v Wisbech Town	L	2-5	70
		Reeve, Webster			

Best Performance: Preliminary Round 2003-2004

HUNGERFORD TOWN

Hellenic Premier (Step 5)

Ex. Prelim.	(H)	v North Leigh	L	0-4	71

Best Performance: 1st Round 1979-1980

HYDE UNITED

N.P.L. Prem (Step 3)

2nd Qual.	(H)	v Lancaster City	W	2-1	333
		Johnson, Jones			
3rd Qual.	(H)	v Barrow	L	2-3	469
		Johnson, Clee			

Best Performance: 1st Round 1954-1955 1983-1984 1994-1995

HYTHE TOWN

Kent (Step 5)

Ex. Prelim.	(H)	v Raynes Park Vale	W	4-1	116
		Brazier(2), Hayes, Winfield			
Prelim.	(A)	v Bashley	L	0-4	76

Best Performance: 4th Qualifying Round 1989-1990

Andy Hall puts Kettering in front against Gravesend in the 4th Qualifying Round. Photo: Peter Barnes.

ILFORD

Southern 1 E (Step 4)

Prelim.	(H) v Brackley Town	L	0-2	68

Best Performance: Preliminary Round 2004-2005 (as new club)

ILFRACOMBE TOWN

Western League 1 (Step 6)

Prelim.	(A) v Bemerton Heath H.	L	0-1	64

Best Performance: 4th Qualifying Round 1952-1953

ILKESTON TOWN

N.P.L. Premier (Step 3)

1st Qual.	(H) v Coalville Town	W	1-0	336
	Swinscoe			
2nd Qual.	(A) v Solihull Borough	L	0-3	237

Best Performance: 2nd Round 1997-1998 1999-2000

IPSWICH WANDERERS

Eastern P (Step 5)

Prelim.	(A) v Stowmarket Town	D	2-2	119
	Grimwood, Martin			
Replay	(H) v Stowmarket Town	W	3-1*	169
	Hetherington, Hurd, Lowe			
1st Qual.	(H) v Hemel Hempstead T.	D	1-1	126
	Hurd			
Replay	(A) v Hemel Hempstead T.	L	1-4	155
	Baker			

Best Performance: 2nd Qualifying Round 2002-2003

JARROW ROOFING BOLDON CA

Northern 1 (Step 5)

Ex. Prelim.	(H) v Sheffield	L	0-4	56

Best Performance: Preliminary Round 2003-2004

KENDAL TOWN

N.P. L. 1 (Step 4)

Prelim.	(A) v Horden CW	W	2-1	79
	Foster (2)			
1st Qual.	(H) v Witton Albion	L	2-3	160

Best Performance: 2nd Round 1963-1964

KETTERING TOWN

Conference North (Step 2)

2nd Qual.	(H) v Stafford Rangers	W	1-0	971
	Moore			
3rd Qual.	(A) v St Albans City	D	0-0	882
Replay	(H) v St Albans City	W	4-0	1220
	Burgess (3), Gould			
4th Qual.	(H) v Gravesend & N'flt	W	3-0	1647
	Gould , Hall, Midgley.			
1st Round	(H) v Stevenage Borough	L	1-3	4548
	Midgley			

Best Performance: 4th Round 1988-1989

KIDDERMINSTER HARRIERS

Nationwide Conference (Step 1)

4th Qual.	(A) v Southport	L	0-1	1108

Best Performance: 5th Round 1993-994

KIDSGROVE ATHLETIC

N.P.L. 1(Step 4)

Prelim.	(A) v Stourbridge	D	2-2	218
	Hancock, Ward			
Replay	(H) v Stourbridge	W	5-2	110
	Hancock, Johnson,			
	Rehead, Vickers, Ward			
1st Qual.	(H) v Leamington	L	0-1	429

Best Performance: 1st Qualifying Round 1995-1996

KINGS LYNN

Southern Premier (Step 3)

1st Qual.	(A) v Banbury United	L	1-2	549
	Jones			

Best Performance: 3rd Round 1961-1962

KINGSBURY TOWN

Ryman 2 (Step 5)

Ex. Prelim.	(A) v Concord Rangers	W	1-0	53
	David			
Prelim.	(A) v Aveley	L	1-5	53
	Otasanyo			

Best Performance: 3rd Qualifying Round 1987-88

KINGSTONIAN

Ryman 1 (Step 4)

Prelim.	(H) v Ringmer	W	2-1	324
	Panter, Sills			
1st Qual.	(A) v Cray Wanderers	L	1-4	225
	Lee			

Best Performance: 4th Round 2000-2001

KIRKLEY

Eastern Co. Prem. (Step 5)

Ex. Prelim.	(A) v Aylesbury Vale	D	2-2	105
	Stokeld (2)			
Replay	(H) v Aylesbury Vale	L	0-3	191

Best Performance: Extra Preliminary Replay 2005-2006

LANCASTER CITY

Conference North (Step 2)

2nd Qual.	(A) v Hyde United	L	1-2	333
	Taylor			

Best Performance: 2nd Round 1946-1947 1972-1973

LANCING

Sussex 2 (Step 6)

Ex. Prelim.	(H) v Whitehawk	L	1-2	95
	Reilly			

Best Performances 4th Qqualifying Round 52-53

LANGFORD

S.S.M. (Step 5)

Ex. Prelim.	(A) v Harefield United	W	3-2	33
	Saunders, Taylor, Warren			
Prelim.	(A) v Stansted	L	1-2	70
	Saunders			

Best Performance: Preliminary Round 2005-2006

LEAMINGTON

Mid. Alliance(Step 5)

Prelim.	(H) v Sutton Town	D	0-0	538
Replay	(A) v Sutton Town	W	2-2*	205
Leamington won 9-8 on pens.		Adams, Blake		
1st Qual.	(A) v Kidsgrove Athletic	W	1-0	429
	Morgan			
2nd Qual.	(H) v Oadby	D	2-2	861
	Blake, Morgan			
Replay	(A) v Oadby	D	1-1*	356
Leamington won 4-2 on pens.		Adams		
3rd Qual.	(H) v Woodford United	W	2-0	1017
	Rodman (2)			
4th Qual.	(A) v Ossett Town	W	4-2	900
	Blake, J Adams (2),Tank			
1st Round	(A) v Colchester United (L1) L	1-9	3513
	R Adams			

Best Performance: 1st Round 2005-2006

LEATHERHEAD

Ryman 1 (Step 4)

Prelim.	(A) v Ash United	D	1-1	111
	Stevens			
Replay	(H) v Ash United	W	3-2	235
	Morrhouse, Stevens (2)			
1st Qual.	(A) v Chatham Town	W	4-3	251
	Alighirri, Hendry, Stevens (2)			
2nd Qual.	(A) v Hampton & R.Boro'	D	1-1	357
	O'Connor			
Replay	(H) v Hampton & R. Boro'	W	2-1	273
	Stevens (2)			
3rd Qual.	(H) v Farnborough Town	L	0-2	600

Best Performance: 4th Round 1974-1975

LEEK CSOB

N.W. Counties 2 (Step 6)

Prelim.	(A) v Belper Town	L	0-1	148

Best Performance: 3rd Qualifying Round 1998-1999

Action from the game between Hampton & Richmond Borough and Leatherhead, which finsihed in a 1-1 draw. Here Leatherhead defenders and 'keeper combine to stop this attack.

Photo: Gordon Whittington.

LEEK TOWN

N.P.L. Prem. (Step 3)

1st Qual.	(H)	v Long Eaton United	W	7-0	193
		Brown, Eldershaw, Kinsey (3), Nagington (2)			
2nd Qual.	(H)	v Grantham Town	W	1-0	371
		Nagington			
3rd Qual.	(H)	v Thornaby	W	2-1	211
		Whittaker, Nagington			
4th Qual.	(A)	v Burton Albion	L	0-2	1467

Best Performance: 2nd Round 1990-1991

LEIGH RMI

N.L. P. Prem (Step 3)

2nd Qual.	(A)	v Chester-Le-Street T.	W	3-1	193
		Simm, Smith, Thompson			
3rd Qual.	(H)	v Gainsborough Trinity	D	1-1	165
		Smith			
Replay	(A)	v Gainsborough Trinity	L	1-2	385
		Smith			

Best Performance: 1st Round 1928-1929 1982-1983 1998-1999

LEIGHTON TOWN

Southern 1 W (Step 4)

Prelim.	(H)	v Wroxham	D	1-1	113
		Perry			
Replay	(A)	v Wroxham	L	1-4	180
		Perry			

Best Performance: 3rd Qualifying Round 1970-1971

LEISTON

Eastern Co. Prem. (Step 5)

Ex. Prelim.	(A)	v Brook House	D	1-1	77
		Inglis			
Replay	(H)	v Brook House	L	1-3	122
		Wright			

Best Performance: Preliminary 2003-2004

LEVERSTOCK GREEN

S.S.M. (Step 5)

Ex. Prelim.	(A)	v Eton Manor	W	1-0	35
		Byfield			
Prelim.	(A)	v Barkingside	D	2-2	111
		Byfield, McKane			
Replay	(H)	v Barkingside	L	3-4	64
		Armstrong (3)			

Best Performance: Preliminary Replay 2005-2006

LEWES

Conference South (Step 2)

2nd Qual.	(A)	v Leyton	W	1-0	162
		Beckford			
3rd Qual.	(H)	v Dulwich Hamlet	W	1-0	539
		Beckford			
4th Qual.	(A)	v Cambridge City	L	1-2	588
		Watts			

Best Performance: 1st Round 2001-2002

LEYTON

Ryman Prem. (Step 3)

1st Qual.	(A)	v Potton United	W	1-0	84
		Bajada			
2nd Qual.	(H)	v Lewes	L	0-1	162

Best Performance: 2nd Round 1951-1952

LINCOLN MOORLANDS

N.Co.E. 1(Step 6)

Prelim.	(H)	v Eastwood Town	D	0-0	74
Replay	(A)	v Eastwood Town	L	2-3*	116
		Robinson, Wilkinson			

Best Performance: Preliminary Replay 2005-2006

LINCOLN UNITED

N.P.L. Prem. (Step 3)

1st Qual.	(A)	v Grantham Town	L	0-4	413

Best Performance: 1st Round 1991-1992 1997-1998

LISKEARD ATHLETIC

S.Western (Step 7)

Prelim.	(H)	v Brislington	W	2-0	73
		Nute, Richardson			
1st Qual.	(H)	v Bitton	D	1-1	102
Replay	(A)	v Bitton	L	0-1	140

Best Performance: 3rd Qualifying Round 1982-1983

LITTLEHAMPTON TOWN

Sussex 1 (Step 5)

Prelim.	(H)	v Tunbridge Wells	D	1-1	131
		Davies			
Replay	(A)	v Tunbridge Wells	D	2-2*	122
Tunbridge won 16-15 on pens.				Brackley, Kamara	

Best Performance: 1st Round 199-1991

LIVERSEDGE

N.Co.E. Prem. (Step 5)

Ex. Prelim.	(A)	v Skelmersdale United	L	0-1	132

Best Performance: 4th Qualifying Round 2004-2005

LONDON APSA

Essex (Step 5)

Ex. Prelim.	(H)	v Halstead Town	L	0-2	94

Best Performance: Extra Preliminary Round 2005-2006

LONDON COLNEY

S.S.M. (Step 5)

Prelim.	(H)	v Rothwell Town	L	2-3	50
		Flain, Ross			

Best Performance: 1st Qualifying Round

LONG BUCKBY

Utd.Co. Prem. (Step5)

Ex. Prelim.	(A)	v Fakenham Town	L	0-2	52

Best Performance: 1st Qualifying Round 1992-1993

LONG EATON UNITED

N.Co.E Prem. (Step 5)

Ex. Prelim.	(H)	v Quorn	W	2-1	93
		Downie, Eaton			
Prelim.	(H)	v Boston Town	W	4-2	63
		Downie, Eaton, Tansley, Young			
1st Qual.	(A)	v Leek Town	L	0-7	193

Best Performance: 3rd Qual Rd 1965-66 67-68 70-711 76-77

LONG MELFORD

E.Co 1 (Step 6)

Prelim.	(H)	v AFC Sudbury	L	0-1	448

Best Performance: 2nd Qualifying Round 2004-2005

LORDSWOOD

Kent (Step 5)

Prelim.	(H)	v Saltdean United	W	3-2	60
		Doerr, Richards, Sharp			
1st Qual.	(H)	v AFC Totton	L	1-2	71
		Forster			

Best Performance: 1st Qualifying Round 2005-2006

LOUGHBOROUGH DYNAMO
Mid. Alliance (Step 5)

Ex. Prelim.	(A) v Sutton Town	L	1-5	108
	Miller			

Best Performance: Extra Preliminary 2005-2006

LOWESTOFT TOWN
Eastern Co. Prem (Step 5)

Ex. Prelim.	(A) v Woodbridge Town	D	3-3	121
	Cockrill, Hough (2)			
Replay	(H) v Woodbridge Town	W	5-0	238
	McKenna, Stock (3), Woodrow			
Prelim.	(A) v Oxhey Jets	W	2-1	139
	Cockrill, Woodrow			
1st Qual.	(A) v Halstead Town	W	3-1	142
	Cockrill, McGee, Stokeld			
2nd Qual.	(A) v Burham	D	1-1	110
	Woodrow			
Replay	(H) v Burham	D	1-1*	249
Burham won 4-2 on pens.	OG			

Best Performance: 1st Round 1926-7 38-9 66-7 67-8

LYMINGTON & NEW MILTON
Ryman 1 (Step 4)

Prelim.	(H) v Dover Athletic	L	0-2	172

Best Performance: 4th Qualifying Round 2004-2005

MAIDENHEAD UNITED
Conference South (Step 2)

2nd Qual.	(A) v Yeading	L	0-3	185

Best Performance: 1st Round 1960-61 1962-63

MAIDSTONE UNITED
Kent (Step 5)

Prelim.	(A) v Winchester City	W	3-0	452
	Rowland (2), Takalobighashi			
1st Qual.	(H) v Burnham	L	1-2	347
	Takalobighashi			

Best Performance: 3rd Qualiifying Round 2003-2004 2004-2005

MAINE ROAD
N.W.Co. 1 (Step 5)

Prelim.	(H) v Armthorpe Welfare	L	0-2	40

Best Performance: 2nd Qualifying Round 19889-90 90-91 92-93

MALDON TOWN
Ryman Premier (Step 3)

1st Qual.	(A) v Barkingside	W	6-1	61
	Clarke, Fiddis, Huttley,			
	Parker (2), Rugg			
2nd Qual.	(A) v Sutton United	L	0-2	402

Best Performance: 2nd Qualifying Rounnd 2001-02

MALVERN TOWN
Mid. Alliance (Step 5)

Prelim.	(H) v Mickleover Sports	W	4-3	136
	Owen, Preedy (2), Whittington			
1st Qual.	(A) v Willenhall Town	D	1-1	131
	Shepherd			
Replay	(H) v Willenhall Town	W	1-0	139
	Shepherd			
2nd Qual.	(H) v Histon	L	1-4	196
	Shepherd			

Best Performance: 2rd Qualifying Round 1981-1982 1966-1967

MANGOTSFIELD UNITED
Southern Premier (Step 3)

1st Qual.	(A) v Bournemouth	D	1-1	130
	Corbett			
Replay	(H) v Bournemouth	W	7-0	197
	Claridge, Corbett, Lane,			
	Prince, Seal (3)			
2nd Qual.	(H) v Swindon Supermarine	W	4-2	278
	Ball, Casey, Price			
3rd Qual.	(A) v Bromley	D	0-0	488
Replay	(H) v Bromley	L	0-1	403

Best Performance: 4th Qualifying Round 2001-2002

MARCH TOWN UNITED
Eastern Co. 1 (Step 6)

Prelim.	(H) v Harpenden Town	W	4-1	108
	Brand (2), Cousins, Pepper			
1st Qual.	(A) v Northwood	L	0-3	141

Best Performance: 1st Round 1953-54 1977-78

MARGATE
Ryman Premier (Step 3)

1st Qual.	(H) v Cowes Sports	W	4-0	672
	Brown, Hilaire, Remy,			
	Watson			
2nd Qual.	(H) v Carshalton Athletic	W	1-0	773
	Remy			
3rd Qual.	(H) v Cray Wanderers	L	0-3	807

Best Performance: 3rd Round 1936-37 1972-73

MARINE
N.P.L. Prem. (Step 3)

1st Qual.	(H) v Cheadle Town	W	4-0	191
	Connolly, Rendell, Young (2)			
2nd Qual.	(H) v Cammell Laird	D	1-1	358
	Mullin			
Replay	(A) v Cammell Laird	L	1-3	205
	Rendell			

Best Performance: 3rd Round 1952-1953

MARLOW
Southern 1 W (Step 4)

Prelim.	(H) v Arlesey Town	L	2-3	88
	Brown, Smillie			

Best Performance: 3rd Round 1992-93 1994-95

MARSKE UNITED
Northern 2 (Step 6)

Prelim.	(A) v Ramsbottom United	L	1-3	169
	Hebbron			

Best Performance: 2nd Qualifying Round 2000-2001

MATLOCK TOWN
N.P.L. Prem. (Step 3)

1st Qual.	(H) v Pegasus Juniors	W	4-0	160
	Cropper, Warne (2), Webster			
2nd Qual.	(H) v Corby Town	W	2-0	333
	Cropper, Riley			
3rd Qual.	(H) v Ossett Albion	L	3-6	332
	Webster (2), Cropper			

Best Performance: 3rd Round 1976-1977

MELKSHAM TOWN
Western Prem. (Step 5

Prelim.	(H) v Westbury United	D	2-2	112
	Ridout			
Replay	(A) v Westbury United	W	3-2	190
	Beavis, Price, Rideout			
1st Qual.	(A) v Swindon Supermarine	L	0-1	101

Best Performance: 2nd Qualifying Round 1957-1958

MERSTHAM
Co.Co.(Step 5)

Prelim.	(H) v Ramsgate	L	1-4	85
	Vernon			

Best Performance: 3rd Qualifying Round

Craig Vernon scores Merthan's only goal from the spot against Ramsgate. Photo: Roger Turner.

MERTHYR TYDFIL

Southern Premier(Step 3)

1st Qual.	(H) v St Blazey	W	3-2	407
	Fowler, Shepherd, D Williams			
2nd Qual.	(A) v Taunton Town	D	1-1	414
	Fowler			
Replay	(H) v Taunton Town	W	2-1	370
	Griffiths, Welsh			
3rd Qual.	(H) v Salisbury City	W	2-1	615
	Steins, Sommers			
4th Qual.	(H) v Farnborough Town	W	2-0	1019
	Fowler, Steins			
1st Round	(H) v Walsall (L1)	L	1-2	3046
	S Williams 29.			

Best Performance: 2nd Round Replay 1979-1980

METROPOLITAN POLICE

Isthmian 1 (Step 4)

Prelim.	(H) v Bracknell Town	D	0-0	81
Replay	(A) v Bracknell Town	W	2-0	131
	Cooper (2)			
1st Qual.	(H) v Tunbridge Wells	W	2-0	83
	Cooper, Parma			
2nd Qual.	(A) v Hendon	D	0-0	155
Replay	(H) v Hendon	W	1-0	104
	C Brown			
3rd Qual.	(H) v Eastbourne Borough	D	3-3	201
	Haworth, OG, Cooper			
Replay	(A) v Eastbourne Borough	L	2-3	601
	Cooper (2)			

Best Performance: 1st Round 1931-1932 1984-1985 1993-1994

MICKLEOVER SPORTS

N.Co.E.Prem (Step 5)

Prelim.	(A) v Malvern Town	L	3-4	136
	Conningham, Kettle, Strzyzewski			

Best Performance: 2 Qualifying Round 1998-1999

MILDENHALL TOWN

Eastern Co. Prem (Step5)

Prelim.	(H) v Potters Bar Town	W	3-1	140
	Okay, Paynter, Simpson			
1st Qual.	(A) v Southall	L	3-6	75
	Libam (2), Mitchel-King			

Best Performance: 2nd Qualifying Round

MILE OAK

Sussex 2 (Step 6)

Prelim.	(H) v Camberley Town	D	1-1	61
Tie awarded to Camberley Town.	Gaton			

Best Performance: 2nd Qualifying Round 1982-83 85-86 88-89

MILTON UNITED

Hellenic Prem (Step 5)

Ex. Prelim.	(A) v AFC Totton	L	0-5	80

Best Performance: Extra Preliminary Round 2005-2006

MINEHEAD

Western 1 (Step 6)

Ex. Prelim.	(H) v Alondsbury Town	L	1-2	49
	Hall			

Best Performance: 2nd Round 1976-1977 1977-1978

Leamington's Stuart Herlihy breaks down an Oadby attack with this headed clearance. Photo: Bill Wheatcroft.

MOLE VALLEY (PREDATORS)

Co.Co. (Step 5)

Prelim.	(H) v Gosport Borough	L	0-8	58

Best Performance: Preliminary Round 2005-2006

MOLESEY

Ryman 2 (Step 5)

Prelim.	(H) v Burgess Hill Town	L	2-4	121
	Pym, Ruggles			

Best Performance: 1st Round 1994-1995

MONEYFIELDS

Wessex 1 (Step 5)

Ex. Prelim.	(H) v Abingdon Town	W	6-1	67
	Elias, Mould (2), Wyatt (3)			
Prelim.	(H) v Rye & Iden United	W	4-0	109
	Black, Elias, Gillman, Mould			
1st Qual.	(A) v Banstead Athletic	L	0-3	72

Best Performance: 1st Qualifying Round 2001-2002 2005-2006

MOOR GREEN

Conference North (Step 2)

2nd Qual.	(A) v Hednesford Town	L	0-2	491

Best Performance: 1st Round 1979-19809 2002-2003

MORECAMBE

Conference (Step 1)

4th Qual.	(A) v Bromsgrove Rovers	W	2-0	919
	O'Connor, Walmsley			
1st Round	(H) v Northwich Victoria	L	1-3	2166
	Carlton			

Best Performance: 3rd Round 1961-1962 2000-2001

MORPETH TOWN

Northern 1 (Step 5)

Ex. Prelim.	(A) v Oldham Town	L	0-1	40

Best Performance: 4th QualifyingRound 1998-1999

MOSSLEY

N.P.L. 1 (Step 4)

Prelim.	(A) v Sheffield	D	2-2	229
	Giggs, Morning			
Replay	(H) v Sheffield	W	1-0	268
	Giggs			
1st Qual.	(A) v Armthorpe Welfare	L	1-3	92
	Downey			

Best Performance: 2nd Round 1949-1950 1980-1981

NANTWICH TOWN

N.W.Co. (Step 5)

Prelim.	(H) v Gresley Rovers	W	3-1	131
	Blake, Griggs (2)			
1st Qual.	(A) v Boldmere St Michaels	W	3-0	94
	Griggs, Marrow (2)			
2nd Qual.	(H) v Hucknall Town	L	0-1	190

Best Performance: 5 Qualifying Round 1900-1901 1903 1904

NEEDHAM MARKET

Eastern Co.Prem. (Step 5)

Prelim.	(H) v Diss Town	L	2-5	191
	Clements, Head			

Best Performance: Preliminary Round 2005-2006

NELSON

N.W.Co. 2 (Step 6)

Ex. Prelim.	(H) v Retford United	L	2-4	106
	Brown, Ridehalgh			

Best Performance: 2nd Round 1930-1931

NEW MILLS

N.W.Co.2 (Step 6)

Prelim.	(H) v Salford City	L	0-2	206

Best Performance: 2nd Qual Rd 1971-1972 1976-1977 1978-79

NEWCASTLE BENFIELD BAY PLASTIC

Norther 1 (Step 5)

Ex. Prelim.	(H) v Bedlington Terriers	L	2-4	153
	Chilton (2)			

Best Performance: Extra Preliminary Round 2005-2006

NEWCASTLE BLUE STAR

Northern 1 (Step 5)

Ex. Prelim.	(A)	v Blackpool Mechanics	W	2-1	80
			Graham, Woodhouse		
Prelim.	(H)	v Hallam	W	2-0	62
			Bainbridge, Fenwick		
1st Qual.	(H)	v Whitby Town	L	1-2	208
			Carr		

Best Performance: 1st Round 1984-1985

NEWCASTLE TOWN

N.W.Co 1. (Step 5)

Prelim.	(H)	v Buxton	D	1-1	211
			Lennon		
Replay	(A)	v Buxton	W	2-1	376
			Beeston, Lennon		
1st Qual.	(A)	v Bromsgrove Rovers	L	0-2	242

Best Performance: 1st Round 1996-1997

NEWMARKET TOWN

Eastern Co. Ptrem. (Step 5)

Prelim.	(A)	v Berkhamsted Town	L	0-2	131

Best Performance: 4th Qualifying Round 1992-1993

NEWPORT COUNTY

Conference South (Step 3)

2nd Qual.	(A)	v Chippenham Town	L	0-4	949

Best Performance: 1st Round 2001-2002

NEWPORT PAGNELL TOWN

Utd.Co. P{rem. (Step 5)

Prelim.	(A)	v Harlow Town	L	2-4	119
			Shrieves, Will		

Best Performance: Preliminary Round 2004-2005 2005-2006

NEWPORT(IW)

Isthmian Div 1 (Step4)

Prelim.	(A)	v Oxford City	L	2-3	139
			Greening (2)		

Best Performance: 2nd Round 1935-1936 1945-1946

NEWQUAY

S.Western (Step 7)

Ex. Prelim.	(A)	v Westbury United	L	1-2	78
			Curtis		

Best Performance: 2nd Q. Rd 1950-1 56-7 73-4 76-7 77-8 79-80

NORTH FERRIBY UNITED

N.P.L. Prem. (Step 3)

1st Qual.	(H)	v Brigg Town	W	3-1	213
			Bradshaw (2), Farley		
2nd Qual.	(A)	v Billingham Synthonia	W	3-0	183
			Bradshaw, Forthergill (2)		
3rd Qual.	(A)	v Northwich Victoria	L	0-1	684

Best Performance: 3rd Qualifying Round 1981-1982

NORTH GREENFORD UNITED

Co.Co. (Step 5)

Ex. Prelim.	(A)	v Gorleston	W	4-2	84
			Hill, Hughes (2), Jarvis		
Prelim.	(H)	v Brook House	L	1-6	65
			Reed		

Best Performance: 1st Qualifying Round 2004-2005

NORTH LEIGH

Hellenic Prem. (Step 5)

Ex. Prelim.	(A)	v Hungerford Town	W	4-0	71
			Hope (2), Miller, Murphy		
Prelim.	(A)	v Chatham Town	L	0-2	154

Best Performance: 3rd Qualifying Round 2004-2005

NORTH SHIELDS

Northern 2 (Step 6)

Ex. Prelim.	(A)	v Winterton Rangers	L	0-1	56

Best Performance: 2nd Round 1933-1934 1982-1983

NORTHALLERTON TOWN

Utd.Co. 2 (Step 6)

Prelim.	(H)	v Winsford United	W	4-0	100
			Chillingsworth (4)		
1st Qual.	(A)	v St Helens Town	D	3-3	81
			Charlton, Goodchild, Ryan		
Replay	(H)	v St Helens Town	L	2-3	134
			Curry, Kasonali		

Best Performance: 4th Qualifying Round 1992-1993

NORTHAMPTON SPENCER

Utd.Co.Prem. (Step 5)

Prelim.	(A)	v Ware	W	4-2	103
			Coleman, Frost (2), Gregory		
1st Qual.	(H)	v Aylesbury United	L	1-2	201
			O'Brien		

Best Performance: 1st Qualifying Round 2005-2006

NORTHWICH VICTORIA

Conference North (Step 2)

2nd Qual.	(A)	v Frickley Athletic	W	4-1	392
			Brayson (3), Carr		
3rd Qual.	(H)	v North Ferriby United	W	1-0	684
			Brayson		
4th Qual.	(H)	v Barrow	W	4-1	1116
			Brayson (2), Allan, Carr		
1st Round	(A)	v Morecambe	W	3-1	2166
			Brayson (3)		
2nd Round	(A)	v Woking	D	0-0	2462
Replay	(H)	v Woking	W	2-1	2302
			Elliott, Brayson		
3rd Round	(A)	v Sunderland (Prem)	L	0-3	19323

Best Performance: Quarter Final 1883-1884

NORTHWOOD

Southern Premier (Step 3)

1st Qual.	(H)	v March Town United	W	3-0	141
			Kirkland, Moore (2)		
2nd Qual.	(H)	v Aylesbury United	D	0-0	249
Replay	(A)	v Aylesbury United	L	0-2	262

Best Performance: 4th Qualifying Round 2000-2001

NORTON & STOCKTON ANCIENTS

Northern 2 (Step 6)

Prelim.	(H)	v Great Harwood Town	L	0-4	67

Best Performance: 1st Qualifying Round 1988-89 90-91 92-93

NORTON UNITED

N.W.Co. 2 (Step 6)

Ex. Prelim.	(H)	v Alvechurch	W	1-0	40
			Wowra		
Prelim.	(A)	v Deeping Rovers	D	0-0	77
Replay	(H)	v Deeping Rovers	W	1-0	42
			Callan		
1st Qual	(A)	v Staveley MW	L	1-2	67
			Owen		

Best Performance: 1st Qualifying Round 2005-2006

NORWICH UNITED

Eastern Co.Prem. (Step 5)

Ex. Prelim.	(A)	v Stanway Rovers	L	1-4	80
			Bunn		

Best Performance: 2nd Qualifying Round 1992-1993

NUNEATON BOROUGH

Conference North (Step 2)

2nd Qual.	(H)	v AFC telford United	W	3-1	1174
			Collins, Frew, Staff		
3rd Qual.	(H)	v Chelmsford City	W	1-0	915
			Quailey		
4th Qual.	(H)	v Tiverton Town	D	0-0	1237
Replay	(A)	v Tiverton Town	W	1-0	885
			Quailey		
1st Round	(H)	v Ramsgate	W	2-0	2153
			Oddy, Staff		
2nd Round	(H)	v Histon	D	2-2	3366
			Collins, Quailey		
Replay	(A)	v Histon	W	2-1	3000
			Angus, Oddy		
3rd Round	(H)	v Middlesbrough (Prem)	D	1-1	6000
			Murphy		
Replay	(A)	v Middlesbrough	L	2-5	26255
			Murphy		

Best Performance: 3rd Round Replay 2005-2006

OADBY TOWN

Mid.Alliance: (Step 5)

Ex. Prelim.	(A)	v Studley	W 3-1	67
			Almond, Bacon, Moult	
Prelim.	(H)	v Stamford	D 3-3	175
			Almond, McCathie, Warner	
Replay	(A)	v Stamford	W 1-0*	202
			Warner	
1st Qual.	(H)	v Oldbury United	D 3-3	142
			Almond, McCathie, Warner	
Replay	(A)	v Oldbury United	W 3-0	62
			Almond, Chapman, Warner	
2nd Qual.	(A)	v Leamington	D 2-2	861
			Chapman, Ward	
Replay	(H)	v Leamington	D 1-1*	356
Leamington won 4-2 on pens.			Chapman	

Best Performance: 2nd Qualifying Replay 2005-2006

ODD DOWN

Western Prem. (Step 5)

Ex. Prelim.	(H)	v Portland United	W 2-0	50
			Hopkins, Lucas	
Prelim.	(H)	v Exmouth Town	W 3-2	25
			Bright, Webb (2)	
1st Qual.	(A)	v Taunton Town	L 0-3	283

Best Performance: 1st Qualifying Round 2005-2006

OLDBURY UNITED

Mid. Alliance (Step 5)

Ex. Prelim.	(H)	v Racing Club Warwick	W 2-1	72
			Booth, Dodds	
Prelim.	(H)	v Stone Dominoes	W 4-0	62
			Barnfield, Booth, Dimmock, Smith	
1st Qual.	(A)	v Oadby Town	D 3-3	142
			Barnfield, Dodds	
Replay	(H)	v Oadby Town	L 0-3	62

Best Performance: 4th Qualifying Round 1986-1987

OLDHAM TOWN

N.W.Co. 2 (Step 6)

Ex. Prelim.	(H)	v Morpeth Town	W 1-0	40
			Ogoo	
Prelim.	(H)	v Hall Road Rangers	W 2-0	55
			Scanlon (2)	
1st Qual.	(H)	v Great Harwood Town	L 1-2	65
			Scanlon	

Best Performance: 2nd Qualifying Round 2003-2004

OSSETT ALBION

N.P.L. 1 (Step 4)

Prelim.	(H)	v Dunston Federation B.	L 0-3	103

Best Performance:

OSSETT TOWN

N.P.L. Prem (Step 3)

1st Qual.	(A)	v Stockbridge PS	W 3-1	104
			Walshaw (2)	
2nd Qual.	(A)	v Consett	W 5-1	166
			Hayward (2), Walshaw (2), Wheeler	
3rd Qual.	(A)	v Matlock Town	W 6-2	332
			Walshaw (4), Staton, Briggs	
4th Qual.	(h)	v Leamington	L 2-4	900
			Walshaw (2)	

Best Performance: 4th Qualifying Round 2005-2006

OXFORD CITY

S.S M. (Step 5)

Prelim.	(H)	v Newport (IOW)	W 3-2	139
			Emsden (2), Keen	
1st Qual.	(A)	v Slough Town	L 1-4	312
			Spence	

Best Performance: 2nd Round 1969-1970

OXHEY JETS

S.S.M. (Step 5)

Prelim.	(H)	v Lowestoft Town	L 1-2	139
			Gladdy	

Best Performance: Preliminary Round 2005-2006

PADIHAM

N.W. Co. 2 (Step 6)

Prelim.	(A)	v Tow Law Town	W 3-1	112
			Anderton, Fildes (2)	
1st Qual.	(A)	v Bradford (PA)	D 1-1	198
			Seddon (2)	
Replay	(H)	v Bradford (PA)	L 1-4	305
			Seddon	

Best Performance: 1st Qualifying Round Replay 2005-2006

PAGHAM

Sussex Div 2 (Step 6)

Ex. Prelim.	(A)	v Sidley United	L 1-3	205
			Forden	

Best Performance: 2nd Qual Round 1981-82 85-86 88-89 90-91

PARKGATE

N.Co.E 1 (Step 6)

Prelim.	(A)	v Retford United	L 3-4	197
			Cisworth (2), Marshall	

Best Performance: 2nd Qualifying Round 1997-1998

PAULTON ROVERS

Southern Div 1 W (Step 4)

Prelim.	(A)	v Bridgwater Town	W 1-0	168
			Jefferies	
1st Qual.	(H)	v Barnstaple Town	W 3-2	102
			Burborough (2), Jefferies	
2nd Qual.	(A)	v AFC Totton	L 1-2	150
			Drysdale	

Best Performance: 4th Qualifying 2003-2004

PEGASUS JUNIORS

Hellenic Prem. (Step 5)

Prelim.	(A)	v Teversal	D 1-1	78
Replay	(H)	v Teversal	W 3-2	178
			Harris, Helme, Robbins	
1st Qual.	(A)	v Matlock Town	L 0-4	160

Best Performance: 1st Qualifying Round 2005-2006

PENRITH

Northern Div 2 (Step 6)

Prelim.	(A)	v Warrington Town	D 2-2	84
			Broadley, Douglass	
Replay	(H)	v Warrington Town	L 1-2*	118
			Irving	

Best Performance: 2nd Round 1981-1982

PENZANCE

South Western. (Step 7)

Prelim.	(H)	v Street	D 2-2	158
			Turner (2)	
Replay	(A)	v Street	D 0-0*	135
Penzance won 4-2 on pens.				
1st Qual.	(H)	v Bemerton Heath H.	L 0-1	171

Best Performance: 3rd Qualifying Round 1955-56 1975-76

PETERLEE NEWTOWN

Northern 2 (Step 6)

Prelim.	(A)	v Thornaby	L 0-3	49

Best Performance: 4th Qualifying Round1985-1986

PICKERING TOWN

N. Co. E Prem. (Step 5)

Ex. Prelim.	(A)	v Bacup Borough	W 5-0	40
			Baxter, Ryan (2), Roberts	
Prelim.	(H)	v Ashington	D 2-2	228
			Eeles, Salt	
Replay	(A)	v Ashington	W 2-1	282
			Gray, MaCauly	
1st Qual.	(H)	v Farsley Celtic	L 1-2	146
			Salt	

Best Performance: 2nd Qualifying Round 1999-2000 2001-02

PONTEFRACT COLLIERIES

N.Co.East 1 (Step 6)

Prelim.	(H)	v Bishop Auckland	L 2-3	62
			Amos, Eastwood	

Best Performance: Preliminary Round 2005-2006

PORTHLEVEN

South Western (Step7)

Ex. Prelim.	(A)	v Hallen	L	0-3	78

Best Performance: Preliminary Round 2004-2005

PORTLAND UNITED

Wessex 1 (Step 5)

Ex. Prelim.	(A)	v Odd Down	L	0-2	50

Best Performance: 4th Qualifying Round 1953-1954 1965-1966

POTTERS BAR TOWN

Southern 1E (Step 4)

Prelim.	(A)	v Mildenhall Town	L	1-3	140
		Martin			

Best Performance: Preliminary Round 2004-2005

POTTON UNITED

Utd.Co. P (Step 5)

Prelim.	(A)	v Tiptree United	W	3-2	91
		Byrne (2)			
1st Qual.	(H)	v Leyton	L	0-1	84

Best Performance: 3rd Qualifying 1994-1995

PRESCOT CABLES

N.P.L. Prem. (Step 3)

1st Qual.	(A)	v Woodley Sports	W	4-2	71
		McEwan, O'Donnell,			
		Prescott (2)			
2nd Qual.	(A)	v Blyth Spartans	L	0-1	484

Best Performance: 1st Round 1957-1958 1959-1960

PRUDHOE TOWN

Northern Div 2 (Step 6)

Ex. Prelim.	(H)	v Horden CW	L	1-3	32
		Orysoale			

Best Performance: 2nd Qualifying Round 1990-1991

QUORN

Mid Alliance (Step 5)

Ex. Prelim.	(A)	v Long Eaton United	L	1-2	93
		Jonas			

Best Performance: Preliminary Round

RACING CLUB WARWICK

Mid. Alliance (Step 5)

Ex. Prelim.	(A)	v Oldbury United	L	1-2	72
		Mackey			

Best Performance: 3rd Qualifying Round 1992-1993

RADCLIFFE BOROUGH

N.P.L. Premier (Step 3)

1st Qual.	(A)	v Cammell Laird	L	1-2	175
		Foster			

Best Performance: 1st Round 2000-2001

RAMSBOTTOM UNITED

N.West Co. 1 (Step 5)

Prelim.	(H)	v Marske United	W	3-1	169
		Fletcher, Macdonald (2)			
1st Qual.	(A)	v Whitley Bay	W	2-1	162
		Steele (2)			
2nd Qual.	(A)	v Vauxhall Motors	L	0-2	109

Best Performance: 3rd Qualifying Round 1998-1999

RAMSGATE

Isthmian 1 (Step 4)

Prelim.	(A)	v Merstham	W	4-1	85
		Cory, Suter (2), Welford			
1st Qual.	(A)	v Croydon Athletic	W	3-1	
		Ball, Cory, Welford			
2nd Qual.	(H)	v Southall	W	1-0	251
		Ball			
3rd Qual.	(H)	v Walton & Herstham	W	1-0	301
		Ball			
4th Qual.	(H)	v Cirencester Town	W	3-0	697
		Schulz, Suter, Yianni			
1st Round	(A)	v Nuneaton Borough	L	0-2	2153

Best Performance: 1st Round 1955-1956 2005-2006

RAUNDS TOWN

Utd.Co. Prem. (Step 5)

Prelim.	(H)	v Beaconsfield SYCOB	L	0-2	65

Best Performance: 4th Qualifying Round 1998-1999

RAYNES PARK VALE

Co.Co. (Step 5)

Ex. Prelim.	(A)	v Hythe Town	L	1-4	116
		Emptage			

Best Performance: 1st Qualifying Round 2003-2004 2004-2005

READING TOWN

Co.Co. (Step 5)

Prelim.	(H)	v Eastbourne Town	L	1-3	44
		Clifford			

Best Performance: 1st Qualifying Round

REDBRIDGE

Ryman Prem (Step 3)

1st Qual.	(A)	v Ruislip Manor	D	1-1	97
		Apata			
Replay	(H)	v Ruislip Manor	W	2-1	88
		Skerritt, Stephens			
2nd Qual.	(H)	v Eastbourne Borough	D	2-2	113
		Collins, Wilson			
Replay	(A)	v Eastbourne Borough	L	1-5	359
		Iezeki			

Best Performance: 2nd Qualifying Round Replay 2005-2006

REDDITCH UNITED

Conference South (Step 2)

2nd Qual.	(H)	v Woodford United	D	1-1	316
		Jenkins			
Replay	(A)	v Woodford United	D	2-2	207
Woodford won 10-9 on pens.			Rickards, Wilding		

Best Performance: 1st Round Replay 1971-1972

REDHILL

Sussex (Step 5)

Prelim.	(A)	v Croydon Athletic	L	2-4	76
		Flemming, Guscott			

Best Performance: 1st Round 1957-1958

RETFORD UNITED

N.Co.East 1 (Step 6)

Ex. Prelim.	(A)	v Nelson	W	4-2	106
		Ashton, Harvey, Shaw,			
		Tomlinson			
Prelim.	(H)	v Parkgate	W	4-3	197
		Bonser, Harvey, Shaw,			
		Tyler			
1st Qual.	(A)	v Billingham Synthonia	L	2-4	106
		Harvey, Tyler			

Best Performance: 1st Qualifying Round 2004-2005 2005-2006

RINGMER

Sussex 1 (Step 5)

Prelim.	(A)	v Kingstonian	L	1-2	324
		Tidey			

Best Performance: 1st Round 1970-1971

ROCESTER

Midland Allaince (Step 5)

Prelim.	(A)	v Bedworth United	L	1-3	107
		Baum			

Best Performance: 3rd Qualifying Round 1997-1998

ROMFORD

Essex (Step 5)

Ex. Prelim.	(H)	v Waltham Abbey	L	1-3	107
		Taylor			

Best Performance: 4th Qualifying Round1997-1998 1999-2000

ROMULUS

Mid. Alliance   (Step 5)

Ex. Prelim.	(A)	v Congleton Town	L	0-2	148

Best Performance: Extra Prelim inary Round 2005-2006

ROSSENDALE UNITED

N.P.L. 1 (Step 4)

Prelim.	(H)	v Sunderland Nissan	D	1-1	76
Replay	(A)	v Sunderland Nissan	W	4-1	58
		Cooper (3), Queeley			
1st Qual.	(H)	v Billingham Town	D	2-2	107
		Eatock, Macleen			
Replay	(A)	v Billingham Town	W	3-2	166
		Brookes, Eatock (2)			
2nd Qual.	(A)	v Armsthorpe Welfare	W	2-0	110
		Wilkinson (2)			
3rd Qual.	(A)	v Blyth Spartans	L	0-1	209

Best Performance: 2nd Round 1971-1972

ROSSINGTON MAIN

N.Co.East 1(Step 6)

Ex. Prelim.	(H)	v Garforth Town	D	1-1	79
		Craig			
Replay	(A)	v Garforth Town	L	0-3	88

Best Performance: 2nd Qualifying Round 1925-1926

ROTHWELL TOWN

Southern 1 E (Step 4)

Prelim.	(A)	v London Colney	W	3-2	50
		Hackett, Master (2)			
1st Qual.	(H)	v Wivenhoe Town	L	1-3	93
		Towers			

Best Performance: 4th Qualifying Round 1999-2000

ROYSTON TOWN

S.Midlands (Step 5)

Prelim.	(H)	v Clacton Town	L	1-2	83
		Dobson			

Best Performance: 2nd Qualifying Round1989-1990- 1990-1991

RUGBY TOWN

Southern Prem. (Step 3)

1st Qual.	(A)	v AFC Telford United	D	1-1	1065
		Slinn			
Replay	(H)	v AFC Telford United	L	2-3*	265
		Stone (2)			

Best Performance: 2nd Round 1987-1988(as VS Rugby)

RUISLIP MANOR

S.S.M.(Step 5)

Prelim.	(A)	v Hertford Town	W	2-1	85
		Gritt, Long			
1st Qual.	(H)	v Redbridge	D	1-1	97
		Altomare			
Replay	(A)	v Redbridge	L	1-2	88
		Altomare			

Best Performance: 4th Qualifying Round1990-1991

Peter Baker scores Sidley United's first goal against Pagham in the Extra Preliminary Round. Photo: Roger Turner.

RUNCORN HALTON

N.P.L. Prem. (Step 3)

1st Qual.	(H)	v Skelmersdale United	L	2-3	129
		Taylor, Whalley			

Best Performance: 2nd Round 1985-1986 (as Runcorn F.C.)

RUSHALL OLYMPIC

Southern 1 W (Step 4)

Prelim.	(H)	v Gedling Town	L	0-2	78

Best Performance: 3rd Qualifying Round 1992-1993

RYE & IDEN UNITED

Sussex 1 (Step 5)

Prelim.	(A)	v Moneyfields	L	0-4	109

Best Performance: Preliminary Round 2005-2006

SAFFRON WALDEN TOWN

Eastern 1 (Step 5)

Ex. Prelim.	(H)	v Flackwell Heath	D	1-1	102
		Riches			
Replay	(A)	v Flackwell Heath	L	1-3	82
		Leys			

Best Performance: 2nd Qualifying Round 1984-1985

SALFORD CITY

N.W.Co. 1 (Step 5)

Prelim.	(A)	v New Mills	W	2-0	206
		Badcroft, Whitehead			
1st Qual.	(A)	v Guiseley	W	1-0	192
		Badcroft			
2nd Qual.	(H)	v Gateshead	W	1-0	213
		McNally			
3rd Qual.	(H)	v Farsley Celtic	L	0-1	195

Best Performance: 3rd Qualifying Round 2005 -2006

SALISBURY CITY

Southern Premier (Step 3)

1st Qual.	(A)	v Clevedon Town	D	1-1	264
		Tubbs			
Replay	(H)	v Clevedon Town	W	4-2	506
		Tubbs (2), Turk			
2nd Qual.	(A)	v Yate Town	W	2-0	371
		Tubbs, Widdrington			
3rd Qual.	(A)	v Merthyr Tydfil	L	1-2	615
		Tubbs			

Best Performance: 2nd Round 1959-1960

SALTDEAN UNITED

Sussex 2 (Step 6)

Ex. Prelim.	(H)	v Wantage Town	D	0-0	47
Replay	(A)	v Wantage Town	W	2-0	76
		Martin (2)			
Prelim.	(A)	v Lordswood	L	2-3	60
		Martin			

Best Performance: Preliminary Round 2005-2006

SANDHURST TOWN

Co.Co. (Step 5)

Ex. Prelim.	(A)	v Gosport Borough	L	1-6	138

Best Performance: 2nd Qualifying Round 2004-2005

SAWBRIDGEWORTH TOWN

Essex (Step 5)

Ex. Prelim.	(A)	v Harpenden Town	L	1-2	61
		Robinson			

Best Performance: Preliminary Round 1947-1948 2004-2005

SCARBOROUGH

Conference (Step 1)

4th Qual.	(A)	v Harrogate Town	L	0-1	1591

Best Performance: 4th Round 2003-2004

SEAHAM RED STAR

Northern 2 (Step 6)

Prelim.	(H)	v Atherton Collieries	W	2-0	62
		Hubbard (2)			
1st Qual.	(H)	v Consett	L	0-4	87

Best Performance:3rd Qualifying 1992-1993

SELBY TOWN

N.Co.East Prem (Step 5)

Prelim.	(H) v Billingham Town	L 1-3		150
		Twitchen		

Best Performance: 1st Round 1953-1954

SELSEY

Sussex Co. 2 (Step 6)

Ex. Prelim.	(A) v Fareham Town	D 0-0		90
		Brown, Morey, Price		
Replay	(H) v Fareham Town	W 3-2		250
Prelim.	(A) v Burnham	L 0-2		49

Best Performance: 2ndQualifying Round 1967-68 1991-92

SEVENOAKS TOWN

Kent (Step 5)

Ex. Prelim.	(H) v Chertsey Town	W 4-2		133
		Cable, Clark (2), Hollidge		
Prelim.	(A) v Herne Bay	L 2-3		117
		Clark, Websoal		

Best Performance: Preliminary Round 2005-2006

SHEFFIELD

N.Co.East Prem. (Step 5)

Ex. Prelim.	(A) v Jarrow Roofing B. CA W 4-0			56
		Boulter, Bray, Tevendale, Ward		
Prelim.	(H) v Mossley	D 2-2		229
		Hilton, Smith		
1st Qual.	(A) v Mossley	L 0-1		268

Best Performance: 4th Qualifying Round 2000-2001

SHEPSHED DYNAMO

N.P.L. Div 1 (Step 4)

Prelim.	(H) v Carlton Town	W 4-1		96
		Bourne, Gomm, Morgan (2)		
1st Qual.	(A) v Corby Town	L 0-2		184

Best Performance: 1st Round 1982-1983 1996-1997

SHEPTON MALLET

Western 1 (Step 6)

Prelim.	(H) v Bournemouth	L 0-2		69

Best Performance: 2nd Qualifyng Round 78-79 82-83 84-85

SHILDON

Northern 1 (Step 5)

Ex. Prelim.	(A) v West Auckland Town	L 1-2		125
		Hillery		

Best Performance: 2nd Round 1936-1937

SHIREBROOK TOWN

N.Co.East Prem. (Step 5)

Ex. Prelim.	(H) v Teversal	L 2-3		183
		Johnson, Rowbottom		

Best Performance: 3rdQualifying Round 2002-2003

SHOREHAM

Sussex 1 (Step 5)

Ex. Prelim.	(A) v Three Bridges	L 0-2		55

Best Performance: 1st Qualifying Round 1948-1949 1987-1988

SHORTWOOD UNITED

Hellenic Prem (Step 5)

Ex. Prelim.	(A) v Calne Town	W 2-0		56
		Davis, Haddock		
Prelim.	(H) v Bodmin Town	L 2-3		93
		Haddock (2)		

Best Performance: 2nd Qualifying Round 1989-1990

SIDLESHAM

Sussex Co. Div 2 (Step 6)

Prelim.	(H) v Bedfont	L 1-2		53
		Lester		

Best Performance: Preliminary Round 2005-2006

SIDLEY UNITED

Sussex Co 1 (Step 5)

Ex. Prelim.	(H) v Pagham	W 3-1		205
		Baker (2), Murris		
Prelim.	(H) v Deal Town	D 1-1		104
		Morris		
Replay	(A) v Deal Town	L 1-2		143
		Baker		

Best Performance: 1st Qualifying Round (x 5)

A Shepshed Dynamo players puts pressure on the Corby Town player in possession. Photo: Peter Barnes.

SKELMERSDALE UNITED

N.W.Co. 1 (Step 5)

Ex. Prelim.	(H) v Liversedge	W 1-0		132
		Rudd		
Prelim.	(H) v Colwyn Bay	W 2-0		219
		Osman (2)		
1st Qual.	(A) v Runcorn FC Halton	W 3-2		129
		Cole, Osman, Rudd		
2nd Qual.	(H) v Bishop Auckland	D 0-0		509
Replay	(A) v Bishop Auckland	W 2-1		125
		Rudd (2)		
3rd Qual.	(A) v Vauxhall Motors	L 3-4		243
		Rudd (3)		

Best Performance: 1st Round 1967-1968 1968-1969 1971-1972

SLADE GREEN

Kent (Step 5)

Prelim.	(A) v Ashford Town	L 1-3		169
		Weir		

Best Performance: 2nd Qualifying Round 1992-1993

SLIMBRIDGE

Helleniic Prem (Step 5)

Ex. Prelim.	(H) v Wimborne Town	L 0-1		131

Best Performance: Extra Preliminary Round 2005-2006

SLOUGH TOWN

Ryman Premier (Step 3)

1st Qual.	(H) v Oxford City	W 4-1		312
		Alexis, Carbon (2), Harris		
2nd Qual.	(A) v Wroxham	L 0-2		267

Best Performance: 2nd Round Replay 1985-1986

SOHAM TOWN RANGERS

Eastern prem. (Step 5)

Ex. Prelim.	(H) v Yaxley	W 2-1		151
		Benjamin, Bugg		
Prelim.	(H) v Enfield Town	L 1-2		254
		Williams		

Best Performance: 3rd Qualifying Round 1970-1971

SOLIHULL BOROUGH

Southern 1W (Step 4)

Prelim.	(H) v Eccleshall	W 2-0		115
		Hall, Hawker		
1st Qual.	(A) v Bedworth United	D 1-1		141
		Marsden		
Replay	(H) v Bedworth United	W 3-2		173
		Hawker, Marsden, Orady		
2nd Qual.	(H) v Ilkeston Town	W 3-0		237
		Barry, Petty (2)		
3rd Qual.	(A) v Thurrock	L 0-1		126

Best Performance: 1st Round 1992-1993 1997-1998

St. Margretsbury 'keeper Kris Smithers snatches the ball from the head of Folkstone Invicta's No.12. Photo: Arthur Evans.

SOUTH NORMANTON ATHLETIC
N.Co.East 1 (Step 6)

Prelim.	(H)	v Arnold Town	W 1-0	84
			Roome	
1st Qual.	(A)	v Halesowen Town	L 3-5	279
			Bedward, Peel, Thorpe	

Best Performance: Re-formed 1980. 1st Qualifying Rd 2005-06

SOUTH SHIELDS
Northern 2 (Step 6)

Prelim.	(A)	v Thackley	L 0-2	57

Best Performance:

SOUTHALL
Co.Co. (Step 5)

Prelim.	(H)	v Enfield	W 5-0	48
			De Costa, Glasgow,	
			Martinec, O'Sullivan (2)	
1st Qual.	(H)	v Mildenhall Town	W 6-3	75
			Dussard, Fisher, Moses (2)	
			O'Sullivan (2)	
2nd Qual.	(A)	v Ramsgate	L 0-1	251

Best Performance: 2nd Qualifying Round 2005-2006

SOUTHEND MANOR
Essex (Step 5)

Ex. Prelim.	(H)	v Woodford United	L 0-1	34

Best Performance: 1st Qualifying Round 2004-2005

SOUTHPORT
Conference (Step 1)

4th Qual.	(H)	v Kidderminster Harriers	W 1-0	1108
			Lane	
1st Round	(H)	v Woking	D 1-1	1417
			Leadbetter	
Replay	(A)	v Woking	L 0-1*	2298

Best Performance: 6th Round 1930-1931 (in 3rd Div North)

SPALDING UNITED
N.P.L. 1 (Step 4)

Prelim.	(H)	v Staveley MW	L 0-1	121

Best Performance: 1st Round 1957-1958 1964-1965

SPENNYMOOR TOWN (FORMERLY EVENWOOD TOWN)
Northern (Step 5)

Prelim.	(H)	v Consett	L 0-2	284

Best Performance: Preliminary Round 2005-21006

SPORTING BENGAL UNITED
Kent (Step 5)

Ex. Prelim.	(A)	v Ware	L 0-2	207

Best Performance: Extra Preliminary Round 2005-2006

SQUIRES GATE
N.W.Co 1 (Step 5)

Ex. Prelim.	(A)	v Tow Law Town	L 0-2	108

Best Performance: 2nd Qualifying Round 2004-2005

ST ALBANS CITY
Conference South (Step 2)

2nd Qual.	(A)	v Enfield Town	D 1-1	525
			Martin	
Replay	(H)	v Enfield Town	W 3-0	436
			Seeby, Martin, Cracknell	
3rd Qual.	(H)	v Kettering Town	D 0-0	882
Replay	(A)	v Kettering Town	L 0-4	1220

Best Performance: 2nd Round Replay 1969-1970 1980-1981

ST BLAZEY
South Western (Step 7)

Prelim.	(A)	v Frome Town	D 0-0	211
Replay	(H)	v Frome Town		

Tie awarded to St Blazey, Frome Town unable to fulfil fixture.

1st Qual.	(A)	v Merthyr Tydfil	L 2-3	407
			Band, Hooper	

Best Performance: 3rd Qualifying Rd 53-54 63-64 64-65 70-71

ST HELENS TOWN
N.W.Co 1 (Step 5)

Prelim.	(A)	v Crook Town	W 3-0	103
			Jensen, Obong (2)	
1st Qual.	(H)	v Northallerton Town	D 3-3	81
			Byers, Nexfanya, Robinson	
Replay	(A)	v Northallerton Town	W 3-2	134
			Earley, Jensen, Milsom	
2nd Qual.	(H)	v Alfreton Town	L 0-2	142

Best Performance: 4th Qualifying Round 1985-1986

ST IVES TOWN
Utd Co (Step 5)

Ex. Prelim.	(A)	v St Margaretsbury	L 1-2	60
			Ewles	

Best Performance: Extra Preliminary Round 2005-2006

ST MARGARETSBURY
S.S.M. (Step 5)

Ex. Prelim.	(H)	v St Ives Town	W 2-1	60
			Barker, Petrov	
Prelim.	(A)	v Barking & East Ham Utd	D 1-1	91
			Barker	
Replay	(H)	v Barking & East Ham Utd	W 2-0	94
			Brown, Herod	
1st Qual.	(H)	v Billericay Town	D 0-0	228
Replay	(A)	v Billericay Town	W 3-2*	302
			Brown, Maskell	
2nd Qual.	(H)	v Folkstone Invicta	L 0-1	212

Best Performance: 2nd Qualifying Round Replay 2005-2006

ST NEOTS TOWN
Utd Co. (Step 5

Ex. Prelim.	(A)	v Wembley	W 2-0	87
			Kuhne, Walker	
Prelim.	(H)	v Hemel Hempstead T.	L 1-4	145
			Walker	

Best Performance: 1st Round 1966-1967

STAFFORD RANGERS
Conference North (Step 2)

2nd Qual.	(A)	v Kettering Town	L 0-1	971

Best Performance: 4th Round 1974-1975

STAINES TOWN
Ryman Premier (Step 3)

1st Qual.	(H)	v Dunstable Town	D 1-1	174
			Hunter	
Replay	(A)	v Dunstable Town	W 1-0*	118
			James	
2nd Qual.	(H)	v Croydon	D 1-1	251
			Plummer	
Replay	(A)	v Croydon	W 2-1	82
			Popovic, Muldowney	
3rd Qual.	(A)	v Folkstone Invicta	L 0-2	337

Best Performance: 1st Round 1984-1985

STALYBRIDGE CELTIC
Conference North (Step 2)

2nd Qual.	(H) v Workington	D	0-0	448
Replay	(A) v Workington	L	1-2*	315
		Price		

Last Season: ?
Best Performance: 2nd Round 1993-19994

STAMFORD
Southern Div 1 East (Step 4)

Prelim.	(A) v Oadby Town	D	3-3	175
		Hargreaves, Neil, Wormall		
Replay	(H) v Oadby Town	L	0-1*	202

Best Performance: 5th Qual. Rd 1913-1914 & 4thQ. Rd 73-4

STANSTED
Essex (Step5)

Prelim.	(H) v Langford	W	2-1	70
		Beggs, Mercer		
1st Qual.	(A) v AFC Hornchurch	L	0-2	415

Best Performance: 1st Qualifying Round 2005-2006

STANWAY ROVERS
Eastern Co (Step 5)

Ex. Prelim.	(H) v Norwich United	W	4-1	80
		Newson, Witney (2)		
Prelim.	(A) v Great Yarmouth T.	W	3-2	80
		Turner, Witney (2)		
1st Qual.	(H) v Wealdstone	D	0-0	170
Replay	(A) v Wealdstone	L	0-3	179

Best Performance: 1st Qualifying Round Replay 2005-2006

STAVELEY MW
N.Co. E (Step 6)

Prelim.	(A) v Spalding United	W	1-0	121
		Hurrell		
1st Qual.	(H) v Norton United	W	2-1	67
		Hayes (2)		
2nd Qual.	(A) v Cogenhoe United	L	2-3	91
		Hurrell (2)		

Best Performance: 2nd Qualifying Rd 2005-2006

STEVENAGE BOROUGH
Conference (Step 1)

4th Qual.	(A) v Exeter City	W	1-0	3421
		Laker		
1st Round	(A) v Kettering Town	W	3-1	4548
		Stamp, Boyd, Elding		
2nd Round	(H) v Northampton Town	D	2-2	3937
		Boyd, Elding		
Replay	(A) v Northampton Town	L	0-2	4407

Best Performance: 4th Round Replay 1997-1998

STEYNING TOWN
Sussex 2 (Step 6)

Prelim.	(H) v Cray Wanderers	L	0-6	80

Best Performance: 2nd Qualifying Round 1988-1989

STOCKSBRIDGE PARK STEELS
N.P.L. 1 (Step 4)

Prelim.	(A) v Washington	D	0-0	94
Replay	(H) v Washington	D	1-1*	126
Stocksbridge PS won 4-2 on pens.		Brown		
1st Qual.	(H) v Ossett Town	L	1-3	104
		Bayes		

Best Performance: 4th Qualifying Round 1950-1951 1956-1957

STONE DOMINOES
N.W.Co. (Step 5)

Prelim.	(A) v Oldbury United	L	0-4	62

Best Performance: 2nd Qualifying Round 2004-2005

STOTFOLD
Utd Co. P (Step 5)

Ex. Prelim.	(A) v Bowers & Pitsea	D	2-2	68
		Cashman, Drew		
Replay	(H) v Bowers & Pitsea	D	3-3	95
Stotfold won 4-2 on pens.		Bascombe (2), Cottenden		
Prelim.	(H) v Clapton	L	1-2	70
		Drew		

Best Performance:

STOURBRIDGE
Mid Alliance (Step 5)

Ex. Prelim.	(H) v Glossop North End	W	3-0	211
		Bellingham (3)		
Prelim.	(H) v Kidsgrove Athletic	D	2-2	218
		Broadhurst, Taylor		
Replay	(A) v Kidsgrove Athletic	L	2-5	110
		Brookes, Wright		

Best Performance: 4th Qualifying Rd. 67-68 84-85 85-86 96-97

STOURPORT SWIFTS
Southern Div 1 West (Step 4)

Prelim.	(H) v Stratford Town	L	1-2	71
		Willetts		

Best Performance: 3rd Qualifying Round 2001-2002

STOWMARKET TOWN
Eastern Co. (Step 5)

Prelim.	(H) v Ipswich Wanderers	D	2-2	119
		Brill, Smythe		
Replay	(A) v Ipswich Wanderers	L	1-3*	169
		Smy		

Best Performance: 4th Qualifying Round 1953-1954

STRATFORD TOWN
Mid. Alliance (Step 5)

Prelim.	(A) v Stourport Swifts	W	2-1	71
		Hunter, Niblett		
1st Qual.	(H) v Glapwell	L	1-3	112
		Pountney		

Best Performance: 2nd Qualifying Round 1989-1990

STREET
Western 1 (Step 6)

Prelim.	(A) v Penzance	D	2-2	158
		Njie, White		
Replay	(H) v Penzance	D	0-0*	135
Penzance won 4-2 on pens.				

Best Performance: 1st Round 1947-1948

STUDLEY
Mid Alliance: (Step 5)

Ex. Prelim.	(H) v Oadby Town	L	1-3	67
		Blake		

Best Performance: 1st Qualifying Round 2003-2004

Staveley MW's 'keeper claims this cross well during their 2nd Qualifying Round tie against Cogenhoe. Photo: Peter Barnes.

Thurrock's Terry Bowes gets in a centre against Solihull Borough in teh 3rd Qualifying Round. Photo: Alan Coomes.

SUNDERLAND NISSAN

Northern 1 (Step 6)

Prelim.	(A) v Rossendale United	D	1-1		76
	McCabe				
Replay	(H) v Rossendale United	L	1-4		58
	Cogden				

Best Performance: Prelim Replay 2004-2005

SUTTON COLDFIELD TOWN

Southern Div 1 W (Step 4)

Prelim.	(A) v Westfields	L	0-3		56

Best Performance: 1st Round 1980-1981 1992-1993

SUTTON TOWN

N.Co.East (Step 5)

Ex. Prelim.	(H) v Loughborough Dynamo	W	5-1		108
	Brown, Mitchell (3), Naylor				
Prelim.	(A) v Leamington	D	0-0		538
Replay	(H) v Leamington	D	2-2*		205
Leamington won 9-8 on pens.	Brown, Cockerill				

Best Performance: 1st Round 2004-2005

SUTTON UNITED

Conference South (Step 2)

2nd Qual.	(H) v Maldon Town	W	2-0		402
	Cornwall, Lastledine				
3rd Qual.	(A) v Chippenham Town	L	0-1		727

Best Performance: 4th Round 1969-1970

SWINDON SUPERMARINE

Southern Div 1W (Step 4)

Prelim.	(A) v Hallen	W	3-1		83
	Allen, Davies, Slattery				
1st Qual.	(H) v Melksham Town	W	1-0		101
	Hulbelt				
2nd Qual.	(A) v Mangotsfield United	L	2-4		278
	Rackley (2)				

Best Performance: 2nd Qualifying Round 2005-2006

TADCASTER ALBION

N.Co.E. 1 (Step 6)

Prelim.	(H) v Chorley	D	2-2		110
	Brady (2)				
Replay	(A) v Chorley	L	0-2		176

Best Performance: 2nd Qualifying Roundd 1998-1999

TAMWORTH

Conference (Step 1)

4th Qual.	(H) v Altrincham	W	3-1		801
	Robinson, Edwards (2)				
1st Round	(A) v AFC Bournemouth (L1)	W	2-1		4550
	Ward, Storer				
2nd Round	(A) v Hartlepool United (L1)	W	2-1		3786
	Edwards, Redmile				
3rd Round	(A) v Stoke City (Cham.)	D	0-0		9366
Replay	(H) v Stoke City	D	1-1*		3812
Stoke won 5-4 on pens.	Jackson				

Best Performance: 3rd Round 2005-2006

TAUNTON TOWN

Southern Div 1 West (Step 4)

Prelim	(H) v Bristol Manor Farm	W	1-0		268
	Stevens				
1st Qual.	(H) v Odd Down	W	3-0		283
	lynch, Sheppard (2)				
2nd Qual.	(H) v Merthyr Tydfil	D	1-1		414
	Heath				
Replay	(A) v Merthyr Tydfil	L	1-2		370
	Fisher				

Best Performance: 1st Round 1981-1982

TEAM BATH

Southern Prem (Step 3)

1st Qual.	(A) v Hamworthy United	W	2-0		132
	Adams, Canham				
2nd Qual.	(A) v Dorchester Town	L	2-4		317
	Canham, Tisdale				

Best Performance: 1st Round 2002-2003

TEVERSAL

N.Co.E 1 (Step 6)

Ex. Prelim.	(A) v Shirebrook Town	W	3-2		183
	Matthews, Roe, Walker				
Prelim.	(H) v Pegasus Juniors	D	1-1		78
	Roe				
Replay	(A) v Pegasus Juniors	L	2-3		178
	Cockerill (2)				

Best Performance: Preliminary Round Replay 2005-2006

THACKLEY

N.Co E. Prem. (Step 5)

Prelim.	(H) v South Shields	W	2-0		57
	Johnson (2)				
1st Qual.	(A) v Dunston FB	L	1-4		140

Best Performance: 1st Qualifying Round 2005-2006

THAME UNITED

Southern Div 1 W (Step 4)

Prelim.	(H) v Brentwood Town	L	0-1		49

Best Performance: 3rd Qualifying Round 1991-1992

THAMESMEAD TOWN

Kent (Step 5)

Ex. Prelim.	(H) v Abingdon United	L	2-4		38
	Burns, Kearley				

Best Performance: 2ndQualifying Round 2003-2004 2004-2005

THATCHAM TOWN

Wessex 1 (Step 5)

Prelim.	(H) v Cove	W	3-0		80
	Cook, Davies (2)				
1st Qual.	(A) v Fleet Town	L	2-3		138
	Blackford, Campion				

Best Performance: 4th Qualifying Round 1996-1997

THORNABY

Northern 1(Step 5)

Prelim.	(H) v Peterlee Newtown	W	3-0		49
	Campbell (2), Wilson				
1st Qual.	(H) v West Auckland Town	W	4-3		62
	Campbell, Jameson, Oliver				
	Storr				
2nd Qual.	(A) v Dunston FB	D	1-1		124
	Storr				
Replay	(H) v Dunston FB	W	2-1		126
	Campbell, Storr				
3rd Qual.	(A) v Leek Town	L	1-2		211
	Storr				

Best Performance: 3rd Qualifying Round 2005-2006

THREE BRIDGES

Sussex 1 (Step 5)

Ex. Prelim.	(H) v Shoreham	W	2-0	55
		Burt, Massaro		
Prelim.	(H) v Walton Casuals	W	1-0	84
		Day		
1st Qual.	(H) v Chipstead	L	1-3	59
		Rhodes		

Best Performance: 2nd Qualifying Round 1983-1984

THURROCK

Conference South (Step 2)

2nd Qual.	(H) v Hemel Hempstead T.	W	3-2	93
		Harper, McFarlane, O'Connor		
3rd Qual.	(H) v Solihull Borough	W	1-0	126
		O'Connor		
4th Qual.	(A) v Woking	L	0-3	1486

Best Performance: 1st Round Replay 2003-2004

TILBURY

Essex (Step 5)

Prelim.	(H) v Wivenhoe Town	L	0-3	38

Best Performance: 3rd Round 1977-1978

TIPTREE UNITED

Eastern Co. 1 (Step 6)

Prelim.	(H) v Potton United	L	2-3	91
		Mackey (2)		

Best Performance: 2nd Qualifying Round 1986-87 1991-1992

TIVERTON TOWN

Southern Premier (Step 3)

1st Qual.	(H) v Evesham United	D	1-1	392
		Yetton		
Replay	(A) v Evesham United	W	1-0	130
		Bale		
2nd Qual.	(A) v Highworth Town	W	7-1	284
		Booth (3), Daly, Mudge,		
		Winter, Yetton		
3rd Qual.	(H) v Windsor & Eton	W	2-1	531
		Yetton, Mudge		
4th Qual.	(A) v Nuneaton Borough	D	0-0	1237
Replay	(H) v Nuneaton Borough	L	0-1	885

Best Performance: 1st Rd.90-91 91-92 94-95 97-98 2004-2005

TONBRIDGE ANGELS

Ryman 1 (Step 4)

Prelim.	(H) v Horsham	W	3-1	457
		Carey, Dolby, Huggins		
1st Qual.	(A) v Hastings Town	D	3-3	555
		Huggins, Lye, Powell		
Replay	(H) v Hastings Town	W	2-1	454
		Lye, Powell		
2nd Qual.	(A) v Fisher Athetic	W	3-2	257
		Powell, May (2)		
3rd Qual.	(A) v Worcester City	L	0-3	684

Best Performance: 1st Round Replay 1950-51 51-52 52-53

TOOTING & MITCHAM UNITED

Ryman 1 (Step 4)

Prelim.	(A) v Erith & Belvedere	W	2-1	215
		Grant, Howard		
1st Qual.	(A) v Fisher Athletic	L	2-6	159
		Hastings (2)		

Best Performance: 4th Round 1975-1976

TORRINGTON

Western P (Step 5)

Prelim.	(A) v Elmore	L	0-2	43

Best Performance: 2nd Qualifying Round 1981-1982

TOW LAW TOWN

Northern 1(Step 5)

Ex. Prelim.	(H) v Squires Gate	W	2-0	108
		Martin, Niven		
Prelim.	(H) v Padiham	L	1-3	112
		Thompson		

Best Performance: 2nd Round Replay 1967-1968

TRAFFORD

N.W.Co. 1 (Step 5)

Prelim.	(H) v Silsden	W	3-1	159
		Bromley, Carratt, Eames		
1st Qual.	(H) v Yorkshire Amateurs	W	4-1	117
		Barker, Vaughan (2)		
2nd Qual.	(H) v Whitby Town	D	1-1	164
		Barker		
Replay	(A) v Whitby Town	L	0-6	196

Best Performance: 2nd Qualifying Round Replay 2005-2006

TRING ATHLETIC

S.S.Mids (Step 5)

Prelim.	(H) v Biggleswade United	L	1-2	140
		Humphreys		

Best Performance: Preliminary Round 2005-2006

TUFFLEY ROVERS

Hellenic Prem. (Step 5)

Ex. Prelim.	(H) v Elmore	D	0-0	45
Prelim.	(A) v Elmore	L	0-1	85

Best Performance: Preliminary Round 2005-2006

TUNBRIDGE WELLS

Kent (Step 5)

Prelim.	(A) v Littlehampton Town	D	1-1	131
		McRoberts		
Replay	(H) v Littlehampton Town	D	2-2*	122
		Beaney, Hassett		
1st Qual.	(A) v Met. Police	L	0-2	83

Tunbridge won 16-15 on pens.

Best Performance: 1st Round 1954-19551961-1962

UXBRIDGE

Southern 1E (Step4)

Prelim.	(H) v Great Wakering Rovers	L	2-3	93
		Bamford (2)		

Best Performance: 2nd Round 1873-1874

VAUXHALL MOTORS

Conference North (Step 2)

2nd Qual	(H) v Ramsbottom United	W	2-0	109
		Moogan, Rooney		
3rd Qual.	(A) v Skelmersdale United	W	4-3	243
		Cumiskey (4)		
4th Qual.	(A) v Hednesford Town	L	0-3	628

Best Performance: 2nd Round 2003-2004

VCD ATHLETIC

Kent (Step 5)

Ex. Prelim.	(A) v East Grinstead Town	W	7-0	73
		Abbott (2), Brown, Foley,		
		Gretorex, Probets, Turner		
Prelim.	(H) v Hastings United	L	0-2	122

Best Performance: 1st Qualifying Round 2003-2004 2004-2005

WAKEFIELD-EMLEY

M.P.L. Prem (Step 3)

1st Qual.	(H) v Blyth Spartans	L	1-2	162
		Kenworthy		

Best Performance: 3rd Round 1997-1998

WALTHAM ABBEY

Essex (Step 5)

Ex. Prelim.	(A) v Romford	W	3-1	107
		White (2)		
Prelim.	(H) v Wingate & Finchley	W	6-2	58
		Elmes (2), Page, Sontag,		
		White (2)		
1st Qual.	(A) v Enfield Town	L	0-3	314

Best Performance: 1st Qualifying Round 2005-2006

WALTHAM FOREST

Southern 1E (Step 4)

Prelim.	(A) v Fakenham Town	W	4-1	65
		Belton-McKenzie, Hughes,		
		Thomas (2)		
1st Qual.	(H) v Hitchin Town	L	1-4	168
		Thomas		

Best Performance: 2nd Qualifying Round 2004-2005

WALTON & HERSHAM

Ryman Premier (Step 3)

1st Qual.	(A)	v Burgess Hill Town	W	4-0	169
		Edgar (2), Haylock (2)			
2nd Qual.	(A)	v AFC Wimbledon	W	3-0	1930
		Cartwright, Keevill, Nwokeji			
3rd Qual.	(A)	v Ramsgate	L	0-1	301

Best Performance: 2nd Round 1992-1993

WALTON CASUALS

Ryman 1 (Step 4)

Prelim.	(A)	v Three Bridges	L	0-1	84

Best Performance: 1st Qualifying Round 2002-2003 2003-2004

WANTAGE TOWN

Hellenic Prem. (Step 5)

Ex. Prelim.	(A)	v Saltdean United	D	0-0	47
Replay	(H)	v Saltdean United	L	0-2	76

Best Performance: Extra Preliminary Round 2005-2006

WARE

Ryman 2 (Step 5)

Ex. Prelim.	(H)	v Sporting Bengal Utd	W	2-0	207
		Hanson, Stevens			
Prelim.	(H)	v Northampton Spencer	L	2-4	103
		Hanson, Stevens			

Best Performance: 1st Round 1968-1969

WARRINGTON TOWN

N.P.L. 1 (Step 4)

Prelim.	(H)	v Penrith	D	2-2	84
		Mitchell (2)			
Replay	(A)	v Penrith	W	2-1*	118
		McNally, Randles			
1st Qual.	(A)	v Gateshead	L	0-4	235

Best Performance: 4th Qualifying Round 1994-1995

WASHINGTON

Northern 2 (Step 6)

Prelim.	(H)	v Stocksbridge PS	D	0-0	94
Replay	(A)	v Stocksbridge PS	D	1-1*	126
Stocksbridge won 4-2 on pens.			Burns		

Best Performance: 4th Qualifying Round 1970-1971

WEALDSTONE

Ryman Premier (Step 3)

1st Qual.	(A)	v Stanway Rovers	D	0-0	170
Replay	(H)	v Stanway Rovers	W	3-0	179
		Beckford, Jolly, Ryan			
2nd Qual.	(A)	v Banstead Athletic	W	4-1	164
		Cooper, Harris (2), Jolly			
3rd Qual.	(H)	v Burnham	L	2-4	247
		Beckford (2)			

Best Performance: 3rd Round 1977-1978

WELLING UNITED

Conference South (Step 2)

2nd Qual.	(A)	v Boreham Wood	W	2-0	267
		Perkins, Pinnock			
3rd Qual.	(A)	v Harrow Borough	W	1-0	258
		Bodkin			
4th Qual.	(A)	v Dorchester Town	W	2-1	533
		Bodkin, Kedwell			
1st Round	(A)	v Huddersfield (L1)	L	1-4	5518
		C. Moore			

Best Performance: 3rd Round 1988-1989

WELTON ROVERS

Western Prem.(Step 5)

Prelim.	(A)	v Highworth Town	L	0-1	122

Best Performance: 2nd Round 1964-1965 1966-1967

WELWYN GARDEN CITY

S.S.Mids (Step 5)

Prelim.	(H)	v Aylesbury Vale	W	2-0	76
		Brumwell, Garness			
1st Qual.	(H)	v Beaconsfield SYCOB	W	3-2	71
		Devera, Edgerley, Wardle			
2nd Qual.	(H)	v St Neots Town	W	4-2	304
		Devera, Edgerley, Wardle			
3rd Qual.	(A)	v Histon	L	1-2	373
		Garness			

Best Performance: 2nd Qualifyinmg Round 2005-2006

WEMBLEY

Ryman 2 (Step 5)

Ex. Prelim.	(H)	v St Neots Town	L	0-2	87

Best Performance: 1st Round 1980-1981

WEST ALLOTMENT CELTIC

Northern 1 (Step 5)

Ex. Prelim.	(A)	v Cammell Laird	L	1-4	130
		Douglas			

Best Performance: Extra Preliminary Round 2005-2006

WEST AUCKLAND TOWN

Northern 1 (Step 5)

Ex. Prelim.	(H)	v Shildon	W	2-1	125
		Moffett (2)			
Prelim.	(A)	v Whickham	W	5-1	90
		Bell, Ellison (2), Moffett, Reid			
1st Qual.	(A)	v Thornaby	L	3-4	62
		Fairhurst, Richmond			

Best Performance: 1st Round 1958-1959 1961-1962 1998-1999

WESTBURY UNITED

Western 1 (Step 6)

Ex. Prelim.	(H)	v Newquay	W	2-1	78
		Beavers, Groves			
Prelim.	(A)	v Melksham Town	D	2-2	112
		Wheeler (2)			
Replay	(H)	v Melksham Town	L	2-3	190
		Ayton, Beavers			

Best Performance: 3rd Qualifying Round 1947-1948 1948-1949

WESTFIELD

Co.Co (Step 5)

Ex. Prelim.	(H)	v Godalming Town	L	1-2	61
		Reeves			

Best Performance: 1st Qualifying Round 2004-2005.

WESTFIELDS

Mid. Alliance (Step 5)

Prelim.	(H)	v Sutton Coldfield Town	W	3-0	56
		Aubrey (3)			
1st Qual.	(H)	v Belper Town	L	1-2	122
		Davis			

Best Performance:

WESTON SUPER MARE

Conference South (Step 2)

2nd Qual.	(H)	v Weymouth	D	2-2	744
		Evans, French			
Replay	(A)	v Weymouth	L	0-1	1003

Best Performance: 2nd Round 2003-2004

WEYMOUTH

Conference South (Step 2)

2nd Qual.	(A)	v Weston-Super-Mare	D	2-2	744
		Dutton, Jackson			
Replay	(H)	v Weston-Super-Mare	W	1-0	1003
		Taggart			
3rd Qual.	(H)	v Bath City	W	1-0	1232
		Bound			
4th Qual.	(H)	v Cambridge United	W	2-1	1652
		Jackson, Purser			
1st Round	(A)	v Nottingham Forest (L1)	D	1-1	10305
		Harris			
Replay	(H)	v Nottingham Forest	L	0-2	6500

Best Performance: 4th Round 1961-1962

WHICKHAM

Northern 2 (Step 6)

Prelim.	(H) v West Auckland Town	L	1-5	90
	Elliott			

Best Performance: 1st Qualifying Round 1989-1990

WHITBY TOWN

N.P.L. Prem. (Step 3)

1st Qual.	(A) v Newcastle Blue Star	W	2-1	208
	Atkinson, Nicholson			
2nd Qual.	(A) v Trafford	D	1-1	164
	Raw			
Replay	(H) v Trafford	W	6-0	196
	Raw, Veart, Brown (3),			
	Wilford			
3rd Qual.	(A) v Alfreton Town	L	1-2	231
	McTiernan			

Best Performance: 2nd Rd 1983-1984

WHITEHAWK

Sussex (Step 6)

Ex. Prelim.	(A) v Lancing	W	2-1	95
	Cooper, Gunn			
Prelim.	(H) v AFC Totton	L	0-2	80

Best Performance: 4th Qualifying Round 1988-1989

WHITLEY BAY

Northern 1 (Step 5)

Prelim.	(A) v Bridlington Town	D	2-2	180
	Fairlamb, Johnston			
Replay	(H) v Bridlington Town	W	4-0	189
	Johnston, Leadbitter (2),			
	Walton			
1st Qual.	(H) v Ramsbottom United	L	1-2	162
	Kerr			

Best Performance: 3rd Round 1989-1990

WHITSTABLE TOWN

Kent (Step 5)

Prelim.	(H) v Fleet Town	D	3-3	162
	Constable, Marshall, Prett			
Replay	(A) v Fleet Town	L	1-2	104
	Constable			

Best Performance: 3rd Qualifying Round 1957-1958 86-87 89-90

WHYTELEAFE

Ryman 1 (Step 4)

Prelim.	(A) v Ashford Town (Middx)	L	1-3	102
	Martin			

Best Performance: 1st Round 1999-2000

WICK

Sussex 1 (Step 5

Prelim.	(H) v Arundel	D	1-1	155
	Morrow			
Replay	(A) v Arundel	W	2-1	204
	Christodoulou, Manton			
1st Qual.	(H) v Worthing	L	0-4	283

Best Performance: 2nd Qualifying Round 1981-1982

WILLAND ROVERS

Western Prem. (Step 5)

Ex. Prelim.	(H) v Hamworthy United	L	0-1	167

Best Performance: Extra Preliminary Round 2005-2006

WILLENHALL TOWN

Southern 1W (Step4)

Prelim.	(H) v Blackstones	W	1-0	104
	Holland			
1st Qual.	(H) v Malvern Town	D	1-1	131
	Swann			
Replay	(A) v Malvern Town	L	0-1	139

Best Performance: 1st Round 1981-1982

WIMBORNE TOWN

Wessex 1 (Step 5)

Ex. Prelim.	(A) v Slimbridge	W	1-0	131
	Percival			
Prelim.	(A) v Chard Town	D	0-0	93
Replay	(H) v Chard Town	W	2-0	200
	Cooper, Roast			
1st Qual.	(A) v Cirencester Town	L	3-5	147
	Cannie (2), Walker			

Best Performance: 1st Round 1982-1983

WINCHESTER CITY

Wessex 1 (Step 5)

Prelim.	(H) v Maidstone United	L	0-3	452

Best Performance: 2nd Qualifyinmg Round 2003-2004

WINDSOR & ETON

Ryman Premier (Step 3)

1st Qual.	(A) v Ashford Town	W	3-0	163
	Holsgrove (2), Warner			
2nd Qual.	(A) v Brentwood Town	W	2-1	144
	Holsgrove, Warner			
3rd Qual.	(A) v Tiverton Town	L	1-2	531
	Wallace			

Best Performance: 2nd Round 1083-1984

WINGATE & FINCHLEY

Southern 1 E (Step 4)

Prelim.	(A) v Waltham Abbey	L	2-6	58
	Sloma, Stolerman			

Best Performance: 2nd Qualifying Round 2003-2004

WINSFORD UNITED

N.W.Co. 2 (Step 6)

Ex. Prelim.	(H) v Alsager Town	D	1-1	99
	Arnold			
Replay	(A) v Alsager Town	W	1-0	120
	Wellstead			
Prelim.	(A) v Northallerton Town	L	0-4	100

Best Performance: 2nd Rd 1887-1888 1st Rd 1975-76 19991-92

WINTERTON RANGERS

N.Co.E. 1 (Step 6)

Ex. Prelim.	(H) v North Shields	W	1-0	56
	Keel			
Prelim.	(A) v Hebburn Town	D	1-1	143
	Pindar			
Replay	(H) v Hebburn Town	L	0-2	102

Best Performance: 4th Qualifying Round 1976-1977

WISBECH TOWN

Eastern Co.Prem. (Step 5)

Ex. Prelim.	(A) v Hullbridge Sports	W	5-2	70
	Dunn, Gubberley, Jimson,			
	Nimmo (2)			
Prelim.	(A) v Woodford United	L	0-1	92

Best Performance: 2nd Round 1957-1958

WITHAM TOWN

Ryman 2 (Step 5)

Ex. Prelim.	(H) v Hadleigh United	W	1-0	51
	Hawes			
Prelim.	(A) v Henley Town	W	4-2	78
	Hawes (2), Lunn, Sampson			
1st Qual.	(A) v Hampton & R.Boro'	L	0-3	226

Best Performance: 2nd Qualifying Rd 1988-1989 1989 -1990

WITNEY UNITED

Hellenic Prem. (Step 5)

Prelim.	(H) v Clevedon Town	D	0-0	155
Replay	(A) v Clevedon Town	L	2-3	162
	Keyes (2)			

Best Performance: 1st Round 1971-1972 (as Whitney Town)

WITTON ALBION
N.P.L. Prem. (Step 3)

1st Qual.	(A)	v Kendal Town	W 3-2	160
			Jones, Moseley, Peers	
2nd Qual.	(A)	v Worksop Town	W 1-0	348
			Jones	
3rd Qual.	(A)	v Harrogate Town	L 0-2	402

Best Performance: 2nd Round 1991-1992

WIVENHOE TOWN
Southern 1E (Step 4)

Prelim.	(A)	v Tilbury	W 3-0	38
			Hillier (2), Townrow	
1st Qual.	(A)	v Rothwell Town	W 3-1	93
			Martin (2), Townrow	
2nd Qual.	(H)	v Heybridge Swifts	L 1-4	241
			Hillier	

Best Performance: 4th Qualifying Round 1989-1990 1994-1995

WOKING
Conference (Step 1)

4th Qual.	(H)	v Thurrock	W 3-0	1486
			Oliver, Jackson, Ferguson	
1st Round	(A)	v Southport	D 1-1	1417
			Evans	
Replay	(H)	v Southport	W 1-0*	2298
			McAllister	
2nd Round	(H)	v Northwich Victoria	D 0-0	2462
Replay	(A)	v Northwich Victoria	L 1-2	2302
			Ferguson	

Best Performance: 4th Round 1990-19991

WOODBRIDGE TOWN
E Co. Prem. (Step 5)

Ex. Prelim.	(H)	v Lowestoft Town	D 3-3	121
			Goddard, Snell (2)	
Replay	(A)	v Lowestoft Town	L 0-5	238

Best Performance: 3rd Qualifying Round 1997-1998 2000-2001

No lack of effort as Wootton B.C. and Desborough Town players challenge for the ball. Photo: Peter Barnes.

WOODFORD UNITED
Utd. Co. Prem. (Step 5)

Ex. Prelim.	(A)	v Southend Manor	W 1-0	34
			Dunkey	
Prelim.	(H)	v Wisbech Town	W 1-0	92
			Gordon	
1st Qual.	(H)	v Harwich & Parkeston	W 5-0	76
			Champelovier, Dunkley, Fountain, Gordon, Parkinson	
2nd Qual.	(A)	v Redditch United	D 1-1	316
			Dunkley	
Replay	(H)	v Redditch United	D 2-2	207
			Woodford won 10-9 on pens. Milner, Pearman	
3rd Qual.	(A)	v Leamington	L 0-2	1017

Best Performance: 3rd Qualifying Round 2005-2006

WOODLEY SPORTS
N.P.L. 1 (Step 4)

Prelim.	(A)	v Glasshoughton W.	W 2-0	35
			Wilkinson, Young	
1st Qual.	(H)	v Prescot Cables	L 2-4	71
			Bricknell, Dickinson	

Best Performance: 1st Qualifying Round 1999-2000 2005-2006

WOOTTON BLUE CROSS
Utd.Co. Prem. (Step 5)

Ex. Prelim.	(H)	v Desborough Town	W 2-0	67
			Johnson, Joswiak	
Prelim.	(H)	v Barton Rovers	D 1-1	79
			Deverall	
Replay	(A)	v Barton Rovers	L 1-4*	144
			Joswiak	

Best Performance: 2nd Qualifying Round 1950-1951

WORCESTER CITY
Conference North (League (Step 2)

2nd Qual.	(H)	v Bemberton Heath H.	W 7-0	579
			Colley, Kelly (2), McDonald Webster (2), Wedgbury	
3rd Qual.	(H)	v Tonbridge Angels	W 3-0	684
			Kelly, Webster, Hyde	
4th Qual.	(A)	v Accrington Stanley	D 1-1	940
			Kelly	
Replay	(H)	v Accrington Stanley	W 3-2	1331
			Smith, Webster, Warner	
1st Round	(A)	v Chippenham Town	D 1-1	2815
			Webster	
Replay	(H)	v Chippenham Town	W 1-0	4006
			Webster	
2nd Round	(H)	v Huddersfield Town	L 0-1	4163

Best Performance: 4th Round 1958-1959

WORKINGTON
Conference North (Step 2)

2nd Qual.	(A)	v Stalybridge Celtic	D 0-0	448
Replay	(H)	v Stalybridge Celtic	W 2-1*	315
			Kenney, OG	
3rd Qual.	(A)	v Burscough	L 0-2	303

Best Performance: 4th Round 1933-1934

WORKSOP TOWN
Conference North (Step 2)

2nd Qual.	(H)	v Witton Albion	L 0-1	348

Best Performance: 3rd Round 1955-1956

WORTHING
Ryman Premier (Step 3)

1st Qual.	(A)	v Wick	W 4-0	283
			Browne (2), Francis (2)	
2nd Qual.	(A)	v AFC Hornchurch	W 4-1	544
			Browne, Francis (2), Knee	
3rd Qual.	(H)	v Basingstoke Town	L 2-4	577
			Browne, Cable	

Best Performance: 2nd Round 1982-1983

WROXHAM

Eastern Co P (Step 5)

Prelim.	(A)	v Leighton Town	D	1-1	113
			Coote		
Replay	(H)	v Leighton Town	W	4-1	132
			Coote, Edridge, Furlong		
1st Qual.	(H)	v Diss Town	W	2-0	228
			Gilman (2)		
2nd Qual.	(H)	v Slough Town	W	2-0	267
			Fox, Lennon		
3rd Qual.	(H)	v Aylesbury United	D	1-1	257
			Coote		
Replay	(A)	v Aylesbury United	L	2-4	381
			Gilman (2)		

Best Performance: 4th Qualifying Round

YATE TOWN

Southetr Premier (Step 3)

1st Qual.	(H)	v Bodmin Town	W	2-0	170
			Edwards, Stonehouse		
2nd Qual.	(H)	v Salisbury City	L	0-2	371

Best Performance: 2nd Qualifying Round 2005-2006

YAXLEY

Utd Co. Prem. (Step 5)

Ex. Prelim.	(A)	v Soham Town Rangers L		1-2	151
			Paul		

Best Performance: 1st Qualifying Round 2003-2004

YEADING

Conference South (Step 2)

2nd Qual.	(H)	v Maidenhead United	W	3-0	185
			Saroya, Telemaque,		
			Williams		
3rd Qual.	(H)	v Dorchester Town	D	1-1	151
			Williams		
Replay	(A)	v Dorchester Town	L	2-3	394
			Mapes, Williams		

Best Performance: 3rd Ropund 2004-2005

YORK CITY

Conference (Step 1)

4th Qual.	(A)	v Gainsborough Trinity	W	4-0	1680
			Bishop (2), Donaldson		
			Connery		
1st Round	(H)	v Grays Athletic	L	0-3	3586

Best Performance: Semi-Final 1954 -1955 (In 3rd Div North)

YORKSHIRE AMATEUR

N.Co.E. 1 (Step 6)

Prelim.	(H)	v Bedlington Terriers	W	2-1	45
			Britten (2)		
1st Qual.	(A)	v Trafford	L	1-4	117
			Bingley		

Best Performance: 1st Round 1931-32 1945-1946

ROUND BY ROUND

EXTRA PRELIMINARY ROUND

BIGGEST HOME WIN:	**6-0** BIGGLESWADE UNITED VS HAVERHILL ROVERS
BIGGEST AWAY WIN:	**0-7** EAST GRINSTED TOWN VS VCD ATHLETIC
HIGHEST ATTENDANCE:	**292** DIDCOT TOWN VS ANDOVER
NUMBER OF GAMES:	**86 + 16** (73 + 15)
TOTAL ATTENDANCE:	**9,819** (9,369)
AVERAGE ATTENDANCE:	**96** (106)

Home	Away	Score	Att
AFC Newbury	v Farnham Town	2-2	95
AFC Totton	v Milton United	5-0	80
Andover	v Didcot Town	4-4	190
Aylesbury Vale	v Kirkley	2-2	105
Bacup Borough	v Pickering Town	0-5	40
Biggleswade United	v Haverhill Rovers	6-0	106
Bishops Cleeve	v Corsham Town	1-0	94
Blackpool Mechanics	v Newcastle Blue Star	1-2	80
Borrowash Victoria	v Ford Sports Daventry	1-1	79
Bowers & Pitsea	v Stotfold	2-2	41
Brandon United	v Billingham Synthonia	0-5	71
Brook House	v Leiston	1-1	77
Broxbourne Borough V&Ev Holmer Green		1-4	28
Calne Town	v Shortwood United	0-2	56
Cammell Laird	v West Allotment Celtic	4-1	130
Chalfont St Peter	v Buckingham Town	1-0	67
Cheadle Town	v Abbey Hey	3-1	46
Chichester City United	v East Preston	1-2	65
Concord Rangers	v Kingsbury Town	0-1	53
Congleton Town	v Romulus	2-0	148
Curzon Ashton	v Darwen	2-1	145
East Grinstead Town	v VCD Athletic	0-7	73
Eastbourne Utd Assoc	v Ash United	1-2	68
Erith & Belvedere	v Hamble ASSC	4-2	99
Erith Town	v Hassocks	0-3	46
Esh Winning	v Ashington	4-4	59
Eton Manor	v Leverstock Green	0-1	35
Fakenham Town	v Long Buckby	2-0	52
Fareham Town	v Selsey	0-0	90
Flixton	v Hebburn Town	1-2	64
Formby	v Consett	1-1	57
Gorleston	v North Greenford United	2-4	84
Gosport Borough	v Sandhurst Town	6-1	138
Guisborough Town	v Great Harwood Town	1-1	77
Hallen	v Porthleven	3-0	78
Harefield United	v Langford	2-3	33
Haringey Borough	v Felixstowe & Walton	0-3	73
Harpenden Town	v Sawbridgeworth Town	2-1	61
Horsham YMCA	v Hailsham Town	1-0	80
Hullbridge Sports	v Wisbech Town	2-5	70
Hungerford Town	v North Leigh	0-4	71
Hythe Town	v Raynes Park Vale	4-1	116
Jarrow Roofing Boldon CA v Sheffield		0-4	56
Lancing	v Whitehawk	1-2	95
London APSA	v Halstead Town	0-2	78
Long Eaton United	v Quorn	2-1	93
Minehead	v Almondsbury Town	1-2	49
Moneyfields	v Abingdon Town	6-1	70
Nelson	v Retford United	2-4	106
Newcastle BBP	v Bedlington Terriers	2-4	153
Norton United	v Alvechurch	1-0	40
Odd Down	v Portland United	2-0	50
Oldbury United	v Racing Club Warwick	2-1	72
Oldham Town	v Morpeth Town	1-0	40
Prudhoe Town	v Horden CW	1-3	32
Romford	v Waltham Abbey	1-3	82
Rossington Main	v Garforth Town	1-1	79
Saffron Walden Town	v Flackwell Heath	1-1	102
Saltdean United	v Wantage Town	0-0	47
Sevenoaks Town	v Chertsey Town	4-2	133
Shirebrook Town	v Teversal	2-3	183
Sidley United	v Pagham	3-1	205
Skelmersdale United	v Liversedge	1-0	132
Slimbridge	v Wimborne Town	0-1	131
Soham Town Rangers	v Yaxley	2-1	151

897

Home		Away	Score	Att
Southend Manor	v	Woodford United	0-1	44
St Margaretsbury	v	St Ives Town	2-1	60
Stanway Rovers	v	Norwich United	4-1	80
Stourbridge	v	Glossop North End	3-0	211
Studley	v	Oadby Town	1-3	67
Sutton Town	v	Loughborough Dynamo	5-1	108
Thamesmead Town	v	Abingdon United	2-4	23
Three Bridges	v	Shoreham	2-0	55
Tow Law Town	v	Squires Gate	2-0	108
Tuffley Rovers	v	Elmore	0-0	45
Ware	v	Sporting Bengal United	2-0	207
Wembley	v	St Neots Town	0-2	87
West Auckland Town	v	Shildon	2-1	125
Westbury United	v	Newquay	2-1	78
Westfield	v	Godalming Town	1-2	61
Willand Rovers	v	Hamworthy United	0-1	167
Winsford United	v	Alsager Town	1-1	119
Winterton Rangers	v	North Shields	1-0	56
Witham Town	v	Hadleigh United	1-0	51
Woodbridge Town	v	Lowestoft Town	3-3	121
Wootton Blue Cross	v	Desborough Town	2-0	67

REPLAYS

Home		Away	Score	Att
Ashington	v	Esh Winning	1-0	165
Alsager Town	v	Winsford United	0-1	120
Consett	v	Formby	5-1	104
Didcot Town	v	Andover	2-0	292
Elmore	v	Tuffley Rovers	1-0	85
Farnham Town	v	AFC Newbury	2-3*	90
Flackwell Heath	v	Saffron Walden Town	3-1	82
Ford Sports Daventry	v	Borrowash Victoria	1-2	50
Garforth Town	v	Rossington Main	3-0	58
Great Harwood Town	v	Guisborough Town	3-3*, 4-2p	95
Kirkley	v	Aylesbury Vale	0-3	181
Lesiton	v	Brook House	1-3	122
Lowestoft Town	v	Woodbridge Town	5-0	238
Selsey	v	Fareham Town	3-2	230
Stotfold	v	Bowers & Pitsea	3-3*, 4-2p	65
Wantage Town	v	Saltdean United	0-2	76

PRELIMINARY ROUND

BIGGEST HOME WIN:	**7-0** HALSTEAD TOWN VS CORNARD UNITED
BIGGEST AWAY WIN:	**0-8** ELY CITY VS BURY TOWN
	MOLE VALLEY (PREDATORS) VS GOSPORT BOROUGH
HIGHEST ATTENDANCE:	**538** LEAMINGTON VS SUTTON TOWN
NUMBER OF GAMES:	**182 + 37** (182 + 29)
TOTAL ATTENDANCE:	**27,248** (28,699)
AVERAGE ATTENDANCE:	**124** (386)

Home		Away	Score	Att
AFC Hornchurch	v	Chalfont St Peter	0-0	320
Almondsbury Town	v	Cinderford Town	3-5	81
Ash United	v	Leatherhead	1-1	111
Ashford Town	v	Slade Green	3-1	169
Ashford Town (Mx)	v	Whyteleafe	3-1	102
Atherton LR	v	Goole	1-1	70
Aveley	v	Kingsbury Town	5-1	53
Banstead Athletic	v	Alton Town	1-0	37
Barking & East Ham Utd	v	St Margaretsbury	1-1	91
Barkingside	v	Leverstock Green	2-2	111
Barnstaple Town	v	Clevedon United	4-1	130
Bashley	v	Hythe Town	4-0	76
BAT Sports	v	Abingdon United	0-3	54
Bedworth United	v	Rocester	3-1	107
Belper Town	v	Leek CSOB	1-0	148
Bemerton Heath H	v	Ilfracombe Town	1-0	64
Berkhamsted Town	v	Newmarket Town	2-0	131

Home		Away	Score	Att
Billingham Synthonia	v	Fleetwood Town	2-0	128
Bishops Cleeve	v	Bideford	3-1	107
Bitton	v	Dawlish Town	2-1	127
Boreham Wood	v	Dereham Town	3-0	115
Bridgwater Town	v	Paulton Rovers	0-1	168
Bridlington Town	v	Whitley Bay	2-2	180
Bridport	v	Falmouth Town	0-3	139
Brigg Town	v	Holker Old Boys	4-0	123
Bromsgrove Rovers	v	Bourne Town	4-1	274
Burnham	v	Selsey	2-0	49
Burnham Ramblers	v	Flackwell Heath	4-3	56
Bury Town	v	Ely City	1-1	155
Cammell Laird	v	Alnwick Town	6-0	115
Carterton Town	v	Didcot Town	0-3	109
Chard Town	v	Wimborne Town	0-0	93
Chasetown	v	Causeway United	2-0	111
Chatham Town	v	North Leigh	2-0	154
Cheadle Town	v	Bamber Bridge	2-1	71
Chipstead	v	Brockenhurst	4-2	72
Christchurch	v	Bishop Sutton	5-0	55
Coalville Town	v	Borrowash Victoria	3-0	117
Cobham	v	Egham Town	0-2	45
Cogenhoe United	v	Hanwell Town	4-1	78
Colne	v	Chadderton	1-2	111
Congleton Town	v	Corby Town	1-2	164
Cradley Town	v	Biddulph Victoria	2-1	41
Crook Town	v	St Helens Town	0-3	103
Croydon	v	Frimley Green	1-1	56
Croydon Athletic	v	Redhill	4-2	76
Curzon Ashton	v	Garforth Town	1-0	141
Dartford	v	Dorking	1-2	281
Deeping Rangers	v	Norton United	0-0	77
Durham City	v	Brodsworth Miners Welfare	5-0	127
East Preston	v	Cowes Sports	0-1	51
Eccleshill United	v	Chester Le Street Town	1-2	52
Elmore	v	Torrington	2-0	43
Epsom & Ewell	v	AFC Newbury	6-1	81
Erith & Belvedere	v	Tooting & Mitcham	1-2	215
Fairford Town	v	Devizes Town	0-0	55
Fakenham Town	v	Waltham Forest	1-4	65
Felixstowe & Walton	v	Dunstable Town	1-2	123
Frome Town	v	St Blazey	0-0	211
Frome withdrew from replay - unable to raise a team.				
Glapwell	v	Barwell	3-1	46
Glasshoughton Welfare	v	Woodley Sports	0-2	35
Godalming Town	v	Dulwich Hamlet	1-2	121
Great Yarmouth Town	v	Stanway Rovers	2-3	80
Hallen	v	Swindon Supermarine	1-3	83
Halstead Town	v	Cornard United	7-0	114
Hamworthy United	v	Backwell United	4-0	122
Harlow Town	v	Newport Pagnell Town	4-2	119
Harrogate Railway	v	Clitheroe	1-2	138
Harwich & Parkeston	v	Holmer Green	2-2	110
Hebburn Town	v	Winterton Rangers	1-1	143
Henley Town	v	Witham Town	2-4	78
Herne Bay	v	Sevenoaks Town	3-2	117
Hertford Town	v	Ruislip Manor	1-2	85
Highworth Town	v	Welton Rovers	1-0	122
Hillingdon Borough	v	Hassocks	0-0	64
Holbeach United	v	Boldmere St Michaels	0-2	56
Horden CW	v	Kendal Town	1-2	79
Horsham YMCA	v	Corinthian Casuals	2-0	99
Ilford	v	Brackley Town	0-2	68

Home	Away	Score	Att.
Kingstonian	v Ringmer	2-1	324
Leamington	v Sutton Town	0-0	538
Leighton Town	v Wroxham	1-1	113
Lincoln Moorlands	v Eastwood Town	0-0	74
Liskeard Athletic	v Brislington	2-0	73
Littlehampton Town	v Tunbridge Wells	1-1	131
London Colney	v Rothwell Town	2-3	50
Long Eaton United	v Boston Town	4-2	63
Long Melford	v AFC Sudbury	0-1	448
Lordswood	v Saltdean United	3-2	60
Lymington & New Milton	v Dover Athletic	0-2	172
Maine Road	v Armthorpe Welfare	0-2	40
Malvern Town	v Mickleover Sports	4-3	136
March Town United	v Harpenden Town	4-1	108
Marlow	v Arlesey Town	2-3	88
Melksham Town	v Westbury United	2-2	112
Merstham	v Ramsgate	1-4	85
Metropolitan Police	v Bracknell Town	0-0	81
Mildenhall Town	v Potters Bar Town	3-1	140
Mile Oak	v Camberley Town	1-1	61

Awarded to Camberley - Mile Oak played ineligible player

Home	Away	Score	Att.
Mole Valley Predators	v Gosport Borough	0-8	58
Molesey	v Burgess Hill Town	2-4	121
Moneyfields	v Rye & Iden United	4-0	109
Nantwich Town	v Gresley Rovers	3-1	131
Needham Market	v Diss Town	2-5	191
New Mills	v Salford City	0-2	206
Newcastle Blue Star	v Hallam	2-0	62
Newcastle Town	v Buxton	1-1	211
North Greenford United	v Brook House	1-6	65
Northallerton Town	v Winsford United	4-0	130

Match abandoned 80 mins. Result stands

Home	Away	Score	Att.
Norton & Stockton A.	v Great Harwood Town	0-4	67
Oadby Town	v Stamford	3-3	175
Odd Down	v Exmouth Town	3-2	25
Oldbury United	v Stone Dominoes	4-0	62
Oldham Town	v Hall Road Rangers	2-0	55
Ossett Albion	v Dunston Federation Brewery	0-3	103
Oxford City	v Newport IoW	3-2	139
Oxhey Jets	v Lowestoft Town	1-2	139
Penzance	v Street	2-2	158
Pickering Town	v Ashington	2-2	228
Pontefract Collieries	v Bishop Auckland	2-3	62
Ramsbottom United	v Marske United	3-1	169
Raunds Town	v Beaconsfield SYCOB	0-2	65
Reading Town	v Eastbourne Town	1-3	44
Retford United	v Parkgate	4-3	197
Rossendale United	v Sunderland Nissan	1-1	76
Royston Town	v Clacton Town	1-2	83
Rushall Olympic	v Gedling Town	0-2	78
Seaham Red Star	v Atherton Collieries	2-0	62
Selby Town	v Billingham Town	1-3	150
Sheffield	v Mossley	2-2	229
Shepshed Dynamo	v Carlton Town	4-1	96
Shepton Mallet	v Bournemouth	0-2	69
Shortwood United	v Bodmin Town	2-3	93
Sidlesham	v Bedfont	1-2	53
Sidley United	v Deal Town	1-1	104
Sittingbourne	v Chessington & Hook	2-4	138
Skelmersdale United	v Colwyn Bay	2-0	219
Soham Town Rangers	v Enfield Town	1-2	254
Solihull Borough	v Eccleshall	2-0	115
South Normanton Ath.	v Arnold Town	1-0	84

Home	Away	Score	Att.
Southall	v Enfield	5-0	48
Spalding United	v Staveley MW	0-1	121
Spennymoor Town	v Consett	0-2	284
St Neots Town	v Hemel Hempstead	1-4	145
Stansted	v Langford	2-1	70
Steyning Town	v Cray Wanderers	0-6	80
Stotfold	v Clapton	1-2	70
Stourbridge	v Kidsgrove Athletic	2-2	218
Stourport Swifts	v Stratford Town	1-2	71
Stowmarket Town	v Ipswich Wanderers	2-2	119
Tadcaster Albion	v Chorley	2-2	110
Taunton Town	v Bristol Manor Farm	1-0	268
Teversal	v Pegasus Juniors	1-1	78
Thackley	v South Shields	2-0	57
Thame United	v Brentwood Town	0-1	49
Thatcham Town	v Cove	3-0	80
Thornaby	v Peterlee Newtown	3-0	49
Three Bridges	v Walton Casuals	1-0	84
Tilbury	v Wivenhoe Town	0-3	38
Tiptree United	v Potton United	2-3	91
Tonbridge Angels	v Horsham	3-1	457
Tow Law Town	v Padiham	1-3	112
Trafford	v Silsden	3-1	159
Tring Athletic	v Biggleswade United	1-2	140
Uxbridge	v Great Wakering Rovers	2-3	93
VCD Athletic	v Hastings United	0-2	187
Waltham Abbey	v Wingate & Finchley	6-2	58
Ware	v Northampton Spencer	2-4	103
Warrington Town	v Penrith	2-2	84
Washington	v Stocksbridge PS	0-0	94
Welwyn Garden City	v Aylesbury Vale	2-0	76
Westfields	v Sutton Coldfield Town	3-0	56
Whickham	v West Auckland Town	1-5	90
Whitehawk	v AFC Totton	0-2	80
Whitstable Town	v Fleet Town	3-3	162
Wick	v Arundel	1-1	155
Willenhall Town	v Blackstones	1-0	104
Winchester City	v Maidstone United	0-3	452
Witney United	v Clevedon Town	0-0	155
Woodford United	v Wisbech Town	1-0	92
Wootton Blue Cross	v Barton Rovers	1-1	79
Yorkshire Amateur	v Bedlington Terriers	2-1	45

REPLAYS

Home	Away	Score	Att.
Arundel	v Wick	1-2	204
Ashington	v Pickering Town	1-2	282
Barton Rovers	v Wootton Blue Cross	4-1*	144
Bracknell Town	v Metropolitan Police	0-2	131
Buxton	v Newcastle Town	1-2	376
Chalfont St Peter	v AFC Hornchurch	1-2	104
Chorley	v Tadcaster Albion	2-0	176
Clevedon Town	v Witney United	3-2	162
Deal Town	v Sidley United	2-1	143
Devizes Town	v Fairford Town	0-3	85
Eastwood Town	v Lincoln Moorlands	3-2	116
Ely City	v Bury Town	0-8	218
Fleet Town	v Whitstable Town	2-1	104
Frimley Green	v Croydon	0-2	68
Goole	v Atherton LR	2-0	193
Hassocks	v Hillingdon Borough	2-1*	164
Holmer Green	v Harwich & Parkeston	2-5	104
Ipswich Wanderers	v Stowmarket Town	3-1*	169
Kidsgrove Athletic	v Stourbridge	5-2	110
Leatherhead	v Ash United	3-2	235

Leverstock Green	v Barkingside	3-4	64
Mossley	v Sheffield	1-0	268
Norton United	v Deeping Rangers	1-0	42
Pegasus Juniors	v Teversal	3-2	179
Penrith	v Warrington Town	1-2*	118
St Margaretsbury	v Barking & East Ham United	2-0	94
Stamford	v Oadby Town	0-1*	202
Stocksbridge PS	v Washington	1-1*, 4-2p	126
Street	v Penzance	0-0*, 2-4p	135
Sunderland Nissan	v Rossendale United	1-4	58
Sutton Town	v Leamington	2-2*, 8-9p	205
Tunbridge Wells	v Littlehampton Town	2-2*, 16-15p	122
Westbury United	v Melksham Town	2-3	190
Whitley Bay	v Bridlington Town	4-0	189
Wimbrne Town	v Chard Town	2-0	200
Winterton Rangers	v Hebburn Town	0-2	102
Wroxham	v Leighton Town	4-1	132

FIRST QUALIFYING ROUND

BIGGEST HOME WIN:	9-1 BROOK HOUSE VS CLACTON TOWN
BIGGEST AWAY WIN:	0-6 CRADLEY TOWN VS EASTWOOD TOWN
HIGHEST ATTENDANCE:	1,868 AFC WIMBLEDON VS ASHFORD TOWN (MX)
NUMBER OF GAMES:	124 + 25 (124 + 27)
TOTAL ATTENDANCE:	30,655 (30,159)
AVERAGE ATTENDANCE:	206 (200)

Abingdon United	v Dulwich Hamlet	1-1	102
AFC Hornchurch	v Stansted	2-0	415
AFC Telford United	v Rugby Town	1-1	1065
AFC Wimbledon	v Ashford Town (Mx)	2-2	1868
Armthorpe Welfare	v Mossley	3-1	92
Ashford Town	v Windsor & Eton	0-3	163
Aveley	v Burnham Ramblers	1-2	76
Banbury United	v King's Lynn	2-1	549
Banstead Athletic	v Moneyfields	3-0	72
Barkingside	v Maldon Town	1-6	61
Bashley	v Dover Athletic	0-1	141
Bath City	v Cinderford Town	1-0	404
Bedfont	v Bromley	1-4	128
Bedford Town	v AFC Sudbury	2-2	460
Bedworth United	v Solihull Borough	1-1	141
Berkhamsted Town	v Barton Rovers	3-0	144
Billingham Synthonia	v Retford United	4-2	10

Boldmere St Michaels	v Nantwich Town	0-3	94
Bournemouth	v Mangotsfield United	1-1	130
Bradford Park Avenue	v Padiham	1-1	198
Brentwood Town	v Great Wakering Rovers	3-1	131
Bromsgrove Rovers	v Newcastle Town	2-0	242
Brook House	v Clacton Town	9-1	91
Burgess Hill Town	v Walton & Hersham	0-4	169
Burscough	v Ashton United	3-2	187
Bury Town	v Boreham Wood	2-2	166
Camberley Town	v Epsom & Ewell	1-0	73
Cammell Laird	v Radcliffe Borough	2-1	175
Chasetown	v Gedling Town	2-1	76
Chatham Town	v Leatherhead	3-4	251
Chelmsford City	v Harlow Town	1-1	301
Chesham United	v Brackley Town	0-1	224
Cheshunt	v Braintree Town	1-2	132
Chessington & Hook	v Hassocks	0-3	129
Chippenham Town	v Falmouth Town	4-0	443
Chorley	v Bishop Auckland	0-0	237
Cirencester Town	v Wimborne Town	5-3	147
Clevedon Town	v Salisbury City	1-1	264
Cogenhoe United	v Clapton	4-2	68
Corby Town	v Shepshed Dynamo	2-0	184
Cradley Town	v Eastwood Town	0-6	55
Cray Wanderers	v Kingstonian	4-1	225
Croydon Athletic	v Ramsgate	1-3	101
Curzon Ashton	v Chester Le Street Town	0-2	110
Didcot Town	v Herne Bay	0-0	239
Dorking	v Deal Town	1-3	91
Dunston Federation B.	v Thackley	4-1	140
Durham City	v Hebburn Town	0-2	151
East Thurrock United	v Harrow Borough	1-2	96
Eastbourne Town	v Gosport Borough	1-2	160
Enfield Town	v Waltham Abbey	3-0	314
Fairford Town	v Bishops Cleeve	0-1	75
Fisher Athletic	v Tooting & Mitcham	6-2	159
Fleet Town	v Thatcham Town	3-2	138
Folkestone Invicta	v Egham Town	3-1	212
Frickley Athletic	v Chadderton	2-0	214
Gateshead	v Warrington Town	4-0	235
Gloucester City	v Christchurch	0-0	280
Goole	v Clitheroe	5-3	207
Grantham Town	v Lincoln United	4-0	413
Guiseley	v Salford City	0-1	192
Halesowen Town	v South Normanton Athletic	5-3	279
Halstead Town	v Lowestoft Town	1-3	142
Hampton & Richmond	v Witham Town	3-0	226
Hamworthy United	v Team Bath	0-2	132
Hastings United	v Tonbridge Angels	3-3	555
Hendon	v Biggleswade United	6-0	116
Heybridge Swifts	v Arlesey Town	1-0	169
Highworth Town	v Elmore	2-1	135
Hitchin Town	v Waltham Forest	4-1	168
Horsham YMCA	v Croydon	1-2	72
Ilkeston Town	v Coalville Town	1-0	279
Ipswich Wanderers	v Hemel Hempstead	1-1	126
Kendal Town	v Witton Albion	2-3	160
Kidsgrove Athletic	v Leamington	0-1	429
Leek Town	v Long Eaton United	7-0	193
Liskeard Athletic	v Bitton	1-1	102
Lordswood	v AFC Totton	1-2	71
Maidstone United	v Burnham	1-2	347
Margate	v Cowes Sports	4-0	672

Guiseley's Danny Ellis (white) and Salford City's Nick Robinson battle for the ball. Photo: Darren Thomas.

Marine	v Cheadle Town	4-0	191
Matlock Town	v Pegasus Juniors	4-0	160
Merthyr Tydfil	v St Blazey	3-2	407
Metropolitan Police	v Tunbridge Wells	2-0	83
Newcastle Blue Star	v Whitby Town	1-2	208
North Ferriby United	v Brigg Town	3-1	213
Northampton Spencer	v Aylesbury United	1-2	201
Northwood	v March Town United	3-0	141
Oadby Town	v Oldbury United	3-3	142
Oldham Town	v Great Harwood Town	1-2	65
Paulton Rovers	v Barnstaple Town	3-2	102
Penzance	v Bemerton Heath H	0-1	171
Pickering Town	v Farsley Celtic	1-2	146
Potton United	v Leyton	0-1	84
Rossendale United	v Billingham Town	2-2	107
Rothwell Town	v Wivenhoe Town	1-3	93
Ruislip Manor	v Redbridge	1-1	97
Runcorn FC Halton	v Skelmersdale United	2-3	129
Seaham Red Star	v Consett	0-4	87
Slough Town	v Oxford City	4-1	312
Southall	v Mildenhall Town	6-3	75
St Helens Town	v Northallerton Town	3-3	81
St Margaretsbury	v Billericay Town	0-0	228
Staines Town	v Dunstable Town	1-1	174
Stanway Rovers	v Wealdstone	0-0	170
Staveley MW	v Norton United	2-1	67
Stocksbridge PS	v Ossett Town	1-3	104
Stratford Town	v Glapwell	1-3	112
Swindon Supermarine	v Melksham Town	1-0	101
Taunton Town	v Odd Down	3-0	283
Thornaby	v West Auckland Town	4-3	62
Three Bridges	v Chipstead	1-3	59
Tiverton Town	v Evesham United	1-1	392
Trafford	v Yorkshire Amateur	4-1	117
Wakefield Emley	v Blyth Spartans	1-2	162
Welwyn Garden City	v Beaconsfield SYCOB	3-2	71
Westfields	v Belper Town	1-2	122
Whitley Bay	v Ramsbottom United	1-2	162
Wick	v Worthing	0-4	303
Willenhall Town	v Malvern Town	1-1	131
Woodford United	v Harwich & Parkeston	5-0	76
Woodley Sports	v Prescot Cables	2-4	71
Wroxham	v Diss Town	2-0	228
Yate Town	v Bodmin Town	2-0	170

REPLAYS

AFC Sudbury	v Bedford Town	2-1*	441
Ashford Town (Mx)	v AFC Wimbledon	0-2	720
Billericay Town	v St Margretsbury	2-3*	302
Billingham Town	v Rossendale United	2-3	166
Bishop Auckland	v Chorley	2-1	140
Bitton	v Liskeard Athletic	1-0	140
Boreham Wood	v Bury Town	4-2	128
Christchurch	v Gloucester City	3-0	103
Dulwich Hamlet	v Abingdon United	3-2	115
Dunstable Town	v Staines Town	0-1*	118
Evesham United	v Tiverton Town	0-1	130
Harlow Town	v Chelmsford City	0-1	206
Hemel Hempstead	v Ipswich Wanderers	4-1	155
Herne Bay	v Didcot Town	2-6	211
Malvern Town	v Willenhall Town	1-0	139
Mangotsfield United	v Bournemouth	7-0	197
Northallerton Town	v St Helens Town	2-3	134
Oldbury United	v Oadby Town	0-3	62

Padiham	v Bradford Park Avenue	1-4	305
Redbridge	v Ruislip Manor	2-1	88
Rugby Town	v AFC Telford United	2-3*	265
Salisbury City	v Clevedon Town	4-2	506
Solihull Borough	v Bedworth United	3-2	173
Tonbridge Angels	v Hastings United	2-1	454
Wealdstone	v Stanway Rovers	3-0	179

SECOND QUALIFYING ROUND

BIGGEST HOME WIN:	7-0 WORCESTER CITY VS BEMERTON HEATH H.
BIGGEST AWAY WIN:	1-7 HIGHWORTH TOWN VS TIVERTON TOWN
HIGHEST ATTENDANCE:	1,930 AFC WIMBLEDON VS WALTON & HERSHAM
NUMBER OF GAMES:	84 + 23 (84 + 16)
TOTAL ATTENDANCE:	37,699 (38,261)
AVERAGE ATTENDANCE:	352 (383)

AFC Hornchurch	v Worthing	1-4	544
AFC Totton	v Paulton Rovers	2-1	150
AFC Wimbledon	v Walton & Hersham	0-3	1930
Armthorpe Welfare	v Rossendale United	0-2	110
Banstead Athletic	v Wealdstone	1-4	164
Barrow	v Hebburn Town	5-1	911
Billingham Synthonia	v North Ferriby United	0-3	183
Bishops Cleeve	v Bitton	3-0	211
Blyth Spartans	v Prescot Cables	1-0	484
Bognor Regis Town	v Basingstoke Town	1-1	552
Boreham Wood	v Welling United	0-2	267
Brackley Town	v Banbury United	1-1	680
Braintree Town	v Didcot Town	2-0	306
Brentwood Town	v Windsor & Eton	1-2	144
Bromley	v Chipstead	2-1	407
Bromsgrove Rovers	v Hinckley United	3-1	425
Burnham	v Lowestoft Town	1-1	110
Chasetown	v Belper Town	3-3	167
Chelmsford City	v Dover Athletic	1-0	404
Chester Le Street Town	v Leigh RMI	1-3	193
Chippenham Town	v Newport County	4-0	949
Christchurch	v Cirencester Town	0-2	165
Cogenhoe United	v Staveley MW	3-2	91
Consett	v Ossett Town	1-5	166
Cray Wanderers	v Camberley Town	4-1	169
Deal Town	v Hitchin Town	1-3	211
Dorchester Town	v Team Bath	4-2	317
Droylsden	v Burscough	1-2	316
Dunston Federation B.	v Thornaby	1-1	124
Eastleigh	v Havant & Waterlooville	0-0	470
Eastwood Town	v Cambridge City	1-1	225
Enfield Town	v St Albans City	1-1	525
Farnborough Town	v Berkhamsted Town	3-0	456
Farsley Celtic	v Bradford Park Avenue	2-0	403
Fisher Athletic	v Tonbridge Angels	2-3	257
Fleet Town	v Bishop's Stortford	0-2	201
Frickley Athletic	v Northwich Victoria	1-4	392
Gainsborough Trinity	v Goole	2-2	423
Glapwell	v Halesowen Town	0-1	171
Gosport Borough	v Bath City	3-4	440
Hampton & Richmond	v Leatherhead	1-1	357
Harrogate Town	v Great Harwood Town	3-0	346
Harrow Borough	v Burnham Ramblers	2-1	140
Hassocks	v Dulwich Hamlet	0-1	320
Hayes	v Brook House	1-1	406
Hednesford Town	v Moor Green	2-0	491
Hendon	v Metropolitan Police	0-0	155
Highworth Town	v Tiverton Town	1-7	284
Hyde United	v Lancaster City	2-1	333

Kettering Town	v Stafford Rangers	1-0	971	**THIRD QUALIFYING ROUND**				
Leamington	v Oadby Town	2-2	861	BIGGEST HOME WIN:	**4-0** KETTERING TOWN VS ST ALBANS CITY			
Leek Town	v Grantham Town	1-0	347	BIGGEST AWAY WIN:	**0-4** AFC TOTTON VS BISHOP'S CLEEVE			
Leyton	v Lewes	0-1	162	HIGHEST ATTENDANCE:	**1,232** WEYMOUTH VS BATH CITY			
Malvern Town	v Histon	1-4	196	NUMBER OF GAMES:	**42 + 11** (42 + 6)			
Mangotsfield United	v Swindon Supermarine	4-2	278	TOTAL ATTENDANCE:	**24,380** (22,475)			
Margate	v Carshalton Athletic	1-0	773	AVERAGE ATTENDANCE:	**460** (468)			
Marine	v Cammell Laird	1-1	358	Alfreton Town	v Whitby Town	2-1	231	
Matlock Town	v Corby Town	2-0	333	Banbury United	v Hednesford Town	3-4	1005	
Nantwich Town	v Hucknall Town	0-1	220	Bishop's Cleeve	v AFC Totton	1-1	175	
Northwood	v Aylesbury United	0-0	249	Bromley	v Mangotsfield United	0-0	488	
Nuneaton Borough	v AFC Telford United	3-1	1174	Burscough	v Workington	2-0	303	
Ramsgate	v Southall	1-0	251	Cambridge City	v Hitchin Town	4-1	461	
Redbridge	v Eastbourne Borough	2-2	113	Chippenham Town	v Sutton United	1-0	727	
Redditch United	v Woodford United	1-1	316	Cirencester Town	v Havant & Waterlooville	2-1	278	
Salford City	v Gateshead	1-0	213	Cogenhoe United	v Chasetown	1-1	184	
Skelmersdale United	v Bishop Auckland	0-0	509	Folkestone Invicta	v Staines Town	2-0	337	
Solihull Borough	v Ilkeston Town	3-0	267	Halesowen Town	v Bromsgrove Rovers	0-2	757	
St Helens Town	v Alfreton Town	0-2	142	Harrogate Town	v Witton Albion	2-0	402	
St Margaretsbury	v Folkestone Invicta	0-1	212	Harrow Borough	v Welling United	0-1	258	
Staines Town	v Croydon	1-1	251	Hayes	v Bishop's Stortford	2-0	231	
Stalybridge Celtic	v Workington	0-0	448	Heybridge Swifts	v Braintree Town	1-1	360	
Sutton United	v Maldon Town	2-0	402	Histon	v Welwyn Garden City	2-1	373	
Taunton Town	v Merthyr Tydfil	1-1	414	Hucknall Town	v Cammell Laird	2-2	292	
Thurrock	v Hemel Hempstead	3-2	93	Hyde United	v Barrow	2-3	469	
Trafford	v Whitby Town	1-1	164	Leamington	v Woodford United	2-0	1027	
Vauxhall Motors	v Ramsbottom United	2-0	109	Leatherhead	v Farnborough Town	0-2	609	
Welwyn Garden City	v AFC Sudbury	4-2	304	Leek Town	v Thornaby	2-1	211	
Weston Super Mare	v Weymouth	2-2	744	Leigh RMI	v Gainsborough Trinity	1-1	165	
Wivenhoe Town	v Heybridge Swifts	1-4	241	Lewes	v Dulwich Hamlet	1-0	539	
Worcester City	v Bemerton Heath H	7-0	579	Margate	v Cray Wanderers	0-3	807	
Worksop Town	v Witton Albion	0-1	348	Matlock Town	v Ossett Town	3-6	332	
Wroxham	v Slough Town	2-0	267	Merthyr Tydfil	v Salisbury City	2-1	615	
Yate Town	v Salisbury City	0-2	371	Metropolitan Police	v Eastbourne Borough	3-3	201	
Yeading	v Maidenhead United	3-0	185	Northwich Victoria	v North Ferriby United	1-0	684	
REPLAYS				Nuneaton Borough	v Chelmsford City	1-1	915	
Aylesbury United	v Northwood	2-0	262	Ramsgate	v Walton & Hersham	1-0	301	
Banbury United	v Brackley Town	5-2	960	Rossendale United	v Blyth Spartans	0-1	209	
Basingstoke Town	v Bognor Regis Town	2-1	315	Salford City	v Farsley Celtic	0-1	195	
Belper Town	v Chasetown	1-4	154	St Albans City	v Kettering Town	0-0	882	
Bishop Auckland	v Skelmersdale United	1-2	125	Thurrock	v Solihull Borough	1-0	126	
Brook House	v Hayes	0-4	342	Tiverton Town	v Windsor & Eton	2-1	531	
Cambridge City	v Eastwood Town	3-1	263	Vauxhall Motors	v Skelmersdale United	4-3	243	
Cammell Laird	v Marine	3-1	205	Wealdstone	v Burnham	2-4	241	
Croydon	v Staines Town	2-1	82	Weymouth	v Bath City	1-0	1232	
Eastbourne Borough	v Redbridge	5-1	359	Worcester City	v Tonbridge Angels	3-0	684	
Goole	v Gainsborough Trinity	1-2	298	Worthing	v Basingstoke Town	2-4	571	
Havant & waterlooville	v Eastleigh	4-1	329	Wroxham	v Aylesbury United	1-1	220	
Leatherhead	v Hampton & Richmond	2-1	273	Yeading	v Dorchester Town	1-1	151	
Lowestoft Town	v Burnham	1-1*, 2-4p	249	**REPLAYS**				
Merthyr Tydfil	v Taunton Town	2-1	370	AFC Totton	v Bishops Cleeve	0-4	322	
Metropolitan Police	v Hendon	1-0	104	Aylesbury United	v Wroxham	4-2	384	
Oadby Town	v Leamington	1-1*, 2-4p	356	Braintree Town	v Heybridge Swifts	3-1	479	
St Albans City	v Enfield Town	3-0	436	Cammell Laird	v Hucknall Town	0-1	395	
Thornaby	v Dunston Federation B.	2-1	126	Chasetown	v Cogenhoe United	4-3*	382	
Weymouth	v Weston Super Mare	1-0	1003	Chelmsford City	v Nuneaton Borough	1-2*	379	
Whitby Town	v Trafford	6-0	196	Dorchester Town	v Yeading	3-2	394	
Woodford United	v Redditch United	2-2*, 10-9p	207	Eastbourne Borough	v Metropolitan Police	3-2	601	
Workington	v Stalybridge Celtic	2-1*	315	Gainsborough Trinity	v Leigh RMI	2-1	385	
				Kettering Town	v St Albans City	4-0	1220	
				Mangotsfield United	v Bromley	0-1	403	

FOURTH QUALIFYING ROUND

BIGGEST HOME WIN:	**6-2** BURSCOUGH VS HUCKNALL TOWN		
BIGGEST AWAY WIN:	**0-4** GAINSBOROUGH TRINITY VS YORK CITY		
HIGHEST ATTENDANCE:	**3,421** EXETER CITY VS STEVENAGE BOROUGH		
NUMBER OF GAMES:	**32 + 6** (40 + 6)		
TOTAL ATTENDANCE:	**42,329** (158,904)		
AVERAGE ATTENDANCE:	**1,114** (3,454)		

Accrington Stanley	v Worcester City	1-1	940
Aylesbury United	v Folkestone Invicta	0-2	646
Basingstoke Town	v Chippenham Town	0-1	1072
Bishop's Cleeve	v Eastbourne Borough	0-1	625
Blyth Spartans	v Chasetown	2-2	926
Bromley	v Aldershot Town	0-1	1454
Bromsgrove Rovers	v Morecambe	0-2	919
Burton Albion	v Leek Town	2-0	1467
Cambridge City	v Lewes	2-1	588
Canvey Island	v Burnham	1-1	361
Crawley Town	v Braintree Town	0-1	970
Dorchester Town	v Welling United	1-2	533
Exeter City	v Stevenage Borough	0-1	3421
Forest Green Rovers	v Dagenham & Redbridge	2-3	751
Gainsborough Trinity	v York City	0-4	1680
Grays Athletic	v Cray Wanderers	2-0	135
Halifax Town	v Farsley Celtic	2-0	1469
Harrogate Town	v Scarborough	1-0	1591
Hednesford Town	v Vauxhall Motors	3-0	628
Hereford United	v Alfreton Town	0-0	1768
Histon	v Hayes	3-1	588
Hucknall Town	v Burscough	0-0	690
Kettering Town	v Gravesend & Northfleet	3-0	1647
Merthyr Tydfil	v Farnborough Town	2-0	1019
Northwich Victoria	v Barrow	4-1	1116
Nuneaton Borough	v Tiverton Town	0-0	1237
Ossett Town	v Leamington	2-3	900
Ramsgate	v Cirencester Town	3-0	697
Southport	v Kidderminster Harriers	1-0	1108
Tamworth	v Altrincham	3-1	801
Weymouth	v Cambridge United	2-1	1652
Woking	v Thurrock	3-0	1485

REPLAY

Alfreton Town	v Hereford United	1-1*, 3-4p	740
Burnham	v Canvey Island	2-1	607
Burscough	v Hucknall Town	6-2	415
Chasetown	v Blyth Spartans	1-0	2134
Tiverton Town	v Nuneaton Borough	0-1	885
Worcester City	v Accrington Stanley	3-2	1331

FIRST ROUND PROPER (NON-LEAGUE TIES ONLY)

BIGGEST HOME WIN:	**4-0** HISTON VS HEDNESFORD TOWN		
BIGGEST AWAY WIN:	**1-3** BURNHAM VS ALDERSHOT TOWN		
	MORECAMBE VS NORTHWICH VICTORIA		
HIGHEST ATTENDANCE:	**10,305** NOTTINGHAM FOREST VS WEYMOUTH		

AFC Bournemouth	v Tamworth	1-2	4550
Burnham	v Aldershot Town	1-3	1623
Burscough	v Gillingham	3-2	1927
Cambridge City	v Hereford United	0-1	1116
Chasetown	v Oldham Athletic	1-1*	1997
Chester City	v Folkestone Invicta	2-1	2503
Chippenham Town	v Worcester City	1-1*	2815
Colchester United	v Leamington	9-1	3513
Eastbourne Borough	v Oxford United	1-1*	3770
Halifax Town	v Rushden & Diamonds	1-1*	2303
Hartlepool United	v Dagenham & Redbridge	2-1	3655
Histon	v Hednesford Town	4-0	1080

Huddersfield Town	v Welling United	4-1	5518
Kettering Town	v Stevenage Borough	1-3	4548
Merthyr Tydfil	v Walsall	1-2	3046
Morecambe	v Northwich Victoria	1-3	2166
Nottingham Forest	v Weymouth	1-1*	10305
Nuneaton Borough	v Ramsgate	2-0	2153
Peterborough United	v Burton Albion	0-0*	3856
Shrewsbury Town	v Braintree Town	4-1	2969
Southport	v Woking	1-1*	1417
Torquay United	v Harrogate Town	1-1*	2079
York City	v Grays Athletic	0-3	3586

REPLAYS

Burton Albion	v Peterborough United	1-0	2511
Harrogate Town	v Torquay United	0-0*, 5-6p	3.317
Oldham Athletic	v Chasetown	4-0	7235
Oxford United	v Eastbourne Borough	3-0	4396
Rushden & Diamonds	v Halifax Town	0-0*, 5-4p	2133
Weymouth	v Nottingham Forest	0-2	6500
Woking	v Southport	1-0*	2298
Worcester City	v Chippenham Town	1-0	4006

SECOND ROUND PROPER

BIGGEST HOME WIN:	**4-1** BURTON ALBION VS BURSCOUGH		
BIGGEST AWAY WIN:	**1-2** HARTLEPOOL UNITED VS TAMWORTH		
	HISTON VS NUNEATON BOROUGH		
HIGHEST ATTENDANCE:	**4,499** BURTON ALBION VS BURSCOUGH		

Aldershot Town	v Scunthorpe United	0-1	3548
Burton Albion	v Burscough	4-1	4499
Hartlepool United	v Tamworth	1-2	3786
Hereford United	v Stockport County	0-2	3620
Mansfield Town	v Grays Athletic	3-0	2992
Nuneaton Borough	v Histon	2-2	3366
Stevenage Borough	v Northampton Town	2-2	3937
Woking	v Northwich Victoria	0-0	2462
Worcester City	v Huddersfield Town	0-1	4163

REPLAYS

Histon	v Nuneaton Borough	1-2	3077
Northampton Town	v Stevenage Borough	2-0	4407
Northwich Victoria	v Woking	2-1	2302

Leamington's Leon Morgan in an arial battle with Colchester's Sam Stockley. Photo: Bill Wheatcroft.

THIRD ROUND PROPER

BURTON ALBION	0	MANCHESTER UTD	0
Deeney		Howard	
Sedgemore		Brown	
Tinson		Pique	
Austin		Silvestre	
Corbett		Bardsley	
Chris Hall (Todd 89)		O'Shea	
Stride		Jones	
Ducros		Richardson	
Gilroy		Solskjaer (Ronaldo 59)	
Shaw		Saha	
Harrad (Anderson 80)		Rossi (Rooney 58)	
Subs not used:		**Subs not used:**	
Henshaw		Steele	
Martin Taylor		Eckersley	
Clough		Campbell	
		ATT: 6,191	

MANCHESTER UTD	5	BURTON ALBION	0
Saha 7, Rossi 23, 90			
Richardson 52, Giggs 68			
Howard		Deeney	
Bardsley		Sedgemore	
Pique		Tinson	
Brown (Neville 62)		Austin	
Silvestre		Corbett	
Solskjaer		Chris Hall (Webster 74)	
Fletcher (Giggs 62)		Stride	
O'Shea (Ferdinand 62)		Ducros	
Richardson		Gilroy (Henshaw 86)	
Rossi		Shaw (Anderson 26)	
Saha		Harrad	
Subs not used:		**Subs not used:**	
Van der Sar		Martin Taylor	
van Nistelrooy		Todd	
		ATT: 53,564	

NUNEATON BOROUGH	1	MIDDLESBROUGH	1
Murphy 90 (pen)		Mendieta 15	
Acton		Jones	
Oddy		Parnaby	
Moore		Southgate	
Angus		Bates	
Love		Pogatetz	
Collins		Morrison	
Noon		Doriva	
Fitzpatrick (Reeves 82)		Cattermole	
Staff (Whittaker 23)		Mendieta	
Quailey (Frew 77)		Yakubu	
Murphy		Viduka	
Subs not used:		**Subs not used:**	
Wilkin		Schwarzer	
Poole		Taylor	
		Johnson	
		Wheater	
		Maccarone	
		ATT: 5,780	

MIDDLESBROUGH	5	NUNEATON BOROUGH	2
Riggott 34, Yakubu 42 (pen),58,		Murphy 71, 86 (pen)	
Parnaby 50, Viduka 63		Acton	
Jones		Oddy	
Bates		Moore	
Riggott		Angus	
Pogatetz		Love	
Taylor		Collins (Reeves 81)	
Parnaby (Parlour 63)		Noon	
Mendieta		Fitzpatrick	
Cattermole		Whittaker (Wilkin 77)	
Johnson		Quailey (Frew 59)	
Yakubu		Murphy	
Viduka (Maccarone 64)		**Subs not used:**	
Subs not used:		Poole	
Schwarzer		Rea	
Rochemback			
Wheater			
		ATT: 26,324	

STOKE CITY	0	TAMWORTH	0
Simonsen		Bevan	
Broomes		Ward	
Hoefkens		Smith	
Henry		Redmile	
Buxton		Turner	
Chadwick (Harper 79)		Touhy	
Russell		Bampton (Cooper 83)	
Brammer		Melton	
Kopteff (Sweeney 54)		Anaclet	
Gallagher (Sigurdsson		Edwards	
76) Sidibe		Wright (Storer 64)	
Subs not used:		**Subs not used:**	
Junior		Stamps	
de Goey		Heggs	
		Gayle	
		ATT: 9,366	

TAMWORTH	1* 4p	STOKE CITY	1* 5p
Jackson 42		Gallagher 80	
Bevan		Simonsen	
Touhy		Henry	
Smith		Hoefkens	
Redmile		Duberry	
Anaclet		Broomes (Rooney 80)	
Wright (Turner 66)		Chadwick (Kopteff 45)	
Melton (Storer 83)		Brammer (Junior 45)	
Ward (Stamps 116)		Harper	
Bampton		Buxton	
Heggs		Gallagher	
Jackson		Sidibe	
Subs not used:		**Subs not used:**	
Cooper		Sweeney	
Gayle		Duggan	
		ATT: 9,366	

SUNDERLAND 3	NORTHWICH VICTORIA 0
Neill Collins 6, Whitehead 41,	
Le Tallec 70	
Davis	Rodgers
Hoyte	McCarthy
Neill Collins	Payne
Stubbs	Charnock
Danny Collins	Chapman (Sale 79)
Lawrence	Mayman (Byrne 72)
Whitehead (Welsh 84)	Carr
Miller	Elliott
Arca	Roca (Devlin 83)
Stead	Allan
Le Tallec (Murphy 78)	Brayson
Subs not used:	**Subs not used:**
Nosworthy	Connett
Alnwick	Battersby
Bassila	**ATT: 19.323**

Vics' Danny Mayman heads the ball into the Sunderland penalty area.

Jon Allan challenges Sunderland's Neil Collins.

Photos: Bill Wheatcroft.

Northwich Victoria's Michael Carr heads towards the Sunderland goal. Photo: Bill Wheatcroft.

ROUND BY ROUND STATISTICS
(NON-LEAGUE CLUB ROUNDS ONLY)

Round	Games	Home Win	Away Win	Draws	Home Goals	Away Goals	Att. Total	Att. Ave
Extra Preliminary	86+16	47	39	16	179	164	9,819	96 (-10)
Preliminary	182+37	96	86	37	388	344	27,248	124 (-12)
1st Qualifying	124+25	69	55	25	298	232	30,655	206 (+6)
2nd Qualifying	84+23	50	34	23	179	144	37,699	352 (-31)
3rd Qualifying	42+11	27	15	11	87	72	24,380	460 (-8)
4th Qualifying	32+6	19	13	6	58	37	42,329	1,114 (-98)

(Figure in brackets denotes +/- difference between 04/05 average attendance).

TOP NON-LEAGUE GOAL SCORERS 2005 - 2006

Player	Club	No. goals	Round Reached
J Laidlaw	Gosport Borough	11	Second Qualifying Round
P Brayson	Northwich Victoria	10	Third Round Proper
J Walshaw	Ossett Town	10	Fourth Qualifying Round
L Bullimore	Chasetown	7	First Round Proper
K Edwards	Chasetown	7	First Round Proper
I Concanon	Didcot Town	7	Second Qualifying Round
D Stevens	Leatherhead	7	Third Qualifying Round
S Rudd	Skelmersdale United	7	Third Qualifying Round
M Dunwell	Billingham Synthonia	6	Second Qualifying Round
K Johnstone	Bishop's Cleeve	6	Fourth Qualifying Round
P Booth	Cambridge City	6	First Round Proper
J McGuire	Cammell Laird	6	Third Qualifying Round
M Power	Cray Wanderers	6	Fourth Qualifying Round
K Cooper	Metropolitan Police	6	Third Qualifying Round
A Webster	Worcester City	6	Second Round Proper

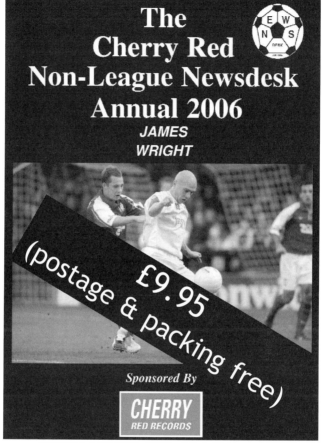

THE F.A. TROPHY
2005/06

The redevelopment of Wembley Stadium will no doubt give the national game a wonderful home ground in the future where many non-league finalists in the F.A. Vase and F.A. Trophy will experience the highlights of their future footballing careers. Creating memories that will stay with them all their lives!

The last six years, however, have seen the finalists of the two famous competitions being sent off to Birmingham or the London suburbs to decide their special cup finals and for the last four years they have also had to compete with the end of season headlines and excitement built up by the Conference play offs to decide who would be the second club promoted to the Football League.

Once a club has reached The Conference, the pinnacle of the non-league pyramid, or indeed has dropped down into it from the Football League, then their only realistic ambition is to gain or regain a place in the country's top football competition (echelons). So the play offs to them are all important.

Without consciously not actually trying, Conference clubs even failed to reach a Trophy final for thee years so the crowds at those games were made up of supporters thrilled to see their teams contesting finals, but not producing attendances that really did the competition justice.

Despite the quite staggeringly depressing stories we read in the press about the Wembley Stadium project and its budget, we must surely soon be welcoming the F.A. knock out competition finals back to a new and glorious Wembley Stadium where every club will be determined to reach a final and crowds of non-league enthusiasts will join the supporters of the contestants and create a special atmosphere.

West Ham hosted last season's excellent final between the holders Grays Athletic and a very solid and hard working, Woking side. An enthusiastic crowd of over 15,000 was an improvement on recent years, but it was played on Grays back doorstep against home counties opposition the day after West Ham had lost a thrilling Cup Final at Cardiff.

There is always at least one club who exceeds all expectations and gives their supporters a special cup run and this season it was Boreham Wood who could have been writing the script for an epic at their nearby Elstree film studios.

The Southern League Division One leaders were drawn at home for their first five ties which included Gravesend & Northfleet, then away games at Crawley Town and Worksop Town and those brought them face to face with Woking in their two legged semi-finals. Their Trophy attendances had developed from 98 to 1,511 before they found the Surrey club's defence too difficult to break through.

Exeter City also reached the semi-finals while battling finally to shake off their financial restrictions. They found Grays just too good but the Devon club has nearly turned the corner and will be challenging seriously on all fronts within a couple of seasons.

Trophy tradition shows that Dagenham & Redbridge enjoy the competition and it took their high flying neighbours from Grays to eliminate them after a replay, while Worksop Town and Stafford Rangers also have Trophy traditions and they too enjoyed good 'runs'. Rangers like their Conference North champions Northwich Victoria eventually enjoyed promotion so their comparative failures in the knock out competition didn't hurt too much.

Two clubs with a special interest in the F.A. Trophy are Tamworth and Forest Green Rovers. They have both won the F.A. Vase and have lost Trophy finals and last season reached the Third Round Proper and both are keen to be the first club to see their name on the two trophies but perhaps they are waiting to do it in style at Wembley!

Next season the competition will be joined by the Step 4 clubs in all five First Divisions of the Southern, Isthmian and Northern Premier Leagues. so it will have its biggest entry. There will be even more chance of the relatively smaller clubs enjoying some serious giant killing and it may well give the competition extra life, especially if there is a visit to Wembley at the end of the journey!

909

CLUB BY CLUB RECORDS

ACCRINGTON STANLEY
Conference National (Step 1)

1st Round	(H)	v Altrincham	W 2-0	810
			Boco, Craney	
2nd Round	(A)	v Carshalton Athletic	D 2-2	618
			Craney, Mullin	
Replay	(H)	v Carshalton Athletic	W 2-0	556
			Mullin (2)	
3rd Round	(H)	v Worksop Town	D 1-1	961
			Brown	
Replay	(A)	v Worksop Town	D 1-1*	733
Worksop won 4-2 on pens.			Craney	

Best Performance: 3rd Round 2003-04, 04-05.

AFC TELFORD UNITED
Northern Premier League Premier Division (Step 3)

1st Qual.	(A)	v Witton Albion	D 1-1	404
			Charie	
Replay	(H)	v Witton Albion	W 2-1	853
			Hamilton, Reynolds	
2nd Qual.	(H)	v Goole	D 1-1	990
			Reynolds	
Replay	(A)	v Goole	W 1-0	330
			Curtis	
3rd Qual.	(A)	v Worksop Town	D 1-1	416
			Reynolds	
Replay	(H)	v Worksop Town	L 1-2	952
			Reynolds	

Best Performance: 3rd Qualifying Round 2004-05.

AFC WIMBLEDON
Isthmian League Premier Division (Step 3)

1st Qual.	(H)	v Kings Lynn	W 1-0	1720
			Howard	
2nd Qual.	(A)	v Ramsgate	D 1-1	1047
			R Butler	
Replay	(H)	v Ramsgate	W 2-1	1140
			R Butler, Smeltz	
3rd Qual.	(A)	v Dartford	D 0-0	1082
Replay	(H)	v Dartford	W 2-0	1086
			Butler, Moore	
1st Round	(H)	v St Albans City	L 2-3	1953
			Butler, Sargent	

Best Performance: 1st Round 2005-06.

Alfreton's Chris Bettney shields the ball from the Histon defender in this first round tie. Photo: Bill Wheatcroft.

ALDERSHOT TOWN
Conference National (Step 1)

1st Round	(H)	v Grays Athletic	D 1-1	1771
			Barnard	
Replay	(A)	v Grays Athletic	L 0-1*	852

Best Performance: Semi-Final 2003-04.

ALFRETON TOWN
Conference North (Step 2)

3rd Qual.	(A)	v Fleetwood Town	W 3-1	552
			White, Clarke, Stevenson	
1st Round	(H)	v Histon	D 1-1	238
			Godber	
Replay	(A)	v Histon	L 1-2	288
			Featherstone	

Best Performance: 4th Round 2004-05.

ALTRINCHAM
Conference National (Step 1)

1st Round	(A)	v Accrington Stanley	L 0-2	810

Best Performance: Winners 1977-78, 1985-86.

ARLESEY TOWN
Southern League Division One East (Step 4)

1st Qual.	(A)	v Leyton	L 0-1	73

Best Performance: 5th Round 2003-04.

ASHFORD TOWN
Isthmian League Division One (Step 4)

1st Qual.	(H)	v Bromley	L 0-2	251

Best Performance: Semi-Final 1972-73.

ASHFORD TOWN (MIDDX)
Southern League Division One West (Step 4)

1st Qual.	(A)	v Marlow	W 2-1	105
			Foulser, Smith	
2nd Qual.	(A)	v Rushall Olympic	W 4-3	88
			Canderton, Harris (3)	
3rd Qual.	(H)	v Bognor Regis Town	L 2-3	140
			Smith, Harris	

Best Performance: 4th Qualifying Round 2004-05.

ASHTON UNITED
Northern League Premier Division (Step 3)

1st Qual.	(A)	v Kidsgrove Athletic	L 1-3	178
			Kilheeney	

Best Performance: 6th Round 1996-97.

AVELEY
Southern League Division One East (Step 4)

1st Qual.	(A)	v Kingstonian	D 2-2	402
			Marsden, Thomas	
Replay	(H)	v Kingstonian	L 0-1	122

Best Performance: 3rd Qualifying Round 1974-75.

AYLESBURY UNITED
Southern League Premier Division (Step 3)

1st Qual.	(A)	v Thame United	W 5-0	294
			Gould (2), Edgeworth, Jaggard, Lazarus	
2nd Qual.	(A)	v Halesowen Town	L 0-2	374

Best Performance: Semi-Final 2002-03.

BAMBER BRIDGE
Northern Premier League Division One (Step 3)

1st Qual.	(H)	v Grantham Town	D 2-2	162
			Newsham, Bain	
Replay	(A)	v Grantham Town	L 0-3	230

Best Performance: 2nd Round 1994-95.

BANBURY UNITED

Southern League Premier Division (Step 3)

1st Qual.	(A) v Brackley Town	D	1-1	494
		Bridges		
Replay	(H) v Brackley Town	W	3-0	479
		Blossom, Lamb, Potter		
2nd Qual.	(H) v Circencester Town	D	2-2	404
		Fuller, McKay		
Replay	(A) v Cirencester Town	W	4-3*	186
		Baird (2), Redknap, Blossom		
3rd Qual.	(A) v Farnborough Town	L	0-2	466

Best Performance: 3rd Round 1970-71, 73-74.

BANSTEAD ATHLETIC

Isthmian League Division One (Step 4)

1st Qual.	(H) v Redbridge	L	1-2	64
		Mitchell		

Best Performance: 1st Round 2003-04, 04-05.

BARKING & EAST HAM UNITED

Southern League Division One East (Step 4)

1st Qual.	(A) v Dulwich Hamlet	D	1-1	228
		Taylor		
Replay	(H) v Dulwich Hamlet	W	2-0	98
		Baptiste, Blaney		
2nd Qual.	(H) v Burgess Hill Town	W	4-1	105
		Blaney, Taylor, Vaughan (2)		
3rd Qual.	(H) v Croydon Athletic	W	2-1	101
		Higgs, Palmer		
1st Round	(A) v Weston-S-Mare	L	2-3	243
		Blaney, Henry		

Best Performance: 2nd Round 1979-80.

BARROW

Conference North (Step 2)

3rd Qual.	(A) v Redditch United	D	1-1	289
		Flitcroft		
Replay	(H) v Redditch United	W	2-0	756
		Rushton, Tarrant		
1st Round	(H) v Clitheroe	W	2-1	897
		Ridley, Rushton		
2nd Round	(H) v Cambridge City	L	1-2	996
		Rushton		

Best Performance: Winners 1989-90.

BARTON ROVERS

Southern League Division One East (Step 4)

1st Qual.	(H) v Potters Bar Town	W	3-2	110
		Morgan, Gray, Case		
2nd Qual.	(A) v Harlow Town	L	1-2	81
		Whyte		

Best Performance: 2nd Round 1998-99, 99-00.

BASHLEY

Isthmian League Division One (Step 3)

1st Qual.	(H) v Margate	L	0-3	95

Best Performance: 2nd Round 1991-92.

BASINGSTOKE TOWN

Conference South (Step 2)

3rd Qual.	(H) v Welling United	L	0-2	313

Best Performance: 3rd Round 1998-99.

BATH CITY

Southern League Premier Division (Step 3)

1st Qual.	(A) v Dunstable Town	D	2-2	122
		Bird, Walsh		
Replay	(H) v Dunstable Town	W	5-0	241
		Bird (2), Holloway (2), Walsh		
2nd Qual.	(H) v Bromsbrove Rovers	W	2-0	423
		Bird, Holloway		
3rd Qual.	(H) v Yeading	L	1-2	393
		Rollo		

Best Performance: 4th Round 1989-90.

BEACONSFIELD SYCOB

Southern League Division One West (Step 4)

1st Qual.	(A) v Bromsgrove Rovers	L	2-3	347
		Gumbs, Gibbs		

Best Performance: 1st Qualifying Round 2005-06.

BEDFORD TOWN

Southern League Premier Division (Step 3)

1st Qual.	(H) v Bracknell Town	W	3-0	420
		Blake, Howe (2)		
2nd Qual.	(A) v Hitchin Town	W	2-1	603
		Dillon (2)		
3rd Qual.	(A) v Weston-S-Mare	L	0-4	221

Best Performance: Semi-Finals 1974-75.

BEDWORTH UNITED

Southern League Division One West (Step 4)

1st Qual.	(A) v Stourport Swifts	W	1-0	113
		Douglas		
2nd Qual.	(H) v Sutton Coldfield Town	L	2-5	146
		Greenway, Douglas		

Best Performance: Semi-final 1974-75.

BELPER TOWN

Northern Premier League Division One (Step 4)

1st Qual.	(A) v Blyth Spartans	L	0-2	372

Best Performance: 3rd Qualifying Round 1997-98.

BERKHAMSTED TOWN

Southern League Division One East (Step 4)

1st Qual.	(A) v Enfield Town	L	0-3	212

Best Performance: 1st Round 1997-98.

BILLERICAY TOWN

Isthmian League Premier Division (Step 3)

1st Qual.	(H) v Wingate & Finchley	W	1-0	317
		Poole		
2nd Qual.	(A) v Heybridge Swifts	L	1-2	326
		OG		

Best Performance: 5th Round 2000-01.

BISHOP AUCKLAND

Northern Premier League Division One (Step 4)

2nd Qual.	(H) v Woodley Sports	L	1-3	85
		Allen		

Best Performance: Quarter Finals 1978-79, 96-97, 99-00.

BISHOP'S STORTFORD

Conference South (Step 2)

3rd Qual.	(A) v Maidenhead United	D	2-2	165
		Essandoh, Forbes		
Replay	(H) v Maidenhead United	W	2-1*	171
		Essandou (2)		
1st Round	(A) v Exeter City	L	1-2	1807
		Essandou		

Best Performance: Winners 1980-81.

BLYTH SPARTANS

Northern Premier League Premier Division (Step 3)

1st Qual.	(H) v Belper Town	W	2-0	372
		Dale, Johnson		
2nd Qual.	(H) v Whitby Town	W	2-0	501
		Leeson, McCabe		
3rd Qual.	(A) v Marine	W	1-0	268
		Williams		
1st Round	(A) v Warrington Town	W	2-1	251
		Forster, Leeson		
2nd Round	(H) v Welling United	L	1-3	784
		Fenton		

Best Performance: 6th Round 1979-80, 82-83.

BOGNOR REGIS TOWN

Conference South (Step 2)

3rd Qual.	(A)	v Ashford Town (Mx)	W 3-2	140
			Murphy, Watson, OG	
1st Round	(H)	v Hereford United	L 1-7	624
			Beck	

Best Performance: 3rd Round 1995-96.

Bognor's Micky Birmingham is out jumped by Hereford's Tamika Mkandawire. Photo: Graham Cotterill.

BOREHAM WOOD

Southern League Division One East (Step 4)

1st Qual.	(H)	v Ilford	W 1-0	98
			Moran	
2nd Qual.	(H)	v Bromley	W 4-1	195
			Archer (2), Bangura, Cooper	
3rd Qual.	(H)	v Stamford	W 3-1	146
			Cooper (2), Archer	
1st Round	(H)	v Leighton Town	W 1-0	165
			Watters	
2nd Round	(H)	v Gravesend & N'fleet	W 3-1	462
			Archer (2), Watters	
3rd Round	(A)	v Crawley Town	W 2-0	929
			Archer, Cooper	
4th Round	(A)	v Worksop Town	W 1-0	1006
			Black	
Semi-Final 1	(H)	v Woking	L 0-1	1511
Semi-Final 2	(A)	v Woking	L 0-2	2080

Best Performance: Semi-Finals 2005-06.

BRACKLEY TOWN

Southern League Division One West (Step 4)

1st Qual.	(H)	v Banbury United	D 1-1	494
			M Murphy	
Replay	(A)	v Banbury United	L 0-3	479

Best Performance: 1st Qualifying Round 1997-98.

BRACKNELL TOWN

Southern League Division One West (Step 4)

1st Qual.	(A)	v Bedford Town	L 0-3	420

Best Performance: 1st Round 2002-03.

BRADFORD (PARK AVENUE)

Northern Premier League Premier Division (Step 3)

1st Qual.	(H)	v Gateshead	D 1-1	191
			Greaves	
Replay	(A)	v Gateshead	L 3-4*	130
			Coubrough, Newton (2)	

Best Performance: 3rd Round 1998-99.

BRAINTREE TOWN

Isthmian League Premier Division (Step 3)

1st Qual.	(H)	v Great Wakering Rovers	W 4-2	210
			Revell (2), Ofori (2)	
2nd Qual.	(A)	v Chelmsford City	W 2-0	436
			Baker (2)	
3rd Qual.	(H)	v Hayes	L 0-1	228

Best Performance: 5th Round 2001-02.

BRIDLINGTON TOWN

Northern Premier League Division One (Step 4)

2nd Qual.	(H)	v Warrington Town	D 2-2	192
			Harper, Palmer	
Replay	(A)	v Warrington Town	L 0-1	135

Best Performance: 3rd Qualifying Round 1993-94.

BRIGG TOWN

Northern Premier League Division One (Step 4)

1st Qual.	(H)	v Matlock Town	L 0-1	214

Best Performance: 2nd Qualifying Round 1971-72, 72-73.

BROMLEY

Isthmian League Premier Division (Step 3)

1st Qual.	(A)	v Ashford Town	W 2-0	251
			Logan, Locke	
2nd Qual.	(A)	v Boreham Wood	L 1-4	195
			McDonnell	

Best Performance: 2nd Round 1991-92.

BROMSGROVE ROVERS

Southern League Division One West (Step 4)

1st Qual.	(H)	v Beaconsfield SYCOB	W 3-2	347
			Szewczyk, Dyer (2)	
2nd Qual.	(A)	v Bath City	L 0-2	423

Best Performance: Quarter-Finals 1975-76, 95-96.

BURGESS HILL TOWN

Isthmian League Division One (Step 4)

1st Qual.	(A)	v Waltham Forest	W 1-0	130
			Musungu	
2nd Qual.	(A)	v Barking & East Ham Utd	L 1-4	105
			Gedling	

Best Performance: 2nd Qualifying Round 2004-05, 05-06.

BURNHAM

Southern League Division One West (Step 4)

1st Qual.	(H)	v Yate Town	W 2-0	75
			Jones, Leacock	
2nd Qual.	(H)	v Leighton Town	L 4-5	103
			Horsted (2), Miller (2)	

Best Performance: 4th Round 1999-2000.

BURSCOUGH

Northern Premier League Premier Division (Step 3)

1st Qual.	(H)	v Leek Town	D 3-3	212
			Gedman, Gray (2)	
Replay	(A)	v Leek Town	W 3-1	175
			Bell, Gray (2)	
2nd Qual.	(H)	v Fleetwood Town	L 1-2	438
			Gray	

Best Performance: Winners 2002-03.

BURTON ALBION

Conference National (Step 1)

1st Round	(H)	v Worksop Town	L	0-1	1359

Best Performance: Runners-up 1986-87.

CAMBRIDGE CITY

Conference South (Step 2)

3rd Qual.	(A)	v Sittingbourne	W	3-1	265
		Booth (2), Simpson			
1st Round	(A)	v Farnborough Town	W	2-0	377
		Gash, Sadler			
2nd Round	(A)	v Barrow	W	2-1	996
		Gash, Simpson			
3rd Round	(A)	v Exeter City	L	0-1	2166

Best Performance: 3rd Round 2005-06.

CAMBRIDGE UNITED

Conference National (Step 1)

1st Round	(A)	v Dorchester Town	L	2-3	426
		Bridges, Morrison			

Best Performance: 1st Round 2005-06.

CANVEY ISLAND

Conference National (Step 1)

1st Round	(H)	v Kingstonian	W	4-1	413
		Boylan, Clarke, Hallett (2)			
2nd Round	(H)	v Salisbury City	L	0-1	534

Best Performance: Winners 2000-01.

CARSHALTON ATHLETIC

Conference South (Step 2)

3rd Qual.	(A)	v Chippenham Town	W	2-0	510
		Fontana, Dundas			
1st Round	(A)	v Yeading	W	2-1	107
		Fontana (2)			
2nd Round	(H)	v Accrington Stanley	D	2-2	618
		Armel, Johnson			
Replay	(A)	v Accrington Stanley	L	0-2	556

Best Performance: 3rd Round 1995-96.

CHATHAM TOWN

Southern League Division One East (Step 4)

1st Qual.	(A)	v Sittingbourne	L	0-3	284

Best Performance: 3rd Round 1970-71.

CHELMSFORD CITY

Isthmian League Premier Division (Step 3)

1st Qual.	(H)	v Horsham	W	6-0	358
		Fiddes, Halle, Lincoln (2)			
		Richards (2)			
2nd Qual.	(H)	v Braintree Town	L	0-2	436

Best Performance: Semi-Finals 1969-70.

CHESHAM UNITED

Southern League Premier Division (Step 3)

1st Qual.	(A)	v Sutton Coldfield Town	L	1-2	107
		Sippetts			

Best Performance: 3rd Round 1979-80.

CHESHUNT

Southern League Premier Division (Step 3)

1st Qual.	(A)	v Tonbridge Wells	L	0-1	430

Best Performance: 2nd Qualifying Round 1974-75, 77-78, 04-05.

CHIPPENHAM TOWN

Southern League Premier Division (Step 3)

1st Qual.	(A)	v Cinderford Town	D	1-1	197
		Allison			
Replay	(H)	v Cinderford Town	W	3-1	309
		De Francescanro, Griffin,			
		Jefferies			
2nd Qual.	(A)	v Hemel Hempstead T.	W	3-2	226
		Adams, Tego, Gilroy			
3rd Qual.	(H)	v Carshalton Athletic	L	0-2	510

Best Performance: 2nd Round 2003-04.

CHORLEY

Northern Premier League Division One (Step 4)

1st Qual.	(A)	v Guiseley	L	1-3	182
		Wright			

Best Performance: Semi-Finals 1995-96.

CINDERFORD TOWN

Southern League Division One West (Step 4)

1st Qual.	(H)	v Chippenham Town	D	1-1	197
		Mayo			
Replay	(A)	v Chippenham Town	L	1-3	309
		Lutz			

Best Performance: 2nd Qualifying Round

CIRENCESTER TOWN

Southern League Premier Division (Step 3)

1st Qual.	(H)	v Gloucester City	W	2-0	322
		Halliday, Crowe			
2nd Qual.	(A)	v Banbury United	D	2-2	404
		Halliday, Griffin			
Replay	(H)	v Banbury United	L	3-4*	186
		Stanley, Morgan, Hopkins			

Best Performance: 3rd Qualifying Round 1999-2000.

CLEVEDON TOWN

Southern League Division One West (Step 4)

1st Qual.	(H)	v Taunton Town	W	2-1	216
		Pitcher, Holly			
2nd Qual.	(A)	v Salisbury City	L	1-2	552
		Pitcher			

Best Performance: 2nd Round 1998-99.

CLITHEROE

Northern Premier League Division One (Step 4)

1st Qual.	(H)	v Spalding United	W	3-1	253
		Sargeson, Evans, Jackson			
2nd Qual.	(A)	v Ossett Town	D	2-2	108
		Stansfield, Kearney			
Replay	(H)	v Ossett Town	D	1-1*	188
Clitheroe won 4-2 on pens.			Stansfield		
3rd Qual.	(H)	v Woodley Sports	W	2-1	205
		Stansfield, Williams			
1st Round	(A)	v Barrow	L	1-2	897
		Evans			

Best Performance: 1st Round 2005-06.

Bracknell Town striker, Neil Selby, under pressure from Bedford captain Eddie Lawley. Photo: Peter Barnes.

COLWYN BAY

Northern League Division One (Step 4)

1st Qual.	(A)	v Lincoln United	L	1-2	113
		Mottram			

Best Performance: Quarter Finals 1996-97.

CORBY TOWN

Southern League Division One East (Step 4)

1st Qual.	(A)	v Hastings United	D	0-0	376
Replay	(H)	v Hastings United	W	2-0	100
		Darby			
2nd Qual.	(A)	v Sittingbourne	L	0-1	178

Best Performance: 3rd Round 1986-87.

CORINTHIAN CASUALS

Isthmian League Division One (Step 4)

1st Qual.	(H)	v Stamford	L	1-4	85
		Corbett			

Best Performance: 2nd Round 2002-03.

CRAWLEY TOWN

Conference National (Step 1)

1st Round	(A)	v Stevenage Borough	W	2-0	951
		Burton, Wormull			
2nd Round	(H)	v Worcester City	W	3-1	862
		Burton, Giles, Scully			
3rd Round	(H)	v Boreham Wood	L	0-2	929

Best Performance: 3rd Round 1998-99, 2005-06.

CRAY WANDERERS

Isthmian League Division One (Step 4)

2nd Qual.	(H)	v Staines Town	W	4-3	131
		Power, Main (3)			
3rd Qual.	(H)	v Kingstonian	D	1-1	239
		Watkins			
Replay	(A)	v Kingstonian	L	1-3	264
		Bremnar			

Best Performance: 3rd Qualifying Round 2005-06.

CROYDON ATHLETIC

Isthmian League Division One (Step 4)

1st Qual.	(A)	v Slough Town	W	3-1	286
		Myton, Suggrin (2)			
2nd Qual.	(H)	v Rothwell Town	D	2-2	88
		Allen, Garrard			
Replay	(A)	v Rothwell Town	W	1-0	98
		Stevens			
3rd Qual.	(A)	v Barking & East Ham Utd	L	1-2	101
		Gibson			

Best Performance: 3rd Qualifying Round 2005-06.

DAGENHAM & REDBRIDGE

Conference National (Step 1)

1st Round	(H)	v Thurrock	W	2-0	737
		Moore, Southam			
2nd Round	(H)	v Kettering Town	W	2-1	931
		Mackail-Smith			
3rd Round	(A)	v Tamworth	D	0-0	920
Replay	(H)	v Tamworth	W	3-0	922
		Moore (2), Southam			
4th Round	(A)	v Grays Athletic	D	1-1	2321
		Mackail-Smith			
Replay	(H)	v Grays Athletic	L	2-4	1526
		Mackail-Smith, Saunders			

Best Performance: Runners-up 1996-97.

DARTFORD

Southern League Division One East (Step 4)

1st Qual.	(A)	v Dover Athletic	D	1-1	615
		McClements			
Replay	(H)	v Dover Athletic	W	3-2	323
		Hafner (2), Martin			
2nd Qual.	(A)	v Margate	W	1-0	549
		Martin			
3rd Qual.	(H)	v AFC Wimbledon	D	0-0	1082
Replay	(A)	v AFC Wimbledon	L	0-2	1086

Best Performance: Runners-up 1974.

Cray Wanderers' Gary Abbott heads clear a Staines Town corner during their 2nd Qualifying round match.
Photo: Alan Coomes.

DORCHESTER TOWN

Conference South (Step 2)

3rd Qual.	(A)	v Lewes	D 2-2	364
			Browne, Keeler	
Replay	(H)	v Lewes	W 3-1	235
			Groves, Keeler (2)	
1st Round	(H)	v Cambridge United	W 3-2	426
			Brown, Keeler, Robinson	
2nd Round	(A)	v Forest Green Rovers	L 1-3	862
			Groves	

Best Performance: 3rd Round 1971-72, 1996-97.

DOVER ATHLETIC

Isthmian League Division One (Step 4)

1st Qual.	(H)	v Dartford	D 1-1	615
			Humphrey	
Replay	(A)	v Dartford	L 2-3	323
			Hogg, Smissen	

Best Performance: Semi-Finals 1997-98.

DROYLSDEN

Conference North (Step 2)

3rd Qual.	(H)	v Grantham Town	W 4-0	251
			Robinson, Fearns, Brodie, Talbot	
1st Round	(A)	v Stalybrideg Celtic	L 0-1	598

Best Performance: 2nd Round 1990-91.

DULWICH HAMLET

Isthmian League Division One (Step 4)

1st Qual.	(H)	v Barking & East Ham Utd D	1-1	228
			Side	
Replay	(A)	v Barking & East Ham Utd L	0-2	98

Best Performance: Quarter Finals 1979-80.

DUNSTABLE TOWN

Southern League Division One West (Step 4)

1st Qual.	(H)	v Bath City	D 2-2	122
			B Smith, Quinn	
Replay	(A)	v Bath City	L 0-5	241

Best Performance: 2nd Qualifying Round 1980-81, 85-86, 89-90.

EAST THURROCK UNITED

Isthmian League Premier Division (Step 3)

1st Qual.	(A)	v Leatherhead	W 1-0	141
			Boot	
2nd Qual.	(H)	v Leyton	W 2-1	109
			West, Harris	
3rd Qual.	(A)	v Tonbridge Angels	D 0-0	288
Replay	(H)	v Tonbridge Angels	W 3-0	130
			Harris, Hayzelden, Tuohy	
1st Round	(H)	v Gravesend & NorthfleetL	0-2	381

Best Performance: 1st Round 2005-06.

EASTBOURNE BOROUGH

Conference South (Step 2)

3rd Qual.	(H)	v Thurrock	L 0-3	368

Best Performance: 3rd Round 2001-02, 02-03, 04-05.

EASTLEIGH

Conference South (Step 2)

3rd Qual.	(A)	v Leighton Town	D 1-1	145
			Thomas	
Replay	(H)	v Leighton Town	L 1-2*	186
			Town	

Best Performance: 2nd Round 2003-04.

EASTWOOD TOWN

Northern Premier League Division One (Step 4)

1st Qual.	(A)	v Whitby Town	L 2-4	228
			Knox, Fisher	

Best Performance: 5th Round 2004-05.

ENFIELD

Southern League Division One East (Step 4)

1st Qual.	(H)	v Fleet Town	L 1-2	88
			Nelson	

Best Performance: Winners 1981-82, 1987-88.

ENFIELD TOWN

Southern League Division One East (Step 4)

1st Qual.	(H)	v Berkhamsted Town	W 3-0	212
			Paul, Hall, Hammatt	
2nd Qual.	(H)	v Redbridge	D 1-1	268
			Hall	
Replay	(A)	v Redbridge	L 1-2	172
			Negus	

Best Performance: 2nd Qualifying Round 2005-06.

EVESHAM UNITED

Southern League Premier Division (Step 3)

1st Qual.	(H)	v Solihull Borough	L 0-2	157

Best Performance: 3rd Qualifying Round 1996-97.

EXETER CITY

Conference National (Step 1)

1st Round	(H)	v Bishop's Stortford	W 2-1	1807
			Jones, Robinson	
2nd Round	(H)	v Histon	W 3-2	2103
			Challinor, Jones, Mackie	
3rd Round	(H)	v Cambridge City	W 1-0	2166
			OG	
4th Round	(H)	v Salisbury City	W 3-1	3653
			Phillips (2), Flack	
Semi-Final 1	(H)	v Grays Athletic	W 2-1	3051
			Todd, Phillips	
Semi-Final 2	(A)	v Grays Athletic	L 0-2	3693

Best Performance: Semi-Finals 2005-06.

FARNBOROUGH TOWN

Conference South (Step 2)

3rd Qual.	(H)	v Banbury United	W 2-0	466
			Gibbs, Harkness	
1st Round	(H)	v Cambridge City	L 0-2	377

Best Performance: 6th Round 1992-03, 2002-03.

FARSLEY CELTIC

Northern Premier League Premier Division (Step 3)

1st Qual.	(H)	v Runcorn FC Halton	W 2-0	223
			Bambrook (2)	
2nd Qual.	(A)	v Prescot Cables	W 2-1	214
			Bambrook, Sanasay	
3rd Qual.	(H)	v Nuneaton Borough	W 3-1	271
			Sanasay (2), Knowles	
1st Round	(A)	v Kettering Town	L 1-2	960
			Iqbal	

Best Performance: 3rd Round 2002-03.

FISHER ATHLETIC

Isthmian League Premier Division (Step 3)

1st Qual.	(H)	v Hendon	W 4-2	189
			Clancey, Walshe, Watts (2)	
2nd Qual.	(H)	v Uxbridge	L 1-2	103
			C Piper	

Best Performance: 3rd Round 1987-88.

FLEET TOWN

Isthmian League Division One (Step 4)

1st Qual.	(A)	v Enfield	W 2-1	88
			Rose (2)	
2nd Qual.	(H)	v Kingstonian	L 0-1	257

Best Performance: 2nd Round 1997-98.

FLEETWOOD TOWN

Northern Premier League Division One (Step 4)

1st Qual.	(A)	v Wakefield-Emley	W	5-0	128
			Stevens (2), Pryers, Booth, Allen		
2nd Qual.	(A)	v Burscough	W	2-1	438
			Saunders (2)		
3rd Qual.	(H)	v Alfreton Town	L	1-3	552
			Pond		

Best Performance: 1st Round 1988-89, 90-91, 91-92.

FOLKESTONE INVICTA

Isthmian League Premier Division (Step 3)

1st Qual.	(H)	v Whyteleafe	D	1-1	265
			Dryden		
Replay	(A)	v Whyteleafe	W	2-1	103
			Dryden, Jones		
2nd Qual.	(H)	v Wealdstone	W	5-3	316
			Myall, Dryden (2), Guest, Flanaghan		
3rd Qual.	(A)	v Harlow Town	L	1-2	184
			Norman		

Best Performance: 3rd Round 1998-99, 00-01.

FOREST GREEN ROVERS

Conference National (Step 1)

1st Round	(A)	v Weymouth	W	1-0	1120
			Gadsby		
2nd Round	(H)	v Dorchester Town	W	3-1	862
			Harding, Hayes, Wanless		
3rd Round	(A)	v Stafford Rangers	L	1-2	1178
			Madjo		

Best Performance: Runners-up 1998-99, 2000-01.

FRICKLEY ATHLETIC

Northern Premier League Premier Division (Step 3)

1st Qual.	(A)	v Warrington Town	D	1-1	132
			Woolford		
Replay	(H)	v Warrington Town	D	1-1*	265
Warrington won 5-4 on pens.			Chambers		

Best Performance: Quarter Finals 1984-85.

GAINSBOROUGH TRINITY

Conference North (Step 2)

3rd Qual.	(A)	v Kettering Town	L	0-2	1132

Best Performance: 4th Round 2002-03.

Gainsborough Trinty 'keeper, James Holmshaw, clips the ball off the head of Kettering midfielder Dave Theobald.
Photo: Peter Barnes.

GATESHEAD

Northern Premier League Premier Division (Step 3)

1st Qual.	(A)	v Bradford (PA)	D	1-1	191
			Lawes		
Replay	(H)	v Bradford (PA)	W	4-3*	130
			Johnson, Taylor, Thompson		
2nd Qual.	(H)	v Kidsgrove Athletic	W	1-0	127
			Thompson		

Best Performance: 6th Round 1992-93.

GLOUCESTER CITY

Southern League Premier Division (Step 3)

1st Qual.	(A)	v Cirencester Town	L	0-2	322

Best Performance: Semi-Finals 1996-97.

GOOLE

Northern Premier League Division One (Step 4)

2nd Qual.	(A)	v AFC Telford United	D	1-1	990
			Jackson		
Replay	(H)	v AFC Telford United	L	0-1	330

Best Performance: Quarter-Finals 1974-75.

GRANTHAM TOWN

Southern League Premier Division (3)

1st Qual.	(A)	v Bamber Bridge	D	2-2	162
			Francis, Julien		
Replay	(H)	v Bamber Bridge	W	3-0	230
			Curruthers, Popple, Smith		
2nd Qual.	(H)	v Lincoln United	W	2-1	308
			White, Sturgess		
3rd Qual.	(A)	v Droylsden	L	0-4	251

Best Performance: 6th Round 1971-72, 97-98.

GRAVESEND & NORTHFLEET

Conference National (Step 1)

1st Round	(A)	v East Thurrock United	W	2-0	381
			MacDonald, Smith		
2nd Round	(A)	v Boreham Wood	L	1-3	462
			MacDonald		

Best Performance: Quarter Finals 2004-05.

GRAYS ATHLETIC (HOLDERS)

Conference National (Step 1)

1st Round	(A)	v Aldershot Town	D	1-1	1771
			Kightly		
Replay	(H)	v Aldershot Town	W	1-0*	852
			Poole		
2nd Round	(A)	v Kidderminster H.	W	1-0	1436
			McLean		
3rd Round	(A)	v Hereford United	W	1-0	1609
			Kightly		
4th Round	(H)	v Dagenham & Redbridge	D	1-1	2321
			Poole		
Replay	(A)	v Dagenham & Redbridge	W	4-2	1526
			Nutter, Oli, Poole, Stuart		
Semi-Final 1	(A)	v Exeter City	L	1-2	3051
			Slabber		
Semi-Final 2	(H)	v Exeter City	W	2-0	3693
			Poole, McLean		
FINAL	(N)	v Woking	W	2-0	13997
			Oli, Poole		

Best Performance: Winners 2004-05, 2005-06

GREAT WAKERING ROVERS

Southern League Division One East (Step 4)

1st Qual.	(A) v Braintree Town	L	2-4	210
			Frankis, Butterworth	

Best Performance: 1st Qualifying Round 2002-03, 04-05, 05-06.

GRESLEY ROVERS

Northern Premier League Division One (Step 4)

1st Qual.	(H) v Ilkeston Town	D	2-2	320
			Barratt, Slater	
Replay	(A) v Ilkeston Town	W	3-2	349
			Barratt (2), Tate	
2nd Qual.	(H) v Mossley	L	1-4	275
			Edwards	

Best Performance: Quarter Finals 1995-96.

GUISELEY

Northern Premier League Premier Division (Step 3)

1st Qual.	(H) v Chorley	W	3-1	182
			Parke, Illingworth, Cooke	
2nd Qual.	(H) v Kendal Town	D	2-2	228
			Connor, Stuart	
Replay	(A) v Kendal Town	L	0-4	183

Best Performance: Semi-Finals 1994-95.

HALESOWEN TOWN

Southern League Premier Division (Step 3)

1st Qual.	(H) v Willenhall Town	D	0-0	326
Replay	(A) v Willenhall Town	W	3-2*	210
			Amos, Forsdick, Preston	
2nd Qual.	(H) v Aylesbury Town	W	2-0	374
			Lamey, Forsdick	
3rd Qual.	(A) v Sutton Coldfield Town	D	1-1	278
			Forinton	
Replay	(H) v Sutton Coldfield Town	W	3-0	245
			Forsdick, Lamey, Pope	
1st Round	(H) v Tamworth	L	1-2	668
			Lamey	

Best Performance: 3rd Round 1994-95.

HALIFAX TOWN

Conference National (Step 1)

1st Round	(H) v Southport	D	0-0	1101
Replay	(A) v Southport	W	1-0	589
			Forrest	
2nd Round	(H) v Hereford United	L	0-1	1220

Best Performance: 5th Round 2002-03.

HAMPTON & RICHMOND BOROUGH

Isthmian League Premier Division (Step 3)

1st Qual.	(H) v Newport (IW)	L	0-2	293

Best Performance: 4th Round 2001-02.

HARLOW TOWN

Southern League Division One East (Step 4)

1st Qual.	(A) v Walton Casuals	W	1-0	92
			Wraight	
2nd Qual.	(H) v Barton Rovers	W	2-1	81
			Ositola (2)	
3rd Qual.	(H) v Folkestone Invicta	W	2-1	184
			Salmon, Ositola	
1st Round	(A) v Salisbury City	L	0-1	731

Best Performance: 2nd Round 1980-81, 1981-82.

HARROGATE TOWN

Conference North (Step 2)

3rd Qual.	(A) v Solihull Borough	L	0-1	199

Best Performance: 3rd Round 1999-2000, 2001-02.

Chris Honey (left) of Hastings United, holds off Corby Town's captain Bobby White. Photo: Roger Turner.

HARROW BOROUGH

Isthmian League Premier Division (Step 3)

2nd Qual.	(H) v Met Police	W	4-2	126
			Le Roux, Haule, Onochie,	
			Leech	
3rd Qual.	(A) v Redbridge	D	1-1	94
			Le Roux	
Replay	(H) v Redbridge	L	2-3*	101
			Fitzsimon, Le Roux	

Best Performance: Semi-Finals 1982-83.

HASTINGS UNITED

Isthmian League Division One (Step 4)

1st Qual.	(H) v Corby Town	D	0-0	376
Replay	(A) v Corby Town	L	0-2	100

Best Performance: 3rd Round 1998-99.

HAVANT & WATERLOOVILLE

Conference South (Step 2)

3rd Qual.	(A) v Weymouth	L	1-2	1018
			Harrison	

Best Performance: Semi-Finals 2002-03.

HAYES

Conference South (Step 2)

3rd Qual.	(A) v Braintree Town	W	1-0	228
			M Bartley	
1st Round	(A) v Worcester City	L	0-1	677

Best Performance: 6th Round 1978-79.

HEDNESFORD TOWN

Conference North (Step 2)

3rd Qual.	(H) v Moor Green	D	1-1	254
			Bell	
Replay	(A) v Moor Green	W	4-2	192
			Brannan (2), Dyer, Marshall	
1st Round	(A) v Solihull Borough	L	1-2	306
			McMahon	

Best Performance: Winners 2003-04.

HEMEL HEMPSTEAD TOWN

Southern League Division One West (Step 4)

1st Qual.	(H) v Swindon Supermarine	D	1-1	130
			Thomas	
Replay	(A) v Swindon Supermarine	W	1-0	86
			Wojtowicz	
2nd Qual.	(H) v Chippenham Town	L	2-3	226
			Thomas, Carney	

Best Performance: 2nd Qualifying 2005-06.

HENDON

Isthmian League Premier Division (Step 3)

1st Qual.	(A)	v Fisher Athletic	L	2-4	189
		Cook, Frendo			

Best Performance: 5th Round 1998-99.

HEREFORD UNITED

Conference National (Step 1)

1st Round	(A)	v Bognor Regis Town	W	7-1	624
		Ipoua, Pitman, Purdle (2),			
		Stanley, Stansfield, Williams			
2nd Round	(A)	v Halifax Town	W	1-0	1220
		Stansfield			
3rd Round	(H)	v Grays Athletic	L	0-1	1609

Best Performance: Semi-Finals 2000-01.

HEYBRIDGE SWIFTS

Isthmian League Premier Division (Step 3)

1st Qual.	(H)	v Walton & Hersham	W	3-0	202
		Glover, Hill, Bradshaw			
2nd Qual.	(H)	v Billericay Town	W	2-1	326
		Lee (2)			
3rd Qual.	(H)	v St Albans City	L	0-1	253

Best Performance: Quarter Finals 1996-97.

HINCKLEY UNITED

Conference North (Step 2)

3rd Qual.	(H)	v Histon	D	2-2	446
		Cluzel, Jackson			
Replay	(A)	v Histon	L	1-2	218
		Story			

Best Performance: 4th Round 1998-99.

HISTON

Conference South (Step 2)

3rd Qual.	(A)	v Hinckley United	D	2-2	446
		I Cambrisge, Haniver			
Replay	(H)	v Hinckley United	W	2-1	218
		Haniver			
1st Round	(A)	v Alfreton Town	D	1-1	238
		Vowden			
Replay	(H)	v Alfreton Town	W	2-1	288
		Barker (2)			
2nd Round	(A)	v Exeter City	L	2-3	2103
		I Cambridge (2)			

Best Performance: 4th Round 2001-01.

HITCHIN TOWN

Southern League Premier Division (Step 3)

1st Qual.	(A)	v Team Bath	W	1-0	86
		Cavill			
2nd Qual.	(H)	v Bedford Town	L	1-2	603
		W Mills			

Best Performance: 5th Round 1998-99.

HORSHAM

Isthmian League Division One (Step 4)

1st Qual.	(A)	v Chelmsford City	L	0-6	358

Best Performance: 1st Round 1976-77.

HUCKNALL TOWN

Conference North (Step 2)

3rd Qual.	(H)	v Northwich Victoria	D	0-0	437
Replay	(A)	v Northwich Victoria	L	1-2	500
		Sucharewycz			

Best Performance: Runners-up 2004-05.

HYDE UNITED

Conference North (Step 2)

3rd Qual.	(H)	v Stalybridge Celtic	L	1-5	906
		Lynch			

Best Performance: Semi-Finals 1988-89, 1994-95, 1995-96.

ILFORD

Southern League Division One East (Step 4)

1st Qual.	(A)	v Boreham Wood	L	0-1	98

2004/05 Season: Competed in the FA Vase.

Best Performance: 3rd Round 1974-75.

ILKESTON TOWN

Northern Premier League Premier Division (Step 3)

1st Qual.	(A)	v Gresley Rovers	D	2-2	320
		Burns, Clifford			
Replay	(H)	v Gresley Rovers	L	2-3	349
		Jemson, Jenkins			

Best Performance: 3rd Round 1982-83, 94-95.

KENDAL TOWN

Northern Premier League Division One (Step 4)

1st Qual.	(A)	v Ossett Albion	W	4-0	87
		Mercer, Cliff, Mayers, Ashcroft			
2nd Qual.	(A)	v Guiseley	D	2-2	228
		Foster, Ashcroft			
Replay	(H)	v Guiseley	W	4-0	183
		Foster, Smith, McKenna,			
		Ashcroft			
3rd Qual.	(A)	v Worcester City	L	0-1	973

Best Performance: 2nd Round 1980-81.

KETTERING TOWN

Conference North (Step 2)

3rd Qual.	(H)	v Gainsborough Trinity	W	2-0	1132
		Midgley, Duffy			
1st Round	(H)	v Farsley Celtic	W	2-1	960
		Moore, Paterson			
2nd Round	(A)	v Dagenham & Redbridge	L	1-2	931
		Burgess			

Best Performance: Runners-up 1978-79, 1999-2000.

KIDDERMINSTER HARRIERS

Conference National (Step 1)

1st Round	(H)	v Scarborough	W	4-0	957
		Blackwood, Christie,			
		Heslop, Thompson			
2nd Round	(H)	v Grays Athletic	L	0-1	1436

Best Performance: Winners 1986-87.

KIDSGROVE ATHLETIC

Northern Premier League Division One (Step 4)

1st Qual.	(H)	v Ashton United	W	3-1	178
		Jones, Miller, Twigg			
2nd Qual.	(A)	v Gateshead	L	0-1	127
3rd Qual.	(A)	v Warrington Town	L	0-4	121

Best Performance: 3rd Qualifying Round 2005-06.

KINGS LYNN

Southern League Premier Division (Step 3)

1st Qual.	(A)	v AFC Wimbledon	L	0-1	1750

Best Performance: 2nd Round 1978-79.

KINGSTONIAN

Isthmian League Division One (Step 4)

1st Qual.	(H)	v Aveley	D	2-2	402
		Ahmed (2)			
Replay	(A)	v Aveley	W	1-0	122
		Ojukwa			
2nd Qual.	(A)	v Fleet Town	W	1-0	257
		Reid			
3rd Qual.	(A)	v Cray Wanderers	D	1-1	239
		Lee			
Replay	(H)	v Cray Wanderers	W	3-1	264
		Alimi, Coke, Lee			
1st Round	(A)	v Canvey Island	L	1-4	413
		Ahmed			

Best Performance: Winners 1998-99, 1999-2000.

LANCASTER CITY

Conference North (Step 2)

3rd Qual.	(H) v Workington	D 0-0		206
Replay	(A) v Workington	W 2-1		326
		Howson, Thomas		
1st Round	(A) v Stafford Rangers	L 2-4		646
		Howson, Taylor		

Best Performance: 3rd Round 1974-75, 1975-76.

LEATHERHEAD

Isthmian League Division One (Step 4)

1st Qual.	(H) v East Thurrock Utd	L 0-1		141

Best Performance: Runners-up 1977-78.

LEEK TOWN

Northern Premier League Premier Division (Step 4)

1st Qual.	(A) v Burscough	D 3-3		212
		Nagington, Hadrell, Whittaker		
Replay	(H) v Burscough	L 1-3		175

Best Performance: Runners-up 1989-90.

LEIGH RMI

Conference North (Step 2)

3rd Qual.	(H) v Stafford Rangers	L 1-4		165
		Simm		

Best Performance: 6th Round 1990-91.

LEIGHTON TOWN

Southern League Division One West (Step 4)

1st Qual.	(H) v Rugby Town	W 2-1		134
		Melissi, Silvestri		
2nd Qual.	(A) v Burnham	W 5-3		103
		Chennells, Burfoot,		
		Rocco, Rawden, OG		
3rd Qual.	(H) v Eastleigh	D 1-1		145
		Chennells		
Replay	(A) v Eastleigh	W 2-1*		186
		Burfoot (2)		
1st Round	(A) v Boreham Wood	L 0-1		165

Best Performance: 1st Round 2005-06.

LEWES

Conference South (Step 2)

3rd Qual.	(H) v Dorchester Town	D 2-2		364
		Hooligan, Sigere		
Replay	(A) v Dorchester Town	L 1-3		235
		Sigere		

Best Performance: 3rd Round 2002-03, 2003-04.

LEYTON

Isthmian League Premier Division (Step 3)

1st Qual.	(H) v Arlesey Town	W 1-0		73
		S Curley		
2nd Qual.	(A) v East Thurrock United	L 1-2		109
		Correria		

Best Performance: 4th Round 2004-05.

LINCOLN UNITED

Northern Premier League Premier Division (Step 3)

1st Qual.	(H) v Colwyn Bay	W 2-1		113
		Miller, Wilkinson		
2nd Qual.	(A) v Grantham Town	L 1-2		308
		Hawley		

Best Performance: 3rd Round.

LYMINGTON & NEW MILTON

Isthmian League Division One (Step 4)

1st Qual.	(H) v Worthing	L 0-4		179

Best Performance: 1st Qualifying Round 2005-06.

MAIDENHEAD UNITED

Conference South (Step 2)

3rd Qual.	(H) v Bishop's Stortford	D 2-2		165
		Newman, Badu		
Replay	(A) v Bishop's Stortford	L 1-2*		171
		Newman		

Best Performance: 3rd Round.

Maidenhead United's 'keeper, Scott Tarr, gathers the ball during the 2-2 draw with Bishop's Stortford.
Photo: Gordon Whittington.

MALDON TOWN

Isthmian League Premier Division (Step 3)

1st Qual.	(A) v Met Police	L 1-4		105
		Ansell		

Best Performance: 2nd Qualifying Round.

MANGOTSFIELD UNITED

Southern League Premier Division (Step 3)

1st Qual.	(A) v Tiverton Town	D 0-0		564
Replay	(H) v Tiverton Town	L 1-2		
		Casey		

Best Performance: 4th Round 2001-02.

MARGATE

Isthmian League Premier Division (Step 3)

1st Qual.	(A) v Bashley	W 3-0		95
		Braithwaite (2), Amoako		
2nd Qual.	(H) v Dartford	L 0-1		549

Best Performance: 6th Round 2001-02.

MARINE

Northern Premier League Premier Division (Step 3)

1st Qual.	(A) v Radcliffe Borough	W 2-1		173
		Nesbitt, Parle		
2nd Qual.	(H) v Matlock Town	W 2-1		239
		Nesbitt, Connolly		
3rd Qual.	(H) v Blyth Spartans	L 0-1		268

Best Performance: Semi-Finals 1983-84, 91-92.

MARLOW

Southern League Division One West (Step 4)

1st Qual.	(H) v Ashford Town (Mx)	L 1-2		105
		OG		

Best Performance: 4th Round 2003-04.

MATLOCK TOWN

Northern Premier League Premier Division (Step 3)

1st Qual.	(A) v Brigg Town	W 1-0		214
		Warne		
2nd Qual.	(A) v Marine	L 1-2		239
		Cropper		

Best Performance: Winners 1974-75.

MERTHYR TYDFIL
Southern League Premier Division (Step 3)
1st Qual.	(H) v Rushall Olympic	L	0-3	403

Best Performance: 3rd Round 1995-96.

METROPOLITAN POLICE
Isthmian League Division One (Step 4)
1st Qual.	(H) v Maldon Town	W	4-1	105
	Daly, King, Johnson, Hamsher			
2nd Qual.	(A) v Harrow Borough	L	2-4	126
	Johnson (2)			

Best Performance: 2nd Round 1989-90.

MOLESEY
Isthmian League Division One (Step 4)
1st Qual.	(A) v Rothwell Town	L	1-3	80
	Ruggles			

Best Performance: 1st Round 1990-91.

MOOR GREEN
Conference North (Step 2)
3rd Qual.	(A) v Hednesford Town	D	1-1	254
	McPhee			
Replay	(H) v Hednesford Town	L	2-4	192
	Trainer (2)			

Best Performance: 1st Round 1990-91, 1996-97.

MORECAMBE
Conference National (Step 1)
1st Round	(A) v Vauxhall Motors	W	4-0	322
	Bentley, Curtis, Twiss (2)			
2nd Round	(A) v Stafford Rangers	L	0-1	

Best Performance: Winners 1973-74.

MOSSLEY
Northern Premier League Division One (Step 4)
1st Qual.	(H) v Shepshed Dynamo	W	3-2	239
	Denney, Giggs, Knight			
2nd Qual.	(A) v Gresley Rovers	W	4-1	275
	Challinor, Kingham,			
	Morning, Downey			
3rd Qual.	(A) v Vauxhall Motors	L	1-2	161
	Goodeve			

Best Performance: Runners-up 1979-80.

NEWPORT COUNTY
Conference South (Step 2)
3rd Qual.	(A) v Salisbury City	L	0-3	806

Best Performance: 3rd Round 1999-2000, 2000-01, 2002-03.

Joe McCormack, the Newport IOW 'keeper, tips a Tonbridge shot over the bar during their 2nd Qualifying round tie. Photo: Roger Turner.

NEWPORT(IW)
Isthmian League Division One (Step 4)
1st Qual.	(A) v Hampton & Richmond B.	W	2-0	293
	P Jones, Quirke			
2nd Qual.	(A) v Tonbridge Angels	L	1-2	358
	OG			

Best Performance: 4th Round 1999-2000.

NORTH FERRIBY UNITED
Northern Premier League Premier Division (Step 3)
1st Qual.	(H) v Prescot Cables	D	1-1	188
	Hartley			
Replay	(A) v Prescot Cables	D	2-2*	192
Prescot Cables won 4-3 on pens.		Fothergill, Lightowler		

Best Performance: 4th Round 2001-02.

NORTHWICH VICTORIA
Conference North (Step 2)
3rd Qual.	(A) v Hucknall Town	D	0-0	437
Replay	(H) v Hucknall Town	W	2-1	500
	Allan, Brayson			
1st Round	(A) v York City	W	2-1	1372
	Allan (2)			
2nd Round	(A) v Woking	D	1-1	1072
	Carr			
Replay	(H) v Woking	L	1-2*	888
	Allan			

Best Performance: Winners 1983-84.

NORTHWOOD
Southern League Premier Division (Step 3)
1st Qual.	(H) v Ramsgate	L	2-4	152
	Kirkland, Clarke			

Best Performance: 3rd Round 2000-01.

NUNEATON BOROUGH
Conference North (Step 2)
3rd Qual.	(A) v Farsley Celtic	L	1-3	271
	Quailey			

Best Performance: Quarter Finals 1976-77.

OSSETT ALBION
Northern Premier League Division One (Step 4)
1st Qual.	(H) v Kendal Town	L	0-4	87

Best Performance: 1st Round 2001-02.

OSSETT TOWN
Northern Premier League Premier Division (Step 3)
1st Qual.	(H) v Stocksbridge P.S.	D	1-1	109
	Walshan			
Replay	(A) v Stocksbridge P.S.	D	2-2*	103
Ossett won 4-1 on pens.		Jones, Walshan		
2nd Qual.	(H) v Clitheroe	D	2-2	108
	O'Brien, Hayward			
Replay	(A) v Clitheroe	D	1-1*	188
Ckitheroe won 4-2 on pens.		Hanson		

Best Performance: 2nd Round 1999-00.

PAULTON ROVERS
Southern League Division One West (Step 4)
1st Qual.	(H) v Salisbury City	D	1-1	285
	Seavill			
Replay	(A) v Salisbury City	L	1-3*	336
	Perry			

Best Performance: 2nd Qualifying Round 1976-77, 77-78.

POTTERS BAR TOWN
Southern League Division One East (Step 4)
1st Qual.	(A) v Barton Rovers	L	2-3	110
	Milne, Winger			

Best Performance: 1st Qualifying Round 2005-06.

PRESCOT CABLES

Northern Premier League Premier Division

1st Qual.	(A) v North Ferriby United	D	1-1	188
		Feeney		
Replay	(H) v North Ferriby United	D	2-2*	192
Prescot Cables won 4-3 on pens.		Flynn, McEwan		
2nd Qual.	(H) v Farsley Celtic	L	1-2	214
		Duffy		

Best Performance: 3rd Qualifying Round 1981-82.

RADCLIFFE BOROUGH

Northern Premier League Premier Division (Step 3)

1st Qual.	(H) v Marine	L	1-2	173
		Foster		

Best Performance: 3rd Round 1995-96.

RAMSGATE

Isthmian League Division One (Step 4)

1st Qual.	(A) v Northwood	W	4-2	152
		Welford, O Schulz, Ball (2)		
2nd Qual.	(H) v AFC Wimbledon	D	1-1	1047
		Welford		
Replay	(A) v AFC Wimbledon	L	1-2	1140
		W Schulz		

Best Performance: 2nd Qualifying Round.

REDBRIDGE

Isthmian League Premier Division (Step 3)

1st Qual.	(A) v Banstead Athletic	W	2-1	64
		Apata, Luck		
2nd Qual.	(A) v Enfield Town	D	1-1	268
		Wattley		
Replay	(H) v Enfield Town	W	2-1	172
		Collins, Wattley		
3rd Qual.	(H) v Harrow Borough	D	1-1	94
		Roberts		
Replay	(A) v Harrow Borough	W	3-2*	101
		Elbi (2), Haan		
1st Round	(A) v Welling United	L	1-4	415
		Kahn		

Best Performance: 1st Round 2005-06.

REDDITCH UNITED

Conference North (Step 2)

3rd Qual.	(H) v Barrow	D	1-1	289
		Rickards		
Replay	(A) v Barrow	L	0-2	756

Best Performance: 4th Round 1998-99.

ROSSENDALE UNITED

Northern Premier League Division One (Step 4)

1st Qual.	(H) v Woodley Sports	L	0-1	112

Best Performance: 2nd Round 1981-82.

ROTHWELL TOWN

Southern League Division One East (Step 4)

1st Qual.	(H) v Molesey	W	3-1	80
		Rice, Master, Mitchell		
2nd Qual.	(A) v Croydon Athletic	D	2-2	88
		Spencer, Morris		
Replay	(H) v Croydon Athletic	L	0-1	98

Best Performance: 2nd Round 1994-95.

RUGBY UNITED

Southern League Premier Division (Step 3)

1st Qual.	(A) v Leighton Town	L	1-2	134
		Squire		

Best Performance: 2nd Round 1972-73.

RUNCORN HALTON

Northern Premier League Premier Division (Step 3)

1st Qual.	(A) v Farsley Celtic	L	0-2	223

Best Performance: Runners-up 1985-86, 92-93, 93-94.

RUSHALL OLYMPIC

Southern League Division One West (Step 4)

1st Qual.	(A) v Merthyr Tydfil	W	3-0	403
		Barnett, O'Connor, Mitchell		
2nd Qual.	(H) v Ashford Town (Mx)	L	3-4	88
		Erraji, O'Connor, Jackson		

Best Performance: 2nd Qualifying Round 2005-06.

SALISBURY CITY

Southern League Premier Division (Step 3)

1st Qual.	(A) v Paulton Rovers	D	1-1	285
		Sales		
Replay	(H) v Paulton Rovers	W	3-1*	336
		Haddow, Heath (2)		
2nd Qual.	(H) v Clevedon Town	W	2-1	552
		Davis, Tubbs		
3rd Qual.	(H) v Newport County	W	3-0	806
		Haddow, Sales, Widdrington		
1st Round	(H) v Harlow Town	W	1-0	731
		Tubbs		
2nd Round	(A) v Canvey Island	W	1-0	534
		Haddow		
3rd Round	(H) v Stalybridge Celtic	D	0-0	1533
Replay	(A) v Stalybridge Celtic	W	1-0	
		Tubbs		
4th Round	(A) v Exeter City	L	1-3	3653
		Matthews		

Best Performance: 4th Round 2005-06.

SCARBOROUGH

Conference National (Step 1)

1st Round	(A) v Kidderminster H.	L	0-4	957
		Goalscorers		

Best Performance: Winners 1972-73, 1975-76, 1976-77.

SHEPSHED DYNAMO

Northern Premier League Division One (Step 4)

1st Qual.	(A) v Mossley	L	2-3	239
		Howell, Gomm		

Best Performance: 3rd Round 1998-99.

SITTINGBOURNE

Southern League Division One East (Step 4)

1st Qual.	(H) v Chatham Town	W	3-0	284
		Marsh, Spice, Neal		
2nd Qual.	(H) v Corby Town	W	1-0	178
		Marsh		
3rd Qual.	(H) v Cambridge City	L	1-3	265
		Spice		

Best Performance: 1st Round 1997-98.

SLOUGH TOWN

Isthmian League Premier Division (Step 3)

1st Qual.	(H) v Croydon Athletic	L	1-3	286
		Hodges		

Best Performance: Semi-Finals 1976-77, 1997-98.

SOLIHULL BOROUGH

Southern League Division One West (Step 4)

1st Qual.	(A) v Evesham United	W	2-0	157
		Marsden, Grady		
2nd Qual.	(H) v Tiverton Town	W	3-1	204
		Pearson (2), Marsden		
3rd Qual.	(H) v Harrogate Town	W	1-0	199
		Pearson		
1st Round	(H) v Hednesford Town	W	2-1	306
		Barry, Pearson		
2nd Round	(A) v Stalybridge Celtic	L	0-1	612

Best Performance: 4th Round 1997-98, 2001-02.

SOUTHPORT

Conference National (Step 1)

1st Round	(A)	v Halifax Town	D	0-0	1101
Replay	(H)	v Halifax Town	L	0-1	589

Best Performance: Runners-up 1997-98.

SPALDING UNITED

Northern Premier League Division One (Step 4)

1st Qual.	(A)	v Clitheroe	L	1-3	253
		Bonser			

Best Performance: 3rd Round 1999-2000.

ST ALBANS CITY

Conference South (Step 2)

3rd Qual.	(A)	v Heybridge Swifts	W	1-0	253
		Cracknell			
1st Round	(A)	v AFC Wimbledon	W	3-2	1953
		Hakim (2)			
2nd Round	(A)	v Tamworth	L	0-1	705

Best Performance: Semi-Finals 1998-99.

STAFFORD RANGERS

Conference North (Step 2)

3rd Qual.	(A)	v Leigh RMI	W	4-1	165
		Talbott (2), Walker, Gibson			
1st Round	(H)	v Lancaster City	W	4-2	646
		Grayson (2), Smith, Walker			
2nd Round	(H)	v Morecambe	W	1-0	1121
		Street			
3rd Round	(H)	v Forest Green Rovers	W	2-1	1178
		Lovatt, Grayson			
4th Round	(A)	v Woking	D	1-1	2020
		Grayson			
Replay	(H)	v Woking	L	2-4	1781
		Talbott, Thomson			

Best Performance: Winners 1971-72, 1978-79.

Stafford Rangers' Paul Groves (right), wins the ball off Woking's Steve Ferguson, in the 4th round.

Photo: Roger Turner.

STAINES TOWN

Isthmian League Premier Division (Step 4)

1st Qual.	(H)	v Wivenhoe Town	W	2-0	201
		Newtown, Nabil			
2nd Qual.	(A)	v Cray Wanderers	L	3-4	131
		Maskell, Hunter, De Lisser			

Best Performance: 2nd Round 1976-77, 2003-04.

STALYBRIDGE CELTIC

Conference North (Step 2)

3rd Qual.	(A)	v Hyde United	W	5-1	906
		Prince (3), Ellington (2)			
1st Round	(H)	v Droylsden	W	1-0	598
		Eastwood			
2nd Round	(H)	v Solihull Borough	W	1-0	612
		Eastwood			
3rd Round	(A)	v Salisbury City	D	0-0	1533
Replay	(H)	v Salisbury City	L	0-1	

Best Performance: 6th Round 2001-02.

STAMFORD

Southern League Division One East (Step 4)

1st Qual.	(A)	v Corinthian Casuals	W	4-1	85
		Neil, Holmes, Stevens,			
		Pritchard			
2nd Qual.	(A)	v Worthing	D	1-1	427
		Pritchard			
Replay	(H)	v Worthing	W	2-0	203
		Wornall (2)			
3rd Qual.	(A)	v Boreham Wood	L	1-3	146
		Maddox			

Best Performance: 5th Round 2004-05.

STEVENAGE BOROUGH

Conference National (Step 1)

1st Round	(H)	v Crawley Town	L	0-2	951

Best Performance: Runners-up 2001-02.

STOCKSBRIDGE PARK STEELS

Northern Premier League Division One (Step 4)

1st Qual.	(A)	v Ossett Town	D	1-1	109
		Zoll			
Replay	(H)	v Ossett Town	D	2-2*	103
Ossett won 4-1 on pens.		Cockerill, Walker			

Best Performance: 3rd Qualifying Round 1996-97.

STOURPORT SWIFTS

Southern League Division One West (Step 4)

1st Qual.	(H)	v Bedworth United	L	0-1	113

Best Performance: 3rd Round 2001-02.

SUTTON COLDFIELD TOWN

Southern League Division One West (Step 4)

1st Qual.	(H)	v Chesham United	W	2-1	107
		Field, Hebberd			
2nd Qual.	(A)	v Bedworth United	W	5-2	146
		Owen, Markman, Rowe,			
		Didd, OG			
3rd Qual.	(H)	v Halesowen Town	D	1-1	278
		Hebberd			
Replay	(A)	v Halesowen Town	L	0-3	245

Best Performance: 1st Round 1989-90.

SUTTON UNITED

Conference South (Step 2)

3rd Qual.	(A)	v Uxbridge	D	2-2	204
		Elliott, Castledine			
Replay	(H)	v Uxbridge	L	0-1	252

Best Performance: Runners-Up 1980-81.

SWINDON SUPERMARINE

Southern League Division One West (Step 4)

1st Qual.	(A)	v Hemel Hempstead T.	D	1-1	130
		Ronincsky			
Replay	(H)	v Hemel Hempstead T.	L	0-1	86

Best Performance: 1st Qualifying Round.

TAMWORTH
Conference National (Step 1)

1st Round	(A)	v Halesowen Town	W 2-1	668
			Anaclet, Ward	
2nd Round	(H)	v St Albans City	W 1-0	705
			Davidson	
3rd Round	(H)	v Dagenham & Redbridge	D 0-0	920
Replay	(A)	v Dagenham & Redbridge	L 0-3	922

Best Performance: Runners-Up 2002-03.

TAUNTON TOWN
Southern League Division One West (Step 4)

1st Qual.	(A)	v Clevedon Town	L 1-2	216
			Peckham	

Best Performance: 1st Round 1980-81.

TEAM BATH
Southern League Premier Division (Step 4)

1st Qual.	(H)	v Hitchin Town	L 0-1	86

Best Performance: 3rd Round 2004-05.

THAME UNITED
Southern League Division One West (Step 4)

1st Qual.	(H)	v Aylesbury United	L 0-5	294

Best Performance: 3rd Round 2002-03.

THURROCK
Conference South (Step 2)

3rd Qual.	(A)	v Eastbourne Borough	W 3-0	368
			Heffer (2), Hodges	
1st Round	(A)	v Dagenham & Red.	L 0-2	737

Best Performance: 2nd Round 1995-96.

TIVERTON TOWN
Southern League Premier Division (Step 3)

1st Qual.	(H)	v Mangotsfield United	D 0-0	564
Replay	(A)	v Mangotsfield United	W 2-1	294
			Daly, Mudge	
2nd Qual.	(A)	v Solihull Borough	L 1-3	204
			Pears	

Best Performance: 5th Round 2000-01.

TONBRIDGE ANGELS
Isthmian League Division One (Step 4)

1st Qual.	(H)	v Cheshunt	W 1-0	430
			Piscine	
2nd Qual.	(H)	v Newport (IW)	W 2-1	358
			Powell, Parks	
3rd Qual.	(H)	v East Thurrock United	D 0-0	288
Replay	(A)	v East Thurrock United	L 0-3	130

Best Performance: 1st Round 1970-71, 71-72.

TOOTING & MITCHAM UNITED
Isthmian League Division One (Step 4)

1st Qual.	(H)	v Weladstone	L 1-2	312
			Pinnock	

Best Performance: 4th Round 1975-76.

UXBRIDGE
Southern League Division One East (Step 4)

1st Qual.	(A)	v Windsor & eton	W 2-1	172
			Feeley (2)	
2nd Qual.	(A)	v Fisher Athletic	W 2-1	103
			Swaysland, Tunnell	
3rd Qual.	(H)	v Sutton United	D 2-2	204
			Nichols, Swaysland	
Replay	(A)	v Sutton United	W 1-0	252
			Swift	
1st Round	(H)	v Woking	L 1-2	471
			Weedon	

Best Performance: 2nd Round 1998-99, 1999-2000, 2000-01.

VAUXHALL MOTORS
Conference North (Step 2)

3rd Qual.	(H)	v Mossley	W 2-1	161
			Rooney, McGivern	
1st Round	(H)	v Morecambe	L 0-4	322

Best Performance: 4th Round 2001-02.

WAKEFIELD-EMLEY
Northern Premier League Premier Division (Step 3)

1st Qual.	(H)	v Fleetwood Town	L 0-5	128

Best Performance: 6th Round 1998-99.

WALTHAM FOREST
Southern League Division One East (Step 4)

1st Qual.	(H)	v Burgess HIll Town	L 0-1	130

Best Performance: 1st Qualifying Round.

WALTON & HERSHAM
Isthmian League Premier Division (Step 3)

1st Qual.	(A)	v Heybridge Swifts	L 0-3	202

Best Performance: 4th Round 1999-2000.

WALTON CASUALS
Isthmian League Division One (Step 4)

1st Qual.	(H)	v Harlow Town	L 0-1	92

Best Performance: 1st Qualifying Round 2005-06.

WARRINGTON TOWN
Northern Premier League Division One (Step 4)

1st Qual.	(H)	v Frickley Athletic	D 1-1	132
			Howard	
Replay	(A)	v Frickley Athletic	D 1-1* 5-4p	132
Warrington won 5-4 o pens.			Latham	
2nd Qual.	(A)	v Bridlington Town	D 2-2	192
			Lacken, Featherstone	
Replay	(H)	v Bridlington Town	W 1-0	135
			Featherstone	
3rd Qual.	(H)	v Kidsgrove Athletic	W 4-0	121
			G Mitchell (2),	
			Featherstone, P Mitchell	
1st Round	(H)	v Blyth Spartans	L 1-2	251
			Tickle	

Best Performance: Quarter Finals 1992-93.

WEALDSTONE
Isthmian League Premier Division (Step 3)

1st Qual.	(A)	v Tooting & Mitcham Utd	W 2-1	312
			Ryan, Tucker	
2nd Qual.	(A)	v Folkestone Invicta	L 3-5	316
			Beckford, Jolly, Montgomery	

Best Performance: Winners 1984-85.

WELLING UNITED
Conference South (Step 2)

3rd Qual.	(A)	v Basingstoke Town	W 2-0	313
			Day, OG	
1st Round	(H)	v Redbridge	W 4-1	415
			Day, Kedwell, Stadhart (2)	
2nd Round	(A)	v Blyth Spartans	W 3-1	784
			Day, Kedwell, Owen	
3rd Round	(A)	v Woking	L 2-3	1244
			Stadhart, Kedwell	

Best Performance: 6th Round 1988-89.

WESTON SUPER MARE
Conference South (Step 2)

3rd Qual.	(H)	v Bedford Town	W 4-0	221
			Rogers (2), Walker, Brown	
1st Round	(H)	v Barking & East Ham Utd	W 3-2	243
			Brown, French (2)	
2nd Round	(H)	v Worksop Town	D 1-1	366
			Walker	
Replay	(A)	v Worksop Town	L 1-2	369
			Rose	

Best Performance: 4th Round 1998-99, 2003-04.

Whytleafe 'keeper, James Wastell, and defedner Lee Sidwell, keep out Folkstone Invicta's Adam Flanagan and Stuart Myall. Photo: Alan Coomes.

WEYMOUTH

Conference South (Step 2)

3rd Qual.	(H)	v Havant & Waterlooville	W	2-1	1018
		Wilkinson, O'Connor			
1st Round	(H)	v Forest Green Rovers	L	0-1	1120

Best Performance: 5th Round 2000-01.

WHITBY TOWN

Northern Premier League Premier Division (Step 3)

1st Qual.	(H)	v Eastwood Town	W	4-2	228
		Wilford (4)			
2nd Qual.	(A)	v Blyth Spartans	L	0-2	501

Best Performance: Quarter Finals 1983-84.

WHYTELEAFE

Isthmian League Division One (Step 4)

1st Qual.	(A)	v Folkestone Invicta	D	1-1	265
		Martin			
Replay	(H)	v Folkestone Invicta	L	1-2	103

Best Performance: 4th Round 1998-99.

WILLENHALL TOWN

Southern League Division One West (Step 4)

1st Qual.	(A)	v Halesowen Town	D	0-0	326
Replay	(H)	v Halesowen Town	L	2-3*	210
		Bishop, Perrow			

Best Performance: 3rd Round 2004-05.

WINDSOR & ETON

Isthmian League Premier Division (Step 3)

1st Qual.	(H)	v Uxbridge	L	1-2	172
		Wallace			

Best Performance: 3rd Round 1968-69.

WINGATE & FINCHLEY

Southern League Division One East (Step 4)

1st Qual.	(A)	v Billericay Town	L	0-1	317

Best Performance: 1st Qualifying Round.

WITTON ALBION

Northern Premier League Division (Step 3)

1st Qual.	(H)	v AFC Telford United	D	1-1	404
		Jones			
Replay	(A)	v AFC Telford United	L	1-2	853

Best Performance: Runners-up 1991-92.

WIVENHOE TOWN

Southern League Division One East (Step 4)

1st Qual.	(A)	v Staines Town	L	0-2	201

Best Performance: 2nd Round 1989-90.

WOKING

Conference National (Step 1)

1st Round	(A)	v Uxbridge	W	2-1	471
		McAllister, Rawle			
2nd Round	(H)	v Northwich Victoria	D	1-1	1072
		Murray			
Replay	(A)	v Northwich Victoria	W	2-1*	888
		Ferguson, Selley			
3rd Round	(H)	v Welling United	W	3-2	1244
		Sharpling, McAllister, Hutchinson			
4th Round	(H)	v Stafford Rangers	D	1-1	2020
		McAllister			
Replay	(A)	v Stafford Rangers	W	4-2	1781
		McAllister, Evans, Ferguson, Smith			
Semi-Final 1	(A)	v Boreham Wood	W	1-0	1511
		Hutchinson			
Semi-Final 2	(H)	v Boreham Wood	W	2-0	2080
		Ferguson (2)			
FINAL	(N)	v Grays Athletic	L	0-2	13997

Best Performance: Winners 1993-94, 1994-95, 1996-97.

WOODLEY SPORTS

Northern Premier League Division One (Step 4)

1st Qual.	(A)	v Rossendale United	W	1-0	112
		Young			
2nd Qual.	(A)	v Bishop Auckland	W	3-1	85
		Bailey, Curley, Headley			
3rd Qual.	(A)	v Clitheroe	L	1-2	205
		Daniel			

Best Performance: 1st Round 2004-05.

WORCESTER CITY

Conference North (Step 2)

3rd Qual.	(H)	v Kendal Town	W	1-0	973
		Webster			
1st Round	(H)	v Hayes	W	1-0	677
		Clegg			
2nd Round	(A)	v Crawley Town	L	1-3	862
		Preece			

Best Performance: 6th Round (x4)

WORKINGTON

Conference North (Step 2)

3rd Qual.	(A)	v Lancaster City	D	0-0	206
Replay	(H)	v Lancaster City	L	1-2	326
		Arnold			

Best Performance: 6th Round 1999-2000.

WORKSOP TOWN

Conference North (Step 2)

3rd Qual.	(H) v AFC Telford United	D 1-1		416
		Jackson		
Replay	(A) v AFC Telford United	W 2-1		952
		Saunders (2)		
1st Round	(A) v Burton Albion	W 1-0		1359
		Saunders		
2nd Round	(A) v Weston-S-Mare	D 1-1		366
		Crane		
Replay	(H) v Weston-S-Mare	W 2-1		369
		Norton, Wilson		
3rd Round	(A) v Accrington Stanley	D 1-1		961
		Crane		
Replay	(H) v Accrington Stanley	D1-1* 4-2p		733
Worksop won 4-2 on pens.		Norton		
4th Round	(H) v Boreham Wood	L 0-1		1006

Best Performance: 6th Round 2000-01.

WORTHING

Isthmian League Premier Division (Step 3)

1st Qual.	(A) v Lymington & New M.	W 4-0		179
		Browne (3), Palquette		
2nd Qual.	(H) v Stamford	D 1-1		427
		Browne		
Replay	(A) v Stamford	L 0-2		203

Best Performance: 3rd Round 1985-86.

YATE TOWN

Southern League Premier Division (Step 3)

1st Qual.	(A) v Burnham	L 0-2		75

Best Performance: 2nd Round 1999-00.

YEADING

Conference South (Step 2)

3rd Qual.	(A) v Bath City	W 2-1		393
		Telemaque (2)		
1st Round	(H) v Carshalton Athletic	L 1-2		107
		Saroya		

Best Performance: 2nd Round 1997-98, 2000-01, 2001-02.

Worksop's Michael Simpson rises above all others to clear this Boreham Wood attack.

Photo: Bill Wheatcroft.

YORK CITY

Conference National (Step 1)

1st Round	(H) v Northwich Victoria	L 1-2		1372
		Bishop		

Best Performance: 1st Round 2004-05, 2005-06.

Woking's Gary McDonald heads towards teh Grays goal in the final.

Photo: Keith Clayton.

ROUND BY ROUND

FIRST QUALIFYING ROUND

BIGGEST HOME WIN:	**6-0** CHELMSFORD CITY VS HORSHAM	
BIGGEST AWAY WIN:	**0-5** WAKEFIELD-EMLEY VS FLEETWOOD TOWN	
HIGHEST ATTENDANCE:	**1,750** AFC WIMBLEDON VS KINGS LYNN	
NUMBER OF GAMES:	**75 + 20**	
TOTAL ATTENDANCE:	**23,048**	
AVERAGE ATTENDANCE:	**243**	

AFC Wimbledon	v Kings Lynn	1-0	1750
Ashford Town	v Bromley	0-2	251
Bamber Bridge	v Grantham Town	2-2	162
Banstead Athletic	v Redbridge	1-2	64
Barton Rovers	v Potters Bar Town	3-2	110
Bashley	v Margate	0-3	95
Bedford Town	v Bracknell Town	3-0	420
Billericay Town	v Wingate & Finchley	1-0	317
Blyth Spartans	v Belper Town	2-0	372
Boreham Wood	v Ilford	1-0	98
Brackley Town	v Banbury United	1-1	494
Bradford (PA)	v Gateshead	1-1	191
Braintree Town	v Great Wakering Rovers	4-2	210
Brigg Town	v Matlock Town	0-1	214
Bromsgrove Rovers	v Beaconsfield SYCOB	3-2	347
Burnham	v Yate Town	2-0	75
Burscough	v Leek Town	3-3	175
Chelmsford City	v Horsham	6-0	358
Cinderford Town	v Chippenham Town	1-1	197
Cirencester Town	v Gloucester City	2-0	322
Clevedon Town	v Taunton Town	2-1	216
Clitheroe	v Spalding United	3-1	253
Corinthian Casuals	v Stamford	1-4	85
Dover Athletic	v Dartford	1-1	615
Dulwich Hamlet	v Barking & East Ham Utd	1-1	224
Dunstable Town	v Bath City	2-2	122
Enfield	v Fleet Town	1-2	88
Enfield Town	v Berkhamsted Town	3-0	212
Evesham United	v Solihull Borough	0-2	157
Farsely Celtic	v Runcorn FC Halton	2-0	223
Fisher Athletic	v Hendon	4-2	189
Folkestone Invicta	v Whyteleafe	1-1	265
Gresley Rovers	v Ilkeston Town	2-2	320
Guiseley	v Chorley	3-1	182
Halesowen Town	v Willenhall Town	0-0	326
Hampton & Richmond	v Newport (IW)	0-2	293
Hastings United	v Corby Town	0-0	376
Hemel Hempstead Town	v Swindon Supermarine	1-1	130
Heybridge Swifts	v Walton & Hersham	3-0	202
Kidsgrove Athletic	v Ashton United	3-1	178
Kingstonian	v Aveley	2-2	402
Leatherhead	v East Thurrock Utd	0-1	141
Leighton Town	v Rugby Town	2-1	134
Leyton	v Arlesey Town	1-0	73
Lincoln United	v Colwyn Bay	2-1	105
Lymington & New	v Worthing	0-4	179
Marlow	v Ashford Town (Mx)	1-2	105
Merthyr Tydfil	v Rushall Olympic	0-3	403
Met Police	v Maldon Town	4-1	80
Mossley	v Shepshed Dynamo	3-2	239
North Ferriby United	v Prescot Cables	1-1	188
Northwood	v Ramsgate	2-4	152
Ossett Albion	v Kendal Town	0-4	87
Ossett Town	v Stocksbridge P.S.	1-1	109
Paulton Rovers	v Salisbury City	1-1	285
Radcliffe Borough	v Marine	1-2	173
Rossendale United	v Woodley Sports	0-1	112
Rothwell Town	v Molesey	3-1	80
Sittingbourne	v Chatham Town	3-0	284
Slough Town	v Croydon Athletic	1-3	286
Staines Town	v Wivenhoe Town	2-0	201
Stourport Swifts	v Bedworth United	0-1	113
Sutton Coldfield Town	v Chesham United	2-1	107

Corby Town's Brett Darby (No.7) fires in a shot but Hastings' 'keeper, John Sullivan, has it covered this time.
Photo: Roger Turner.

Team Bath	v Hitchin Town	0-1	86
Thame United	v Aylesbury United	0-5	394
Tiverton Town	v Mangotsfield United	0-0	564
Tonbridge Angels	v Cheshunt	1-0	430
Tooting & Mitcham Utd	v Weladstone	1-2	312
Wakefield-Emley	v Fleetwood Town	0-5	128
Waltham Forest	v Burgess HIll Town	0-1	130
Walton Casuals	v Harlow Town	0-1	92
Warrington Town	v Frickley Athletic	1-1	132
Whitby Town	v Eastwood Town	4-2	228
Windsor & Eton	v Uxbridge	1-2	172
Witton Albion	v AFC Telford United	1-1	404

REP LAYS

AFC Telford United	v Witton Albion	2-1	853
Aveley	v Kingstonian	0-1	122
Banbury United	v Brackley Town	3-0	479
Barking & East Ham Utd	v Dulwich Hamlet	2-0	98
Bath City	v Dunstable Town	5-0	241
Chippenham Town	v Cinderford Town	3-1	309
Corby Town	v Hastings United	2-0	100
Dartford	v Dover Athletic	3-2	323
Frickley Athletic	v Warrington Town	1-1* 4-5p	265
Gateshead	v Bradford (PA)	4-3*	130
Grantham Town	v Bamber Bridge	3-0	230
Ilkeston Town	v Gresley Rovers	2-3	349
Leek Town	v Burscough	1-3	175
Mangotsfield Utd	v Tiverton Town	1-2	294
Prescot Cables	v North Ferriby United	2-2* 4-3p	192
Salisbury City	v Paulton Rovers	3-1*	336
Stocksbridge P.S.	v Ossett Town	2-2* 1-4p	103
Swindon Supermarine	v Hemel Hempstead T.	0-1	86
Whyteleafe	v Folkestone Invicta	1-2	103
Willenhall Town	v Halesowen Town	2-3*	210

SECOND QUALIFYING ROUND

BIGGEST HOME WIN:	**4-0** KENDAL TOWN VS GUISELEY
BIGGEST AWAY WIN:	**1-4** GRESLEY ROVERS VS MOSSLEY
HIGHEST ATTENDANCE:	**1,161** AFC WIMBLEDON VS RAMSGATE
NUMBER OF GAMES:	**40 + 9**
TOTAL ATTENDANCE:	**14,566**
AVERAGE ATTENDANCE:	**297**

AFC Telford United	v Goole	1-1	990
Banbury United	v Circencester Town	2-2	404
Barking & East Ham Utd	v Burgess Hill Town	4-1	105
Bath City	v Bromsbrove Rovers	2-0	423
Bedworth United	v Sutton Coldfield Town	2-5	146
Bishop Auckland	v Woodley Sports	1-3	85
Blyth Spartans	v Whitby Town	2-0	501
Boreham Wood	v Bromley	4-1	195
Bridlington Town	v Warrington Town	2-2	192
Burnham	v Leighton Town	3-5	103
Burscough	v Fleetwood Town	1-2	438
Chelmsford City	v Braintree Town	0-2	436
Cray Wanderers	v Staines Town	4-3	131
Croydon Athletic	v Rothwell Town	2-2	88
East Thurrock United	v Leyton	2-1	109
Enfield Town	v Redbridge	1-1	268
Fisher Athletic	v Uxbridge	1-2	103
Fleet Town	v Kingstonian	0-1	257
Folkestone Invicta	v Wealdstone	5-3	316

Gateshead	v Kidsgrove Athletic	1-0	127
Grantham Town	v Lincoln United	2-1	308
Gresley Rovers	v Mossley	1-4	275
Guiseley	v Kendal Town	2-2	228
Halesowen Town	v Aylesbury Town	2-0	374
Harlow Town	v Barton Rovers	2-1	81
Harrow Borough	v Met Police	4-2	126
Hemel Hempstead Town	v Chippenham Town	2-3	226
Heybridge Swifts	v Billericay Town	2-1	326
Hitchin Town	v Bedford Town	1-2	603
Margate	v Dartford	0-1	549
Marine	v Matlock Town	2-1	239
Ossett Town	v Clitheroe	2-2	108
Prescot Cables	v Farsley Celtic	1-2	214
Ramsgate	v AFC Wimbledon	1-1	1047
Rushall Olympic	v Ashford Town (Mx)	3-4	88
Salisbury City	v Clevedon Town	2-1	552
Sittingbourne	v Corby Town	1-0	178
Solihull Borough	v Tiverton Town	3-1	204
Tonbridge Angels	v Newport (IW)	2-1	358
Worthing	v Stamford	1-1	427

REPLAYS

AFC Wimbledon	v Ramsgate	2-1	1140
Cirencester Town	v Banbury United	3-4*	186
Clitheroe	v Ossett Town	1-1* 4-2p	188
Goole	v AFC Telford United	0-1	330
Kendal Town	v Guiseley	4-0	183
Redbridge	v Enfield Town	2-1	192
Rothwell Town	v Croydon Athletic	0-1	98
Stamford	v Worthing	2-0	203
Warrington Town	v Bridlington Town	1-0	135

THIRD QUALIFYING ROUND

BIGGEST HOME WIN:	**4-0** DROYLSDEN VS GRANTHAM TOWN
	WARRINGTON TOWN VS KIDSGROVE ATH. WESTON S MARE VS BEDFORD TOWN
BIGGEST AWAY WIN:	**1-5** HYDE UNITED VS STALYBRIDGE CELTIC
HIGHEST ATTENDANCE:	**1,143** KETTERING TOWN VS GAINSBOROUGH T.
NUMBER OF GAMES:	**42 + 15**
TOTAL ATTENDANCE:	**20,983**
AVERAGE ATTENDANCE:	**368**

Ashford Town (Mx)	v Bognor Regis Town	2-3	140
Barking & East Ham Utd	v Croydon Athletic	2-1	101
Basingstoke Town	v Welling United	0-2	313
Bath City	v Yeading	1-2	393
Boreham Wood	v Stamford	3-1	146
Braintree Town	v Hayes	0-1	228
Chippenham Town	v Carshalton Athletic	0-2	510
Clitheroe	v Woodley Sports	2-1	205
Cray Wanderers	v Kingstonian	1-1	239
Dartford	v AFC Wimbledon	0-0	1082
Droylsden	v Grantham Town	4-0	251
Eastbourne Borough	v Thurrock	0-3	368
Farnborough Town	v Banbury United	2-0	466
Farsley Celtic	v Nuneaton Borough	3-1	271
Fleetwood Town	v Alfreton Town	1-3	552
Harlow Town	v Folkestone Invicta	2-1	184
Hednesford Town	v Moor Green	1-1	254
Hinckley United	v Histon	2-2	446
Hucknall Town	v Northwich Victoria	0-0	437
Hyde United	v Stalybridge Celtic	1-5	906
Kettering Town	v Gainsborough Trinity	1-0	1132
Lancaster City	v Workington	0-0	206
Leigh RMI	v Stafford Rangers	1-4	165
Leighton Town	v Eastleigh	1-1	145

Lewes	v Dorchester Town	2-2	364
Maidenhead United	v Bishop's Stortford	2-2	165
Marine	v Blyth Spartans	0-1	268
Redbridge	v Harrow Borough	1-1	94
Redditch United	v Barrow	1-1	289
Salisbury City	v Newport County	3-0	806
Sittingbourne	v Cambridge City	1-3	265
Solihull Borough	v Harrogate Town	1-0	199
Sutton Coldfield Town	v Halesowen Town	1-1	278
Tonbridge Angels	v East Thurrock United	0-0	288
Uxbridge	v Sutton United	2-2	204
Vauxhall Motors	v Mossley	2-1	161
Warrington Town	v Kidsgrove Athletic	4-0	121
Weston-S-Mare	v Bedford Town	4-0	221
Weymouth	v Havant & Waterlooville	2-1	1018
Worcester City	v Kendal Town	1-0	973
Worksop Town	v AFC Telford United	1-1	416

REPLAYS

AFC Telford United	v Worksop Town	1-2	952
AFC Wimbledon	v Dartford	2-0	1086
Barrow	v Redditch United	2-0	756
Bishop's Stortford	v Maidenhead United	2-1*	171
Dorchester Town	v Lewes	3-1	235
East Thurrock United	v Tonbridge Angels	3-0	130
Eastleigh	v Leighton Town	1-2*	186
Halesowen Town	v Sutton Coldfield Town	3-0	245
Harrow Borough	v Redbridge	2-3*	101
Histon	v Hinckley United	2-1	218
Kingstonian	v Cray Wanderers	3-1	264
Moor Green	v Hednesford Town	2-4	192
Northwich Victoria	v Hucknall Town	2-1	500
Sutton United	v Uxbridge	0-1	252
Workington	v Lancaster City	1-2	326

FIRST ROUND PROPER

BIGGEST HOME WIN:	**4-0** KIDDERMINSTER HARRIERS VS SCARBOROUGH
BIGGEST AWAY WIN:	**1-7** BOGNOR REGIS TOWN VS HEREFORD UNITED
HIGHEST ATTENDANCE:	**1,953** AFC WIMBLEDON VS ST ALBSN CITY
NUMBER OF GAMES:	**32 + 3** (32 + 10)
TOTAL ATTENDANCE:	**25,628** (29,654)
AVERAGE ATTENDANCE:	**732** (706)

Accrington Stanley	v Altrincham	2-0	810
AFC Wimbledon	v St Albans City	2-3	1953
Aldershot Town	v Grays Athletic	1-1	1771
Alfreton Town	v Histon	1-1	238
Barrow	v Clitheroe	2-1	897
Bognor Regis Town	v Hereford United	1-7	624
Boreham Wood	v Leighton Town	1-0	165
Burton Albion	v Worksop Town	0-1	1359
Canvey Island	v Kingstonian	4-1	413
Dagenham & Redbridge	v Thurrock	2-0	737
Dorchester Town	v Cambridge United	3-2	426
East Thurrock United	v Gravesend & Northfleet	0-2	381
Exeter City	v Bishop's Stortford	2-1	1807
Farnborough Town	v Cambridge City	0-2	377
Halesowen Town	v Tamworth	1-2	668
Halifax Town	v Southport	0-0	1101
Kettering Town	v Farsley Celtic	2-1	960
Kidderminster Harriers	v Scarborough	4-0	957
Salisbury City	v Harlow Town	1-0	731
Solihull Borough	v Hednesford Town	2-1	306
Stafford Rangers	v Lancaster City	4-2	646
Stalybridge Celtic	v Droylsden	1-0	598
Stevenage Borough	v Crawley Town	0-2	951
Uxbridge	v Woking	1-2	471
Vauxhall Motors	v Morecambe	0-4	322
Warrington Town	v Blyth Spartans	1-2	251
Welling United	v Redbridge	4-1	415

Weston-S-Mare	v Barking & East Ham Utd	3-2	243
Weymouth	v Forest Green Rovers	0-1	1120
Worcester City	v Hayes	1-0	677
Yeading	v Carshalton Athletic	1-2	107
York City	v Northwich Victoria	1-2	1372

REPLAYS

Grays Athletic	v Aldershot Town	1-0*	852
Histon	v Alfreton Town	2-1	288
Southport	v Halifax Town	0-1	589

SECOND ROUND PROPER

BIGGEST HOME WIN:	**2-0** ACCRINGTON VS CARSHALTON
	3-1 BOREHAM W. VS GRAVESEND, FOREST G. VS DORCHESTER, CRAWLEY VS WORCESTER
BIGGEST AWAY WIN:	**1-3** BLYTH SPARTANS VS WELLING UNITED
HIGHEST ATTENDANCE:	**2,103** EXETER CITY VS HISTON
NUMBER OF GAMES:	**16 + 3** (16 + 2)
TOTAL ATTENDANCE:	**16,497** (14,855)
AVERAGE ATTENDANCE:	**868** (825)

Barrow	v Cambridge City	1-2
Blyth Spartans	v Welling United	1-3
Boreham Wood	v Gravesend & N'fleet	3-1
Canvey Island	v Salisbury City	0-1
Carshalton Athletic	v Accrington Stanley	2-2
Crawley Town	v Worcester City	3-1
Dagenham & Redbridge	v Kettering Town	2-1
Exeter City	v Histon	3-2
Forest Green Rovers	v Dorchester Town	3-1
Halifax Town	v Hereford United	0-1
Kidderminster Harriers	v Grays Athletic	0-1
Stafford Rangers	v Morecambe	1-0
Stalybridge Celtic	v Solihull Borough	1-0
Tamworth	v St Albans City	1-0
Weston-S-Mare	v Worksop Town	1-1
Woking	v Northwich Victoria	1-1

REPLAYS

Accrington Stanley	v Carshalton Athletic	2-0
Northwich Victoria	v Woking	1-2*
Worksop Town	v Weston-S-Mare	2-1

THIRD ROUND PROPER

BIGGEST HOME WIN:	**3-0** DAGENHAM & REDBRIDGE VS TAMWORTH
BIGGEST AWAY WIN:	**0-2** CRAWLEY TOWN VS BOREHAM WOOD
HIGHEST ATTENDANCE:	**2,166** EXETER CITY VS CAMBRIDGE CITY
NUMBER OF GAMES:	**8 + 3** (8 + 2)
TOTAL ATTENDANCE:	**12,919** (10,910)
AVERAGE ATTENDANCE:	**1,174** (1,091)

Accrington Stanley	v Worksop Town	1-1	961
Crawley Town	v Boreham Wood	0-2	929
Exeter City	v Cambridge City	1-0	2166
Hereford United	v Grays Athletic	0-1	1609
Salisbury City	v Stalybridge Celtic	0-0	1533
Stafford Rangers	v Forest Green Rovers	2-1	1178
Tamworth	v Dagenham & Redbridge	0-0	920
Woking	v Welling United	3-2	1264

REPLAYS

Dagenham & Redbridge	v Tamworth	3-0	922
Stalybridge Celtic	v Salisbury City	0-1	704
Worksop Town	v Accrington Stanley	1-1* 4-2p	733

QUARTER FINALS

NUMBER OF GAMES:	**4 + 2** (4 + 2)
TOTAL ATTENDANCE:	**12,307** (9,091)
AVERAGE ATTENDANCE:	**2,051** (1,515)

Exeter City	v Salisbury City	3-1	3653
Grays Athletic	v Dagenham & Redbridge	1-1	2321
Woking	v Stafford Rangers	1-1	2020
Worksop Town	v Boreham Wood	0-1	1006

REPLAYS

Dagenham & Redbridge	v Grays Athletic	2-4	1526
Stafford Rangers	v Woking	2-4	1781

SEMI FINALS			
TOTAL ATTENDANCE:	**9,335** (6,977)		
AVERAGE ATTENDANCE:	**2,334** (1,744)		
SEMI-FINAL 1ST LEGS			
Boreham Wood	v Woking	0-1	1511
Exeter City	v Grays Athletic	2-1	3051
SEMI-FINAL 2ND LEGS			
Grays Athletic	v Exeter City	2-0	3693
Woking	v Boreham Wood	2-0	2080

Above: Gray's Jamie Slabber shields the ball from Exeter's Dean Moxey, whilst (left) Jon Challinor fires in a shot during their second leg match.

Photos: Bill Wheatcroft and Alan Coomes.

Right: Chris Watters takes on Woking players Paul Watson and Karl Murray, while below, 'keeper Shwan Jalal collects the ball as team mates Stuart Nethercott and Tom Hutchinson hold off Boreham Wood's Chris Bangura.

Photo: Roger Turner.

THE FINAL

GRAYS ATHLETIC 2   WOKING   0
at the Boleyn Ground, West Ham United
Attendance 13,997
Report by: Arthur Evans

Just like its big brother, the F A Cup Final played the day before, this was one of those finals where both teams emerged with credit, whatever the result, as they made a competitive spectacle with plenty of attacking, not the frightened chess movements beloved by some so called technicians, where not losing is more important than winning.

Paramount among the players was the effervescent Stuart Thurgood, Grays skipper. He was motion personified, covering in defence one moment and the next on the heels of his own attackers. His short passing, concentration, urging of his team mates, wise positioning and yet seemingly permanent pursuit of the ball made one think of a fit Roy Keane. It will be remarkable if Thurgood, the undisputed man of this match, is not snapped up by some wealthier club during the close season.   His fellow midfielder, John Martin, was similarly present at the scene of action, drawn as if magnetically to the place where the important interception or change of direction could be most effective. And up front Grays had the pacy Aaron McLean whose shambling gait belies his athleticism and speed. He and Dennis Oli formed an impressive spearhead,

Gray's Michael Kightly and Woking's Steve Ferguson challenge for the ball. Photo: Roger Turner.

able to turn seemingly innocuous receipt of the ball into a scoring chance with a flick of the foot or a deft body feint. No defence can relax when they are on song and they were certainly in tune on this occasion, especially when orchestrated by their midfield duo.

Gray's skipper, Stuart Thurgood, bends the ball around the wall in this attempt on goal. Photo: Peter Barnes.

Strange to say though that Woking made some splendid chances and gave Ashley Bayes the opportunity to make his own telling contribution in the Grays goal. In only the second minute he was in action to force away a well worked free kick from Steve Evans. This was followed by a less assured flap out of danger when Justin Richards headed Simon Jackson's deep cross goalward. Then he had to rush out more assuredly to prevent Craig McAllister fastening on to Richards' through ball as Woking counter attacked. With half time approaching Woking were unlucky when a Richards shot wrong footed Bayes only to pass inches wide and again the gods were not on their side when McLean had to head over his own bar to prevent Karl Murray from scoring.

With the interval almost reached Grays struck. Michael Kightly picked up a clearance, raced down the right and found Oli with a precise pass. As if he was in a beach game, Oli, without any fuss, just diverted the ball past the helpless Shwan Jalal. The Sky Blues were in the lead. Immediately Thurgood was left with only Bayes between him and a second goal but lifted the ball over both keeper and bar. Not to worry for next second Thurgood placed a pass accurately on Glen Poole's head for him to send Woking in two down.

There was no recovery from that. In fact Thurgood headed wide when well placed, hit the inside of a post with a left footer and saw Oli go close on a couple of occasions. Woking continued to be denied whenever they looked like opening their account as Bayes, with a mixture of good judgement and fortune, somehow kept out all their efforts, on one occasion even diverting a Richards shot with his feet over his cross bar. Just prior he had made a miraculous save, also from Richards, who had been only two yards away from the target, thanks to a smart pass

from McAllister, who had himself been similarly denied by Bayes diving to his left to execute a wonderful push away.

Thus Grays, in denying Woking a fourth success, took the Trophy for the second consecutive year and brought some joy to the neutral, as well as consolation to East London for the Hammers' defeat the previous day.

Grays Athletic: Ashley Bayes, Andy Sambrook, John Nutter, Jamie Stuart, Christian Hanson, Michael Kightly (sub Tom Williamson 90th min), Stuart Thurgood, John Martin, Glenn Poole, Dennis Oli, Aaron McLean. Subs not used: Nicky Eyre (g/k), Gary Hooper, Ade Olayinka and Cameron Mawer.
Woking: Shwan Jalal, Simon Jackson, Gary MacDonald, Stuart Nethercott (sub Paul Watson 60th min), Tom Hutchinson, Karl Murray, Neil Smith (sub Liam Cockerill 60th min), Steve Evans (sub Lloyd Blackman 85th min), Steve Ferguson, Craig McAllister, Justin Richards. Subs not used: Clint Davis (g/k) and Karim El-Salahi.
Referee, Howard Webb (Sheffield), assisted by Trevor Massey (Manchester) and Gavin Ward (Kent). Fourth official, Keith Stroud (Hampshire)

Stuart Thurgood with the Trophy. Photo: Eric Marsh.

ROUND BY ROUND STATISTICS

Round	Games	Home Win	Away Win	Draws	Home Goals	Away Goals	Att. Total	Att. Ave
1st Qualifying	75+20	41	34	20	153	132	23,048	243
2nd Qualifying	40+9	23	17*	9	92	77	14,566	297
* Tie awarded to Kidsgrove Athletic.								
3rd Qualifying	42+15	24	18	15	87	71	20,983	368
First Round	32+3	18	14	3	51	48	25,628	732 (26)
Second Round	16+3	10	6	3	28	21	16,497	868 (43)
Third Round	8+3	5	3	3	11	9	12,919	1,174 (83)
Fourth Round	4+2	1	3	2	9	12	12,307	2,051 (536)
Semi-Finals	4	3	1	0	6	2	9,335	2,334 (590)

(Figure in brackets denotes +/- difference between 04/05 average attendance).

TOP GOAL SCORERS 2005 - 2006

Player	Club	No. goals	Round Reached
Leon Archer	Boreham Wood	6	Semi-Finals
T Gray	Burscough	5	Second Qualifying Round
G Poole	Grays Athletic	5	Winners
N Grayson	Stafford Rangers	5	Fourth Round
L Reynolds	AFC Telford	4	Third Qualifying Round
S Harris	Ashford Town (Middlesex)	4	Third Qualifying Round
T Bird	Bath City	4	Third Qualifying Round
R Essandou	Bishop's Stortford	4	First Round
I Cooper	Boreham Wood	4	Semi-Finals
J Keller	Dorchester Town	4	Second Round
J Dryden	Folkstone Invicta	4	Third Qualifying Round
J Allan	Northwich Victoria	4	Second Round
D Pearson	Solihull Borough	4	Second Round
A Wilford	Whitby Town	4	Second Qualifying Round
S Ferguson	Woking	4	Runners-up
C McAllister	Woking	4	Runners-up
S Browne	Worthing	4	Second Qualifying Round

Aaron McLean (Gray's) breaks through the Woking defence.

Photo: Keith Clayton.

PAST F.A. TROPHY FINALS

1970   MACCLESFIELD TOWN 2 (Lyond, B Fidler)   TELFORD UNITED 0   Att: 28,000
Northern Premier League   Southern League
Macclesfield: Cooke, Sievwright, Bennett, Beaumont, Collins, Roberts, Lyons, B Fidler,Young, Corfield, D Fidler.
Telford: Irvine, Harris, Croft, Flowers, Coton, Ray,Fudge, Hart, Bentley, Murray, Jagger.   Ref: K Walker

1971   TELFORD UTD 3 (Owen, Bentley, Fudge)   HILLINGDON BORO. 2 (Reeve, Bishop)   Att: 29,500
Southern League   Southern League
Telford: Irvine, Harris, Croft, Ray, Coton, Carr, Fudge, Owen, Bentley, Jagger ,Murray.
Hillingdon B.: Lowe, Batt, Langley, Higginson, Newcombe, Moore, Fairchild,Bishop, Reeve, Carter, Knox.   Ref: D Smith

1972   STAFFORD RANGERS 3 (Williams 2, Cullerton)   BARNET 0   Att: 24,000
Northern Premier League   Southern League
Stafford R.: Aleksic, Chadwick, Clayton, Sargeant, Aston, Machin, Cullerton, Chapman,Williams, Bayley, Jones.
Barnet: McClelland, Lye, Jenkins, Ward, Embrey, King, Powell, Ferry, Flatt, Easton, Plume .   Ref: P Partridge

1973   SCARBOROUGH 2 (Leask, Thompson)   WIGAN ATHLETIC 1 (Rogers) aet   Att:23,000
Northern Premier League   Northern Premier League
Scarborough: Garrow, Appleton, Shoulder, Dunn, Siddle, Fagan, Donoghue, Franks,Leask (Barmby), Thompson, Hewitt.
Wigan: Reeves, Morris, Sutherland, Taylor,Jackson, Gillibrand, Clements, Oats (McCunnell), Rogers, King, Worswick.   Ref: H Hackney

1974   MORECAMBE 2 (Richmond, Sutton)   DARTFORD 1 (Cunningham)   Att: 19,000
Northern Premier League   Southern League
Morecambe: Coates, Pearson, Bennett, Sutton, Street, Baldwin, Done, Webber,Roberts (Galley), Kershaw, Richmond.
Dartford: Morton, Read, Payne, Carr, Burns,Binks, Light, Glozier, Robinson (Hearne), Cunningham, Halleday.   Ref: B Homewood

1975 **1**   MATLOCK TOWN 4 (Oxley, Dawson, T Fenoughty, N Fenoughty)   SCARBOROUGH 0   Att: 21,000
Northern Premier League   Northern Premier League
Matlock: Fell, McKay, Smith, Stuart, Dawson, Swan, Oxley, N Fenoughy, Scott, T Fenoughty, M Fenoughty.
Scarborough: Williams, Hewitt, Rettitt, Dunn, Marshall, Todd, Houghton, Woodall, Davidson, Barnby, Aveyard.   Ref: K Styles

1976   SCARBOROUGH 3 (Woodall, Abbey, Marshall(p))   STAFFORD R. 2 (Jones 2) aet   Att: 21,000
Northern Premier League   Northern Premier League
Scarborough: Barnard, Jackson, Marshall, H Dunn, Ayre (Donoghue), HA Dunn, Dale,Barmby, Woodall, Abbey, Hilley.
Stafford: Arnold, Ritchie, Richards, Sargeant,Seddon, Morris, Chapman, Lowe, Jones, Hutchinson, Chadwick.   Ref: R Challis

1977   SCARBOROUGH 2 (Dunn(p), Abbey)   DAGENHAM 1 (Harris)
Northern Premier League   Ishthmian League   Att: 21,500
Scarborough: Chapman, Smith, Marshall (Barmby), Dunn, Ayre, Deere, Aveyard,Donoghue, Woodall, Abbey, Dunn.
Dagenham: Hutley, Wellman, P Currie, Dunwell,Moore, W Currie, Harkins, Saul, Fox, Harris, Holder.   Ref: G Courtney

1978   ALTRINCHAM 3 (King, Johnson, Rogers)   LEATHERHEAD 1 (Cook)
Northern Premier League   Isthmian League   Att: 20,000
Altrincham: Eales, Allan, Crossley, Bailey, Owens, King, Morris, Heathcote,Johnson, Rogers, Davidson (Flaherty).
Leatherhead: Swannell, Cooper, Eaton, Davies,Reid, Malley, Cook, Salkeld, Baker, Boyle (Bailey).   Ref: A Grey

1979   STAFFORD RANGERS 2 (A Wood 2)   KETTERING TOWN 0
Northern Premier League   Isthmian League   Att: 32,000
Stafford: Arnold, F Wood, Willis, Sargeant, Seddon, Ritchie, Secker, Chapman, A Wood, Cullerton, Chadwick (Jones).
Kettering: Lane, Ashby, Lee, Eastell, Dixey,Suddards, Flannagan, Kellock, Phipps, Clayton, Evans (Hughes).   Ref: D Richardson

1980 **2**   DAGENHAM 2 (Duck, Maycock)   MOSSLEY 1 (Smith)
Northern Premier League   Isthmian League   Att : 26,000
Dagenham: Huttley, Wellman, Scales, Dunwell, Mooore, Durrell, Maycock, Horan,Duck, Kidd, Jones (Holder).
Mossley: Fitton, Brown, Vaughan, Gorman, Salter, Polliot, Smith, Moore, Skeete, O'Connor, Keelan (Wilson).   Ref: K Baker

1981 **3**   BISHOP'S STORTFORD 1 (Sullivan)   SUTTON UNITED 0
Isthmian League   Isthmian League   Att:22,578
Bishop's Stortford: Moore, Blackman, Brame, Smith (Worrell), Bradford, Abery, Sullivan,Knapman, Radford, Simmonds, Mitchell.
Sutton Utd.: Collyer, Rogers, Green, J Rains,T Rains, Stephens (Sunnucks), Waldon, Pritchard, Cornwell, Parsons, Dennis.   Ref: J Worrall

1982
ENFIELD 1 (Taylor)   ALTRINCHAM 0
Isthmian League   Alliance Premier League   Att:18.678
Enfield: Jacobs, Barrett, Tone, Jennings, Waite, Ironton, Ashford, Taylor,Holmes, Oliver (Flint), King.   Ref: B Stevens
Altrincham: Connaughton, Crossley, Davison, Bailey, Cuddy, King (Whitbread), Allan, Heathcote, Johnson, Rogers, Howard.

Notes:
1   The only occasion three members of the same family played in the same FA Trophy Final team.
2   The first of the Amateurs from the Isthmian League to win the FA Trophy
3   Goalkeeper Terry Moore had also won an Amateur Cup Winners Medal with Bishop's Stortford in 1974

1983   TELFORD UTD 2 (Mather 2)   NORTHWICH VICTORIA 1 (Bennett)   Att: 22,071
Alliance Premier League   Alliance Premier League
Telford: Charlton, Lewis, Turner, Mayman (Joseph), Walker, Easton, Barnett,Williams, Mather, Hogan, Alcock.
Northwich: Ryan, Fretwell, Murphy, Jones, Forshaw, Ward, Anderson, Abel (Bennett), Reid, Chesters, Wilson.   Ref: B Hill

1984   NORTHWICH VICTORIA 1 (Chester)   BANGOR CITY 1 (Whelan)   Att: 14,200
Replay NORTHWICH VICTORIA 2 (Chesters(p), Anderson) BANGOR CITY 1 (Lunn)   Att: 5,805 (at Stoke)
Alliance Premier League   Alliance Premier League
Northwich: Ryan, Fretwell, Dean, Jones, Forshaw (Power 65), Bennett, Anderson,Abel, Reid, Chesters, Wilson.   Ref: J Martin
Bangor: Letheren, Cavanagh, Gray, Whelan, Banks,Lunn, Urqhart, Morris, Carter, Howat, Sutcliffe (Westwood 105) . Same in replay.

1985   WEALDSTONE 2 (Graham, Holmes)   BOSTON UNITED 1 (Cook)   Att: 20,775
Alliance Premier League   Alliance Premier League
Wealdstone: Iles, Perkins, Bowgett, Byatt, Davies, Greenaway, Holmes, Wainwright,Donnellan, Graham (N Cordice 89), A Cordice.
Boston: Blackwell, Casey, Ladd,Creane, O'Brien, Thommson, Laverick (Mallender 78), Simpsom, Gilbert, Lee, Cook.   Ref: J Bray

1986   ALTRINCHAM 1 (Farrelly)   RUNCORN 0   Att: 15,700
Gola League   Gola League
Altrincham: Wealands, Gardner, Densmore, Johnson, Farrelly, Conning, Cuddy,Davison, Reid, Ellis, Anderson. Sub: Newton.
Runcorn: McBride, Lee, Roberts,Jones, Fraser, Smith, S Crompton (A Crompton), Imrie, Carter, Mather, Carrodus.   Ref: A Ward

1987   KIDDERMINSTER HARRIERS 0   BURTON ALBION 0   Att: 23,617
Replay KIDDERMINSTER HARRIERS 2 (Davies 2)   BURTON ALBION 1 (Groves)   Att: 15,685 (at West Brom)
Conference   Southern League
Kidderminster: Arnold, Barton, Boxall, Brazier (sub Hazlewood in rep), Collins (subPearson 90 at Wembley), Woodall, McKenzie,
O'Dowd, Tuohy, Casey, Davies. sub:Jones.
Burton: New, Essex, Kamara, Vaughan, Simms, Groves, Bancroft, Land, Dorsett, Redfern, (sub Wood in replay), Gauden.
Sub: Patterson.   Ref: D Shaw

1988   ENFIELD 0   TELFORD UNITED 0   Att: 20,161, Ref: L Dilkes
Replay ENFIELD 3 (Furlong 2, Howell)   TELFORD 2 (Biggins, Norris(p))   Att: 6,912 (at W Brom)
Conference   Conference
Enfield: Pape, Cottington, Howell, Keen (sub Edmonds in rep), Sparrow (sub Hayzleden at Wembley), Lewis (sub Edmonds at
Wembley), Harding, Cooper, King,Furlong, Francis.
Telford: Charlton, McGinty, Storton, Nelson, Wiggins, Mayman (sub Cunningham in rep (sub Hancock)), Sankey, Joseph, Stringer (sub
Griffiths at Wembley, Griffiths in replay), Biggins, Norris.

1989   TELFORD UNITED 1 (Crawley)   MACCLESFIELD TOWN 0   Att: 18,102
Conference   Conference
Telford: Charlton, Lee, Brindley, Hancock, Wiggins, Mayman, Grainger, Joseph, Nelson, Lloyd, Stringer. Subs: Crawley, Griffiths.
Macclesfield: Zelem, Roberts, Tobin, Edwards, Hardman, Askey, Lake, Hanton, Imrie, Burr, Timmons. Subs: Devomshire, Kendall.
                                                Ref: T Holbrook

1990   BARROW 3 (Gordon 2, Cowperthwaite)   LEEK TOWN 0   Att: 19,011
Conference   Northern Premier League
Barrow: McDonnell, Higgins, Chilton, Skivington, Gordon, Proctor, Doherty (Burgess), Farrell (Gilmore), Cowperthwaite, Lowe, Ferris.
Leek: Simpson, Elsby (Smith), Pearce, McMullen, Clowes, Coleman (Russell),Mellor, Somerville, Sutton, Millington, Norris   Ref: T Simpson

1991   WYCOMBE W. 2 (Scott, West)   KIDDERMINSTER H. 1 (Hadley)   Att: 34,842
Conference   Conference
Wycombe: Granville, Crossley, Cash, Kerr, Creaser, Carroll, Ryan, Stapleton,West, Scott, Guppy (Hutchinson).   Ref: J Watson
Kidderminster: Jones, Kurila, McGrath, Weir, Barnett, Forsyth, Joseph (Wilcox), Howell (Whitehouse), Hadley, Lilwall, Humphries

1992   COLCHESTER UTD* 3 (Masters, Smith, McGavin) WITTON ALBION 1 (Lutkevitch)   Att: 27,806
Conference   Conference
Colchester: Barrett, Donald, Roberts, Knsella, English, Martin, Cook, Masters,McDonough (Bennett 65), McGavin, Smith.   Ref: K P Barratt
Witton: Mason, Halliday, Coathup, McNeilis, Jim Connor, Anderson, Thomas, Rose, Alford, Grimshaw (Joe Connor), Lutkevitch (McCluskie)

1993   WYCOMBE W*. 4 (Cousins, Kerr, Thompson, Carroll) RUNCORN 1 (Shaughnessy)   Att: 32,968
Conference   Conference
Wycombe: Hyde, Cousins, Cooper, Kerr, Crossley, Thompson (Hayrettin 65),Carroll, Ryan, Hutchinson, Scott, Guppy. Sub: Casey.
Runcorn: Williams, Bates, Robertson, Hill, Harold (Connor 62), Anderson, Brady (Parker 72), Brown, Shaughnessy, McKenna, Brabin
                                                Ref: I J Borritt

1994   WOKING 2 (D Brown, Hay)   RUNCORN 1 (Shaw (pen))   Att: 15,818
Conference   Conference
Woking: Batty, Tucker, L Wye, Berry, Brown, Clement, Brown (Rattray 32), Fielder, Steele, Hay (Puckett 46), Walker.   Ref: Paul Durkin
Runcorn: Williams, Bates, Robertson, Shaw, Lee, Anderson, Thomas, Connor, McInerney (Hill 71), McKenna, Brabin. Sub: Parker

1995   WOKING 2 (Steele, Fielder)   KIDDERMINSTER H. 1 aet (Davies)   Att: 17,815
Conference   Conference
Woking: Batty, Tucker, L Wye, Fielder, Brown, Crumplin (Rattray 42), S Wye, Ellis, Steele, Hay (Newberry 112), Walker. (Sub: Read(gk)
Kidderminster: Rose, Hodson, Bancroft, Webb, Brindley (Cartwright 94), Forsyth, Deakin, Yates, Humphreys (Hughes 105), Davies,
Purdie. Sub: Dearlove (gk)   Ref: D J Gallagher

THE F.A. TROPHY

1996   MACCLESFIELD TOWN 3 (Payne, OG, Hemmings) NORTHWICH VICTORIA 1 (Williams)   Att: 8,672
Conference   Conference
Macclesfield: Price, Edey, Gardiner, Payne, Howarth(C), Sorvel, Lyons, Wood (Hulme 83), Coates, Power, Hemmings (Cavell 88).
Northwich: Greygoose, Ward, Duffy, Burgess (Simpson 87), Abel (Steele), Walters, Williams, Butler (C), Cooke, Humphries, Vicary.
Ref: M Reed

1997   WOKING 1 (Hay 112)   DAGENHAM & REDBRIDGE 0   Att: 24,376
Conference   Isthmian League
Woking: Batty, Brown, Howard, Foster, Taylor, S Wye, Thompson (sub Jones 115), Ellis, Steele (L Wye 108), Walker, Jackson (Hay 77).
Dagenham: Gothard, Culverhouse, Connor, Creaser, Jacques (sub Double 75), Davidson, Pratt (Naylor 81), Parratt, Broom, Rogers, Stimson (John 65).   Ref: J Winter

1998   CHELTENHAM TOWN 1 (Eaton 74)   SOUTHPORT 0   Att: 26,387
Conference   Conference
Cheltenham: Book, Duff, Freeman, Banks, Victory, Knight (Smith 78), Howells, Bloomer, Walker (sub Milton 78), Eaton, Watkins. Sub: Wright.
Southport: Stewart, Horner, Futcher, Ryan, Farley, Kielty, Butler, Gamble, Formby (sub Whittaker 80), Thompson (sub Bollard 88), Ross. Sub: Mitten.   Ref: G S Willard

1999   KINGSTONIAN 1 (Mustafa 49)   FOREST GREEN ROVERS 0   Att: 20,037
Conference   Conference
Kingstonian: Farrelly, Mustafa, Luckett, Crossley, Stewart, Harris, Patterson, Pitcher, Rattray, Leworthy (Francis 87), Akuamoah. Subs (not used): John, Corbett, Brown, Tranter
Forest Green Rovers: Shuttlewood, Hedges, Forbes, Bailey (Smart 76), Kilgour, Wigg (Cook 58), Honor (Winter 58), Drysdale, McGregor, Mehew, Sykes. Subs (not used): Perrin, Coupe   Ref: A B Wilkie

2000   KINGSTONIAN 3 (Akuamoah 40, 69, Simba 75)   KETTERING TOWN 2 (Vowden 55, Norman 64p)   Att: 20,034
Conference   Conference
Kingstonian: Farelly, Mustafa, Luckett, Crossley, Stewart (Saunders 77), Harris, Kadi (Leworthy 83), Pitcher, Green (Basford 86), Smiba, Akuamoah. Subs (not used): Hurst, Allan
Kettering Town: Sollit, McNamara, Adams, Perkins, Vowden, Norman (Duik 76), Fisher, Brown, Shutt, Watkins (Hudson 46), Setchell (Hopkins 81). Subs (not used): Ridgway, Wilson   Ref: S W Dunn

2001   CANVEY ISLAND 1 (Chenery)   FOREST GREEN ROVERS 0   at Villa Park Att: 10,007
Isthmian League   Conference
Forest Green Rovers: Perrin, Cousins, Lockwood, Foster, Clark, Burns, Daley, Drysdale (Bennett 46), Foster (Hunt 75), Meecham, Slater. Subs (not used): Hedges, Prince, Ghent
Canvey Island: Harrison, Duffy, Chenery, Bodley, Ward, Tilson, Stimson (Tanner 83), Gregory, Vaughan (Jones 76), Parmenter. Subs (not used): Bennett, Miller, Thompson.   Ref: A G Wiley

2002   YEOVIL TOWN 2 (Alford, Stansfield)   STEVENAGE BOROUGH 0   at Villa Park Att: 18,809
Conference   Conference
Yeovil Town: Weale, Lockwood, Tonkin, Skiverton, Pluck (White 51), Way, Stansfield, Johnson, Alford (Giles 86), Crittenden (Lindegaard 83), McIndoe. Subs (not used): O'Brien, Sheffield
Stevenage Borough: Wilkerson, Hamsher, Goodliffe, Trott, Fraser, Fisher, Wormull (Stirling 71), Evers (Williams 56), Jackson, Sigere (Campbell 74), Clarke. Subs (not used): Campbell, Greygoose   Ref: N S Barry

2003   BURSCOUGH 2 (Martindale 25, 55)   TAMWORTH 1 (Cooper 78)   at Villa Park Att: 14,265
Northern Premier   Southern Premier
Burscough: Taylor, Teale, Taylor, Macauley (White 77), Lawless, Bowen, Wright, Norman, Martindale (McHale 80), Byrne (Bluck 84), Burns. Subs (not used): McGuire (g/k) Molyneux.
Tamworth: Acton, Warner, Follett, Robinson, Walsh, Cooper, Colley, Evans (Turner 64), Rickards (Hatton 88), McGorry, Sale (Hallam 54). Subs (not used): Grocutt, Barnes (g/k).   Ref: U D Rennie

2004   HEDNESFORD TOWN 3 (Maguire 28, Hines 53, Brindley 87) CANVEY ISLAND 2 (Boylan 46, Brindley 48 og) at Villa Park   Att: 6,635
Southern Premier   Isthmian Premier Champions
Hednesford Town: Young, Simkin, Hines, King, Brindley, Ryder (Barrow 59), Palmer, Anthrobus, Danks (Piearce 78), Maguire, Charie (Evans 55). Subs (not used): Evans (g/k) McGhee.
Canvey Island: Potter, Kennedy, Duffy, Chenery, Cowan, Gooden (Dobinson 89), Minton, Gregory (McDougald 80), Boylan, Midgley (Berquez 73), Ward. Subs (not used): Theobald, Harrison (g/k).   Ref: M L Dean

2005   GRAYS ATHLETIC 1 (Martin 65) Pens: 6   HUCKNALL TOWN 1 (Ricketts 75) Pens: 5   at Villa Park Att: 8,116
Conference South   Conference North
Grays Athletic: Bayes, Brennan, Nutter, Stuart, Matthews, Thurgood, Oli (Powell 80), Hopper (Carthy 120), Battersby (sub West 61), Martin, Cole. Subs (not used): Emberson, Bruce..
Hucknall Town: Smith, Asher, Barrick (Plummer 30), Hunter, Timons, Cooke, Smith (Ward 120), Palmer (Heathcote 94), Ricketts, Bacon, Todd. Subs (not used): Winder, Lindley.   Ref: P Dowd

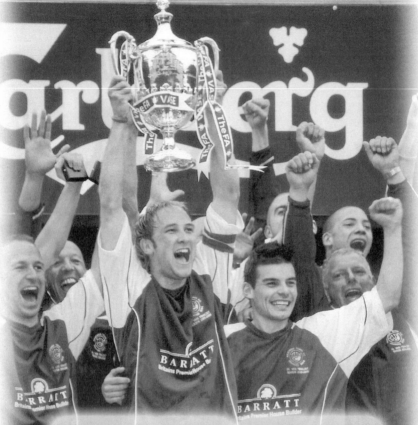

THE F.A. VASE
2005/06

Although the glamour and excitement of the F.A.Cup may have been reduced with the massive financial rewards of the Premier League and the quality of the European Champions clashes, young players with non-league clubs of all levels still look forward to playing in the famous knock-out competition.

However, if their club cannot reasonably expect to last very long in the top competition, the smaller clubs have a very special knock out challenge of their own and to many of them their F.A. Challenge Vase matches are the highlight of their season.

I can personally remember the thrill of two Vase runs all the way to the two legged semi-finals with Hungerford Town, a tiny club on the Berkshire/Wiltshire border that lifted average crowds of about seventy to over a thousand amidst unbearable local tension.

To play clubs from different parts of the country, perhaps staying away for a Friday night in preparation for the big game, and then the added interest of the local press and sometimes even the national media will always be remembered. A Vase run was something special, even the tension of waiting to hear if you had been given a home draw and if you had avoided the favourites was a situation you never forgot.

A Vase run was something special, even the tension of waiting to hear if you had been given a home draw and if you had avoided the favourites was a situation you never forgot.

Of course in those days there was the wonderful prospect of your little club actually walking out at Wembley and hopefully that possibility will again be opened up in the new stadium very soon.

Unfortunately Hungerford Town never made it past the semi-finals but I have seen the joy on the faces of many life long supporters of little clubs who have realised their dreams.

Last season both Nantwich Town and a re-formed Hillingdon Borough brought just such rewards to their members, who would hardly have forecast an appearance for their clubs in the Vase Final before the competition started. In fact Borough started out in the 2nd Qualifying Round and played eleven ties before walking out at St.Andrews. A previous Hillingdon Borough had lost one of the first F.A.Trophy finals so they joined Tamworth and Forest Green Rovers, who have also played in both finals, although so far no club has won both competitions.

Cammel Laird had appeared to have more financial backing than most Vase clubs and they, along with regular finalists AFC Sudbury and Bury Town, were perhaps more fancied clubs as they entered the quarter finals. Indeed the Eastern Counties League had shown up well in the competition as Newmarket Town was a third representative in the last eight while famous Amateur Cup fighters Crook Town represented the North East and Squires Gate brought the North's total to an impressive six.

The competition received excellent coverage in the Football Association's Competitions bulletin and it was perhaps the Fifth Round when the competition really opened up to the outsiders. AFC Sudbury were knocked out at home by fellow Eastern Leaguers Bury Town and much fancied Winchester City, winners in 2005, lost after extra time at home to Newmarket Town.

The South West had enjoyed a proud record in recent F.A.Vase competitions but not a single representative was to be found in the last sixteen last season. Perhaps this wasn't surprising when you note that only St. Blazey had survived the incredible Third Round draw when all seven representatives of the area were drawn away!

This season the competition has a massive entry of 490 from 30 different leagues and once again the small clubs who enter the competition in the early rounds will hope for luck in the draws early on and a chance to get a cup run going with the chance of some exciting trips and possible giant killing. Vase ties are very important to the 'minnows'.

For example, three Devon County League clubs are thrilled to be accepted into the competition and dream about exciting cup runs. Vase games are important, so when very young referees are given Vase matches (presumably for encouragement and experience) it can completely ruin a season for the small club. I saw Budleigh Salterton's Vase tie with Witney United completely ruined for everyone involved with the home club by poor decisions and the game was reduced to a one sided farce on a day which should have been a highlight of the season. The young referee got experience, but for the small club, their special day in a special competition was ruined.

Another Vase campaign will probably have started by the time you are reading this review and all over the country supporters will be wondering and hoping that this could just be their year.

Headlines, big crowds, local media and possibly even Wembley!

Could it be your club ?

CLUB BY CLUB RECORDS

ABBEY HEY
N.W.Co 1 (Step 6)

2nd Qual.	(H) v Formby	W	6-1	35
	Lomas, Moore (3),			
	Simpson, Watson			
1st Round	(A) v Sunderland Nissan	L	0-1	42

2004/05 Season: Ist Q

Best Performance: 3rd Rd 2002-2003

ABINGDON TOWN
Hellenic Premier (Step 5)

2nd Qual.	(A) v Blackfield & Langley	W	5-4	55
	Ankcliffe, Jezzaro (2),			
	Larman (2)			
1st Round	(H) v Egham Town	L	0-2	84

2004/05 Season: 3rd Rd

Best Performance: 5th Rd Replay 1989-90

ABINGDON UNITED
Hellenic Premier (Step 5)

2nd Qual.	(H) v Sandhurst Town	W	4-1	69
	Herbert, Hooper,			
	Odihambo, Peirson			
1st Round	(A) v Brockenhurst	L	1-2	51
	Curtin			

2004/05 Season: 1st Rd

Best Performance: 3rd Rd 1988-89

AFC KEMPSTON ROVERS
Utd.Co.Div 1 (Step 6)

2nd Qual.	(H) v Colney Heath	L	0-3	40

2004/05 Season: 2Q

Best Performance: 5th Rd 1974-75 1980-81

AFC HORNCHURCH
Essex (Step 5)

1st Round	(A) v Cogenhoe United	W	1-0	180
	Heale			
2nd Round	(H) v Soham Town Rangers	L	1-3	469
	Heale			

2004/05 Season: F.A.Trophy

Best Performance: 5th Rd 1974-75

AFC NEWBURY
Wessex 1 (Step 5)

2nd Round	(A) v Winchester City	L	0-5	184

2004/05 Season: Quarter Final

Best Performance: Quarter Final 2004-05

AFC SUDBURY
Eastern Premier (Step 5)

2nd Round	(H) v Romford	W	4-0	331
	Abrahams (2), Owen, Rayner			
3rd Round	(H) v Bodmin Town	W	3-1	331
	Hayes, Head (2)			
4th Round	(H) v Bedlington Terriers	D	1-1*	611
	Head			
Replay	(A) v Bedlington Terriers	W	3-1	434
	Abrahams (2), Head			
5th Round	(H) v Bury Town	L	0-2*	1016

2004/05 Season: Runners-up.

Best Performance: Runners Up 2002-03, 2003-04 & 2004-05

AFC TOTTON
Wessex 1 (Step 5)

1st Qual.	(H) v Mole Valley (Predators)	W	3-1	87
	Osman, West (2)			
2nd Qual.	(A) v Shoreham	L	2-6	72
	Osman, Whitcher			

2004/05 Season: 2Q

Best Performance: 5th Rd. 1982-83 1999-2000

Wallingford's Sheikh Jarju out wits Harpenden's Ben Graham. Photo: Bill Wheatcroft.

AFC WALLINGFORD
Co.Co 1 (Step 6)

1st Qual.	(A) v Harpenden Town	W	2-1	60
	Tana (2)			
2nd Qual.	(H) v March Town United	W	1-0	63
	Baker			
1st Round	(H) v Wisbech Town	L	1-4	99
	Elmore			

2004/05 Season: 1st Rd.

Best Performance: 3rd Rd 2001-02

ALMONDSBURY TOWN
Hellenic Premier (Step 5)

2nd Qual.	(H) v Dawlish Town	L	0-1	56

2004/05 Season: 2nd Q. Rd.

Best Performance: Finalists 1978-79..

ALNWICK TOWN
Northern 2 (Step 6)

2nd Qual.	(A) v Shildon	D	1-1*	139
	Cockburn			
Replay	(H) v Shildon	W	5-2	89
	Jeffrey (2), Marshall (2),			
	Swordy			
1st Round	(H) v Glasshoughton	L	1-3	66
	Keen			

2004/05 Season: 2nd Q Rd.

Best Performance: 2nd Rd 1975-76

ALSAGER TOWN
N.W.Co. (Step 5)

2nd Qual.	(H) v Newcastle Benfield BP	L	2-4*	81
	Brotherton, Mitchell			

2004/05 Season: 2nd Q

Best Performance: 2nd Rd 2003-2004

ALTON TOWN
Wessex Div 1 (Step 5)

1st Qual.	(A) v Hartley Wintney	L	0-1	55

2004/05 Season: 2nd Rd

Best Performance: 3rd Rd 1978-1979

ALVECHURCH

Mid Alliance (Step 5)

1st Qual.	(A) v Gedling MW	W	2-1	56
		Hewitt, Rostill		
2nd Qual.	(A) v Kimberley Town	W	4-1	42
		Litching, Rostill (3)		
1st Round	(A) v Wellington	W	1-0	122
		Redhead		
2nd Round	(A) v Buxton	L	0-4	246

2004/05 Season: 2nd Rd

Best Performance: 2nd Rd. Replay 1993-94

AMESBURY TOWN

Wesex Div 2 (Step 6)

1st Qual.	(H) v Bishop Sutton	L	0-1	48

2004/05 Season: 1st Rd

Best Performance: 2nd Rd 1996-1997

Andover's Callum Earl (left) gets in a tackle against Mo Takalobighashi of Maidstone. Photo: Alan Coomes.

ANDOVER

Wessex Div 1(Step 5)

2nd Qual.	(A) v Guildford United	W	5-1	73
		Bennett (3), Turpin, Vine		
1st Round	(A) v Whitstable Town	W	3-1	180
		Andrews (2), Bennett		
2nd Round	(A) v Maidstone United	L	0-4	423

2004/05 Season: 2nd Rd

Best Performance: 6th Rd 2003-04

ANDOVER NEW STREET

Wessex Div 2 (Step 6)

2nd Qual.	(A) v Erith Town	L	2-3	86
		Edwards, Tobin		

2004/05 Season: 2nd Qualifying Round.

Best Performance: 2nd Qualifying Round 2005-06

ANSTEY NOMADS

Leics. (Step 7)

2nd Qual.	(A) v Dudley Town	L	0-1	70

2004/05 Season: 2nd Qualifying Round.

Best Performance: 5th Round 1995-1996

ARDLEY UNITED

Hellenic Prem.(Step 5)

2nd Qual.	(H) v Carterton	L	1-3	58

2004/05 Season: N/A

Best Performance: 2nd Qualifying Round. 2005-2006

ARLESEY ATHLETIC

S.S.M. 1 (Step 5)

2nd Qual.	(H) v Concord Rangers	L	3-5*	67
		Gilbert, Thorne		

2004/05 Season: N/A

Best Performance: 2nd Qualifying Round 2004-2005

ARMTHORPE WELFARE

N.Co E Prem (Step 5)

1st Qual.	(A) v Easington Colleries	W	6-0	39
		Carchedi, Hilred, Hyslop,		
		Jones (2), Soames		
2nd Qual.	(A) v Cheadle Town	W	4-2	41
		Carchedi, Hildred (2), Jones		
1st Round	(H) v Norton & Stockton A.	L	0-1	52

2004/05 Season: 2nd Qualifying Round

Best Performance: 3rd Rd 1984-85

ARNOLD TOWN

N.Co.E.Prem (Step 5)

2nd Qual.	(A) v Ibstock United	W	1-0	145
		Screaton		
1st Round	(A) v Heanor Town	W	2-0	190
		Screaton, Starbuck		
2nd Round	(H) v Pelsall Villa	W	2-0	108
		Hutchinson (2)		
3rd Round	(A) v Coalville Town	D	3-3*	102
		Hutchinson, Mabon (2)		
Replay	(H) v Coalville Town	W	3-0	124
		Mabon, Screaton, Wilkins		
4th Round	(A) v Thackley	W	2-0	216
		Huckerby, Wilkins		
5th Round	(H) v Crook Town	L	0-1	560

2004/05 Season: 2nd Rd Qualifying Round.

Best Performance: 5th Rd 2001-02

ARUNDEL

Sussex 1 (Step 5)

2nd Qual.	(H) v Frimley Green	W	5-1	96
		Blake, Huckett (3), Norgate		
1st Round	(H) v Croydon	W	4-2	103
		Barnard, Boxall, Huckett (2)		
2nd Round	(A) v Three Bridges	W	1-0	92
		Huckett		
3rd Round	(H) v VCD Athletic	L	1-2	188
		Walker		

2004/05 Season: 2nd Q ualifying Round

Best Performance: 4thRd 2002-2003

Arundel 'keeper, Ben O'Connor, pushes this VCD cross away during their 3rd Round tie. Photo: Graham Cotterill

ASH UNITED

Co.Co Prem(Step 5)

1st Qual.	(A)	v Bedfont Green	D	1-1*	37
		Bartley			
Replay	(H)	v Bedfont Green	W	4-0	101
		Bartley (2), Dallaway, Smith			
2nd Qual.	(A)	v Hassocks	L	1-3	126
		Short			

2004/05 Season: 2nd Qualifying Round.

Best Performance: 4th Round 1998-1999

ASHINGTON

Northern 1(Step 5)

2nd Qual.	(A)	v South Shields	W	3-1	105
		Atkinson, Hogg (2)			
1st Round	(H)	v Thornaby	D	3-3*	151
Replay	(A)	v Thornaby	L	3-4	105
		Hollier, Lawson, Timmons			

2004/05 Season: 2nd Qualifying Round.

Best Performance: 3rd Round Replay.1990-19991

ASHVILLE

West Cheshire (Step 7)

2nd Qual.	(A)	v Silsden	W	3-1	108
		Bennett, McDermott, Mort			
1st Round	(H)	v Penrith	W	3-1*	130
		McDermott, Speed (2)			
2nd Round	(A)	v Nelson	W	1-0	110
		Mort			
3rd Round	(H)	v Racing Club Warwick	D	3-3*	160
		Bennett, Crosbie, Mort			
Replay	(A)	v Racing Club Warwick	D	2-2*	125
Ashville won 4-3p on pens.			Crosbie, White		
4th Round	(A)	v Buxton	L	0-1	572

2004/05 Season: N/A

Best Performance: 4th Round. 2004-05

ATHERSTONE TOWN

Mid Ciomb. (Step 7)

1st Qual.	(H)	v Ludlow Town	W	4-2	
		Dunkley (3), Gaunt			
2nd Qual.	(A)	v Ford Sports Daventry	L	0-1	110

2004/05 Season: N/A

Best Performance: 2nd Qualifying Round 2005-2006

ATHERTON COLLIERIES

N.W.Co 1 (Step 5)

2nd Qual.	(A)	v Cammell Laird	L	0-4	74

2004/05 Season: 1st Q Rd.

Best Performance: 3rd Round 1992-1993

ATHERTON LR

N.W.Co 1 (Step 5)

2nd Qual.	(H)	v Marske United	D	1-1*	71
		Doyle			
Replay	(A)	v Marske United	L	2-4	168
		Bennet, Grimes			

2004/05 Season: 2nd Q Rd.

Best Performance: Semi-Final Replay 1993-1994

AYLESBURY VALE

S.S.M. Premier (Step 5)

1st Round	(H)	v Bicester Town	L	1-2	89
		Talbot			

2004/05 Season: N/A

Best Performance: ist Round 2005-2006

BACKWELL UNITED

Western Premier. (Step 5)

2nd Round	(A)	v Tavistock	L	2-4*	60
		Brown, Gould			

2004/05 Season: 5th Round

Best Performance: 5th Rd 2004-05

BACUP BOROUGH

N.W.Co. 1 (Step 5)

1st Qual.	(A)	v Horden CW	W	3-2	48
		Carroll, Thornley (2)			
2nd Qual.	(A)	v Liversedge	L	0-1	102

2004/05 Season: 1st Round.

Best Performance: 3rd Round 1993-1994

BARKINGSIDE

Essex (Step 5)

1st Qual.	(A)	v Buckingham Town	L	1-3	92
		Bennett			

2004/05 Season: 2nd Qualifying Round

Best Performance: 3rd Rd 1974-1975 1998-1999

BARNSTAPLE TOWN

Western Premier (Step 5)

1st Qual.	(A)	v Radstock Town	L	1-3	79
		Hevingham			

2004/05 Season: 2nd Qualifying Round

Best Performance: 4th Rd. 1994-1995

BARNT GREEN SPARTAK

Mid.Comb, (Step 7)

2nd Qual.	(H)	v Coleshill Town	L	2-4	26
		Sewell, Taylor			

2004/05 Season: 2nd Qualifying Round

Best Performance: 2nd Round 2004-2005

BARROW TOWN

Leics. (Step 7)

2nd Qual.	(H)	v Congleton Town	W	3-2*	132
		Dunkley (2), Pitman			
1st Round	(H)	v Borrowash Victoria	W	4-3	130
		Boyles, Dunkley, Groves, Moreira			
2nd Round	(H)	v Quorn	L	1-3	420
		Osborne			

2004/05 Season: 1st Round.

Best Performance: 2nd Round 2000-2001 & 2001-2002

1st Qualifying Round action from Bedford United & Valerio against Basildon United. Photo: Peter Barnes.

BARWELL

Mid. Alliance (Step 5)

2nd Qual.	(H) v Leek CSOB	W	3-2	66
		Noble (2), Spencer		
1st Round	(A) v Racing Club Warwick	L	0-1	131

2004/05 Season: 1st Rd.

Best Performance: 5th Rd 1995-1996

BASILDON UNITED

Essex (Step 5)

1st Qual.	(A) v Bedford Utd & Valerio	W	4-0	15
		Church, Downer (2), McArdle		
2nd Qual.	(H) v Buckingham Athletic	W	2-1	31
		Allen, St Halaire		
1st Round	(A) v Stanway Rovers	L	3-4	75
		Allen (2), Smith		

2004/05 Season: N/A

Best Performance: 6th Round Replay 1980-1981

BAT SPORTS

Wessex 1 (Step 5)

2nd Qual.	(A) v Mile Oak	L	0-2	52

2004/05 Season: 1st Rd

Best Performance: 3rd Rd Replay 1999-2000

BEDFONT

Co.Co.Prem. (Step 5)

1st Qual.	(H) v Littlehampton Town	L	1-2	47
		Danahar		

2004/05 Season: N/A

Best Performance: 3rd Round 1993-1994 & 1999-2000

BEDFONT GREEN

Co.Co Prem. (Step 5)

1st Qual.	(H) v Ash United	D	1-1*	37
		Williams		
Replay	(A) v Ash United	L	0-4	101

2004/05 Season: N/A

Best Performance: 1st Q ualifying Round Replay. 2005-2006

BEDFORD UNITED & VALERIO

S.S.M. 1 (Step 6)

1st Qual.	(H) v Basildon United	L	0-4	15

2004/05 Season: 1st Qualifying Round

Best Performance: 2nd Round 2001-2002

BEDLINGTON TERRIERS

Northern 1 (Step 5)

2nd Round	(A) v Sunderland Nissan	D	3-3*	94
		Cockburn, Gibb, Preen		
Replay	(H) v Sunderland Nissan	W	2-1	152
		Laing, McAlindon		
3rd Round	(A) v Newcastle Town	W	3-1	151
		Preen, Robinson, Shandran		
4th Round	(A) v AFC Sudbury	D	1-1*	611
		McAlindon		
Replay	(H) v AFC Sudbury	L	1-3	434
		Kitchen		

2004/05 Season: Semi-Final

Best Performance: Finalists 1998-99

BEMERTON HEATH HARLEQUINS

Wessex 1 (Step 5)

2nd Qual.	(A) v Liskeard Athletic	W	4-1	83
		Cole, Jones (3)		
1st Round	(A) v Wellington Town	W	2-1	45
		Chalk, Palmer		
2nd Round	(H) v St Blazey	L	2-3	134
		Cole, Waite		

2004/05 Season: 1st Rd

Best Performance: 5th Rd 1998-1999

BICESTER TOWN

Hellenic Div 1E (Step6)

2nd Qual.	(H) v Buckingham Town	W	2-0	85
		Wickens (2)		
1st Round	(A) v Aylesbury Vale	W	2-1	89
		Currie		
2nd Round	(H) v Dorking	L	0-1	52

2004/05 Season: 2nd Qualifying Round

Best Performance: .4th Round 1978-1979

BIDDULPH VICTORIA

Mid.Alliance (Step 5)

1st Qual.	(H) v Brierley & Hagley	W	3-0	
		Heath (2), Pope		
2nd Qual.	(A) v Stone Dominoes	w/o		

Walkover for Biddulph Victoria.

1st Round	(H) v Castle Vale	W	2-1	76
		Alcock, McCarthy		
2nd Round	(H) v Leamington	L	1-2	86
		Burge		

2004/05 Season: 1st Round

Best Performance: 1st Rd 2003-2004 & 2004-2005

A missed opportunity for visitors Bideford during their 3rd Round tie verses Hillingdon Borough.
Photo: Gordon Whittington.

BIDEFORD

Western Prem (Step 5)

1st Round	(A) v Poole Town	W	2-1	226
		Groves, Harris		
2nd Round	(A) v Dawlish Town	W	2-1*	162
		Laight (2)		
3rd Round	(A) v Hillingdon Borough	L	1-2	91
		Groves		

2004/05 Season: 2nd Round.

Best Performance: Semi-Final 2003-04

BIGGLESWADE TOWN

S.S.M. Prem (Step 5)

1st Qual.	(A) v Brimsdown Rovers	W	2-1	60
		Fontenelle, Furness		
2nd Qual.	(H) v Tiptree United	L	1-3	41
		Fisher		

2004/05 Season: 1st Qualifying Round

Best Performance: 3rd Rd 2000-2001

BIGGLESWADE UNITED

S.S.M. Prem. (Step 5)

1st Qual.	(H) v Walsham Le Willows	L	1-2	48
		O'Dell		

2004/05 Season: 2nd Q.ualifying Round

Best Performance: 1st Round 2003-2004

BILLINGHAM SYNTHONIA

Northern 1. (Step 5)

1st Round	(A)	v West Auckland Town	W	2-0	88
		Lake, Wells			
2nd Round	(A)	v Liversedge	L	4-5*	144
		Dunwell, Lake, Radigan, Wells			

2004/05 Season: 3rd Round

Best Performance: 4th Round 2003 - 2004

BILLINGHAM TOWN

Northern 1 (Step 5)

2nd Round	(A)	v Crook Town	L	0-4	161

2004/05 Season: 4th Rd.

Best Performance: 5th Rd.1997-1998

BIRSTALL UNITED

Leics. (Step 7)

2nd Qual.Rd.	(A)	v Romulus	L	0-5	65

2004/05 Season: 4th Round

Best Performance: 5th Round 1997-1998

BISHOP SUTTON

Western Premier (Step 5)

1st Qual.	(A)	v Amesbury Town	W	1-0	48
		Chaffey			
2nd Qual.	(H)	v Hallen	L	0-2	43

2004/05 Season: 2nd Qualifying Round

Best Performance: 3rd Round 1995-1996

BISHOP'S CLEEVE

Hellenic Premier (Step 5)

1st Round	(A)	v Shortwood United	W	3-0	70
		Davis, Goodwin,Slack			
2nd Round	(H)	v Newton Abbot	W	3-0	65
		Slack (2), Verecsi			
3rd Round	(A)	v Wimborne Town	L	1-4	287
		Slack			

2004/05 Season: 1st Round

Best Performance: 2nd Round 2003-2004

BITTON

Western Premier (Step 5)

2nd Round	(A)	v Bodmin Town	L	0-3	190

2004/05 Season: 4th Round

Best Performance: 4th Rd 2004-05

BLABY & WHETSTONE ATHLETIC

Leics (Step 7)

1st Qual.	(H)	v Loughborough D.	W	3-1	88
		Allen, Brewin, Griffin			
2nd Qual.	(H)	v Heanor Town	L	2-5*	85
		Brewin, Wright			

2004/05 Season: 2nd Q

Best Performance: 3rd Round 2003-2004

BLACKFIELD & LANGLEY

Wessex 2 (Step 6)

2nd Qual.	(H)	v Abingdon Town	L	4-5	55
		Hommer (2), Mockridge, Morant			

2004/05 Season: 2nd Qualifying Round

Best Performance: 2nd Qualifying Round 2002-2003

BLACKPOOL MECHANICS

N.W.Co. Div 2 (Step 6)

2nd Qual.	(A)	v Brodsworth MW	L	0-2	70

2004/05 Season: 1st Qualifying Roun

Best Performance: 2nd Round 1977-78, 90-91, 2002-02 & 03-04

BLACKSTONES

U.Co. Premier (Step 5)

1st Qual.	(H)	v Dunkirk	W	1-0	41
		Stevens			
2nd Qual.	(H)	v Racing Club Warwick	L	1-2	60
		Foley			

2004/05 Season: 2nd Qualifying Round

Best Performance: 2nd Round. 2001-2002

BLACKWELL MW

Central Midlands (Step 5)

2nd Qual.	(H)	v Shirebrook Town	L	0-3	155

2004/05 Season: 1st Rd.

Best Performance: 1st Round 2004-2005

BLIDWORTH WELFARE

Central Midlands (Step 7)

2nd Qual.	(A)	v St Andrews	L	1-5	22
		Russell			

2004/05 Season: 2nd Qualifying Round

Best Performance: 1st Round 1997-1998

BODMIN TOWN

S.W.Co. (Step 7)

2nd Round	(H)	v Bitton	W	3-0	190
		Fice, Gilbert, Ohagan			
3rd Round	(A)	v AFC Sudbury	L	1-3	331
		Swiggs			

2004/05 Season: 4th Round.

Best Performance: 4th Round 1997-1998, 2004-05 & 2005-2006

BOLDMERE ST MICHAELS

Midland Combination (Step 7)

2nd Qual.	(H)	v Meir KA	W	4-2	63
		Charlley (3), Quiggan			
1st Round	(A)	v Nantwich Town	L	0-1	123

2004/05 Season: 2nd Qualifying Round

Best Performance: 3rd Round Replay 1974-75, 88-89

BOLEHALL SWIFTS

Midland Combination (Step 7)

1st Qual.	(H)	v Buxton	L	1-5	91
		Allmark			

2004/05 Season: 1st Q.ualifying Round

Best Performance: 2nd Round 1998-1999

BORROWASH VICTORIA

Northern Counties East Division 1 (Step 5)

2nd Qual.	(A)	v Tividale	D	1-1*	60
		Langford			
Replay	(H)	v Tividale	W	4-0	71
		Adul (3), Nikov			
1st Round	(A)	v Barrow Town	L	3-4	130
		Moss, Pitt (2)			

2004/05 Season: 2nd Round

Best Performance: 4th Round 1990-91 2000-01

BOSTON TOWN

United Counties Premier Division (Step 7)

1st Qual.	(H)	v Nuneaton Griff	L	0-2	70

2004/05 Season: 1st Q

Best Performance: Semi-Final 1993-1994

BOTTESFORD TOWN

Central Midlands (Step 7)

1st Qual.	(A)	v Brandon United	L	3-4	54
		Elston, Leech (2)			

2004/05 Season: N/A

Best Performance: 1st Qualifying Round 2001-2002

BOURNE TOWN

United Counties Premier Division (Step 5)

1st Qual.	(H)	v Shirebrook Town	L 1-2	68
			Mason	

2004/05 Season: 1st Qualifying Round

Best Performance: 4th Round Replay 1989-90

BOURNEMOUTH

Wessex 1 (Step 5)

2nd Qual.	(A)	v Ilfracombe Town	W 4-2	79
			Joyce (2), Saadi, Swann	
1st Round	(H)	v Odd Down	W 4-1	69
			Joyce (3), McCabe	
2nd Round	(H)	v Frome Town	W 1-0*	101
			Joyce	
3rd Round	(H)	v Brockenhurst	L 1-2	83
			Joyce	

2004/05 Season: 2nd Round

Best Performance: 3rd Round 1994-1995

BOWERS & PITSEA

Essex (Step 5)

1st Qual.	(A)	v Ipswich Wanderers	L 0-2	67

2004/05 Season: 2nd Qualifying Round

Best Performance: 2nd Qualifying Ropund 2004-2005

BRANDON UNITED

Northern League Division 1 (Step 5)

1st Qual.	(H)	v Bottesford Town	W 4-3	54
			Ebdon, Richardson, Shoulder (2)	
2nd Qual.	(A)	v Squires Gate	L 1-2	62
			McNullen	

2004/05 Season: 2nd Qualifying Round

Best Performance: 6th Round 1982-1983 & 1983-1984

BRENTWOOD TOWN

Essex (Step 5)

2nd Qual.	(A)	v Southend Manor	L 0-3	21

2004/05 Season: 2nd Qualifying Round

Best Performance: 3rd Round 1995-1996

BRIDGNORTH TOWN

Midland Comb. (Step 7)

2nd Qual.	(A)	v Pershore Town	W 2-0	66
			Broome, Handley	
1st Round	(A)	v Westfields	L 0-1	64

2004/05 Season: 1st Round

Best Performance: 5th Round 1975-1976 1993-1994

BRIDGWATER TOWN

WesternPremeier (Step 5)

2nd Round	(H)	v Slimbridge	L 0-1	189

2004/05 Season: 2nd Rd

Best Performance: 5th Round 2004-2005

BRIDPORT

Western 1 (Step 6)

2nd Qual.	(A)	v Odd Down	L 0-3	29

2004/05 Season: 2nd Qualifying Round.

Best Performance: 2nd Qualifying Round.

BRIERLEY & HAGLEY

West Midlands (Step 7)

1st Qual.	(A)	v Biddulph Victoria	L 0-3	60

2004/05 Season: 1st Qualifying Round.

Best Performance: 1st Qualifying Round.

BRIMSDOWN ROVERS

SSM 1 (Step 5)

1st Qual.	(H)	v Biggleswade Town	L 1-2	60
			Blackett	

2004/05 Season: 1st Qualifying Round

Best Performance: 3rd Round 1993-1994

BRISLINGTON

Western Premier (Step 5)

2nd Round	(A)	v Devizes Town	L 1-2	54
			Bishop	

2004/05 Season: 4th Round

Best Performance: 4th Round 2004-2005

BRISTOL MANOR FARM

Western Premier (Step 5)

2nd Qual.	(H)	v Minehead	W 2-1	37
			Bennett, Thomas	
1st Round	(H)	v Highworth Town	L 2-3	43
			Cook, Wilson	

2004/05 Season: 2nd Qualifying Round

Best Performance: 5th Round 1983-1984

BROCKENHURST

Wessex 1 (Step 5)

2nd Qual.	(A)	v Chipstead	W 2-1	53
			Mills, Totczyk	
1st Round	(H)	v Abingdon United	W 2-1	51
			Kemp (2)	
2nd Round	(H)	v Egham Town	D 2-2*	70
			Burden, Saunders	
Replay	(A)	v Egham Town	W 1-0	45
			Gibbons	
3rd Round	(A)	v Bournemouth	W 2-1	83
			Gibbons (2)	
4th Round	(H)	v Bury Town	L 0-2	195

2004/05 Season: 2nd Qualifying Round

Best Performance: 5th Round 1974-1975

BRODSWORTH MW

N.Co E Premier (Step 5)

2nd Qual.	(H)	v Blackpool Mechanics	W 2-0	95
			Radford (2)	
1st Round	(A)	v Retford United	L 0-4	180

2004/05 Season: 2nd Qualifying Round

Best Performance: 1st Round 2001-2002

BROMYARD TOWN

W.Mids (Step 7)

2nd Qual.	(H)	v Heath Hayes	W 2-1	35
			Baylis, Woodward	
1st Round	(H)	v Chasetown	L 0-1	72

2004/05 Season: 2nd Qualifying Round

Best Performance: 2nd Round 2001-2002

BROOK HOUSE

Ryman Div 2 (Step 5)

2nd Round	(A)	v Thamesmead Town	W 4-0	63
			Deriera, Fermie, Kirkland,	
			Rouco	
3rd Round	(A)	v Wisbech Town	D 4-4*	371
			Jones, Papali (3)	
Replay	(H)	v Wisbech Town	W 2-0	155
			Firmie, Dereira	
4th Round	(A)	v Hillingdon Borough	L 0-2	259

2004/05 Season: 5th Round

Best Performance: 5th Round 2004-2005

BROXBOURNE BOROUGH V&E

S.S.M.(Step 5)

2nd Qual.	(H)	v St Margaretsbury	W 2-1	43
			Tezel (2)	
1st Round	(H)	v Woodford United	W 4-3	48
			Aiken (2), Newman (2)	
2nd Round	(A)	v Stanway Rovers	D 5-5*	65
			Aiken, Norman, Osborne,	
			Tungatt	
Replay	(H)	v Stanway Rovers	W 3-0	41
			Newman (3)	
3rd Round	(A)	v Maidstone United	D 2-2*	411
			Aiken, Tungatt	

Broxbourne Borough V&E continued....

Replay	(H)	v Maidstone United	D	3-3*	153
Broxbourne won 5-4 on pens.			Tezel (2), Ward		
4th Round	(A)	v VCD Athletic	L	0-1	257

2004/05 Season: 4th Rd
Best Performance: 4th Rd 2004-05 & 2005-2006

Broxbourne's Nick Sawkins gets in a good challenge against VCD's Mark Greatorex. Photo: Alan Coomes.

BUCKINGHAM ATHLETIC

S.S.M.1 (Step 6)

2nd Qual.	(A)	v Basildon United	L	1-2	31
			Carrol		

2004/05 Season: N/A
Best Performance: 2nd Round 1998-1999

BUCKINGHAM TOWN

U.Co.Premier (Step 5)

1st Qual.	(H)	v Barkingside	W	3-1	92
			Max Grant, McKenzie (2)		
2nd Qual.	(A)	v Bicester Town	L	0-2	87

2004/05 Season: 2nd Q
Best Performance: 2nd Round 1990-1991

BUDLEIGH SALTERTON

Devon League (Step 7)

1st Qual.	(H)	v Falmouth Town	D	1-1*	91
			Lock		
Replay	(A)	v Falmouth Town	W	1-0	120
			Squire		
2nd Qual.	(H)	v Witney United	L	0-6	86

2004/05 Season: 1st Qualifying Round
Best Performance: 1st Round 2003-2004

BUGBROOKE ST MICHAELS

U.Co 1 (Step 6)

2nd Qual.	(H)	v Long Melford	L	0-4	45

2004/05 Season: 2nd Qualifying Round
Best Performance: 1st Round 1999-2000

BURNHAM RAMBLERS

Essex (Step 5)

1st Round	(A)	v Tilbury	L	1-2	71
			Jones		

2004/05 Season: 1st Rd.
Best Performance: 5th Round 1988-1989

BURY TOWN

Eastern Premeir (Step 5)

2nd Round	(H)	v Hanwell Town	W	3-0	148
			Parker, Stokes (2)		
3rd Round	(A)	v Soham Town Rangers	W	2-1	202
			McGavin (2)		
4th Round	(A)	v Brockenhurst	W	2-0	195
			Miller, Wood		
5th Round	(A)	v AFC Sudbury	W	2-0*	1016
			Miller, Wood		
Q. Final	(A)	v Crook Town	W	1-0	1946
			Tatham.		
Semi-Final 1	(H)	v Hillingdon Borough	D	1-1	1173
			McGavin		
Semi-Final 2	(A)	v Hillingdon Borough	L	1-2	723
			Thrower		

2004/05 Season: 6th Round
Best Performance: Semi-Final 2005-06

BUXTON

N.Co E P (Step 5)

1st Qual.	(A)	v Bolehall Swifts	W	5-1	91
			Copnell, Doxey, Knapper (2), Lukic		
2nd Qual.	(H)	v Lincoln Moorlands	W	2-1	208
			Copnell, Reed		
1st Round	(A)	v Deeping Rangers	W	4-0	165
			Brady (2), Brownrigg, Knapper		
2nd Round	(H)	v Alvechurch	W	4-0	246
			Copnell (2), Reed (2)		
3rd Round	(A)	v Selby	W	1-0	160
			Riley		
4th Round	(H)	v Ashville	W	1-0	572
			Reed		
5th Round	(A)	v Nantwich Town	L	0-1	987

2004/05 Season: 1st Round
Best Performance: 5th Rd 2005-06

CALNE TOWN

Western Premier (Step 5)

1st Qual.	(A)	v Wellington Town	L	1-3	68
			Pratley		

2004/05 Season: 2nd Qualifying Round
Best Performance: 2nd Round 1977-1978 1974-1975

CAMBERLEY TOWN

Ryman 2 (Step 5)

1st Qual.	(H)	v Godalming Town	L	2-4	51
			Williams (2)		

2004/05 Season: 1st Q
Best Performance: 6th Round 1985-1986

CAMMELL LAIRD

N.W.Co. 1 (Step 5)

1st Qual.	(A)	v North Shields	W	4-1	121
			Clampitt, Cooke (2), McGuire		
2nd Qual.	(H)	v Atherton Colliers	W	4-0	74
			Cooke, Couch, McGuire(2)		
1st Round	(A)	v Consett	W	1-0	176
			Morgan		
2nd Round	(A)	v Harrogate Railway	W	1-0	124
			Hargreaves		
3rd Round	(H)	v Retford United	W	3-0	122
			Hargreaves, Morgan (2)		
4th Round	(A)	v Chessington & H.Utd	W	2-1	393
			Jebb, McGuire		
5th Round	(H)	v VCD Athletic	W	1-0	283
			McGuire.		
Q. Final	(A)	v Newmarket Town	W	2-1	750
			Morgan, Collins.		
Semi-Final 1	(H)	v Nantwich Town	L	0-1	528
Semi-Final 2	(A)	v Nantwich Town	L	0-4	1420

2004/05 Season: 1st Rd
Best Performance: Semi-Final 2005-06

CARLTON TOWN

N.Co.E 1 (Step 6)

2nd Qual.	(H)	v Holbrook MW	W	2-1	63
			Ball, Brindley		
1st Round	(A)	v Rocester	W	2-0	66
			Jeffries, Pickard		
2nd Round	(A)	v Glossop North End	W	4-3	106
			Brindley , Chaplin (2), Jeffries		
3rd Round	(A)	v Gedling Town	L	3-4	50
			Bignall, Chaplin		

2004/05 Season: 2nd Round

Best Performance: 3rd Rd 2004-05 2005-06

CARTERTON

Hellenic League P (Step 5)

2nd Qual.	(A)	v Ardley United	W	3-1	58
			Joyce, Mortimer-Jones		
1st Round	(H)	v Hungerford Town	W	1-0	42
			Odom		
2nd Round	(A)	v Chessington & H. Utd	L	0-2	81

2004/05 Season: 2nd Qualifying Round

Best Performance: 3rd 2000-2001

CASTLE VALE

Midland Comb. (Step 7)

1st Qual.	(A)	v Ellistown	W	4-1	30
			Benjamin (2), Cheale, Power		
2nd Qual.	(A)	v Malvern Town	W	3-1	84
			King, Smith, Spence		
1st Round	(A)	v Biddulph Victoria	L	1-2	76
			Spence		

2004/05 Season: 2nd Qualifying Round

Best Performance: 1st Round   2005-2006

CAUSEWAY UNITED

Midland Alliance (Step 5)

1st Qual.	(H)	v Graham St Prims	W	2-0	75
			Busby, Drakeley		
2nd Qual.	(H)	v Kirby Muxloe	L	2-3*	64
			Busby, Drakeley		

2004/05 Season: 2nd Round

Best Performance: 3rd Round Replay 2002-2003

CHADDERTON

N.W.Co 2 (Step 6)

2nd Qual.	(A)	v Whickham	L	1-5	68

2004/05 Season: 2nd Qualifying Round

Best Performance: 3rd Round 1095-1976

CHALFONT ST PETER

Ryman 2 (Step 5)

2nd Qual.	(A)	v Swabridgeworth	W	3-1	34
			Goddard, Needham		
1st Round	(A)	v Felixstowe & W	D	1-1*	134
			Carroll, Ghattaora, Goddard		
Replay	(H)	v Felixstowe & W	W	2-1	67
			Proverbs		
2nd Round	(A)	v Leverstock Green	W	2-0	74
			Cochrane, Goddard		
3rd Round	(A)	v Hythe Town	L	1-2	202
			Goddard		

2004/05 Season: 2nd Qualifying Round

Best Performance: 4th Round 1987-1988

CHARD TOWN

Western 1 (Step 6)

2nd Qual.	(H)	v Melksham Town	W	4-1	78
			Foster (3), Henbest		
1st Round	(H)	v Dawlish Town	D	1-1*	89
			Delahaye		
Replay	(A)	v Dawlish Town	L	2-3*	77
			Henbest, Nicholls		

2004/05 Season: 2nd Qualifying Round

Best Performance: 4th Round 1989-1990

CHASETOWN

Midland Alliance (Step 5)

1st Round	(A)	v Bromyard Town	W	1-0	72
			Bullimore		
2nd Round	(H)	v Nantwich Town	L	0-1	284

2004/05 Season: 2nd Qualifying Round

Best Performance: 4th Round Replay 1999-2000

CHEADLE TOWN

N.W.Co. 2 (Step 6)

2nd Qual.	(H)	v Armthorpe Welfare	L	2-4	41
			Flanaghan, Linden		

2004/05 Season: 2nd Qualifying Roumd

Best Performance: 3rd Round 1983-1984

CHERTSEY TOWN

Isthmian 2 (Step 5)

1st Qual.	(A)	v Greenwich Borough	L	0-2	88

2004/05 Season: 3rd Round

Best Performance: 6th Round 1987-1988 & 1991-19992

CHESSINGTON & HOOK UNITED

Combined Co. (Step 5)

1st Round	(H)	v Horsham YMCA	W	1-0	101
			Burns		
2nd Round	(H)	v Carterton	W	2-0	81
			Burns, Nichols		
3rd Round	(A)	v London Colney	W	2-1	85
			Burns, Nichols		
4th Round	(H)	v Cammell Laird	L	1-2	393
			Nichols		

2004/05 Season: 1st Qualifying Round

Best Performance: 4th Round 2005-2006

CHESTER-LE-STREET TOWN

Northern League 1 (Step 5)

1st Qual.	(A)	v Glasshoughton Welfare	L	0-2	60

2004/05 Season: 1st Qualifying Round

Best Performance: 5th Round 3rd Replay 1984-1985

CHICHESTER CITY UNITED

Sussex 1 (Step 5)

1st Qual.	(H)	v Colliers Wood United	D	2-2*	70
			Barnard, Ward		
Replay	(A)	v Colliers Wood United	L	1-2	54
			Stevens		

2004/05 Season: 1st Qualifying Round

Best Performance: 2nd Round 2000-2001 & 2001-2002

CHIPPING NORTON TOWN

Hellenic Premier (Step 5)

1st Qual.	(A)	v Slimbridge	L	0-3	60

2004/05 Season: 2nd Round

Best Performance: 4th Round 1974-1975 & 1980-1981

CHIPSTEAD

Combined Co. (Step 5)

2nd Qual.	(H)	v Brockenhurst	L	1-2	53
			Cassidy		

2004/05 Season: 2nd Qualifying Round

Best Performance: 3rd Rd Replay 1998-1999

CHRISTCHURCH

Wessex 1 (Step 5)

2nd Qual.	(A)	v Wootton Bassett Town	D	1-1*	65
			Roberts		
Replay	(H)	v Wootton Bassett Town	W	1-0	105
			Till		
1st Round	(A)	v Street	W	2-0	78
			Czastka, Till		
2nd Round	(H)	v Truro City	W	3-2	142
			Czastka (2), Sotoudeh		
3rd Round	(A)	v Dorking	L	2-5	164
			Sotoudeh, Till		

2004/05 Season: 2nd Round

Best Performance: 4th Round 2002-2003

CLACTON TOWN
Eastern Prem. (Step 5)
2nd Qual.	(A) v Hullbridge Sports	L	0-4	36

2004/05 Season: 2nd Qualifying Round
Best Performance: 4th Round Replay 1974-1975 & 1999-2000

CLAPTON
Isthmian 2 (Step 5)
2nd Qual.	(H) v Haringey Borough	L	1-2

2004/05 Season: 2nd Qualifying Round
Best Performance: 2nd Round 1989-90 92-93 & 2003-2004

CLEVEDON UNITED
Western 1 (Step 5)
2nd Qual.	(A) v Saltash United	W	2-1*	51
	Price, Thorne			
1st Round	(H) v St Blazey	L	2-4*	194
	Cheeseman, Thorne			

2004/05 Season: 1st round
Best Performance: 1st Round 2005-2006

CLIPSTONE WELFARE
Central Midlands (Step 7)
1st Qual.	(A) v Penrith	L	0-3	54

2004/05 Season: 2nd Qualifying Round
Best Performance: 3rd Round 1992-1993

COALVILLE TOWN
Midland Alliance (Step 5)
1st Round	(H) v Dudley Town	W	7-0	160
	Bunce, Geary, Knight,			
	McGlinchey, Saunders,			
	Tonge, Wilson			
2nd Round	(A) v Desborough	W	1-0	108
	Weafer			
3rd Round	(H) v Arnold Town	D	3-3*	102
	Fox, Russell, Tonge			
Replay	(A) v Arnold Town	L	0-3	124

2004/05 Season: 1st Qualifying Round
Best Performance: 3rd Round Replay 2005-2006

COBHAM
Combined Co. (Step 5)
1st Qual.	(H) v Sevenoaks Town	L	0-2	23

2004/05 Season: 2nd Qualifying Round
Best Performance: 3rd Round 1998-1999

No lack of effort from both sides in the second half at Compton Park, as Cogenhoe and Hornchurch players demonstrate with this midfield challenge. Photo: Peter Barnes.

COCKFOSTERS
S.S.Mids. (Step5)
2nd Qual.	(H) v Holmer Green	W	4-1	67
	Montiatis, Pigden, Steward			
(2)				
1st Round	(H) v Ipswich Wanderers	L	0-3	91

2004/05 Season: 1st Qualifying Round
Best Performance: 2nd Round 1991-1992

COGENHOE UNITED
Utd.Co. (Step 5)
1st Round	(H) v AFC Hornchurch	L	0-1	180

2004/05 Season: 2nd Qualifying Round
Best Performance: 4th Round 1993-1994 & 1996-1997

COLESHILL TOWN
Midland Combination (Step 7)
2nd Qual.	(A) v Barnt Green Spartak	W	4-2	26
	Brush, Campbell,			
	Dance(2)			
1st Round	(A) v Oldbury United	W	4-0	56
	Brush, Campbell (2),			
	Wagstaff			
2nd Round	(A) v Ford Sports Daventry	L	2-4	40
	Campbell, Wright			

2004/05 Season: 2nd QualifyingRound
Best Performance: 2nd Round 1976-1977

COLLIERS WOOD UNITED
Co.Co. (Step 5)
1st Qual.	(A) v Chichester City Utd	D	2-2*	70
	Flemming, Hughes			
Replay	(H) v Chichester City Utd	W	2-1	60
	Flemming (2)			
2nd Qual.	(H) v Raynes Park Vale	W	3-0	65
	Bedj-Badj, Finn, Hudson			
1st Round	(A) v Greenwich Borough	W	3-1	31
	Davies, Hudson, Hughes			
2nd Round	(H) v VCD Athletic	L	2-3	63
	Flemming, Griffiths			

2004/05 Season: 2nd Qualifying Round
Best Performance:2nd Round 1976-1977

COLNE
N.W.Co. (Step 5)
2nd Round	(H) v Norton & SA P	W	4-0	127
	Cunningham, Howarth (2),			
	Simpson			
3rd Round	(A) v Thackley	L	1-2	200
	Forsyth			

2004/05 Season: 5th Round
Best Performance: Semi-Final 2002-2003

COLNEY HEATH
S.S.Mids(Step 5)
2nd Qual.	(A) v AFC Kempston R.	W	3-0	40
	Farrow (2), Hemmingway			
1st Round	(A) v AFC Wallingford	L	1-4	53
	Sissons			

2004/05 Season: 2nd Qualifying Round
Best Performance:2nd Round 2001-2001

CONCORD RANGERS
Essex (Step 5)
2nd Qual.	(A) v Arlesey Athletic	W	5-3*	67
	Collins, Gillam (2), Ing,			
	Stevens			
1st Round	(H) v Halstead Town	W	2-0	51
	Chapman, Stevens			
2nd Round	(H) v Welwyn Garden City	L	1-2*	61
	Ing			

2004/05 Season: 1st Qualifying Round
Best Performance: 2nd Round 2995-2006

Colliers Wood captain, Marc Hudson, coolly slots home a penalty against Greenwich Borough in the 1st Round.
Photo: Alan Coomes.

CONGLETON TOWN
N.W.Co. 1 (Step 5)
2nd Qual.   (A) v Barrow Town   L   2-3*   150

2004/05 Season: 2nd Round
Best Performance: 4th Round 1976-1977 & 1980-1981

CONSETT
Northern 2 (Step 6)
2nd Qual.   (H) v Worsborough Bridge   W   5-0   87
                                        Forbes, Ormston, Tate (3)
1st Round   (H) v Cammell Laird   L   0-1   176
2004/05 Season: 1st Round
Best Performance: 4th Round 1999-2000

CORNARD UNITED
Essex (Step 5)
1st Qual.   (A) v Hullbridge Sports   L   1-3   25
                                        Wiffin
2004/05 Season: 2nd Qualifying Round
Best Performance: 1st Round 1993-1994 & 2002-2003

CORSHAM TOWN
Western P (Step 5)
1st Round   (A) v Newton Abbot   L   0-1   106
2004/05 Season: 1st Round
Best Performance: 2nd Round 2002-2003

COVE
Co.Co. (Step 5)
2nd Qual.   (A) v Hailsham Town   W   5-2   107
                                        Bazen, Crittenden,
                                        Finnieston, Turner, Watson
1st Round   (H) v VCD Athletic   L   0-2   72
2004/05 Season: 1st Qualifying Round
Best Performance: 5th Round 2000-2001

COVENTRY COPSEWOOD
Midalns Combination (Step 7)
1st Qual.   (A) v Shifnal Town   L   0-4   73
2004/05 Season: 1st Qualifying Round
Best Performance: 1st Qualifying Round 2005-2006

COVENTRY SPHINX
Midalnd Com. (Step 7)
2nd Qual.   (A) v Newark Town   L   2-4   61
                                        Gordon (2)

2004/05 Season: 2nd Round
Best Performance: 2nd Round 2003-2004 & 2004-2005

COWES SPORTS
Wessex 1 (Step 5)
1st Qual.   (A) v Maidstone United   L   2-4*   290
                                        Smeeton, Taylor
2004/05 Season: 2nd Round
Best Performance: 5th Round 1999-2000

CRADLEY TOWN
Mid.Alliance (Step 5)
2nd Qual.   (H) v Lye Town   W   2-1   89
                                        How, Whyte
1st Round   (H) v Newark Town   W   4-2*   53
                                        How (3)
2nd Round   (A) v Newcastle Town   L   0-1   96
2004/05 Season: 2nd Qualifying Round
Best Performance: 1st Round Replay

CRANFIELD UNITED
S.S.Mids. (Step 5)
1st Qual.   (A) v Northampton Spencer L   0-3   68
2004/05 Season: 1st Qualifying Round
Best Performance: 1st Qualifying Round 2005-2006

CROOK TOWN
Northern 2 (Step 6)
1st Qual.   (A) v Ryton   W   2-1   61
                                        Allen, Mellanby
2nd Qual.   (A) v Spennymoor Town   W   4-1   255
                                        Everett, McQuine, Vennalls (2)
1st Round   (H) v Winsford United   W   2-0   106
                                        Allen, Millroy
2nd Round   (H) v Billingham Town   W   4-0   161
                                        Allen (2), Gordon, Stout
3rd Round   (H) v Ford Sports Daventry W   8-2   179
                                        Allen (3), Beckett, Harwood,
                                        McGuine, Mellanby (2)

Crook Town continued....

4th Round	(H) v St Blazey	W	3-0	494
		Allen, Millroy, Stone		
5th Round	(A) v Arnold Town	W	1-0	560
		Allen		
Q. Finals	(H) v Bury Town	L	0-1	1946

2004/05 Season: Ist Round

Best Performance: 6th Round 2005-2006

CROYDON

Ryman 2 (Step 5)

1st Round	(A) v Arundel	L	2-4	103
		Jenry, Murdoch		

2004/05 Season: N/A

Best Performance: 4th Round 1994-1995

CULLOMPTON RANGERS

Devon (Step 7)

2nd Qual.	(A) v Shortwood United	L	0-5	64

2004/05 Season: 1st round

Best Performance: 1st Round 2004-2005

CURZON ASHTON

N.W.Co. 1 (Step 5)

1st Qual.	(H) v Newcastle Benfield B.P	L	0-1	87

2004/05 Season: 2nd Round

Best Performance: Semi-Final 1979-1980

Desborough mount an attack against Coalville Town in this 2nd Round tie. Photo: Peter Barnes.

DAISY HILL

N.W.Co. 2 (Step 6)

2nd Qual.	(A) v Maine Road	W	3-2*	57
		Arlher (2), Cartridge		
1st Round	(H) v Nelson	L	0-1	46

2004/05 Season: N/A

Best Performance: 2nd Round

DARLINGTON RAILWAY ATHLETIC

Northern 2 (Step 6)

2nd Qual.	(A) v Pontefract Colleries	W	3-2	100
		Byrne (2), Radmore		
1st Round	(H) v Dunston Federation B.D	2-2*		290
		Freary (2)		
Replay	(A) v Dunston Federation B. L	0-3		167

2004/05 Season: N/A

Best Performance: 2nd Round 1978-1979

DARWEN

N.W.Co 2 (Step 6)

2nd Qual.	(A) v Willington	W	4-2	56
		Clarke (2), Fogarty (2)		
1st Round	(H) v Harrogate Railway	L	2-4	102
		Clarke, Power		

2004/05 Season: 1st Qualifying Round

Best Performance: 3rd Round 1989-1990

DAVENTRY TOWN

Utd.Co 1 (Step 6)

2nd Qual.	(H) v Wellington	D	0-0*	30
Wellington won 4-2 on pens.				

2004/05 Season: 2nd Qualifying Round

Best Performance: 2nd Round 2002-2003

DAWLISH TOWN

Western 1 (Step 6)

2nd Qual.	(A) v Alondsbury Town	W	1-0	56
		Veale		
1st Round	(A) v Chard Town	D	1-1*	89
		Veale		
Replay	(H) v Chard Town	W	3-2*	77
		Cliff-Brown, Slough, Vickery		
2nd Round	(H) v Bideford	L	1-2*	162
		Forrester		

2004/05 Season: 2nd Qualifying Round

Best Performance: 6thRound1986-1987

DEAL TOWN

Kent (Step 5)

2nd Round	(A) v Mile Oak	W	3-1*	107
		Bathgate, Robinson, Utterson		
3rd Round	(H) v Tavistock	L	2-4	148
		Bathgate, Utterson		

2004/05 Season: 4th Round

Best Performance: Winners 1999-2000

DEEPING RANGERS

Utd.Co. P (Step 5)

1st Qual.	(H) v Stapenhill	W	2-1	63
		Lovelace, Oldacre		
2nd Qual.	(A) v Rainworth MW	W	1-0	51
		Lovelace		
1st Round	(H) v Buxton	L	0-4	165

2004/05 Season: 1st Qualifying Round

Best Performance: 1st Round 2002-2003

DEREHAM TOWN

Eastern Premier (Step 5)

1st Qual.	(A) v Hertford Town	W	2-1	99
		Bacon, Willis		
2nd Qual.	(A) v Kirkley	W	2-0	232
		Nichols, Wright		
1st Round	(A) v Needham Market	L	0-1	122

2004/05 Season: 2nd Qualifying

Best Performance: 4th Rd 2001-2002

DESBOROUGH TOWN

Utd.Co. (Step 5)

2nd Round	(H) v Coalville Town	L	0-1	108

2004/05 Season: 4th Round

Best Performance: 5th Round1979-1980

DEVIZES TOWN

Western (Step 5)

2nd Qual.	(H) v Penzance	W	1-0	43
		Mooney		
1st Round	(H) v Pewsey Vale	D	0-0*	164
Replay	(A) v Pewsey Town	D	1-1*	142
Devizes won 3-0 on pens.		Drewitt		
2nd Round	(H) v Brislington	W	2-1	54
		Mullings, Sartin		
3rd Round	(A) v Needham Market	L	0-3	120

2004/05 Season: 2nd Round

Best Performance: 6th Round 1980-1981 & 2002-2003

DIDCOT TOWN (HOLDERS)

Hellenic (Step 5)

2nd Round	(H)	v Herne Bay	W 7-0	340
			Barrott, Beavon, Campbell, Concanon, Jack, Powell(2)	
3rd Round	(H)	v Mildenhall Town	D 4-4*	352
			Beavon, Concanon, King, Powell	
Replay	(A)	v Mildenhall Town	L 1-2	320
			Beavon	

2004/05 Season: Winners.

Best Performance: Winners 2004-2005

DISS TOWN

Eastern (Step 5)

2nd Qual.	(A)	v Mildenhall Town	L 0-4	190

2004/05 Season: 1st Round

Best Performance: Winners 1994

DORKING

Ryman 2 (Step 5)

1st Round	(H)	v Hamble ASSC	W 4-1	131
			Smith (2), Terry, Wills	
2nd Round	(A)	v Bicester Town	W 1-0	52
			Phillpott	
3rd Round	(H)	v Christchurch	W 5-2	164
			Duffell (3), Smith, Terry	
4th Round	(H)	v Mildenhall Town	L 1-3	449
			Vaughan	

2004/05 Season:

Best Performance: 4th Round Replay

DOWNES SPORTS

Leics. (Step7)

2nd Qual.	(A)	v Highfield Rangers	L 1-2*	31
			Moore	

2004/05 Season: 2nd Qualifying Round

Best Performance: 1st Round

DOWNHAM TOWN

Eastern 1 (Step 6)

2nd Qual.	(H)	v Leverstock Green	D 1-1*	55
			Wren	
Replay	(A)	v Leverstock Green	L 1-5	44
			Bush	

2004/05 Season: 2nd Qualifying Round

Best Performance: 3rd Round 1986-1987

DOWNTON

Wessex 2 (Step 6)

1st Qual.	(H)	v Street	L 1-2	77
			Robertson	

2004/05 Season: 2nd Qualifying Round

Best Performance: 1st Round 1996-97 7 2003-2004

DUDLEY TOWN

West Mids. (Step 7)

2nd Qual.	(H)	v Anstey Nomads	W 1-0	70
			Dudley	
1st Round	(A)	v Coalville Town	L 0-7	160

2004/05 Season: 1st Round

Best Performance: 1st Round 2000-2001 & 2004-2005

DUNKIRK

Central Mids. (Step 7)

1st Qual.	(A)	v Blackstones	L 0-1	41

2004/05 Season: 2nd Qualifying Round
Best Performance: 5th Round 1993-1994

Action from the 4th Round tie between Dorking and Mildenhall Town, which the visitors won 3-1. Photo: Neil Thaler.

DUNSTABLE TOWN 98

Spartan South Midlands Division One (Step 6)

2nd Qual.	(H)	v Wisbech Town	L 1-7	101
			Quinn	

2004/05 Season: N/A

Best Performance: 2nd Round 2000-2001

DUNSTON FEDERATION BREWERY

Northern (Step 5)

1st Round	(A)	v Darlington RA	D 2-2*	290
			Benjamin, Howe	
Replay	(H)	v Darlington RA	W 3-0	167
			Armstrong, Benjamin, Shore	
2nd Round	(A)	v St Helens Town	W 3-1	84
			Armstrong, Pickering, Young	
3rd Round	(A)	v Pickering Town	L 0-1	131

2004/05 Season: 2nd Round

Best Performance: 6th Round 1992-1993

DURHAM CITY

Northern (Step 5)

1st Qual.	(H)	v Eccleshill United	W 1-0	135
			Brunskill	
2nd Qual.	(H)	v Trafford	L 2-4	148
			Mackey, Pearson	

2004/05 Season: 3rd Round

Best Performance: Semi-Final 2001-2002

EASINGTON COLLIERY

N.Alliance (Step 7)

1st Qual.	(H)	v Armthorpe Welfare	L 0-6	39

2004/05 Season: 2nd Qualifying Round

Best Performance: 4th Round Replay 1982-83

EAST GRINSTEAD TOWN

Sussex 2 (Step 6)

2nd Qual.	(H)	v Lancing	W 3-1	52
			Burns, Gellatly, Thompson	
1st Round	(H)	v Rye Iden United	L 3-5	95
			Leete, Tadman, Thorpe	

2004/05 Season: 1st Qualifying Round Replay

Best Performance: 3rd Round 1973-1974

EAST PRESTON

Sussex 1 (Step 5)

1st Qual.	(H)	v Redhill	W 4-1	41
			Biggs (2), Dick, Hall	
2nd Qual.	(A)	v Slade Green	L 1-2	74
			Ryan	

2004/05 Season: 2nd Round

Best Performance: 2nd Round 2002-2003 & 2004-2005

EASTBOURNE TOWN
Sussex 1 (Step 5)
2nd Qual.   (H) v Maidstone United   L   0-3   324
2004/05 Season: 2nd Qualifying Round
Best Performance:5th Round 1975-1976

EASTBOURNE UNITED
Sussex 1 (Step 5)
1st Qual.   (H) v Mile Oak   L   1-3   65
                                         McDonald
2004/05 Season: 2nd Qualifying Round
Best Performance: 6th Round 1978-1979

ECCLESHALL
N.W.Co. 2 (Step 5)
1st Qual.   (A) v Racing Club Warwick L   0-1   45
2004/05 Season: 2nd Qualifying Round
Best Performance: 2nd Round 1991-92

ECCLESHILL UNITED
N.Co. E P (Step 5)
1st Qual.   (A) v Durham City   L   0-1   135
2004/05 Season: 1st Round
Best Performance: 5th Round 1999-2000

EGHAM TOWN
Ryman 2 (Step 5)
1st Round   (A) v Abingdon Town   W   2-0   84
                                         Coleman, Martin
2nd Round   (A) v Brockenhurst   D   2-2*   70
                                         Coleman, Georgiou
Replay   (H) v Brockenhurst   L   0-1   45
2004/05 Season:
Best Performance: 4th Round 1984-1985

ELLISTOWN
Leics. (Step 7)
1st Qual.   (H) v Castle Vale   L   1-4   30
                                         Laurence
2004/05 Season: 2nd Qualifying Round
Best Performance: 1st Round 2003-2004

ELMORE
Western 1 (Step 6)
2nd Qual.   (A) v Willand Rovers   L   1-4   112
                                         Tapp
2004/05 Season: 2nd Qualifying Round
Best Performance: 4th Round 1993-1994

Jamie Lewis, Eastbourne United, skips over Mile Oak's Ryan
Sergeant in teh 1st Qualifying Round. Photo: Roger Turner.

ELY CITY
Eastern 1 (Step 6)
2nd Qual.   (A) v Henley Town   L   2-3   52
2004/05 Season: 2nd Qualifying Round
Best Performance: 3rd Round 1997-1998

EPSOM & EWELL
Ryman 2 (Step 5)
1st Qual.   (H) v Petersfield Town   W   3-1   57
                                         Goodwin, Pritchard, Tacey
2nd Qual.   (H) v Milton United   W   3-0   58
                                         Gay (2), Marvell
1st Round   (A) v Herne Bay   L   2-4   145
                                         Marvell, Read
2004/05 Season: 1st Round
Best Performance: Finalists 1874-1975

ERITH & BELVEDERE
Kent (Step 5)
1st Round   (H) v Hillingdon Borough   L   1-5   82
                                         Dickson
2004/05 Season: N/A
Best Performance: 3rd Round 1976-1977

ERITH TOWN
Kent (Step 5)
2nd Qual.   (H) v Andover New Street   W   3-2   86
                                         Hamilton, Russell, Usherwood
1st Round   (H) v Whitehawk   W   2-0   30
                                         Fagan, McNally
2nd Round   (A) v Sidley United   L   2-4   92
                                         Garland (2)
2004/05 Season: 2nd Round
Best Performance: 2nd Round 99-00 02-03 03-04 04-05

ESH WINNING
Northern 1 (5) (Step 5)
1st Qual.   (H) v Flixton   L   0-1*   53
2004/05 Season: 2nd Round
Best Performance: 2nd Round 83-84 92-93 01-02 04-05

ETON MANOR
Essex (Step 5)
2nd Qual.   (H) v Kingsbury Town   L   1-4   20
                                         Reading
2004/05 Season: 2nd Round
Best Performance: 2nd Round 75-76 76-77 77-78 04-05

EXMOUTH TOWN
Western Prem.(Step 5)
1st Qual.   (H) v St Blazey   L   1-4*   125
                                         Bingham
2004/05 Season: 3rd Round
Best Performance: semi-Finalists 1984-1985

EYNESBURY ROVERS
Utd.Co. 1 (Step 6)
1st Qual.   (A) v London Colney   L   1-4   40
                                         Harper
2004/05 Season: 2nd Qualifying Round
Best Performance: 3rd Round 1994-1995

FAIRFORD TOWN
Hellenic Prem. (Step 5)
1st Qual.   (H) v Portland United   W   5-0   48
                                         Clark, Hill, Stoddart (3)
2nd Qual.   (H) v Radstock Town   L   1-2*   45
                                         Coles
2004/05 Season: 2nd Qualifying Round
Best Performance: 2nd Round 77-8 79-80 83-4 85-98-9 03-04

FAKENHAM TOWN

Eastern 1 (Step 6)

2nd Qual.	(H) v Newport Pagnell	L	0-4	80

2004/05 Season: 1st Qualifying Round

Best Performance: 3rd Round 1998-1999 1999-2000

FALMOUTH TOWN

South Western (Step 7)

1st Qual.	(A) v Budleigh Salterton	D	1-1*	91
		Chambers		
Replay	(H) v Budleigh Salterton	L	0-1	169

2004/05 Season: 1st Qualifying Round

Best Performance: 6th Round Replay 1986-1987

FAREHAM TOWN

Wessex 1 (Step 5)

1st Qual.	(H) v Ringmer	L	0-1	101
		Goalscorers		

2004/05 Season: 3rd Round

Best Performance: 3rd Round2003-2004 2004-2005

FARNHAM TOWN

Co.Co. (Step 5

1st Qual.	(H) v Wantage Town	L	1-2	36

2004/05 Season: 2nd Qualifying Round

Best Performance: 4th Round 1976-1977

FELIXSTOWE & WALTON UNITED

Eastern 1 (Step 6

2nd Qual.	(A) v Sporting Bengal	W	4-1	85
		Crump(2), Morgan, Phillips		
1st Round	(H) v Chalfont St Peter	D	3-3*	134
		Buckle, Drury, Phillips		
Replay	(A) v Chalfont St Peter	L	1-2	67
		Edwards		

2004/05 Season: 1st Qualifying Round

Best Performance: 1st Round 2002-2003.

FLACKWELL HEATH

Ryman 2 (Step 5)

1st Qual.	(H) v Gorleston	L	1-2	65
		Suarez		

2004/05 Season: 1st Qualifying Round

Best Performance: 3rd Qualifying Round

FLIXTON

N.W.Co. 2 (Step 6)

1st Qual.	(A) v Eash Winning	W	1-0*	53
		Barnes		
2nd Qual.	(A) v Nelson	L	2-3	117
		Butterworth, Tobin		

2004/05 Season: 2nd Qualifying Round

Best Performance: Semi-Final 1995-1996

FORD SPORTS DAVENTRY

Utd. Co. P (Step 5)

2nd Qual.	(H) v Atherstone Town	W	1-0	110
		Foster		
1st Round	(H) v Sutton Town	W	2-1	45
		Foster, Trill		
2nd Round	(H) v Coleshill Town	W	4-2	40
		Evans, Foster, Trill (2)		
3rd Round	(A) v Crook town	L	2-8	179
		Foster, Trill		

2004/05 Season: 1st Qualifying Round

Best Performance: 3rd Round 2002-2003

FORMBY

N.W.Co. 1 (Step 5)

2nd Qual.	(A) v Abbey Hey	L	1-6	35

2004/05 Season: 2nd Qualifying Round

Best Performance: 2nd Round 1996-1997

FRIAR LANE & EPWORTH

Leics. (Step 7)

1st Qual.	(H) v Holwell Sports	W	5-1	91
		Gibbons, Roper (2),		
		Stevenson (2)		
2nd Qual.	(A) v Oadby Town	W	3-1*	291
		Connolly, Kendrick, Roper		
1st Round	(H) v Shirebrook Town	W	5-1	229
		Kendrick (2), Marsh, Roper		
2nd Round	(H) v Stourbridge	L	1-5	208
		Stevenson		

2004/05 Season: 2nd Round

Best Performance: Semi-Final 1974-1975

FRIMLEY GREEN

Co.Co.P (Step 5)

2nd Qual.	(A) v Arundel	L	1-5	96
		Gomma		

2004/05 Season: 2nd Qualifying Round

Best Performance: 2nd Round 1979-1980

FROME TOWN

Western Prem. (Step 5)

2nd Round	(A) v Bournemouth	L	0-1*	101

2004/05 Season: 6th Round

Best Performance: 6th Round 2004-2005

GARFORTH TOWN

N.Co.E 1 (Step 5)

1st Qual.	(A) v Pontefract Colleries	L	2-3	82
		Kelly, McCargo		

2004/05 Season: 2nd Qualifying Round

Best Performance: 6th Round 1986-1987

GEDLING MW

Central Mids (Step 7)

1st Qual.	(H) v Alvechurch	L	1-2*	56
		Matthews		

2004/05 Season: N/A

Best Performance: 1st Qua;lifying Round

GEDLING TOWN

N.Co. E 1 (Step 6)

2nd Round	(A) v Highfield Rangers	W	3-2	37
		Back, Massingham, Newton		
3rd Round	(H) v Carlton Town	W	4-3	50
		Clark, Massingham,		
		Saunders, Westcarr		
4th Round	(A) v Squires Gate	L	1-2*	75
		Saunders		

2004/05 Season: 4th Round

Best Performance: 4th Round 2003--2004 2004-2005

GLAPWELL

N.Co.E P (Step 5)

2nd Qual.	(A) v Shawbury United	W	4-0	47
		Hardwick, Robinson,		
		Trodden, Wilson		
1st Round	(A) v Newcastle Town	L	2-3	101
		Brown, Clarke		

2004/05 Season: 1st Round

Best Performance: 2nd Round 1996-1997

GLASSHOUGHTON WELFARE

N.Co. E P (Step 5)

1st Qual.	(H) v Chester-le-Street	W	2-0	60
		King, Newton		
2nd Qual.	(H) v Rossington Main	W	7-1	38
		Downes, Higgins (2),		
		King, Seed (3)		
1st Round	(A) v Alnwick Town	W	3-1	66
		King (2), Seed		
2nd Round	(H) v Squires Gate	L	1-2	75
		Parker		

2004/05 Season: 2nd Qualifying Round

Best Performance: 2nd Round 2000-2001

GLOSSOP NORTH END

N.W.Co.1 (Step 5)

2nd Qual.	(H) v Staveley MW	W	3-2*	118
	Hind, Kharas (2)			
1st Round	(H) v Romulus	W	6-4	118
	Hamilton, Hind, Kharas (3)			
	Woodcock			
2nd Round	(H) v Carlton Town	L	3-4	106
	Kharas (2), Yates			

2004/05 Season: 2nd Round

Best Performance: 4th Round (Extra Time)1999-2000

GODALMING TOWN

CoCo.Prem (Step 5)

1st Qual.	(A) v Camberley Town	W	4-2	51
	Dear, Stanley, Tchankou(2)			
2nd Qual.	(A) v Peacehaven Town	W	4-1*	65
	Douglas, Mariner,			
	Newman, Tchankou			
1st Round	(H) v Hassocks	L	1-4	102
	Newman			

2004/05 Season: 1st Qualifying Round

Best Performance: 2nd Round 1993-1994 1995-1996

GODMANCHESTER ROVERS

Eastern 1 (Step 6

1st Qual.	(H) v St Neots Town	L	1-2	85
	Nicholls			

2004/05 Season: 1st Round

Best Performance: 1st Round 2004-2005+-*

GORLESTON

Eastern 1 (Step 6)

1st Qual.	(A) v Flackwell Heath	W	2-1	65
	Gil, Stone			
2nd Qual.	(A) v Stotfold	W	4-1	67
	Coe, Fergusson (2), Savage			
1st Round	(H) v Raunds Town	W	1-0	106
	Savage			
2nd Round	(H) v Mildenhall Town	D	0-0*	112
Replay	(A) v Mildenhall Town	L	0-2	123

2004/05 Season: 2nd Qualifying Round

Best Performance: 5th Round 2002-2003

GORNAL ATHLETIC

West Midlands (Step 7)

1st Qual.	(A) v Leek CSOB	L	1-2	87

2004/05 Season: 2nd Qualifying Round

Best Performance: 1st Round 75-6 76-7 78-9 79-80 98-9 99-00

GOSPORT BOROUGH

Wessex (Step 5)

2nd Qual.	(H) v Greenwich Borough	L	0-1*	138

2004/05 Season: 3rd Round

Best Performance: 6th Round Replay 1976-1977

GRAHAM ST PRIMS

Central Mids. (Step 7)

1st Qual.	(A) v Causeway United	L	0-2	75

2004/05 Season: 2nd QualifyingRound

Best Performance: 1st Round 1983-1984

GREAT HARWOOD TOWN

N.W.Co. 2 (Step 6)

2nd Qual.	(H) v Thornaby	L	0-3	75

2004/05 Season: 1st Round

Best Performance: 6th Round 1990-1991

GREAT YARMOUTH TOWN

Eastern 1 (Step 6)

2nd Qual.	(H) v Stanway Rovers	L	0-1	99

2004/05 Season: 2nd Qualifying Round

Best Performance: Semi-Final 1982-1983

GREENWICH BOROUGH

Kent (Step 5)

1st Qual.	(H) v Chertsey Town	W	2-0	44
	Dowling, White			
2nd Qual.	(A) v Gosport Borough	W	1-0*	138
	O'Connell			
1st Round	(H) v Colliers Wood	L	1-3	31
	Smith			

2004/05 Season: 2nd Round

Best Performance: 4th Ropund Replay 1989-1990

GUILDFORD UNITED

Co.Co P (Step 5)

2nd Qual.	(H) v Andover	L	1-5	73
	Azeem			

2004/05 Season: N/A

Best Performance: 2nd Qualifying Round

GUISBOROUGH TOWN

Northern 2 (Step 6)

1st Qual.	(A) v Winterton Rangers	L	1-3	70

2004/05 Season: 3rd Round

Best Performance: Finalists 1979-1980

HADLEIGH UNITED

Eastern 1 (Step 6)

2nd Qual.	(A) v London Colney	L	1-2	56
	Curtis			

2004/05 Season: 2nd Qualifying Round

Best Performance: 5th Round 1994-1995

HAILSHAM TOWN

Sussex 1 (Step 5)

2nd Qual.	(H) v Cove	L	2-5	107
	Skan			

2004/05 Season: 1st Round Proper.

Best Performance:

HALL ROAD RANGERS

N.Co.E 1 (Step 6)

1st Qual.	(H) v Morpeth Town	L	3-5	55
	Dale, Medcalfk, N-Jie			

2004/05 Season: 2nd Qualifying Round

Best Performance: 3rd Round 1999-2000

HALLAM

N.Co.E P League (Step 5)

1st Qual.	(H) v Padiham	L	1-2	40

2004/05 Season: 1st Round

Best Performance: 5th Round 1980-1981

HALLEN

Western Prem. (Step5)

2nd Qual.	(A) v Bishop Sutton	W	2-0	43
	Beecham, Collett			
1st Round	(H) v Slimbridge	L	0-1	49

2004/05 Season: 1st Round

Best Performance: 5th Round 2000-2001

HALSTEAD TOWN

Eastern P (Step 5)

1st Round	(A) v Concord Rangers	L	0-2	51

2004/05 Season: 1st Round

Best Performance: 4th Round Replay 1994-1995

HAMBLE ASSC

Wessex 1 (Step 5)

2nd Qual.	(H) v Steyning Town	W	4-0	68
	Bottomley, Eagle,			
	McClements, Morse			
1st Round	(A) v Dorking	L	1-4	131
	Thompson			

2004/05 Season: 2nd Qualifying Round

Best Performance: 1st Round 2005-2006

HAMWORTHY UNITED
Wessex 1 (Step 5)
1st Qual.	(H) v Tuffley Rovers	w/o		

Tuffley Rovers withdrawn.
2nd Qual.	(A) v Penryn Athletic	L	1-2*	121
	Lucas			

2004/05 Season: 2nd Qualifying Round

Best Performance: 2nd Round 2003-2004

HANWELL TOWN
S.S.M. (Step 5)
1st Round	(H) v Colney Heath	W	4-1	53
	Jaso (2), Mills, Tucker			
2nd Round	(A) v Bury Town	L	0-3	148

2004/05 Season: 1st Round

Best Performance: 3rd Round 1985-1986 2002-2003

HAREFIELD UNITED
S.S.M. (Step 5)
1st Qual.	(H) v Witham Town	L	2-3	71
	Chase, Totton			

2004/05 Season: 3rd Round

Best Performance: 6th Round 1989-1990

HARINGEY BOROUGH
S.S.M. (Step 5)
2nd Qual.	(A) v Clapton	W	2-1	45
	Ake, Kavanagh			
1st Round	(A) v Kingsbury Town	L	0-2	28

2004/05 Season: 2nd Qualifying Round

Best Performance: 6th Round 1977-1978

HARPENDEN TOWN
S.S.M. (Step 5)
1st Qual.	(H) v AFC Wallingford	L	1-2	74
	Gregory			

2004/05 Season: 2nd Qualifying Round

Best Performance: 2nd Round 1976-1977

HARROGATE RAILWAY
N.Co.E. P (Step 5)
1st Round	(A) v Darwen	W	4-2	102
	Henderson, Howarth,			
	Ryan, Stevenson			
2nd Round	(H) v Cammell Laird	L	0-1	124

2004/05 Season: 2nd Qualifying Round

Best Performance: 3rd Round 2002-2003

HARROW HILL
Hellenic 1W (Step 6)
1st Qual.	(H) v Penryth Athletic	L	2-5	35
	Hook, Weyman			

2004/05 Season: 1st Qualifying Round

Best Performance: 1st round 1988-1989

HARTLEY WINTNEY
C.Co. 1 (Step 6)
1st Qual.	(H) v Alton Town	W	1-0	55
	Orgar			
2nd Qual.	(H) v Hungerford Town	D	1-1*	65
	Brownlie			
Replay	(A) v Hungerford Town	L	1-2	72
	Elms			

2004/05 Season: 2nd Qualifying Round

Best Performance: 3rd Round 1992-1993

HARWICH & PARKESTON
Eastern P (Step 5)
1st Qual.	(A) v Woodbridge Town	L	2-4	84
	Lyness, Meadows			

2004/05 Season: 2nd Round

Best Performance: 5th Round 1990-1991

HASSOCKS
Aussex 1 (Step 5)
2nd Qual.	(H) v Ash United	W	3-1	126
	Laing, Simpson, Thompson			
1st Round	(A) v Godalming Town	W	4-1	102
	Harding, Laing (3)			
2nd Round	(A) v Kingsbury Town	L	0-1	37

2004/05 Season: 1st Round

Best Performance: 2nd Round 1998-1999

HAVERHILL ROVERS
Eastern 1 (Step 6)
1st Qual.	(H) v Welwyn Garden City	L	2-4	139
	Hunt, lyons			

2004/05 Season: 1st Round

Best Performance: 6th Round 1986-1987

HEANOR TOWN
Central Mids (Step 7)
2nd Qual.	(A) v Bladby & Whetstone A.	W	5-2*	85
	Davis (2), Hall, Nicholls,			
	Vickerton			
1st Round	(H) v Arnold Town	L	0-2	190

2004/05 Season: 1st Round

Best Performance: 4th Round Replay 1988-1989

HEATH HAYES
West Nids. (Step 7)
2nd Qual.	(A) v Bromyard Town	L	1-2	84
	Latham			

2004/05 Season: 2nd Qualifying Round

Best Performance: 1st Round Replay

HEBBURN TOWN
Northern 2 (Step 6
2nd Qual.	(H) v Prudhoe Town	L	0-2	90

2004/05 Season: 1st Qualifying Round

Best Performance: 2nd Qualifying Round 2003-2004

HENLEY TOWN
Hellenic Prem. (Step 5
2nd Qual.	(H) v Ely City	W	3-2	52
	Small-King, Wilson (2)			
1st Round	(A) v Leiston	L	2-3	133
	Bixby, Jones			

2004/05 Season: 1st Qualifying Round

Best Performance: 2nd Qualifying Round 2003-2004

HERNE BAY
Kent (Step 5)
1st Round	(H) v Epsom & Ewell	W	4-2	145
	Brown, Denly (2), King			
2nd Round	(A) v Didcot Town	L	0-7	340

2004/05 Season: 1st Qualifying Round

Best Performance: 5th Round 1996-1997

HERTFORD TOWN
Ryman 2 (Step 5)
1st Qual.	(H) v Dereham Town	L	1-2	99
	Goss			

2004/05 Season: 1st Round

Best Performance: 3rd Round Replay 2003-2004

HIGHFIELD RANGERS
Leics. (Step 5)
2nd Qual.	(H) v Downes Sports	W	2-1*	31
	Laws, O'Brien			
1st Round	(H) v St Andrews	W	2-0	48
	Amoo, Potter			
2nd Round	(H) v Gedling Town	L	2-3	37
	Julian, Taylor			

2004/05 Season: 2nd Qualifying Round

Best Performance: 3rd Round 1998-1999

HIGHGATE UNITED

Midland Comb. (Step 7)

1st Qual.	(A)	v Tividale	L	1-4	50
				Turner	

2004-/05 Season: 2nd Round

Best Performance: 2nd Round 2004-2005

HIGHWORTH TOWN

Hellenic Prem. (Step 5)

1st Round	(A)	v Bristol Manor Farm	W	3-2	43
			Bellinger, Corcoran, McCrae		
2nd Round	(H)	v Wimborne Town	L	0-1	138

2004/05 Season: 2nd Qualifying Round

Best Performance: 2nd Round 2003-2004

HILLINGDON BOROUGH

S.S.M (Step 5)

2nd Qual.	(A)	v Littlehampton Town	D	1-1*	68
			Tilbury		
Replay	(H)	v Littlehampton Town	W	3-1	60
			Kidson, O'Brien (2)		
1st Round	(A)	v Erith & Belvedere	W	5-1	82
			Lawrence (2), O'Brien,		
			Tilbury (2)		
2nd Round	(A)	v Rye & Iden United	D	2-2*	86
			Lawrence, Tilbury		
Replay	(H)	v Rye & Iden United	W	1-0	62
			Lawrence		
3rd Round	(H)	v Bideford	W	2-1	91
			Lawrence, Phillips		
4th Round	(H)	v Brook House	W	2-0	259
			Lawrence (2)		
5th Round	(H)	v Mildenhall Town	W	4-0	233
			Tilbury, Craft, Lawrence(2)		
Q. Final	(H)	v Squires Gate	W	2-0	428
			Lawrence, Tilbury.		
Semi-Final 1	(A)	v Bury Town	D	1-1	1773
			Craft		
Semi-Final 2	(H)	v Bury Town	W	2-1	723
			Rundell, Tilbury		

2004/05 Season: 3rd Round

Best Performance: 2005-2006

Hillingdon's Chris Phillips puts Rye & Iden's Colin Johnson under pressure in the 2nd Round . Photo: Roger Turner.

HODDESDON TOWN

S.S.M. 1 (Step 6)

1st Qual.	(H)	v Yaxley	L	0-1	68

2004/05 Season: 1st Round

Best Performance: First Winners in 1974-1975

HOLBEACH UNITED

Utd.Co. Prem. (Step 5)

1st Round	(H)	v Leamington	L	0-2	269

2004/05 Season: 3rd Round

Best Performance: 5th Round 1988-1989

HOLBROOK MINERS WELFARE

Central Mids. (Step 7)

2nd Qual.	(A)	v Carlton Town	L	1-2	63
			Hallsworth		

2004/05 Season: 2nd Qualifying Round

Best Performance: 3rd Round 1996-1997

HOLKER OLD BOYS

N.W.Co 2 (Step 6)

2nd Qual.	(A)	v Retford United	L	2-4	155
			Round (2)		

2004/05 Season: 1st Round

Best Performance: 3rd Round 1996-1997

HOLMER GREEN

S.S.M. (Step 5)

2nd Qual.	(A)	v Cockfosters	L	1-4	67
			Graham		

2004/05 Season: 1st Qualifying Round

Best Performance: 1st round Rep[lay 1999-2000

HOLWELL SPORTS

Leics (Step 5)

1st Qual.	(A)	v Friar Lane & Epworth	L	1-5	91
			Keast		

2004/05 Season: 1st Round

Best Performance: 2nd Round 1900-91 1993-94 1998-99

HORDEN CW

Northern 1 (Step 5)

1st Qual.	(H)	v Bacup Borough	L	2-3	48
			Ainsley, O'Riordan		

2004/05 Season: 2nd Round

Best Performance: 2nd Round 90-91 02- 03 04-05

HORLEY TOWN

Co.Co. (Step 5)

2nd Qual.	(A)	v North Leigh	L	0-2	74

2004/05 Season: 2nd Qualifying Round

Best Performance: 2nd Round 1974-1975 1975-1976

HORSHAM YMCA

Sussex 1 (Step 5)

1st Round	(A)	v Chessington & H. Utd	L	0-1	101

2004/05 Season: 1st Qualifying Round

Best Performance: 4th Round 1999-2000

HULLBRIDGE SPORTS

Essex (Step 5)

1st Qual.	(H)	v Cornard United	W	3-1	25
			Cheeswright (2), Hughes		
2nd Qual.	(H)	v Clacton Town	W	4-0	36
			Cheeswright (2), Hughes,		
			Kreyling		
1st Round	(H)	v Mildenhall Town	L	0-8	74

2004/05 Season: 2nd Qualifying Round

Best Performance: 1st Round 2001-2002

HUNGERFORD TOWN

Hellenic Prem (Step 5)

1st Qual.	(A)	v Westfield	W	2-0	45
			Lucas (2)		
2nd Qual.	(A)	v Hartley Wintney	D	1-1*	65
			Lucas		
Replay	(H)	v Hartley Wintney	W	2-1	
			Brewer, Philpott		
1st Round	(A)	v Carterton	L	0-1	42

2004/05 Season: 1st Round

Best Performance: Semi-Final 1977-78 1978-79 1988-89

Hullbridge Sports put the Conard United defence under pressure from this corner, however, it's Conard's Ian Campbell (5) who heads clear. Photo: Alan Coomes.

HUNTINGDON TOWN
Utd Co.1 (Step 6)
1st Qual.	(H)	v St Margaretsbury	L	1-3	53
		Edwards			

2004/05 Season: N/A
Best Performance: 1st Qualifying Round 2005-2005

HYTHE TOWN
Kent (Step 5)
1st Qual.	(A)	v Pagham	W	6-2	55
		Godden (2), Porter, Sinden (2), Winfield			
2nd Qual.	(H)	v Moneyfields	W	2-1	101
		Fisk, Sinden			
1st Round	(A)	v VT	W	2-1	95
		Abel, Godden			
2nd Round	(H)	v Thatcham Town	W	3-2	130
		Abel, Fisk, Godden			
3rd Round	(H)	v Chalfont St Peter	W	2-1	202
		Abel, Godden			
4th Round	(H)	v Winchester City	L	1-3	441
		Sinden			

2004/05 Season: 2nd Qualifying Round
Best Performance: Semi-Final 1989-1990

IBSTOCK WELFARE
Leics. (Step 7)
2nd Qual.	(H)	v Arnold Town	L	0-1	145

2004/05 Season: 2nd Qualifying Round
Best Performance: 2nd Rd 1998-1999

ILFRACOMBE TOWN
Western 1 (Step 6)
2nd Qual.	(H)	v Bournemouth	L	2-4	79
		Langmead, Yeo			

2004/05 Season: 1st Qualifying Round
Best Performance: 2nd Round 1992-1993 1989-1990

IPSWICH WANDERERS
Eastern Prem. (Step 5)
1st Qual.	(H)	v Bowers & Pitsea	W	2-0	67
		Hetherington, Swann			
2nd Qual.	(A)	v Northampton Spencer	W	3-1	66
		Baker, Hurd, Tracey			
1st Round	(A)	v Cockfosters	W	3-0	91
		Baker, Swann			

Ipswich Wanderers continued....
2nd Round	(A)	v London Colney	L	3-6	55
		Hetherington, Swann, Tracey			

2004/05 Season: 1st Round
Best Performance: 1st Round 1996-97 2001-02 02-03 04-05

JARROW ROOFING BOLDON CA
Northern 1 (Step 5)
2nd Round	(A)	v Thackley	L	0-3	67

2004/05 Season: Semi-Final
Best Performance: Semi-Final 2004-2005

KIMBERLEY TOWN
Central Mids. (Step 7())
2nd Qual.		v Alvechurch	L	1-4	42
		Ahmed			

2004/05 Season: 1st Round
Best Performance:2nd Round 1981-1982 1986-1987

KINGSBURY TOWN
Ryman 2 (Step 5)
1st Qual.	(H)	v Saffron Walden	W	3-1	38
		Boateng, Cronin, David			
2nd Qual.	(A)	v Eton Manor	W	4-1	20
		Cooper, Cronin (2), Kpaka			
1st Round	(H)	v Haringey Borough	W	2-0	28
		Bouton, Mathieu			
2nd Round	(H)	v Hassocks	W	1-0	37
		Fitzpatrick			
3rd Round	(A)	v Lowestoft Town	L	0-2	265

2004/05 Season: 3rd Round
Best Performance: 4th Round 1983-1984

KIRBY MUXLOE
Leics. (Step 5)
1st Qual.	(H)	v Sandiacre Town	D	2-2*	48
		Pietrykz, Taylor			
Replay	(A)	v Sandiacre Town	W	2-1	78
		Mason (2)			
2nd Qual.	(A)	v Causeway United	W	3-2*	93
		King, Mason, Taylor			
1st Round	(H)	v Pelsall Villa	L	0-2	72

2004/05 Season: 1st Round
Best Performance: 1st Round Replay 1999-2000

KIRKLEY

Eastern Prem. (Step 5)

2nd Qual.	(H)	v Dereham Town	L 0-2	232

2004/05 Season: 2nd Round

Best Performance: 2nd Round 1995-1996

LANCING

Sussex 2 (Step 6)

2nd Qual.	(A)	v East Grinstead	L 1-3	52
			Carter	

2004/05 Season: 1st Qualifying Round

Best Performance: 2nd Round 2001-2002

LANGFORD

S.S.M. (Step 5)

2nd Qual.	(H)	v Leiston	L 0-3	70

2004/05 Season: 1st Qualifying Round

Best Performance: 2nd Round 1995-1996

LARKHALL ATHLETIC

Western 1 (Step 6)

2nd Qual.	(H)	v Poole Town	L 1-4	115
			Edwards	

2004/05 Season: 1st Qualifying Round

Best Performance: 2nd Round Replay1980-1981

LAUNCESTON

South Western (Step 7)

1st Qual.	(A)	v Truro City	L 1-3	109
			Doncaster	

2004/05 Season: 1st Round disqualification.

Best Performance: 1st Round 2004-2005

LEAMINGTON

Midland Alliance (Step 5)

1st Qual.	(A)	v Studley	W 1-0	230
			Adams	
2nd Qual.	(H)	v Radcliffe Olympic	w/o	

Walkover for Leamington.

1st Round	(A)	v Holbeach United	W 2-0	269
			Morgan (2)	
2nd Round	(A)	v Biddulph Victoria	W 2-1	86
			Adams, Morgan	
3rd Round	(H)	v Liversedge	W 2-1	518
			Adams, Titterton	
4th Round	(H)	v Wimborne Town	L 2-3	746
			Adams, Titterton	

2004/05 Season: 3rd Round

Best Performance: 4th Round 2003-=-2004 2005-2006

LEDBURY TOWN

West Midlands (Step 7)

2nd Round	(H)	v Willand Rovers	L 0-4	72

2004/05 Season: 4th Round

Best Performance:4th Round 2003-2004 2005-2006

LEEK CSOB

N.W.Co 2 (Step 6)

1st Qual.	(H)	v Gornal Athletic	W 2-1	87
			Johnson (2)	
2nd Qual.	(A)	v Barwell	L 2-3	66
			Bradbury, Fower	

2004/05 Season: 2nd Qualifying Round

Best Performance: 2nd Round Replay 2000-2001

LEISTON

Eastern Prem. (Step 5)

1st Qual.	(H)	v Ruislip Manor	W 3-1	122
			Dennett, Jennings	
2nd Qual.	(A)	v Langford	W 3-0	70
			Driver, Ryland, Stanley	
1st Round	(H)	v Henley Town	W 3-2	133
			Dennett, Inglis, Wright	
2nd Round	(A)	v Wisbech Town	L 1-8	330
			Dennett	

2004/05 Season: 1st Qualifying Round

Best Performance: 1st Round 2003-2004

LEVERSTOCK GREEN

S.S.M. (Step 5)

2nd Qual.	(A)	v Downham Town	D 1-1*	55
			Armstrong	
Replay	(H)	v Downham Town	W 5-1	44
			Armstrong (3), Board, Welling	
1st Round	(H)	v North Greenford	W 3-1	56
			Byfield (2), Nick	
2nd Round	(H)	v Chalfont St Peter	L 0-2	74

2004/05 Season: 1st Round

Best Performance: 1st Round 1993-94 1996-7 2002-33 20004 -5

LINCOLN MOORLANDS

N.Co.E. 1 (Step 6)

1st Qual.	(H)	v Nettleham	W 4-1	90
			Coupland (2), Ranshaw, Robinson	
2nd Qual.	(A)	v Buxton	L 1-2	208
			Robinson	

2004/05 Season: 1st Qualifying Round

Best Performance: 3rd Rd 2003-2004

LISKEARD ATHLETIC

S.Western (Step 7)

2nd Qual.	(H)	v Bemerton Harlequins	L 1-4	83
			Williams	

2004/05 Season: 2nd Round

Best Performance: 4th Round 1994-1995

LITTLEHAMPTON TOWN

Sussex 1 (Step 5)

1st Qual.	(A)	v Bedfont	W 2-1	
			Hill, Miller	
2nd Qual.	(H)	v Hillingdon Borough	D 1-1*	
			Davies	
Replay	(A)	v Hillingdon Borough	L 1-3	
			Davies	

2004/05 Season: 2nd Qualifying Round

Best Performance: Semi-Final 1990-1991

LIVERSEDGE

N.Co E Prem. (Step 5)

2nd Qual.	(H)	v Bacup Borough	W 1-0	102
1st Round	(A)	v Parkgate	D 3-3*	72
			Borland, Farrand, Lowe	
Replay	(H)	v Parkgate	W 3-0	117
			Hamlet, Markham, Walker	
2nd Round	(H)	v Billingham Synthonia	W 5-4*	144
			Farrand, Marshall (2), Stansfield, Walker	
3rd Round	(A)	v Leamington	L 1-2	518
			Marshall	

2004/05 Season: 2nd Qualifying Round

Best Performance: 3rd Round 1875 -1976

LONDON APSA

Essex (Step 5)

1st Qual.	(A)	v Tiptree United	L 1-2	68
			Dakri	

2004/05 Season: 2nd Qualifying Round

Best Performance: 2nd Qualifying Round 2004-2005

LONDON COLNEY

Spartan South Midlands Premier (Step 5)

1st Qual.	(H)	v Eynesbury Rovers	W	4-1	40
		Flain, Jowle, McCafferty, Parkinson			
2nd Qual.	(H)	v Hadleigh United	W	2-1	66
		Flain, Parkinson			
1st Round	(H)	v Tiptree United	W	5-3*	60
		Deacon, Flain, Hunt, Jowle, Rogers			
2nd Round	(H)	v Ipswich Wanderers	W	6-3	55
		Flain (2), Hunt, Jowle, Parkinson, Ross			
3rd Round	(H)	v Chessington & H. Utd	L	1-2	85
		Deacon			

2004/05 Season: 2nd Round

Best Performance: 4th Round 1999-2000

LONG BUCKBY

Utd.Co. P (Step 5)

1st Qual.	(A)	v Sawbridgeworth	L	0-2	39

2004/05 Season: 1st Qualifying Round

Best Performance: 2nd Round 1985-1986

LONG EATON UNITED

N.Co.E Prem (Step 5)

1st Qual.	(A)	v Malvern Town	L	2-4	99
		Downie (2)			

2004/05 Season: 2nd Round

Best Performance: 2nd Round 1984-85 2002-2003 2004-2005

LONG MELFORD

Eastern 1 (Step6)

2nd Qual.	(A)	v Bugbrooke St Michaels	W	4-0	
		Balaam, Boardley, Jones, Taylor			
1st Round	(H)	v Newmarket Town	L	1-2	97
		Taylor			

2004/05 Season: 3rd Round

Best Performance: 3rd Round Replay 2004-2005

LORDSWOOD

Kent League (Step 5)

2nd Qual.	(A)	v Selsey	D	2-2*	220
		Cunningham, Sharp			
Replay	(H)	v Selsey	L	0-2	106

2004/05 Season: 1st Round

Best Performance: 1st Rd. 2001-2002 2003-2004 2004-2005

LOUGHBOROUGH DYNAMO

Kent (Step 5)

1st Qual.	(A)	v Blaby & Whetstone Ath.	L	1-3	88
		Miller			

2004/05 Season: 2nd Round

Best Performance: 2nd Round Replay 2004-2005

LOWESTOFT TOWN

Easrtern Prem. (Step 5)

2nd Round	(H)	v Wootton BC	W	2-0	240
		Cockrill, McGee			
3rd Round	(H)	v Kingsbury Town	W	2-0	265
		McGee			
4th Round	(A)	v Newcastle Benfield (BP)	L	1-3	239
		McGee			

2004/05 Season: 4th Round

Best Performance: 4th Round Replay 2004-2005

LUDLOW TOWN

West Midlands (Step 7)

1st Qual.	(A)	v Atherstone Town	L	2-4	184
		Lodgers (2)			

2004/05 Season: 1st Round

Best Performance: 1st Replay 2004-2005

LYE TOWN

West Midlands (Step 7)

2nd Qual.	(A)	v Cradley Town	L	1-2	89
		Blakemore			

2004/05 Season: 1st Qualifying Round

Best Performance: 4th Round 1995-1996

LYMINGTON TOWN

Wesssex 2 (Step 6)

1st Qual.	(H)	v Sidlesham	W	3-0	102
		Egerton, Veal, Young			
2nd Qual.	(H)	v Thamesmead	L	2-4	115
		Veal, Young			

2004/05 Season: 2nd Round

Best Performance: 2nd Round 2004-2005

MAIDSTONE UNITED

Kent (Step 5)

1st Qual.	(H)	v Cowes Sports	W	4-2	290
		Rowland, Sperring, Takalobighashi (2)			
2nd Qual.	(A)	v Eastbourne Town	W	3-0	324
		Rowland (3)			
1st Round	(A)	v North Leigh	W	4-0	276
		Takalobighashi (4)			
2nd Round	(H)	v Andover	W	4-0	423
		Hegley, Royston, Takalobighashi (2)			
3rd Round	(H)	v Broxbourne Borough	D	2-2*	411
		Strouts, Takalobighashi			
Replay	(A)	v Broxbourne Borough	D	3-3*	153
Broxbourne won 5-4 on pens.			Rowland, Royston, Takalobighashi		

2004/05 Season: 2nd Round

Best Performance: 3rd Round 2003-2004

MAINE ROAD

N.W.Co 1 (Step 5)

2nd Qual.	(H)	v Daisy Hill	L	2-3*	57
		Morrison, Simms			

2004/05 Season: 1st Qualifying Round

Best Performance: 4th Rouund 194-1995

MALMESBURY VICTORIA

Hellenic 1W (Step 6)

2nd Qual.	(H)	v Slimbridge	L	0-2	

2004/05 Season: 2nd Qualifying Round

Best Performance: 3rd Round 1976-1977

MALVERN TOWN

Midland Alliance (Step 5)

1st Qual.	(H)	v Long Eaton United	W	4-2	99
		Bullock, Owen, Preedy, Shepherd			
2nd Qual.	(H)	v Castle Vale	L	1-3	84
		Halion			

2004/05 Season: 3rd Round

Best Performance: 4th Round Replay 1974-1975

MARCH TOWN UNITED

Eastern 1 (Step 6)

2nd Qual.	(A)	v AFC Wallingford	L	0-1	63

2004/05 Season: 1st Round

Best Performance: 3rd Round1975-1976 1988-1989

MARSKE UNITED

Northern 2 (Step 6)

2nd Qual.	(A)	v Atherton LR	D	1-1*	71
		Bythway			
Replay	(H)	v Atherton LR	W	4-2	168
		Boldison (2), Metcalf, Onions			
1st Round	(H)	v St Helens Town	L	2-3	138
		Boldison, Onions			

2004/05 Season: 1st Round

Best Performance: 6th Round Replay 2000-2001

MEIR KA

Midland Comb. (Step 7)

2nd Qual.	(A)	v Boldmere St Michaels	L 2-4	63
		Borthwick (2)		

2004/05 Season: 2nd Qualifying Round

Best Performance: 2nd Round Replay

MELKSHAM TOWN

Western Premier (Step 5)

2nd Qual.	(A)	v Chard Town	L 1-4	78
		Brigham		

2004/05 Season: 1st Qualifying Round

Best Performance: 3rd Round Replay 1974-1975

MERSTHAM

Co.Co. (Step 5)

2nd Qual.	(H)	v Reading Town	W 4-0	57
		Carr (2), Davis (2)		
1st Round	(H)	v Three Bridges	L 1-2	106
		Nugent		

2004/05 Season: 2nd Qualifying Round

Best Performance: 4th Round 1989-1990

MICKLEOVER SPORTS

N.Co.E. Prem. (Step 5)

1st Qual.	(H)	v Pershore Town	L 1-2	84
		McCaul		

2004/05 Season: 3rd Round

Best Performance: 3rd Round Replay 2002-2003

MILDENHALL TOWN

Eastern Prem. (Step 5)

2nd Qual.	(H)	v Diss Town	W 4-1	190
		Hammond, Libam (2)		
1st Round	(A)	v Hullbridge Sports	W 8-0	74
		Bocking (2), Inman, Libam,		
		Paynter (3), Summerscales		
2nd Round	(A)	v Gorleston	D 0-0*	112
Replay	(H)	v Gorleston	W 2-0	123
		Hobbs, Simpson		
3rd Round	(A)	v Didcot Town	D 4-4*	352
		Docking, Paynter		
Replay	(H)	v Didcot Town	W 2-1	320
		Hobbs, North		
4th Round	(A)	v Dorking	W 3-1	449
		Docking, Pell, Simpson		
5th Round	(A)	v Hillingdon Borough	L 0-4	233

2004/05 Season: 2nd Round

Best Performance: 5th Round 2005-2006

MILE OAK

Sussex 2 (Step 6)

1st Qual.	(A)	v Eastbourne United	W 3-1	65
		Carden, Eaton, Kimbangi		
2nd Qual.	(H)	v BAT Sports	W 2-0	52
		Curram, Whittington		
1st Round	(H)	v Slade Green	D 0-0*	72
Replay	(A)	v Slade Green	W 4-1	67
		Burnett, Curram, Porter (2)		
2nd Round	(H)	v Deal Town	L 1-3*	107

2004/05 Season: 1st Round

Best Performance: 2nd Round 2005-2006

MILLBROOK

South Western (Step 7)

2nd Qual.	(H)	v Newton Abbot	L 2-3	45
		Cooke, Stacey		

2004/05 Season: 2nd Qualifying Round

Best Performance: 2nd Qualifying Round 2005-2006

MILTON UNITED

Hellenic Prem. (Step 5)

2nd Qual.	(A)	v Epsom & Ewell	L 0-3	58

2004/05 Season: 2nd Round

Best Performance: 2nd Round 93-94 94-95 04-05

MINEHEAD

Westyern 1 (Step 6)

2nd Qual.	(A)	v Bristol Manor Farm	L 1-2	37
		Hall		

2004/05 Season: 2nd Qualifying Round

Best Performance: 2nd Round 1998-1999

MOLE VALLEY (PREDATORS)

Co.Co. Prem (Step 5)

1st Qual.	(A)	v AFC Totton	L 1-3	87
		Cheadle		

2004/05 Season: N/A

Best Performance: 1st Qualifying Round 2005-2006

MONEYFIELDS

Wessex 1 (Step 5)

1st Qual.	(A)	v Tunbridge Wells	D 0-0*	110
Replay	(H)	v Tunbridge Wells	W 5-0	96
		Elias, Gee, Mould (2), Singh		
2nd Qual.	(A)	v Hythe Town	L 1-2	101
		Mould		

2004/05 Season: 1st Round

Best Performance: 4th Round 1985-1986

MORPETH TOWN

Northern 1(Step 5)

1st Qual.	(A)	v Hall Road Rangers	W 5-3	55
		Bowman (2), Edgcombe(3)		
2nd Qual.	(H)	v Salford City	D 1-1*	45
		Pitt		
Replay	(A)	v Salford City	L 0-5	116

2004/05 Season: 1st Round

Best Performance: 4th Round 2003-2004

NANTWICH TOWN

N..W.Co. 1 (Step 5)

2nd Qual.	(A)	v Shifnal Town	W 1-0	99
		Grice		
1st Round	(H)	v Boldmere St Michaels	W 1-0	123
		Adlington		
2nd Round	(A)	v Chasetown	W 1-0	284
		Blake		
3rd Round	(A)	v Quorn	W 1-0	182
		Schuber		
4th Round	(A)	v Needham Market	W 6-3*	223
		Beasley, Blake, Griggs,		
		Kinsey (2), Scarlett		
5th Round	(H)	v Buxton	W 1-0	987
		Blake		
6th Round	(H)	v Pickering Town	W 2-0	700
		Blake, Griggs		
Semi-Final	(A)	v Cammell Laird	W 1-0	528
		Blake		
Semi-Final	(H)	v Cammel Laird	W 4-0	1,420
		Beasley, Kinsey, Schuber		

2004/05 Season: 2nd Round

Best Performance: Winners 2005-2006

NEEDHAM MARKET

Eastern Prem. (Step 5)

1st Qual.	(A)	v Stowmarket Town	W 5-0	188
		Brothers, Clements (2),		
		Jopling (2)		
2nd Qual.	(A)	v Wembley	W 4-0	56
		Clements (2), Jopling, Mann		
1st Round	(H)	v Dereham United	W 1-0	122
		Jopling		
2nd Round	(H)	v Potton United	W 3-1	122
		Brothers (2), Howlett		

Needham Market continued....

3rd Round	(H) v Devizes Town	W	3-0	120
		Brothers, Clements, Norfolk		
4th Round	(H) v Nantwich Town	L	3-6*	223
		Clements (3)		

2004/05 Season: 2nd Qualifying Round

Best Performance: 4th Round 2005-2006

NELSON

N.W.Co. 2 (Step 6)

2nd Qual.	(H) v Flixton	W	3-2	115
		Holt, Jones, Smith		
1st Round	(A) v Daisy Hill	W	1-0	46
		Holt		
2nd Round	(H) v Ashville	L	0-1	110

2004/05 Season: 2nd Qualifying Round

Best Performance: 2ndRound Replay 2001-2002

NETTLEHAM

Central Mids. (Step 7)

1st Qual.	(A) v Lincoln Moorlands	L	1-4	90
		Szendrey		

2004/05 Season: 1st Qualifying Round.

Best Performance: 1st Qualifying Round.

NEW MILLS

N.W.Co 2 (Step 6)

2nd Qual.	(H) v Penrith	L	1-2	140
		Dignan		

2004/05 Season: 1st Qualifying Round.

Best Performance:

NEWARK TOWN

Central Mids. (Step 7)

2nd Qual.	(H) v Coventry Sphinx	W	4-2	61
		Ellison (3), Purves		
1st Round	(A) v Cradley Town	L	2-4*	53
		Ellison, McNamara		

2004/05 Season: Did not take part.

Best Performance: 1st Round 2005-06

NEWCASTLE BENFIELD BAY PLASTIC

Northern 1 (Step 5)

1st Qual.	(A) v Curzon Ashton	W	1-0	87
		Errington		
2nd Qual.	(A) v Alsager Town	W	4-2*	81
		Scope, Young (2)		
1st Round	(H) v Whickham	W	3-1	97
		Bell, Chilton, Young		
2nd Round	(H) v Thornaby	W	5-1	65
		Bell (3), Chilton (2)		
3rd Round	(H) v Stourbridge	W	2-1	82
		Bangura, Chilton		
4th Round	(H) v Lowestoft Town	W	3-1	239
		Chilton (2), Fuller		
5th Round	(A) v Squires Gate	L	1-2	146
		Chilton.		

2004/05 Season: 1st Round

Best Performance: 2nd Round 2000-2001

NEWCASTLE BLUE STAR

Northern 1 (Step 5)

1st Qual.	(A) v Yorkshire Amateurs	W	3-0	48
		Russell, Southern (2)		
2nd Qual.	(H) v Seaham Red Star	L	1-2	88
		Southern		

2004/05 Season: 1st Round

Best Performance: Winners 1977-1978

NEWCASTLE TOWN

N.W.Co. 1 (Step 5)

1st Round	(H) v Glapwell	W	3-2	101
		Gillick, Lennon (2)		
2nd Round	(H) v Cradley Town	W	1-0	96
		Lennon		
3rd Round	(H) v Bedlington Terriers	L	1-3	151
		Diskin		

2004/05 Season: 2nd Round

Best Performance: Semi-Final 1999-2000

NEWMARKET TOWN

Eastern Prem. (Step 5)

2nd Qual.	(H) v Walsham Le Willows	W	2-1	91
		Marshall, Mee		
1st Round	(A) v Long Melford	W	2-1	97
		Mee, Shaw		
2nd Round	(H) v Tilbury	W	2-1*	93
		Mee, Reed		
3rd Round	(H) v Willand Rovers	W	1-0	105
		Murray		
4th Round	(H) v Welwyn Garden City	D	2-2*	284
		Reed, Shaw		
Replay	(A) v Welwyn Garden City	L	1-2*	353
		Olive		

(tie awarded to Newmarket - Welwyn Garden City removed for playing ineligible player)

5th Round	(A) v Winchester City	W	4-3*	532
		Reed, Jones, Mee, Olive.		
Q. Final	(H) v Cammell Laird	L	1-2	750
		Shaw.		

2004/05 Season: 1st Round

Best Performance: 6thh Round 2005-2006

NEWPORT PAGNELL TOWN

Utd.Co. Prem. (Step 5)

1st Qual.	(A) v Ware	W	3-1	89
		Dean, Hill, Rowe		
2nd Qual.	(A) v Fakenham Town	W	4-0	80
		Dean, Kelly, Lyon (2)		
1st Round	(H) v Romford	L	0-1	235

2004/05 Season: 1st Qualifying Round

Best Performance: 2nd Round 1984-1985 1994-1995

NEWQUAY

South Western (Step 7)

2nd Qual.	(H) v Street	L	1-2	120
		Rabone		

2004/05 Season: 2nd Qualifying Round

Best Performance: 4th Round Replay 1990-1991

NEWTON ABBOT

Devon (Step 7)

2nd Qual.	(A) v Millbrook	W	3-2	45
		Clark, Friend, McDermott		
1st Round	(H) v Corsham Town	W	1-0	106
		Bowker		
2nd Round	(A) v Bishop's Cleeve	L	0-3	65

2004/05 Season: 2nd Qualifying Round

Best Performance: 1st Round 2002-2003 2003-2004

NORTH GREENFORD UNITED

Co.Co.Prem. (Step 5)

1st Round	(A) v Leverstock Green	L	1-3	56
		Hill		

2004/05 Season: 1st Round

Best Performance: 1st Round 2004-2005 2005-2006

NORTH LEIGH

Hellenic Prem. (Step 5)

2nd Qual.	(H) v Horley Town	W	2-0	74
		Futcher, Hope		
1st Round	(H) v Maidstone United	L	0-4	276

2004/05 Season: N/A

Best Performance: 4th Round 2003-2004

NORTH SHIELDS
Northern 2 (Step 6)
1st Qual.	(H) v Cammell Laird	L	1-4	121
			Matthews	

2004/05 Season: 2nd Qualifying Round

Best Performance: 2nd Qual Rd 2002-03 2003-04 2005-06

NORTHALLERTON TOWN
Northern 2 (Step 6)
1st Qual.	(H) v Sunderland Nissan	L	0-1	64

2004/05 Season: 2nd Qualifying Round

Best Performance: 4th Round 2002-2003

NORTHAMPTON SPENCER
Utd Co. Prem (Step 5)
1st Qual.	(H) v Cranfield United	W	3-0	68
			Frost (2), Wigley	
2nd Qual.	(H) v Ipswich Wanderers	L	1-3	66
			Coleman	

2004/05 Season: 2nd Qualifying Round
Best Performance: 4th Round 1987-1988

Jerry Moss, Northampton Spencer, strides away from this Ipswich Wanderers' challenge. Photo: Peter Barnes.

NORTON & STOCKTON ANCIENTS
Northern 2 (Step 6)
2nd Qual.	(H) v Sheffield	W	2-0	85
			Laing, Masters	
1st Round	(A) v Armthorpe Welfare	W	1-0	52
			Baverstock	
2nd Round	(A) v Colne	L	0-4	127

2004/05 Season: 2nd Qualifying Round

Best Performance: 2nd Round 1983-1984

NORTON UNITED
N.W.Co. 2 (Step 6)
1st Qual.	(A) v Teversal	D	1-1*	69
			Callan	
Replay	(H) v Teversal	W	1-0	60
			Powell	
2nd Qual.	(H) v Oldbury Town	D	1-1*	40
			Pugh	
Replay	(A) v Oldbury Town	L	0-2	48

2004/05 Season: 2nd Qualifying Round

Best Performance: 2nd Round 2002-2003

NORWICH UNITED
Eastern Co. Prem. (Step 5)
2nd Qual.	(A) v Royston Town	L	0-1	70

2004/05 Season: 1stQualifying Round

Best Performance: 3rd Round 1992-1993 2002-2003

NUNEATON GRIFF
Midland Comb.(Step 7)
1st Qual.	(A) v Boston Town	W	2-0	70
			Aston, Wilson	
2nd Qual.	(A) v Sutton Town	D	0-0*	111
Replay	(H) v Sutton Town	D	0-0*	160

Sutton won 4-1 on pens.

2004/05 Season: 2nd Qualifying Round

Best Performance:2nd Round 2003-2004

OADBY TOWN
Mid. Alliance (Step 5)
2nd Qual.	(H) v Friar Lane & Epworth	L	1-3*	291
			Hart	

2004/05 Season: 3rd Round

Best Performance: Semi-Final 2002-2003

OAKWOOD
Sussex 2 (Step 6)
1st Qual.	(H) v VCD Atheletic	L	1-4	32
			Newman	

2004/05 Season: 1st Round

Best Performance: 1st Round 1988-1989 2004-2005

ODD DOWN
Western Prem.(Step 5)
1st Qual.	(H) v Wadebridge Town	W	2-1	37
			Bright, Hewby	
2nd Qual.	(H) v Bridport	W	3-0	29
			Duggah (2), Hewby	
1st Round	(A) v Bournemouth	L	1-4	69
			Bright	

2004/05 Season: 2nd Qualifying Round

Best Performance: 4th Round 1981-1982

OLDBURY UNITED
Mid. Aliance (Step 5)
2nd Qual.	(A) v Norton United	D	1-1*	40
			Lawley	
Replay	(H) v Norton United	W	2-0	48
			Barhfield, Booth	
1st Round	(H) v Coleshill Town	L	0-4	56

2004/05 Season: 3rd Round

Best Performance: 5th Round 1977-1978

OLDHAM TOWN
N.W.Co 2 (Step 6
2nd Qual.	(H) v Winterton Rangers	W	3-1	45
			Melia (2), Taylor	
1st Round	(H) v Seaham Red Star	W	3-1	40
			Curley, Scanlon (2)	
2nd Round	(A) v Pickering Town	L	0-1*	115

2004/05 Season: 1st Qualifying Round
Best Performance: 2nd Round 1994-1995

OTTERY ST MARY
Devon (Step 7)
2nd Qual.	(H) v Tavistock	L	2-5	78
			Gill, Mowarth	

2004/05 Season: 1st Qualifying Round

Best Performance: 3rd Round 1980-1981

OXFORD CITY
S.S.M. (Step 5)
1st Round	(H) v Welwyn Garden City	L	1-3	162
			Durrant	

2004/05 Season: N/A

Best Performance: Finalists 1994-1995

OXHEY JETS
S.S.M. (Step5)
2nd Qual.	(A) v Romford	L	0-2	108

2004/05 Season: 2nd Qualifying Round

Best Performance: 2nd Qualifying Round 2003-2004 2005-2006

PADIHAM

N.W.Co. 2 (Step 6)

1st Qual.	(A) v Hallam	W	2-1	40
		Seddon (2)		
2nd Qual.	(A) v Winsford United	L	1-2*	97
		Filds		

2004/05 Season: 1st Round

Best Performance: 3rd Round Replay 1981-1982

PAGHAM

Sussex 2 (Step 6)

1st Qual.	(H) v Hythe Town	L	2-6	55
		Bamfo, Gibbs		

2004/05 Season: 1st Round

Best Performance: 4th Round 1980-1981

PARKGATE

N.Co E 1 (Step 6)

1st Qual.	(H) v Tadcaster Albion	W	2-0	26
		Cusworth (2)		
2nd Qual.	(A) v Poulton Victoria	W	3-1	49
		Outram (2), Petch		
1st Round	(H) v Liversedge	D	3-3*	72
		Cusworth (2), Whitehead		
Replay	(A) v Liversedge	L	0-3	117

2004/05 Season: 2nd Qualifying Round

Best Performance: 1st Rd 1994-95 1996-97 1999-2000

PEACEHAVEN & TELSCOMBE

Susex 3 (Step7)

2nd Qual.	(H) v Godalming Town	L	1-4*	65
		Walton		

2004/05 Season: 2nd Qualifying Round

Best Performance: 6th Round 1995-1996

PEGASUS JUNIORS

Hellenic Prem. (Step 5)

1st Qual.	(A) v Pilkington XXX	W	6-3	66
		Aldrich, Brown, Hyde (2),		
		Mortlock, Price		
2nd Qual.	(A) v Westfields	L	0-3	202

2004/05 Season: 2nd Qualifying Round

Best Performance: 2nd Round Replay 2000-2001

PELSALL VILLA

West Midlands (Step 7)

2nd Qual.	(A) v Radford	W	2-1	52
		Cartwright (2)		
1st Round	(A) v Kirby Muxloe	W	2-0	72
		Battisson, Mason		
2nd Round	(A) v Arnold Town	L	0-2	108

2004/05 Season: 2nd Qualifying Round

Best Performance: 5th Round 1992-1993

PENRITH

Northern 2 (Step 6)

1st Qual.	(H) v Clipstone Welfare	W	3-0	73
		Broadley, Paul, Reed		
2nd Qual.	(A) v New Mills	W	2-1	140
		Paul, Rooke		
1st Round	(A) v Ashville	L	1-3*	130
		Strong		

2004/05 Season: 1st Round

Best Performance: 3rd Round 1991-1992 1993-1994

PENRYN ATHLETIC

SouthWestern (Step 7)

1st Qual.	(A) v Harrow Hill	W	5-2	35
		Goldring, Rowson, Thwaits		
		Young (2)		
2nd Qual.	(H) v Hamworthy United	W	2-1*	121
		Drummond, Salmon		
1st Round	(A) v Tavistock	L	0-3	90

2004/05 Season: N/A

Best Performance: 1st Round 2005-2006

PENZANCE

South Western (Step 7)

2nd Qual.	(A) v Devizes Town	L	0-1	43

2004/05 Season: 2nd Qualifying Round

Best Performance: 2nd Qualifying Round 2004-2005 2005-2006

PERSHORE TOWN

Midland Comb. (Step 7)

1st Qual.	(A) v Mickleover Sports	W	2-1	84
		Bellamy, Biddle		
2nd Qual.	(H) v Bridgnorth Town	L	0-2	66

2004/05 Season: 1st Qualifying Round

Best Performance: 1st Round Replay 1974-1975

PETERLEE NEWTOWN

Northern 2 (Step 6)

1st Qual.	(H) v Retford United	L	2-6	66
		Winspear (2)		

2004/05 Season: 1st Round

Best Performance: 3rd Round 1981-82 1982-83 1989-1990

PETERSFIELD TOWN

Wessex 2 (Step 6)

1st Qual.	(A) v Epsom & Ewell	L	1-3	57
		Keogh		

2004/05 Season: 1st Round

Best Performance: 2nd Round 1994-1995

PEWSEY VALE

Hellenic 1W (Step 6)

2nd Qual.	(H) v Westbury United	W	1-0	63
		Field		
1st Round	(A) v Devizes Town	D	0-0*	164
Replay	(H) v Devizes Town	D	1-1*	142

Devizes won 3-0 on pens.

2004/05 Season: 2nd Qualifying Round

Best Performance: 1st Round Rep[lay 2005-2006

PICKERING TOWN

N.Co.East P (Step5)

2nd Round	(H) v Oldham Town	W	1-0*	115
		Salt		
3rd Round	(H) v Dunston Federation B.W		1-0	131
		Nogan		
4th Round	(H) v Tavistock	W	3-0	290
		Drinkall, Nogan, Swales		
5th Round	(A) v Wimborne Town	W	2-1	983
		Drinkall, Salt.		

2004/05 Season: 4th Round

Best Performance: 5th Round 2005-2006

PILKINGTON XXX

Mid. Comb.(Step 7)

1st Qual.	(H) v Pegasus Juniors	L	3-6	66
		McKenzie (2), Ruck		

2004/05 Season: N/A

Best Performance: 1st Qualifying Round

PONTEFRACT COLLIERIES

N.Co.East 1 (Step 6)

1st Qual.	(H) v Garforth Town	W	3-2	82
		Cuss, Lanes, Rimmington		
2nd Qual.	(H) v Darlington Railway	L	2-3	100
		Duckworth, Rimmington		

2004/05 Season: 2nd Qualifying Round

Best Performance: 2nd Round 2002-2003

POOLE TOWN

Wesex 1 (Step 5)

2nd Qual.	(A) v Larkhall Athletic	W	4-1	115
		Brown (2), Chivers, Funnell		
1st Round	(H) v Bideford	L	1-2	226
		Richardson		

2004/05 Season: N/A

Best Performance: 1st Round 2005-2006

PORTHLEVEN

South Western (Step 7)

2nd Qual.	(H)	v St Blazey	L	0-3	197

2004/05 Season: 2nd Qualifying Round

Best Performance: 6th Round 1997-1998

PORTLAND UNITED

Wessex 1 (Step 5)

1st Qual.	(A)	v Fairford Town	L	0-5	48

2004/05 Season: 2nd Qualifying Round

Best Performance: 2nd Round 2001-2002

POTTON UNITED

Utd. Co. P (Step 5)

2nd Round	(A)	v Needham Market	L	1-3	122
		Crook			

2004/05 Season: 4th Round

Best Performance: 5th Round 1989-1990

POULTON VICTORIA

West Cheshire (Step 7)

2nd Qual.	(H)	v Parkgate	L	1-3	49
		Burrows			

2004/05 Season: 1st Qualifying Round

Best Performance: 3rd Rd 1986-87 1988-89 1996-97 1997-98

PRUDHOE TOWN

Northern 2 (Step 6)

2nd Qual.	(A)	v Hebburn Town	W	2-0	90
		Bulford, Drysdale			
1st Round	(A)	v Trafford	L	0-1	138

2004/05 Season: 1st Round

Best Performance: 3rd Round 1995-1996

QUORN

Mid. Alliance (Step 5)

2nd Round	(A)	v Barrow Town	W	3-1	420
		Jonas, Nurse, Turner			
3rd Round	(H)	v Nantwich Town	L	0-1	182

2004/05 Season: 4th Round

Best Performance: 4th Round 2004-2005

RACING CLUB WARWICK

Mid Alliance (Step 5)

1st Qual.	(H)	v Eccleshall	W	1-0	45
		Mackey			
2nd Qual.	(A)	v Blackstones	W	2-1	81
		Mackey, Olanipekun			
1st Round	(H)	v Barwell	W	1-0	131
		Wood			
2nd Round	(A)	v Tipton Town	W	2-0	80
		Gordon, Mackey			
3rd Round	(A)	v Ashville	D	3-3*	160
		Beckett, Gordon, Olanipekun			
Replay	(H)	v Ashville	D	2-2*	125
Ashville won 4-3 on pens.		Pringle, Wood			

2004/05 Season: 2nd Qualifying Round

Best Performance: 4th Round Replay 1977-1978

RADCLIFFE OLYMPIC

Central Mids. (Step 7)

2nd Qual.	(A)	v Leamington	withdrawn	

Walkover for Leamington.

2004/05 Season: N/A

Best Performance: 2nd Qualifying Round 2005-2006

RADFORD

Cental Mids (Step 7)

2nd Qual.	(H)	v Pelsall Villa	L	1-2	52
		Garmston			

2004/05 Season: N/A

Best Performance: 2nd Qualifying Round 1996-1997 2005-2006

RADSTOCK TOWN

Western 1 (Step 6)

1st Qual.	(H)	v Barnstaple Town	W	3-1	79
		Billings, Boys, Schuster			
2nd Qual.	(A)	v Fairford Town	W	2-1*	45
		Bryant, Schuster			
1st Round	(A)	v Wimborne Town	L	1-3	244

2004/05 Season: N/A

Best Performance: 2nd Round Replay 1988-1989

RAINWORTH MW

Central Mids (Step 7)

2nd Qual.	(H)	v Deeping Rangers	L	0-1	51

2004/05 Season: 1st Round

Best Performance: Finalists 1981-1982

RAMSBOTTOM UNITED

N.W.Co. 1 (Step 5)

1st Qual.	(H)	v Squires Gate	L	1-3	151
		MacDonald			

2004/05 Season: 2nd Round

Best Performance: 3rd Round 2003-2004

RAUNDS TOWN

U.Co P (Step 5)

2nd Qual.	(A)	v Woodbridge Town	W	4-1	71
		Curtis (2), Hanock, Tallents			
1st Round	(A)	v Gorleston	L	0-1	106

2004/05 Season: 2nd Qualifying Round

Best Performance: Semi-Final 1994-1995

RAYNES PARK VALE

Co.Co. (Step 5)

2nd Qual.	(A)	v Colliers Wood United	L	0-3	65

2004/05 Season: 1st Qualifying Round

Best Performance: 2ndQ. 95-6 96-7 97-8 98-9 02-3 03-4 95-6

READING TOWN

Co.Co (Step 5)

2nd Qual.	(A)	v Merstham	L	0-4	57

2004/05 Season: 1st Round

Best Performance: 4th Round 18996-1997

REDHILL

Sussex 1 (Step 5)

1st Qual.	(A)	v East Preston	L	1-4	41
		Braver-Jones			

2004/05 Season: 2nd Qualifying Round

Best Performance: 4th Round Replay 1976-77

RETFORD UNITED

N.Co. E. 1 (Step 6)

1st Qual.	(A)	v Peterlee Newtown	W	6-2	66
		Ashton (3), Harvey, Tomlinson, Tyler			
2nd Qual.	(H)	v Holker OB	W	4-2	
		Ashton, Harvey, Parks, Shaw			
1st Round	(H)	v Brodsworth MW	W	4-0	180
		Ashton (2), Harvey (2)			
2nd Round	(H)	v Trafford	W	2-1	249
		Ashton, Parks			
3rd Round	(A)	v Cammell Laird	L	0-3	122

2004/05 Season: 2nd Qualifying Round

Best Performance: 3rd Round 2005-2006

RINGMER

Sussex 1 (Step 5)

1st Qual.	(A)	v Fareham Town	W	1-0	101
		Green			
2nd Qual.	(A)	v Wantage Town	L	2-3	81
		Moore, Shepherd			

2004/05 Season: 2nd Qualifying Round

Best Performance: 3rd Round 1977-1978

Romford desperately hang on to a slender 1-0 advantage over Newport Pagnell in the First Round.

Photo: Steve Ayre.

RINGWOOD TOWN

Wessex 2 (Step 6)

2nd Qual.	(A)	v Wellington Town	L 0-1	35

2004/05 Season: 2nd Qualifying Round

Best Performance: 2nd Qualifying Round 2004-2005 2005-2006

ROCESTER

Mid. Alliance (Step 5)

1st Round	(H)	v Carlton Town	L 0-2	66

2004/05 Season: N/A

Best Performance: 5th Round 1986-1987

ROLLS ROYCE LEISURE

Central Mids. (Step 7)

1st Qual.	(A)	v St Andrews	L 1-3	23
			Peel	

2004/05 Season: 2nd Qualifying Round

Best Performance: 2nd Round 1979-1980

ROMFORD

Essex (Step 5)

2nd Qual.	(H)	v Oxhey Jets	W 2-0	198
			Gallen, Howe	
1st Round	(A)	v Newport Pagnell	W 1-0	235
			Hall	
2nd Round	(A)	v AFC Sudbury	L 0-4	331

2004/05 Season: 1st Round

Best Performance: 2nd Round 2001-2002

ROMULUS

Mid. Alliance (Step 5)

2nd Qual.	(H)	v Birstall United	W 5-0	65
			Batchelor, Fagan (2),	
			Hamilton, Lanns	
1st Round	(A)	v Glossop North End	L 4-6	118
			Batchelor, Hamilton, Knott (2)	

2004/05 Season: 1st Qualifying Round

Best Performance: 1st 2005-2006

ROSSINGTON MAIN

N.Co E 1 (Step 6)

2nd Qual.	(A)	v Glasshoughton	L 1-7	38
			Hickey	

2004/05 Season: 2nd Qualifying Round

Best Performance: 2nd Rouns 1988-1989

ROTHWELL CORINTHIANS

Utd. Co. 1 (Step 6)

2nd Qual.	(H)	v Welwyn Garden City	L 1-3	49
			Nandson	

2004/05 Season: 1st Qualifying Round

Best Performance: 1st Round Replay 2002-2003

ROYSTON TOWN

S.S.M (Step 5)

1st Qual.	(H)	v Whitton United	D 0-0*	81
Replay	(A)	v Whitton United	W 2-0	79
			McMurough	
2nd Qual.	(H)	v Norwich United	W 1-0	70
			Dove	
1st Round	(A)	v Wootton BC	L 1-2	64
			Saunders	

2004/05 Season: 1st Round

Best Performance: 4th Round 1978-79 1982-83

RUISLIP MANOR

S.S.M (Step 5)

1st Qual.	(A)	v Leiston	L 1-3	122
			Pierre	

2004/05 Season: 1st Qualifying Round

Best Performance: 3rd Round Replay 1979-1980

RYE & IDEN UNITED

Sussex 1 (Step 6)

1st Round	(A)	v East Grinstead Town	W 5-3	95
			Bradley, Cusden (2),	
			Johnson, Playford	
2nd Round	(H)	v Hillingdon Borough	D 2-2*	86
			Chenery, Johnson	
Replay	(A)	v Hillingdon Borough	L 0-1	62

2004/05 Season: 1st Round

Best Performance: 2ndt Round Replay 2004-2005

RYTON

Northern 2 (Step 6)

1st Qual.	(H)	v Crook Town	L 1-2	61
			Piecha	

2004/05 Season: 1st Round

Best Performance: 1st Round 2004-2005

SAFFRON WALDEN TOWN

Eastern 1(Step 6)

1st Qual.	(A)	v Kingsbury Town	L	2-3	38
			Green (2)		

2004/05 Season: 2nd Qualifying Round

Best Performance: 5th Round 1990-1991

SALFORD CITY

N.W.Co. 1 (Step 5)

2nd Qual.	(A)	v Morpeth Town	D	1-1*	45
			Burke		
Replay	(H)	v Morpeth Town	W	5-0	116
			Burke (2), Massay,		
			Robinson (2)		
1st Round	(A)	v Squires Gate	L	0-3	66

2004/05 Season: 3rd Round

Best Performance: 3rd rOund 2004-2005

SALTASH UNITED

Western 1 (Step 6)

2nd Qual.	(H)	v Clevedon United	L	1-2*	51
			Jefferis		

2004/05 Season: 2nd Qualifying Round

Best Performance: 3rd Round 1996-1997

SALTDEAN UNITED

Sussex 2 (Step 6)

2nd Qual.	(H)	v VCD Athletic	L	0-3	43

2004/05 Season: 2nd Qualifying Round

Best Performance: 4th Round 1999-2000

SANDHURST TOWN

Co.Co. (Step 5)

2nd Qual.	(A)	v Abingdon United	L	1-4	69
			Anderson		

2004/05 Season: 3rd Round

Best Performance: 3rd Round 2004-2005

SANDIACRE TOWN

Central Mids. (Step 7)

1st Qual.	(A)	v Kirby Muxloe	D	2-2*	48
			Aldred, Potter		
Replay	(H)	v Kirby Muxloe	L	1-2	78
			Saxton		

2004/05 Season: 1st Qualifying Round

Best Performance: 1st Round 1997-1998 2003-2004

SAWBRIDGEWORTH TOWN

Essex (Step 5)

1st Qual.	(H)	v Long Buckby	W	2-0	39
			Hughes, Pike		
2nd Qual.	(H)	v Chalfont St Peter	L	1-3	34
			Smith		

2004/05 Season: 2nd Round

Best Performance: 3rd Round Replay 1980-1981

SEAHAM RED STAR

Northern 2 (Step 6)

1st Qual.	(H)	v Shotton Comrades	w/o		
Shotton withdrew.					
2nd Qual.	(A)	v Newcastle Blue Star	W	2-1	88
			Hubbard, Jennings		
1st Round	(A)	v Oldham Town	L	1-3	40
			Blackett		

2004/05 Season: 2nd Round

Best Performance: 3rd Round 1995--1996 1997-1998 1998-1999

SELBY TOWN

N.Co.Esat P (Step 5)

1st Round	(H)	v South Normanton	W	3-1	85
			Croad, Graham, Matthews		
2nd Round	(H)	v Westfields	D	3-3*	65
			Reid, Roughley, Wash		
Replay	(A)	v Westfields	L	2-3*	28
			Matthews, Twitchen, Wash		
3rd Round	(H)	v Buxton	L	0-1	

2004/05 Season: 1st Round

Best Performance: 4th Round 2nd Replay 1995-1996

SELSEY

Sussex 2 (Step 6)

2nd Qual.	(H)	v Lordswood	D	2-2*	220
			More, Rishman		
Replay	(A)	v Lordswood	W	2-0	106
			More, Ridley		
1st Round	(A)	v Thatcham Town	L	2-4	108
			Brown, More		

2004/05 Season: 1st Qualifying Road

Best Performance: 3rd Round 1975-1976 2001-2002 2002-2003

SEVENOAKS TOWN

Kent P (Step 5)

1st Qual.	(A)	v Cobham	W	2-0	23
			Grant (2)		
2nd Qual.	(H)	v VT	L	2-3*	65
			Bartley, Forster		

2004/05 Season: 2nd Qualifying Round

Best Performance: 2nd Qualifying Round 2004-2005 2005-2006

Carl Bartley, of Sevenoaks, gets in a powerful harder against VT FC. Photo: Alan Coomes.

SHAFTESBURY

Wessex 2 (Step 6)

1st Qual.	(A)	v Westbury	L	0-4	86

2004/05 Season: N/A

Best Performance: 1st Qualifying Round 2005-2006

SHAWBURY UNITED

West Mids (Step 7)

2nd Qual.	(H)	v Glapwell	L	0-4	47

2004/05 Season: 1st Qualifying Round

Best Performance: 2nd Qualifying Rd. 2001-2002 02-03 03-04

SHEFFIELD

N.Co East P. (Step 5)

2nd Qual.	(A)	v Norton & Stockton A.	L	0-2	85

2004/05 Season: 1st Round

Best Performance: Semi-Final 1976-1977

Sidley United's Dominic Clarke (centre), lobs the ball over Johnny Betteridge the United Services 'keeper, during their 2nd Qualifying Round tie. Photo: Roger Turner.

SHEPTON MALLET

Western 1(Step 6)

2nd Qual.	(A) v Wimborne Town	L	0-3	213

2004/05 Season: 1st Round

Best Performance: 2nd Round 1985-1986 1975-1976

SHERBORNE TOWN

Dorset Prem. (Step 7)

2nd Qual.	(A) v Welton Rovers	L	0-5	72

2004/05 Season: N/A

Best Performance: 1st Rd. 1991-1992 1993-1994 19905-1996

SHIFNAL TOWN

Mid. Comb. (Step 7)

1st Qual.	(H) v Coventry Copsewood	W	4-0	73
	Bates, Currier, Dovey, Joshua			
2nd Qual.	(H) v Nantwich Town	L	0-1	0-1

2004/05 Season: 2nd Qualifying Round

Best Performance: 4th Round Replay 1981-1982

SHILDON

Northern 1 (Step 5)

2nd Qual.	(H) v Alnwick Town	D	1-1*	139
	Howarth			
Replay	(A) v Alnwick Town	L	2-5	89

2004/05 Season: 1st Round

Best Performance: 3rd Round 2003-2004

SHIREBROOK TOWN

N.Co East P (Step 5)

1st Qual.	(A) v Bourne Town	W	2-1	68
	Johnson (2)			
2nd Qual.	(A) v Blackwell MW	W	3-0	155
	Hall, Roberts, Wilson			
1st Round	(A) v Friar Lane & E	L	1-5	229
	Johnson			

2004/05 Season: 2nd Qualifying Round

Best Performance: 3rd Round 2002-2003

SHOREHAM

Sussex 1 (Step 6)

2nd Qual.	(H) v AFC Totton	W	6-2	72
	Annis, Boiling, Gainsford, Sadough, Venton (2)			
1st Round	(A) v Sidley United	L	0-3	97

2004/05 Season: 2nd Qualifying Round

Best Performance: 4th Rd. 1981-19842

SHORTWOOD UNITED

Hellenic Prem. (Step 5)

2nd Qual.	(H) v Cullompton Rangers	W	5-0	64
	Greenough, Haddock, Harmer, Singh (2)			
1st Round	(H) v Bishop's Cleeve	L	0-3	70

2004/05 Season: 2nd Qualifying Round

Best Performance: 5th Round 1981-1982

SHOTTON COMRADES

Wearside (Step 7

1st Qual.	(A) v Seaham Red Star		withdrew	

Walkover for Seaham Red Star.

2004/05 Season: 1st Qualifying Round

Best Performance: 2nd Round 1992-1993

SIDLESHAM

Susssex 2 (Step 6)

1st Qual.	(A) v Lymington Town	L	0-3	102

2004/05 Season: 2nd Qualifying Round

Best Performance: 2nd Round 2002-2003

SIDLEY UNITED

Sussex 1 (Step 5)

2nd Qual.	(A) v Utd Services Portsmouth	W	2-0	52
	Wood, Wooler			
1st Round	(H) v Shoreham	W	3-0	97
	Baker (2), Miles			
2nd Round	(H) v Erith Town	W	4-2	92
	Barham (4)			
3rd Round	(H) v St Blazey	L	1-2	146
	Wood			

2004/05 Season: 2nd Qualifying Round

Best Performance: 3rd Round 1998-1999 2005-2006

SILSDEN

N.W.Co 1 (Step 5)

2nd Qual.	(H) v Ashville	L	1-3	108

2004/05 Season: 2nd Round

Best Performance: 4th Round 1991-1992 1992-1993

SKELMERSDALE UNITED

N.W.Co 1 (Step 5)

2nd Round	(H) v West Allotment C.	W	4-3	141
	Cole, Rudd, Thompson, Wallace			
3rd Round	(A) v Squire Gate	L	1-2	102
	Wallace			

2004/05 Season: 4th Round

Best Performance: 4th Round 1999-2000 2004-2005

SLADE GREEN

Kent (Step 5)

2nd Qual.	(H) v East Preston	W	2-1	74
	McTaggart, Weir			
1st Round	(A) v Mile Oak	D	0-0*	72
Replay	(H) v Mile Oak	L	1-4	67
	McTaggart			

2004/05 Season: 1st Round

Best Performance: 3rd Round

SLIMBRIDGE

Hellenic Premier (Step 5)

1st Qual.	(H) v Chipping Norton	W	3-0	60
	Colwell, Meadows (2)			
2nd Qual.	(A) v Malnesbury Victoria	W	2-0	40
	Morford (2)			
1st Round	(A) v Hallen	W	1-0	49
	Colwell			
2nd Round	(A) v Bridgwater Town	W	1-0	189
	Green			
3rd Round	(A) v Welwyn Garden City	L	1-3	93
	Varnam			

2004/05 Season: 3rd Round

Best Performance: 3rd Round 2004-2005 2005-2006

SOHAM TOWN RANGERS

Eastern Prem. (Step 5)

2nd Round	(A) v AFC Hornchurch	W	3-1	469
	Bugg (2), Robinson			
3rd Round	(H) v Bury Town	L	1-2	202
	Simpson			

2004/05 Season: 5th Round

Best Performance: 5th Round 2004-2005

SOUTH NORMANTON ATHLETIC

N.Co.E 1 (Step6)

2nd Qual.	(H) v Wolverhampton C.	W	2-1	39
	Hatton, Robinson			
1st Round	(A) v Selby Town	L	1-3	85
	Russle			

2004/05 Season: N/A

Best Performance: 1st Round 2002- 2003 2005-2006

SOUTH SHIELDS

Northern 2 (Step 6)

2nd Qual.	(H) v Ashington	L	1-3	105
	Marfleet			

2004/05 Season: 2nd Qualifying Round

Best Performance: 6th Round 1975-1976

SOUTHALL

Co.Co. (Step 5)

1st Qual.	(H) v Wroxham	L	2-3	50
	Moses, O'Sullivan			

2004/05 Season: 2nd Qualifying Round

Best Performance: Finalists 1985-1986

SOUTHEND MANOR

Essex (Step 5)

2nd Qual.	(H) v Brentwood Town	W	3-0	21
	Kemp (2), Shelly			
1st Round	(A) v Yaxley	L	1-8	93
	Kemp			

2004/05 Season: 1st Round

Best Performance: 4th Round 1996-1997

SPENNYMOOR TOWN (FORMERLY EVENWOOD T.)

Norther 2 (Step 6)

2nd Qual.	(H) v Crook Town	L	1-4	255
	Dinsley			

2004/05 Season: N/A

Best Performance: 2nd Qualifying Round

SPORTING BENGAL UNITED

Kent (Step 5)

2nd Qual.	(H) v Felixstowe & W.	L	1-4	85
	Pipim			

2004/05 Season: 2nd Round

Best Performance: 2nd Round 2004-2005

SQUIRES GATE

N.W.Co. 1(Step 5)

1st Qual.	(A) v Ramsbottom United	W	3-1	151
	Ashall, Sugden (2)			
2nd Qual.	(H) v Brandon United	W	2-1	62
	Beattie, Walsh			
1st Round	(H) v Salford City	W	3-0	66
	Ashall, Cairns, Morris			
2nd Round	(A) v Glasshoughton	W	2-1	75
	Butler, Pearson			
3rd Round	(H) v Skelmersdale United	W	2-1	102
	Beattie, Catlow			
4th Round	(H) v Gedling Town	W	2-1*	75
	Beattie, Butler			
5th Round	(H) v Newcastle Benfield (BP)	W	2-1	428
	Palmer, Cairns			
Q. Final	(A) v Hillingdon Borough	L	0-2	428

2004/05 Season: 1st Qualifying Round

Best Performance: 6th Round 2005-2006

ST ANDREWS

Leics. (Step 7)

1st Qual.	(H) v Rolls Royce Leisure	W	3-1	23
	Hollis (2), Johnson			
2nd Qual.	(H) v Blidworth Welfare	W	5-1	22
	Hollis (3), Johnson, Shepherd			
1st Round	(A) v Highfield Rangers	L	0-2	48

2004/05 Season: 2nd Qualifying Round

Best Performance: 5th Round 1994-1995

ST BLAZEY

South Western (Step 7)

1st Qual.	(A) v Exmouth Town	W	4-1*	125
	Harrington (2), Hooper, Vercesi			
2nd Qual.	(A) v Porthleven	W	3-0	197
	Band, Harrington, Hodge			
1st Round	(A) v Clevedon United	W	4-2*	194
	Madden, Street, Vercesi			
2nd Round	(A) v Bemerton Heath H.	W	3-2	134
	Harrington (2), Hooper			
3rd Round	(A) v Sidley United	W	2-1	146
	Harrington, Street			
4th Round	(A) v Crook Town	L	0-3	494

2004/05 Season: 2nd Qualifying Round

Best Performance: 3rd Round 1998-1999

ST HELENS TOWN

N.W. Co. (Step 5)

1st Round	(A) v Marske United	W	3-2	138
	Jensen (3)			
2nd Round	(H) v Dunston Federation B.	L	1-3	84
	Gibiliru (Jnr)			

2004/05 Season: 3rd Round

Best Performance: Winners 1986-1987

ST IVES TOWN

Utd.Co. (Step 5)

2nd Qual.	(H) v Woodford United	L	0-2	43

2004/05 Season: 1st Qualifying Round

Best Performance: 2nd Round 1989-1990

ST MARGARETSBURY

S.S.M. (Step 5)

1st Qual.	(A) v Huntingdon Town	W	3-1	53
	Barker, Birnie, Herod			
2nd Qual.	(A) v Broxbourne Borough	L	1-2	43

2004/05 Season: 1st Round

Best Performance: 3rd Round 1985-1986

ST NEOTS TOWN

Utd.Co. (Step 5)

1st Qual.	(A) v Godmanchester R.	W	2-1	85
	Kuhne, Walker			
2nd Qual.	(H) v Witham Town	D	0-0*	124
Replay	(A) v Witham Town	L	2-4	96
	Kuhne, Reynolds			

2004/05 Season: 3rd Round

Best Performance: 5th Round 2001-2003

STANSTED

Essex (Step 5)

1st Qual.	(A) v Wootton Blue Cross	L	0-2	41

2004/05 Season: 1st Round

Best Performance: Winners 1983-1984

STANWAY ROVERS

Eastern 1(Step 6)

2nd Qual.	(A) v Great Yarmouth Town	W	1-0	99
	Turner			
1st Round	(H) v Basildon United	W	4-3	75
	Callander, Newson, Symes			
	Turner			
2nd Round	(H) v Broxbourne Borough	D	5-5*	65
	Callander, Howard (2),			
	Newson (2)			
Replay	(A) v Broxbourne Borough	L	0-3	41

2004/05 Season: 1st Qualifying Round

Best Performance: 2nd Round Replay

STAPENHILL

Leics. (Step 7)

1st Qual.	(A) v Deeping Rangers	L	1-2	63
	Akers			

2004/05 Season: 1st Qualifying Round

Best Performance: 2nd Round Replay 1992-93 1996-97

STAVELEY MW

N.Co.East 1 (Step 6)

2nd Qual.	(A) v Glossop North End	L	2-3*	118
	Johnson			

2004/05 Season: 1st Round

Best Performance: 3rd Round

STEYNING TOWN

Sussex 2 (Step 6)

2nd Qual.	(A) v Hamble ASSC	L	0-4	68

2004/05 Season: 1st Qualifying Round

Best Performance: 5th Round 1984-1985

STONE DOMINOES

N.W.Co 1 (Step 5)

2nd Qual.	(H) v Biddulph Victoria	withdrawn	
Walkover for Biddulph Victoria.			

2004/05 Season: 3rd Round Replay

Best Performance: 5th Round Replay

STOTFOLD

Utd Co. P (Step 5)

1st Qual.	(A) v Tring Athletic	D	1-1*	83
	Bascombe			
Replay	(H) v Tring Athletic	W	2-0	60
	Mills, Thomas			
2nd Qual.	(H) v Gorleston	L	1-4	67
	Blackett			

2004/05 Season: 2nd Round

Best Performance: 4th Round 95-96 97-98 00-01

STOURBRIDGE

Mid Alliance (Step 5)

2nd Round	(A) v Friar Lane & E	W	5-1	208
	Bellingham (3), Broadhurst			
	Rogers (2)			
3rd Round	(A) v Newcastle Benfield (BP)	L	1-2	82
	Bennett			

2004/05 Season: 6th Round

Best Performance: 6th Round 2004-2005

STOWMARKET TOWN

Eastern 1 (Step 6)

1st Qual.	(H) v Needham Market	L	0-5	188

2004/05 Season: 2nd Qualifying Round

Best Performance: 4th Round 1982-1983

STRATFORD TOWN

Mid Alliance (Step 5)

1st Qual.	(A) v Westfields	L	1-2	76
	Bailey			

2004/05 Season: 1st Round

Best Performance:4th Round 1975-1976

STREET

Western 1 (Step 6)

1st Qual.	(A) v Downton	W	2-1	77
	Ashton, Dovey			
2nd Qual.	(A)v Newquay	W	2-1	120
	Amghar, Luke			
1st Round	(H) v Christchurch	L	0-2	78

2004/05 Season: 1st Round

Best Performance: 2nd Round 2000-2001

STUDLEY

Mid Alliance (Step 5)

1st Qual.	(H) v Leamington	L	0-1	230

2004/05 Season: 3rd Round

Best Performance: 5th Round Replay

SUNDERLAND NISSAN

Northern 1 (Step 5)

1st Qual.	(A) v Northallerton Town	W	1-0	64
2nd Qual.	(H) v Whitley Bay	W	4-2	43
	Rice, Sankey, Stewart, Tait			
1st Round	(H) v Abbey Hey	W	1-0	42
	Sankey			
2nd Round	(H) v Bedlington Terriers	D	3-3*	94
	Cogdon, Tait			
Replay	(A) v Bedlington Terriers	L	1-2	
	Cogdon			

2004/05 Season: N/A

Best Performance: 2nd Round 2004-2005

SUTTON TOWN

N.Co. E. Pem. (Step 5)

2nd Qual.	(H) v Nuneaton Griffin	D	0-0*	111
Replay	(A) v Nuneaton Griffin	D	0-0*	160
Sutton won 4-1 on pens.				
1st Round	(A) v Ford Sports Daventry	L	1-2	45
	Brown			

2004/05 Season: 2nd Round

Best Performance: 2nd Round 1989-1990 2004-2005

TADCASTER ALBION

N.Co.E. 1 (Step 6)

1st Qual.	(A) v Parkgate	L	0-2	26

2004/05 Season: 1st Round

Best Performance: 5th Round 1977-1978

TAVISTOCK

South Western (Step 7)

2nd Qual.	(A) v Ottery St Mary	W	5-2	55
	Conday (2), Hadjiyianni, Hobbs, Krac			
1st Round	(H) v Penryn Athletic	W	3-0	90
2nd Round	(H) v Backwell United	W	4-2*	60
	Conday, Gosling, Hobbs, Stringer			
3rd Round	(A) v Deal Town	W	4-2	148
	Conday, Hallett, Steer, Stringer			
4th Round	(A) v Pickering Town	L	0-3	290

2004/05 Season: 2nd Qualifying Round

Best Performance: 4th Round 2005-1006

TEVERSAL

N.Co.E 1 (Step 6)

1st Qual.	(H) v Norton United	D	1-1*	69
	Rhodes			
Replay	(A) v Norton United	L	0-1	60

2004/05 Season: 2nd Qualifying Round

Best Performance: 2nd Qualifying Round2004-2005

THACKLEY

N.Co E Prem. (Step 5)

2nd Round	(H) v Jarrow Roofing	W	3-0	67
	King (2), Reilly			
3rd Round	(H) v Colne	W	2-1	200
	Johnson, Walters			
4th Round	(H) v Arnold Town	L	0-2	216

2004/05 Season: 4th Round

Best Performance: 5th Round 1980-1981

Thackley's Shiz Iqbal is challenged from behind by an Arnold Town player. Photo: Darren Thomas.

THAMESMEAD TOWN

Kent (Step 5)

2nd Qual.	(A) v Lymington Town	W	4-2	115
	Deadman, Kearley, Williams (2)			
1st Round	(A) v Wantage Town	W	3-1	52
	Collins, Knight, Thomas			
2nd Round	(H) v Brook House	L	0-4	63

2004/05 Season: 3rd Round

Best Performance: 5th Round 1995-1996

THATCHAM TOWN

Wessex Prem. (Step 5)

1st Round	(H) v Selsey	W	4-2	108
	Green (2), Parfitt, Witt			
2nd Round	(A) v Hythe Town	L	2-3	130
	Campion, Green			

2004/05 Season: 2nd Qualifying Round

Best Performance: 6th Round 1988-1989

THETFORD TOWN

Eastern 1(Step 6)

2nd Qual.	(H) v Wootton BC	L	1-4	42
	Bray			

2004/05 Season: 2nd Qualifying Round

Best Performance: 4th Round 1990-1991

THORNABY

Northern 1 (Step 5)

2nd Qual.	(A) v Great Harwood Town	W	3-0	86
	Campbell (2), Storr			
1st Round	(A) v Ashington	D	3-3*	151
	Campbell (2), Jameson			
Replay	(H) v Ashington	W	4-3	105
	Jameson, Larkin, Storr (2)			
2nd Round	(A) v Newcastle Benfield	L	1-5	65
	Campbell			

2004/05 Season: 2nd Round

Best Performance: 2nd Round Replay 2002-2003

THREE BRIDGES

Sussex 1 (Step 5)

2nd Qual.	(A) v Worthing United	W	5-0	58
	Chamel, Jones, Pearce, Rhodes (2)			
1st Round	(A) v Merstham	W	2-1	106
	Massaro (2)			
2nd Round	(H) v Arundel	L	0-1	92

2004/05 Season: 2nd Round Replay

Best Performance: 5th Round 1981-1982

TILBURY

Essex(Step 5)

1st Round	(H) v Burnham Ramblers	W	2-1	71
	Dosser (2)			
2nd Round	(A) v Newmarket Town	L	1-2*	93
	Dosser			

2004/05 Season: Competed in FA Trophy.

Best Performance: 4th Roujnd 1988-1989 1999-2000

TIPTON TOWN

Mid Alliance (Step 5)

2nd Round	(H) v Racing Club Warwick	L	0-2	80

2004/05 Season: 5th Round Replay

Best Performance: 5th Round Replay 2004-2005

TIPTREE UNITED

Eastern 1 (Step 6)

1st Qual.	(H) v London APSA	W	2-1	68
	Hill, Rochester			
2nd Qual.	(A) v Biggleswade Town	W	3-1	41
	Coe, Hill, Robinson			
1st Round	(A) v London Colney	L	3-5*	60
	Carmichael, Robinson (2)			

2004/05 Season: 1st Round Replay

Best Performance: FInalists 2001-2002

VCD Athletic's Paul Foley beats Broxbourne's defender Nick Sawkins and 'keeper Will Viner to the ball, but sees his powerful header go just past the post in the 4th round. Photo: Alan Coomes.

TIVIDALE

West Midlands (Step 7)

1st Qual.	(H) v Highgate United	W	4-1		50
2nd Qual.	(H) v Borrowash Victoria	D	1-1*		65
Replay	(A) v Borrowash Victoria	L	0-4		71

2004/05 Season: 2nd Qualifying Round

Best Performance: 4th Round Replay

TORRINGTON

Western Prem. (Step 5)

2nd Qual.	(H) v Turo City	L	0-4		101

2004/05 Season: 2nd Round

Best Performance: 5th Round 1984-1985

TOW LAW TOWN

Northern 1 (Step 5)

1st Qual.	(H) v Trafford	L	1-2		144

2004/05 Season: 2nd Qualifying Round

Best Performance: 6th Round Replay 19971998

TRAFFORD

N.W.Co. (Step 5)

1st Qual.	(A) v Tow Law Town	W	2-1		144
	Carratt				
2nd Qual.	(A) v Durham City	W	4-2		148
	Carratt, Vaughan (3)				
1st Round	(H) v Prudhoe Town	W	1-0		138
2nd Round	(A) v Retford United	L	1-2		249
	Goalscorers				

2004/05 Season: 2nd Qualifying Replay

Best Performance: 5th Round 1995-1996

TRING ATHLETIC

S.S.M. (Step 5)

1st Qual.	(H) v Stotfold	D	1-1*		83
	Meehan				
Replay	(A) v Stotfold	L	0-2		60

2004/05 Season: 2nd Qualifying Round

Best Performance: 2nd Qualifying Round 2004-2005

TRURO CITY

South Western (Step 7)

1st Qual.	(H) v Launceston	W	3-1		109
	Ash, Wolstencroft, Wort				
2nd Qual.	(A) v Torrington	W	4-0		101
	Ash, Bowker, Burchell, Cain				
1st Round	(H) v Witney United	W	3-1		235
	Bowker, Yetton (2)				
2nd Round	(A) v Christchurch	L	2-3		142
	Ash, Yetton				

2004/05 Season: N/A

Best Performance: 2nd Round 2004-2005

TUFFLEY ROVERS

Hellenic Prem.(Step 5)

1st Qual.	(A) v Hamworthy United	withdrawn	

Walkover for Hamworthy.

2004/05 Season: 1st Qualifying Round

Best Performance: 4th Round 1984-1985

TUNBRIDGE WELLS

Kent (Step 5)

1st Qual.	(H) v Moneyfields	D	0-0*		110
Replay	(A) v Moneyfields	L	0-5		96

2004/05 Season: 3rd Round

Best Performance: 4th Round.1974-5 75-76 78-79 84-85 92-93

UNITED SERVICES PORTSMOUTH

Wessex 2 (Step 6)

2nd Qual.	(H) v Sidley United	L	0-2		52

2004/05 Season: 2ndQualifying Round

Best Performance: 2nd Qlalifing Round 2004-2005 2005-2006

VCD ATHLETIC

Kent (Step 5)

1st Qual.	(A) v Oakwood	W	4-1		32
	Abbott, Coburn (3)				
2nd Qual.	(A) v Saltdean United	W	3-0		43
	Foley, Frost, Probets				
1st Round	(A) v Cove	W	2-0		72
	Foley, Turner				
2nd Round	(A) v Colliers Wood	W	3-2		63
	Coburn, Greatorex (2)				
3rd Round	(A) v Arundel	W	2-1		188
	Abbott, Driscoll				
4th Round	(H) v Broxbourne Borough	W	1-0		257
	Penny				
5th Round	(A) v Cammell Laird	L	0-1		283

2004/05 Season: 2nd Round

Best Performance: 5th Round 2005-2006

VT

Wessex 1 (Step 5)

1st Qual.	(H) v Wick	W	4-3	56
		Gary, McClean		
2nd Qual.	(A) v Sevenoaks Town	W	3-2*	65
		Gibbens, Spinney		
1st Round	(H) v Hythe Town	L	1-2	95

2004/05 Season: N/A

Best Performance: 1st Round 2005-2006

WADEBRIDGE TOWN

SouthWestern (Step 7)

1st Qual.	(A) v Odd Down	L	1-2	37
		Cook		

2004/05 Season: 1st Qualifying Round

Best Performance: 3rd Round Replay

WALSHAM LE WILLOWS

Esatern 1 (Step6)

1st Qual.	(A) v Biggleswade United	W	2-1	48
		Newman, Wake		
2nd Qual.	(A) v Newmarket Town	L	1-2	91
		Wake		

2004/05 Season: N/A

Best Performance: 2nd Qualifying Round 2005-2006

WALTHAM ABBEY

Essex (Step 5)

1st Round	(A) v Witham Town	L	3-5	131
		Elems, Sontag		

2004/05 Season 1st Round

Best Performance: 2nd Rd. 1997-1998

WANTAGE TOWN

Hellenic Prem. (Step 5)

1st Qual.	(A) v Farnham Town	W	2-1	36
		Jones (2)		
2nd Qual.	(H) v Ringmer	W	3-2	81
		Day, Giles (2)		
1st Round	(H) v Thamesmead	L	1-3	52
		Day		

2004/05 Season: 2nd Qualifying Round

Best Performance: 3rd Round 1974-1975 1983-1984 1986-1987

WARE

Ryman 2 (Step 5)

1st Qual.	(H) v Newport Pagnell Town	L	1-3	89

2004/05 Season: 2nd Qualifying Round

Best Performance: 4th Round 2002-2003

WASHINGTON

Northern 2 (Step 6)

2nd Qual.	(H) v West Auckland Town	L	1-2*	65
		Burns		

2004/05 Season: 1st Round

Best Performance: 3rd Round 1977-1978

WELLINGTON

West Midlands (Step 7)

2nd Qual.	(A) v Daventry Town	D	0-0*	30
Wellington won 4-2 on pens.				
1st Round	(H) v Alvechurch	L	0-1	122

2004/05 Season: 1st Qualifying Round

Best Performance: 3rd Round 1991-92 2003-2004

WELLINGTON TOWN

Western 1 (Step 6)

1st Qual.	(H) v Calne Town	W	3-1	68
		Gage, Norman, Woon		
2nd Qual.	(H) v Ringwood Town	W	1-0	35
		Piper		
1st Round	(H) v Bemerton Heath H.	L	1-2	45
		Butler		

2004/05 Season: 1st Round

Best Performance: 2nd Round 1998-1999

WELTON ROVERS

Wesstern Premier (Step 5)

2nd Qual.	(H) v Sherbourne Town	W	5-0	72
		Kington, Riccio (2),		
		Simpson, Stewart		
1st Round	(H) v Willand Rovers	L	2-3	88
		Hughes		

2004/05 Season: 2nd Round

Best Performance: 4th Round 1988-1989 21991-1992

WELWYN GARDEN CITY

S.S.M (Step 5)

1st Qual.	(A) v Haverhill Rovers	W	4-2	139
		Devera, Mehmet (2), Wardle		
2nd Qual.	(A) v Rothwell Corinthians	W	3-1	49
		Brindley (2), Edgerley		
1st Round	(A) v Oxford City	W	3-1	162
		Collins, Garness, Wardle		
2nd Round	(A) v Concord Rangers	W	2-1*	61
		Pritchard, Yates		
3rd Round	(H) v Slimbridge	W	3-1	93
		Devera, Wardle (2)		
4th Round	(A) v Newmarket Town	D	2-2*	284
		Kinsley, Seller		
Replay	(H) v Newmarket Town	W	2-1*	353
		Kinsley, Medley		

(tie awarded to Newmarket - Welwyn Garden City removed for playing ineligible player)

2004/05 Season: 1st Qualifying Round

Best Performance: 2nd Rd 2nd Replay 1974-1975

WEMBLEY

Isthmian 2 (Step 5

2nd Qual.	(H) v Needham Market	L	0-4	56

2004/05 Season: 2nd Quallifying Round

Best Performance: 3rd Round 1999-2000

WEST ALLOTMENT CELTIC

Northern 1 (Step 5)

2nd Round	(A) v Skelmersdale United	L	3-4	141
		Hay, Potts, Rasmussen		

2004/05 Season: 4th Round

Best Performance: 4th Round 2003-2004 2004-2005

WEST AUCKLAND TOWN

Northern 1 (Step 5)

2nd Qual.	(A) v Washington	W	2-1*	81
		Maddison, Reid		
1st Round	(H) v Billingham Synthonia	L	0-2	88

2004/05 Season: 1st Qualifying Round

Best Performance: 4th Round 1997-98 2001-2002

WESTBURY UNITED

Western 1 (Step 6)

1st Qual.	(H) v Shaftesbury	W	4-0	86
		Billett, Wheeler (3)		
2nd Qual.	(A) v Pewsey Vale	L	0-1	63

2004/05 Season: 1st Round

Best Performance: 3rd Round 1977-1978 1994-95 2003-04

WESTFIELD

Co.Co. (Step 5)

1st Qual.	(H) v Hungerford Town	L	0-2	45

2004/05 Season: 2nd Qualifying Round

Best Performance: 4th Round 2000-2001

WESTFIELDS

Mid Alliance (Step 5)

1st Qual.	(H) v Stratford Town	W	2-1	76
	Burton, Jackson			
2nd Qual.	(H) v Pegasus Juniors	W	3-0	202
	Davis (2), Hibbard			
1st Round	(H) v Bridgnorth Town	W	1-0	64
2nd Round	(A) v Selby Town	D	3-3*	65
	Davis (2), Hibbard			
Replay	(H) v Selby Town	W	3-2*	28
	Davis, Jordan			

2004/05 Season: 1st Round

Best Performance: 3rd Round 1986-1987

WHICKHAM

Northrn 2 (Step 6)

2nd Qual.	(H) v Chadderton	W	5-1	68
	Brodie (2), Elliot, Robson (2)			
1st Round	(A) v Newcastle Benfield	L	1-3	97

2004/05 Season: 1st Round

Best Performance: Winners 1980-1981

WHITEHAWK

Sussex 1 (Step 5)

1st Round	(A) v Erith Town	L	0-2	30

2004/05 Season: 1st Round

Best Performance: 5th Round 1993-1994

WHITLEY BAY

Northern 1 (Step 5)

2nd Qual.	(A) v Sunderland Nissan	L	2-4	43
	Kerr, Robinson			

2004/05 Season: 2nd Round

Best Performance: Winners 2001-2002

WHITSTABLE TOWN

Kent (Step 5)

1st Round	(H) v Andover	L	1-3	180
	Perona			

2004/05 Season: 1st Round

Best Performance: 5th Round 1996-1997

WHITTON UNITED

Esatern 1(Step 6

1st Qual.	(A) v Royston United	D	0-0*	81
Replay	(H) v Royston United	L	0-2	79

2004/05 Season: 1st Round

Best Performance: 1st Round 1996-97 97-98 99-00 2004-05

WICK

Sussex 1 (Step 5)

1st Qual.	(A) v VT	L	3-4	56
	Burton, Christodoulou, Howard			

2004/05 Season: 1st Round

Best Performance:4th Rd 1998-99

WILLAND ROVERS

Western Prem. (Step 5)

2nd Qual.	(H) v Elmore	W	4-1	112
	Ansell, Ebdy, Jee, Steele			
1st Round	(A) v Welton Rovers	W	3-2	88
	Ebdy (2), Shore			
2nd Round	(A) v Ledbury Town	W	4-0	72
	Ebdy, Everett (2), Steele			
3rd Round	(A) v Newmarket Town	L	0-1	105

2004/05 Season: 1st Round Replay

Best Performance:3rd Round 2002-2003

WILLINGTON

Wearside (Step 7)

2nd Qual.	(H) v Darwen	L	2-4	56
	Bussey, Pickering			

2004/05 Season: 2nd Qualifying Round

Best Performance: 3rd Round 1994-1995

WIMBORNE TOWN

Wesex 1e (Step 5)

2nd Qual.	(H) v Shepton Mallet	W	3-0	213
	Clements (3)			
1st Round	(H) v Radstock Town	W	3-1	244
	Cannie, Oldbury, Roast			
2nd Round	(A) v Highworth Town	W	1-0	138
	Arnold			
3rd Round	(H) v Bishop's Cleeve	W	4-1	287
	Arnold (2), Rideout (2)			
4th Round	(A) v Leamington	W	3-2	746
	Percival, Rideout, Roast			
5th Round	(H) v Pickering Town	L	1-2	983
	Percival.			

2004/05 Season: 2nd Round

Best Performance: Winners 1991-1992

Shaun Dyke (No.7) heads past Hythe Town goalkeeper, Kevin Readings, for Winchester City's first goal during this 4th Round tie. Photo: Roger Turner.

WINCHESTER CITY
Wessex Prem. (Step 5)

2nd Round	(H)	v AFC Newbury	W	5-0	184
			Green, Jones, Kneller,		
			Mancey (2)		
3rd Round	(A)	v Yaxley	W	4-2	212
			Buckman, Maceey,		
			Mancey, Wakefield		
4th Round	(A)	v Hythe Town	W	3-1	441
			Dyke, Musselwhite (2)		
5th Round	(H)	v Newmarket Town	L	3-4*	581
			Mancey, Keneller, Green.		

2004/05 Season: 4th Round

Best Performance: Winners 2003-2004

WINSFORD UNITED
N.W.Co.2 (Step 6)

2nd Qual.	(H)	v Padiham	W	2-1*	97
			Hanley, Stanton		
1st Round	(A)	v Crook Town	L	0-2	106

2004/05 Season: 2nd Qualifying Round

Best Performance: 2nd Round 2001-2002

WINTERTON RANGERS
N.Co.East 1 (Step 6)

1st Qual.	(H)	v Guisborough Town	W	3-1	70
			Barnwell, Northern,		
			Whitehouse		
2nd Qual.	(A)	v Oldham Town	L	1-3	45
			Whitehouse		

2004/05 Season: 1st Qualifying Round

Best Performance: 6th Round 1976-1977

WISBECH TOWN
Eastern Prem. (Step 5)

2nd Qual.	(A)	v Dunstable Town 98	W	7-1	101
			Cubberley, Dunn (3), Edey,		
			Harrold, Nimmo		
1st Round	(A)	v AFC Wallingford	W	4-1	99
			Appleby, Cubberley,		
			Harris, Harold		
2nd Round	(H)	v Leiston	W	8-1	330
			Appleby, Harris, Harold,		
			Jimson (2), Nimmo (2)		
3rd Round	(H)	v Brook House	D	4-4*	371
			Dunn, Cubberley, Nimmo (2)		
Replay	(A)	v Brook House	L	0-2	155

2004/05 Season: 1st Qualifying Round

Best Performance: 1984-1985 replay 1985-1986

WITHAM TOWN
Isthmian 2 (Step 5)

1st Qual.	(A)	v Harefield United	W	3-2	71
			Bennett (3)		
2nd Qual.	(A)	v St Neots Town	D	0-0*	124
Replay	(H)	v St Neots Town	W	4-2	96
			Budge (3), Hawes		
1st Round	(H)	v Waltham Abbey	W	5-3	131
			Bennett (2), McDonald (3)		
2nd Round	(A)	v Yaxley	L	0-3	126

2004/05 Season: 1st Round

Best Performance: 5th Round 1986-1987

WITNEY UNITED
Hellenic Premier (Step 5)

2nd Qual.	(A)	v Budleigh Salterton	W	6-0	86
			Butler, Cook, Keyes (3),		
			McMahon		
1st Round	(A)	v Truro City	L	1-3	235
			Keyes		

2004/05 Season: 2nd Round

Best Performance: 2nd Round 2005-2006

WOLVERHAMPTON CASUALS
West Mids (Step 6)

2nd Qual.	(A)	v South Normanton Ath.	L	1-2	39
			Butler		

2004/05 Season: N/A

Best Performance: 1st Round 1989-1990

WOODBRIDGE TOWN
Eastern Prem. (Step 5)

1st Qual.	(H)	v Harwich & Parkeston	W	4-2	84
			Berry, Francis (2), Snell		
2nd Qual.	(H)	v Raunds Town	L	1-4	71
			Goddard		

2004/05 Season: 2nd Qualifying Round

Best Performance: 5th Round 1998-99 1999-2000

WOODFORD UNITED
Utd.Co. Prem. (Step 5)

2nd Qual.	(A)	v St Ives Town	W	2-0	43
			Dunkley, Milner		
1st Round	(H)	v Broxbourne Borough	L	3-4	48
			Dunkley, Gordon, Milner		

2004/05 Season: 3rd Round

Best Performance: 3rd Round 2004-2005

WOOTTON BASSETT TOWN
H.Jellenic 1W (Step 6)

2nd Round	(H)	v Christchurch	D	1-1*	65
			Bennett		
Replay	(A)	v Christchurch	L	0-1	81

2004/05 Season: 1st Qualifying Round

Best Performance: 1st Round 2001-2002

WOOTTON BLUE CROSS
Utd Co. P (Step 5)

1st Qual.	(H)	v Stansted	W	2-0	41
			Joswiak, Smith		
2nd Qual.	(A)	v Thetford Town	W	4-1	42
			Deverell, Joswaik, Snaylam (2)		
1st Round	(H)	v Royston Town	W	2-1	64
			Gentle, Joswiak		
2nd Round	(A)	v Lowestoft Town	L	0-2	240

2004/05 Season: 2nd Qualifying Round

Best Performance: 4th Round 2002-2003

WORSBROUGH BRIDGE MW
N.Co.E. 1 (Step 6)

2nd Qual.	(A)	v Consett	L	0-5	87

2004/05 Season: 1st Qualifying Round

Best Performance: 3rd Round 1990-1991

WORTHING UNITED
Sussex 1 (Step 5)

2nd Qual.	(H)	v Three Bridges	L	0-5	58

2004/05 Season: N/A

Best Performance: 3rd Round 1991-1992

WROXHAM
Eastern Prem. (Step 5)

1st Qual.	(A)	v Southall	W	3-2	50
			Howes, Johnson, Tjirimuje		
2nd Qual.	(A)	v Yaxley	L	0-2	126

2004/05 Season: 3rd Round

Best Performance: 6th Round 2001-2002

YAXLEY
Utd.Co. Prem.(Step 5)

1st Qual.	(A)	v Hoddesdon Town	W	1-0	68
			Hailstone		
2nd Qual.	(A)	v Wroxham	W	2-0	126
			Acton, Paul		
1st Round	(H)	v Southend Manor	W	8-1	93
			Challinorr (2), Gospel,		
			Paul (3), Picillo		
2nd Round	(H)	v Witham Town	W	3-0	126
			Hailstone (2), Lenton		
3rd Round	(H)	v Winchester City	L	2-4	212
			Paul, Picillo		

2004/05 Season: 2nd Qualifying Replay

Best Performance: 3rd Round 2002-2003 2005-2006

YORKSHIRE AMATEUR
N.Co.E 1 (Step 6)

1st Qual.	(H)	v Newcastle Blue Star	L	0-3	48

2004/05 Season: 2nd Round Replay

Best Performance: 2nd Round Replay 2004-2005

ROUND BY ROUND

FIRST QUALIFYING ROUND

BIGGEST HOME WIN:	5-0 FAIRFORD TOWN VS PORTLAND UTD.
	MONEYFIELDS VS TUNBRIDGE WELLS (REPLAY)
BIGGEST AWAY WIN:	0-6 ARMTHORPE WELFARE VS EASINGTON COL.
HIGHEST ATTENDANCE:	290 MAIDSTONE UNITED VS COWES SPORTS
NUMBER OF GAMES:	104* + 8 *INCLUDES TWO WALKOVERS (74 + 5)
TOTAL ATTENDANCE:	8,382 (5,959)
AVERAGE ATTENDANCE:	75 (75)

Home		Away	Score	Att
AFC Totton	v	Mole Valley (Predators)	3-1	87
Amesbury Town	v	Bishop Sutton	0-1	48
Atherstone Town	v	Ludlow Town	4-2	184
Bedfont	v	Littlehampton Town	1-2	47
Bedfont Green	v	Ash United	1-1*	37
Bedford United & Valerio	v	Basildon United	0-4	15
Biddulph Victoria	v	Brierley & Hagley	3-0	60
Biggleswade United	v	Walsham Le Willows	1-2	48
Blaby & Whetstone Ath.	v	Loughborough Dynamo	3-1	88
Blackstones	v	Dunkirk	1-0	41
Bolehall Swifts	v	Buxton	1-5	91
Boston Town	v	Nuneaton Griff	0-2	70
Bourne Town	v	Shirebrook Town	1-2	68
Brandon United	v	Bottesford Town	4-3	54
Brimsdown Rovers	v	Biggleswade Town	1-2	60
Buckingham Town	v	Barkingside	3-1	92
Budleigh Salterton	v	Falmouth Town	1-1*	91
Camberley Town	v	Godalming Town	2-4	51
Causeway United	v	Graham St Prims	2-0	75
Chichester City United	v	Colliers Wood United	2-2*	70
Cobham	v	Sevenoaks Town	0-2	23
Curzon Ashton	v	Newcastle Benfield (Bay Plastics)	0-1	87
Deeping Rangers	v	Stapenhill	2-1	63
Downton	v	Street	1-2	77
Durham City	v	Eccleshill United	1-0	135
Easington Colliery	v	Armthorpe Welfare	0-6	39
East Preston	v	Redhill	4-1	41
Eastbourne United	v	Mile Oak	1-3	65
Ellistown	v	Castle Vale	1-4	30
Epsom & Ewell	v	Petersfield Town	3-1	57
Esh Winning	v	Flixton	0-1*	53
Exmouth Town	v	St Blazey	1-4*	125
Fairford Town	v	Portland United	5-0	48
Fareham Town	v	Ringmer	0-1	101
Farnham Town	v	Wantage Town	1-2	36
Flackwell Heath	v	Gorleston	1-2	65
Friar Lane & Epworth	v	Holwell Sports	5-1	91
Gedling MW	v	Alvechurch	1-2*	56
Glasshoughton Welfare	v	Chester-Le-Street Town	2-0	60
Godmanchester Rovers	v	St Neots Town	1-2	85
Greenwich Borough	v	Chertsey Town	2-0	56
Hall Road Rangers	v	Morpeth Town	3-5	55
Hallam	v	Padiham	1-2	40
Hamworthy United	v	Tuffley Rovers		
(walkover for Hamworthy United - Tuffley Rovers withdrawn)				
Harefield United	v	Witham Town	2-3	71
Harpenden Town	v	AFC Wallingford	1-2*	46
Harrow Hill	v	Penryn Athletic	2-3	45
Hartley Wintney	v	Alton Town	1-0	55
Haverhill Rovers	v	Welwyn Garden City	2-4	139
Hertford Town	v	Dereham Town	1-2	99
Hoddesdon Town	v	Yaxley	0-1	68
Horden CW	v	Bacup Borough	2-3	48
Hullbridge Sports	v	Cornard United	3-1	25
Huntingdon Town	v	St Margaretsbury	1-3*	53
Ipswich Wanderers	v	Bowers & Pitsea	2-0	67
Kingsbury Town	v	Saffron Walden Town	3-1	38
Kirby Muxloe	v	Sandiacre Town	2-2*	48
Leek CSOB	v	Gornal Athletic	2-0	87
Leiston	v	Ruislip Manor	3-1	122
Lincoln Moorlands	v	Nettleham	4-1	90
London Colney	v	Eynesbury Rovers	4-1	40
Lymington Town	v	Sidlesham	3-0	102
Maidstone United	v	Cowes Sports	4-2	290
Malvern Town	v	Long Eaton United	4-2	99
Mickleover Sports	v	Pershore Town	1-2	84
North Shields	v	Cammell Laird	1-4	121
Northallerton Town	v	Sunderland Nissan	0-1	64
Northampton Spencer	v	Cranfield United	3-0	68
Oakwood	v	VCD Athletic	1-4	32
Odd Down	v	Wadebridge Town	2-1	37

Cornard 'keeper, Darren Moyes, makes a point blank save from Scott Wheeler of Hullbridge Sports (stripes). Photo: Alan Coomes.

Pagham	v Hythe Town	2-6	55
Parkgate	v Tadcaster Albion	2-0	26
Penrith	v Clipstone Welfare	3-0	73
Peterlee Newtown	v Retford United	2-6	66
Pilkington XXX	v Pegasus Juniors	3-6	66
Pontefract Collieries	v Garforth Town	3-2	82
Racing Club Warwick	v Eccleshall	1-0	45
Radstock Town	v Barnstaple Town	3-1	79
Ramsbottom United	v Squires Gate	1-3	151
Royston Town	v Whitton United	0-0*	79
Ryton	v Crook Town	1-2	61
Sawbridgeworth Town	v Long Buckby	2-0	39
Seaham Red Star	v Shotton Comrades		
(walkover for Seaham Red Star - Shotton Comrades withdrawn)			
Shifnal Town	v Coventry Copsewood	4-0	73
Slimbridge	v Chipping Norton Town	3-0	60
Southall	v Wroxham	2-3	50
St Andrews	v Rolls Royce Leisure	3-1	23
Stowmarket Town	v Needham Market	0-5	188
Studley	v Leamington	0-1	230
Teversal	v Norton United	1-1*	69
Tiptree United	v London APSA	2-1	68
Tividale	v Highgate United	4-1	50
Tow Law Town	v Trafford	1-2	144
Tring Athletic	v Stotfold	1-1*	83
Truro City	v Launceston	3-1	109
Tunbridge Wells	v Moneyfields	0-0*	110
VT	v Wick	4-3	56
Ware	v Newport Pagnell Town	1-3	89
Wellington Town	v Calne Town	3-1	68
Westbury United	v Shaftesbury	4-0	86
Westfield	v Hungerford Town	0-2	45
Westfields	v Stratford Town	2-1*	76
Winterton Rangers	v Guisborough Town	3-1	70
Woodbridge Town	v Harwich & Parkeston	4-2	84
Wootton Blue Cross	v Stansted	2-0	41
Yorkshire Amateur	v Newcastle Blue Star	0-3	48

REPLAYS

Ash United	v Bedfont Green	4-0	106
Colliers Wood United	v Chichester City United	2-1	30
Falmouth Town	v Budleigh Salterton	0-1	169
Moneyfields	v Tunbridge Wells	5-0	86
Norton United	v Teversal	1-0	58
Sandiacre Town	v Kirby Muxloe	1-2	78
Stotfold	v Tring Athletic	2-0	60
Whitton United	v Royston Town	0-2	73

SECOND ROUND QUALIFYING

BIGGEST HOME WIN:	**7-1** GLASSHOUGHTON VS ROSSINGTON MAIN
BIGGEST AWAY WIN:	**1-7** DUNSTABLE TOWN 98 VS WISBECH TOWN
	0-6 WITNEY UNITED VS BUDLEIGH SALTERTON
HIGHEST ATTENDANCE:	**324** EASTBOURNE TOWN VS MAIDSTONE UNITED
NUMBER OF GAMES:	**159* + 12** *INCLUDES TWO WALKOVERS (117 + 10)
TOTAL ATTENDANCE:	**14,065** (14,250)
AVERAGE ATTENDANCE:	**82** (112)

Abbey Hey	v Formby	6-1
Abingdon United	v Sandhurst Town	4-1
AFC Kempston Rovers	v Colney Heath	0-3
AFC Wallingford	v March Town United	1-0
Almondsbury Town	v Dawlish Town	0-1
Alsager Town	v Newcastle Benfield (Bay Plastics)	2-4*
Ardley United	v Carterton	1-3
Arlesey Athletic	v Concord Rangers	3-5*
Arundel	v Frimley Green	5-1
Atherton LR	v Marske United	1-1*

Maidstone's Lynden Rowland fires in a shot past Andover's Bobby Swayne. Photo: Alan Coomes.

Barnt Green Spartak	v Coleshill Town	2-4
Barrow Town	v Congleton Town	3-2*
Barwell	v Leek CSOB	3-2
Basildon United	v Buckingham Athletic	2-1
Bicester Town	v Buckingham Town	2-0
Biggleswade Town	v Tiptree United	1-3
Bishop Sutton	v Hallen	0-2
Blaby & Whetstone Ath	v Heanor Town	2-5
Blackfield & Langley	v Abingdon Town	4-5
Blackstones	v Racing Club Warwick	1-2
Blackwell MW	v Shirebrook Town	0-3
Boldmere St Michaels	v Meir KA	4-2
Bristol Manor Farm	v Minehead	2-1
Brodsworth MW	v Blackpool Mechanics	2-0
Bromyard Town	v Heath Hayes	2-1
Broxbourne Borough V&E	v St Margaretsbury	2-1
Budleigh Salterton	v Witney United	0-6
Bugbrooke St Michaels	v Long Melford	0-4
Buxton	v Lincoln Moorlands	2-1
Cammell Laird	v Atherton Collieries	4-0
Carlton Town	v Holbrook Miners Welfare	2-1
Causeway United	v Kirby Muxloe	2-3*
Chard Town	v Melksham Town	4-1
Cheadle Town	v Armthorpe Welfare	2-4
Chipstead	v Brockenhurst	1-2
Clapton	v Haringey Borough	1-2
Cockfosters	v Holmer Green	4-1
Colliers Wood United	v Raynes Park Vale	3-0
Consett	v Worsborough Bridge MW	5-0
Cradley Town	v Lye Town	2-1
Daventry Town	v Wellington	0-0*
(Wellington won 4-2 on kicks from the penalty mark)		
Devizes Town	v Penzance	1-0
Downham Town	v Leverstock Green	1-1*
Dudley Town	v Anstey Nomads	1-0
Dunstable Town 98	v Wisbech Town	1-7
Durham City	v Trafford	2-4
East Grinstead Town	v Lancing	3-1
Eastbourne Town	v Maidstone United	0-3
Epsom & Ewell	v Milton United	3-0
Erith Town	v Andover New Street	3-2
Eton Manor	v Kingsbury Town	1-4
Fairford Town	v Radstock Town	1-2*
Fakenham Town	v Newport Pagnell Town	0-4

Ford Sports Daventry	v Atherstone Town	1-0
Glasshoughton Welfare	v Rossington Main	7-1
Glossop North End	v Staveley MW	3-2*
Gosport Borough	v Greenwich Borough	0-1*
Great Harwood Town	v Thornaby	0-3
Great Yarmouth Town	v Stanway Rovers	0-1
Guildford United	v Andover	1-5
Hailsham Town	v Cove	2-5
Hamble ASSC	v Steyning Town	4-0
Hartley Wintney	v Hungerford Town	1-1*
Hassocks	v Ash United	3-1
Hebburn Town	v Prudhoe Town	0-2
Henley Town	v Ely City	3-2
Highfield Rangers	v Downes Sports	2-1*
Hullbridge Sports	v Clacton Town	4-0
Hythe Town	v Moneyfields	2-1
Ibstock United	v Arnold Town	0-1
Ilfracombe Town	v Bournemouth	2-4
Kimberley Town	v Alvechurch	1-4
Kirkley	v Dereham Town	0-2
Langford	v Leiston	0-3
Larkhall Athletic	v Poole Town	1-4
Leamington	v Radcliffe Olympic	
(walkover for Leamington - Radcliffe Olympic withdrawn)		
Liskeard Athletic	v Bemerton Heath Harlequins	1-4
Littlehampton Town	v Hillingdon Borough	1-1*
Liversedge	v Bacup Borough	1-0
London Colney	v Hadleigh United	2-1
Lymington Town	v Thamesmead Town	2-4
Maine Road	v Daisy Hill	2-3*
Malmesbury Victoria	v Slimbridge	0-2
Malvern Town	v Castle Vale	1-3
Merstham	v Reading Town	4-0
Mildenhall Town	v Diss Town	4-0
Mile Oak	v BAT Sports	2-0
Millbrook	v Newton Abbot	2-3
Morpeth Town	v Salford City	1-1*
Nelson	v Flixton	3-2
New Mills	v Penrith	1-2
Newark Town	v Coventry Sphinx	4-2*
Newcastle Blue Star	v Seaham Red Star	1-2
(at Seaham Red Star FC)		
Newmarket Town	v Walsham Le Willows	2-1
Newquay	v Street	1-2
North Leigh	v Horley Town	2-0
Northampton Spencer	v Ipswich Wanderers	1-3
Norton & Stockton Ancients	v Sheffield	2-0
Norton United	v Oldbury United	1-1*
Oadby Town	v Friar Lane & Epworth	1-3*
Odd Down	v Bridport	3-0
Oldham Town	v Winterton Rangers	3-1
Ottery St Mary	v Tavistock	2-5
Peacehaven & Telscombe	v Godalming Town	1-4*
Penryn Athletic	v Hamworthy United	2-1*
Pershore Town	v Bridgnorth Town	0-2
Pewsey Vale	v Westbury United	1-0
Pontefract Collieries	v Darlington Railway Athletic	2-3
Porthleven	v St Blazey	0-3
Poulton Victoria	v Parkgate	1-3
Radford	v Pelsall Villa	1-2
Rainworth MW	v Deeping Rangers	0-1
Retford United	v Holker Old Boys	4-2
Romford	v Oxhey Jets	2-0
Romulus	v Birstall United	5-0

Rothwell Corinthians	v Welwyn Garden City	1-3
Royston Town	v Norwich United	1-0
Saltash United	v Clevedon United	1-2*
Saltdean United	v VCD Athletic	0-3
Sawbridgeworth Town	v Chalfont St Peter	1-3
Selsey	v Lordswood	2-2*
Sevenoaks Town	v VT	2-3*
Shawbury United	v Glapwell	0-4
Shifnal Town	v Nantwich Town	0-1
Shildon	v Alnwick Town	1-1*
Shoreham	v AFC Totton	6-2
Shortwood United	v Cullompton Rangers	5-0
Silsden	v Ashville	1-3
Slade Green	v East Preston	2-1
South Normanton Ath.	v Wolverhampton Casuals	2-1
South Shields	v Ashington	1-3
Southend Manor	v Brentwood Town	3-0
Spennymoor Town	v Crook Town	1-4
Sporting Bengal United	v Felixstowe & Walton United	1-4
Squires Gate	v Brandon United	2-1
St Andrews	v Blidworth Welfare	5-1
St Ives Town	v Woodford United	0-2
(at Woodford United FC)		
St Neots Town	v Witham Town	0-0*
Stone Dominoes	v Biddulph Victoria	
(walkover for Biddulph Victoria - Stone Dominoes withdrawn)		
Stotfold	v Gorleston	1-4
Sunderland Nissan	v Whitley Bay	4-2
Sutton Town	v Nuneaton Griff	0-0*
Thetford Town	v Wootton Blue Cross	1-4
Tividale	v Borrowash Victoria	1-1*
Torrington	v Truro City	0-4
United Services Portsmouth	v Sidley United	0-2
Wantage Town	v Ringmer	3-2
Washington	v West Auckland Town	1-2*
Wellington Town	v Ringwood Town	1-0
Welton Rovers	v Sherbourne Town	5-0
Wembley	v Needham Market	0-4
Westfields	v Pegasus Juniors	3-0
Whickham	v Chadderton	5-1
Willand Rovers	v Elmore	4-1
Willington	v Darwen	2-4
Wimborne Town	v Shepton Mallet	3-0
Winsford United	v Padiham	2-1*
Woodbridge Town	v Raunds Town	1-4
Wootton Bassett Town	v Christchurch	1-1*
Worthing United	v Three Bridges	0-5
Wroxham	v Yaxley	0-2

REPLAYS

Alnwick Town	v Shildon	5-2
Borrowash Victoria	v Tividale	4-0
Christchurch	v Wootton Bassett Town	1-0
Hillingdon Borough	v Littlehampton Town	3-1
Hungerford Town	v Hartley Wintney	2-1
Leverstock Green	v Downham Town	5-1
Lordswood	v Selsey	0-2
Marske United	v Atherton LR	4-2
Nuneaton Griff	v Sutton Town	0-0*
(Sutton Town won 4-1 on penalties)		
Oldbury United	v Norton United	2-0
Salford City	v Morpeth Town	5-0
Witham Town	v St Neots Town	4-2

THE F.A. VASE

1ST ROUND PROPER

BIGGEST HOME WIN:	**8-1** YAXLEY VS SOUTHEND MANOR.	
	7-0 COALVILLE TOWN VS DUDLEY TOWN	
BIGGEST AWAY WIN:	**0-8** MILDENHALL TOWN VS HULLBRIDGE SPORTS	
HIGHEST ATTENDANCE:	**290** DARLINGTON R. ATH VS MAIDSTONE UTD (REPLAY)	
NUMBER OF GAMES:	**98 + 6** (101 + 5)	
TOTAL ATTENDANCE:	**11,359** (10,710)	
AVERAGE ATTENDANCE:	**109** (101)	

Abingdon Town	v Egham Town	0-2	84
AFC Wallingford	v Wisbech Town	1-4	99
Alnwick Town	v Glasshoughton Welfare	1-3	66
Armthorpe Welfare	v Norton & Stockton Ancients	0-1	52
Arundel	v Croydon	4-2	103
Ashington	v Thornaby	3-3*	151
Ashville	v Penrith	3-1*	130
Aylesbury Vale	v Bicester Town	1-2	89
Barrow Town	v Borrowash Victoria	4-3*	130
Biddulph Victoria	v Castle Vale	2-1	76
Bournemouth	v Odd Down	4-1	69
Bristol Manor Farm	v Highworth Town	2-3	43
Brockenhurst	v Abingdon United	2-1	51
Bromyard Town	v Chasetown	0-1	72
Carterton	v Hungerford Town	1-0	42
Chard Town	v Dawlish Town	1-1*	89
Chessington & Hook United	v Horsham YMCA	1-0	101
Clevedon United	v St Blazey	2-4*	194
Coalville Town	v Dudley Town	7-0	160
Cockfosters	v Ipswich Wanderers	0-3	91
Cogenhoe United	v AFC Hornchurch	0-1	180
Concord Rangers	v Halstead Town	2-0*	51
Consett	v Cammell Laird	0-1	176
Cove	v VCD Athletic	0-2	72
Cradley Town	v Newark Town	4-2	53

Greenwich Borough 'keeper, Michael Holder, punches clear against Colliers Wood. Photo: Alan Coomes.

Crook Town	v Winsford United	2-0	106
Daisy Hill	v Nelson	0-1	46
Darlington Railway Athletic	v Dunston FB	2-2*	290
Darwen	v Harrogate Railway	2-4	102
Deeping Rangers	v Buxton	0-4	165
Devizes Town	v Pewsey Vale	0-0*	164
Dorking	v Hamble ASSC	4-1	131
East Grinstead Town	v Rye Iden United	3-5	95
Erith & Belvedere	v Hillingdon Borough	1-5	82
Erith Town	v Whitehawk	2-0	30
Felixstowe & Walton Utd	v Chalfont St Peter	3-3*	134
Ford Sports Daventry	v Sutton Town	2-1	45
Friar Lane & Epworth	v Shirebrook Town	5-1	229
Glossop North End	v Romulus	6-4	118
Godalming Town	v Hassocks	1-4	102
Gorleston	v Raunds Town	1-0	106
Greenwich Borough	v Colliers Wood United	1-3	67
Hallen	v Slimbridge	0-1	49
Hanwell Town	v Colney Heath	4-1	53
Heanor Town	v Arnold Town	0-2	190
Herne Bay	v Epsom & Ewell	4-2*	145
Highfield Rangers	v St Andrews	2-0	48
Holbeach United	v Leamington	0-2	269
Hullbridge Sports	v Mildenhall Town	0-8	74
Kingsbury Town	v Haringey Borough	2-0	28
Kirby Muxloe	v Pelsall Villa	0-2	72
Leiston	v Henley Town	3-2	133
Leverstock Green	v North Greenford United	3-1	56
London Colney	v Tiptree United	5-3*	60
Long Melford	v Newmarket Town	1-2	97
Marske United	v St Helens Town	2-3	138
Merstham	v Three Bridges	1-2	106
Mile Oak	v Slade Green	0-0*	72
Nantwich Town	v Boldmere St Michaels	1-0	123
Needham Market	v Dereham Town	1-0	122
Newcastle Benfield (Bay Plastics)	v Whickham	3-1	97
Newcastle Town	v Glapwell	3-2	101
Newport Pagnell Town	v Romford	0-1	235
Newton Abbot	v Corsham Town	1-0	106
North Leigh	v Maidstone United	0-4	276
Oldbury United	v Coleshill Town	0-4	56
Oldham Town	v Seaham Red Star	3-1	40
Oxford City	v Welwyn Garden City	1-3	162
Parkgate	v Liversedge	3-3*	72
Poole Town	v Bideford	1-2	226
Racing Club Warwick	v Barwell	1-0	131
Retford United	v Brodsworth MW	4-0	180
Rocester	v Carlton Town	0-2	66
Selby Town	v South Normanton Athletic	3-1	85
Shortwood United	v Bishop's Cleeve	0-3	70
Sidley United	v Shoreham	3-0	97
Squires Gate	v Salford City	3-0	66
Stanway Rovers	v Basildon United	4-3	75
Street	v Christchurch	0-2	78
Sunderland Nissan	v Abbey Hey	1-0	42
Tavistock	v Penryn Athletic	3-0	90
Thatcham Town	v Selsey	4-2*	108
Tilbury	v Burnham Ramblers	2-1	71
Trafford	v Prudhoe Town	1-0	138
Truro City	v Witney United	3-1	235
VT	v Hythe Town	1-2	95
Wantage Town	v Thamesmead Town	1-3	52
Wellington	v Alvechurch	0-1	122

976

Home	Away	Score	Att
Wellington Town	v Bemerton Heath Harlequins	1-2	45
Welton Rovers	v Willand Rovers	2-3*	88
West Auckland Town	v Billingham Synthonia	0-2	88
Westfields	v Bridgnorth Town	1-0	64
Whitstable Town	v Andover	1-3	180
Wimborne Town	v Radstock Town	3-1	244
Witham Town	v Waltham Abbey	5-3	131
Woodford United	v Broxbourne Borough V&E	3-4	48
Wootton Blue Cross	v Royston Town	2-1	64
Yaxley	v Southend Manor	8-1	93

REPLAYS

Home	Away	Score	Att
Chalfont St Peter	v Felixstowe & Walton United	2-1	43
Dawlish Town	v Chard Town	3-2*	77

(1/11 tie abandoned after 70 mins due to waterlogged pitch, 5-0)

Home	Away	Score	Att
Dunston FB	v Darlington Railway Athletic	3-0	167
Liversedge	v Parkgate	3-0	117
Pewsey Vale	v Devizes Town	1-1*	142

(Devizes Town won 3-0 on kicks from the penalty mark)

Home	Away	Score	Att
Slade Green	v Mile Oak	1-4	67
Thornaby	v Ashington	4-3	105

SECOND ROUND PROPER

BIGGEST HOME WIN:	8-1 WISBECH TOWN VS LEISTON.
	7-0 DIDCOT TOWN VS HERNE BAY.
BIGGEST AWAY WIN:	1-5 FRIAR LANE & EPWORTH VS STOURBRIDGE
0-4 BROOK HOUSE VS THAMESMEAD TOWN, WILLAND ROVERS VS LEDBURY T.	
HIGHEST ATTENDANCE:	468 AFC HORNCHURCH VS SOHAM TOWN.
NUMBER OF GAMES:	64 + 6 (64 + 8)
TOTAL ATTENDANCE:	9,275 (9,483)
AVERAGE ATTENDANCE:	132 (132)

Home	Away	Score	Att
AFC Hornchurch	v Soham Town Rangers	1-3	469
AFC Sudbury	v Romford	4-0	331
Arnold Town	v Pelsall Villa	2-0	108
Barrow Town	v Quorn	1-3	420
Bemerton Heath Harlequins	v St Blazey	2-3	134
Bicester Town	v Dorking	0-1	52
Biddulph Victoria	v Leamington	1-2	86
Bishop's Cleeve	v Newton Abbot	3-0	65

(19/11 tie abandoned after 48 mins due to fog, 1-0)

Home	Away	Score	Att
Bodmin Town	v Bitton	3-0	190
Bournemouth	v Frome Town	1-0*	101
Bridgwater Town	v Slimbridge	0-1	189
Brockenhurst	v Egham Town	2-2*	70
Bury Town	v Hanwell Town	3-0	148
Buxton	v Alvechurch	4-0	246
Chasetown	v Nantwich Town	0-1	284
Chessington & Hook United	v Carterton	2-0	81
Christchurch	v Truro City	3-2	142
Colliers Wood United	v VCD Athletic	2-3	65
Colne	v Norton & Stockton Ancients	4-0	127
Concord Rangers	v Welwyn Garden City	1-2*	61
Crook Town	v Billingham Town	4-0	161
Dawlish Town	v Bideford	1-2*	162
Desborough Town	v Coalville Town	0-1	108
Devizes Town	v Brislington	2-1	54
Didcot Town	v Herne Bay	7-0	340
Ford Sports Daventry	v Coleshill Town	4-2	40
Friar Lane & Epworth	v Stourbridge	1-5	208
Glasshoughton Welfare	v Squires Gate	1-2	75
Glossop North End	v Carlton Town	3-4	106
Gorleston	v Mildenhall Town	0-0*	112
Harrogate Railway	v Cammell Laird	0-1	124
Highfield Rangers	v Gedling Town	2-3	37
Highworth Town	v Wimborne Town	0-1	138
Hythe Town	v Thatcham Town	3-2	130

Home	Away	Score	Att
Kingsbury Town	v Hassocks	1-0	37
Ledbury Town	v Willand Rovers	0-4	72

(19/11 tie abandoned after 86 mins due to fog, 2-1)

Home	Away	Score	Att
Leverstock Green	v Chalfont St Peter	0-2	74
Liversedge	v Billingham Synthonia	5-4*	144
London Colney	v Ipswich Wanderers	6-3	55
Lowestoft Town	v Wootton Blue Cross	2-0	240
Maidstone United	v Andover	4-0	423
Mile Oak	v Deal Town	1-3*	107
Needham Market	v Potton United	3-1	122
Nelson	v Ashville	0-1	110
Newcastle Benfield (Bay Plastics)	v Thornaby	5-1	65
Newcastle Town	v Cradley Town	1-0	96
Newmarket Town	v Tilbury	2-1*	93
Pickering Town	v Oldham Town	1-0*	115
Retford United	v Trafford	2-1	249
Rye & Iden United	v Hillingdon Borough	2-2*	86
Selby Town	v Westfields	3-3*	65
Sidley United	v Erith Town	4-2	92
Skelmersdale United	v West Allotment Celtic	4-3	141
St Helens Town	v Dunston FB	1-3	84
Stanway Rovers	v Broxbourne Borough V&E	5-5*	65
Sunderland Nissan	v Bedlington Terriers	3-3*	94
Tavistock	v Backwell United	4-2*	67
Thackley	v Jarrow Roofing Boldon CA	3-0	67
Thamesmead Town	v Brook House	0-4	63
Three Bridges	v Arundel	0-1	92
Tipton Town	v Racing Club Warwick	0-2	80
Winchester City	v AFC Newbury	5-0	184
Wisbech Town	v Leiston	8-1	330
Yaxley	v Witham Town	3-0	126

REPLAYS

Home	Away	Score	Att
Bedlington Terriers	v Sunderland Nissan	2-1	
Broxbourne Borough V&E	v Stanway Rovers	3-0	41
Egham Town	v Brockenhurst	0-1	45
Hillingdon Borough	v Rye & Iden United	1-0	62
Mildenhall Town	v Gorleston	2-0	123

(22/11 tie abandoned after 15 mins due to fog, 1-0)

Home	Away	Score	Att
Westfields	v Selby Town	2-3*	28

THIRD ROUND PROPER

BIGGEST HOME WIN:	8-2 CROOK TOWN VS FORD SPORTS DAVENTRY.
BIGGEST AWAY WIN:	2-4 WINCHESTER CITY VS YAXLEY.
	2-4 TAVISTOCK VS DEAL TOWN.
	1-3 BEDLINGTON TERRIERS VS NEWCASTLE TOWN.
HIGHEST ATTENDANCE:	518 LEAMINGTON VS LIVERSEDGE.
NUMBER OF GAMES:	32 + 5 (32 + 2)
TOTAL ATTENDANCE:	6,927 (6,001)
AVERAGE ATTENDANCE:	187 (177)

Home	Away	Score	Att
AFC Sudbury	v Bodmin Town	3-1	331
Arundel	v VCD Athletic	1-2	188
Ashville	v Racing Club Warwick	3-3*	160
Bournemouth	v Brockenhurst	1-2	83
Cammell Laird	v Retford United	3-0	122
Coalville Town	v Arnold Town	3-3*	102
Crook Town	v Ford Sports Daventry	8-2	179
Deal Town	v Tavistock	2-4	148
Didcot Town	v Mildenhall Town	4-4*	352
Dorking	v Christchurch	5-2	164
Gedling Town	v Carlton Town	4-3	50
Hillingdon Borough	v Bideford	2-1	91
Hythe Town	v Chalfont St Peter	2-1	202
Leamington	v Liversedge	2-1	518
London Colney	v Chessington & Hook United	1-2	85
Lowestoft Town	v Kingsbury Town	2-0	265

Crook Town's No.6, Phil Stout, sends his header towards the Arnold goal, during their 5th Round victory.

Photo: Bill Wheatcroft.

Maidstone United	v Broxbourne Borough V&E	2-2*	411
Needham Market	v Devizes Town	3-0	120
Newcastle Benfield (Bay Plastics)	v Stourbridge	2-1	82
Newcastle Town	v Bedlington Terriers	1-3	151
Newmarket Town	v Willand Rovers	1-0	105
Pickering Town	v Dunston FB	1-0	131
Quorn	v Nantwich Town	0-1	182
Selby Town	v Buxton	0-1	
Sidley United	v St Blazey	1-2	146
Soham Town Rangers	v Bury Town	1-2	202
Squires Gate	v Skelmersdale United	2-1	102
Thackley	v Colne	2-1	200
Welwyn Garden City	v Slimbridge	3-1	93
Wimborne Town	v Bishop's Cleeve	4-1	287
Wisbech Town	v Brook House	4-4*	371
Yaxley	v Winchester City	2-4	212

REPLAYS

Arnold Town	v Coalville Town	3-0	124
Brook House	v Wisbech Town	2-0	155
Broxbourne Borough V&E	v Maidstone United	3-3*	153
(Broxbourne won 5-4 on pens)			
Mildenhall Town	v Didcot Town	2-1	320
Racing Club Warwick	v Ashville	2-2*	125
(Ashville won 4-3 on pens)			

FOURTH ROUND PROPER

BIGGEST HOME WIN:	**3-0** PICKERING TOWN VS TAVISTOCK.
	3-0 CROOK TOWN VS ST. BLAZEY.
BIGGEST AWAY WIN:	**3-6** NANTWICH TOWN VS NEEDHAM MARKET (AET).
HIGHEST ATTENDANCE:	**746** LEAMINGTON VS WIMBORNE TOWN.
NUMBER OF GAMES:	**16 + 2** (16 + 1)
TOTAL ATTENDANCE:	**6,529** (5,622)
AVERAGE ATTENDANCE:	**363** (331)

AFC Sudbury	v Bedlington Terriers	1-1*	611
Brockenhurst	v Bury Town	0-2	195
Buxton	v Ashville	1-0	572
Chessington & Hook United	v Cammell Laird	1-2	393
Crook Town	v St Blazey	3-0	494

Dorking	v Mildenhall Town	1-3	449
Hillingdon Borough	v Brook House	2-0	259
Hythe Town	v Winchester City	1-3	441
Leamington	v Wimborne Town	2-3	746
Needham Market	v Nantwich Town	3-6*	223
Newcastle Benfield (Bay Plastics)	v Lowestoft Town	3-1	239
Newmarket Town	v Welwyn Garden City	2-2*	284
Pickering Town	v Tavistock	3-0	290
Squires Gate	v Gedling Town	2-1*	75
Thackley	v Arnold Town	0-2	216
VCD Athletic	v Broxbourne Borough V&E	1-0	257

REPLAY

Bedlington Terriers	v AFC Sudbury	1-3	434
Welwyn Garden City	v Newmarket Town	2-1*	353

(Tie awarded to Newmarket Town - Welwyn Garden City removed for playing an ineligible player)

FIFTH ROUND PROPER

NUMBER OF GAMES:	**8** (8 + 1)
TOTAL ATTENDANCE:	**4,735** (4,801)
AVERAGE ATTENDANCE:	**676** (533)

AFC Sudbury	v Bury Town	0-2	1016
Arnold Town	v Crook Town	0-1	560
Cammell Laird	v VCD Athletic	1-0	283
Hillingdon Borough	v Mildenhall Town	4-0	233
Nantwich Town	v Buxton	1-0	987
Squires Gate	v Newcastle Benfield (Bay Plastics)	2-1	146
Wimborne Town	v Pickering Town	1-2	983
Winchester City	v Newmarket Town	3-4*	533

QUARTER-FINALS

NUMBER OF GAMES:	**4** (4)
TOTAL ATTENDANCE:	**3,822** (3,129)
AVERAGE ATTENDANCE:	**956** (782)

Crook Town	v Bury Town	0-1	1946
Hillingdon Borough	v Squires Gate	2-0	428
Nantwich Town	v Pickering Town	2-0	700
Newmarket Town	v Cammell Laird	1-2	750

SEMI-FINALS

TOTAL ATTENDANCE:	**4,444** (5,256)		
AVERAGE ATTENDANCE:	**1,111** (1,314)		
FIRST LEG			
Bury Town	v Hillingdon Borough	1-1	1773
Cammell Laird	v Nantwich Town	0-1	528
SECOND LEG			
Hillingdon Borough	v Bury Town	2-1	723
Nantwich Town	v Cammell Laird	4-0	1420

Action from the Cammell Laird v Nantwich Semi-Final 1st Leg. Photo: Mark Wood.

Nantwich Town's, Matt Blake, is closly marked by a Cammell Laird defender. Photo: Mark Wood.

Above, Nick Rundell scores the winning goal for Hillingdon Borough in extra-time, after Daniel Thrower's equaliser in the final minutes of normal time (right). Photos: Eric Marsh and Roger Turner.

THE FINAL

HILLINGDON BOROUGH 1   NANTWICH TOWN   3
(Spartan South Midlands Premier)   (North West Counties Division 1)

at St. Andrews, Birmingham City F.C.
Attendance 3,286

There is no doubt the F.A.Vase and F.A.Trophy competitions have missed Wembley Stadium. Yes, it is a thrill for any non-league clubs to reach a national final and there's no doubt that both Nantwich Town and Hillingdon Borough football clubs and their supporters enjoyed the thrill of their final at St Andrews, but it will be very different next year in the new Wembley Stadium, when the whole of football at this level will celebrate a special climax to their season.

The Nantwich fans were noisy and, although many, who were probably not regular Dabber supporters, were keener to jeer the opposition rather than lift their own lads, they were at least in good voice. Hillingdon had tripled their normal support and they enjoyed the day, but hopefully next year, with good marketing, the two national non-league club finals will attract not only the supporters of the finalists, but many genuine followers of the non-league game, who will be thrilled to sample the end of season finals at the wonderful new Wembley Stadium.

From the start, Nantwich took control and a wonderfull passing movement involving nine of their side showed exactly how they wanted to play and Steve Davis's well drilled and mobile squad must have been thrilled that they could produce a commanding start on such an important occasion. Using the wings to stretch the

A Hillingdon player shields the ball from the in coming Natntwich player. Photo: Peter Barnes.

Hillingdon defence, the central strikers of Andy Kinsey and Matt Blake received an excellent service and it wasn't long before the Dabbers were rewarded for their pressure, skipper Kinsey crashing in a low drive to the keeper's right after good work from mid field dynamo Stuart Scheuber and Blake.

A second superb strike was a reward for constant pressure from the North West Counties club and the lively Danny Griggs combined with Kinsey to give Scheuber the opportunity to crash home another unstoppable shot and half time came with only one team in contention.

Full marks to Borough manager Steve Ringrose as his team came out with a couple of changes and much improved form that brought greater possession and pressure, which tested the Nantwich defence without actually creating many clear chances. Dabbers' keeper Robert Hackney did save well from Dave Lawrence, but it was skipper Kinsey who put the game out of Hillingdon's reach at the other end by cutting in from the left and hammering another glorious cross shot that screamed in to ensure the Vase was going back to the North West.

Hillingdon never gave up, although their possession very rarely produced a cutting edge but they deserved their consolation goal scrambled in by Leon Nelson in the dying minutes.

Hillingdon's Leon Nelson tries to direct the ball towards the Nantwich goal. Photo: Roger Turner.

Nantwich's Stuart Scheuber scores his
sides second goal on there way to the
celebrations below.
Photos: Bill Wheatcroft & Eric Marsh
respectively.

Andy Kinsey was selected as 'man of the match' for his leadership and two great goals, but the captain found himself in the embarrassing situation of receiving the Vase and his personal award with one hand, as he had dislocated a shoulder attempting to throw his shirt into the crowd after scoring his side's vital third goal! He must be the only captain to celebrate at a prize giving draped in a blanket, but how many footballers will be able to look back year after year at two such quality goals as the Nantwich skipper scored in his club's triumphant national final?

The game was played in an excellent spirit with no problems for the match officials, who should have enjoyed their day,while the Spartan South Midlands and North West Counties League must also have been proud of their representatives and Birmingham City officials made everyone feel welcome with cheerful organisation despite their own personal disappointments. So it was another good Vase day and now we can look forward to returning to Wembley.

Hillingdon Borough: Harris, Brown, Rundell (Fenton 80),Kidson, Phillips, Croft, Lawrence, Duncan (Nelson 46), Tilbury, Hibbs, Wharton (Lyons 38). Substitutes not used: O'Grady and White.

Nantwich Town: Hackney, A.Taylor, T.Taylor, Smith, Davis, Donnelly, Beasley, Scheuber (Parkinson 69), Kinsey (Marrow 69), Blake (Scarlett 86) and Griggs. Substitutes not used: O'Connor and Read.

ROUND BY ROUND STATISTICS

Round	Games	Home Win	Away Win	Draws	Home Goals	Away Goals	Att. Total	Att. Ave
1st Qualifying	104*+8	53	51	8	209	191	8,382	75 (0)
* Two walkovers.								
2nd Qualifying	159*+12	79	80	12	321	318	14,065	82 (+6)
* Two walkovers.								
First Round	98+6	53	44	7	201	184	11,359	109 (+8)
Second Round	64+6	37	27	6	155	104	9,275	132 (0)
Third Round	32+5	21	11	5	87	61	6,927	187 (+10)
Fourth Round	16+2	7	9*	2	29	30	6,529	363 (+32)
*Tie awarded to Newmarket Town.								
Fifth Round	8	4	4	0	12	10	4,735	676 (+143)
Six Round	4	2	2	0	5	3	3,822	956 (+174)
Semi-Finals	4	2	1	1	7	3	4,444	1,111 (-203

(Figure in brackets denotes +/- difference between 04/05 average attendance).

TOP GOAL SCORERS 2005 - 2006

Player	Club	No. goals	Round Reached
D Lawrence	Hillingdon Borough	10	Runners-up
M Takalobighashi	Maidstone United	10	Third Round
R Allen	Crook Town	9	Sixth Round
M Clements	Needham Market	8	Sixth Round
S Joyce	Bournemouth	7	Third Round
G Kharas	Glossop North End	7	Second Round
D Tilbury	Hillingdon Borough	7	Runners-up
M Chilton	Newcastle Benfield (Bay Plastics)	7	Fifth Round
M Ashton	Retford United	7	Third Round
M Huckett	Arundel	6	Third Round
A Kinsey	Nantwich Town	6	Winners
J Harrington	St. Blazey	6	Fourth Round

Maidstone's Mo Takalobighashi is challenged by Andover's Callum Earl. Photo: Alan Coomes.

Sports Lighting

Specialists in the Lighting of all Sports Applications

Tel: 01803 844 833   Fax: 01803 844 835

www.sportslighting.co.uk

Sports Lighting has been a family run business for the last 15yrs.

We do nationwide installations.

All our work comes with a 12months parts and labour guarantee.

We make on site surveys and advise for installation to suit your needs.

We make life easy for you, by supplying all the lux and spillage charts for your planning application FREE OF CHARGE.

Our light fittings are all asymmetric which cut out any possibility of light pollution and spillage.

All out work comes with the backing of the NICEIC as we are an approved contractor.

We are the main floodlighting contractor for Torquay Utd.

Sports lighting is always prepared to put money back into local sports by means of sponsorships tailored to meet the requirements of both parties.

The FA

YOUTH CUP

Non-League Clubs Involvement only.

Liverpool beat Manchester City 5-0 on Agg. in the final.

PRELIMINARY ROUND

AFC Kempston Rovers	v St Margaretsbury	3-1
AFC Newbury	v Westfield	0-5
AFC Telford United (wo)	v Mickleover Sports	
Aylesbury United	v Chesham United	1-3
Belper Town	v Eccleshal	1-0
Blackstones	v Corby Town	6-2
Bugbrooke St Michaels	v Histon	0-6
Burnham Ramblers	v Hitchin Town	1-3
Burton Albion	v Redditch United	4-0
Bury Town	v Diss Town	12-0
Camberley Town	v AFC Wimbledon	0-4
Carshalton Athletic	v Erith Town	4-1
Carterton	v Oxford City	3-5*
Chadderton	v Marine	2-2*, 7-8p
Chasetown	v Tamworth	3-2
Cobham	v Ash United	2-2*, 3-5p
Colney Heath	v Bedford Town	1-2
Concord Rangers	v Grays Athletic	3-0
East Thurrock United	v Woodbridge Town	2-5
Godalming Town	v Fleet Town	2-0
Halstead Town (wo)	v Stansted	
Hampton & Richmond B.	v Hayes (at Hayes FC)	0-7
Harefield United	v Royston Town	3-2
Harlow Town	v Brentwood Town	2-3*
Harrow Borough	v Enfield Town	2-1
Harwich & Parkeston	v Dereham Town	6-1
Herne Bay (wo)	v Ashford Town	
Kings Lynn	v Raunds Town	2-1
Leigh RMI	v Frickley Athletic	5-0
Long Buckby (wo)	v Thame United	
Long Melford	v Southend Manor	4-0
Matlock Town	v Ford Sports Daventry	3-3*, 6-7p
Newport Pagnell Town	v Barton Rovers	1-3
North Greenford United	v Boreham Wood	3-1
Nuneaton Borough	v Sutton Coldfield Town	4-0
Reading Town	v Ashford Town (Middx)	1-3
Redbridge	v Berkhamsted Town	2-0
Ruislip Manor	v Leighton Town	0-1*
Sawbridgeworth Town	v Wealdstone	0-4
Stotfold	v St Albans City	3-2
Teversal	v Eastwood Town	1-1*, 6-5p
Thamesmead Town	v Bedfont	3-2
Three Bridges (wo)	v Havant & Waterlooville	
Tring Athletic	v Buckingham Town	5-0
Whitton United	v Great Yarmouth Town	1-1*, 2-4p
Woodley Sports	v Lancaster City	1-2

FIRST ROUND QUALIFYING

AFC Emley	v Morecambe	1-6
AFC Hornchurch	v Harefield United	1-2
AFC Wallingford	v Henley Town	1-2*
AFC Wimbledon	v Erith & Belvedere	3-0
Aldershot Town	v Bromley	6-0
Alvechurch	v Bourne Town	1-0
Atherton LR	v Vauxhall Motors	0-3
Barking & East Ham U.	v Leyton	5-3
Basingstoke Town	v Molesey	6-1
Bath City	v Bishop's Cleeve	2-0
Beaconsfield SYCOB	v Aveley	1-0
Bedford Town	v Brentwood Town	5-2
Bedworth United	v Nuneaton Griff	4-2
Bishop's Stortford	v Woodbridge Town	2-1
Bitton	v Bridgwater Town	3-1
Blackstones	v Stafford Rangers	1-3
Bracknell Town	v Eastleigh	4-2*
Bradford (Park Avenue)	v Thackley	1-0
Bromsgrove Rovers	v Belper Town	6-1
Burnham	v Milton United	6-1
Bury Town	v Long Melford	3-0
Canvey Island	v Leighton Town	1-2
Castle Vale	v Boldmere St Michaels	1-3
Chalfont St Peter	v Brook House	0-2
Chelmsford City	v Braintree Town	1-0*
Chester-Le-Street Town	v Farsley Celtic	1-1*, 4-5p
Chippenham Town	v Poole Town	0-4
Chipstead	v Lewisham Borough	6-0
Cinderford Town	v Bristol Manor Farm	2-4
Cirencester Town	v Merthyr Tydfil	1-2

Clacton Town	v Great Wakering Rovers	2-1
Clapton	v Marlow	0-0*, 2-4p
Coleshill Town	v Congleton Town	3-1
Concord Rangers	v Harrow Borough	0-1
Coventry Sphinx	v Glossop North End	1-0
Dagenham & Redbridge	v Waltham Forest	0-1
Dartford	v Gravesend & Northfleet	1-6
Dover Athletic	v Chatham Town	2-1*
Dulwich Hamlet	v Epsom & Ewell	6-1
Dunston Federation B.	v Gateshead	2-1
East Grinstead Town	v Maidstone United	0-3
Evesham United	v Worcester City	1-5
Fakenham Town	v Ware	6-5
Farnborough Town	v Steyning Town	4-1
Fisher Athletic	v Maidenhead United	2-3
Folkestone Invicta	v Croydon Athletic	3-3*, 5-4p
Ford Spots Daventry	v Deeping Rangers	0-3
Formby	v Lancaster City	1-2
Goole	v Guiseley	3-2
Gornal Athletic	v Leek Town	0-3
Great Yarmouth Town	v Witham Town	3-1
Gresley Rovers	v Kidderminster Harriers	0-3
Halifax Town	v North Ferriby United	0-3
Halstead Town	v Buntingford Town	0-3
Haringey Borough	v AFC Kempston Rovers	7-3*
Hayes	v Cheshunt	1-1*, 3-4p
Hednesford Town	v Newcastle Town	14-0
Hemel Hempstead T.	v Thurrock	1-3
Hendon	v Kingsbury Town	3-0
Hereford United	v Malmesbury Victoria	4-0
Herne Bay	v Peacehaven & Telscombe	7-1
Heybridge Swifts	v Chesham United	0-1
Hillingdon Borough	v Crawley Town	2-0
Hitchin Town	v Uxbridge	1-1*, 3-4p
Horsham YMCA	v Ash United	2-1
Hucknall Town	v Arnold Town	1-6
Ilford	v Rothwell Corinthians	0-1
Kettering Town	v Malvern Town	1-0
Kimberley Town	v Alfreton Town	1-6
Kings Lynn	v Ely City	1-2
London Colney	v Barton Rovers	0-2
Long Eaton United	v AFC Telford United	3-4
Lowestoft Town	v Long Buckby	1-0
Lye Town	v Chasetown	2-4
Mangotsfield United	v Gloucester City	0-2
Mile Oak	v Alton Town	5-1
Mole Valley (Predators)	v Corinthian Casuals	1-3
Moneyfields	v Godalming Town	3-1
Moor Green	v Hinckley United	4-3*
Nantwich Town	v Burton Albion	1-9
Newmarket Town	v Histon	0-3
North Greenford United	v Cambridge City	0-3
Northampton Spencer	v March Town United	5-1
Northwich Victoria	v Burscough	0-3
Northwood	v Romford	3-2
Nuneaton Borough	v Oadby Town	3-1
Ossett Albion	v Retford United	1-2*
Oxford City	v Burgess Hill Town	9-1
Pagham	v Walton & Hersham	1-1*, 4-2
Paulton Rovers	v Brislington	3-2
Penrith	v Workington (wo)	
Potters Bar Town	v Cogenhoe United	1-7
Prescot Cables	v Daisy Hill	0-2
Racing Club Warwick	v Cradley Town	4-2
Radcliffe Borough	v Southport	1-2
Radstock Town	v Forest Green Rovers	0-1
Ramsgate	v Tonbridge Angels	2-1
Rugby Town	v Pershore Town	14-0
Rushall Olympic	v Wellington	3-2
Ryton	v Scarborough	4-3
Saltdean United	v Horsham	2-1
Sandhurst Town	v Thatcham Town	1-0
Selby Town	v Altrincham	2-1
Sevenoaks Town	v Three Bridges	3-4*
Skelmersdale United	v Alsager Town	11-1
South Park	v Thamesmead Town	2-4
Staines Town	v Stotfold	4-1
Stalybridge Celtic	v Pontefract Collieries	1-2

Stevenage Borough	v	Redbridge	4-0
Stocksbridge Park Steels	v	Leigh RMI	2-3
Stourbridge	v	Carlton Town	2-0
Stratford Town	v	Teversa	2-2*, 3-0p
Sutton United	v	Chertsey Town	4-1
Taunton Town	v	Salisbury City	3-1
Tiverton Town	v	Exeter City	2-2*, 9-8p
Trafford	v	Eccleshill United	4-3
Tring Athletic	v	Harwich & Parkeston	1-0
Walsham Le Willows	v	Hullbridge Sports	2-3
Waltham Abbey	v	Billericay Town	0-3
Wealdstone	v	Banbury United	6-1
(at Ruislip Manor FC)			
Westfield	v	Andover	2-1
Weston Super Mare	v	Newport County	2-5
Weymouth	v	Westbury United	1-1*, 3-1p
Whitley Bay	v	Kendal Town	3-0
Whyteleafe	v	Carshalton Athletic	3-4
Wick	v	Eastbourne Borough	2-3*
Wingate & Finchley	v	Cambridge United	0-10
Winsford United	v	Warrington Town	1-4
Witton Albion	v	Yorkshire Amateur	0-1
Wivenhoe Town	v	Broxbourne Borough V&E	5-6*
Woking	v	Ashford Town (Middx)	4-0
Wootton Bassett Town	v	Witney United	3-0
Worksop Town	v	Garforth Town	0-3
Worthing	v	Lewes	5-2
Yate Town	v	Bournemouth	1-0
York City	v	Marine	4-1

SECOND ROUND QUALIFYING

Alfreton Town	v	Leek Town	2-5
Alvechurch	v	Rugby Town	3-2
Arnold Town	v	Kidderminster Harriers	4-0
Barking & East Ham U.	v	Marlow	2-0
Basingstoke Town	v	Maidstone United	5-3
Bath City	v	Bristol Manor Farm	4-2
Beaconsfield SYCOB	v	Cheshunt	1-0
Bedford Town	v	Cogenhoe United	1-2
Billericay Town	v	Tring Athletic	9-0
Bitton	v	Tiverton Town	1-4
Boldmere St Michaels	v	Stratford Town	1-4
Bracknell Town	v	Woking	0-4
Bradford (Park Avenue)	v	Southport	1-4
Bromsgrove Rovers	v	AFC Telford United	2-3
Brook House	v	Bury Town	0-3
Broxbourne Boro' V&E	v	Histon	1-2
Buntingford Town	v	Henley Town	1-0
Cambridge City	v	Cambridge United	1-0
Chasetown	v	Rushall Olympic	3-3*, 4-2p
Chipstead	v	Moneyfields	2-0
Clacton Town	v	Waltham Forest	0-3
Corinthan Casuals	v	Burgess Hill Town	6-0
Coventry Sphinx	v	Stourbridge	2-1
Daisy Hill	v	Retford United	3-1
Deeping Rangers	v	Burton Albion	1-4
Eastbourne Borough	v	Burnham	0-1
Fakenham Town	v	Barton Rovers	1-7
Farsley Celtic	v	Warrington Town	2-1
Folkestone Invicta	v	Carshalton Athletic	2-2*, 6-5p
Forest Green Rovers	v	Worcester City	1-3
Great Yarmouth Town	v	Chesham United	1-2
Haringey Borough	v	Harefield United	1-1*, 6-5p
Harrow Borough	v	Chelmsford City	1-4
Hendon	v	Wealdstone	1-2
Hereford United	v	Paulton Rovers	5-0
Hillingdon Borough	v	Horsham YMCA	3-3*, 3-1
Hullbridge Sports	v	Rothwell Corinthians	0-2
Lancaster City	v	Selby Town	1-1*, 4-1p
Leighton Town	v	Ely City	2-3
Maidenhead United	v	Ramsgate	0-4
Mile Oak	v	Dover Athletic	2-1
Moor Green	v	Hednesford Town	0-1
Morecambe	v	Leigh RMI	2-1
Newport County	v	Yate Town	2-1
North Ferriby United	v	Garforth Town	3-0
Northwood	v	Lowestoft Town	7-1
Nuneaton Borough	v	Coleshill Town	0-1
Pagham	v	Farnborough Town	1-3
Pontefract Collieries	v	Workington	1-2
Poole Town	v	Merthyr Tydfil	3-2
Racing Club Warwick	v	Bedworth United	1-2*
Ryton	v	Burscough	0-3
Saltdean United	v	Gravesend & Northfleet	1-8*
Sandhurst Town	v	AFC Wimbledon	1-1*, 12-11p
Skelmersdale United	v	Yorkshire Amateur	6-0
Stafford Rangers	v	Kettering Town	1-3
Staines Town	v	Bishop's Stortford	10-0
Stevenage Borough	v	Uxbridge	6-1
Sutton United	v	Herne Bay	4-0
Thamesmead Town	v	Dulwich Hamlet	2-0
Three Bridges	v	Worthing	2-4
Thurrock	v	Northampton Spencer	1-3
Trafford	v	York City	2-2*, 1-4p
Vauxhall Motors	v	Goole	2-1*

Westfield	v	Aldershot Town	0-2
Weymouth	v	Gloucester City	0-1
Whitley Bay	v	Dunston Federation Brewery	0-3
Wootton Bassett Town	v	Taunton Town	1-2*

THIRD ROUND QUALIFYING

Arnold Town	v	Alvechurch	2-1
Barking & East Ham U.	v	Bury Town	4-3
Beaconsfield SYCOB	v	Chelmsford City	3-2*
Bedworth United	v	Stratford Town	0-2
Billericay Town	v	Waltham Forest	2-3
Buntingford Town	v	Rothwell Corinthians	1-0
Burnham	v	Worthing	1-1*, 2-4p
Burton Albion	v	AFC Telford United	7-0
Chasetown	v	Coleshill Town	1-2
Chesham United	v	Staines Town	3-2
Daisy Hill	v	Farsley Celtic	4-3
Dunston FB	v	York City	3-2
Farnborough Town	v	Sandhurst Town	2-0
Folkestone Invicta	v	Basingstoke Town	3-2
Hednesford Town	v	Leek Town	4-3*
Hereford United	v	Bath City	1-5
Hillingdon Borough	v	Gravesend & Northfleet	0-5
Histon	v	Cogenhoe United	2-3
Kettering Town	v	Coventry Sphinx	3-1
Morecambe	v	Lancaster City	1-1*, 4-1p
Newport County	v	Worcester City	2-0
Northampton Spencer	v	Cambridge City	1-2
Northwood	v	Barton Rovers	1-5
Poole Town	v	Gloucester City	0-3
Ramsgate	v	Aldershot Town	0-4
Skelmersdale United	v	Vauxhall Motors	5-4
Southport	v	North Ferriby United	4-4*, 4-2p
Stevenage Borough	v	Haringey Borough	8-0
Sutton United	v	Mile Oak	5-1
Taunton Town	v	Tiverton Town	2-3
Thamesmead Town	v	Chipstead	2-4
Wealdstone	v	Ely Town	3-2
Woking	v	Corinthian Casuals	9-3
Workington	v	Burscough	0-11

FIRST ROUND PROPER

AFC Bournemouth	v	Tiverton Town	2-0	335
Aldershot Town	v	**Buntingford Town**	3-3*, 6-7	125
Barking & East Ham U.	v	**Sutton United**	2-0	98
Beaconsfield SYCOB	v	Colchester United	1-5*	92
Bradford City	v	**Dunston FB**	1-2	
Brentford	v	Worthing	4-1	454
Burton Albion	v	Port Vale	3-4	119
Chipstead	v	**Chesham United**	3-2	84
Cogenhoe United	v	**Boston United**	2-1	143
Coleshill Town	v	**Arnold Town**	0-2	76
Daisy Hill	v	Doncaster Rovers	2-4	137
Gloucester City	v	Bath City	1-2*	
Hednesford Town	v	Cambridge City	2-3	74
Huddersfield Town	v	Burscough	3-0	351
Kettering Town	v	Nottingham Forest	0-3	275
Milton Keynes Dons	v	Farnborough Town	4-0	234
Morecambe	v	Darlington	1-3	156
Newport County	v	Swindon Town	3-4	119
Rochdale	v	**Southport**	0-1	183
Southend United	v	Barton Rovers	3-1	237
Stevenage Borough	v	**Woking**	2-1	180
Stratford Town	v	Northampton Town	1-2	101
Waltham Forest	v	**Leyton Orient**	4-2	425
Wealdstone	v	Folkestone Invicta	1-1*, 6-7p	45
Wrexham	v	Skelmersdale United	3-0	147
Wycombe Wanderers	v	Gravesend & Northfleet	1-0	147

SECOND ROUND PROPER

Bath City	v	Cheltenham Town	0-1	147
Brentford	v	Buntingford Town	3-1	358
Cogenhoe United	v	**Southport**	3-0	125
Colchester United	v	Barking & East Ham United	3-2	292
Dunston FB	v	**Arnold Town**	1-7	242
Folkestone Invicta	v	**Chipstead**	1-2	232
Milton Keynes Dons	v	Stevenage Borough	1-0	316
Waltham Forest	v	**Yeovil Town**	2-0	124

THIRD ROUND PROPER

Arnold Town	v	Sheffield United	0-4	565
Cogenhoe United	v	Derby County	1-3	318
Carlisle United	v	Chipstead	5-1	250
Waltham Forest	v	**West Bromwich Albion**	1-0	296

FOURTH ROUND PROPER

Brentford	v	Waltham Forest	2-0	685

F.A. COUNTY YOUTH CUP

FIRST ROUND

Durham	v	Leicestershire & Rutland	4-1
Cheshire	v	Isle of Man	6-0
West Riding	v	Birmingham	0-3
Lincolnshire	v	Westmorland	4-1
Manchester	v	Nottinghamshire	3-1
Sheffield & Hallamshire	v	Cumberland	2-1
Essex	v	Hertfordshire	2-0
Gloucestershire	v	Huntingdonshire	0-1
Middlesex	v	Army	4-2
London	v	Berks & Bucks	0-3
Worcestershire	v	Dorset	2-3
Cambridgeshire	v	Wiltshire	0-3
Guernsey	v	Herefordshire	4-2*
Devon	v	Surrey	2-3*
Kent	v	Bedfordshire	0-3

Byes: Cornwall, Derbyshire, East Riding, Hampshire, Jersey, Lancashire, Liverpool, Northamptonshire, Northumberland, Oxfordshire, Norfolk, North Riding, Shropshire, Somerset, Staffordshire, Suffolk (**H**), Sussex.

SECOND ROUND

Sheffield & Hallamshire	v	Birmingham	1-4
Shropshire	v	Lancashire	1-5
Manchester	v	Northumberland	3-2*
Lincolnshire	v	East Riding	2-1
Liverpool	v	Durham	1-7
Cheshire	v	North Riding	2-1*
Derbyshire	v	Staffordshire	4-0
Jersey	v	Surrey	0-1
Suffolk (**H**)	v	Guernsey	2-1
Cornwall	v	Bedfordshire	2-3
Sussex	v	Norfolk	3-1
Middlesex	v	Hampshire	1-5
Berks & Bucks	v	Somerset	1-0
Huntingdonshire	v	Wiltshire	1-2
Dorset	v	Northamptonshire	0-1
Oxfordshire	v	Essex	4-3

THIRD ROUND

Lincolnshire	v	Derbyshire	2-0
Berks & Bucks	v	Cheshire	0-3
Bedfordshire	v	Lancashire	2-1
Hampshire	v	Wiltshire	1-5
Northamptonshire	v	Manchester	2-0
Oxfordshire	v	Sussex	1-2
Surrey	v	Durham	2-3*
Birmingham	v	Suffolk (**H**)	4-2

FOURTH ROUND

Durham	v	Sussex	3-1
Wiltshire	v	Northants	3-2
Cheshire	v	Lincolnshire	1-2
Bedfordshire	v	Birmingham	1-0

SEMI FINALS

Durham	v	Wiltshire	0-0*, 5-4p
Lincolnshire	v	Bedfordshire	0-0*, 1-3p

THE FINAL

Durham	v	Bedfordshire	2-3
Forrest 60, Brown 73		Cunnington 11, Grieve 84, Lewis 85	

LAST TEN FINALS

1996	Durham	v	Gloucestershire	1-0
1997	Cambridgeshire	v	Lancashire	1-0
1998	Northumberland	v	West Riding	2-1
1999	Durham	v	Sussex	1-0
2000	Birmingham	v	Surrey	2-1
2001	Northamptonshire	v	Birmingham	3-0
2002	Birmingham	v	Durham	2-1
2003	Northumberland	v	Liverpool	1-0
2004	Durham	v	North Riding	4-0
2005	Suffolk	v	Hampshire	2-1

F.A. SUNDAY CUP

PRELIMINARY ROUND

Allerton	v Blessed Sacrament	5-2*
The Warby	v Whetley Lane WMC	1-2
Bartley Green Sunday	v AC Sportsman	2-1
Wainscott Arrows	v Howbridge Swifts	2-0
Treble Chance	v Grange Athletic	0-2
Broad Plain House	v Holt	2-1

FIRST ROUND

Allerton	v AFC Pudsey	6-0
James Cropper	v Harrington Portland	1-2
Bolton Woods	v Carrs Hotel	1-2
BRNESC	v Britannia	1-7
Buttershaw Whitestar	v Brow	0-1
Home & Bargain	v Canada Edinburgh Park	2-1
Elland	v Nicosia	0-3
Clifton	v Fairweather Green WMC	6-6*, 1-4p
Oakenshaw	v Queens Park	1-3
Elmhouse Canon	v Rawdon	3-0
Queensbury	v Hartlepool Athletic Rugby	2-1
Dock	v Lobster	3-5
Redoubt	v Orchard Park	1-2
Seaburn	v Pablo Derby Arms	1-0
Halton Arms Sports	v Ring O'Bells (Shipley)	1-2
Hartlepool Rovers Quoit	v Paddock	0-1
Seymour KFCA	v Shipley Town	5-2
Smith & Nephew	v Thornaby Town	2-0
Whetley Lane WMC	v Hartlepool Supporters Athletic	2-0
Bruce Ennis Square	v St Aloysius 'E	1-6
Western Approaches	v Shankhouse United	1-3
Hetton Lyons Cricket Club	v Seaton Sluice SC	4-1
Maryport	v Sunderland JWS Construction	2-3
Taxi Club	v Hessle Rangers (wo)	
Melling Victoria	v Irlam MS	1-1*, 2-4p
Sandon Dock	v Norcoast	3-4*
Hartlepool Lion Hillcarter	v North Mersey Lions	1-2
61 FC (Sunday)	v George & Dragon	4-1
Austin Ex Apprentices	v Birstall Stamford	1-2
Scots Grey	v Tally Ho	5-3
Bartley Green Sunday	v Loff Style St Andrews	0-2
AFC Hornets (Studham)	v Pioneer	1-6
Brache Green Man	v Dun Cow	3-1
Ashlyn's United	v Grosvenor Park	1-4
Crawley Green (Sunday)	v Belstone	2-3
Belt Road	v Lodge Cottrell	0-1
Casino	v St Margarets	2-0
Hammer	v Lewsey Social	2-1
Wainscott Arrows	v Nicholas Wybacks	2-0
The Clifton	v Lashings	7-1
Diffusion	v Lebeq Tavern Courage	1-2
Travellers	v Moggerhanger Sunday	3-1
Rettendon Athletic	v Snodland Working Mens Club	3-5*
Rainham Sports	v Toby	2-1
UK Flooring	v Moat	5-2
FC Fellowship	v Venceremos	3-1
Grange Athletic	v Wernley	2-3
Green Baize	v CB Hounslow United	4-2*
Broad Plain House	v Woolston T&L	2-1
Bowood	v Sandford	0-3*
Risden Wood	v Skew Bridge	3-1
London Maccabi Lions	v The Well	5-3*
VS Villa	v Hanham Sunday	3-2
Dees	v Greyhound	0-2
Reading Irish	v Shireway Sports (wo)	
St Josephs (Luton)	v Trooper	2-0
Bournemouth Electric	v Bedfont Sunday	3-2
Richfield Rovers	v Team Bristol	0-4
The Cutters Friday	v Mackadown Lane S&S	0-4
Queensmen	v Celtic SC (Luton)	2-3
FC Houghton Centre	v Nirankari Sports Sabha	2-8
Red Star ICL	v Enfield Rangers	0-3

SECOND ROUND

Harrington Portland	v Allerton	1-2
(Reversed tie)		
Carrs Hotel	v Home & Bargain	3-2
Fairweather Green WMC	v Britannia	1-9
Brow	v Nicosia	1-4
Queens Park	v Lobster	2-4*
Elmhouse Canon	v Queensbury	0-0*, 2-4p
Orchard Park	v Paddock	5-4
Seaburn	v Ring O'Bells (Shipley)	5-0
Smith & Nephew	v St Aloysius 'E	1-2*
Seymour KFCA	v Whetley Lane WMC	5-1
Shankhouse United	v Hetton Lyons Cricket Club	1-8
Sunderland JWS Construction	v Albion Sports	3-2
Hessle Rangers	v North Mersey Lions	2-2*, 4-2p
Irlam MS	v Norcoast	2-1
Birstall Stamford	v Gossoms End (H)	1-0
61 FC (Sunday)	v Scots Grey	1-2
Pioneer	v FC Fellowship	6-2
Loft Style St Andrews	v Grosvenor Park	3-6
Lodge Cottrell	v Belstone	1-2
Casino	v UK Flooring	1-2
The Clifton	v London Maccabi Lions	0-2
Wainscott Arrows	v VS Villa	2-1
Risden Wood	v Travellers	2-1*
Greyhound	v Lebeq Tavern Courage	0-2
(Reversed tie)		
Snodland WMC	v Brache Green Man	0-2
Rainham Sports	v Hammer	3-1
Wernley	v Green Baize	3-0
Sandford	v Broad Plain House	3-3*, 7-8p
Reading Irish	v St Josephs (Luton)	1-1*, 4-5p
Bournemouth Electric	v Team Bristol	2-0
Mackadown Lane S&S	v Enfield Rangers	2-2*, 6-5p
Celtic SC (Luton)	v Nirankari Sports Sabha	6-3

THIRD ROUND

Queensbury	v Hetton Lyons Cricket Club	0-5
Allerton	v Nicosia	0-2
Sunderland JWS Construction	v Orchard Park	0-1
Britannia	v Lobster	2-5
Hessle Rangers	v Carrs Hotel	2-0
Seymour KFCA	v Irlam MS	2-1
Seaburn	v St Aloysius 'E	2-2*, 2-4p
Birstall Stamford	v Grosvenor Park	3-1
Scots Grey	v Mackadown Lane S&S	5-4
Brache Green Man	v Wernley	0-2
Belstone	v Wainscott Arrows	0-5
Pioneer	v Celtic SC (Luton)	3-3*, 3-4p
Rainham Sports	v St Josephs (Luton)	2-6
London Maccabi Lions	v Risden Wood	3-1
UK Flooring	v Bournemouth Electric	0-1
Lebeq Tavern Courage	v Broad Plain House	5-0

FOURTH ROUND

Nicosia	v Hetton Lyons Cricket Club	2-5
Hessle Rangers	v Seymour KFCA	0-1
Orchard Park	v Scots Grey	3-2
St Aloysius 'E	v Lobster	3-5
Wernley	v Birstall Stamford	0-1
St Josephs (Luton)	v London Maccabi Lions	2-1
Wainscott Arrows	v Lebeq Tavern Courage	1-0
Bournemouth Electric	v Celtic SC (Luton)	0-2

FIFTH ROUND

Seymour KFCA	v Hetton Lyons Cricket Club	0-2
Orchard Park	v Lobster	0-2
Wainscott Arrows	v Birstall Stamford	1-3
Celtic SC (Luton)	v St Josephs (Luton)	0-1

SEMI-FINALS

Hetton Lyons Cricket Club	v Birstall Stamford	2-1
(Durham Sunday League)	(Charnwood Sunday League)	Att: 448
Lobster	v St. Josephs (Luton)	0-2
(Liverpool & Dist. Sun. Lge)	(North Home Counties Sunday Lge)	Att: 629

THE FINAL

Hetton Lyons Cricket Club	v St. Josephs (Luton)	5-3
		Att: 1,127

F.A. NATIONAL LEAGUE SYSTEMS CUP

In its second campaign, the F.A.National League Systems Cup attracted 33 leagues including the Isle of Man, and Guernsey and Jersey from the Channel Islands.

All these leagues were represented by squads of players from their member clubs who had never been contract professionals and were between the ages of 19 and 32. So in England this opened the way for Step 7 leagues and of course the Island representatives.

The strength of the competing sides really depends on how much pride the respective competition administrators take in their league's reputation. The appointment of an enthusiastic, knowledgeable manager is important. He must have pride in his league also needing the support of his league officials, who must ensure the right host clubs are chosen for home matches and the right players are available.The league and the county, or geographical area it represents, will benefit from a squad that conducts itself with style, sportsmanship and enough talent to make an impression on the competition.

The earlier rounds had produced some thrilling games with The Dorset County league certainly amongst the goals as they beat the Gloucester County League 3-2 before losing a thriller 4-5 at home to Guernsey. Two of the quarter finals went

to extra time with the previous competition's beaten finalists, Cambridgeshire County League, beating Liverpool Combination after penalty kicks.

Anyone lucky enough to watch last season's semi-finals, played over one week-end at the end of the season, will have realised that everything we love about the game was on show.

Cambridge entertained Guernsey's Priaux League at Cambridge City's Milton Road ground but were relieved to take the tie to penalties, having trailed for most of the game and seen Guernsey miss a penalty in normal time. However, their experience and never say die spirit saw them through to a second final after another penalty shoot out so it was off to Chatham Town to see who they would face in the final - The Kent County League or the Isle of Man.

The Manxmen were playing their fourth away tie but the squad had thrived on the away trips, the spirit was clear to see and certainly boosted by the incredible support of a bunch of Wolverhampton University students who had decided to support the Isle of Man team having chosen them after a few drinks and the use of a blindfold and a pin!

The students' noisy and amusing support had given the Island lads a lift in previous games but

The Isle of Man team celebrate their victory in the FA National League System Cup. Photo: Gordon Whittington.

PRELIMINARY ROUND

Northamptonshire Comb.	v Midland Football Comb.	1-0*	
Middlesex County League	v North Berks League	3-0	

FIRST ROUND

Wearside League	v Northern Alliance	0-2	
West Cheshire League	v Isle of Man League	1-3	75
Liverpool County Comb	v Manchester Football League	3-0*	87
Northampton Town Lge	v Cambridgeshire County	1-3	98
Northamptonshire Comb	v Central Midlands League	1-2	70
Spartan South Mid. D2	v Bedford & District League	0-1	35
Anglian Combination	v Peterborough & District	3-1	80
Somerset County Lge	v Wiltshire Football League	4-1	52
Guernsey League	v Reading Football League	3-2*	130
South Western League	v Jersey Combination	2-0	116
Dorset Premier League	v Gloucestershire County	3-2	42
Hertfordshire Senior Co.	v Essex & Suffolk Border	2-0	45
Sussex County Lge D3	v Kent County League	1-4	96
Essex Olympian League	v Middlesex County League	3-1	22
Brighton Hove & District	v Mid Sussex League	5-1	69

SECOND ROUND

Northern Alliance	v Isle of Man League	1-4	76
Liverpool Combination	v Mid Cheshire League (H)	1-0	
Anglian Combination	v Bedford & District Lge	4-0	62
Central Midlands Lge	v Cambridgeshire County	0-2	67
Dorset Premier League	v Guernsey Prilaux Lge	4-5	39
South Western League	v Somerset Senior League	4-0	89
Essex Olympian Lge	v Herts County Senior	0-0*, 5-6p	47
Brighton Hove & District	v Kent County League	1-3	

THIRD ROUND

Cambridgeshire County	v Liverpool Combination	2-2*, 4-3p	
Anglian Combination	v Isle of Man League	1-3*	
South Western League	v Guernsey Prilaux League	0-2	
Kent County League	v Hertfordshire Senior Lge	3-0	

SEMI-FINAL

Cambridgeshire League	v Guernsey Prilaux Lg	3-3*, 4-2p	
Kent County League	v Isle of Man League	1-2	

on a heavy pitch against lively opponents who had already enjoyed the privilege of representing England in the European competition on invitation three years ago, their non-stop encouragement probably made all the difference as legs were seen to get tired and both sides fought for a vital winning goal. The Islanders scored in the very last minute and a wonderful week-end of football came to an end with a bar full of yellow and red clad students celebrating with their unlikely heroes.

Both semi-finals had been full of bright attacking football, played in an excellent competitive but sporting spirit, which brought the best out of two very sound referees. Gracious losers were appreciated by two very happy and equally gracious winners while everyone present must have wondered why this excellent spirit was acting as such a breath of fresh air for us all.

The Final was played on the day after The F.A.Vase Final and once again we returned to Cambridge, but this time to United's Abbey Stadium. The Wolverhampton University lads were in great voice and decked out in full colour but as last year's finalists, the Cambridge League were favourites to win at the second attempt.

Another excellent game was dominated throughout by the lively Islanders who produced splendid attacking football using the wings to great effect with Nicky Hurt dominant in mid field and Callum Morrisey always dangerous up front.

Chris Bass must have covered every blade of grass up and down the left flank while manager Kevin Manning takes great credit for his inspired work throughout the season.

The Isle of Man's, not so secret, '12th man' celebrate their adopted team's triumph!

Photo: Gordon Whittington.

The Isle of Man officials were obviously thrilled with their success and the thought of a European Competition has thrilled the whole Island.

We couldn't have more worthy representatives who played good football in the right spirit with a smile and it's hard not to create the right spirit when supported by their special 'Barmy Army' whose words to one of their songs " The Isles of Man is full of Men" proved exactly right in this competition!

FINAL RESULT

Cambridgeshire League v Isle of Man League 0-4

Hurt 60, Morrisey 70, 75, Myers 82

UEFA REGIONS CUP DRAW FOR THE ISLE OF MAN LEAGUE
Preliminary Round - Central West Group
Northern Ireland, Finland, Scotland, Latvia
Intermediary Round - Group 4
Czech Republic, Winners Central West, England , Slovakia
Eight group winners will qualify for the Final which will be staged in June 2007.

PRELIMINARY ROUND

Braintree Town	v	Eastbourne Borough	3-2
Basildon Town	v	Crowborough Athletic	0-2

FIRST ROUND QUALIFYING

AFC Bournemouth Ladies	v	Poole Town	5-1
AFC Kempston Rovers	v	Littlehampton Town	3-2
AFC Newbury Ladies	v	Kings Sports	4-1
Aldershot Town	v	Stevenage Borough	3-1
Aylesbury Vale	v	Haywards Heath Town	2-3*
Banbury United	v	Brentwood Town	3-2
Barnsley	v	Darlington RA	5-0
Bath City	v	Holway United	5-2
Battersea	v	Woking	1-2
Billericay	v	Saffron Walden Town	2-1
Blyth Town	v	Wakefield Hall Green	3-2
Bolton Ambassodors	v	Blyth Spartans	2-6
Bradford City	v	Buxton	7-1
Broughton Rangers	v	Sandiacre Town	6-4
Bury Girls & Ladies	v	Wigan	4-0
Cambridge Rangers	v	Dudley United	1-5
Carterton	v	Corinthian Casuals	2-2*, 3-1p
Chelmsford City	v	Abbey Rangers	3-2
Clapton Orient	v	Lewes	1-2
Concord Rangers	v	Hendon	0-2
Corby S&L	v	AFC Telford United Ladies	2-4*
Darwen	v	Macclesfield Town	10-0
Denton Town	v	Gateshead Cleveland Hall	3-1
Dover Athletic	v	Arlesey Town	5-3
Durham City	v	Teeside Athletic	0-6
Dynamo North London	v	Croydon Athletic	4-3
Eastbourne Town	v	Whitehawk	0-9
Exeter City	v	Frome Town	1-2
Florence	v	Peterborough	1-0
Gloucester City	v	Alphington	12-0
Haringey Borough	v	Kent Magpies	7-3
Hastings United (wo)	v	Leighton Linslade	
Henley Town	v	UKP	6-5*
Hereford Pegasus	v	Brize Norton	9-0
Hoddesdon Owls	v	Crowborough Athletic	0-1
Huddersfield Town	v	Bolton Wanderers	6-2*
Ilminster Town	v	Saltash United	1-6
Kettering Town	v	Birstall FL&E Ladies	5-4
Kettering United	v	Solihull Ladies	1-9
Launceston	v	Penzance	2-4
Launton	v	Staines Town	0-10
Leicester City Womens	v	Cambridge United	5-0
Liverpool Manweb Feds	v	Warrington Town	4-0
London Women	v	Woodbridge Town	0-3
Lordswood	v	Aylesbury United	7-0
Loughborough Dynamo	v	Cambridge University	3-1
Lumley Ladies	v	Killingworth YPC	11-1
Mansfield Road	v	Ross Town	2-3
Met Ladies	v	Newport Pagnell Town	1-3
MK Wanderers	v	Gravesend & Northfleet	2-3
Ossett Albion	v	Morley Spurs	0-4
Penrith United	v	Windscale	2-4*
Peterborough Azure	v	Lichfield Diamonds	2-5
Reading	v	Chinnor Youth Ladies	4-2*
Rushcliffe Eagles	v	Creswell Wanderers	5-0
Sawbridgeworth Town	v	Tottenham Hotspur	1-0
Shanklin	v	St Peter's	2-0

Slough	v	Brentford	3-2
South Notts	v	Colchester Town	5-0
Southam United	v	Kirkley	7-0
Stoke City	v	University of Birmingham	0-1
Tamworth Lionesses	v	Copsewood (Coventry)	0-2
Team Bath	v	Central	3-2
Thatcham Town	v	Braintree Town	3-1
Thurrock & Tilbury	v	Swale Magpies	0-4
Tring Athletic	v	Acton Sports Club	1-3
Upper Beeding	v	Barking	1-4
Walsall	v	Notts County	4-4*, 4-3p
Worcester City	v	Yeovil Town	0-5
Wycombe Wanderers	v	Harlow Athletic	3-1
Wyrley	v	Stratford Town	5-1
York City	v	Kirklees	11-0

SECOND ROUND QUALIFYING

AFC Kempston Rovers	v	Woking	1-2
AFC Newbury Ladies	v	Lewes	2-6
Aldershot Town	v	Thatcham Town	2-3
Bath City	v	Frome Town	2-4
Billericay	v	Lordswood	2-1
Blyth Town	v	Bradford City	4-3
Chelmsford City	v	Newport Pagnell Town	9-0
Copsewood (Coventry)	v	Solihull Ladies	1-2
Crowborough Athletic	v	Barking	2-0
Dudley United	v	Lichfield Diamonds	2-3
Florence	v	Broughton Rangers	2-1
Gloucester City	v	Team Bath	2-3
Gravesend & Northfleet	v	Carterton	6-1
Haringey Borough	v	Banbury United	10-1
Hastings United	v	Dover Athletic	9-2
Hendon	v	Woodbridge Town	2-4
Henley Town	v	Dynamo North London	0-1
Huddersfield Town	v	Darwen	4-0
Liverpool Manweb Feds	v	Bury Girls & Ladies	3-5
Loughborough Dynamo	v	Leicester City Womens	0-6
Lumley Ladies	v	Blyth Spartans	1-3
Penzance	v	Saltash United	11-0
Reading	v	Yeovil Town	0-7
Ross Town	v	Hereford Pegasus	3-4
Rushcliffe Eagles	v	Kettering Town	1-2
Sawbridgeworth Town	v	Whitehawk	2-4
Shanklin	v	AFC Bournemouth Ladies	1-1*, 4-2p
Slough	v	Haywards Heath Town	5-0
South Notts	v	University of Birmingham	1-3
Southam United	v	AFC Telford United Ladies	2-3
Staines Town	v	Acton Sports Club	4-2
Swale Magpies	v	Wycombe Wanderers	5-1
Teeside Athletic	v	Morley Spurs	1-7
Windscale	v	Barnsley	1-3
Wyrley	v	Walsall	4-2
York City	v	Denton Town	2-2*, 5-4p

FIRST ROUND PROPER

Barnsley	v	Blyth Spartans	1-2
Billericay	v	Hastings United	1-6
Blackpool Wren Rovers	v	Sheffield Wednesday	1-7
Blyth Town	v	Leeds City Vixens	4-6
Bury Girls & Ladies	v	Huddersfield Town	2-4
Chesham United	v	Barnet FC Ladies	3-4
Chesterfield	v	Shrewsbury Town	2-1
Colchester United	v	Dynamo North London	7-0
Crewe	v	York City	1-2
Crowborough Athletic	v	Queens Park Rangers	0-4
Dagenham & Redbridge	v	Chelmsford City	5-2
Doncaster Parkland Rovers	v	Chester Le Street Town	0-2
Enfield Town	v	Luton Town Belles	3-1
Florence	v	Morley Spurs	2-3
Forest Green Rovers	v	Newton Abbot	1-0
Gillingham	v	Leyton Orient	1-2*
Gravesend & Northfleet	v	Woking	4-0
Haringey Borough	v	Staines Town	2-5
Ipswich Town	v	Kettering Town	7-0
Keynsham Town	v	Shanklin	4-1
Leafield Athletic Triplex	v	Derby County	5-4*
Leicester City Womens	v	Solihull Ladies	12-1
Lewes	v	Thatcham Town	7-0
Lichfield Diamonds	v	Wyrley	4-2
Loughborough Students	v	Stafford Rangers	7-0
Newquay AFC Ladies	v	Team Bath	5-3
Northampton Town	v	Coventry City	2-1
Norwich City Ladies	v	Leicester City Ladies	0-0*, 5-6p
Oxford City	v	Frome Town	2-4
Penzance	v	Clevedon Town	2-1*
Plymouth Argyle	v	Hereford Pegasus	0-4
Preston North End	v	South Durham Royals	8-0
Rotherham United	v	Chester City	6-1
Scunthorpe United	v	Garswood Saints	0-0*, 2-4p
Sophtlogic	v	Bedford Town Bells	4-2
Swindon Town	v	Yeovil Town	1-0
TNS Ladies	v	AFC Telford United Ladies	8-0
University or Birmingham	v	Long Eaton Villa	1-5
Whitehawk	v	Swale Magpies	3-1
Woodbridge Town	v	Slough	2-3*

SECOND ROUND PROPER

Barnet FC Ladies	v	Dagenham & Redbridge	1-0
Blyth Spartans	v	Chester Le Street Town	3-2*
Chesterfield	v	Northampton Town	0-2
Frome Town	v	Swindon Town	6-1
Gravesend & Northfleet	v	Colchester United	0-1
Hereford Pegasus	v	Penzance	3-0
Leeds City Vixens	v	York City	6-1
Leicester City Womens	v	Litchfield Diamonds	3-2
Leyton Orient	v	Hastings United	5-3
Long Eaton Villa	v	Ipswich Town	3-3*, 4-5p
Loughborough Students	v	Leicester City Ladies	1-2
Morley Spurs	v	Huddersfield Town	0-0*, 2-4p
Newquay AFC Ladies	v	Keynsham Town	1-5
Preston North End	v	Garswood Saints	8-1
Queens Park Rangers	v	Lewes	6-0
Sheffield Wednesday	v	Rotherham United	1-2
Slough	v	Forest Green Rovers	1-0
Sophtlogic	v	Staines Town	1-4
TNS Ladies	v	Leafield Athletic Triplex	1-1*, 3-1p
Whitehawk	v	Enfield Town	3-0

THIRD ROUND PROPER

AFC Wimbledon Ladies	v	Crystal Palace	3-1
Aston Villa	v	Wolverhampton Wanderers	1-0
Barnet FC Ladies	v	West Ham United	4-1
Blackburn Rovers	v	Lincoln City	3-1
Brighton & Hove Albion	v	Leyton Orient	3-0
Cardiff City	v	Keynsham Town	2-0
Colchester United	v	Staines Town	3-2*
Curzon Ashton	v	Blyth Spartans	6-0
Hereford Pegasus	v	Frome Town	3-3*, 1-3p
Ipswich Town	v	Leicester City Ladies	2-0
Langford	v	Whitehawk	2-1

Leeds City Vixens	v	Rotherham United	5-1
Liverpool	v	Tranmere Rovers	2-1
Middlesbrough	v	Manchester City	1-2
Newcastle Utd Women's	v	Huddersfield Town	7-2
Northampton Town	v	TNS Ladies	2-1
Nottingham Forest	v	Leicester City Women's	3-1
Portsmouth	v	Millwall Lionesses	2-1
Preston North End	v	Stockport County	1-2*
Reading Royals	v	Bristol City	2-4
Southampton Saints	v	Slough	3-1
Watford	v	Queens Park Rangers	3-0

FOURTH ROUND PROPER

AFC Wimbledon Ladies	v	Watford	1-3
Blackburn Rovers	v	Chelsea	1-2*
Bristol City	v	Charlton Athletic (H)	1-4
Cardiff City	v	Arsenal	1-4
Everton	v	Nottingham Forest	2-0
Fulham	v	Southampton Saints	6-0
Ipswich Town	v	Birmingham City	0-7
Langford	v	Brighton & Hove Albion	0-1*
Leeds City Vixens	v	Aston Villa	4-5*
Leeds United	v	Doncaster Rovers Belles	2-1
Liverpool	v	Colchester United	1-0
Manchester City	v	Barnet FC Ladies	0-2
Newcastle Utd Women's	v	Northampton Town	3-1
Portsmouth	v	Bristol Academy	5-5*, 5-6p
Stockport County	v	Frome Town	7-1
Sunderland AFC Ladies	v	Curzon Ashton	2-2*, 3-4p

FIFTH ROUND PROPER

Aston Villa	v	Arsenal	0-3
Barnet FC Ladies	v	Liverpool	2-3
Brighton & Hove Albion	v	Bristol Academy	1-2
Fulham	v	Charlton Athletic (H)	0-3
Leeds United	v	Everton	3-1
Newcastle Utd Women's	v	Curzon Ashton	2-0
Stockport County	v	Birmingham City	0-2
Watford	v	Chelsea	0-1*

SIXTH ROUND PROPER

Birmingham City	v	Leeds United	1-3
Bristol Academy	v	Charlton Athletic (H)	0-5
Chelsea	v	Arsenal	1-6
Newcastle United	v	Liverpool	2-2*, 8-9p

SEMI-FINALS

Leeds United	v	Liverpool	2-0
			Att: 1,050
Arsenal	v	Charlton Athletic (H)	2-1*
			Att: 1,095

THE FINAL

Arsenal	v	Leeds United	5-0

Ward 3 (og), Fleeting 34,
Yankey 35, Smith 73 (pen),
Sanderson 77

Att: 13,452

Team Line-ups:
Arsenal Ladies: Byrne, Scott, Philliip, White, Champ, Ludlow, Smith, Anita Asante, Yankey, Fleeting, Sanderson.
Leeds Ladies: Fay, Burke, Cook, Preston, Emmanuel, Smith, Walker, Ward, Clarke, Haigh, Culvin.

F.A. FUTSAL CUP

GROUP STAGES

GROUP A		P	W	D	L	F	A	Pts
Kickers		3	2	1	0	20	3	7
Ravenous Taverners		3	2	1	0	8	3	7
Salford Victoria		3	1	0	2	10	20	3
Sporting Shropshire		3	0	0	3	8	20	0

Kickers	v	Sporting Shropshire	7-0
Ravenous Taverners	v	Sporting Shropshire	5-2
Salford Victoria	v	Ravenous Taverners	0-2
Slaford Victoria	v	Kickers	2-12
Ravenous Taverners	v	Kickers	1-1
Sporting Shropshire	v	Salford Victoria	6-8

GROUP B		P	W	D	L	F	A	Pts
Baltic		3	3	0	0	20	2	9
White Bear		3	2	0	1	18	9	6
Norwich Union		3	1	0	2	7	18	3
FCF Corinthians		3	0	0	3	7	23	0

FCF Corinthians	v	Baltic	1-8
Norwich Union	v	Baltic	1-8
White Bear	v	Norwich Union	7-2
White Bear	v	FCF Corinthians	11-3
Baltic	v	White Bear	4-0
Norwich Union	v	FCF Corinthians	4-3

GROUP C		P	W	D	L	F	A	Pts
Team United		3	3	0	0	16	9	9
Doncaster College (H)		3	2	0	1	20	9	6
Barsa		3	0	1	2	11	17	1
Trydovie Res		3	0	1	2	4	16	1

Barsa	v	Doncaster College	4-8
Team United	v	Doncaster College	5-4
Trydovie Res	v	Team United	1-5
Trydovie Res	v	Barsa	3-3
Barsa	v	Team United	4-6
Doncaster College	v	Trydovie Res	8-0

GROUP B		P	W	D	L	F	A	Pts
Tranmere Victoria		3	2	1	0	17	5	7
Ipswich Wolves		3	1	1	1	13	12	4
Nicol Magpies		3	1	0	2	12	21	3
Vaughan's		3	0	2	1	10	12	2

Nicol Magpies	v	Vaughan's	7-5
Nicol Magpies	v	Tranmere Victoria	1-8
Tranmere Victoria	v	Ipswich Wolves	7-2
Vaughan's	v	Ipswich Town	3-3
Ipswich Wolves	v	Nicol Magpies	8-4
Vaughan's	v	Tranmere Victoria	2-2

QUARTER-FINALS

Kickers	v	White Bear	1-3
Ravenous Taverners	v	Baltic	1-5
Team United	v	Ipswich Wolves	2-4
Tranmere Victoria	v	Doncaster College (H)	6-2

SEMI FINALS

White Bear	v	Ipswich Wolves	4-3
Baltic	v	Tranmere Victoria	3-2

THE FINAL

White Bear	v	Baltic	5-0

PLATE COMPETITION

QUARTER-FINALS

Sporting Shropshire	v	Norwich Union	7-8
Barsa	v	Vaughan's	3-11
Salford Victoria	v	FCF Corinthians	2-4
Trydovie Res	v	Nicol Magpies	4-10

SEMI FINALS

FCF Corinthians	v	Vaughan's	0-4
Norwich Union	v	Nicol Magpies	4-7

THE FINAL

Vaughan's	v	Nicol Magpies	8-7

COUNTY FOOTBALL ASSOCIATIONS

BEDFORDSHIRE F.A.

Tel: 01582 565111 (B)   Fax: 01582 565222   Email: peter.brown@bedfordshirefa.com
Century House, Skimpot Road, Dunstable, Bedfordshire LU5 4JU
Secretary: Peter D Brown
Other executives: **President:** Ray Berridge **Chairman:** Richard Robinson
Chief Executive: Peter D Brown   **Development Manager:** Simon Macqueen
Coaching: Kevin England **Discipline:** Secretary   **Registration:** Secretary   **Referees:** Nicholas Snelson
Grants: Secretary   **Courses:** Secretary   **Womens:** Charlene Ward   **Press&PR:** Secretary
Number of Affiliated Clubs   Senior: 39   Junior: 238   Womens: 12
County Representative Teams U18 & U16 Senior Coach: Kevin Thorburn   Womens Manager: Noel Lewis
Inter County Competitions: East Anglia Counties ChampionshipU18 U16
Trophies won in season 2004-05: None

COUNTY CUP FINALS

Senior Cup	Biggleswade United	v	Leighton Town	1-0
Senior Trophy	Brache Sports	v	Kent Athletic	1-0
Intermediate Cup	A.F.C. Kempston T.	v	Biggleswade U Res	2-3

BERKS & BUCKS F.A. LIMITED

Tel: 01367 242 099   Fax: 01367 242 158
email: secretary@berks-bucksfa.com www.berks-bucksfa.com
15a London Street, Faringdon, Oxon SN7 7HD
Chief Executive: Brian Moore   **Chairman:** Jim Atkins **President:** Bill Gosling

County Development Manager: Liz Verrall   **Football Development Officer:** Freya Coombe
Discipline: Tracey Bannon & Leigh Priest   **Coaching**: development@berks-bucksfa.com   **Registration:** Caroline Terry
Courses: development@berks-buckfa.com **Referees:** Tracey Bannon/Leigh Priest **Press & PR:** Brian Moore
Number of Affiliated Clubs Senior: 30   Junior: 432   Womens: 17
Intermediate:183   Youth: 218
County Representative Teams (Senior Coach responsible): Youth Under-18 & 16 and Women
Inter County Competitions: South West Counties (Youth)
Trophies won in season 2005-06: None

COUNTY CUP FINALS
Senior Cup

Wycombe Wanderers	v	MK Dons	2-1	at the Causeway Stadium.
Trophy				
Didcot Town	v	Sandhurst Town	5-1	at Thatcham Town F.C.
Intermediate Cup				
Chalfont Wasps	v	Eton Wick	3-1	at ThatchamTown F.C.

BIRMINGHAM COUNTY F.A.

Tel: 0121 357 4278   **Fax**: 0121 358 1661   **Email**: info@birminghamfa.com

County Offices: Ray Hall Lane, Great Barr, Birmingham B43 6JF

County Secretary: David Shelton.   **Company Secretary**: Michael Pennick

President: Jim Blower **Chariman:** Roger Wood

County Development Officer: Natalie Justice (includes Grants)

Discipline: Michael Fellows   **Womens:** Heather Cowan **Press & PR:** Antonia Lacey & Sunny Sahota

Coaching Courses: BCFDS 0121 682 2525 **Referees:** Mike Penn

Number of Affiliated Clubs   Senior: 1,675   Minor: 643

Number of Affiliated Leagues: Senior: 55   Minor   18

County Representative Teams: U18, U16,

Inter County Competition: B oys U18, U16 , FA Youth Cup and Midland Youth Championships

County Publications: A new newsletter will be launched in August 2006

COUNTY CUP FINALS

Senior	Willenhall Town.	v	Stourbridge	1-0

CAMBRIDGESHIRE F.A. LTD

Tel: 01223 576 770x201   Fax: 01223 576 780   Email: secretary@cambridgeshirefa.com

City Ground, Milton Road, Cambridge CB4 1FA

Secretary: Roger Pawley

Other executives: **President:** T.B.A.   **Chairman:** J W Coad

Chief Executive: R K Pawley   **Development Officer:** J F Hill

Coaching: **Discipline:** R K Pawley   **Registration:**   **Referees:** R K Nichols

Grants: **Courses:** Beverly Clarkson **Womens:** Victoria Morley   **Press&PR:** R.K.Pawley

Number of Affiliated Clubs   Senior: 30   Junior: 280   Womens: 15

County Representative Teams (Senior Coach responsible): (Andrew Ross)

Inter County Competitions: East Anglian

Trophies won in season 2004-05: None

COUNTY CUP FINALS

Professional Cup	Soham Town Rangers	v		Great Shelford	1-0

CHESHIRE F.A.

Tel: 01606 871166   Fax: 01606 871292   Football Development: 01606 871155

Hartford House, Hartford Moss Recreation Centre, Winnington, Northwich CW8 4BG

Secretary: Maureen Dunford

Other executives: **President:** Eddie Crabtree   **Chairman:** Dave Edmunds

Chief Executive: Maureen Dunford   **Development Officer:** John Ackerley

Coaching: John Ackerley **Discipline:** Steve Mundy   **Registration:** Steve Mundy   **Referees:** Trevor Massey

Grants: John Ackerley   **Courses:** John Ackerley   **Womens:** Zoe Harp   **Press&PR:** Secretary

Number of Affiliated Clubs   Senior: 1,197   Junior: 262   Womens: 42

County Representative Teams: (Senior Coach responsible): Correspondence to Dave Edmunds

Inter County Competitions: Northern Counties Senior, Northern Counties Youth, F.A.County Youth

COUNTY CUP FINALS

Senior Cup	Stalybridge Celtic	v	Witton Albion	0-2	Att 427 at Altrincham

CORNWALL F.A.

Tel: 01726 74080   Fax: 01726 76174   Email: secretary@cornwallfa.com

1 High Cross Street, St Austell, Cornwall PL25 4AB Website: www.cornwallfa.com

President: B F Conyon M.B.E. **Chairman:** D G Champion. **Secretary:** Barry Cudmore

Executives (Responsibility): David Bray (Youth Secretary). Ray Brown (Referees)

Phil Cardew (Football Development Officer) **Football Development Office:** Andy Mitchell

Number of Affiliated Clubs   Senior: 311   U.18:   75

Number of Affiliated Leagues: Senior: 25   Youth: 3

County Representative Teams: Senior, Youth U18, Seniopr Women, Womens Under 18

Inter County Competitions: S.W.t Counties Senior, Youth & Womens, FA County Youth Cup & Womens U 18

COUNTY CUP FINALS

Senior Cup   Bodmin Town   v   Truro City   1-4

CUMBERLAND F.A.

Tel: 01900 872310   Fax: 01900 61647

17 Oxford Street, Workington, Cumbria CA14 2AL Email: secretary@cumberlandfa.com

Secretary: G Turrell

Other executives: **President:** B Taylor   **Chairman:** J.Williamson

Company Secretary: J A Murphy   **County Development Manager:** P Devlin

Coaching: P Devlin   **Discipline:** G Turrell   **Registration:** G Turrell   **Referees:** J Williamson

Grants: W Wilson   **Courses:** E.Bassett   **Womens:** H.Aitchison   **Press&PR:** S.Durham

Number of Affiliated Clubs   Senior: 186   Junior: 209   Womens: 4

County Representative Teams: (Senior Coach responsible) B.Snowden

Inter County Competitions: Northern Counties

COUNTY CUP FINALS

Senior Cup   Penrith   v   Carlisle City   1-0

DERBYSHIRE F.A.

Tel: 01332 361 422   Fax: 01332 360 130   Email: info@derbyshirefa.com

Nos 8-9 Stadium Business Court, Millennium Way, Pride Park, Derby DE24 8HP

Website: www.derbyshirefa.com

Chairman: R F Johnson   **Secretary:** K Compton

President: T.Brocklehurst   **Development Officer:** J.Woodward

Coaching: **Discipline:**   **Registration:**   **Referees:** D N Harwood

Grants: **Courses:**   **Womens D.O.-** K.Brown   **Press&PR:** K Compton

Number of Affiliated Clubs   Senior: 450   Junior: 250   Womens: 12

County Representative Teams (Senior Coach responsible): J.Chambers

Inter County Competitions: Midlands County Youth

COUNTY CUP FINAL

Senior Cup   Mickleover Sports (1) v   Ilkeston Town (2)   1st Leg 1-1   2nd Leg: 1-0

DEVON F.A.

Tel: 01626 332077   Fax: 01626 336814   Email: info@devonfa.com

County Headquarters, Coach Road, Newton Abbot, Devon TQ12 1EJ

Secretary: Paul Morrison

Other executives: **President:** A.Beer   **Chairman:** D Smith

Chief Executive: Paul Morrison   **County Development Manager:** Ms H Buckley

Coaching& Courses: D Keast   **Discipline:** T.B.A.   **Press&PR:** D.Richardson   **Referees:** G.Gordon

Womens: L.Rider   **Registration**: Ms.M.Oxley.   **Referees**: G.Gordon   **Grants**: Ms H.Buckley

Number of Affiliated Clubs Senior: 350   Junior: 220   Womens: 36

County Representative Teams: (Senior Coach responsible) R.Brown

Inter County Competitions: South West Counties Championship

Trophies won in season 2005-06: None

COUNTY CUP FINALS

St Lukes College Bowl	Tiverton Town	v	Bideford Town		2-1aet
Premier Cup	Ivybridge Town	v	Plymouth Parkway		1-0

DORSET F.A.

Tel: 01202 682 375   Fax: 01202 666 577   Email: secretary@dorsetfa.com

County Ground, Blandford Close, Hamworthy, Poole BH15 4BF

President: Spencer Miles. **Chairman:** Doug Smurthwaite. **Chief Executive:** Sue Hough

Cup & Competitions Manager: Colin Chainey. **Secretary:** Peter Hough

Gary Knight (Football Development Manager). Referees Training Officer: L.Nethercott

County Representative Teams: Senior Men, U18 Boys, U16 Boys, Senior Women & Under 16 Girls

Inter County Competitions: South West Championship for all the above

COUNTY CUP FINALS

Senior Cup	Hamworthy United	v	Poole Town	2-1

DURHAM F.A.

Tel: 0191 3872929 Fax: 0191 387 1919 Email: john.topping@durhamfa.com

"Codeslaw', Riverside South, Chester le Street,Co. Durham DH3 3SJ

Secretary: John Topping   **President & Chairman:** Mr F D Pattison

County Development Manager: Phillip Woodward

Coaching: P. Woodward   **Discipline:** Robert Strophair **Registration:** John Topping   **Referees:** Tom Harvey

Courses: P. Woodward   **Womens:** P.Woodward   **Press&PR:** John Topping

Number of Affiliated Clubs   Senior: 1000   Junior: 350   Womens: 60

County Representative Teams (Senior Coach responsible): James Thompson

Inter County Competitions: Association of Northern Counties

COUNTY CUP FINALS

Challenge Cup	Whickham F.C.	v	Billingham Synthonia F.C.	2-1
County Trophy	Brandon Prince Bishop	v	Chester le Street Whitehills	5-0

EAST RIDING F.A. LTD

Tel: 01482 221158   Fax: 01482 221159   E.Mail: info@eastridingfa.com

50 Boulevard, Hull HU3 2TB

Secretary: Dennis R Johnson

Other executives: **President:** C Bodsworth   **Chairman:** J.Suddards

Development Officer: Andy Foster

Coaching: A Lowthorpe   **Referees:** Peter Summerbell   **Courses:** Liz Shipp

Womens: Hannah Simpson   **Press&PR:** D R Johnson

Number of Affiliated Clubs   Senior: 335   Junior: 314   Womens: 6

County Representative Teams: (Senior coach responsible) Andy Foster (Youth XI)

Inter County Competitions: Northern Counties Senior & Youth, Ridings Cup - Ladies

COUNTY CUP FINALS

Senior Cup   Sculcoates Ams.   v   Hull City   2-2 (3-2 after penalties)

ESSEX F.A.

The County Office, Springfield Lyons Approach,Springfield, Chelmsford CM2 5LB

Tel No: 01245 465271   **Fax**: 01245 393089   **Email**: info@essexfa.com

Chief Executive: Phil Sammons   **Chairman:** Mike Game

County Development Manager: Nick Perchard   **Governance Manager**: Greg Hart

Development Officers: Sharon Brownlie (clubs) & Lana Bond (schools)   **Coaching:** Gary Piggott Sue Hammond
& Simon Thomas   **Press & PR:** Matt Phillips   **Womens:** Emma Wake   **Cups:** Mark Wallis & Chris Evans

Discipline: Nicola Bruce   **Referees:** Terry Thacker/Greg Hart

Number of Affiliated Clubs   Senior: 46 Step 7: 77   Junior: 1,126   Youth 434 Womens:34 Girls 68

Inter County Competitions: East Anglian Counties

Trophies won in 2005-2006: East Anglian Under 16

COUNTY CUP FINALS

Premier Cup	Harold Wood Athletic	v	Witham Town	0-0(aet 1-3 pens)	12th April at Thurrock F.C.
Junior Cup	Brightlingsea Regent	v	Potter Street	1-2	5th April at Billericay TownF.C

GLOUCESTERSHIRE F.A. LIMITED

Tel: 01454 615888   Fax: 01454 618088

Oaklands Park, Almondsbury, Bristol BS32 4AG

Chief Executive: D.Neale

Other executives: **President:** D.C.Watts   **Chairman:** Mr R F Burden

Development Manager: N Baker   **Coaching:**R.Skinner   **Discipline:** D.Jones & r.Gray

Registration/Administration: C.Bellamy   **Referees:** K E Fry   **Grants:** N Baker   **Courses:** T.Elsbury

Womens: R.Skinner   **Press & PR:** D.Neale

Number of Affiliated Clubs   Senior:880   Junior:140   Womens:37

County Representative Teams (Senior Coach responsible): Adult Women, Womens U18 & Uner 16 (males)

Inter County Competitions: South West Counties Championship Competition

COUNTY CUP FINALS

Senior	Yate Town	v	Bristol Rovers	2-0
Trophy	Hallen	v	Harrow Hill	1-3

HAMPSHIRE F.A. Tel: 02380 791 110 Fax: 02380 788 340

Email: secretary@hampshirefa.com www.hampshirefa.com

Units 8/9 Summerlea Court, Herriard Business Park, Herriard, Hampshire. RG25 2PN

President: John Benfield **Chairman:** John Ward

Chief Executive: Neil Cassar **Office/Marketing Manager** Keith Stroud

Development Officer: Sacha Nicholas

Coaching: Lee Burch **Discipline:** Debbie Sowton **Registration:** Darren Parker **Referees:** Matt Parfect

Grants: Sacha Nicholas **Courses:** jJackie Elkin **Womens:** Kathryn Holland **Press & PR:** Paul Creeden

Number of Affiliated Clubs Senior: 1650 Junior: 450 Womens: 50

County Representative Teams (Senior Coach responsible): U21, U18, u17 Women's & U18 Girls

Inter County Competitions: South West Counties Championship Competition

Trophies won in season 2005-06: Women & Girls U18s and Men Under 18

COUNTY CUP FINALS

Senior Cup Farnborough Town v Basington Town 1-0 Bournemouth

HEREFORDSHIRE F.A.

Tel: 01432 342179 Fax: 01432 279265 Email: herefordfa@ukonline.co.uk

County Ground Offices, Widemarsh Common, Hereford HR4 9NA

Secretary: Jim Lambert

Other executives: **President:** Sir Colin Shephard **Chairman:** W E Shorten

Chief Executive: N/A **Development Officer:** Paul Carpenter

Coaching: Secretary **Discipline:** Secretary **Registration:** Secretary **Referees:** Secretary

Grants: Secretary **Courses:** Secretary **Womens:** Secretary **Press&PR:** Secretary

Number of Affiliated Clubs Senior: 31 Junior: 126 Womens: 3

County Representative Teams (Senior Coach responsible): (Jack Perks)

Inter County Competitions: Midland Counties

COUNTY CUP FINALS

Challenge Cup Hinton v Westfields 0-1 aet

HERTFORDSHIRE F.A.

Tel: 01462 677622 Fax: 01462 677624 E.Mail: info@hertfordshirefa.com

County Ground, Baldock Road, Letchworth, Herts SG6 2EN

Company Secretary: Mr E W J King **Office Manager:** Linda Ennis

Other executives: J **President:** Mr R G Kibble **Chairman:** Mr W H Dance

Chief Executive: John Marchant **Development Manager:**

Coaching: Mr Alan Ackrell **Discipline:** Mr G R Norman **Registration:** Secretary **Referees:** Mr R G Dowden

Grants: Secretary **Courses:** Gill Collins **Womens:** Mr Karl Lingham **Press&PR:** Mr S R Trulock

Number of Affiliated Clubs Senior: 4 Junior: 664 Womens: 14

County Representative Teams (Senior Coach responsible): (Mr E T Dowber)

Inter County Competitions: East Anglian Counties Championship - U16, U18 and Womens

Trophies won in season 2005-06: East Anglian CC - Womens

COUNTY CUP FINALS

Senior Cup Bishop's Stortford v Stevenage Borough 1-0 County Ground

HUNTINGDONSHIRE F.A.

Tel: 01480 414422   Fax: 01480 447489   Email: Mark.Frost@HuntsFA.com   www.HuntsFA.com

Cromwell Chambers, 8 St Johns Street, Huntingdon, Cambs. PE29 3DD

Secretary: Mark Frost

Other executives: **President:** Doug Roberts   **Chairman:** Eric Heads

Chief Executive: N/A   **Development Officer:** Kirsty Frior

Coaching: Kirsty Fior   **Discipline:** Valerie Bryant   **Press&PR:** Mark Frost   **Referees:** Mike Hair

Grants: info@HuntsFA.com **Courses:** Susan Brydon   **Womens:** Victoria Morley

Number of Affiliated Clubs Senior: 120   Junior: 30   Womens: 6

County Representative Teams (c/o County Office):

Inter County Competitions: East Midlands Youth U18 & U16 - FA County Youth Cup-Womens E.Anglian Co.

COUNTY CUP FINALS

Senior Cup	Ortonians	v	St.Neots Town	1-0

KENT F.A. Limited

Tel: 01634 843 824   Fax: 01634 815 369   E.Mail: secretary@kentfa.com

69 Maidstone Road, Chatham, Kent ME4 6DT

Secretary: Keith Masters

Other executives: **President:** N Chatfield   **Chairman:** B W Bright

Chief Executive: K Masters   **Development Officer:** N Rice

Coaching: A Walker   **Discipline:** S Tillman   **Registration:**   **Referees:** J Newson

Grants: **Courses:** L.Suter   **Womens:** L Symons   **Press&PR:** T Hudd

Number of Affiliated Clubs   Senior: 37 Intermediate 3   Junior: 856 Women & Girls: 30: Youth:193

County Representative Teams (Senior Coach responsible): (B Bull)

Inter County Competitions: Home Counties

COUNTY CUP FINALS

Senior Cup	Bromley	v	Gravesend & Northfleet	3-2	
Senior Trophy	Tunbridge Wells	v	VCD	1-1	(VCD won after penalties)

LANCASHIRE F.A.

Tel: 01772 624000   Fax: 01772 624700

The County Ground, Thurston Road, Leyland PR25 2LF

Company Secretary: David Burgess

Other executives: **President:** G Howard   **Chairman:** W.B. Warburton

Chief Executive: David Burgess   **Development Manager:** Derek Egan

Coaching: Derek Egan   **Discipline Officer:** Miss Hayley Mather   **Registration:** Linda Threlfall

Referees Officer: Eddie Wolstenholme   **Grants:** David Burgess **Courses:** Derek Egan

Girls & Womens' Officer: Simon Gerrard   **Press & PR:** David Burgess

Number of Affiliated Clubs   Senior: 3,000   Junior: 2,500   Womens: 1,300

County Representative Teams: David Wilson (Chairman of Youth Committee) and BillShaw (Chairman of Competitions Committee)

Inter County Competitions: Linda Threlfall

COUNTY CUP FINALS

United Co-operatives Challenge Trophy: Southport F.C.v Lancaster City F.C. 1-0

LEICESTERSHIRE & RUTLAND F.A.

Te.lNo: 0116 284 7828   Fax: 0116 286 4858   Email: secretary@leicestershirefa.com

Holmes Park, Dog & Gun Lane, Whetstone LE8 6FA

Chief Executive: John Folwell

Other executives: **President:** Gerry Cooper   **Chairman:** David Jamieson

Chief Executive: Paul Morrison   **County Development Manager:** Steve Savva

Discipline: Chris Parkin   **R egistration:** Matt Edkins   **Referees:** Jamie Snashall

Number of Affiliated Clubs   Senior: 520   Junior: 180   Womens: 21

County Representative Teams (Senior Coach responsible): Under 18/16 Boys, Under 16 Girls

Inter County Competitions: Midland Youth Championship - as above

Trophies won in season 2005-06: Midland Youth Championship U16 Cup winners & U16 League Winners

COUNTY CUP FINALS

Challenge Cup	Rocester	v	Coalville	3-2 aet

LINCOLNSHIRE F.A.

Tel: 01522 524917   Fax: 01522 528859

PO Box 26, 12 Dean Road, Lincoln LN2 4DP

Secretary: John Griffin

Other executives: **President:** Norman Saywell   **Chairman:** Roy Teanby

Chief Executive: N/A   **Development Officer:** Robert King

Coaching: Secretary   **Discipline:** Secretary   **Registration:** Secretary   **Referees:** Reg Jackson

Grants: Secretary   **Press&PR:** Keith Weaver

Number of Affiliated Clubs   Senior: 638   Junior: 284   Womens: 15

County Representative Teams (Senior Coach responsible): Under 18

Inter County Competitions: Midland Youth Football Championships

COUNTY CUP FINALS

Shield	Brigg Town	v	Lincoln United	0-1
Senior Cup	Boston United	v	Scunthorpe United	2-1
Senior 'A'	Bourne Town	v	Deeping Rangers	1-0

LIVERPOOL F.A.

Tel: 0151 523 4488   Fax: 0151 523 4477   Email: info@liverpoolfa.com

Liverpool Soccer Centre, Walton Hall Park, Walton Hall Avenue, Liverpool L4 9XP

Secretary: T.B.A. **Acting County Secretary**: Alan

Other executives: **President:** G.S. Winnett   **Chairman:** C.Welsh

Chief Executive: F Hunter   **Development Manager:** M McGlynn   **Website Officer**:A.Smith

Devlopment Officer: C Smith   **Discipline:** W Flanagan   **Registration:** Miss L Edwards   **Referees:** D Cleveland

Grants: M McGlynn   **Courses:** C Smith   **Womens:** Miss J. O'Donnell   **Press & PR:** B Phillips

Number of Affiliated Clubs   Senior: 400   **Junior**:   500   **Womens:**   26

County Representative Teams (Senior Coach responsible): (P.Hackney)

Inter County Competitions: Northern Counties

COUNTY CUP FINALS

Senior Cup	Marine	v	Tranmere Rovers	Not yet played
Challenge Cup	Aintre VIlla	v	Waterloo Dock	0-4

LONDON F.A.

Tel: 00870 7743010   Fax: 020 8690 9471   Email: info@londonfa.com

11 Hurlingham Business Park, Sulivan Rd., Fulham, London SW6 3DU

Other executives: **President:** L.J.Seymour **Chairman:** T.B.A.

Chief Executive: David Fowkes   **Development Manager:** Josie Clifford

Coaching: John Drabwell **Discipline:** Pam Coleman   **Registration:** Pam Coleman **Referees:** Andy Porter

Treasurer: Basil Stallard   **Courses:** Neil Fowkes   **Womens:** Caroline McRoyall **Press&PR:** N/A

Number of Affiliated Clubs   Senior: 1457   Junior: 461   Womens: 42

County Rep. Teams : Adult Men-Lester Newham, Adult Women-Nigel Coppewheat & Youth-Alan Clarke

Inter County Competitions: Lester Newham

Trophies won in season 2004-05: London Yth U16, Southern CC

COUNTY CUP FINALS

Senior Cup	FisherAthletic	v	Wingate & Finchley	4-0	6th May - Met Police F.C.

MANCHESTER F.A.

Tel: 0161604 7620   Fax: 0161 604 7622   Email:steve rooke@manchesterfa.com

Salford Sports Village, Littleton Road, Lower Kersal, Salford Manchester M7 3NQ

Chief Executive//Company Secrtary: Steve Rooke **President/Chairman:** Frank Hannah

Office Manager: Joan Harris   **Discipline& Finance:** David Harris

Chief Executive responsible for: **Coaching, Governance, Grants, Press & PR, Marketing, Referees,**

Affiliations and staffing. Development Manager: Philip Heap **Development Administration:** Colin Bridgford

Development Officer: Paul Bright **Child Protection Officer**: John Taylor **Disability Officer**: Gilly Cunningham

Social Inclusion Projects Officer: TBA **Women's Officer**: Anita Blair

Number of Affiliated Clubs: Full Members 29 Associate Members 465 Youth 182 Women 32

County Representative Teams Youth U18s only **Manager:** Danny Johnson **Coach:** Paul Fletcher.

Trophies won in season 2005-05: Northern Counties Division 2 Champions

COUNTY CUP FINALS

Premier Cup	Droysden	v	Hyde United	1-2
Senior Cup	Oldham Athletic	v	Manchester United	2-3
Amateur Cup	East Manchester	v	Old Stretfordians	3-1

MIDDLESEX COUNTY F.A.

Tel: 0208 5151919 Fax: 0208 5151910 E.Mail: chief.exec@middlesexfa.com

39 Roxborough Road, Harrow, Middlesex HA1 1NS

Chief Executive: Peter Clayton

Other executives: **President:** Derek Mennell   **Chairman:** Jim Taylor

County Development Manager: Stuart Allen **Development Officer:** Leigh O'Connor

Coaching: Leigh O'Connor **Discipline:** Chris Hartley   **Registration:** Mark Larner **Referees:** Mark Sennett

Grants: Stuart Allen   **Courses:** Leigh O'Connor **Womens:** Charlotte Edwards **Press&PR:** Geoff Harrison

Number of Affiliated Clubs   Senior: 600   Junior: 225   Womens: 30

County Representative Teams (Senior Coach responsible):

Inter County Competitions: Pip Axtell

COUNTY CUP FINAL

Senior Cup	Hayes	v	Hampton & Richmond B	H& B won after penalties

NORFOLK F.A.

Tel: 01603 704050   Fax: 01603 704059   E.mail: info@norfolkfa.com

11 Meridian Way,Thorpe St.Andrew, Norwich NF7 0TA

Chief Executive : Shaun Turner

Other executives: **President:** Ray Kiddell   **Chairman:** Stuart Dracup

Football Association Representative: Roger Howlett

Football Administrative Officer: Richard King   **County Development Manager:** Gavin Lemmon

Discipline: Richard King   **Referees:** Steve Clover

For any other matters please contact the Chief Executive.

Number of Affiliated Clubs   Male Adults:408   Male Youth:154   Womens: 18   Girls: 32

County Representative Teams (Senior Coach responsible): John Musgrove U18's & Womens: Darren Moss

COUNTY CUP FINALS

Senior Cup	Dereham Town	v	Norwich United	1-0

NORTH RIDING F.A.

Tel: 01642 717770 Fax: 01642 318604

Broughton Road, Stokesley, Middlesbrough TS9 5NY

Chief Executibe/Secretary: Tom Radigan

Other executives: **President:** T.B.A.   **Chairman:** Len Scott

Development Manager: Mark Coulson   **Referees:** C Dale/J Campbell

Coaching: Paul Stephenson,/G Grainger/S.Wade & D.Burns   **Courses:**Paul Stephenson

Discipline: Chief Executive **Registration: Grants:** Office   **Womens:** G Grainger   **Press&PR:** Office

Number of Affiliated Clubs   Senior: 337   Junior: 95   Womens: 33

County Representative Teams (Senior Coach responsible): J Wattis

Inter County Competitions: FA, Northern Counties, Ridings Ladies

COUNTY CUP FINALS

Senior Cup	York City	v	North Allerton Town	3-1

NORTHAMPTONSHIRE F.A.

Tel: 01604 670741   Fax: 01604 670742   E.mail: info@northamptonshirefa.com

9 Duncan Close, Redhouse Square, Moulton Park, Northampton NN3 6WL

Chief Executive: David Payne   **President:** D Vernum **Chairman:** Robert Cotter

Football Administrator: Sue Ainge **Football Development Off:** Jamie Leeson

County Development Manager: T.B.A.   **Finance Assitsant:** Nicola Dodds

County Development Manager: Joanne Ashworth **Referees:** Mrs Sue Ainge **Grants:** David Payne

Courses: Mrs Debbie Preston   **Press & PR:** David Payne   **Disciplinary Office:** Miss Rebecca Greaves

Girls & Women's Football Development Officer: Miss Jackie Bushell

Number of Affiliated Clubs: Senio:15, Jun/Sat:110 ,Jun/Sun:199,Youth/Boys 126,Youth/Girls 36 Mini Soccer 85

County Rep. Teams: (Senior Coach): U18 Boys.(Paul Curtis) U16 Girls (Jackie Bushell & Caroline Moran)

Inter County Competitions: Boys FA County Youth Champs & Midland County Champs. U16 Girls Midland Co. Youth Champs.

COUNTY CUP FINALS

Maunsell Cup	Rushden & Diamonds	v	Peterborough United	1-1 (32- after pens)
Hillier Senior Cup	Northampton Spencer	v	Corby Town	1-0
Les Underwood Junior	Wellingborough Town	v	Peterborough Northern Star	2-0 aet
Lower Junior Cup:	Bugbrooke St.Michael	v	Corby Grampian	1-0

NORTHUMBERLAND F.A.

Tel: 0191 2 700 700

Whitley Park, Whitley Road, Newcastle upon Tyne NE12 9FA

Secretary: See Chief Executive

Other executives: **President:** E A Wright   **Chairman:** T.B.A.

Chief Executive: Rowland E Maughan   **Development Officer:** S W Leason

Coaching: M Woodhall   **Discipline:** R.E.Maughan   **Referees:** R E Maughan

Grants: S W Leason   **Courses:** S W Leason   **Womens:** S W Leason   **Press&PR:** W Gardiner

Number of Affiliated Clubs   Senior: 477   Junior: 508   Womens: 19

County Representative Teams (Senior Coach responsible): J.Carron

Inter County Competitions: Associate Northern Counties

COUNTY CUP FINALS

Senior Cup	Blyth Spartans	v	Newcastle Unityed Reserves	1-2
Bowl	Seaton Delaval Am.	v	Ponteland United	2-3

NOTTINGHAMSHIRE F.A. LIMITED

Tel: 0115 941 8954   Fax: 0115 941 5254   Email: info@nottinghamshirefa.com

7 Clarendon Street, Nottingham NG1 5HS

Secretary: Mike Kilbee

Other executives: **President:** David Woolrich   **Chairman:** Alec Thompson

Chief Executive: N/A   **Development Officer:** Ricky Stephenson (CDM), Craig Lee (FDO)

Coaching: R.Stephenson   **Discipline:** Helen Bennett   **Referees:** David Coote   **Womens:** Malcolm Fox

Grants: Ricky Stephenson **Courses:** Ricky Stephensopn

Number of Affiliated Clubs Senior:561   Junior: 198   Womens: 13

County Representative Teams (Senior Coach responsible): U18 (Steve Pritchard)

Inter County Competitions: East Midlands Youth

Senior Cup	Eastwood Town	v	Sutton Town	3-1	April 26th, Meadow Lane

OXFORDSHIRE F.A.

Tel: 01993 778 586   Fax: 01993 772 191   Email: secretary@oxfordshirefa.com

PO Box 62, Witney, Oxon OX28 1HA

President: J Webb. **Chairman:** T Williams. **Secretary:** Ian Mason

Executives (Responsibility): Kirsty Brammer (Football Development)

Trevor Spindler (Coaching Exams/Courses) Gavin Hawkey (Development Manager)

Paul Faulkner (Referees)   Liz Verrall (Womens Football)

Number of Affiliated Clubs   320

Number of Affiliated Leagues: 12

County Representative Teams: Under 18, Under 16

Inter County Competitions: Under 18, Under 16

COUNTY CUP FINALS

Senior Cup	Carterton	v	Banbury United	0-3

SHEFFIELD & HALLAMSHIRE F.A.

Tel: 0114 241 4999   Fax: 0114 241 4990   Email: secretary@sheffieldfa.com

Clegg House, 69 Cornish Place, Cornish Street, Sheffield S6 3AF

Secretary: Mr J P Hope-Gill

Other executives: **President:** Mr C L Milner   **Chairman:** Mr M Matthews

Chief Executive: Mr J P Hope-Gill   **Development Officer:** Marc Birkett

Head of Development: Brian Peck **Discipline:**   **Registration:**   **Referees:** Craig Grundy

Grants: Brian Peck   **Courses:** Lisa Pembrook   **Womens:** Julie Callaghan   **Press&PR:** Hayley Roach

Number of Affiliated Clubs   Senior: Junior: Womens:

County Representative Teams (Senior Coach responsible)**:** (Brian Peck/Julie Callaghan - Girls)

Inter County Competitions:

COUNTY CUP FINALS

Senior Cup	Parkgate		
	v	Sheffield	0-1

SHROPSHIRE F.A.

Tel: 01743 362769   Fax: 01743 240474

Gay Meadow, Abbey Foregate, Shrewsbury, Shropshire SY2 6AB

Other executives: **President:** A E Munt **Chairman:** S T Farmer

Chief Executive: David Rowe

Coaching & Development Manager: Mick Murphy (01743 255092)   **Discipline:** Janet Highfield

Registration: Neil Sambrook **Referees:** G A Arrowsmith   **Grants:** Mick Murphy

Courses: Andrea Goodall (01743 255074)   **Womens:** Eve Bailey (01743 255083) **Press & PR:** Neil Sambrook

Number of Affiliated Clubs   Senior: 320   Junior: 110   Womens: 6

Inter County Competitions: U18 Midland Counties Youth Championship

COUNTY CUP FINALS

Senior Cup	Shrewsbury Town v Telford United	4-1	29th July 05 - at Gay Meadow

SOMERSET F.A.

Tel: 01761 410 280   Fax: 01761 410 477   Email: secretary@somersetfa.com

Drvelopment: 01761 410287

30 North Road, Midsomer Norton, Radstock, Somerset BA3 2QD

Secretary: Mrs H Marchment

Other executives: **President:** F P Hillier   **Chairman:** A J Hobbs

Chief Executive: N/A   **Development Officers:** T.McCallum & J.Smedley

Discipline: R J Fox   **Registration:** County Office   **Referees:** B.Braithwaite

Grants: County Office   **Courses:** County Office   **Womens:** R Stone   **Press&PR:**

Number of Affiliated Clubs: Premier 27 **Senior:**52   **Junior:** 296   **Womens:** 19   **Youth:** 122 **Mini:** 83

County Representative Teams (Managers responsible): Youth (B Simms?/R Stone) Women U18 (D Prior)

Inter County Competitions: FA County Youth Cup, South West Co. Champ. Competition - Youth & U18 Women

Trophies won in season 2005-06: S.W.Counties Chammpionship-Under 18 Women Runners Up

COUNTY CUP FINAL6

Premier Cup	Mangotsfield United	v	Taunton Town	2-3	25th April - Weston-s-Mare
Senior Cup	Broad Plain House	v	Westland Sports	2-0	1st May - Paulton Rovers

STAFFORDSHIRE F.A.

Tel: 01785 256 994   Fax: 01785 279837 Email: secretary@staffordshirefa.com

Dyson Court, Staffordshire Technology Park, Beaconside, Syafford ST180LQ

Secretary: Adam Evans

Other executives: **President:** D.M.Bathurst **Chairman:** D.E.Ramsbotham

Chief Executive: B J Adshead   **Development Manager:** A Weston

Coaching: G Thomas   **Discipline:** Sarah Davies   **Registration:** Sarah Davies   **Referees:** R A Vaughan

Grants: A Weston   **Courses:** J.Reynolds   **Womens:** K.Staples   **Press&PR:** A C Evans

Number of Affiliated Clubs   Senior: Junior: Womens:

County Representative Teams (Senior Coach responsible): U18/U16 boys, U16 girls, Ladies

Inter County Competitions: Midland Counties Youth Foortball Championship

COUNTY CUP FINALS

Senior Cup	Rushall Olympic	v	Stoke City	1-0	at Stoke City F.C.

SUFFOLK F.A.

Tel: 0144 4616606 Fax: 01449 616607 Email: info@suffolkfa.com

The Buntings, Cedars Park, Stowmarket, Suffolk IP14 5GZ

Secretary: Martin Head

Other executives: **President:** Gordon Blake   **Chairman:** Dave Porter

Chief Executive: N/A   **Development Officer:** Will Cook

Coaching: Phil Woolnough**Discipline:** Martin Head   **Registration:** James Payne   **Referees:** Brian Chapman

Grants: William Steward   **Courses:** Sharon O'Connell**Womens:** Kate Steed   **Press&PR:** Martin Head

Number of Affiliated Clubs   Senior: 470   Junior: 145   Womens: 15

County Representative Teams (Senior Coach responsible): (Andy Laws)

Inter County Competitions: East Anglian League

COUNTY CUP FINALS

Premier Cup	Lowestoft Town	v	Leiston	3-2 aet

SURREY F.A.

Tel: 01372 373543   Fax: 01372 361310   Website: www.surreyfa.co.uk   Email: info@surreyfa.com

Connaught House, 36 Bridge Street, Leatherhead, Surrey KT22 8BZ

Secretary: Ray Ward Assistant County **Secretary**: Mark Wood

Other executives: **President:** Peter Adams   **Chairman:** Ray Lewis

County Development Officer: Jason Kilby

Coaching: Keith Boanas   **Discipline:** Fiona Cheesman   **Referees:** David Crick

Grants: Jason Kilby   **Courses:** Pauline Harrison **Womens:** Clair Nicholls   **Press&PR:**

Number of Affiliated Clubs   Senior: 39   Junior:509   Womens: 22 Youth 264

County Representative Teams (Senior Coach responsible): (Bryan Croucher)

Inter County Competitions: Bryan Croucher

COUNTY CUP FINALS

Senior Cup	AFC Wimbledon	v	Kingstonian F.C.	0-1

SUSSEX F.A.

Culver Road, Lancing, West Sussex BN15 9AX

Tel: 01903 753547   Fax: 01903 761608   Email: info@sussexfa.com

Development/Coaching: 01903 766855 Governance: 01903 753547

Website: www.sussexfa.com

President: John Davey **Chairman:** Peter Bentley **Chief Executive:** Ken Benham

Development/Coaching: Kevin Tharme/ Emma Mead/Keveena Mosen and Julie Tobinn

Community Sports Coach: Adrian Penrose **Women & Girls Football Co ordinator**: Michelle Lawrence

Number of Affiliated Clubs   Senior: 468   Junior: 219   Womens: 72

County Representative Teams (Administrator): Brian Shacklock

Inter County Competitions: South West County Championship & Home CountiesYouth & Ladies Competitions

COUNTY CUP FINALS

Senior Cup	Horsham	v	Lewes	1-3

WEST RIDING F.A.

Tel: 0113 282 1222   Fax: 0113 282 1525   Email: info@wrcfa.com

Fleet Lane, Woodlesford, Leeds LS26 8NX

President: Peter Marsden **Chairman:** Bob Secker **Secretary & Press Officer:** Roy Carter

Executives (Responsibility): Dean Grice (Development Manager)

Development Officers: Julie Grundy, Nicola Copley and Andrew Shuttleworth

Number of Affiliated Clubs   Senior: 892   U.18:   229

Number of Affiliated Leagues: Senior: 33   Junior: 1

County Representative Teams: Senior, Womens, Junior U18, Junior U16

Inter County Competitions:

Association of Northern Counties Senior, Ridings Ladies League,

Association of Northern Counties Youth, Midland Youth, FA County Youth.

COUNTY CUP FINALS

County Cup	Farsley Celtic	v	Harrogate Town	2-1	12th April
Challenge Cup	Bay Athletic	v	Sherburn White Rose	1-0	5th May
	(Sherburn awarded tie as Bay played an ineligible player)				
Sunday Cup	Walkers Arms	v	Silsden	3-0	2nd May

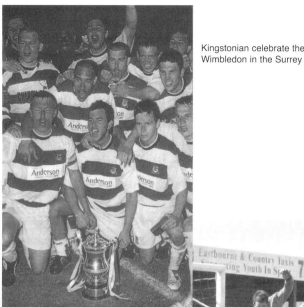

Kingstonian celebrate their 1-0 win over AFC Wimbledon in the Surrey Cup. Photo: Eric Marsh.

Lewes goalkeeper Paul Wilkerson punches clear as Horsham push for goal in the Sessex Senior Cup Final.
Whilst left, Lewes celebrate their 3-1 win over Horsham.
Photos: Roger Turner.

WESTMORLAND F.A.

Tel: 01539 730946   Fax: 01539 730946   Email: info@westmorlandfa.com

Unit 1, Riverside Business Park, Natland Road, Kendal, Cumbria LA9 7SX

Executive Officer: Peter G Ducksbury

Other executives: **President:** Tommy Huck   **Chairman:** P.J.Nicholls

Executive Officer: Peter G Ducksbury **Football Development Officer:** P.J.Nicholls

Coaching: P.J.Nicholls   **Courses**: F.D.O   **Girls & Womens Development Officer:** H.Aitchison

All other matters will be handled by the Executive Officer.

Number of Affiliated Clubs Senior: 45   Junior: 28   Womens: 8

County Representative Teams (Senior Coach responsible): Senior, U18 (P.B.Hogson & I.A.Carradus)

U16 (G Nicholson)

Inter County Competitions: Association of Northern Counties

COUNTY CUP FINALS

Senior Cup	Kendal County	v	Windeeermere SC	2-1

WILTSHIRE F.A.

Tel: 01793 486047 or 525245   Fax: 01793 692699   Email: mike.benson@wiltsfa.com

18 Covingham Square, Covingham, Swindon, Wilts SN3 5AA

Secretary: Mike Benson

Other executives: **President:** Air Cdr.C.A.B.McLaren   **Chairman:** R J Gardiner

Chief Executive: N/A   **Development Officer:** B J Stephens

Coaching: A K Riddiford   **Discipline:** M A Edmonds   **Registration:** M G Benson   **Referees:** I Whitehouse

Grants: M G Benson   **Courses:** A K Riddiford   **Womens:** B Maull   **Press&PR:** M G Benson

Number of Affiliated Clubs   Senior: 32   Junior: 406   Womens: 9

County Representative Teams (Senior Coach responsible): (Mel Gingell)

Inter County Competitions: South West Counties Championship

COUNTY CUP FINALS

Premier Shield	Salisbury City	v	Chippenham Town	0-1
Senior Cup	Corsham Town	v	Melksham Town 2-2 (5-4 on pens)	

WORCESTERSHIRE F.A.

Tel: 01905 827137 Fax:01905 798963 Email: secretary@worcestershirefa.com

Craftsman House, De Salis Drive, Hampton Lovett Ind. Estate, Droitwich, Worcs WR9 0QE

Secretary: Mervyn Leggett

Other executives: **President:** Percy Rushton **Chairman:** Ken Clifford

Chief Executive: N/A   **Football Development Officer:** Matt Jones

Coaching: Andy Norman **Discipline:** John Lovegrove   **Referees:** Bill Allsopp   **Womens:** Louise Thornton

Grants: M Leggett/A Norman **Courses:** Lisa Hollis   **Press & PR:** Mervyn Leggett

Number of Affiliated Clubs   Senio:18   Junio: 220   Womens:14   Youth: 123 (Boys & girls)

County Representative Teams (Senior Coach responsible): U18 (Ivor Chambers)

Inter County Competitions: FA County Youth Cup, MIdland Youth Football Championships

COUNTY CUP FINALS

Senior Cup	Moor Green	v	Halesowen Town	1st Leg: 4-1	2nd Leg: 1-1
Senior Urn	Worcester City Res	v	Lye Town.	2-0	

WELSH PREMIER

SPONSORED BY: PRINCIPALITY BUILDING SOCIETY

President: D W Shanklin
Secretary: J C Deakin **Chief Executive:** D G Collins

FINAL LEAGUE TABLE 2005-06

		P	W	D	L	F	A	Pts
1.	Total Network Solutions (Champions 04-05)	34	27	5	2	89	17	86
2.	Llanelli AFC	34	21	5	8	64	28	68
3.	Rhyl FC	34	18	10	6	65	30	64
4.	Carmarthen Town	34	17	6	11	62	42	57
5.	Port Talbot Town	34	15	11	8	47	32	56
6.	Welshpool Town	34	15	9	10	59	48	54
7.	Aberystwyth Town	34	14	10	10	59	48	52
8.	Haverfordwest County	34	12	14	8	49	36	50
9.	Bangor City	34	14	3	17	51	54	45
10.	Caersws FC	34	11	12	11	44	56	45
11.	Porthmadog FC	34	12	8	14	57	59	44
12.	Connah's Quay Nomads	34	10	8	16	36	46	38
13.	Caernarfon Town	34	9	10	15	47	55	37
14.	NEWI Cefn Druids	34	7	11	16	42	58	32
15.	Airbus UK	34	8	8	18	35	60	32
16.	Newtown AFC (-5)	34	10	6	18	42	61	31
17.	Cwmbran Town (-13)	34	8	8	18	42	73	19
18.	Grange Harlequins (-1) (2nd Welsh Lge D1 04-05)	34	4	4	26	23	110	15

		1	2	3	4	5	6	7	8	9	10	11	12	13	14	15	16	17	18
1	Aberystwyth Town		2-2	1-0	1-1	0-0	1-1	1-2	3-1	0-0	1-1	4-1	2-1	3-1	0-3	4-1	1-2	2-0	6-2
2	Airbus UK	0-1		2-1	1-2	1-1	1-3	2-2	1-3	3-0	1-2	1-0	3-2	0-2	0-1	0-1	1-2	0-5	0-2
3	Bangor City	3-1	1-2		1-0	1-2	1-2	0-2	3-0	5-1	0-1	1-3	2-1	0-1	3-2	1-2	0-3	2-3	2-4
4	Caernarfon Town	4-2	0-1	1-1		6-0	0-2	4-2	2-2	2-1	0-2	0-3	1-1	0-0	0-1	1-2	0-2	1-3	1-1
5	Caersws FC	1-1	3-1	0-6	3-4		1-2	1-0	1-2	2-2	1-0	1-4	1-0	2-1	1-1	2-1	1-1	0-2	0-2
6	Carmarthen Town	1-0	2-1	0-2	1-1	1-3		1-1	1-1	8-0	2-3	0-1	3-0	6-0	1-1	3-1	1-1	2-1	2-0
7	Connah's Quay Nomads	1-0	3-0	0-1	2-1	1-3	0-1		2-2	1-0	1-1	1-0	1-0	0-2	0-1	0-2	0-1	0-2	2-0
8	Cwmbran Town	1-3	1-1	1-2	0-1	2-2	3-2	2-1		1-1	3-2	0-1	1-2	0-1	2-5	3-1	1-7	1-4	1-2
9	Grange Harlequins	2-5	0-1	2-3	4-1	0-5	0-6	1-4	1-1		1-0	0-5	3-1	0-5	0-2	0-2	0-3	0-5	
10	Haverfordwest County	1-1	1-1	1-1	1-2	0-2	1-2	0-3	2-0	7-0		0-2	0-0	1-1	1-3	1-1	2-2	0-1	2-1
11	Llanelli AFC	2-1	3-0	5-0	3-1	5-0	0-2	2-0	0-1	1-0	0-1		1-0	2-2	3-1	2-2	1-1	0-2	0-0
12	NEWI Cefn Druids	2-2	0-0	2-2	3-2	2-0	1-2	2-2	0-0	7-0	0-1	2-5		3-0	0-0	1-1	1-1	0-6	1-1
13	Newtown AFC	1-3	0-3	0-1	1-2	0-2	2-1	1-1	4-1	5-0	2-3	0-3	2-3		0-1	3-1	1-4	0-3	1-1
14	Port Talbot Town	0-0	4-0	0-2	1-1	0-0	3-0	0-0	2-1	0-1	1-1	0-1	1-0	3-2		2-1	1-0	1-1	1-1
15	Porthmadog FC	0-2	3-1	1-2	2-3	3-3	3-0	2-2	5-1	4-0	1-4	1-2	5-0	1-1	1-1		2-1	2-2	2-0
16	Rhyl FC	4-1	1-1	4-1	2-1	0-0	1-0	2-1	1-2	5-2	1-1	0-1	1-1	3-1	3-0	3-0		0-0	3-0
17	Total Network Solutions	5-0	3-0	2-0	2-1	2-0	4-1	2-0	1-0	7-0	2-0	0-0	4-1	3-1	3-0	7-0	1-0		1-1
18	Welshpool Town	1-4	3-3	2-0	0-0	2-2	3-0	4-1	5-1	2-1	1-1	3-2	3-2	1-2	2-1	1-0	3-1	1-2	

THE FAW WELSH CUP

FIRST ROUND

fan Lido	v	West End	0-3
AFC Llwydcoed	v	Blaenrhondda	5-0
AFC Porth	v	Pontyclun	0-1
Bethesda Athletic	v	Mynydd Isa	1-5
Bridgend Town	v	UWIC	1-4
Briton Ferry Athletic	v	Llantwit Fadre	5-2
Buckley Town	v	Flint Town United	4-2
Caerleon	v	Bettws	5-6*
Caerwys	v	Llanrwst United	0-2
Caldicot Town	v	Porthcawl Town	4-0
Cefn United	v	Connah's Quay Nomads	0-2
Chirk AAA	v	Brynteg Village	3-2
Coedpoeth United	v	Caernarfon Town	0-3
Conwy United	v	Y Felinheli	H w/o
Corwen	v	Glantraeth	0-6
Croesyceiliog	v	Garden Village	2-1
Cwmbran Celtic	v	Ystradgynlais	2-4
Denbigh Town	v	Prestatyn Town	1-4
Dinas Powys	v	Port Talbot Town	0-2
Ely Rangers	v	Cambrian & Clydach B & G Club	4-2*
Ento Aberaman	v	Barry Town	2-0
Garw Athletic	v	Taffs Well	0-3
Glan Conwy	v	Bala Town	0-3
Goytre United	v	Llanwern	7-1
Grange Harlequins	v	Penrhiwceiber Rangers	2-0*
Gresford Athletic	v	Bodedern	2-1
Hawarden Rangers	v	Mold Alexandra	2-3
Holywell Town	v	NEWI Cefn Druids	0-1
Knighton Town	v	Penrhyncoch	0-4
Llandudno Junction	v	Airbus UK	0-3
Llandyrnog United	v	Llanrhaeadr YM Mochnant	3-2
Llanfairpwll	v	Llangefni Town	1-3
Llanfyllin Town	v	Carno	2-1
Llangollen Town	v	Llanberis	0-2
Llanidloes Town	v	Guilsfield	0-7
Llanrug United	v	Llandudno	2-6
Maesteg Park Ath.	v	Ammanford	7-0
Morriston Town	v	Bryntirion Athletic	0-1
Neath Athletic	v	Llanelli	0-1
Nefyn United	v	Halkyn United	1-0
Newcastle Emlyn	v	Cardiff Corinthians	1-6
Newport YMCA	v	Caerau Ely	2-1
Penmaenmawr Pheonix	v	Summerhill Brymbo	1-1*, 4-5p
Penrhiwfer	v	Risca United	2-4
Pontypridd Town	v	Pontardawe Town	3-2
Presteigne St An.	v	Meifod	H w/o
Rhayader Town	v	Four Crosses	5-1
Rhydymwyn	v	Holyhead Hotspur	0-6
Ruthin Town	v	Lex XI	3-4
Sealand Rovers	v	Rhos Aelwyd	0-4
Tredegar Town	v	Ton Pentre	0-4
Treharris Athletic	v	Goytre	4-2
Troedyrhiw	v	Treowen Stars	3-0*

SECOND ROUND

Aberystwyth Town	v	Bettws FC	2-0
Airbus UK	v	Conwy United	4-1
Bala Town	v	Penrhyncoch	3-2*
Bangor City	v	Llanberis	4-0
Caersws FC	v	Cardiff Grange Quins	5-3
Caldicot Town	v	Cwmbran Town	1-3
Cardiff Corinthians	v	Carmarthen Town	0-11
Chirk AAA	v	Nefyn United	1-2
Croesyceiliog FC	v	West End	3-2

Second continued...

Ento Aberaman	v	Briton Ferry Athletic	0-1
Glantraeth	v	Guilsfield	6-1
Gresford Athletic	v	Porthmadog FC	1-2
Haverfordwest Co.	v	Goytre United	1-2
Holyhead Hotspur	v	Caernarfon Town	1-3
Lex XI	v	Connah's Quay Nomads	4-2
Llanelli AFC	v	Risca United	8-2
Llanfyllin Town	v	Buckley Town	1-3
Llanrwst United	v	Llandudno	3-2
Mold Alexandra	v	Mynydd Isa	4-3
Newtown AFC	v	Llandyrnog United	5-1
Pontyclun	v	Maesteg Park Athletic	2-1*
Pontypridd Town	v	Ton Pentre	2-2*, 7-6p
Port Talbot Town	v	Newport YMCA	3-2
Presteigne St An.	v	Prestatyn Town	2-4*
Rhayader Town	v	Llangefni Town	2-4
Rhyl FC	v	Sealand Rovers	4-0
Summerhill Brymbo	v	NEWI Cefn Druids	2-3*
Total Network S.(H)	v	Welshpool Town	4-1
Treharris Athletic	v	Ely Rangers	1-3
Troedyrhiw	v	Taffs Well	3-2*
UWIC	v	AFC Llwydcoed	2-1
Ystradgynlais	v	Bryntirion Athletic	2-3

THIRD ROUND

Bala Town	v	Buckley Town	4-3*
Bangor City	v	Airbus UK	4-2
Caersws FC	v	Croesceiliog	3-1
Carmarthen Town	v	Briton Ferry Athletic	4-0
Ely Rangers	v	Cwmbran Town	1-4
Glantraeth	v	Rhyl FC	2-5
Goytre United	v	Troedyrhiw	6-3
Llangefni Town	v	Llanrwst	3-0
Mold Alexandra	v	Prestatyn Town	0-5
NEWI Cefn Druids	v	Nefyn United	3-1
Newtown AFC	v	Pontyclun	6-0
Pontypridd Town	v	Aberystwyth Town	1-0*
Port Talbot Town	v	Bryntirion Athletic	3-0
Porthmadog FC	v	Caernarfon Town	0-3
Total Network S.(H)	v	Lex XI	4-0
UWIC	v	Llanelli AFC	1-3

FOURTH ROUND

Bangor City	v	Newtown AFC	2-1
Caernarfon Town	v	Bala Town	4-0
Caersws FC	v	Llangefni Town	1-3
Cwmbran Town	v	Port Talbot Town	1-3
Llanelli AFC	v	Total Network Solutions (H)	1-0
NEWI Cefn Druids	v	Rhyl FC	3-5
Pontypridd Town	v	Goytre United	0-5
Prestatyn Town	v	Carmarthen Town	1-2

FIFTH ROUND

Bangor City	v	Carmarthen Town	1-0
Llanelli AFC	v	Caernarfon Town	3-0
Port Talbot Town	v	Llangefni Town	3-0
Rhyl FC	v	Goytre United	5-2

SEMI-FINALS

Llanelli AFC	v	Bangor City	0-1
Rhyl FC	v	Port Talbot Town	2-2*, 5-4p

THE FINAL at the Racecourse Ground, Wrexham

Bangor City	v	Rhyl FC	0-2

WELSH CLUBS IN EUROPE

CHAMPIONS LEAGUE

Two legs - home and away

FIRST QUALIFYING ROUND

			1st	2nd
Liverpool	v	Total Network Sol.	3-0	3-0

INTERTOTO CUP

Two legs - home and away

FIRST ROUND

			1st	2nd
Bangor City	v	FC Dinaburg	1-2	0-2

WELSH PREMIER

WELSH LEAGUE

DIVISION ONE

		P	W	D	L	F	A	Pts
1.	Goytre United	34	22	9	3	82	42	75
2.	Neath Athletic	34	22	7	5	76	32	73
3.	Pontardawe Town	34	18	9	7	57	35	63
4.	Maesteg Park	34	18	9	7	61	40	63
5.	UWIC	34	16	6	12	61	52	54
6.	Bridgend Town	34	16	6	12	55	47	54
7.	Afan Lido	34	13	8	13	46	41	47
8.	Dinas Powys	34	13	8	13	42	44	47
9.	Newport YMCA	34	11	11	12	48	54	44
10.	Barry Town	34	11	10	13	39	50	43
11.	Bryntirion Athletic (-3)	34	13	6	15	62	58	42
12.	Ely Rangers	34	12	5	17	47	59	41
13.	Ton Pentre	34	11	5	18	51	60	38
14.	Caerleon	34	11	4	19	33	58	37
15.	Taffs Well	34	9	9	16	46	62	36
16.	Bettws	34	10	5	19	46	63	35
17.	Briton Ferry	34	9	6	19	43	64	33
18.	AFC Llwydcoed	34	8	3	23	35	69	27

CYMRU ALLIANCE

		P	W	D	L	F	A	Pts
1.	Glantraeth	34	21	7	6	83	36	70
2.	Buckley Town	34	20	7	7	85	52	67
3.	Flint Town United	34	19	12	3	77	40	66
4.	Guilsfield	34	16	12	6	73	44	60
5.	Llangefni Town	34	17	7	10	68	46	58
6.	Llandudno	34	17	8	9	64	42	56
7.	Bala Town	34	14	9	11	63	52	51
8.	Lex X1	34	13	9	12	72	75	48
9.	Bodedern	34	13	6	15	40	55	45
10.	Penrhyncoch	34	13	4	17	62	78	43
11.	Queens Park	34	11	8	15	36	59	41
12.	Llanfair PG	34	11	6	17	58	73	39
13.	Llandyrnog United	34	10	8	16	51	64	38
14.	Gresford Athletic	34	9	9	16	45	64	36
15.	Ruthin Town	34	7	13	14	43	55	34
16.	Holyhead Hotspur	34	8	9	17	44	67	33
17.	Holywell Town	34	5	12	17	49	72	24
18.	Halkyn United	34	5	8	21	47	83	23

Carmarthen Town v Bangor City, which the visiting side won 0-2.

WELSH PREMIER LEAGUE ACTION

Newly promoted Grange Harlequins take on T.N.S., however, the defending champions came away 3-0 winners. Photos: Mark Wood.

SCOTLAND

Compiled by Bill Mitchell with thanks to Stewart Davidson

SENIOR NON-LEAGUE REVIEW

AS the main honours went the rounds in all four regions of the senior Scottish Non-League scene it is not easy to find a team of the season, so it seems best to look at the outstanding Scottish Cup achievements again of Spartans and nominate them, as they beat Berwick Rangers(1-0 at home) in the First Round, thrashed Lossiemouth (5-0) on their own patch in the next, ousted Queen's Park at home in the Third Round (3-2) and then held high-flying St Mirren in a goalless Fourth Round home tie, before bowing out in Paisley in the replay.

However, Spartans did not win the East of Scotland Premier Division as, possibly due to fixture congestion, the team could only finish fourth six points behind Edinburgh City, who also suffered a 6-1 hammering at Spartans' expense in the King Cup Final, with the Image Printers East of Scotland Qualifying Cup and South Qualifying Cup also taking their places on the Spartans sideboard, so 'Team of the Year' does seem appropriate, but why did they have to wait six months to complete the process of winning the former from the Second Round to the semi-finals? Can anyone explain how that makes sense?

It should also be noted in connection with the East of Scotland League that Heriot Watt University beat off a top set of challengers - Spartans included - to win the East of Scotland League Cup, Lothian Thistle took the Alex Jack Cup and Craigroyston only lost one match in winning the First Division title with brave Selkirk keeping the Borders flag flying by joining them in the ascent to Premiership.

The South of Scotland League was a dog-fight between Threave Rovers (more in their element geographically) and Annan Athletic's second string and the former also won the Cree Lodge Cup with the latter taking the Haig Gordon Trophy and the Southern Counties Challenge Cup, and other knock-out honours went to Creetown (South of Scotland League Cup), Abbey Vale (Tweedie Cup) and Nithsdale Wanderers (Potts Cup).

The Highland League was won by Deveronvale for the second time in the new century, but after a tough struggle with runners-up Inverurie Loco Works (whose talented side must be one of the favourites for the new campaign) and Buckie Thistle, but the various cups all went to different places with the North Qualifying Cup Final at Keith being won by Loco Works after an epic struggle with (perhaps luckless) Forres Mechanics (2-1 after extra-time), while 'Cancans' had the small consolation of winning the Inverness Cup, but also lost another final (the North of Scotland Cup) surprisingly to Nairn County (1-3), a greatly improved side these days.

The two Aberdeenshire competitions - the Cup and the Shield - also had different winners in Buckie Thistle, who won on a penalty shoot out after a 2-2 draw against Deveronvale, and Keith respectively, who beat Loco Works in their Shield final.

Fraserburgh later on reached the Highland League Cup Final after two penalty shoot-outs and then demolished holders Cove Rangers in the ultimate contest (4-1), after the latter had been somewhat unluckily reduced to ten men, a possibly involuntary hand ball on a hard and bouncy pitch by skipper Livingstone being subjected to the severe punishments of a penalty and red card. It certainly was not - as one national Sunday paper called it - 'violent conduct'.

The North Caledonian League - reduced to only nine clubs - carries on bravely and was won comfortably by Balintore, whose colours were only lowered once in the competition - by second placed Dornoch, who won the SWL Cup with third placed Halkirk United winning the Port Services Cup and PCT Cup and Invergordon beating Golspie Sutherland after extra-time (3-1) to triumph in the Football Times Cup.

At the end of each campaign Scotland's semi-professionals take part in an alleged competition against similar players from England (mostly full-timers from the Conference), Wales (likewise mostly Conference full-timers) and the Republic of Ireland, who play their Under 21 selection, which all means that, if Scotland restricts its selection to players from the four senior non-league competitions, the chances of winning the event are similarly reduced, so are we satisfied by being described in the press in an insultingly patronising fashion as being 'plucky' or should the side be selected from all the semi-professional players n the country, which would mean some actual Scottish League players, Juniors and the existing performers, who lack nothing in courage?

With the next competition scheduled for Wales, the holders, the task will be very difficult and a review of the availability and selection situation will need to be carefully examined if a plausible and winning challenge is to be made. Who wants to end up in third place out of four?

Finally, this review is mostly about winners, so spare a thought for three clubs, who bravely completed their scheduled fixtures despite dreadful results and` the first of them is Fleet Star from the South of Scotland League, who lost all 26 league matches for a 17 for and 171 goals against story and lost in the First Round of all the five cup competitions entered, albeit not badly in every case.

Fort William in the Highland League drew one of their 28 fixtures and beat Cove Rangers' second string in their final match (Cove rested their top men for the Highland League Cup Final), but otherwise were brave underdogs, while Bunillidh of the North Caledonian League lost all their sixteen league matches (12 for 84 against) and there were three immediate heavy defeat exits from cup competitions (they did not play in he fourth).

Such courage in the face of adversity is as praiseworthy as is the winning of big trophies and they are to be congratulated for persistence and wished 'better luck in the future'.

NORTH OF SCOTLAND

HIGHLAND LEAGUE

	P	W	D	L	F	A	Pts
Deveronvale	28	20	4	4	77	29	64
Inverurie Loco Works	28	19	3	6	72	26	60
Buckie Thistle	28	16	8	4	48	23	56
Forres Mechanics	28	17	3	8	76	37	54
Keith	28	16	4	8	63	41	52
Huntly	28	15	6	7	66	41	51
Fraserburgh	28	13	6	9	68	45	45
Cove Rangers	28	12	6	10	55	46	42
Clachnacuddin	28	12	5	11	56	57	41
Nairn County	28	12	4	12	57	46	40
Rothes	28	9	1	19	48	75	28
Wick Academy	28	7	4	17	39	67	25
Lossiemouth	28	7	4	17	40	97	25
Brora Rangers	28	4	1	23	31	83	13
Fort William	28	1	1	2618		104	4

SCOTTISH QUALIFYING CUP NORTH
First Round
(matches played on Saturday, 27th August 2005)
Clachnacuddin 3 Keith 0
Cove Rangers 1 Deveronvale 0
Forres Mechanics 3 Brora Rangers 1
Fraserburgh 4 Fort William 0
Golspie Sutherland 0 Lossiemouth 2
Huntly 0 Rothes 1
Nairn County 1 Buckie Thistle 2
Wick Academy 1 Inverurie Locos 6
Second Round
(Saturday, 19th September 2005)
Cove Rangers 2 Clachnacuddin 1
Forres Mechanics 3 Fraserburgh 2
Inverurie Loco Works 3 Buckie Thistle 1
Rothes 1 Lossiemouth 2
Semi-finals
(Saturday, 15th October 2005)
Forres Mechanics 2 Cove Rangers 2
Lossiemouth 2 Inverurie Loco Works 2

Replays
(Saturday, 22nd October 2005)
Cove Rangers 0 Forres Mechanics 3
Inverurie Loco Works 3 Lossiemouh 1
FINAL
(Sat, 5thNovember 2005. At Kynoch Park, Keith)

FORRES MECHANICS 1 INVERURIE LOCO WORKS 2
Whyte 108 minutes   Mackay 103 minutes,
                        Ross 116 minutes

An excellent final produced some end-to-end play but no goals in normal time, although there were plenty of chances with Forres having, perhaps, slightly more of the play (and leading marksman McMillan being off target), which should have meant victory, while in the added time Mackay gave Locos the lead with a fine cross shot, only for Whyte to level matters after 108 minutes, which i itslef suggested penalties before Ross, unfairly booked for a most harmless challenge earlier on, settled affairs with only three minutes remaining.

Cancans were unlucky to lose, but the fans were the winners with two hours of very lively entertainment to keep them on tenterhooks.

Teams:
FORRES MECHANICS: Rae; Black, Morrison, Grant, McKinnon, Campbell, Whyte (captain), Brown, McMillan, Sanderson, Mackay. Substitutes: Rogers for McMillan 75 minutes, Matheson for Sanderson 115 minutes. Booked: Grant 43 minutes.

INVERURIE LOCO WORKS: Gray; Graham, Buchan, Wilson (captain), Simpson, Young, Singer, Ross, Roddie, McKay, McLean. Substitutes: Milne for McLean 73 minutes, Walker for Roddie 112 minutes, Booked: Ross 82 minutes.

Referee: S Duff.

FOSTERS HIGHIAND LEAGUE CUP

First Round

(Saturday, 25th March 2006)

Forres Mechanics 2 Deveronvale 0

Huntly 0 Buckie Thistle 2

Lossiemouth 0 Fort William 2

Rothes 1 Nairn County 4

Second Round

(Saturday, 8th April 2006)

Brora Rangers 1 Cove Rangers 3

Inverurie Loco Works 1 Clachnacuddin 0

Wick Academy 0 Keith 7

Bye: Fraserburgh

Semi-finals

(Saturday, 22 nd April 2006)

Cove Rangers 2 Forres Mechanics 0

Fraserburgh 1 Nairn County 1

(Fraserburgh won 5-4 on penalties)

FINAL

(Saturday, 6th May 2006. At Kynoch Park, Keith)

FRASERBURGH 4	COVE RANGERS 1

Johnston 44 pen, West 47, Milne 90 Half-time: 1-0.
Stephen 49, S Main 74

FRASERBURGH: Gordon; Milne, N Main, Dickson, McBride (capt), S Main, Norris, West, Wemyss, Stephen, Johnston. Substitutes: Cowie for Stephen 80 minutes, Elrick for S Main 88 minutes, Geddes for Wemyss 89 minutes.

COVE RANGERS: Pirie; Cruickshank, Livingstone (capt), Hendry, S Fraser, Tindal, Bain, Duncan, Ord, Cadger, Coutts. Substitutes: Gordon for Ord 53 minutes, Milne for Cadger 53 minutes, Steele for Hendry 65 minutes. Sent off: Livingstone 43 minutes. Yellow cards: Cadger 43 minutes, Duncan 77 minutes.

Referee: M Ritchie.

Man of the Match: Dickson (Fraserburgh)

THE CRUCIAL moment on a beautiful day at Kynoch Park in this final arrived two minutes before half-time, when a free kick from the right taken by Dickson caused confusion in the Cove defence with Pirie flapping at the ball and a scramble resulted during the course of which a ball, which might have been goal bound, took an awkward bounce and struck gthe fore-arm of Skipper Richie Livingstone.

Referee Mike Ritchie was caught between a rock and a hard face and decided that the hand ball was deliberate, which meant 'the long walk' for the wretched captain and a penalty for Broch, which was taken by Johnston and almost saved by Pirie, who otherwise was not having a good game.

Was Ritchie correct? The penalty was right as the ball had hit the 'culprit's' hand, but a red card in a match played on a rock hard pitch with numerous awkward bounces appeared to be very harsh.

Withhin four minutes of the restart Broch had settled the result in effect thanks to a disorganised Cove defence being caught out by a free kick, which Pirie spilled to the feet of West, and a huge gap being left down the middle, which was well exploited by Stephen..

Effectively that was game, set and match and a shot after 74 minutes by Steven Main, which was deflected inside Pirie's near post, was just another piece of misortune for Cove, whose late consolation goal by Milne was well deserved if only for effort.

Despite the red card and yellows for Cadger and Duncan (both of Cove and for dissent) this was a game mosttly played in a sporting spirit, and on the whole Broch were worthy winners of a cup they last won in 1959 and which was achieved with a young side that had been handicapped by two suspensions and injuries.

CALEDONIA BROADBAND
NORTH OF SCOTLAND CUP

Semi-finals
Elgin City 'A' 0 Forres Mechanics 2
Wick Academy 2 Nairn County 4

FINAL
(Sun, 30th Oct 2005. At Grant Street Park, Inverness)

FORRES MECHANCICS 1-3 NAIRN COUNTY
Rogers 77 minutes   McRae 19, 49 minutes,
                           Jones 40 minutes
Half-time: 0-2   Attendance: 950

NIARN County, who are not regular recipients ofi awards, shocked the Qualifying Cup finallists with a comprehensive victory in the North of Scotland Cup Final at Clachnacuddin's Inverness ground, to taste success in the competition for the first time in 40 years after a blazing first half, which saw goals bt McRae and Jones, and when the former added a third soon after the tea break Cancans were chasing the game and could only convert one of the chances that came their way - by Rogers in 77 minutes - and thus their near neighbours deprived them of victory in the first of two unsuccessful bids for knock-out honours.

Teams:
FORRES MECHANICS: Rae; Black, Morrison, Grant, McKinnon, Campbell, Whyte, Brown, McMillain, A Matheson, Sanderson. Substitutes: Mackay for Morrison 46 minutes, Rogers for Black 61 minutes, S Matheson for A Matheson 61 minutes.
NAIRN COUNTY: Calder: Seaton, MacAskill, Macleod, M Sanderson, Jones, Kellacher, MacRae, Barron, Brooks, Low. Sustitutes: MacDonald for McRae 71 minutes, S Sanderson for Seaton 76 minutes, MacIntosh for Jones 89 minutes.

ABERDEENSHIRE CUP
Semi-finals
(matches played on 16th/17th August 2005)
Fraserburgh 0 Buckie Thistle 2 (after extra-time)
Deveronvale 3 Keith 1 (after extra-time)

FINAL
(Wedesday, 31st August 2005. At Christie Park, Huntly)

BUCKIE THISTLE 2-2 DEVERONVALE
Angus, Small
          Attendance: 820.
(afterextra-time - score at 90 minutes 1-1 - Buckie Thistle won 3-2 on penalties)

BUCKIE THISTLE: Main; Murray, Lamberton, Angus, Davidson, Small, Shewan, Munro, Scott, Coutts, McDonald. Substitute: Smith for Scott.
DEVERONVALE: Bl'anchard; Urquhart, Mc William, Chisholm, Dlugonski (catain), Brown, Smith, Kidd, McKenzie, Murray, Watt. Substitutes: Munro for McKenzie 30 minutes, Craib for Urquhart 71 minutes, Noble for Watt 81 minutes.
Referee: M Ritc h.

ABERDEENSHIRE SHIELD
FINAL
(Wed, 26th Octr 2005. At Princess Royal Park, Banff)
INVERURIE LOCO WORKS 1-2 KEITH

INVERNESS CUP
Semi-final
Forres Mechanics 3 Nairn County 1
FINAL
FORRES MECHANICS 4-2 CLACHNACUDDIN

EAST OF SCOTLAND

TENNENT'S SCOTTISH QUALIFYING CUP
(EAST & SOUTH)
First Round
(matches played on Saturday, 27th August 2005)
Glasgow University 2 Spartans 4
Quarter-finals
(Saturday, 15th October 2005)
Edinburgh City 1 Spartans 1
Preston Athletic 4 St Cuthbert Wanderers 0
Selkirk 3 Girvan 3
Threave Rovers 2 Annan Athletic 1
Replays
(Saturday, 22nd October 2005)
Girvan 1 Selkirk 4
Spartans 3 Edinburgh City 1
Semi-finals
(Saturday, 11th March 2006 at Raedale Park, Gretna)
Preston Athletic 1 Threave Rovers 3
Selkirk 1 Spartans 4
FINAL (Saturday, 29th April 2006)
SPARTANS 2-0 THREAVE ROVERS
McLeod, Thomson

HIGHLAND LEAGUE

PREMIER DIVISION	P	W	D	L	F	A	Pts
Edinburgh Cit y	22	12	7	3	44	27	43
Heriot Watt University	22	13	2	7	54	35	412
Lothian Thistle	22	11	6	5	49	30	39
Spartans	22	10	7	5	39	19	37
Whitehill Welfare	22	10	7	5	40	24	37
Annan Athletic	22	11	4	7	37	31	37
Preston Athletic	22	9	5	8	30	32	32
Edinburgh University	22	6	5	11	25	28	23
Easthouses Lily	22	7	4	11	24	37	19*
Civil Service Strollers	22	4	7	11	23	44	19
Dalbeattie Star	22	4	5	13	28	51	17
Kelso United	22	4	3	15	18	53	15

* Denotes six points deducted

Division One	P	W	D	L	F	A	Pts
Craigroyston	20	14	5	1	42	18	47
Selkirk	20	10	7	3	38	21	37
Edinburgh Athletic	20	8	7	5	36	30	31
Vale of Leithen	20	7	8	5	41	35	29
Ormiston	20	8	3	9	34	31	27
Coldstream	20	8	3	9	31	40	27
Peebles Rovers	20	6	7	7	38	39	25
Eyemouth United	20	7	3	10	34	37	24
Tynecastle	20	7	3	10	31	40	24
Gala Fairydean	20	4	5	11	32	41	17
Hawick Royal Albert	20	3	5	12	36	53	14

EAST OF SCOTLAND LEAGUE CUP

Semi-finals
Edinbugh Athletic 2 Easthouses Lily 3
Heriot Watt Uiversity 3 Preston Athletic 1
FINAL
(Sunday, 29th January 2006 att Whitehill Welfare FC)

HERIOT WATT UNIVERSITY 2-0 EASTHOUSES LILY
Stoddart 2
Attendance: 300 (approximately)

ALEX JACK CUP
Semi-finals
Kelso United 4 Peebles Rovers 1
Ormiston 0 Lothian Thistle 5

FINAL
(Sunday, 6th November 2005 at Preston Athletic FC)

KELSO UNITED 1-2 LOTHIAN THISTLE
Porter   McIntosh Ogilvie

KING CUP

Semi-finals

Easthouses Lily 1 Edinburgh City 2

Spartans 3 Whitehill Welfare 1

FINAL

(Tuesday, 30th May 2006 at Whitehill Welfare FC)

SPARTANS 6-1 EDINBURGH CITY

IMAGE PRINTERS EAST OF SCOTLAND
QUALIFYING CUP
Semi-finals

Preston Athletic 3 Lothian Thistle 1 (after extra-time)

Spartans 1 Edinburgh Athletic 0

FINAL

(Sunday, 14th May 2006 at Civil Service Sportsground, Edinburgh)

SPARTANS 6-4 PRESTON ATHLETIC
(after extra-time - score at 90 minutes - 3-3))
Johnson, Thomson, Wilson 2, Lockhart, Cowie
Scott og, Henretty,
Seeley, McLeod

SOUTH OF SCOTLAND

SOUTH OF SCOTLAND LEAGUE

	P	W	D	L	F	A	Pts
Threave Rovers	26	20	4	2	87	21	64
Annan Athletic 'A'	26	20	2		490	31	62
Abbey Vale	26	18	1	7	62	43	55
Stranraer Athletic	26	16	4	6	97	34	52
Creetown	26	15	2	9	66	43	47
St Cuthbert Wanderers	26	14	5	7	66	43	47
Nithsdale Wanderers	26	13	1	12	48	61	40
Wigtown & Bladnoch	26	12	3	11	68	44	39
Mid Annandale	26	10	5	11	48	52	35
Dalbeattie Star 'A'	26	9	2	15	55	69	29
Chrichton Royal	26	8	4	13	49	91	28
Newton Stewart	26	6	1	19	39	98	19
Dumfries FC	26	3	2	21	31	79	11
Fleet Star	26	0	0	2617		171	0
Craigroyston	20	14	5	1	42	18	47

SOUTH OF SCOTLAND LEAGUE CUP

Semi-finals
Threave Rovers 3 Stranraer Athletic 4
Wigtown & Bladnoch disqualified - Creetown w/o
FINAL
Saturday, 10th September 2005 at Creetown FC)

CREETOWN 1-0 STRANRAER ATHLETIC
Wilson

SOUTHERN COUNTIES CHALLENGE CUP
Semi-finals
Dalbeattie Star 'A' 4 Annan Athletic 'A' 5
Nithsdale Wanderers 2 Creetown 3
FINAL
(Wednesday, 10th May 2006 at Annan Athletic FC)

ANNAN ATHLETIC 'A' 3-1 CREETOWN
Moffat, McMenamin,   Houston
Parker

CREE LODGE CUP
Semi-finals
Creetown 2 Threave Rovers 2 (Threave won 4-2 on pens)
Dumfries FC 3 Wigtown & Bladnoch 7
FINAL (Mon, 8th May 2006 at Wigtown & Bladnoch FC)
WIGTOWN & BLADNOCH 1-2 THREAVE ROVERS
G McClymont   Rudd 2

POTTS CUP
Semi-finals
Mid Annandale 2 Threave Rovers 5
Nithsdale Wanderers 5 Abbey Vale 1
FINAL (Sat, 8th April 2006 at Nithsdale Wanderers FC)
NITHSDALE WANDERERS 2-0 THREAVE ROVERS
Fingland og, Jardine

HAIG GORDON TROPHY
Semi-finals
Annan Athletic 'A' 3 Creetown 0
Stranraer Athletic 1 Wigtown & Badenoch 3
FINAL (Sat, 15th April 2006 (at Wigtown & Bladnoch FC)r)
WIGTOWN & BLADNOCH 2-3 ANNAN ATHLETIC 'A'
Paterson og, A McClymont pen   Johnstone pen,
Parker 2

TWEEDIE CUP
Semi-finals
Newton Stewart 0 Abbey Vale 5
Wigtown & Bladnoch 5 St Cuthbert Wanderers 0
FINAL (Saturday, 1th March 2006 at Abbey Vale FC)
ABBEY VALE 2-1 WIGTOWN & BLADNOC H
Cameron, Copland   A McClymont pen

Leading Scorers (all competitions)
Alan Murdoch (Stranraer Athletic)(39), Craig Little
(Abbey Vale)(36), Alan McClymont (Wigtown &
Bladnoch(31)), Craig Rudd (Threave Rovers)(26),
Roman Soltys (Mid Annnadale (24)

NORTH CALEDONIAN EAGUE

	P	W	D	L	F	A	Pts
Balintore	16	12	3	1	46	13	39
Dornoch	16	11	2	3	48	26	35
Halkirk United	15	9	1	5	44	22	28
Golspie Sutherland	16	8	3	5	48	29	27
Thurso	16	8	2	6	48	33	26
Invergordon	16	7	3	6	41	40	24
Alness nited	16	5	1	10	36	36	16
Bonar Bridge	16	3	1	11	25	66	10
BunillidhThistle	16	0	0	16	12	84	0

One match not played

PORT SERVICES CUP
Semi-finals
Halkirk United 5 Allness United 3 (after extra-time)
Thurso 0 Balintore 2
FINAL (Sat, 29th Oct 2004 at Golspie Sutherland FC)
BALINTORE 2-3HALKIRK UNITED

PCT NORTH CALEDONIAN CUP
Semi-finals
Halkirk Uited 2 Thurso 1
Invergordon 0 Allness United 2

FINAL (Saturday, 15th April 2006 at Balintore)
HALKIRK UNITED 3-1 ALNESS UNITED

FOOTBALL TIMES CUP
Semi-finals
Halkirk 0 Glspie Sutherland 22
Thurso 2 Invergordon 3

FINAL
(Saturday, 6th May 2006 at Dudgeon Park, Brora)

GOLSPIE SUTHERLAND 1-3 INVERGORDON
(after extra-time)

NON-LEAGUE TEAMS IN THE SCOTTISH CUP
First Round (Saturday, 19th November 2005)
Dumbarton 4 Forres Mechanics 1
Preston Athletic 2 Gretna 6
Saturday, 26th November 2005
Dumbarton 4 Forres Mechanics 1
Spartans 1 Berwick Rangers 0
(Monday, 28th November 2005)
Alloa 9 Selkirk 0
Second Round (Saturday, 10th December 2005)
Gretna 6 Cove Rangers 1
Lossiemouth 0 Spartans 5
Stirling Albion 1 Inverndess Loco Works 0
Threave Rovers 0 Forfar Athletic 4
Third Round (Saturday, 10th January 2006)
Spartans 3 Queen's Park 2
Fourth Round (Saturday, 4th February 2006)
Spartans 0 St Mirren 0 (atttendance 3,346)
Replay
St Mirren 3 Spartans 0 (attendance 3,612)

AMATEURS

SCOTTISH AMATEUR CUP
Semi-finals
Newmilns Vesuvius 1 Falkrk Amateurs 3 (after extra-time)
St Patricks FP 4 Eddlewood 1 (after extra-time)

FINAL
Sunday, 14th May 2006 at Hampden Park, Glasgow)

ST PATRICKS FP 3-2 FALKIRK AMATEURS

AMATEUR LEAGUE WINNERS

Scottish Amateur Lge Premier Division: St Patricks FP
Premier One: Cambria
Premier Two Inverclyde AFC
Ayrshire Amateur League Premier Division: Newmilns
Vesuvius
Fife Amateur FA Premier League: Fysart
Caledonan League Premier Division: Dumbarton
Academy
Caledonian League Division One: Links United
Division Two: Milton

Scottish Non League Review

Often referred to as the 'bible' of non league football in Scotland, the Review of 2005/2006 is the 19th in the series and like the previous editions gives all the league tables and results and cup results from each of the junior regions and the Highland, East and South of Scotland Leagues as well as details from many minor leagues.

Order the 2005/2006 edition now for £3 plus 60p postage. Add 40p postage for each back issue - any excess sent will be refunded.

SCOTTISH NON-LEAGUE REVIEW OF 2005/2006

All final tables, league and cup result from each Junior region and the three Senior Leagues from 2005/2006 Season

Includes a Junior Club Directory

£3

Cheques made payable to Stewart Davidson.

Many other publications on Scottish non-league football also available. See the website @ www.snlr.co.uk or send an SAE to 84 Gallowhill Road, Paisley PA3 4TJ

JUNIOR NON-LEAGUE REVIEW

FOUR clubs dominated the Junior scene in 2005-06 - Auchinleck, Talbot, Tayport, Bathgate Thistle and Irvine Meadow and each deserves a separate paragraph on its own. Team of the season must be Auchinleck Talbot, since the club did the double of Junior Cup and West Region champions - on goal difference from gallant Renfrew. In a bizarre final at Rugby Park, Kilmarnock,they scored the odd goal in three against first-timers Bathgate Thistle and in the process won the competition for a seventh time, while it also meant that the East's recent dominance had been- for the moment at least - halted.

Tayport were the Junior Cup holders and lost their grip on the last ever OVD Cup in a superb semi-final against the eventual winners, a match at Firhill Park which went to extra-time, while they too had to rely on goal difference to take the East Region Superleague title from Bathgate Thistle with Fife's Hill of Beath Hawthorn a point adrift of the pair. Tayport also won the local Findlay & Co Cup, which confirms them as one of the country's teams to beat.

Bathgate Thistle reached the Junior Cup semi-final for the first time and then needed to go to extra-time to beat Irvince Meadow in a very hard fought and at time ill-tempered macth at Firhill Park, which saw two red cards and numerous yellows, and the defeat at Rugby Park meant no silverware this time for Bathgate, but the side is good enogh for better things.

This leaves the story about Irvine Meadow, whose recent poor form had brought a descent to the Ayrshire League, where the only blemishes this past campaign were two draws with 87 goals scored and only sixteen conceded, so they return to the West Region First Division, and as they also won the Evening Times Cup Winners Cup (1-0 against Maryhill at Pollok) they will be taken very seriously in the new season.

Other notable Junior achievements saw the prestigeous White & Mackay West of Scotland Cup also go to Ayrshire with Glenafton Athletic and Maryhill (they won thwe Central League Cup and their bigger day must come soon) sharing two goals in the final at Pollokand the penalty shoot out going in the former's favour.

Lesmahagow and East Kilbride Thistle were the Central League top dogs with the former edging the title by a single point and both are now West First Division members, while Blantyre Victoria and Port Glasgow go up to the league's First Division

Over in the East the achievements of Tayport, Bathgate Thistle and Hill of Beath Hawthorn have been mentioned, the last named doing well to keep the Kingdom's flag flying and it remains to be seen whether the latter's champion club, Oakley United, and St Andrews United can trouble the best, a question which will also be asked of the Lothians' Camelon, who have p layed at a much higher level and did well to win the Fife & Lothians Cup and lose the Dem Master Demolition Cup final to Arniston Rangers (one from bottom of the East Regioal Superleague) on penalties, but the East of Scotland Cup showed up Bonnyrigg Rose as a team to beat and they also grabbed the Dechmont Forklift Cup, so a Superleague challenge should not be ruled out.

On Tayside Kinnoull took the major Premier honours from Montrose Roselea with Jeanfield Swifts ascending from the First Division, while further north Culter took the Premier Division honours comfortably from Formartine United and grabbed the Grill Cup into the bargain, but the latter took thde Acorn Heating Cup as consolation, while the Premier Division will welcome promoted Dyce and Islavale, who once again won 'their' trophy - the Rollstud Cup - but Banks o'Dee without winning anything fielded a young and talented side, which may just be ready to take off.

There were no international fixtures for the SJFA's representatives and they may well have to search hard for opposition, which is a pity since the new annual Semi-Professional tournament involving England (usually full timers despite the competition's title), Wales, Republic of Ireland and Scotland has yet to be won and there is a plausible school of thought that suggests that the Juniors would at least do as well as the under performaing but brave men from the Scottish Senior Non-League clubs.

There also appears to be no sign of some Junior clubs being admitted to the Qualifying Cup, which iis also sad, particularly as it would be interesting to see how they would fare, but should we hold our respective breaths?

OVD SCOTTISH JUNIOR CUP

FOURTH ROUND
Armadale Thistle 0 Irvine Meadow 1
Arthurlie 2 Kilbirnie Ladeside0
Bellshill Athletic 0 St Andrews United 2
Clydebank 2 Vale of Leven 1
Glasgow Perthshire 0 Auchenleck Talbot 4
Glenafton Athletic 0 Kirkcaldy YM 1
Harthill Royal 0 Bonnyrigg Rose 1
Kilsyth Rangers 2 Fauldhouse United 3
Linlithgow Rose 0 Beith 1
Lochee United 1 Rutherglen Glecairn 1
Maryhill 0 Neilston 1
Glenrothes 1 Montrose Roselea 0
Petershill 1 Largs Thistle 0
Shotts Bon Accord 0 Bo'ness United 2
Tayport 2 Renfrew 0
Troon 1 Bathgate Thistle 1

Replays
(Saturday, 21st January 2006)
Rutherglen Glencairn 1 Lochee United 1(Lochee United won 3-1 on penalties)
Troon Juniors 1 Bathgate Thistle 3

FIFTH ROUND
Arthurlie 2 Tayport 6
Beith 5 St Andrews United 1
Bo'oness United 4 Neilston 0
Clydebank 1 Bonnyrigg Rose 0
Fauldhouse United 0 Auchenleck Talbot 4
Irvine Meadow 3 Glenrothes 0
Kirkcaldy YM 0 Petershill 1
Replay, Saturday, 18th February 2006
Lochee United 1 Bathgate Thistle 2
Bo'oness United disqualified for fielding unregistered players.

QUARTER-FINALS
(Saturday, 11th March 2006)
Bathgate Thistle 1 Beith 0
Petershill 0 Irvine Meadow 3
Tayport 1 Clydebank 1
Auchenleck Talbot walked over

Replay
(Saturday, 18th March 2006)
Clydebank 1 Tayport 1 (Tayport won 3-1 on penalties)

SEMI-FINALS
Friday, 14th April 2006. At Firhill Park, Glasgow.
BATHGATE THISTLE 2-1 IRVINE MEADOW
Elliot, Grant   Turner
(after extra-time - score at half-time and 90 minutes - 1-1 - score at 105 minutes - 2-1)
This was the first time Bathgate Thistle had progressed beyond the semi-finals of the competition.
Friday, 21st April 2006. At Firhill Park, Glasgow.
AUCHINLECK TALBOT 2-1 TAYPORT
Slavin, Mallan   Henderson
(after extra-time - score at half-time - 0-1 - score at 90 minutes - 1-1 - score at 105 minutes - 2-1.)

FINAL
(Suday, 21st Ma`y 2006. At Rugby Park, Kilmarnock)

AUCHINLECK TALBOT 2-1 BATHGATE THISTLE
Mallan 31, Boyle 80   McVey own goal 78
Half-time: 1-0   Attendance: 7,479

AUCHINLECK TALBOT: McIntosh (capt); Latta, McVey, Anderson, Collins, Davidson, Young, Slavin, Gillies, Mallan, Gilmour. Substitutes: Spence for Davidson 38 minutes, Boyle for Gillies 68 minutes, Robertson for Mallan 86 minutes. Not used: Traynor, Feroz. Booked: Mallan, Boyle.

BATHGATE THISTLE: Godfrey; Wilson, Harty, G Love, Sweeney, Neill (capt), Bradley, F Love, Elliot, Murphy, Smith. Substitutes: Grant for Murphy 58 minutes, Maxwell for F Love 58 minutes, Annand for Elliot 73 miutes. Booked: Harty, F Love, Maxwell, Elliot.
Referee: S Nicholls. Man of the Matvh: S Mallan (Auchinleck Talbot).

KILMARNOCK'S splendid Rugby Park stadium was the scene of the latest OVD Scottish Junior Cup Final as a result of which Talbot became the record holders for successes with their seventh win, which also meant that the club had completed a league and cup double as the had also won the West Superleague.

On the whole their victory was deserved against a West Lothian outfit, which had done well in the East Superleague, but was appearing in a national final for the first time.

The match was distinguished as much for its bizarre goals as for not too much skilled football, as nerves seemed to play a big part in the fare on offer, but there have been few more extraordinary opening goals as the effort for which Stephen Mallon was credited with the first score as he followed up his own speculative header from some way out to make no further contact but still see the ball bounce over a prone Godfrey, who had slipped, and roll into an empty net.

Bathgate could have drawn level almost immediately but a corner kick was eventually cleared by McIntosh and the Talbot defence after an almighty scramble, and the latter might have gone further ahead after the breeak when an effort by Man of the Match Mallan hit the woodwork, but the next goal was another personal disaster - this time forMcVey (who had otherwise played very well), whose attempt to clear a Bradley free kick sailed off his head past the helpless McIntosh and into the net.

By now there were twelve minutes to go and John Boyle was on the park and he it was who finished off a rather hectic move by Mallan to steer the ball into Godfrey's left hand of the net for the winner, while for his 'excessive' celebrations the scorer received one of the game's six yellow cards.

This was by no means a great game, but all the players deserved fullmarks for effort, which meant that there were not too many dull moments and most neutrals came away satisfied with what they had seen.

SJFA SUPER CUP

Semi-finals

Culter 0 Lochee United 5

Tayport 0 Pollok 0

(after extra-time - Pollok won 3-2 on penalties)

FINAL (Sat, 30th July 2005 at Dundee North End JFC)

LOCHEE UNITED 0-1 POLLOK

Attendance: 275   McLauchlan

WHYTE & MACKAY WEST OF SCOTLAND CUP

Semi-finals

Artgurlie 0 Maryhill 1

Hurlford United 0 Glenafton Athletic 1

FINAL (Sat, 6th May 2006 at Newlandsfield Park, Glasgow)

GLENAFTON ATHLETIC 1-1 MARYHILL

McGregor   Murray

(A.E.T. -Glenafton Athletic won 4-3 on penalties)

WEST REGION

STAGECOACH SUPER LEAGUE

	P	W	D	L	F	A	Pts
Auchinleck Talbot	22	12	5	5	46	29	41
Renfrew	22	12	5	3	40	27	41
Pollok	22	11	5	6	43	30	38
Shotts Bon Accord	22	9	8	7	39	39	33
Cumnock Juniors	22	8	5	9	33	35	29
Maryhill	22	7	7	8	37	33	28
Kilsyth Rangers	22	6	10	6	28	28	28
Larkhall Thistle	22	10	3	9	40	37	33
Glenafton Athletic	22	5	10	7	24	2	25
Bellshill Athletic	22	6	7	9	24	31	25
Johnstone Borough	22	6	2	14	19	37	20
Arthurlie	20	10	3	7	27	27	18
Larkhall Thistle	21	2	8	11	27	47	14

NB: Arthurlie started the new season with a deficit of 12 points and they were also fined £3,000 for failing to assist the West Region officials in an investigation into an alleged head butting incident at Auchuneck in a league match, while their accused player, Mark Ross, received a five year suspension for his alleged misdeed. Arthurle were also fined three points for fielding an ineligible player.

DIVISION ONE

	P	W	D	L	F	A	Pts
Neilston	26	16	6	4	54	23	54
Petershill	26	14	5	7	46	35	47
Largs Thistle	26	13	6	7	51	33	45
Beith	26	11	8	7	60	39	41
Troon	26	12	3	11	48	39	39
Vale of Clyde	26	11	5	11	52	47	38
Kilwinning Rangers	26	11	4	11	51	49	37
Hurlford United	26	11	4	11	51	54	37
Lugar Boswell Thistle	26	10	6	10	37	45	36
Annbank United	26	10	5	11	34	49	35
Kirkintilloch Rob Roy	26	8	7	11	33	42	31
Maybole	26	8	5	13	31	44	29
Dunipace	26	6	4	16	33	53	22
Cambuslang Rangers	26	4	6	16	23	52	18

EVENING TIMES CUP WINNERS CUP

Sem-finals

Irvine Meadow 2 Neilston 0

Maryhill 5 Lesmahagow 0

FINAL (Friday, 2nd June 2006 at Pollok JFC)

IRVINE MEADOW 1-0 MARYHILL

Davidson   Att: 1,200 (approx.)

CENTRAL LEAGUE CUP

Semi-finals

Greenock 1 Petershill 1

(Greenock won 4-2 on penalties)

Johnstone Borough 1 Maryhill 3

FINAL (Saturday, 20th May 20066 at Pollok JFC)

MARYHILL 2-1 GREENOCK

Dingwall 2   Dingwall og   Att: 500 (approx.)

CLYDESDALE CUP

Semi-finals

Carluke Rovers 4 Forth Wanderers 0

Lanark United 1 Lesmahagow 0 Carluke Rovers 0

FINAL (Monday, 1st August 2005 at Lanark United JFC)

LANARK UNITED 0-1 CARLUKE ROVERS

Thompson

CENTRAL LGE DIVISION 1

	P	W	D	L	F	A	Pts
Lesmahagow	22	12	6	4	37	24	42
East Kilbride Thistle	22	12	5	5	40	28	41
Rutherglen Glencairn	22	11	6	5	43	31	39
Yoker Athletic	22	10	4	8	40	28	34
Cumbernauld United	22	10	4	8	32	35	34
Lanark United	22	9	6	7	51	35	33
Vale of Leven	22	10	3	9	39	29	33
Clydebank	22	10	2	10	35	34	32
St Anthonys	22	10	2	10	40	41	32
Greenock	22	7	3	12	32	46	24
Thorniewood United	22	5	3	14	35	65	18
Shettleston	22	4	3	15	21	53	15

NB: Top two were promoted and the tast three were relegated.

DIVISION 2

(top six place - first three promoted)

	P	W	D	L	F	A	Pts
Blantyre Victoria	20	16	1	3	57	27	49
Port Glasgow	20	11	7	2	48	23	40
Glasgow Perthshire	20	10	7	3	44	24	37
Ashfield	20	11	3	6	46	26	36
St Rochs	20	11	2	7	36	28	35
Stonehouse Violet	20	10	2	8	45	36	32

Other positions: Carluke Rovers 27pts; Benburb 26 pts; Forth Wanderers 15 pts; Royal Albert 9 pts; Wishaw 7 pts. Coltness Uited Withdrew after 17 matches and their record was expunged.

CARLSBERG SECTIONAL LEAGUE CUP
Semi-finals
East Kilbride Thistle 3 Dunipace 0
Maryhill 1 Neilston 2
FINAL (Tues, 4th October 2005 at Ffirhill Park, Glasgow)
NEILSTON 0-0 EAST KILBRIDE THISTLE
(Neilston won 4-3 on penalties)

AYRSHIRE LEAGUE

	P	W	D	L	F	A	Pts
Irvine Meadow	24	22	2	0	87	16	68
Girvan	24	18	0	6	66	38	54
Kilbirnie Ladeside	24	13	5	6	69	35	44
Craigmark Bruntonians	24	13	2	9	45	46	41
Ardeer Thistle	24	13	2	9	42	39	39
Kello Rovers	24	10	5	9	55	40	35
Whitletts Victoria	24	10	4	10	49	34	34
Dalry Thistle	24	9	4	11	51	47	31
Ardrossan Winton Rovers	24	8	3	13	47	53	27
Irvine Victoria	24	7	6	11	44	52	27
Saltcoats Victoria	24	6	7	11	39	74	25
Darvel Juniors	24	2	4	18	36	85	10
Muirkirk	24	0	6	18	24	95	6

ROCKWARE GLASS AYRSHIRE LEAGUE CUP
Semi-finals
Cumnock 3 Largs Thistle 2
Glenafton Athletic 1 Beith 1
(Glenafton Athletic won 5-4 on penalties)
FINAL (Wed, 5th October 2005 at Somerset Park, Ayr)
GLENAFTON ATHLETIC 4-3 CUMNOCK
Agnew 2, Blair, Deeney   McGowan, Muir pen,
                          Henderson

AYRSHIRE WEEKLY PRESS CUP
Semi-finals
Irvne Meadow 2 Beith 0
Kilwinning Rangers 1 Whitletts Victoria 1
(Kilwinning Rangers won 4-2 on penalties)
FINAL (Thursday, 18th May 2006 at Cumnock JFC)
IRVINE MEADOW 2-1 KILWINNING RANGERS
Davidson, Kerr   Armstrong

NORTH AYRSHIRE CUP
Semi-finals
Irvine Meadow 1 Kilwinning rangers 0
Largs Thistle 2 Saltcoats Victoria 0
FINAL (Tuesday, 6th June 2006. At Ardeer Thistle JFC)
LARGS THISTLE 1-1 IRVINE MEADOW
McGlone   Moore
(Largs Thistle won 5-4 on penalties)

SOUTH AYRSHIRE CUP
Semi-finals
Maybole 1 Annbank United 0
Troon 1 Girvan 2
FINAL (Thursday, 1st June 2006 at Maybole JFC)
MAYBOLE 1-0 GIRVAN
Love

EAST REGION

WHYTE & MACKAY EAST REGION

SUPER LEAGUE	P	W	D	L	F	A	Pts
Tayport	22	10	9	3	32	23	39
Bathgate Thistle	22	11	6	5	27	22	30
Hill o'Beath Hawthorn	22	11	5	6	34	26	38
Whitburn	22	10	5	7	34	24	35
Linlithgow Rose	22	9	7	6	37	33	34
Bonnyrigg Rose	22	9	5	8	43	38	32
Bo'ness United	22	8	8	6	36	29	32
Carnoustie Panmure	22	8	6	8	31	33	30
Lochee United	22	8	4	10	33	33	28
Carnoustie Panmure	22	7	6	9	32	36	27
Glenrothes	22	5	7	10	23	31	22
Arniston Rangers	22	5	6	11	35	51	21
Dundee NE	22	2	4	16	19	42	10

LOTHIAN LEAGUE

DIVISION ONE	P	W	D	L	F	A	Pts
Camelon	18	11	4	3	34	17	37
Penicuik Athletic	18	10	3	5	42	31	35
Musseburh Athletic	18	10	3	5	40	28	33
Armadale Thistle	18	9	3	6	35	24	30
Fauldhouse Uited	18	9	1	8	26	25	28
Edinburgh United	18	8	3	7	21	16	27
Newtongrange Star	18	5	8	5	28	27	23
Sauchie	18	4	5	9	21	34	17
Pumpherston	18	4	3	11	19	29	15
West Calder United	18	2	2	14	13	48	8

LOTHIAN LEAGUE

DIVISION TWO	P	W	D	L	F	A	Pts
Broxburn Athletic	16	10	3	3	28	11	33
Harthill Royal	16	9	4	3	33	18	31
Blackburn United	16	9	2	5	34	27	29
Haddington Athltic	16	9	1	1	6	29	28
Stoneyburn	16	8	2	6	26	18	26
Tranent	16	7	2	7	26	30	23
Dunbar United	16	5	2	9	25	34	17
Livingston United	16	3	1	12	13	41	10
Dalkeith Thistle	16	1	5	10	17	33	8

DEM MASTER DEMOLITION ST MICHAEL'S CUP
Semi-finals
Bathgazte Thistle 0 Arniston Rangers 3
Bo'ness United 1 DCamelon 1
(Camelon won 4-3 on penaltie)
FINAL (Saturday, 3rd June 2006. At Whitburn JFC)
ARNISTON RANGERS 1-1 CAMELON
Mitchell   Thomson
(Arniston Rangers won 5-4 on penalties)

DECHMONT FORKLIFT CUP (BROWN CUP)
Semi-finals
Newtongrange Star 0 Arniston Rangers 0
(Newtongrange Star won 2-0 on penalties)
Whitburn 1 Bonnyrigg Rose 4

FINAL (Saturday, 27th May 2006 at Broxburn JFC)
BONNYRIGG ROSE 3-0 NEWTONGRANGE STAR
Elliot 3

Irvine Meadow X1. Champions Ayrshire District League. Lost to Bathgate Thistle in the semi-final of the OVD Scottish Junior Cup (Original picture by R. Mackenzie final image by John B Vass) Irvine Meadow also won the Ayrshire Weekly Press Cup Result: Irvine Meadow 2 -v- 1 Kilwinning Rangers.

Glenafton Athletic winners of the Rockware Glass Ayrshire Sectional Cup.
They beat near neighbours Cumnock 4 - 3 at Somerset Park, Ayr. Glenafton Athletic also won the Whyte & Mackay West of Scotland Cup - beat Marryhill 4 - 3 on penalties after 1 - 1 draw in ninety minutes.

Photo: John B Vass.

FIFE & LOTHIANS CUP
Semi-finals
Camelon 1 Whitburn 1
(after extra-time - Camelon won 7-6 on penalties)
Newtongrange Star 2 Kelty Hearts 4
FINAL (Saturday, 20th May 2006 at Whitburn JFC)
CAMELON 2-1 KELTY HEARTS
Cringean,   Lawrie
Findlay og
(after extra-time - score at 90 mins - 1-1)

JOHN WALKER EAST OF SCOTLAND CUP
(formerly KIA Cup)
Semi-finals
Hill of Beath Hawthorn 2 Oakley United 0
Musselburgh Athletic 1 Bonnyrigg Rose 4
FINAL (Sat, 10th June 2006 at Armadale Thistle RFC)
BONNYRIGG ROSE 2-1 HILL OF BEATH HAWTHORN
Killen, Elliot   Thomson

FIFE LEAGUE

	P	W	D	L	F	A	Pts
Oakley United	24	18	3	3	73	18	57
St Andrews United	24	17	2	5	80	39	53
Rosyth Recreation	24	15	4	5	55	25	49
Kelty Hearts	24	14	5	5	57	26	47
Kirkcaldy YM	24	11	5	8	54	55	38
Dundonald Bluebell	24	10	4	10	45	48	34
Ballingry Rovers	24	9	3	12	43	55	30
Thornton Hibs	24	7	5	12	35	54	26
Lochgelly Albert	24	8	2	14	38	58	26
Newburgh	24	8	2	14	31	54	26
Crossgates Prmirose	24	6	5	13	40	51	23
Lochore Welfare	24	7	1	16	40	49	22
Steelend Victoria	23	2	5	16	27	87	11

PEDDIE SMITH MALOCO CUP
Semi-finals
Kelty Hearts 1 Dundonald Bluebell 4
Lochore Welfare 0 Hill of Beath Hawthorn 2
FINAL (Fri, 26th May 2006. At Rosyth Recreation JFC)
HILL OF BEATH HAWTHORN 3-2 DUNDONALD BLUEBELL
Meikle, Wright, & og   McQuade, Balfour pen

FIFE LEAGUE CUP
Semi-finals
Kelty Hearts 2 St Andrews United 2
(Kelty Hearts won 3-1 on penalties)
Oakley United 3 Dundonald Bluebell 3
(Oakley United won 5-4 on penalties)
FINAL (Sun, 11th December 2005 at Rosyth Recreation JFC)
KELTY HEARTS 1-1 OAKLEY UNITED
Rollo   Smart
(Oakley United won 4-3 on penalties)

KINGDOM KEGS CUP
Semi-finals
Dundonald Bluebell 3 St Andrews United 6
Osakley United 3 Thornton Hibs 2
FINAL (Fri, 2nd June 2006 at Dundonald Bluebell JFC)
OAKLEY UNITED 4-5 ST ANDREWS UNITED
Morrison, Lammie,   Blackadder 2, Juskowiak,
Herkes, Nicoll   Ewing, Newbiggins

FIFE/TAYSIDE REDWOOD LEISURE CUP
Semi-finals
Dundonald Bluebell 0 Tayport 5
Lochee United 4 Kirkcaldy YM 1
FINAL (Sat, 3rd June 2006, at Dundee Violet JFC)
LOCHEE UNITED 3-1 TAYPORT
Robertson,   Duell
Bonella 2 pens

TAYSIDE

PREMIER DIVISION	P	W	D	L	F	A	Pts
Kinnoull	18	14	1	3	49	24	43
Montrose Roselea	18	12	3	3	45	20	39
Scone Thistle	18	11	3	4	50	31	36
Lochee Harp	18	10	3	5	58	29	33
Violet	18	9	3	6	43	31	30
Forfar West End	18	9	2	7	34	24	29
Arbroath SC	18	9	1	8	32	35	28
Downfield	18	2	3	13	22	50	9
Coupar Angus	18	3	0	15	11	57	9
East Craigie	18	1	1	16	16	57	4

FIRST DIVISION
(leading five positions)

	P	W	D	L	F	A	Pts
Jeanfield Swifts	16	12	2	2	50	18	38
Luncarty	16	11	1	4	26	16	34
Blairgowrie	16	8	4	4	39	23	28

Other positions: Kirrie Thistle (28pts); Broughty Athletic (26pts); Bankfoot Athletic (15pts); Forfar Albion (13pts); Arbroath Victoria (13pts); Brechin Victoria (7pts)

TAYSIDE LEAGUE CUP
Semi-Finals
Jeanfield Swifts 2 Scone Thistle 2
(Scone Thistle won 5-3 on penalties)
Kinnoull 2 2 Violet 3
FINAL (Sun, 7th May 2006 at Carnoustie Panmure JFC)
SCONE THISTLE 4-1 VIOLET
Anderson, Scott 2,   Neilson
S Gardiner

CHALLENGE CUP
Semi-finals
Lochee Harp 3 Tayport 1
Lochee United 1 Violet 1
(Lochee United won 4-2 on penalties)
FINAL (Sat, 10th June 2006 at Glenesk Park, Dundee)
LOCHEE HARP 2-3 LOCHEE UNITED
Craik 2   Robertson, Bonella, Thoson

FINDLAY & CO CUP

Semi-Finals

Montrose Roselea 0 Forfar West End 3

Tayport 4 Carnoustie Panmure 1

FINAL (Friday, 9th June 20056 Thomson Park, Lochee)

FORFAR WEST END 0-4 TAYPORT

Morris 2 (1 pen),

Duell, Kenneth

DUG OUT CUP

Semi-finals

Lochee United 1 Lochee Harp 0

Turriff United 0 Montrose Roselea 1

FINAL (Sat, 20th May 2006 at Dundee North End JFC)

LOCHEE UNITED 3 - 2 MONTROSE ROSELEA

Unnamed, Robertson   Simpson, Watson

Blackwood

NORTH EAST LEAGUES

SOCCER WORLD SUPER LEAGUE

SUPER LEAGUE	P	W	D	L	F	A	Pts
Culter	26	20	1	5	65	33	61
Formartine United	26	17	2	769		36	53
Banks o'Dee	26	15	5	6	46	34	50
Wilson's XI	26	14	4	8	51	33	46
Sunnybank	26	12	5	9	55	41	41
Hermes	26	12	4	10	51	39	40
Ellon United	26	11	6	9	48	43	39
Turriff United	26	11	3	12	45	46	36
Glentanar	26	10	4	12	49	52	34
Stonehaven	26	8 5		13	33	43	29
Longside	26	8	4	14	35	58	28
Parkvale	26	7	5	14	42	69	26
Fraserburgh United	26	5	7	14	32	64	22
FC Stoneywood	26	3	3	20	35	65	12

Fraserburgh United and FC Stoneywood relegated

SOCCER WORLD DIVISION ONE

(first six positions)

	P	W	D	L	F	A	Pts
Dyce Juniors	26	19	4	3	61	34	61
Islavale	26	17	4	5	73	31	55
Maud	26	17	3	6	65	37	54
Lewis United	26	17	1	8	58	43	52
East End	26	15	2	9	54	30	47
Banchory St Ternan	26	13	6	7	62	38	45

Dyce and Islavale promoted

Other positions: Lads Club (43pts); Cruden Bay (39pts); Strathspey Thistle (27pts);Deveronside (26pts); Dufftown (2pts); Buchanhaven Hearts (18pts); Hall Russell United (16pts), Burghead Thistle (11pts), Buchanhaven Hearts deducted three points.

SCOTSCOUP DIVISION TWO

(first five places)

	P	W	D	L	F	A	Pts
New Elgin	27	22	2	3	79	14	68
Forres Thistle	27	17	7	3	76	30	58
Fochabers	27	13	8	6	59	36	47
Nairn St Ninian	27	14	4	9	64	48	46
Buckie Rovers	27	10	8	9	51	46	38

Other places: Lossiemouth United (35pts) Bishopmill United (32pts); RAF Lossiemouth (26pts); Kinloss (18pts); Whitehills (8pts). Kinloss withdrew from league with four fixtures remaining and points were awarded to the teams they still had to play.

New Elgin refused promotion, but Forres Thistle beat Burghead Thistle (4-2) in a play-off for promotion and take their place in Division One.

GRILL BAR LEAGUE CUP

Semi-Finals

Banchory St Ternan 0 Culter 1

Ellon United 1 Formartine United 1

(Formartine United won 3-1 on penalties)

FINAL (Sun, 20th November 2005. At Heathryfold, Aberdeen)

CULTER 2-0 FORMARTINE UNITED

Stewart, Calder   H.T. 0-0

Teams:

CULTER: Pirie, Sim, Rattray, Calder, Scott, Smith, Morrison, Shand, Stewart, Christie, Craik. Substitutes: Ogbloe for Shand 65 minutes, Farmer for Stewart 69 minutes, Robertson for Craik 86 minutes. Booked: Smith, Stewart.

FORMARTINE UNITED: Christie; Graffin, Bisset, Cameron, Binnie, K Fraser, McLeod, Corser, Cormie, Reid, Gauld. Substitutes: Craib for Fraser 55 minutes, R Fraser for Binnie 67 minutes, Findlater for Reid 75 minutes. Booked: Graffin.

Referee: G Duncan.

ROLLSTUD REGIONAL CUP

Semi-Finals

Stoneywood 1 Longside 3

Wilsons XI 0 Islavale 1

FINAL (Saturday, 6th May 2006. At Turriff United JFC)

LONGSIDE 1-3 ISLAVALE

ACORN HEATING CUP

Semi-finals

Culter 1 Formartine United 2

Turriff United 0 Parkvale 1

FINAL (Wed, 31st May 2006. At Heathryfold, Aberdeen).

FORMATINE UNITED 3-0 PARKVALE

Gauld 2, 1 pen, Corser

Half-time: 3-0

FORMARTINE UNITED: Christie; Cunningham, R Fraser, Cameron, Binnie, Craib, McLeod, Corser, Cormie, Reid, Gauld. Substitutes: Allsop 61 for Binnie, Graffin 71 for McLeod, K Fraser 77 for Cunningham.

PARKVALE: Hopkin; Cowperthwaite, Jappy, Long, Paul, Greig, Fettes, Small, Brooks, Felber, McKay. Substitutes: Keith for Brooks 45 minutes, Horne 63 for McKay, Robb 77 for Fettes.

Referee: S McKenzie.

IN A superb start Formartine were three goals ahead after 36 minutes and the game was over, although Parkvale tries hard after the break to redress the balance, but to no avail.

GORDON WILLIAMSON TROPHY

Semi-finals

Kinloss scratched - New Elgin w/o

RAF Lossiemouth 1 Forres Thistle 1

(A.E.T. - RAF Lossiemouth won 4-3 on penalties)

FINAL

(Friday, 12th May 2006 at Mosset Park, Forres)

NEW ELGIN 1-1 RAF LOSSIEMOUTH

Sim   Lamberton

MORRISON TROPHY

Semi-finals

Lewis United 4 Lads Club 1

Maud disqualified - Banchory St Ternan w/o

FINAL (Friday, 26th May 2006 at Dyce JFC)

LEWIS UNITED 1-2 BANCHORY ST TERNAN

Gove   Courage, Robertson

SCOTTISH NON-LEAGUE ACTION

Left: West Superleague First Division. Troon - - Neilston. Result 1 - 3. Neilston - promoted as Champions.
Below: Girvan -v- Irvine Meadow. Ayrshire District League. (The two promoted teams) 20 May 06 Result: 0 - 3.

Above: Whyte & Mackay West of Scotland Cup Round One. Annbank United -v- Maybole.

Right: OVD Scottish Junior Cup Final Auchinleck Talbot -v- Bathgate Thistle 21 May 06 Result: 2 - 1.

Top: Auchinleck Talbot -v- Bellshill Athletic West Superleague Premier Division. Result 1 - 0. The crucial winning goal for Talbot in their bid for the championship.
Above left: OVD Scottish Junior Cup Round Two. Whitletts Victoria -v- Pumpherson. Result 2 - 2. Pumpherson won the replay 4 - 3.
Above: OVD Scottish Junior Cup Round Four. Troon -v- Bathgate Thistle. Result 1 - 1.
Left: OVD Scottish Junior Cup Round One. Lugar Boswell Thistle -v- Craigmark Burntonians. The underdogs from the Ayrshire District League (CB) beat their opponents from the Superleague First Division (LBT) 1 - 2.

ALL PHOTOS BY: JOHN B. VASS

GUERNSEY F.A.

Email: neil.laine@guernseyfa.com
Corbet Field, grand Fort Road, St Sampson's GY2 4DT. Tel: 01481 200443 Fax: 01481 200451.
Secretary: Neil Laine

Other executives: **President:** David Nussbaumer   **Chairman:** David Nussbaumer

Vice-Chairman: Jeff Vidamour   **Development Officer:** Chris Pringle

Coaching: Steve Ogier   **Discipline:** Secretary   **Registration:** Secretary   **Referees:** Graham Skuse

Grants: Secretary   **Courses:** Secretary   **Womens:** Vacant   **Press&PR:** Steve Dewsnip

Number of Affiliated Clubs   Senior: 10   Junior: 7   Womens: 5

County Representative Teams (Senior Coach responsible): (Steve Ogier)

Inter County Competitions: South West Counties Championship (Senior, U18), FA County Youth Cup

PRIAULX LEAGUE

	P	W	D	L	F	A	Pts
Belgrave Wanderers	24	18	4	2	64	24	58
Northerners	24	12	4	8	49	36	40
Rangers	24	12	2	10	54	53	38
Vale Recreation	24	9	6	9	37	36	33
St Martin's	24	7	8	9	43	39	29
Sylvans	24	7	6	11	46	58	27
Rovers	24	3	2	19	27	74	11

JACKSON LEAGUE

	P	W	D	L	F	A	Pts
Belgrave Wanderers	18	13	4	1	63	31	43
Northerners	18	14	0	4	64	26	42
Sylvans	18	9	2	7	45	44	29
St Martin's	18	7	3	8	47	52	24
Vale Recreation	18	7	2	9	29	36	23
Rangers	18	4	1	13	30	51	13
Rovers	18	3	0	15	25	63	9

RAILWAY LEAGUE

	P	W	D	L	F	A	Pts
Rangers	18	14	0	4	55	30	42
Rovers	18	12	1	5	49	22	37
Northerners	18	11	3	4	54	27	36
Sylvans	18	10	3	5	63	39	33
Bavaria Nomads	18	8	4	6	42	37	28
Vale Recreation	18	8	4	6	45	48	28
St Martin's	18	7	2	9	40	41	23
Port City	18	5	1	12	40	76	16
Belgrave Wanderers	18	5	0	13	49	63	15
Police	18	1	0	17	29	83	3

YOUTH DIVISION ONE

	P	W	D	L	F	A	Pts
Northerners	18	17	1	0	77	18	52
Sylvans	18	12	4	2	65	35	40
Belgrave Wanderers	18	10	3	5	45	33	33
Vale Recreation	18	8	2	8	37	34	26
St Martin's	18	5	2	11	34	44	17
Rovers	18	2	4	12	18	52	10
Rangers	18	0	2	16	14	74	2

YOUTH DIVISION TWO

	P	W	D	L	F	A	Pts
Northerners	12	10	1	1	45	12	31
Belgrave Wanderers	12	9	0	3	27	14	27
Sylvans	12	8	2	2	31	14	26
Vale Recreation	12	5	2	5	22	18	17
St Martin's	12	3	1	8	25	36	10
Rangers	12	2	2	8	13	31	8
Rovers	12	0	2	10	5	43	2

YOUTH DIVISION THREE (Brian Mercer Trophy)

	P	W	D	L	F	A	Pts
Rovers	12	10	0	2	68	14	30
Northerners	12	8	4	0	40	9	28
Belgrave Wanderers	12	6	2	4	40	27	20
Sylvans	12	5	3	4	31	21	18
Rangers	12	4	0	8	24	56	12
Vale Rec	12	3	2	7	18	32	11
St Martin's	12	0	1	11	11	73	1

WOMEN'S LEAGUE

	P	W	D	L	F	A	Pts
Sylvans	15	15	0	0	91	14	45
Rangers	15	12	0	3	92	17	36
St Martin's	15	7	1	7	48	49	22
Rovers	15	6	1	8	29	26	19
Northerners	15	3	2	10	23	64	11
Vale Rec	15	0	0	15	8	121	0

PORTHOLME CORBET CUP

	P	W	D	L	F	A	Pts
Northerners	12	12	0	0	108	7	36
Rovers	12	9	1	2	64	20	28
Sylvans	12	8	0	4	60	25	24
Vale Rec	12	6	1	5	59	42	19
Belgrave Wanderers	12	4	0	8	44	56	12
St Martin's	12	2	0	10	38	72	6
Rangers	12	0	0	12	7	158	0

CUP WINNERS

Upton Park: Belgrave Wanderers.
Jeremie Cup: Trinity.
FletcherSports GFA Cup: Northerners.
Stranger: Northerners.
Rawlinson: Rangers.
Collins: Belgrave Wanderers.
Mauger (Jackson): Sylvans.
Rouget (railway): St Martin's.
Old Vic (Y1): Northerners.
Loveridge (Y1 Sports Fed.): Northerners.
Normandie (Y2): Vale Recreation.
Duquemin (Y2 Sports Fed): Belgrave Wanderers.
Le Prevost (Y3): Rangers.
Le Vallee (Y3 Sports Fed.): Belgrave Wanderers.
Corbet: Northerners.
Women's KO: Northerners.
Women's Secondary: Rangers.

The Guernsey Priaulx League team who representated their County in teh semi-finals of the National League Systems Cup. Photo: Arthur Evans.

JERSEY F.A.

Tel: 01534 449765 Email: nicky.martini@jerseyfa.com

Springfield Stadium, St Helier, Jersey JE2 4LF.

Secretary: Nicky Martini

Other executives: **President:** C Tostevin   **Chairman:** N/A

Chief Executive: N/A   **Development Officer:** Brian Oliver

Coaching: Brian Oliver   **Discipline:** J Gasston   **Registration:**   **Referees:** P Daniel

Grants: **Courses:**   **Womens:**   **Press&PR:**

Number of Affiliated Clubs   Senior: 19   Junior: 55 teams   Womens: 8 teams

County Representative Teams (Senior Coach responsible): Senior/u21/u18/u16/Sen.Ladies. Yr 7,8&9 boys & girls

Inter County Competitions: South West Counties Championship (Senior men). FA County Youth Cup.

FLYBE COMBINATION

Division One

	P	W	D	L	F	A	Pts
Trinity	18	13	5	0	45	13	44
Jersey Scottish	18	12	4	2	59	18	40
St. Pauls	18	7	4	7	29	32	25
St. Peter	18	7	3	8	30	28	24
First Tower Utd	18	8	0	10	36	40	24
Magpies	18	6	5	7	22	30	23
Portuguese Club	18	6	4	8	35	49	22
Jersey Wanderers	18	5	5	8	33	41	20
Grouville	18	5	3	10	26	35	18
St. Clement	18	3	3	12	19	48	12

Division Two

	P	W	D	L	F	A	Pts
Sporting Accies	16	13	1	2	59	22	40
Rozel Rovers	16	11	0	5	46	21	33
St. John	16	10	3	3	43	18	33
St. Martin	16	9	0	7	49	50	27
St. Ouen	16	8	2	6	34	26	26
St. Brelade	16	6	2	8	46	41	20
Beeches	16	6	1	9	35	46	19
St. Lawrence	16	2	1	13	14	62	7
S.C.F.	16	1	2	13	8	48	5

Division One Reserves

	P	W	D	L	F	A	Pts
Trinity	18	12	0	6	62	28	36
Grouville	18	10	5	3	51	23	35
Jersey Scottish	18	11	1	6	53	24	34
St. Pauls	18	10	1	7	36	43	31
First Tower Utd	18	9	3	6	33	31	30
St. Clement	18	7	4	7	31	36	25
St. Peter	18	6	3	9	37	47	21
Jersey Wanderers	18	5	5	8	35	43	20
Rozel Rovers	18	4	2	12	31	45	14
Magpies	18	3	2	13	15	54	11

Division Two Reserves

	P	W	D	L	F	A	Pts
St. Brelade	16	10	3	3	54	28	33
St. John	16	9	4	3	51	34	31
Portuguese	16	10	0	6	55	27	30
Sporting Academics	16	8	2	6	42	43	26
St. Ouen	16	7	2	7	46	32	23
Beeches	15	6	4	5	39	31	22
St. Martin	16	6	1	9	36	59	19
S.C.F.	16	5	0	11	29	65	15
St. Lawrence	15	2	0	13	24	57	6

Division C

	P	W	D	L	F	A	Pts
Jersey Wanderers	18	15	2	1	70	24	47
St. Brelade	18	12	0	6	45	29	37
Grouville	18	11	1	5	57	27	34
St. Peter	18	10	3	5	54	36	33
Trinity	15	10	1	4	63	30	31
St. Clement	18	6	3	9	33	53	21
Sporting Academics	18	5	3	10	35	56	18
St. John	17	4	1	12	29	70	13
Rozel Rovers	17	3	2	12	32	50	11
St. Ouen	18	2	2	14	30	74	8

ISLE OF MAN FOOTBALL LEAGUE

OSA DIVISION ONE

	P	W	D	L	F	A	Gd	Pts
Laxey C	24	20	4	0	103	15	88	64
St Georges	24	18	1	5	87	29	58	55
Peel	24	17	3	4	73	32	41	54
St Marys	24	15	4	5	72	33	39	49
St Johns	24	11	3	10	53	52	1	36
Douglas Royal	24	10	3	11	39	56	-17	33
Gymnasium	24	9	2	13	56	75	-19	29
Rushen United	24	8	3	13	44	47	-3	27
Ramsey	24	8	2	14	48	64	-16	26
Ayre United	24	8	1	15	50	80	-30	25
Marown	24	7	3	14	50	88	-38	24
DHSOB R	24	6	5	13	42	66	-24	23
Castletown R	24	1	2	21	19	99	-80	5

CFS DIVISION TWO

	P	W	D	L	F	A	Gd	Pts
Union Mills	26	22	1	3	137	29	108	64
Braddan	26	18	5	3	96	35	61	59
Police	26	18	2	6	82	50	32	56
Colby	26	17	2	7	87	35	52	53
Michael	26	15	2	9	82	51	31	47
Pulrose	26	13	5	8	99	63	36	44
Corinthians	26	13	5	8	81	53	28	44
Onchan	26	14	2	10	90	66	24	44
Foxdale	26	11	2	13	63	67	-4	35
RYCOB	26	7	3	16	58	128	-70	24
Doug and Dist	26	6	1	19	48	112	-64	19
Malew	26	5	0	21	44	92	-48	15
Ronaldsway	26	4	1	21	50	138	88	13
Jurby	26	3	1	22	39	137	-98	10

Last year Laxey AFC's first team won every competition they entered, winning Division One, The Hospital Cup, the Railway Cup, The FA Cup and the Charity Shield so becoming only the fifth side/fourth club ever to win the Grand Slam. They also went undefeated throughout their entire campaign, so wrestling the title of the Island's strongest club from previous league champions St George's.

The Isle of Man squad before their FA National League Systems final victory over Cambridgeshire County.
Photo: Gordon Whittington.

AMATEUR FOOTBALL ALLIANCE

President: W H Evans
General Secretary: Mike Brown, 55 Islington Park Street, London N1 1QB
Tel: 020 7359 3493   Fax: 020 7359 5027
Website: www.amateur-fa.com   Email: secretary@amateur-fa.com

A F A S E N I O R C U P
Sponsored by Alan Day Volkswagen

1ST ROUND PROPER
Wood Green Old Boys 4 Old Finchleians 5
West Wickham 3 Hon Artillery Company 2
Old Reptonians 2 Old Wilsonians 4
Chislehurst Sports 1 William Fitt 3
Old Esthameians 7 Old Sedcopians 1
BB Eagles 1 Southgate Olympic 2
Bradfield Old Boys 0 Civil Service 5
Old Camdenians 1 Bromleians Sports 3
Alleyn Old Boys 4 Glyn Old Boys 0
Lloyds TSB Bank 2 Broomfield 8
Southgate County 6 Old Tiffinians 3
Enfield Old Grammarians w/o Old Chigwellians w/d
Weirside Rangers 3 Old Salvatorians 2
Bank of England 2 Brent 0
Centymca 1 Old Actonians Association 0
Old Suttonians 1 Carshalton 0
Old Woodhousians 0 Wake Green 4
Old Meadonians 2 Alexandra Park 0
Old Foresters 2 Old Brentwoods 8
Old Aloysians 3 Old Latymerians 2
Old Hamptonians 5 Old Wokingians 1
Old Challoners 0 Polytechnic 1
Winchmore Hill 4 Parkfield 1
Old Danes 0 South Bank Cuaco 3
Norsemen 7 Old Manorians 2
Old Parmiterians 0 Albanian 3
UCL Academicals 2 HSBC 0
Old Guildfordians 4 Cardinal Manning Old Boys 2
Sinjuns Gramm'ns 3 E Barnet Old Grammarians 4
Nottsborough 4 Old Bealonians 1
Old Isleworthians 3 Old Stationers 2
Old Salesians 0 Old Owens 1

2ND ROUND PROPER
Bank of England 1 Wake Green 2
Old Hamptonians 2* Old Guildfordians 0*
Bromleians Sports 2 Nottsborough 1

Old Finchleians 0 Old Owens 4
Southgate County 2 Old Suttonians 0
Albanian 3 Polytechnic 5
Norsemen 1*:4p Civil Service 1*:2p
Centymca 0 West Wickham 4
Old Isleworthians 1 William Fitt 2
South Bank Cuaco 1*:5p Southgate Olympic 1*:4p
Enfield Old Grammarians 1 Winchmore Hill 2
Bromleians Sports 2 Nottsborough 1
Broomfield 2 UCL Academicals 1
Alleyn Old Boys 5 E Barnet Old Grammarians 6
Old Meadonians 2 Old Aloysians 1
Old Esthameians 2 Old Brentwoods 1
Old Wilsonians 2*:10p Weirside Rangers 2*:9p

3RD ROUND PROPER
Polytechnic 3 Old Hamptonians 2
William Fitt 1 Old Owens 3
Norsemen 0 West Wickham 4
South Bank Cuaco 4 Old Wilsonians 1
Broomfield 2*:2p E Barnet Old Grammarians 2*:4p
Wake Green 5 Southgate County 0
Winchmore Hill 4 Old Esthameians 1
Old Meadonians 3 Bromleians Sports 1

4TH ROUND PROPER
South Bank Cuaco 0 Old Owens 2
West Wickham 0 Winchmore Hill 1
Old Meadonians 4 E Barnet Old Grammarians 1
Polytechnic 2 Wake Green 3

SEMI-FINALS
Old Meadonians 1*:2p Old Owens 1*:4p
Wake Green 0 Winchmore Hill 4

FINAL
Old Owens 0 Winchmore Hill 1

OTHER CUP FINALS

Middlesex / Essex Senior
Broomfield 0 Old Meadonians 5
Surrey / Kent Senior
Clapham Old Xaverians 2* Old Salesians 0*
Intermediate
Civil Service Res 0 Mill Hill Village 1st 4
Junior
Civil Service 3rd 1*:4p Winchmore Hill 3rd 1*:3p
Minor
Old Actonians 4th 5 Old Haileyburians 1st 4
Veterans
William Fitt "A" 1 Sinjuns Grammarians 2
Open Veterans
Port of London Authority 2 Chelsea Diamonds 1

Middlesex / Essex Intermediate
Old Actonians Ass'n Res 1 Old Meadonians Res 3
Surrey / Kent Intermediate
Dresdner Kleinwort Wasserstein 3 Marsh 1
Greenland
Old Owens 3 UCL Academicals 0
Senior Novets
Civil Service 5th 1 Nat'l Westminster Bank 2
Intermediate Novets
Old Actonians 6th 3 Old Meadonians 6th 1
Junior Novets
Old Actonians 7th 3 Old Meadonians 8th 0
Women's Cup
East Barnet Old Grammarians 4 Alexandra Park 0

SATURDAY   **YOUTH**
U-18
Provident House 4 Hale End Athletic 0
U-17
Field Crusaders 2 Norsemen 1
U-16
Forty Hill 1 Norsemen 1
U-15
Bethwin SE 2* Old Bealonians 4*
U-14
Prydun 3 Norsemen "B" 2
U-13
Providence House 1*:5p Mill Hill Village 1*:3p
U-12
Cheshunt 2 Whitewebbs Eagles 1
U-11
Old Bealonians 0*:2p West Essex Colts 0*:4p
U-12 Girls
Potters Bar United 5 Flamingoes 1

SUNDAY
U-18
Chase Side 2*:3p Barnet 2*:5p
U-17
Cheshunt 3 Field Crusaders 4
U-16
Cheshunt 3 Forty Hill 1
U-15
Cheshunt 1 Whitewebbs Eagles 6
U-14
Prydun 2 Potters Bar United 0
U-13 (Tesco)
Chase Side 1 Broomfield PL 2
U-12
Whitewebbs Eagles 2 Southgate Adelaide 0
U-11
Trent Park 1 Potters Bar United 3
U-14 Girls
William Fitt 2 Flamingoes 1

AMATEUR FOOTBALL COMBINATION

PREMIER DIVISION	P	W	D	L	F	A	Pts
Old Meadonians	18	12	6	0	53	15	42
Old Hamptonians	18	12	3	3	42	17	39
Honourable Artillery Company	18	11	4	3	62	19	37
Albanian	18	10	3	5	35	33	33
Old Bealonians	18	8	5	5	26	22	29
Parkfield	18	5	3	10	24	38	18
UCL Academicals	18	5	2	11	26	31	17
Old Aloysians	18	5	2	11	28	41	17
Hale End Athletic	18	5	1	12	21	42	16
Latymer Old Boys	18	1	3	14	19	78	3

SENIOR DIVISION 1	P	W	D	L	F	A	Pts
Southgate County	18	12	3	3	51	26	39
Old Parmiterians	18	11	5	2	41	18	38
Enfield Old Grammarians	18	11	4	3	44	23	37
Glyn Old Boys	18	9	2	7	46	30	29
Old Salvatorians	18	8	5	5	43	36	29
Old Danes	18	6	6	6	24	34	24
Wood Green Old Boys	18	5	2	11	26	40	17
Old Tiffinians	18	4	3	11	22	38	15
Old Wokingians	18	4	2	12	27	45	14
Old Ignatians	18	3	2	13	16	50	11

SENIOR DIVISION 2	P	W	D	L	F	A	Pts
Sinjuns Grammarians	20	15	3	2	71	32	48
Old Challoners	20	14	3	3	50	26	45
Economicals	20	13	2	5	56	30	41
Old Suttonians	20	12	4	4	54	36	40
Clapham Old Xaverians	20	11	2	7	45	32	35
Shene Old Grammarians	20	9	4	7	50	47	31
Old Vaughanians	20	6	2	12	31	44	20
Old Aloysians Res	20	4	4	12	35	49	16
Old Dorkinians	20	3	4	13	38	57	13
Old Tenisonians	20	2	6	12	39	58	12
Old Isleworthians	20	2	4	14	22	80	10

SENIOR DIVISION 3 NORTH	P	W	D	L	F	A	Pts
Old Meadonians Res	18	12	3	3	46	21	39
Old Salvatorians Res	18	12	3	3	50	27	39
Albanians Res	18	12	1	5	50	32	37
UCL Academicals Res	18	11	2	5	40	20	35
Hale End Athletic Res	18	9	3	6	50	36	30
Old Minchendenians	18	6	5	7	48	49	23
Old Manorians	18	6	3	9	32	42	21
Parkfield Res	18	4	3	11	37	42	15
Old Buckwellians	18	4	2	12	29	54	14
Pegasus*	18	1	1	16	16	75	3

SENIOR DIVISION 3 SOUTH	P	W	D	L	F	A	Pts
King's Old Boys	20	14	4	2	65	26	46
Old Paulines	20	11	4	5	54	34	37
Wandsworth Borough	20	11	4	5	52	38	37
Old Hamptonians Res	20	9	4	7	35	35	31
Hampstead Heathens	20	7	7	6	40	39	28
Fitzwilliam Old Boys	20	8	4	8	40	41	28
Old Guildfordians	20	8	3	9	34	37	27
John Fisher Old Boys	20	8	2	10	41	48	26
Old Reigatians	20	5	4	11	35	42	19
Queen Mary College Old Boys	20	5	2	13	29	42	17
Old Sedcopians	20	4	2	14	27	70	14

INTERMEDIATE DIV. NORTH	P	W	D	L	F	A	Pts
Mill Hill Village	20	17	2	1	77	25	53
Southgate County Res	20	13	3	4	52	39	42
Enfield Old Grammarians Res	20	12	2	6	57	37	38
Old Bealonians Res	20	8	5	7	33	28	29
Old Woodhouseians	20	7	4	9	43	43	25
Egberthan	20	6	6	8	39	44	24
UCL Academicals 3rd	20	7	3	10	42	50	24
Old Camdenians	20	7	2	11	33	48	23
Old Edmontonians	20	6	4	10	39	48	22
Old Buckwellians Res	20	4	4	12	34	59	16
Old Parmiterians Res	20	2	7	11	36	64	13

INTERMEDIATE DIV. SOUTH	P	W	D	L	F	A	Pts
H A C Res	20	13	6	1	65	23	45
Old Belgravians	20	12	2	6	78	44	38
Centymca	20	9	5	6	43	44	32
Witan	20	8	6	6	52	50	30
Kings Old Boys Res	20	8	5	7	50	41	29
Old Thorntonians	20	7	6	7	37	39	27
Old Suttonians Res	20	7	5	8	35	39	26
Old Josephians	20	7	3	10	60	63	24
Mickleham Old Boxhillians	20	6	6	8	46	53	24
Old Tenisonians Res	20	5	5	10	41	73	20
Old St Mary's	20	1	5	14	31	69	8

INTERMEDIATE DIV. WEST	P	W	D	L	F	A	Pts
Old Meadonians 3rd	20	14	1	5	64	37	43
Old Manorians Res	20	13	3	4	63	36	42
Brent	20	13	2	5	66	33	41
London Welsh	20	10	6	4	52	40	36
Cardinal Manning Old Boys	20	11	1	8	48	39	34
Old Challoners Res	20	10	2	8	40	32	32
Old Vaughanians Res	20	6	3	11	47	51	21
Parkfield 3rd	20	5	4	11	29	46	19
Old Danes Res	20	5	5	10	42	86	20
Old Salvatorians 3rd	20	3	4	13	34	58	13
Phoenix Old Boys	20	3	3	14	25	52	12

* - Pts deducted - breach of Rule

OTHER DIVISIONS

	Teams	Won by
Intermediate Division North	11	Mill Hill Village
Intermediate Division South	11	Honourable Artillery Company Res
Intermediate Division West	11	Old Meadonians 3rd

Northern Regional:

Division 1	11	Old Parmiterians 3rd
Division 2	10	Old Aloysians 4th
Division 3	10	Ravenscroft Old Boys
Division 4	10	Mill Hill County Old Boys
Division 5	10	Old Parmiterians 5th
Division 6	10	Old Buckwellians 4th
Division 7	10	Old Tollingtonians Res
Division 8	9	Wood Green Old Boys 5th
Division 9	8	Old Parmiterians 7th

Southern Regional:

Division 1	10	Economicals Res
Division 2	11	Chertsey Old Salesians
Division 3	10	Old Tenisonians 3rd
Division 4	10	Witan Res
Division 5	10	OldJosephians 3rd
Division 6	10	Shene Old Grammarians 3rd
Division 7	10	Old Paulines 3rd
Division 8	10	Old Guildfordians 4th
Division 9	10	Economicals 4th
Division 10	10	John Fisher Old Boys 5th
Division 11	8	Kings Old Boys 3rd

Western Regional:

Division 1	10	Old Vaughanians 3rd
Division 2	10	Old Uffingtonians Res
Division 3	11	Old Challoners 3rd
Division 4	9	Phoenix Old Boys 3rd
Division 5	10	Ealing Association Res

SPRING CUP FINALS

Senior	Old Aloysians 4	Old Manorians 2
Intermediate	Leyton County Old Boys 5	Old Uxonians Res 1
Junior North	Enfield Old Gramm'ns 4th 2	Leyton County OB 3rd 1
Junior South	Clapham Old Xaverians 4th 2	Old Sedcopians Res 0
Minor North	Davenant Wanderers Res 9	Old Edmontonians 5th 2
Minor South	Old Wokingians 6th 3	Economicals 4th 5
Minor West	Phoenix Old Boys 4	Shene Old Gramm'ns 3rd 0

ARTHUR DUNN CUP
Old Carthusians 2   Old Westminsters 0

ARTHURIAN LEAGUE

PREMIER DIVISION	P	W	D	L	F	A	Pts
Old Carthusians	18	15	1	2	68	22	46
Old Harrovians	18	13	1	4	70	26	40
Old Etonians	18	11	4	3	52	24	37
Old Brentwoods	18	9	4	5	36	26	31
Lancing Old Boys	18	7	5	6	36	33	26
Old Foresters	18	7	3	8	40	43	24
Old Salopians	18	5	8	5	42	33	23
Old Reptonians*	18	2	5	11	25	65	8
Old Bradfieldian*	18	3	1	14	23	65	7
Old Chigwellians	18	1	2	15	14	69	5

DIVISION 1	P	W	D	L	F	A	Pts
Old Westminsters	14	9	3	2	40	24	30
Old Cholmeleians	14	9	0	5	29	23	27
Old Aldenhamians	14	7	4	3	40	27	25
Old Wykehamists	14	5	5	4	23	19	20
Old Malvernians	14	4	3	7	23	29	15
Old Haileyburians	14	2	7	5	23	27	13
Old Tonbridgians*	14	4	1	9	29	41	10
Old Haberdashers*	14	4	1	9	24	41	-5

DIVISION 2	P	W	D	L	F	A	Pts
Old Salopians Res	16	10	2	4	49	29	32
Old Foresters Res	16	10	2	4	46	29	32
Old Etonians 3rd	16	9	2	5	31	26	29
Old Chigwellians Res	16	7	3	6	38	28	24
Old Carthusians Res	16	7	3	6	35	29	24
Old Etonians Res	16	5	5	6	25	39	20
Old Westminsters Res	16	5	2	9	30	41	17
Old Carthusians 3rd	16	5	1	10	20	40	16
Old Cholmeleians Res*	16	3	2	11	21	34	11

DIVISION 3	P	W	D	L	F	A	Pts
Old Brentwoods Res	12	9	1	2	43	18	28
Old Radleians	12	8	2	2	33	16	26
Old Bradfieldians Res	12	6	1	5	29	30	19
Old Wellingtonians	12	4	2	6	25	33	14
Old Aldenhamians Res	12	4	2	6	26	36	14
Lancing Old Boys Res	12	2	4	6	23	33	10
Old Brentwoods 3rd	12	1	4	7	16	29	7

DIVISION 4	P	W	D	L	F	A	Pts
Old Chigwellians 3rd	14	10	2	2	33	16	32
Old Oundelians	14	8	1	5	32	17	25
Old Foresters 3rd	14	8	1	5	32	22	25
Old Malvernians Res*	14	7	2	5	30	29	20
Old Eastbournians	14	6	1	7	29	23	19
Old Brentwoods 4th	14	5	2	7	25	21	17
Old Berkhamstedians	14	5	1	8	29	36	16
Old Cholmeleians 3rd	14	1	2	11	11	57	5

DIVISION 5	P	W	D	L	F	A	Pts
Old Westminsters 3rd	15	9	2	4	31	21	29
Old Harrovians Res	15	7	4	4	30	32	25
Old Chigwellians 4th	15	6	5	4	24	14	23
Old Wykehamists Res*	15	8	1	6	32	25	22
Old Foresters 4th	15	5	2	8	25	25	17
Old Cholmeleians 4th*	15	2	2	11	20	45	8

* - Points deducted breach of rules

JUNIOR LEAGUE CUP
Old Harrovians Res 5   Old Chigwellians Res 2 aet

DERRIK MOORE VETERANS' CUP
Old Cholmeleians 3   Old Carthusians 1

JIM DIXSON SIX-A-SIDE CUP
Lancing Old Boys

LONDON FINANCIAL FOOTBALL ASSOCIATION

DIVISION ONE	P	W	D	L	F	A	Pts
Marsh	16	11	4	1	41	15	37
National Westminster Bank Res	16	8	5	3	38	31	29
Dresdner Kleinwort Wasserstein	16	5	4	7	29	33	19
Chislehurst Sports	16	4	5	7	26	36	17
National Westminster Bank	16	0	6	10	16	35	6

DIVISION TWO	P	W	D	L	F	A	Pts
Credit Suisse First Boston	14	11	2	1	54	17	35
Royal Bank of Scotland	14	10	3	1	38	23	33
Chislehurst Sports Res	14	6	5	3	39	25	23
Coutts & Co.	14	5	2	7	39	41	17
Zurich Eagle Star	14	5	2	7	39	41	17
Marsh Res	14	4	3	7	31	39	15
National Westminster Bank 3rd	14	4	2	8	41	55	14
JP Morgan Chase	14	1	1	12	24	64	4

DIVISION THREE	P	W	D	L	F	A	Pts
National Westminster Bank 4th	16	13	3	0	47	12	42
Royal Bank of Scotland Res	16	10	3	3	36	16	33
Chislehurst Sports 3rd	16	7	6	3	31	25	27
British Council	16	7	2	7	25	30	23
Citigroup CIB	16	6	2	8	29	30	20
Royal Sun Alliance	16	6	2	8	24	32	20
Temple Bar	16	5	3	8	34	38	18
Foreign & Commonwealth Office	16	4	1	11	26	53	13
Royal Sun Alliance Res	16	2	2	12	25	41	8

CHALLENGE CUP
HSBC 0*:4p   Weirside Rangers 0*:3p
SENIOR CUP
Marsh 2   Dresdner Kleinwort Wasserstein 1
JUNIOR CUP
Chislehurst Sports 0   Credit Suisse 1
VETERANS' CUP
National Westminster Bank 3   Zurich Eagle Star 1

LONDON LEGAL LEAGUE

DIVISION I	P	W	D	L	F	A	Pts
Linklaters	18	13	2	3	39	26	41
Slaughter & May	18	11	4	3	39	22	37
Stephenson Harwood	18	11	1	6	50	33	34
Macfarlanes	18	10	2	6	48	32	32
Watson Farley & Williams	18	8	4	6	24	23	28
Simmons & Simmons	18	8	1	9	37	37	25
Dechert*	18	5	5	8	34	36	19
Richards Butler	18	4	5	9	35	44	17
Clifford Chance	18	4	3	11	23	46	15
KPMG London*	18	2	1	15	26	56	6

DIVISION II	P	W	D	L	F	A	Pts
Financial Service A	18	14	2	2	57	17	44
Nabarro Nathanson	18	14	2	2	58	20	44
Gray's Inn	18	9	2	7	30	34	29
Allen & Overy	18	8	3	7	44	37	27
Barlow Lyde & Gilbert	18	7	1	10	48	46	22
Baker & McKenzie	18	7	0	11	31	45	21
Herbert Smith	18	6	3	9	31	47	21
Ashurst Morris Crisp*	18	6	4	8	30	31	20
Norton Rose	18	6	0	12	24	58	18
CMS Cameron McKenna*	18	3	3	12	24	42	8

LONDON LEGAL LEAGUE continued...

DIVISION III

	P	W	D	L	F	A	Pts
Lovells	16	11	1	4	48	29	34
Pegasus	16	9	3	4	47	32	30
Kirkpatrick & Lockhart N G	16	9	3	4	39	27	30
Withers	16	8	4	4	30	24	28
Freshfields Bruckhaus Deringer	16	7	1	8	39	34	22
Field Fisher Waterhouse	16	5	3	8	45	37	18
BBC Post Production	16	4	4	8	30	34	16
Denton Wilde Sapte	16	5	1	10	24	45	16
Taylor Wessing	16	3	2	11	12	52	11

Farrer & Co withdrawn and record expunged
* - Points deducted - breach of Rule

LEAGUE CHALLENGE CUP
Stephenson Harwood 4 Watson Farley Williams 1

WEAVERS ARMS CUP
Macfarlanes 2 Lovells 4

INVITATION CUP
Field Fisher Waterhouse 3 Taylor Wessing 1

LONDON OLD BOYS CUP

Senior
Old Meadonians 3 Southgate County 2

Challenge
Old Kolsassions 0*:5p Fulham Compton Old B. 0*:4p

Intermediate
Albanian Res 3 King's Old Boys Res 1

Junior
OldVaughanians 3rd 1 UCL Academicals 3rd 2

Minor
Old Aloysians 4th 2 Parkfield 4th 3

Drummond
Southgate County 4th 0 Albanian 5th 3

Nemean
Old Meadonians 8th 1*:2p Cardinal Manning Res 2*:4p

Olympian
Old Guildfordians Res 2 Old Bromleians 3rd 3

Jack Perry Veterans
Old Meadonians "A" 2 Old Woodhousians 3

OLD BOYS' INVITATION CUPS

Senior:
Old Owens 2 Old Salesians 1

Junior:
Old Owens Res 1 Old Finchleians Res 0

Minor:
Old Tenisonians 3rd 3 Old Owens 3rd 1

4th XIs:
Old Finchleians 4th 1 Old Owens 4th 2

5th XIs:
Old Parmiterians 5th 1*:2p E Barnet Old Grammarians 5th 1*:3p

6th XIs:
Glyn Old Boys 6th 2 Old Parmiterians 6th 1

7th XIs:
Old Bealonians 7th 2 Old Suttonians 7th 5

Veterans'
Old Aloysians 3 Old Woodhousians 0

MIDLAND AMATEUR ALLIANCE

PREMIER DIVISION

	P	W	D	L	F	A	Pts
Underwood Villa	24	21	0	3	119	47	63
Racing Athletic	24	15	4	5	58	30	49
Ashland Rovers	24	15	4	5	58	40	49
Woodborough United	24	14	2	8	87	48	44
Beaufort United	24	13	5	6	68	39	44
Steelers	24	13	3	8	61	39	42
Old Elizabethans	24	11	6	7	49	46	39
Wollaton 3rd	24	10	4	10	66	59	34
Beeston Old Boys Assn	24	9	4	11	48	53	31
Lady Bay	24	6	2	16	47	80	20
Bassingfield	24	5	2	17	29	99	17
Derbyshire Amateurs Res	24	2	4	18	32	78	10
Sherwood Forest	24	1	2	21	25	89	5

DIVISION 1

	P	W	D	L	F	A	Pts
Monty Hind Old Boys	26	19	7	0	73	27	64
County NALGO	26	17	5	4	64	34	56
Brunts Old Boys	26	14	3	9	66	64	45
Clinphone	26	11	7	8	61	50	40
Radcliffe Olympic 3rd	26	11	4	11	47	45	37
PASE	26	10	7	9	59	63	37
Old Bemrosians	26	11	3	12	46	40	36
Nottinghamshire Res	26	11	3	12	50	53	36
Old Elizabethans Res	26	11	1	14	57	62	34
Keyworth United 3rd	26	8	7	11	56	58	31
Southwell Amateurs	26	7	6	13	47	58	27
Wollaton 4th	26	7	6	13	44	59	27
Broadmeadows	26	6	5	15	57	60	23
West Bridgford United	26	5	4	17	40	94	19

DIVISION 2

	P	W	D	L	F	A	Pts
FC 05	26	26	0	0	178	20	78
Acorn Athletic	26	20	2	4	128	62	62
Top Club	26	19	3	4	105	54	60
Calverton Miners Welfare 3rd	26	15	1	10	80	62	46
Ashland Rovers Res	26	14	3	9	75	80	45
Hickling	26	14	1	11	88	69	43
EMTEC	26	12	3	11	86	67	39
Nottinghamshire 3rd	26	10	4	12	60	70	34
Cambridge Knights	26	9	1	16	93	80	28
Derbyshire Amateurs 3rd	26	8	3	15	50	98	27
Ashfield Athletic	26	5	6	15	68	105	21
Old Bemrosians Res	26	6	2	18	34	92	20
Tibshelf Old Boys	26	5	3	18	47	110	18
Hare and Hounds	26	2	2	22	41	164	8

LEAGUE SENIOR CUP
Underwood Villa 3 Racing Athletic 1

LEAGUE INTERMEDIATE CUP
PASE 2 Clinphone 1

LEAGUE MINOR CUP
FC05 6 Hickling 1

SOUTHERN AMATEUR LEAGUE

SENIOR SECTION:

DIVISION 1	P	W	D	L	F	A	Pts
Old Owens	20	14	1	5	51	19	43
West Wickham	20	12	6	2	41	15	42
Nottsborough	20	12	5	3	43	20	41
Winchmore Hill	20	13	2	5	31	15	41
Broomfield	20	7	6	7	26	35	27
Old Salesians	20	6	6	8	28	33	24
East Barnet Old Grammarians	20	6	5	9	27	34	23
Civil Service	20	4	5	11	31	40	17
Old Lyonians	20	5	2	13	22	47	17
Old Esthameians	20	2	10	8	23	42	16
Old Actonians Association	20	2	6	12	18	41	12

DIVISION 2	P	W	D	L	F	A	Pts
Alleyn Old Boys	20	12	2	6	48	26	38
Old Wilsonians	20	11	5	4	38	26	38
Norsemen	20	11	3	6	44	24	36
Ibis	20	11	2	7	51	42	35
Carshalton	20	8	6	6	46	41	30
Bank of England	20	7	5	8	31	33	26
Weirside Rangers	20	7	5	8	37	41	26
Polytechnic	20	7	4	9	36	39	25
HSBC	20	7	4	9	24	31	25
South Bank Cuaco	20	4	3	13	33	53	15
Old Finchleians	20	4	3	13	28	60	15

DIVISION 3	P	W	D	L	F	A	Pts
Merton	20	13	3	4	58	26	42
BB Eagles	20	11	7	2	55	27	40
Alexandra Park	20	12	3	5	59	35	39
Old Westminster Citizens	20	10	6	4	44	37	36
Old Parkonians	20	9	5	6	50	38	32
Crouch End Vampires	20	8	3	9	38	45	27
Old Stationers	20	7	4	5	46	52	25
Old Latymerians	20	7	2	13	27	43	23
Lloyds TSB Bank	20	6	3	16	39	62	21
Kew Association	20	3	3	10	28	59	12
Southgate Olympic	20	2	5	12	25	45	11

RESERVE TEAM SECTION: Teams Won by:

Division 1	11	Old Actonians Ass. Res
Division 2	11	Old Wilsonians Res
Division 3	11	Old Westminster Citizens
Res		

THIRD TEAM SECTION

Division 1	11	Winchmore Hill 3rd
Division 2	11	Old Stationers 3rd
Division 3	11	Southgate Olympic 3rd

MINOR SECTION

Division 3 North	11	Old Owens 6th
Division 3 South	10	BB Eagles 4th
Division 4 North	11	Winchmore Hill 7th
Division 4 South	10	Old Actonians Ass. 7th
Division 5 North	10	Winchmore Hill 9th
Division 5 South	11	Wearside Rangers 5th
Division 6 South	11	Merton 5th
Division 7 South	11	Lloyds TSB Bank 8th

CHALLENGE CUPS

Junior: Southgate Olympic 3rd 0 O Actonians Ass'n 3rd 1
Minor: Old Owens 4th 2*:6p Kew Association 4th 2*:7p
Senior Novets: Civil Service 5th 9 Old Stationers 5th 4
Inter' Novets: Old Actonians Ass'n 6th 4 Crouch End V'ps 6th 1
Junior Novets: Winchmore Hill 7th 2*:3 Crouch End V'ps 7th 2*:2

UNIVERSITY OF LONDON MEN'S INTER-COLLEGIATE LEAGUE

WEEKEND ONE DIVISION	P	W	D	L	F	A	Pts
London School of Economics	11	9	2	0	44	6	29
Queen Mary College	11	6	4	1	27	11	22
Royal Holloway College	11	5	4	2	24	14	19
University College	11	5	3	3	21	22	18
Imperial College	11	4	3	4	20	14	15
King's College	11	4	4	3	27	22	16
R Free, Mx & Univ Coll Hosp MS	11	5	2	4	16	17	17
St Bart's & R London Hosps MS	11	3	3	5	11	17	12
Sch of Oriental & African Studies	11	4	0	7	15	31	12
London Sch Economics Res	11	2	3	6	12	19	9
Imperial College Res	11	2	1	8	6	34	7
University College Res	11	2	1	8	20	36	4

WEEKEND TWO DIVISION	P	W	D	L	F	A	Pts
Royal Holloway CollegeRes	10	8	2	0	30	7	26
Imperial College Medicals	10	6	3	1	31	14	21
Guy's, King's, St Thomas's MS	10	6	2	2	30	12	20
Royal Holloway College 3rd	10	5	3	2	32	13	18
University College 3rd	10	5	1	4	17	21	16
St Georges Hospital MS	10	4	3	3	33	23	15
Queen Mary College Res	10	3	1	6	19	35	10
Imperial College 3rd	10	3	0	7	12	26	9
King's College Res	10	2	2	6	18	23	8
Imperial Medicals Res	10	2	2	6	9	31	8
St Georges Hospital Res	10	1	1	8	8	34	4

DIVISION ONE	P	W	D	L	F	A	Pts
Goldsmiths' College	22	18	3	1	73	27	57
London School of Economics 3rd	22	14	6	2	68	29	48
University College 5th	22	12	3	7	44	30	39
Royal Holloway College 4th	22	9	3	10	45	54	30
King's College 3rd	22	9	4	9	39	40	31
Royal Veterinary College	22	8	4	10	38	44	28
R Free, Mx & Univ Coll Hosp MS Res	22	8	3	11	53	54	27
Imperial College 5th	22	9	3	10	29	61	30
Guy's, King's, St Thomas's MS Res	22	12	2	8	52	25	38
University College 4th	22	6	5	11	43	42	23
Imperial College 4th	22	5	5	12	34	55	20
R Free, Mx & Univ Coll Hosp MS 3rd	22	1	1	20	17	74	4

DIVISION TWO	P	W	D	L	F	A	Pts
University College 6th	22	20	1	1	82	21	61
Queen MaryCollege 3rd	22	15	1	6	61	31	46
London School of Economics 4th	22	12	2	8	43	37	38
London School of Economics 5th	22	11	4	7	62	39	37
St Bart's & R London Hosps MS Res	22	10	5	7	40	26	35
Royal HollowayCollege 5th	22	9	2	11	45	49	29
Guy's, King's, St Thomas's MS 3rd	22	8	2	12	36	32	26
University College 7th	22	8	1	13	43	64	25
King's College 4th	22	7	4	11	39	63	25
Imperial Medicals3rd	22	6	5	11	40	54	23
Royal School of Mines (IC)	22	6	4	12	39	63	22
King's College 5th	22	3	3	16	24	75	12

DIVISION THREE	P	W	D	L	F	A	Pts
Royal HollowayCollege 6th	20	13	2	5	61	33	41
King's College 6th	20	10	6	4	49	28	36
St Bart's & R London Hosps MS 3rd	20	10	4	6	52	38	34
Guy's, King's, St Thomas's MS 4th	20	8	8	4	51	43	32
Imperial College 6th	20	9	2	9	31	29	29
Guy's, King's, St Thomas's Hosp MS 5th	20	9	2	9	25	34	29
London School of Economics 7th	20	7	4	9	37	33	25
London School of Economics 6th	20	7	4	9	24	37	25
Goldsmiths' College Res	20	7	2	11	50	61	23
R Free, Mx & Univ Coll Hosp 4th	20	5	5	10	22	33	20
Queen Mary College 4th	20	4	3	13	31	64	15

UNIVERSITY OF LONDON MEN'S INTER-COLLEGIATE LEAGUE continued...

DIVISION FOUR	P	W	D	L	F	A	Pts
University of the Arts	18	14	1	3	85	25	43
School of Pharmacy	18	13	1	4	81	40	40
Imperial College 7th	18	13	0	5	48	29	39
Sch of Oriental & African Studies Res	18	12	2	4	77	38	38
Sch Slavonic & E European Studies	18	7	3	8	34	53	24
Goldsmiths' College 3rd	16	6	2	8	47	61	20
Queen MaryCollege 5th	18	6	1	11	37	51	19
Royal Veterinary College Res	18	5	3	10	37	72	18
Imperial Medicals 4th	18	4	1	13	40	87	13
St Georges Hospital MS 3rd	18	1	2	15	16	46	5

CHALLENGE CUP
University College 1 Royal Free & UCH Med Sch 3
RESERVES CHALLENGE CUP
R Holloway 3rd 2 University College 4th 1
RESERVES PLATE
University College 6th 3 Queen Mary College 3rd 2
VASE
St Barts & R London Med Coll 3rd 6* King's College 3rd 3*

UNIVERSITY OF LONDON WOMEN'S INTER-COLLEGIATE LEAGUE

PREMIER DIVISION	P	W	D	L	F	A	Pts
Guy's, King's, St. Thomas's Hosp MS	10	8	1	1	77	21	25
Royal Holloway College	10	7	1	2	35	15	22
London School Economics	10	6	2	2	43	13	20
Queen Mary College	10	3	0	7	35	59	9
University College	10	3	1	6	27	29	10
King's College	10	0	1	9	6	86	1

UNIVERSITY OF LONDON WOMEN'S INTER-COLLEGIATE LEAGUE continued...

DIVISION ONE	P	W	D	L	F	A	Pts
Goldsmiths' College	8	6	1	1	34	10	19
Imperial College Medicals	8	4	3	1	29	9	15
R Free, Mx & Univ Coll Hosp MS	8	3	1	4	16	16	10
Royal Veterinary College	8	3	1	4	20	21	10
University College Res	8	1	0	7	7	50	3

DIVISION TWO	P	W	D	L	F	A	Pts
Guy's, King's, St Thomas's MS Res	8	6	1	1	28	16	19
Imperial Medicals Womens 1st	8	5	2	1	54	11	17
School of Oriental & African Studies	8	4	1	3	12	21	13
St George's Hospital MS	8	1	2	5	21	24	5
R Free, Mx & Univ Coll Hosp MS Res	8	0	2	6	6	49	2

WOMEN'S CHALLENGE CUP
Guy's King's StThomas' 9 LSE 1

U-16 GIRLS
CENTRE OF EXCELLENCE LEAGUE

	P	W	D	L	F	A	Pts
Southampton	20	14	3	3	67	32	45
Arsenal	20	13	5	2	39	15	44
Millwall	20	14	1	5	50	25	43
Chelsea	20	13	3	4	50	19	42
Charlton Athletic	20	10	4	6	39	31	34
Reading	20	8	4	8	38	43	28
Watford	20	8	2	10	35	44	26
Colchester United	20	6	3	11	28	47	21
Fulham	20	6	2	12	37	43	20
Leyton Orient	20	2	2	16	16	44	8
Brighton	20	1	1	18	13	69	4

ARMED FORCES FOOTBALL

INTER SERVICES CUP

MEN'S COMPETITION

Army	5	-	1	Royal Navy
RAF	1	-	2	Army
Royal Navy	3	-	2	RAF

	P	W	D	L	F	A	Pts
Army	2	2	0	0	7	2	6
Royal Navy	2	1	0	1	4	7	3
RAF	2	0	0	2	3	5	0

Inter Service Champions 2004/05:   Army
Inter Service Champions 2003/04:   Royal Navy
Inter Service Champions 2002/03:   Army

WOMEN'S COMPETITION

	P	W	D	L	F	A	Pts
RAF	2	2	0	0	5	3	6
Army	2	1	0	1	3	2	3
Royal Navy	2	0	0	2	2	5	0

Inter Service Champions 2004/05:   Army
Inter Service Champions 2003/04:   Army
Inter Service Champions 2002/03:   Army

ARMY INTER CORPS LEAGUE

MEN'S COMPETITION (UK)

	P	W	D	L	F	A	Pts
Royal Signals (C)	11	10	1	0	38	8	31
Royal Artillery	11	8	2	1	35	12	26
Royal Logistic Corps	11	8	1	2	30	11	25
Royal Engineers	11	7	1	3	26	19	22
Royal Electrical & M.E.	11	6	1	4	19	10	19
Infantry	11	6	1	4	18	12	19
Army Medical Services	11	4	1	6	21	30	13
Army Physical Training Corps	11	3	1	7	12	27	10
Royal Armoured Corps	11	3	0	8	21	31	9
Army Air Corps	11	2	1	8	12	24	7
Adjutant Generals Corps	11	1	2	8	10	27	5
Intelligence Corps	11	0	4	7	9	39	4

(C) - Champions 04-05

ARMY CHALLENGE CUP

QUARTER FINALS

1 Irish Guards	v	4 Royal Irish	0-2
3 (UK) Div HQ & Signal Regt	v	4 LS regt RLC	0-3
2 Signal Regt	v	30 Signal Regt	6-2
28 Engineer Regt	v	7 Signal Regt	0-1

2004/05

| 6 Battalion REME | v | LS Regiment RLC | 2-2*, 4-2p |

2003/04 FINAL

| 2 Royal Irish | v | 6 Battalion REME | 1-0 |

2002/03 FINAL

| 6 Battalion REME | v | 11 Signal Regiment | 4-0 |

SEMI FINALS

| 4 LS Regt RLC | v | 2 Signal Regt | 2-0 |
| 4 R Irish | v | 7 Signal Regt | 4-3 |

FINAL

| 4 Logistic Support Regt RLC | v | 4th Battalion The Royal Irish Regt | 5-5*, 5-3p |

2001/02 FINAL

| 28 Engineer Regt | v | 1 Kings | 2-1 |

2000/01 FINAL

| 28 Engineer Regt | v | 3 RSME Regiment | 3-3*, 5-4p |

SOUTH AND WEST COUNTIES CHAMPIONSHIP

O nce again Hampshire dominated the South West Counties competitions, winning four of the five Championships they entered, The Mick Parry Cup, the Under 18's Youth, the Women's and the girls Under 18's. That only left the Senior Championship for Cornwall who defeated Sussex in a close final (2-1) played at St Blazey and the Under 12's Championship which was won on a league basis by the Army.

Unfortunately the Under 12 competition will not be running this season due to lack of entries but a new Under 16 competition has been created with entries from Gloucestershire, Dorset, Berks and Bucks and Guernsey.

The Competition has now changed it's title to the South and West Counties Championships to better reflect the entries which include Gwent from the Welsh F.A. and the Channel Islands.

The Championship welcomes a new Chairman this season in David Dorey who has taken over from Peter Hough who retired at the end of last season.

Further information on fixtures and results can be obtained from the Press Officer, John moody at jm-southwestcounties@tiscali.co.uk.

MENS SENIOR COMPETITION

GROUP A

Sussex	v	Dorset	HW
Royal Navy	v	Dorset	5-1
Guernsey	v	Sussex	1-2
Royal Navy	v	Army	1-1
Dorset	v	Army	HW
Sussex	v	Royal Navy	1-1
Army	v	Guernsey	4-3
Guernsey	v	Royal Navy	2-0
Army	v	Sussex	1-1
Dorset	v	Guernsey	0-3

	P	W	D	L	F	A	Pts
Sussex	4	2	2	0	4	3	8
Guernsey	4	2	0	2	9	6	6
Royal Navy	4	1	2	1	7	5	5
Army	4	1	2	1	6	5	5
Dorset	4	1	0	3	1	8	3

GROUP B

Cornwall	v	Jersey	3-2
Jersey	v	Royal Air Force	1-3
Gloucestershire	v	Royal Air Force	2-4
Jersey	v	Gloucestershire	1-0
Gloucestershire	v	Cornwall	1-4
Cornwall	v	Royal Air Force	2-1

	P	W	D	L	F	A	Pts
Cornwall	3	3	0	0	9	4	9
Royal Air Force	3	2	0	1	8	5	6
Jersey	3	1	0	2	4	6	3
Gloucestershire	3	0	0	3	3	9	0

CHAMPIONSHIP FINAL

Cornwall	v	Sussex	2-1

MENS SENIOR WINNERS - 1974 - 2006

1974/75	Wiltshire	1985/86	Hampshire	1996/97	Devon
1975/76	Army	1986/87	Devon	1997/98	Royal Navy
1976/77	Hampshire	1987/88	Army	1998/99	Army
1977/78	Hampshire	1988/89	Army	1999/2000	Sussex
1978/79	Somerset & Avon	1989/90	Sussex	2000/01	No Competition
1979/80	Somerset & Avon	1990/91	Sussex	2001/02	Sussex
1980/81	Somerset & Avon	1991/92	Somerset & Avon	2002/03	Devon
1981/82	Sussex	1992/93	Army	2003/04	Cornwall
1982/83	Somerset & Avon	1993/94	Royal Navy	2004/05	Army
1983/84	Royal Navy	1994/95	Sussex	2005/06	Cornwall
1984/85	Sussex	1995/96	Royal Navy		

MENS SENIOR WINNERS LEADER BOARD

Sussex	7	championships	Devon	3
Army	5		Hampshire	3
Somerset & Avon	5		Cornwall	2
Royal Navy	4		Wliltshire	1

WOMENS SENIOR COMPETITION

GROUP A

Dorset	v Gloucestershire		3-1
Dorset	v Cornwall		2-6
Cornwall	v Gloucestershire		3-1
Gloucestershire	v Cornwall		1-9
Gloucestershire	v Dorset		4-2
Cornwall	v Dorset		5-0

	P	W	D	L	F	A	Pts
Cornwall	4	4	0	0	23	4	12
Dorset	4	1	0	3	7	16	3
Gloucestershire	4	1	0	3	7	17	3

GROUP B

Hampshire	v Royal Navy		7-1
Royal Navy	v Army		0-3
Army	v Hampshire		1-6
Army	v Royal Navy		10-0
Royal Navy	v Hampshire		0-4
Hampshire	v Army		HW

	P	W	D	L	F	A	Pts
Hampshire	4	4	0	0	17	2	12
Army	4	2	0	2	14	6	6
Royal Navy	4	0	0	4	1	24	0

CHAMPIONSHIP FINAL

Hampshire	v Cornwall		6-1

MENS UNDER 21 COMPETITION

Army	v Royal Navy		AW
Royal Navy	v Hampshire		1-1
Royal Navy	v Army		1-3
Hampshire	v Royal Navy		0-0
Hampshire	v Army		1-3
Army	v Hampshire		4-2

	P	W	D	L	F	A	Pts
Army	4	3	0	1	10	4	9
Royal Navy	4	1	2	1	2	4	5
Hampshire	4	0	2	2	4	8	2

MENS YOUTH COMPETITION

GROUP A

Oxfordshire	v Hampshire		3-8
Oxfordshire	v Cornwall		3-1
Devon	v Oxfordshire		2-4
Wiltshire	v Gloucestershire		1-2
Hampshire	v Wiltshire		0-0
Cornwall	v Devon		4-0
Devon	v Wiltshire		2-0
Gloucestershie	v Cornwall		1-1
Hampshire	v Devon		4-1
Gloucestershire	v Oxfordshire		1-0
Devon	v Gloucestershire		2-1
Oxfordshire	v Wiltshire		1-2
Wiltshire	v Cornwall		3-6
Hampshire	v Gloucestershire		5-0
Cornwall	v Hampshire		0-0

	P	W	D	L	F	A	Pts
Hampshire	5	3	2	0	17	4	11
Cornwall	5	2	2	1	12	7	8
Gloucestershire	5	2	1	2	5	9	7
Oxfordshire	5	2	0	3	11	14	6
Devon	5	2	0	3	7	13	6
Wiltshire	5	1	1	3	6	11	4

GROUP B

Berks & Bucks	v Gwent		4-0
Dorset	v Somerset		4-1
Gwent	v Guernsey		2-1
Somerset	v Guernsey		3-1
Dorset	v Army		5-1
Gwent	v Army		4-2
Berks & Bucks	v Dorset		4-2
Army	v Berks & Bucks		1-7
Somerset	v Gwent		1-2
Guernsey	v Dorset		1-7
Army	v Guernsey		6-4
Berks & Bucks	v Somerset		2-0
Gwent	v Dorset		0-2
Army	v Somerset		0-2
Guernsey	v Berks & Bucks		3-1

	P	W	D	L	F	A	Pts
Dorset	5	4	0	1	20	7	12
Berks & Bucks	5	4	0	1	18	6	12
Gwent	5	3	0	2	8	10	9
Somerset	5	2	0	3	7	9	6
Guernsey	5	1	0	4	10	19	3
Army	5	1	0	4	10	22	3

CHAMPIONSHIP FINAL

Dorset	v Hampshire		1-2

WOMENS UNDER 18 COMPETITION

GROUP A

Hampshire	v	Wiltshire	6-0
Hampshire	v	Gloucestershire	4-1
Wiltshire	v	Hampshire	2-0
Gloucestershire	v	Wiltshire	2-0
Gloucestershire	v	Hampshire	2-4
Wiltshire	v	Gloucestershire	AW

	P	W	D	L	F	A	Pts
Hampshire	4	3	0	1	14	5	9
Gloucestershire	4	2	0	2	5	8	6
Wiltshire	4	1	0	3	2	8	3

GROUP B

Somerset	v	Cornwall	8-1
Devon	v	Somerset	4-5
Devon	v	Dorset	9-0
Somerset	v	Dorset	5-1
Cornwall	v	Devon	2-3
Dorset	v	Cornwall	5-2

	P	W	D	L	F	A	Pts
Somerset	3	3	0	0	18	6	9
Devon	3	2	0	1	16	7	6
Dorset	3	1	0	2	6	16	3
Cornwall	3	0	0	3	5	16	0

CHAMPIONSHIP FINAL

| Somerset | v | Hampshire | 0-1 |

MICK PARRY MEMORIAL TROPHY

Wiltshire	v	Dorset	2-0
Hampshire	v	Devon	2-0
Army	v	Berks & Bucks	3-4
Jersey	v	Oxfordshire	0-1

Semi-Finals

| Oxfordshire | v | Hampshire | 0-3 |
| Wiltshire | v | Berks & Bucks | 1-1*, 4-3p |

Final

| Hampshire | v | Wiltshire | 2-0 |

TOTAL CHAMPIONSHIP TITLES WON - 1974-2006

	SENIOR	YOUTH	MICK PARRY	U21	WOMEN'S	U-18	TOTAL
Hampshire	3	7	1	3	6	3	23
Army	6	-	-	2	-	-	8
Devon	3	3	-	-	1	1	8
Sussex	7	-	-	-	1	-	8
Wiltshire	1	5	1	-	1	-	8
Gloucestershire	-	6	-	-	-	1	7
Somerset & Avon	5	1	-	-	-	-	6
Royal Navy	4	1	-	-	-	-	5
Berks & Bucks	-	3	2	-	-	-	5
Cornwall	2	2	1	-	-	-	4
Dorset	-	1	1	-	-	-	2
Somerset	-	1	-	-	-	-	1
Somerset & Glos.	-	1	-	-	-	-	1

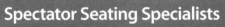

BRITISH UNIVERSITIES FOOTBALL

1ST TEAM FOOTBALL CHAMPIONSHIP 2005

FIRST ROUND

Strathclyde	v	Northumbria	1-2
Hertfordshire	v	MMU Cheshire	0-3
Loughborough	v	Leeds Metropolitan	3-3
Heriot-Watt	v	Edge Hill	3-0
Warwick	v	UW Swansea (H)	1-0
Lincoln	v	Southampton	4-0
Bath	v	Brighton	2-1
Brunel	v	Gloucestershire	4-1

SECOND ROUND

Northumbria	v	MMU Cheshire	1-2
Loughborough	v	Heriot-Watt	3-1
Warwick	v	Lincoln	1-0
Bath	v	Brunel	7-2

SEMI-FINALS

Bath	v	Warwick	5-2
MMU Cheshire	v	Loughborough	0-1

THE FINAL

Bath	v	Loughborough	1-2

PREMIER LEAGUE CONFERENCE

NORTH

	P	W	D	L	F	A	Pts
(C) Northumbria	10	7	2	1	25	10	23
(C) Loughborough	10	7	1	2	31	12	22
(C) Lincoln	10	5	1	4	22	19	16
(C) Edge Hill College	10	4	1	5	14	21	13
(C) MMU Cheshire	10	2	3	5	21	24	9
(R) Nottingham Trent	10	1	0	9	9	36	3

MIDLANDS 1A

	P	W	D	L	F	A	Pts
(C) Warwick	10	7	2	1	26	13	23
(T) Birmingham	10	7	2	1	26	12	23
(T) Northampton	10	4	2	4	16	18	14
(T) Nottingham	10	3	3	4	16	20	12
(R) Cambridge	10	3	0	7	12	20	9
(R) Coventry	10	1	1	8	12	25	4

NORTHERN 1A

	P	W	D	L	F	A	Pts
(C) Leeds Metropolitan	10	6	2	2	28	9	20
(T) Sheffield	10	6	1	3	20	10	19
(T) Manchester	9*	3	3	3	13	19	15
(T) Sheffield Hallam	10	4	1	5	13	12	13
(T) (R) Liverpool John Moores	10	1	4	5	9	22	7
(R) Teeside	9*	1	5	3	8	19	5

*walkover for Manchester over Teeside.

SOUTH

	P	W	D	L	F	A	Pts
(C) Bath	10	9	1	0	34	10	28
(C) UW Swansea	10	5	4	1	13	6	19
(C) Hertfordshire	10	4	2	4	22	19	14
(C) Brunel	10	3	2	5	16	22	11
(C) Southampton	10	3	1	6	15	25	10
(R) Greenwich	10	1	0	9	14	32	3

SOUTH EASTERN 1A

	P	W	D	L	F	A	Pts
(C) Brighton	10	9	0	1	44	12	27
(T) St. Mary's	10	6	1	3	16	14	19
(T) Portsmouth	10	6	0	4	20	15	18
(T) Kingston	10	4	1	5	21	20	13
(R) London	10	2	1	7	13	29	7
(R) Canterbury Christ Church	10	1	1	8	15	39	4

WESTERN 1A

	P	W	D	L	F	A	Pts
(C) Gloucestershire	10	7	1	2	29	16	22
(T) UWIC	10	6	0	4	24	27	18
(T) Bath 2nds	10	5	0	5	24	24	15
(T) UWE Hartpury	10	4	2	4	30	20	14
(T) (R) Exeter	9*	2	2	5	16	22	11
(R) St. Mark & St. John	9*	2	1	6	15	29	4

*walkover for Exeter over St. Mark & St. John

C = qualified for Championship. T = qualified for Trophy. R = Relegated

SCOTTISH CONFERENCE 1A	P	W	D	L	F	A	Pts
(C) Heriot-Watt	10	7	1	2	27	16	22
(C) Strathclyde	10	4	4	2	29	21	16
(T) Glasgow	9*	4	1	4	10	15	16
(T) Dundee	10	4	1	5	17	20	13
(R) Edinburgh	9*	2	4	3	17	19	7
(R) Stirling	10	2	1	7	14	23	7

*walkover for Glasgow over Edinburgh.

TROPHY FINAL

UWE Hartpury	v	St. Mary's	6-1

SHIELD FINAL

De Monfort, Bedford	v	Cardiff	1-0

PLATE FINAL

Essex 2nds	v	Leeds Metropolitan 2nds	1-2

WOMEN'S 1ST TEAM FOOTBALL

CHAMPIONSHIP QUARTER-FINALS

Loughborough	v	Birmingham	3-1
Sheffield Hallam	v	Edinburgh	1-1
Brighton	v	Leeds Metropolitan	2-0
UWIC	v	Bath(H)	1-1

SEMI-FINALS

Loughborough	v	Brighton	4-2
UWIC	v	Sheffield Hallam	3-0

FINAL

Loughborough	v	UWIC	3-1

TROPHY FINAL

Loughborough 2nds	v	Cardiff	0-1

SHIELD FINAL

Liverpool Hope	v	West of England	0-13

PLATE FINAL

Sunderland	v	Manchester Metropolitan	3-0

WOMEN'S PREMIER LEAGUE CONFERENCE

NORTH

	P	W	D	L	F	A	Pts
(C) Loughborough	10	9	0	1	37	6	27
(C) MMU Cheshire	10	6	1	3	25	11	19
(C) Leeds Metropolitan	10	4	2	4	25	14	14
(C) De Monfort, Bedford	10	3	2	5	15	43	11
(C) Birmingham	10	2	4	4	14	16	10
(R) Manchester	10	0	3	7	9	35	3

SOUTH

	P	W	D	L	F	A	Pts
(C) UWIC	10	8	2	0	31	8	26
(C) Brighton	10	7	2	1	37	5	23
(C) Hertfordshire	10	5	0	5	26	21	15
(C) Bath	10	5	0	5	27	17	15
(C) Chichester	10	2	0	8	8	33	6
(R) Oxford	10	1	0	9	11	56	3

MIDLANDS 1A

	P	W	D	L	F	A	Pts
(C) Loughborough 2nds	10	9	0	1	76	5	27
(T) Nottingham Trent	10	7	0	3	47	25	21
(T) Nottingham	10	4	1	5	17	16	13
(T) East Anglia	10	4	1	5	24	30	13
(T) (R) Warwick	10	3	2	5	26	56	11
(R) Worcester	10	1	0	9	11	69	3

SOUTH EASTERN 1A

	P	W	D	L	F	A	Pts
(C) Brunel	10	7	1	2	38	14	22
(T) Portsmouth	10	7	1	2	44	16	22
(T) Brighton 2nds	10	6	2	2	31	21	20
(T) St. Mary's	10	5	1	4	28	27	16
(R) Roehampton	10	1	1	8	15	32	4
(R) London	10	1	0	9	8	54	3

NORTHERN 1A

	P	W	D	L	F	A	Pts
(C) Sheffield Hallam	9*	7	2	0	36	16	26
(T) Leeds	10	6	0	4	25	18	18
(T) Edge Hill	9*	4	1	4	42	24	16
(T) Northumbria	10	5	0	5	21	36	15
(T) (R) Liverpool John Moores	10	4	1	5	22	26	13
(R) York	8*	0	0	8	5	31	-6

*walkover for Sheffield Hallam and Edge Hill over York.

WESTERN 1A

	P	W	D	L	F	A	Pts
(C) Bristol	10	9	0	1	32	11	27
(T) Cardiff	10	8	0	2	16	6	24
(T) St. Mark & St. John	10	7	0	3	28	11	21
(T) Gloucestershire	10	2	1	7	14	25	7
(R) Exeter	10	2	0	8	12	24	6
(R) UWIC 2nds	10	1	1	8	9	34	4

C = qualified for Championship. T = qualified for Trophy. R = Relegated

BRITISH UNIVERSITY GAMES 2006

MENS	P	W	D	L	F	A	Pts
England	3	3	0	0	8	0	9
Wales	3	1	1	1	6	5	4
Scotland	3	0	2	1	4	5	2
Northern Ireland	3	0	0	3	4	12	0

WOMENS	P	W	D	L	F	A	Pts
Scotland	2	1	0	1	3	2	3
Wales	2	1	0	1	1	0	3
England	2	1	0	1	2	3	3

RESULTS

England	v	Scotland	1-0
England	v	Wales	1-0
England	v	Northern Ireland	6-0
Scotland	v	Wales	2-2
Scotland	v	Northern Ireland	2-2
Wales	v	Northern Ireland	4-2

RESULTS

England	v	Scotland	1-3
England	v	Wales	1-0
Scotland	v	Wales	0-1

ENGLAND'S SQUAD (MENS):

1	Ryan Northmore	Bath
2	Alan Fitzpatrick	Edge Hill
3	Glen Steele	Loughborough
4	Matt Taylor	Sheffield Hallam
5	Kes Metitiri	Bath
6	Chris Jenkinson	Leeds Metropolitan
7	Andrew Reilly	Durham
8	Murray McColloch	MMU Cheshire
9	Luke Buttery	UWE Hartpury
10	Mark Noon	Coventry
11	Marc Richards	UWE Hartpury
12	Marc Canham	Bath
13	Steve Abbott	Edge Hill
14	Leon McSweeney	Loughborough
15	Robbie Simpson	Loughborough
16	Colin Iley	Teesside
17	Paul Dixon	Northumbria
18	Sean Canham	Bath

ENGLAND'S SQUAD (WOMENS):

1	Carla Ward	Bath
2	Caroline Collie	Brighton
3	Sophie Perry	Brighton
4	Cori Daniels	Hertfordshire
5	Carla Baxby	Leeds Met
6	Sarah Dobby	Leeds Met
7	Sarah Manning	Liverpool John Moores
8	Denise Campbell	Liverpool John Moores
9	Milly Durrant	Loughborough
10	Rebecca Francis	MMU Cheshire
11	Natalie Smith	MMU Cheshire
12	Rania Ramadan	MMU Cheshire
13	Stacey Aisthorpe	Sheffield Hallam
14	Dawna Dennett	St Mark & St John
15	Vanessa Leat	York St John
16	Lucy Whatley	Sheffield Hallam
17	Una Harkin	MMU Cheshire
18	Holly Sandow	Bath

ENGLISH SCHOOLS' FOOTBALL ASSOCIATION

Chief Executive : John Read, 1-2 Eastgate Street, Stafford ST16 2NQ
Telephone :01785 251142; Fax : 01785 255485; Website : www.esfa.co.uk
Publicity for Non-League Directory : Mike Simmonds
19 The Spinney, Bulcote, Burton Joyce, Nottingham NG14 5GX
Telephone : 0115 931 3299; Fax : 0115 931 2758;
e.mail : msimmonds@waitrose.com
Photos : RWT Photography Telephone: 01733 204445

THE INTERNATIONAL SEASON: E.S.F.A. UNDER 18 SQUAD

The English Schools' F.A. Under 18 international squad had a more limited programme of fixtures than in most previous years although the long selection process included a practice match against Australia during the last coaching week-end which ended in a 2-2 draw with the visitors equalising late on. The match was arranged to fit in with the Australians' European tour schedule which was before the England squad preparations were complete but all the players in the chosen squad were 'capped' at this game which was played at Stafford Rangers ground.

There were several encouraging signs for the coaching staff which were built upon when the squad visited Valencia for further development during the half-term break. They were thus fully prepared for the opening fixture in the Centenary Shield against Northern Ireland at Glenavon F.C. on 25th February. First half goals from the appropriately named Lewis Irish and Lewis Brooks put England in control. In the second half, the England defence kept the home side at bay and Craig Heenigham made the final score 3-0.

A crowd of over 3,000 at Home Park, Plymouth saw England continue in good form with a 2-0 victory over Scotland on 24th March. Irish headed in a Richard Chetcuti cross after 20 minutes for his second of the season and Shaun Taylor made it 2-0 three minutes after half time. Taylor is the first boy from the Isle of Wight to win an England Schools' cap at this level and his goal was a spectacular one as he hit a 25 yard shot past a helpless Scotland keeper, Jamie Barclay.

England went into their last match against the Republic of Ireland in front of another crowd approaching 3,000 at Crawley hoping to clinch the Centenary Shield but a 0-0 draw meant that they had to wait for the last game of the tournament to decide their fate. The Republic dominated the opening exchanges but it was England who seemed to have broken the deadlock when Ryan Sammons and Taylor combined to set up Chetcuti whose effort was denied by an offside decision.

The Republic's best chance came early in the second half but Willem Puddy made a fine save from Timmy Purcell while England came closest in the last minute when Carl Reynolds inswinging corner clipped the bar. The visitors thus went into their last match against Northern Ireland needing to win to take the Shield but they could only manage to draw 1-1 so England took the title, a fitting reward for the players and Team Manager, Peter Chisholm whose three years in charge ended in triumph.

INTERNATIONAL CAPS AWARDED SEASON 2005-06

	A	B	C	D	E	F
Dan Barker (Somerset)	1	1	1	1	1s	
Karanjit Aujla (Dorset)	1	1s	1s	1g	1s	1s
John Brayford (Staffordshire)	1	1	1	1	1	1
Lewis Brooks (Lincolnshire)	1	1	1g	1s	1	1
Richard Chetcuti (Gt.Manchester)	1s	1	1	1	1	1
Craig Heenighan (Cheshire)	1g	1	1g	1	1	1
Matthew Hollyoak (Kent)	1s	1s	1s	1	1s	1s
Lewis Irish (Somerset)	1g	1	1g	1s	1g	1
Alex Johnson (Leicestershire)	1s	1g	1s	1	1s	1s
Joe Melllings (Warwickshire)	1s	1	1s	1	1s	1s
Anthony Moulds (Bedfordshire)	1s	1	1	1	1	1
Ian Parkes (Kent)	1	1	1	1s	1	1
Willem Puddy (Gloucestershire)	1	1s	1	1s	1	1
Carl Reynolds (Gloucestershire)	1	1s	1s	1	1s	1s
Ryan Sammons (Essex)	1	1	1	1s	1	1
Shaun Taylor (Hampshire)	1	1	1	1g	1g	1
Robert Blackledge-Younger (Lincolnshire)	1	1s	1	1	1	

Key : 1 Full appearance; 1g Goalscorer; 1s Substitute
A v. Australia
B v. Valencia Juvenil
C v. Northern Ireland
D v. Cambridge University
E v. Scotland
F v. Republic of Ireland
International Goalscorers :Lewis Irish 3; Craig Heenighan 2; Shaun Taylor 1; Lewis Brooks 1.
Other Matches :
v. Valencia Juvenil (Spain)Lost 1-2
v. Cambridge University (Cambridge) Won 2-1
Team Manager: Peter Chisholm. Assistant Manager: Tony Martin.
Goalkeeping Coach: Alan Thompson. Physio: Mike Hewitt. Doctor: Arthur Tabor

ENGLAND SCHOOLS' UNDER-18 SQUAD 2005-06

Back Row L to R: Lewis Irish, Lewis Brooks, Matthew Hollyoak, Carl Reynolds, John Brayford, Antony Moulds, Alex Johnson, Ryan Sammons. **Middle Row L to R:** Dr Arthur Tabor (Team Doctor), Mike Hewitt (Physiotherapist), Robert Younger, Shaun Taylor, Joe Mellings, Willem Puddy, Ian Parkes, Craig Heenighan, Alan Thomson (Coach), Tony Martin (Assistant Manager). **Front Row L to R:** Richard Chetcuti, Peter Chisholm (Manager), Kevin Wilbur (Chairman), John Read (Chief Executive), Dave Woollaston (International Selection Committee Chairman), Karanjit Aujla

THE INTER-ASSOCIATION COMPETITIONS

E.S.F.A./N.U.T. UNDER 15 INTER-ASSOCIATION TROPHY

THE FINAL

| 1st Leg | Swansea | 0 | Liverpool | 1 | (at Libity Stadium, Swansea F.C.) |
| 2nd Leg | Liverpool | 1 | Swansea | 0 | (at Anfield) |

Liverpool win 2-0 on aggregate

2ND LEG TEAMS :

LIVERPOOL : P. Kennedy, J. Richardson, L. Corrigan, J. Kennedy, P. Rawlings, R. Fraughan, T. McInerery, J. Mcauley, M. Conchie, D. Torpey, D. Price
Subs: D. Barlow, J. Rooney, L. Molyneux, J. Kennedy, A. Johnson

SWANSEA : D. Cornwell, D. Sheehan, L. James, J. Richards, S. Berry, M. Watkins, K. Hayes, K. Howard, S. Rees, S. Davey, S. Sullivan
Subs : K. Cullen, A. Finselbach, S. Rees, L. Chappell, B. James

An impressive crowd of 3,929 saw Liverpool win the 1st leg of the longest established E.S.F.A. competition with a single goal from Dominic Price. The talk during the build-up to the game was that Wayne Rooney's younger brother, midfielder John, would be appearing for Liverpool but from a large Liverpool squad, he was an unused substitute. It was the Merseysiders' strikers who settled the game after Swansea had started the brighter side. On the stroke of half-time, Josh Macauley found Dominic Price in space and he ran on to slot the ball past a helpless David Cornell.

After the break, Swansea found it difficult to break down the Liverpool defence and it was the visitors who missed the best chance of the half when Louis Corrigan volleyed over from three yards after a deep cross from Price. Swansea came close to equalising, however when Peter Kennedy turned Kieran Howard's effort round the post.

The second leg provided a better spectacle than the first with Liverpool making an early bid to double their aggregate lead. Swansea's Jazz Richards cleared off the line while Welsh international Howard headed away courageously under pressure. The visitors weathered the storm with captain Kieran Hayes to the fore and both he and Howard went close. Ironically, it was during this spell against the run of play when the two key figures from the first leg again combined well for Price to fire in from the edge of the penalty box after he had been set up by Macauley.

In the second half, Swansea threw caution to the wind and Stephen Davey had three chances but missed them all before Morley Watkins also shot wide. Swansea, however, battled to the end with Davey again twice going close and then Howard brought the save of the game from Kennedy who then recovered brilliantly to save at the feet of Richards. Despite their brave second half performance, it was Liverpool who took the Trophy for the 15th time in their history.

ROUTES TO THE FINAL

SWANSEA :

Round 1	Bye		
Round 2	v. West Gloucs.	(A)	2-0
Round 3	v. Poole	(A)	6-0
Round 4	v. Newport	(H)	2-1 *
Round 5	v. Milton Keynes	(A)	3-1
Round 6	v. Southampton	(A)	2-2 *
Replay	v. Southampton	(H)	3-0
Semi-Final	v. Cambridge	(H)	4-3 *

LIVERPOOL :

Round 1	Bye		
Round 2	v. Burnley	(A)	2-1
Round 3	v. Macclesfield	(H)	4-0
Round 4	v. Redditch	(H)	3-1
Round 5	v. Sefton	(A)	4-1
Round 6	v. Bishop Auckland	(A)	1-0
Semi-Final	v. Barnsley	(A)	3-1

Action from the Under 15 Inter-Association Trophy final between Liverpool and Swansea.

Liverpool Schools Under 15 squad 2005-2006

E.S.F.A./F.A. PREMIER LEAGUE
UNDER 18 COUNTY CHAMPIONSHIP

SEMI-FINALS
Shropshire 1 Merseyside 2
Essex 0 Bedfordshire 3

T H E   F I N A L
MERSEYSIDE 3 BEDFORDSHIRE 2
(at Anfield)

Merseyside Under 18 squad; Winners of Under 18 Premier League Cup

ENGLISH SCHOOLS' F.A. PREMIER LEAGUE
UNDER 16 COUNTY CHAMPIONSHIP (BOYS)

QUARTER-FINALS
Nottingham 0 Lancashire 2
Greater Manchester 1 Leicestershire 2
Suffolk 1 Hampshire 2
Devon 1 Sussex 0

SEMI-FINALS
Lancashire 3 Leicestershire 1
Hampshire 0 Devon 3

T H E   F I N A L
LANCASHIRE 1   DEVON 2
(at Ewood Park, Blackburn Rovers F.C.)

After many near misses with several semi-final appearances, Devon Under 16's at last reached the Under 16 Inter-County Final with an impressive 3-0 win over Hampshire at the B.A.T. Sports Club, Totton. They continued in this form in the first half of the final with Ben Joyce scoring twice, his second being a 'screamer' from outside the penalty box. Lancashire were unable to reduce the arrears until second half added time when Dean Stott netted from the penalty spot.

Devon : James Wannell, Aiden Way, Ben Tozer, Reece Moseley, Shane White, Mitchell O'Donnell, Jamie Hatch, Bobby Hopkinson, Ben Joyce, Dabnile Gosling, Liam Sercombe, Stuart Davies, Jake Wannell, Sean Szabo, Luke Cole, Karl Baker, Nick Gidley, Craig Russell

Lancashire : Chris Thompson, Dean Stott, Ashley Holt, Lewis Field, Rory Winters, Tom Wilson, Dominic Merella, Adam Kay, Rob Turner, Alex Smith, Nathan Fairhurst, Michael Aspin, Lewis Craig, Adam Crossley, Ross Lloyd, Ben Simmonds, Jack Bilsborough

The Devon Squad who brought the county the Under 16 Premier title.

ENGLISH SCHOOLS' F.A.
UNDER 16 GIRLS COUNTY CHAMPIONSHIP (GIRLS)

HAMPSHIRE WIN AGAIN

Hampshire Under 16 Girls, making their 6th final appearance in the eight year history of the competition, won the trophy for the fourth time when they defeated Leicestershire 3-2 at AFC Bournemouth. Hampshire had shared the trophy after extra time when they drew 2-2 with Merseyside in the most exciting of last season's E.S.F.A. finals and they again needed the additional 20 minutes to overcome a determined Leicestershire side. Indeed, it was the visitors who went ahead in the 9th minute through Courtney Sweetman-Kirk, an advantage they kept until half-time although Kelly Sims did hit the post. It took Hampshire only 30 seconds to draw level when Molly Clarke drove in an excellent shot. Despite near misses at both ends, neither side could get the winner in normal time but it was Hampshire who quickly asserted their authority in an exciting ten minute period which featured three goals. Ciara Allen from Sandown in the Isle of Wight struck first amid the bedlam that followed a corner and two minutes later another Island player, Cherelle Khassal from Cowes ran at the defence, drew Hannah Kershaw off her line and lobbed the ball over her into the net. Although Leicestershire pulled a goal back, the Hampshire defence held firm in the second half to ensure that the trophy stayed with the county.

THE SQUADS
Hampshire : Stacey Parkinson, Rose Glendinning, Alice Wheeler, Jo Morris,
Ciara Allen, Jade Holes, Kelly Sims, Molly Clarke, Cherelle Khassal, Sophie Jackson, Kirby Anderson, Leigh Holes, Beth Chilvers, Jansa Schofield, Isobel Kent, Kayleigh Merritt, Kimberley Williams

Leicestershire : Hannah Kershaw, Katy Morris, Suzy Eassom, Leah Rawle, Kirsty Abbott,
Jen Pearson, Lacie Nutt, Remi Allen, Courtney Sweetman-Kirk, Zira Handley, Lucy Haines,
Natasha Meade, Harriet Crofts, Natlaie Nye, Lauren Turner

The victorious Hampshire squad which retained the N.U.T. Trophy

THE INDIVIDUAL SCHOOLS' COMPETITIONS

ENGLISH SCHOOLS' F.A.
UNDER 18 COLLEGES CHAMPIONSHIP

T H E   F I N A L
WILBERFORCE COLLEGE (Hull) 1   KINGSTON COLLEGE 0 (Surrey)
(at Boston United F.C.)

Ten man Wilberforce College defied all the odds to beat Kingston after Scott Phillips was sent off for retaliation 10 minutes into the second half. They had Adam Scott and Robert Fowler to thank in particular for their narrow victory with Scott producing a series of crucial saves before and after his side was down to 10 men. He had good support from Phillips and Andy Kaye who blocked goal bound chances while Kingston also rued missed chances. Fowler's winner after 68 minutes came when Kaye floated in a teasing cross which Kingston's keeper Rodney Chiwese came to meet only for Fowler to beat him with a header as he found himself stranded.

ENGLISH SCHOOLS' F.A.
UNDER 18 INDIVIDUAL SCHOOLS' CUP
THE FINAL

MONKSEATON SCHOOL 2   **WEST LONDON ACADEMY 1**
(Northumberland)   (Surrey)
(at Meadow Lane, Notts County F.C.)

In the 15th minute, Lee Novak sent the large band of Monkseaton supporters wild when he opened the scoring after a fine passing move with Alan Patterson. 20 minutes later, David Campbell was put clear down the right and hit a fine shot which struck the underside of the bar and bounced in off goalkeeper Philip Robinson's heel. The second half produced numerous chances, fine saves from Robinson and Michael Power-Simpson and goalmouth incident at each end. Ten minutes from time, however, Power-Simpson rushed from his goal to cover a break by Monkeaton but substitute Sean Foster reached the ball just before him and from a narrow angle cleverly flicked the ball over the keeper and into the net just before the retreating defenders could reach it.

ROUTES TO THE FINAL

MONKSEATON				WEST LONDON ACADEMY			
Round 1	Bye			Round 1	Bye		
Round 2	v. Hermitage School (Chester-le-Street)	(H)	3-0	Round 2	v. Gunnersbury R.C. School (Brentford)	(A)	7-0
Round 3	v. Durham Gillespie School (Durham)	(A)	6-2	Round 3	v. King's Langley School (Hertfordshire)	(A)	3-0
Round 4	v. St. Joseph's R.C. School (Hebburn)	(H)	2-1	Round 4	v. Dame Alice Owens School (Herts)	(A)	4-1
Round 5	v. Keswick School (Cumbria)	(A)	2-0	Round 5	v. Parmiter's School (Watford)	(A)	41-1
Round 6	v. Whitley Bay High School (Northumld)	(H)	4-1	Round 6	v. Langley Grammar School (Slough)	(A)	3-2
Round 7	v. Hanson School (Bradford)	(H)	6-0	Round 7	v. Wye Valley School (Bourne End)	(H)	3-1
Quarter-final	v. Balby Carr Sports College (Doncaster)	(H)	4-0	Quarter-final	v. Bishop Wordsworth School	(H)	5-1
Semi-final	v. Wilmslow High School (Cheshire)	(A)	2-0	Semi-final	v. Sharnbrook Upper School (Bedford)	(H)	3-1

Balletic action from Wilberforce (stripes) and Kingston players in the Final

ENGLISH SCHOOLS' F.A./R.A.F
UNDER 16 INDIVIDUAL SCHOOLS' CUP
THE FINAL

IMPINGTON VILLAGE COLLEGE 3 **ST. MARGARET'S C OF E H SCH 1**
(Cambridgeshire.) (Merseyside)
(at The Hawthorns, West Bromwich Albion F.C.)

Impington Village College who had never before reached the national stages of the competition, let alone the final, reached the heights when they won the R.A.F. Cup. This competition, like the girls' one, needs a school to win or be runners-up in their own county competition before the first national round and Team Manager and Director of Sport at the college, Nick Morley, summed up what the achievement meant : "It's unbelievable. The boys have been a credit to themselves, their parents, the school and the community. It's absolutely fantastic."

Impington virtually had the game won by half-time, making a dream start when Lewis Trimmer's swerving shot squirmed past Nathan Elliott in the 9th minute. They doubled their advantage when Chris Medd put a loose ball into the bottom corner while four minutes before half-time, Aidan Litterick and Trimmer exchanged passes and the latter found the top corner. In the 47th minute, St. Margaret's pulled a goal back through Matthew Hughes but with Adam Dalby in fine form at the heart of the Impington defence, there was never any danger of the Cambridgeshire side losing their grip on the Trophy. There was a nice touch when injured players who missed the final, Jack Watson and Andreas Constantinides went up with skipper Will Cook to collect the Cup

The Squads :

Impington : William Cook, Steven Kirkys, Adam Coles, Adam Dalby, Julian Austin, Luke Thulbourn, Philip Carringtoin, James Tyrell, Lewis Trimmer, Aidan Litterick, Sam Allan, Nick Thears, Tom Gray, Jack Watson and Andreas Constantinides

St. Margaret's : Nathan Elliott, Joshua Smith, Matthew Hudson, Jonathan Crossdale, Philip McCaughran, Anthony Williams, Ben McHugh, Andrew Durans, Matthew Hughes, Paul McManus, Charles Jones, Michael Jones, Chris Lloyd, Simon Murphy, Andrew McGral, Jonathan Monks

ROUTES TO THE FINAL

IMPINGTON				ST. MARGARET'S			
Qualified through the Cambridgeshire competition.				Qualified through the Merseyside competition.			
National Rounds ;				National Rounds:			
Round 1	v. Northgate School (Norfolk)	(A)	3-2	Round 1	v. Ripley St. Thomas School (Lancashire)(A)		2-0
Round 2	v. Thurleston High School (Suffolk)	(H)	3-1	Round 2	v. King James' School (West Yorkshire)	(H)	2-1
Round 3	v. Forest Hill School (Inner London)	(H)	2-1	Round 3	v. West Derby School (Merseyside)	(H)	1-0
Round 4	v. Hurstmere School (Kent)	(A)	1-0	Round 4	v. Nunthorpe School (Cleveland)	(A)	2-1
Semi-final	v. Goffs School (Hertfordshire) at R.A.F. Cosford	3-1*		Semi-final	v. Verdin School (Cheshire) at R.A.F. Cosford		1-0

Impington Village College.

Meadowhead School.

E.S.F.A./R.A.F
UNDER 16 GIRLS INDIVIDUAL SCHOOLS' CUP

THE FINAL

MEADOWHEAD SCHOOL 3   **AYLSHAM HIGH SCHOOL 0**
(South Yorkshire)   (Norfolk)
(at The Hawthorns, West Bromwich Albion F.C.)

Meadowhead School Under 16 Girls team created their own bit of sporting history as they became the first South Yorkshire team to win a national 11-a-side schools' competition outright. They are now proud owners of the E.S.F.A. R.A.F. Cup after their 3-0 win over Aylsham School.

Over 400 of Meadowhead's pupils, parents and staff travelled to the game to support their team and they were in raptures when the team raced into a two goal lead in the first seven minutes. First, Anna Kelsey crashed in an unstoppable shot which hit the cross bar and then bounced into the net and then, five minutes later, Emily Rumsby scored her ninth goal of the competition as she lifted the ball over the advancing goalkeeper Hayley Clark.

Aylsham, to ther credit, worked hard to get back into the game led by 'player of the match' Dawn Mallett. The Meadowhead defence remained firm and in the 55th minute Nicola Swift, living up to her name as a quick and elusive winger, confirmed her school's superiority when she swept home a left foot shot past Clark.

All 15 available players featured in the final exemplifying that Meadowhead's achievement in winning all 13 of their games during the season was a true team performance.

Meadowhead : Georgia Ward, Lauran Taylor, Jane Watkinson, Giselle Smith, Eleana Kallis, Zoe Ellison, Nicola Swift, Gemma White, Emily Rumsby, Anna Kelsey, Claire Watkinson, Ellie Brightmore, Lauren Brown, Anna Myers, Jane McInnes, Laura Mann

Aylsham : Hayley Clark, Logan Shepherd, Samantha Ede, Frances Ellis, Charlotte Bunn, Abby Timmins, Katy Smith, Dawn Mallett, Rebecca Chambelin, Amy Walsh, Gemma Reeve, Rebecca Burton, Emily Simmonds, Stephanie Barnes, Lauren Dunthorne

ROUTES TO THE FINAL

MEADOWHEAD			AYLSHAM		
Qualified from South Yorkshire competition.			Qualified from Norfolk competition.		
National rounds			National rounds		
Round 1	v. Ivy Bank Business College Lancashire)(A)	6-4	Round 1	v. Knights Templar School (Hertfordshire)(H)	4-4*
					4-3p
Round 2	v. Chesterfield High School (Derbyshire) (H)	5-4	Round 2	v. East Bergholt School (Suffolk) (H)	2-1
Round 3	v. Notre Dame Catholic College (Merseyside)(A)	3-2	Round 3	v. Kesgrave High School (Suffolk) (A)	3-0
Round 4	v. Laurence Jackson School (Cleveland) (H)	3-2	Round 4	v. St. Angela's School (Essex) (A)	6-3
Semi-final	v. Church Stretton School (Shropshire)		Semi-final v. Tavistock Community College at R.A.F. Cosford		2-3*
at R.A.F. Cosford		4-1	Aylsham were reinstated after Tavistock fielded ineligible players		

E.S.F.A. FOUR ACES
UNDER 14 INDIVIDUAL SCHOOLS' CUP
T H E   F I N A L

THOMAS TELFORD SCHOOL 3   **PARMITER'S SCHOOL 1**
(Shropshire)   (Hertfordshire)

(at Molineux, Wolverhampton Wanderers F.C.)

A hot and sunny afternoon which presaged the June and July to follow plus the large pitch at Molineux provided a stern test for both sides which they passed with honours. A large and enthusiastic crowd saw an excellent match which was closer that the score indicates. Jake Jervis gave the Telford school the lead in the first minute before Josh Jones equalised for Parmiter's with a header. Telford went on to win with two goals at crucial times, one in added time at the end of the first half through Samy Morsy and the second with virtually the last kick of the game, a second for Jervis.

E.S.F.A. UNDER 13 BOYS' COCA-COLA CUP

Nearly 2,600 boys teams and 1,400 girls' teams originally entered the Coca-Cola Cups revealing the magnitude of the achievement of those teams reaching the final. They were much encouraged by the sponsors who gave such excellent support to the E.S.F.A. throughout the competition which saw county competitions , regional rounds,regional semi-finals and finals and then national semi-finals. The finalists thus had survived nine or ten matches to get to the last two. Both the girls' and boys' finals provided dramatic matches in front of large numbers of noisy fans at the magnificent Ricoh Stadium, the new home of Coventry City

T H E   F I N A L

NEWLANDS SCHOOL 3   **IVYBRIDGE COMMUNITY COL. 2**
(Middlesbrough)   (Devon)

The first player to catch the eye in an evenly contested final was Newlands' keeper Sean Cuff who saved convincingly from a corner and a good shot by Ben Hill. Chances occurred at both ends but Newlands came closest with a shot from 25 yards by captain Sam Hargan that came back off a post and was then headed straight into the arms of Ivybridge keeper Hyslop. Play went immediately to the other end with Ben Bowen racing into Newlands' box and being stopped by a heavy challenge which could have brought a penalty on another day.

Newlands opened the scoring after 20 minutes when Anthony Brown broke down the right and laid on a cross for Christos Chalilopolous to tap in. Ivybridge equalised almost immediately when Ben Meads created space on the left and his low cross gave Leon Fricker the chance to net at the far post. Newlands regained the lead on the stroke of half-time when Sam Hargan released Matt Robinson who timed his run to perfection and shot low past Hyslop.

Ivybridge began the second period at a high tempo and deserved their second equaliser again through Fricker who latched on to a lofted pass from midfield and rolled the ball through Cusp's legs. Matt Walker of Newlands and Ben Bowen both shot narrowly wide before Newlands launched a late bid for victory with Brown and Jordan List missing opportunities before Brown beat the advancing Matt Hyslop who had earlier kept his side in the game and slotted the ball into an empty net for the winner.

Squads
Newlands : Sean Cuff, Josh Allan, Deanile Hawkins, Jordan List, Josh Wall, John Pawass, Zak Wilkinson, Sam Hargan, Christos Chalilopolous, Anthony Brown, Matthew Robinson, Sam Henry, Kristofer Gething, John Roddy, Kyle Frost, Patrick Wright

Ivybridge : Matt Hyslop, George Yates, Mike Williams, Matt Walker, Dan Evans, Bill Farleigh, Jake Norrie, Luke Young, Ben Bowen, Leon Fricker, Ben Meads, Bill Hill, Guy Alford, Brolin Stevenson-Twontoo, Sam Marker, Tom Spencer.

Newlands School

E.S.F.A. UNDER 13 GIRLS' COCA-COLA CUP

T H E   F I N A L

WINSTON CHURCHILL 2
(Surrey)

ARCHBISHOP BECK SPORT COL. 1
(Merseyside)

Winston Churchill School

E.S.F.A. JETIX UNDER 12
INDOOR 5-A-SIDE CHAMPIONSHIPS
Boys' Winners: Mosslands School, Wallasey
Girls' Winners: Matthew Arnold School, Staines

The finals of this season long indoor competition had a magnificent prize; not only did the winners get the Jetix Cup but also a trip to Germany to represent England in the Jetix World Cup run concurrently with the World Cup in Germany

The boys' winners were Mosslands School from Wallasey in the Wirral who had seemed likely to be making their way home after losing their first group game in the finals at the JJB Soccerdome in Derby against Lancaster School (Leicester) and trailing 1-0 to John Hampden School (High Wycombe) with only 3 minutes left. In a sensational spell, however, Andrew Mitchell, Ryan Astles and David Webb scored three quick goals to gain their first win. Astle and Webb with two goals each helped Mosslands towards a 4-1 win over St. Ignatius College (Enfield) which put their team top of the qualifying group on goal difference with three of the four sides in the group finishing on six points each. The semi-finals saw Mosslands beat Yeovil School, King Arthur's 2-1 with goals from Webb and Sean Santos which took them through to the final against Nunthorpe (Middlesbrough). A tense game was eventually settled by a goal from Santos early in the second half.

Mosslands squad : Declan Morgan (GK), David Webb (captain), Ryan Adstles, Sean Santos, Andrew Mitchell, Harry Lamb, Ryan Clarke, Tom Mole

In the girls' competition which also took place at the JJB Soccerdome at the same time, Matthew Arnold School (Staines) defeated Witton Middle School from Droitwich 3-0 in the final. With the finals organised in the same way as in the boys' section, Matthew Arnold reached the national finals by winning the Spelthorne local round and the South-East Regional round and in their qualifying group at Derby, they made an excellent start by beating Trinity School (Isle of Wight) 4-0 with goals from Jess Barnes (2), Rachel Watkins and Kelly Smith. They continued their high scoring in the second game against William Farr (Lincoln) with another four goals although this time their opponents scored once.

Barnes and Watkins both netted twice for the Staines school. They had thus won their group before they met Our Lady's School from Preston in the final game, drawing 0-0. In the semifinal, Watkins was again their heroine with two goals as they overcame St. Michael's (Watford) 2-1.

Watkins made her total for Finals Day eight with a hat-trick as they comprehensively defeated Witton to ensure that they too would represent England in Munich. Despite the attention given to the goalscorers, Matthew Arnold's was a real team performance as in all three competitions, they conceded only two goals, a fine tribute to their defence.Squad : Chloe Poole (GK), Vicky Stanford, Jewss Barnes, Rachel Watkins (captain), Patsy Cooper, Mary Symons, Kelly Smith, Kelly Baker

ESFA JETIX KIDS U12 INDOOR 5-A-SIDE CUP FOR BOYS 2005-2006
WINNERS: MOSSLANDS SCHOOL (MERSEYSIDE CSFA)

E.S.F.A. SAINSBURY'S PRIMARY COMPETITIONS
SAINSBURY'S SUPER SOCCER SATURDAY
(June 17th at Keele University)

A glorious summers' day brought the English Schools' F.A. season to a close when 32 teams, 272 players and hundreds of supporters ranging from one to 90 produced another memorable day. Eight teams who had won local, county and regional rounds to reach Finals Day took part in four competitons, each of which had two qualifying groups and then semi-finals and finals. The Chief Executive of Sainsbury's, Justin King, welcomed all the players at the Opening Ceremony and all the winning schools' were treated to an open top bus ride around their city or town as a reward for their victories.

E.S.F.A. SAINSBURY'S INTER-ASSOCIATION UNDER 11 7-A-SIDE CHAMPIONSHIP
Semi-finals :   Poole and East Dorset 0 St. Albans 0 (St. Albans won 3-2 on penalties
                Leicester 2   Chester-le-Street 0
Final :   Leicester 1 Poole and East Dorset 0
A single goal by Liam Canavan brough the Sainsburys' Trophy to Leicester in a pulsating game. The Dorset side had the consolation of winning the Fair play Trophy

E.S.F.A. SAINSBURY'S INDIVIDUAL SCHOOLS UNDER 11 7-A-SIDE CHAMPIONSHIP FOR BOYS
Semi-Finals :   St. Augustine's RC School (Nottinghamshire) 1 Bentley High Street School (SouthYorkshire) 0
                St. Hugh's School (Lincolnshire) 3   Hextable Junior School (Kent) 1
Final :   St. Augustine's 3   St. Hugh's   1
St. Augustine's completed a magnificent season in which they swept all before them in Nottingham and Nottinghamshire with a convincing win in the final. Louis Greenway-Tambini was the St. Augustine's hero with two goals to make him top scorer in the boys' competition with five in total and Joseph Dadoo added a third but they would be the first to give credit to the school's excellent defence which conceded only two goals in their five games at Finals Day.

E.S.F.A. SAINSBURY'S INDIVIDUAL SCHOOLS' UNDER 11 6-A-SIDE CHAMPIONSHIP FOR GIRLS
Semi-Finals :   Abbey Road Primary School (Nottinghamshire) 3 Stafford Primary School (Sussex) 0
                Our Lady of Lourdes Catholic School (Greater Manchester) 1 Sandal Endowed School 0
Final :   Abbey Road 4 Our Lady of Lourdes School 1
 The strong and skilful Amelia Colgan gave Our Lady of Lourdes an early lead but Abbey Road fought back well to equalise through Hannah McLennaghan. In the second half, Abbey Road pressed forward to add three more goals with McLennagahn completing her hat-trick and Fiona Worts her eighth goal of the day to finish as leading scorer.

E.S.F.A. SAINSBURY'S SMALL PRIMARY SCHOOLS' UNDER 11 6-A-SIDE CHAMPIONSHIP
Semi-finals: Three Oaks Schooll (Shropshire) 2 10 pens
St. Swithun Wells School (Hampshire) 2 9 pens
                (Three Oaks won 10-9 on penalties)
                Holy Family and St. Michael's School(W.Yorks) 2
                Ludlow Primary School (Cheshire) 0
Final : Holy Family and St. Michael's 1
         Three Oaks School 3
After being involved in a dramatic nineteen penalty shoot-out in the semi-final, Three Oaks School might perhaps have been shattered but they showed no sign of it in beating the West Yorkshire school. Bradley Mezen's hat-trick proved too much for Holy Family and St. Michael's although Rhys Oates dids net a consolation goal for them.

ESFA SAINSBURY'S U11 6-A-SIDE SCHOOLS' CUP
FOR GIRLS 2005-2006
WINNERS: ABBEY ROAD PRIMARY SCHOOL
(NOTTINGHAMSHIRE CSFA)

WOMEN'S FOOTBALL

NATIONAL DIVISION 2005-06

		P	W	D	L	F	A	Pts
1.	Arsenal	18	16	2	0	83	20	50
2.	Everton	18	14	2	2	46	20	44
3.	Charlton Athletic WFC	18	12	3	3	41	13	39
4.	Doncaster Rovers Belles LFC	18	7	2	9	32	34	23
5.	Bristol Academy WFC	18	4	8	6	19	29	20
6.	Birmingham City LFC	18	6	2	10	24	40	20
7.	Leeds United LFC	18	4	6	8	27	36	18
8.	Fulham LFC	18	4	2	12	24	45	14
9.	Sunderland WFC	18	3	4	11	22	57	13
10.	Chelsea LFC	18	3	3	12	22	46	12

NORTHERN DIVISION 2005-06

		P	W	D	L	F	A	Pts
1.	**Blackburn Rovers LFC**	22	20	2	0	55	12	62
2.	Liverpool LFC	22	15	3	4	39	17	48
3.	Tranmere Rovers LFC	22	13	4	5	41	29	43
4.	Lincoln City LFC	22	11	3	8	40	31	36
5.	Nottingham Forest LFC	22	8	6	8	33	30	30
6.	Wolverhampton Wanderers WFC	22	6	10	6	29	33	28
7.	Aston Villa LFC	22	8	2	12	33	38	26
8.	Newcastle United LFC	22	6	7	9	32	33	25
9.	Stockport County LFC	22	5	7	10	24	31	22
10.	Curzon Ashton LFC	22	4	6	12	27	64	18
11.	Manchester City LFC	22	3	7	12	19	31	16
12.	Middlesbrough LFC	22	3	3	16	18	41	12

SOUTHERN DIVISION 2005-06

		P	W	D	L	F	A	Pts
1.	**Cardiff City LFC**	22	14	7	1	53	17	49
2.	Bristol City WFC	22	16	1	5	51	30	49
3.	Watford LFC	22	14	5	3	59	28	47
4.	Portsmouth LFC	22	12	4	6	58	39	40
5.	Millwall Lionesses LFC	22	11	5	6	51	31	38
6.	West Ham United LFC	22	8	4	10	31	33	28
7.	AFC Wimbledon LFC	22	8	3	11	39	52	27
8.	Reading Royals LFC	22	7	2	13	34	42	23
9.	Crystal Palace LFC	22	7	1	14	38	52	22
10.	Southampton Saints WFC	22	6	0	16	30	70	18
11.	Brighton & Hove Albion WFC	22	4	5	13	33	53	17
12.	Langford LFC	22	4	5	13	30	60	17

NORTHERN COMB.	P	W	D	L	F	A	Pts
Preston North End	20	17	1	2	88	23	52
Leeds City Vixens	20	17	1	2	72	17	52
Sheffield Wednesday	19	14	2	3	53	12	44
Chester-le-Street Tn L.	18	9	1	8	43	37	28
Caernarfon Town	17	9	0	8	34	43	27
Blackpool Wren R. Ladies	19	7	4	8	31	43	25
Chester City Ladies	18	7	2	9	24	36	23
Scunthorpe Utd Ladies	19	5	4	10	28	38	19
South Durham Royals FC	18	5	0	13	24	47	15
Doncaster Parklands Rov.	20	3	2	15	20	59	11
Garswood Saints Womens	18	1	1	16	10	71	4

SOUTH EAST COMB.	P	W	D	L	F	A	Pts
Barnet Ladies	22	19	1	2	72	19	58
Ipswich Town	22	17	1	4	66	19	52
Northampton Town	22	16	4	2	55	24	52
Colchester United	22	12	3	7	40	26	39
Bedford Town Bells	22	8	6	8	37	42	30
Enfield Town Ladies	22	8	4	10	38	42	28
Rushden & Diamonds	22	8	2	12	58	57	26
Norwich City	22	6	6	10	38	61	24
Leyton Orient Women FC	22	7	2	13	28	51	23
Gillingham Ladies	22	6	5	11	36	68	23
Dagenham & Redbridge	22	3	3	16	25	50	12
Sophtlogic Ladies FC	22	3	1	18	24	56	10

MIDLAND COMBINATION	P	W	D	L	F	A	Pts
Leafield Athletic	20	12	6	2	61	24	42
Crewe Ladies	17	12	2	3	44	19	38
Derby County Ladies FC	20	9	5	6	49	33	32
Rotherham United LFC	16	10	1	5	49	26	31
Loughborough Students	20	9	3	8	46	39	30
TNS (Total Network Solutions)	18	9	3	6	41	37	30
Long Eaton Villa	17	5	5	7	27	37	20
Coventry City Ladies	16	5	3	8	23	24	18
Lichfield Diamonds	16	5	2	9	31	46	17
Leicester City A	17	4	3	10	33	39	15
Chesterfield Ladies FC	15	3	5	7	24	34	14
Shrewsbury Town	18	2	2	14	17	87	8

SOUTH WEST COMB.	P	W	D	L	F	A	Pts
Keynsham Town	22	19	3	0	90	20	60
Chesham United	22	17	3	2	88	27	54
Newquay Ladies	22	13	4	5	72	22	43
Queens Park Rangers	22	12	3	7	44	30	39
Forest Green Rovers	22	9	5	8	52	38	32
Plymouth Argyle	22	8	6	8	45	57	30
Luton Town Belles	22	7	5	10	45	51	26
Newton Abbot	22	7	3	12	41	45	24
Swindon Town Ladies FC	22	6	6	10	35	54	24
Clevedon Town SBW	22	5	5	12	24	49	20
Oxford City Womens FC	22	5	2	15	36	80	17
Launton	22	1	1	20	9	108	4

WOMEN'S PYRAMID OF FOOTBALL

FAWPL

NAT

N   S

Two relegated from National Division

Winners of Northern and Southern promoted to National Division

No relegation from Northern and Southern. Therefore increase to twelve teams in the North and South

COMBINATION

N   M   SE   SW

Winners of N, M, SE & SW promoted

N - two relegated, three promoted

M - Winners of two feeder Regional promoted

SE - two relegated, three promoted

SW - one relegated, two promoted

REGIONAL

YH   NW   N   WM   EM   E   L   SE   S   SW

Winners of all ten Leagues automatically promoted

COUNTIES

COUNTIES

NON LEAGUE PROGRAMME OF THE YEAR AWARDS 2005/06
Conducted by "Programme Monthly" magazine
PO Box 3236, Norwich, NR7 7BE   email : progm@hotmail.com
Tel : 01603-449237   website : www.pmfc.co.uk

The Wirral Programme Club announced that they would no longer be conducting the annual Non League Programme of the Year awards in 2005, and "Programme Monthly", the leading magazine for football programme and memorabilia collectors, has taken up the task.

The results of the 2005/06 judging are included in this leaflet. The transition from the Wirral Programme Club has been difficult ; several Leagues did not pass on details to their clubs, and as a result the spread of the awards is not as extensive as we would have liked.   However, steps will be taken to overcome these hurdles from 2006/07 onwards, so please bear with us in this transitional season.

For the third successive season, the Non League Programme of the Year is EXETER CITY, followed by their fellow Conference National members CAMBRIDGE UNITED in second place, and KIDDERMINSTER HARRIERS in third position.

The top 100 programmes are as follows:

1	Exeter City	491	35	Accrington Stanley	282	69	Felixstowe & W.U.	238
2	Cambridge United	416	36	Curzon Ashton	280	70	Gt Harwood Town	238
3	Kidderminster H.	406	37	Braintree Town	279	71	North Ferriby Utd.	238
4	Morecambe	392	38	Gloucester City	279	72	St Albans City	238
5	Dagenham	378	39	Blyth Spartans	278	73	Burton Albion	237
6	Wealdstone	378	40	Ossett Albion	278	74	Clacton Town	237
7	Aldershot Town	376	41	Marine	273	75	Runcorn	237
8	York City	363	42	Winsford United	273	76	Bridgwater	236
9	Stevenage Boro.	360	43	Arlesey Town	270	77	Southport	236
10	Woking	350	44	Dartford	269	78	Abingdon United	235
11	FC United of M/ctr	347	45	Hitchin Town	266	79	Halifax Town	235
12	Banbury United	332	46	Sittingbourne	266	80	Salisbury City	235
13	Warrington Town	331	47	Newport County	264	81	Brackley Town	234
14	Willenhall Town	330	48	Altrincham	263	82	Gateshead	234
15	Rushall Olympic	326	49	Padiham	263	83	Silsden	233
16	Bamber Bridge	318	50	Ilkeston Town	262	84	Chadderton	232
17	New Mills	313	51	Leek Town	262	85	Hednesford Town	232
18	Scarborough	311	52	Witton Albion	262	86	Rossendale United	230
19	Crawley Town	305	53	Mangotsfield U	255	87	Sutton United	230
20	AFCTellford United	304	54	Dulwich Hamlet	253	88	Chorley	229
21	Atherton L.R.	303	55	Enfield	252	89	Tiverton Town	229
22	Maine Road	301	56	Lincoln United	252	90	Billericay Town	225
23	Molesey	301	57	Wakefield-Emley	252	91	Ilford	225
24	Radcliffe Borough	299	58	Chippenham Town	250	92	Hereford United	223
25	Leek CSOB	298	59	Atherton Collieries	248	93	AFC Sudbury	221
26	Skelmersdale Utd	298	60	Windsor & Eton	248	94	Boreham Wood	221
27	Bath City	296	61	Stone Dominoes	247	95	Hendon	221
28	Frickley Athletic	295	62	Canvey Island	245	96	Cambridge City	220
29	Shepshed Dynamo	295	63	Grays Athletic	241	97	Newcastle Town	220
30	Ashford Town	290	64	Heybridge Swifts	240	98	Stourport Swifts	220
31	Prescot Cables	290	65	Slough Town	240	99	Team Bath	220
32	Tonbridge Angels	288	66	Worksop Town	240	100	Alsager Town	218
33	Gravesend & N.	285	67	Tamworth	239			
34	Trafford	285	68	Enfield Town	238			

CONFERENCE (NATIONAL)

1	Exeter City	491
2	Cambridge United	416
3	Kidderminster H.	406
4	Morecambe	392
5	Dagenham	378
6	Aldershot Town	376
7	York City	363
8	Stevenage Boro.	360
9	Woking	350
10	Scarborough	311
11	Crawley Town	305
12	Gravesend & N.	285
13	Accrington Stanley	282
14	Altrincham	263
15	Canvey Island	245
16	Grays Athletic	241
17	Tamworth	239
18	Burton Albion	237
19	Southport	236
20	Halifax Town	235
21	Hereford United	223
22	Forest Green R.	213

CONFERENCE SOUTH *

1	Newport County	264
2	St Albans City	238
3	Sutton United	230
4	Cambridge City	220
5	Weymouth	218
6	Hayes	217
7	Havant & Water.	216
8	Thurrock	209
9	Basingstoke	195
10	Welling	190
11	Weston S-Mare	175
12	Maidenhead	168
13	Eastleigh	165

CONFERENCE NORTH *

1	Worksop Town	240
2	Hednesford Town	232
3	Nuneaton Borough	213
4	Stafford Rangers	195
5	Stalybridge Celtic	193
6	Harrogate Town	180
7	Kettering Town	170
8	Vauxhall Motors	166
9	Barrow	164
10	Gainborough Trin.	152
11	Alfreton	141

SOUTHERN LEAGUE

PREMIER

1	Banbury United	332
2	Bath City	296
3	Gloucester City	279
4	Hitchin Town	266
5	Mangotsfield U	255
6	Chippenham Town	250
7	Salisbury City	235
8	Tiverton Town	229
9	Team Bath	220
10	Cirencester Town	213
11	Evesham United	204
12	Yate Town	203
13	Bedford Town	164

FIRST DIVISION (EAST)

1	Arlesey Town	270
2	Dartford	269
3	Sittingbourne	266
4	Enfield	252
5	Enfield Town	238
6	Ilford	225
7	Boreham Wood	221
8	Barton Rovers	206
9	Corby Town	195
10	Wivenhoe Town	193
11	Chatham Town	190
12	Great Wakering R	189
13	Stamford	184
14	Berkhamsted T.	183
15	Barking	169
16	Potters Bar Town	168
17	Harlow Town	147
18	Aveley	143

FIRST DIVISION (WEST)

1	Willenhall Town	330
2	Rushall Olympic	326
3	Brackley Town	234
4	Stourport Swifts	220
5	Dunstable Town	199
6	Taunton Town	195
7	Hemel Hempstead	194
8	Bedworth United	192
9	Ashford T. (Mdx)	177
10	Beaconsfield SY	165

Due to the incomplete response from clubs in these divisions, no full awards (winners, 2nd and 3rd) have been made this season.

UNIBOND LEAGUE

PREMIER DIVISION

1	AFCTellford United	304
2	Radcliffe Borough	299
3	Frickley Athletic	295
4	Prescot Cables	290
5	Blyth Spartans	278
6	Marine	273
7=	Ilkeston Town	262
7=	Leek Town	262
7=	Witton Albion	262
10=	Lincoln United	252
10=	Wakefield-Emley	252
12	North Ferriby Utd.	238
13	Runcorn	237
14	Gateshead	234
15	Burscough	215
16	Matlock Town	211
17	Ashton United	183
18	Farsley Celtic	110

DIVISION ONE

1	Warrington Town	331
2	Bamber Bridge	318
3	Shepshed Dynamo	295
4	Ossett Albion	278
5	Rossendale United	230
6	Chorley	229
7	Spalding United	211
8	Gresley Rovers	201
9	Woodley Sports	175
10	Belper Town	172
11	Bridlington Town	158
12	Eastwood Town	157
13	Colwyn Bay	155
14	Bishop Auckland	137

SPARTAN SOUTH MIDLANDS LEAGUE

PREMIER DIVISION *

1	Welwyn Garden City
2	Holmer Green
3	Leverstock Green

DIVISION 1

1	Hoddesdon Town
2	Cockfosters
3=	Brimsdown Rovers
4=	Kentish Town

RYMAN (ISTHMIAN) LEAGUE
PREMIER DIVISION

1	Wealdstone	378
2	Braintree Town	279
3	Windsor & Eton	248
4=	Heybridge Swifts	240
4=	Slough Town	240
6	Billericay Town	225
7	Hendon	221
8	Folkestone Invicta	197
9	Bromley	195
10	Leyton	162
11	Walton & Hersham	149
12	Fisher Athletic	143

DIVISION ONE

1	Molesey	301
2	Ashford Town	290
3	Tonbridge Angels	288
4	Dulwich Hamlet	253
5	Cray Wanderers	217
6	Kingstonian	169
7	Newport (IOW)	138
8	Ramsgate	116

DIVISION TWO

1	Ware	197
2	Witham Town	193
3	Chalfont St Peter	191
4	Wembley	183
5	Hertford Town	164

ESSEX SENIOR LEAGUE *

Waltham Abbey	195
Tilbury	194
Burnham Ramblers	166
Bowers & Pitsea	123
Concord	112

MIDLAND COMBINATION *

1	Coventry Sphinx	139
2	Bolehall Swifts	132
3	Brocton	131
4	Pikington XXX	123
5	Feckenham	102

HELLENIC LEAGUE
PREMIER

1	Abingdon United	235
2	Witney United	160
3	Henley Town	143
4	Carterton Town	142
5=	Almondbury Town	138
5=	Slimbridge Town	138
7=	Pegasus Juniors	132
7=	Wantage Town	132
9	Kidlington	127
10	Highworth Town	125
11=	Bishop's Cleeve	122
11=	Didcot Town	122
13	Abingdon Town	119
14	Milton United	116
15	Shrivenham	109
16	Chipping Norton	107
17	Ardley United	103
18	North Leigh	100
19	Shortwood United	90
20	Fairford Town	86
21	Hungerford Town	81

FIRST DIVISION (WEST)

1	Wootton Bassett	191
2	Tytherington Rocks	170
3	Trowbridge Town	163
4	Headington Ams.	146
5=	Cirencester United	133
5=	Hook Norton	133
7	Clanfield	129
8	Easington Sports	122
9	Winterbourne Utd	121
10	Old Woodstock T.	118
11	Ross Town	117
12=	Cricklade Town	115
12=	Purton	115
14	Harrow Hill	110
15	Letcombe	109
16	Cheltenham S.	105
17	Malmesbury Vics	88
18	Pewsey Vale	71

KENT LEAGUE *

Maidstone United	177
Deal Town	167
Herne Bay	165
Hythe Town	150

HELLENIC LEAGUE
FIRST DIVISION (EAST)

1	Binfield	191
2	Finchampstead	139
3	Badshot Lea	137
4	Prestwood	133
5	Rayners Lane	129
6	Bisley Sports	127
7	Bicester Town	126
8	Chalfont Wasps	119
9	Englefield Green R	114
10	Oxford Quarry N.	106
11	Hounslow Borough	105
12	Chinnor	104
13	Wokingham & Em.	101
14=	Eton Wick	90
14=	Penn & Tylers G.	89
16=	Holyport	84
16=	Kintbury R.	84
18	Banbury Utd. Res.	62

SUSSEX COUNTY LGE.
DIVISION ONE

1	Redhill	172
2	East Preston	153
3	Ringmer	150
4	Three Bridges	142
5	Hassocks	132
6	Horsham YMCA	123
7	Whitehawk	104
8	Southwick	98
9	Crowborough A.	88
10	Rye & Iden United	85
11	Wick	84
12	Shoreham	77
13	Littlehampton Town	75
14	Chichester City Utd	54

DIVISION TWO

1	East Grinstead T	189
2	Crawley Down	182
3	Lancing	156
4	Mile Oak	142
5	St Francis Rangers	91
6	Midhurst & Ease.	67
7	Pagham	64

UNITED COUNTIES LEAGUE *

St Neots Town	169
Raunds Town	136
Newport Pagnell	114

NORTH WEST COUNTIES LEAGUE
DIVISION ONE

1	Atherton L.R.	303
2	Maine Road	301
3	Skelmersdale Utd	298
4	Trafford	285
5	Curzon Ashton	280
6	Atherton Collieries	248
7	Stone Dominoes	247
8	Silsden	233
9	Newcastle Town	220
10	Alsager Town	218
11	Ramsbottom Utd.	216
12	Colne	208
13=	Congleton Town	200
13=	St Helens Town	200
15	Salford City	194
16	Abbey Hay	190
17	Formby	184
18	Glossop North End	168
19	Bacup Borough	162
20	Cammell Laird	149
21	Nantwich Town	140
22	Squires Gate	130

DIVISION TWO

1	FC United of M/ctr	347
2	New Mills	313
3	Leek CSOB	298
4	Winsford United	273
5	Padiham	263
6	Gt Harwood Town	238
7	Chadderton	232
8	Norton United	192
9	Eccleshall	156
10	Cheadle Town	155
11	Blackpool Mechs.	147
12	Darwen	141
13	Nelson	140
14	Castleton Gabriels	131
15	Oldham Town	125
16	Flixton	120
17	Holker Old Boys	111
18	Ashton Town	89

EASTERN COUNTIES LEAGUE
PREMIER DIVISION

1	Clacton Town	237
2	AFC Sudbury	221
3	Wroxham	208
4	Mildenhall Town	170
5	Kirkley	157
6	Newmarket Town	152
7	Halstead	149
8	Woodbridge	147
9	Leiston	139
10	Dereham Town	135
11	Harwich & Park.	133
12	Needham Market	132
13	Soham Town R.	130
14	Ipswich Wand'rs	112
15	Wisbech Town	95

DIVISION ONE

1	Felixstowe & W.U.	238
2	Debenham LC	192
3	Fulbourn Institute	146
4	Thetford Town	132
5	Stowmarket Town	131
6	Ely City	121
7	Stanway Rovers	105
8	Whitton United	103
9	Tiptree United	102
10	Hadleigh	70

WESSEX LEAGUE
DIVISION ONE

1	Poole Town	202
2	Winchester City	199
3	Bournemouth	173
4	Moneyfield	135
5	Gosport Borough	104

DIVISION TWO

1	Fawley	137
2	Amesbury Town	131
3	Farnborough N.E.	111
4	United Servs Port.	107
5	Shaftesbury	104

COMBINED CO's LEAGUE
PREMIER DIVISION

1	Chipstead	154
2	Merstham	144
3	Farnham Town	130
4	Ash United	105
5	Reading Town	100

DIVISION ONE

1	Hartley Wintney	148
2	Staines Lammas	146
3	Farleigh R.	92

CENTRAL MIDLANDS LEAGUE *

Rainworth MW	216
Forest Town	152

ANGLIAN COMBINATION *

Brandon Town	110

LIVERPOOL COMBINATION*

South Liverpool	119

MIDLAND ALLIANCE *

Loughborough D.	177

NORTHERN COUNTIES EAST *

Winterton	207
Sutton Town	190
Gedling	130

NOTTS SENIOR LEAGUE *

Linby Colliery W.	108

WESTERN LEAGUE *

Bridgwater	236
Dawlish	120

WEST MIDLANDS (REGIONAL) LEAGUE *

Goodrich	115

NON LEAGUE PROGRAMME OF THE YEAR SURVEY 2006/07
Clubs are asked to send a copy of their programme (for a match dated around early October 2006) to
Programme Monthly, PO Box 3236, Norwich, NR7 7BE

SOCCER CLUB SWAP SHOP

Programme Awards Annually
Design and Produce Badges
Buy Sell and Exchange Programmes
Buy Sell and Exchange other memorbilia
Involved with Speedway as well

Web site   http://pages.zdnet.com/nonleague/thecatalogue
e.mail   philwatkins@soccerclubswapshop.co.uk
tel   0208 861 3016
121 Sefton Avenue Harrow Weald HA3 5JP

NON-LEAGUE PUBLICATIONS

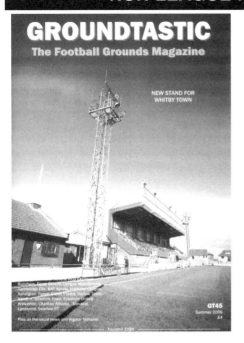

GROUNDTASTIC
The Football Grounds Magazine

NEW STAND FOR
WHITBY TOWN

GT45
Summer 2006
£4

www.nonleaguedigest.co.uk

Non-League Digest
The UK & Overseas Groundhoppers Magazine

Issue 2   22 Aug - 4 Sept 2006   £1.50

West Australia
Football League
Feature - Part 2

Club Focus

* Feniton
* Ascot United
* Newcastle Benfield
* Biddulph Victoria

Programme Review

TOOTING & MITCHAM
UNITED'S SANDY LANE
REVISITED : FORGOTTEN
GROUNDS

Woodsy's World :
MKS POGON
SZCZECIN
(Poland)
REPORT AND
PHOTOS!

YOUR LETTERS

PROGRAMME
MONTHLY
& Football Collectable

No. 302   May 2006   £2

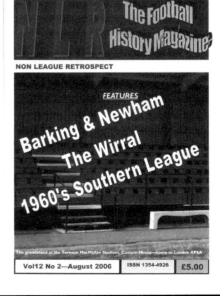

NON LEAGUE RETROSPECT

The Football History Magazine

FEATURES

Barking & Newham
The Wirral
1960's Southern League

The grandstand at the Terence MacMillan Stadium, Custom House—home to London APSA

Vol12 No 2—August 2006   ISSN 1354-4926   £5.00

For further information on the above titles please email:
twpublications@tiscali.co.uk

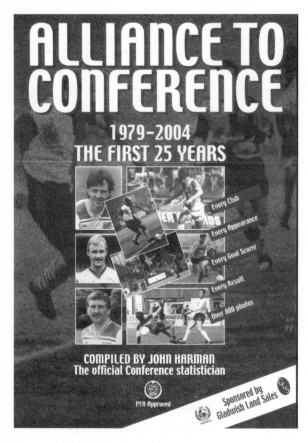

AVAILABLE END OF JULY 2006

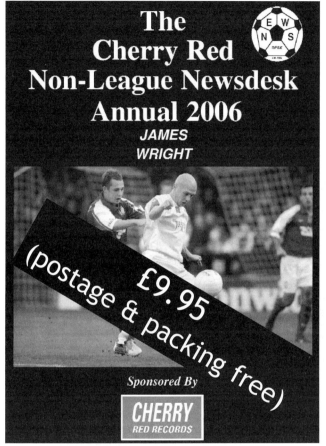

The
Cherry Red
Non-League Newsdesk
Annual 2006

JAMES
WRIGHT

£9.95
(postage & packing free)

Sponsored By

CHERRY
RED RECORDS

EXPANDED TO 304 PAGES

In its seventh year, featuring over 9,500 teams with an extensive round-up
of last season plus club movements/league constitutions for 2006/7,
this is a *MUST* for followers of the non-League scene

Guarantee your copy by ordering from the publishers:-
Non-League Newsdesk Annual
6 Harp Chase
Taunton TA1 3RY
(cheques payable to **Non-League Newsdesk Annual**)
www.nlnewsdesk.co.uk

NON-LEAGUE DIRECTORY

Vase & Trophy CLUB INDEX

Club	Page	League	FA
Abbey Hey FC	606-621	North West Counties 1	Manchester FA
Abingdon Town FC	568-589	Hellenic P	Berks & Bucks FA
Abingdon United FC	388	Southern 1S&W	Berks & Bucks FA
AFC Emley	622-635	Northern Counties East 1	
AFC Hornchurch	486	Isthmian 1N	Essex FA
AFC Kempston Rovers FC	683-699	United Counties 1	Bedfordshire FA
AFC Sudbury	487	Isthmian 1N	Suffolk FA
AFC Telford United	270	Northern Prem. P	Shropshire FA
AFC Totton	700-715	Wessex P	Hampshire FA
AFC Wallingford	568-589	Hellenic P	Berks & Bucks FA
AFC Wimbledon	440	Isthmian P	London FA
Aldershot Town FC	37	Conference	Hampshire FA
Alfreton Town FC	176	Conference North	Derbyshire FA
Almondsbury Town FC	568-589	Hellenic P	Gloucestershire FA
Alnwick Town FC	636-649	Northern 2	Northumberland FA
Alsager Town FC	316	Northern Prem. 1	Cheshire FA
Alton Town FC	700-715	Wessex P	Hampshire FA
Altrincham FC	43	Conference	Cheshire FA
Alvechurch FC	598-605	Midland Alliance	Birmingham FA
Amesbury Town FC	700-715	Wessex 1	Wiltshire FA
Andover FC	389	Southern 1S&W	Hampshire FA
Andover New Street F.C.	700-715	Wessex 1	Hampshire FA
Anstey Nomads FC	776-777	Leicestershire Senior P	Leics. & Rutland FA
Ardley United	568-589	Hellenic P	Oxfordshire FA
Arlesey Athletic FC	650-665	Spartan South Midlands 1	Bedfordshire FA
Arlesey Town FC	488	Isthmian 1N	Bedfordshire FA
Armthorpe Welfare FC	622-635	Northern Counties East P	W. Riding FA
Arnold Town FC	622-635	Northern Counties East P	Nottinghamshire FA
Arundel FC	666-682	Sussex 1	Sussex FA
Ash United FC	532-544	Combined Counties P	Surrey FA
Ashford Town (Middx) FC	442	Isthmian P	Middlesex FA
Ashford Town FC	508	Isthmian 1S	Kent FA
Ashington FC	636-649	Northern 1	Northumberland FA
Ashton Town	606-621	North West Counties 2	
Ashton United FC	272	Northern Prem. P	Manchester FA
Ashville FC	826-827	West Cheshire	Cheshire FA
Atherstone Town FC	794-798	Midland Combination P	Birmingham FA
Atherton Collieries FC	606-621	North West Counties 1	Lancashire FA
Atherton LR FC	606-621	North West Counties 1	Lancashire FA
Aveley FC	489	Isthmian 1N	Essex FA
Aylesbury United FC	412	Southern M	Berks & Bucks FA

Aylesbury Vale	650-665	Spartan South Midlands P	Berks & Bucks FA
Backwell United FC	716-729	Western 1	Somerset FA
Bacup Borough FC	606-621	North West Counties 1	Lancashire FA
Bamber Bridge FC	317	Northern Prem. 1	Lancashire FA
Banbury United FC	344	Southern P	Oxfordshire FA
Banstead Athletic FC	532-544	Combined Counties P	Surrey FA
Barkingside	560-566	Essex Senior	Essex FA
Barnstaple Town FC	716-729	Western P	Devon FA
Barnt Green Spartans	794-798	Midland Combination P	Worcestershire FA
Barrow FC	178	Conference North	Lancashire FA
Barrow Town FC	776-777	Leicestershire Senior P	Leics. & Rutland FA
Barton Rovers FC	413	Southern M	Bedfordshire FA
Barwell FC	598-605	Midland Alliance	Leics. & Rutland FA
Bashley FC	390	Southern 1S&W	Hampshire FA
Basingstoke Town FC	222	Conference South	Hampshire FA
Baslidon United	560-566	Essex Senior	Essex FA
Bath City FC	346	Southern P	Somerset FA
Beaconsfield SYCOB FC	391	Southern 1S&W	Berks & Bucks FA
Bedfont FC	532-544	Combined Counties P	Middlesex FA
Bedfont Green FC	532-544	Combined Counties P	Surrey FA
Bedford Town FC	224	Conference South	Bedfordshire FA
Bedford United & Valerio FC	650-665	Spartan South Midlands	Bedfordshire FA
Bedlington Terriers FC	636-649	Northern 1	Northumberland FA
Bedworth United FC	414	Southern M	Birmingham FA
Belper Town FC	318	Northern Prem. 1	Derbyshire FA
Bemerton Heath Harlequins FC	700-715	Wessex P	Wiltshire FA
Berkhamsted Town FC	415	Southern M	Hertfordshire FA
Bicester Town FC	568-589	Hellenic P	Oxfordshire FA
Biddulph Victoria FC	598-605	Midland Alliance	Staffordshire FA
Bideford FC	716-729	Western P	Devon FA
Biggleswade Town FC	650-665	Spartan South Midlands	Bedfordshire FA
Biggleswade United FC	650-665	Spartan South Midlands	Bedfordshire FA
Billericay Town FC	444	Isthmian P	Essex FA
Billingham Synthonia FC	636-649	Northern 1	Durham FA
Billingham Town FC	636-649	Northern 1	Durham FA
Binfield	568-589	Hellenic 1E	
Birstall United FC	776-777	Leicestershire Senior P	Leics. & Rutland FA
Bishop Auckland FC	636-649	Northern 1	Durham FA
Bishop Sutton FC	716-729	Western P	Somerset FA
Bishop's Cleeve	416	Southern M	Gloucestershire FA
Bishop's Stortford FC	226	Conference South	Hertfordshire FA
Bitton AFC	716-729	Western P	Gloucestershire FA
Blaby & Whetstone Athletic FC	776-777	Leicestershire Senior P	Leics. & Rutland FA
Blackfield & Langley FC	700-715	Wessex 1	Hampshire FA
Blackpool Mechanics FC	606-621	North West Counties 2	Lancashire FA

Burnham FC	394	Southern 1S&W	Berks & Bucks FA
Burnham Ramblers FC	560-566	Essex Senior	Essex FA
Burscough FC	274	Northern Prem. P	Liverpool FA
Burton Albion FC	49	Conference	Birmingham FA
Bury Town FC	490	Isthmian 1N	Suffolk FA
Buxton FC	322	Northern Prem. 1	Derbyshire FA
Cadbury Heath	794-798	Midland Combination P	
Calne Town FC	716-729	Western P	Wiltshire FA
Calverton M.W.	743-747	Central Midlands P	
Camberley Town FC	532-544	Combined Counties P	Surrey FA
Cambridge City FC	232	Conference South	Cambridgeshire FA
Cambridge United	55	Conference	Cambridgeshire FA
Cammell Laird FC	323	Northern Prem. 1	Cheshire FA
Canvey Island FC	491	Isthmian 1N	Essex FA
Carlton Town FC	622-635	Northern Counties East P	Nottinghamshire FA
Carshalton Athletic FC	450	Isthmian P	Surrey FA
Carterton Town FC	568-589	Hellenic P	Oxfordshire FA
Castle Vale KH FC	794-798	Midland Combination P	Birmingham FA
Castleton Gabriels	606-621	North West Counties 2	
Causeway United FC	598-605	Midland Alliance	Birmingham FA
Chadderton FC	606-621	North West Counties 2	Manchester FA
Chalfont St Peter FC	650-665	Spartan South Midlands P	Berks & Bucks FA
Chard Town FC	716-729	Western P	Somerset FA
Chasetown FC	419	Southern M	Staffordshire FA
Chatham Town FC	510	Isthmian 1S	Kent FA
Cheadle Town FC	606-621	North West Counties 2	Cheshire FA
Chelmsford City FC	452	Isthmian P	Essex FA
Chertsey Town FC	532-544	Combined Counties P	Surrey FA
Chesham United FC	395	Southern 1S&W	Berks & Bucks FA
Cheshunt FC	348	Southern P	Hertfordshire FA
Chessington & Hook United FC	532-544	Combined Counties P	Surrey FA
Chester-Le-Street Town FC	636-649	Northern 1	Durham FA
Chippenham Town FC	350	Southern P	Wiltshire FA
Chipping Norton Town FC	568-589	Hellenic P	Oxfordshire FA
Chipstead FC	532-544	Combined Counties P	Surrey FA
Chorley FC	324	Northern Prem. 1	Lancashire FA
Christchurch FC	700-715	Wessex P	Hampshire FA
Cinderford Town FC	420	Southern M	Gloucestershire FA
Cirencester Town FC	352	Southern P	Gloucestershire FA
Clacton Town FC	545-559	Eastern Counties P	Essex FA
Clanfield 85	568-589	Hellenic 1W	
Clapton FC	560-566	Essex Senior	London FA
Clevedon Town FC	354	Southern P	Somerset FA
Clevedon United FC	716-729	Western 1	Somerset FA
Clipstone Welfare	743-747	Central Midlands S	Notts FA

Clitheroe FC	325	Northern Prem. 1	Lancashire FA
Coalville Town FC	598-605	Midland Alliance	Leics. & Rutland FA
Cobham FC	532-544	Combined Counties P	Surrey FA
Cockfosters FC	650-665	Spartan South Midlands	London FA
Cogenhoe United FC	683-699	United Counties P	Northants. FA
Coleshill Town	794-798	Midland Combination P	Birmingham FA
Colliers Wood United	532-544	Combined Counties P	Surrey FA
Colne FC	606-621	North West Counties 1	Lancashire FA
Colney Heath FC	650-665	Spartan South Midlands	Hertfordshire FA
Colwyn Bay FC	326	Northern Prem. 1	Wales
Concord Rangers FC	560-566	Essex Senior	Essex FA
Congleton Town FC	606-621	North West Counties 1	Cheshire FA
Consett FC	636-649	Northern 1	Durham FA
Copeswood	794-798	Midland Combination P	Birmingham FA
Corby Town FC	355	Southern P	Northants. FA
Corinthian Casuals FC	511	Isthmian 1S	London FA
Cornard United FC	545-559	Eastern Counties 1	Suffolk FA
Corsham Town FC	716-729	Western P	Wiltshire FA
Cove FC	532-544	Combined Counties P	Hampshire FA
Coventry Sphinx FC	794-798	Midland Combination P	Birmingham FA
Cowes Sports FC	700-715	Wessex P	Hampshire FA
Cradley Town FC	598-605	Midland Alliance	Birmingham FA
Cranfield United	650-665	Spartan South Midlands	Bedfordshire FA
Crawley Town FC	61	Conference	Sussex FA
Cray Wanderers FC	512	Isthmian 1S	Kent FA
Crook Town FC	636-649	Northern 2	Durham FA
Crowborough Athletic	666-682	Sussex 1	
Croydon Athletic FC	513	Isthmian 1S	London FA
Croydon FC	590-597	Kent Lge	Surrey FA
Cullompton Rangers FC	750-753	Devon	Devon FA
Curzon Ashton FC	606-621	North West Counties 1	Manchester FA
Dagenham & Redbridge FC	67	Conference	Essex FA
Daisy Hill	606-621	North West Counties 2	Lancashire FA
Darlington RA	636-649	Northern 1	Durham FA
Dartford FC	514	Isthmian 1S	Kent FA
Darwen FC	606-621	North West Counties 2	Lancashire FA
Daventry Town FC	683-699	United Counties P	Northants. FA
Dawlish Town FC	716-729	Western P	Devon FA
Deal Town FC	590-597	Kent Lge	Kent FA
Debenham LC	545-559	Eastern Counties 1	
Deeping Rangers FC	683-699	United Counties P	Lincolnshire FA
Dereham Town FC	545-559	Eastern Counties P	Norfolk FA
Desborough Town FC	683-699	United Counties P	Northants. FA
Devizes Town FC	716-729	Western P	Wiltshire FA
Didcot Town FC	396	Southern 1S&W	Berks & Bucks FA

Dinning Town	622-635	Northern Counties East 1	
Diss Town FC	545-559	Eastern Counties P	Norfolk FA
Dorchester Town FC	234	Conference South	Dorset FA
Dorking FC	532-544	Combined Counties P	Surrey FA
Dover Athletic FC	515	Isthmian 1S	Kent FA
Downes Sports FC	776-777	Leicestershire Senior P	Leics. & Rutland FA
Downham Town	545-559	Eastern Counties 1	Norfolk FA
Downton FC	700-715	Wessex P	Wiltshire FA
Droylsden FC	182	Conference North	Manchester FA
Dudley Town FC	832-835	West Midlands P	Birmingham FA
Dulwich Hamlet FC	516	Isthmian 1S	London FA
Dunkirk FC	743-747	Central Midlands S	Nottinghamshire FA
Dunstable Town FC	421	Southern M	Bedfordshire FA
Dunston Federation Brewery FC	636-649	Northern 1	Durham FA
Durham City FC	636-649	Northern 1	Durham FA
Easington Colliery FC	806-809	Northern Alliance	Durham FA
East Grinstead Town FC	666-682	Sussex 2	Sussex FA
East Preston FC	666-682	Sussex 1	Sussex FA
East Thurrock United FC	454	Isthmian P	Essex FA
Eastbourne Borough FC	236	Conference South	Sussex FA
Eastbourne Town FC	666-682	Sussex 1	Sussex FA
Eastbourne United FC	666-682	Sussex 1	Sussex FA
Eastleigh FC	238	Conference South	Hampshire FA
Eastwood Town FC	327	Northern Prem. 1	Nottinghamshire FA
Eccleshall	606-621	North West Counties 2	Staffordshire FA
Eccleshill United FC	622-635	Northern Counties East P	W. Riding FA
Edgware Town	650-665	Spartan South Midlands	
Egham Town FC	532-544	Combined Counties P	Surrey FA
Ellistown	776-777	Leicestershire Senior P	Leics. & Rutland FA
Elmore FC	716-729	Western 1	Devon FA
Ely City FC	545-559	Eastern Counties 1	Cambridgeshire FA
Enfield FC	492	Isthmian 1N	Middlesex FA
Enfield Town FC	493	Isthmian 1N	Middlesex FA
Epsom & Ewell FC	532-544	Combined Counties P	Surrey FA
Erith & Belvedere FC	590-597	Kent Lge	Kent FA
Erith Town FC	590-597	Kent Lge	London FA
Esh Winning FC	636-649	Northern 2	Durham FA
Eton Manor FC	560-566	Essex Senior	Essex FA
Evesham United FC	422	Southern M	Worcesters. FA
Exeter City	73	Conference	Devon FA
Eynesbury Rovers FC	683-699	United Counties 1	Huntingdonshire FA
Fairford Town FC	568-589	Hellenic P	Gloucestershire FA
Fakenham Town FC	545-559	Eastern Counties 1	Norfolk FA
Falmouth Town AFC	816-819	South Western	Cornwall FA
Fareham Town FC	700-715	Wessex P	Hampshire FA

Hailsham Town FC	666-682	Sussex 1	Sussex FA
Halesowen Town FC	358	Southern P	Birmingham FA
Halifax Town FC	97	Conference	W. Riding FA
Hall Road Rangers FC	622-635	Northern Counties East 1	E. Riding FA
Hallam FC	622-635	Northern Counties East P	Sheff. & Hallams. FA
Hallen FC	716-729	Western P	Gloucestershire FA
Halstead Town FC	545-559	Eastern Counties P	Essex FA
Hamble Asociation FC	700-715	Wessex P	Hampshire FA
Hampton & Richmond Bor. FC	458	Isthmian P	Middlesex FA
Hamworthy United FC	700-715	Wessex P	Dorset FA
Hanwell Town FC	397	Southern 1S&W	Middlesex FA
Harefield United FC	650-665	Spartan South Midlands	Middlesex FA
Haringey Borough FC	650-665	Spartan South Midlands	London FA
Harlow Town FC	496	Isthmian 1N	Essex FA
Harpenden Town FC	650-665	Spartan South Midlands	Hertfordshire FA
Harrogate Railway FC	330	Northern Prem. 1	W. Riding FA
Harrogate Town FC	188	Conference North	W. Riding FA
Harrow Borough FC	460	Isthmian P	Middlesex FA
Harrow Hill FC	568-589	Hellenic P	Gloucestershire FA
Hartley Wintney FC	532-544	Combined Counties 1	Hampshire FA
Harwich & Parkeston FC	545-559	Eastern Counties P	Essex FA
Hassocks FC	666-682	Sussex 1	Sussex FA
Hastings United FC	519	Isthmian 1S	Sussex FA
Havant & Waterlooville Hampshire FA	240	244	Conference South
Haverhill Rovers FC	545-559	Eastern Counties 1	Suffolk FA
Hayes FC	246	Conference South	Middlesex FA
Haywards Heath	666-682	Sussex 3	
Heanor Town FC	743-747	Central Midlands S	Derbyshire FA
Heather Athletic	794-798	Midland Combination 1	
Hebburn Town FC	636-649	Northern 2	Durham FA
Hednesford Town FC	286	Northern Prem. P	Birmingham FA
Hemel Hempstead Town FC	360	Southern P	Hertfordshire FA
Hendon FC	462	Isthmian P	Middlesex FA
Henley Town FC	568-589	Hellenic 1E	Oxfordshire FA
Herne Bay FC	590-597	Kent Lge	Kent FA
Hertford Town FC	650-665	Spartan South Midlands	Hertfordshire FA
Heybridge Swifts FC	464	Isthmian P	Essex FA
Highfield Rangers FC	776-777	Leicestershire Senior P	Leics. & Rutland FA
Highgate United FC	794-798	Midland Combination P	Birmingham FA
Highworth Town FC	568-589	Hellenic P	Wiltshire FA
Hillingdon Borough FC	398	Southern 1S&W	Middlesex FA
Hinckley United FC	190	Conference North	Leics. & Rutland FA
Histon FC	248	Conference South	Cambridgeshire FA
Hitchin Town FC	362	Southern P	Hertfordshire FA

Hoddesdon Town FC	650-665	Spartan South Midlands	Hertfordshire FA
Holbeach United FC	683-699	United Counties P	Lincolnshire FA
Holbrook Miners Welfare	743-747	Central Midlands S	Derbyshire FA
Holker Old Boys FC	606-621	North West Counties 2	Lancashire FA
Holmer Green FC	650-665	Spartan South Midlands	Berks & Bucks FA
Holwell Sports	776-777	Leicestershire Senior P	Leics. & Rutland FA
Horden Colliery W elfare FC	636-649	Northern 1	Durham FA
Horley Town	532-544	Combined Counties 1	Surrey FA
Horsham FC	466	Isthmian P	Sussex FA
Horsham YMCA FC	520	Isthmian 1S	Sussex FA
Hounslow Borough	568-589	Hellenic P	
Hucknall Town FC	192	Conference North	Nottinghamshire FA
Hullbridge Sports FC	560-566	Essex Senior	Essex FA
Hungerford Town FC	568-589	Hellenic P	Berks & Bucks FA
Huntingdon FC	683-699	United Counties 1	Huntingdonshire FA
Hyde United FC	194	Conference North	Cheshire FA
Hythe Town FC	590-597	Kent Lge	Kent FA
Ibstock Welfare FC	776-777	Leicestershire Senior P	Leics. & Rutland FA
Ilford FC	497	Isthmian 1N	Essex FA
Ilfracombe Town FC	716-729	Western 1	Devon FA
Ilkeston Town FC	288	Northern Prem. P	Derbyshire FA
Ipswich Wanderers FC	545-559	Eastern Counties P	Suffolk FA
Jarrow Roofing Boldon CA FC	636-649	Northern 1	Durham FA
Kendal Town FC	290	Northern Prem. P	Westmorland FA
Kettering Town FC	196	Conference North	Northants. FA
Keysham Town	716-729	Western P	
Kidderminster Harriers	103	Conference	Birmingham FC
Kidlington	568-589	Hellenic P	
Kidsgrove Athletic FC	331	Northern Prem. 1	Staffordshire FA
Kimberley Town FC	743-747	Central Midlands S	Nottinghamshire FA
Kings Lynn FC	364	Southern P	Norfolk FA
Kingsbury Town FC	650-665	Spartan South Midlands	Middlesex FA
Kingstonian FC	521	Isthmian 1S	Surrey FA
Kirby Muxloe FC	776-777	Leicestershire Senior P	Leics. & Rutland FA
Kirkley	545-559	Eastern Counties P	Suffolk FA
Lancaster City FC	198	Conference North	Lancashire FA
Lancing FC	666-682	Sussex 2	Sussex FA
Langford FC	650-665	Spartan South Midlands	Bedfordshire FA
Larkhall Athletic	716-729	Western 1	Somerset FA
Launceston FC	816-819	South Western	Cornwall FA
Leamington FC	598-605	Midland Alliance	Birmingham FA
Leatherhead FC	522	Isthmian 1S	Surrey FA
Ledbury Town FC	832-835	West Midlands P	Herefordshire FA
Leek CSOB FC	606-621	North West Counties 2	Staffordshire FA
Leek Town FC	292	Northern Prem. P	Staffordshire FA

Leigh RMI FC	200	Conference North	Lancashire FA
Leighton Town FC	423	Southern M	Bedfordshire FA
Leiston	545-559	Eastern Counties P	Suffolk FA
Leverstock Green FC	650-665	Spartan South Midlands	Hertfordshire FA
Lewes FC	250	Conference South	Sussex FA
Lewisham Borough FC	768-775	Kent County	Kent FA
Leyton FC	468	Isthmian P	London FA
Lincoln Moorlands FC	622-635	Northern Counties East 1	Lincolnshire FA
Lincoln United FC	294	Northern Prem. P	Lincolnshire FA
Lingfield	666-682	Sussex 2	
Liskeard Athletic FC	816-819	South Western	Cornwall FA
Littlehampton Town FC	666-682	Sussex 1	Sussex FA
Liversedge FC	622-635	Northern Counties East P	W. Riding FA
London APSA	560-566	Essex Senior	Essex FA
London Colney FC	650-665	Spartan South Midlands	Hertfordshire FA
Long Buckby FC	683-699	United Counties P	Northants. FA
Long Eaton United FC	622-635	Northern Counties East P	Derbyshire FA
Long Melford FC	545-559	Eastern Counties 1	Suffolk FA
Lordswood FC	590-597	Kent Lge	Kent FA
Loughborough Dynamo FC	598-605	Midland Alliance	Leics & Rutland FA
Lowestoft Town FC	545-559	Eastern Counties P	Suffolk FA
Lye Town FC	832-835	West Midlands P	Birmingham FA
Lymington & New Milton FC	399	Southern 1S&W	Hampshire FA
Lymington Town	700-715	Wessex P	Hampshire FA
Maidenhead United FC	366	Southern P	Berks & Bucks FA
Maidstone United FC	523	Isthmian 1S	Kent FA
Maine Road FC	606-621	North West Counties 1	Manchester FA
Maldon Town FC	498	Isthmian 1N	Essex FA
Malmesbury Victoria	568-589	Hellenic 1W	Wiltshire FA
Maltby Main FC	622-635	Northern Counties East P	Sheff. & Hallams. FA
Malvern Town FC	424	Southern M	Worcesters. FA
Mangotsfield United FC	368	Southern P	Gloucestershire FA
March Town United FC	545-559	Eastern Counties 1	Cambridgeshire FA
Margate FC	470	Isthmian P	Kent FA
Marine FC	296	Northern Prem. P	Liverpool FA
Market Drayton Town	598-605	Midland Alliance	
Marlow FC	400	Southern 1S&W	Berks & Bucks FA
Marske United FC	636-649	Northern 2	N. Riding FA
Matlock Town FC	298	Northern Prem. P	Derbyshire FA
Meir KA FC	794-798	Midland Combination P	Staffordshire FA
Melksham Town FC	716-729	Western P	Wiltshire FA
Merstham FC	532-544	Combined Counties P	Surrey FA
Merthyr Tydfil FC	370	Southern P	Wales
Metropolitan Police FC	524	Isthmian 1S	London FA
Mickleover Sports FC	622-635	Northern Counties East P	Derbyshire FA

Mildenhall Town FC	545-559	Eastern Counties P	Suffolk FA
Mile Oak	666-682	Sussex 2	Sussex FA
Milton United FC	568-589	Hellenic P	Berks & Bucks FA
Minehead Town FC	716-729	Western 1	Somerset FA
Molesey FC	525	Isthmian 1S	Surrey FA
Moneyfields FC	700-715	Wessex 1	Hampshire FA
Moor Green FC	202	Conference North	Birmingham FA
Morecambe FC	109	Conference	Lancashire FA
Morpeth Town FC	636-649	Northern 1	Northumberland FA
Mossley AFC	300	Northern Prem. P	Manchester FA
Nantwich Town FC	606-621	North West Counties 1	Cheshire FA
Needham Market FC	545-559	Eastern Counties P	Suffolk FA
Nelson FC	606-621	North West Counties 1	Lancashire FA
Nettleham FC	743-747	Central Midlands S	Lincolnshire FA
New Mills FC	606-621	North West Counties 2	Derbyshire FA
Newark Town	743-747	Central Midlands P	Nottingham FA
Newcastle Benfield Saints FC	636-649	Northern 1	Northumberland FA
Newcastle Blue Star FC	636-649	Northern 1	Northumberland FA
Newcastle Town FC	606-621	North West Counties 1	Staffordshire FA
Newmarket Town FC	545-559	Eastern Counties P	Suffolk FA
Newport County FC	252	Conference South	Wales
Newport Pagnell Town FC	683-699	United Counties P	Berks & Bucks FA
Newport(IW) FC	401	Southern 1S&W	Hampshire FA
Newquay FC	816-819	South Western	Cornish FA
Newton Abbot FC	750-753	Devon	Devon FA
North Ferriby United FC	302	Northern Prem. P	E. Riding FA
North Greenford United FC	532-544	Combined Counties P	Middlesex FA
North Leigh FC	568-589	Hellenic P	Oxfordshire FA
North Shields FC	636-649	Northern 2	Northumberland FA
Northallerton Town FC	636-649	Northern 1	N. Riding FA
Northampton Spencer FC	683-699	United Counties P	Northants. FA
Northwich Victoria FC	115	Conference	Cheshire FA
Northwood FC	372	Southern P	Middlesex FA
Norton & Stockton Ancients FC	636-649	Northern 2	Durham FA
Norton United FC	606-621	North West Counties 2	Staffordshire FA
Norwich United FC	545-559	Eastern Counties P	Norfolk FA
Nuneaton Borough FC	204	Conference North	Birmingham FA
Nuneaton Griff FC	794-798	Midland Combination P	Birmingham FA
Oadby Town FC	598-605	Midland Alliance	Leics. & Rutland FA
Oakwood FC	666-682	Sussex 1	Sussex FA
Odd Down FC	716-729	Western P	Somerset FA
Oldbury United FC	598-605	Midland Alliance	Birmingham FA
Oldham Town FC	606-621	North West Counties 2	Manchester FA
Ossett Albion FC	332	Northern Prem. 1	W. Riding FA
Ossett Town FC	304	Northern Prem. P	W. Riding FA

Ottery St.Mary	750-753	Devon	Devon FA
Oxford City FC	402	Southern 1S&W	Oxfordshire FA
Oxford United	119	Conference	Herefordshire FA
Oxhey Jets	650-665	Spartan South Midlands	Hertfordshire FA
Padiham	606-621	North West Counties 2	Lancashire FA
Pagham FC	666-682	Sussex 2	Sussex FA
Parkgate FC	622-635	Northern Counties East 1	Sheff. & Hallams. FA
Paulton Rovers FC	403	Southern 1S&W	Somerset FA
Peacehaven & Telscombe FC	666-682	Sussex 2	Sussex FA
Pegasus Juniors FC	568-589	Hellenic P	Herefordshire FA
Pelsall Villa FC	832-835	West Midlands P	Staffordshire FA
Penrith FC	636-649	Northern 2	Cumberland FA
Penryn Athletic	816-819	South Western	Cornwall FA
Penzance	816-819	South Western	Cornwall FA
Pershore Town FC	794-798	Midland Combination P	Worcesters. FA
Peterlee Newtown FC	806-809	Northern Alliance P	Durham FA
Pewsey Vale FC	568-589	Hellenic 1W	Wiltshire FA
Pickering Town FC	622-635	Northern Counties East P	N. Riding FA
Pickering XXX	794-798	Midland Combination	Birmingham FA
Plymouth Parkway	816-819	South Western	
Pontefract Collieries FC	622-635	Northern Counties East 1	W. Riding FA
Poole Town FC	700-715	Wessex P	Dorset FA
Porthleven FC	816-819	South Western	Cornwall FA
Portland United FC	700-715	Wessex 1	Dorset FA
Potters Bar Town FC	499	Isthmian 1N	Hertfordshire FA
Potton United FC	683-699	United Counties P	Bedfordshire FA
Poulton Victoria	826-827	West Cheshire 1	Cheshire FA
Prescot Cables FC	306	Northern Prem. P	Liverpool FA
Prudhoe Town FC	636-649	Northern 2	Northumberland FA
Quorn FC	598-605	Midland Alliance	Leics. & Rutland FA
Racing Club Warwick FC	598-605	Midland Alliance	Birmingham FA
Radcliffe Borough FC	308	Northern Prem. P	Lancashire FA
Radcliffe Olympic FC	743-747	Central Midlands	Nottinghamshire FA
Radford FC	743-747	Central Midlands	Nottinghamshire FA
Radstock Town	716-729	Western P	Somerset FA
Rainworth MW FC	743-747	Central Midlands S	Nottinghamshire FA
Ramsbottom United FC	606-621	North West Counties 1	Lancashire FA
Ramsgate FC	473	Isthmian P	Kent FA
Ratby Sports	776-777	Leicstershire Senior	
Raunds Town FC	683-699	United Counties P	Northants. FA
Raynes Park Vale FC	532-544	Combined Counties P	Surrey FA
Reading Town FC	532-544	Combined Counties P	Berks & Bucks FA
Redbridge FC	500	Isthmian 1N	London FA
Redditch United FC	206	Conference North	Birmingham FA
Redhill FC	666-682	Sussex 1	Surrey FA

Retford United FC	622-635	Northern Counties East P	Nottinghamshire FA
Ringmer FC	666-682	Sussex 1	Sussex FA
Ringwood Town FC	700-715	Wessex P	Hampshire FA
Rocester FC	598-605	Midland Alliance	Staffordshire FA
Rolls Royce Leisure FC	743-747	Central Midlands S	Nottinghamshire FA
Romford FC	560-566	Essex Senior	Essex FA
Romulus FC	598-605	Midland Alliance	Birmingham FA
Rossendale United FC	333	Northern Prem. 1	Lancashire FA
Rossington Main FC	622-635	Northern Counties East 1	Sheff. & Hallams. FA
Rothley Imperial	776-777	Leicestershire Senior	
Rothwell Corinthians FC	683-699	United Counties 1	Northants. FA
Rothwell Town FC	425	Southern M	Northants. FA
Royston Town FC	650-665	Spartan South Midlands	Hertfordshire FA
Rugby Town FC	374	Southern P	Birmingham FA
Ruislip Manor FC	650-665	Spartan South Midlands	Middlesex FA
Rushall Olympic FC	426	Southern M	Staffordshire FA
Rushden & Diamonds	123	Conference	Lancashire FA
Rye & Iden United FC	666-682	Sussex 1	Sussex FA
Ryton FC	636-649	Northern 2	Durham FA
Saffron Walden Town	545-559	Eastern Counties 1	Essex FA
Salford City FC	606-621	North West Counties 1	Manchester FA
Salisbury City FC	254	Conference South	Wiltshire FA
Saltash United FC	816-819	South Western	Cornwall FA
Saltdean United FC	666-682	Sussex 2	Sussex FA
Sandhurst Town FC	532-544	Combined Counties P	Berks & Bucks FA
Sandiacre Town FC	743-747	Central Midlands P	Derbyshire FA
Sawbridgeworth Town FC	560-566	Essex Senior	Hertfordshire FA
Scarborough FC	208	Conference North	N. Riding FA
Seaham Red Star FC	636-649	Northern 2	Durham FA
Selby Town FC	622-635	Northern Counties East P	W. Riding FA
Selsey FC	666-682	Sussex 1	Sussex FA
Sevenoaks Town	590-597	Kent Lge	Kent FA
Shaftsbury FC	700-715	Wessex 1	Dorset FA
Shawbury United FC	832-835	West Midlands P	Shropshire FA
Sheffield FC	622-635	Northern Counties East P	Sheff. & Hallams. FA
Shepshed Dynamo FC	334	Northern Prem. 1	Leics. & Rutland FA
Shepton Mallet AFC	716-729	Western 1	Somerset FA
Sherbourne Town FC	716-729	Western 1	Dorset FA
Shifnal Town FC	794-798	Midland Combination P	Shropshire FA
Shildon FC	636-649	Northern 1	Durham FA
Shirebrook Town FC	622-635	Northern Counties East P	Derbyshire FA
Shoreham	666-682	Sussex 1	Sussex FA
Shortwood United FC	568-589	Hellenic P	Gloucestershire FA
Shrewton Town	716-729	Western 1	
Shrivenham	568-589	Hellenic P	

Sidlesham FC	666-682	Sussex 2	Sussex FA
Sidley United FC	666-682	Sussex 1	Sussex FA
Sileby Rangers	683-699	United Counties 1	
Silsden FC	606-621	North West Counties 1	West Riding FA
Sittingbourne FC	526	Isthmian 1S	Kent FA
Skelmersdale United FC	335	Northern Prem. 1	Liverpool FA
Slade Green FC	590-597	Kent Lge	Kent FA
Slimbridge	568-589	Hellenic P	Gloucestershire FA
Slough Town FC	474	Isthmian P	Berks & Bucks FA
Soham Town Rangers FC	545-559	Eastern Counties P	Cambridgeshire FA
Solihull Borough FC	427	Southern M	Birmingham FA
South Normanton Athletic	622-635	Northern Counties East 1	Derbyshire FA
South Shields FC	636-649	Northern 2	Durham FA
Southam United	794-798	Midland Combination P	
Southend Manor FC	560-566	Essex Senior	Essex FA
Southport FC	127	Conference	Lancashire FA
Spalding United FC	428	Southern M	Lincolnshire FA
Spennymoor Town FC	636-649	Northern 2	Durham FA
Sporting Bengal United	590-597	Kent Lge	Kent FA
Squires Gate FC	606-621	North West Counties 1	Lancashire FA
St Albans City FC	133	Conference	Hertfordshire FA
St Andrews FC	776-777	Leicestershire Senior P	Leics. & Rutland FA
St Blazey FC	816-819	South Western	Cornwall FA
St Helens Town FC	606-621	North West Counties 1	Liverpool FA
St Ives Town FC	683-699	United Counties P	Huntingdonshire FA
St Margaretsbury FC	650-665	Spartan South Midlands	Hertfordshire FA
St Neots Town FC	683-699	United Counties P	Huntingdonshire FA
Stafford Rangers FC	137	Conference	Staffordshire FA
Staines Town FC	476	Isthmian P	Middlesex FA
Stalybridge Celtic FC	210	Conference North	Cheshire FA
Stamford AFC	376	Southern P	Lincolnshire FA
Stansted FC	560-566	Essex Senior	Essex FA
Stanway Rovers FC	545-559	Eastern Counties 1	Essex FA
Stapenhill FC	776-777	Leicestershire Senior P	Leics. & Rutland FA
Staveley MW FC	622-635	Northern Counties East 1	Derbyshire FA
Stevenage Borough FC	141	Conference	Hertfordshire FA
Stewarts & Lloyds	683-699	United Counties P	
Stocksbridge Park Steels FC	336	Northern Prem. 1	Sheff. & Hallams. FA
Stone Dominoes FC	606-621	North West Counties 1	Staffordshire FA
Stotfold FC	683-699	United Counties P	Bedfordshire FA
Stourbridge FC	429	Southern M	Birmingham FA
Stourport Swifts FC	430	Southern M	Worcesters. FA
Stowmarket Town FC	545-559	Eastern Counties 1	Suffolk FA
Stratford Town FC	598-605	Midland Alliance	Birmingham FA
Street FC	716-729	Western P	Somerset FA

Studley FC	598-605	Midland Alliance	Birmingham FA
Sun Postal	650-665	Spartan South Midlands	
Sunderland Nissan FC	636-649	Northern 1	Durham FA
Sunderland RCA	636-649	Northern 2	
Sutton Coldfield Town FC	431	Southern M	Birmingham FA
Sutton Town FC	622-635	Northern Counties East P	Nottinghamshire FA
Sutton United	256	Conference South	Surrey FA
Swindon Supermarine FC	404	Southern 1S&W	Wiltshire FA
Tadcaster Albion FC	622-635	Northern Counties East 1	W. Riding FA
Tamworth FC	147	Conference	Birmingham FA
Taunton Town FC	405	Southern 1S&W	Somerset FA
TavistockTown	816-819	South Western	Devon FA
Team Bath FC	378	Southern P	Somerset FA
Team Northumbria	636-649	Northern 2	
Teversal	622-635	Northern Counties East 1	Derbyshire FA
Thackley FC	622-635	Northern Counties East P	W. Riding FA
Thame United FC	568-589	Hellenic P	Oxfordshire FA
Thamesmead Town FC	590-597	Kent Lge	London FA
Thatcham Town FC	406	Southern 1S&W	Berks & Bucks FA
Thetford Town FC	545-559	Eastern Counties 1	Norfolk FA
Thornaby FC	636-649	Northern 2	N. Riding FA
Three Bridges FC	666-682	Sussex 1	Sussex FA
Thurnby Rangers	776-777	Leicestershire Senior	
Thurrock FC	258	Conference South	Essex FA
Tilbury FC	501	Isthmian 1N	Essex FA
Tipton Town FC	598-605	Midland Alliance	Birmingham FA
Tiptree United FC	545-559	Eastern Counties 1	Essex FA
Tiverton Town FC	380	Southern P	Devon FA
Tividale FC	832-835	West Midlands P	Birmingham FA
Tonbridge Angels FC	478	Isthmian P	Kent FA
Tooting & Mitcham United FC	527	Isthmian 1S	Surrey FA
Torrington FC	716-729	Western P	Devon FA
Tow Law Town FC	636-649	Northern 1	Durham FA
Trafford FC	606-621	North West Counties 1	Manchester FA
Tring Athletic	650-665	Spartan South Midlands	Hertfordshire FA
Truro City	816-819	South Western	Cornwall FA
Tunbridge Wells FC	590-597	Kent Lge	Kent FA
United Services Portsmouth	700-715	Wessex 1	Hampshire FA
Uxbridge FC	407	Southern 1S&W	Middlesex FA
Vauxhall Motors FC	212	Conference North	Cheshire FA
VCD Athletic FC	590-597	Kent Lge	Kent FA
VT FC	700-715	Wessex P	Hampshire FA
Wadebridge Town	816-819	South Western	Lancashire FA
Wakefield	337	Northern Prem. 1	Sheff. & Hallams. FA
Walsham Le Willows	545-559	Eastern Counties 1	Suffolk FA

INDEX

Waltham Abbey	502	Isthmian 1N	Essex FA
Waltham Forest FC	503	Isthmian 1N	Essex FA
Walton & Hersham FC	480	Isthmian P	Surrey FA
Walton Casuals FC	528	Isthmian 1S	Surrey FA
Wantage Town FC	568-589	Hellenic P	Berks & Bucks FA
Ware FC	504	Isthmian 1N	Hertfordshire FA
Warrington Town FC	338	Northern Prem. 1	Cheshire FA
Washington FC	636-649	Northern 2	Durham FA
Wealdon	666-682	Sussex 2	
Wealdstone FC	382	Southern P	Middlesex FA
Welling United FC	260	Conference South	London FA
Wellingborough Town	683-699	United Counties P	
Wellington FC	832-835	West Midlands P	Herefordshire FA
Wellington Town FC	716-729	Western 1	Somerset FA
Welton Rovers FC	716-729	Western P	Somerset FA
Welwyn Garden City	650-665	Spartan South Midlands	Hertfordshire FA
Wembley FC	532-544	Combined Counties P	Middlesex FA
West Allotment Celtic FC	636-649	Northern 1	Northumberland FA
West Auckland Town FC	636-649	Northern 1	Durham FA
Westbury United FC	716-729	Western 1	Wiltshire FA
Westfield FC	532-544	Combined Counties 1	Surrey FA
Westfields FC	598-605	Midland Alliance	Herefordshire FA
Weston Super Mare FC	262	Conference South	Somerset FA
Weymouth FC	153	Conference	Dorset FA
Whickham FC	636-649	Northern 2	Durham FA
Whitby Town FC	310	Northern Prem. P	N. Riding FA
Whitehawk FC	666-682	Sussex 1	Sussex FA
Whitley Bay FC	636-649	Northern 1	Northumberland FA
Whitstable Town FC	590-597	Kent Lge	Kent FA
Whitton United FC	545-559	Eastern Counties 1	Suffolk FA
Whyteleafe FC	529	Isthmian 1S	Surrey FA
Wick FC	666-682	Sussex 1	Sussex FA
Willand Rovers FC	716-729	Western P	Devon FA
Willenhall Town FC	432	Southern M	Birmingham FA
Willington FC	823-825	Wearside	Durham FA
Wimborne Town FC	700-715	Wessex P	Dorset FA
Winchester City FC	408	Southern 1S&W	Hampshire FA
Windsor & Eton FC	409	Southern 1S&W	Berks & Bucks FA
Wingate & Finchley FC	505	Isthmian 1N	London FA
Winsford United FC	606-621	North West Counties 2	Cheshire FA
Winterton Rangers FC	622-635	Northern Counties East 1	Lincolnshire FA
Wisbech Town FC	545-559	Eastern Counties P	Cambridgeshire FA
Witham Town FC	506	Isthmian 1N	Essex FA
Witney United	568-589	Hellenic P	Oxfordshire
Witton Albion FC	312	Northern Prem. P	Cheshire FA

Waltham Abbey - Yorkshire Amateur

INDEX

Published by Tony Williams Publications Ltd
Helland, North Curry, Taunton
Somerset TA3 6DU

Tel: 01823 490 080 / 490 684
emila: twpublications@tiscali.co.uk